Y0-BXH-212

Organic Electronic Spectral Data
Volume XXI 1979

Organic Electronic Spectral Data

Volume XXI 1979

JOHN P. PHILLIPS, DALLAS BATES
HENRY FEUER & B. S. THYAGARAJAN

EDITORS

CONTRIBUTORS

Dallas Bates
H. Feuer
L. D. Freedman
C. M. Martini
F. C. Nachod
J. P. Phillips

AN INTERSCIENCE ® PUBLICATION
JOHN WILEY & SONS
New York • Chichester • Brisbane • Toronto • Singapore

An Interscience ® Publication

Library of Congress Catalog Card Number: 60-16428

ISBN 0-471-83047-X

Printed in the United States of America

10 9 8 7 6 5 4 3 2 1

INTRODUCTION TO THE SERIES

In 1956 a cooperative effort to abstract and publish in formula order all the ultraviolet-visible spectra of organic compounds presented in the journal literature was organized through the enterprise and leadership of M.J. Kamlet and H.E. Ungnade. Organic Electronic Spectral Data was incorporated in 1957 to create a formal structure for the venture, and coverage of the literature from 1946 onward was then carried out by chemists with special interests in spectrophotometry through a page by page search of the major chemical journals. After the first two volumes (covering the literature from 1946 through 1955) were produced, a regular schedule of one volume for each subsequent period of two years was introduced. In 1966 an annual schedule was inaugurated.

Altogether, more than fifty chemists have searched a group of journals totalling more than a hundred titles during the course of this sustained project. Additions and subtractions from both the lists of contributors and of journals have occurred from time to time, and it is estimated that the effort to cover all the literature containing spectra may not be more than 95% successful. However, the total collection is by far the largest ever assembled, amounting to nearly half a million spectra in the twenty-one volumes so far.

Volume XXII is in preparation

PREFACE

Processing of the data provided by the contributors to Volume XXI as to the last several volumes was performed at the University of Louisville.

John P. Phillips
Dallas Bates
Henry Feuer
B.S. Thyagarajan

ORGANIZATION AND USE OF THE DATA

The data in this volume were abstracted from the journals listed in the reference section at the end. Although a few exceptions were made, the data generally had to satisfy the following requirements: the compound had to be pure enough for satisfactory elemental analysis and for a definite empirical formula; solvent and phase had to be given; and sufficient data to calculate molar absorptivities had to be available. Later it was decided to include spectra even if solvent was not mentioned. Experience has shown that the most probable single solvent in such circumstances is ethanol.

All entries in the compilation are organized according to the molecular formula index system used by Chemical Abstracts. Most of the compound names have been made to conform with the Chemical Abstracts system of nomenclature.

Solvent or phase appears in the second column of the data lists, often abbreviated according to standard practice; there is a key to less obvious abbreviations on the next page. Anion and cation are used in this column if the spectra are run in relatively basic or acidic conditions respectively but exact specifications cannot be ascertained.

The numerical data in the third column present wavelength values in nanometers (millimicrons) for all maxima, shoulders and inflections, with the logarithms of the corresponding molar absorptivities in parentheses. Shoulders and inflections are marked with a letter s. In spectra with considerable fine structure in the bands a main maximum is listed and labelled with a letter f. Numerical values are given to the nearest nanometer for wavelength and nearest 0.01 unit for the logarithm of the molar absorptivity. Spectra that change with time or other common conditions are labelled "anom." or "changing", and temperatures are indicated if unusual.

The reference column contains the code number of the journal, the initial page number of the paper, and in the last two digits the year (1979). A letter is added for journals with more than one volume or section in a year. The complete list of all articles and authors thereof appears in the References at the end of the book.

Several journals that were abstracted for previous volumes in this series have been omitted, usually for lack of useful data, and several new ones have been added. Most Russian journals have been abstracted in the form of the English translation editions.

ABBREVIATIONS

s	shoulder or inflection
f	fine structure
n.s.g.	no solvent given in original reference
$C_6H_{11}Me$	methylcyclohexane
C_6H_{12}	cyclohexane
DMF	dimethylformamide
DMSO	dimethylsulfoxide
THF	tetrahydrofuran

Other solvent abbreviations generally follow the practice of Chemical Abstracts.

Underlined data were estimated from graphs.

JOURNALS ABSTRACTED

Journal	No.	Journal	No.
Acta Chem. Scand.	1	Talanta	86
Indian J. Chem.	2	J. Med. Chem.	87
Anal. Chem.	3	Tetrahedron Letters	88
J. Heterocyclic Chem.	4	Angew. Chem.	89
Ann. Chem. Liebigs	5	J. Inorg. Nucl. Chem.	90
Ann. chim. (Rome)	7	J. Applied Chem. U.S.S.R.	93
Appl. Spectroscopy	9	Chem. Pharm. Bull. Japan	94
Australian J. Chem.	12	J. Pharm. Soc. Japan	95
Steroids	13	Z. Chemie	97
Bull. Chem. Soc. Japan	18	J. Agr. Food Chem.	98
Bull. Acad. Polon. Sci.	19	Theor. Exptl. Chem.	99
Bull. soc. chim. Belges	20	J. Natural Products	100
Bull. soc. chim. France	22	J. Organometallic Chem.	101
Can. J. Chem.	23	Phytochemistry	102
Chem. Ber.	24	Khim. Geterosikl. Soedin.	103
Chem. and Ind. (London)	25	Zhur. Organ. Khim.	104
Chimia	27	Khim. Prirodn. Soedin.	105
Compt. rend.	28	Die Pharmazie	106
Doklady Akad. Nauk S.S.S.R.	30	Synthetic Comm.	107
Experientia	31	Israel J. Chem.	108
Gazz. chim. ital.	32	Russian J. Phys. Chem.	110
Helv. Chim. Acta	33	European J. Med. Chem.	111
J. Chem. Eng. Data	34	Spectroscopy Letters	112
J. Am. Chem. Soc.	35	Acta Chim. Acad. Sci. Hung.	114
J. Pharm. Sci.	36	Macromolecules	116
J. Chem. Soc., Perkin Trans. II	39B	Org. Preps. and Procedures	117
J. Chem. Soc., Perkin Trans. I	39C	Synthesis	118
Nippon Kagaku Kaishi	40	S. African J. Chem.	119
J. Chim. Phys.	41	Pakistan J. Sci. Ind. Research	120
J. Indian Chem. Soc.	42	J. Macromol. Sci.	121
J. Org. Chem.	44	Moscow U. Chem. Bull.	123
J. Phys. Chem.	46	Ukrain. Khim. Zhur.	124
J. Polymer Sci., Polymer Chem. Ed.	47	Inorg. Chem.	125
J. prakt. Chem.	48	Makromol. Chem.	126
Monatsh. Chem.	49	Croatica Chem. Acta	128
Naturwiss.	51	Bioorg. Chem.	130
Rec. trav. chim.	54	J. Mol. Structure	131
Polish J. Chem.	56	Pharm. Acta Helv.	133
Spectrochim. Acta	59	J. Appl. Spectroscopy S.S.S.R.	135
J. Chem. Soc., Faraday Trans. II	60	Carbohydrate Research	136
Ber. Bunsen Gesell. Phys. Chem.	61	Finnish Chem. Letters	137
Z. phys. Chem.	62	Chemistry Letters	138
Z. physiol. Chem.	63	P,S and Related Elements	139
Z. Naturforsch.	64	J. Anal. Chem. S.S.S.R.	140
Zhur. Obshchei Khim.	65	Heterocycles	142
Biochemistry	69	Mol. Photochem.	144
Izvest. Akad. Nauk S.S.S.R.	70	Arzneimittel Forsch.	145
Coll. Czech. Chem. Comm.	73	J. Chem. Tech. Biotech.	146
Mikrochim. Acta	74	Photochem. Photobiol.	149
J. Chem. Soc., Chem. Comm.	77	J. Chem. Research	150
Tetrahedron	78	J. Photochem.	151
Revue Roumaine Chim.	80	Nouveau J. Chim.	152
Arch. Pharm.	83	Bull. Univ. Osaka Prefect., Sec. A	153

Organic Electronic Spectral Data
Volume XXI 1979

Compound	Solvent	λ_{max}(log ε)	Ref.
CHN_3S_2			
1,2,3,4-Thiatriazole-5-thiol	pH 0	272(3.72),310(3.85)	86-0081-79
anion	pH >3	230s(--),313(3.87)	86-0081-79
CH_3NO_2			
Methane, nitro-	neat	271(1.18)	39-0907-79B
	isooctane	278(1.25)	39-0907-79B
	MeOH	273(1.18)	39-0907-79B
	$CF_3CHOHCF_3$	265(1.20)	39-0907-79B
$C_2Cl_3N_2S_2$			
1,2,3,5-Dithiadiazol-1-ium, 4-(trichloromethyl)-, chloride	MeCN	228(3.88),262s(3.37)	39-1192-79C
$C_2Cl_4N_3P$			
1,3,5,2-Triazaphosphorine, 2,2,4,6-tetrachloro-2,2-dihydro-	hexane	275.0(3.53)	99-0055-79
$C_2Cl_4S_2$			
Carbonothioic dichloride dimer	EtOH	207(4.10),230(3.77), 246s(3.67)	59-0509-79
$C_2H_3ClN_2O$			
3H-Diazirine, 3-chloro-3-methoxy-	gas	340-358(1.65)	39-1298-79B
	hexane	342(1.70),362(1.70)	39-1298-79B
$C_2H_3NO_4$			
Acetic acid, nitro-	4M HCl	274(1.47)	118-0666-79
	0.12M NaOH	275(4.04)	118-0666-79
$C_2H_4Cl_3Pt$			
Platinate(1-), trichloro(η^2-ethene)-	n.s.g.	235(3.5),320(2.1)	101-0223-79R
$C_2H_4Cl_6Pt$			
Platinate(2-), pentachloro-(2-chloroethyl)-	n.s.g.	470(3.3)	101-0223-79R
$C_2H_5NO_2$			
Ethane, nitro-	neat	275(1.28)	39-0907-79B
	isooctane	278(1.31)	39-0907-79B
	MeOH	274(1.26)	39-0907-79B
$C_2H_6N_2S$			
Thioacethydrazide	MeOH	266(4.18)	1-0137-79A
$C_2H_7N_3$			
Ethanimidic acid hydrazide, monohydrochloride	H_2O	209(3.51)	104-2066-79
	pH 13	223(3.51)	104-2066-79

Compound	Solvent	λ_{max}(log ε)	Ref.
$C_3Br_3N_3$			
1,2,3-Triazine, 4,5,6-tribromo-	CH_2Cl_2	226(4.28),255s(--), 291s(--)	24-1529-79
$C_3Cl_3N_3$			
1,2,3-Triazine, 4,5,6-trichloro-	CH_2Cl_2	238(3.72),285s(--), 317s(--)	24-1529-79
$C_3Cl_6N_3P$			
1,3,5,2-Triazaphosphorine, 2,2,4-trichloro-2,2-dihydro-6-(trichloromethyl)-	hexane	285.0(3.60)	99-0055-79
C_3H_2BrNS			
Thiazole, 2-bromo-	H_2O	246(3.73)	39-0163-79B
protonated	H_2O	259(3.94)	39-0163-79B
Thiazole, 5-bromo-	H_2O	244(3.69)	39-0163-79B
protonated	H_2O	257(3.70)	39-0163-79B
$C_3H_2BrN_3O_2$			
1H-Imidazole, 4-bromo-5-nitro-	pH 1	218(3.72),312(3.85)	4-0811-79
	pH 13	275(3.45),354(3.99)	4-0811-79
C_3H_2ClNS			
Isothiazole, 3-chloro-	n.s.g.	207(3.40),248(3.83)	44-1118-79
Thiazole, 2-chloro-	H_2O	243(3.70)	39-0163-79B
protonated	H_2O	253(3.84)	39-0163-79B
Thiazole, 5-chloro-	H_2O	242(3.66)	39-0163-79B
protonated	H_2O	252(3.66)	39-0163-79B
$C_3H_2N_2O_2S$			
Thiazole, 2-nitro-	H_2O	313(3.72)	39-0163-79B
protonated	H_2O	301(3.81)	39-0163-79B
Thiazole, 5-nitro-	H_2O	283(3.86)	39-0163-79B
protonated	H_2O	260(3.87)	39-0163-79B
$C_3H_2N_2S$			
2H-Imidazole-2-thione	pH 1	252(4.19)	4-1185-79
	H_2O	252(4.18)	4-1185-79
	pH 11	251(4.13)	4-1185-79
	MeOH	257.5(4.15)	4-1185-79
$C_3H_3BrN_2$			
1H-Imidazole, 4-bromo-	pH 1	215(3.70)	4-0811-79
	pH 13	213s(3.58)	4-0811-79
$C_3H_3BrN_4O$			
1,2,4-Triazin-5(2H)-one, 3-amino-6-bromo-	H_2O	205(4.08),259(3.36)	4-0555-79
$C_3H_3BrO_2$			
Propanedial, bromo-	EtOH	262(4.15)	102-0617-79
	EtOH-base	216(4.25),278(4.36)	102-0617-79
$C_3H_3N_3$			
1,3,5-Triazine	EtOH	272(2.95)	44-4243-79
$C_3H_3N_3OS$			
1,2,3-Thiadiazole-5-carboxaldehyde, oxime, sodium salt	pH 13	318(3.86)	87-1306-79

Compound	Solvent	$\lambda_{max}(\log \epsilon)$	Ref.
$C_3H_3N_3O_2$			
Propanamide, 2-diazo-3-oxo-	EtOH	240(4.05),270s(--)	5-1518-79
1,2,4-Triazine-3,5(2H,4H)-dione	H_2O	259(3.16)	4-1649-79
	base	288(3.62)	4-1649-79
1H-1,2,3-Triazole-4-carboxaldehyde, 4,5-dihydro-5-oxo-	EtOH	270(3.53),396s(--)	5-1518-79
sodium salt	H_2O	228(3.37),297(3.88)	5-1518-79
$C_3H_3N_3O_2S$			
1H-Imidazole-4-thiol, 5-nitro-, monoammonium salt	pH 1	230(4.06),265s(3.58), 410(4.01)	4-0811-79
	pH 13	237(4.08),318(3.91), 442(3.95)	4-0811-79
$C_3H_3N_3O_2S_3$			
Compd., m. 82-3°	EtOH	276(4.54),335(3.91)	4-1009-79
$C_3H_3N_7O$			
Tetrazolo[5,1-f][1,2,4]triazin-8(5H)-one, 6-amino-	3M HCl	211(4.19),246(3.64), 278s(3.45)	4-0555-79
	H_2O	206(4.34),245(3.80)	4-0555-79
$C_3H_4Cl_2O$			
Ethene, 1,1-dichloro-2-methoxy-	C_6H_{12}	208(4.01)	70-1610-79
$C_3H_4N_2$			
1H-Imidazole	EtOH	206(3.54)	44-4243-79
$C_3H_4N_4$			
1,2,4-Triazin-3-amine	H_2O	226(3.22),321(2.50)	4-0555-79
$C_3H_4N_4O$			
1,2,4-Triazin-5(2H)-one, 3-amino-	H_2O	204(3.82),252(3.15)	4-0555-79
$C_3H_4N_4O_2$			
1,2,4-Triazine-3,5(2H,4H)-dione, 6-amino-	pH 1-7	298(3.69)	124-0048-79
	pH 13	290(3.63)	124-0048-79
$C_3H_4N_4O_4S$			
1H-Imidazole-4-sulfonamide, 5-nitro-	pH 1	225(3.65),297(3.73)	4-0811-79
	pH 13	227(3.49),283(3.46), 357(3.89)	4-0811-79
$C_3H_4O_2$			
1,3-Dioxole	MeCN	219(3.61)	24-0577-79
$C_3H_4O_2S$			
Thiiranecarboxylic acid, (R)-	EtOH	212(2.66),281(1.90)	39-1852-79C
C_3H_5NOS			
2-Oxazolidinethione	MeOH	243(4.28),277s(2.40)	4-0945-79
	CH_2Cl_2	247(4.32),283s(2.30)	4-0945-79
$C_3H_5NO_3$			
2-Propanone, 1-nitro-, dicyclohexylamine salt of enol	isoPrOH	331(4.02)	118-0295-79
$C_3H_5NS_2$			
2-Thiazolidinethione	MeOH	274(4.19),323(2.09)	4-0945-79
	CH_2Cl_2	279(4.18),339(2.05)	4-0945-79

Compound	Solvent	λ_{max}(log ε)	Ref.
2-Thiazolidinethione (cont.)	CCl_4	283(4.14),347(2.18)	4-0945-79
lithium salt	EtOH	273(4.18)	104-1166-79
potassium salt	EtOH	275(4.38)	104-1166-79
sodium salt	EtOH	273(4.17)	104-1166-79
$C_3H_5N_3O_2S$			
2H-1,2,6-Thiadiazin-5-amine, 1,1-dioxide	pH 7	224(3.68),300(3.96)	44-4191-79
$C_3H_5N_3O_3S$			
Sulfamide, 3-isoxazolyl-	isoPrOH	207(3.69)	44-4191-79
$C_3H_6N_2S$			
2-Imidazolidinethione	MeOH	239(4.23)	78-0511-79
	CH_2Cl_2	248(4.29)	78-0511-79
$C_3H_6N_6O$			
1,2,4-Triazine-5,6-dione, 3-amino-1,2-dihydro-, 6-hydrazone	H_2O	204(3.81),231(3.63), 302(3.29)	4-0555-79
$C_3H_7MoNO_6$			
Molybdenum, (N,N-dimethylformamido-O)-oxodiperoxy-	EtOH	335(3.9)	39-2481-79C
$C_3H_7NO_2$			
Propane, 1-nitro-	neat	277(1.36)	39-0907-79B
	isooctane	279(1.37)	39-0907-79B
	MeOH	275(1.35)	39-0907-79B
	$CF_3CHOHCF_3$	269(1.48)	39-0907-79B
Propane, 2-nitro-	isooctane	279(4.34)	39-0907-79B
	MeOH	278(4.32)	39-0907-79B
	$CF_3CHOHCF_3$	270(4.45)	39-0907-79B
$C_3H_9N_3$			
Ethanimidic acid, 2-methylhydrazide, monohydrochloride	H_2O	209(3.51)	104-2066-79
	pH 13	225(3.69)	104-2066-79

Compound	Solvent	$\lambda_{max}(\log \epsilon)$	Ref.
$C_4Cl_2F_6N_3P$			
1,3,5,2-Triazaphosphorine, 2,2-dichloro-2,2-dihydro-4,6-bis(trifluoromethyl)-	hexane	293.4(3.48)	99-0055-79
$C_4Cl_8N_3P$			
1,3,5,2-Triazaphosphorine, 2,2-dichloro-2,2-dihydro-4,6-bis(trichloromethyl)-	hexane	293.5(3.67)	99-0055-79
C_4HBrCl_4			
1,3-Butadiene, 1-bromo-1,2,4,4-tetrachloro-	EtOH	217(4.05),230(3.96), 263(3.79)	104-0615-79
$C_4H_2Cl_4$			
1,3-Butadiene, 1,1,3,4-tetrachloro-, (E)-	EtOH	212(3.81),260(3.76)	104-0615-79
(Z)-	EtOH	256(4.1),250(4.04)[sic], 264(4.03)	104-0615-79
$C_4H_2FNO_3$			
2H-1,3-Oxazine-2,6(3H)-dione, 5-fluoro-	pH 5.0	270(3.89)	87-0592-79
	pH 6.0	272(3.77),308s(3.50)	87-0592-79
	pH 7.0	307(3.89)	87-0592-79
$C_4H_2F_3N_3OS$			
Formamide, N-[5-(trifluoromethyl)-1,3,4-thiadiazol-2-yl]-	n.s.g.	282(3.97)	87-0028-79
$C_4H_2N_4O_2$			
1H-Pyrazole-3-carbonitrile, 4-nitro-	EtOH	209(3.93),263(3.79)	4-1113-79
$C_4H_2OS_3$			
2-Cyclobuten-1-one, 2,3-dimercapto-4-thioxo-, dipotassium salt	H_2O	234(4.11),254s(3.85), 290(4.01),338(4.14), 406(4.53)	24-0990-79
$C_4H_2O_2S_2$			
3-Cyclobutene-1,2-dione, 3,4-dimercapto-, dipotassium salt	H_2O	248(4.12),320s(4.27), 346(4.38)	24-0990-79
2-Cyclobuten-1-one, 3-hydroxy-2-mercapto-4-thioxo-, dipotassium salt	H_2O	230(3.93),276(3.84), 394(4.79)	24-0990-79
$(C_4H_2S)_n$			
Thiophene polymer	EtOH	213s(--),238(3.53), 267s(--),269s(--), 278s(--),300s(--)	47-1963-79
$C_4H_3BrN_4O_4$			
1H-Pyrazole, 4-bromo-1-methyl-3,5-dinitro-	$CHCl_3$	280(5.62)	12-1727-79
$C_4H_3FN_2O_2$			
2,4(1H,3H)-Pyrimidinedione, 5-fluoro-	H_2O	265.6(3.86)	47-0351-79
	H_2O	265.6(3.86)	121-0351-79
$C_4H_3F_3N_2$			
1H-Imidazole, 2-(trifluoromethyl)-	H_2O	217(3.85)	44-2902-79
cation	H_2O	219(3.87)	44-2902-79
anion	H_2O	220(--)(unstable)	44-2902-79

Compound	Solvent	$\lambda_{max}(\log \epsilon)$	Ref.
$C_4H_3NO_3$			
Furan, 2-nitro-	EtOH	226(3.56),302(3.95)	70-1282-79
$C_4H_3N_3$			
1H-Imidazole-2-carbonitrile	H_2O	247(4.03)	44-2902-79
anion	H_2O	256(4.07)	44-2902-79
Propanedinitrile, (aminomethylene)-	hexane	263(--)	131-0077-79D
	EtOH	268(4.24)	131-0077-79D
$C_4H_4BrN_3O$			
2(1H)-Pyrimidinone, 4-amino-5-bromo-	H_2O	282(3.67)	44-4385-79
$C_4H_4BrN_3O_2$			
1H-Imidazole, 4-bromo-1-methyl-5-nitro-	MeOH	240(3.58),307(3.86)	4-0811-79
1H-Imidazole, 5-bromo-1-methyl-4-nitro-	MeOH	223(3.76),299(3.85)	4-0811-79
C_4H_4ClN			
1H-Pyrrole, 3-chloro-	H_2O	246(3.18)	152-0115-79
$C_4H_4ClN_3OS$			
Acetamide, 2-chloro-N-1,3,4-thiadiazol-2-yl-	n.s.g.	251(3.95)	87-0028-79
$C_4H_4F_2N_6O_9$			
Ethanamine, 2-fluoro-N-(2-fluoro-2,2-dinitroethyl)-2,2-dinitro-N-nitroso-	$C_2H_4Cl_2$	242(3.48),376(1.93)	70-0944-79
$C_4H_4N_2OS$			
4(1H)-Pyrimidinone, 2,3-dihydro-2-thioxo-	pH 8.0	264(4.02)	12-0545-79
bisulfite addition compd.	pH 8.0	274(4.14)	12-0545-79
$C_4H_4N_2OS_2$			
4H,6H-Thieno[3,4-c][1,2,5]thiadiazole, 5-oxide	MeOH	264(3.89),320s(2.37)	88-4493-79
$C_4H_4N_2O_2$			
1H-Imidazole-2-carboxylic acid	H_2O	236(4.06)	44-2902-79
cation	H_2O	238(4.06)	44-2902-79
anion	H_2O	248(4.08)	44-2902-79
Uracil	pH 8.0	258(3.89)	12-0545-79
$C_4H_4N_2O_2S$			
3-Isothiazolecarboxylic acid, 4-amino-, hydrochloride	MeCN	240(3.73),339(3.60)	5-1534-79
$C_4H_4N_2O_2S_2$			
1-Imidazolidinecarbodithioic acid, 2,4-dioxo-	EtOH	254(4.21),298(4.07), 331s(3.34)	39-0692-79C
$C_4H_4N_2S_2$			
4H,6H-Thieno[3,4-c][1,2,5]thiadiazole	MeOH	258(4.05),318(2.26)	88-4493-79
$C_4H_4N_2S_3$			
3H-Imidazo[2,1-c]-1,2,4-dithiazole-3-thione, 5,6-dihydro-	EtOH	225(3.95),280(4.26)	39-2909-79C
$C_4H_4N_4$			
1H-Pyrazole-3-carbonitrile, 4-amino-	MeOH	205(3.84),276(3.53)	4-1113-79

Compound	Solvent	λmax(log ε)	Ref.
$C_4H_4N_4O_2S$			
Imidazo[4,5-e]-1,2,4-thiadiazine, 2,5-dihydro-, 1,1-dioxide	pH 1	225(3.48),262(3.43)	44-4046-79
	pH 8	228(3.43),271(3.65)	44-4046-79
	pH 13	230s(3.45),272(3.58)	44-4046-79
$C_4H_4N_4O_3$			
Cytosine, 5-nitro-	pH 2	254(3.88),312(3.93)	73-2846-79
Propanamide, N-(aminocarbonyl)-2-diazo-3-oxo-	EtOH	234(4.02)	5-1518-79
1H-1,2,3-Triazole-1-carboxamide, 4-formyl-4,5-dihydro-5-oxo-, Na salt	H_2O	231(3.22),298(3.65)	5-1518-79
potassium salt	H_2O	237(3.77),292(3.88)	5-1518-79
$C_4H_4N_6O$			
4H-Imidazo[4,5-d]-1,2,3-triazin-4-one, 3-amino-3,5-dihydro-	H_2O	233(3.93),297(3.63)	103-0805-79
1,2,4-Triazolo[3,4-f][1,2,4]triazin-8(5H)-one, 6-amino-	H_2O	213(4.17),274(3.07)	4-0555-79
$C_4H_4N_8O_{13}$			
Ethanamine, 2,2,2-trinitro-N-nitroso-N-(2,2,2-trinitroethyl)-	$C_2H_4Cl_2$	241(3.90),380(1.96)	70-0944-79
$C_4H_4O_2$			
1,2-Cyclobutanedione	MeCN	475(1.53)	88-2347-79
C_4H_5NO			
2H-Pyrrol-2-one, 1,3-dihydro-	H_2O	198(4.02)	104-0535-79
	EtOH	225(3.49)	104-0535-79
C_4H_5NOS			
Thiazole, 2-methoxy-	H_2O	234(3.64)	39-0163-79B
protonated	H_2O	239(3.67)	39-0163-79B
Thiazole, 5-methoxy-	H_2O	250(3.53)	39-0163-79B
protonated	H_2O	267(3.58)	39-0163-79B
$C_4H_5NOS_2$			
4H-1,3-Thiazin-4-one, tetrahydro-2-thioxo-	EtOH	258(4.16),309(4.17)	150-0212-79S
$C_4H_5NO_2$			
2,4-Pyrrolidinedione	aq NaOH	259(4.05)	142-0477-79B
$C_4H_5NO_2S_2$			
Thiazole, 2-(methylsulfonyl)-	H_2O	256(3.83)	39-0163-79B
protonated	H_2O	260(3.91)	39-0163-79B
Thiazole, 5-(methylsulfonyl)-	H_2O	230(3.84)	39-0163-79B
protonated	H_2O	235(3.79)	39-0163-79B
$C_4H_5N_3OS$			
1H-Imidazole-4-carbothioamide, 5-hydroxy-	pH 1	209(3.78),256(3.65), 273(3.70),331(4.32)	103-0807-79
1,2,4-Thiadiazole-5-carboxaldehyde, 3-methyl-, sodium salt of oxime	pH 13	305(3.93)	87-1306-79
1,3,4-Thiadiazole-2-carboxaldehyde, 5-methyl-, sodium salt of oxime	pH 13	298(3.98)	87-1306-79
$C_4H_5N_3O_2$			
1H-Pyrazole, 1-methyl-3-nitro-	EtOH	218(4.28),264(4.01)	12-2203-79
1H-Pyrazole, 1-methyl-4-nitro-	$CHCl_3$	274(3.72)	12-1727-79

Compound	Solvent	$\lambda_{max}(\log \epsilon)$	Ref.
$C_4H_5N_3O_2S$			
1H-Imidazole-4-thiol, 1-methyl-5-nitro-	pH 1	224s(4.00),234s(4.00), 407(3.88)	4-0811-79
	pH 13	227(4.00),293(3.73), 434(3.87)	4-0811-79
1H-Imidazole-5-thiol, 1-methyl-4-nitro-	pH 1	221s(3.76),238(3.86), 267s(3.32)	4-0811-79
	pH 13	237(4.01),285(3.42), 420(3.82)	4-0811-79
$C_4H_5N_5$			
1,2,4-Triazolo[4,3-b][1,2,4]triazine, 1,7-dihydro-	EtOH	269(3.92)	4-0427-79
$C_4H_5N_5O_2$			
4H-Imidazo[1,2-c][1,2,3]triazole, 5,6-dihydro-3-nitro-	EtOH	225(4.10),332(3.88)	39-2361-79C
$C_4H_6BrN_3O_2$			
Sydnone, 4-bromo-3-(dimethylamino)-	benzene	314(3.90)	5-0063-79
	MeOH	307(3.92)	5-0063-79
	CH_2Cl_2	312(3.93)	5-0063-79
	MeCN	309(3.92)	5-0063-79
$C_4H_6Cl_2O_2S$			
Ethene, 1,1-dichloro-2-(ethylsulfonyl)-	C_6H_{12}	217(4.05)	70-1610-79
$C_4H_6Cl_2S$			
Ethene, 1,1-dichloro-2-(ethylthio)-	C_6H_{12}	230(3.88),257s(3.85)	70-1610-79
$C_4H_6N_2O_2$			
5-Isoxazolol, 3-(aminomethyl)-, hydrate	MeOH	251(3.89)	1-0294-79
1H-Pyrazole-3-methanol, 5-hydroxy-	EtOH	223(3.53)	4-0505-79
$C_4H_6N_2O_3S$			
2H-1,2,6-Thiadiazin-3(6H)-one, 4-methyl-, 1,1-dioxide	isoPrOH	210(3.72),280(3.61)	44-4191-79
$C_4H_6N_2O_4$			
2-Butene, 1,4-di-aci-nitro- sodium salt	acetone	328(3.51),343(3.51)	104-0784-79
	H_2O	361(3.51)	104-0784-79
$C_4H_6N_2S$			
1H-Imidazole, 2-(methylthio)-	pH 1	250(3.82)	4-1185-79
	H_2O	245.5(3.70)	4-1185-79
	pH 11	245(3.70)	4-1185-79
	MeOH	248.5(3.65)	4-1185-79
2H-Imidazole-2-thione, 1,3-dihydro-1-methyl-	pH 1	251(4.21)	4-1185-79
	H_2O	251(4.18)	4-1185-79
	pH 11	250.5(4.18)	4-1185-79
	MeOH	257.5(4.20)	4-1185-79
	EtOH	260(4.13)	4-1185-79
	$CHCl_3$	260(4.23)	4-1185-79
2H-Imidazole-2-thione, 1,3-dihydro-4-methyl-	H_2O	257(4.18)	4-1185-79
	EtOH	263(4.17)	4-1185-79
	$CHCl_3$	271(4.14)	4-1185-79
$C_4H_6N_4O_2$			
4,5-Pyrimidinediol, 2,6-diamino- (plus dithiothreitol)	pH 8.1	281(4.1)	35-6144-79

Compound	Solvent	λ_{max}(log ε)	Ref.
1,2,4-Triazine-3,5(2H,4H)-dione,	pH 1-7	307(3.72)	124-0048-79
6-amino-2-methyl-	pH 13	296(3.72)	124-0048-79
1,2,4-Triazine-3,5(2H,4H)-dione,	pH 1-7	298(3.68)	124-0048-79
6-amino-4-methyl-	pH 13	321(3.82)	124-0048-79
1,2,4-Triazine-3,5(2H,4H)-dione,	pH 1-7	308(3.61)	124-0048-79
6-(methylamino)-	pH 13	298(3.57)	124-0048-79
$C_4H_6N_4O_4S$			
1H-Imidazole-4-sulfonamide, 1-methyl-	pH 1	235(3.59),303(3.80)	4-0811-79
5-nitro-	pH 13	235(3.53),317(3.72)	4-0811-79
1H-Imidazole-5-sulfonamide, 1-methyl-	pH 1	230s(3.67),300(3.74)	4-0811-79
4-nitro-	pH 13	317(3.66)	4-0811-79
$C_4H_6O_2$			
1,3-Dioxole, 2-methyl-	MeCN	218(3.62)	24-0577-79
$C_4H_6O_2S$			
1,3-Butadiene-1-sulfinic acid, lithium salt, (Z)-	H_2O	232(4.15)	70-0594-79
Thiiranecarboxylic acid, methyl ester, (S)-	EtOH	211(2.85),279(2.08)	39-1852-79C
$C_4H_6O_6$			
Tartaric acid	pH 6.5	207(2.7)	140-1489-79
$C_4H_7ClN_2S$			
Isothiazolium, 3-amino-2-methyl-, chloride	n.s.g.	207(3.43),283(3.97)	44-1118-79
C_4H_7NO			
3-Buten-2-one, 4-amino-	hexane	282(4.08)	131-0077-79D
	EtOH	291(4.27)	131-0077-79D
$C_4H_7NO_2$			
2,3-Butanedione, monooxime, (E)-	C_6H_{12}	219(4.00),323(1.30)	39-0156-79B
	EtOH	229(4.01)	39-0156-79B
	EtOH-NaOH	280(4.16),370s(1.78)	39-0156-79B
C_4H_7NS			
2-Pyrrolidinethione	MeOH	266(4.15),316(1.85)	4-0945-79
	CH_2Cl_2	270(4.18),338(1.68)	4-0945-79
	CCl_4	273(4.19),334(1.96)	4-0945-79
$C_4H_7NS_2$			
Thiazole, 4,5-dihydro-2-(methylthio)-	EtOH	230(3.80)	4-0945-79
2-Thiazolidinethione, 3-methyl-	MeOH	271(4.17),323(2.07)	4-0945-79
	EtOH	267(4.22)	104-1166-79
	CH_2Cl_2	273(4.19),334(2.08)	4-0945-79
	CCl_4	281(4.16),345(2.14)	4-0945-79
$C_4H_7N_2O_3P$			
1,3,2-Diazaphosphorin-4(1H)-one, 2,3-dihydro-2-hydroxy-6-methyl-, 2-oxide	M HCl	274(4.00)	103-1142-79
	EtOH	272(4.00)	103-1142-79
anion	pH 5-12	274(4.00)	103-1142-79
dianion	2M KOH	279(3.81)	103-1142-79
$C_4H_7N_3O_3S$			
Sulfamide, (4-methyl-5-isoxazolyl)-	isoPrOH	234(3.77)	44-4191-79

Compound	Solvent	λ$_{max}$(log ε)	Ref.
$C_4H_7N_5O$			
1H-Imidazole-4-carboximidic acid, 5-hydroxy-, hydrazide	H_2O	285(4.2)	103-0807-79
4(1H)-Pyrimidinone, 2,5,6-triamino-	pH 1	264(--)	35-6144-79
	pH 8.10	288(4.00)	35-6144-79
$C_4H_8N_2O$			
Ethanedial, mono(dimethylhydrazone)	$CHCl_3$	295(4.40)	150-1451-79
$C_4H_8N_2S$			
2-Imidazolidinethione, 1-methyl-	MeOH	240(4.20)	78-0511-79
	CH_2Cl_2	247(4.27)	78-0511-79
1H-1,2,4-Triazolium, 4-amino-4,5-dihydro-2,3-dimethyl-5-thioxo-, hydroxide, inner salt	n.s.g.	241(4.12)	39-0724-79C
$C_4H_8O_2S$			
Sulfoxonium, dimethyl-, 2-oxoethylide	hexane	248(--)	99-0573-79
	MeOH	250(3.5)	99-0573-79
$C_4H_9NO_2$			
Butane, 1-nitro-	neat	277(1.39)	39-0907-79B
	isooctane	278(1.38)	39-0907-79B
	MeOH	273(1.40)	39-0907-79B
	$CF_3CHOHCF_3$	267(1.58)	39-0907-79B
Propane, 2-methyl-2-nitro-	isooctane	280(1.38)	39-0907-79B
	MeOH	279(1.35)	39-0907-79B
	$CF_3CHOHCF_3$	271(1.50)	39-0907-79B
$C_4H_9NO_3$			
Nitric acid, 1,1-dimethylethyl ester	n.s.g.	272s(1.32)	39-1159-79C
$C_4H_9N_3O_3$			
Carbamic acid, [(methylnitrosoamino)-methyl]-, methyl ester	EtOH	230(3.89),354(1.93)	94-0682-79
$C_4H_{10}S_2Si$			
1,3-Dithia-2-silacyclopentane, 2,2-dimethyl-	hexane	198(3.58),233(2.38)	114-0407-79A
$C_4H_{11}N_3$			
Ethanimidic acid, 2,2-dimethylhydrazide,	H_2O	207(3.47)	104-2066-79
hydrochloride	pH 13	225(3.49)	104-2066-79
hydriodide	H_2O	227(4.09)	104-2073-79
Ethanimidic acid, 2-ethylhydrazide,	H_2O	208(3.42)	104-2066-79
hydrochloride	pH 13	226(3.58)	104-2066-79
$C_4H_{12}Cl_2OSi_2$			
Disiloxane, 1,3-dichloro-1,1,3,3-tetramethyl-	heptane	185.8(1.90)	65-1333-79
	MeCN	186.0(2.40)	65-1333-79

Compound	Solvent	λ max(log ε)	Ref.
C_5HO_5Re			
Rhenium, pentacarbonylhydro-, (OC-6-21)-	isooctane	272(3.42),300s(--)	35-3847-79
$C_5H_3ClN_4$			
1,2,4-Triazolo[4,3-a]pyrazine, 8-chloro-	EtOH	296(3.61)	44-1028-79
$C_5H_3F_3N_2OS$			
Acetamide, 2,2,2-trifluoro-N-2-thiazolyl-	n.s.g.	298(3.98)	87-0028-79
$C_5H_3N_3O_2$			
2-Furancarboxaldehyde, 5-azido-	MeOH	216(4.12),313(4.91)	73-3301-79
$C_5H_4Br_2O_2$			
2,4-Pentadienal, 2,4-dibromo-5-hydroxy-, sodium salt	EtOH	221s(--),237(3.38), 379(4.55)	78-1523-79
C_5H_4ClNO			
1H-Pyrrole-2-carboxaldehyde, 3-chloro-	H_2O	291(4.27)	152-0115-79
1H-Pyrrole-2-carboxaldehyde, 4-chloro-	H_2O	253(3.88),300(4.12)	152-0115-79
$C_5H_4Cl_2N_2O$			
Pyridazinium, 3,4-dichloro-5-hydroxy-1-methyl-, hydroxide, inner salt	EtOH	273(3.72),324(3.79)	39-1199-79C
$C_5H_4Cl_2O_2$			
2,4-Pentadienal, 2,4-dichloro-5-hydroxy-, sodium salt	EtOH	215s(--),238(3.57), 379(4.62)	78-1523-79
$C_5H_4F_4O_2$			
2,4-Pentanedione, 1,1,5,5-tetrafluoro-	hexane	277(2.48)	65-0188-79
$C_5H_4N_2$			
1H-Pyrrole-2-carbonitrile	H_2O	225(3.88),249(4.23)	152-0115-79
$C_5H_4N_2O$			
Propanedinitrile, (methoxymethylene)-	EtOH	250.5(4.08)	65-0188-79
$C_5H_4N_2O_3$			
4-Pyrimidinecarboxaldehyde, 1,2,3,6-tetrahydro-2,6-dioxo-	pH 1.0	261(3.97)	136-0235-79B
	pH 7.0	259(3.97)	136-0235-79B
	pH 11.0	267(3.76),285(3.72)	136-0235-79B
$C_5H_4N_2O_4$			
Acetic acid, (2-amino-4-oxo-5(4H)-oxazolylidene)-	H_2SO_4	250(4.36)	103-0794-79
5-Pyrimidinecarboxylic acid, 1,2,3,4-tetrahydro-2,4-dioxo-	pH 5-6	278(3.81)	90-0549-79
$C_5H_4N_4O$			
2-Purinol	pH 2	308(3.78),314(3.70)	73-2846-79
$C_5H_4N_4O_2$			
1H-Pyrazolo[4,3-d]pyrimidine-3,7(2H,4H)-dione	pH 1	230(4.04),271(3.59), 288(3.66),332(3.61)	18-0208-79
	H_2O	231(4.02),288(3.67), 332(3.79)	18-0208-79
	pH 11	238(4.02),285s(3.58), 315(3.71),332(3.85)	18-0208-79

Compound	Solvent	$\lambda_{max}(\log \epsilon)$	Ref.
$C_5H_4N_4O_3S$			
Pyrazino[1,2-b][1,2,4,6]thiatriazin-3(2H)-one, 1,1-dioxide	MeOH	231(3.60),323(3.40)	142-0815-79
$C_5H_4N_6O_2$			
Pyrimido[5,4-e]-1,2,4-triazine-3,5-dione, 7-amino-1,2-dihydro-	pH 13	257(4.38),429(3.70)	44-1125-79
$C_5H_4O_3$			
1,3-Dioxolan-2-one, 4,5-bis(methylene)-	dioxan	244(4.03)	24-0862-79
4H-Pyran-4-one, 3-hydroxy-	EtOH	214(3.96),272(3.86)	2-0298-79
	EtOH-NaOH	262(3.28),317(3.78)	2-0298-79
$C_5H_5BrN_2O$			
4(1H)-Pyridinone, 3-amino-5-bromo- (protonated)	pH 0.29	246(3.91),269(3.78)	44-3256-79
$C_5H_5BrN_2O_4$			
2-Butenoic acid, 4-[(aminocarbonyl)amino]-2-bromo-4-oxo-	H_2SO_4	220(3.88)	103-0794-79
2-Butenoic acid, 4-[(aminocarbonyl)amino]-3-bromo-4-oxo-	H_2SO_4	216(3.90),250(3.79)	103-0794-79
5-Oxazoleacetic acid, 2-amino-α-bromo-4,5-dihydro-4-oxo-	H_2SO_4	217(4.33)	103-0794-79
$C_5H_5BrO_2$			
2,4-Pentadienal, 2-bromo-5-hydroxy-, sodium salt	EtOH	218(--),235(2.46), 369(4.64)	78-1523-79
$C_5H_5ClN_2OS$			
Acetamide, 2-chloro-N-2-thiazolyl-	n.s.g.	276(4.00)	87-0028-79
$C_5H_5ClO_2$			
2,4-Pentadienal, 2-chloro-5-hydroxy-, sodium salt	EtOH	222s(--),238(3.43), 372(4.68)	78-1523-79
$C_5H_5FN_2O_2$			
2,4(1H,3H)-Pyrimidinedione, 5-fluoro-1-methyl-	pH 1	274(3.92)	1-0515-79
	pH 13	271(3.80)	1-0515-79
2,4(1H,3H)-Pyrimidinedione, 5-fluoro-3-methyl-	pH 1	266(3.82)	1-0515-79
	pH 13	292(3.99)	1-0515-79
$C_5H_5F_3N_2$			
1H-Imidazole, 4-methyl-2-(trifluoromethyl)-	H_2O	225(3.74)	44-2902-79
cation	H_2O	228(3.78)	44-2902-79
anion	H_2O	228(--)(unstable)	44-2902-79
$C_5H_5IO_2$			
2,4-Pentadienal, 5-hydroxy-2-iodo-	EtOH	225(3.79),370(4.77)	78-1523-79
sodium salt	EtOH	231(3.70),368(4.69)	78-1523-79
C_5H_5NO			
1H-Pyrrole-2-carboxaldehyde	H_2O	287(4.16)	152-0115-79
$C_5H_5NO_2$			
2,3-Pyridinediol	EtOH	241(3.6),296(3.9)	77-0285-79
$C_5H_5NO_3$			
2H-1,3-Oxazine-2,4(3H)-dione, 5-methyl-	0.05M HCl	209(3.761),233(3.731)	73-0269-79
	0.05M borax	233(3.924)	73-0269-79

Compound	Solvent	λ max (log ε)	Ref.
2H-1,3-Oxazine-2,6(3H)-dione, 5-methyl-	EtOH	271(3.81)	87-0592-79
$C_5H_5NS_2$			
3,5-Pyridinedithiol	hexane	226(4.18),243s(3.96), 300(3.51)	56-0503-79
	EtOH	223(4.08),288(4.11)	56-0503-79
	EtOH-acid	248(4.36),327(3.64)	56-0503-79
	EtOH-base	264(4.40),336(3.67)	56-0503-79
2(1H)-Pyridinethione, 4-mercapto-	EtOH	264(4.28),284(4.08), 349(4.15)	56-0701-79
	EtOH-HCl	264(4.34),289(4.08), 358(3.85)	56-0701-79
$C_5H_5N_3$			
1H-Imidazole-2-carbonitrile, 4-methyl-	H_2O	258(4.19)	44-2902-79
anion	H_2O	265(4.19)	44-2902-79
Propanedinitrile, (1-aminoethylidene)-	hexane	269(--)	131-0077-79D
	EtOH	271(4.21)	131-0077-79D
$C_5H_5N_3O_2S$			
3-Isothiazolecarboxamide, 4-amino-5-formyl-	MeCN	246(3.85),379(3.94)	5-1534-79
$C_5H_5N_5$			
Adenine	EtOH	260(4.16)	151-0313-79B
$C_5H_5N_5O$			
Adenine 1-oxide	EtOH	235(4.15)	39-2481-79C
4H-Imidazo[4,5-d]-1,2,3-triazin-4-one, 3,5-dihydro-5-methyl-	pH 1	252(3.46),277(4.56)	103-0685-79
$C_5H_6BrN_3O$			
1H-Pyrazole-3-carboxamide, 5-(bromomethyl)-	EtOH	218(4.13)	87-0807-79
$C_5H_6Br_2N_2O_4$			
Butanoic acid, 4-[(aminocarbonyl)amino]-2,3-dibromo-4-oxo-	H_2SO_4	214(3.84)	103-0794-79
$C_5H_6Cl_5N_4P$			
1,3,5,2-Triazaphosphorine, 2,2-dichloro-4-(dimethylamino)-2,2-dihydro-6-(trichloromethyl)-	hexane	283.1(3.89)	99-0055-79
$C_5H_6N_2$			
1H-Imidazole, 1-ethenyl-	isooctane	231.5(4.06)	65-1225-79
	pH 1	220(3.93)	65-1225-79
	H_2O	228.5(3.98)	65-1225-79
	EtOH	229.5(4.00)	65-1225-79
	EtOH	230(4.04)	70-1931-79
$C_5H_6N_2OS$			
Acetamide, N-4-isothiazolyl-	MeCN	273(3.63)	5-1534-79
Acetamide, N-2-thiazolyl-	H_2O	264(3.95)	39-0163-79B
protonated	H_2O	269(4.01)	39-0163-79B
6H-Isothiazolo[1,5-b][1,2,5]oxathiazole-7-S^{IV}, 6-methyl-	MeOH	216(4.03),243(3.10), 335(4.00)	39-2340-79C
Methanamine, N-(5-isothiazolylmethylene)-, N-oxide	MeOH	212(3.80),247(3.35), 300(4.10),312s(4.05)	39-2340-79C
4(1H)-Pyrimidinone, 2,3-dihydro-5-methyl-2-thioxo-	MeOH	216(4.19),276(4.25)	73-2426-79

Compound	Solvent	$\lambda_{max}(\log \epsilon)$	Ref.
4(1H)-Pyrimidinone, 2,3-dihydro-6-methyl-2-thioxo-	MeOH	214(4.19),277(4.18)	73-2426-79
$C_5H_6N_2O_2$			
1H-Imidazole-2-carboxylic acid, methyl ester	H_2O	260(4.08)	44-2902-79
cation	H_2O	249(4.04)	44-2902-79
anion	H_2O	276(4.12)	44-2902-79
1H-Imidazole-2-carboxylic acid, 4-methyl-	H_2O	248(3.90)	44-2902-79
cation	H_2O	251(3.90)	44-2902-79
anion	H_2O	258(3.93)	44-2902-79
1H-Pyrazole-4-carboxylic acid, 1-methyl-	EtOH	223(3.99)	73-0781-79
	ether	222(4.02)	73-0781-79
2,4(1H,3H)-Pyrimidinedione, 5-methyl-	MeOH	264.5(3.97)	73-2426-79
2,4(1H,3H)-Pyrimidinedione, 6-methyl-	MeOH	260.0(3.92)	73-2426-79
$C_5H_6N_2O_2S_2$			
1-Imidazolidinecarbodithioic acid, 2,4-dioxo-, methyl ester	dioxan	265(4.20),298(3.99)	39-0692-79C
$C_5H_6N_2O_3S$			
2,4(1H,3H)-Pyrimidinedione, 5-(methylsulfinyl)-	MeOH	270(3.89)	44-1737-79
$C_5H_6N_2O_4S$			
2,4(1H,3H)-Pyrimidinedione, 5-(methylsulfonyl)-	MeOH	262(3.93)	44-1737-79
$C_5H_6N_2O_5S$			
5-Pyrimidinemethanesulfonic acid, 1,2,3,4-tetrahydro-2,4-dioxo-, sodium salt	pH 7	266(3.91)	69-0632-79
	pH 13	290.5(3.94)	69-0632-79
$C_5H_6N_2S$			
Imidazo[1,2-b]isothiazole, 2,3-dihydro-, monohydrochloride	n.s.g.	205(3.69),222(3.42), 302(3.85)	44-1118-79
Isothiazole, 3-(1-aziridinyl)-	n.s.g.	208(3.19),261(3.44)	44-1118-79
$C_5H_6N_2S_3$			
3H,5H-1,2,4-Dithiazolo[4,3-a]pyrimidine-3-thione, 6,7-dihydro-	CH_2Cl_2	274(4.33)	39-2909-79C
$C_5H_6N_2Se$			
Selenonium, dimethyl-, dicyanomethylide	$CHCl_3$	226(3.77)	104-0541-79
$C_5H_6N_4O$			
Cyanamide, (1,4,5,6-tetrahydro-4-oxo-2-pyrimidinyl)-	H_2O	216(4.22),239(4.17)	23-2593-79
Ethanone, 1-(3-amino-1,2,4-triazin-6-yl)-	EtOH	274(4.24),319(3.62), 380s(2.78)	39-1120-79C
$C_5H_6N_4O_2$			
Sydnone, 4-cyano-3-(dimethylamino)-	CH_2Cl_2	307(3.94)	5-0063-79
$C_5H_6N_4O_2S$			
Imidazo[4,5-e]-1,2,4-thiadiazine, 2,5-dihydro-3-methyl-, 1,1-dioxide	pH 1	225(3.54),257(3.49)	44-4046-79
	pH 8	225(3.52),267(3.72)	44-4046-79
	pH 13	230s(3.51),269(3.66)	44-4046-79
Imidazo[4,5-e]-1,2,4-thiadiazine, 2,5-dihydro-5-methyl-, 1,1-dioxide	pH 1	218s(3.40),266(3.53)	44-4046-79
	pH 8	225s(3.46),273(3.66)	44-4046-79

Compound	Solvent	$\lambda_{max}(\log \epsilon)$	Ref.
Imidazo[4,5-e]-1,2,4-thiadiazine, 2,7-dihydro-7-methyl-, 1,1-dioxide	pH 1	232(3.56),263(3.40)	44-4046-79
	pH 8	244(3.56),265(3.49)	44-4046-79
$C_5H_6N_4O_3$			
1H-Imidazole-1-carboxaldehyde, 4-nitro-, O-methyloxime, (Z)-	EtOH	282(4.03)	4-1545-79
$C_5H_6N_4O_5$			
1H-Purine-2,6,8(3H)-trione, tetrahydro-4,5-dihydroxy-	H_2O	199(4.19),220(3.84), 250(3.41)	88-4781-79
Urea, (hexahydro-5-hydroxy-2,4,6-tri-oxo-5-pyrimidinyl)-	H_2O	199(4.23),220s(3.91)	88-4781-79
$C_5H_6N_6O$			
1,2,4-Triazolo[3,4-f][1,2,4]triazin-8(5H)-one, 6-amino-3-methyl-	H_2O	217(4.02),276(2.99)	4-0555-79
$C_5H_6N_6OS$			
1,2,4-Triazolo[3,4-f][1,2,4]triazin-8(5H)-one, 6-amino-3-(methylthio)-	H_2O	207(4.14),226(4.10), 238s(4.04),275s(3.38)	4-0555-79
$C_5H_6O_2$			
2-Cyclopenten-1-one, 5-hydroxy-	n.s.g.	220(3.53)	39-0274-79C
1,3-Dioxolane, 4,5-bis(methylene)-	dioxan	245(4.06)	24-0862-79
2(5H)-Furanone, 5-methyl-	MeOH	214(3.99)	35-1544-79
$C_5H_6O_3$			
2-Pentenoic acid, 4-oxo-	H_2O	220(4.7)	104-0043-79
$C_5H_7ClN_4$			
2,4-Pyrimidinediamine, 5-chloro-6-methyl-	pH 1.99	207(4.27),233(4.16), 281(3.68)	12-2049-79
	pH 8.95	199(4.32),234(4.01)	12-2049-79
$C_5H_7ClN_4O$			
2-Pyrimidinamine, 5-chloro-1,4-dihydro-4-imino-1-methyl-, 3-oxide	pH 4.0	237(4.49),292(3.72)	12-2049-79
	pH 10.6	240(4.41),276(3.62), 326(3.43)	12-2049-79
$C_5H_7ClN_4O_2$			
2,4-Pyrimidinediamine, 5-chloro-6-methyl-, 1,3-dioxide	pH -2.28	201(4.25),229(4.08), 300(3.91)	12-2049-79
	pH 6.44	217(4.13),241(4.37), 333(3.77)	12-2049-79
C_5H_7N			
1H-Pyrrole, 2-methyl-	C_6H_{12}	217(3.86)	104-0535-79
$C_5H_7NOS_2$			
1-Pyrrolidinecarbodithioic acid, 2-oxo-	EtOH	229s(3.63),276(4.09), 341(4.01)	39-0692-79C
1,3-Thiazin-4(3H)-one, 5,6-dihydro-5-methyl-2-thioxo-	EtOH	259(4.33),310(4.35)	150-0212-79S
1,3-Thiazin-4(3H)-one, 5,6-dihydro-6-methyl-2-thioxo-	EtOH	258(4.10),309(4.13)	150-0212-79S
$C_5H_7NO_2$			
2,4-Pyrrolidinedione, 5-methyl-	aq NaOH	261(4.04)	142-0477-79B
$C_5H_7NS_2$			
2(3H)-Thiazolethione, 4,5-dimethyl-	EtOH	333(3.876)	48-0249-79

Compound	Solvent	λ_{max}(log ε)	Ref.
$C_5H_7N_2OS$			
Isothiazolium, 5-[(hydroxyimino)methyl]-2-methyl-, perchlorate	MeOH	216(3.93),249(3.15), 334(3.93)	39-2340-79C
	MeOH-HClO$_4$	216s(3.52),263s(3.53), 301(3.96),332s(3.45)	39-2340-79C
Methanaminium, N-hydroxy-N-(5-isothiazolylmethylene)-, perchlorate	MeOH-HClO$_4$	213(3.91),248(3.08), 317(4.03),327s(3.99)	39-2340-79C
$C_5H_7N_2O_3$			
2-Pyrrolidinone, 1-methyl-3-nitro-, ion(1-), potassium	H_2O	210(3.71),290(3.90)	4-0481-79
$C_5H_7N_3OS$			
1H-Imidazole-4-carboximidothioic acid, 5-hydroxy-, methyl ester	H_2O	215(3.97),327(4.27)	103-0807-79
Urea, N-methyl-N'-2-thiazolyl-	n.s.g.	257(4.09)	87-0028-79
$C_5H_7N_3O_2S$			
Carbamic acid, 1,3,4-thiadiazol-2-yl-, ethyl ester	n.s.g.	242(3.93)	87-0028-79
$C_5H_7N_3O_2S_2$			
Sulfilimine, S,S-dimethyl-N-(5-nitro-2-thiazolyl)-	EtOH	260(3.85),418(4.26)	139-0195-79
$C_5H_7N_3O_4S$			
Cytosine 5-methylenesulfonate	pH 1	285(3.97)	69-0632-79
	pH 7	274(3.76)	69-0632-79
$C_5H_7N_5$			
Cyanamide, (4-amino-5,6-dihydro-2-pyrimidinyl)-	H_2O	253(4.31)	23-2593-79
1,2,4-Triazolo[4,3-b][1,2,4]triazine, 1,7-dihydro-6-methyl-	EtOH	271(3.75)	4-0427-79
$C_5H_7N_5O_2$			
[1,2,3]Triazolo[1,5-a]pyrimidine, 4,5,6,7-tetrahydro-3-nitro-	EtOH	224(4.13),343(3.98)	39-2361-79C
C_5H_8			
2,3-Pentadiene, (R)-(-)-	gas	190(3.8)	35-2284-79
	3-Mepentane	196(3.4)	35-2284-79
$C_5H_8Cl_2O$			
Propane, 2-[(2,2-dichloroethenyl)oxy]-	C_6H_{12}	209(3.98)	70-1610-79
$C_5H_8Cl_2S$			
Propane, 1-[(2,2-dichloroethenyl)thio]-	C_6H_{12}	248(3.88),256s(3.86)	70-1610-79
Propane, 2-[(2,2-dichloroethenyl)thio]-	C_6H_{12}	248(3.83),257s(3.81)	70-1610-79
$C_5H_8N_2$			
1H-Imidazole, 1-ethyl-	EtOH	217(3.71)	70-1931-79
Pyrimidine, 1,4-dihydro-4-methyl-	EtOH	286(3.94)	39-1228-79C
$C_5H_8N_2O$			
1H-Pyrazolium, 4-hydroxy-1,2-dimethyl-, hydroxide, inner salt	H_2O	285(3.60)	23-0904-79
Pyridine, 1,2,3,4-tetrahydro-1-nitroso-	H_2O	206(3.65),281(3.93)	44-4511-79

Compound	Solvent	λ$_{max}$(log ε)	Ref.
$C_5H_8N_2OS_2$			
1-Imidazolidinecarbodithioic acid, 2-oxo-, methyl ester	EtOH	214(3.75),268(4.26), 289(4.14)	39-0692-79C
$C_5H_8N_2O_2$			
2(5H)-Furanone, 4-(1-methylhydrazino)-	EtOH	264(4.36)	4-0505-79
1H-Pyrazole-3-methanol, 5-hydroxy-α-methyl-	EtOH	224(3.56)	4-0505-79
$C_5H_8N_2S$			
1H-Imidazole, 1-methyl-2-(methylthio)-	pH 1	251(3.74)	4-1185-79
	H_2O	223(3.82),246(3.68)	4-1185-79
	pH 11	245.5(3.70)	4-1185-79
	MeOH	223(3.81),249(3.65)	4-1185-79
2-Thiazolamine, 4,5-dimethyl-	EtOH	263(3.785)	48-0249-79
$C_5H_8N_2S_2$			
2H-1,3,4-Thiadiazine-2-thione, 3,6-dihydro-5,6-dimethyl-	EtOH	278(3.619),319(3.993)	48-0959-79
2H-1,3,4-Thiadiazine-2-thione, 3,6-dihydro-6,6-dimethyl-	EtOH	322(3.807)	48-0959-79
$C_5H_8N_4O$			
Ethanone, 2-amino-1-(5-amino-1H-imidazol-4-yl)-, dihydrochloride	H_2O	304(4.07)	35-6127-79
$C_5H_8N_4O_2$			
1,2,4-Triazine-3,5(2H,4H)-dione,	pH 1-7	312(3.58)	124-0048-79
6-(dimethylamino)-	pH 13	298(3.53)	124-0048-79
1,2,4-Triazine-3,5(2H,4H)-dione,	pH 1-7	314(3.71)	124-0048-79
2-methyl-6-(methylamino)-	pH 13	302(3.70)	124-0048-79
1,2,4-Triazine-3,5(2H,4H)-dione,	pH 1-7	305(3.63)	124-0048-79
4-methyl-6-(methylamino)-	pH 13	324(3.77)	124-0048-79
$C_5H_8N_6O_3$			
2,4-Pyrimidinediamine, 1,6-dihydro-	pH 0.09	221(4.28),316(3.94)	12-2049-79
6-imino-1-methyl-5-nitro-, 3-oxide	pH 9.6	207(4.33),256(3.77), 302(3.70)	12-2049-79
C_5H_8O			
3-Penten-2-one, cis	hexane	254(0.99),313(1.35)	144-0227-79
3-Penten-2-one, trans	hexane	254(1.50),313(1.40)	144-0227-79
$C_5H_8O_2$			
1,3-Dioxole, 2,2-dimethyl-	MeCN	216(3.65)	24-0577-79
2-Propenal, 3-ethoxy-	EtOH	242(4.3)	94-0403-79
$C_5H_8O_2S$			
1,3-Butadiene-1-sulfinic acid, 2-methyl-, lithium salt, (Z)-	H_2O	238(4.38)	70-0594-79
Thiiranecarboxylic acid, ethyl ester, (S)-	EtOH	215(2.72),280(2.04)	39-1852-79C
$C_5H_9ClN_2O$			
Piperidine, 3-chloro-1-nitroso-	EtOH	355(1.93)	44-4511-79
C_5H_9NO			
2-Propenal, 3-(ethylamino)-	EtOH	279(4.49)	49-0613-79
$C_5H_9NO_2$			
Cyclopentane, nitro-	neat	278(1.41)	39-0907-79B

Compound	Solvent	λ max(log ε)	Ref.
Cyclopentane, nitro- (cont.)	isooctane	280(1.38)	39-0907-79B
	MeOH	277(1.35)	39-0907-79B
	$CF_3CHOHCF_3$	269(1.49)	39-0907-79B
$C_5H_9NO_2S_2$			
Glycine, N-methyl-N-[(methylthio)thioxomethyl]-	CH_2Cl_2	250(3.95),277(4.05), 335(1.83)	5-0650-79
$C_5H_9N_3O$			
3-Pyrazolol, 5-(aminomethyl)-1-methyl-, dihydrochloride	MeOH	233(3.60)	1-0294-79
3-Pyrazolol, 5-(aminomethyl)-2-methyl-, (hydrate)	MeOH	245(3.69)	1-0294-79
dihydrochloride	MeOH	222(3.66)	1-0294-79
$C_5H_{10}N_2O$			
Propanal, 2-oxo-, 1-(dimethylhydrazone)	$CHCl_3$	296(4.28)	150-1451-79
$C_5H_{10}N_2S$			
2-Imidazolidinethione, 1,3-dimethyl-	MeOH	239(4.33)	78-0511-79
	CH_2Cl_2	245(4.35)	78-0511-79
2-Imidazolidinethione, 1-ethyl-	MeOH	240(4.23)	78-0511-79
	CH_2Cl_2	248(4.27)	78-0511-79
$C_5H_{10}N_2S_2$			
Propanedithioamide, N,N'-dimethyl-	EtOH	230(1.65),263(2.30), 340(0.40)	48-0001-79
$C_5H_{11}NO_2$			
Pentane, 1-nitro-	neat	277(1.44)	39-0907-79B
	isooctane	278(1.40)	39-0907-79B
	MeOH	274(1.39)	39-0907-79B
	$CF_3CHOHCF_3$	269(1.58)	39-0907-79B
$C_5H_{11}N_3O_3$			
Carbamic acid, [(methylnitrosoamino)-methyl]-, ethyl ester	EtOH	229(3.94),353(1.92)	94-0682-79
$C_5H_{12}GeS$			
Germane, (ethenylthio)trimethyl-	hexane	237(3.66)	70-1479-79
$C_5H_{12}SSi$			
Silane, (ethenylthio)trimethyl-	hexane	233(3.71)	70-1479-79
$C_5H_{12}SSn$			
Stannane, (ethenylthio)trimethyl-	hexane	238(3.76)	70-1479-79
$C_5H_{12}S_2Si$			
1,3-Dithia-2-silacyclohexane, 2,2-dimethyl-	hexane	195(3.58),228(2.82)	114-0407-79A
1,4-Dithia-2-silacyclohexane, 2,2-dimethyl-	hexane	200(3.70),238s(2.46)	114-0407-79A
1,3-Dithia-2-silacyclopentane, 2,2,4-trimethyl-	hexane	198(3.54),233(2.33)	114-0407-79A
$C_5H_{12}Si$			
Silane, ethenyltrimethyl-	heptane	181(4.2)	65-0916-79
$C_5H_{13}N_3$			
Ethanimidic acid, 2-(1-methylethyl)hydrazide, monohydrochloride	H_2O	210(3.52)	104-2066-79
	pH 13	224(3.74)	104-2066-79

Compound	Solvent	$\lambda_{max}(\log \epsilon)$	Ref.
Ethanimidic acid, 2-propylhydrazide, monohydrochloride	H_2O	208(3.33)	104-2066-79
	pH 13	225(3.72)	104-2066-79
Ethanimidic acid, trimethylhydrazide, monohydriodide	H_2O	226(4.14)	104-2073-79
$C_5H_{14}SSi$			
Silane, (ethylthio)trimethyl-	hexane	223(2.49)	114-0407-79A

Compound	Solvent	λ_{max}(log ε)	Ref.
$C_6Cl_2N_6O_2$			
2,5-Cyclohexadiene-1,4-dione, 2,5-diazido-3,6-dichloro-	MeCN	213(4.07),262(4.29), 338(4.30),430(2.98)	59-0663-79
$C_6Cl_4O_2$			
4-Cyclopentene-1,3-dione, 4,5-dichloro-2-(dichloromethylene)-	isoPrOH	250(4.23)	104-0454-79
C_6Cl_8			
Cyclobutane, 1,1,2,2-tetrachloro-3,4-bis(dichloromethylene)-	C_6H_{12}	298s(4.13),310(4.24), 323s(4.12)	39-2995-79C
C_6F_5NOS			
Benzenamine, 2,3,4,5,6-pentafluoro-N-sulfinyl-	pentane	238(3.66),286(3.53), 345(3.41)	70-2352-79
$C_6H_2Br_2O_4$			
2,5-Cyclohexadiene-1,4-dione, 2,5-dibromo-3,6-dihydroxy-	n.s.g.	312(4.26),455(2.36)	86-0341-79
	anion	315(4.20),523(2.94)	86-0341-79
	dianion	334(4.42),520(2.83)	86-0341-79
$C_6H_2ClF_4NO$			
2,4-Cyclohexadien-1-one, 3-amino-6-chloro-2,4,5,6-tetrafluoro-	heptane	381(3.64)	104-1934-79
$C_6H_2Cl_2N_2Se$			
2,1,3-Benzoselenadiazole, 5,6-dichloro-	H_2O	347(4.29)	86-0015-79
monoprotonated	H_2O	363.5(4.33)	86-0015-79
diprotonated	H_2O	400(4.29)	86-0015-79
$C_6H_2Cl_2O_4$			
2,5-Cyclohexadiene-1,4-dione, 2,5-dichloro-3,6-dihydroxy-	n.s.g.	302(4.31),460(2.30)	86-0349-79
	anion	310(4.21),530(2.94)	86-0349-79
	dianion	332(4.43),525(2.28)	86-0349-79
$C_6H_3ClN_2Se$			
2,1,3-Benzoselenadiazole, 5-chloro-	H_2O	338(4.23)	86-0015-79
monoprotonated	H_2O	350(4.27)	86-0015-79
diprotonated	H_2O	376(4.32)	86-0015-79
$C_6H_3Cl_4NO$			
2(1H)-Pyridinone, 3,4,5,6-tetrachloro-1-methyl-	MeOH	333(3.83)	39-2756-79C
$C_6H_3N_3O_2Se$			
2,1,3-Benzoselenadiazole, 5-nitro-	H_2O	344(4.22)	86-0015-79
monoprotonated	H_2O	348.5(4.23)	86-0015-79
$C_6H_3N_3O_5$			
4-Benzofurazanol, 7-nitro-, 3-oxide	8M HCl	300s(3.75),320(3.75), 435(3.87)	23-2512-79
potassium salt	pH 10.3	312(3.91),371(3.92), 484(4.07)	23-2512-79
5-Benzofurazanol, 4-nitro-, 1-oxide	7M HCl	277(3.77),320(3.86), 402(3.86)	23-2512-79
potassium salt	pH 10.3	312(4.19),394(3.83)	23-2512-79
$C_6H_3N_3O_7$			
Phenol, 2,4,6-trinitro- (picric acid)	EtOH	360(4.19)	56-0415-79

Compound	Solvent	λ_{max}(log ε)	Ref.
$C_6H_3N_5S_2$			
1H-Pyrazolo[3,4-d]pyrimidine-3-carbonitrile, 4,5,6,7-tetrahydro-4,6-dithioxo-	EtOH	204(4.10),257(4.05), 262(4.05),300(4.04)	103-1361-79
C_6H_4AsN			
4-Arsenincarbonitrile	EtOH	222(4.05),286(4.16)	88-3141-79
$C_6H_4Br_3NO_2Te$			
Tellurium, tribromo(2-nitrophenyl)-, (T-4)-	EtOH	285(3.71),306(4.22)	44-3957-79
$C_6H_4ClF_2OP$			
Phosphonic difluoride, (4-chlorophenyl)-	C_6H_{12} or dioxan	228.0(4.19)	65-0068-79
$C_6H_4ClF_2PS$			
Phosphonothioic difluoride, (4-chlorophenyl)-	C_6H_{12} or dioxan	239(4.13)	65-0068-79
$C_6H_4ClNOS_2$			
3H-1,2,3-Benzodithiazole, 5-chloro-, 2-oxide	50% H_2SO_4	360(4.2),540(3.2)	103-0978-79
$C_6H_4ClNO_2S$			
Benzenesulfenyl chloride, 2-nitro-	MeOH-HCl	395(3.37)	70-1271-79
$C_6H_4ClN_3$			
7H-Pyrrolo[2,3-d]pyrimidine, 4-chloro-	MeOH	222(4.39),275(3.63), 280s(3.62)	24-3526-79
$C_6H_4Cl_2N_2O_2$			
Pyrazinecarboxylic acid, 3,6-dichloro-5-methyl-	EtOH	225(3.98),291(3.83)	94-2027-79
$C_6H_4Cl_3N_5O$			
7H-1,2,3-Triazolo[4,5-d]pyrimidin-7-one, 1,4-dihydro-1-methyl-5-(trichloromethyl)-	n.s.g.	283(3.93)	39-0922-79C
$C_6H_4Cl_3OP$			
Phosphonic dichloride, (4-chlorophenyl)-	C_6H_{12} or dioxan	234.5(4.22)	65-0068-79
$C_6H_4Cl_3PS$			
Phosphonothioic dichloride, (4-chlorophenyl)-	C_6H_{12} or dioxan	237(4.21)	65-0068-79
$C_6H_4Cl_8N_3P$			
1,3,5,2-Triazaphosphorin, 2,2-dichloro-2,2-dihydro-4,6-bis(1,1,2-trichloroethyl)-	hexane	293.2(3.61)	99-0055-79
$C_6H_4F_3NO_2$			
2H-Pyrrol-2-one, 1,3-dihydro-1-(trifluoroacetyl)-	ether	228(3.98)	44-2798-79
$C_6H_4N_2O$			
1H-Pyrrole-3-carbonitrile, 2-formyl-	H_2O	265(3.62),300(4.17)	152-0115-79
1H-Pyrrole-3-carbonitrile, 5-formyl-	H_2O	281(4.15)	152-0115-79

Compound	Solvent	λ_{max}(log ε)	Ref.
$C_6H_4N_2OS$			
Benzene, 1-nitroso-2-(thionitroso)-	C_6H_{12}?	490(3.95)	88-0745-79
$C_6H_4N_2OSe$			
Benzene, 1-nitroso-2-(selenonitroso)-	C_6H_{12}	526-540(3.85)(changing)	88-0745-79
$C_6H_4N_2O_2$			
4,5'-Bioxazole	MeOH	242(4.2)	5-1370-79
5,5'-Bioxazole	MeOH	259(4.23),266(4.20), 278(3.91)	5-1370-79
$C_6H_4N_2O_4S$			
Benzenethiol, 2,4-dinitro-	isooctane	304(3.91)	104-1462-79
	DMF	476(4.33)	104-1462-79
	MeCN	458(4.30)	104-1462-79
	DMSO	473(4.36)	104-1462-79
potassium salt	DMF	476(4.33)	104-1462-79
	MeCN	458(4.32)	104-1462-79
	DMSO	473(4.36)	104-1462-79
$C_6H_4N_2S$			
Thieno[3,2-c]pyridazine	EtOH	234(4.97),277(3.75), 304(3.40)	78-2027-79
$C_6H_4N_2Se$			
2,1,3-Benzoselenadiazole	H_2O	331.5(4.24)	86-0015-79
monoprotonated	H_2O	341(4.30)	86-0015-79
diprotonated	H_2O	362.5(4.38)	86-0015-79
$C_6H_4N_4O_2$			
Pyrazino[2,3-d]pyridazine-5,8-diol	pH -3.0	229s(3.575),264(3.965), 306(3.43)	12-0459-79
	pH 2.0	225s(3.55),261(4.01), 317(3.41)	12-0459-79
	pH 7.0	211(4.14),271(4.01), 330(3.36)	12-0459-79
$C_6H_4N_4O_2S$			
Isothiazolo[4,5-d]pyrimidine-3-carboxamide, 4,7-dihydro-7-oxo-	DMF	312(3.90),321s(3.82)	5-1534-79
4,7(1H,8H)-Pteridinedione, 2,3-dihydro-2-thioxo-	pH 0.0	207(4.39),252(3.94), 287(4.14),342(4.27)	24-1499-79
	pH 5.0	214(4.29),230(4.28), 261(4.16),295(4.05), 339(4.30),353(4.28)	24-1499-79
	pH 11.0	240(4.33),256(4.39), 305(4.11),342(4.21)	24-1499-79
	2M NaOH	232(4.51),268(4.26), 353(4.21)	24-1499-79
$C_6H_4N_8O_2$			
2,5-Cyclohexadiene-1,4-dione, 2,5-diamino-3,6-diazido-	MeOH	215(4.29),245(4.01), 337(4.44),520(2.52)	59-0663-79
$C_6H_4OS_4$			
1,3-Dithiole, 2-(1,3-dithiol-2-ylidene)-, 1-oxide	n.s.g.	395(3.97)	39-0862-79B
$C_6H_4S_4$			
1,3-Dithiole, 2-(1,3-dithiol-2-ylidene)-	MeCN	306(4.10),315(4.11), 355s(3.30),446(2.44)	44-0880-79

Compound	Solvent	$\lambda_{max}(\log \epsilon)$	Ref.
C_6H_5Br			
Benzene, bromo-	n.s.g.	193(4.54),215(3.90), 261(2.43)	73-0873-79
$C_6H_5BrCl_2O$			
2-Propenal, 2-bromo-3-(2,2-dichloro-cyclopropyl)-	n.s.g.	257(4.05)	70-2452-79
$C_6H_5BrN_2O_2$			
Pyridine, 3-bromo-4-methyl-5-nitro-	EtOH	220(4.1),284(3.1)	103-0076-79
2,4(1H,3H)-Pyrimidinedione, 5-(2-bromo-ethenyl)-	EtOH	251(4.24),290(4.00)	88-4415-79
$C_6H_5BrN_2O_4$			
1(2H)-Pyrimidineacetic acid, 5-bromo-3,4-dihydro-2,4-dioxo-	H_2O	285(3.93)	73-1634-79
	pH 8.7	282(3.87)	73-1634-79
	pH 12	281(3.85)	73-1634-79
C_6H_5Cl			
Benzene, chloro-	n.s.g.	189(4.79),214(3.90), 261(2.43)	73-0873-79
radical	MeOH	255(1.70)	49-1367-79
$C_6H_5ClN_2O_2$			
2,4(1H,3H)-Pyrimidinedione, 5-(2-chloro-ethenyl)-	EtOH	248(4.17),291(3.98)	88-4415-79
$C_6H_5ClN_4$			
1,2,4-Triazolo[4,3-a]pyrazine, 8-chloro-3-methyl-	EtOH	305(3.61)	44-1028-79
$C_6H_5Cl_2OP$			
Phosphonic dichloride, phenyl-	C_6H_{12}	194(4.48),221(4.03), 262(2.88),267(3.04), 275(2.93)	65-0275-79
	C_6H_{12}	222(4.03)	65-0068-79
	$C_2H_4Cl_2$	224(4.08),262(2.94), 268(3.08),274(3.04)	65-0275-79
	MeCN	223(4.08),261(2.91), 267(3.08),274(3.00)	65-0275-79
$C_6H_5Cl_2P$			
Phosphonous dichloride, phenyl-	hexane	265(3.18)	22-0241-79I
$C_6H_5Cl_2PS$			
Phosphonothioic dichloride, phenyl-	C_6H_{12} or dioxan	225.5(4.10)	65-0068-79
$C_6H_5Cl_3N_2O_3$			
Oxazole, 4,5-dihydro-2-(2,3,3-tri-chloro-1-aci-nitro-2-propenyl)-	EtOH	215(4.19),323(4.21)	104-0240-79
$C_6H_5Cl_3P$			
Phosphorus(1+), trichlorophenyl-, (T-4)-, hexachlorophosphate	MeCN	240(4.11),270(3.81), 345(2.00)	65-0275-79
	$MeNO_2$	242(4.12),270(3.81), 345(2.00)	65-0275-79
	$C_2H_4Cl_2$	244(4.13),270(3.81), 345(2.00)	65-0275-79
tetrachloroaluminate	MeCN	277(3.26)	65-0275-79
	$C_2H_4Cl_2$-MeCN	242(4.10),278(3.28)	65-0275-79

Compound	Solvent	λ_{max}(log ε)	Ref.
$C_6H_5Cl_4P$			
Phosphorane, tetrachlorophenyl-	C_6H_{12}	197(4.48),228(4.03), 267s(3.08)	65-0275-79
	$C_2H_4Cl_2$	229(4.03),267s(3.08)	65-0275-79
	MeCN	201(4.40),227(4.02), 267s(3.08)	65-0275-79
C_6H_5F			
Benzene, fluoro-	n.s.g.	182(4.68),203(3.86), 260(3.04)	73-0873-79
$C_6H_5FN_2O_4$			
1(2H)-Pyrimidineacetic acid, 5-fluoro-3,4-dihydro-2,4-dioxo-	H_2O	266(4.00)	73-1634-79
	pH 8.7	266(3.98)	73-1634-79
	pH 12	264(3.93)	73-1634-79
$C_6H_5F_2OP$			
Phosphonic difluoride, phenyl-	C_6H_{12} or dioxan	214.5(3.93)	65-0068-79
$C_6H_5F_2PS$			
Phosphonothioic difluoride, phenyl-	C_6H_{12} or dioxan	230.0(3.93)	65-0068-79
C_6H_5I			
Benzene, iodo-	n.s.g.	178(4.48),194(4.45), 230(4.10),260(2.85)	73-0873-79
$C_6H_5IN_2O_2$			
2,4(1H,3H)-Pyrimidinedione, 5-(2-iodoethenyl)-	EtOH	250(4.18),294(4.00)	88-4415-79
$C_6H_5IN_2O_4$			
1(2H)-Pyrimidineacetic acid, 3,4-dihydro-5-iodo-2,4-dioxo-	H_2O	293(3.88)	73-1634-79
	pH 8.7	288(3.83)	73-1634-79
	pH 12	284(3.78)	73-1634-79
$C_6H_5NO_2$			
Benzene, nitro-	n.s.g.	175(4.49),198(4.26), 252(3.95),280(3.18)	73-0873-79
2-Pyridinecarboxylic acid	$CHCl_3$	263(3.57)	131-0165-79D
	MeCN	223(3.77),263(3.55)	131-0165-79D
$C_6H_5NO_2S$			
Benzenethiol, 2-nitro-	pH 7.8	413(3.10)	70-1271-79
Benzenethiol, 4-nitro-	benzene	318(4.1)	70-1585-79
Thiophene, 2-(2-nitroethenyl)-	EtOH	350(4.24)	104-1859-79
$C_6H_5NO_3$			
Phenol, 4-nitro-	benzene	300(4.03)	70-1585-79
Furan, 2-(2-nitroethenyl)-	EtOH	348(4.28)	104-1859-79
$C_6H_5NO_3S$			
4-Thia-1-azabicyclo[3.2.0]hept-2-ene-2-carboxylic acid, 7-oxo-, (R)-	EtOH	257(3.45),310(3.81)	35-6306-79
(S)-	EtOH	256(3.45),310(3.80)	35-6306-79
$C_6H_5NO_4$			
1H-Pyrrole-2,5-dione, 3-acetyl-4-hydroxy-	EtOH	253(4.24),328(3.45)	94-1792-79

Compound	Solvent	λ_{max}(log ε)	Ref.
$C_6H_5N_3$			
3-Pyridinecarbonitrile, 2-amino-	CH_2Cl_2	320(3.81)	118-0376-79
$C_6H_5N_3O_3S$			
Pyrido[1,2-b][1,2,4,6]thiatriazin-3(2H)-one, 1,1-dioxide	MeOH	235(4.08),302(3.82)	142-0815-79
$C_6H_5N_3O_4$			
Benzenamine, 2,4-dinitro-	EtOH	227(4.04),259(3.99), 338(4.15),385(3.84)	73-1613-79
Benzenamine, 2,6-dinitro-	EtOH	223(4.38),251(4.06), 426(3.97)	73-1613-79
$C_6H_5N_3O_6S$			
Benzenesulfonamide, 2,4-dinitro-	EtOH	259(3.68),340(3.92)	80-1027-79 +80-1329-79
$C_6H_5N_3S$			
Acetonitrile, (2-pyrimidinthio)-	pH -2.8	247(3.97),299(3.57)	12-2713-79
	pH 7	238(4.03),274(3.31)	12-2713-79
$C_6H_5N_3S_3$			
Thiazolo[5,4-d]pyrimidine-7(4H)-thione, 2-(methylthio)-	EtOH	262(4.19),332(4.38)	2-0307-79B
$C_6H_5N_3S_4$			
Thiazolo[5,4-d]pyrimidine-5,7(4H,6H)-dithione, 2-(methylthio)-	pH 13	290(4.24),335(4.11)	2-0307-79B
$C_6H_5N_5O$			
Pyridine, 4-(3-cyano-1-triazeno)-, 1-oxide, potassium salt	EtOH	225(3.83),255(3.50), 370(4.41)	94-1824-79
$C_6H_6ClNO_2S$			
Thiophene, 2-(1-chloroethyl)-4-nitro-	MeOH	226(4.06),269(3.85)	12-2647-79
Thiophene, 2-(1-chloroethyl)-5-nitro-	MeOH	317(3.51)	12-2647-79
$C_6H_6Cl_2N_2O$			
Pyrazine, 2,5-dichloro-3,6-dimethyl-, 1-oxide	EtOH	215(4.23),236(4.30), 272(3.96),309(3.45), 314(3.46),320(3.46)	94-2027-79
$C_6H_6Cl_2N_2O_2$			
2,5-Pyrazinedimethanol, 3,6-dichloro-	EtOH	222(4.05),293(3.40)	94-2980-79
$C_6H_6Cl_2N_4$			
1H-Purine, 2,6-dichloro-7,8-dihydro-7-methyl-	MeOH	317(3.8)	31-1418-79
$C_6H_6Cl_3N_3O_2$			
1H-Imidazole, 4,5-dihydro-2-(2,3,3-trichloro-1-aci-nitro-2-propenyl)-	EtOH	214(4.16),325(4.24)	104-0240-79
$C_6H_6Cl_6N_3P$			
1,3,5,2-Triazaphosphorine, 2,2-dichloro-4,6-bis(1,1-dichloroethyl)-2,2-dihydro-	hexane	292.6(3.59)	99-0055-79
$C_6H_6FNO_3S$			
Benzenesulfonic acid, 2-amino-4-fluoro-	MeOH	250(4.22),282(3.41)	73-2108-79

Compound	Solvent	$\lambda_{max}(\log \epsilon)$	Ref.
$C_6H_6N_2$			
7,8-Diazatetracyclo[3.3.0.0^{2,4}.0^{3,6}]-oct-7-ene	n.s.g.	371f(2.5),380(2.3)	144-0111-79
$C_6H_6N_2O_2$			
1H-Pyrrole, 2-(2-nitroethenyl)-	EtOH	398(4.30)	104-1859-79
$C_6H_6N_2O_2S$			
4-Pyrimidinecarboxaldehyde, 1,6-dihydro-2-(methylthio)-6-oxo-	pH 1.0	259(3.95)	136-0235-79B
	pH 7.0	255(3.95)	136-0235-79B
	pH 10.0	265(3.75),282(3.72)	136-0235-79B
$C_6H_6N_2O_3$			
Phenol, 2-amino-4-nitro-, tetrafluoroborate	pH 11	274(3.83),443(4.14)	69-1019-79
$C_6H_6N_2O_4$			
Acetic acid, (2-amino-4-oxo-5(4H)-oxazolylidene)-, methyl ester	H_2SO_4	250(4.25)	103-0794-79
2-Propenoic acid, 3-(methylfurazanyl)-, N-oxide	EtOH	233(4.38)	88-4399-79
1H-Pyrazole-4,5-dicarboxylic acid, 1-methyl-	EtOH	240(3.92)	73-0781-79
	ether	249(3.92)	73-0781-79
1(2H)-Pyrimidineacetic acid, 3,4-dihydro-2,4-dioxo-	H_2O	269(4.00)	73-1634-79
	pH 8.7	269(3.98)	73-1634-79
	pH 12	267(3.95)	73-1634-79
4-Pyrimidinecarboxylic acid, 1,2,3,6-tetrahydro-2,6-dioxo-, methyl ester	n.s.g.	283(3.86)	149-0447-79A
4-Pyrimidinecarboxylic acid, 1,2,3,6-tetrahydro-1-methyl-2,6-dioxo-	pH 1	283(3.83)	44-0970-79
	pH 2.1	280.5(3.81)	149-0447-79A
	pH 13	298(3.84)	44-0970-79
4-Pyrimidinecarboxylic acid, 1,2,3,6-tetrahydro-3-methyl-2,6-dioxo-	pH 3.3	272(3.96)	149-0447-79A
$C_6H_6N_2O_4S$			
Benzenesulfonamide, 2-nitro-	EtOH	261(3.32),307(3.69)	80-1027-79
Benzenesulfonamide, 3-nitro-	EtOH	256(3.69),306(2.75)	80-1027-79
Benzenesulfonamide, 4-nitro-	pH 10	262(3.99),350(3.04)	80-1329-79
	EtOH	262(4.00),340(3.65)	80-1027-79
$C_6H_6N_4O$			
Imidazo[4,5-d][1,3]diazepin-8(1H)-one, 4,7-dihydro-	MeOH	227(4.24),300(3.53)	35-6127-79
Imidazo[1,5-a]-1,3,5-triazin-4(3H)-one, 8-methyl-	EtOH	265(3.88),292s(3.56)	44-3835-79
6-Purinol, 8-methyl-	pH 1	248(3.34)	44-1450-79
	pH 12	261(3.40)	44-1450-79
7H-Pyrazolo[4,3-d]pyrimidin-7-one, 1,6-dihydro-3-methyl-	pH 1	281(3.81)	18-0208-79
	pH 11	226(3.95),281(3.93), 288(3.94),300s(3.75)	18-0208-79
	EtOH	226(3.81)	18-0208-79
1,2,4-Triazolo[4,3-a]pyrazin-8(7H)-one, 3-methyl-	EtOH	280(3.67)	44-1028-79
$C_6H_6N_4OS$			
Imidazo[1,5-a]-1,3,5-triazin-4(1H)-one, 2,3-dihydro-8-methyl-2-thioxo-	EtOH	240(3.89),299(4.17)	44-3835-79
$C_6H_6N_4O_4$			
Hydrazinecarboxamide, 2-[(5-nitro-2-furanyl)methylene]-	EtOH	264(4.10),367(4.28)	70-1282-79

Compound	Solvent	λ max(log ε)	Ref.
$C_6H_6N_4O_5$			
1H-Imidazole-1-acetic acid, α-(hydroxy-imino)-4-nitro-, methyl ester, (E)-	EtOH	282(3.96)	4-1545-79
(Z)-	EtOH	282(3.93)	4-1545-79
1H-Imidazole-1-acetic acid, α-(methoxy-imino)-4-nitro-, (E)-	EtOH	287(3.92)	4-1545-79
(Z)-	EtOH	282(3.86)	4-1545-79
$C_6H_6N_4S$			
1,2,4-Triazolo[4,3-a]pyrazine-8(7H)-thione, 3-methyl-	EtOH	272(3.86),356(4.11)	44-1028-79
$C_6H_6N_6O$			
6(5H)-Pteridinone, 2,4-diamino-	pH 1	245(4.13),275(3.64), 354(3.86),367(3.82)	44-0302-79
C_6H_6O			
Phenol	H_2O	200(2.80),210(2.92), 224(2.99),262(2.89), 276(2.88)	135-1004-79B
	pH 12	215(3.48),224(3.42), 236(3.86),268(2.95), 288(3.36)	135-1004-79B
	MeOH	273(3.23)	36-1306-79
	n.s.g.	189(4.75),211(3.81), 270(3.30)	73-0873-79
$C_6H_6O_3$			
6,8-Dioxabicyclo[3.2.1]oct-2-en-4-one (levoglucosenone)	EtOH	218(3.88)	136-0169-79D
2-Furancarboxaldehyde, 5-(hydroxymeth-yl)-	EtOH	282(4.00)	32-0151-79
$C_6H_6O_4$			
3,8,9-Trioxabicyclo[4.2.1]non-4-en-2-one	EtOH	212(3.69)	136-0169-79D
C_6H_6S			
Benzenethiol	C_6H_{12}	280(2.82)	39-0217-79B
	n.s.g.	185(4.20),203(4.34), 235(3.93),276(2.85)	73-0873-79
$C_6H_7BrN_2O_4$			
2-Butenoic acid, 4-[(aminocarbonyl)am-ino]-2-bromo-4-oxo-, methyl ester, (Z)-	H_2SO_4	250(3.71)	103-0794-79
5-Oxazoleacetic acid, α-bromo-4,5-di-hydro-4-oxo-2-amino-, methyl ester	H_2SO_4	219(4.28),248s(3.77)	103-0794-79
$C_6H_7ClN_2O_2$			
Pyrazine, 3-chloro-2,5-dimethyl-, 1,4-dioxide	EtOH	242(4.40),308(4.33)	94-2027-79
2(1H)-Pyrazinone, 5-chloro-1-hydroxy-3,6-dimethyl-	EtOH	236(4.30),335(3.89)	94-2027-79
Pyridazinium, 3-chloro-5-hydroxy-4-methoxy-1-methyl-, hydroxide, inner salt	EtOH	328(3.64)	39-1199-79C
$C_6H_7Cl_3N_6O$			
1H-1,2,3-Triazole-5-carboxamide, 1-	n.s.g.	289(4.19)	39-0922-79C

Compound	Solvent	λ$_{max}$(log ε)	Ref.
methyl-4-[(2,2,2-trichloro-1-imino-ethyl)amino]- (cont.)			39-0922-79C
$C_6H_7FN_2O_3$			
2,4(1H,3H)-Pyrimidinedione, 5-fluoro-1-(2-hydroxyethyl)-	pH 1	274(3.94)	1-0515-79
	pH 13	272(3.80)	1-0515-79
C_6H_7N			
Aniline	MeOH	234(3.99),285(3.11)	36-1306-79
	n.s.g.	176(4.18),198(4.48), 235(3.90),285(3.20)	73-0873-79
C_6H_7NO			
Ethanone, 1-(1H-pyrrol-2-yl)-	H_2O	256(3.68),291(4.18)	152-0115-79
Phenol, 2-amino-	MeOH	233(3.79),287(3.49)	36-1306-79
Phenol, 3-amino-	MeOH	233(3.77),285(3.32)	36-1306-79
Phenol, 4-amino-	H_2O	226(3.76),296(3.20)	36-1306-79
	MeOH	232(3.86),300(3.36)	36-1306-79
	MeOH	235(3.90),300(3.57)	36-1306-79
	EtOH	301(3.40)	36-1306-79
	PrOH	299(3.36)	36-1306-79
	$CHCl_3$	303(3.36)	36-1306-79
1H-Pyrrole-2-carboxaldehyde, 3-methyl-	H_2O	295(4.21)	152-0115-79
1H-Pyrrole-2-carboxaldehyde, 4-methyl-	H_2O	258(3.78),300(4.13)	152-0115-79
1H-Pyrrole-2-carboxaldehyde, 5-methyl-	H_2O	253(3.65),306(4.32)	152-0115-79
1H-Pyrrole-3-carboxaldehyde, 2-methyl-	H_2O	258(3.97),283(3.81)	152-0115-79
C_6H_7NOS			
2-Cyclobuten-1-one, 2-(dimethylamino)-4-thioxo-	CH_2Cl_2	319(4.34),439(1.77)	118-0361-79
6H-[1,2]Oxathiolo[3,2-e]isothiazole-7-S^{IV}, 6-methyl-	C_6H_{12}	235(3.74),374(4.13)	39-2340-79C
$C_6H_7NOS_4$			
1,3-Pyrrolidinedicarbodithioic acid, 2-oxo-	EtOH	262(3.75),311(3.96), 408(4.40)	39-0692-79C
$C_6H_7NO_2$			
3-Pyridinol, 6-methoxy-	H_2O	220(3.93),294(3.64)	152-0115-79
2(1H)-Pyridinone, 5-methoxy-	H_2O	224(3.82),306(4.00)	152-0115-79
4(1H)-Pyridinone, 3-hydroxy-1-methyl-	neutral	282(4.12)	18-0111-79
	base	309(3.97)	18-0111-79
1H-Pyrrole-2-carboxaldehyde, 3-methoxy-	H_2O	294(4.30)	152-0115-79
1H-Pyrrole-2-carboxaldehyde, 5-methoxy-	H_2O	251(3.38),315(4.36)	152-0115-79
1H-Pyrrole-2-carboxylic acid, methyl ester	H_2O	236(3.65),266(4.19)	152-0115-79
2,4-Pyrrolidinedione, 5-ethylidene-	aq NaOH	264(4.28),322(3.62)	142-0477-79B
$C_6H_7NO_3$			
2-Propenoic acid, 2-cyano-3-methoxy-, methyl ester	EtOH	250.0(4.07)	73-1423-79
4(1H)-Pyridinone, 5-hydroxy-2-(hydroxy-methyl)-	acid	276(3.70)	18-0107-79
	neutral	278(3.90)	18-0107-79
	base	298(3.75)	18-0107-79
$C_6H_7NO_3S$			
Benzenesulfonic acid, 2-amino-, sodium salt	$NaHCO_3$	240(3.84)	104-0887-79
Benzenesulfonic acid, 4-amino-, sodium salt	$NaHCO_3$	249.5(4.18)	104-0887-79

Compound	Solvent	λ max(log ε)	Ref.
2-Pyridinol, methanesulfonate	EtOH	211(3.83),258(3.69)	150-1579-79
2-Thiophenemethanol, α-methyl-4-nitro-	MeOH	224(4.05),270(3.90)	12-2647-79
2-Thiophenemethanol, α-methyl-5-nitro-	MeOH	324(4.01)	12-2647-79
$C_6H_7NO_4$			
3-Pyrrolidinecarboxylic acid, 2,4-di-oxo-, methyl ester	H_2O	227(4.13),261(4.05)	142-0477-79B
$C_6H_7NS_2$			
4H-Cyclopent[c]isothiazole-3-thiol, 5,6-dihydro-, ammonium salt	EtOH	256(3.83),309(4.07)	150-0410-79S
3H-Cyclopent[c]isothiazole-3-thione, 3a,4,5,6-tetrahydro-	EtOH	286(3.62),302(3.64), 394(4.03)	150-0410-79S
2(1H)-Pyridinethione, 4-(methylthio)-	EtOH	277(4.51),356(3.90)	56-0701-79
	EtOH-HCl	275(4.51),354(3.90)	56-0701-79
$C_6H_7N_3$			
Propanedinitrile, [(dimethylamino)meth-ylene]-	EtOH	281(4.32)	131-0077-79D
	hexane	279(--)	131-0077-79D
$C_6H_7N_3OS$			
Acetamide, 2-(2-pyrimidinylthio)-	pH -2.3	214(3.58),249(4.08), 301(3.62)	12-2713-79
	pH 7	244(4.10),276(3.57)	12-2713-79
$C_6H_7N_3O_2$			
Glycine, N-4-pyrimidinyl-	pH 1	257(4.23)	39-2672-79C
Pyrazolo[4,3-d][1,3]oxazin-5(1H)-one, 4,7-dihydro-3-methyl-	EtOH	227(3.78)	118-0584-79
$C_6H_7N_3O_2S$			
3-Isothiazolecarboxamide, 5-acetyl-4-amino-	MeCN	244(3.91),379(3.96)	5-1534-79
$C_6H_7N_3O_3$			
1(2H)-Pyrimidineacetic acid, 4-amino-2-oxo-	pH 1	280(4.02)	73-3023-79
	pH 7-10.5	275(3.88)	73-3023-79
	pH 12	275(3.88)	73-3023-79
4-Pyrimidinecarboxamide, 1,2,3,6-tetra-hydro-1-methyl-2,6-dioxo-	pH 1	280(3.78)	44-0970-79
	pH 13	313(3.82)	44-0970-79
4-Pyrimidinecarboxamide, 1,2,3,6-tetra-hydro-3-methyl-2,6-dioxo-	pH 1	273(3.93)	44-0970-79
	pH 13	271(3.80)	44-0970-79
$C_6H_7N_3O_4$			
1H-Imidazole-1-acetic acid, 4-nitro-, methyl ester	EtOH	286(3.87)	4-1545-79
1H-Pyrazole-3-carboxylic acid, 4,5-di-hydro-4-nitroso-5-oxo-, ethyl ester	pH 1	261(3.98),357(3.56)	18-0208-79
	pH 11	300(4.02),369(3.72)	18-0208-79
	EtOH	261(3.93),357(3.62)	18-0208-79
$C_6H_7N_3S_2$			
2-Thiophenecarbonitrile, 3,4-diamino-5-(methylthio)-	EtOH	300(4.07),325(4.00)	95-1081-79
hydrochloride	EtOH	300(4.07),325(3.99)	95-1081-79
$C_6H_7N_5$			
1,2,4-Triazolo[4,3-a]pyrazin-8-amine, 3-methyl-	EtOH	229(4.08),297(3.79)	44-1028-79

Compound	Solvent	λ_{max}(log ε)	Ref.
$C_6H_7N_5O$			
Imidazo[1,5-a]-1,3,5-triazin-4(1H)-one, 2-amino-8-methyl-	EtOH	267(3.94)	44-3835-79
$C_6H_7N_5O_2$			
Imidazo[5,1-f][1,2,4]triazine-4,7-(1H,6H)-dione, 2-amino-5-methyl-	EtOH-NaOH	223(4.17),242(4.17), 317(3.62)	39-1120-79C
1H-Pyrazole-4-carbonyl azide, 3-(hydroxymethyl)-5-methyl-	EtOH	256(4.15)	118-0584-79
$C_6H_7N_5O_4$			
Glycine, N-(6-amino-1,4-dihydro-5-nitroso-4-oxo-2-pyrimidinyl)-	pH 0.25	209(3.99),270(4.17), 310s(4.03)	18-2933-79
	pH 5.0	214(3.85),230(3.98), 260(3.74),326(4.41)	18-2933-79
	pH 10.0	211(3.89),327(4.43)	18-2933-79
$C_6H_7N_5S$			
5H-Imidazo[4,5-d]-1,2,3-triazine, 5-methyl-4-(methylthio)-	MeOH	210(4.2),238(4.04), 298(4.0)	103-0685-79
7H-Imidazo[4,5-d]-1,2,3-triazine, 7-methyl-4-(methylthio)-	MeOH	210(4.14),235(3.98), 284(3.88),305(3.88)	103-0685-79
$C_6H_7N_5S_2$			
Thiazolo[5,4-d]pyrimidin-7(4H)-one, 2-(methylthio)-, hydrazone	EtOH	244(4.32),288(4.30)	2-0307-79B
C_6H_7P			
Phosphine, phenyl-	hexane	258(2.74),265(2.74), 272(2.59)	22-0241-79I
	C_6H_{12}	220s(3.87),237s(3.72), 266f(2.75)	39-0501-79B
	12M HCl	222(4.00),267f(3.06)	39-0501-79B
C_6H_8			
Cyclobutane, 1,2-bis(methylene)-	dioxan	247(3.99)	24-0862-79
1,3,5-Hexatriene	C_6H_{12}	289(1.40),298(1.38), 308s(1.23)	44-4254-79
C_6H_8BrNO			
2H-Pyrrol-2-one, 4-bromo-1,5-dihydro-5,5-dimethyl-	EtOH	221(4.04)	12-2041-79
$C_6H_8BrN_2O$			
Pyrimidinium, 5-bromo-3,4-dihydro-1,3-dimethyl-4-oxo-	pH 0.29	245(3.84),277(3.72)	44-3256-79
$C_6H_8BrN_3O$			
2(1H)-Pyrimidinone, 5-bromo-1-methyl-4-(methylamino)-	H_2O	287(3.89)	44-4385-79
$C_6H_8Br_2N_2O_2$			
1-Cyclohexen-1-amine, 6,6-dibromo-2-nitro-	EtOH	230(3.64),371(4.13)	44-3410-79
$C_6H_8Cl_2N_4O_2$			
1,3-Propanediol, 2-[(4,6-dichloro-1,3,5-triazin-2-yl)amino]-	EtOH	236(4.17)	104-1144-79

Compound	Solvent	λ max (log ε)	Ref.
$C_6H_8N_2$			
1,4-Diazocine, 1,4-dihydro-	MeCN	254s(3.77),263(3.82), 282s(4.39)	89-0964-79
1H-Imidazole, 1-ethenyl-2-methyl-	isooctane	236(4.03)	65-1225-79
	pH 1	222(3.98)	65-1225-79
	H_2O	229(3.98)	65-1225-79
	EtOH	236(4.03)	65-1225-79
$C_6H_8N_2O$			
Ethanone, 1-cyclobutyl-2-diazo-	MeOH	246(3.91),272(4.05)	73-2426-79
1H-Imidazole-2-methanol, 1-ethenyl-	EtOH	237.4(4.09)	70-1931-79
4(3H)-Pyrimidinone, 3,6-dimethyl-	EtOH	224(3.75),268(3.56)	39-1199-79C
$C_6H_8N_2OS$			
4(1H)-Pyrimidinone, 2,3-dihydro-5,6-dimethyl-2-thioxo-	MeOH	218(4.19),279(4.25)	73-2426-79
4(1H)-Pyrimidinone, 5-ethyl-2,3-dihydro-2-thioxo-	MeOH	216(4.23),277(4.30)	73-2426-79
$C_6H_8N_2O_2$			
Isoxazolo[3,4-c]pyridin-3-ol, 4,5,6,7-tetrahydro- (zwitterion)	MeOH	260(3.97)	111-0157-79
2-Propenoic acid, 3-amino-2-cyano-, ethyl ester	hexane	271(--)	131-0077-79D
	EtOH	272(4.23)	131-0077-79D
2,4(1H,3H)-Pyrimidinedione, 5,6-dimethyl-	MeOH	267.0(4.00)	73-2426-79
2,4(1H,3H)-Pyrimidinedione, 5-ethyl-	MeOH	264.5(3.92)	73-2426-79
4(3H)-Pyrimidinone, 6-(hydroxymethyl)-3-methyl-	EtOH	224(3.75),270(3.53)	39-1199-79C
$C_6H_8N_2O_2S$			
Benzenesulfonamide, 4-amino-	pH 7.4	260(4.16)	149-0531-79A
Carbamic acid, 2-thiazolyl-, ethyl ester	n.s.g.	256(4.05)	87-0028-79
1H-Imidazole-5-carboxylic acid, 1-methyl-4-(methylthio)-	EtOH	278(3.94)	2-0222-79A
2,4(1H,3H)-Pyrimidinedione, 6-methyl-5-(methylthio)-	MeOH	235(3.87),253(3.89), 276(3.92)	4-0567-79
$C_6H_8N_2O_2S_2$			
1-Imidazolidinecarbodithioic acid, 3-methyl-2,4-dioxo-, methyl ester	EtOH	242(3.40),265(4.34), 301(4.09)	39-0692-79C
1-Piperazinecarbodithioic acid, 2,5-dioxo-, methyl ester	EtOH	267(4.04),310(3.90)	39-0692-79C
$C_6H_8N_2O_3$			
2(1H)-Pyrazinone, 1-hydroxy-3,6-dimethyl-, 4-oxide	EtOH	230(4.36),279(3.93), 335(3.79)	94-2027-79
1H-Pyrazole-3-carboxylic acid, 4,5-dihydro-5-oxo-, ethyl ester	pH 1	211(3.95),256(3.60)	18-0208-79
	pH 11	225(4.06),295(3.39)	18-0208-79
	EtOH	223(4.00),260(3.46)	18-0208-79
1H-Pyrrole, 2-methoxy-1-methyl-4-nitro-	MeOH	280(3.84),359(3.62)	44-4420-79
1H-Pyrrole, 3-methoxy-1-methyl-4-nitro-	MeOH	297(3.98)	44-4420-79
$C_6H_8N_2O_3S$			
4(1H)-Pyrimidinone, 6-(1,2-dihydroxyethyl)-2,3-dihydro-2-thioxo-, (S)-	pH 1.0	220(4.23),275(4.24)	136-0235-79B
	pH 7.0	217(4.23),270(4.22)	136-0235-79B
	pH 11.0	257(4.08),300(3.86)	136-0235-79B

Compound	Solvent	λ_{max}(log ε)	Ref.
$C_6H_8N_2O_4$			
2,4(1H,3H)-Pyrimidinedione, 6-(1,2-dihydroxyethyl)-	pH 0.25	212(3.90),263(3.96)	136-0235-79B
	pH 6.0	208(4.00),263(3.99)	136-0235-79B
	pH 13.0	226(3.85),269(3.83)	136-0235-79B
$C_6H_8N_2O_5$			
2-Hexenoic acid, 4-(hydroxyimino)-5-nitro-	EtOH	253(4.26)	88-4399-79
$C_6H_8N_2S$			
4(1H)-Pyrimidinethione, 2,6-dimethyl-	EtOH	292(4.00),333(3.85)	150-1579-79
$C_6H_8N_2S_2$			
Cyclopenta[1,3,4]thiadiazine-3(2H)-thione, 4a,5,6,7-tetrahydro-	EtOH	323(4.027)	48-0959-79
4(1H)-Pyrmidinethione, 6-methyl-2-(methylthio)-	EtOH	254(4.17),302(3.81)	150-1579-79
$C_6H_8N_2S_3$			
Carbamodithioic acid, (3-methyl-2(3H)-thiazolylidene)-, methyl ester	EtOH	221(4.30),314(4.00), 359(4.31)	94-2879-79
$C_6H_8N_4O_2S$			
Formamide, N-(4-amino-1,2,5,6-tetrahydro-5-methyl-6-oxo-2-thioxo-5-pyrimidinyl)-	EtOH	261(3.92),317(3.78)	44-3835-79
C_6H_8O			
2-Cyclohexen-1-one	H_2SO_4	271(4.02)	124-1093-79
$C_6H_8O_2$			
2-Cyclopenten-1-one, 5-hydroxy-3-methyl-	n.s.g.	219(3.87)	39-0274-79C
1,4-Dioxane, 2,3-bis(methylene)-	dioxan	254(3.73)	24-0862-79
$C_6H_8O_3$			
6,8-Dioxabicyclo[3.2.1]octan-7-one, (+)-(1R,5R)-, hexamer	MeCN	215(2.86)	35-4013-79
2-Furancarboxaldehyde, 4,5-dihydro-5-(hydroxymethyl)-	EtOH	257(3.92)	136-0169-79D
$C_6H_8O_5$			
Butanedioic acid, oxo-, dimethyl ester	MeOH	259(3.48)	107-0603-79
$C_6H_9Br_2N_3O_2$			
2(1H)-Pyrimidinone, 5,5-dibromo-5,6-dihydro-6-hydroxy-1-methyl-4-(methylamino)-	0.5M HCl	229(3.89)	44-4385-79
	pH 1	229(3.87)	44-4385-79
	pH 2	229(3.80),280s(3.50)	44-4385-79
	pH 4	267(3.82)	44-4385-79
	pH 6	267(3.82)	44-4385-79
	pH 7	264(3.82)	44-4385-79
	pH 8	252(3.89)	44-4385-79
	pH 9	251(3.98)	44-4385-79
	MeOH	266(3.77)	44-4385-79
	H_2O	267(3.81)	44-4385-79
$C_6H_9Cl_3N_3P$			
1,3,5,2-Triazaphosphorine, 2,2,4-trichloro-6-(1,1-dimethylethyl)-2,2-dihydro-	hexane	274.5(3.54)	99-0055-79

Compound	Solvent	λ_{max}(log ε)	Ref.
$C_6H_9FN_2O_4S_2$			
Isothiazolium, 2-methyl-5-[methyl(oxido)iminiomethyl]-, fluorosulfonate	MeOH	218(3.95),260(3.44), 331(3.96)	39-2340-79C
C_6H_9NO			
2H-Pyrrol-2-one, 1,5-dihydro-5,5-dimethyl-	EtOH	230(3.46)	12-2035-79
$C_6H_9NOS_2$			
1-Pyrrolidinecarbodithioic acid, 2-oxo-, methyl ester	EtOH	269(4.22),304(4.05)	39-0692-79C
4H-1,3-Thiazin-4-one, tetrahydro-6,6-dimethyl-2-thioxo-	EtOH	259(4.14),310(4.17)	150-0212-79S
$C_6H_9NO_2$			
2,4-Pentanedione, 3-(aminomethylene)-	hexane	280(--)	131-0077-79D
	EtOH	280(4.17)	131-0077-79D
1H-Pyrrole-1-carboxaldehyde, 4,5-dihydro-5-hydroxy-2-methyl-	H_2O	238(3.95)	152-0115-79
2,4-Pyrrolidinedione, 5-ethyl-	aq NaOH	262(4.08)	142-0477-79B
$C_6H_9NO_2S_3$			
2-Propenenitrile, 2-(methylsulfonyl)-3,3-bis(methylthio)-	EtOH	225(3.57),326(4.13)	95-1234-79
$C_6H_9NO_3$			
2,3-Butanedione, mono(O-acetyloxime), (E)-	C_6H_{12}	215(4.10),326(1.30)	39-0156-79B
	EtOH	215(4.06),316(1.34)	39-0156-79B
$C_6H_9NS_2$			
2(3H)-Thiazolethione, 3,4,5-trimethyl-	EtOH	321(3.865)	48-0249-79
$C_6H_9N_2O$			
Pyrimidinium, 1,4-dihydro-1,3-dimethyl-4-oxo-	pH 0.29	231(4.06),262(3.47)	44-3256-79
$C_6H_9N_3O$			
2H-Pyrazolo[3,4-c]pyridin-3-ol, 4,5,6,7-tetrahydro-, dihydrobromide	MeOH	226(3.55),250(2.92)	111-0157-79
$C_6H_9N_3OS$			
1H-Imidazole-5-carboxamide, 1-methyl-4-(methylthio)-	EtOH	271(3.77)	2-0222-79A
$C_6H_9N_3OS_2$			
2-Thiophenecarboxamide, 3,4-diamino-5-(methylthio)-	EtOH	315(4.10)	95-1081-79
monohydrochloride	EtOH	317(4.11),325(4.03)	95-1081-79
$C_6H_9N_3O_3$			
1H-Pyrazole-3-carboxylic acid, 4-amino-4,5-dihydro-5-oxo-, ethyl ester, monohydrochloride	pH 1	281(3.91)	18-0208-79
	pH 11	253(3.88),288s(3.74)	18-0208-79
	EtOH	281(3.90)	18-0208-79
1,2,3-Triazine, 4,5,6-trimethoxy-	CH_2Cl_2	259(3.73),270s(--)	24-1529-79
$C_6H_9N_3O_5$			
4-Pyridinol, 1,2,3,6-tetrahydro-1-methyl-3,5-dinitro-	50% EtOH	304(3.35),364(3.54), 410(3.62)	4-0481-79
dipotassium salt	50% EtOH	234(3.70),308(3.61), 390(4.01)	4-0481-79

Compound	Solvent	λ_{max}(log ε)	Ref.
$C_6H_9N_3S$			
Isothiazolo[5,1-e][1,2,3]thiadiazole-7-S^{IV}, 1,6-dihydro-1,6-dimethyl-	C_6H_{12}	223(4.01),283(2.41), 386(4.11)	39-2340-79C
$C_6H_9N_5$			
1,2,4-Triazolo[4,3-b][1,2,4]triazine, 1,7-dihydro-3,7-dimethyl-	EtOH	271(3.62)	4-0427-79
1,2,4-Triazolo[4,3-b][1,2,4]triazine, 1,7-dihydro-6,7-dimethyl-	EtOH	216(3.86),267(2.95)	4-0427-79
1,2,4-Triazolo[4,3-b][1,2,4]triazine, 1,7-dihydro-7,7-dimethyl-	EtOH	265(3.88)	4-0427-79
$C_6H_9N_5O_2$			
Formamide, N-(2,6-diamino-4,5-dihydro-5-methyl-4-oxo-5-pyrimidinyl)-	EtOH	234(4.31),271(3.93)	44-3835-79
$C_6H_{10}BrN_3O_2$			
2(1H)-Pyrimidinone, 5-bromo-5,6-dihydro-6-hydroxy-1-methyl-4-(methylamino)-	H_2O	263(3.89)	44-4385-79
$C_6H_{10}Cl_2O$			
Butane, 1-[(2,2-dichloroethenyl)oxy]-	C_6H_{12}	210(4.07)	70-1610-79
$C_6H_{10}Cl_2S$			
Butane, 1-[(2,2-dichloroethenyl)thio]-	C_6H_{12}	248(3.89),256s(3.86)	70-1610-79
Propane, 2-[(2,2-dichloroethenyl)thio]-2-methyl-	C_6H_{12}	247(3.85),256s(3.79)	70-1610-79
	MeCN	246(3.89),256s(3.82)	70-1610-79
$C_6H_{10}N_2$			
Pyrazole, 3-propyl-	EtOH	222(3.66)	150-3782-79
$C_6H_{10}N_2O$			
1H-Imidazole-2-methanol, 1-ethyl-	EtOH	219.7(3.87)	70-1931-79
$C_6H_{10}N_2O_2$			
2(5H)-Furanone, 5-methyl-4-(1-methylhydrazino)-	EtOH	263(4.38)	4-0505-79
3-Pyrazolemethanol, 5-hydroxy-α,α-dimethyl-	EtOH	223(3.58)	4-0505-79
$C_6H_{10}N_2O_3$			
Pyrrolidine, α-acetoxy-N-nitroso-	H_2O	231(3.68),350(1.88)	44-4511-79
$C_6H_{10}N_2O_3S$			
2H-1,2,6-Thiadiazin-3(6H)-one, 6-ethyl-5-methyl-, 1,1-dioxide	isoPrOH	218(3.68),293(3.89)	44-4191-79
$C_6H_{10}N_2O_4S$			
L-Cysteine, N-acetyl-, methyl ester, nitrite	MeOH	338(2.98),510(1.08), 545(1.34)	39-1969-79C
$C_6H_{10}N_2S_2$			
2-Butenenitrile, 3-amino-2,4-bis(methylthio)-	EtOH	280(4.07)	39-2708-79C
2H-1,3,4-Thiadiazine-2-thione, 3,6-dihydro-5,6,6-trimethyl-	EtOH	278(3.748),319(3.976)	48-0959-79
$C_6H_{10}N_3S$			
Sulfonium, methyl(2-pyrimidinylamino)-, salt with trifluoroacetic acid	EtOH	273(4.37),304(3.57)	139-0195-79

Compound	Solvent	λ_{max}(log ε)	Ref.
$C_6H_{10}N_4O_2$			
1H-Pyrazole-4-carboxylic acid, 3-(hydroxymethyl)-5-methyl-, hydrazide	EtOH	230(3.84)	118-0584-79
1,2,4-Triazine-3,5(2H,4H)-dione, 6-(dimethylamino)-2-methyl-	pH 1-7	318(3.73)	124-0048-79
	pH 13	302(3.69)	124-0048-79
1,2,4-Triazine-3,5(2H,4H)-dione, 6-(dimethylamino)-4-methyl-	pH 1-7	310(3.72)	124-0048-79
	pH 13	324(3.79)	124-0048-79
$C_6H_{10}N_6O_2$			
1,2,4-Triazine-6-acetic acid, 3-amino-2,5-dihydro-α-methyl-5-oxo-, hydrazide	EtOH-NaOH	253(3.71)	39-1120-79C
$C_6H_{10}N_6O_9$			
1-Propanamine, N-(2,2-dinitropropyl)-2,2-dinitro-N-nitroso-	$C_2H_4Cl_2$	242(3.60),375(1.95)	70-0944-79
$C_6H_{10}O$			
Cyclobutanone, 2,2-dimethyl-	EtOH	277(1.70)	44-0989-79
$C_6H_{10}OS$			
2-Oxepanethione	$CHCl_3$	255(3.99),388(1.23)	88-1477-79
$C_6H_{10}O_2S$			
1,3-Butadiene, 2-methyl-1-(methylsulfonyl)-	EtOH	240(4.37)	70-0594-79
Thiiranecarboxylic acid, propyl ester, (S)-	EtOH	219(2.72),279(2.15)	39-1852-79C
Thiiranecarboxylic acid, 3,3-dimethyl-, methyl ester, (R)-	EtOH	212(2.93),259s(2.23)	39-1852-79C
$C_6H_{10}O_3$			
2,5-Hexanedione, 1-hydroxy-	EtOH	276(3.60)	136-0055-79B
$C_6H_{10}S$			
3-Pentene-2-thione, 4-methyl-	$CHCl_3$	582(1.0)	88-2677-79
$C_6H_{11}N$			
2,4-Hexadien-1-amine	MeOH	227(4.44)	44-3451-79
$C_6H_{11}NO_2$			
2,3-Butanedione, mono(O-ethyloxime)	C_6H_{12}	234(4.03)	39-1025-79B
(E)-	C_6H_{12}	234(4.03),318(1.43)	39-0151-79B
	EtOH	238(4.08)	39-0151-79B
(Z)-	C_6H_{12}	244(3.51),328(1.79)	39-0151-79B
Cyclohexane, nitro-	neat	278(1.52)	39-0907-79B
	isooctane	280(1.46)	39-0907-79B
	MeOH	277(1.48)	39-0907-79B
	$CF_3CHOHCF_3$	270(1.76)	39-0907-79B
2-Pentenoic acid, 4-amino-4-methyl-	H_2O	206(3.70)	12-2507-79
3=Pentenoic acid, 2-amino-4-methyl-	H_2O	210(3.46)(end abs.)	12-2507-79
$C_6H_{11}NO_2S_2$			
Glycine, N-methyl-N-[(methylthio)thioxomethyl]-, methyl ester	CH_2Cl_2	249(3.96),277(4.06), 337(1.82)	5-0650-79
$C_6H_{11}NO_3$			
2-Butanone, 3,3-dimethyl-1-nitro-	EtOH	230(2.78),303(2.15)	44-4116-79
	EtOH-NaOH	234(3.54),331(4.21)	44-4116-79

Compound	Solvent	$\lambda_{max}(\log \epsilon)$	Ref.
$C_6H_{11}N_2O_3P$			
1,3,2-Diazaphosphorin-4(1H)-one, 2-ethoxy-2,3-dihydro-6-methyl-, 2-oxide	pH 1-6	264(4.05)	103-1142-79
	EtOH	260(4.05)	103-1142-79
	anion	267(3.87),292(3.57)	103-1142-79
	dianion	290(4.01)	103-1142-79
$C_6H_{11}N_3O$			
Acetamide, N-(4,5-dihydro-1-methyl-1H-pyrazol-3-yl)-	$CHCl_3$	269.5(3.93)	150-0801-79
1,2,4-Triazin-3(2H)-one, 4,5-dihydro-5,5,6-trimethyl-	EtOH	238(3.51),271(2.95)	4-0427-79
$C_6H_{11}N_3O_2S$			
2H-1,2,6-Thiadiazin-5-amine, 2-ethyl-3-methyl-, 1,1-dioxide	isoPrOH	243(3.76),289(4.05)	44-4191-79
$C_6H_{11}N_3O_3S$			
Sulfamide, N-ethyl-N'-(3-methyl-5-isoxazolyl)-	isoPrOH	232(4.00)	44-4191-79
$C_6H_{11}O_4P$			
Phosphoric acid, dimethyl 1-methylene-2-propenyl ester	MeOH	220(4.22)	33-0442-79
C_6H_{12}			
1-Butene, 3,3-dimethyl-	heptane	181(4.1)	65-0916-79
$C_6H_{12}N_2$			
1H-Imidazole, 4,5-dihydro-2-(1-methylethyl)-	EtOH	223(3.72)	39-2289-79C
$C_6H_{12}N_2O$			
2,3-Butanedione, mono(dimethylhydrazone)	$CHCl_3$	305(3.83)	150-1451-79
$C_6H_{12}N_2O_2$			
Acetaldehyde, (butylnitrosoamino)-	EtOH	236(3.84),352(1.93)	94-0541-79
Diazene, cyclohexylhydroxy-, 1-oxide	EtOH	228.5(3.86)	88-2457-79
$C_6H_{12}O$			
Butane, 1-(ethenyloxy)-	C_6H_{12}	194(3.99)	70-1610-79
$C_6H_{12}OSi$			
2-Propenal, 3-(trimethylsilyl)-, (E)-	EtOH	220(4.04)	78-0621-79
$C_6H_{12}O_3Si$			
Acetic acid, oxo(trimethylsilyl)-, methyl ester	C_6H_{12}	227(2.41),455(2.00)	88-0871-79
$C_6H_{12}S$			
Propane, 2-(ethenylthio)-2-methyl-	hexane	241(3.67)	70-1479-79
$C_6H_{12}S_2$			
1,3-Dithiolane, 2,2,4-trimethyl-	hexane	194(3.65),249(2.20)	114-0407-79A
$C_6H_{12}S_4Si$			
1,4,6,9-Tetrathia-5-silaspiro[4.4]nonane, 2,7-dimethyl-	hexane	235(3.03)	114-0407-79A
$C_6H_{13}N_3O_3$			
Carbamic acid, [(methylnitrosoamino)-methyl]-, 1-methylethyl ester	EtOH	227(3.92),353(1.94)	94-0682-79

Compound	Solvent	λ_{max}(log ε)	Ref.
$C_6H_{14}ClPS$			
Phosphonochloridothious acid, ethyl-, butyl ester	hexane	190(3.67),215(4.15), 250(3.32)	65-1760-79
$C_6H_{14}S_2Si$			
1,4-Dithia-2-silacyclohexane, 2,2,5-trimethyl-	hexane	200(3.56),240s(2.42)	114-0407-79A
$C_6H_{15}N_3$			
Ethanehydrazonamide, N,N,N',N'-tetra-methyl-, monohydrochloride	H_2O	215(3.95)	104-2066-79
	pH 13	232(3.80)	104-2066-79
Ethanimidic acid, 2-(1,1-dimethylethyl)-hydrazide, monohydrochloride	H_2O	208(3.51)	104-2066-79
	pH 13	224(3.72)	104-2066-79
Ethanimidic acid, 2-methyl-2-(1-methyl-ethyl)hydrazide, monohydriodide	H_2O	226(4.15)	104-2073-79
$C_6H_{15}PS$			
Phosphinothious acid, diethyl-, ethyl ester	hexane	198(4.02),208(3.99), 223(3.84)	65-1760-79
$C_6H_{15}PS_2$			
Phosphonodithious acid, ethyl-, diethyl ester	hexane	215(4.31),254s(3.34)	65-1760-79
$C_6H_{15}PS_3$			
Phosphorotrithious acid, triethyl ester	hexane	202(4.13),228s(3.87), 278s(3.31)	65-1760-79
$C_6H_{16}Cl_2OSi_2$			
Disiloxane, 1,3-bis(chloromethyl)-1,1,3,3-tetramethyl-	heptane	189.3(3.48)	65-1333-79
	MeCN	189.2(3.50)	65-1333-79
$C_6H_{16}S_2Si$			
Silane, bis(ethylthio)dimethyl-	hexane	224(3.14)	114-0407-79A
$C_6H_{18}OSi_2$			
Disiloxane, hexamethyl-	heptane	185.7(2.86)	65-1333-79
	MeCN	185.7(2.95),198s(--)	65-1333-79
$C_6H_{18}O_3Si_3$			
Cyclotrisiloxane, hexamethyl-	heptane	185.5(2.26),202s(--)	65-1333-79
$C_6H_{18}Si_2$			
Disilane, hexamethyl-	heptane	193(3.7)	65-0916-79
$C_6H_{19}NSi_2$			
Silanamine, 1,1,1-trimethyl-N-(trimeth-ylsilyl)-	heptane	202.8(3.40)	65-1333-79
$C_6H_{20}O_2Si_3$			
Trisiloxane, 1,1,3,3,5,5-hexamethyl-	heptane	185.2(1.78)	65-1333-79
	MeCN	186(2.34),198s(--)	65-1333-79
$C_6H_{21}N_3Si_3$			
Cyclotrisilazane, 2,2,4,4,6,6-hexa-methyl-	heptane	198.3(3.76)	65-1333-79
$C_6H_{24}O_6Si_6$			
Cyclohexasiloxane, 2,4,6,8,10,12-hexa-methyl-	heptane	198.4(1.65)	65-1333-79

Compound	Solvent	$\lambda_{max}(\log \epsilon)$	Ref.
$C_6N_{12}O_2$			
2,5-Cyclohexadiene-1,4-dione, 2,3,5,6-tetraazido-	hexane	215(4.26),278(4.55), 380(4.26),570(2.42)	59-0663-79
	C_6H_{12}	210(4.18),281(4.41), 382(4.14),570(2.39)	59-0663-79
	MeOH	205(4.47),268(4.41), 355(4.11),540(2.50)	59-0663-79
	MeCN	215(4.43),275(4.40), 368(4.12),550(2.48)	59-0663-79

Compound	Solvent	λ_{max}(log ϵ)	Ref.
$C_7H_3Cl_2NS$			
2,1-Benzisothiazole, 3,5-dichloro-	EtOH	225(4.41),293(3.90), 306(3.98),334(3.80), 347s(3.7)	33-0391-79
$C_7H_3F_5OS$			
Benzenesulfenic acid, pentafluoro-, methyl ester	n.s.g.	217(3.91),276(3.16), 313(3.06)	70-0315-79
C_7H_3NO			
2-Propynenitrile, 3-(2-furanyl)-	EtOH	212(3.90),279(4.13), 291(4.11)	22-0651-79
2-Propynenitrile, 3-(3-furanyl)-	EtOH	209(3.73),215(3.67), 256(3.89),270(3.88)	22-0651-79
C_7H_3NS			
2-Propynenitrile, 3-(2-thienyl)-	EtOH	220(3.99),265(4.03), 292(4.18)	22-0651-79
2-Propynenitrile, 3-(3-thienyl)-	EtOH	214(4.15),228(3.83), 266(4.21),280(4.15)	22-0651-79
$C_7H_4BrClO_2$			
1,3-Benzodioxole, 5-bromo-4-chloro-	n.s.g.	208(4.39),238(3.44), 295(3.27)	103-0961-79
$C_7H_4BrNO_4$			
1,3-Benzodioxole, 6-bromo-4-nitro-	n.s.g.	205(4.11),240(3.97), 272(3.65)	103-0961-79
$C_7H_4BrN_3O_2$			
Imidazo[1,5-a]pyridine, 3-bromo-1-nitro-	MeOH	234(4.01),275(3.57), 390(4.15)	39-1833-79C
Sydnone, 4-bromo-3-(3-pyridinyl)-	MeOH	246(3.77),322(3.90)	4-1059-79
$C_7H_4Br_2O_2$			
1,3-Benzodioxole, 4,5-dibromo-	n.s.g.	213(4.54),238(3.71), 296(3.50)	103-0961-79
$C_7H_4ClNO_4$			
1,3-Benzodioxole, 4-chloro-5-nitro-	n.s.g.	206(4.20),250(3.78), 320(3.45)	103-0961-79
1,3-Benzodioxole, 4-chloro-6-nitro-	n.s.g.	205(4.45),217(4.28), 247(4.08),333(3.75)	103-0961-78
C_7H_4ClNS			
2,1-Benzisothiazole, 3-chloro-	EtOH	222(4.15),290(3.78), 303(3.88),327(3.65), 341s(3.5)	33-0391-79
$C_7H_4ClN_3OS$			
1,2,3,4-Oxatriazolium, 3-(4-chlorophenyl)-2,5-dihydro-5-oxo-, hydroxide, inner salt	n.s.g.	232s(3.81),261(4.26), 274s(4.19),388(3.54)	39-0732-79C
1,2,3,4-Thiatriazolium, 3-(4-chlorophenyl)-2,5-dihydro-5-oxo-, hydroxide, inner salt	n.s.g.	223(3.96),288(4.00), 338s(3.65)	39-0732-79C
$C_7H_4ClN_3O_2$			
Sydnone, 4-chloro-3-(3-pyridinyl)-	MeOH	235(3.76),255s(3.69), 317(3.84)	4-1059-79

Compound	Solvent	λ_{max}(log ϵ)	Ref.
$C_7H_4ClN_3S_2$			
1,2,3,4-Thiatriazolium, 3-(4-chloro-phenyl)-2,5-dihydro-5-thioxo-, hydroxide, inner salt	n.s.g.	236(3.79),297(4.42), 456(3.32)	39-0732-79C
$C_7H_4Cl_2O_4$			
Benzoic acid, 2,3-dichloro-5,6-di-hydroxy-	EtOH	218(3.68),284(3.64)	104-1740-79
$C_7H_4Cl_2S_2$			
Carbonochloridodithioic acid, 2-chloro-phenyl ester	C_6H_{12}	303(4.06),450(1.31)	97-0289-79
Carbonochloridodithioic acid, 3-chloro-phenyl ester	C_6H_{12}	306(3.96),452(1.38)	97-0289-79
Carbonochloridodithioic acid, 4-chloro-phenyl ester	C_6H_{12}	307(3.97),451(1.42)	97-0289-79
$C_7H_4F_8O_2$			
3,5-Heptanedione, 1,1,2,2,6,6,7,7-octa-fluoro-	hexane	279(3.52)	65-0188-79
$C_7H_4IN_3O_2$			
Sydnone, 4-iodo-3-(3-pyridinyl)-	MeOH	255(3.63),327(3.85)	4-1059-79
$C_7H_4N_2O_2S$			
2-Propenenitrile, 2-nitro-3-(2-thienyl)-	EtOH	375(4.25)	104-1859-79
$C_7H_4N_2O_3$			
2-Propenenitrile, 3-(2-furanyl)-2-nitro-	EtOH	371(4.33)	104-1859-79
$C_7H_4N_2O_3S$			
Oxazole, 5-(5-nitro-2-thienyl)-	EtOH	250(3.88)	94-0793-79
$C_7H_4N_2O_4$			
Oxazole, 5-(5-nitro-2-furanyl)-	EtOH	238(4.05),351(4.16)	94-0793-79
$C_7H_4N_2O_6$			
1,3-Benzodioxole, 4,5-dinitro-	n.s.g.	208(4.04),233(4.05), 345(3.70)	103-0961-79
$C_7H_4OS_4$			
1,3-Dithiole-4-carboxaldehyde, 2-(1,3-dithiol-2-ylidene)-	MeCN	238(3.21),285(4.12), 298(4.12),312(4.11), 462(3.35)	44-1476-79
$C_7H_4O_2S_4$			
1,3-Dithiole-4-carboxylic acid, 2-(1,3-dithiol-2-ylidene)-	pH 13	301(3.84),313(3.85), 420(2.00)	44-1476-79
$C_7H_4S_3$			
3H-1,2-Benzodithiole-3-thione	MeOH	225(4.07),270(4.08), 445(4.11)	2-0131-79B
$C_7H_5BrN_2$			
1H-Pyrrolo[2,3-c]pyridine, 4-bromo-	EtOH	375(3.7)	103-0076-79
$C_7H_5BrN_2O_3S$			
2H-1,2,4-Benzothiadiazin-3(4H)-one, 6-bromo-, 1,1-dioxide	EtOH	222(4.50),245s(4.01), 295(3.37)	39-1043-79C

Compound	Solvent	$\lambda_{max}(\log \epsilon)$	Ref.
2H-1,2,4-Benzothiadiazin-3(4H)-one, 8-bromo-, 1,1-dioxide	EtOH	220(4.37),249(3.92), 298(3.42)	39-1043-79C
$C_7H_5BrO_2$			
1,3-Benzodioxole, 4-bromo-	n.s.g.	207(4.55),286(3.47)	103-0961-79
$C_7H_5ClN_2O_3S$			
2H-1,2,4-Benzothiadiazin-3(4H)-one, 7-chloro-, 1,1-dioxide	EtOH	215(4.16),251(4.13), 304(3.23)	39-1043-79C
$C_7H_5ClN_2S_2$			
1,2,3,5-Dithiadiazol-1-ium, 4-phenyl-, chloride	CH_2Cl_2	396(2.84)	39-1192-79C
$C_7H_5ClO_2$			
1,3-Benzodioxole, 4-chloro-	n.s.g.	207(4.49),233(3.53), 285(3.49)	103-0961-79
$C_7H_5ClS_2$			
Carbonochloridodithioic acid, phenyl ester	C_6H_{12}	306(3.94),458(1.52)	97-0289-79
$C_7H_5FN_2O_2$			
2,4(1H,3H)-Pyrimidinedione, 5-fluoro-1-(2-propynyl)-	pH 1	270(3.96)	1-0515-79
	pH 13	269(3.78)	1-0515-79
$C_7H_5F_4N_3$			
Guanidine, 1-(2,3,4,6-tetrafluorophenyl)-, mononitrate	MeOH	203(4.29),261(3.38)	83-0426-79
C_7H_5N			
Benzonitrile	C_6H_{12}	221(4.10),225(4.08), 230(4.05),264(2.70), 270(2.85),277(2.85)	65-0479-79
	n.s.g.	192(4.72),223(4.11), 270(2.81)	73-0873-79
C_7H_5NO			
Benzene, isocyanato-	n.s.g.	263(3.6),270(3.8), 278(3.6)	65-1828-79
1,2-Benzisoxazole	EtOH	229s(3.88),234(3.98), 240(3.91),280(3.44)	33-0314-79
2,1-Benzisoxazole	EtOH	256(3.04),261(3.09), 267(3.27),273(3.27), 279(3.42),304(3.70)	33-0271-79
C_7H_5NOS			
Oxazole, 5-(2-thienyl)-	EtOH	286(4.16)	94-0793-79
Thiazolo[3,2-a]pyridinium, 3-hydroxy-, hydroxide, inner salt	MeOH	260(3.9),390(3.9)	103-1081-79
$C_7H_5NOS_2$			
3H-1,2-Benzodithiol-3-one, oxime	EtOH	345(3.65)	2-0131-79B
$C_7H_5NO_2$			
Furo[3,4-c]pyridin-1(3H)-one	EtOH	223(3.73),278(3.85)	150-4801-79
Oxazole, 5-(2-furanyl)-	EtOH	275(4.03)	94-0793-79
$C_7H_5NO_4$			
1,3-Benzodioxole, 4-nitro-	n.s.g.	205(3.85),233(4.01), 272(3.89),360(3.43)	103-0961-79

Compound	Solvent	λ_{max}(log ϵ)	Ref.
1,3-Benzodioxol-5-ol, 6-nitroso-	0.7M HCl	226(3.98),315(4.02), 370(3.49),395(3.48)	94-2442-79
	H_2O	225(3.93),315(4.01), 370(3.49),395(3.48)	94-2442-79
	pH 12	240(3.96),345(4.08), 423(3.82)	94-2442-79
$C_7H_5NO_6$			
Benzoic acid, 2,3-dihydroxy-4-nitro-	EtOH	230(3.53),314(3.66)	104-1740-79
Benzoic acid, 2,3-dihydroxy-5-nitro-	EtOH	211(4.12),235(4.06), 270(3.81),350(3.82)	104-1740-79
Benzoic acid, 2,3-dihydroxy-6-nitro-	EtOH	213(4.25),355(3.64)	104-1740-79
$C_7H_5N_2S_2$			
1,2,3,5-Dithiadiazol-1-ium, 4-phenyl-, chloride	CH_2Cl_2	396(2.84)	39-1192-79C
$C_7H_5N_3$			
1,2,4-Benzotriazine	EtOH	232(4.78),305(3.57), 321s(3.45),434(2.46)	4-1005-79
Pyrido[3,2-c]pyridazine	EtOH	263(3.59),306(3.62), 318(3.65)	78-2027-79
Pyrido[3,4-c]pyridazine	EtOH	284(3.58)	78-2027-79
$C_7H_5N_3O$			
Benzaldehyde, 2-azido-	EtOH	239(4.27),258(4.09), 317(3.51)	33-0271-79
1,2,3-Benzotriazin-4(1H)-one	EtOH	223(3.28),278(2.77)	83-0842-79
$C_7H_5N_3OS$			
1,2,3,4-Oxatriazolium, 2,5-dihydro-3-phenyl-5-thioxo-, hydroxide, inner salt	n.s.g.	259(4.34),394(3.42)	39-0732-79C
1,2,3,4-Thiatriazolium, 2,5-dihydro-5-oxo-3-phenyl-, hydroxide, inner salt	n.s.g.	215s(3.99),280(4.04), 330s(3.71)	39-0732-79C
$C_7H_5N_3O_2$			
Imidazo[1,2-a]pyridine, nitro-	neutral	215(4.2),253(4.1), 264(4.1),292(3.7), 361(4.1)	9-0561-79
2-Propenenitrile, 2-nitro-3-(1H-pyrrol-2-yl)-	EtOH	420(4.67)	104-1859-79
$C_7H_5N_3O_2S$			
Isothiazolo[4,3-d]pyrimidin-7(4H)-one, 3-acetyl-	DMF	345(3.97)	5-1534-79
$C_7H_5N_3O_3$			
2,1-Benzisoxazole, 3-amino-6-nitro-	MeOH	232(4.16),272(4.10), 313(3.82),435(3.49)	94-2775-79
$C_7H_5N_3S_2$			
1,2,3,4-Thiatriazolium, 2,5-dihydro-3-phenyl-5-thioxo-, hydroxide, inner salt	n.s.g.	233(3.60),292(4.31), 450(3.23)	39-0732-79C
$C_7H_5N_5O$			
3H-Imidazo[1,2-c]pyrazolo[4,3-e]pyrimidin-2(7H)-one	H_2O	287(4.12)	39-2672-79C
	H_2O	287(4.08)	39-2672-79C

Compound	Solvent	$\lambda_{max}(\log \epsilon)$	Ref.
$C_7H_6Br_4N_2O$			
Ethanol, 2-[(2,3,5,6-tetrabromo-4-pyridinyl)amino]-	EtOH	234(4.47)	103-0764-79
$C_7H_6Br_4N_2O_3S$			
4-Pyridinesulfonamide, 2,3,5,6-tetra-bromo-N-(2-hydroxyethyl)-	EtOH	222(4.35),320(3.85)	103-0764-79
$C_7H_6ClN_3$			
1H-Benzotriazole, 5-chloro-1-methyl-	EtOH	258(3.73),292(3.61)	33-2129-79
1H-Benzotriazole, 6-chloro-1-methyl-	EtOH	270(3.87)	33-2129-79
$C_7H_6ClN_3S$			
1H-Pyrrolo[2,3-d]pyrimidine, 4-chloro-2-(methylthio)-	MeOH	222(4.08),248(4.39), 271(3.79),310(3.81)	24-3432-79
$C_7H_6ClN_5O$			
Acetamide, 2-chloro-N-1H-pyrazolo-[3,4-d]pyrimidin-4-yl-	pH 1	260.5(4.07)	39-2672-79C
$C_7H_6Cl_2N_2O_2$			
Pyrazinecarboxylic acid, 3,6-dichloro-5-methyl-, methyl ester	EtOH	227(4.05),295(3.90)	94-2027-79
C_7H_6FNO			
Benzene, 4-fluoro-2-methyl-1-nitroso-	$CHCl_3$	760(1.44)	44-2087-79
$C_7H_6F_3NO_2S_2$			
Thiazolium, 5-hydroxy-3-methyl-2-(meth-ylthio)-4-(trifluoroacetyl)-, hydroxide, inner salt	CH_2Cl_2	247(4.00),310(3.87), 358(4.16)	5-0650-79
$C_7H_6N_2$			
1H-Benzimidazole	pH 1	241(3.62),253(3.60), 261(3.71),267(3.88), 273(3.84)	65-1225-79
	H_2O	243(3.77),248(3.75), 265(3.65),271(3.75), 277(3.73)	65-1225-79
	EtOH	244(3.82),249(3.79), 266(3.66),272(3.80), 279(3.82)	65-1225-79
$C_7H_6N_2O$			
2-Propenenitrile, 3-amino-2-(2-furan-yl)-	EtOH	215(4.06),242(3.72), 299(4.14)	22-0651-79
2-Propenenitrile, 3-amino-2-(3-furan-yl)-	EtOH	206(3.86),252(3.82), 289(3.97)	22-0651-79
$C_7H_6N_2O_3S$			
2H-1,2,4-Benzothiadiazin-3(4H)-one, 1,1-dioxide	EtOH	214(4.08),243(4.01), 290(3.26)	39-1043-79C
$C_7H_6N_2S$			
2-Propenenitrile, 3-amino-2-(2-thien-yl)-	EtOH	206(3.96),312(4.11)	22-0651-79
2-Propenenitrile, 3-amino-2-(3-thien-yl)-	EtOH	208(4.11),280(4.15)	22-0651-79
1H-Thieno[2,3-c]-1,2-diazepine	EtOH	250(4.04)	94-2183-79
1H-Thieno[3,2-c]-1,2-diazepine	EtOH	277(4.00)	94-2183-79

Compound	Solvent	λ_{max}(log ε)	Ref.
Thieno[2,3-b]pyridin-6-amine	EtOH	240(4.34),322(3.78)	94-2183-79
Thieno[3,2-b]pyridin-5-amine	EtOH	254(4.15),328(3.78)	94-2183-79
$C_7H_6N_2S_2$			
3H-1,2-Benzodithiol-3-one, hydrazone	EtOH	348(3.70)	2-0131-79B
$C_7H_6N_2Se$			
2,1,3-Benzoselenadiazole, 5-methyl-	H_2O	335(4.23)	86-0015-79
monoprotonated	H_2O	348.5(4.31)	86-0015-79
diprotonated	H_2O	370(4.39)	86-0015-79
$C_7H_6N_4$			
1H-Tetrazole, 5-phenyl-, potassium salt	H_2O	240(4.1)	104-0751-79
	MeCN	248(4.1)(anom.)	104-0751-79
$C_7H_6N_4O_2$			
Pyrazino[2,3-d]pyridazin-5(6H)-one, 8-hydroxy-6-methyl-	pH 2.0	225s(3.61),263(4.12), 315(3.47)	12-0459-79
	pH 8.0	210(--),271(4.10), 328(3.47)	12-0459-79
$C_7H_6N_4O_2S$			
4,7(1H,8H)-Pteridinedione, 2,3-dihydro-1-methyl-2-thioxo-	pH 0.0	210(4.35),233s(4.00), 252(4.02),290(4.12), 339(4.22)	24-1499-79
	pH 6.0	236(4.37),261(4.24), 296(4.02),339(4.35), 353(4.32)	24-1499-79
	pH 13.0	223(4.47),252(4.25), 335(4.32),358(4.30)	24-1499-79
4,7(1H,8H)-Pteridinedione, 2,3-dihydro-3-methyl-2-thioxo-	pH 0.0	209(4.38),234s(3.92), 256s(3.93),280(4.09), 344(4.26)	24-1499-79
	pH 6.0	218s(4.20),234(4.36), 262(4.14),293(4.01), 340(4.28),354(4.27)	24-1499-79
	pH 12.0	242(4.41),257(4.37), 305(4.09),344(4.17), 353s(4.14)	24-1499-79
4,7(3H,8H)-Pteridinedione, 2-(methylthio)-	pH 2.1	220(4.34),244s(3.97), 295(3.97),339(4.18)	24-1499-79
	pH 7.33	215(4.31),244(4.25), 295(3.78),336(4.08), 345(4.10)	24-1499-79
	pH 11.0	232(4.54),254(4.21), 336(4.13),348s(4.08)	24-1499-79
$C_7H_6N_4O_3$			
1,2-Benzisoxazol-3(2H)-one, 5-nitro-, hydrazone	EtOH	268(4.05),294s(3.81), 331s(3.57)	94-0452B-79
3(2H)-Furazanone, 4-(6-methoxy-3-pyridazinyl)-	EtOH	243s(3.86),259(3.93), 314s(3.36)	4-0689-79
1,2,4-Oxadiazol-5(2H)-one, 3-(6-methoxy-3-pyridazinyl)-	EtOH	238(4.08)	4-0689-79
C_7H_6O			
Benzaldehyde	H_2O	201(4.33),250(4.15), 282s(3.20)	23-0506-79
	MeOH	247(4.09),281(3.09)	23-0506-79
	dioxan	245(4.14),281(3.13)	23-0506-79

Compound	Solvent	λmax(log ε)	Ref.
Benzaldehyde (cont.)	n.s.g.	198(4.43),241(4.15), 281(3.11)	73-0873-79
$C_7H_6OS_4$			
1,3-Dithiole-4-methanol, 2-(1,3-dithiol-2-ylidene)-	MeCN	309(4.12),316(4.13), 353(3.36),452(2.39)	44-1476-79
$C_7H_6O_2$			
Benzoic acid	H_2SO_4	193(4.64),228(4.03), 272(2.93)	114-0421-79B
	n.s.g.	196(4.56),232(4.18), 275(3.00)	73-0873-79
protonated	H_2SO_4	198(4.00),262(4.30), 303(3.18)	114-0421-79B
$C_7H_6O_3$			
Benzaldehyde, 2,3-dihydroxy-	EtOH	267(4.07),349(3.38)	33-0314-79
Benzaldehyde, 2,5-dihydroxy-	EtOH	257(3.86),363(3.61)	33-0314-79
C_7H_7			
Cycloheptatrienylium (tetrafluoroborate)	10% HCl	218(4.70),274(3.61), 281s(--)	39-1005-79B
$C_7H_7BrCl_2O$			
2-Propenal, 2-bromo-3-(2,2-dichloro-3-methylcyclopropyl)-	n.s.g.	260(4.08)	70-2452-79
$C_7H_7ClN_2O$			
Benzenamine, 4-chloro-N-methyl-N-nitroso-	EtOH	277(3.99)	104-1915-79
$C_7H_7ClN_2O_2$			
Benzenamine, 2-chloro-N-methyl-4-nitro-	30% t-BuOH	390(3.91)	104-1915-79
Benzenamine, 4-chloro-N-methyl-2-nitro-	EtOH	440(3.82)	104-1915-79
$C_7H_7Cl_2OPS$			
Phosphonothioic dichloride, (4-methoxyphenyl)-	C_6H_{12} or dioxan	254(4.16)	65-0068-79
$C_7H_7Cl_2O_2P$			
Phosphonic dichloride, (4-methoxyphenyl)-	C_6H_{12} or dioxan	246.0(4.25)	65-0068-79
$C_7H_7FN_2O_3$			
2,4(1H,3H)-Pyrimidinedione, 5-fluoro-1-(2-oxopropyl)-	pH 1	270(3.90)	1-0515-79
	pH 13	269(3.80)	1-0515-79
$C_7H_7F_2N_3$			
Guanidine, (2,4-difluorophenyl)-, mononitrate	MeOH	202(4.30),260(3.04), 265(3.05)	83-0426-79
Guanidine, (2,5-difluorophenyl)-, mononitrate	MeOH	202(4.35),268(3.65)	83-0426-79
$C_7H_7F_2OPS$			
Phosphonothioic difluoride, (4-methoxyphenyl)-	C_6H_{12} or dioxan	247(4.22)	65-0068-79
$C_7H_7F_2O_2P$			
Phosphonic difluoride, (4-methoxyphenyl)-	C_6H_{12} or dioxan	238.0(4.14)	65-0068-79

Compound	Solvent	$\lambda_{max}(\log \epsilon)$	Ref.
C_7H_7NO			
Benzamide	dioxan	224(4.07),263(2.90), 270(2.90),277(2.75)	4-0225-79
C_7H_7NOS			
2-Propenal, 3-(2-thienyl)-, oxime, (E)-	n.s.g.	308(4.45)	83-0282-79
(Z)-	n.s.g.	315(4.25)	83-0282-79
5H-Thiazolo[3,2-a]pyridin-5-one, 2,3-dihydro-	EtOH	243(3.92),328(4.11)	39-1150-79C
$C_7H_7NO_2$			
1,3-Benzodioxol-4-amine	n.s.g.	215(4.46),234(3.91)	103-0961-79
Benzohydroxamic acid	80% MeOH	227(3.92)	140-1562-79
ion	80% MeOH	270(3.69)	140-1562-79
2-Propenal, 3-(2-furanyl)-, oxime, (E)-	n.s.g.	298(4.52)	83-0282-79
(Z)-	n.s.g.	308(4.33)	83-0282-79
$C_7H_7NO_2S$			
Acetic acid, (2-pyridinylthio)-	MeOH	251(4.0),293(3.7)	103-1081-79
$C_7H_7NO_3$			
2(1H)-Pyridinone, 5-acetoxy-	EtOH	231(4.05),306(3.83)	36-0816-79
$C_7H_7NO_3S$			
Glycine, N-(2-thienylcarbonyl)-	toluene	250(4.08)	103-1303-79
4-Thia-1-azabicyclo[3.2.0]hept-2-ene-2-carboxylic acid, 3-methyl-7-oxo-	EtOH	260(3.59),302(3.78)	35-6296-79
(R)-	pH 7.4	258(3.68),297(3.81)	35-6301-79
	EtOH	261(3.55),305(3.82)	35-6301-79
$C_7H_7NO_4$			
Glycine, N-(2-furanylcarbonyl)-	toluene	255(4.25)	103-1303-79
2-Pyridinecarboxylic acid, 1,4-dihydro-5-hydroxy-1-methyl-4-oxo-	neutral	284(4.04)	18-0111-79
	base	312(3.90)	18-0111-79
$C_7H_7N_3$			
1H-Benzotriazole, 1-methyl-	EtOH	260(3.79),281(3.67)	33-2129-79
Imidazo[1,2-a]pyrimidine, 2-methyl-	MeOH	252(4.12),336(3.97)	9-0561-79
	base	317(4.36),444(4.29)	9-0561-79
3-Pyridinecarbonitrile, 2-amino-4-methyl-	CH_2Cl_2	318(3.84)	118-0376-79
7H-Pyrrolo[2,3-b]pyridin-7-amine	EtOH	238(4.28),308(4.00)	94-2183-79
$C_7H_7N_3O$			
1H-Benzotriazole, 1-methoxy-	EtOH	260(3.79),282(3.60)	33-2129-79
2H-Imidazo[4,5-b]pyridin-2-one, 1,4-dihydro-4-methyl-	CH_2Cl_2	328(4.0)	64-1473-79B
6H-Pyrazolo[3,4-b]pyridin-6-one, 1,7-dihydro-4-methyl-	MeOH	207(4.00),260(4.15)	48-0881-79
1H-Pyrrolo[2,3-d]pyrimidine, 4-methoxy-	MeOH	216(4.28),262(3.89)	24-3526-79
4H-Pyrrolo[3,2-d]pyrimidin-4-one, 1,5-dihydro-7-methyl-	pH 1	242(4.43),266s(3.86)	44-3826-79
	pH 7	263(4.40)	44-3826-79
	pH 13	270(3.86)	44-3826-79
$C_7H_7N_3OS$			
4H-Pyrrolo[2,3-d]pyrimidin-4(3H)-one, 1,2,3,7-tetrahydro-5-methyl-2-thioxo-	MeOH	242(3.93),302(4.26)	24-0799-79
$C_7H_7N_3OS_2$			
Formamide, N-[4-amino-5-cyano-2-(methylthio)-3-thienyl]-	EtOH	224(4.06),293(4.06), 299(3.96)	95-1081-79

Compound	Solvent	λmax(log ε)	Ref.
$C_7H_7N_3O_2$			
Imidazo[1,5-b]pyridazin-3-one, 2,3-dihydro-6-methoxy-	EtOH	233(4.43),376(3.28)	4-0689-79
1H-Pyrazole-5-carboxylic acid, 4-cyano-1-methyl-, methyl ester	MeOH	239(3.98)	24-1719-79
$C_7H_7N_3O_3$			
1H-Pyrazole-3-carboxylic acid, 5-cyano-4-hydroxy-, ethyl ester	EtOH	283(3.88),329(3.18)	23-0904-79
	EtOH-NaOH	329(3.93)	23-0904-79
$C_7H_7N_3O_4$			
Benzenamine, N-methyl-2,4-dinitro-	EtOH	261(3.96),351(4.21), 403(3.80)	73-1613-79
Benzenamine, N-methyl-2,6-dinitro-	EtOH	231(4.33),263(3.75), 427(3.85)	73-1613-79
$C_7H_7N_3S_3$			
Thiazolo[5,4-d]pyrimidine, 2,7-bis(methylthio)-	EtOH	258(4.32),300(4.31), 306(4.35)	2-0307-79B
$C_7H_7N_5$			
1-Triazene-1-carbonitrile, 3-(1-methyl-4(1H)-pyridinylidene)-	EtOH	230(3.80),245(3.88), 376(4.59)	94-1824-79
$C_7H_7N_5O_2$			
Glycine, N-1H-pyrazolo[3,4-d]pyrimidin-4-yl-	pH 1	268(4.01)	39-2672-79C
	pH 13	267(3.97)	39-2672-79C
C_7H_8			
1,3-Cyclohexadiene, 5-methylene-	isooctane	303(3.64)	44-0907-79
1,2,4,6-Heptatetraene	hexane	250s(4.49),257(4.60), 268(4.52)	89-0396-79
Toluene	n.s.g.	188(4.72),205(3.90), 262(2.40)	73-0873-79
$C_7H_8Br_2$			
Cyclopropane, 1,1-dibromo-2-(1,3-butadienyl)-, cis	hexane	231(4.26)	89-0396-79
trans	hexane	229.5(4.35)	89-0396-79
$C_7H_8Br_2Si$			
Silane, dibromomethylphenyl-	hexane	192(--),218(3.73), 255s(2.39),260(2.55), 266(2.64),273(2.52)	114-0195-79D
$C_7H_8ClNO_2$			
4(1H)-Pyridinone, 2-(chloromethyl)-5-hydroxy-1-methyl-	neutral	283(4.00)	18-0111-79
	base	312(3.89)	18-0111-79
$C_7H_8Cl_2Si$			
Silane, dichloromethylphenyl-	hexane	191(--),216(3.88), 254s(2.37),259(2.56), 265(2.68),272(2.58)	114-0195-79D
$C_7H_8FN_3$			
Guanidine, (4-fluorophenyl)-, nitrate	MeOH	203(4.35)	83-0426-79
$C_7H_8F_2Si$			
Silane, difluoromethylphenyl-	hexane	185(--),211(3.83), 253s(2.39),258(2.60), 264(2.74),270(2.66)	114-0195-79D

Compound	Solvent	λ_{max}(log ε)	Ref.
$C_7H_8N_2O$			
Benzenamine, N-methyl-N-nitroso-	EtOH	270(3.87)	104-1915-79
2,5-Cyclohexadien-1-one, 2-amino-4-imino-5-methyl-, protonated	H_2O	508(3.66)	39-0304-79B
6-Oxa-1-azabicyclo[3.1.0]hex-3-ene-5-carbonitrile	EtOH	233(2.90)	12-2035-79
2H-Pyrrole-5-carbonitrile, 2,2-dimethyl-, 1-oxide	EtOH	213(3.83),322(3.73)	12-1785-79
$C_7H_8N_2OS$			
4(1H)-Pyrimidinone, 5-cyclopropyl-2,3-dihydro-2-thioxo-	MeOH	218(4.17),278(4.29)	73-2426-79
4(1H)-Pyrimidinone, 6-cyclopropyl-2,3-dihydro-2-thioxo-	MeOH	274.5(4.29)	73-2426-79
$C_7H_8N_2O_2$			
Acetamide, N-(1,2-dihydro-2-oxo-4-pyridinyl)-	H_2O	219(4.35),250(4.06), 294(3.72)	152-0115-79
Acetamide, N-(2-formyl-1H-pyrrol-3-yl)-	H_2O	298(4.23)	152-0115-79
Acetamide, N-(3-hydroxy-4-pyridinyl)-	H_2O	254(4.06),320(3.57)	152-0115-79
Benzenamine, N-methyl-4-nitro-	30% t-BuOH	405(4.28)	104-1915-79
2,4(1H,3H)-Pyrimidinedione, 5-cyclopropyl-	MeOH	269.0(3.88)	73-2426-79
2,4(1H,3H)-Pyrimidinedione, 6-cyclopropyl-	MeOH	267.0(3.96)	73-2426-79
2,4(1H,3H)-Pyrimidinedione, 1-(2-propenyl)-	pH 1	266.0(4.05)	18-0259-79
	pH 7	266.0(4.00)	18-0259-79
	pH 13	265.0(3.84)	18-0259-79
	n.s.g.	266(3.94)	128-0281-79
1H-Pyrrole, 1-methyl-2-(2-nitroethenyl)-	EtOH	400(4.67)	104-1859-79
2H-Pyrrole-5-carbonitrile, 3,4-dihydro-2,2-dimethyl-4-oxo-, 1-oxide	EtOH	280(4.16)	12-1785-79
$C_7H_8N_2O_2S$			
Pyrido[2,1-c][1,2,4]thiadiazine, 3,4-dihydro-, 1,1-dioxide	MeOH	248(4.04),320(3.71)	44-3847-79
$C_7H_8N_2O_3$			
2(1H)-Pyridinone, 3-[[(methylamino)-carbonyl]oxy]-	EtOH	227(3.77),297(3.81)	36-0816-79
$C_7H_8N_2O_4$			
4-Pyrimidinecarboxylic acid, 1,2,3,6-tetrahydro-1,3-dimethyl-2,6-dioxo-	pH 1	272(3.90)	44-0970-79
	pH 13	271(3.94)	44-0970-79
$C_7H_8N_2O_5$			
1H-Pyrazole-3,5-dicarboxylic acid, 4-hydroxy-, dimethyl ester	EtOH	275(3.90)	23-0904-79
	EtOH-NaOH	318(c.3.9)	23-0904-79
$C_7H_8N_4O$			
Imidazo[1,5-a]-1,3,5-triazin-4(3H)-one, 3,8-dimethyl-	EtOH	267(3.98),294s(3.64)	44-3835-79
Imidazo[1,5-a]-1,3,5-triazin-4(3H)-one, 6,8-dimethyl-	EtOH	263s(3.62),267(3.63), 294s(3.23)	44-3835-79
1H-Purine, 6-methoxy-8-methyl-	pH 7	256(3.86)	44-1450-79
6H-Purin-6-one, 3,7-dihydro-2,3-dimethyl-	pH 1	255(3.90)	44-1450-79
$C_7H_8N_4OS$			
Imidazo[1,5-a]-1,3,5-triazin-4(1H)-one, 2,3-dihydro-6,8-dimethyl-2-thioxo-	EtOH	264s(3.99),289(4.14)	44-3835-79

Compound	Solvent	λ_{max}(log ϵ)	Ref.
7H-Pyrimido[4,5-b][1,4]thiazin-6-amine, 4-methoxy-	pH 3.02	247(4.46),275(3.60), 285(3.67),305(3.72)	103-0041-79
	pH 7.12	253(4.34),290(3.88), 317(3.83)	103-0041-79
$C_7H_8N_4O_2S$			
Isothiazolo[3,4-d]pyrimidine-4,6-(5H,7H)-dione, 3-amino-5,7-dimethyl-	EtOH	233(4.37),268(4.12)	95-0989-79
$C_7H_8N_4O_5$			
1H-Imidazole-1-acetic acid, α-(methoxy-imino)-4-nitro-, methyl ester, (E)-	EtOH	281(3.96)	4-1545-79
(Z)-	EtOH	281(3.89)	4-1545-79
$C_7H_8N_4S$			
1H-Purine, 1-methyl-2-(methylthio)-	pH 7	247(4.46),278(3.77)	12-2771-79
1H-Purine, 8-methyl-6-(methylthio)-	pH 7	292(3.72)	44-1450-79
7H-Purine, 7-methyl-2-(methylthio)-	pH 7	240(4.34),313(3.70)	12-2771-79
$C_7H_8N_6O_2$			
Acetamide, N-(4,7-dihydro-3-methyl-7-oxo-1,2,4-triazolo[3,4-f][1,2,4]-triazin-5-yl)-	H_2O	224(4.00),254(3.45)	4-0555-79
C_7H_8O			
Benzene, methoxy- (anisole)	C_6H_{12}	220(3.89),265(3.15), 271(3.33),278(3.30)	65-2000-79
	heptane	220(3.89),265(3.13), 271(3.30),278(3.27)	65-2000-79
	MeOH	219(3.90),266(3.12), 271(3.25),277(3.12)	65-2000-79
	dioxan	221(3.94),268(3.16), 272(3.28),278(3.20)	65-2000-79
	AmOAc	266(3.14),272(3.28), 278(3.23)	65-2000-79
	MeCN	220(3.84),266(3.19), 271(3.28),278(3.18)	65-2000-79
	DMF	266(3.12),272(3.23), 278(3.15)	65-2000-79
	CH_2Cl_2	221(3.91),267(3.16), 272(3.29),278(3.22)	65-2000-79
	$CHCl_3$	266(3.15),272(3.28), 278(3.20)	65-2000-79
	CCl_4	268(3.22),273(3.33), 280(3.28)	65-2000-79
	n.s.g.	192(4.70),217(3.93), 272(3.30)	73-0873-79
3,5-Cycloheptadien-1-one	C_6H_{12}	231(3.78),290s(2.38)	44-4254-79
$C_7H_8OS_2$			
3-Furancarbodithioic acid, ethyl ester	EtOH	311(4.10),491(1.72)	44-2807-79
$C_7H_8O_2$			
Bicyclo[3.2.0]heptane-2,6-dione	MeOH	292(1.57)	44-4557-79
Phenol, 4-methoxy-	MeOH	205(3.23),228(3.33), 294(2.91)	106-0022-79
	EtOH	205(3.21),223(3.63), 291(3.22)	106-0188-79
2H-Pyran-2-one, 3,4-dimethyl-	EtOH	224(3.26),287(3.87)	35-7510-79
2H-Pyran-2-one, 3,6-dimethyl-	EtOH	221(3.49),298(3.93)	35-7510-79

Compound	Solvent	λ_{max}(log ε)	Ref.
2H-Pyran-2-one, 4,5-dimethyl-	EtOH	216(3.25),293(3.72)	35-7510-79
2H-Pyran-2-one, 4,6-dimethyl-	EtOH	221(3.41),294(3.86)	35-7510-79
2H-Pyran-2-one, 5,6-dimethyl-	EtOH	219(3.47),308(3.82)	35-7510-79
4H-Pyran-4-one, 2,5-dimethyl-	EtOH	211(4.00),252(4.13)	35-7510-79
$C_7H_8O_3$			
2-Cyclopenten-1-one, 5-acetoxy-	n.s.g.	223(4.31)	39-0274-79C
$C_7H_8O_4$			
Compd., m. 140-143°	MeOH	288(4.10)	39-2048-79C
4H-Furo[2,3-b]pyran-2(3H)-one, 3a,7a-dihydro-4-hydroxy-, (3aα,4α,7aα)-	n.s.g.	215(3.11),284(2.62)	102-1886-79
$C_7H_8O_4S_2$			
1,3-Dithiole-4,5-dicarboxylic acid, dimethyl ester	CH_2Cl_2	296s(4.23),351(4.67)	44-0930-79
$C_7H_8O_5S$			
4H-Cyclopenta-1,3,2-dioxathiol-4-one, 3a,6a-dihydro-3a,5-dimethyl-, 2,2-dioxide	EtOH	223(3.93),339(1.63)	35-7510-79
C_7H_8S			
Benzene, (methylthio)-	C_6H_{12}	284(3.00)	39-0217-79B
	C_6H_{12}	255(4.02)	65-2000-79
	heptane	254.5(3.99)	65-2000-79
	MeOH	254(4.00)	65-2000-79
	dioxan	255(4.05)	65-2000-79
	AmOAc	254(3.99)	65-2000-79
	MeCN	253(4.05)	65-2000-79
	DMF	256(3.99)	65-2000-79
	CH_2Cl_2	256(4.01)	65-2000-79
	CHCl	257(3.99)	65-2000-79
	CCl_4	259(3.96)	65-2000-79
	n.s.g.	184(4.41),203(4.15), 254(3.99),280(3.18)	73-0873-79
Benzenethiol, 4-methyl-	C_6H_{12}	285(2.85)	39-0217-79B
C_7H_8Se			
Benzene, (methylseleno)-	C_6H_{12}	251(3.80),272(3.55)	65-2000-79
	heptane	250(3.79),271(3.51)	65-2000-79
	MeOH	248(3.80),264(3.61)	65-2000-79
	dioxan	249(3.82),264(3.66)	65-2000-79
	AmOAc	249(3.76),265(3.77)	65-2000-79
	MeCN	248(3.80),263(3.66)	65-2000-79
	DMF	263(3.62)	65-2000-79
	CH_2Cl_2	249(3.82),265(3.71)	65-2000-79
	CCl_4	254(3.80)	65-2000-79
C_7H_8Te			
Benzene, (methyltelluro)-	heptane	223(3.99),269(3.99), 331(2.84)	65-2000-79
	MeOH	220(3.95),267(3.70), 325(2.79)	65-2000-79
	dioxan	222(4.02),269(3.79), 324(2.94)	65-2000-79
	MeCN	268(3.76),322(2.88)	65-2000-79
	DMF	270(3.77),323(2.89)	65-2000-79
	CH_2Cl_2	220(4.13),270(3.76), 326(2.88)	65-2000-79
	$CHCl_3$	326(2.77)	65-2000-79

Compound	Solvent	$\lambda_{max}(\log \epsilon)$	Ref.
Benzene, (methyltelluro)- (cont.)	CCl_4	273(3.90),331(2.68)	65-2000-79
$C_7H_9BrN_2O_2$			
1H-Pyrazole-3-carboxylic acid, 5-(bromomethyl)-, ethyl ester	EtOH	222(4.07)	87-0807-79
$C_7H_9ClO_2$			
2-Heptenal, 2-chloro-6-oxo-, (E)-	isoPrOH	236(4.08),286s(2.75)	44-0447-79
$C_7H_9IN_2O_3$			
2,4(1H,3H)-Pyrimidinedione, 1-(2-hydroxy-3-iodopropyl)-	EtOH	263(4.19)	128-0051-79
C_7H_9N			
Benzenamine, 4-methyl-	EtOH	237(3.9),295(3.3)	94-0403-79
1H-Pyrrole, 1-ethenyl-2-methyl-	C_6H_{12}	202(4.00),248(4.10)	104-0535-79
C_7H_9NO			
Phenol, 2-aminomethyl-	M HCl	274(3.30)	102-1547-79
	M NaOH	293(3.48)	102-1547-79
$C_7H_9NO_2$			
2(1H)-Pyridinone, 3-methoxy-1-methyl-	EtOH	243(3.7),296(3.8)	77-0285-79
4(1H)-Pyridinone, 5-hydroxy-1,2-dimethyl-	neutral	278(4.08)	18-0111-79
	base	304(3.96)	18-0111-79
$C_7H_9NO_3$			
2-Propenoic acid, 2-cyano-3-ethoxy-, methyl ester	EtOH	250.5(4.06)	73-1423-79
2-Propenoic acid, 2-cyano-3-methoxy-, ethyl ester	EtOH	250.0(4.11)	73-1423-79
2(1H)-Pyridinone, 5-acetoxy-5,6-dihydro-	n.s.g.	207(4.10),241(3.30)	78-0437-79
4(1H)-Pyridinone, 5-hydroxy-2-(hydroxymethyl)-1-methyl-	acid	281(3.75)	18-0107-79
	neutral	285(4.08)	18-0107-79
	neutral	283(4.11)	18-0111-79
	base	312(3.96)	18-0107-79
	base	311(3.99)	18-0111-79
4(1H)-Pyridinone, 2-(hydroxymethyl)-5-methoxy-	acid	275(3.63)	18-0107-79
	neutral	277(3.99)	18-0107-79
2H-Pyrrol-2-one, 1-acetyl-1,5-dihydro-4-methoxy-	EtOH	218(4.00),238(4.04)	35-0240-79
$C_7H_9NO_3S$			
Benzenesulfonic acid, 2-(methylamino)-, monosodium salt	$NaHCO_3$	247(3.63)	104-0887-79
Benzenesulfonic acid, 4-(methylamino)-, monosodium salt	$NaHCO_3$	259(4.23)	104-0887-79
2-Propenoic acid, 3-[(4-oxo-2-azetidinyl)thio]-, methyl ester, (Z)-	EtOH	277(4.12)	35-6306-79
$C_7H_9NO_4$			
3-Pyrrolidinecarboxylic acid, 1-methyl-2,4-dioxo-, methyl ester	MeOH	227(4.06),260s(3.59)	142-0477-79B
3-Pyrrolidinecarboxylic acid, 5-methyl-2,4-dioxo-, methyl ester	H_2O	228(4.13),263(4.04)	142-0477-79B
$C_7H_9NS_2$			
Pyridine, 2,4-bis(methylthio)-	EtOH	252(4.43)	56-0701-79
	EtOH-HCl	251(4.20),298(4.20), 314s(4.18)	56-0701-79

Compound	Solvent	λ_{max}(log ε)	Ref.
Pyridine, 3,5-bis(methylthio)-	hexane	247(4.18),308(3.63)	56-0503-79
	EtOH	249(4.26),313(3.65)	56-0503-79
2(1H)-Pyridinethione, 1-methyl-4-(methylthio)-	EtOH	277(4.51),351(3.89)	56-0701-79
	EtOH-HCl	275(4.51),350(3.89)	56-0701-79
$C_7H_9N_3O$			
2(1H)-Pyrimidinone, 4-amino-1-(2-propenyl)-	pH 1	282.0(4.19)	18-0259-79
	pH 7	274.0(4.01)	18-0259-79
	pH 13	274.0(4.00)	18-0259-79
$C_7H_9N_3OS$			
Propanamide, 2-(2-pyrimidinylthio)-	pH 7	244(4.18),278(3.17)	12-2713-79
$C_7H_9N_3O_2$			
5H-Pyrazolo[4,3-d][1,3]oxazepin-5-one, 1,4,7,8-tetrahydro-3-methyl-	EtOH	230(3.86)	118-0584-79
Pyrazolo[4,3-d][1,3]oxazin-5(1H)-one, 4,7-dihydro-3,7-dimethyl-	EtOH	227(3.85)	118-0584-79
$C_7H_9N_3O_3$			
1H-Pyrazole-3-carboxylic acid, 5-methyl-4-nitroso-, ethyl ester	pH 1	273s(3.79),303(4.00)	18-0208-79
	pH 11	329(4.17),333(4.20)	18-0208-79
	EtOH	212(3.92),275s(3.81), 303(4.01)	18-0208-79
$C_7H_9N_3O_3S$			
5-Isothiazolecarboxylic acid, 4-amino-3-(aminocarbonyl)-, ethyl ester	MeCN	239(4.01),361(3.96)	5-1534-79
$C_7H_9N_3O_4$			
Acetic acid, cyano[(2-ethoxy-2-oxoethyl)hydrazono]-, (Z)-	EtOH	302.5(4.17)	23-0904-79
1H-Pyrazole-3-carboxylic acid, 5-(aminocarbonyl)-4-hydroxy-, ethyl ester	EtOH	271(c.4.1)	23-0904-79
2H-Pyrrole-5-carbonitrile, 3,4-dihydro-2,2-dimethyl-4-(nitrooxy)-, 1-oxide	EtOH	269(4.10)	12-1785-79
2H-Pyrrole-5-carbonitrile, 3,4-dihydro-3,3-dimethyl-4-(nitrooxy)-, 1-oxide	EtOH	270(4.10)	12-1785-79
$C_7H_9N_3S_2$			
Carbamodithioic acid, (1-methyl-2(1H)-pyrimidinylidene)-, methyl ester	EtOH	220(3.96),256(3.92), 310(4.13)	94-2879-79
$C_7H_9N_5O$			
Imidazo[1,5-a]-1,3,5-triazin-4(1H)-one, 2-amino-6,8-dimethyl-	EtOH	269(3.93)	44-3835-79
$C_7H_9N_5O_2$			
1H-Pyrazole-4-carbonyl azide, 3-(1-hydroxyethyl)-5-methyl-	EtOH	256(4.15)	118-0584-79
1H-Pyrazole-4-carbonyl azide, 3-(2-hydroxyethyl)-5-methyl-	EtOH	255(4.21)	118-0584-79
$C_7H_9N_5O_2S$			
1H-Pyrimido[4,5-e][1,3,4]thiadiazine-5,7(6H,8H)-dione, 3-amino-6,8-dimethyl-	MeOH	250(4.13),281s(3.64), 358(3.36)	94-1965-79
$C_7H_9N_5O_4$			
D-Alanine, N-(6-amino-1,4-dihydro-	pH 0.25	209(3.96),271(4.13),	18-2933-79

Compound	Solvent	λmax(log ε)	Ref.
5-nitroso-4-oxo-2-pyrimidinyl)-		310s(4.00)	18-2933-79
(cont.)	pH 5.0	215(3.82),230(3.93), 261(3.68),327(4.37)	18-2933-79
	pH 10.0	214(3.89),328(4.38)	18-2933-79
L-Alanine, N-(6-amino-1,4-dihydro-5-nitroso-4-oxo-2-pyrimidinyl)-	pH 0.25	209(3.96),271(4.13), 310s(3.99)	18-2933-79
	pH 5.0	214(3.83),230(3.93), 261(3.68),326(4.37)	18-2933-79
	pH 10.0	213(3.89),328(4.40)	18-2933-79
β-Alanine, N-(6-amino-1,4-dihydro-5-nitroso-4-oxo-2-pyrimidinyl)-	pH 0.25	211(3.98),269(4.16)	18-2933-79
	pH 5.0	215(3.85),230(3.98), 257(3.75),326(4.40)	18-2933-79
	pH 10.0	213(3.92),327(4.44)	18-2933-79
C_7H_9P			
Phosphine, methylphenyl-	C_6H_{12}	208s(4.11),220s(3.91), 245(3.73),266f(3.23)	39-0501-79B
	12M HCl	222(3.97),267f(3.02)	39-0501-79B
Phosphine, (2-methylphenyl)-	C_6H_{12}	217s(4.00),227s(3.81), 237s(3.72),272f(2.86)	39-0501-79B
Phosphine, (3-methylphenyl)-	C_6H_{12}	216s(4.15),237s(3.70), 272f(2.89)	39-0501-79B
Phosphine, (4-methylphenyl)-	C_6H_{12}	209s(3.95),225s(3.72), 235s(3.66),272f(2.46)	39-0501-79B
C_7H_{10}			
Cyclopentane, 1,2-bis(methylene)-	dioxan	250(4.02)	24-0862-79
$C_7H_{10}Cl_2N_4O_2$			
1,3-Propanediol, 2-[(4,6-dichloro-1,3,5-triazin-2-yl)amino]-2-methyl-	EtOH	236(4.21)	104-1144-79
$C_7H_{10}Cl_2N_4O_3$			
1,3-Propanediol, 2-[(4,6-dichloro-1,3,5-triazin-2-yl)amino]-2-(hydroxymethyl)-	EtOH	236(4.24)	104-1144-79
$C_7H_{10}Cl_5N_4P$			
1,3,5,2-Triazaphosphorine, 2,2-dichloro-4-[(1,1-dimethylethyl)amino]-2,2-dihydro-6-(trichloromethyl)-	hexane	277.3(3.83)	99-0055-79
$C_7H_{10}N$			
Pyridinium, 1,2-dimethyl-, iodide	EtOH	265(3.78)	4-1583-79
$C_7H_{10}N_2$			
1H-Imidazole, 1-ethenyl-2-ethyl-	isooctane	235.5(4.04)	65-1225-79
	pH 1	222(3.98)	65-1225-79
	H_2O	229.5(3.99)	65-1225-79
	EtOH	232.5(4.02)	65-1225-79
$C_7H_{10}N_2O$			
Azetidine, 1-(cyanocarbonyl)-2,2-dimethyl-	EtOH	233(3.78)	12-1775-79
6-Oxa-1-azabicyclo[3.1.0]hexane-5-carbonitrile, 2,2-dimethyl-	EtOH	214(2.54),231s(--)	12-1775-79
$C_7H_{10}N_2OS$			
4(1H)-Pyrimidinone, 2,3-dihydro-5-(1-methylethyl)-2-thioxo-	pH 1	280(4.02)	73-2426-79
	pH 13	260(3.96),302s(3.73)	73-2426-79
	MeOH	217(4.18),277(4.29)	73-2426-79

Compound	Solvent	$\lambda_{max}(\log \epsilon)$	Ref.
4(1H)-Pyrimidinone, 2,3-dihydro-5-propyl-2-thioxo-	MeOH	216(4.20),277(4.27)	73-2426-79
$C_7H_{10}N_2OS_4$			
1,3-Imidazolidinedicarbodithioic acid, 2-oxo-, dimethyl ester	dioxan	303(4.76)	39-0692-79C
$C_7H_{10}N_2O_2$			
2-Butenoic acid, 3-amino-2-cyano-, ethyl ester	EtOH	274(4.21)	131-0077-79D
	hexane	274(--)	131-0077-79D
2,4(1H,3H)-Pyrimidinedione, 5-(1-methylethyl)-	MeOH	264.5(3.97)	73-2426-79
2,4(1H,3H)-Pyrimidinedione, 5-propyl-	MeOH	263.0(3.92)	73-2426-79
2H-Pyrrole-5-carbonitrile, 3,4-dihydro-4-hydroxy-2,2-dimethyl-, 1-oxide	EtOH	269(4.01)	12-1785-79
2H-Pyrrole-5-carbonitrile, 3,4-dihydro-4-hydroxy-3,3-dimethyl-, 1-oxide	EtOH	270(4.03)	12-1785-79
$C_7H_{10}N_2O_2S$			
1H-Imidazole-5-carboxylic acid, 4-mercapto-1-methyl-, ethyl ester	EtOH	275(3.96),314(3.74)	2-0222-79A
$C_7H_{10}N_2O_3S$			
4(1H)-Pyrimidinone, 6-(1,2-dihydroxyethyl)-2-(methylthio)-, (S)-	pH 1.0	235(3.92),283(3.89)	136-0235-79B
	pH 7.0	236(3.92),287(3.91)	136-0235-79B
	pH 11.0	242(3.92),275(3.79)	136-0235-79B
$C_7H_{10}N_2O_3S_2$			
4-Pyrimidinol, 6-methyl-2-(methylthio)-, methanesulfonate	EtOH	256(4.04),280s(3.50)	150-1579-79
$C_7H_{10}N_2O_4$			
2,4(1H,3H)-Pyrimidinedione, 1-(2,3-dihydroxypropyl)-	n.s.g.	267(3.95)	128-0281-79
$C_7H_{10}N_2S$			
2-Benzothiazolamine, 4,5,6,7-tetrahydro-	EtOH	263(3.805)	48-0249-79
$C_7H_{10}N_2S_2$			
3H-4,1,2-Benzothiadiazine-3-thione, 2,4a,5,6,7,8-hexahydro-	EtOH	323(4.101)	48-0959-79
$C_7H_{10}N_4O_2S$			
Acetamide, N-(4-amino-1,2,5,6-tetrahydro-5-methyl-6-oxo-2-thioxo-5-pyrimidinyl)-	EtOH	261(3.92),317(3.82)	44-3835-79
5-Pyrimidinecarbothioamide, 6-amino-1,2,3,4-tetrahydro-1,3-dimethyl-2,4-dioxo-	EtOH	257(4.27),308(4.21)	95-0515-79
$C_7H_{10}N_4O_3$			
1,2,4-Triazine-3,5(2H,4H)-dione, 6-morpholino-	pH 1-7	304(3.68)	124-0048-79
	pH 13	294(3.64)	124-0048-79
$C_7H_{10}O$			
2-Cyclopenten-1-one, 2,3-dimethyl-	MeOH	238(3.93)	146-0100-79
$C_7H_{10}O_2$			
Acetic acid, cyclopentylidene-	EtOH	221(4.03)	12-2507-79

Compound	Solvent	λ_{max}(log ε)	Ref.
2-Cyclohexen-1-one, 3-hydroxy-5-methyl-	EtOH	281.5(4.19)	83-0240-79
2-Cyclopenten-1-one, 5-hydroxy-3,4-di-methyl-, cis	n.s.g.	229(3.96)	39-0274-79C
trans	n.s.g.	230(3.96)	39-0274-79C
1,3-Dioxolane, 2,2-dimethyl-4,5-bis-(methylene)-	dioxan	248(3.92)	24-0862-79
Ethanone, 1-(5-hydroxy-1-cyclopenten-1-yl)-	EtOH	230(3.99)	30-0046-79
2-Propanone, 1-(dihydro-2(3H)-furan-ylidene)-	EtOH	263(4.23)	44-2073-79
$C_7H_{10}O_3$			
2-Cyclohexen-1-one, 3-hydroxy-5-(hy-droxymethyl)-	EtOH	282.5(4.15)	83-0240-79
2,4-Pentanedione, 3-(methoxymethylene)-	EtOH	262(3.97)	39-0464-79C
2H-Pyran-3(6H)-one, 2-ethyl-6-hydroxy-	EtOH	216(3.92)	56-0265-79
$C_7H_{10}O_3S$			
2,3-O-Isopropylidene-4-thio-D-ery-throno-1,4-lactone	EtOH	238(3.57)	136-0101-79H
$C_7H_{10}O_4$			
Butanoic acid, 2-(methoxymethylene)-3-oxo-, methyl ester	EtOH	253(4.01)	39-0464-79C
$C_7H_{10}O_5$			
Propanedioic acid, (methoxymethylene)-, dimethyl ester	EtOH	242(4.08)	39-0464-79C
$C_7H_{11}Br_2N_3O_2$			
2(1H)-Pyrimidinone, 5,5-dibromo-5,6-di-hydro-6-methoxy-1-methyl-4-(methyl-amino)-	H_2O	268(3.81)	44-4385-79
	MeOH	266(3.79)	44-4385-79
2(1H)-Pyrimidinone, 5,5-dibromotetra-hydro-4-imino-6-methoxy-1,3-dimethyl-	H_2O	243(3.74)	44-4385-79
	MeOH	242(3.73)	44-4385-79
$C_7H_{11}N$			
1H-Pyrrole, 2-ethyl-3-methyl-	C_6H_{12}	213(3.94)	104-0535-79
$C_7H_{11}NO$			
2H-Pyrrol-2-one, 1,5-dihydro-3,5,5-tri-methyl-	EtOH	214(3.81)	12-2041-79
2H-Pyrrol-2-one, 1,5-dihydro-4,5,5-tri-methyl-	EtOH	219(3.61)	12-2035-79
$C_7H_{11}NOS$			
1,4-Pentadiene-3-thione, 1-methoxy-5-(methylamino)-, (E,Z)-	C_6H_{12}	335s(4.15),349(4.16), 406(4.02)	39-2340-79C
$C_7H_{11}NOS_2$			
1H-Azepine-3-carbodithioic acid, hexa-hydro-2-oxo-	EtOH	345(4.30)	39-0692-79C
$C_7H_{11}NO_2$			
Acetic acid, (2-aminocyclopentyli-dene)-, (E)-	H_2O	210(3.94)	12-2507-79
1H-Azepine-4-carboxylic acid, 2,3,6,7-tetrahydro-, hydrobromide	MeOH	210(3.98)	111-0157-79
1H-Azepine-4-carboxylic acid, 2,5,6,7-tetrahydro-, hydrobromide	MeOH	210(3.93)	111-0157-79

Compound	Solvent	λ_{max}(log ϵ)	Ref.
1-Cyclopentene-1-acetic acid, α-amino-	H_2O	210(3.45)(end abs.)	12-2507-79
$C_7H_{11}NO_2S$			
2,4-Pyrrolidinedione, 5-[2-(methylthio)ethyl]-	aq NaOH	262.5(4.04)	142-0477-79B
$C_7H_{11}NS_2$			
Cyclohexanecarbodithioic acid, 2-imino-	EtOH	305(3.96),388(4.56)	150-1732-79
$C_7H_{11}N_3O$			
1H-Pyrazolo[3,4-c]pyridin-3-ol, 4,5,6,7-tetrahydro-1-methyl-	MeOH	233(3.59),260(3.19)	111-0157-79
hydrobromide	MeOH	233(3.70),260s(--)	111-0157-79
2H-Pyrazolo[3,4-c]pyridin-3-ol, 4,5,6,7-tetrahydro-2-methyl-	MeOH	249(3.79)	111-0157-79
$C_7H_{11}N_3O_2$			
1H-Pyrazole-3-carboxylic acid, 4-amino-5-methyl-, ethyl ester	pH 1	218(3.82)	18-0208-79
	pH 11	236(3.80)	18-0208-79
	EtOH	208(3.76),296(3.69)	18-0208-79
$C_7H_{11}N_5$			
1,2,4-Triazolo[3,4-c][1,2,4]triazine, 1,5-dihydro-5,5,6-trimethyl-	EtOH	237(3.76)	4-0427-79
1,2,4-Triazolo[4,3-b][1,2,4]triazine, 1,7-dihydro-6,7,7-trimethyl-	EtOH	216(3.56),269(2.85)	4-0427-79
$C_7H_{11}N_5O_2$			
Acetamide, N-(2,6-diamino-4,5-dihydro-5-methyl-4-oxo-5-pyrimidinyl)-	EtOH	234(4.20),269(3.85)	44-3835-79
$C_7H_{11}N_5O_2S$			
Uracil-5-carbothiohydrazide, 6-amino-1,3-dimethyl-	EtOH	262(4.22),295(4.24)	95-0515-79
C_7H_{12}			
Cycloheptene, compd. with Cu(1+) trifluoromethanesulfonate, cis	dioxan	230(3.67),260s(3.27)	54-0423-79
trans	dioxan	236(3.94),288(3.18)	54-0423-79
$C_7H_{12}BrN_3O_2$			
2(1H)-Pyrimidinone, 5-bromo-4-(dimethylamino)-5,6-dihydro-6-hydroxy-1-methyl-	H_2O	276(3.96)	44-4385-79
$C_7H_{12}BrN_5$			
1,2,3-Triazine-4,6-diamine, 5-bromo-N,N,N',N'-tetramethyl-	CH_2Cl_2	272(4.27)	24-1529-79
$C_7H_{12}ClN_5$			
1,2,3-Triazine-4,6-diamine, 5-chloro-N,N,N',N'-tetramethyl-	CH_2Cl_2	267(4.26),325s(--)	24-1529-79
tetrafluoroborate	CH_2Cl_2	369(3.32)	24-1535-79
$C_7H_{12}N_2$			
1H-Pyrazole, 3-methyl-5-propyl-	EtOH	222(3.72)	150-3782-79
$C_7H_{12}N_2O$			
2,3-Diazabicyclo[3.2.1]hept-2-ene, 7-(methoxymethyl)-, anti	MeCN	343(2.05)	35-3315-79
syn	MeCN	343(2.02)	35-3315-79

Compound	Solvent	$\lambda_{max}(\log \epsilon)$	Ref.
1H-Pyrazolium, 4-hydroxy-1,2,3,5-tetramethyl-, hydroxide, inner salt	H_2O	289(3.90)	23-0904-79
$C_7H_{12}N_2O_2$			
1-Azetidineacetamide, 2,2-dimethyl-α-oxo-	EtOH	220(3.74)	12-1775-79
2(5H)-Furanone, 5,5-dimethyl-4-(1-methylhydrazino)-	EtOH	263(4.37)	4-0505-79
2(5H)-Furanone, 5,5-dimethyl-4-(2-methylhydrazino)-	EtOH	256(4.35)	4-0505-79
2(5H)-Oxazolone, 4-(dimethylamino)-5,5-dimethyl-	EtOH	234(4.26)	33-1236-79
1H-Pyrazole-3-methanol, 5-hydroxy-α,α,1-trimethyl-	EtOH	248(3.72)	4-0505-79
$C_7H_{12}N_2O_3$			
1H-Imidazole, 2-(trimethoxymethyl)-	H_2O	214(3.86)	44-2902-79
2-Piperidinol, 1-nitroso-, acetate	EtOH	230(3.67),365(1.95)	44-4511-79
$C_7H_{12}N_2S$			
4H-Pyrazole-4-thione, 3,5-dihydro-3,3,5,5-tetramethyl-	EtOH	530(--),550(0.92)	39-2401-79C
$C_7H_{12}N_4O_2$			
1H-Pyrazole-4-carboxylic acid, 3-(1-hydroxyethyl)-5-methyl-, hydrazide	EtOH	230(3.86)	118-0584-79
1H-Pyrazole-4-carboxylic acid, 3-(2-hydroxyethyl)-5-methyl-, hydrazide	EtOH	230(3.64)	118-0584-79
$C_7H_{12}OS_2$			
2-Oxa-6,9-dithiaspiro[3.6]decane	EtOH	210(2.96)	49-0279-79
$C_7H_{12}O_2$			
Cyclohexanone, 3-hydroxy-3-methyl-	EtOH	285(1.48)	22-0627-79
$C_7H_{12}O_2S$			
Sulfonium, dimethyl-, 1-acetyl-2-oxopropylide	hexane	244(--),268(--)	99-0573-79
	MeOH	230(--),269(--)	99-0573-79
	EtOH	232(3.8),273(4.1)	99-0573-79
	MeCN	237(3.8),270(4.1)	99-0573-79
	ether	240(--),269(--)	99-0573-79
$C_7H_{12}O_3S$			
Sulfoxonium, dimethyl-, 1-acetyl-2-oxopropylide	MeOH	216(3.9)	99-0573-79
	MeCN	218(3.8)	99-0573-79
$C_7H_{13}N$			
Methanamine, N-(2-methyl-2-pentenylidene)-	MeOH	229(4.33)	44-1417-79
$C_7H_{13}N_2O_3P$			
1,3,2-Diazaphosphorin-4(1H)-one, 2,3-dihydro-2-methoxy-1,3,6-trimethyl-, 2-oxide	H_2O	275(4.02)	103-1142-79
	EtOH	271(4.02)	103-1142-79
$C_7H_{13}N_3O$			
1,2,4-Triazine, 2,5-dihydro-3-methoxy-5,5,6-trimethyl-	EtOH	228(3.61),263(3.43)	4-0427-79
1,2,4-Triazin-3(2H)-one, 4,5-dihydro-2,5,5,6-tetramethyl-	EtOH	244(3.66)	4-0427-79

Compound	Solvent	λ_{max}(log ϵ)	Ref.
1,2,4-Triazin-3(2H)-one, 4,5-dihydro-4,5,5,6-tetramethyl-	EtOH	244(3.71)	4-0427-79
$C_7H_{14}N_2$			
1H-Imidazole, 2-butyl-4,5-dihydro-	EtOH	223(3.69)	39-2289-79C
1-Propen-1-amine, N-ethyl-3-(ethylimino)-, carbonate (1:1)	EtOH	299(4.64)	49-0613-79
$C_7H_{14}N_2O$			
1H-Imidazole, 2,5-dihydro-2,2,5,5-tetramethyl-, 3-oxide	EtOH	230(4.00)	103-0092-79
$C_7H_{14}N_2O_2$			
1-Buten-2-amine, N,3,3-trimethyl-1-nitro-	isooctane	237(3.32),343(4.20)	44-4116-79
Cyclohexanamine, N-methoxy-N-nitroso-	EtOH	235.8)3.78)	88-2457-79
Diazene, cyclohexylmethoxy-, 1-oxide	EtOH	234.8(3.96)	88-2457-79
Diazene, hydroxy(4-methylcyclohexyl)-, 2-oxide	EtOH	228.3(3.80)	88-2457-79
Propanal, 3-(butylnitrosoamino)-	EtOH	235(3.86),352(1.97)	94-0541-79
$C_7H_{14}N_2S$			
2-Imidazolidinethione, 1,3-diethyl-	MeOH	240(4.33)	78-0511-79
	CH_2Cl_2	247(4.36)	78-0511-79
$C_7H_{14}O_3Si$			
Acetic acid, oxo(trimethylsilyl)-, ethyl ester	C_6H_{12}	230(2.59),455(1.99)	88-0871-79
$C_7H_{14}Si$			
Silane, diethenylethylmethyl-	heptane	181(4.5)	65-0916-79
$C_7H_{15}Cl_2N_2O_2P$			
2H-1,3,2-Oxaphosphorin-2-amine, N,N-bis(2-chloroethyl)tetrahydro-, 2-oxide	45% MeOH	198(2.67)	36-1144-79
$C_7H_{15}N_3O_3$			
Carbamic acid, [(ethylnitrosoamino)-methyl]-, 1-methylethyl ester	EtOH	231(3.87),356(1.86)	94-0682-79
Carbamic acid, [(methylnitrosoamino)-methyl]-, butyl ester	EtOH	229(3.80),353(1.87)	94-0682-79
$C_7H_{16}BrN$			
1-Propanamine, 1-bromo-N-(1,1-dimethylethyl)- (type spectrum)	C_6H_{12}	224(4.04)	88-3319-79
$C_7H_{16}IN_3$			
1H-1,2,4-Triazolium, 4,5-dihydro-1,1,3,5,5-pentamethyl-, iodide	H_2O	226(4.20)	104-2073-79
$C_7H_{16}N_3$			
1H-1,2,3-Triazolium, 1-(1,1-dimethylethyl)-4,5-dihydro-3-methyl-, perchlorate	MeOH	272(3.88)	24-0445-79
$C_7H_{17}N_3$			
Ethanimidic acid, 2-(1,1-dimethylethyl)-2-methylhydrazide, monohydriodide	H_2O	226(4.17)	104-2073-79

Compound	Solvent	λ_{max}(log ϵ)	Ref.
$C_7H_{18}N_3$			
Hydrazinium, 2-[1-(dimethylamino)ethylidene]-1,1,1-trimethyl-, iodide	H_2O	228(4.36)	104-2073-79
$C_7H_{18}S_3Si$			
Silane, tris(ethylthio)methyl-	hexane	225(3.26)	114-0407-79A
$C_7H_{18}Si$			
Silane, butyltrimethyl-	EtOH	231(4.34)	78-0621-79
$C_7H_{18}Si_2$			
Disilane, ethynylpentamethyl-	heptane	225(3.7)	65-0916-79
$C_7H_{28}O_7Si_7$			
Cycloheptasiloxane, 2,4,6,8,10,12,14-heptamethyl-	heptane	200.0(1.78)	65-1333-79

Compound	Solvent	λ_{max}(log ϵ)	Ref.
$C_8Cl_4O_3$			
Cyclopenta[b]pyran-2,5-dione, 3,4,6,7-tetrachloro-	hexane	228(4.16),240s(4.04), 332(3.93),488(2.72)	18-0811-79
$C_8Cl_6O_2$			
Cyclopenta[b]pyran-2(5H)-one, 3,4,5,5,6,7-hexachloro-	hexane	230s(3.75),305s(3.66), 317(3.74),330(3.71), 380(3.85)	18-0811-79
Cyclopenta[b]pyran-5(2H)-one, 2,2,3,4,6,7-hexachloro-	hexane	254(4.11),302(3.76), 445(2.97)	18-0811-79
4-Cyclopentene-1,3-dione, 4,5-dichloro-2-(1,2,3,3-tetrachloro-2-propenylidene)-	hexane	230s(4.16),248(4.32), 256(4.32),267s(4.21), 277s(4.16),288s(4.05), 300s(3.84),330s(3.33)	18-0811-79
C_8Cl_8O			
2-Cyclopenten-1-one, 2,3,4,4-tetrachloro-5-(1,2,3,3-tetrachloro-2-propenylidene)-, (E)-	hexane	224(4.30),262s(3.91), 272(3.98),281(3.99), 290s(3.86),310s(3.39), 322s(3.30)	18-0811-79
(Z)-	hexane	240(4.00),330(3.30)	18-0811-79
C_8Cl_{10}			
Cyclopentene, 1,2,3,3,5,5-hexachloro-4-(1,2,3,3-tetrachloro-2-propenylidene)-	hexane	221(4.41),285(3.09)	18-0811-79
$C_8HCl_6N_3O_2$			
1H-Benzimidazole, 4,5,6,7-tetrachloro-2-(dichloronitromethyl)-	n.s.g.	206(4.45),296(3.83)	104-0361-79
$C_8H_2O_8Re_2$			
Rhenium, octacarbonyldi-μ-hydrodi-, (Re-Re)- (also spectrum at 77°K)	isooctane	250(3.83),310s(--), 340(3.59),360s(--), 392(3.38)	35-3847-79
$C_8H_3F_4NO_2$			
2H-1,4-Benzoxazin-3(4H)-one, 5,6,7,8-tetrafluoro-	EtOH	209(4.18),240(4.83)	18-0516-79
$C_8H_3F_5N_2O_3$			
Benzene, pentafluoro(2-nitro-1-nitrosoethyl)- (dimer)	EtOH	217(4.10),281(3.78)	104-2179-79
Ethanone, 2-nitro-1-(pentafluorophenyl)-, oxime	EtOH	220(4.12),319(2.95)	104-2179-79
$C_8H_3F_6I$			
Benzene, 1-iodo-3,5-bis(trifluoromethyl)-	C_6H_{12}	242(4.01),275(2.92), 285(2.77)	12-1521-79
$C_8H_3N_5O$			
Propanedinitrile, [(5-azido-2-furanyl)-methylene]-	MeOH	207(3.80),242(4.10), 395(4.18)	73-3301-79
$C_8H_4BrCl_3$			
Benzene, 1-(2-bromoethenyl)-2,3,4-trichloro-	EtOH	224(4.34),269(4.27)	78-1177-79
$C_8H_4BrN_3$			
3,5-Pyridinedicarbonitrile, 2-bromo-6-methyl-	n.s.g.	286(3.51)	73-3288-79

Compound	Solvent	$\lambda_{max}(\log \epsilon)$	Ref.
$C_8H_4ClN_3$			
3,5-Pyridinedicarbonitrile, 2-chloro-6-methyl-	n.s.g.	284(3.52)	73-3288-79
$C_8H_4Cl_2N_4O_4$			
1H-Benzimidazole, 2-(dichloronitromethyl)-5-nitro-	n.s.g.	245(4.28),300(4.04)	104-0361-79
$C_8H_4F_3HgNO_4$			
Mercury, (4-nitrophenyl)(trifluoroacetato-O)-	$CHCl_3$	262(4.13)	12-1521-79
$C_8H_4F_5NS$			
Aziridine, 1-[(pentafluorophenyl)thio]-	n.s.g.	217(3.96),277(3.20), 309(3.26)	70-0315-79
$C_8H_4IN_3$			
3,5-Pyridinedicarbonitrile, 2-iodo-6-methyl-	n.s.g.	277(3.86)	73-3288-79
$C_8H_4N_2S_3$			
3H-1,2,4-Dithiazolo[4,3-a]benzimidazole-3-thione	CH_2Cl_2	269(4.54),305(4.01), 358(3.68)	39-2909-79C
$C_8H_4O_3$			
4,7-Isobenzofurandione	EtOH	235(4.16),340(3.42)	33-2211-79
	ether	235(4.18),335(3.45)	33-2211-79
$C_8H_5BrN_4O_2$			
1H-1,2,3-Triazole, 4-(4-bromophenyl)-5-nitro-	EtOH	236(4.33),303(3.76)	104-1168-79
$C_8H_5BrO_3$			
1,3-Benzodioxole-4-carboxaldehyde, 5-bromo-	n.s.g.	211(4.33),240(4.32), 253(4.12),360(3.66)	103-0961-79
1,3-Benzodioxole-4-carboxaldehyde, 6-bromo-	n.s.g.	211(4.19),232(4.17), 360(3.53)	103-0961-79
$C_8H_5BrO_4$			
1,3-Benzodioxole-4-carboxylic acid, 5-bromo-	n.s.g.	212(4.86),300(3.83)	103-0961-79
1,3-Benzodioxole-4-carboxylic acid, 6-bromo-	n.s.g.	216(4.28),237(3.76), 320(3.51)	103-0961-79
$C_8H_5ClFHgN$			
Mercury, (chlorocyanofluoromethyl)-phenyl-	EtOH	209(4.02),216(4.04)	33-1401-79
$C_8H_5ClN_2OS$			
1,2,3-Thiadiazolium, 4-chloro-5-hydroxy-3-phenyl-, hydroxide, inner salt	EtOH	260(3.78),350(3.78)	39-0956-79C
$C_8H_5ClN_4O_2$			
1H-1,2,3-Triazole, 4-(3-chlorophenyl)-5-nitro-	EtOH	234(4.22),290(3.75)	104-1168-79
$C_8H_5Cl_2N_5O$			
Pyrido[3,2-d]pyrimidine-6-carboxamide, 4-amino-2,8-dichloro-	pH 1	238(4.37),317(4.00), 330s(3.92)	44-0435-79

Compound	Solvent	$\lambda_{max}(\log \epsilon)$	Ref.
Pyrido[3,2-d]pyrimidine-6-carboxamide, 4-amino-2,8-dichloro- (cont.)	pH 7	238(4.38),317(4.00), 330(3.92)	44-0435-79
	pH 11	238(4.37),317(3.97), 330s(3.90)	44-0435-79
$C_8H_5Cl_4NO_2$			
2(1H)-Pyridinone, 3,4,5,6-tetrachloro-1-(2-propenyloxy)-	MeOH	334(3.85)	39-2756-79C
$C_8H_5NO_2$			
1H-Isoindole-1,3(2H)-dione (phthalimide)	EtOH	219(4.63),230(4.21), 238(4.02),292(3.27)	4-0225-79
	dioxan	216(4.60),229s(4.18), 237(3.99),290(4.23)	4-0225-79
$C_8H_5NO_5$			
1,3-Benzodioxole-4-carboxaldehyde, 5-nitro-	n.s.g.	228(3.86),251(3.63), 360(3.48)	103-0961-79
$C_8H_5NO_6$			
1,3-Benzodioxole-4-carboxylic acid, 5-nitro-	n.s.g.	211(4.65),245(4.47), 345(4.30)	103-0961-79
$C_8H_5N_3O$			
Propanedinitrile, [(5-amino-2-furanyl)-methylene]-	MeOH	230(4.20),447(4.82)	73-3301-79
$C_8H_5N_3OS$			
1,3,4-Thiadiazolo[3,2-a]benzimidazol-6-ol	pH 1	317(3.81),382(3.75)	18-2033-79
	pH 13	310(3.66),465(3.67)	18-2033-79
	EtOH	237(4.33),260(3.81), 365(3.62)	18-2033-79
$C_8H_5N_3O_3$			
Pyrido[3,2-d]pyrimidine-6-carboxylic acid, 3,4-dihydro-4-oxo-	pH 1	282(3.26),283(4.11), 285(3.99),305(3.92), 313(3.73)	44-0435-79
	pH 7	229(4.20),274(3.96), 304(3.79),315(3.65)	44-0435-79
	pH 11	243(4.35),314(3.91)	44-0435-79
$C_8H_5N_3O_4$			
Sydnone, 3-(4-nitrophenyl)-	CH_2Cl_2	335(3.48)	5-0063-79
$C_8H_5N_5O$			
Imidazo[1,2-c]pteridin-6(4H)-one	pH -0.5	230(4.02),262(3.60), 337(4.19),350(4.15)	18-0867-79
	pH 5.0	218(4.16),240(3.89), 278(3.38),343(4.21)	18-0867-79
	pH 9.5	223(4.42),256(3.99), 283s(3.58),363(4.16)	18-0867-79
$C_8H_5N_5O_4$			
1H-1,2,3-Triazole, 4-nitro-5-(3-nitrophenyl)-	EtOH	233(4.29),268(4.07)	104-1168-79
$C_8H_6ClN_3$			
3,5-Pyridinedicarbonitrile, 2-chloro-1,4-dihydro-6-methyl-	n.s.g.	341(3.59)	73-3288-79

Compound	Solvent	$\lambda_{max}(\log \epsilon)$	Ref.
$C_8H_6ClN_3O_2$			
1H-Benzimidazole, 2-(chloronitromethyl)-	n.s.g.	208(4.53),268(3.64), 373(4.42)	104-0361-79
$C_8H_6Cl_2S$			
Benzene, [(2,2-dichloroethenyl)thio]-	C_6H_{12}	253(4.03),271(3.98)	70-1610-79
$C_8H_6Cl_4O_2$			
Benzenemethanol, 5-chloro-2-hydroxy-α-(trichloromethyl)-	EtOH	230(3.83),291(3.48)	118-0824-79
$C_8H_6D_6O_2$			
3,5-Heptadienoic-2,4,5,6,7,7-d_6 acid, methyl ester, (E,Z)-	EtOH	231(4.14)	104-0618-79
$C_8H_6FNO_4$			
Benzeneacetic acid, 4-fluoro-2-nitro-	MeOH	255(3.70),292s(3.31)	73-2108-79
$C_8H_6N_2O$			
Pyridine, 2-(5-oxazolyl)-	EtOH	256(4.14),289(4.00)	94-0793-79
Pyridine, 3-(5-oxazolyl)-	EtOH	261(4.88)	94-0793-79
Pyridine, 4-(5-oxazolyl)-	EtOH	271(4.60)	94-0793-79
$C_8H_6N_2OS$			
1,2,3-Oxadiazolium, 5-mercapto-3-phenyl-, hydroxide, inner salt	EtOH	262(4.33),396(3.81)	39-0956-79C
1,2,3-Thiadiazolium, 5-hydroxy-3-phenyl-, hydroxide, inner salt	EtOH	264(3.99),342(3.58)	39-0956-79C
$C_8H_6N_2O_2$			
Isoindole-1,3(2H)-dione, 4-amino-	EtOH	224(4.35),236(4.29), 258(3.89),389(3.71)	4-0225-79
	dioxan	224(4.37),235(4.32), 256(3.95),378(3.75)	4-0225-79
$C_8H_6N_2S_2$			
1,2,3-Thiadiazolium, 5-mercapto-3-phenyl-, hydroxide, inner salt	EtOH	285(3.99),440(3.22)	39-0956-79C
$C_8H_6N_3O_6S_2$			
1,4-Dithiaspiro[4.5]deca-6,8-trinitro-, ion(1-), potassium salt	MeCN	445(4.47),530(4.08)	104-0487-79
silver salt	MeOH	370(3.86)	104-0487-79
$C_8H_6N_3O_8$			
1,4-Dioxaspiro[4.5]deca-6,8-diene, 6,8,10-trinitro-, ion(1-), potassium salt	MeCN	414(4.49),486(4.33)	104-0487-79
silver salt	MeOH	414(4.57),486(4.40)	104-0487-79
$C_8H_6N_4O_2$			
1H-Pyrazole-5-carboxylic acid, 3,4-dicyano-1-methyl-, methyl ester	MeOH	238.5s(3.84)	24-1719-79
1H-1,2,3-Triazole, 4-nitro-5-phenyl-	EtOH	234(4.13),293(3.70)	104-1168-79
$C_8H_6N_4O_4Se_2$			
2,4(1H,3H)-Pyrimidinedione, 5,5'-diselenobis-	pH 1	260(3.92)	87-0618-79
	pH 7.2	267(4.05)	87-0618-79
	pH 12	293(4.33)	87-0618-79

Compound	Solvent	λmax(log ε)	Ref.
$C_8H_6N_4O_5$			
2,4-Imidazolidinedione, 1-[[(5-nitro-2-furanyl)methylene]amino]-	EtOH	366(4.29)	70-1282-79
$C_8H_6N_6$			
Imidazo[1,2-c]pteridin-6-amine	pH -3.0	224(4.37),270(4.01), 337s(3.68),354(3.82), 392(4.08)	18-0867-79
	pH 1.0	214(4.32),251(4.11), 273(3.91),354(4.01)	18-0867-79
	pH 5.0	228(4.43),255(3.96), 280s(3.58),357(4.13)	18-0867-79
$C_8H_6N_6O_4$			
2,5-Cyclohexadiene-1,4-dione, 2,5-diazido-3,6-dimethoxy-	MeOH	210(4.16),263(4.15), 332(4.11),485(2.49)	59-0663-79
$C_8H_6OS_2$			
[2,3'-Bithiophen]-5'(2'H)-one	MeOH	277(3.96),327(4.19)	18-1126-79
$C_8H_6OS_4$			
Ethanone, 1-[2-(1,3-dithiol-2-ylidene)-1,3-dithiol-4-yl]-	MeCN	235(3.75),285(3.98), 300(3.99),312(4.01), 455(3.29)	44-1476-79
$C_8H_6O_2$			
1,2-Benzenedicarboxaldehyde (initial)	H_2O	222(4.46),263(3.92), 300(3.41)	23-0506-79
(final spectrum)	H_2O	222s(3.40),259(3.03), 300(2.41)	23-0506-79
	MeOH	251(2.93),281s(2.18), 292s(2.06)	23-0506-79
	dioxan	222(4.43),256(3.93), 297(3.34)	23-0506-79
1,3-Benzenedicarboxaldehyde	H_2O	196(4.20),228(4.45), 248s(4.12),292(3.05)	23-0506-79
	MeOH	203(4.27),224(4.16), 243(4.08),285(3.03)	23-0506-79
	dioxan	224(4.48),246s(4.06), 290(3.00),299(2.98)	23-0506-79
1,4-Benzenedicarboxaldehyde	H_2O	198(4.30),261(4.33), 268s(4.30),296(3.29)	23-0506-79
	MeOH	202(4.27),253(4.20), 266s(3.95),290(3.14)	23-0506-79
	dioxan	259(4.33),266s(4.28), 296(3.33)	23-0506-79
$C_8H_6O_2S$			
1,3-Benzoxathiol-2-one, 5-methyl-	hexane	222(4.02),273s(--), 278s(--),282(3.47), 289(3.55)	44-1977-79
$C_8H_6O_3$			
1,3-Isobenzofurandione, 3a,7a-dihydro-, cis	90% EtOH	256(3.68),264(3.66)	12-2659-79
$C_8H_6S_3$			
4H-Thiopyran, 4-(1,3-dithiol-2-ylidene)-	MeCN	348s(4.4),359(4.5)	44-0880-79

Compound	Solvent	λmax(log ε)	Ref.
$C_8H_7AsO_2$			
2-Propenoic acid, 3-(4-arseninyl)-	EtOH	225(3.86),240(3.76), 320(4.16)	88-3141-79
$C_8H_7BrO_2$			
1,3-Benzodioxole, 5-bromo-4-methyl-	n.s.g.	208(4.45),241(3.56), 289(3.40)	103-0961-79
$C_8H_7BrO_3$			
1,3-Benzodioxole, 4-bromo-7-methoxy-	n.s.g.	212(4.62),276(3.87)	103-0961-79
$C_8H_7ClN_4O$			
3H-1,2,4-Triazol-3-one, 4-amino-5-(4-chlorophenyl)-	EtOH	272(3.79)	4-0403-79
$C_8H_7ClN_6O$			
Pyrido[3,2-d]pyrimidine-6-carboxamide, 2,4-diamino-8-chloro-	pH 1	230(4.57),260(4.48), 310(3.87),323(3.98), 335(3.90)	44-0435-79
	pH 7	228(4.40),248(4.44), 265(4.19),307(4.02), 350(3.95)	44-0435-79
	pH 11	232(4.32),248(4.40), 265(4.18),307(4.02), 350(3.95)	44-0435-79
C_8H_7ClO			
Ethanone, 1-(4-chlorophenyl)-	C_6H_{12}	250(4.24)	56-2251-79
	EtOH	251(4.14)	56-2251-79
$C_8H_7ClOS_2$			
[2,2'-Bithiophen]-5(2H)-one, 5'-chloro-3,4-dihydro-	MeOH	244(4.09)	18-1126-79
[2,3'-Bithiophen]-5'(2'H)-one, 5-chloro-3',4'-dihydro-	MeOH	242(4.07)	18-1126-79
$C_8H_7ClS_2$			
Carbonochloridodithioic acid, 3-methylphenyl ester	C_6H_{12}	308(3.97),454(1.25)	97-0289-79
Carbonochloridodithioic acid, 4-methylphenyl ester	C_6H_{12}	307(4.23),454(1.52)	97-0289-79
$C_8H_7Cl_3O_2$			
Benzenemethanol, 2-hydroxy-α-(trichloromethyl)-	EtOH	220(3.78),283(3.48)	118-0824-79
$C_8H_7Cl_3O_3$			
1,3-Benzenediol, 4-(2,2,2-trichloro-1-hydroxyethyl)-	EtOH	225(3.89),294(3.98)	118-0824-79
C_8H_7NO			
1,2-Benzisoxazole, 3-methyl-	EtOH	231s(3.85),236(3.91), 243(3.80),280(3.46), 297s(3.31)	33-0314-79
2,1-Benzisoxazole, 3-methyl-	EtOH	256(3.03),261(3.05), 267(3.16),273(3.13), 279(3.28),314(3.88)	33-0271-79
Benzoxazole, 2-methyl-	EtOH	231(3.96),263(3.42), 268s(3.48),270(3.60), 276(3.63)	33-0314-79

Compound	Solvent	$\lambda_{max}(\log \epsilon)$	Ref.
C_8H_7NOS			
2,1-Benzisothiazole, 3-methoxy-	EtOH	222(4.62),281(3.74), 294(3.74),337(3.88)	33-0391-79
5H-Thiazolo[3,2-a]pyridin-5-one, 3-methyl-	EtOH	235(3.89),268(3.72), 277s(3.60),364(4.09), 382(4.08)	39-1150-79C
$C_8H_7NO_2$			
Benzene, (2-nitroethenyl)-	MeOH	310(4.2)	104-1859-79
1H-Isoindole-1,3(2H)-dione, 3a,7a-dihydro-	MeCN	262(3.57),271(3.55)	44-0604-79
2-Propenoic acid, 3-(3-pyridinyl)-	MeOH	206(4.09),252(4.26)	35-5370-79
$C_8H_7NO_2S$			
6(3aH)-Benzothiazolone, 3a-hydroxy-2-methyl-	MeOH	226(4.08),245(4.17), 317(3.63)	44-0120-79
$C_8H_7NO_3$			
Ethanone, 1-(4-nitrophenyl)-	C_6H_{12}	258.5(4.13)	56-2251-79
	EtOH	260.5(4.14)	56-2251-79
$C_8H_7NO_4$			
1,3-Benzodioxole, 4-methyl-5-nitro-	n.s.g.	204(4.24),248(4.24), 309(3.89),341(3.91)	103-0961-79
1,3-Benzodioxole, 4-methyl-6-nitro-	n.s.g.	207(3.81),215(3.84), 245(3.79),304(3.43), 347(3.67)	103-0961-79
1,3-Benzodioxole-4-carboxylic acid, 5-amino-, hydrochloride	EtOH	204(4.29),229(4.23), 236(4.04)	87-1354-79
2H-1,4-Benzoxazin-3(4H)-one, 2,4-dihydroxy-	EtOH	254(3.6),283(3.5), 288(3.5)	39-2481-79C
$C_8H_7N_3$			
1,2,4-Benzotriazine, 3-methyl-	EtOH	234(4.40),303(3.59), 330s(3.44),438(2.48)	4-1005-79
1H-Benzotriazole, 1-ethenyl-	EtOH	218(4.19),262(3.83), 270(3.81),296(3.78)	33-2129-79
1H-Pyrido[2,3-c]-1,2-diazepine	EtOH	234(4.28),313(3.30)	94-2183-79
1H-Pyrido[3,2-c]-1,2-diazepine	EtOH	232(4.20),306(3.48)	94-2183-79
Pyrido[3,2-c]pyridazine, 3-methyl-	EtOH	265(3.67),276(3.60), 314(3.75),327(3.80)	78-2027-79
$C_8H_7N_3O$			
Acetophene, 2-azido-	EtOH	232(4.18),256(4.03), 305(3.42)	33-0271-79
$C_8H_7N_3OS$			
1,2,3,4-Oxatriazolium, 2,5-dihydro-3-(4-methylphenyl)-5-thioxo-, hydroxide, inner salt	n.s.g.	256(4.23),285(4.14), 395(3.43)	39-0732-79C
Pyrido[3,4-d]pyrimidin-4(1H)-one, 2,3-dihydro-6-methyl-2-thioxo-	EtOH	207(4.23),227(4.18), 296(3.75)	4-0133-79
Pyrido[2,3-d]pyrimidin-4(1H)-one, 2-(methylthio)-	H_2O	310(3.85)	102-1265-79
	0.2M HCl	297(3.71),336(4.15)	102-1265-79
	0.2M NaOH	323(3.91)	102-1265-79
1,2,3,4-Thiatriazolium, 2,5-dihydro-3-(4-methylphenyl)-5-oxo-, hydroxide, inner salt	n.s.g.	217s(3.91),294(3.99), 333s(3.71)	39-0732-79C
$C_8H_7N_3O_2$			
1H-Benzimidazole, 2-(nitromethyl)-	n.s.g.	210(4.53),370(4.42)	104-0361-79

Compound	Solvent	$\lambda_{max}(\log \epsilon)$	Ref.
$C_8H_7N_3O_2$			
2-Propenenitrile, 3-(1-methyl-1H-pyrrol-2-yl)-2-nitro-	EtOH	430(4.54)	104-1859-79
$C_8H_7N_3O_2S$			
1,2,3,4-Oxatriazolium, 2,5-dihydro-3-(4-methoxyphenyl)-5-thioxo-, hydroxide, inner salt	n.s.g.	251(4.12),323(4.11)	39-0732-79C
1,2,3,4-Thiatriazolium, 2,5-dihydro-3-(4-methoxyphenyl)-5-oxo-, hydroxide, inner salt	n.s.g.	216s(3.99),235s(3.88), 326(4.11)	39-0732-79C
$C_8H_7N_3O_2S_3$			
2H-Pyrimido[4,5-d][1,3]thiazine-5,7(1H,6H)-dione, 4,8-dihydro-6,8-dimethyl-2,4-dithioxo-	EtOH	285(4.47),330(4.40), 422(4.10)	95-0515-79
$C_8H_7N_3O_3S$			
Isothiazolo[4,3-d]pyrimidine-3-carboxylic acid, 4,7-dihydro-7-oxo-, ethyl ester	DMF	336(3.97)	5-1534-79
$C_8H_7N_3O_6$			
Benzene, 1-(1,1-dinitroethyl)-4-nitro-	hexane	249(4.11)	12-1487-79
$C_8H_7N_3O_7$			
1,4-Dioxaspiro[4.5]deca-6,9-dien-8-one, 6,10-dinitro-, oxime	MeOH	294(4.26)	104-0487-79
compd. with triethylamine	EtOH	400(4.26),436s(3.99)	104-0586-79
$C_8H_7N_3S_2$			
1,2,3,4-Thiatriazolium, 2,5-dihydro-3-(4-methylphenyl)-5-thioxo-, hydroxide, inner salt	n.s.g.	239(3.84),298(4.40), 448(3.37)	39-0732-79C
$C_8H_7N_5O$			
Pyrido[3,2-d]pyrimidine-6-carboxamide, 4-amino-	pH 1	239(4.38),312(4.08), 329(4.06)	44-0435-79
	pH 7	248(4.36),322(3.91)	44-0435-79
	pH 11	247(4.37),322(3.91)	44-0435-79
$C_8H_7N_5O_2$			
Pyrido[3,2-d]pyrimidine-6-carboxamide, 4-amino-1,2-dihydro-2-oxo-	pH 1	265(4.16),315(3.83), 326(3.83)	44-0435-79
	pH 7	258(4.19),315(3.88), 325(3.84)	44-0435-79
	pH 11	241(4.25),301(4.00), 329s(3.86)	44-0435-79
$C_8H_7N_5O_3$			
Glycine, N-(1,4-dihydro-4-oxo-2-pteridinyl)-	pH -4.0	209(4.06),235(4.02), 280s(3.70),318(3.72), 390(3.43)	18-2933-79
	pH -1.0	209(4.13),235(4.08), 280s(3.73),315(3.78), 384(3.44)	18-2933-79
	pH 2.0	214(4.09),234(4.06), 273(4.12),342(3.76)	18-2933-79
	pH 5.5	221(4.07),275(4.19), 347(3.78)	18-2933-79
	pH 10.0	261(4.34),365(3.84)	18-2933-79

Compound	Solvent	λ_{max}(log ϵ)	Ref.
$C_8H_7N_5S_2$			
1H-Pyrazolo[3,4-d]pyrimidine-3-carbonitrile, 4,6-bis(methylthio)-	EtOH	202(4.20),249(4.41), 288(4.09)	103-1361-79
C_8H_8			
Cyclooctatetraene	gas	262(2.4)	61-0776-79
Pentalene, 1,2-dihydro-	gas	238(c.4)	61-0776-79
Pentalene, 1,5-dihydro-	gas	250(3.40)	61-0776-79
Semibullvalene	gas	280f(3.64)	61-0776-79
$C_8H_8BrNO_3$			
Furo[3,4-c]pyridine-1,7-diol, 4-bromo-1,3-dihydro-6-methyl-	MeOH	225(3.98),288(3.82)	88-2603-79
$C_8H_8Br_2O_4$			
Carbonic acid, 2,4-dibromo-5-oxo-1,3-pentadienyl ethyl ester, (Z,Z)-	EtOH	301(4.15),378(3.30)	78-1523-79
$C_8H_8Br_4N_2O$			
1-Propanol, 3-[(2,3,5,6-tetrabromo-4-pyridinyl)amino]-	EtOH	234(4.57)	103-0764-79
$C_8H_8Br_4N_2O_3S$			
4-Pyridinesulfonamide, 2,3,5,6-tetrabromo-N-(3-hydroxypropyl)-	EtOH	222(4.48),320(3.86)	103-0764-79
C_8H_8ClNO			
Benzaldehyde, 5-chloro-2-(methylamino)-	EtOH	271(3.80),266s(--), 396(3.71)	33-0234-79
$C_8H_8ClN_3$			
1H-Pyrazolo[3,4-b]pyridine, 4-chloro-1,6-dimethyl-	MeOH	216(4.49),273(3.79), 298(3.83)	48-0881-79
2H-Pyrazolo[3,4-b]pyridine, 4-chloro-2,6-dimethyl-	MeOH	215(4.56),287(4.00), 308s(3.83)	48-0881-79
2H-Pyrazolo[3,4-b]pyridine, 6-chloro-2,4-dimethyl-	MeOH	215(4.52),284(4.00), 309s(3.91)	48-0881-79
$C_8H_8ClN_3S$			
Hydrazinecarbothioamide, 2-[(4-chlorophenyl)methylene]-	$CHCl_3$	272s(--),320(4.55), 330s(--)	90-0815-79
$C_8H_8ClN_5O$			
6H-Purin-6-one, 2-[(2-chloro-1-propenyl)amino]-1,7-dihydro-	pH 1 and 13	272(4.44)	88-1177-79
$C_8H_8Cl_2N_2O_2$			
Pyrazinemethanol, 3,6-dichloro-5-methyl-, acetate	EtOH	220(4.04),280s(3.87), 292(3.97)	94-2027-79
$C_8H_8Cl_2N_2O_3$			
Pyrazinemethanol, 3,6-dichloro-5-methyl-, acetate, 1-oxide	EtOH	217(4.22),239(4.29), 274(3.97),310(3.36), 321(3.33)	94-2027-79
$C_8H_8Cl_2O_4$			
Carbonic acid, 2,4-dichloro-5-oxo-1,3-pentadienyl ethyl ester, (Z,Z)-	EtOH	293(4.23),378(2.61)	78-1523-79

Compound	Solvent	$\lambda_{max}(\log \epsilon)$	Ref.
$C_8H_8F_3NO_3S$			
Oxazolium, 2-(ethylthio)-5-hydroxy-3-methyl-4-(trifluoroacetyl)-, hydroxide, inner salt	CH_2Cl_2	246(3.77),325s(2.69)	5-0650-79
$C_8H_8F_3N_3$			
Guanidine, [3-(trifluoromethyl)phenyl]-, mononitrate	MeOH	203(4.46),231(3.95), 268(3.43)	83-0426-79
$C_8H_8N_2$			
1H-Benzimidazole, 2-methyl-	pH 1	235(3.63),262(3.72), 268(3.90),274(3.92)	65-1225-79
	H_2O	241(3.74),246(3.71), 266(3.65),272(3.76), 278(3.74)	65-1225-79
	EtOH	243(3.79),248(3.76), 268(3.68),273(3.79), 280(3.80)	65-1225-79
Imidazo[1,2-a]pyridine, methyl- (same in acid or base)	MeOH	220(4.4),267s(--), 278(3.7),293(3.6)	9-0561-79
$C_8H_8N_2O$			
Imidazo[1,5-a]pyridin-3(2H)-one, 1-methyl-	EtOH	216(4.43),269(3.82), 276(3.82),388(3.34)	4-0689-79
Oxazole, 5-(1-methyl-1H-pyrrol-2-yl)-	EtOH	282(4.12)	94-0793-79
Pyrimidine, 4-(2-furanyl)-1,4-dihydro-	EtOH	281(3.18)	39-2393-79C
$C_8H_8N_2O_2$			
Benzenemethanamine, α-(nitromethylene)-, (Z)-	EtOH	203(3.85),248(3.83), 350(4.32)	28-0255-79B
Ethenamine, 2-nitro-2-phenyl-, (Z)-	EtOH	211(4.01),247(4.00), 353(4.02)	28-0255-79B
$C_8H_8N_2O_2S$			
2H-1,2,4-Benzothiadiazine, 3-methyl-, 1,1-dioxide	EtOH	212(4.31),264(3.97)	104-0121-79
$C_8H_8N_2O_3S$			
2H-1,2,4-Benzothiadiazin-3(4H)-one, 4-methyl-, 1,1-dioxide	EtOH	215(4.16),246(4.03), 290(3.30)	39-1043-79C
2H-1,2,4-Benzothiadiazin-3(4H)-one, 5-methyl-, 1,1-dioxide	EtOH	215(4.27),242(3.98), 290(3.33)	39-1043-79C
2H-1,2,4-Benzothiadiazin-3(4H)-one, 7-methyl-, 1,1-dioxide	EtOH	215(4.16),245(4.08), 298(3.24)	39-1043-79C
$C_8H_8N_2O_4S$			
2H-1,2,4-Benzothiadiazin-3(4H)-one, 7-methoxy-, 1,1-dioxide	EtOH	216(4.13),251(4.12), 311(3.36)	39-1043-79C
$C_8H_8N_2O_5S$			
2-Thiophenecarboxaldehyde, 5-(1-methyl-1-nitroethyl)-4-nitro-	MeOH	226(4.09),255(3.97), 273(3.91)	12-1709-79
$C_8H_8N_2S$			
Pyrimidine, 1,4-dihydro-4-(2-thienyl)-	EtOH	240(3.97),281(3.36)	39-2393-79C
Pyrimidine, 1,4-dihydro-4-(3-thienyl)-	EtOH	240(3.70),285(3.11)	39-2393-79C
Thieno[2,3-b]pyridin-4-amine, 6-methyl-	DMF	271(4.05),278(4.05), 302(3.80),310(3.83)	49-1189-79

Compound	Solvent	λ_{max}(log ε)	Ref.
$C_8H_8N_3O_8$			
1,3-Cyclohexadiene, 6,6-dimethoxy-1,3,5-trinitro-, ion(1-), sodium salt	MeCN	419(4.45),490(4.24)	104-0487-79
silver salt	MeOH	419(4.36),490(4.17)	104-0487-79
$C_8H_8N_4$			
6H-Cyclopenta[e]-1,2,4-triazolo[4,3-b]-pyridazine, 7,8-dihydro-	MeOH	219(4.64),296(3.51)	39-1816-79C
Diimidazo[1,2-a:2',1'-c]pyrazine, 5,6-dihydro-	EtOH	283(4.18),290(4.19)	44-4243-79
$C_8H_8N_4O$			
Pyrido[3,4-d]pyrimidin-4(1H)-one, 2-amino-6-methyl-	pH 13	234(4.15),269(4.03), 346(3.57)	4-0133-79
4H-1,2,4-Triazol-5-one, 4-amino-2-phenyl-	EtOH	265(3.95)	4-0403-79
$C_8H_8N_4OS_2$			
2(1H)-Pteridinone, 3,4,7,8-tetrahydro-1,3-dimethyl-4,7-dithioxo-	pH -5.5	215(4.27),237(4.21), 253s(4.03),299(4.00), 355(3.90),378s(3.89), 438(4.04)	24-1499-79
	pH -1.0	210(4.33),238s(3.88), 278(3.96),314s(3.90), 326(3.92),395(4.15), 407(4.13),440s(3.91), 462s(3.83)	24-1499-79
	pH 5	215(4.36),247(3.93), 286s(3.68),312(3.92), 432(4.38)	24-1499-79
4(1H)-Pteridinone, 2,3,7,8-tetrahydro-1,3-dimethyl-2,7-dithioxo-	pH -5.5	226(4.01),261(4.29), 296(4.23),354s(3.75), 415(4.03)	24-1499-79
	pH -1.0	240(4.09),250s(4.13), 273(4.31),290s(4.20), 368(4.17),420s(3.58)	24-1499-79
	pH 5.0	274(4.39),310s(3.90), 391(4.32)	24-1499-79
7(8H)-Pteridinone, 1,2,3,4-tetrahydro-1,3-dimethyl-2,4-dithioxo-	pH -4.9	226(3.98),276(4.38), 320(4.05),420(4.05)	24-1499-79
	pH 0.0	225(4.09),268(4.25), 309(4.33),385(4.17), 395s(4.11)	24-1499-79
	pH 5.0	242(4.23),272s(4.15), 310(4.36),383(4.32), 400(4.37)	24-1499-79
$C_8H_8N_4O_2$			
Pyrazino[2,3-d]pyridazine, 5,8-dimethoxy-	pH -1.0	228(4.31),255(3.73), 314(3.83)	12-0459-79
	pH 4	254(4.23),305s(3.28)	12-0459-79
Pyrazino[2,3-d]pyridazine-5,8-dione, 6,7-dihydro-6,7-dimethyl-	pH -3.0	229s(3.73),274(4.03), 314(3.52)	12-0459-79
	pH 1.0	224s(3.72),272(4.05), 320(3.53)	12-0459-79
Pyrazino[2,3-d]pyridazin-5(6H)-one, 8-methoxy-6-methyl-	pH -3.0	266(4.06),309(3.42)	12-0459-79
	pH 1.0	229s(3.47),264(4.15), 314(3.43)	12-0459-79

Compound	Solvent	λ max (log ε)	Ref.
$C_8H_8N_4O_2S$			
2,4(1H,3H)-Pteridinedione, 7,8-dihydro-1,3-dimethyl-7-thioxo-	pH -6.8	242(4.36),265(4.02), 320s(3.49),380s(4.14), 391(4.16),426s(3.37)	24-1499-79
	pH -1.0	223(4.32),255s(3.87), 354(4.12),386s(3.71), 412s(3.58)	24-1499-79
	pH 5.0	225(4.36),240s(4.14), 281(3.66),300(3.76), 379(4.30)	24-1499-79
2,7(1H,8H)-Pteridinedione, 3,4-dihydro-1,3-dimethyl-4-thioxo-	pH -4.0	207(4.46),247(3.88), 292(4.16),325(3.92), 410(3.90)	24-1499-79
	pH 0.0	240(3.84),282(4.16), 373(4.18),385s(4.08)	24-1499-79
	pH 6.0	209(4.46),283(4.25), 373(4.37),388(4.36)	24-1499-79
4,7(1H,8H)-Pteridinedione, 2,3-dihydro-1,3-dimethyl-2-thioxo-	pH -4.9	213(4.32),247s(3.82), 277(4.23),380(4.00)	24-1499-79
	pH 0.0	212(4.39),240(4.04), 258(4.08),289(4.10), 341(4.23)	24-1499-79
	pH 6.0	239(4.16),260(4.24), 296(3.99),340(4.34), 354(4.29)	24-1499-79
$C_8H_8N_4O_3$			
2,4,7(1H,3H,8H)-Pteridinetrione, 1,3-dimethyl-	pH -4.3	253(4.21),348(4.05)	24-1499-79
	pH 1.0	238(4.04),263(3.81), 325(4.10)	24-1499-79
	pH 6.0	240s(3.86),277(3.96), 329(4.23)	24-1499-79
$C_8H_8N_4S_3$			
2,4,7(1H,3H,8H)-Pteridinetrithione, 1,3-dimethyl-	pH -5.5	238(3.97),267(4.42), 319(4.13),362s(3.72), 453(4.10),407s(4.12), 480s(3.75)	24-1499-79
	pH -1.0	250s(4.14),270(4.23), 296(4.21),350(4.02), 423(4.12)	24-1499-79
	pH 5.0	224s(4.01),277(4.41), 324(4.16),350(4.39)	24-1499-79
$C_8H_8N_6O$			
Pyrido[3,2-d]pyrimidine-6-carboxamide, 2,4-diamino-	pH 1	220(4.49),253(4.35), 307(3.87),319(4.00), 331(3.91)	44-0435-79
	pH 7	220(4.35),249(4.36), 304(3.94),336(3.90)	44-0435-79
	pH 11	248(4.34),301(3.91), 346(3.87)	44-0435-79
$C_8H_8N_6O_2$			
Pyrido[3,2-d]pyrimidine-6-carboxamide, 2,4-diamino-5,8-dihydro-8-oxo-	pH 1	245(4.60),290(3.83), 315(3.74),326(3.62)	44-0435-79
	pH 7	226(4.39),246(4.38), 257(4.38),325(3.80)	44-0435-79
	pH 11	245(4.29),340(3.95)	44-0435-79

Compound	Solvent	$\lambda_{max}(\log \epsilon)$	Ref.
C_8H_8O			
Ethanone, 1-phenyl- (acetophenone)	C_6H_{12}	239(3.86),278(2.76)	56-2251-79
	EtOH	242(4.08),279(3.02)	56-2251-79
	n.s.g.	198(4.49),239(4.11), 280(3.00)	73-0873-79
$C_8H_8O_2$			
Ethanone, 1-(4-hydroxyphenyl)-	EtOH	279(4.15)	12-2071-79
	EtOH-NaOH	331(4.17)	12-2071-79
$C_8H_8O_3$			
Benzaldehyde, 3-hydroxy-5-methoxy-	EtOH	230(3.73),270(3.77), 327(3.36)	150-0301-79
Benzaldehyde, 4-hydroxy-3-methoxy- (vanillin)	H_2O	200(3.27),212(3.03), 230(3.27),258(2.69), 276(3.10),310(3.06)	135-1004-79B
	pH 12	215(4.10),228(3.67), 250(4.02),296(3.57), 322(?),350(4.38)	135-1004-79B
	EtOH	232(3.76),258(3.56), 279(4.05),312(4.07)	135-1004-79B
Ethanone, 1-(2,3-dihydroxyphenyl)-	EtOH	264(4.00),346(3.39)	33-0314-79
Ethanone, 1-(2,5-dihydroxyphenyl)-	EtOH	255(3.84),363(3.61)	33-0314-79
4H-Pyran-3,5-dicarboxaldehyde, 4-methyl-	EtOH	212(4.13),232s(3.77), 295(3.80)	49-0613-79
$C_8H_8O_4$			
2(6H)-Benzofuranone, 7,7a-dihydro-6,7-dihydroxy- (dasycarponilide)	MeOH	252(4.13)	100-0500-79
Benzoic acid, 3-hydroxy-5-methoxy-	EtOH	224(3.68),250(3.72), 307(3.44)	150-0301-79
Benzoic acid, 4-hydroxy-3-methoxy-	H_2O	200(3.18),212(3.14), 228(2.64),248(2.80), 262(2.80),290(2.65)	135-1004-79B
	pH 12	215(4.30),228(4.25), 255(3.69),275(4.06), 300(4.24)	135-1004-79B
	EtOH	230(3.27),250(3.64), 262(3.83),290(3.62)	135-1004-79B
$C_8H_8S_2$			
Benzeneethane(dithioic) acid	EtOH	300(3.91),340(3.28)	44-0569-79
C_8H_9			
Cycloheptatrienylium, methyl-, perchlorate	10% HCl	227(4.70),287(3.68), 300s(--)	39-1005-79B +78-0949-79
$C_8H_9BrN_2O_2$			
Quinazoline, 8-bromo-5,6,7,8-tetrahydro-, 1,3-dioxide	EtOH	271(4.37),298(4.09)	103-1025-79
$C_8H_9BrN_2O_3$			
2,4(1H,3H)-Pyrimidinedione, 5-bromo-1-(1-methyl-2-oxopropyl)-	MeOH	280(4.22)	44-1737-79
2,4(1H,3H)-Pyrimidinedione, 5-bromo-1-(tetrahydro-2-furanyl)-	pH 1	278(3.93)	94-0899-79
	pH 7	278(3.93)	94-0899-79
	pH 12	278(3.81)	94-0899-79
$C_8H_9BrN_3$			
Imidazo[1,5-a]pyridinium, 2-amino-1-bromo-3-methyl-, bromide	MeOH	230s(3.99),260s(3.5), 399(4.13)	39-1833-79C

Compound	Solvent	λ_{max}(log ϵ)	Ref.
$C_8H_9BrO_4$			
Carbonic acid, 2(or 4)-bromo-5-oxo-1,3-pentadienyl ethyl ester	EtOH	289(4.29),368(3.18)	78-1523-79
$C_8H_9ClHgO_2$			
Bicyclo[2.2.1]hept-5-ene-2-carboxylic acid, 3-(chloromercuri)-	MeOH	215(4.669)	94-0870-79
$C_8H_9ClN_2O_2$			
Benzenamine, 3-chloro-N,N-dimethyl-4-nitro-	30% t-BuOH	395(4.24)	104-1915-79
Benzenamine, 4-chloro-N,N-dimethyl-2-nitro-	EtOH	252(4.26),425(3.45)	104-1915-79
$C_8H_9ClN_2O_3$			
2,4(1H,3H)-Pyrimidinedione, 5-chloro-1-(tetrahydro-2-furanyl)-	pH 1	275(3.95)	94-0899-79
	pH 7	273(3.90)	94-0899-79
	pH 12	272(3.80)	94-0899-79
$C_8H_9ClO_4$			
Carbonic acid, 2(or 4)-chloro-5-oxo-1,3-pentadienyl ethyl ester, (Z,E)-	EtOH	286(4.44),370(3.25)	78-1523-79
$C_8H_9FN_2O_3$			
2,4(1H,3H)-Pyrimidinedione, 5-fluoro-1-(tetrahydro-2-furanyl)-	pH 1 and 7	270(3.95)	94-0899-79
	pH 12	270(3.83)	94-0899-79
2,4(1H,3H)-Pyrimidinedione, 5-fluoro-3-(tetrahydro-2-furanyl)-	pH 1 and 7	271(3.80)	94-0899-79
	pH 12	303.5(3.97)	94-0899-79
$C_8H_9HgIO_2$			
Bicyclo[2.2.1]hept-5-ene-2-carboxylic acid, 3-(iodomercuri)-	MeOH	217(4.363)	94-0870-79
$C_8H_9IO_2$			
Bicyclo[2.2.1]hept-5-ene-2-carboxylic acid, 3-iodo-	MeOH	220(4.131)	94-0870-79
$C_8H_9IO_4$			
Carbonic acid, ethyl 2(or 4)-iodo-5-oxo-1,3-pentadienyl ester, (Z,E)-	EtOH	250(--),287s(3.94), 308(4.15)	78-1523-79
C_8H_9NO			
Acetamide, N-phenyl-	MeOH	228(4.11)	36-1306-79
2-Azabicyclo[2.2.0]hex-5-en-3-one, 2-(1-trans-propenyl)-	EtOH	242(4.06)	35-3607-79
Ethanone, 1-(3-aminophenyl)-	hexane	325(3.4)	18-1601-79
	2-MeTHF	340(3.4)	18-1601-79
Ethanone, 1-(4-aminophenyl)-	H_2O	311(4.30)	65-2189-79
	MeOH	317(4.29)	65-2189-79
	BuOH	319(4.30)	65-2189-79
	$CHCl_3$	299(4.27)	65-2189-79
C_8H_9NOS			
Benzene, 2-methyl-4-(methylthio)-1-nitroso-	$CHCl_3$	770(1.72)	44-2087-79
2-Cyclobuten-1-one, 2-(1-pyrrolidinyl)-4-thioxo-	CH_2Cl_2	327(4.58),430(2.13)	118-0361-79
1,3-Oxathiolo[4,5-b]pyridine, 2,5-dimethyl-	EtOH-HCl	247(3.57),344(4.00)	1-0299-79
	EtOH-NaOH	243(3.71),315(3.94)	1-0299-79
5H-Thiazolo[3,2-a]pyridin-5-one, 2,3-dihydro-8-methyl-	EtOH	250(3.45),334(3.57), 345s(3.48)	39-1150-79C

Compound	Solvent	$\lambda_{max}(\log \epsilon)$	Ref.
$C_8H_9NOS_2$			
2H-3,1-Benzothiazin-2-one, 1,4,5,6,7,8-hexahydro-4-thioxo-	EtOH	219(3.98),267(3.41), 317(3.19),377(4.11)	150-1732-79
$C_8H_9NO_2$			
Acetamide, N-(4-hydroxyphenyl)-	MeOH	248(4.20)	36-1303-79
Benzaldehyde, 5-hydroxy-2-(methylamino)-	EtOH	265(3.62),424(3.68)	33-0234-79
Benzene, 4-methoxy-2-methyl-1-nitroso-	$CHCl_3$	750(1.63)	44-2087-79
Ethanone, 1-(2-amino-3-hydroxyphenyl)-	EtOH	232(4.31),269(3.82), 370(3.64)	33-0271-79
Ethanone, 1-(2-amino-5-hydroxyphenyl)-	EtOH	229(4.30),257s(--), 392(3.67)	33-0234-79
	EtOH	229(4.30),255s(3.71), 392(3.67)	33-0271-79
Furo[3,4-c]pyridin-7-ol, 1,3-dihydro-6-methyl-, hydrochloride	pH 1	282(3.92)	5-1657-79
	pH 13	243(3.90),292(3.85)	5-1657-79
3,5-Pyridinedicarboxaldehyde, 1,4-dihydro-4-methyl-	EtOH	244(4.15),254(3.68), 375(3.95)	49-0613-79
$C_8H_9NO_2S$			
2-Cyclobuten-1-one, 2-morpholino-4-thioxo-	CH_2Cl_2	322(4.59),455s(2.20)	118-0361-79
Thiophene, 2-(2-methyl-1-propenyl)-4-nitro-	MeOH	253(4.06)	12-1709-79
Thiophene, 2-(2-methyl-1-propenyl)-5-nitro-	MeOH	246(3.93),385(4.16)	12-2647-79
$C_8H_9NO_3$			
6-Oxa-1-azabicyclo[5.2.0]non-4-ene-3,9-dione, 5-methyl-	EtOH	268(4.08)	88-0391-79
2(1H)-Pyridinone, 3-acetoxy-1-methyl-	EtOH	237(3.65),298(3.94)	36-0816-79
2(1H)-Pyridinone, 3-acetyl-6-hydroxy-4-methyl-	aq HOAc	324(4.22)	5-0769-79
	aq base	337(4.28)	5-0769-79
2(1H)-Pyridinone, 3-(1-oxopropoxy)-	EtOH	226(3.79),297(3.81)	36-0816-79
1H-Pyrrole-2-butanoic acid, γ-oxo-	EtOH	203(3.80),256s(3.67), 287(4.18)	103-0747-79
$C_8H_9NO_3S$			
4-Thia-1-azabicyclo[3.2.0]hept-2-ene-2-carboxylic acid, 3-ethyl-7-oxo-, potassium salt	H_2O	257(3.59),300(3.71)	77-0663-79
$C_8H_9NO_4$			
3-Pyrrolidinecarboxylic acid, 5-ethylidene-2,4-dioxo-, methyl ester	MeOH	277(4.15)	142-0477-79B
$C_8H_9NO_4S$			
2-Thiophenemethanol, α-methyl-4-nitro-, acetate	MeOH	269(3.88)	12-2647-79
2-Thiophenemethanol, α-methyl-5-nitro-, acetate	MeOH	316(3.97)	12-2647-79
$C_8H_9N_3$			
1H-Benzotriazole, 5,6-dimethyl-	EtOH	260(3.80),282(3.75)	33-2129-79
2H-Benzotriazole, 2-ethyl-	hexane	273(4.32),278(4.36), 284(4.29)	33-2129-79
Propanedinitrile, (1-pyrrolidinylmethylene)-	MeCN	287(4.59)	80-1143-79
3-Pyridinecarbonitrile, 2-amino-4-ethyl-	CH_2Cl_2	317(3.80)	118-0376-79
Pyrido[4,3-c]pyridazine, 1,4-dihydro-7-methyl-	EtOH	225(3.99),300(3.74)	78-2027-79

Compound	Solvent	λmax(log ε)	Ref.
$C_8H_9N_3O$			
Aziridine, 2-methyl-1-(pyrazinylcarbonyl)-, (S)-	isooctane	214(3.89),268(3.96), 330(2.70)	39-2881-79C
	EtOH	214(3.91),269(3.96), 323(2.85)	39-2881-79C
	MeCN	215(3.92),270(4.03), 322(2.78)	39-2881-79C
Propanedinitrile, (4-morpholinylmethylene)-	MeCN	289(4.42)	80-1143-79
4H-Pyrazolo[3,4-b]pyridin-4-one, 1,2-dihydro-2,6-dimethyl-	MeOH	213(4.38),260(4.07), 309(4.26)	48-0881-79
4H-Pyrazolo[3,4-b]pyridin-4-one, 1,7-dihydro-1,6-dimethyl-	MeOH	212(4.42),255(3.89), 285(4.10),294s(4.02)	48-0881-79
6H-Pyrazolo[3,4-b]pyridin-6-one, 1,2-dihydro-2,4-dimethyl-	MeOH	206(4.08),304(4.23), 319s(4.00)	48-0881-79
6H-Pyrazolo[3,4-b]pyridin-6-one, 1,7-dihydro-1,4-dimethyl-	MeOH	212(4.30),231s(3.93), 299(4.18)	48-0881-79
$C_8H_9N_3OS$			
1H-Pyrrolo[2,3-d]pyrimidine, 4-methoxy-2-(methylthio)-	MeOH	233(4.26),282(4.09)	24-3432-79
4H-Pyrrolo[2,3-d]pyrimidin-4-one, 1,7-dihydro-5-methyl-2-(methylthio)-	MeOH	223(4.21),287(4.00)	24-0799-79
4H-Pyrrolo[3,2-d]pyrimidin-4-one, 1,2,3,5-tetrahydro-3,7-dimethyl-2-thioxo-	pH 1 and 7	268(4.45)	44-3826-79
	pH 13	256(4.55),285s(4.08)	44-3826-79
$C_8H_9N_3OS_2$			
Acetamide, N-[4-amino-5-cyano-2-(methylthio)-3-thienyl]-	EtOH	294(4.06),315(3.97)	95-1081-79
Thieno[3,2-d]pyrimidin-4(1H)-one, 7-amino-2-methyl-6-(methylthio)-	EtOH	246(4.08),305(3.76), 342(3.89)	95-1081-79
$C_8H_9N_3O_2$			
Pyrrolo[3,2-d]pyrimidine-2,4(3H,5H)-dione, 1,3-dimethyl-	EtOH	225s(4.05),266(3.97)	44-3830-79
Pyrrolo[3,2-d]pyrimidine-2,4(3H,5H)-dione, 3,7-dimethyl-	pH 1 and 7	272(4.15)	44-3826-79
	pH 13	268(3.96),301(4.77)	44-3826-79
$C_8H_9N_3O_2S_2$			
Isothiazolo[3,4-d]pyrimidine-4,6(5H,7H)-dione, 5,7-dimethyl-3-(methylthio)-	EtOH	294(4.26)	95-0989-79 +142-0485-79
$C_8H_9N_3O_3$			
1(2H)-Pyrimidinebutanenitrile, 3,4-dihydro-β-hydroxy-2,4-dioxo-	EtOH	262(4.05)	128-0051-79
$C_8H_9N_3O_3S$			
3-Isothiazolecarboxamide, 4-(diacetylamino)-	MeCN	247(4.10),314(3.73)	5-1534-79
$C_8H_9N_3O_4$			
Benzenamine, N,N-dimethyl-2,4-dinitro-	EtOH	370(4.24)	73-1613-79
Benzenamine, N,N-dimethyl-2,6-dinitro-	EtOH	235(4.11),410(2.88)	73-1613-79
Benzenamine, N-ethyl-2,4-dinitro-	EtOH	262(3.94),350(4.21), 403s(3.81)	73-1613-79
Benzenamine, N-ethyl-2,6-dinitro-	EtOH	232(4.36),265s(3.76), 427(3.83)	73-1613-79
Cytosine, 1-carboxymethyl-N^4-acetyl-	pH 1	242(3.89),307(4.00)	73-3023-79
	pH 7-10.5	247(4.09),300(3.87)	73-3023-79

Compound	Solvent	λ_{max}(log ε)	Ref.
$C_8H_9N_3O_4S_2$			
Isothiazolo[3,4-d]pyrimidine-4,6(5H,7H)-dione, 5,7-dimethyl-3-(methylsulfonyl)-	EtOH	220(4.35),260(3.82), 328(3.82)	95-0989-79
$C_8H_9N_3S$			
Hydrazinecarbothioamide, 2-(phenylmethylene)-	$CHCl_3$	300s(--),315(4.33), 322s(--)	90-0815-79
$C_8H_9N_3S_4$			
Thiazolo[5,4-d]pyrimidine, 2,5,7-tris-(methylthio)-	EtOH	269(4.09),338(4.10)	2-0307-79B
$C_8H_9N_5$			
3H-Purin-6-amine, 3-(2-propenyl)-	pH 1	274.0(4.22)	18-0259-79
	pH 7	274.0(4.10)	18-0259-79
	pH 13	274.0(4.06)	18-0259-79
9H-Purin-6-amine, 9-(2-propenyl)-	pH 1	259.5(4.11)	18-0259-79
	pH 7 and 13	261.0(4.11)	18-0259-79
$C_8H_9N_5O$			
Cyanamide, [1-(2-cyanoethyl)-1,4,5,6-tetrahydro-4-oxo-2-pyrimidinyl]-	H_2O	218(4.16),244(4.17)	23-2593-79
9H-Purin-6-amine, 9-(2-propenyl)-, 1-oxide	pH 1	259(4.09)	18-0259-79
	pH 7	232(4.66),262(3.91), 292(3.32)	18-0259-79
	pH 13	232(4.46),269(3.94), 305(3.61)	18-0259-79
	EtOH	235(4.63),263(3.90), 300(3.32)	18-0259-79
$C_8H_9N_5O_2$			
4(1H)-Pteridinone, 2-amino-6-(1-hydroxyethyl)-, (R)-	pH 0.0	247(3.89),321(3.75)	18-0181-79
	pH 5.5	235(3.91),273(3.98), 345(3.62)	18-0181-79
	pH 10.5	253(4.19),363(3.69)	18-0181-79
(S)-	pH 0	246(3.89),320(3.76)	18-0181-79
	pH 5.5	235(3.93),273(3.99), 345(3.64)	18-0181-79
	pH 10.5	253(4.19),363(3.70)	18-0181-79
$C_8H_9N_5O_2$ (cont.)			
Pyrimido[4,5-d]pyrimidine-2,4(1H,3H)-dione, 5-amino-1,3-dimethyl-	EtOH	236(4.58),294(3.74)	95-0515-79 +142-0503-79
$C_8H_9N_5O_3$			
4(1H)-Pteridinone, 2-amino-6-(1,2-dihydroxyethyl)-, (R)-	pH 0.0	247(3.91),321(3.77)	18-0181-79
	pH 5.5	235(3.92),274(3.99), 345(3.63)	18-0181-79
	pH 10.5	254(4.21),363(3.70)	18-0181-79
(S)-	pH 0.0	247(3.92),321(3.78)	18-0181-79
	pH 5.5	235(3.95),274(4.02), 345(3.66)	18-0181-79
	pH 10.5	254(4.24),363(3.73)	18-0181-79
$C_8H_{10}Cl_2N_2$			
Pyrazine, 2,5-dichloro-3,6-diethyl-	EtOH	221(3.95),280s(3.69), 297(3.82)	94-2027-79
$C_8H_{10}Cl_2N_2O$			
Pyrazine, 2,5-dichloro-3,6-diethyl-,	EtOH	217(4.23),239(4.30),	94-2027-79

Compound	Solvent	λmax(log ε)	Ref.
1-oxide (cont.)		274(3.96),311(3.50), 319(3.52)	94-2027-79
$C_8H_{10}Cl_2N_2O_2$			
Pyrazine, 2,5-dichloro-3,6-diethyl-, 1,4-dioxide	EtOH	215(4.24),254(4.47), 314(4.28)	94-2027-79
$C_8H_{10}Cl_2O$			
1,5-Heptadien-3-one, 1,6-dichloro-2-methyl-, (E,Z)-	EtOH	234(3.90)	12-2545-79
$C_8H_{10}F_3NO_3S_2$			
Butanoic acid, 4,4,4-trifluoro-2-[methyl[(methylthio)thioxomethyl]amino]-3-oxo-, methyl ester	CH_2Cl_2	248(4.18),275(4.10)	5-0650-79
$C_8H_{10}NO$			
Oxazolo[3,2-a]pyridinium, 2,3-dihydro-2-methyl-, perchlorate	H_2O	285(3.68)	35-3607-79
Pyridinium, 2-hydroxy-1-(1-propenyl)-, perchlorate	MeOH-$HClO_4$	281(3.89)	35-3607-79
$C_8H_{10}N_2O$			
Benzenamine, N,N-dimethyl-4-nitroso-	EtOH	273(3.80),428(4.47), 660(1.85)	104-1915-79
2,4,6-Cycloheptatrien-1-one, 2-(1-methylhydrazino)-	MeOH	259(4.17),362(3.95), 418(3.85)	18-2447-79
2,5-Cyclohexadien-1-one, 4-imino-5-methyl-2-(methylamino)-, cation	H_2O	512(3.76)	39-0304-79B
1H-Imidazole, 1-ethenyl-2-[(ethenyloxy)methyl]-	EtOH	238(4.06)	70-1931-79
6-Oxa-1-azabicyclo[3.1.0]hex-3-ene-5-carbonitrile, 2,2,3-trimethyl-	EtOH	230(3.28)	12-2035-79
2H-Pyrrole-5-carbonitrile, 2,2,3-trimethyl-, 1-oxide	EtOH	217(3.97),332(3.76)	12-1785-79
$C_8H_{10}N_2OS$			
4(1H)-Pyrimidinone, 5-cyclobutyl-2,3-dihydro-2-thioxo-	MeOH	218(4.18),279(4.27)	73-2426-79
4(1H)-Pyrimidinone, 5-cyclopropyl-2,3-dihydro-6-methyl-2-thioxo-	MeOH	220(4.12),281(4.26)	73-2426-79
4(1H)-Pyrimidinone, 6-cyclopropyl-2,3-dihydro-5-methyl-2-thioxo-	MeOH	220(4.09),278(4.24)	73-2426-79
$C_8H_{10}N_2O_2$			
Benzenamine, N,N-dimethyl-2-nitro-	EtOH	250(4.08),420(3.26)	104-1915-79
Benzenamine, N,N-dimethyl-4-nitro-	30% t-BuOH	410(4.32)	104-1915-79
Carbamic acid, (4-cyano-1,3-butadienyl)-, ethyl ester, (Z,Z)-	EtOH	303(4.4)	142-0263-79
2,4(1H,3H)-Pyrimidinedione, 5-cyclobutyl-	MeOH	266.0(3.93)	73-2426-79
2,4(1H,3H)-Pyrimidinedione, 5-cyclopropyl-6-methyl-	MeOH	268.0(3.96)	73-2426-79
2,4(1H,3H)-Pyrimidinedione, 6-cyclopropyl-5-methyl-	MeOH	272.0(4.06)	73-2426-79
2,4(1H,3H)-Pyrimidinedione, 5-methyl-1-(2-propenyl)-	pH 1	272.0(3.96)	18-0259-79
	pH 7	272.0(3.95)	18-0259-79
	pH 13	272.0(3.82)	18-0259-79
	n.s.g.	271(3.99)	128-0281-79
2H-Pyrrole-5-carbonitrile, 3,4-dihydro-2,2,3-trimethyl-4-oxo-, 1-oxide	EtOH	212(3.60)	12-1785-79

Compound	Solvent	λ_{max}(log ε)	Ref.
Quinazoline, 5,6,7,8-tetrahydro-, 1,3-dioxide	EtOH	262(4.40),278s(4.13), 340(2.82)	103-1025-79
$C_8H_{10}N_2O_2S$			
Acetic acid, (2-pyrimidinylthio)-, ethyl ester	pH -2.3	251(4.11),302(3.61)	12-2713-79
	pH 7	245(4.07),274(3.34)	12-2713-79
$C_8H_{10}N_2O_3$			
Benzoic acid, 3-hydroxy-5-methoxy-, hydrazide	EtOH	224(3.74),249(3.62), 295(3.42)	150-0301-79
2H-Indazole-6-carboxylic acid, 3,3a,4,5,6,7-hexahydro-3-oxo-	EtOH	238s(3.62),250(3.75)	39-2099-79C
1H-Pyrazole-3-carboxylic acid, 2,5-dihydro-2-methyl-5-oxo-, 2-propenyl ester	MeOH	229(3.98),273(3.43)	5-1696-79
1H-Pyrazole-3-carboxylic acid, 5-hydroxy-1-methyl-, 2-propenyl ester	MeOH	224(4.17)	5-1696-79
2,4(1H,3H)-Pyrimidinedione, 1-(tetrahydro-2-furanyl)-	pH 1	265(4.03)	94-0899-79
	pH 7	265(4.00)	94-0899-79
	pH 12	225(3.81)	94-0899-79
2,4(1H,3H)-Pyrimidinedione, 3-(tetrahydro-2-furanyl)-	pH 1	263(3.85)	94-0899-79
	pH 7	263(3.86)	94-0899-79
	pH 12	291.5(4.01)	94-0899-79
$C_8H_{10}N_2O_3S$			
Acetamide, N-[(2-aminophenyl)sulfonyl]-	EtOH	213(4.36),247(4.04), 287(3.48)	104-1495-79
Ceph-2-em-4-carboxylic acid, 7-amino-3-methyl-, (4R,6R,7R)-	H_2O	226(3.69)	39-1629-79C
3-Isothiazolecarboxylic acid, 5-acetyl-4-amino-, ethyl ester	MeCN	249(3.90),379(3.97)	5-1534-79
$C_8H_{10}N_2O_4$			
4-Pyrimidinecarboxylic acid, 1,2,3,6-tetrahydro-2,6-dioxo-, 1-methylethyl ester	pH 6.1	285(3.86)	149-0447-79A
1(2H)-Pyrimidinepropanoic acid, 3,4-dihydro-5-methyl-2,4-dioxo-	n.s.g.	273(3.95)	47-1737-79
$C_8H_{10}N_2O_4S$			
Propanoic acid, 3-[(1,2,3,4-tetrahydro-2,4-dioxo-5-pyrimidinyl)thio]-, methyl ester	MeOH	274(3.77)	4-0567-79
Thiophene, 2-(2-methyl-2-nitropropyl)-4-nitro-	MeOH	271(3.91)	12-2647-79
Thiophene, 2-(2-methyl-2-nitropropyl)-5-nitro-	MeOH	322(3.92)	12-2647-79
$C_8H_{10}N_2S_2$			
1,4-Benzenediamine, N,N-dimethyl-N'-sulfinothioyl-	MeOH	538(4.59)	88-0745-79
Carbamodithioic acid, (1-methyl-2(1H)-pyridinylidene)-, methyl ester	EtOH	220(3.96),308(3.98), 374(4.07)	94-2879-79
Carbamodithioic acid, (1-methyl-4(1H)-pyridinylidene)-, methyl ester	EtOH	220(4.18),318(4.01), 384(4.23)	94-2879-79
$C_8H_{10}N_4O$			
Imidazo[1,5-a]-1,3,5-triazin-4(3H)-one, 3,6,8-trimethyl-	EtOH	266s(3.88),270(3.89), 294s(3.51)	44-3835-79

Compound	Solvent	$\lambda_{max}(\log \epsilon)$	Ref.
$C_8H_{10}N_4O_2S$			
Isothiazolo[3,4-d]pyrimidine-4,6(5H,7H)-dione, 5,7-dimethyl-3-(methylamino)-	EtOH	232(4.45),269(4.45), 292(3.95)	95-0989-79
1,2,3-Thiadiazolo[4,5-d]pyrimidine-5,7(4H,6H)-dione, 4,6-diethyl-	MeOH	217(4.15),240s(3.49), 331(3.59)	94-1965-79
$C_8H_{10}N_4S$			
1H-Purine, 1,8-dimethyl-2-(methylthio)-	pH 7	246(4.45),274(3.82)	12-2771-79
9H-Purine, 8,9-dimethyl-2-(methylthio)-	pH 7	235(4.26),259(3.89), 301(3.92)	12-2771-79
$C_8H_{10}N_6$			
Cyanamide, [4-amino-1-(2-cyanoethyl)-5,6-dihydro-2(1H)-pyrimidinylidene]-	H_2O	255(4.42)	23-2593-79
Guanidine, N'-cyano-N,N-bis(2-cyanoethyl)-	H_2O	223(4.29)	23-2593-79
$C_8H_{10}O$			
2-Cyclohexen-1-one, 3-methyl-4-methylene-	EtOH	272(4.18)	39-1837-79C
1,3-Cyclopentadiene, 5-(ethoxymethylene)-	EtOH	208(3.42),284(4.05), 340(2.57)	104-1594-79
2-Cyclopenten-1-one, 2,3-dimethyl-5-methylene-	MeOH	242(4.00),263s(3.90)	44-4212-79
2-Propyn-1-one, 1-cyclopentyl-	EtOH	214(3.54),218s(3.51)	33-0852-79
Tricyclo[3.2.1.0^{3,6}]octan-2-one, (+)-	isooctane	280s(1.18),294(1.28), 304s(1.26),316s(1.04)	44-0016-79
$C_8H_{10}OS$			
Phenol, 3-methyl-4-(methylthio)-	MeOH	232(3.94)	98-0699-79
$C_8H_{10}O_2$			
Cyclopentadieneacetic acid, α-methyl-	CH_2Cl_2	249(3.51)	1-0307-79
Ethanone, 1-(5-ethyl-2-furanyl)-	EtOH	222(3.34),283(4.17)	35-7510-79
2,4-Heptadienal, 2-methyl-6-oxo-, (Z,E)-	isoPrOH	288(4.05)	54-0316-79
Methylenomycin B	MeOH	240(3.88),270s(--)	142-0353-79B
6-Oxabicyclo[3.1.0]hexen-2-one, 1,5-dimethyl-3-methylene-	MeOH	229(3.85)	44-4212-79
4H-Pyran-4-one, 2-ethyl-3-methyl-	EtOH	210(3.97),255(4.13)	35-7510-79
$C_8H_{10}O_2S$			
1,2-Benzenediol, 3-methyl-4-(methylthio)-	MeOH	290(3.36)	98-0699-79
1,2-Benzenediol, 4-methyl-5-(methylthio)-	MeOH	298(3.49)	98-0699-79
Phenol, 3-methyl-4-(methylsulfinyl)-	MeOH	246(4.03)	98-0699-79
7-Thiabicyclo[4.2.1]nona-2,4-diene, 7,7-dioxide	EtOH	259(3.69)	88-4789-79
$C_8H_{10}O_3$			
Benzenemethanol, 4-hydroxy-3-methoxy-	H_2O	200(3.21),210(2.89), 230(2.99),262(2.16), 280(2.88)	135-1004-79B
	pH 12	215(4.00),230(3.45), 248(4.11),278(3.37), 294(3.37)	135-1004-79B
	EtOH	215(3.47),230(3.69), 262(2.40),280(3.33)	135-1004-79B
Benzenemethanol, 3-hydroxy-5-methoxy-	EtOH	229(3.80),276(3.44), 281(3.44)	150-0301-79

Compound	Solvent	λ_{max}(log ε)	Ref.
2,4-Pentadienoic acid, 2-acetyl-, methyl ester	EtOH	258(4.00)	70-0758-79
$C_8H_{10}O_4$			
2(4H)-Benzofuranone, 5,6,7,7a-tetrahydro-6,7-dihydroxy- (dihydrodasycarponilide)	MeOH	216(3.97)	100-0500-79
Carbonic acid, ethyl 5-oxo-1,3-pentadienyl ester, (E,E)-	EtOH	274(4.57)	1-0305-79
(Z,E)-	EtOH	275(4.30)	1-0305-79
3-Furancarboxylic acid, 5-(hydroxymethyl)-2-methyl-, methyl ester	EtOH	215(4.77),248(3.64)	136-0055-79B
Griffonilide, dihydro-	MeOH	211(4.09)	100-0500-79
$C_8H_{10}O_4S$			
2-Furanacetic acid, 2,5-dihydro-2-methyl-3-(methylthio)-5-oxo-	MeOH	264(4.11)	98-0699-79
2-Furanacetic acid, 2,5-dihydro-4-methyl-3-(methylthio)-5-oxo-	MeOH	274(4.02)	98-0699-79
$C_8H_{10}S$			
Benzene, (ethylthio)-	C_6H_{12}	283(3.08)	39-0217-79B
	hexane	210(--),256(3.90), 270s(3.40)	114-0195-79D
Benzene, 1-methyl-4-(methylthio)-	C_6H_{12}	290(2.93)	39-0217-79B
$C_8H_{11}BrN_2O$			
2H-Pyrrole-5-carbonitrile, 4-bromo-3,4-dihydro-2,2,3-trimethyl-, 1-oxide	EtOH	277(4.11)	12-1785-79
$C_8H_{11}BrN_4O$			
Pyrido[2,3-d]pyrimidin-4(1H)-one, 2-amino-4a-bromo-4a,5,6,7-tetrahydro-6-methyl-	pH 1	218(4.0),245(3.8), 300(3.9)	35-6068-79
	pH 8.06	269(3.9)	35-6068-79
$C_8H_{11}ClN_2O$			
Pyrazine, 3-chloro-2,5-diethyl-, 1-oxide	EtOH	233(4.27),273(4.08), 302(3.62),312(3.58)	94-2027-79
2H-Pyrrole-5-carbonitrile, 4-chloro-3,4-dihydro-2,2,3-trimethyl-, 1-oxide	EtOH	272(4.06)	12-1785-79
$C_8H_{11}ClN_2O_2$			
Pyrazine, 3-chloro-2,5-diethyl-, 1,4-dioxide	EtOH	244(4.40),311(4.31)	94-2027-79
2(1H)-Pyrazinone, 5-chloro-3,6-diethyl-1-hydroxy-	EtOH	242(4.27),352(3.88)	94-2027-79
Pyridine, 3-chloro-1,4-dihydro-1-methyl-4-(1-nitroethyl)-	$CHCl_3$	303(3.59),354(3.06)	44-1761-79
	DMSO	303(3.59),355(3.11)	44-1761-79
$C_8H_{11}ClN_2O_3$			
2(1H)-Pyrazinone, 5-chloro-3,6-diethyl-1-hydroxy-, 4-oxide	EtOH	234(4.17),245(4.16), 264(4.15),299(3.79), 375(3.91)	94-2027-79
$C_8H_{11}ClN_4O$			
Pyrido[2,3-d]pyrimidin-4(1H)-one, 2-amino-4a-chloro-4a,5,6,7-tetrahydro-6-methyl-	pH 1	230(3.9),288(4.0)	35-6068-79
	pH 8.06	259(4.1),309(3.8)	35-6068-79

Compound	Solvent	λmax(log ε)	Ref.
$C_8H_{11}ClO_2$			
3-Octene-2,7-dione, 3-chloro-, (E)-	isoPrOH	238(4.04)	44-0447-79
$C_8H_{11}IN_2O_3$			
2,4(1H,3H)-Pyrimidinedione, 1-(2-hydroxy-3-iodopropyl)-5-methyl-	EtOH	271(3.95)	128-0051-79
$C_8H_{11}N$			
Benzenamine, N,N-dimethyl-	n.s.g.	177(4.14),201(4.34), 250(4.15),296(3.30)	73-0873-79
$C_8H_{11}NO$			
3-Azanoradamantan-6-one	hexane	230(2.14),300(1.36)	142-0343-79
3-Azanoradamantan-9-one	hexane	229(3.15),290s(1.48)	142-0343-79
5(1H)-Indolizinone, 2,3,6,7-tetrahydro-	ether	237(4.04)	24-0734-79
5(6H)-Indolizinone, 2,3,7,8-tetrahydro-	ether	252(3.69)	24-0734-79
1(4H)-Pyridinecarboxylic acid, ethyl ester ($C_8H_{11}NO_2$)	isooctane	228(4.26)	44-2522-79
$C_8H_{11}NO_3$			
1,3-Cyclohexadiene, 1-methoxy-5-methyl-4-nitro-	hexane	362(3.96)	44-2087-79
2-Propenoic acid, 2-cyano-3-ethoxy-, ethyl ester	EtOH	250.5(4.17)	73-1423-79
2-Pyridinemethanol, 4,5-dimethoxy-	MeOH	234(3.77),274(3.44)	18-0107-79
4(1H)-Pyridinone, 1-ethyl-5-hydroxy-2-(hydroxymethyl)-	acid	281(3.72)	18-0107-79
	neutral	286(4.08)	18-0107-79
	base	312(4.00)	18-0107-79
	MeOH	226(4.22),290(4.10)	18-0107-79
4(1H)-Pyridinone, 2-(hydroxymethyl)-5-methoxy-1-methyl-	acid	275(3.70)	18-0107-79
	neutral	278(4.04)	18-0107-79
$C_8H_{11}NO_3S$			
Benzenesulfonic acid, 2-(dimethylamino)-, sodium salt	$NaHCO_3$	255(4.45)	104-0887-79
Benzenesulfonic acid, 4-(dimethylamino)-, sodium salt	$NaHCO_3$	270(4.27)	104-0887-79
Benzenesulfonic acid, 2-(ethylamino)-, sodium salt	$NaHCO_3$	252(3.71)	104-0887-79
Benzenesulfonic acid, 4-(ethylamino)-, sodium salt	$NaHCO_3$	266(4.25)	104-0887-79
Pyridinium, 1-(3-sulfopropyl)-, hydroxide, inner salt	H_2O	210(3.68),254s(--), 257(3.61),265s(--)	1-0695-79
$C_8H_{11}NO_4$			
3-Pyrrolidinecarboxylic acid, 5-ethyl-2,4-dioxo-, methyl ester	H_2O	229(4.15),263(4.05)	142-0477-79B
$C_8H_{11}NO_4S$			
Thiazole, 5-C-(β-D-ribofuranosyl)-	acid	244(3.70)	44-4351-79
	pH 7	236(3.73)	44-4351-79
	base	236(3.83)	44-4351-79
$C_8H_{11}NO_5S$			
2(3H)-Thiazolone, 5-β-D-ribofuranosyl-	acid	245(3.86)	44-4351-79
	pH 7.0	245(3.86)	44-4351-79
	base	257(3.87)	44-4351-79
$C_8H_{11}NO_6S$			
2,4-Thiazolidinedione, 3-β-D-ribofuranosyl-	H_2O	228(3.50)	73-1475-79

Compound	Solvent	λmax(log ε)	Ref.
$C_8H_{11}N_3$			
Ethanimidic acid, 2-phenylhydrazide, monohydrochloride	H_2O	228(3.96),274(3.24)	104-2066-79
	pH 13	234(3.82),288(3.60), 309(3.50)	104-2066-79
$C_8H_{11}N_3OS$			
Propanamide, 2-methyl-2-(2-pyrimidinylthio)-	pH 7	244(4.05),278(3.32)	12-2713-79
$C_8H_{11}N_3O_2$			
1,3-Benzenediamine, 4,6-dimethyl-5-nitro-	MeOH	239s(3.96),295(3.49), 359(2.70)	48-0175-79
5H-Pyrazolo[4,3-d][1,3]oxazepin-5-one, 1,4,7,8-tetrahydro-3,7-dimethyl-	EtOH	230(3.89)	118-0584-79
$C_8H_{11}N_3O_2S_2$			
5-Pyrimidinecarbodithioic acid, 6-amino-1,2,3,4-tetrahydro-1,3-dimethyl-2,4-dioxo-, methyl ester	EtOH	239(4.07),261(4.01), 343(4.34)	95-0515-79 +142-0485-79
$C_8H_{11}N_3O_3$			
1H-Imidazole-2-acetic acid, α-(hydroxyimino)-1-methyl-, ethyl ester, (E)-	EtOH	271(3.36)	4-1385-79
(Z)-	EtOH	276(4.05)	4-1385-79
6H-Pyrazolo[3,4-c]pyridine-6-carboxylic acid, 2,4,5,7-tetrahydro-3-hydroxy-, methyl ester	MeOH	229(3.55),250(3.52)	111-0157-79
$C_8H_{11}N_3O_4$			
1H-Pyrazole-3-carboxylic acid, 4-(acetylamino)-4,5-dihydro-5-oxo-, ethyl ester	pH 1	245(3.81),288(3.65)	18-0208-79
	pH 11	234(3.76),302(3.47)	18-0208-79
	EtOH	245(3.82),290(3.66)	18-0208-79
$C_8H_{11}N_3S$			
Guanidine, [2-(methylthio)phenyl]-, mononitrate	MeOH	207(4.33),251(4.01)	83-0426-79
Guanidine, [3-(methylthio)phenyl]-, mononitrate	MeOH	201(4.29),221(4.27), 255(4.13)	83-0426-79
Guanidine, [4-(methylthio)phenyl]-, mononitrate	MeOH	202(4.45),263(4.22)	83-0426-79
$C_8H_{11}N_5$			
1H-Imidazol-2-amine, 4,5-dihydro-N-(1-methyl-2(1H)-pyrimidinylidene)-, monohydriodide	EtOH	220(4.22),268(4.53)	94-2879-79
$C_8H_{11}N_5O_2$			
1H-Pyrazole-4-carbonyl azide, 3-(2-hydroxypropyl)-5-methyl-	EtOH	255(4.19)	118-0584-79
$C_8H_{11}N_5O_4$			
Butanoic acid, 4-[(6-amino-1,4-dihydro-5-nitroso-4-oxo-2-pyrimidinyl)amino]-	pH 0.25	212(3.92),270(4.10), 310s(3.81)	18-2933-79
	pH 5.0	215(3.82),230(3.93), 257(3.70),326(4.36)	18-2933-79
	pH 10.0	213(3.86),327(4.39)	18-2933-79
$C_8H_{11}P$			
Phosphine, dimethylphenyl-	C_6H_{12}	210s(4.11),220s(3.88), 252(3.70)	39-0501-79B

Compound	Solvent	$\lambda_{max}(\log \epsilon)$	Ref.
Phosphine, dimethylphenyl- (cont.)	C_6H_{12}	251(3.74)	65-0479-79
	12M HCl	220(3.96),266f(2.93)	39-0501-79B
Phosphine, ethylphenyl-	C_6H_{12}	208s(4.11),220s(3.83), 242(3.70),266f(3.23)	39-0501-79B
	12M HCl	222(4.00),267f(3.05)	39-0501-79B
C_8H_{12}			
Cyclohexane, 1,2-bis(methylene)-	dioxan	214(3.81)	24-0862-79
1,3,5-Heptatriene, 3-methyl-	EtOH	266(4.51)	104-1037-79
1,3,5-Heptatriene, 6-methyl-	EtOH	260(4.40),271(4.49), 281(4.43)	39-0810-79B
$C_8H_{12}ClN_2O$			
Cyclobutenylium, 1-chloro-2,3-bis(dimethylamino)-4-oxo-, hexachloroantimonate	MeCN	258(4.45),272s(4.29), 342(3.26)	118-0361-79
$C_8H_{12}Cl_2N_4O_2$			
1,3-Propanediol, 2-[(4,6-dichloro-1,3,5-triazin-2-yl)amino]-2-ethyl-	EtOH	236(4.20)	104-1144-79
$C_8H_{12}CrO_7$			
Chromate(1-), bis(2-hydroxy-2-methylpropanoato(2-)-O^1,O^2)oxo-, sodium	H_2O	250(3.80),350(3.11), 512(2.24),750(1.55), 800(1.50)	35-3206-79
$C_8H_{12}N_2$			
2,3-Diazabicyclo[2.2.2]oct-2-ene, 1-ethenyl-	n.s.g.	381(2.38)	44-4233-79
1H-Imidazole, 1-ethenyl-2-propyl-	isooctane	233(4.08)	65-1225-79
	pH 1	222.5(3.99)	65-1225-79
	H_2O	229.5(4.04)	65-1225-79
	EtOH	231.5(4.07)	65-1225-79
Pyrimidine, 1,4-dihydro-4-(2-methyl-1-propenyl)-	EtOH	235(3.65),278(3.24)	39-1228-79C
$C_8H_{12}N_2O$			
Azetidine, 1-(cyanocarbonyl)-2,2,3-trimethyl-	EtOH	234(3.72)	12-1775-79
1H-Imidazole, 2-[(ethenyloxy)methyl]-1-ethyl-	EtOH	219.7(3.97)	70-1931-79
6-Oxa-1-azabicyclo[3.1.0]hexane-5-carbonitrile, 2,2,3-trimethyl-	EtOH	213(2.40)	12-1775-79
Pyrazine, 2,5-diethyl-, 1-oxide	EtOH	226(4.19),269(4.04), 295s(3.61),304s(3.51)	94-2027-79
$C_8H_{12}N_2OS$			
4(1H)-Pyrimidinone, 2,3-dihydro-5-methyl-6-(1-methylethyl)-2-thioxo-	MeOH	220(4.17),282(4.30)	73-2426-79
4(1H)-Pyrimidinone, 2,3-dihydro-6-methyl-5-(1-methylethyl)-2-thioxo-	MeOH	220(4.24),279(4.33)	73-2426-79
4(1H)-Pyrimidinone, 5-(1,1-dimethylethyl)-2,3-dihydro-2-thioxo-	MeOH	215(4.13),277(4.23)	73-2426-79
$C_8H_{12}N_2O_2$			
2-Propenoic acid, 2-cyano-3-[(1-methylethyl)amino]-, methyl ester	MeCN	295(4.27)	80-1143-79
Pyrazine, 2,5-diethyl-, 1,4-dioxide	EtOH	236(4.27),308(4.20)	94-2027-79
2(1H)-Pyrazinone, 3,6-diethyl-, 4-oxide	EtOH	226(4.21),231(4.22), 274(3.83),330(3.84)	94-2027-79

Compound	Solvent	λ_{max}(log ε)	Ref.
3-Pyridazinecarboxylic acid, 2,5-dihydro-5,5-dimethyl-, methyl ester	MeOH	247(3.66),278(3.20)	44-1202-79
2,4(1H,3H)-Pyrimidinedione, 5-(1,1-dimethylethyl)-	MeOH	260.0(3.90)	73-2426-79
2,4(1H,3H)-Pyrimidinedione, 5-methyl-6-(1-methylethyl)-	MeOH	267.0(3.97)	73-2426-79
2,4(1H,3H)-Pyrimidinedione, 6-methyl-5-(1-methylethyl)-	MeOH	267.0(3.99)	73-2426-79
2H-Pyrrole-5-carbonitrile, 3,4-dihydro-4-hydroxy-2,2,3-trimethyl-, 1-oxide	EtOH	211(3.24),269(4.01)	12-1785-79
1H-Pyrrole-2-carboxylic acid, 3-amino-4-methyl-, ethyl ester	pH 1	270(4.23)	44-3826-79
	pH 7 and 13	270(4.30)	44-3826-79
$C_8H_{12}N_2O_2S$			
Benzenesulfonamide, 4-(dimethylamino)-	EtOH	276(4.39)	80-1027-79
1H-Imidazole-5-carboxylic acid, 1-methyl-4-(methylthio)-, ethyl ester	EtOH	286(3.76)	2-0222-79A
$C_8H_{12}N_2O_2S_2$			
Sulfilimine, N-[(4-aminophenyl)sulfonyl]-S,S-dimethyl-	EtOH	211(4.21),265(4.39)	139-0195-79
Sulfilimine, N-[4-(aminosulfonyl)phenyl]-S,S-dimethyl-	70% EtOH	203(4.36),286(4.37)	139-0195-79
2-Thiophenecarboxylic acid, 3,4-diamino-5-(methylthio)-, ethyl ester	EtOH	305(4.11)	95-1081-79
$C_8H_{12}N_2O_3$			
2(1H)-Pyrazinone, 3,6-diethyl-1-hydroxy-, 4-oxide	EtOH	230(4.35),282(3.93), 336(3.84)	94-2027-79
1H-Pyrazole-3-carboxylic acid, 5-hydroxy-1-methyl-, 1-methylethyl ester	MeOH	223(4.05)	5-1696-79
$C_8H_{12}N_2O_4$			
2,4(1H,3H)-Pyrimidinedione, 1-(2,3-dihydroxypropyl)-5-methyl-	n.s.g.	271(4.01)	128-0281-79
$C_8H_{12}N_2O_4S$			
1H-Imidazole-5-carboxylic acid, 1-methyl-4-(methylsulfonyl)-, ethyl ester	EtOH	246(3.94)	2-0222-79A
2H-Imidazole-2-thione, 1,3-dihydro-1-β-D-ribofuranosyl-	MeOH	259(4.20)	4-1185-79
	EtOH	265(4.20)	4-1185-79
2-Thiazolamine, 5-C-(α-D-ribofuranosyl)-	acid	258(3.98)	44-4351-79
	pH 7.0	261(3.94)	44-4351-79
	base	261(3.96)	44-4351-79
2-Thiazolamine, 5-C-(β-D-ribofuranosyl)-	acid	257(3.98)	44-4351-79
	pH 7.0	259(3.93)	44-4351-79
	base	261(3.94)	44-4351-79
$C_8H_{12}N_2O_5$			
2,4(1H,3H)-Pyrimidinedione, 1-(D-threo-2,3,4-trihydroxybutyl)-	pH 2	260(3.99)	73-0593-79
$C_8H_{12}N_2S_2$			
Cyclobutenediylium, 1,3-bis(dimethylamino)-2,4-dimercapto-, dihydroxide, bis(inner salt)	CH_2Cl_2	278(3.94),352(4.10), 430(4.71),496s(2.77)	5-0595-79
$C_8H_{12}N_4O$			
Pyrido[2,3-d]pyrimidin-4(1H)-one, 2-amino-5,6,7,8-tetrahydro-6-methyl-	pH 1	272(4.3)	35-6068-79
	pH 8.06	218(4.4),277(4.2)	35-6068-79

Compound	Solvent	λ max (log ε)	Ref.
$C_8H_{12}N_4O_2$			
Pyrido[2,3-d]pyrimidin-4(1H)-one, 2-amino-4a,5,6,7-tetrahydro-4a-hydroxy-6-methyl-	pH 1	222(4.1),275(4.1)	35-6068-79
	pH 8.06	247(4.2),295(3.8)	35-6068-79
$C_8H_{12}N_4O_2S$			
5-Pyrimidinecarbothioamide, 6-amino-1,2,3,4-tetrahydro-N,1,3-trimethyl-2,4-dioxo-	EtOH	259(4.34),300(4.19)	95-0515-79
$C_8H_{12}N_4O_3$			
1,2,4-Triazine-3,5(2H,4H)-dione, 2-methyl-6-morpholino-	pH 1-7	309(3.75)	124-0048-79
	pH 13	293(3.67)	124-0048-79
1,2,4-Triazine-3,5(2H,4H)-dione, 4-methyl-6-morpholino-	pH 1-7	302(3.64)	124-0048-79
	pH 13	321(3.83)	124-0048-79
$C_8H_{12}N_4O_5$			
1,3,5-Triazin-2(1H)-one, 4-amino-1-β-D-arabinofuranosyl-	H_2O	243(3.83)(changing)	87-1230-79
	pH 8	242(3.87)	87-1230-79
1H-1,2,3-Triazole-4-carboxamide, 1-β-D-arabinofuranosyl-	MeOH	211(4.12)	44-1424-79
$C_8H_{12}N_4O_6$			
1,2,4-Triazine-3,5(2H,4H)-dione, 6-amino-2-β-D-ribofuranosyl-	pH 1-7	298(3.71)	124-0048-79
	pH 13	293(3.57)	124-0048-79
$C_8H_{12}N_4S_3$			
5H-2a-Thia(2a-S^{IV})-2,3,4a,7a-tetraaza-cyclopent[cd]indene-1,4(2H,3H)-dithione, 6,7-dihydro-2,3-dimethyl-	EtOH	242(4.23),261(4.54)	39-2909-79C
$C_8H_{12}O$			
2-Cyclohepten-1-one, 2-methyl-	C_6H_{12}	232(4.10),291(2.04)	44-2722-79
2-Cyclohepten-1-one, 6-methyl-	EtOH	228(3.96)	44-4481-79
2-Cyclopenten-1-one, 2-ethyl-3-methyl-	MeOH	236(4.00)	146-0100-79
2-Cyclopenten-1-one, 2,4,4-trimethyl-	n.s.g.	229(4.03)	39-0274-79C
Ethanone, 1-(3-cyclohexen-1-yl)-	C_6H_{12}	283(1.62)	54-0346-79
1-Pentalenol, 1,2,3,3a,4,6a-hexahydro-	MeOH	197(3.63)(end abs.)	44-0452-79
$C_8H_{12}OS$			
Cyclobutanone, 2,2,4,4-tetramethyl-3-thioxo-	C_6H_{12}	244(3.4),272(2.6), 324(2.1),525(0.9)	88-4787-79
	MeOH	512(0.9)	88-4787-79
$C_8H_{12}O_2$			
2-Butanone, 1-(dihydro-2(3H)-furanylidene)-, (E)-	EtOH	263(4.11)	44-2073-79
2-Cyclopenten-1-one, 5-(hydroxymethyl)-2,3-dimethyl-	MeOH	236(4.10)	44-4212-79
2-Cyclopenten-1-one, 2-hydroxy-3,5,5-trimethyl-	n.s.g.	260(3.2)	39-0274-79C
2-Cyclopenten-1-one, 5-hydroxy-2,4,4-trimethyl-	n.s.g.	230(4.84)	39-0274-79C
2-Cyclopenten-1-one, 5-hydroxy-3,4,4-trimethyl-	n.s.g.	231(4.14)	39-0274-79C
Ethanone, 1,1'-(1,2-cyclobutanediyl)-bis-, cis	C_6H_{12}	283(1.70)	54-0346-79
trans	C_6H_{12}	282(1.72)	54-0346-79
Ethanone, 1-(3,4-dihydro-6-methyl-2H-pyran-2-yl)-	C_6H_{12}	210(3.34),283(1.56)	54-0346-79

Compound	Solvent	$\lambda_{max}(\log \epsilon)$	Ref.
2(5H)-Furanone, 5-butyl-	MeOH	217(4.16)	35-1544-79
2(5H)-Furanone, 5,5-diethyl-	MeOH	215(4.19)	35-1544-79
3-Hexenoic acid, 2-methylene-, methyl ester, (Z)-	heptane	247(3.4)	24-3480-79
2H-Pyran-2-carboxaldehyde, 3,4-dihydro-2,5-dimethyl-	C_6H_{12}	212(3.64),311(1.61)	54-0346-79
$C_8H_{12}O_3$			
2-Butenoic acid, 2-acetyl-, ethyl ester	n.s.g.	220.5(3.59)	33-2630-79
Cyclopentaneacetic acid, 3-oxo-, methyl ester, (S)-	MeOH	205s(2.00),287(1.36)	44-0452-79
Ethanone, 1-(6-hydroxy-1-cyclohexen-1-yl)-	EtOH	228(3.92)	30-0046-79
3,4(2H,5H)-Furandione, 2,2,5,5-tetramethyl-	isooctane	290(2.23),301(2.04), 314(1.70),333(1.20), 521(1.34),536(1.34), 561(1.28)	19-0665-79
	H_2O	317(1.46)	19-0665-79
2-Hexenoic acid, 6-oxo-, ethyl ester, (E)-	n.s.g.	208(4.09),300s(3.43)	118-0279-79
(Z)-	n.s.g.	210(4.02),300s(3.43)	118-0279-79
2H-Pyran-3(6H)-one, 2-ethyl-6-methoxy-, cis	EtOH	212(3.93)	56-0265-79
trans	EtOH	210(3.92)	56-0265-79
2H-Pyran-3(6H)-one, 6-hydroxy-2-(1-methylethyl)-	EtOH	215(3.92)	56-0265-79
$C_8H_{12}O_5$			
2-Cyclobuten-1-one, 2,3,4,4-tetramethoxy-	MeOH	249(4.05),294s(2.32)	44-1208-79
Pentanoic acid, 2-acetyl-5-hydroxy-4-oxo-, methyl ester, (±)-	EtOH	206(3.49),254(3.84)	136-0055-79B
$C_8H_{12}S_2$			
1,3-Cyclobutanedithione, 2,2,4,4-tetramethyl-	C_6H_{12}	254(3.00),315f(2.3), 500f(1.0)	88-4787-79
	MeOH	427(0.8),492(1.1)	88-4787-79
$C_8H_{12}S_3$			
1,2,5-Trithiepin, 3,4,6,7-tetramethyl-	$CHCl_3$	217(4.12),231(4.18), 260s(4.0),329(3.01), 362s(2.96)	5-1702-79
$C_8H_{12}S_5$			
2-Cyclobutene-1-thione, 2,3,4,4-tetrakis(methylthio)-	CH_2Cl_2	274(3.94),314s(3.71), 395(3.92),507(2.15) (changing)	5-0595-79
$C_8H_{13}ClN_4O_2$			
1,3,5-Triazin-2(1H)-one, 1-(2-chloroethyl)-4-(dimethylamino)-6-methoxy-	EtOH	235(4.12)	103-0111-79
$C_8H_{13}NO$			
2-Pyrrolidinone, 3-ethylidene-5,5-dimethyl-	EtOH	220(4.12)	12-2041-79
$C_8H_{13}NOS_2$			
1H-Azepine-3-carbodithioic acid, hexahydro-2-oxo-, methyl ester	EtOH	310(4.01)	39-0692-79C

Compound	Solvent	λ_{max}(log ϵ)	Ref.
$C_8H_{13}NO_2$			
Acetic acid, (2-aminocyclohexylidene)-, (E)-	H_2O	206(3.79)	12-2507-79
3-Buten-2-one, 4-morpholino-	EtOH	301(4.39)	4-0217-79
1-Cyclohexene-1-acetic acid, α-amino-	H_2O	210(3.32)(end abs.)	12-2507-79
$C_8H_{13}NO_5$			
Heptanoic acid, 7-nitro-6-oxo-, methyl ester, dicyclohexylamine salt	isoPrOH	332(4.04)	118-0295-79
$C_8H_{13}NS_2$			
Cycloheptanecarbodithioic acid, 2-imino-	EtOH	304(4.00),385(4.28)	150-1732-79
Cyclohexanecarbodithioic acid, 2-imino-, methyl ester	EtOH	315(3.98),384(4.44)	150-1732-79
Cyclohexanecarbodithioic acid, 2-imino-4-methyl-	EtOH	305(4.00),388(4.29)	150-1732-79
$C_8H_{13}N_2O_4PS_2$			
Phosphorothioic acid, O-[1,6-dihydro-1-methyl-5-(methylthio)-6-oxo-4-pyridazinyl] O,O-dimethyl ester	MeOH	211(4.22),238(3.70), 320(3.86)	73-1761-79
$C_8H_{13}N_2O_7P$			
2,4(1H,3H)-Pyrimidinedione, 1-[3-hydroxy-2-(phosphonooxy)propyl]-5-methyl-, barium salt	n.s.g.	271(3.09)	128-0281-79
$C_8H_{13}N_3$			
Cyclooctene, 5-azido-	EtOH	286(1.49)	56-0027-79
4-Pyrimidinamine, N,N,2,6-tetramethyl-	EtOH	249(4.22),273(3.70)	150-1579-79
$C_8H_{13}N_3O_2S$			
Sydnone, 4-(methylthio)-3-piperidino-	CH_2Cl_2	318(3.89)	5-0063-79
$C_8H_{13}N_3O_3$			
L-Histidine, 3-(2-hydroxyethyl)-	pH 7.0	213(3.76)	1-0277-79
$C_8H_{13}N_3S$			
4-Pyrimidinamine, N,N,6-trimethyl-2-(methylthio)-	EtOH	239(4.21),254(4.05), 292(3.72)	150-1579-79
$C_8H_{13}N_4OS$			
Oxazolo[3,2-a]-1,3,5-triazin-5-ium, 2-(dimethylamino)-6,7-dihydro-4-(methylthio)-, chloride	H_2O	240(4.00)	103-0111-79
$C_8H_{13}N_4O_2$			
Oxazolo[3,2-a]-1,3,5-triazin-5-ium, 2-(dimethylamino)-6,7-dihydro-4-methoxy-, chloride	H_2O	235(4.46)	103-0111-79
$C_8H_{14}Br_2N_2O$			
1H-Imidazole, 4-(dibromomethyl)-2,5-dihydro-2,2,5,5-tetramethyl-	EtOH	267(3.85)	103-0092-79
$C_8H_{14}IN_2O_2$			
1H-Imidazol-1-yloxy, 2,5-dihydro-4-(iodomethyl)-2,2,5,5-tetramethyl-, 3-oxide	EtOH	218(3.77),274(3.77)	70-2521-79

Compound	Solvent	λ_{max}(log ε)	Ref.
$C_8H_{14}N_2O$			
2-Cyclohexen-1-one, 3-(2,2-dimethyl-hydrazino)-	MeOH	291(4.60)	64-0102-79B
$C_8H_{14}N_2O_2$			
1-Azetidineacetamide, 2,2,3-trimethyl-α-oxo-	EtOH	226(3.70)	12-1775-79
Cyclohexanone, 2-[(methyleneamino)meth-yl]-, oxime, N^2-oxide	EtOH	238(3.98)	103-1025-79
$C_8H_{14}N_2O_3$			
2-Propenamide, N-[(dimethylamino)carbo-nyl]-3-methoxy-2-methyl-	MeOH	251.0(4.105)	73-0269-79
2H-Pyrrole-5-carboxamide, 3,4-dihydro-4-hydroxy-2,2,3-trimethyl-, 1-oxide	EtOH	264(4.00)	12-1785-79
$C_8H_{14}N_2O_4S$			
Methionine, N-acetyl-N-nitroso-, methyl ester	MeOH	241(3.81),377s(1.61), 390(1.76),404(1.92), 423(1.91)	39-1969-79C
S-oxide	MeOH	242(--),387(--), 403(--),422(--)	39-1969-79C
$C_8H_{14}N_3O_3$			
1H-Imidazol-1-yloxy, 4-(aminocarbonyl)-2,5-dihydro-2,2,5,5-tetramethyl-, 3-oxide	EtOH	260(4.01)	70-0214-79
$C_8H_{14}N_4O$			
4H-Imidazole-2-carboxamide, 5-(dimeth-ylamino)-4,4-dimethyl-	EtOH	297.5(3.84)	33-0768-79
$C_8H_{14}N_4O_2$			
1H-Pyrazole-4-carboxylic acid, 3-(2-hy-droxypropyl)-5-methyl-, hydrazide	EtOH	230(3.69)	118-0584-79
$C_8H_{14}N_4O_3$			
1H-Imidazole-4-carboxaldehyde, 2,5-di-hydro-2,2,5,5-tetramethyl-1-nitroso-, oxime, 3-oxide	EtOH	238(4.00)	103-0092-79
$C_8H_{14}N_4O_5$			
1,3,5-Triazin-2(1H)-one, 4-amino-5,6-dihydro-1-β-D-arabinofuranosyl-hydrochloride	pH 2	232(3.75)	87-1230-79
	MeOH	233(3.69)	87-1230-79
	pH 8	232(3.72)(changing)	87-1230-79
$C_8H_{14}N_5O_2$			
1H-Imidazol-1-yloxy, 4-(azidomethyl)-2,5-dihydro-2,2,5,5-tetramethyl-, 3-oxide	EtOH	242(4.00)	70-2521-79
$C_8H_{14}O$			
Ethanone, 1-cyclohexyl-	C_6H_{12}	286(1.30)	54-0346-79
$C_8H_{14}O_2$			
1,3-Butadiene, 2,3-diethoxy-	dioxan	225(4.28)	24-0862-79
Ethanone, 1-(tetrahydro-6-methyl-2H-pyran-2-yl)-	C_6H_{12}	283(1.40)	54-0346-79
3(2H)-Furanone, dihydro-2,2,5,5-tetra-methyl-	isooctane	301(1.11),310(1.08), 321(0.85)	19-0665-79
	H_2O	294(1.62)	19-0665-79

Compound	Solvent	λmax(log ε)	Ref.
$C_8H_{14}S_2$			
6,9-Dithiaspiro[3.6]decane	EtOH	213(3.02)	49-0279-79
$C_8H_{15}ClN_5$			
1,2,3-Triazinium, 5-chloro-4,6-bis(dimethylamino)-2-methyl-, perchlorate	CH_2Cl_2	425(2.97)	24-1535-79
$C_8H_{15}N_2$			
4H-Pyrazolium, 1,3,4,4,5-pentamethyl-, iodide	EtOH	222(4.15)	23-1186-79
$C_8H_{15}N_2O_3$			
1H-Imidazol-1-yloxy, 2,5-dihydro-4-methoxy-2,2,5,5-tetramethyl-, 3-oxide	EtOH	234(3.83)	70-0214-79
$C_8H_{15}N_2O_3P$			
1,3,2-Diazaphosphorin-4(1H)-one, 2-ethoxy-2,3-dihydro-1,3,6-trimethyl-, 2-oxide	H_2O	275(3.95)	103-1142-79
	EtOH	270(3.95)	103-1142-79
$C_8H_{15}N_3$			
2-Pentenenitrile, 3-(2-aminoethylamino)-4-methyl-	EtOH	263(4.18)	39-2289-79C
$C_8H_{15}N_3O$			
1,2,4-Triazin-3(2H)-one, 4,5-dihydro-2,4,5,5,6-pentamethyl-	EtOH	255(3.64)	4-0427-79
$C_8H_{15}N_3O_2$			
1H-Imidazole, 2,5-dihydro-2,2,4,5,5-pentamethyl-1-nitroso-, 3-oxide	EtOH	234(4.25)	103-0092-79
1H-Imidazole-4-carboxaldehyde, 2,5-dihydro-2,2,5,5-tetramethyl-, oxime, 3-oxide	EtOH	286(4.12)	103-0092-79
$C_8H_{16}N_2$			
1H-Imidazole, 4,5-dihydro-4,4-dimethyl-2-(1-methylethyl)-	EtOH	220(3.72)	39-2289-79C
1H-Imidazole, 2-(1-ethylpropyl)-4,5-dihydro-	EtOH	223(3.72)	39-2289-79C
$C_8H_{16}N_2O$			
1H-Imidazole, 2,5-dihydro-2,2,4,5,5-pentamethyl-, 3-oxide	EtOH	230(4.00)	103-0092-79
$C_8H_{16}N_2O_2$			
Butanal, 4-(butylnitrosoamino)-	EtOH	234(3.87),352(1.95)	94-0541-79
Diazene, methoxy(4-methylcyclohexyl)-, 2-oxide, cis	EtOH	235.2(3.94)	88-2457-79
$C_8H_{16}N_4O_5$			
Bis(2-methyl-2-nitro-1-propyl)amine, N-nitroso-	$C_2H_4Cl_2$	240(3.70),371(1.98)	70-0944-79
$C_8H_{16}S_2$			
Cyclohexane, 1,1-bis(methylthio)-	hexane	238(3.0)	114-0407-79A
$C_8H_{17}NO_2$			
Pentane, 2,2,4-trimethyl-4-nitro-	isooctane	280(1.39)	39-0907-79B
	MeOH	280(1.41)	39-0907-79B
	$CF_3CHOHCF_3$	271(1.63)	39-0907-79B

Compound	Solvent	λ_{max}(log ε)	Ref.
$C_8H_{17}N_2$			
1H-Imidazolium, 1-(1,1-dimethylethyl)-4,5-dihydro-3-methyl-, perchlorate	MeOH	220(3.75)	24-0445-79
$C_8H_{17}N_3O$			
1H-Imidazol-1-amine, 2,5-dihydro-2,2,4,5,5-pentamethyl-, 3-oxide	EtOH	231(4.01)	103-0092-79
$C_8H_{17}N_3O_3$			
Carbamic acid, [(nitrosopropylamino)-methyl]-, 1-methylethyl ester	EtOH	233(3.84),359(1.87)	94-0682-79
$C_8H_{18}NO$			
Nitroxide, bis(1,1-dimethylethyl)	pentane	238(3.41),460(0.95)	35-1904-79
2-Propanaminium, N-(1-ethoxyethylidene)-N-methyl-, fluorosulfate, (E)-	H_2O	225(2.76)	35-7323-79
1:1 E:Z	H_2O	225(2.82)	35-7323-79
$C_8H_{18}N_2O$			
1-Propanamine, 2-methyl-N-(2-methyl-propyl)-N-nitroso-	$C_2H_4Cl_2$	241(3.89),362(2.05)	70-0944-79
$C_8H_{18}SSn$			
Stannane, (ethenylthio)triethyl-	hexane	238(3.76)	70-1479-79
$C_8H_{18}SeSi_2$			
Etheneselone, bis(trimethylsilyl)-	isooctane	226(4.78),255(4.66), 463(3.94)	54-0055-79
$C_8H_{18}Si_2$			
Disilane, diethenyltetramethyl-	heptane	230(4.0)	65-0916-79
$C_8H_{19}N_3$			
Ethanehydrazonamide, N-butyl-N',N'-dimethyl-, monohydrochloride	H_2O	213(3.90)	104-2066-79
	pH 13	226(3.79)	104-2066-79
$C_8H_{20}Cl_2O_3Si_4$			
Disiloxane, 1,3-bis(chloromethyl)-1,3-diethoxy-1,3-dimethyl-	heptane	185.3(1.78)	65-1333-79
	MeCN	186.6(2.28)	65-1333-79
$C_8H_{20}S_4Si$			
Thiosilicic acid, tetraethyl ester	hexane	227(3.48)	114-0407-79A
$C_8H_{24}O_2Si_3$			
Trisiloxane, octamethyl-	heptane	185.5(2.62)	65-1333-79
	MeCN	185.8(2.78),188s(--)	65-1333-79
$C_8H_{24}O_4Si_4$			
Cyclotetrasiloxane, octamethyl-	heptane	186(2.34),200s(--)	65-1333-79
	MeCN	185.8(2.48)	65-1333-79
Cyclotetrasiloxane, 2,4,6,8-tetraethyl-	heptane	186(1.0),200(0.78)	65-1333-79

Compound	Solvent	λ_{max}(log ϵ)	Ref.
$C_9H_2Cl_4O_3$			
2H,5H-4a,7a-Methanocyclopenta[b]pyran-2,5-dione, 3,4,6,7-tetrachloro-	hexane	257(4.08)	18-0811-79
$C_9H_3Cl_3FNO_2$			
1H-Indene, 1,1,3-trichloro-2-fluoro-6-nitro-	hexane	256(3.97),308(3.57)	104-1121-79
$C_9H_3F_9O_6S_3$			
Benzene, 1,3,5-tris[(trifluoromethyl)-sulfonyl]-	MeOH	210(4.14)(changing)	150-0272-79S
methanol adduct	MeOH	225(4.27),260(4.33), 357(4.15)	150-0272-79S
$C_9H_4Cl_2O$			
1H-Inden-1-one, 2,3-dichloro-	hexane	237(4.63),400(2.84)	39-1686-79B
$C_9H_4Cl_3F$			
1H-Indene, 1,1,3-trichloro-2-fluoro-	hexane	275(2.98),312(2.95)	104-1121-79
$C_9H_4Cl_3N_3O_2$			
Pyrido[3,2-d]pyrimidine-6-carboxylic acid, 2,4,8-trichloro-, methyl ester	pH 1	231(4.49),295(3.95), 308(3.86),320(3.74)	44-0435-79
	pH 7	223(4.49),295(3.93), 307(3.85),320(3.74)	44-0435-79
	pH 11	247(4.18),332(3.97), 345(3.88)	44-0435-79
$C_9H_4Cl_5F$			
1H-Indene, 1,1,2,3,3-pentachloro-2-fluoro-2,3-dihydro-	hexane	262(2.48),269(2.54)	104-1121-79
$C_9H_4Cl_5N_3O_2$			
1H-Benzimidazole, 4,5,7-trichloro-2-(dichloronitromethyl)-6-methyl-	n.s.g.	207(4.38),290(3.76)	104-0361-79
$C_9H_4F_6HgO_2$			
Mercury, (trifluoroacetato-O)[3-(trifluoromethyl)phenyl]-	$CHCl_3$	258(2.66),264(2.75), 270(2.65)	12-1521-79
Mercury, (trifluoroacetato-O)[4-(trifluoromethyl)phenyl]-	$CHCl_3$	265(2.89),271(2.83)	12-1521-79
$C_9H_4O_2S$			
4H-Cyclopenta[2,1-b:3,4-b']dithiophen-4-one	C_6H_{12}	266(4.51),285s(3.85), 297s(3.74),472(3.11)	39-0393-79B
	CF_3COOH	304(3.70),335s(3.54), 545(2.78)	39-0393-79B
4H-Cyclopenta[2,1-b:3,4-c']dithiophen-4-one	C_6H_{12}	268(4.64),295s(3.51), 306s(3.34),380(2.78)	39-0393-79B
	CF_3COOH	270(4.65),290s(3.86), 323(3.32),339s(3.23), 437(2.60)	39-0393-79B
7H-Cyclopenta[1,2-b:3,4-b']dithiophen-7-one	C_6H_{12}	298(3.168),321(3.43), 334s(3.38),459(2.60)	39-0393-79B
	CF_3COOH	313(3.83),346(3.86), 510(2.30)	39-0393-79B
7H-Cyclopenta[1,2-b:3,4-c']dithiophen-7-one	C_6H_{12}	279(3.81),290(3.88), 300(3.57),312(3.65), 319(3.52),326(3.54), 377(2.90)	39-0393-79B

Compound	Solvent	λ max (log ε)	Ref.
7H-Cyclopenta[1,2-b:3,4-c']dithiophen-7-one (cont.)	CF_3COOH	302(3.73),315s(3.66), 338s(3.77),421(3.90)	39-0393-79B
7H-Cyclopenta[1,2-b:4,3-b']dithiophen-7-one	C_6H_{12}	311(3.83),321(4.01), 330(3.77),337(4.01), 418(2.30)	39-0393-79B
	CF_3COOH	347s(3.93),362(3.96), 485(2.60)	39-0393-79B
7H-Cyclopenta[1,2-c:3,4-c']dithiophen-7-one	C_6H_{12}	275s(3.94),281(3.81), 286s(3.76),291(3.83), 299(3.60),305(3.72), 342(3.04)	39-0393-79B
	CF_3COOH	288(3.67),335(3.79), 400s(2.78)	39-0393-79B
$C_9H_5AsN_2$			
Propanedinitrile, (4-arseninylmethylene)-	EtOH	238(3.99),360(4.45)	88-3141-79
$C_9H_5ClN_2$			
Pyrazino[2.1.6-cd]pyrrolizine, 5-chloro-	EtOH	205(4.14),248(4.52), 299(3.71),370(3.43)	24-2465-79
$C_9H_5FN_2O_3$			
1,2,4-Oxadiazole-3-carboxylic acid, 5-(4-fluorophenyl)-	n.s.g.	256(4.46)	4-1153-79
$C_9H_5FN_4O_4$			
1H-Imidazole, 2-(4-fluoro-3-nitrophenyl)-4-nitro-	MeOH	252(4.25),311(3.99)	4-1153-79
1H-Imidazole, 2-(4-fluorophenyl)-4,5-dinitro-	MeOH	240(4.17),277(4.01), 328(3.85)	4-1153-79
$C_9H_5F_5S$			
Benzene, pentafluoro(2-propenylthio)-	n.s.g.	212(4.04),282(3.32)	70-0315-79
$C_9H_5F_7$			
Benzene, 1-ethyl-2,3,5,6-tetrafluoro-4-(1-trifluoromethyl)-	EtOH	213(3.86),275(3.30)	65-0464-79
C_9H_5N			
2-Propynenitrile, 3-phenyl-	EtOH	207(4.36),211(4.35), 249(4.14),262(4.34), 275(4.20)	39-2289-79C
$C_9H_5N_3O_4$			
Quinoline, 2,5-dinitro-	EtOH	231(3.87)	94-2627-79
Quinoline, 2,8-dinitro-	EtOH	236(3.91)	94-2627-79
Quinoline, 3,5-dinitro-	EtOH	248(4.13),305(3.64)	94-2627-79
Quinoline, 3,8-dinitro-	EtOH	229(4.03),285(3.67), 384(3.61),430(3.91)	94-2627-79
Quinoline, 4,5-dinitro-	EtOH	249(3.78),382(3.68)	94-2627-79
Quinoline, 4,8-dinitro-	EtOH	250(3.77),320(3.64)	94-2627-79
Quinoline, 5,7-dinitro-	EtOH	241(3.93),295(3.64)	94-2627-79
Quinoline, 6,7-dinitro-	EtOH	249(3.84),257s(3.81), 293(3.43)	94-2627-79
Quinoline, 7,8-dinitro-	EtOH	251(3.86)	94-2627-79
$C_9H_6BrN_3OS$			
1,3,5-Triazin-2(1H)-one, 6-(4-bromophenyl)-3,4-dihydro-4-thioxo-	dioxan	271.5(4.42)	18-3728-79

Compound	Solvent	λ_{max}(log ε)	Ref.
C_9H_6ClNO			
Benzenepropanenitrile, 4-chloro-β-oxo-	C_6H_{12}	258(4.20)	56-2251-79
	EtOH	254(4.10),308(4.38)	56-2251-79
$C_9H_6ClN_3OS$			
1,3,5-Triazin-2(1H)-one, 6-(2-chloro-phenyl)-3,4-dihydro-4-thioxo-	dioxan	260(4.29)	18-3728-79
$C_9H_6ClN_3O_2S$			
Benzamide, 2-chloro-N-(2,3-dihydro-3-oxo-1,2,4-thiadiazol-5-yl)-	dioxan	231(4.23),309(3.76)	18-3728-79
$C_9H_6Cl_2N_4O_2$			
Pyrido[3,2-d]pyrimidine-6-carboxylic acid, 4-amino-2,8-dichloro-, methyl ester	pH 1	250(4.32),327(4.02)	44-0435-79
	pH 7	250(4.32),327(4.00), 340s(3.95)	44-0435-79
	pH 11	247(4.30),301(3.86), 324(3.93),337(3.84)	44-0435-79
$C_9H_6FN_3O_2$			
1H-Imidazole-4,5-dione, 2-(4-fluoro-phenyl)-, 5-oxime	MeOH	232(4.01),238(4.00), 271(4.20),333(4.04)	4-1153-79
$C_9H_6F_4N_2O$			
2H-Benzimidazol-2-one, 4,5,6,7-tetra-fluoro-1,3-dihydro-1,3-dimethyl-	EtOH	210(4.23),224(3.94), 277(3.49)	18-2657-79
$C_9H_6F_4N_2S$			
2H-Benzimidazole-2-thione, 4,5,6,7-tetrafluoro-1,3-dihydro-1,3-dimethyl-	EtOH	218(4.08),248(4.24), 302(4.35)	18-2657-79
isomer	EtOH	220(4.41),263(3.80), 290(3.44)	18-2657-79
$C_9H_6N_2O_2$			
Benzeneacetonitrile, α-(nitromethyl-ene)-, (Z)-	MeCN	323(4.04)	4-1611-79
2-Propenenitrile, 2-nitro-3-phenyl-	n.s.g.	327(4.2)	104-1859-79
$C_9H_6N_2O_2S$			
1,3-Dioxolo[4,5-g]quinazoline-8(5H)-thione	EtOH	226s(4.35),228(4.36), 258s(3.95),272(4.03), 346s(3.66),353s(3.99), 365(4.17),377(4.10)	1-0079-79
$C_9H_6N_2O_3$			
Benzenepropanenitrile, 4-nitro-β-oxo-	EtOH	262.5(4.16)	56-2251-79
$C_9H_6N_4O$			
5H-Pyrazolo[4,3-g]quinazolin-5-one, 1,6-dihydro-	EtOH	232(4.45),247(4.52), 254(4.56),263(4.44), 312(3.76)	44-4609-79
$C_9H_6N_6$			
Triimidazo[1,2-a:1',2'-c:1",2"-e]-[1,3,5]triazine	EtOH	228(4.52),235(4.50), 255(3.77)	44-4243-79
C_9H_6OSSe			
Benzo[b]thiophene-2-carboxaldehyde, 3-selenyl-	EtOH	225(4.30)	103-0731-79
	$CHCl_3$	243(4.31)	103-0731-79
Benzo[b]thiophene-3-carboxaldehyde, 2-selenyl-	EtOH	228(4.27)	103-0731-79
	$CHCl_3$	243(4.30)	103-0731-79

Compound	Solvent	λmax(log ε)	Ref.
$C_9H_6O_3$			
2H-1-Benzopyran-2-one, 7-hydroxy- (umbelliferone)	EtOH	217(4.06),245(3.52), 255(3.40),329(4.12)	105-0426-79
4H-Pyran-3,5-dicarboxaldehyde, 4-ethynyl-	EtOH	211(4.10),286(3.76)	49-0613-79
$C_9H_7BrCl_3NOS$			
Carbamothioic acid, dimethyl-, 2-bromo-3,4,6-trichlorophenyl ester	MeOH	211(4.74),224(--), 248(4.16)	73-0918-79
$C_9H_7BrCl_3NO_2$			
Carbamic acid, dimethyl-, 2-bromo-3,4,6-trichlorophenyl ester	MeOH	210(4.77),224(--)	73-0918-79
$C_9H_7BrN_2OS$			
4(5H)-Thiazolone, 2-[(4-bromophenyl)-amino]-	MeOH	272(4.24)	104-1344-79
	70% dioxan	275(4.21)	104-1344-79
$C_9H_7BrN_4$			
1H-Imidazole, 2-[(4-bromophenyl)azo]-	MeOH	240(3.97),364(4.50), 372(4.49),463s(3.36)	19-0249-79
$C_9H_7BrO_2$			
2-Propenoic acid, 3-(3-bromophenyl)-	neutral	278(4.31)	19-0045-79
	cation	323(4.40)	19-0045-79
2-Propenoic acid, 3-(4-bromophenyl)-	neutral	294(4.33)	19-0045-79
	cation	351(4.43)	19-0045-79
$C_9H_7BrO_3$			
Ethanone, 1-[6-bromo-1,3-benzodioxol-5-yl)-	EtOH	231(4.17),277(3.57), 305(3.56)	39-0829-79C
$C_9H_7BrO_4$			
Benzoic acid, 3-acetyl-5-bromo-4-hydroxy-	EtOH	234(4.45),258s(3.96), 330(3.50)	39-0677-79C
	EtOH-HCl	234(4.47),256s(3.98), 330(3.51)	39-0677-79C
	EtOH-NaOH	251(4.34),283(4.12), 372(3.78)	39-0677-79C
$C_9H_7ClN_2O_2S$			
1,2,3-Thiadiazolium, 5-chloro-4-hydroxy-3-(4-methoxyphenyl)-, hydroxide, inner salt	EtOH	226(4.25),313(3.88), 397(4.18)	39-2349-79C
$C_9H_7ClO_2$			
2-Propenoic acid, 3-(2-chlorophenyl)-	neutral	275(4.25)	19-0045-79
	cation	328(4.34)	19-0045-79
2-Propenoic acid, 3-(3-chlorophenyl)-	neutral	278(4.30)	19-0045-79
	cation	323(4.39)	19-0045-79
2-Propenoic acid, 3-(4-chlorophenyl)-	neutral	290(4.31)	19-0045-79
	cation	347(4.39)	19-0045-79
$C_9H_7Cl_2N_5O_2$			
Acetamide, 2-chloro-N-[1-(chloroacetyl)-1H-pyrazolo[3,4-d]pyrimidin-4-yl]-	EtOH	268(4.00)	39-2672-79C
	EtOH-HCl	260(3.97)	39-2672-79C
$C_9H_7Cl_3INOS$			
Carbamothioic acid, dimethyl-, 3,4,6-trichloro-2-iodophenyl ester	MeOH	217(4.58),242(4.32)	73-0918-79

Compound	Solvent	λ_{max}(log ε)	Ref.
$C_9H_7Cl_3INO_2$			
Carbamic acid, dimethyl-, 3,4,6-trichloro-2-iodophenyl ester	MeOH	218(4.50),240(--)	73-0918-79
$C_9H_7Cl_3N_2O_3S$			
Carbamothioic acid, dimethyl-, 3,4,6-trichloro-2-nitrophenyl ester	MeOH	209(4.56),248(4.12)	73-0918-79
$C_9H_7Cl_3N_2O_4$			
Carbamic acid, dimethyl-, 3,4,6-trichloro-2-nitrophenyl ester	MeOH	209(4.55),292(3.42)	73-0918-79
$C_9H_7FN_2O_5$			
2-Butenoic acid, 4-(5-fluoro-3,4-dihydro-2,4-dioxo-1(2H)-pyrimidinyl)-4-oxo-, methyl ester	dioxan	275.5(3.90)	121-0351-79
$C_9H_7F_6N_3$			
Guanidine, [3,5-bis(trifluoromethyl)-phenyl]-, mononitrate	MeOH	204(4.49),239(4.01)	83-0426-79
C_9H_7Li			
Lithium, 1H-indenyl-	$MeOCH_2CH_2OMe$	340(3.15)	104-2023-79
C_9H_7N			
Isoquinoline	EtOH	262(3.57),371(3.54)	44-3244-79
C_9H_7NO			
Benzeneacetonitrile, α-(hydroxymethylene)-	EtOH	262(4.16)	22-0017-79
Benzenepropanenitrile, β-oxo-	C_6H_{12}	245(4.13),284(3.05)	56-2251-79
	EtOH	244(4.13),278(3.41)	56-2251-79
Benzonitrile, 4-acetyl-	C_6H_{12}	246(4.32),286(3.16)	56-2251-79
	EtOH	247(4.36),287(3.34)	56-2251-79
8-Quinolinol	n.s.g.	243(4.68),310(3.73)	93-1271-79
C_9H_7NOS			
2(3H)-Thiazolone, 4-phenyl-	EtOH	223(4.28),271(3.18)	2-0082-79B
$C_9H_7NOS_2$			
Thiazole, 2-(phenylsulfinyl)-	H_2O	258(3.94)	39-0163-79B
protonated	H_2O	270(4.01)	39-0163-79B
$C_9H_7NO_2$			
1H-2-Benzopyran-1-one, 5-amino-	MeOH	217(3.04),236(3.27),244(3.31),275(3.00),360(2.69)	94-0946-79
	MeOH-HCl	228(--),242(--),257(--),276(--),321(--)	94-0946-79
4H-1-Benzopyran-4-one, 2-amino-	EtOH	225(4.22),293(4.20)	56-0229-79
Phenol, 2-(5-isoxazolyl)-	MeOH	218(4.14),260(4.16),271(4.10),305(3.94)	56-0229-79
3,5-Pyridinedicarboxaldehyde, 4-ethynyl-1,4-dihydro-	EtOH	229(4.33),245s(3.81),365(4.03)	49-0613-79
sodium deriv.	EtOH	229(4.13),246(4.03),367(3.56),447(3.65)	49-0613-79
$C_9H_7NO_2S$			
Thiazolo[2,3-a]pyridinium, 2-acetyl-3-hydroxy-, hydroxide, inner salt	EtOH	272(4.10),410(4.36)	150-2935-79

Compound	Solvent	λmax(log ε)	Ref.
$C_9H_7NO_2S_2$			
2,2'-Bithiophene, 5-methyl-5'-nitro-	EtOH	411.3(4.25)	103-0864-79
2,2'-Bithiophene, 5'-methyl-3-nitro-	EtOH	382(4.04)	103-0864-79
Thiazole, 2-(phenylsulfonyl)-	H_2O	266(4.08)	39-0163-79B
protonated	H_2O	278(4.11)	39-0163-79B
$C_9H_7NO_3$			
5-Norbornen-7-one-2,3-dicarboximide	MeCN	253(2.11),274(1.48)	44-0604-79
$C_9H_7NO_4$			
2-Furancarboxylic acid, 5-(5-oxazolyl)-, methyl ester	EtOH	297(4.36)	94-0793-79
2-Propenal, 3-(2-hydroxy-5-nitrophenyl)-	MeOH	278(3.93),376(3.88), 417(3.90)	104-1715-79
	dioxan	280(4.20),312(4.03)	104-1715-79
	DMSO	280(4.22),320(4.10), 393(3.81),455(4.01)	104-1715-79
2-Propenoic acid, 3-(2-nitrophenyl)-	neutral	250(4.18)	19-0045-79
	cation	303(4.07)	19-0045-79
2-Propenoic acid, 3-(3-nitrophenyl)-	neutral	263(4.40)	19-0045-79
	cation	302(4.42)	19-0045-79
2-Propenoic acid, 3-(4-nitrophenyl)-	cation	345(4.40)	19-0045-79
$C_9H_7NS_2$			
Benzothiazole, 2-(ethenylthio)-	THF	225(4.31),285(4.21), 293(4.21),303(4.15)	121-0001-79
polymer at 60°	THF	226(4.24),285(4.01), 294(4.00),303(3.92)	121-0001-79
$C_9H_7N_3O$			
3,5-Pyridinedicarbonitrile, 1,2-dihydro-1,6-dimethyl-2-oxo-	n.s.g.	340(4.02)	73-3288-79
3,5-Pyridinedicarbonitrile, 2-methoxy-6-methyl-	EtOH	222(4.57),280(4.41), 333(4.16)	39-0677-79C
$C_9H_7N_3OS$			
1,3,4-Thiadiazolo[3,2-a]benzimidazol-6-ol, 2-methyl-	pH 1	312(3.80),376(3.71)	18-2033-79
	pH 13	303(3.57),453(3.61)	18-2033-79
	EtOH	241(4.21),255(3.80), 371(3.85)	18-2033-79
1,3,5-Triazin-2(1H)-one, 3,4-dihydro-6-phenyl-4-thioxo-	dioxan	260(4.36),330(3.90)	18-3728-79
$C_9H_7N_3O_2$			
3-Quinolinamine, 8-nitro-	EtOH	211(4.26),223s(4.19), 345(4.01),404s(3.66)	94-2627-79
$C_9H_7N_3O_2S$			
Benzamide, N-(2,3-dihydro-3-oxo-1,2,4-thiadiazol-5-yl)-	dioxan	245(4.28),311(4.04)	18-3728-79
$C_9H_7N_3O_3S$			
4(5H)-Thiazolone, 2-[(4-nitrophenyl)amino]-	H_2O	319(4.13)	104-1344-79
	MeOH	316(4.19)	104-1344-79
	dioxan	316(4.19)	104-1344-79
	70% dioxan	320(4.19)	104-1344-79
$C_9H_7N_3O_5$			
Pyrido[3,2-d]pyrimidine-6-carboxylic acid, 1,2,3,4,5,8-hexahydro-2,4,8-trioxo-, methyl ester	pH 1	240(4.33),248(4.29), 257(4.18),326(3.86)	44-0435-79
	pH 7	248(4.44),256(4.34),	44-0435-79

Compound	Solvent	λmax(log ε)	Ref.
(cont.)		325(3.93)	44-0435-79
	pH 11	248(4.44),315(3.83)	44-0435-79
$C_9H_7N_3S$			
Propanedinitrile, [[(5-methyl-2-thien-yl)amino]methylene]-	DMF	348(4.22)	49-1189-79
Thieno[2,3-b]pyridine-5-carbonitrile, 4-amino-2-methyl-	DMF	287(3.96),322(3.77), 330(3.75)	49-1189-79
$C_9H_7N_5O$			
Imidazo[1,2-c]pteridine, 6-methoxy-	pH -4	215(4.22),255s(3.71), 352(3.97),365s(3.92)	18-0867-79
	pH 0.0	215(4.19),235s(3.90), 263(3.46),329(3.93), 342s(3.83)	18-0867-79
	pH 4.5	230(4.19),247s(3.75), 289(3.27),343(3.93)	18-0867-79
1,2,4-Triazino[5,6-c]cinnolin-3(2H)-one, 4,6-dihydro-	EtOH	213(4.33),237(4.03), 267(3.79),275(3.86), 305(4.08),313(3.93)	73-2438-79
$C_9H_7N_5OS$			
Isothiazolo[4,5-b]pyridine-3-carbox-amide, 5-amino-6-cyano-7-methyl-	DMF	292(3.81),299s(3.77), 390(3.78)	5-1534-79
$C_9H_7N_5O_2$			
1H-Imidazole, 2-[(4-nitrophenyl)azo]-	MeOH	216(3.93),276(3.84), 385(4.44),460s(3.40)	19-0249-79
$C_9H_7N_5O_3S$			
Urea, N-(4-nitrophenyl)-N'-1,3,4-thia-diazol-2-yl-	n.s.g.	318(4.32)	87-0028-79
$C_9H_7N_5S$			
Imidazo[1,2-c]pteridine, 6-(methylthio)-	pH -4.0	241(4.19),270s(4.03), 290(4.00),386(4.09)	18-0867-79
	pH 0.0	225(4.21),253(4.23), 287s(4.03),294(4.04), 343(4.06),355s(4.00)	18-0867-79
	pH 4.5	232(4.29),255(4.30), 292s(3.76),303(3.78), 350(4.09)	18-0867-79
C_9H_8			
1H-Indene, lithium deriv.	$MeOCH_2CH_2OMe$	340(3.15)	104-2023-79
sodium deriv.	$MeOCH_2CH_2OMe$	359(3.17)	104-2023-79
potassium deriv.	$MeOCH_2CH_2OMe$	366(3.14)	104-2023-79
cesium deriv.	$MeOCH_2CH_2OMe$	371(3.13)	104-2023-79
$C_9H_8BrClO_4$			
Benzoic acid, 4-bromo-5-chloro-2,3-di-methoxy-	EtOH	214(4.68),295(3.27)	104-1740-79
$C_9H_8BrNO_2$			
2-Propenoic acid, 2-bromo-3-(2-pyridin-yl)-, methyl ester	MeOH	240(4.02),286(4.02)	22-0559-79
$C_9H_8BrN_3$			
Benzene, (1-azido-2-bromo-1-propenyl)-	C_6H_{12}	257(4.08)	44-3281-79

Compound	Solvent	λmax(log ε)	Ref.
$C_9H_8BrN_3O_2S$			
Benzamide, N-[[(aminocarbonyl)amino]-thioxomethyl]-4-bromo-	dioxan	256(4.38),287(4.19)	18-3728-79
C_9H_8ClN			
1H-Indole, 5-chloro-3-methyl-	EtOH	231(4.36),281(3.69), 287(3.72),296(3.67)	39-0829-79C
$C_9H_8ClN_3$			
1H-1,2,4-Triazole, 3-(4-chlorophenyl)-5-methyl-	MeOH	248(4.26)	44-0084-79
$C_9H_8ClN_3O_2$			
1H-Benzimidazole, 2-(chloronitromethyl)-5-methyl-	n.s.g.	211(4.49),275(3.48), 375(4.41)	104-0361-79
$C_9H_8ClN_3O_2S$			
Benzamide, N-[[(aminocarbonyl)amino]-thioxomethyl]-4-chloro-	dioxan	236(4.24),286(4.17)	18-3728-79
$C_9H_8Cl_2OS$			
Benzene, 1-[(2,2-dichloroethenyl)thio]-4-methoxy-	C_6H_{12}	233(4.10),253(4.12), 270s(4.02)	70-1610-79
$C_9H_8Cl_2S$			
Benzene, 1-[(2,2-dichloroethenyl)thio]-4-methyl-	C_6H_{12}	253(4.07),272(4.01)	70-1610-79
$C_9H_8N_2$			
1H-Benzimidazole, 1-ethenyl-	isooctane	238(4.33),275(3.72), 282(3.80),291(3.76)	65-1225-79
	EtOH	232(4.15),250(3.95), 280(3.66),288(3.58)	65-1225-79
	EtOH	227(4.22),233(4.23), 253(4.04),281(3.71)	70-1931-79
1H-Pyrazole, 4-phenyl-	EtOH	248(4.14),304s(3.11)	103-0501-79
$C_9H_8N_2O$			
8(1H)-Cycloheptapyrazolone, 3-methyl-	MeOH	235(4.35),296(3.82), 308(3.81),365(3.85)	18-1972-79
5-Isoxazolamine, 4-phenyl-	MeOH	262(4.20)	4-1611-79
1(2H)-Phthalazinone, 2-methyl-	EtOH	287(4.03)	39-1199-79C
8-Quinolinol, 2-amino-	acid	234(4.04),262(4.49), 306(3.87)	123-0070-79
	neutral	239(4.19),257(4.32), 280(4.26),330(3.58)	123-0070-79
	base	269(4.51),304(3.48), 354(3.39)	123-0070-79
$C_9H_8N_2OS$			
1,2,3-Oxadiazolium, 5-mercapto-3-methyl-4-phenyl-, hydroxide, inner salt	EtOH	252(3.74),341(3.49), 428(2.88)	39-0956-79C
1,2,3-Oxadiazolium, 5-mercapto-4-methyl-3-phenyl-, hydroxide, inner salt	EtOH	253(4.14),387(3.92)	39-0956-79C
1,2,3-Thiadiazolium, 5-hydroxy-3-methyl-4-phenyl-, hydroxide, inner salt	EtOH	255(3.76),342(3.63)	39-0956-79C
1,2,3-Thiadiazolium, 5-hydroxy-4-methyl-3-phenyl-, hydroxide, inner salt	EtOH	233(3.88),340(3.75)	39-0956-79C
4(5H)-Thiazolone, 2-(phenylamino)-	H_2O	260(4.19)	104-1344-79
	MeOH	264(4.19)	104-1344-79
	dioxan	269(3.96)	104-1344-79

Compound	Solvent	λ_{max}(log ε)	Ref.
4(5H)-Thiazolone, 2-(phenylamino)-	70% dioxan	265(4.12)	104-1344-79
$C_9H_8N_2O_2$			
Benzonitrile, 5-acetyl-2-amino-4-hydroxy-	EtOH and EtOH-HCl	233s(4.46),239(4.55), 271(3.95),300(4.18), 328(4.10)	39-0677-79C
	EtOH-NaOH	259(4.69),280s(4.23), 350(3.89)	39-0677-79C
1H-Isoindole-1,3(2H)-dione, 2-(aminomethyl)-, monohydrobromide	isoPrOH	217(4.65),235(3.98), 293(3.28),301(3.25)	4-0339-79
3-Pyridinecarbonitrile, 5-acetyl-1,2-dihydro-6-methyl-2-oxo-	EtOH	213(4.23),218(4.15), 274(4.17),334(3.97)	39-0677-79C
	CF_3COOH	267(4.12),309(4.11)	39-0677-79C
$C_9H_8N_2O_3$			
Benzoic acid, 4-amino-3-cyano-6-hydroxy-, methyl ester	EtOH and EtOH-HCl	234(4.66),257(4.07), 285(4.26),318(3.83)	39-0677-79C
	EtOH-NaOH	251(4.75),273(4.19), 330(3.83)	39-0677-79C
2-Propenoic acid, 3-(5-amino-2-furanyl)-2-cyano-, methyl ester	EtOH	227(4.08),447(4.64)	73-3301-79
3-Pyridinecarboxylic acid, 5-cyano-1,6-dihydro-2-methyl-6-oxo-, methyl ester	EtOH	208(4.22),215s(4.14), 261(4.19),331(3.98)	39-0677-79C
$C_9H_8N_2O_4$			
[4,5'-Bioxazole]-4'-carboxylic acid, 5-methyl-	MeOH	263(3.93)	5-1370-79
$C_9H_8N_2O_6$			
Benzeneacetic acid, 5-methyl-2,4-dinitro-	MeOH	251(4.19)	73-2677-79
$C_9H_8N_2S$			
2(1H)-Quinazolinethione, 4-methyl-	EtOH	262(3.96),291(4.35), 395(3.67)	118-0120-79
$C_9H_8N_2S_2$			
2H-1,3,4-Thiadiazine-2-thione, 3,6-dihydro-5-phenyl-	EtOH	274(3.945),318(4.031)	48-0959-79
1,2,3-Thiadiazolium, 5-mercapto-4-methyl-3-phenyl-, hydroxide, inner salt	EtOH	272(3.82),428(2.99)	39-0956-79C
$C_9H_8N_4$			
1H-Imidazole, 2-(phenylazo)-	MeOH	230(3.90),356(4.38), 368(4.35),426s(3.25)	19-0249-79
$C_9H_8N_4OS$			
Urea, N-phenyl-N'-1,3,4-thiadiazol-2-yl-	n.s.g.	257(4.41)	87-0028-79
$C_9H_8N_4O_3$			
1H-1,2,3-Triazole, 4-(4-methoxyphenyl)-5-nitro-	EtOH	242(4.13),330(3.62)	104-1168-79
$C_9H_8N_6$			
Imidazo[1,2-c]pteridin-6-amine, N-methyl-	pH -3.0	228(4.37),278(4.07), 295s(3.92),402(4.15)	18-0867-79
	pH 0.5	217(4.32),230s(4.20), 259(4.12),277(4.07), 364(4.01)	18-0867-79

Compound	Solvent	λ_{max}(log ϵ)	Ref.
Imidazo[1,2-c]pteridin-6-amine, N-methyl- (cont.)	pH 5.0	228(4.44),260s(3.97), 290s(3.72),361(4.14)	18-0867-79
C_9H_8O			
Bicyclo[4.2.1]nona-2,4,7-trien-9-one	EtOH	216(3.49),269(3.60), 277(3.58),325(2.75)	44-1294-79
$C_9H_8O_2$			
2-Propenoic acid, 3-phenyl-	neutral	278(4.25)	19-0045-79
	cation	322(4.35)	19-0045-79
$C_9H_8O_2S_4$			
1,3-Dithiole-4-carboxylic acid, 2-(1,3-dithiol-2-ylidene)-, ethyl ester	MeCN	292s(4.07),303(4.11), 314(4.13),424(3.28)	44-1476-79
$C_9H_8O_3$			
2,4,6-Cycloheptatrien-1-one, 3-acetyl-2-hydroxy-	MeOH	245(4.25),350(3.80), 415(3.75)	18-1972-79
2-Propenoic acid, 3-(2-hydroxyphenyl)-	neutral	278(4.13)	19-0045-79
	cation	319(4.24)	19-0045-79
2-Propenoic acid, 3-(3-hydroxyphenyl)-	neutral	278(4.27)	19-0045-79
	cation	323(4.36)	19-0045-79
2-Propenoic acid, 3-(4-hydroxyphenyl)-	neutral	306(4.26)	19-0045-79
	cation	357(4.45)	19-0045-79
2H-Pyran-2-one, 6-methyl-4-(2-propynyloxy)-	MeOH	284(3.97)	150-0110-79S
$C_9H_8O_3S$			
Benzo[b]thiophene, 3-methoxy-, 1,1-dioxide	EtOH	224(4.07),290(4.27)	95-0038-79
$C_9H_8O_4$			
1,3-Benzodioxole-4,7-dione, 5,6-dimethyl-	MeCN	295(4.18),486(2.65)	64-0624-79B
$C_9H_8O_5$			
1,2-Benzenedicarboxaldehyde, 3,4-dihydroxy-5-methoxy-	EtOH	260(4.17),293(3.82), 335(3.71),424s(3.38)	20-0883-79
1,2-Benzenedicarboxaldehyde, 3,5-dihydroxy-4-methoxy-	EtOH	264(4.13),298(3.74), 340(3.63),432(3.31)	20-0883-79
1,3-Benzodioxole-5-carboxylic acid, 7-methoxy- (myristicic acid)	MeOH	265(3.8),310(2.9), 340(1.8)	102-0352-79
1,3-Benzodioxole-4,7-dione, 5-methoxy-6-methyl-	MeCN	302(4.03),500(3.42)	64-0624-79B
2-Propenoic acid, 3-(5-methoxy-4-oxo-4H-pyran-2-yl)-	MeOH	233(4.27),277(4.31)	4-1281-79
$C_9H_9BrN_2$			
Pyridine, 3-bromo-5-(3,4-dihydro-2H-pyrrol-5-yl)-	EtOH	237(3.88),286(3.73)	44-4332-79
$C_9H_9Br_2NO$			
1H-Pyrrole-2-carboxaldehyde, 4-(1,2-dibromoethenyl)-3,5-dimethyl-	MeOH	305(4.34)	65-0767-79
$C_9H_9Br_2NO_2$			
2-Pyridinepropanoic acid, α,β-dibromo-, dimethyl ester	MeOH	226(3.62),260(3.68)	22-0559-79
C_9H_9Cl			
Bicyclo[6.1.0]nona-2,4,6-triene, 9-	EtOH	248(3.57)	33-0718-79

Compound	Solvent	λ$_{max}$(log ε)	Ref.
anti-chloro-, cis (cont.)			33-0718-79
$C_9H_9ClN_2O$			
8-Azabicyclo[3.2.1]oct-3-ene-6-carbonitrile, 1-chloro-8-methyl-2-oxo-	$CHCl_3$	200(3.02)	39-2528-79C
$C_9H_9ClN_2S_2$			
Hydrazinecarbodithioic acid, [(4-chlorophenyl)methylene]-, methyl ester	$CHCl_3$	255s(--),293s(--), 305s(--),325s(--), 337(4.59),347s(--)	90-0815-79
zinc chelate	$CHCl_3$	260(4.14),325s(--), 343s(--),353(4.47)	90-0815-79
$C_9H_9ClN_3OS$			
1,2,3,4-Thiatriazolium, 3-(4-chlorophenyl)-5-ethoxy-, tetrafluoroborate	n.s.g.	217s(3.15),236s(3.94), 285s(4.00),324(4.30)	39-0732-79C
C_9H_9ClO			
Bicyclo[2.2.1]heptan-2-one, 3-chloro-5,6-bis(methylene)-, endo	isooctane	264(3.84),299s(2.42), 308(2.53),319(2.52), 330s(2.27)	33-0511-79
	EtOH	306(2.49)	33-0511-79
Bicyclo[3.2.2]nona-3,6-dien-2-one, 1-chloro-	MeOH	227(3.82),330(1.97)	18-3355-79
Bicyclo[3.2.2]nona-3,6-dien-2-one, 3-chloro-	MeOH	238(3.69),265s(3.44), 330(1.94)	18-3355-79
2-Propanone, 1-(2-chlorophenyl)-	MeOH	266(2.60),274(2.53)	56-0849-79
2-Propanone, 1-(4-chlorophenyl)-	MeOH	261(2.70),268(2.69), 276(2.59)	56-0849-79
$C_9H_9Cl_2N_3S$			
Sulfur, dichloro(1-methyl-4-phenyl-1H-1,2,4-triazolium-3-yl)-	MeOH	250(3.88),294(2.77)	70-2526-79
$C_9H_9Cl_3O_2$			
Benzenemethanol, 2-hydroxy-3-methyl-α-(trichloromethyl)-	EtOH	222(3.83),287(3.56)	118-0824-79
Benzenemethanol, 2-hydroxy-5-methyl-α-(trichloromethyl)-	EtOH	222(3.83),290(3.56)	118-0824-79
$C_9H_9FN_2O_4$			
2,2'-Anhydro-1-(5-deoxy-β-D-arabinofuranosyl)-5-fluorouracil	MeOH	227(3.86)	87-1330-79
$C_9H_9FN_2O_5$			
2-Furancarboxylic acid, 5-(6-fluoro-3,4-dihydro-2,4-dioxo-1(2H)-pyrimidinyl)tetrahydro-	pH 2	263(3.96)	103-0926-79
	pH 7	264(3.96)	103-0926-79
	pH 10	263(3.86)	103-0926-79
Uridine, 4',5'-didehydro-5'-deoxy-5-fluoro-	MeOH	205(4.25)	87-1330-79
C_9H_9N			
2-Azatricyclo[6.2.0.0^{3,6}]deca-1,3(6),7-triene	EtOH	290(3.91)	88-0143-79
	EtOH	286s(3.94),289(3.97), 292s(3.95),299s(3.74)	89-0411-79
C_9H_9NO			
Benzene, 1-cyclopropyl-2-nitroso-	EtOH	290(3.89),313(3.83), 356(3.43),760(3.04)	104-0847-79
1,2-Benzisoxazole, 3,5-dimethyl-	EtOH	232s(3.87),237(3.92),	33-0314-79

Compound	Solvent	λ_{max}(log ε)	Ref.
1,2-Benzisoxazole, 3,5-dimethyl- (cont.)		243(3.83),289(3.51), 297s(3.36)	33-0314-79
1,2-Benzisoxazole, 3,6-dimethyl-	EtOH	240(3.98),246s(3.89), 280(3.55),289s(3.46)	33-0314-79
2,1-Benzisoxazole, 3,4-dimethyl-	EtOH	256(2.95),267(3.00), 279(3.15),317(3.81)	33-0271-79
2,1-Benzisoxazole, 3,5-dimethyl-	EtOH	258(2.97),269(3.06), 281(3.15),318(3.75)	33-0271-79
2,1-Benzisoxazole, 3,7-dimethyl-	EtOH	257(2.96),268(3.10), 281(3.26),316(3.80)	33-0271-79
Propanal, 3-imino-2-phenyl-	EtOH	277(4.24)	22-0017-79
C_9H_9NOS			
5H-Thiazolo[3,2-a]pyridin-5-one, 3,8-dimethyl-	EtOH	234(3.83),272(3.55), 370(3.94),383(3.93)	39-1150-79C
$C_9H_9NO_2$			
Acetamide, N-(2-formylphenyl)-	EtOH	233(4.47),260(4.00), 268(3.99),326(3.62)	33-0271-79
Bicyclo[2.2.1]hept-5-ene-2-carboxylic acid, 3-cyano-	MeOH	220(4.265)	94-0870-79
1,2-Propanedione, 1-phenyl-, 1-oxime,	EtOH	211(4.04),244s(3.73)	39-0156-79B
(E)-	EtOH-NaOH	239(3.82),291(4.15), 400(1.91)	39-0156-79B
(Z)-	EtOH	250(4.03)	39-0156-79B
	EtOH-NaOH	227(3.93)	39-0156-79B
1,2-Propanedione, 1-phenyl-, 2-oxime,	EtOH	248(3.98),330s(2.18)	39-0156-79B
(E)-	EtOH-NaOH	295(4.26),4.0s(2.00)	39-0156-79B
(Z)-	EtOH	248(4.14),330s(1.95)	39-0156-79B
	EtOH-NaOH	245(4.22)	39-0156-79B
2-Propenoic acid, 3-(4-aminophenyl)-	neutral	278(4.32)	19-0045-79
	cation	313(4.39)	19-0045-79
2-Propenoic acid, 3-(3-pyridinyl)-, methyl ester	MeOH	206(4.12),257(4.27)	35-5370-79
$C_9H_9NO_3$			
Benzenepropanal, 2-hydroxy-β-oxo-, α-oxime	MeOH	216(4.11),254(4.02), 327(3.59)	56-0229-79
Cyclopropanecarboxylic acid, 1,2-dihydro-2-oxo-3-pyridinyl ester	EtOH	227(3.79),298(3.81)	36-0816-79
Ethanone, 1-(3-methyl-2-nitrophenyl)-	EtOH	285(3.14)	33-0271-79
Ethanone, 1-(5-methyl-2-nitrophenyl)-	EtOH	272(3.80)	33-0271-79
2-Propanone, 1-(2-nitrophenyl)-	MeOH	260(3.76)	56-0849-79
2-Propanone, 1-(3-nitrophenyl)-	MeOH	264(3.87)	56-0849-79
2-Propanone, 1-(4-nitrophenyl)-	MeOH	273(3.96)	56-0849-79
$C_9H_9NO_4S$			
4-Thia-1-azabicyclo[3.2.0]hept-2-ene-2-carboxylic acid, 7-oxo-, 2-oxopropyl ester	EtOH	317(3.89)	35-6306-79
(R)-	EtOH	317(3.89)	35-6306-79
(S)-	EtOH	318(3.90)	35-6306-79
C_9H_9NSSe			
Pyrrolo[2,1-b]thiazole-5-carboselenoaldehyde, 6,7-dimethyl-	C_6H_{12}	229(4.19),348(3.86), 465(4.52),622(2.40), 667(2.66)	39-2334-79C
Pyrrolo[2,1-b]thiazole-7-carboselenoaldehyde, 5,6-dimethyl-	C_6H_{12}	236(4.25),255(3.97), 305(3.61),442(4.26), 451(4.28),630(2.36), 651(2.43)	39-2334-79C

Compound	Solvent	$\lambda_{max}(\log \epsilon)$	Ref.
$C_9H_9NS_2$			
Benzothiazole, 2-(ethylthio)-	THF	230(4.30),284(3.97), 293(4.06),303(3.95)	121-0001-79
2(3H)-Benzothiazolethione, 3-ethyl-	THF	233(4.18),245(4.16), 329(4.44)	121-0001-79
$C_9H_9N_3$			
1H-Benzotriazole, 1-propenyl-, (E)-	EtOH	228(4.15),263(3.83), 270(3.81),295(3.82)	33-2129-79
Pyrimidine, 1,4-dihydro-4-(3-pyridinyl)-	EtOH	260(3.37),294s(3.02)	39-2393-79C
$C_9H_9N_3O$			
Ethanone, 1-(2-azido-3-methylphenyl)-	EtOH	229(4.20),253s(3.86), 290s(3.49)	33-0271-79
Ethanone, 1-(2-azido-5-methylphenyl)-	EtOH	234(4.16),259(4.01), 313(3.50)	33-0271-79
Ethanone, 1-(2-azido-6-methylphenyl)-	EtOH	240s(3.96),252(3.99)	33-0271-79
2(1H)-Quinolinone, 8-hydroxy-, hydrazone	pH 3	266(4.62)	86-0297-79
	pH 9	278(4.67)	86-0297-79
	pH 12	262(4.64)	86-0297-79
$C_9H_9N_3O_2$			
1H-Benzimidazole, 5-methyl-2-(nitromethyl)-	n.s.g.	210(4.59),368(4.46)	104-0361-79
$C_9H_9N_3O_2S$			
Benzamide, N-[[(aminocarbonyl)amino]-thioxomethyl]-	dioxan	244(4.29),286(4.19)	18-3728-79
1,2,3,4-Oxatriazolium, 3-(4-ethoxyphenyl)-2,5-dihydro-5-thioxo-, hydroxide, inner salt	n.s.g.	252(4.19),325(4.13)	39-0732-79C
1,2,3,4-Thiatriazolium, 3-(4-ethoxyphenyl)-2,5-dihydro-5-oxo-, hydroxide, inner salt	n.s.g.	222s(3.94),240s(3.81), 330(4.08)	39-0732-79C
$C_9H_9N_3O_2S_2$			
Hydrazinecarbodithioic acid, [(4-nitrophenyl)methylene]-, methyl ester	$CHCl_3$	263s(--),340s(--), 360(4.43)	90-0815-79
$C_9H_9N_3O_2S_3$			
4H-Pyrimido[4,5-d][1,3]thiazine-5,7(6H,8H)-dione, 6,8-dimethyl-2-(methylthio)-4-thioxo-	EtOH	226(4.29),247(4.16), 283(4.16),376(4.04)	95-0515-79
$C_9H_9N_3O_3$			
5-Pyrimidinecarbonitrile, 1,2,3,4-tetrahydro-2,4-dioxo-1-(tetrahydro-2-furanyl)-	pH 1	280(4.07)	94-0899-79
	pH 7	280(4.08)	94-0899-79
	pH 12	280(4.06)	94-0899-79
1H-Pyrrolo[3,2-d]pyrimidine-6-carboxaldehyde, 2,3,4,5-tetrahydro-1,3-dimethyl-2,4-dioxo-	EtOH	229(4.36),278(4.29), 330(3.88)	44-3830-79
$C_9H_9N_3O_6S_2$			
Benzene, 2-[[2-(methylthio)ethyl]thio]-1,3,5-trinitro-	MeCN	350(3.83)	104-0487-79
$C_9H_9N_3O_8$			
1,4-Dioxaspiro[4.5]deca-6,8-diene, 8-(methyl-aci-nitro)-6,10-dinitro-	MeOH	224(4.06),366(4.38)	104-0487-79
1,4-Dioxaspiro[4.5]deca-6,8-diene, 10-(methyl-aci-nitro)-6,8-dinitro-	MeOH	310(4.03),468(4.13)	104-0487-79

Compound	Solvent	λ_{max}(log ε)	Ref.
$C_9H_9N_3S$			
2(1H)-Quinazolinethione, 3,4-dihydro-4-imino-3-methyl-	MeOH	206(4.04),221(4.06), 238(4.08),290(4.27)	44-0173-79
1H-1,2,4-Triazolium, 2,3-dihydro-1-methyl-4-phenyl-3-thioxo-,	MeOH	219(4.14),250(3.86), 294(3.31)	70-2526-79
hydroxide, inner salt	MeCN	219(4.13),244(4.00), 265(3.75),308(3.34)	70-2526-79
$C_9H_9N_5O_2S$			
Pyrido[3,2-d]pyrimidine-6-carboxamide, 4-amino-1,2-dihydro-8-(methylthio)-2-oxo-	pH 1	262(4.23),348(3.81)	44-0435-79
	pH 7	251(4.37),348(3.90), 360(3.72)	44-0435-79
	pH 11	258(4.37),357(3.90)	44-0435-79
$C_9H_9N_5O_3$			
9H-Purine-9-acetaldehyde, 6-amino-α-(2-oxoethoxy)-, (R)-	pH 7.0	259(4.16)	69-2838-79
(S)-	pH 7.0	259(4.18)	69-2838-79
2,4(1H,3H)-Pyrimidinedione, 1-(5-azido-2,3,5-trideoxy-β-D-glycero-pent-2-enofuranosyl)-	EtOH	260(3.97)	136-0113-79F
C_9H_9S			
Benzo[b]thiophenium, 1-methyl-, tetrafluoroborate	CH_2Cl_2	230(4.32),270(3.40), 300(3.43)	4-0471-79
C_9H_{10}			
Bicyclo[4.2.1]nona-2,4,7-triene	pentane	260(3.64)	44-2034-79
3-Nonene-1,5-diyne, (E)-	EtOH	257(4.37),260(4.35), 271(4.33)	39-2136-79C
$C_9H_{10}BrIO$			
1,2-Benziodoxole, 1-bromo-1,3-dihydro-3,3-dimethyl-	pentane	204(4.02),235(3.79)	44-1779-79
$C_9H_{10}BrN_3O$			
Pyridine, 3-bromo-5-(1-nitroso-2-pyrrolidinyl)-	EtOH	240(3.82),272(3.61), 280s(3.52)	44-4332-79
$C_9H_{10}BrN_3O_2$			
Ethenamine, 2-(3-bromo-5-nitro-4-pyridinyl)-N,N-dimethyl-	EtOH	218(4.1),346(4.2), 432(3.5)	103-0076-79
$C_9H_{10}BrN_5O_5$			
2,4(1H,3H)-Pyrimidinedione, 1-(5-azido-5-deoxy-β-D-arabinofuranosyl)-5-bromo-	pH 2	281(3.91)	87-1273-79
	pH 12	278(3.91)	87-1273-79
$C_9H_{10}Br_2O_2$			
2(5H)-Furanone, 4-bromo-5-(bromomethylene)-3-butyl-	hexane	286(4.2)	88-1649-79
$C_9H_{10}ClIO$			
1,2-Benziodoxole, 1-chloro-1,3-dihydro-3,3-dimethyl-	pentane	200(4.20),232(4.18), 329(2.28)	44-1779-79
$C_9H_{10}ClN_3$			
1H-Pyrazol-3-amine, 1-(4-chlorophenyl)-4,5-dihydro-	EtOH	283(4.20)	150-0801-79

Compound	Solvent	λ_{max}(log ε)	Ref.
$C_9H_{10}ClN_3O_4$			
2,2'-Anhydro-1-β-D-arabinofuranosyl-5-chlorocytosine, hydrochloride	pH 1	230s(3.91),275(3.97)	87-0514-79
	pH 7	230s(3.91),275(3.97)	87-0514-79
	pH 11	231(3.91),286(3.83)	87-0514-79
$C_9H_{10}Cl_2N_4$			
1,4-Benzenediamine, 2,6-dichloro-N[1]-(4,5-dihydro-1H-imidazol-2-yl)-, dihydrochloride	EtOH	254(3.26),304(3.40)	22-0520-79
$C_9H_{10}FN_3O_3$			
2,2'-Anhydro-1-(5-deoxy-β-D-arabinofuranosyl)-5-fluorocytosine, hydrochloride	H_2O	214(3.91),230(3.95), 267(4.06)	87-1330-79
2(1H)-Pyrimidinone, 4-amino-1-(2,3-anhydro-5-deoxy-β-D-lyxofuranosyl)-5-fluoro-	MeOH	240(3.94),281(3.86)	87-1330-79
$C_9H_{10}FN_3O_4$			
2,2'-Anhydro-1-β-D-arabinofuranosyl-5-fluorocytosine, hydrochloride	pH 1	228(3.96),268(4.06)	87-0514-79
	H_2O	228(3.96),268(4.06)	87-0514-79
	pH 11	240(4.00),274(3.92)	87-0514-79
$C_9H_{10}IN_5O_5$			
2,4(1H,3H)-Pyrimidinedione, 1-(5-azido-5-deoxy-β-D-arabinofuranosyl)-5-iodo-	pH 2	289(3.88)	87-1273-79
	pH 12	279(3.77)	87-1273-79
$C_9H_{10}NOP$			
Benzonitrile, 4-(dimethylphosphinyl)-	dioxan	230(4.21),276(3.11), 284(3.11)	65-0479-79
$C_9H_{10}NO_2$			
Pyridinium, 3-hydroxy-1-(3-oxo-1-butenyl)-, chloride	EtOH	215(4.59),255(4.88)	56-0057-79
$C_9H_{10}NP$			
Benzonitrile, 4-(dimethylphosphino)-	C_6H_{12}	227(4.13),282(3.85)	65-0479-79
	12M HCl	235(4.29),241(4.27), 280(3.30),288(3.28)	65-0479-79
$C_9H_{10}N_2$			
1H-Benzimidazole, 1-ethyl-	EtOH	248(3.76),254(3.76), 275(3.66),283(3.68)	65-1225-79
	EtOH	249(3.78),255(3.79), 267(3.62),276(3.68), 282(3.71)	70-1931-79
1H-Benzimidazole, 2-ethyl-	pH 1	236(3.66),263(3.78), 268(3.94),275(3.97)	65-1225-79
	H_2O	242(3.74),246(3.71), 268(3.72),272(3.81), 277(3.80)	65-1225-79
	EtOH	243(3.81),248(3.79), 269(3.73),274(3.86), 280(3.88)	65-1225-79
Benzonitrile, 4-(dimethylamino)-	heptane	280(4.43)	65-0479-79
1H-Imidazole, 4,5-dihydro-2-phenyl-	EtOH	205(4.13),226(4.26), 275(3.82)	39-2289-79C
Pyrrolo[1,2-b]pyridazine, 2,7-dimethyl-	C_6H_{12}	238(4.09),245(4.28), 252(4.32),298(3.20), 380(3.31)	4-0839-79

Compound	Solvent	λ_{max}(log ε)	Ref.
$C_9H_{10}N_2O$			
2-Propenenitrile, 3-(dimethylamino)-3-(2-furanyl)-	EtOH	218s(3.81),240s(3.85), 285(4.08)	22-0651-79
2-Propenenitrile, 3-(dimethylamino)-3-(3-furanyl)-	EtOH	207(3.99),275(4.18)	22-0651-79
$C_9H_{10}N_2OS_2$			
Ethanethioic acid, S-(2,3,6,7-tetrahydro-2-iminocyclopenta[d][1,3]-thiazin-4-yl) ester	EtOH	230(4.38),244s(4.20), 314(3.98),424(3.94)	150-1732-79
$C_9H_{10}N_2O_2$			
Benzenemethanamine, N-methyl-α-(nitromethylene)-, (Z)-	EtOH	203(3.83),243(3.73), 354(4.30)	28-0255-79B
Ethenamine, N-methyl-2-nitro-2-phenyl-, (Z)-	EtOH	210(3.96),249(3.96), 367(4.01)	28-0255-79B
1H-Pyrrole-3-carboxylic acid, 4-cyano-2,5-dimethyl-, methyl ester	n.s.g.	211(4.18),263(3.94)	23-0044-79
$C_9H_{10}N_2O_3$			
2-Azetidinecarboxylic acid, N-(2-pyridinyl)-, N-oxide, (S)-(-)-	MeOH	330(3.63)	4-0591-79
Phenol, 2-[4,5-dihydro-5-(hydroxyamino)-3-isoxazolyl]-	EtOH	219(4.19),259(3.94), 308(3.58)	56-0229-79
$C_9H_{10}N_2O_3S$			
4-Thiazolidinecarboxylic acid, 3-(2-pyridinyl)-, N-oxide, (R)-(-)-	MeOH	325(3.53)	4-0591-79
$C_9H_{10}N_2O_4$			
2,4(1H,3H)-Pyrimidinedione, 1-(2,3-dideoxy-β-D-glycero-threo-pent-2-enofuranosyl)-	H_2O	261(4.00)	44-1404-79
$C_9H_{10}N_2O_5$			
2-Furancarboxylic acid, 5-(3,4-dihydro-2,4-dioxo-1(2H)-pyrimidinyl)-tetrahydro-, trans-(±)-	pH 2	262(4.00)	103-0926-79
	pH 7	263(4.02)	103-0926-79
	pH 10	262(4.00)	103-0926-79
$C_9H_{10}N_2O_6$			
Butanedioic acid, [(3,4-dihydro-2,4-dioxo-1(2H)-pyrimidinyl)methyl]-	MeOH	263(4.04)	126-2323-79
$C_9H_{10}N_2S$			
2-Propenenitrile, 3-(dimethylamino)-3-(2-thienyl)-, (E)-	EtOH	245(4.13),280(4.06)	22-0651-79
2-Propenenitrile, 3-(dimethylamino)-3-(3-thienyl)-, (E)-	EtOH	213(4.03),243(4.09), 277(4.10)	22-0651-79
Pyrimidine, 1,4-dihydro-5-methyl-4-(2-thienyl)-, monohydrochloride	EtOH	235(3.82),280s(3.39)	24-0001-79
$C_9H_{10}N_2S_2$			
Hydrazinecarbodithioic acid, (phenylmethylene)-, methyl ester	$CHCl_3$	250s(--),290s(--), 305s(--),322s(--), 331(4.56),343s(--)	90-0815-79
zinc chelate	$CHCl_3$	244(4.30),315s(--), 335s(--),348(4.51), 360s(--)	90-0815-79

Compound	Solvent	λ_{max}(log ε)	Ref.
$C_9H_{10}N_3$			
1H-1,2,3-Triazolium, 1-methyl-3-phenyl-, perchlorate	MeOH	251(3.89)	24-0445-79
$C_9H_{10}N_3OS$			
1,2,3,4-Thiatriazolium, 5-ethoxy-3-phenyl-, tetrafluoroborate	n.s.g.	229s(3.71),278s(3.83), 313(4.02)	39-0732-79C
$C_9H_{10}N_4$			
8(1H)-Cycloheptapyrazolone, 3-methyl-, hydrazone	MeOH	215(4.42),335(3.98)	18-1972-79
Phthalazine, 1-(1-methylhydrazino)-	MeCN	218(4.44),262s(3.43), 322(3.66)	103-0443-79
$C_9H_{10}N_4O$			
3H-1,2,4-Triazol-3-one, 4-amino-2,4-dihydro-5-(4-methylphenyl)-	EtOH	265(4.07)	4-0403-79
$C_9H_{10}N_4OS_2$			
2,4(1H,3H)-Pteridinedithione, 7-methoxy-1,3-dimethyl-	pH -4.9	232(4.02),276(4.33), 290s(4.27),322(4.05), 420(4.02)	24-1499-79
	pH 1.0	225(4.10),269(4.23), 309(4.33),383(4.15), 395s(4.12)	24-1499-79
2(1H)-Pteridinone, 3,4-dihydro-1,3-dimethyl-7-(methylthio)-4-thioxo-	pH -4.0	219(4.25),240(4.12), 256s(4.04),307(4.05), 383(3.88),444(4.18)	24-1499-79
	pH 5.0	212(4.41),295(4.08), 330(3.82),397(4.36), 410(4.31),418(4.27)	24-1499-79
4(1H)-Pteridinone, 2,3-dihydro-1,3-dimethyl-7-(methylthio)-2-thioxo-	pH -5.5	227(3.97),278(4.42), 298s(4.18),424(4.16)	24-1499-79
	pH 1.0	211(4.11),272(4.39), 295(4.14),376(4.29)	24-1499-79
$C_9H_{10}N_4O_2$			
1,2,4-Triazol-3-one, 4-amino-2,4-dihydro-5-(4-methoxyphenyl)-	EtOH	265(4.23)	4-0403-79
$C_9H_{10}N_4O_2S$			
2,4(1H,3H)-Pteridinedione, 7,8-dihydro-1,3,8-trimethyl-7-thioxo-	pH -5.5	246(4.15),320(4.20), 436(4.07)	24-1499-79
	pH 6.0	212(4.02),231(4.03), 323(4.01),397(4.15)	24-1499-79
2,4(1H,3H)-Pteridinedione, 1,3-dimethyl-7-(methylthio)-	pH -4.3	244(4.32),280(3.97), 393(4.15)	24-1499-79
	pH 5.0	226(4.33),268(3.85), 280s(3.83),360(4.29)	24-1499-79
4,7(1H,8H)-Pteridinedione, 2,3-dihydro-1,3,6-trimethyl-2-thioxo-	pH -4.9	214(4.32),275(4.21), 292s(4.14),382(4.06)	24-1499-79
	pH 1.0	213(4.34),239(4.02), 257(4.03),293(4.11), 341(4.21)	24-1499-79
	pH 6.0	237(4.41),258(4.18), 298(4.05),339(4.33), 354(4.26)	24-1499-79
4,7(1H,8H)-Pteridinedione, 2,3-dihydro-1,3,8-trimethyl-2-thioxo-	pH -5.5	225(4.30),266(4.13), 305s(3.58),397(4.18)	24-1499-79
	pH 6.0	223(4.25),240s(4.10), 308s(3.89),350(4.22)	24-1499-79

Compound	Solvent	$\lambda_{max}(\log \epsilon)$	Ref.
2(1H)-Pteridinone, 3,4-dihydro-7-methoxy-1,3-dimethyl-4-thioxo-	pH -4.0	247(3.91),294(4.16), 322s(3.89),410(3.92)	24-1499-79
	pH 1.0	241(3.93),282(4.16), 372(4.22),385s(4.15)	24-1499-79
4(1H)-Pteridinone, 2,3-dihydro-7-methoxy-1,3-dimethyl-2-thioxo-	pH -5.5	213(4.29),223(4.26), 248s(3.85),280(4.21), 382(3.99)	24-1499-79
	pH 0.0	215(4.38),240s(4.00), 255(4.08),290(4.12), 338(4.21)	24-1499-79
$C_9H_{10}N_4O_3$			
2,4(1H,3H)-Pteridinedione, 7-methoxy-1,3-dimethyl-	pH -5.5	213(4.38),255(4.19), 347(4.03)	24-1499-79
	pH 5.0	239(4.09),262(3.84), 322(4.13)	24-1499-79
2,4,7(1H,3H,8H)-Pteridinetrione, 1,3,8-trimethyl-	pH -6.9	216(4.33),267(4.02), 282s(3.89),372(4.15)	24-1499-79
	pH 6.0	285(4.13),336(4.02)	24-1499-79
$C_9H_{10}N_4S$			
1H-1,2,4-Triazolium, 4-amino-2,3-dihydro-1-methyl-5-phenyl-3-thioxo-, hydroxide, inner salt	n.s.g.	245(4.20),309(3.39)	39-0724-79C
1H-1,2,4-Triazolium, 4-amino-2,3-dihydro-5-methyl-1-phenyl-3-thioxo-, hydroxide, inner salt	n.s.g.	243(4.26),288(3.77)	39-0724-79C
4H-1,2,4-Triazolium, 4-amino-5-methyl-1-phenyl-3-thioxo-, hydroxide, inner salt	EtOH	242(4.29),280(3.59)	94-1683-79
$C_9H_{10}N_4S_3$			
2,4(1H,3H)-Pteridinedithione, 1,3-dimethyl-7-(methylthio)-	pH -5.5	238(3.93),275(4.48), 328(4.10),380s(3.80), 459(4.22)	24-1499-79
	pH 0.0	260s(4.28),269(4.28), 311(4.29),419(4.33), 430(4.32)	24-1499-79
$C_9H_{10}N_8O_4$			
2,4(1H,3H)-Pyrimidinedione, 1-(2,5-diazido-2,5-dideoxy-β-D-arabinofuranosyl)-	MeOH	261(4.01)	88-0605-79
$C_9H_{10}O$			
Bicyclo[2.2.1]hept-2-en-7-ol, 5,6-bis(methylene)-, syn	isooctane	232(4.00),246(4.03)	33-0511-79
	EtOH	243.5(4.04)	33-0511-79
Bicyclo[4.2.1]nona-2,4-dien-7-one	pentane	258(3.58)	44-2034-79
Bicyclo[4.2.1]nona-2,4-dien-9-one	EtOH	264(3.52),313(2.70)	44-1294-79
Ethanone, 1-(4-methylphenyl)-	C_6H_{12}	247.5(4.30)	56-2251-79
	EtOH	251(4.09)	56-2251-79
2-Propanone, 1-phenyl-	MeOH	254(2.64),260(2.68), 266(2.66),280(2.65)	56-0849-79
$C_9H_{10}O_2$			
2,5-Cyclohexadiene-1,4-dione, 2,3,5-trimethyl-	DMF	441(3.78)	104-1621-79
4,11-Dioxatricyclo[5.3.1.0^{3,5}]undeca-1,6-diene	EtOH	231(2.73)	35-3893-79
	MeCN	230s(2.93)	35-3893-79
Ethanone, 1-(4-methoxyphenyl)-	C_6H_{12}	265(4.26)	56-2251-79
	EtOH	271(4.26)	56-2251-79

Compound	Solvent	λ_{max}(log ε)	Ref.
2-Propenoic acid, 3-(1,4-cyclohexadien-1-yl)-, (E)-	hexane	267(4.11)	69-1431-79
	pH 2.3	272(4.20)	69-1431-79
	pH 7.0	262(4.20)	69-1431-79
	EtOH	265(4.20)	69-1431-79
Tropolone, 3,7-dimethyl-	MeOH	244(4.50),251s(4.43), 305s(3.65),320(3.72), 334s(3.68),357(3.71), 369(3.76),398s(2.85)	88-1113-79
$C_9H_{10}O_3$			
2,4-Cyclohexadiene-1-carboxylic acid, 1-methyl-6-oxo-, methyl ester	MeOH	302(3.61)	35-2470-79
Ethanone, 1-(2,3-dihydroxy-4-methyl-phenyl)-	EtOH	228(4.10),273(4.14), 344(3.41)	33-0314-79
Ethanone, 1-(2,3-dihydroxy-5-methyl-phenyl)-	EtOH	268(4.00),353(3.45)	33-0314-79
Ethanone, 1-(2,5-dihydroxy-4-methyl-phenyl)-	EtOH	265(4.01),358(3.71)	33-0314-79
4H-Pyran-3,5-dicarboxaldehyde, 4-ethyl-	EtOH	213(4.01),233s(3.67), 295(3.67)	49-0613-79
$C_9H_{10}O_4$			
3,5-Cycloheptadiene-1,2-dione, 7,7-di-methoxy-	THF	303(3.76)	138-0855-79
2,5-Cyclohexadiene-1,4-dione, 2,3-di-methoxy-5-methyl-	DMF	417(4.89)	104-1621-79
6-Oxabicyclo[3.1.0]hexane-2-carboxylic acid, 1,5-dimethyl-3-methylene-4-oxo-(methylenomycin A)	MeOH	224(3.80)	142-0353-79B
C_9H_{11}			
Cycloheptatrienylium, 1,2-dimethyl-, perchlorate	10% HCl	232(4.66),297(3.71)	39-1005-79B +78-0949-79
Cycloheptatrienylium, 1,3-dimethyl-, perchlorate	10% HCl	234(4.68),289(3.79), 295s(--)	39-1005-79B +78-0949-79
Cycloheptatrienylium, 1,4-dimethyl-, perchlorate	10% HCl	231(4.63),302(3.84)	78-0949-79
$C_9H_{11}BrN_2$			
Pyridine, 3-bromo-5-(2-pyrrolidinyl)-	EtOH	275(3.53)	44-4332-79
$C_9H_{11}BrN_2O_2$			
Quinazoline, 8-bromo-5,6,7,8-tetrahydro-2-methyl-, 1,3-dioxide	EtOH	267(4.37),301(4.05), 361(3.21)	103-1025-79
$C_9H_{11}BrN_2O_5$			
Uridine, 5-bromo-2'-deoxy-	EtOH	278(3.92)	73-0439-79
$C_9H_{11}BrN_2O_6$			
2,4(1H,3H)-Pyrimidinedione, 1-β-D-ara-binofuranosyl-5-bromo-	pH 2	281(3.91)	87-1273-79
	pH 12	278(3.82)	87-1273-79
$C_9H_{11}ClO$			
Bicyclo[2.2.1]heptan-2-ol, 3-chloro-5,6-bis(methylene)-, (2-exo,3-endo)-	isooctane	237s(3.95),243(4.00), 251s(3.83)	33-0511-79
	EtOH	238s(3.92),244(3.96), 252s(3.80)	33-0511-79
$C_9H_{11}FN_2O_5$			
2,4(1H,3H)-Pyrimidinedione, 1-(5-deoxy-β-D-arabinofuranosyl)-5-fluoro-	MeOH	204(4.03),270(3.97)	87-1330-79

Compound	Solvent	$\lambda_{max}(\log \epsilon)$	Ref.
2,4(1H,3H)-Pyrimidinedione, 1-(5-deoxy-α-L-lyxofuranosyl)-5-fluoro-	MeOH	207(3.94),270(3.93)	87-1330-79
2,4(1H,3H)-Pyrimidinedione, 1-(5-deoxy-β-D-lyxofuranosyl)-5-fluoro-	H_2O	203(4.03),270(3.95)	87-1330-79
Uridine, 5'-deoxy-5-fluoro-	MeOH	269(3.93)	87-1330-79
$C_9H_{11}FN_2O_6$			
2,4(1H,3H)-Pyrimidinedione, 1-α-D-arabinofuranosyl-5-fluoro-	pH 1	269(3.94)	4-0353-79
	pH 7	269(3.94)	4-0353-79
	pH 13	270(3.82)	4-0353-79
$C_9H_{11}IO_2$			
1,2-Benziodoxole, 1,3-dihydro-1-hydroxy-3,3-dimethyl-	pentane	205(4.11),235(4.02)	44-1779-79
$C_9H_{11}NO$			
2-Azabicyclo[2.2.0]hex-5-en-3-one, 2-(2-methyl-1-propenyl)-	EtOH	228(4.11)	35-3607-79
Benzaldehyde, 2-amino-3,5-dimethyl-	EtOH	262s(--),267(3.81), 380(3.66)	33-0234-79
Benzaldehyde, 3-methyl-2-(methylamino)-	EtOH	267(3.75),367(3.51)	33-0234-79
Benzaldehyde, 5-methyl-2-(methylamino)-	EtOH	263(3.85),395(3.76)	33-0234-79
Ethanone, 1-(2-amino-3-methylphenyl)-	EtOH	227(4.41),254(3.79), 259(3.80),362(3.75)	33-0271-79
Ethanone, 1-(2-amino-5-methylphenyl)-	EtOH	228(4.39),256(3.80), 369(3.70)	33-0271-79
Ethanone, 1-(2-amino-6-methylphenyl)-	EtOH	232(4.20),256s(3.48), 350(3.27)	33-0271-79
Phenol, 2-(1-aziridinylmethyl)-, hydrochloride	H_2O	215s(4.06),238s(3.52), 273(3.49)	150-3801-79
$C_9H_{11}NO_2$			
Benzaldehyde, 2-amino-3-ethoxy-	EtOH	269(3.74),372(3.54)	33-0234-79
Benzaldehyde, 5-methoxy-2-(methylamino)-	EtOH	264s(--),408(3.76)	33-0234-79
Carbamic acid, phenyl-, ethyl ester	C_6H_{12}	233(4.23),274(3.00)	78-0063-79
Ethanone, 1-(2-amino-3-methoxyphenyl)-	EtOH	266(3.71),366(3.68)	33-0234-79
Ethanone, 1-(2-amino-5-methoxyphenyl)-	EtOH	257s(--),390(3.66)	33-0234-79
Ethanone, 1-[5-hydroxy-2-(methylamino)-phenyl]-	EtOH	260s(--),415(3.68)	33-0234-79
3,5-Pyridinedicarboxaldehyde, 4-ethyl-1,4-dihydro-	EtOH	233(4.16),254(3.67), 378(3.93)	49-0613-79
$C_9H_{11}NO_2S$			
Thiophene, 2-(1,2-dimethyl-1-propenyl)-5-nitro-	MeOH	242(3.72),353(3.96)	12-2647-79
$C_9H_{11}NO_3$			
2,5-Cyclohexadiene-1,4-dione, 2-(dimethylamino)-5-methoxy-	MeOH	218(4.27),305(4.14), 490(3.59)	142-0411-79B
2(1H)-Pyridinone, 3-acetyl-6-hydroxy-1,4-dimethyl-	acid	325(4.21)	5-0769-79
	base	339(4.22)	5-0769-79
1H-Pyrrole-2-butanoic acid, 1-methyl-γ-oxo-	EtOH	203(3.84),256s(3.78), 287(4.20)	103-0747-79
$C_9H_{11}NO_4$			
Phenylalanine, 2,3-dihydroxy-	H_2O	277.5(3.3)	5-0564-79
	pH 12	288(--)(decomposes)	5-0564-79

Compound	Solvent	λ_{max}(log ϵ)	Ref.
$C_9H_{11}NO_5S_2$			
4H-1,3-Thiazin-4-one, 2,3-dihydro-6-β-D-ribofuranosyl-2-thioxo-	pH 1	248(4.21),313(4.13)	44-4854-79
	pH 13	267(4.35),325(3.80)	44-4854-79
$C_9H_{11}NTe$			
Benzenecarbotelluroamide, N,N-dimethyl-	CCl_4	387(3.99),540(2.91)	77-1102-79
$C_9H_{11}N_3$			
Propanedinitrile, [3-(dimethylamino)-1-methyl-2-propenylidene]-	CH_2Cl_2	388(4.66)	118-0376-79
Propanedinitrile, (1-piperidinylmethylene)-	MeCN	290(4.48)	80-1143-79
1H-Pyrazol-3-amine, 4,5-dihydro-1-phenyl-	EtOH	275(4.07)	150-0801-79
Pyrimidine, 1,4-dihydro-4-(1-methyl-1H-pyrrol-2-yl)-	EtOH	249(3.53),286s(3.23)	39-2393-79C
$C_9H_{11}N_3O$			
2-Oxazolamine, 4,5-dihydro-N-(1-methyl-2(1H)-pyridinylidene)-, monohydriodide	EtOH	220(4.23),262(4.18), 320(4.24)	94-2879-79
$C_9H_{11}N_3OS$			
Hydrazinecarbothioamide, 2-[(4-methoxyphenyl)methylene]-	$CHCl_3$	288s(--),303s(--), 323(4.62),335s(--)	90-0815-79
1H-Pyrrolo[2,3-d]pyrimidine, 4-methoxy-5-methyl-2-(methylthio)- (also spectra at several pH values)	MeOH	240(4.31),285(4.03)	24-0799-79
$C_9H_{11}N_3O_2$			
Formamide, N-[[nitroso(phenylmethyl)-amino]methyl]-	EtOH	236(3.88),368(1.80)	94-0682-79
3-Pyridinecarbonitrile, 1,4-dihydro-1-methyl-4-(1-nitroethyl)-	$CHCl_3$	324(3.76)	44-1761-79
	DMSO	326(3.74)	44-1761-79
1H-Pyrrolo[3,2-d]pyrimidine-2,4(3H,5H)-dione, 1,3,5-trimethyl-	EtOH	225s(4.20),262(4.26)	44-3830-79
1H-Pyrrolo[3,2-d]pyrimidine-2,4(3H,5H)-dione, 1,3,6-trimethyl-	EtOH	220s(3.61),273(3.67)	44-3830-79
$C_9H_{11}N_3O_2S$			
Benzenesulfonamide, 4-(diazomethyl)-N,N-dimethyl-	EtOH	229(4.02),310(4.18), 465(1.67)	118-0531-79
Ethenamine, N-(1-methyl-2(1H)-pyridinylidene)-1-(methylthio)-2-nitro-	EtOH	220(4.01),233(4.22), 260(4.01),340(4.08), 420(4.35)	94-2879-79
$C_9H_{11}N_3O_3$			
L-Alanine, N-(pyrazinylcarbonyl)-, methyl ester	isooctane	208(4.04),266(3.94), 332f(2.78)	39-2881-79C
	EtOH	210(4.07),269(3.97), 316(3.85)	39-2881-79C
	MeCN	208(4.03),268(3.92), 320(2.78)	39-2881-79C
Cytosine, 1-(5-hydroxy-2,3-dideoxy-β-D-glyceropent-2-enofuranosyl)-	MeOH	272(3.93)	44-1404-79
1(2H)-Pyrimidinebutanenitrile, 3,4-dihydro-β-hydroxy-5-methyl-2,4-dioxo-	EtOH	269(3.96)	128-0051-79
1H-Pyrrolo[3,2-d]pyrimidine-2,4(3H,5H)-dione, 6-(hydroxymethyl)-1,3-dimethyl-	EtOH	220(4.17),273(4.10)	44-3830-79
8(5H)-Quinazolinone, 6,7-dihydro-2-methyl-, oxime, 1,3-dioxide	EtOH	273(4.33),330(4.10), 349(3.99)	103-1025-79

Compound	Solvent	λ_{max}(log ϵ)	Ref.
$C_9H_{11}N_3O_4$			
Benzenamine, 2,4-dinitro-N-propyl-	EtOH	262(3.97),350(4.23), 403s(3.81)	73-1613-79
Benzenamine, N-(1-methylethyl)-2,4-di-nitro-	EtOH	262(3.98),350(4.25), 403s(3.83)	73-1613-79
1(2H)-Pyridinecarboxamide, N-methyl-3-[[(methylamino)carbonyl]oxy]-2-oxo-	EtOH	220s(--),306(3.70)	36-0816-79
5-Pyrimidinecarboxamide, 1,2,3,4-tetra-hydro-2,4-dioxo-1-(tetrahydro-2-fur-anyl)-	pH 1	280(4.11)	94-0899-79
	pH 7	280(4.11)	94-0899-79
	pH 12	280(3.99)	94-0899-79
$C_9H_{11}N_3O_8$			
2,4(1H,3H)-Pyrimidinedione, 1-β-D-ara-binofuranosyl-5-nitro-	pH 1	240(3.93),306(4.01)	87-0316-79
	pH 6	237(3.89),310(4.04)	87-0316-79
	pH 12	280s(--),324(4.23)	87-0316-79
$C_9H_{11}N_3S$			
Hydrazinecarbothioamide, 2-[(4-methyl-phenyl)methylene]-	$CHCl_3$	310s(--),318(4.55), 327s(--)	90-0815-79
$C_9H_{11}N_4O_2$			
1H-1,2,3-Triazolium, 4,5-dihydro-1-methyl-3-(4-nitrophenyl)-, perchlor-ate	MeOH	335(4.27)	24-0445-79
$C_9H_{11}N_5O_2$			
1H-Imidazo[2,1-f]purine-2,4(3H,6H)-di-one, 7,8-dihydro-1,3-dimethyl-	EtOH	296(3.96)	118-0581-79
4(1H)-Pteridinone, 2-amino-7,8-dihydro-6-(1-oxopropyl)-	pH -1.0	232(4.14),284(4.10), 330s(3.35),395(3.89)	24-2750-79
	pH 5.0	213(4.22),265(4.23), 286s(3.89),410(4.01)	24-2750-79
	pH 13.0	267(4.22),312(3.28), 430(4.10)	24-2750-79
$C_9H_{11}N_5O_2S$			
Pyrimido[4,5-d]pyrimidine-2,4(1H,3H)-dione, 5-amino-1,3-dimethyl-7-(meth-ylthio)-	EtOH	239(4.56),281(4.22), 292(4.21)	142-0503-79
$C_9H_{11}N_5O_3$			
4(1H)-Pteridinone, 2-amino-7,8-dihydro-6-(2-hydroxy-1-oxopropyl)- (sepiapterin)	pH -1.0	233(4.12),283(4.07), 330s(3.38),400(3.89)	24-2750-79
	pH 5.0	212(4.23),266(4.24), 287s(3.88),417(4.04)	24-2750-79
	pH 13.0	266(4.23),313(3.38), 438(4.15)	24-2750-79
$C_9H_{11}N_5O_5$			
2,4(1H,3H)-Pyrimidinedione, 1-(2-azido-2-deoxy-arabinofuranosyl)-	MeOH	261(4.01)	88-0605-79
2,4(1H,3H)-Pyrimidinedione, 1-(3-azido-3-deoxy-β-D-xylofuranosyl)-	MeOH	264(3.99)	136-0331-79A
C_9H_{12}			
1,3,6-Heptatriene, 4-ethenyl-	EtOH	254(4.52),264(4.62), 275(4.55)	39-0717-79B
$C_9H_{12}BrN_3O_5$			
2,4(1H,3H)-Pyrimidinedione, 1-(5-amino-	pH 2	278(3.84)	87-1273-79

Compound	Solvent	$\lambda_{max}(\log \epsilon)$	Ref.
5-deoxy-β-D-arabinofuranosyl)-5-bromo- (cont.)	pH 12	274(3.90)	87-1273-79
$C_9H_{12}BrN_7$			
1H-Pyrazol-5-amine, 4-[(4-bromo-5-methyl-1H-pyrazol-3-yl)azo]-1,3-dimethyl-	MeOH	380(4.70),410(4.71)	103-0657-79
$C_9H_{12}Cl_2N_4O_2$			
1,3,5-Triazin-2-amine, 4,6-dichloro-N-(2,2-dimethyl-1,3-dioxan-5-yl)-	EtOH	236(4.35)	104-1144-79
$C_9H_{12}FN_3O_4$			
Cytidine, 5'-deoxy-5-fluoro-	H_2O	238(3.90),281(3.90)	87-1330-79
2(1H)-Pyrimidinone, 4-amino-1-(5-deoxy-β-D-arabinofuranosyl)-5-fluoro-	H_2O	212(3.97),237(3.89), 282(3.92)	87-1330-79
$C_9H_{12}F_3NO_4S$			
Butanoic acid, 2-[[(ethylthio)carbonyl]-methylamino]-4,4,4-trifluoro-3-oxo-, methyl ester	CH_2Cl_2	245(3.60)	5-0650-79
$C_9H_{12}IN_3O_5$			
2,4(1H,3H)-Pyrimidinedione, 1-(5-amino-5-deoxy-β-D-arabinofuranosyl)-5-iodo-	pH 2	281(3.87)	87-1273-79
	pH 12	274(3.87)	87-1273-79
$C_9H_{12}NO$			
Oxazolo[3,2-a]pyridinium, 2,3-dihydro-2,2-dimethyl-, perchlorate	H_2O	285(3.71)	35-3607-79
Pyridinium, 2-hydroxy-1-(2-methyl-1-propenyl)-, perchlorate	MeOH-$HClO_4$	285(3.72)	35-3607-79
$C_9H_{12}N_2$			
Pyrrolo[1,2-b]pyridazine, 3,4-dihydro-2,7-dimethyl-	C_6H_{12}	263(3.98),370(2.06)	4-0839-79
$C_9H_{12}N_2O$			
2,4,6-Cycloheptatrien-1-one, 4-methyl-2-(1-methylhydrazino)-	MeOH	265(4.22),363(3.93), 412(3.83)	18-2447-79
2,4,6-Cycloheptatrien-1-one, 6-methyl-2-(1-methylhydrazino)-	MeOH	260(4.24),363(3.94), 411(3.86)	18-2447-79
$C_9H_{12}N_2OS$			
4(1H)-Pyrimidinone, 5-cyclopentyl-2,3-dihydro-2-thioxo-	MeOH	218(4.19),278(4.24)	73-2426-79
$C_9H_{12}N_2O_2$			
5H-Cyclopentapyrazine, 6,7-dihydro-2,3-dimethyl-, 1,4-dioxide	EtOH	242(4.44),306(4.33)	70-0848-79
2-Propenoic acid, 2-cyano-3-pyrrolidino-, methyl ester, (E)-	MeCN	290(4.37)	80-1143-79
2,4(1H,3H)-Pyrimidinedione, 5-cyclopentyl-	MeOH	265(3.87)	73-2426-79
Quinazoline, 5,6,7,8-tetrahydro-2-methyl-, 1,3-dioxide	EtOH	259(4.41),283(4.03), 340(3.03)	103-1025-79
Quinoxaline, 5,6,7,8-tetrahydro-2-methyl-, 1,4-dioxide	EtOH	238(4.41),306(4.31)	70-0848-79
$C_9H_{12}N_2O_2S_4$			
1-Piperazinecarbodithioic acid, 3-[bis-(methylthio)methylene]-2,5-dioxo-, methyl ester	EtOH	250s(3.99),286(4.13), 313s(4.04),384(4.11)	39-0692-79C

Compound	Solvent	λ_{max}(log ε)	Ref.
$C_9H_{12}N_2O_3$			
2,4(3H,5H)-Furandione, 3-(1-aminoethylidene)-5-[(dimethylamino)methylene]-	EtOH	242(4.06),288(4.21), 352(4.28)	4-1335-79
2-Propenoic acid, 2-cyano-3-morpholino-, methyl ester, (E)-	MeCN	287(4.42)	80-1143-79
2,4(1H,3H)-Pyrimidinedione, 5-methyl-1-(tetrahydro-2-furanyl)-	pH 1 and 7	269(3.99)	94-0899-79
	pH 12	269(3.86)	94-0899-79
4(1H)-Pyrimidinone, 6-(2,2-dimethyl-1,3-dioxolan-4-yl)-, (S)-	pH 1	222(3.89),263(3.55)	136-0235-79B
	pH 7.0	220(3.87),265(3.58)	136-0235-79B
	pH 11.0	230(4.06),265(3.54)	136-0235-79B
8-Quinazolinol, 5,6,7,8-tetrahydro-2-methyl-, 1,3-dioxide	EtOH	262(4.40),287(4.01), 349(3.15)	103-1025-79
$C_9H_{12}N_2O_3S$			
4(1H)-Pyrimidinone, 6-(2,2-dimethyl-1,3-dioxolan-4-yl)-2,3-dihydro-2-thioxo-	pH 1.0	214(4.20),273(4.28)	136-0235-79B
	pH 7.0	214(4.20),272(4.23)	136-0235-79B
	pH 11.0	260(4.08),300(3.88)	136-0235-79B
$C_9H_{12}N_2O_4$			
4-Pyrimidinecarboxylic acid, 1,2,3,6-tetrahydro-1-methyl-2,6-dioxo-3-propyl-	pH 1	274(3.96)	44-0970-79
	pH 13	270(3.97)	44-0970-79
$C_9H_{12}N_2O_4S$			
3,5-Isothiazoledicarboxylic acid, 4-amino-, diethyl ester	MeCN	241(3.97),364(3.96)	5-1534-79
Thiophene, 2-(1,2-dimethyl-2-nitropropyl)-4-nitro-	MeOH	269(3.89)	12-2647-79
Thiophene, 2-(1,2-dimethyl-2-nitropropyl)-5-nitro-	MeOH	320(4.00)	12-2647-79
$C_9H_{12}N_2O_5S$			
4(1H)-Pyrimidinone, 2,3-dihydro-6-β-D-ribofuranosyl-2-thioxo-	pH 3.58	271(4.20)	44-4854-79
	pH 14	260(4.07),290(3.79)	44-4854-79
$C_9H_{12}N_2O_6$			
2,4(1H,3H)-Pyrimidinedione, 6-β-D-ribofuranosyl-	pH 7	262(4.27)	44-4854-79
	pH 14	279(4.20)	44-4854-79
Uridine, 2'-deoxy-5-hydroxy-	pH 2	280(3.90)	33-1677-79
	pH 7	281(3.85)	33-1677-79
	pH 12	303(--)	33-1677-79
$C_9H_{12}N_2O_7$			
2,4(1H,3H)-Pyrimidinedione, 1-β-D-arabinofuranosyl-5-hydroxy-	pH 1	282(3.95)	87-0316-79
	pH 11	305(3.83)	87-0316-79
Uridine, 5-hydroxy-	pH 2	279(3.92)	33-1677-79
	pH 7	281(3.88)	33-1677-79
	pH 12	303(--)	33-1677-79
$C_9H_{12}N_2S_2$			
Carbamodithioic acid, (1,3-dimethyl-2(1H)-pyridinylidene)-	EtOH	220(4.08),240(4.00), 300(3.98)	94-2879-79
Carbamodithioic acid, (1,5-dimethyl-2(1H)-pyridinylidene)-	EtOH	220(4.05),306(4.00)	94-2879-79
Carbamodithioic acid, (1,6-dimethyl-2(1H)-pyridinylidene)-	EtOH	220(4.02),308(3.95), 374(4.08)	94-2879-79
$C_9H_{12}N_3$			
1H-1,2,3-Triazolium, 4,5-dihydro-1-methyl-3-phenyl-, perchlorate	MeOH	235(3.78),242(3.69), 326(4.05)	24-0445-79

Compound	Solvent	λ_{max}(log ϵ)	Ref.
$C_9H_{12}N_4$			
1H-Imidazol-2-amine, 4,5-dihydro-N-(1-methyl-2(1H)-pyridinylidene)-, monohydriodide	EtOH	220(4.28),272(4.17), 330(4.11)	94-2879-79
$C_9H_{12}N_4O$			
Ethanol, 2-[(2-methyl-1H-pyrrolo[2,3-d]pyrimidin-4-yl)amino]-	pH 1	280(4.12)	102-0217-79
	H_2O	278(4.12)	102-0217-79
	pH 13	277(4.18)	102-0217-79
$C_9H_{12}N_4O_6S$			
Imidazo[4,5-e]-1,2,4-thiadiazine, 2,7-dihydro-7-β-D-ribofuranosyl-, 1,1-dioxide	pH 3	232(3.58),263(3.40)	44-4046-79
	pH 9	245(3.59),267(3.57)	44-4046-79
$C_9H_{12}N_6O_2$			
9H-Purine-9-propanoic acid, α,6-diamino-, methyl ester, dihydrochloride	n.s.g.	260(4.15)	65-0989-79
$C_9H_{12}O$			
Bicyclo[3.2.0]hepta-2,6-diene, 3-ethoxy-	EtOH	232.5(3.72)	78-2311-79
Bicyclo[4.2.1]nona-2,4-dien-7-ol, endo	pentane	260(2.91)	44-2034-79
Bicyclo[4.2.1]nona-2,4-dien-7-ol, exo	pentane	257(3.40)	44-2034-79
Bicyclo[4.2.1]non-2-en-9-one	hexane	308(1.88)	33-2174-79
Bicyclo[4.2.1]non-3-en-9-one	hexane	297(1.20)	33-2174-79
Bicyclo[4.2.1]non-7-en-9-one	hexane	296(1.24)	33-2174-79
3-Cyclohexene-1-acetaldehyde, 2-methylene-	EtOH	231(4.44)	35-2383-79
1H-Inden-1-one, 3a,4,5,6,7,7a-hexahydro-	EtOH	224(3.90)	33-0852-79
2,5-Methanopentalen-7-one, octahydro-	hexane	290(1.23)	142-0343-79
1(2H)-Pentalenone, 4,5,6,6a-tetrahydro-6a-methyl-	EtOH	222(3.92)	33-0852-79
2-Propyn-1-one, 1-(1-methylcyclopentyl)-	EtOH	213(3.58),217s(3.52)	33-0852-79
Tricyclo[3.3.1.0^{3,6}]nonan-2-one, (-)-	isooctane	291(1.36),301s(1.30), 312s(1.00)	44-0016-79
Tricyclo[4.2.1.0^{3,7}]nonan-2-one, (+)-	isooctane	282s(1.20),272(1.34), 307s(1.32),318s(1.11)	44-0016-79
$C_9H_{12}O_2$			
Bicyclo[3.2.0]heptane-2,6-dione, 1,5-dimethyl-	MeOH	294(1.71)	44-4557-79
Bicyclo[2.2.1]hept-2-ene-2-carboxaldehyde, 3-(hydroxymethyl)-	ether	250(3.82)	88-0561-79
	isooctane	249(--),280s(--)	88-0561-79
	EtOH	256(--)	88-0561-79
Bicyclo[3.2.0]hept-5-en-3-one, 1-ethoxy-	EtOH	303(1.97)	78-2311-79
Cyclopropaneacetic acid, α-cyclopropylidene-, methyl ester	EtOH	230(5.70)	44-0989-79
Ethanone, 1-(2,6-dimethyl-2H-pyran-5-yl)-	EtOH	213(3.62),280(4.17)	70-0758-79
$C_9H_{12}O_2S$			
1-Thiaspiro[4.5]decane-4,6-dione	n.s.g.	235(2.83),255s(2.51), 296(2.53),306(2.54)	44-0825-79
$C_9H_{12}O_3$			
1-Cyclohexene-1-carboxylic acid, 6-oxo-, ethyl ester	EtOH	227(3.79),290s(2.62)	33-2630-79
Ethanone, 1-[5-(methoxymethyl)-2-methyl-3-furanyl]-	MeOH	268(3.37)	136-0055-79B

Compound	Solvent	λmax(log ε)	Ref.
2H-Pyran-5-carboxylic acid, 2,6-dimethyl-, methyl ester	EtOH	230s(4.30),268(4.11)	70-0758-79
$C_9H_{12}O_3S_2$			
Acetic acid, [[(2-oxocyclohexyl)thioxomethyl]thio]-	EtOH	324(4.15),364(4.18)	150-1732-79
$C_9H_{12}S$			
Benzene, [(ethylthio)methyl]-	hexane	240(3.90),260s(2.58), 265(2.40)	114-0195-79D
Benzene, 1-(ethylthio)-4-methyl-	C_6H_{12}	290(2.86)	39-0217-79B
Benzene, [(1-methylethyl)thio]-	C_6H_{12}	282(3.11)	39-0217-79B
$C_9H_{12}S_2Si$			
1,3-Dithia-2-silacyclopentane, 2-methyl-2-phenyl-	hexane	194(4.52),220s(3.86), 245s(3.13),266(2.61), 274(2.45)	114-0195-79D
$C_9H_{13}ClN_4O_4$			
2-Pyrimidinamine, 1-β-D-arabinofuranosyl-5-chloro-1,4-dihydro-4-imino-, hydrochloride	pH 1	282(3.85)	87-0514-79
	pH 7	282(3.86)	87-0514-79
	pH 14	296(3.54)	87-0514-79
$C_9H_{13}FN_4O_4$			
2-Pyrimidinamine, 1-β-D-arabinofuranosyl-5-fluoro-1,4-dihydro-4-imino-, sulfate(1:1)	pH 1	278(3.85)	87-0514-79
	pH 14	305s(--)(changing)	87-0514-79
	MeOH	278(3.84)	87-0514-79
$C_9H_{13}N$			
Benzenamine, N,N,3-trimethyl-	MeCN	255(4.19),300(3.34)	18-1573-79
1H-Pyrrole, 1-ethenyl-2-ethyl-3-methyl-	C_6H_{12}	202(4.08),254(4.10)	104-0535-79
$C_9H_{13}NO$			
2-Propen-1-amine, N-[(3,4-dihydro-2H-pyran-2-yl)methylene]-	EtOH	346(0.72)	103-0488-79
5H-Pyrrolo[1,2-a]azepin-5-one, 1,2,3,6,7,8-hexahydro-	ether	244(3.87)	24-0734-79
5H-Pyrrolo[1,2-a]azepin-5-one, 2,3,6,7,8,9-hexahydro-	ether	240(4.10)	24-0734-79
2H-Quinolizin-2-one, 1,6,7,8,9,9a-hexahydro-, (±)-	EtOH	320(4.19)	88-4587-79
$C_9H_{13}NOS_4$			
1-Pyrrolidinecarbodithioic acid, 3-[bis(methylthio)methylene]-2-oxo-, methyl ester	EtOH	216(3.29),249(3.46), 285s(3.67),364(4.29)	39-0692-79C
$C_9H_{13}NO_2$			
5(1H)-Indolizinone, 2,3,6,7-tetrahydro-6-hydroxy-6-methyl-	ether	252(3.62)	24-0734-79
$C_9H_{13}NO_3$			
4(1H)-Pyridinone, 1-ethyl-2-(hydroxymethyl)-5-methoxy-	acid	281(3.72)	18-0107-79
	neutral	285(4.11)	18-0107-79
	MeOH	224(4.21),287(4.13)	18-0107-79
$C_9H_{13}NO_4S$			
3-Pyrrolidinecarboxylic acid, 5-[2-(methylthio)ethyl]-2,4-dioxo-, methyl ester	H_2O	228(4.19),263(4.07)	142-0477-79B

Compound	Solvent	λmax(log ε)	Ref.
D-Ribitol, 1-C-(2-methyl-5-thiazolyl)-, (R)-	acid	247(3.81)	44-4351-79
	pH 7	240(3.82)	44-4351-79
	base	238(3.90)	44-4351-79
$C_9H_{13}NS_2$			
2(3H)-Cyclooctathiazolethione, 4,5,6,7,8,9-hexahydro-	EtOH	326(3.909)	48-0249-79
$C_9H_{13}N_3$			
Ethanimidic acid, 2-methyl-2-phenyl-, hydrazide, monohydriodide	H_2O	227(4.37),275(3.00)	104-2073-79
monohydrochloride	H_2O	233(4.05),272(3.24)	104-2066-79
	pH 13	253(4.08)	104-2066-79
$C_9H_{13}N_3O$			
Pyrazinecarboxamide, N-(1-methylprop-yl)-, (S)-	isooctane	208(3.99),266(3.88), 332f(2.70)	39-2881-79C
	EtOH	211(4.01),269(3.91), 320(2.78)	39-2881-79C
	MeCN	208(4.08),268(3.97), 322(2.85)	39-2881-79C
$C_9H_{13}N_3O_2$			
5H-Pyrazolo[4,3-d][1,3]oxazepin-5-one, 1,4,7,8-tetrahydro-3,7,7-trimethyl-	EtOH	230(3.94)	118-0584-79
$C_9H_{13}N_3O_3$			
1H-Pyrazole-3-carboxylic acid, 4-(acet-ylamino)-5-methyl-, ethyl ester	pH 1	217(3.91),259s(3.67)	18-0208-79
	pH 11	230(3.96),253(4.11)	18-0208-79
	EtOH	217(3.90),254s(3.63)	18-0208-79
6H-Pyrazolo[3,4-c]pyridine-6-carboxylic acid, 1,4,5,7-tetrahydro-3-hydroxy-1-methyl-, methyl ester	MeOH	232(3.61),260(2.93)	111-0157-79
6H-Pyrazolo[3,4-c]pyridine-6-carboxylic acid, 2,4,5,7-tetrahydro-3-hydroxy-2-methyl-, methyl ester	MeOH	235s(--),250(3.72)	111-0157-79
4(1H)-Pyrimidinone, 2-amino-6-(2,2-di-methyl-1,3-dioxolan-4-yl)-, (S)-	pH 1.0	237(3.59),257(3.85)	136-0235-79B
	pH 7.0	220(3.95),282(3.92)	136-0235-79B
	pH 11.0	215(3.30),277(3.78)	136-0235-79B
$C_9H_{13}N_3O_4$			
1H-Pyrazole-3,5-dicarboxylic acid, 4-amino-, diethyl ester	EtOH	312(3.92)	23-0904-79
	EtOH-NaOH	296(3.80)	23-0904-79
$C_9H_{13}N_3O_4Se$			
Cytidine, 2-seleno-	pH 1	235(4.22)	77-0271-79
	pH 11	251(4.27),299(4.10)	77-0271-79
	MeOH	252(4.07),303(4.10)	77-0271-79
$C_9H_{13}N_3O_5$			
2(1H)-Pyrimidinone, 4-amino-1-α-D-ara-binofuranosyl)-	pH 1	280(4.13)	4-0353-79
	pH 7	271(3.93)	4-0353-79
	pH 13	272(3.96)	4-0353-79
2(1H)-Pyrimidinone, 4-amino-6-β-D-ribo-furanosyl-	pH 1	279(3.99)	44-4854-79
	pH 7	271(3.83)	44-4854-79
	pH 13	284(3.82)	44-4854-79
4(1H)-Pyrimidinone, 2-amino-6-β-D-ribo-furanosyl-	pH 1	261(3.86)	44-4854-79
	pH 7	286(3.85)	44-4854-79
	pH 13	276(3.78)	44-4854-79
Uridine, 5-amino-2'-deoxy-	pH 1	265(3.90)	87-0621-79

Compound	Solvent	$\lambda_{max}(\log \epsilon)$	Ref.
Uridine, 5-amino-2'-deoxy- (cont.)	pH 12	289(3.74)	87-0621-79
$C_9H_{13}N_3O_6$			
1H-1,2,3-Triazole-4-carboxylic acid, 1-β-D-ribofuranosyl-, methyl ester	MeOH	214(3.98)	44-1424-79
$C_9H_{13}N_3O_6S$			
1,2,4-Triazin-5(2H)-one, 3,4-dihydro-2-[4-C-(hydroxymethyl)-β-D-erythro-pentofuranosyl]-3-thioxo-	pH 1	218(4.16),270(4.22)	44-1301-79
$C_9H_{13}N_5$			
Imidazo[5,1-f][1,2,4]triazin-2-amine, 5-methyl-7-propyl-, monohydrochloride	EtOH	247(4.14),315(2.70), 360s(2.43)	39-1120-79C
$C_9H_{13}N_5O$			
Imidazo[1,5-a]-1,3,5-triazin-4(1H)-one, 2-(dimethylamino)-6,8-dimethyl-	MeCN	278(3.91)	44-3835-79
Imidazo[5,1-f][1,2,4]triazin-4(1H)-one, 2-amino-5-methyl-7-propyl-	pH 1	221(4.52),227(3.75)	39-1120-79C
	EtOH	227(4.51),265(3.75)	39-1120-79C
$C_9H_{13}N_5O_2$			
1H-Pyrazole-4-carbonyl azide, 3-(2-hydroxy-2-methylpropyl)-5-methyl-	EtOH	255(4.17)	118-0584-79
3H-Pyrazolo[3',4':3,4]pyrrolo[2,3-d]-pyrimidine-7,9(3aH,8H)-dione, 4,5,5a,6-tetrahydro-6,8-dimethyl-, (3aα,5aβ,9aS*)-(±)-	EtOH	212(3.45)	4-0293-79
5H-Pyrido[1,2-c][1,2,3]triazolo[1,5-a]-pyrimidine, 6,6a,7,8,9,10-hexahydro-1-nitro-	EtOH	229(4.34),356(4.00)	39-2361-79C
$C_9H_{13}N_5O_3$			
Adenine, 9-(D-erythro-2,3,4-trihydroxybutyl)-	pH 2 and 12	262(4.10)	73-0593-79
L-	pH 2 and 12	262(4.09)	73-0593-79
Adenine, 9-(D-thre-2,3,4-trihydroxybutyl)-	pH 2 and 12	262(4.17)	73-0593-79
$C_9H_{13}P$			
Phosphine, dimethyl(2-methylphenyl)-	C_6H_{12}	210s(4.20),216s(4.11), 254(3.68),272f(3.44)	39-0501-79B
	12M HCl	220(3.92),272f(3.11)	39-0501-79B
Phosphine, dimethyl(3-methylphenyl)-	C_6H_{12}	210s(4.18),216s(4.08), 253(3.63),272f(3.40)	39-0501-79B
	12M HCl	220(3.90),272f(3.15)	39-0501-79B
Phosphine, dimethyl(4-methylphenyl)-	C_6H_{12}	210s(4.00),225s(3.76), 253(3.56),272f(3.22)	39-0501-79B
	12M HCl	225(4.11),267f(2.86)	39-0501-79B
Phosphine, ethylmethylphenyl-	C_6H_{12}	208s(4.10),220s(3.92), 253(3.48),266f(3.36)	39-0501-79B
	12M HCl	219(3.93),266f(2.90)	39-0501-79B
Phosphine, (1-methylethyl)phenyl-	C_6H_{12}	209s(4.09),220s(3.83), 243(3.68),266f(3.21)	39-0501-79B
	12M HCl	222(4.02),267f(3.06)	39-0501-79B
Phosphine, (2,4,6-trimethylphenyl)-	C_6H_{12}	205(4.59),237(3.91), 275s(2.99)	39-0501-79B
C_9H_{14}			
1,2-Cyclononadiene, (R)-	gas	188(4.1)	35-2284-79

Compound	Solvent	λmax(log ε)	Ref.
1,3-Heptadiene, 4-ethenyl-	EtOH	255(4.43),265(4.54), 276(4.43)	39-0717-79B
2,4,6-Octatriene, 2-methyl-	EtOH	272(4.51)	104-1037-79
$C_9H_{14}ClF_2N$			
1-Cyclopropen-1-amine, 2-chloro-3,3-difluoro-N,N-bis(1-methylethyl)-	CH_2Cl_2	268(4.42),310(4.24)	24-1529-79
$C_9H_{14}NO_3$			
1-Pyrrolidinyloxy, 3-formyl-2,2,5,5-tetramethyl-4-oxo-	C_6H_{12}	279(3.89)	88-0941-79
	MeOH	267(4.00)	88-0941-79
	MeOH-HCl	267(4.08)	88-0941-79
	MeOH-NaOH	225(3.52),295(4.25)	88-0941-79
copper chelate	MeOH	224(4.05),243(4.14), 315(4.28),324s(4.10), 410s(2.46),660(1.75)	88-0941-79
$C_9H_{14}N_2O$			
Azetidine, 1-(cyanocarbonyl)-2,2,4,4-tetramethyl-	EtOH	234(3.75)	12-1775-79
$C_9H_{14}N_2OS$			
1,3-Diazaspiro[4.5]decan-4-one, 3-methyl-2-thioxo-	80% H_2SO_4	223(4.01),238s(3.87)	23-1980-79
$C_9H_{14}N_2O_2S$			
Methanesulfonamide, N-[4-(dimethylamino)phenyl]-	EtOH	265(4.29)	80-1027-79
$C_9H_{14}N_2O_3$			
1H-Pyrazole-3-carboxylic acid, 5-hydroxy-1-methyl-, 1,1-dimethylethyl ester	MeOH	223(4.06)	5-1696-79
1H-Pyrazole-4-carboxylic acid, 3-(hydroxymethyl)-1,5-dimethyl-, ethyl ester	EtOH	232(3.91)	4-1117-79
1H-Pyrazole-4-carboxylic acid, 5-(hydroxymethyl)-1,3-dimethyl-, ethyl ester	EtOH	235(3.93)	4-1117-79
1H-Pyrrole, 1-(1,1-dimethylethyl)-2-methoxy-4-nitro-	MeOH	277(3.89),360(3.69)	44-4420-79
1H-Pyrrole, 1-(1,1-dimethylethyl)-3-methoxy-4-nitro-	MeOH	300(4.01)	44-4420-79
$C_9H_{14}N_2O_4$			
Carbamic acid, [(4,5-dihydro-5-oxo-3-isoxazolyl)methyl]-, 1,1-dimethylethyl ester	MeOH	252(3.58)	1-0294-79
2,4(1H,3H)-Pyrimidinedione, 1-(2,4-dihydroxybutyl)-5-methyl-	EtOH	268(3.83)	128-0051-79
$C_9H_{14}N_2O_5$			
2,3-Piperidinediol, 1-nitroso-, diacetate, trans	EtOH	239(3.91),368(1.91)	44-4511-79
$C_9H_{14}N_2S$			
2-Cyclooctathiazolamine, 4,5,6,7,8,9-hexahydro-	EtOH	266(4.808)	48-0249-79
$C_9H_{14}N_2S_2$			
3H-Cycloocta[e][1,3,4]thiadiazine-3-thione, 2,4a,5,6,7,8,9,10-octahydro-	EtOH	323(4.120)	48-0959-79

Compound	Solvent	$\lambda_{max}(\log \epsilon)$	Ref.
$C_9H_{14}N_3O_2S$			
1H-Imidazol-1-yloxy, 2,5-dihydro-2,2,5,5-tetramethyl-4-(thiocyanatomethyl)-, 3-oxide	EtOH	254(3.88)	70-2521-79
$C_9H_{14}N_4O_3S$			
5-Pyrimidinecarbothioamide, 6-amino-1,2,3,4-tetrahydro-N-(2-hydroxyethyl)-1,3-dimethyl-2,4-dioxo-	EtOH	259(4.43),301(4.27)	95-0515-79
$C_9H_{14}N_4O_7$			
1,2,4-Triazine-3,5(2H,4H)-dione, 6-amino-2-β-D-glucopyranosyl-	pH 1-7	300(3.70)	124-0048-79
	pH 13	290(3.63)	124-0048-79
$C_9H_{14}N_6O_5$			
Urea, [5-[4-(aminocarbonyl)-1H-1,2,3-triazol-1-yl]-5-deoxy-β-D-ribofuranosyl]-	MeOH	210(4.15)	44-1424-79
$C_9H_{14}O$			
2-Cyclohexen-1-one, 2,3,4-trimethyl-	MeOH	246(3.98)	44-4042-79
2-Cycloocten-1-one, 2-methyl-	EtOH	242(3.83),285(2.88)	44-2722-79
2-Cycloocten-1-one, 3-methyl-	EtOH	245(3.88)	44-2722-79
2-Cyclopenten-1-one, 3-methyl-2-(1-methylethyl)-	MeOH	237(3.90)	146-0100-79
2-Cyclopenten-1-one, 3-methyl-2-propyl-	MeOH	239(3.91)	146-0100-79
$C_9H_{14}O_2$			
Cyclobutane, 1,2-diacetyl-1-methyl-, trans	C_6H_{12}	290(1.72)	54-0346-79
3-Hexenoic acid, 5-methyl-2-methylene-, methyl ester	heptane	248(3.4)	24-3480-79
3-Penten-1-yne, 4-(1-ethoxyethoxy)-, (Z)-	isoPrOH	233(4.16)	54-0316-79
1-Propanone, 1-(3,4-dihydro-6-methyl-2H-pyran-2-yl)-	C_6H_{12}	208(3.32),282(1.58)	54-0346-79
4H-Pyran, 2-acetyl-2,3-dihydro-2,5-dimethyl-	C_6H_{12}	211(3.49),292(1.61)	54-0346-79
4H-Pyran, 2-acetyl-2,3-dihydro-2,6-dimethyl-	C_6H_{12}	210(3.43),291(1.59)	54-0346-79
$C_9H_{14}O_3$			
2-Heptenoic acid, 7-oxo-, ethyl ester, (E)-	n.s.g.	212(3.94),290(1.48)	118-0279-79
(Z)-	n.s.g.	214(3.88),290(1.43)	118-0279-79
2-Hexenoic acid, 2-methyl-6-oxo-, ethyl ester, (E)-	n.s.g.	215(4.06),290(1.58)	118-0279-79
(Z)-	n.s.g.	217(3.95),290(1.52)	118-0279-79
2-Hexenoic acid, 3-methyl-6-oxo-, ethyl ester	EtOH	220(3.686)	70-0353-79
$C_9H_{14}O_4$			
Butanoic acid, 2-(ethoxymethylene)-3-oxo-, ethyl ester	EtOH	254(4.05)	39-0464-79C
$C_9H_{14}O_5$			
Pentanoic acid, 2-acetyl-5-hydroxy-4-oxo-, ethyl ester, (±)-	EtOH	208(3.58),254(5.16)	136-0055-79B

Compound	Solvent	λ_{max}(log ε)	Ref.
$C_9H_{14}Si$			
Silane, trimethylphenyl-	hexane	211(4.00),252(2.23), 258(2.26),265(2.24), 270(2.10)	114-0195-79D
$C_9H_{15}Br_2N_2O_2$			
1H-Imidazol-1-yloxy, 4-(1,2-dibromoethyl)-2,5-dihydro-2,2,5,5-tetramethyl-, 3-oxide	EtOH	260(3.85)	70-2521-79
$C_9H_{15}ClN_4O_2$			
1,3,5-Triazin-2-amine, 4-(2-chloroethoxy)-6-ethoxy-N,N-dimethyl-	EtOH	229(4.49)	103-0111-79
1,3,5-Triazin-2(1H)-one, 1-(2-chloroethyl)-4-(dimethylamino)-6-ethoxy-	EtOH	236(4.37)	103-0111-79
$C_9H_{15}N$			
1H-Pyrrole, 3-ethyl-2-propyl-	C_6H_{12}	222(3.89)	104-0535-79
$C_9H_{15}NO$			
Acetamide, N-1,3-butadienyl-N-(1-methylethyl)-	MeOH	259(4.14)	88-0981-79
Morpholine, 4-(1-cyclopenten-1-yl)-	MeCN	218(3.9)	24-2997-79
2-Propanone, 1-(4,4-dimethyl-2-pyrrolidinylidene)-	MeOH	203(3.43),305(4.32)	83-0498-79
2-Pyrrolidinone, 5,5-dimethyl-3-propylidene-	EtOH	223(3.98)	12-2041-79
2H-Pyrrol-2-one, 1,5-dihydro-5,5-dimethyl-3-(1-methylethyl)-	EtOH	213(3.89)	12-2041-79
$C_9H_{15}NOS_2$			
2H-Azepin-2-one, 3-[bis(methylthio)-methylene]dihydro-	EtOH	250(3.98)	39-0692-79C
$C_9H_{15}NO_2$			
Cyclohexanamine, N-(oxiranylmethylene)-, N-oxide	EtOH	246(4.02),310(2.18)	33-0205-79
$C_9H_{15}NS_4$			
2-Cyclobutene-1-thione, 3-(dimethylamino)-2,4,4-tris(methylthio)-	CH_2Cl_2	272(3.87),352(4.38), 428(2.59)	5-0595-79
$C_9H_{15}N_2O_2$			
1H-Imidazol-1-yloxy, 4-ethenyl-2,5-dihydro-2,2,5,5-tetramethyl-, 3-oxide	EtOH	234(3.81),282(4.06)	70-2521-79
$C_9H_{15}N_2O_4PS_2$			
Phosphorothioic acid, O-[1,6-dihydro-1-methyl-5-(methylthio)-6-oxo-4-pyridazinyl] O-ethyl O-methyl ester	MeOH	211(4.13),237(3.75), 319(3.84)	73-1761-79
$C_9H_{15}N_2O_5PS$			
Phosphorothioic acid, O-(5-ethoxy-1,6-dihydro-1-methyl-6-oxo-4-pyridiazinyl) O,O-dimethyl ester	MeOH	213(4.31),286(3.72)	73-1761-79
$C_9H_{15}N_3O_3$			
Carbamic acid, [3-(2-hydroxyethyl)-5-methyl-1H-pyrazol-4-yl]-, ethyl ester	EtOH	220(3.60)	118-0584-79

Compound	Solvent	λ_{max}(log ε)	Ref.
$C_9H_{15}N_3S_3$			
1,2,3-Triazine, 4,5,6-tris(ethylthio)-	CH_2Cl_2	276(4.41)	24-1529-79
$C_9H_{15}N_4O_2$			
Oxazolo[3,2-a]-1,3,5-triazin-5-ium, 2-(dimethylamino)-4-ethoxy-6,7-dihydro-, chloride	H_2O	236(4.41)	103-0111-79
$C_9H_{15}N_4O_7P$			
2-Pyrimidinamine, 1,4-dihydro-4-imino-1-(3-O-phosphono-β-D-arabinofuranosyl)-	pH 1	269(3.91)	87-0514-79
	pH 7	269(3.91)	87-0514-79
	pH 14	295(3.45)	87-0514-79
$C_9H_{15}N_5$			
Imidazo[5,1-f][1,2,4]triazin-2-amine, 1,4-dihydro-5-methyl-7-propyl-	EtOH	250(4.03)	39-1120-79C
$C_9H_{15}N_5O_2$			
Acetamide, N-[6-amino-2-(dimethylamino)-4,5-dihydro-5-methyl-4-oxo-5-pyrimidinyl]-	EtOH	260(4.37)	44-3835-79
Butanamide, N-[1-(3-amino-2,5-dihydro-5-oxo-1,2,4-triazin-6-yl)ethyl]-	pH 1	259(3.75)	39-1120-79C
	pH 13	290(3.79)	39-1120-79C
$C_9H_{16}N_2O$			
2-Cyclohexen-1-one, 3-(2,2-dimethylhydrazino)-5-methyl-	MeOH	290(4.52)	64-0102-79B
$C_9H_{16}N_2O_2$			
1-Azetidineacetamide, 2,2,4,4-tetramethyl-α-oxo-	EtOH	217(3.77),235s(--)	12-1775-79
Cyclohexanone, 2-[(ethylideneamino)-methyl]-, oxime, N^2-oxide	EtOH	235(3.95)	103-1025-79
1-Cyclopenten-1-amine, N-(1,1-dimethylethyl)-2-nitro-	EtOH	241s(--),366(4.39)	44-3410-79
$C_9H_{16}N_2O_4$			
2-Butenedioic acid, 2-(1-methylhydrazino)-, diethyl ester, (E)-	MeOH	281(4.35)	24-1712-79
$C_9H_{16}N_3O_2$			
1-Imidazolidinyloxy, 2,2,3,5,5-pentamethyl-4-(nitromethylene)-	EtOH	322(4.35)	104-0364-79
$C_9H_{16}N_4O_2$			
1H-Pyrazole-4-carboxylic acid, 3-(2-hydroxy-2-methylpropyl)-5-methyl-, hydrazide	EtOH	230(3.71)	118-0584-79
$C_9H_{16}N_5O_2$			
1H-Imidazol-1-yloxy, 4-(1-azidoethyl)-2,5-dihydro-2,2,5,5-tetramethyl-, 3-oxide	EtOH	238(4.05)	70-2521-79
$C_9H_{16}S_2$			
2,5-Dithiaspiro[4.6]undecane	EtOH	213(3.02)	49-0279-79
$C_9H_{17}NO_3$			
3-Heptanone, 2,2-dimethyl-4-nitro-	EtOH	236(3.26),295(2.18)	44-4116-79
	EtOH-NaOH	230(3.88),320(3.38)	44-4116-79

Compound	Solvent	λ_{max}(log ϵ)	Ref.
$C_9H_{17}N_3$			
2-Heptenenitrile, 3-[(2-aminoethyl)amino]-	EtOH	261(4.30)	39-2289-79C
2-Hexenenitrile, 3-[(2-aminoethyl)amino]-4-methyl-	EtOH	261(4.25)	39-2289-79C
$C_9H_{17}N_3O_2$			
1H-Imidazole-4-carboxaldehyde, 2,5-dihydro-1,2,2,5,5-pentamethyl-, oxime, 3-oxide	EtOH	290(4.08)	103-0092-79
$C_9H_{17}O_4PS_3$			
Phosphoro(dithioperoxo)thioic acid, S-(1-acetyl-2-oxopropyl) O,O-diethyl ester	EtOH	231(3.1)	65-1964-79
$C_9H_{17}O_4PS_4$			
2,4-Pentanedione, 3-[(diethoxyphosphinothioyl)trithio]- (type spectrum)	EtOH	240(3.9)	65-1964-79
$C_9H_{18}N_2$			
1H-Imidazole, 4,5-dihydro-4,4-dimethyl-2-(1-methylpropyl)-	EtOH	220(3.73)	39-2289-79C
1H-Imidazole, 2-butyl-4,5-dihydro-4,4-dimethyl-	EtOH	217(3.60)	39-2289-79C
$C_9H_{18}N_2O$			
1H-Imidazole, 4-ethyl-2,5-dihydro-2,2,5,5-tetramethyl-, 3-oxide	EtOH	234(4.01)	103-0092-79
$C_9H_{18}N_2O_2$			
3-Heptanimine, 2,2-dimethyl-N-nitro-	isooctane	269(2.75)	44-4116-79
3-Heptanimine, 2,2-dimethyl-4-nitro-	isooctane	251(2.83)	44-4116-79
3-Hepten-3-amine, 2,2-dimethyl-N-nitro-	isooctane	231(3.53)	44-4116-79
$C_9H_{19}N_3O_3$			
Carbamic acid, [(butylnitrosoamino)-methyl]-, 1-methylethyl ester	EtOH	232(3.89),357(1.86)	94-0682-79
Carbamic acid, [[(1-methylpropyl)nitrosoamino]methyl]-, 1-methylethyl ester	EtOH	233(3.88),365(1.84)	94-0682-79
$C_9H_{19}O_5PS$			
Sulfoxonium, dimethyl-, 1-(diethoxyphosphinyl)-2-oxopropylide	hexane	239(--)	99-0573-79
	EtOH	242(--)	99-0573-79
$C_9H_{22}IN_3$			
Ethanimidic acid, N-butyl-, trimethylhydrazide, monohydriodide	H_2O	225(4.37)	104-2073-79

Compound	Solvent	$\lambda_{max}(\log \epsilon)$	Ref.
$C_{10}AsClCr_2O_{10}$			
Chromium, [μ-[arsinous chloridato(2-)]]-decacarbonyldi-	n.s.g.	594(4.15)	89-0233-79
$C_{10}F_{14}$			
Bicyclo[5.2.0]nona-1(7),2-diene, 3,4,4,5,5,6,6,8,8,9,9-undecafluoro-2-(trifluoromethyl)-	n.s.g.	245(4.13)	77-1062-79
1,4-Cycloheptadiene, 3-(difluoromethylene)-1,5,6,6,7,7-hexafluoro-2,4-bis(trifluoromethyl)-	n.s.g.	241(3.68)	77-1062-79
Cycloheptene, 6,7-bis(difluoromethylene)-2,3,3,4,4,5,5-heptafluoro-1-(trifluoromethyl)-	n.s.g.	228(3.57)	77-1062-79
$C_{10}HF_7O_2$			
1(4H)-Naphthalenone, 2,4,4,5,6,7,8-heptafluoro-3-hydroxy-	C_6H_{12} or heptane	221(4.08),231(4.00), 247(3.94),291(3.83)	104-1934-79
$C_{10}H_2F_7NO$			
1(4H)-Naphthalenone, 3-amino-2,4,4,5,6,7,8-heptafluoro-	heptane	230(4.18),303(3.84), 323(3.89)	104-1934-79
$C_{10}H_2N_4S$			
Propanedinitrile, 2,2'-(2,5-thiophenediylidene)bis-	MeCN	394(4.45),413(4.49)	77-1030-79
radical ion, lithium salt	MeCN	265(3.72),405(3.63), 468(4.49),481(4.62), 610(3.59),662(4.18), 732(4.38)	77-1030-79
$C_{10}H_3F_9HgO_2$			
Mercury, [3,5-bis(trifluoromethyl)phenyl](trifluoroacetato-O)-	MeOH	263(2.73),270(2.60)	12-1521-79
$C_{10}H_4Br_3NO_4$			
Furan, 2-bromo-5-[1,2-dibromo-2-(5-nitro-2-furanyl)ethenyl]-, cis	EtOH	300(4.30),375(4.00)	94-3078-79
trans	EtOH	300(4.30),375(4.08)	94-3078-79
$C_{10}H_4ClN_5S$			
1,2,3,4-Thiatriazolium, 3-(4-chlorophenyl)-5-(dicyanomethyl)-, hydroxide, inner salt	n.s.g.	238(3.77),298(4.50), 471(3.56)	39-0744-79C
$C_{10}H_4Cl_2O_2$			
1,4-Naphthalenedione, 2,3-dichloro-	hexane	245(4.12),279(4.25), 252(4.12),332(3.42)	39-1686-79B
$C_{10}H_4Cl_2O_4$			
1H-Indene-3-carboxylic acid, 2,4-dichloro-7-hydroxy-1-oxo-	EtOH	240(3.51),265(3.53), 400(3.72)	107-0129-79
$C_{10}H_4Cl_4O$			
Cycloprop[a]inden-6(1H)-one, 1,1,1a,6a-tetrachloro-1a,6a-dihydro-	hexane	241(4.50),290(3.62), 298(3.65),310(3.52)	39-1686-79B
1(2H)-Naphthalenone, 2,2,3,4-tetrachloro-	hexane	242(4.44),250(4.49), 296(3.09),353(3.38)	39-1686-79B
	hexane	255(4.17),293(3.65)	46-1821-79
1(4H)-Naphthalenone, 2,3,4,4-tetrachloro-	hexane	255(4.17),363(1.30) 262(4.16),293(3.65),	39-1686-79B

Compound	Solvent	λmax(log ε)	Ref.
1(4H)-Naphthalenone, 2,3,4,4-tetrachloro- (cont.)		400(0.52)	39-1686-79B
	hexane	242(4.44),296(3.09), 353(3.38)	46-1821-79
$C_{10}H_4N_4Se_2$			
Naphtho[1,8-cd:4,5-c'd']bis[1,2,6]-selenadiazine	dioxan	263(4.33),280s(4.19), 328(3.76),341s(3.66), 490s(4.12),523(4.32)	35-3306-79
$C_{10}H_5ClN_2O$			
Pyrazino[2,1,6-cd]pyrrolizine-5-carboxaldehyde, 6-chloro-	EtOH	205(4.14),252(4.32), 300(3.60),320(3.45), 390(3.17)	24-2465-79
$C_{10}H_5Cl_3N_2O_3$			
Benzoxazole, 2,3-dihydro-2-(2,3,3-trichloro-1-nitro-2-propenylidene)-	EtOH	208(4.15),360(4.53)	104-0240-79
$C_{10}H_5Cl_3O$			
1-Naphthalenol, 2,3,4-trichloro-	hexane	290(3.71),302(3.77), 318(3.59),334(3.42)	39-1686-79B
$C_{10}H_5Cl_3O_4$			
2-Butenoic acid, 2,3-dichloro-4-(5-chloro-2-hydroxyphenyl)-4-oxo-, (Z)-	EtOH	228(4.23),237(4.10), 292(4.19),365(3.77)	107-0129-79
$C_{10}H_5NO_4$			
1,4-Naphthalenedione, 6-nitro-	MeOH	214(4.36),253(4.40), 328(3.53)	12-0575-79
$C_{10}H_5N_5S$			
1,2,3,4-Thiatriazolium, 5-(dicyanomethyl)-3-phenyl-, hydroxide, inner salt	n.s.g.	232s(3.79),293(4.58), 465(3.60)	39-0744-79C
$C_{10}H_6BrF_6IO$			
1,2-Benziodoxole, 1-bromo-1,3-dihydro-5-methyl-3,3-bis(trifluoromethyl)-	pentane	200(4.27),235(4.12), 332(2.13)	44-1779-79
$C_{10}H_6BrNO_2S$			
6H-1,3-Thiazin-6-one, 5-bromo-4-hydroxy-2-phenyl-	EtOH	248(4.33)	103-0037-79
$C_{10}H_6BrN_3O_4S$			
2-Thiophenamine, N-(2-bromophenyl)-3,5-dinitro-	MeOH	394(4.24)	39-0219-79B
$C_{10}H_6ClF_6IO$			
1,2-Benziodoxole, 1-chloro-1,3-dihydro-5-methyl-3,3-bis(trifluoromethyl)-	pentane	200(4.21),223(4.29), 329(2.00)	44-1779-79
$C_{10}H_6ClN_3O_4S$			
2-Thiophenamine, N-(2-chlorophenyl)-3,5-dinitro-	MeOH	394(4.25)	39-0219-79B
$C_{10}H_6Cl_3N_3O_2$			
1H-Benzimidazole, 2,3-dihydro-2-(2,3,3-trichloro-1-nitro-2-propenylidene)-	EtOH	212(4.30),365(4.53)	104-0240-79
$C_{10}H_6FN_3O_4S$			
2-Thiophenamine, N-(2-fluorophenyl)-3,5-dinitro-	MeOH	394(4.24)	39-0219-79B

Compound	Solvent	λ_{max}(log ε)	Ref.
$C_{10}H_6F_4O$			
Benzofuran, 4,5,6,7-tetrafluoro-2,3-dimethyl-	C_6H_{12}	247(4.11)	18-2657-79
$C_{10}H_6F_7IO$			
1,2-Benziodoxole, 1-fluoro-1,3-dihydro-5-methyl-3,3-bis(trifluoromethyl)-	pentane	209(3.95),223(3.95), 325(1.60)	44-1779-79
$C_{10}H_6INO_2S$			
6H-1,3-Thiazin-6-one, 4-hydroxy-5-iodo-2-phenyl-	EtOH	248(4.21)	103-0037-79
$C_{10}H_6N_2$			
1,3,5,7-Cyclooctatetraene-1,4-dicarbonitrile	EtOH	217(4.43),307(2.86)	138-1427-79
$C_{10}H_6N_2O$			
Benzenepropanenitrile, 4-cyano-β-oxo-	EtOH	238(4.36),345(3.85)	56-2251-79
$C_{10}H_6N_2OS$			
[1,4]Oxathiino[3,2-b:5,6-b']dipyridine	MeOH	213(4.30),229(4.23), 311(3.97)	88-5035-79
$C_{10}H_6N_2O_2$			
1,4-Dioxino[2,3-b:5,6-b']dipyridine	MeOH	219(4.17),220s(--), 298(4.13)	88-5035-79
$C_{10}H_6N_2O_6$			
Furan, 2,2'-(1,2-ethenediyl)bis[5-nitro-, (E)-	MeOH	245(4.23),288(3.94), 415(4.54)	73-2511-79
$C_{10}H_6N_2S$			
Naphtho[1,8-de]-1,2,3-thiadiazine	hexane	269(3.83),278(3.83), 289(3.74),321(3.73), 326(3.72),336(3.65), 352(3.60),450(3.08), 474s(3.00),506s(2.67), 516s(2.49)	35-7684-79
$C_{10}H_6N_2S_2$			
[1,4]Dithiino[2,3-b:5,6-b']dipyridine	MeOH	225s(--),255(4.10), 300(3.74)	88-5035-79
$C_{10}H_6N_2Se$			
Naphtho[2,3-c][1,2,5]selenadiazole	H_2O	378.5(4.26)	86-0015-79
protonated	H_2O	397.5(4.24)	86-0015-79
diprotonated	H_2O	404(4.14)	86-0015-79
$C_{10}H_6O_2$			
1,2-Naphthalenedione	MeOH	249(4.28),337(3.30), 396(3.23)	18-1796-79
	heptane	245(--),251(--), 326(--),338(--), 382(--)	18-1796-79
$C_{10}H_6O_3$			
4H-1-Benzopyran-2-carboxaldehyde, 4-oxo-	EtOH	228(4.09),300(3.90)	118-0889-79
$C_{10}H_6S$			
Benzo[3,4]cyclobuta[1,2-b]thiophene	EtOH	207(3.80),226(3.90),	88-3571-79

Compound	Solvent	$\lambda_{max}(\log \epsilon)$	Ref.
Benzo[3,4]cyclobuta[1,2-b]thiophene (cont.)		272(3.53),283(3.55), 301(3.40),327(3.08)	88-3571-79
$C_{10}H_6S_2$			
Benzo[1,2-b:4,5-b']dithiophene	EtOH	247(4.62),254(4.69), 290(3.95),300(3.88), 320(3.83),334(3.99)	117-0247-79
$C_{10}H_7ClN_2O$			
1H-Imidazole-4-carboxaldehyde, 5-chloro-1-phenyl-	EtOH	267(4.1)	103-0544-79
	$CHCl_3$	268(4.2)	103-0544-79
$C_{10}H_7ClN_4$			
1,2,4,5-Tetrazino[6,1-a]isoindole, 6-chloro-3-methyl-	C_6H_{12} and MeOH	253(4.13),274(3.74), 307(4.06),334(3.75), 341(3.83),345(3.77), 459(3.61)	24-1981-79
$C_{10}H_7ClO_2$			
1H-2-Benzopyran-1-one, 6-chloro-3-methyl-	EtOH	227(5.21),266(4.54)	2-0295-79A
1H-2-Benzopyran-1-one, 8-chloro-3-methyl-	EtOH	225(5.2),260(4.49)	2-0295-79A
1H-Inden-1-one, 4-chloro-2,3-dihydro-7-hydroxy-2-methylene-	$CHCl_3$	275(3.86),348(3.57)	107-0129-79
$C_{10}H_7Cl_3O$			
1H-Indene, 1,1,3-trichloro-2-methoxy-	hexane	287(3.46),324(3.18)	104-1121-79
$C_{10}H_7F_6IO$			
Benzenemethanol, 2-iodo-5-methyl-α,α-bis(trifluoromethyl)-	pentane	199(4.31),229(3.99), 275(3.10)	44-1779-79
$C_{10}H_7F_9N_2O_2$			
Pyrimidine, 2,4-dimethoxy-5-(nonafluorobutyl)-	pH 1	265(--)	48-0449-79
	pH 14	264.5(3.88)	48-0449-79
2,4(1H,3H)-Pyrimidinedione, 1,3-dimethyl-5-(nonafluorobutyl)-	pH 1	269(--)	48-0449-79
	pH 14	270(3.86)	48-0449-79
$C_{10}H_7NO_2$			
2-Quinolinecarboxylic acid	pH 1	322(4.22)	149-0251-79B
	pH 4.5	318(3.08)	149-0251-79B
	pH 12	285(3.90)	149-0251-79B
$C_{10}H_7NO_2S$			
6H-1,3-Thiazin-6-one, 4-hydroxy-2-phenyl-	EtOH	246(4.38)	103-0037-79
$C_{10}H_7NO_2S_4$			
1,2-Dithiolo[4,3-b][1,4]benzothiazine-3(9H)-thione, 9-methyl-, 4,4-dioxide	DMSO	260(3.3),355(3.4), 400(3.2)	83-0302-79
$C_{10}H_7NO_3$			
2H-1-Benzopyran-2,4(3H)-dione, 3-(aminomethylene)-	EtOH	311(4.24)	131-0077-79D
2-Quinolinecarboxylic acid, 4-hydroxy-(kynurenic acid)	pH -0.3	310(3.98)	149-0251-79B
	pH 7	332(4.15)	149-0251-79B
	pH 12	320(4.01)	149-0251-79B

Compound	Solvent	λ_{max}(log ϵ)	Ref.
$C_{10}H_7NO_3S$			
Furan, 2-nitro-5-[2-(2-thienyl)ethenyl]-, (E)-	MeOH	221(4.06),297(4.07), 414(4.36)	73-2096-79
$C_{10}H_7NO_4$			
3-Isoxazolecarboxylic acid, 5-(2-hydroxyphenyl)-	EtOH	220(4.10),263(3.68), 272(4.05),305(4.02)	56-0229-79
$C_{10}H_7N_3$			
Propanedinitrile, [(phenylamino)methylene]-	hexane	223(--),313(--)	131-0077-79D
	EtOH	315(4.42)	131-0077-79D
5H-Pyrimido[5,4-b]indole	EtOH	212(4.41),239(4.33), 257(4.31),298(4.16), 349(3.41)	103-0808-79
$C_{10}H_7N_3O$			
3-Quinolinecarbonitrile, 4-amino-1,2-dihydro-2-oxo-	DMF	303s(3.92),315(3.99), 329s(3.84),345s(3.71)	48-0695-79
$C_{10}H_7N_3O_2$			
1,2,4-Triazino[4,5-a]indole-1,4-dione, 2,3-dihydro-	dioxan	250(4.01),299(4.07), 311(4.05),326(4.00)	4-1217-79
$C_{10}H_7N_3O_2S$			
1,2,3-Thiadiazolium, 5-cyano-4-hydroxy-3-(4-methoxyphenyl)-, hydroxide, inner salt	EtOH	223(4.25),325(3.60), 412(4.15)	39-2349-79C
$C_{10}H_7N_3O_3$			
Sydnone, 4-cyano-3-(4-methoxyphenyl)-	CH_2Cl_2	315(4.10)	5-0063-79
$C_{10}H_7N_3S_2$			
Pyridinium, 1-(4-amino-5-cyano-2-mercapto-3-thienyl)-, hydroxide, inner salt	EtOH	239(4.10),296(4.03), 355(4.28)	95-1081-79
Pyridinium, 1-[1-cyano-2-[(cyanomethyl)-thio]-2-mercaptoethenyl]-, hydroxide, inner salt	EtOH	256(3.93),315(4.28)	95-1081-79
$C_{10}H_7N_5OS$			
Urea, N-(4-cyanophenyl)-N'-(1,3,4-thiadiazol-2-yl)-	n.s.g.	272(4.53)	87-0028-79
$C_{10}H_7N_5O_3$			
1,2,4,5-Tetrazino[6,1-a]isoindol-6(2H)-one, 3-methyl-7-nitro-	MeOH	410(3.05)	24-1981-79
	MeOH-NaOH	237(3.72),500(3.20)	24-1981-79
1,2,4,5-Tetrazino[6,1-a]isoindol-6(2H)-one, 3-methyl-10-nitro-	MeOH	271(--),375(--), 440(--)	24-1981-79
	MeOH-NaOH	445(3.80),530(3.34)	24-1981-79
$C_{10}H_8$			
Naphthalene	gas at 120°	258(3.76),265(3.75), 268(3.81),276(3.64), 279(3.68)	46-2176-79
	gas at 400°	261(3.71),267(3.74)	46-2176-79
	hexane	256(3.60),265(3.74), 275(3.78),285(3.62)	46-2176-79
$C_{10}H_8AsNO_2$			
2-Propenoic acid, 3-(4-arseninyl)-2-cyano-, methyl ester, (E)-	EtOH	247(4.00),350(4.48)	88-3141-79

Compound	Solvent	$\lambda_{max}(\log \epsilon)$	Ref.
$C_{10}H_8BrNO$			
Oxazole, 5-(4-bromophenyl)-2-methyl-	EtOH	273(4.33),279(4.35)	18-3597-79
$C_{10}H_8Br_2O_2$			
Furo[2,3-b]benzofuran, 2,3-dibromo-2,3,3a,8a-tetrahydro-, trans	CH_2Cl_2	239(3.58),285(3.51), 291(3.47)	39-2664-79C
$C_{10}H_8ClNO$			
Oxazole, 5-(4-chlorophenyl)-2-methyl-	EtOH	271(4.36),280(4.37)	18-3597-79
2-Propenenitrile, 3-(4-chlorophenyl)-3-methoxy-, (E)-	C_6H_{12}	268(4.03)	56-0839-79
	EtOH	269(3.97)	56-0839-79
(Z)-	C_6H_{12}	274(4.22)	56-0839-79
	EtOH	275(4.20)	56-0839-79 +56-2251-79
2(1H)-Quinolinone, 3-chloro-1-methyl-	EtOH	334(3.88)	4-0065-79
$C_{10}H_8ClNOS_2$			
4H-1,3-Thiazin-4-one, 6-(2-chlorophenyl)tetrahydro-2-thioxo-	EtOH	220s(3.78),254(3.88), 297(4.14)	150-0212-79S
4H-1,3-Thiazin-4-one, 6-(4-chlorophenyl)tetrahydro-2-thioxo-	EtOH	230(4.12),260(4.07), 311(4.15)	150-0212-79S
$C_{10}H_8ClN_3OS$			
Urea, N-(4-chlorophenyl)-N'-2-thiazolyl-	n.s.g.	243(4.02),268(4.43)	87-0028-79
$C_{10}H_8Cl_2O_2$			
Furo[2,3-b]benzofuran, 2,3-dichloro-2,3,3a,8a-tetrahydro-	CH_2Cl_2	230(3.30),277(3.49), 284(3.43)	39-2664-79C
$C_{10}H_8Cl_3NO_3$			
4-Cyclopentene-1,3-dione, 4,5-dichloro-2-(chloro-4-morpholinylmethylene)-	isoPrOH	249(4.21),324(4.32)	104-0454-79
$C_{10}H_8FN_3OS$			
Urea, N-(4-fluorophenyl)-N'-2-thiazolyl-	n.s.g.	233(3.93),266(4.38)	87-0028-79
$C_{10}H_8F_5NOS$			
Morpholine, 4-[(pentafluorophenyl)-thio]-	n.s.g.	212(4.00),279(3.34)	70-0315-79
$C_{10}H_8N_2$			
Bicyclo[4.2.0]octa-1,5-diene-2,5-dicarbonitrile	EtOH	302(4.12),315(4.21), 330(4.05)	138-1427-79
$C_{10}H_8N_2OS$			
Formamide, N-(4-phenyl-2-thiazolyl)-	EtOH	212(3.90),223(3.88), 267(3.65)	2-0082-79B
1H-Imidazole-4-carboxaldehyde, 5-mercapto-1-phenyl-	EtOH	297(3.6),363(3.9)	103-0544-79
	$CHCl_3$	303(3.7),385(3.5)	103-0544-79
5-Thiazolecarboxaldehyde, 2-amino-4-phenyl-	EtOH	207(4.3),226(4.4), 232(4.4),267(4.2)	2-0082-79B
Thiazolo[3,2-a]benzimidazol-6-ol, 2-methyl-	pH 1	321(3.37),370(3.5)	18-3096-79
	pH 13	310(3.48),427(3.35)	18-3096-79
	EtOH	244(3.80),272(3.74), 355(3.40)	18-3096-79
Thiazolo[3,2-a]benzimidazol-6-ol, 3-methyl-	pH 1	310(3.43),366(3.71)	18-3096-79
	pH 13	305(3.54),435(3.43)	18-3096-79
	EtOH	236(4.01),253(3.95), 357(3.56)	18-3096-79

Compound	Solvent	λ_{max}(log ε)	Ref.
$C_{10}H_8N_2O_2$			
Benzeneacetonitrile, α-(1-nitroethylidene)-, (Z)-	MeCN	300(3.75)	4-1611-79
1H-Imidazole-4-carboxaldehyde, 5-hydroxy-1-phenyl-	EtOH	225(4.1),315(4.2)	103-0544-79
	$CHCl_3$	327(3.9)	103-0544-79
4,5-Pyrimidinediol, 2-phenyl-	pH 1	244(3.98),290(4.05)	4-1423-79
	pH 11	222s(4.18),315(4.06)	4-1423-79
5-Pyrimidinol, 4-phenyl-, 3-oxide	EtOH	204(4.00),251(4.23), 319(3.72)	103-0677-79
$C_{10}H_8N_2O_2S$			
1,3-Dioxolo[4,5-g]quinazoline-8(5H)-thione, 6-methyl-	EtOH	223s(4.47),228(4.49), 260s(4.12),271(4.18), 354s(4.04),370(4.22), 381(4.15),385(4.15)	1-0079-79
1(4H)-Pyridinecarbothioamide, 4-ethynyl-3,5-diformyl-	EtOH	212(4.11),261(4.22), 299(4.34),340(3.87)	49-0613-79
2,4(1H,3H)-Pyrimidinedione, 5-(phenylthio)-	MeOH	246(4.31),300s(3.74)	4-0567-79
$C_{10}H_8N_2O_2Se$			
2,4(1H,3H)-Pyrimidinedione, 5-(phenylseleno)-	MeOH	243(4.02),263s(3.94), 300(3.42)	4-0567-79
$C_{10}H_8N_2O_3$			
Acetamide, N-(2,3-dihydro-1,3-dioxo-1H-isoindol-4-yl)-	dioxan	225(4.50),252(4.16), 342(3.66)	4-0225-79
Oxazole, 2-methyl-5-(3-nitrophenyl)-	EtOH	262(4.42)	18-3597-79
Oxazole, 2-methyl-5-(4-nitrophenyl)-	EtOH	233(4.02),327(4.26)	18-3597-79
2-Propenenitrile, 3-methoxy-3-(4-nitrophenyl)-, (E)-	C_6H_{12}	226(4.13),292(4.05)	56-2251-79
	EtOH	226(4.08),295(3.98)	56-2251-79
(Z)-	C_6H_{12}	225(4.13),296(4.06)	56-2251-79
	EtOH	229(4.08),299(4.07)	56-2251-79
1(4H)-Pyridinecarboxamide, 4-ethynyl-3,5-diformyl-	EtOH	226(4.21),255(4.17), 261s(4.14),300(3.82)	49-0613-79
$C_{10}H_8N_2O_3S$			
1,2,3-Thiadiazolium, 5-formyl-4-hydroxy-3-(4-methoxyphenyl)-	EtOH	232(4.25),305(3.71), 405(3.95)	39-2349-79C
$C_{10}H_8N_2O_3S_2$			
Acetamide, N-(3'-nitro[2,2'-bithiophen]-5-yl)-	EtOH	424.8(3.85)	103-0864-79
Acetamide, N-(4-nitro[2,2'-bithiophen]-5-yl)-	EtOH	400(4.04)	103-0864-79
Acetamide, N-(5'-nitro[2,2'-bithiophen]-5-yl)-	EtOH	451.2(4.29)	103-0864-79
$C_{10}H_8N_2O_4$			
[2,2'-Bipyridine]-3,3',4,4'-tetrol	pH 1	213(--),250(--), 305(--)	88-1931-79
	pH 13	243(--),260(--), 285(--),385(--), 407(--)	88-1931-79
	MeOH	219(4.35),344(3.90), 390(3.38)	88-1931-79
$C_{10}H_8N_2O_4S$			
2,1,3-Benzothiadiazole-5,6-dicarboxylic acid, dimethyl ester	MeOH	238(4.39),311(4.04)	88-4493-79

Compound	Solvent	$\lambda_{max}(\log \epsilon)$	Ref.
$C_{10}H_8N_2O_6$			
[5,5'-Bioxazole]-4,4'-dicarboxylic acid, dimethyl ester	MeOH	276(3.92)	5-1370-79
[2,2'-Bipyridine]-3,3',4,4'-tetrol, 1,1'-dioxide (orellanine)	MeOH	219(4.34),248(4.12), 282(3.92),352(3.86)	88-1931-79
	pH 1	213(--),265(--), 290(--)	88-1931-79
	pH 13	234(--),292(--), 319(--)	88-1931-79
Furan, 2,2'-(1,2-ethanediyl)bis[5-nitro-	MeOH	206(4.13),228(3.99), 321(4.40)	73-2511-79
$C_{10}H_8N_4O$			
1,2,4,5-Tetrazino[6,1-a]isoindol-6(2H)-one, 3-methyl-	MeOH	225(4.20),260(4.00), 340(3.64),417(3.36)	24-1981-79
	MeOH-NaOH	382(3.69),502(3.44)	24-1981-79
$C_{10}H_8N_4O_3S$			
Acetamide, 2-cyano-2-[[[(4-nitrophenyl)methyl]thio]imino]-	MeCN	277(4.04),328(4.05)	5-1534-79
3-Isothiazolecarboxamide, 4-amino-5-(4-nitrophenyl)-	MeCN	250s(3.90),279(3.94), 387(4.03)	5-1534-79
Urea, N-(4-nitrophenyl)-N'-2-thiazolyl-	n.s.g.	245(4.07),324(4.38)	87-0028-79
$C_{10}H_8N_4O_4$			
2,6(1H,3H)-Pyridinedione, 5-amino-3-(5-amino-1,6-dihydro-2,6-dioxo-3(2H)-pyridinylidene)-	pyridine	268(4.06),602(4.37)	118-0948-79
$C_{10}H_8N_6O$			
1,2,4-Triazolo[3,4-f][1,2,4]triazin-8(5H)-one, 6-amino-3-phenyl-	H_2O	247(4.38)	4-0555-79
$C_{10}H_8N_6OS$			
1,2,4-Triazolo[3,4-b]-1,3,4-thiadiazolium, 3-methyl-6-(nitrosoamino)-2-phenyl-, hydroxide, inner salt	EtOH	312(4.03)	94-1688-79
$C_{10}H_8O$			
1H-Inden-1-one, 2-methyl-	hexane	236(4.64),242(4.70), 306(3.00),316(3.04), 330(2.99),388(2.76), 396(2.75)	18-1796-79
	benzene	319(3.10),331(2.97), 397(2.75)	18-1796-79
	MeOH	237(4.63),242(4.68), 319(3.14),402(2.69)	18-1796-79
$C_{10}H_8OSSe$			
Benzo[b]thiophene-2-carboxaldehyde, 3-(methylseleno)-	$CHCl_3$	308(4.18)	103-0731-79
Benzo[b]thiophene-3-carboxaldehyde, 2-(methylseleno)-	$CHCl_3$	318(3.85)	103-0731-79
$C_{10}H_8O_2$			
4H-Pyran, 4-(4H-pyran-4-ylidene)-	MeCN	316(4.60),332(4.71)	44-0880-79
$C_{10}H_8O_3$			
1H-2-Benzopyran-1-one, 7-hydroxy-3-methyl-	EtOH	227s(4.5),270(4.0), 350(3.70)	2-0360-79A

Compound	Solvent	λ_{max}(log ε)	Ref.
2H-1-Benzopyran-2-one, 7-hydroxy-4-methyl-	MeOH	323(4.18)	73-2211-79
	NH_3	365(4.31)	73-2211-79
4H-1-Benzopyran-4-one, 2-(hydroxymethyl)-	EtOH	230(4.04),296(3.87)	118-0889-79
Cyclopenta[c]pyran-7-carboxaldehyde, 4-(hydroxymethyl)-	EtOH	287(4.19)	83-0555-79
$C_{10}H_8O_3S_3$			
Benzo[b]thiophene-2-carbodithioic acid, 3-hydroxy-, methyl ester, 1,1-dioxide	EtOH	244(4.05),287(3.83), 325(3.94)	95-0038-79
$C_{10}H_8O_4$			
4H-1-Benzopyran-4-one, 5,7-dihydroxy-2-methyl-	MeOH	255(4.16),295(3.91)	102-0181-79
$C_{10}H_8O_5$			
2H-1-Benzopyran-2-one, 7,8-dihydroxy-6-methoxy- (fraxetin)	MeOH	218(3.34),260s(2.54), 341(3.07)	36-0247-79
	MeOH	213(4.44),230s(4.11), 256(3.65),340(3.89)	102-0688-79
1(3H)-Isobenzofuranone, 3-acetyl-5,7-dihydroxy-	MeOH	258(4.03),295(3.62)	39-0337-79C
$C_{10}H_8S_2$			
Thiophene, 2,2'-(1,2-ethenediyl)bis-	DMF	353(4.34)	61-0417-79
	KBr	352(--)	61-0417-79
4H-Thiopyran, 4-(4H-thiopyran-4-ylidene)-	MeCN	346s(4.25),367(4.63), 386(4.81)	44-0880-79
$C_{10}H_9BrN_2$			
Pyrimidine, 5-bromo-1,4-dihydro-4-phenyl-	EtOH	293(3.63)	39-1228-79C
$C_{10}H_9BrN_2OS$			
4(5H)-Thiazolone, 2-[(4-bromophenyl)-methylamino]-	MeOH	253(4.33)	104-1344-79
	70% dioxan	255(4.35)	104-1344-79
$C_{10}H_9BrN_2O_2$			
2-Pyrrolidinone, 3-[(5-bromo-3-pyridinyl)carbonyl]-	EtOH	234(3.76),285(3.45)	44-4332-79
$C_{10}H_9BrN_4$			
1H-Imidazole, 2-[(4-bromophenyl)azo]-1-methyl-	MeOH	242(3.85),368(4.24), 380(4.20),440s(3.41)	19-0249-79
$C_{10}H_9BrO_2$			
1,2-Propanedione, 1-[2-(bromomethyl)-phenyl]-	CCl_4	415(1.6)	39-0508-79C
$C_{10}H_9BrO_3$			
2,5-Cyclohexadien-1-one, 2-bromo-6-methoxy-4-(2-oxopropylidene)-	EtOH	345(4.15)	39-1326-79C
Furo[2,3-b]benzofuran-2-ol, 3-bromo-2,3,3a,8a-tetrahydro-	CH_2Cl_2	233(3.48),281(3.55), 287(3.50)	39-2664-79C
$C_{10}H_9ClN_2O$			
Pyrazole, 4-chloro-5-methyl-3-phenyl-, 1-oxide	$CHCl_3$	256(4.34),347(3.17)	44-4438-79
1H-Pyrrolo[2,3-b]pyridine, 1-acetyl-6-chloro-4-methyl-	n.s.g.	233(4.25),256(3.97)	103-0310-79

Compound	Solvent	$\lambda_{max}(\log \epsilon)$	Ref.
4(1H)-Quinazolinone, 6-chloro-1,2-dimethyl-	80% EtOH	230(4.63),272-316(4.2-3.8)	42-0708-79
4(1H)-Quinazolinone, 7-chloro-1,2-dimethyl-	80% EtOH	233(4.54),274s(4.15), 307(3.87)	42-0708-79
$C_{10}H_9ClN_4$			
1H-Pyrazole, 3-chloro-5-methyl-4-(phenylazo)-	EtOH	222(4.47),329(4.85)	48-0127-79
$C_{10}H_9ClN_4O_3$			
Pyrido[3,2-d]pyrimidine-6-carboxylic acid, 4-amino-8-chloro-2-methoxy-, methyl ester	pH 1	220(4.55),239(4.45), 308(3.92),318(4.05)	44-0435-79
	pH 7	224(4.44),248(4.45), 308(3.89),336(4.00)	44-0435-79
	pH 11	244(4.40),295(3.83), 336(3.91)	44-0435-79
$C_{10}H_9ClO_2$			
1H-2-Benzopyran-1-one, 6-chloro-3,4-dihydro-3-methyl-	EtOH	242(4.29),282(2.98)	2-0295-79A
1H-2-Benzopyran-1-one, 8-chloro-3,4-dihydro-3-methyl-	EtOH	237(3.85),292(3.00)	2-0295-79A
2-Propenoic acid, 3-(4-chlorophenyl)-, methyl ester, (E)-	MeCN	282(4.39)	88-0863-79
$C_{10}H_9ClO_3$			
Furo[2,3-b]benzofuran-2-ol, 3-chloro-2,3,3a,8a-tetrahydro-	CH_2Cl_2	233(3.29),282(3.51), 288(3.44)	39-2664-79C
$C_{10}H_9F_3N_2O_4S$			
Ceph-2-em-4-carboxylic acid, 3-methyl-7-(trifluoroacetamido)-, (4R,6R,7R)-	THF	222(3.76),249s(3.62)	39-1629-79C
Ceph-3-em-4-carboxylic acid, 3-methyl-7-(trifluoroacetamido)-, (6R,7R)-	EtOH	259(3.86)	39-1629-79C
$C_{10}H_9F_6N_3O_3$			
Acetamide, 2,2,2-trifluoro-N-methyl-N-[4-methyl-2-[[(trifluoroacetyl)amino]methyl]-5-oxazolyl]-	MeOH	208(3.99),212(4.02)	5-0973-79
Ethanimidic acid, 2,2,2-trifluoro-N-[4-methyl-2-[[(trifluoroacetyl)amino]-methyl]-5-oxazolyl-, methyl ester	MeOH	216(3.93),285(4.07)	5-0973-79
$C_{10}H_9N$			
Bicyclo[4.2.1]nona-2,4,7-triene-9-carbonitrile, anti	$CHCl_3$	257(3.64),266(3.62), 276(3.38)	24-0175-79
syn	EtOH	215(3.49),225s(3.38), 246s(3.53),255(3.65), 264(3.61),275(3.36)	24-0175-79
Bicyclo[6.1.0]nona-2,4,6-triene-9-carbonitrile, (1α,8α,9α)-	EtOH	242(3.63)	24-0175-79
$C_{10}H_9NO$			
Benzeneacetonitrile, α-(hydroxymethylene)-4-methyl-	EtOH	265(4.31)	22-0017-79
Benzenepropanenitrile, 4-methyl-β-oxo-	C_6H_{12}	256(4.23)	56-2251-79
	EtOH	256(4.20)	56-2251-79
1H-Indole-7-carboxaldehyde, 1-methyl-	MeOH	226(4.38),247(4.34), 340(3.92)	103-0276-79
Oxazole, 2-methyl-5-phenyl-	EtOH	265(4.29),272(4.29)	18-3597-79

Compound	Solvent	λ_{max}(log ε)	Ref.
2-Propenenitrile, 3-methoxy-3-phenyl-, (E)-	C_6H_{12}	265(3.96)	56-0839-79
	EtOH	263(4.06)	56-0839-79
(Z)-	C_6H_{12}	269(4.15)	56-0839-79
	EtOH	269(4.21)	56-0839-79
			56-2251-79
$C_{10}H_9NOS$			
4H-1,4-Benzothiazine, 4-acetyl-	EtOH	213(3.89),238(4.03), 265(3.98),290(3.59)	94-1982-79
$C_{10}H_9NOS_2$			
Acetamide, N-[2,2'-bithiophen]-5-yl-	EtOH	334.2(4.23)	103-0864-79
4H-1,3-Thiazin-4-one, tetrahydro-6-phenyl-2-thioxo-	EtOH	220s(4.16),260(4.18), 311(4.27)	150-0212-79S
$C_{10}H_9NO_2$			
Benzenepropanenitrile, 4-methoxy-β-oxo-	C_6H_{12}	278(4.10)	56-2251-79
	EtOH	280(4.22)	56-2251-79
2H-1-Benzopyran-2-one, 7-amino-4-methyl-	MeOH	353(4.26)	73-2211-79
	MeOH-HCl	308(3.86)	73-2211-79
	NH_3	266(4.03)	73-2211-79
5H-1,3-Dioxolo[4,5-f]indole, 7-methyl-	EtOH	228(4.11),286(3.64), 312(3.90)	39-0829-79C
1H-Isoindole-1,3(2H)-dione, 4,5-dimethyl-	EtOH	206s(4.29),224(4.65), 242s(4.12),311(3.62)	33-1525-79
3,5-Pyridinedicarboxaldehyde, 4-ethynyl-1,4-dihydro-1-methyl-	EtOH	207s(4.05),232(4.34), 253(3.91),377(4.03)	49-0613-79
2,4-Pyrrolidinedione, 5-phenyl-	EtOH-NaOH	267(4.35)	142-0477-79B
$C_{10}H_9NO_3$			
2H-1-Benzopyran-2-one, 4-(aminomethyl)-7-hydroxy-	MeOH	322(4.16)	73-2211-79
	NH_3	365(4.28)	73-2211-79
hydrochloride	MeOH	326(4.13)	73-2211-79
2-Propenoic acid, 3-(3-isocyano-6-oxabicyclo[3.1.0]hex-3-en-1-yl)-, methyl ester, (E)-	MeOH	225(4.19)	77-1061-79
$C_{10}H_9NO_3S$			
3H-Thiazolo[3,4-a]pyridine-1-carboxylic acid, 3-oxo-, ethyl ester	EtOH	240(3.85),305(3.8), 395(3.85)	2-0486-79B
$C_{10}H_9NO_4$			
2-Propenoic acid, 3-(4-nitrophenyl)-, methyl ester, (E)-	MeCN	303(4.30)	88-0863-79
(Z)-	MeCN	298(4.16)	88-0863-79
$C_{10}H_9NSe$			
3-Indolizinecarboselenoaldehyde, 2-methyl-	C_6H_{12}	236(4.31),263(3.90), 271(3.97),316s(3.83), 327(4.01),350(3.60), 360s(3.57),371(3.53), 467(4.42),472(4.40), 645(2.28),700(2.55)	39-2334-79C
$C_{10}H_9N_3O$			
3,5-Pyridinedicarbonitrile, 2-ethoxy-6-methyl-	n.s.g.	298(3.83)	73-3288-79
$C_{10}H_9N_3OS$			
Acetamide, 2-cyano-2-[[(phenylmethyl)-thio]imino]-	MeCN	256(3.47),325(3.97)	5-1534-79

Compound	Solvent	λ_{max}(log ε)	Ref.
1,3,4-Thiadiazolo[3,2-a]benzimidazol-6-ol, 2-ethyl-	pH 1	305(3.73),370(3.65)	18-2033-79
	pH 13	307(3.58),460(3.61)	18-2033-79
	EtOH	232(4.27),251(3.75), 359(3.71)	18-2033-79
1,3,5-Triazin-2(1H)-one, 3,4-dihydro-6-(4-methylphenyl)-4-thioxo-	dioxan	260(4.15),294(4.37)	18-3728-79
Urea, N-phenyl-N'-2-thiazolyl-	n.s.g.	234(4.02),267(4.43)	87-0028-79
$C_{10}H_9N_3OS_2$			
Pyridinium, 1-[4-amino-5-(aminocarbonyl)-2-mercapto-3-thienyl]-, hydroxide, inner salt	EtOH	248(4.19),293(4.04), 352(4.35)	95-1081-79
Pyridinium, 1-[2-[(2-amino-2-oxoethyl)thio]-1-cyano-2-mercaptoethenyl]-, hydroxide, inner salt	EtOH	267(4.59),325(4.66)	95-1081-79
1H-Thieno[3,4-b][1,4]diazepine-6-carbonitrile, 2,3-dihydro-4-methyl-8-(methylthio)-2-oxo-	EtOH	230(4.19),312(4.05)	142-0401-79
1H-Thieno[3,4-b][1,4]diazepine-6-carbonitrile, 4,5-dihydro-2-methyl-8-(methylthio)-4-oxo-	EtOH	253(4.11),280(4.17), 338(4.01)	142-0401-79
$C_{10}H_9N_3O_2$			
1H-Imidazole, 2-methyl-1-(4-nitrophenyl)-	EtOH	279(3.98)	78-1331-79
2,4(1H,3H)-Pyrimidinedione, 5-(2-aminophenyl)-	EtOH	238(4.05),264(3.96)	39-2902-79C
$C_{10}H_9N_3O_2S$			
1,3-Dioxolo[4,5-g]quinazoline-8(7H)-thione, 7-amino-6-methyl-	EtOH	226s(4.32),230(4.34), 254s(4.08),276(4.17), 342s(3.91),358(4.07), 370s(4.03),375(4.05)	1-0079-79
1,3,5-Triazin-2(1H)-one, 3,4-dihydro-6-(4-methoxyphenyl)-4-thioxo-	dioxan	260(4.18),295(4.41)	18-3728-79
$C_{10}H_9N_3O_3S$			
Benzamide, N-(2,3-dihydro-3-oxo-1,2,4-thiadiazol-5-yl)-4-methoxy-	dioxan	229(4.06),269(3.88), 317(3.96)	18-3728-79
1,2,3-Thiadiazolium, 5-(aminocarbonyl)-4-hydroxy-3-(4-methoxyphenyl)-, hydroxide, inner salt	EtOH	225(4.0),320(3.0), 405(3.78)	39-2349-79C
1,2,3-Thiadiazolium, 4-hydroxy-5-[(hydroxyimino)methyl]-3-(4-methoxyphenyl)-, hydroxide, inner salt	EtOH	234(3.70),318(2.78), 413(3.48)	39-2349-79C
4-Thiazolidinone, 3-methyl-2-[(4-nitrophenyl)imino]-	H_2O	316(4.07)	104-1344-79
	MeOH	310(4.15)	104-1344-79
	dioxan	315(4.15)	104-1344-79
	70% dioxan	315(4.14)	104-1344-79
4(5H)-Thiazolone, 2-[methyl(4-nitrophenyl)amino]-	H_2O	235(4.26)	104-1344-79
	MeOH	230(4.23)	104-1344-79
	dioxan	228(4.19),300(3.96)	104-1344-79
	70% dioxan	232(4.25)	104-1344-79
$C_{10}H_9N_3O_4$			
Benzenamine, N-(1-methyl-2-propynyl)-2,4-dinitro-, (R)-	C_6H_{12}	261(3.98),325(4.22), 388(3.71)	78-2413-79
	MeOH	263(3.99),342(4.22), 395s(3.79)	78-2413-79
Sydnone, 4-[(hydroxyimino)methyl]-3-(4-methoxyphenyl)-	CH_2Cl_2	227(4.11),275(3.87), 335(3.96)	5-0063-79

Compound	Solvent	λ max (log ε)	Ref.
$C_{10}H_9N_3O_5$			
1H-Pyrrolo[3,2-d]pyrimidine-6-acetic acid, 2,3,4,5-tetrahydro-1,3-dimethyl- ,2,4-trioxo-	EtOH	230(3.34),285(3.30), 330(3.06)	44-3830-79
$C_{10}H_9N_3S$			
Thieno[2,3-b]pyridine-2-carbonitrile, 3-amino-4,6-dimethyl-	EtOH	232(4.01),274(4.38), 342(3.71)	103-1070-79
$C_{10}H_9N_5O$			
Imidazo[1,2-c]pteridine, 6-ethoxy-	pH -4.0	218(4.31),255s(3.82), 354(4.05)	18-0867-79
	pH 0.0	215(4.14),235s(3.97), 263(3.56),330(4.00), 345s(3.90)	18-0867-79
	pH 4.5	220(4.34),250s(3.82), 278(3.37),342(4.01)	18-0867-79
Imidazo[1,2-c]pteridin-6(4H)-one, 2,3-dimethyl-	pH -0.5	209(4.22),232(4.11), 262(3.75),270s(3.67), 341(4.25),354(4.22)	18-0867-79
	pH 4.5	217(4.29),241(3.93), 270s(3.51),346(4.26)	18-0867-79
	pH 10.0	222(4.48),254(3.99), 280s(3.71),365(4.20)	18-0867-79
$C_{10}H_9N_5O_2$			
1H-Imidazole, 1-methyl-2-[(4-nitrophenyl)azo]-	MeOH	224(4.10),274(4.00), 362(4.26),384(4.32), 460s(3.53)	19-0249-79
$C_{10}H_9N_5O_3$			
9H-Purine-9-acetaldehyde, 6-amino-α-[(1-formylethenyl)oxy]-, (R)-	pH 7.0	260(4.13)	69-2838-79
$C_{10}H_9N_7O_2S$			
1,2,4-Triazolo[4,3-a]pyrazine, 3-methyl-8-[(1-methyl-4-nitro-1H-imidazol-5-yl)thio]-	EtOH	245(4.21),300(4.03)	44-1028-79
$C_{10}H_{10}$			
Naphthalene, 1,2-dihydro-	gas at 120°	251(4.04)	46-2176-79
	gas at 400°	251(3.98)	46-2176-79
	hexane	258(3.96)	46-2176-79
$C_{10}H_{10}BrNO_2$			
2-Propenoic acid, 2-bromo-3-(2-pyridinyl)-, ethyl ester, (E)-	MeOH	200(4.01),244(3.97)	22-0559-79
(Z)-	MeOH	258(4.06),286(3.92)	22-0559-79
$C_{10}H_{10}BrNO_4$			
Benzene, 1-bromo-4,5-dimethoxy-2-(2-nitroethenyl)-	MeOH	260(4.39),365(4.5)	2-0198-79
$C_{10}H_{10}BrN_3$			
1H-1,2,3-Triazole, 4-(bromomethyl)-1-(phenylmethyl)-	EtOH	236(3.36)	87-0496-79
$C_{10}H_{10}BrN_3OS$			
1,3,4-Thiadiazolo[3,2-a]benzimidazolium, 9-ethyl-6-hydroxy-, bromide	EtOH	285(4.15),505(3.80)	18-2033-79

Compound	Solvent	λ_{max}(log ε)	Ref.
$C_{10}H_{10}Br_2$			
3a,7a-Methano-1H-indene, 8,8-dibromo-2,3-dihydro-	C_6H_{12}	235(3.20)	88-4141-79
$C_{10}H_{10}ClNO_2$			
Acetamide, N-[4-(chloroacetyl)phenyl]-	MeOH	295(4.32)	65-2189-79
Benzene, 1-(1-chloro-2-methyl-1-propenyl)-3-nitro-	MeOH	253(4.15),300(3.04)	12-1949-79
$C_{10}H_{10}ClN_3$			
1H-1,2,3-Triazole, 4-(chloromethyl)-1-(phenylmethyl)-	EtOH	231(3.10)	87-0496-79
$C_{10}H_{10}Cl_2$			
Benzene, 1,3-dichloro-5-(2-methyl-1-propenyl)-	MeOH	253(4.13)	44-1458-79
$C_{10}H_{10}Cl_2N_2O_4$			
2,5-Pyrazinedimethanol, 3,6-dichloro-, diacetate	EtOH	222(4.13),293(3.93)	94-2980-79
$C_{10}H_{10}Cl_2Zr$			
Zirconium, dichlorobis(η^5-2,4-cyclopentadien-1-yl)-	$CHCl_3$	254(4.25),292(4.25), 332(3.95)	101-0353-79S
$C_{10}H_{10}Cl_3N_3O_2$			
Acetamide, 2,2,2-trichloro-N-[[nitroso-(phenylmethyl)amino]methyl]-	EtOH	236(4.14),368(1.80)	94-0682-79
$C_{10}H_{10}FN_3$			
1H-1,2,3-Triazole, 4-(fluoromethyl)-1-(phenylmethyl)-	EtOAc	228(3.00)	87-0496-79
$C_{10}H_{10}F_3N_3O_2$			
Acetamide, 2,2,2-trifluoro-N-[[nitroso-(phenylmethyl)amino]methyl]-	EtOH	236(3.96),369(1.81)	94-0682-79
$C_{10}H_{10}F_5NS$			
Benzenesulfenamide, N,N-diethyl-2,3,4,5,6-pentafluoro-	n.s.g.	216(3.87),271(3.35)	70-0315-79
$C_{10}H_{10}IN_3$			
1H-1,2,3-Triazole, 4-(iodomethyl)-1-(phenylmethyl)-	EtOH	241(3.60)	87-0496-79
$C_{10}H_{10}N_2$			
1H-Benzimidazole, 1-ethenyl-2-methyl-	isooctane	242(4.33),280(3.73), 290(3.65)	65-1225-79
	EtOH	232(4.11),255(3.85), 277(3.59)	65-1225-79
$C_{10}H_{10}N_2O$			
1H-Benzimidazole-2-methanol, 1-ethenyl-	EtOH	232(4.22),260(3.96), 283(3.73),292(3.54)	70-1931-79
Butyrophenone, γ-azido-	heptane	240(4.00),278(3.00), 325(1.70)	35-0378-79
5-Isoxazolamine, 3-methyl-4-phenyl-	MeOH	255(4.15)	4-1611-79
4(1H)-Quinazolinone, 1,2-dimethyl-	80% EtOH	229(4.24),265-305(3.7-3.9)	42-0708-79
8-Quinolinol, 2-(methylamino)-	acid	240(4.14),266(4.45), 308(3.91)	123-0070-79

Compound	Solvent	λ_{max}(log ε)	Ref.
8-Quinolinol, 2-(methylamino)- (cont.)	neutral	244(4.23),263(4.33), 281(4.29),332(3.64)	123-0070-79
	base	234(4.20),275(4.50), 360(3.37)	123-0070-79
$C_{10}H_{10}N_2OS$			
Acetamide, N-(6-methylthieno[2,3-b]pyridin-4-yl)-	DMF	294(3.96)	49-1189-79
Formamide, N-(4,6-dimethylthieno[2,3-b]pyridin-3-yl)-	EtOH	237(4.35),288(4.24)	103-1074-79
4-Thiazolidinone, 3-methyl-2-(phenylimino)-	H_2O	217(4.34),267(3.79)	104-1344-79
	MeOH	268(3.80)	104-1344-79
	dioxan	269(3.83)	104-1344-79
	70% dioxan	270(3.77)	104-1344-79
4(5H)-Thiazolone, 2-(methylphenylamino)-	H_2O	250(4.29)	104-1344-79
	MeOH	252(4.28)	104-1344-79
	dioxan	255(4.20)	104-1344-79
	70% dioxan	252(4.25)	104-1344-79
3-Thiophenecarbonitrile, 2-[(1-methyl-3-oxo-1-butenyl)amino]-	EtOH	227(4.01),250(3.59), 359(4.11)	49-1189-79
$C_{10}H_{10}N_2OS_2$			
Carbamothioic acid, (3-methyl-2(3H)-benzothiazolylidene)-, S-methyl ester	EtOH	283(3.68),319(4.55)	94-2879-79
$C_{10}H_{10}N_2O_2$			
2(5H)-Furanone, 4-(2-phenylhydrazino)-	EtOH	257(4.36)	4-0505-79
3-Pyridinecarbonitrile, 5-acetyl-2-methoxy-6-methyl-	EtOH	220(4.52),241s(3.99), 259(4.16),294(4.06)	39-0677-79C
$C_{10}H_{10}N_2O_2S$			
2,6-Methano-4H-1,3,5-benzoxadiazocine-4-thione, 2,3,5,6-tetrahydro-9-hydroxy-	EtOH	250(4.20),276s(3.52), 281s(3.42)	24-0001-79
4(5H)-Thiazolone, 2-[(4-methoxyphenyl)-amino]-	MeOH	265s(4.15),277(4.17)	104-1344-79
	70% dioxan	265s(4.12),275(4.13)	104-1344-79
$C_{10}H_{10}N_2O_3$			
3-Pyridinecarboxylic acid, 5-cyano-6-methoxy-2-methyl-, methyl ester (same in acid or base)	EtOH	210(4.51),212(4.51), 250(4.11),290(3.87), 294(3.86)	39-0677-79C
$C_{10}H_{10}N_2O_4$			
2-Propanone, O-(3-nitrobenzoyl)oxime	MeOH	222(4.38),250(3.91)	12-1949-79
$C_{10}H_{10}N_2O_5$			
1-Propanone, 2-methyl-2-nitro-1-(3-nitrophenyl)-	MeOH	219(3.40),258s(2.86)	12-1949-79
1-Propanone, 2-methyl-2-nitro-1-(4-nitrophenyl)-	MeOH	260(4.15)	12-1487-79
$C_{10}H_{10}N_2S$			
2H-[1,3]Thiazino[3,2-a]benzimidazole, 3,4-dihydro-	CH_2Cl_2	235(4.12),264(3.95), 270(3.97),292(4.13), 300(4.16)	18-0930-79
2-Thiazolamine, N-methyl-4-phenyl-	EtOH	206(4.2),234(4.4), 288(3.8)	2-0082-79B
$C_{10}H_{10}N_2S_2$			
6H-1,3,4-Thiadiazine, 2-(methylthio)-5-phenyl-	EtOH	274(3.985),321(4.069)	48-0959-79

Compound	Solvent	λ max(log ε)	Ref.
$C_{10}H_{10}N_3OS$			
1,3,4-Thiadiazolo[3,2-a]benzimidazol-ium, 4-ethyl-6-hydroxy-, bromide	EtOH	285(4.15),505(3.80)	18-2033-79
$C_{10}H_{10}N_4$			
1H-Imidazole, 1-methyl-2-(phenylazo)-	MeOH	232(3.84),360(4.28), 372(4.24),430s(3.28)	19-0249-79
3,5-Pyridinedicarbonitrile, 2-(dimeth-ylamino)-6-methyl-	n.s.g.	343(3.67)	73-3288-79
$C_{10}H_{10}N_4O$			
2H-Furo[2,3-b]indole, 3a-azido-3,3a,8,8a-tetrahydro-	EtOH	242(3.81),304(3.36)	39-3061-79C
1H-Imidazole, 2-[(4-methoxyphenyl)azo]-	MeOH	248(3.88),368(4.40), 380(4.41),406s(4.10)	19-0249-79
1,2,4,5-Tetrazino[6,1-a]isoindol-6(2H)-one, 1,10b-dihydro-3-methyl-	MeOH	223(4.06),247(3.62), 313(3.74)	24-1981-79
hydrochloride	MeOH	223(4.03),254(3.50), 280(3.51),295(3.52)	24-1981-79
$C_{10}H_{10}N_4OS$			
Hydrazinecarbothioamide, 2-(1,3-dihydro-3-oxo-2H-indol-2-ylidene)-N-methyl-	EtOH	242(4.12),267(4.27), 340(4.13),460(3.99)	104-0765-79
2,4-Pyrimidinediamine, 6-(phenylthio)-, 3-oxide	pH 0.09	197(4.51),239(4.37), 298(4.24)	12-2049-79
	pH 9.6	236(4.59),298(4.09)	12-2049-79
[1,3,4]Thiadiazino[5,6-b]indol-4a(9H)-ol, 3-(methylamino)-	EtOH	242(4.24),269s(3.73), 336(3.97),414(3.95)	104-0765-79
$C_{10}H_{10}N_4O_3$			
Pyrido[3,2-d]pyrimidine-6-carboxylic acid, 4-amino-2-methoxy-, methyl ester	pH 1	219(4.45),240(4.39), 316(4.05),330(3.99)	44-0435-79
	pH 7	249(4.49),296s(3.95), 327(4.07)	44-0435-79
	pH 11	246(4.49),295(3.94), 325(3.96)	44-0435-79
$C_{10}H_{10}N_4O_3S$			
4-Pyrimidinesulfinic acid, 2,6-diamino-, phenyl ester, 1-oxide	pH -1.22	199(4.73),234(4.50), 313(4.12)	12-2049-79
	pH 6.0	234(4.76),308(4.03)	12-2049-79
$C_{10}H_{10}N_4O_3S_3$			
5-Thia-1-azabicyclo[4.2.0]oct-2-ene-2-carboxylic acid, 7-amino-8-oxo-3-[(1,2,3-thiadiazol-5-ylthio)methyl]-, (6R-trans)-	MeOH	273(3.83),305(3.65)	87-1214-79
$C_{10}H_{10}N_4O_4$			
Hypoxanthine, 9-(5-deoxy-β-D-erythro-pent-4-enofuranosyl)-	MeOH	244(4.04),250(4.03), 267s(3.67)	44-0400-79
	MeOH-NaOH	254(4.06)	44-0400-79
$C_{10}H_{10}N_4O_4S$			
1H-Imidazole-4-sulfonamide, 5-nitro-1-(phenylmethyl)-	pH 13	310(3.75)	4-0811-79
	MeOH	235(3.69),297(3.79)	4-0811-79
1H-Imidazole-5-sulfonamide, 4-nitro-1-(phenylmethyl)-	pH 1	231s(3.67),297(3.73)	4-0811-79
	pH 13	255s(3.53),315(3.66)	4-0811-79

Compound	Solvent	$\lambda_{max}(\log \epsilon)$	Ref.
$C_{10}H_{10}N_4O_4Se_2$			
2,4(1H,3H)-Pyrimidinedione, 5,5'-diselenobis[1-methyl-	pH 1	277(3.92)	87-0618-79
	pH 7.2	277(4.10)	87-0618-79
	pH 12	272(4.03)	87-0618-79
in dithiothreitol		339(3.55)	87-0618-79
$C_{10}H_{10}N_4S$			
2,4-Pyrimidinediamine, 6-(phenylthio)-	pH 1.06	195(4.93),205(3.91), 291(4.56)	12-2049-79
	pH 9.6	206(4.82),234(4.79), 287(4.45)	12-2049-79
$C_{10}H_{10}N_5S$			
1,2,4-Triazolo[3,4-b][1,3,4]thiadiazolium, 6-amino-3-methyl-2-phenyl-, bromide	EtOH	256(4.21)	94-1688-79
$C_{10}H_{10}N_6$			
Imidazo[1,2-c]pteridin-6-amine, 2,3-dimethyl-	pH -2.5	224(4.46),270(4.06), 290s(3.91),396(4.25)	18-0867-79
	pH 1.5	219(4.41),251(4.17), 275(3.99),285s(3.96), 356(4.12)	18-0867-79
	pH 5.5	227(4.54),255(4.00), 282(3.73),358(4.22)	18-0867-79
Imidazo[1,2-c]pteridin-6-amine, N-ethyl-	pH -3.0	228(4.35),279(4.08), 293s(3.97),403(4.15)	18-0867-79
	pH 1.0	217(4.30),230s(4.17), 260(4.13),279(4.09), 282s(4.08),367(4.00)	18-0867-79
	pH 5.0	223(4.42),260s(4.01), 285s(3.76),362(4.13)	18-0867-79
$C_{10}H_{10}N_6O$			
Ethanol, 2-(imidazo[1,2-c]pteridin-6-ylamino)-	pH -3.0	228(4.37),277(4.09), 293s(3.94),399(4.17)	18-0867-79
	pH 1.0	217(4.31),258(4.14), 278(4.08),283s(4.06), 363(4.01)	18-0867-79
	pH 5.0	228(4.43),260s(4.00), 285s(3.75),361(4.14)	18-0867-79
$C_{10}H_{10}N_6O_2$			
Benzoic acid, 2-(3-amino-2,5-dihydro-5-oxo-1,2,4-triazin-6-yl)hydrazide	H_2O	224(4.48),270(3.91)	4-0555-79
$C_{10}H_{10}O$			
3-Buten-2-one, 4-phenyl-	EtOH	220(4.09),286(4.35)	12-2523-79
Tricyclo[4.3.1.0^{7,9}]deca-2,4-dien-10-one, exo	EtOH	196(3.53),257(3.41), 266(3.60),277(3.58), 318(2.74)	44-1294-79
Tricyclo[5.2.1.0^{2,4}]deca-5,8-dien-10-one, exo	EtOH	198(3.75),214s(3.51)	44-1294-79
$C_{10}H_{10}O_2$			
2-Propenal, 3-(4-methoxyphenyl)-	EtOH	326(4.43)	104-1669-79
2-Propenoic acid, 3-phenyl-, methyl ester, (E)-	MeCN	276(4.34)	88-0863-79
(Z)-	MeCN	267(3.99)	88-0863-79
2-Propenoic acid, 3-(2-methylphenyl)-	neutral	271(4.21)	19-0045-79
	cation	328(4.37)	19-0045-79

Compound	Solvent	λ_{max}(log ϵ)	Ref.
2-Propenoic acid, 3-(3-methylphenyl)-	neutral	279(4.26)	19-0045-79
	cation	337(4.41)	19-0045-79
2-Propenoic acid, 3-(4-methylphenyl)-	neutral	294(4.35)	19-0045-79
	cation	352(4.46)	19-0045-79
Tricyclo[4.2.2.0^{2,5}]dec-7-ene-3,4-dione	MeCN	275(2.25),507(1.42)	88-2347-79
$C_{10}H_{10}O_2S_2$			
Benzeneacetic acid, α-((1-thioxoethyl)-thio]-	dioxan	303(4.11),455(1.66)	24-1650-79
$C_{10}H_{10}O_2S_4$			
1,3-Dithiole-4-carboxylic acid, 2-(4-methyl-1,3-dithiol-2-ylidene)-, ethyl ester	MeCN	214(4.00),294(4.04), 303(4.06),313(4.08), 432(3.18)	44-1476-79
$C_{10}H_{10}O_3$			
1H-2-Benzopyran-1-one, 3,4-dihydro-8-hydroxy-3-methyl-, (R)- (mellein)	MeOH	246(3.73),314(3.57)	39-2048-79C
2,4,6-Cycloheptatrien-1-one, 2-acetyl-7-methoxy-	MeOH	235(4.24),330(3.84), 365(3.83)	18-1972-79
2,4,6-Cycloheptatrien-1-one, 3-acetyl-2-methoxy-	MeOH	235(4.21),330(3.87)	18-1972-79
Ethanone, 1,1'-(4-hydroxy-1,3-phenylene)bis-	EtOH-H_2SO_4	240(4.41),272(4.09), 318(3.48)	39-0478-79C
	EtOH-KOH	247(4.14),320(4.38)	39-0478-79C
2-Propenoic acid, 3-(2-methoxyphenyl)-	neutral	278(4.13)	19-0045-79
	cation	322(4.22)	19-0045-79
2-Propenoic acid, 3-(3-methoxyphenyl)-	neutral	270(4.24)	19-0045-79
	cation	323(4.33)	19-0045-79
2-Propenoic acid, 3-(4-methoxyphenyl)-	neutral	311(4.35)	19-0045-79
	cation	357(4.45)	19-0045-79
$C_{10}H_{10}O_4$			
Benzenepropanoic acid, 4-hydroxy-β-oxo-, methyl ester	EtOH	281(4.16)	12-2071-79
	EtOH-NaOH	332(4.19)	12-2071-79
1,4-Benzodioxin-5,8-dione, 2,3-dihydro-6,7-dimethyl-	MeCN	281(4.26),440(2.69)	64-0624-79B
Benzoic acid, 3-acetyl-4-hydroxy-, methyl ester	EtOH and EtOH-HCl	231(4.51),254(3.99), 321(3.45)	39-0677-79C
	EtOH-H_2SO_4	232(4.54),254(4.05), 320(3.43)	39-0478-79C
	EtOH-NaOH	227s(4.01),245(4.27), 296(4.37),357(3.79)	39-0677-79C
	EtOH-KOH	245(4.33),296(4.42), 360(3.90)	39-0478-79C
1H-2-Benzopyran-1-one, 3,4-dihydro-6,8-dihydroxy-3-methyl- (6-hydroxymellein)	EtOH	270(4.11),305(3.76)	33-1129-79
(R)-	EtOH	270(4.11),305(3.76)	33-1785-79
2-Propenoic acid, 3-(4-hydroxy-3-methoxyphenyl)- (ferulic acid)	pH 12	215(4.10),230(3.99), 248(3.81),274(3.41), 292(3.88),318(3.96), 350(4.05)	135-1004-79B
	MeOH	235(4.36),321(4.45)	106-0841-79
	EtOH	210(3.68),227(4.05), 244(3.96),265(3.65), 288(4.02),320(4.16)	135-1004-79B
$C_{10}H_{10}O_5$			
1,2-Benzenedicarboxaldehyde, 3-hydroxy-4,5-dimethoxy-	EtOH	242(4.13),250s(4.11), 300(3.83)	20-0883-79

Compound	Solvent	λ_{max}(log ε)	Ref.
1,3-Benzodioxole-5-carboxylic acid, 7-methoxy-, methyl ester	MeOH	250(3.2),280(3.5), 350(2.8)	102-0352-79
Benzoic acid, 5-acetyl-2,4-dihydroxy-, methyl ester	EtOH	243(4.60),268(4.02), 313(3.69)	39-0464-79C
$C_{10}H_{10}O_6$			
2H-Pyran-3,5-dicarboxylic acid, 6-methyl-2-oxo-, dimethyl ester	EtOH	248(3.96),320(3.90)	39-0677-79C
	EtOH-HCl	247(3.97),319(3.90)	39-0677-79C
	EtOH-NaOH	265(4.15),342(4.37)	39-0677-79C
$C_{10}H_{11}$			
Cycloheptatrienylium, cyclopropyl-, tetrafluoroborate	10% HCl	248(4.42),330(4.11)	39-1005-79B
$C_{10}H_{11}BrN_2O_4$			
Benzene, 1-(1-bromo-2-methyl-2-nitropropyl)-3-nitro-	MeOH	262(3.87)	12-1949-79
$C_{10}H_{11}BrN_2O_4S$			
Butanamide, N-[2-(aminosulfonyl)-5-bromophenyl]-3-oxo-	EtOH	226(4.45),247(4.15), 283(3.72),317(3.40)	104-1495-79
$C_{10}H_{11}BrO_4$			
Benzoic acid, 3-bromo-5,6-dimethoxy-, methyl ester	EtOH	218(4.11),306(3.24)	104-1740-79
$C_{10}H_{11}Br_2NO_2$			
2-Pyridinepropanoic acid, α,β-dibromo-, ethyl ester	MeOH	248(3.69),260(3.72)	22-0559-79
$C_{10}H_{11}Cl$			
Benzene, 1-chloro-4-(2-methyl-1-propenyl)-	MeOH	251(4.24)	44-1458-79
$C_{10}H_{11}ClF_4O_4Si$			
Silane, [(chlorotetrafluorophenoxy)-methyl](trimethoxy)-	heptane	217(4.00),268s(2.76)	70-2602-79
$C_{10}H_{11}ClN_2O$			
1H-Pyrrolo[2,3-b]pyridine, 1-acetyl-6-chloro-2,3-dihydro-4-methyl-	n.s.g.	250(4.09),300(4.09)	103-0310-79
$C_{10}H_{11}ClN_2O_4$			
Benzene, 1-(1-chloro-2-methyl-2-nitropropyl)-3-nitro-	EtOH	259(3.90)	12-1949-79
2,5-Pyrazinedimethanol, 3-chloro-, diacetate	EtOH	247s(4.15),257(4.18), 309(4.10)	94-2980-79
$C_{10}H_{11}ClN_2O_4S$			
Butanamide, N-[2-(aminosulfonyl)-5-chlorophenyl]-3-oxo-	EtOH	220(4.44),248(4.06), 282(3.69),317(3.38)	104-1495-79
$C_{10}H_{11}ClN_2O_5$			
2,5-Pyrazinedimethanol, 3-chloro-, diacetate, 1-oxide	EtOH	238(4.30),275(4.03)	94-2980-79
$C_{10}H_{11}ClN_4O$			
1,2,4-Triazin-6(1H)-one, 3-[5-chloro-2-(methylamino)phenyl]-4,5-dihydro-	MeOH	265(4.16),300(3.71), 357(3.80)	44-0088-79

Compound	Solvent	$\lambda_{max}(\log \epsilon)$	Ref.
$C_{10}H_{11}Cl_2F_3O_4Si$			
Silane, [(dichlorotrifluorophenoxy)-methyl]trimethoxy-	heptane	220(4.09),273(2.88)	70-2602-79
$C_{10}H_{11}Cl_2NO$			
2(1H)-Quinolinone, 3,8-dichloro-5,6,7,8-tetrahydro-1-methyl-	EtOH	326(4.00)	4-0065-79
$C_{10}H_{11}Cl_2NOS$			
2-Butanesulfenamide, N-(3,5-dichloro-4-oxo-2,5-cyclohexadien-1-ylidene)-	hexane	425(4.34)	138-1077-79
2-Propanesulfenamide, N-(3,5-dichloro-4-oxo-2,5-cyclohexadien-1-ylidene)-2-methyl-	hexane	424(4.53)	138-1077-79
$C_{10}H_{11}Cl_2N_5O$			
Adenine, 9-(3,5-dichloro-2,3,5-trideoxy-β-D-threo-pentofuranosyl)-	pH 1	257(4.20)	44-3100-79
	pH 13	259(4.27)	44-3100-79
$C_{10}H_{11}Cl_2N_5O_2$			
Adenine, 9-(3,5-dichloro-3,5-dideoxy-β-D-ribofuranosyl)-	MeOH	258(4.19)	23-0274-79
$C_{10}H_{11}Cl_5O_4Si$			
Silane, trimethoxy[(pentachlorophenoxy)methyl]-	heptane	215(4.98),227s(4.36), 290(2.69),300(2.72)	70-2602-79
$C_{10}H_{11}FN_2O_5$			
2-Furancarboxylic acid, 5-(5-fluoro-3,4-dihydro-2,4-dioxo-1(2H)-pyrimidinyl)tetrahydro-, methyl ester	pH 2	263(3.96)	103-0926-79
	pH 7	266(3.96)	103-0926-79
	pH 10	270(3.86)	103-0926-79
$C_{10}H_{11}F_2NO_2$			
Phenylalanine, α-(difluoromethyl)-	H_2O	251(2.15),257(2.23), 262(2.11)	44-2732-79
$C_{10}H_{11}F_2NO_3$			
Tyrosine, α-(difluoromethyl)-	M HCl	224(3.91),274(3.13), 279(3.07)	44-2732-79
$C_{10}H_{11}F_2NO_4$			
Tyrosine, α-(difluoromethyl)-3-hydroxy-	H_2O	220(3.79),280(3.43)	44-2732-79
$C_{10}H_{11}F_2NO_4S_2$			
1,1-Ethenedisulfonyl difluoride, 2-[4-(dimethylamino)phenyl]-	EtOH	435(4.75)	104-2187-79
$C_{10}H_{11}F_4O_3P$			
Phosphonic acid, (2,3,5,6-tetrafluorophenyl)-, diethyl ester	EtOH	215(3.67),279(3.12)	65-0464-79
$C_{10}H_{11}F_5O_4Si$			
Silane, trimethoxy[(pentafluorophenoxy)methyl]-	heptane	202(3.63),207(3.62), 258(2.45)	70-2602-79
$C_{10}H_{11}IN_4O_4$			
Inosine, 5'-deoxy-5'-iodo-	MeOH	245(4.08),250(4.08), 268(3.73)	44-0400-79
$C_{10}H_{11}IO_3$			
2,5-Cyclohexadiene-1,4-dione, 3-iodo-	EtOH	268(4.02),435(3.04)	44-0428-79

Compound	Solvent	λ_{max}(log ε)	Ref.
2-methyl-5-(1-methylethyl)- (cont.)			44-0428-79
$C_{10}H_{11}N$			
2,4,6-Cycloheptatriene-1-carbonitrile, 1,2-dimethyl-	C_6H_{12}	270(3.59)	24-1168-79
2,4,6-Cycloheptatriene-1-carbonitrile, 1,4-dimethyl-	C_6H_{12}	263(3.56)	24-1168-79
$C_{10}H_{11}NO$			
2,1-Benzisoxazole, 3,5,7-trimethyl-	EtOH	260(3.13),271(3.20), 283(3.30),320(3.89)	33-0271-79
Propanal, 3-imino-2-(4-methylphenyl)-	EtOH	277(4.25)	22-0017-79
2-Propenal, 3-[(4-methylphenyl)amino]-	benzene	350(4.3)	94-0403-79
	EtOH	228(3.9),296s(4.2), 324(4.5)	94-0403-79
5H-2-Pyrindine-4-carboxaldehyde, 6,7-dihydro-7-methyl-, (R)-	MeOH	232s(3.33),261(3.16), 269(3.16)	106-0577-79
$C_{10}H_{11}NO_2$			
Acetamide, N-(2-acetylphenyl)-	EtOH	258(4.07),266(4.00), 323(3.71)	33-0271-79
Acetamide, N-(4-acetylphenyl)-	MeOH	284(4.27)	65-2189-79
Acetamide, N-(2-formyl-4-methylphenyl)-	EtOH	263(3.97),271(3.96), 339(3.64)	33-0234-79
Benzene, 1-(2-methyl-1-propenyl)-4-nitro-	MeOH	316(4.08)	44-1458-79
6-Isoquinolinol, 3,4-dihydro-7-methoxy-	pH 6.0	389(4.11)	39-2744-79C
Propanoic acid, 3-(3-isocyano-2-cyclopenten-1-ylidene)-, methyl ester	ether	270(4.08)	77-1061-79
2-Propenoic acid, 3-(2-pyridinyl)-, ethyl ester	MeOH	204(3.88),248(3.88), 284(3.89)	22-0559-79
5H-2-Pyrindine-4-carboxylic acid, 6,7-dihydro-7-methyl-, (R)-	MeOH	270(3.45)	106-0577-79
$C_{10}H_{11}NO_3$			
Acetamide, N-(2-formyl-4-methoxyphenyl)-	EtOH	267(3.87),275s(--), 354(3.61)	33-0234-79
Benzaldehyde, 5-acetoxy-2-amino-3-methyl-	EtOH	260(3.86),378(3.76)	33-0234-79
Benzene, (2-ethoxy-1-nitroethenyl)-	EtOH	210(3.98),232(3.97), 298(3.66)	28-0255-79B
Ethanone, 1-(3,5-dimethyl-2-nitrophenyl)-	EtOH	290(3.31)	33-0271-79
1H-Indole-2-carboxylic acid, 4,5,6,7-tetrahydro-4-oxo-, methyl ester	MeOH	227(4.33),246(4.12), 284(4.27)	64-0102-79B
2H-Indol-2-one, 1,3-dihydro-3-hydroperoxy-1,3-dimethyl-	EtOH	257(3.78),288(3.08)	35-7332-79
1,2-Propanedione, 1-(2-methoxyphenyl)-, 1-oxime	EtOH	220(4.20),270s(3.43)	39-0156-79B
	EtOH-NaOH	284(4.23),390(1.89)	39-0156-79B
2-Pyridinepropanoic acid, β-oxo-, ethyl ester	MeCN	242(4.15),290(4.52), 324(2.78)	22-0559-79
2(1H)-Pyridinone, 3,5-diacetyl-6-methyl-	EtOH and EtOH-acid	278(4.21),345(4.00)	39-0677-79C
	EtOH-KOH	237s(4.09),298(4.34), 348(4.08)	39-0677-79C
$C_{10}H_{11}NO_4$			
Benzoic acid, 5-acetyl-2-amino-4-hydroxy-, methyl ester	EtOH and EtOH-HCl	226s(4.00),245(4.50), 277(4.03),304(4.20), 330(4.14)	39-0677-79C
	EtOH-NaOH	270(4.65),346(3.94)	39-0677-79C

Compound	Solvent	λmax(log ε)	Ref.
4-Oxa-1-azabicyclo[3.2.0]heptane-2-carboxylic acid, 7-oxo-3-(2-propenylidene)-, methyl ester	EtOH	246(4.22)	88-1889-79
3-Pyridinecarboxylic acid, 5-acetyl-1,2-dihydro-6-methyl-2-oxo-, methyl ester	EtOH and EtOH-HCl	274(4.09),327(3.85)	39-0677-79C
	EtOH-NaOH	228s(4.07),298(4.23), 320(4.12)	39-0677-79C
3-Pyridinecarboxylic acid, 5-acetyl-1,6-dihydro-2-methyl-6-oxo-, methyl ester	EtOH and EtOH-acid	264(4.18),340(3.95)	39-0677-79C
	EtOH-KOH	234s(4.18),282(4.38), 348(4.21)	39-0677-79C
$C_{10}H_{11}NO_5$			
1,3-Benzenedicarboxylic acid, 4-amino-6-hydroxy-, dimethyl ester	EtOH and EtOH-HCl	241(4.62),261(4.08), 288(4.26),320(4.10)	39-0677-79C
	EtOH-NaOH	260(4.73),278s(4.33), 322(3.91)	39-0677-79C
2H-Pyran-5-carboxylic acid, 6-methyl-3-[(methylamino)carbonyl]-2-oxo-,	EtOH and EtOH-HCl	208(4.21),258(4.08), 330(3.93)	39-0686-79C
	EtOH-NaOH	266(4.11),348(3.87)	39-0686-79C
3,5-Pyridinedicarboxylic acid, 1,2-dihydro-6-methyl-2-oxo-, dimethyl ester	EtOH and EtOH-HCl	206(4.30),260(4.23), 329(3.92)	39-0677-79C
	EtOH-NaOH	209(4.58),278(4.35), 331(4.00)	39-0677-79C
$C_{10}H_{11}N_2O_3P$			
1,3,2-Diazaphosphorin-4(1H)-one, 2,3-dihydro-6-methyl-2-phenoxy-, 2-oxide	pH 1-6	264(4.05)	103-1142-79
	pH 13	269(3.85),292s(3.66)	103-1142-79
	EtOH	260(4.05)	103-1142-79
dianion	n.s.g.	289(4.06)	103-1142-79
$C_{10}H_{11}N_3$			
1H-Benzotriazole, 1-isobutenyl-	EtOH	264(3.68),310(3.37)	33-2129-79
1H-Benzotriazole, 1-(1-methyl-1-propenyl)- (E/Z mixture)	EtOH	261(3.77),287(3.68)	33-2129-79
4,5,6-Triazaspiro[2.4]hept-4-ene, 6-phenyl-	ether	214(4.04),288(4.03), 307(4.01)	44-1202-79
$C_{10}H_{11}N_3O$			
Ethanone, 1-(2-azido-3,5-dimethylphenyl)-	EtOH	229(4.29),253s(3.95), 305(3.46)	33-0271-79
$C_{10}H_{11}N_3O_2$			
2,6-Methano-2H-1,3,5-benzoxadiazocin-9-ol, 4-amino-3,6-dihydro-, hydrochloride	EtOH	277(3.31),283(3.27)	24-0001-79
Sydnone, 3-[4-(dimethylamino)phenyl]-	CH_2Cl_2	245(4.06),320s(4.11), 350(4.19)	5-0063-79
$C_{10}H_{11}N_3O_2S$			
Benzamide, N-[[(aminocarbonyl)amino]-thioxomethyl]-4-methyl-	dioxan	254(4.36),286(4.21)	18-3728-79
$C_{10}H_{11}N_3O_2S_2$			
Acetamide, N,N'-[2-cyano-5-(methylthio)-3,4-thiophenediyl]bis-	EtOH	224(4.17),316(4.02)	95-1081-79
$C_{10}H_{11}N_3O_3S$			
Benzamide, N-[[(aminocarbonyl)amino]-thioxomethyl]-4-methoxy-	dioxan	255(4.37),287(4.21)	18-3728-79
Sydnone, 3-(dimethylamino)-4-(phenyl-	CH_2Cl_2	307(3.96)	5-0063-79

Compound	Solvent	$\lambda_{max}(\log \epsilon)$	Ref.
sulfinyl)- (cont.)			5-0063-79
$C_{10}H_{11}N_3O_4$			
Benzenamine, N-(1-methyl-2-propenyl)-2,4-dinitro-, (R)-	C_6H_{12}	257(3.99),329(4.26), 397(3.74)	78-2413-79
	MeOH	264(3.95),347(4.22), 400s(3.79)	78-2413-79
1H-Pyrrolo[3,2-d]pyrimidine-7-carboxylic acid, 2,3,4,5-tetrahydro-1,3-dimethyl-2,4-dioxo-, methyl ester	EtOH	232(4.54),273(3.91)	44-3830-79
$C_{10}H_{11}N_3O_5$			
Morpholine, 4-(2,6-dinitrophenyl)-	EtOH	380(3.16)	73-1613-79
Uridine, 5-cyano-2'-deoxy-	pH 1	278(4.10)	87-0621-79
	pH 12	278(4.00)	87-0621-79
$C_{10}H_{11}N_3O_6$			
2-Butenedioic acid, 2-[(1,2,3,4-tetrahydro-2,4-dioxo-5-pyrimidinyl)amino]-, dimethyl ester, (Z)-	pH 1	260(3.92)	44-0435-79
	pH 7	320(4.09)	44-0435-79
	pH 11	292(4.13)	44-0435-79
5-Pyrimidinecarbonitrile, 1-β-D-arabinofuranosyl-1,2,3,4-tetrahydro-2,4-dioxo-	H O	276(4.14)	87-0316-79
$C_{10}H_{11}N_3O_8$			
1,4-Dioxaspiro[4.5]deca-6,8-diene, 8-(ethyl-aci-nitro)-6,10-dinitro-	MeOH	223(4.03),367(4.35)	104-0487-79
$C_{10}H_{11}N_5OS_2$			
Pyrido[3,2-d]pyrimidine-6-carboxamide, 4-amino-2,8-bis(methylthio)-	pH 1	277(4.48),346(4.14)	44-0435-79
	pH 7	277(4.44),350(4.18)	44-0435-79
	pH 11	277(4.42),350(4.09)	44-0435-79
$C_{10}H_{11}N_5O_2$			
Adenosine, 2',3'-didehydro-2',3'-dideoxy-	MeOH	260(4.19)	44-1404-79
1H-1,2,3-Triazol-5-amine, N,1-dimethyl-4-nitro-N-phenyl-	EtOH	234(4.24),355(3.21)	39-2361-79C
$C_{10}H_{11}N_5O_2S$			
8,2'-Anhydro-8-thio-9-(β-D-5'-deoxyarabinofuranosyl)adenine	pH 1	278(4.28)	94-2647-79
	H_2O	276.5(4.29)	94-2647-79
	pH 13	278(4.29)	94-2647-79
$C_{10}H_{11}N_5O_3$			
8,2'-Anhydro-8-oxy-9-(β-D-5'-deoxyarabinofuranosyl)adenine	pH 1	259(4.14)	94-2647-79
	H_2O	257(4.13)	94-2647-79
	pH 13	265(4.08)	94-2647-79
Glycine, N-(1,4-dihydro-6,7-dimethyl-4-oxo-2-pteridinyl)-	pH -4.0	221(4.12),252(4.08), 287(3.68),336(3.87), 391(3.41)	18-2933-79
	pH -0.75	219(4.11),255(4.05), 285(3.98),323(3.72), 387(3.82)	18-2933-79
	pH 2.5	220(4.20),275(4.15), 343(3.83)	18-2933-79
	pH 6.0	222(4.21),278(4.23), 350(3.86)	18-2933-79
	pH 10.5	259(4.25),360(3.89)	18-2933-79
9H-Purine-9-acetaldehyde, α-(1-methyl-2-oxoethoxy)- (several isomers)	pH 7.0	259(4.18)	69-2838-79

Compound	Solvent	λ_{max}(log ϵ)	Ref.
Thymidine, 5'-azido-2',3'-didehydro-3',5'-dideoxy-	MeOH	265(3.94)	136-0113-79F
$C_{10}H_{11}N_5O_4$			
3,3'-Anhydro-9-β-D-xylofuranosylguanine	pH 1	245(4.14)	24-0625-79
	pH 7	262(4.07)	24-0625-79
	pH 10	262(4.08)	24-0625-79
Butanedioic acid, [(6-amino-9H-purin-9-yl)methyl]-	pH 13	262(4.18)	126-2323-79
Guanine, 9-(2,3-anhydro-β-D-ribofuranosyl)-	H_2O	252(4.13),270s(4.01)	24-0625-79
Guanine, 9-(5-deoxy-β-D-erythro-pent-4-enofuranosyl)-	MeOH-NaOH	267(4.05)	44-0400-79
9H-Purine-9-acetaldehyde, 6-amino-α-(1-formyl-2-hydroxyethoxy)-	pH 7.0	258(4.18)	69-2838-79
isomer	pH 7.0	259(4.16)	69-2838-79
$C_{10}H_{12}$			
Naphthalene, 1,2,3,4-tetrahydro-	gas at 120°	259(2.55),261(2.57), 265(2.66),273(2.63)	46-2176-79
	gas at 400°	265(2.64)	46-2176-79
	hexane	261(2.54),263(2.56), 267(2.70),275(2.75)	46-2176-79
Naphthalene, 1,4,4aα,8aβ-tetrahydro-	EtOH	198(3.77),259(3.55)	44-1294-79
Tricyclo[3.2.1.0^{2,4}]octane, 6,7-bis-(methylene)-, (1α,2β,4β,5α)-	isooctane	237(3.94),243(3.97), 251s(3.77)	33-2341-79
	EtOH	237(3.88),243(3.90), 251s(3.71)	33-2341-79
	gas	232s(--),238(--), 246s(--)	33-2341-79
$C_{10}H_{12}BrNO_2$			
Benzene, 1-bromo-4-(1,1-dimethylethyl)-	C_6H_{12}	281(2.9),335s(2.5)	5-0554-79
	MeOH	281(2.9),330s(2.5)	5-0554-79
Benzene, 1-bromo-2-methyl-2-nitropropyl)-	MeOH	250s(2.81),265s(2.77), 275s(2.61)	12-1949-79
$C_{10}H_{12}BrN_5O_3$			
Adenosine, 8-bromo-5'-deoxy-	pH 1	263(4.17)	94-2647-79
	H_2O	265.5(4.12)	94-2647-79
	pH 13	265.5(4.11)	94-2647-79
$C_{10}H_{12}ClNO$			
2(1H)-Quinolinone, 3-chloro-5,6,7,8-tetrahydro-1-methyl-	EtOH	325(4.00)	4-0065-79
$C_{10}H_{12}ClNO_3$			
8-Azabicyclo[3.2.1]oct-3-ene-6-carboxylic acid, 1-chloro-8-methyl-2-oxo-, methyl ester	$CHCl_3$	267(4.74)	39-2528-79C
$C_{10}H_{12}ClN_2$			
Pyrrolizinium, 1-chloro-5-[)dimethylamino)methylene]-3,5-dihydro-, perchlorate	MeOH	206(3.96),241(4.06), 377(5.27)	24-2465-79
$C_{10}H_{12}ClN_5O_2$			
Adenosine, 5'-chloro-2',5'-dideoxy-	pH 1	257(4.16)	44-3100-79
	pH 13	260(4.18)	44-3100-79

Compound	Solvent	λ_{max}(log ε)	Ref.
$C_{10}H_{12}ClN_5O_3$			
9H-Purin-6-amine, 9-(5-chloro-5-deoxy-β-D-xylofuranosyl)-	H_2O	258(4.17)	23-0274-79
$C_{10}H_{12}Cl_2N_2O_2$			
4-Cyclopentene-1,3-dione, 2-[bis(dimethylamino)methylene]-4,5-dichloro-	isoPrOH	248(4.78),289(4.44)	104-0454-79
$C_{10}H_{12}Cl_3NO_2$			
Benzenemethanol, 4-(dimethylamino)-2-hydroxy-α-(trichloromethyl)-	EtOH	226(4.04),267(4.07), 295(3.80)	118-0824-79
$C_{10}H_{12}Cl_3N_3O_2$			
1,3-Butadiene-1,1-diamine, 3,4,4-trichloro-2-nitro-N,N'-di-2-propenyl-	EtOH	219(4.16),340(4.10)	104-0039-79
$C_{10}H_{12}FNO$			
Benzene, 2-butyl-4-fluoro-1-nitroso-	$CHCl_3$	760(1.59)	44-2087-79
$C_{10}H_{12}FNO_2$			
Phenylalanine, α-(fluoromethyl)-	H_2O	251(2.16),257(2.27), 263(2.15)	44-2732-79
$C_{10}H_{12}F_4O_4Si$			
Silane, trimethoxy[(tetrafluorophenoxy)methyl]-	heptane	202(3.96),210(3.93), 263(2.72)	70-2602-79
$C_{10}H_{12}IN_5O_4$			
Guanosine, 5'-deoxy-5'-iodo-	MeOH-HCl	260(4.15),273s(3.79)	44-0400-79
	MeOH-NaOH	265(4.12)	44-0400-79
$C_{10}H_{12}N_2$			
1H-Benzimidazole, 1-ethyl-2-methyl-	isooctane	253(3.89),270(3.92), 277(4.02),284(4.01)	65-1225-79
	EtOH	248(3.80),251(3.81), 267(3.61),275(3.73), 282(3.82)	65-1225-79
1H-Benzimidazole, 2-(1-methylethyl)-	EtOH	207(4.63),245(3.98), 274(3.98),281(4.03)	39-2289-79C
1H-Benzimidazole, 2-propyl-	pH 1	236(3.64),262(3.77), 268(3.96),275(4.00)	65-1225-79
	H_2O	242(3.75),246(3.72), 268(3.74),272(3.82), 279(3.80)	65-1225-79
	EtOH	243(3.80),249(3.78), 269(3.74),274(3.86), 281(3.85)	65-1225-79
$C_{10}H_{12}N_2O$			
Benzeneacetaldehyde, α-oxo-, aldehydo-(dimethylhydrazone)	$CHCl_3$	319(4.23)	150-1451-79
1H-Benzimidazole-2-methanol, 1-ethyl-	EtOH	250(3.86),256(3.89), 270(3.78),278(3.84), 286(3.74)	70-1931-79
$C_{10}H_{12}N_2OS_2$			
Ethanethioic acid, S-(5,6,7,8-tetrahydro-2-imino-2H-3,1-benzothiazin-4-yl) ester	EtOH	231(4.38),290s(3.79), 309(3.93),420(3.93)	150-1732-79
Hydrazinecarbodithioic acid, [(4-methoxyphenyl)methylene]-, methyl ester	$CHCl_3$	260s(--),295s(--), 305s(--),333s(--),	90-0815-79

Compound	Solvent	$\lambda_{max}(\log \epsilon)$	Ref.
(cont.)		343(4.45),355s(--)	90-0815-79
$C_{10}H_{12}N_2O_2$			
Benzenemethanamine, N,N-dimethyl-α-(nitromethylene)-, (Z)-	EtOH	206(4.03),244(3.77), 353(4.30)	28-0255-79B
2-Pyrrolidinone, 1-methyl-5-(3-pyridinyl)-, N-oxide	MeOH	215(2.38),268(1.22)	150-3901-79
$C_{10}H_{12}N_2O_3$			
2-Butanone, 3-(4-nitrophenyl)-, oxime	hexane	266(4.08)	12-1487-79
3-Pyridinecarboxylic acid, 5-cyano-1,4-dihydro-6-hydroxy-2-methyl-, sodium salt	EtOH	242(4.23),263s(--), 350(4.07)	56-1913-79
3-Pyridinecarboxylic acid, 5-cyano-1,4,5,6-tetrahydro-2-methyl-, ethyl ester	EtOH	275(4.10)	56-1913-79
2-Pyrrolidinecarboxylic acid, 1-(2-pyridinyl)-, N-oxide, (S)-(-)-	MeOH	335(3.59)	4-0591-79
$C_{10}H_{12}N_2O_4$			
Benzene, 1-(1,1-dimethylethyl)-2,4-dinitro-	hexane	256(4.0),330s(2.5)	5-0554-79
	EtOH	261(4.0),330s(2.6)	5-0554-79
Benzene, 1-(1-methyl-2-nitropropyl)-4-nitro-	hexane	260(4.09)	12-1487-79
2-Pyrrolidinecarboxylic acid, 4-hydroxy-1-(2-pyridinyl)-, N-oxide	MeOH	335(3.61)	4-0591-79
$C_{10}H_{12}N_2O_4S$			
Butanamide, N-[2-(aminosulfonyl)phenyl]-3-oxo-	EtOH	210(4.31),245(3.94), 281(3.59),316(3.28)	104-1495-79
Butanamide, N-[4-(aminosulfonyl)phenyl]-2-oxo-	EtOH	208(4.37),265(4.38), 280(4.16),298(3.78)	104-1495-79
5-Thia-1-azabicyclo[4.2.0]oct-2-ene-2-carboxylic acid, 7-(formylamino)-3-methyl-8-oxo-, methyl ester, (6R-trans)-	EtOH	270(3.79)	39-2455-79C
$C_{10}H_{12}N_2O_5$			
2-Furancarboxylic acid, 5-(3,4-dihydro-2,4-dioxo-1(2H)-pyrimidinyl)tetrahydro-, methyl ester, trans-(±)-	pH 2	262(3.88)	103-0926-79
	pH 7	263(3.88)	103-0926-79
	pH 10	264(3.76)	103-0926-79
2-Furancarboxylic acid, 5-(3,4-dihydro-5-methyl-2,4-dioxo-1(2H)-pyrimidinyl)tetrahydro-	pH 2	264(3.99)	103-0926-79
	pH 7	265(3.99)	103-0926-79
	pH 10	263(3.90)	103-0926-79
2,5-Pyrazinedimethanol, diacetate, 1-oxide	EtOH	226(4.29),269(4.03)	94-2980-79
5-Pyrimidinecarboxylic acid, 1,2,3,4-tetrahydro-2,4-dioxo-1-(tetrahydro-2-furanyl)-, methyl ester	pH 1	278(4.13)	94-0899-79
	pH 7	278(4.15)	94-0899-79
	pH 12	278(3.96)	94-0899-79
$C_{10}H_{12}N_2O_5S$			
6H-Furo[2',3':4,5]oxazolo[3,2-a]pyrimidin-6-one, 2,3,3a,9a-tetrahydro-3-hydroxy-2-(hydroxymethyl)-7-(methylthio)-, [2R-(2α,3β,3aβ,9aβ)]-	pH 2	252(3.65),289(3.59)	4-1049-79
	H_2O	253(3.76),291(3.71)	4-1049-79
	pH 12	283(3.65)	4-1049-79
$C_{10}H_{12}N_2O_6$			
Butanedioic acid, (3,4-dihydro-5-methyl-2,4-dioxo-1(2H)-pyrimidinyl)-	MeOH	269(3.97)	126-0325-79
2,5-Pyrazinedimethanol, diacetate, 1,4-dioxide	EtOH	232(4.35),311(4.32)	94-2980-79

Compound	Solvent	λmax(log ε)	Ref.
$C_{10}H_{12}N_2S$			
Thieno[2,3-b]pyridin-4-amine, 2,3,6-trimethyl-	DMF	282(4.02),303(3.86), 313(3.83)	49-1189-79
$C_{10}H_{12}N_2S_2$			
Hydrazinecarbodithioic acid, [(4-methylphenyl)methylene]-, methyl ester	$CHCl_3$	253s(--),293s(--), 323s(--),334(4.70), 345s(--)	90-0815-79
zinc chelate	$CHCl_3$	250s(--),308(4.34), 347(4.43)	90-0815-79
$C_{10}H_{12}N_3OS$			
1,2,3,4-Thiatriazolium, 5-ethoxy-3-(4-methylphenyl)-, tetrafluoroborate	n.s.g.	237s(3.79),285s(3.77), 332(4.22)	39-0732-79C
$C_{10}H_{12}N_4$			
Propanedinitrile, (3,5-dihydro-3,3,5,5-tetramethyl-4H-pyrazol-4-ylidene)-	EtOH	242(4.00)	39-2401-79C
1H-Pyrrolo[2,3-d]pyrimidin-4-amine, 2-methyl-N-2-propenyl-	pH 1	280(4.11)	102-0217-79
	H_2O	279(4.11)	102-0217-79
	pH 13	277(4.16)	102-0217-79
$C_{10}H_{12}N_4O$			
4H-Pyrazolo[3,4-d]pyrimidin-4-one, 1-cyclopentyl-1,5-dihydro-	MeOH	211(4.24),253(3.67)	83-0586-79
$C_{10}H_{12}N_4O_2S$			
4,7(1H,8H)-Pteridinedione, 2,3-dihydro-1,3,6,8-tetramethyl-2-thioxo-	pH -4.9	225(4.31),268(4.15), 302s(3.68),390(4.23)	24-1499-79
	pH 6.0	223(4.27),265s(3.92), 340(4.29)	24-1499-79
4(1H)-Pteridinone, 2,3-dihydro-7-methoxy-1,3,6-trimethyl-2-thioxo-	pH -4.0	214(4.33),276(4.23), 292s(4.20),376(4.06)	24-1499-79
	pH 1.0	215(4.39),240s(4.04), 255(4.12),294(4.23), 338(4.24)	24-1499-79
Pyrimido[4,5-d]pyrimidine-2,4(1H,3H)-dione, 5,6-dihydro-1,3,6,7-tetramethyl-5-thioxo-	EtOH	258(3.91),270(3.91), 316(3.99)	95-0515-79
$C_{10}H_{12}N_4O_3$			
5(4H)-Isoxazolone, 4-[(3,4-dimethyl-5-isoxazolyl)azo]-3,4-dimethyl-	MeOH	297(4.20)	33-1570-79
$C_{10}H_{12}N_4O_3S$			
1,2,4-Triazolo[4,3-a]pyrazine-8(7H)-thione, 3-(2-deoxy-β-D-erythro-pentofuranosyl)-	EtOH	268(4.04),351(4.20)	44-1028-79
$C_{10}H_{12}N_4O_4$			
Acetic acid, (2-amino-1,5-dihydro-4-oxo-4H-pyrimido[4,5-b][1,4]oxazin-6(7H)-ylidene)-, ethyl ester	M NaOH	269(3.90),316(3.96)	4-1455-79
DL-Pentose, 2,3-dideoxy-3-(1,6-dihydro-6-oxo-7H-purin-7-yl)-	neutral	256(3.91)	69-2843-79
	base	263(--)	69-2843-79
DL-Pentose, 2,3-dideoxy-3-(1,6-dihydro-6-oxo-9H-purin-9-yl)-	neutral	250(4.01)	69-2843-79
	base	254(--)	69-2843-79
Thymine, 5,6-dihydro-5-(α-thyminyl)-	pH 6	265(3.90)	44-1414-79
	pH 10	290(3.90)	44-1414-79
1,2,4-Triazolo[4,3-a]pyrazin-8(7H)-one, 3-(2-deoxy-β-D-erythro-pentofuranosyl)-	EtOH	280(3.80)	44-1028-79

Compound	Solvent	$\lambda_{max}(\log \epsilon)$	Ref.
$C_{10}H_{12}N_4O_4S$			
Pyrazolo[1,5-a]-1,3,5-triazine-4(1H)-thione, 8-β-D-ribofuranosyl-	pH 1	277(4.28),310s(--)	44-4547-79
	pH 7-12	273(4.03),320(4.05)	44-4547-79
1,2,4-Triazolo[4,3-a]pyrazine-8(7H)-thione, 3-β-D-ribofuranosyl-	EtOH	268(4.10),351(4.25)	44-1028-79
$C_{10}H_{12}N_4O_5$			
3,6-Epoxyimidazo[1,5-a][1,3]diazocine-10-carboxamide, 1-formyl-1,2,3,4,5,6-hexahydro-4,5-dihydroxy-, [3R-(3α,4α-5α,6α)]-	H_2O	253(3.83)	44-0400-79
Inosine	pH -1.0	250(4.06)	5-1872-79
	pH 4.0	243s(4.07),248(4.10), 272s(3.55)	5-1872-79
	pH 12	252(4.13)	5-1872-79
2H-Purin-2-one, 1,9-dihydro-9-β-D-ribofuranosyl-	pH 2	312(3.70)	73-2846-79
	pH 7	310(3.83)	73-2846-79
	pH 12	310(3.92)	73-2846-79
1,2,4-Triazolo[4,3-a]pyrazin-8(7H)-one, 3-α-D-arabinofuranosyl-	H_2O	270(3.72)	111-0375-79
1,2,4-Triazolo[4,3-a]pyrazin-8(7H)-one, 3-β-D-ribofuranosyl-	EtOH	280(3.88)	44-1028-79
$C_{10}H_{12}N_4S$			
3H-Pyrazolium, 4,5-dihydro-3,3,5,5-tetramethyl-4-thioxo-, dicyanomethylide	EtOH	235(3.79),347(4.03), 508(1.11)	39-2401-79C
$C_{10}H_{12}N_6O_2$			
9H-Purin-6-amine, 9-(2,3-dideoxy-2,3-imino-β-D-lyxofuranosyl)-	MeOH	259(4.16)	44-1317-79
9H-Purin-6-amine, 9-(2,3-dideoxy-2,3-imino-β-D-ribofuranosyl)-	MeOH	259(4.14)	44-1317-79
$C_{10}H_{12}N_8O_3$			
9H-Purin-6-amine, 9-(2-azido-2-deoxy-α-D-arabinofuranosyl)-	pH 7.4	259(4.10)	136-0263-79C
β-	pH 7.4	259(4.13)	136-0263-79C
$C_{10}H_{12}N_8O_4$			
6H-Purin-6-one, 2-amino-7-(2-azido-2-deoxy-β-D-arabinofuranosyl)-1,7-dihydro-	H_2O	218(4.24),241s(3.80), 286(3.83)	136-0263-79C
$C_{10}H_{12}O$			
Bicyclo[3.2.2]nona-3,6-dien-2-one, 1-methyl-	MeOH	228(3.90),326(2.17)	18-3355-79
Bicyclo[3.2.2]nona-3,6-dien-2-one, 3-methyl-	MeOH	232(3.82),255s(3.68), 330(2.10)	18-3355-79
3-Buten-2-ol, 4-phenyl-	EtOH	251(4.23)	12-2523-79
Phenol, 2-(2-butenyl)-	EtOH	225(3.87),278(3.36)	39-2027-79C
2-Propanone, 1-(2-methylphenyl)-	MeOH	263(2.59),272(2.53)	56-0849-79
2-Propanone, 1-(4-methylphenyl)-	MeOH	259(2.89),265(2.85), 273(2.70)	56-0849-79
$C_{10}H_{12}OS_4$			
Tetrathiafulvalene, tetramethyl-, S-oxide	n.s.g.	369(3.72)	39-0862-79B

Compound	Solvent	λ_{max}(log ε)	Ref.
$C_{10}H_{12}O_2$			
2H-1-Benzopyran-3-ol, 3,4-dihydro-4-methyl-	EtOH	213(3.77),278(3.24), 285(3.27)	2-0011-79B
Bicyclo[3.2.2]nona-3,6-dien-2-one, 1-methoxy-	MeOH	228(3.77),340(2.22)	18-3355-79
Bicyclo[3.2.2]nona-3,6-dien-2-one, 3-methoxy-	MeOH	235(3.64),277(3.68), 335s(2.43)	18-3355-79
4,12-Dioxatricyclo[5.4.1.0^{3,5}]dodeca-1,6-diene	EtOH	216(2.87)	35-3893-79
2,5-Ethanopentalene-1,4-dione, hexahydro-	MeOH	298(1.72)	44-4557-79
1H-Indene-1,5(6H)-dione, 2,3,7,7a-tetrahydro-7a-methyl-, (7aS)-(+)-	EtOH	236(4.01)	54-0496-79
Phenol, 2-methoxy-4-propenyl-	pH 12	215(3.84),227(3.52), 250(3.62),270(3.28), 290(3.88),322(3.40), 350(3.02)	135-1004-79B
	EtOH	210(3.90),225(3.97), 245(3.76),262(3.98), 280(3.53),300(3.55)	135-1004-79B
2-Propanone, 1-(2-methoxyphenyl)-	MeOH	274(3.32),279(3.29)	56-0849-79
2-Propanone, 1-(4-methoxyphenyl)-	MeOH	278(3.35),284(3.31)	56-0849-79
	MeOH	205(3.00),228(2.95), 276(2.24)	106-0022-79
2-Propen-1-ol, 3-(3-methoxyphenyl)-	MeOH	253(4.09),292(3.53)	13-0361-79A
$C_{10}H_{12}O_2S$			
1H-2-Benzothiopyran-4,7(3H,4aH)-dione, 5,6-dihydro-4a-methyl-, (S)-	EtOH	218s(3.91),239(4.01), 284(3.43)	39-0990-79C
$C_{10}H_{12}O_3$			
4,11-Dioxatricyclo[5.3.1.0^{3,5}]undeca-1,6-diene,(3α,5α,9α)-	EtOH	232s(2.79)	44-0999-79
	MeCN	232s(2.79)	44-0999-79
Phenol, 2-methoxy-, propanoate	pH 12	215(3.74),225(3.65), 240(4.03),272(3.13), 290(3.73)	135-1004-79B
	EtOH	212(3.89),225(3.72), 260(2.92),274(3.50)	135-1004-79B
2-Propanone, 1-(3-hydroxy-5-methoxyphenyl)-	EtOH	206(3.64),209s(3.14)	150-0301-79
2-Propanone, 1-(2-methoxyphenoxy)-	pH 12	215(3.86),225(3.42), 248(3.97),294(3.61), 318(3.57),348(4.26)	135-1004-79B
	EtOH	212(3.50),230(4.30), 256(3.53),274(4.09), 305(4.03)	135-1004-79B
$C_{10}H_{12}O_4$			
3,5-Cyclohexadiene-1,2-dione, 4,5-diethoxy-	EtOH	289(4.14),416(2.73)	18-2169-79
$C_{10}H_{12}O_5$			
Acetic acid, (3-methoxy-4-methyl-5-oxo-2(5H)-furanylidene)-, ethyl ester, (Z)-	$CHCl_3$	271(4.24)	39-0062-79C
Benzeneacetic acid, 2-hydroxy-4,5-dimethoxy-	MeOH	289(3.7)	63-0721-79
$C_{10}H_{12}O_6$			
α-D-glycero-Hex-3-enopyranos-2-ulose, 1,6-di-O-acetyl-3,4-dideoxy-	EtOH	223(4.00)	136-0169-79D

Compound	Solvent	λ_{max}(log ε)	Ref.
$C_{10}H_{13}$			
Cycloheptatrienylium, (1-methylethyl)-, perchlorate	10% HCl	228(4.52),294(3.70), 302s(--)	39-1005-79B
Cycloheptatrienylium, 1,2,3-trimethyl-, perchlorate	10% HCl	240(4.73),293(3.75), 300s(--)	78-0949-79 +39-1005-79B
Cycloheptatrienylium, 1,2,4-trimethyl-, perchlorate	10% HCl	239(4.71),293(3.73), 298(3.73),309s(--)	78-0949-79
Cycloheptatrienylium, 1,2,5-trimethyl-, perchlorate	10% HCl	236(4.70),302s(--), 307(3.93)	78-0949-79
Cycloheptatrienylium, 1,3,5-trimethyl-, perchlorate	10% HCl	239(4.73),289s(--), 296(3.83),305s(--)	78-0949-79
$C_{10}H_{13}BrN_2$			
Pyridine, 3-bromo-5-(1-methyl-2-pyrrolidinyl)-	EtOH	229(3.24),267s(3.48), 275(3.53),281s(3.44)	44-4332-79
$C_{10}H_{13}BrO$			
4-Adamantanone, 1-bromo-	MeCN	291(1.30)	107-0825-79
$C_{10}H_{13}Br_3O_4Si$			
Silane, trimethoxy[(tribromophenoxy)-methyl]-	heptane	212(4.80),220s(--), 283(3.00),291(3.04)	70-2602-79
$C_{10}H_{13}ClN_4O_2$			
Glycine, N-[5-chloro-2-(methylamino)-benzoyl]-, hydrazide	MeOH	263(4.26),360(3.78)	44-0088-79
$C_{10}H_{13}Cl_3O_4Si$			
Silane, trimethoxy[(trichlorophenoxy)-methyl]-	heptane	205(4.91),220s(--), 280(2.98),290(3.04)	70-2602-79
$C_{10}H_{13}FN_2O_6$			
2,4(1H,3H)-Pyrimidinedione, 5-fluoro-1-(2-O-methyl-β-D-arabinofuranosyl)-	pH 1	268(3.96)	4-0353-79
	pH 7	268(3.94)	4-0353-79
	pH 13	269(3.86)	4-0353-79
$C_{10}H_{13}FN_2O_7$			
Uridine, 5-fluoro-4'-C-(hydroxymethyl)-	pH 1	269(4.00)	44-1301-79
$C_{10}H_{13}IN_2O_4$			
2,4(1H,3H)-Pyrimidinedione, 1-(2-O-acetyl-3-iodopropyl)-5-methyl-	EtOH	268(3.96)	128-0051-79
$C_{10}H_{13}NO$			
Benzaldehyde, 3,5-dimethyl-2-(methylamino)-	EtOH	269(3.75),392(3.74)	33-0234-79
Benzene, 1-butyl-2-nitroso-	$CHCl_3$	775(1.57)	44-2087-79
Benzene, 1-butyl-4-nitroso-	$CHCl_3$	745(1.64)	44-2087-79
Ethanone, 1-(2-amino-3,5-dimethylphenyl)-	EtOH	229(4.41),257(3.80), 372(3.73)	33-0271-79
$C_{10}H_{13}NOS$			
2,5-Cyclohexadiene-1,4-dione, mono-[S-(1,1-dimethylethyl)thiooxime]	hexane	401(4.43)	138-1077-79
$C_{10}H_{13}NO_2$			
Acetamide, N-(4-ethoxyphenyl)-	MeOH	250(4.18)	36-1303-79
6-Azaspiro[2.5]octa-4,7-diene-6-carboxylic acid, ethyl ester	isooctane	239(4.38)	44-2522-79
Benzaldehyde, 2-amino-6-methoxy-3,5-dimethyl-	EtOH	274(3.92),386(3.67)	33-0234-79

Compound	Solvent	λ_{max}(log ϵ)	Ref.
Benzaldehyde, 5-methoxy-4-methyl-2-(methylamino)-	EtOH	271(3.79),410(3.78)	33-0234-79
Benzene, 1-(1,1-dimethylethyl)-2-nitro-	hexane	250s(3.2),270s(2.9), 332(2.4)	5-0554-79
	EtOH	250s(3.2),275s(2.9), 334(2.4)	5-0554-79
Benzene, (2-methyl-1-nitropropyl)-	hexane	252(2.43),258(2.51), 263(2.54),269(2.48)	12-1487-79
2-Pyridinepropanoic acid, ethyl ester	MeOH	202(3.73),260(3.54)	22-0559-79
$C_{10}H_{13}NO_3$			
Benzenemethanol, α-(1-methyl-1-nitroethyl)-	EtOH	256(2.56),264(2.53)	4-1525-79
Phenol, 3-(1,1-dimethylethyl)-4-nitro-	C_6H_{12}	233s(3.6),243s(3.4), 270(3.4),280s(3.3), 338(2.8)	5-0554-79
	MeOH	220s(3.8),242s(3.5), 275(3.4),350(3.1)	5-0554-79
	MeOH-NaOH	237(3.9),265(3.6), 292(3.4),403(3.9)	5-0554-79
Phenol, 4-(1,1-dimethylethyl)-3-nitro-	C_6H_{12}	282(3.1),296s(3.0)	5-0554-79
	MeOH	240s(3.4),273(3.1), 315s(2.8)	5-0554-79
	MeOH-NaOH	236(4.2),288(3.4), 360(2.9)	5-0554-79
2(1H)-Pyridinone, 3-acetyl-4-methoxy-1,6-dimethyl-	EtOH	213(4.34),312(3.86)	94-0242-79
$C_{10}H_{13}NO_6$			
Homoshowdomycin	MeOH	222(4.01)	142-0141-79B
2-Pyrrolidinepropanoic acid, 4-(methoxycarbonyl)-3,5-dioxo-, methyl ester	H_2O	229(4.16),263(4.06)	142-0477-79B
$C_{10}H_{13}N_2$			
1H-Imidazolium, 4,5-dihydro-1-methyl-3-phenyl-, iodide	MeOH	272(4.10)	24-0445-79
1H-Indazolium, 2-ethyl-1-methyl-, tetrafluoroborate	EtOH	257(3.73),265(3.72), 298(3.56)	33-0234-79
$C_{10}H_{13}N_3$			
Propanedinitrile, [(cyclohexylamino)-methylene]-	MeCN	289(4.40)	80-1143-79
Propanedinitrile, [3-(dimethylamino)-1-ethyl-2-propenylidene]-	CH_2Cl_2	390(4.67)	118-0376-79
1H-Pyrazol-3-amine, 4,5-dihydro-1-(4-methylphenyl)-	EtOH	275(4.05)	150-0801-79
$C_{10}H_{13}N_3O$			
Aziridine, 2-(1-methylethyl)-1-(pyrazinylcarbonyl)-, (S)-	isooctane	211(3.91),267(3.92), 331(2.78)	39-2881-79C
	EtOH	212(3.91),268(3.90), 320(3.04)	39-2881-79C
	MeCN	212(3.90),268(3.88), 320(3.00)	39-2881-79C
$C_{10}H_{13}N_3O_2$			
3-Pyrrolidinemethanol, 1-nitroso-2-(3-pyridinyl)-, trans	EtOH	246(3.63),259s(3.58), 264s(3.53)	44-4332-79
hemisuccinate	EtOH	242(3.70),262s(3.52)	44-4332-79
1H-Pyrrolo[3,2-d]pyrimidine-2,4(3H,5H)-dione, 6-ethyl-1,3-dimethyl-	EtOH	230s(4.17),274(4.25)	44-3830-79

Compound	Solvent	$\lambda_{max}(\log \epsilon)$	Ref.
$C_{10}H_{13}N_3O_3$			
Carbamic acid, [(methylnitrosoamino)-methyl]-, phenylmethyl ester	EtOH	229(3.88),354(1.90)	94-0682-79
2H,6H-Cyclopent[4,5]oxazolo[3,2-a]pyrimidine-7-methanol, 5a,7,8,8a-tetrahydro-8-hydroxy-2-imino-, monoformate	pH 1	232(3.95),269(3.98)	36-0668-79
$C_{10}H_{13}N_3O_4$			
Benzenamine, N-butyl-2,4-dinitro-	EtOH	261(3.97),350(4.23), 403s(3.83)	73-1613-79
Benzenamine, N,N-diethyl-2,4-dinitro-	EtOH	376(4.20)	73-1613-79
Benzenamine, N,N-diethyl-2,6-dinitro-	EtOH	233(4.05),413(2.86)	73-1613-79
Benzenamine, N-(1-methylpropyl)-2,4-dinitro-, (R)-	C_6H_{12}	256(3.99),333(4.26), 403(3.74)	78-2413-79
	MeOH	264(3.97),352(4.24), 410s(3.79)	78-2413-79
Benzenamine, N-(2-methylpropyl)-2,4-dinitro-	EtOH	261(3.97),350(4.22), 403s(3.81)	73-1613-79
1H-Pyrazole-5-acetic acid, 3-cyano-4,5-dihydro-5-(methoxycarbonyl)-1-methyl-, methyl ester	MeOH	295.5(4.11)	24-1719-79
$C_{10}H_{13}N_3O_5$			
1(2H)-Pyrimidineacetic acid, α-(acetylamino)-3,4-dihydro-2,4-dioxo-, ethyl ester	pH 1	259(4.01)	44-2019-79
	pH 12	263(3.85)	44-2019-79
	MeOH	259(4.00)	44-2019-79
$C_{10}H_{13}N_3O_8$			
1,4-Cyclohexadiene, 3-(ethyl-aci-nitro)-6,6-dimethoxy-1,5-dinitro-	MeOH	218(4.26),365(4.40)	104-0487-79
$C_{10}H_{13}N_3S$			
Imidazo[1,2-c]quinazoline-5(3H)-thione, 2,6,7,8,9,10-hexahydro-	EtOH	270(4.41),340(3.74)	106-0390-79
	EtOH-HCl	246(3.92),278(4.21)	106-0390-79
	EtOH-NaOH	266(4.35),334(4.02)	106-0390-79
$C_{10}H_{13}N_5O$			
6H-Purin-6-imine, 1-ethoxy-1,9-dihydro-9-(2-propenyl)-, monohydrobromide	pH 1 and 7	260(4.11)	142-1543-79
	pH 13	258(4.13),265s(4.08)	142-1543-79
	EtOH	259(4.10)	142-1543-79
$C_{10}H_{13}N_5O_2$			
3H-Pyrazolo[3',4':3,4]pyrrolo[2,3-d]-pyrimidine-7,9(3aH,8H)-dione, 4,5,5a,6-tetrahydro-5-(2-propenyl)-	EtOH	214(3.68)	4-0293-79
Pyrimido[2,1-f]purine-2,4(1H,3H)-dione, 6,7,8,9-tetrahydro-1,3-dimethyl-	EtOH	292(3.02)	118-0581-79
$C_{10}H_{13}N_5O_3$			
Adenosine, 2'-deoxy-	H_2O	260(4.18)	23-0274-79
Adenosine, 3'-deoxy-	H_2O	260(4.16)	23-0274-79
D-erythro-Pentitol, 1-C-(8-amino-1,2,4-triazolo[4,3-a]pyrazin-3-yl)-1,4-anhydro-2-deoxy-	EtOH	227(4.15),290(3.81)	44-1028-79
$C_{10}H_{13}N_5O_4$			
Adenosine	pH 1.0	257(4.18)	5-1872-79
	pH 7.0	259(4.19)	5-1872-79
Guanosine, 3'-deoxy-	pH 1	255(4.07),275s(3.89)	24-0625-79
	pH 7	252(4.09),270s(3.97)	24-0625-79

Compound	Solvent	λ_{max}(log ε)	Ref.
9H-Purin-6-amine, 9-β-D-arabinofuranosyl- (vidarabine)	pH 13	260(4.2)	36-0499-79
1,2,4-Triazolo[4,3-a]pyrazin-8-amine, 3-β-D-ribofuranosyl-	EtOH	228(4.18),290(3.86)	44-1028-79
$C_{10}H_{13}N_5O_4S$			
7H-Imidazo[4,5-d]-1,2,3-triazine, 4-(methylthio)-7-β-D-ribofuranosyl-	pH 1	208(4.04),233(4.03), 282(3.96),305(3.93)	103-0685-79
	MeOH	208(4.01),233(4.11), 280(4.01),301(3.99)	103-0685-79
$C_{10}H_{13}N_5O_5$			
Pyrazolo[1,5-a]-1,3,5-triazin-4(1H)-one, 2-amino-8-β-D-ribofuranosyl-	pH 0	246(3.93)	44-4547-79
	pH 7	263(3.96)	44-4547-79
	pH 14	264(3.99)	44-4547-79
Pyrazolo[1,5-a]-1,3,5-triazin-4(1H)-one, 8-β-D-ribofuranosyl-, oxime	pH 0	235(4.07),250s(--), 300s(--)	44-4547-79
	pH 7	248(4.10),305s(--)	44-4547-79
	pH 14	267(4.01)	44-4547-79
$C_{10}H_{13}OS$			
Sulfonium, dimethyl(2-oxo-2-phenylethyl)-, tetrafluoroborate	MeOH	250(3.84),290(3.61)	47-2877-79
tetraphenylborate	n.s.g.	237s(4.322),271s(3.602), 283s(3.055)	104-0332-79
$C_{10}H_{13}OSe$			
Selenonium, dimethyl(2-oxo-2-phenylethyl)-, tetraphenylborate	n.s.g.	237s(4.398),271s(3.63)	104-0332-79
$C_{10}H_{13}O_7P$			
Benzoic acid, 2-(dimethoxyphosphinyl)-3,6-dihydroxy-, methyl ester	EtOH	209(4.21),322(3.84)	33-2350-79
$C_{10}H_{14}$			
Benzene, (1,1-dimethylethyl)-	hexane	208(3.98),251(2.14), 257(2.20),263(2.13), 266(2.07)	114-0195-79D
1,3,5(and 7)-Cyclodecatriene	EtOH	198(4.08)	44-1294-79
1,3,5-Cycloheptatriene, 3,7,7-trimethyl-	EtOH	270(3.70)	105-0691-79
p-Mentha-1,4,8-triene	hexane	230(4.03)	12-0217-79
4,5-Methano-1H-indene, 2,3,3a,4,5,7a-hexahydro-	EtOH	207(3.73)	88-0711-79
2,6-Octadien-4-yne, 2,7-dimethyl-	hexane	260(4.15),272(4.28), 287(4.21)	39-2429-79C
$C_{10}H_{14}BrN_5O_2$			
1H-Purine-2,6-dione, 7-(3-aminopropyl)-8-bromo-3,7-dihydro-1,3-dimethyl-, monohydrobromide	EtOH	279(3.91)	118-0581-79
$C_{10}H_{14}Br_2$			
p-Mentha-3,8-diene, 1,6-dibromo-, (1RS,6RS)-	hexane	230(4.11)	12-0217-79
$C_{10}H_{14}ClN_5O_2$			
1H-Purine-2,6-dione, 7-(3-aminopropyl)-8-chloro-3,7-dihydro-1,3-dimethyl-, monohydrochloride	EtOH	278(3.90)	118-0581-79

Compound	Solvent	$\lambda_{max}(\log \epsilon)$	Ref.
$C_{10}H_{14}ClOP$			
Phosphine oxide, (4-chlorophenyl)diethyl-	C_6H_{12} or dioxan	226.0(4.08)	65-0068-79
$C_{10}H_{14}ClPS$			
Phosphine sulfide, (4-chlorophenyl)diethyl-	C_6H_{12} or dioxan	225(4.27)	65-0068-79
$C_{10}H_{14}Cl_2$			
1,3,7-Octatriene, 2,6-dichloro-3,7-dimethyl-, (E)-	hexane	238(4.27)	12-2735-79
$C_{10}H_{14}Cl_2N_4O_2$			
1,3,5-Triazin-2-amine, 4,6-dichloro-N-(2,2,5-trimethyl-1,3-dioxan-5-yl)-	EtOH	236(4.32)	104-1144-79
$C_{10}H_{14}NO_6P$			
Phosphonic acid, [2-(5-nitro-2-furanyl)ethenyl]-, diethyl ester	EtOH	204s(3.81),232(4.20), 335(4.23)	48-0353-79
$C_{10}H_{14}N_2$			
2,3-Diazabicyclo[2.2.2]oct-2-ene, 1,4-diethenyl-	hexane	382(2.15)	44-4233-79
Dispiro[cyclopropane-1,5'-[2,3]diazabicyclo[2.2.2]oct[2]ene-6',1"-cyclopropane]	C_6H_{12}	344(1.26),370(1.60), 382(1.72)	88-0779-79
$C_{10}H_{14}N_2O$			
Benzenamine, N,N-diethyl-4-nitroso-	EtOH	427(4.59),658(1.81)	104-1437-79
Pyridine, 2-(2-methyl-1-pyrrolidinyl)-, 1-oxide, (R)-	MeOH	330(3.52)	4-0591-79
Pyridine, 2-(3-methyl-1-pyrrolidinyl)-, 1-oxide, (R)-	MeOH	342(3.61)	4-0591-79
3-Pyrrolidinemethanol, 2-(3-pyridinyl)-, trans	EtOH	259s(3.31),265(3.34), 270s(3.24)	44-4332-79
$C_{10}H_{14}N_2O_2$			
Benzenamine, 3-(1,1-dimethylethyl)-4-nitro-	C_6H_{12}	291(3.6),352(3.4)	5-0554-79
	MeOH	241(3.9),298(3.4), 384(3.7)	5-0554-79
Benzenamine, 4-(1,1-dimethylethyl)-3-nitro-	hexane	232(4.2),269(3.1), 284(3.1),330s(2.9)	5-0554-79
	EtOH	240(4.2),289(3.2), 342(2.8)	5-0554-79
Benzenamine, N-ethyl-3,5-dimethyl-2-nitro-	EtOH	238(4.19),292(3.56), 423(3.57)	103-0087-79
Benzenamine, N-ethyl-3,5-dimethyl-4-nitro-	EtOH	246(3.92),305(3.45), 392(3.79)	103-0087-79
Benzenamine, N,N,3,5-tetramethyl-4-nitro-	EtOH	249(3.98),308(3.47), 393(3.79)	103-0087-79
5H-Cycloheptapyrazine, 6,7,8,9-tetrahydro-2-methyl-, 1,4-dioxide	EtOH	241(4.27),307(4.40)	70-0848-79
2,5-Cyclohexadiene-1,4-dione, 2,5-bis(dimethylamino)-	MeOH	222(4.38),365(5.33), 513(2.61)	142-0411-79B
2-Propenoic acid, 2-cyano-3-(1-piperidinyl)-, methyl ester, (E)-	MeCN	289(4.42)	80-1143-79
Pyrazinemethanol, 5-ethyl-α-methyl-, acetate	EtOH	275(3.90),297s(3.80)	94-2027-79
Pyrazinol, 3,6-diethyl-, acetate	EtOH	270(3.91),275(3.89), 304(3.04)	94-2027-79

Compound	Solvent	λ$_{max}$(log ε)	Ref.
Quinoxaline, 5,6,7,8-tetrahydro-2,3-dimethyl-, 1,4-dioxide	EtOH	241(4.53),302(4.34)	70-0848-79
$C_{10}H_{14}N_2O_3$			
Benzenemethanol, 3-amino-α-(1-methyl-1-nitroethyl)-	EtOH	235(3.97),292(3.31)	4-1525-79
2H-Indazole-6-carboxylic acid, 3,3a,4,5,6,7-hexahydro-3-oxo-, ethyl ester	EtOH	239s(3.63),250(3.74)	39-2099-79C
1H-Pyrazole-3-carboxylic acid, 5-hydroxy-1-methyl-, cyclopentyl ester	MeOH	223(4.06)	5-1696-79
7H-Pyrazolo[1,5-c][1,3]oxazine-3-carboxylic acid, 4,5-dihydro-2-methyl-, ethyl ester	EtOH	231(3.97)	118-0440-79
$C_{10}H_{14}N_2O_3S$			
4(1H)-Pyrimidinone, 6-(2,2-dimethyl-1,3-dioxolan-4-yl)-2-(methylthio)-, (S)-	pH 1.0	238(3.90),286(3.92)	136-0235-79B
	pH 7.0	240(3.90),287(3.93)	136-0235-79B
	pH 11.0	243(3.95),277(3.78)	136-0235-79B
$C_{10}H_{14}N_2O_3S_2$			
Sulfilimine, N-[4-(acetylamino)sulfonyl]phenyl-S,S-dimethyl-	EtOH	275(4.27),300(4.22)	139-0195-79
$C_{10}H_{14}N_2O_4$			
2,5,8,11-Tetraoxa-13,15-diazabicyclo[10.3.1]hexadeca-1(16),12,14-triene	EtOH	240(3.51)	44-3812-79
$C_{10}H_{14}N_2O_4S_2$			
Uridine, 2'-deoxy-5-(methylthio)-4-thio-	pH 2	256(3.86),308(3.86), 353(4.07)	4-1049-79
	H_2O	255(3.85),308(3.86), 352(4.07)	4-1049-79
	pH 12	253(3.95),312(4.01), 334(4.03)	4-1049-79
$C_{10}H_{14}N_2O_5$			
2,4(1H,3H)-Pyrimidinedione, 1-(2-acetoxy-3-hydroxypropyl)-5-methyl-	n.s.g.	269(3.90)	128-0281-79
Uridine, deoxy-3-methyl-	pH 1 and 7	262.5(4.12)	18-0204-79
	pH 13	263.0(4.13)	18-0204-79
$C_{10}H_{14}N_2O_5S$			
2(1H)-Pyrimidinone, 4-(methylthio)-6-β-D-ribofuranosyl-	pH 1	270(3.63),320(4.25), 330s(--)	44-4854-79
	pH 7	270(4.13),302s(--)	44-4854-79
2-Thiazoleacetamide, 5-β-D-ribofuranosyl-	acid	252(3.78)	44-4351-79
	pH 7	246(3.81)	44-4351-79
	base	244(3.86)	44-4351-79
$C_{10}H_{14}N_2O_5S_2$			
4(1H)-Pyrimidinone, 1-β-D-arabinofuranosyl-2,3-dihydro-5-(methylthio)-2-thioxo-	pH 2	293(4.10)	4-1049-79
	H_2O	293(4.09)	4-1049-79
	pH 12	249(4.17),280(4.18)	4-1049-79
$C_{10}H_{14}N_2O_6$			
2,4(1H,3H)-Pyrimidinedione, 5-(2-C-methyl-β-D-ribofuranosyl)-	M HCl	266(3.85)	88-3669-79
	M NaOH	285(3.85)	88-3669-79
	MeOH	265(3.85)	88-3669-79
2,4(1H,3H)-Pyrimidinedione, 5-(4-C-methyl-β-D-ribofuranosyl-	pH 1	264(3.88)	88-2897-79
	pH 13	286(3.88)	88-2897-79

Compound	Solvent	λ_{max}(log ε)	Ref.
(cont.)	MeOH	264(3.89)	88-2897-79
$C_{10}H_{14}N_2O_6S$			
Uridine, 5-(methylthio)-	pH 2	288(3.60)	4-1049-79
	H_2O	286(3.72)	4-1049-79
	pH 12	282(3.70)	4-1049-79
$C_{10}H_{14}N_2O_7$			
Uridine, 4'-C-(hydroxymethyl)-	MeOH	257(3.97)	44-1309-79
$C_{10}H_{14}N_2S$			
2-Benzothiazolamine, 4,5,6,7-tetrahydro-N-2-propenyl-	EtOH	270(3.911)	48-0249-79
$C_{10}H_{14}N_2Se$			
Benzocarboselenoic acid, trimethylhydrazide	CCl_4	316(4.09),442(2.6)	77-1102-79
$C_{10}H_{14}N_2Te$			
Benzenecarbotelluroic acid, trimethylhydrazide	CCl_4	375(4.00),540(3.02)	77-1102-79
$C_{10}H_{14}N_3$			
1H-1,2,3-Triazolium, 4,5-dihydro-1-methyl-3-(4-methylphenyl)-, perchlorate	MeOH	240(3.74),247(3.65), 335(4.05)	24-0445-79
$C_{10}H_{14}N_3O$			
1H-1,2,3-Triazolium, 4,5-dihydro-1-(4-methoxyphenyl)-3-methyl-	MeOH	224(3.84),244(3.76), 349(4.09)	24-0445-79
$C_{10}H_{14}N_4O_3S$			
Isothiazolo[3,4-d]pyrimidine-4,6(5H,7H)-dione, 3-[(2-hydroxypropyl)amino]-5,7-dimethyl-	EtOH	233(4.36),270(4.09), 294(3.88)	95-0989-79
$C_{10}H_{14}N_4O_4$			
1H-Purine-2,6-dione, 7-(2,3-dihydroxypropyl)-3,7-dihydro-1,3-dimethyl-	pH 2,7,12	274(4.00)	73-2550-79
1(2H)-Pyrimidineacetic acid, α-(acetylamino)-4-amino-2-oxo-, ethyl ester	MeOH	238(3.87),269(3.87)	44-2019-79
$C_{10}H_{14}N_6O_2$			
9H-Purine-9-propanoic acid, α,6-diamino-, ethyl ester, dihydrochloride	n.s.g.	260(4.16)	65-0989-79
$C_{10}H_{14}N_6O_3$			
9H-Purin-6-amine, 9-(2-amino-2-deoxy-β-D-arabinofuranosyl)-	pH 7.4	259.5(4.11)	136-0263-79C
$C_{10}H_{14}N_6O_4$			
Guanine, 9-(2-amino-2-deoxy-β-D-arabinofuranosyl)-	H_2O	253(4.13),273s(3.98)	136-0263-79C
$C_{10}H_{14}O$			
2-Butyn-1-one, 1-(1-methylcyclopentyl)-	EtOH	219(3.76),222s(3.75)	33-0852-79
3-Butyn-2-one, 1-cyclohexyl-	EtOH	213(3.49)	33-0852-79
2-Cyclohepten-1-one, 6-(1-methylethenyl)-	EtOH	228(3.95)	44-4481-79
1,3-Cyclohexadiene-1-carboxaldehyde, 2,6,6-trimethyl-	MeOH	312(3.91)	39-1597-79C

Compound	Solvent	λ max(log ε)	Ref.
2-Cyclopenten-1-one, 3-cyclopentyl-	EtOH	230(4.17)	33-0852-79
2-Cyclopenten-1-one, 4-cyclopentyl-	EtOH	223(4.02)	33-0852-79
1H-Inden-1-one, 3a,4,5,6,7,7a-hexahydro-7a-methyl-	EtOH	224(3.88)	33-0852-79
1(3aH)-Pentalenone, 4,5,6,6a-tetrahydro-2,6a-dimethyl-	EtOH	230(3.96)	33-0852-79
1-Pentyn-3-one, 5-cyclopentyl-	EtOH	213(3.57)	33-0852-79
[3,3,2]Propellan-9-one	MeOH	304(1.54)	44-4557-79
Spiro[4.5]dec-2-en-1-one	EtOH	220(3.93)	33-0852-79
$C_{10}H_{14}OSi$			
Silane, benzoyltrimethyl-	C_6H_{12}	386(1.66),404(1.92), 424(2.01),444(1.76)	35-0083-79
$C_{10}H_{14}O_2$			
2(3H)-Benzofuranone, hexahydro-7a-methyl-3-methylene-	EtOH	213(3.93)	33-0205-79
3H-2-Benzopyran-3-one, 1,5,6,7,8,8a-hexahydro-4-methyl-	MeOH	232(4.00)	146-0031-79
Bicyclo[3.2.0]hepta-3,6-diene, 6-ethoxy-1-methoxy-	EtOH	218(3.90)	78-2311-79
1,3,5-Cycloheptatriene, 1-ethoxy-6-methoxy-	EtOH	227(4.12),260(3.42), 340(3.59)	78-2311-79
1,3,5-Cycloheptatriene, 3-ethoxy-1-methoxy-	EtOH	222(4.03),264(3.61), 321(3.61)	78-2311-79
2-Cyclohexen-1-one, 4-acetyl-3,4-dimethyl-	EtOH	235.5(4.01)	39-0990-79C
2(5H)-Furanone, 4-ethenyldihydro-3-methyl-5-(1-methylethenyl)-	EtOH	207(2.57)	44-3113-79
1-Oxaspiro[4.5]decan-2-one, 3-methylene-	EtOH	212(3.91)	33-0205-79
2H-Pyran-2-one, 5-acetyl-2,2,6-trimethyl-	EtOH	215(3.95),250(3.83), 295(4.13)	70-0758-79
$C_{10}H_{14}O_2S$			
1H-2-Benzothiopyran-7(3H)-one, 4,4a,5,6-tetrahydro-4α-hydroxy-4aβ-methyl-	EtOH	239.5(3.79)	39-0990-79C
$C_{10}H_{14}O_2S_3$			
Benzenesulfono(dithioperoxoic) acid, 1,1-dimethylethyl ester	dioxan	225(4.13),254(3.90)	44-0610-79
$C_{10}H_{14}O_3$			
2(4H)-Benzofuranone, 5,6,7,7a-tetrahydro-7a-hydroxy-3,6-dimethyl-	MeOH	219(4.21)	18-1964-79
2H-1-Benzopyran-5-one, 2,3,4,6,7,8-hexahydro-7-hydroxy-2-methyl-	MeOH	263(4.07)	39-1154-79C
1,2-Butanediol, 3-(2-hydroxyphenyl)-	EtOH	211(3.89),283(3.31)	2-0011-79B
1-Cyclohexene-1-carboxylic acid, 2,5-dimethyl-6-oxo-, methyl ester	EtOH	237(4.00)	152-0785-79
2-Cyclopenten-1-one, 5-acetoxy-2,4,4-trimethyl-	n.s.g.	231(3.95)	39-0274-79C
2,4-Hexadienoic acid, 2-acetyl-5-methyl-, methyl ester, (E)-	EtOH	205(4.00),236(3.81), 294(3.81)	70-0758-79
(Z)-	EtOH	215(3.64),295(4.23)	70-0758-79
2H-Oxecin-2,4(3H)-dione, 7,8,9,10-tetrahydro-10-methyl-, (E)-	MeOH	232(3.86),310(2.04)	39-0323-79C
	MeOH	232(3.82)	39-1154-79C
2-Propenoic acid, 3-(4-ethylidenetetrahydro-2-furanyl)-2-methyl-	EtOH	218(3.25)	102-0463-79

Compound	Solvent	λmax(log ε)	Ref.
$C_{10}H_{14}O_4$			
Benzeneethanol, 2-hydroxy-4,5-dimethoxy-	MeOH	289(3.6)	63-0721-79
2,5-Cyclohexadien-1-one, 4,4,5-trimeth- oxy-2-methyl-	EtOH	234(4.09),293(3.54)	35-6767-79
1,3-Dioxane-4,6-dione, 2,2-dimethyl- 5-(2-methyl-1-propenyl)-	C_6H_{12}	<220(>3.5)	24-3293-79
2,5-Furandione, 3-methoxy-4-pentyl-	EtOH	286(3.75)	39-0089-79C
Propanedioic acid, (3-methyl-2-buten- ylidene)-, dimethyl ester	EtOH	287(4.25)	70-0758-79
$C_{10}H_{14}O_5$			
Cyclopentaneacetic acid, 2-(methoxy- carbonyl)-3-oxo-, methyl ester, (-)-	MeOH	237s(2.60),252(2.69), 290s(1.74)	44-0452-79
Propanedioic acid, (3-ethoxy-2-propen- ylidene)-, dimethyl ester, (E)-	EtOH	210(3.84),300(4.40)	70-0758-79
1,3,6-Trioxaspiro[4.4]non-7-ene-8-carb- oxylic acid, 2,2,7-trimethyl-, (±)-	EtOH	224(4.17)	136-0055-79B
$C_{10}H_{14}O_5S$			
D-Ribonic acid, 2,3-O-(1-methylethyli- dene)-5-thio-, γ-lactone, acetate	EtOH	228(3.65)	136-0101-79H
$C_{10}H_{14}S$			
Benzene, [2-(ethylthio)ethyl]-	hexane	212(3.95),248(2.22), 253(2.28),259(2.35), 265(2.25),268(2.15)	114-0195-79D
Benzene, 1-[[(1-methylethyl)thio]meth- yl]-	C_6H_{12}	290(2.76)	39-0217-79B
$C_{10}H_{14}S_2Si$			
1,3-Dithia-2-silacyclohexane, 2-methyl- 2-phenyl-	hexane	198(4.51),218(4.14), 236s(3.43),272(2.55)	114-0195-79D
1,3-Dithia-2-silacyclopentane, 2,4-di- methyl-2-phenyl-	hexane	192(4.44),217(3.88), 245s(3.05),266(2.58), 272(2.44)	114-0195-79D
$C_{10}H_{15}Cl$			
1,3,7-Octatriene, 6-chloro-3,7-dimeth- yl-, (E)-	hexane	231(4.23)	12-2735-79
$C_{10}H_{15}ClNP$			
Phosphonamidous chloride, N,N-diethyl- P-phenyl-	hexane	243(3.71)	22-0241-79I
$C_{10}H_{15}N$			
4,6-Heptadienenitrile, 3,3,6-trimethyl-	EtOH	222s(4.18),228(4.24), 234s(4.09)	101-0211-79N
1H-Pyrrolizine, 2,3-dihydro-2,2,6-tri- methyl-	MeOH	209(3.73)	83-0896-79
Quinoline, 1,2,3,5,6,7-hexahydro-1- methyl-	C_6H_{12}	224(3.92),237(3.51)	44-3576-79
$C_{10}H_{15}NO$			
Benzenemethanol, α-(1-amino-1-methyl- ethyl)-	EtOH	221(4.08),259(2.51)	4-1525-79
Ethanone, 1-(9-azabicyclo[3.3.1]non- 2-en-2-yl)-	EtOH	224(3.99)	56-0027-79
Ferruginine	EtOH	233(4.00)	12-2537-79

Compound	Solvent	$\lambda_{max}(\log \epsilon)$	Ref.
$C_{10}H_{15}NOS_4$			
1-Piperidinecarbodithioic acid, 3-[bis-(methylthio)methylene]-2-oxo-, methyl ester	EtOH	213(4.22),281(4.13), 322(4.39),355(4.39)	39-0692-79C
$C_{10}H_{15}NO_2$			
Adamantane, 1-nitro-	isooctane	281(1.49)	39-0907-79B
	MeOH	280(1.59)	39-0907-79B
	$CF_3CHOHCF_3$	270s(1.84)	39-0907-79B
Adamantane, 2-nitro-	isooctane	282(1.58)	39-0907-79B
	MeOH	279(1.51)	39-0907-79B
5H-3,1-Benzoxazin-5-one, 1,2,4,6,7,8-hexahydro-2,4-dimethyl-	pH 1	291(4.30)	39-1593-79C
	H_2O	298(4.35)	39-1593-79C
Bicyclo[2.2.1]heptane-2,3-dione, 4,6,6-trimethyl-, 3-oxime, (E)-	C_6H_{12}	228(3.93),346(1.48)	39-0156-79B
(Z)-	C_6H_{12}	264(3.36),380(1.88)	39-0156-79B
isomer undesignated	EtOH	242(3.76),383(1.73)	39-0156-79B
1,5-p-Menthadiene, 2-nitro-, (R)-(-)-	EtOH	230(3.75),336(3.70)	33-2061-79
1(7),2-p-Menthadiene, 6-nitro-	EtOH	229(4.31)	33-2061-79
2-Propenal, 3-[(1-methoxy-2-propynyl)-(1-methylethyl)amino]-	EtOH	280(4.54)	49-0613-79
$C_{10}H_{15}NO_3$			
2,4-Pentanedione, 3-(4-morpholinyl-methylene)-	hexane	291(4.12)	131-0077-79D
	EtOH	306(--)	131-0077-79D
$C_{10}H_{15}NO_3S$			
Benzenesulfonic acid, 2-(diethylamino)-, sodium salt	$NaHCO_3$	265(3.53)	104-0887-79
Benzenesulfonic acid, 4-(diethylamino)-, sodium salt	$NaHCO_3$	284(4.33)	104-0887-79
$C_{10}H_{15}NO_4$			
1,3,6-Trioxaspiro[4.4]non-7-ene-8-carb-oxamide, 2,2,7-trimethyl-, (±)-	EtOH	246(4.04)	136-0055-79B
$C_{10}H_{15}NO_5$			
α-D-glycero-Hex-4-enopyranosiduronic acid, 3-acetamido-2,3,4-trideoxy-, methyl ester	EtOH	241(3.92)	136-0059-79C
$C_{10}H_{15}NO_5S_2$			
Benzenesulfonamide, N,N-dimethyl-4-[[(methylsulfonyl)oxy]methyl]-	EtOH	230(4.04),268(2.98), 274(2.84)	118-0531-79
$C_{10}H_{15}NS_2$			
4H-3,1-Benzothiazine-4-thione, 1,2,5,6,7,8-hexahydro-2,2-dimethyl-	EtOH	234s(3.46),339(3.61), 406(4.41)	150-1732-79
2(3H)-Cyclooctathiazolethione, 4,5,6,7,8,9-hexahydro-3-methyl-	EtOH	323(4.174)	48-0249-79
$C_{10}H_{15}N_2O_2$			
1H-Benzimidazol-1-yloxy, 2,6,7,7a-tetrahydro-2,2,7a-trimethyl-, 3-oxide	EtOH	235(3.80),280(4.01)	70-2521-79
$C_{10}H_{15}N_2O_3S_2$			
Sulfonium, [[4-(acetylamino)sulfonyl]-phenyl]amino]dimethyl-, salt with trifluoroacetic acid	EtOH	273(3.98),288(4.09), 302(4.19)	139-0195-79

Compound	Solvent	λmax(log ε)	Ref.
$C_{10}H_{15}N_3$			
Ethanimidic acid, 1,2-dimethyl-2-phenylhydrazide, monohydriodide	H_2O	230(4.42),275(3.50)	104-2073-79
$C_{10}H_{15}N_3O_2$			
Pyrazinecarboxamide, N-[1-(hydroxymethyl)-2-methylpropyl]-, (S)-	EtOH	210(4.03),268(3.93), 320(2.85)	39-2881-79C
	MeCN	209(4.00),267(3.91), 322(2.70)	39-2881-79C
$C_{10}H_{15}N_3O_2S$			
1H-Pyrrole-2-carboxylic acid, 4-methyl-3-[[(methylamino)thioxomethyl]amino]-, ethyl ester	pH 7	236(4.30),275(4.32)	44-3826-79
$C_{10}H_{15}N_3O_3$			
1H-Pyrrole-2-carboxylic acid, 4-methyl-3-[[(methylamino)carbonyl]amino]-, ethyl ester	pH 7	275(4.10)	44-3826-79
$C_{10}H_{15}N_3O_4$			
2(1H)-Pyrimidinone, 4-amino-1-(2,5-dideoxy-α-D-erythro-hexofuranosyl)-	H_2O	228s(--),272(3.91)	136-0079-79J
	H_2SO_4	214(4.00),280(4.11)	136-0079-79J
β-	H_2O	228s(3.88),272(3.94)	136-0079-79J
	H_2SO_4	214(4.15),280(4.10)	136-0079-79J
2(1H)-Pyrimidinone, 4-amino-1-[2,3-dihydroxy-4-(hydroxymethyl)cyclopentyl]-	pH 1	214(4.00),283(4.16)	36-0668-79
	pH 7 or 13	225s(--),274(4.00)	36-0668-79
$C_{10}H_{15}N_3O_4S$			
Cytosine, 1-(2-deoxy-β-erythro-pentofuranosyl)-5-(methylthio)-	pH 2	284(3.94)	4-1049-79
	H_2O	279(3.81)	4-1049-79
	pH 12	277(3.81)	4-1049-79
$C_{10}H_{15}N_3O_5$			
2(1H)-Pyrimidinone, 4-amino-1-(5-deoxy-β-D-ribohexofuranosyl)-	H_2O	230s(3.87),272(3.92)	136-0079-79J
	H_2SO_4	214s(3.93),278(4.08)	136-0079-79J
4(1H)-Pyrimidine, 2-amino-5-(2-C-methyl-β-D-ribofuranosyl)-	pH 1	221(3.94),262(3.81)	88-2897-79
	pH 13	230(4.04),278(3.92)	88-2897-79
4(1H)-Pyrimidinone, 2-amino-5-[(β-D-ribofuranosyl)methyl]-, hydrochloride	M HCl	223(4.09),264(3.98)	88-3669-79
	M NaOH	232(4.05),281(3.96)	88-3669-79
	MeOH	224(4.06),263(3.89)	88-3669-79
Uridine, 5-(aminomethyl)-2'-deoxy-	pH 1	266(3.96)	87-0621-79
	pH 12	266(3.83)	87-0621-79
$C_{10}H_{15}N_3O_5S$			
2(1H)-Pyrimidinone, 5-(methylthio)-1-α-D-ribofuranosyl-4-amino-	pH 2	286(3.74)	4-1049-79
	H_2O	231(3.61),281(3.79)	4-1049-79
	pH 12	232(3.78),281(3.61)	4-1049-79
$C_{10}H_{15}N_3O_6$			
Cytidine, 4'-C-(hydroxymethyl)-	MeOH	263(3.89),272(3.91)	44-1309-79
1H-Pyrazole-5-carboxamide, 4-hydroxy-3-[(β-D-ribofuranosyl)methyl]-	H_2O	223(3.94),266(3.71)	142-0141-79B
	pH 13	235(3.64),311(3.74)	142-0141-79B
$C_{10}H_{15}N_5O_2$			
2H-Pyrazolo[3,4-d]pyrimidine-4,6(5H,7H)-dione, 5,7-diethyl-3-(methylamino)-	MeOH	218(4.34),245s(3.82), 274(3.79)	94-1328-79
$C_{10}H_{15}N_5O_4$			
Hexanoic acid, 6-[(6-amino-1,4-dihydro-5-nitroso-4-oxo-2-pyrimidinyl)amino]-	pH 0.25	212(3.90),268(4.06), 310s(3.96)	18-2933-79

Compound	Solvent	λ_{max}(log ε)	Ref.
(cont.)	pH 5.5	216(3.77),230(3.89), 258(3.66),326(4.34)	18-2933-79
	pH 10.5	214(3.82),328(4.36)	18-2933-79
$C_{10}H_{15}N_5O_6$			
Urea, [5-deoxy-5-[4-(methoxycarbonyl)-1H-1,2,3-triazol-1-yl]-β-D-ribofuranosyl]-	MeOH	214(4.04)	44-1424-79
$C_{10}H_{15}OP$			
Phosphine oxide, diethylphenyl-	C_6H_{12} or dioxan	213(3.89)	65-0068-79
	dioxan	214(3.89),263(2.72), 270(2.70)	65-0479-79
$C_{10}H_{15}O_3P$			
Phosphonic acid, phenyl-, diethyl ester	C_6H_{12} or dioxan	215.5(3.92)	65-0068-79
$C_{10}H_{15}O_4P$			
Phosphonic acid, 2-[(2-furanyl)ethenyl]-, diethyl ester	EtOH	203(3.56),230s(3.34), 286(4.36)	48-0353-79
$C_{10}H_{15}P$			
Phosphine, diethylphenyl-	C_6H_{12}	208s(4.11),219s(3.93), 255(3.43),266f(3.36)	39-0501-79B
	C_6H_{12}	255(3.52)	65-0479-79
	hexane	253(3.50)	22-0241-79I
	12M HCl	218(3.95),266f(2.91)	39-0501-79B
Phosphine, (1,1-dimethylethyl)phenyl-	C_6H_{12}	209s(4.04),218s(3.92), 248(3.58),266f(3.30)	39-0501-79B
	12M HCl	223(4.02),267f(3.08)	39-0501-79B
$C_{10}H_{15}PS$			
Phosphine sulfide, diethylphenyl-	C_6H_{12} or dioxan	214.0(4.19)	65-0068-79
$C_{10}H_{16}$			
1,3-Cyclohexadiene, 5,5,6,6-tetramethyl-	C_6H_{12}	258(3.60)	88-0779-79
1,3,6-Octatriene, 4,5-dimethyl-	EtOH	232(4.13)	104-1037-79
2,4,6-Octatriene, 2,6-dimethyl-	EtOH	276(4.73)	104-1037-79
2,4,6-Octatriene, 2,7-dimethyl-	C_6H_{12}	269(4.59),280(4.74), 292(4.59)	44-4254-79
two isomers	EtOH	269(4.44),279(4.55), 291(4.45)	39-0810-79B
$C_{10}H_{16}BrNO$			
6-Oxa-1-azabicyclo[3.1.0]hex-3-ene, 3-bromo-5-(1,1-dimethylethyl)-2,2-dimethyl-	EtOH	228(3.40)	12-2041-79
2H-Pyrrole, 3-bromo-5-(1,1-dimethylethyl)-2,2-dimethyl-, 1-oxide	EtOH	318(3.78)	12-1795-79
$C_{10}H_{16}BrNO_2$			
3H-Pyrazol-3-one, 4-bromo-2-(1,1-dimethylethyl)-4,5-dihydro-5,5-dimethyl-, 1-oxide	EtOH	213(3.36),286(4.03)	12-1795-79
$C_{10}H_{16}BrN_2O_2$			
1H-Benzimidazol-1-yloxy, 4-bromo-2,4,5,6,7,7a-hexahydro-2,2,7a-trimethyl-	EtOH	260(3.87)	70-2521-79

Compound	Solvent	λ_{max}(log ϵ)	Ref.
$C_{10}H_{16}Br_4$			
p-Menth-3-ene, 1,6,8,9-tetrabromo-, (1RS,6RS,8RS)-	hexane	251(2.35)	12-0217-79
$C_{10}H_{16}Cl_3N_3O_2$			
1,3-Butadiene-1,1-diamine, 3,4,4-trichloro-N,N'-bis(1-methylethyl)-2-nitro-	EtOH	218(4.08),338(4.01)	104-0039-79
1,3-Butadiene-1,1-diamine, 3,4,4-trichloro-2-nitro-N,N'-dipropyl-	EtOH	213(4.13),337(4.07)	104-0039-79
$C_{10}H_{16}NO_3$			
1-Piperidinyloxy, 3-formyl-2,2,6,6-tetramethyl-4-oxo-	C_6H_{12}	238(3.47),284(3.89), 420s(1.46)	88-0941-79
	MeOH	230(3.45),282(3.87)	88-0941-79
	MeOH-HCl	220s(3.48),270(3.90)	88-0941-79
	MeOH-NaOH	230(3.45),303(4.16)	88-0941-79
copper chelate	C_6H_{12}	241(3.85),312(4.04), 325s(3.90),500s(1.70), 655(1.60)	88-0941-79
$C_{10}H_{16}N_2$			
3,4-Diazatricyclo[5.4.1.0^{1,5}]dodec-3-ene	EtOH	322(2.5)	33-2025-79
Pyrazine-2,5- $^{14}C_2$, 2,5-diethyl-3,6-dimethyl-	EtOH	282(3.70),297(3.30)	39-2411-79C
$C_{10}H_{16}N_2O$			
Benzenemethanol, 3-amino-α-(1-amino-1-methylethyl)-	EtOH	236(3.91),288(3.27)	4-1525-79
$C_{10}H_{16}N_2O_2S_3$			
Sulfur, [μ-[4-aminobenzenesulfonamidato(4-)-N^1:N^4]]tetramethyldi-	70% EtOH	204(4.52),289(4.35)	139-0195-79
$C_{10}H_{16}N_2O_3$			
1H-Pyrazole-4-carboxylic acid, 3-(1-hydroxyethyl)-1,5-dimethyl-, ethyl ester	EtOH	234(3.95)	4-1117-79
1H-Pyrazole-4-carboxylic acid, 3-(2-hydroxyethyl)-1,5-dimethyl-, ethyl ester	EtOH	233(3.91)	4-1117-79
1H-Pyrazole-4-carboxylic acid, 5-(1-hydroxyethyl)-1,3-dimethyl-, ethyl ester	EtOH	234(3.97)	4-1117-79
1H-Pyrazole-4-carboxylic acid, 5-(2-hydroxyethyl)-1,3-dimethyl-, ethyl ester	EtOH	234(3.95)	4-1117-79
1-Pyrrolidinecarboxamide, N-(3-methoxy-2-methyl-1-oxo-2-propenyl)-	MeOH	252.5(4.121)	73-0269-79
$C_{10}H_{16}N_2O_4$			
4-Morpholinecarboxamide, N-(3-methoxy-2-methyl-1-oxo-2-propenyl)-	MeOH	252.0(4.135)	73-0269-79
$C_{10}H_{16}N_2S_2$			
6H-Cycloocta[e][1,3,4]thiadiazine, 4a,5,7,8,9,10-hexahydro-3-(methylthio)-	EtOH	291(3.506)	48-0959-79
$C_{10}H_{16}N_3O_2S$			
1H-Imidazol-1-yloxy, 2,5-dihydro-2,2,5,5-tetramethyl-4-(1-thiocyanatoethyl)-, 3-oxide	EtOH	250(3.90)	70-2521-79

Compound	Solvent	λ_{max}(log ε)	Ref.
$C_{10}H_{16}N_3O_7P$			
2(1H)-Pyrimidinone, 4-amino-1-(2,5-dideoxy-6-O-phosphono-β-D-erythro-hexofuranosyl)-	H_2O	275(4.07)	136-0079-79J
$C_{10}H_{16}N_4$			
1H-Imidazole-5-carbonitrile, 1-(1-methylethyl)-4-[(1-methylethyl)amino]-	MeOH	211(4.01),230(3.69), 279(4.00)	44-1273-79
$C_{10}H_{16}N_4O_7$			
1,2,4-Triazine-3,5(2H,4H)-dione, 2-β-D-glucopyranosyl-6-(methylamino)-	pH 1-7	311(3.71)	124-0048-79
	pH 13	299(3.68)	124-0048-79
$C_{10}H_{16}N_6O_2$			
1H-Imidazole-5-carboxamide, 4-(3,3-dimethyl-1-triazenyl)-1-(tetrahydro-2-furanyl)-	pH 1	275s(3.97),322(4.35)	87-1422-79
	pH 11	239(4.18),326(4.29)	87-1422-79
	MeOH	237(4.22),323(4.30)	87-1422-79
1,3-Propanediol, 2-[[4,6-bis(1-aziridinyl)-1,3,5-triazin-2-yl]amino]-	EtOH	222(4.70)	104-1144-79
1H-Pyrazole-4-carboxamide, 3-(3,3-dimethyl-1-triazenyl)-1-(tetrahydro-2-furanyl)-	pH 1	314(4.18)	87-1422-79
	pH 11	236(4.15),309(4.14)	87-1422-79
	MeOH	308(4.15)	87-1422-79
$C_{10}H_{16}O$			
2-Cycloocten-1-one, 2,3-dimethyl-	EtOH	250(3.64)	44-2722-79
2-Cyclopenten-1-one, 2-butyl-3-methyl-	MeOH	239(3.85)	146-0100-79
2-Cyclopenten-1-one, 3-methyl-2-(2-methylpropyl)-	MeOH	239(4.15)	146-0100-79
1(7),5-p-Menthadien-2-ol, (2R,4R)-(+)-	EtOH	230(4.02)	33-2061-79
(-)-	EtOH	230(4.33)	33-2061-79
(2S,4R)-	EtOH	233(4.26)	33-2061-79
1,5,7-Octatrien-3-ol, 3,7-dimethyl-, (E)-	EtOH	230(4.41)	107-0317-79
$C_{10}H_{16}OS_2$			
Spiro[2H,6H-cyclopenta[b][1,4]dithiepin-3(4H),3'-oxetane], tetrahydro-, trans	EtOH	211(2.97)	49-0279-79
$C_{10}H_{16}O_2$			
2-Cyclohexen-1-one, 2-(1-hydroxy-1-methylethyl)-5-methyl-	MeOH	234(3.90)	18-1964-79
Ethanone, 1,1'-(1,2-dimethyl-1,2-cyclobutanediyl)bis-, trans	C_6H_{12}	295(1.76)	54-0346-79
4,6-Heptadienoic acid, 3,3,6-trimethyl-	EtOH	224s(4.24),228(4.28), 237s(4.13)	101-0211-79N
2-Heptenal , 3-(1-methylethyl)-6-oxo-, (Z)-	pentane	223(4.10),285(1.48), 348(1.54)	5-0608-79
(Z/E)-	pentane	221(4.09),290(1.48), 347(1.54)	5-0608-79
2,7-Octanedione, 3-methyl-6-methylene-	C_6H_{12}	219(3.98),288(1.70)	54-0346-79
2-Octenal, 3,7-dimethyl-6-oxo-, (E)-	pentane	221(4.08),292(1.42), 335(1.56),348(1.42)	5-0608-79
(Z)-	pentane	231(4.19),289(1.40), 333(1.68),348(1.60)	5-0608-79
2-Propanone, 1-(2-acetylcyclopentyl)-	EtOH	275(1.96)	126-0079-79
2-Propenal, 3-[3-(hydroxymethyl)-2,2-dimethylcyclopropyl]-2-methyl-, [1R-[1α(E),3β]]-	EtOH	257(4.25)	44-2441-79
2H-Pyran, 2-acetyl-3,4-dihydro-2,5,6-trimethyl-	C_6H_{12}	217(3.34),290(1.61)	54-0346-79

Compound	Solvent	$\lambda_{max}(\log \epsilon)$	Ref.
$C_{10}H_{16}O_3$			
2-Cyclohexen-1-one, 2,6-dihydroxy-3-methyl-6-(1-methylethyl)-	MeOH	275(3.63)	18-2372-79
2-Heptenoic acid, 2-methyl-7-oxo-, ethyl ester, (E)-	n.s.g.	217(3.93),290s(--)	118-0279-79
(Z)-	n.s.g.	217(3.86),290(1.54)	118-0279-79
2-Hexenoic acid, 2-ethyl-6-oxo-, ethyl ester, (E)-	n.s.g.	216(4.06),290(1.61)	118-0279-79
(Z)-	n.s.g.	215(4.03),290(1.63)	118-0279-79
2,4-Oxecanedione, 10-methyl-	MeOH	210s(2.88)	39-1154-79C
2H-Oxocin-3(4H)-one, 8-ethyl-7,8-dihydro-2-(hydroxymethyl)-, cis	isooctane	304s(2.12),312(2.22), 321(2.21),332s(1.98)	18-0127-79
2H-Pyran-3(6H)-one, 2-(1,1-dimethylethyl)-6-methoxy-	EtOH	210(3.89),285(1.85), 350(1.70)	56-0265-79
$C_{10}H_{17}ClN_4O_2$			
1,3,5-Triazin-2-amine, 4-(2-chloroethoxy)-N,N-dimethyl-6-propoxy-	EtOH	228(4.20)	103-0111-79
1,3,5-Triazin-2(1H)-one, 1-(2-chloroethyl)-4-(diethylamino)-6-methoxy-	EtOH	238(4.21)	103-0111-79
1,3,5-Triazin-2(1H)-one, 1-(2-chloroethyl)-4-(dimethylamino)-6-propoxy-	EtOH	237(4.37)	103-0111-79
$C_{10}H_{17}N$			
Pyrrolidine, 1-(2,4-hexadienyl)-	EtOH	228(4.43)	104-1041-79
$C_{10}H_{17}NO$			
Morpholine, 4-(1-cyclohexen-1-yl)-	MeCN	223(3.6)	24-2997-79
Morpholine, 4-(2,4-hexadienyl)-	EtOH	228(4.67)	104-1041-79
$C_{10}H_{17}NO_2$			
Carbamic acid, (3-methyl-1,3-butadienyl)propyl-, methyl ester	MeOH	257(4.43)	88-0981-79
2,4-Pyrrolidinedione, 5-hexyl-	EtOH-NaOH	262.5(4.07)	142-0477-79B
$C_{10}H_{17}NO_4$			
Pentanoic acid, 5-[(1,1-dimethylethyl)amino]-3,5-dioxo-, methyl ester	MeOH-NaOH	275(4.29)	35-2171-79
Propanedioic acid, [[(1,1-dimethylethyl)amino]methylene]-, dimethyl ester	MeCN	282(4.32)	80-1143-79
$C_{10}H_{17}NO_9S_2$			
β-D-Glucopyranose, 1-thio-, 1-[N-(sulfooxy)-3-butenimidate] (sinigrin)	n.s.g.	227(3.89)	51-0364-79
$C_{10}H_{17}N_2O_2S_3$			
Sulfilimine, N-[[4-[(dimethylsulfonio)amino]phenyl]sulfonyl]-S,S-dimethyl-, salt with trifluoroacetic acid	70% EtOH	202(4.45),290(4.08)	139-0195-79
$C_{10}H_{17}N_2O_3PS_2$			
Phosphonothioic acid, ethyl-, O-[1,6-dihydro-1-methyl-5-(methylthio)-6-oxo-4-pyridazinyl] O-ethyl ester	MeOH	212(4.20),238(3.72), 320(3.79)	73-1761-79
$C_{10}H_{17}N_2O_4$			
1H-Imidazol-1-yloxy, 4-(acetoxymethyl)-2,5-dihydro-2,2,5,5-tetramethyl-, 3-oxide	EtOH	240(4.06)	70-0208-79
	EtOH	238(4.08)	70-2521-79

Compound	Solvent	$\lambda_{max}(\log \epsilon)$	Ref.
$C_{10}H_{17}N_2O_4PS_2$			
Phosphorothioic acid, O-[1,6-dihydro-1-methyl-5-(methylthio)-6-oxo-4-pyridazinyl] O,O-diethyl ester	MeOH	212(4.20),238(3.72), 320(3.82)	73-1761-79
$C_{10}H_{17}N_2O_5PS$			
Phosphoric acid, 1,6-dihydro-1-methyl-5-(methylthio)-6-oxo-4-pyridazinyl diethyl ester	MeOH	212(4.18),238(3.66), 321(3.81)	73-1761-79
Phosphorothioic acid, O-(5-ethoxy-1,6-dihydro-1-methyl-6-oxo-4-pyridazin-yl) O-ethyl O-methyl ester	MeOH	212(4.28),287(3.70)	73-1761-79
$C_{10}H_{17}N_3$			
4-Pyrimidinamine, N,N-diethyl-2,6-di-methyl-	EtOH	251(4.15),275(3.69)	150-1579-79
$C_{10}H_{17}N_3O_2$			
1H-Benzimidazole, 2,4,5,6,7,7a-hexa-hydro-2,2,7a-trimethyl-1-nitroso-, 3-oxide	EtOH	234(4.28)	103-0092-79
1,4-Diazaspiro[4.4]non-1-ene, 2,3,3-trimethyl-4-nitroso-, 1-oxide	EtOH	234(4.23)	103-0092-79
$C_{10}H_{17}N_3O_3$			
Carbamic acid, [3-(2-hydroxypropyl)-5-methyl-1H-pyrazol-4-yl]-, ethyl ester	EtOH	220(3.60)	118-0584-79
$C_{10}H_{17}N_3S$			
4-Pyrimidinamine, N,N-diethyl-6-methyl-2-(methylthio)-	EtOH	239(4.17),253s(3.93), 292(3.61)	150-1579-79
$C_{10}H_{17}N_4OS$			
Oxazolo[3,2-a]-1,3,5-triazin-5-ium, 2-(diethylamino)-6,7-dihydro-4-(methylthio)-, chloride	H_2O	243(4.13)	103-0111-79
$C_{10}H_{17}N_4O_2$			
Oxazolo[3,2-a]-1,3,5-triazin-5-ium, 2-(diethylamino)-6,7-dihydro-4-methoxy-, chloride	H_2O	238(4.63)	103-0111-79
Oxazolo[3,2-a]-1,3,5-triazin-5-ium, 2-(dimethylamino)-6,7-dihydro-4-propoxy-, chloride	H_2O	237(4.12)	103-0111-79
$C_{10}H_{17}N_5O_2S$			
Hydrazinecarbothioamide, 2-(1,3-dieth-yl-1,2,3,6-tetrahydro-2,6-dioxo-4-pyrimidinyl)-N-methyl-	MeOH	245(4.22),267(4.23)	94-1328-79
$C_{10}H_{18}$			
4,6-Decadiene	EtOH	231(4.29)	39-2136-79C
$C_{10}H_{18}NS_4$			
Methanaminium, N-methyl-N-[2,3,4,4-tetrakis(methylthio)-2-cyclobuten-1-ylidene]-, iodide	CH_2Cl_2	265(4.01),336(3.91), 366(3.96)	5-0595-79
$C_{10}H_{18}N_2$			
1H-Benzimidazole, 3a,4,5,6,7,7a-hexa-	EtOH	220(3.52)	39-2289-79C

Compound	Solvent	λ max (log ε)	Ref.
hydro-2-(1-methylethyl)- (cont.)			39-2289-79C
2,3-Diazabicyclo[2.2.2]oct-2-ene, 5,5,6,6-tetramethyl-	C_6H_{12}	334(1.08),344(1.26), 370(1.77),382(2.05)	88-0779-79
2-Hexenenitrile, 3-(2-aminoethyl)-4-ethyl-	EtOH	262(4.27)	39-2289-79C
3H-Pyrazole, 4,5-dihydro-3,3,5,5-tetramethyl-4-(1-methylethylidene)-	$C_{16}H_{34}$	328(2.36)	39-2401-79C
$C_{10}H_{18}N_2O$			
1H-Benzimidazole, 2,4,5,6,7,7a-hexahydro-2,2,7a-trimethyl-, 3-oxide	EtOH	235(4.04)	103-0092-79
2-Cyclohexen-1-one, 3-(2,2-dimethylhydrazino)-5,5-dimethyl-	MeOH	292(4.59)	64-0102-79B
1,4-Diazaspiro[4.4]non-1-ene, 2,3,3-trimethyl-, 1-oxide	EtOH	232(4.00)	103-0092-79
1H-Imidazole, 2,5-dihydro-1,2,2,4,5,5-hexamethyl-, 3-oxide	EtOH	230(4.00)	103-0092-79
$C_{10}H_{18}N_2O_2$			
Cyclohexanone, 2-[[(1-methylethylidene)amino]methyl]-, oxime, N^2-oxide	EtOH	238(3.95)	103-1025-79
1-Cyclohexen-1-amine, N-(1,1-dimethylethyl)-2-nitro-	EtOH	246s(--),370(4.31)	44-3410-79
$C_{10}H_{18}N_2S$			
1-Thia-5,6-diazaspiro[2.4]hept-5-ene, 2,2,4,4,7,7-hexamethyl-	EtOH	320(2.18)	39-2401-79C
$C_{10}H_{18}N_3O_4PS$			
Phosphoroamidothioic acid, (1-methylethyl)-, O-(2,3-dihydro-5-methoxy-2-methyl-3-oxo-4-pyridazinyl) O-methyl ester	MeOH	213(4.19),237(3.74), 321(3.80)	73-1761-79
$C_{10}H_{18}N_4$			
Butanedinitrile, 2,3-bis[(1-methylethyl)amino]-	hexane	202(2.92)	44-1273-79
	MeCN	204(--)	44-1273-79
$C_{10}H_{18}N_4S$			
4-Thia-1,2,7,8-tetraazaspiro[4.4]nona-1,7-diene, 3,3,6,6,9,9-hexamethyl-	EtOH	275(2.73),290(2.81)	39-2401-79C
$C_{10}H_{18}O_2$			
Ethanone, 1-(tetrahydro-2,5,6-trimethyl-2H-pyran-2-yl)-	C_6H_{12}	286(1.42)	54-0346-79
$C_{10}H_{18}S_2$			
Bicyclo[1.1.0]butane, 2,2,4,4-tetramethyl-1,3-bis(methylthio)-	hexane	243(3.25)	88-4457-79
2,4-Hexadiene, 2,5-dimethyl-3,4-bis(methylthio)-	C_6H_{12}	230(3.91),264(3.61)	88-4457-79
$C_{10}H_{19}N_3$			
2-Hexenenitrile, 3-[(2-aminoethyl)amino]-4-ethyl-	EtOH	262(4.27)	39-2289-79C
$C_{10}H_{20}N_2$			
1H-Imidazole, 2-(1-ethylpropyl)-4,5-dihydro-4,4-dimethyl-	EtOH	221(3.75)	39-2289-79C

Compound	Solvent	λ_{max}(log ϵ)	Ref.
$C_{10}H_{20}N_2O_2$			
1,3-Butadiene-1,3-diamine, 4,4-dimethoxy-N,N,N',N'-tetramethyl-	CH_2Cl_2	269(4.2)	88-0921-79
2-Penten-1-amine, 2-(1,1-dimethylethyl)-N-methyl-N-nitro-	isooctane	238(3.72)	44-4116-79
$C_{10}H_{20}N_6O_2$			
1,3-Propanediol, 2-[[4,6-bis(dimethylamino)-1,3,5-triazin-2-yl]amino]-	EtOH	223(4.74)	104-1144-79
$C_{10}H_{23}PS_2$			
Phosphinodithioic acid, ethyl-, dibutyl ester	hexane	216(4.20),266s(3.10)	65-1760-79
$C_{10}H_{24}NPS_2$			
Phosphoroamidodithious acid, dimethyl-, dibutyl ester	hexane	195(4.22),234s(3.63), 260s(3.30)	65-1760-79
$C_{10}H_{24}N_3$			
Hydrazinium, 2-[(dimethylamino)methylene]-1-methyl-1,1-bis(1-methylethyl)-, iodide	H_2O	226(4.42)	104-2073-79
$C_{10}H_{25}N_2OP$			
Phosphorodiamidous acid, tetraethyl-, ethyl ester	hexane	230(3.21)	22-0241-79I
$C_{10}H_{30}O_3Si_4$			
Tetrasiloxane, decamethyl-	heptane	186.5(2.58)	65-1333-79
	MeCN	186(2.76),189s(--)	65-1333-79
$C_{10}H_{30}O_5Si_5$			
Cyclopentasiloxane, decamethyl-	heptane	186(2.45),200s(--)	65-1333-79
Cyclopentasiloxane, 2,4,6,8,10-pentaethyl-	heptane	187(1.48),198(1.08)	65-1333-79

Compound	Solvent	λ max(log ε)	Ref.
$C_{11}H_3F_7O_2$			
1(4H)-Naphthalenone, 2,4,4,5,6,7,8-heptafluoro-3-methoxy-	heptane or C_6H_{12}	220(4.37),240(4.31), 246(4.30),293(4.21)	104-1934-79
$C_{11}H_4O_5$			
4H-Furo[3,2-g][1]benzopyran-4,7,9-trione	MeOH	270(4.0),285s(4.0), 315(3.8),350(3.1)	102-0352-79
$C_{11}H_5ClOS$			
3H-Naphtho[1,8-bc]thiophen-3-one, 2-chloro-	MeOH	234(4.5),266(4.5), 284(4.2),337(4.3), 371(4.2)	5-0965-79
$C_{11}H_5Cl_3O_2$			
2H-Pyran-2-one, 3,4,6-trichloro-5-phenyl-	MeOH	203(4.22),235(3.64), 310(3.75)	24-2741-79
$C_{11}H_6ClNO_2S$			
4H-[1]Benzothiopyrano[3,4-d]oxazol-4-one, 2-(chloromethyl)-	EtOH	230(4.52),302(3.87), 330(3.82)	25-0478-79
$C_{11}H_6Cl_2OS$			
2H-Naphtho[1,8-bc]thiophene-3-ol, 6,8-dichloro-	MeOH	233(4.1),255(4.1), 322(3.5),363(3.5), 354(3.4)	24-0349-79
$C_{11}H_6Cl_2O_2$			
2H-Pyran-2-one, 3,4-dichloro-5-phenyl-	MeOH	203(4.4),238(4.0), 310(3.8)	24-2741-79
2H-Pyran-2-one, 4,5-dichloro-3-phenyl-	MeOH	203(4.4),315(3.9)	24-2741-79
$C_{11}H_6Cl_2O_4$			
4H-1-Benzopyran-2-carboxylic acid, 3,6-dichloro-4-oxo-, methyl ester	EtOH	244(3.91),280(4.18), 291(4.21),355(3.57)	107-0129-79
$C_{11}H_6Cl_2S$			
2H-Naphtho[1,8-bc]thiophene, 6,8-dichloro- (25% 5H isomer)	MeOH	220(4.4),241(4.2), 250(4.2),326(3.9), 351(3.7)	24-0349-79
$C_{11}H_6N_4O_3S$			
Isothiazolo[4,5-d]pyrimidin-7(4H)-one, 3-(4-nitrophenyl)-	DMF	308s(4.08),335(4.19)	5-1534-79
$C_{11}H_6N_4S$			
1,2,3-Thiadiazolium, 5-(dicyanomethyl)-3-phenyl-, hydroxide, inner salt	EtOH	287(4.33),464(3.91)	39-0956-79C
$C_{11}H_6O_2S$			
2H-Naphtho[1,8-bc]thiophen-2-one, 3-hydroxy-	MeOH	236(4.5),265(4.5), 284(4.2),337(4.4), 371(4.2),382(4.2), 414(3.9)	5-0965-79
$C_{11}H_6O_3$			
Benzocycloheptene-5,6,7-trione	CH_2Cl_2	250(4.44),358(3.83), 522(1.45)	138-0859-79
hydrate	CH_2Cl_2	246(4.44),345(3.85)	138-0859-79
Psoralen	EtOH	291(4.1),328(3.8)	149-0645-79B

Compound	Solvent	λmax(log ε)	Ref.
$C_{11}H_6O_5$			
Psoralen, 5,8-dihydroxy-	MeOH	280(3.9),315(3.7), 350(3.2)	102-0352-79
$C_{11}H_6O_5S_6$			
1,3-Dithiole-4,5-dicarboxylic acid, 2-(5-oxo[1,3]dithiolo[4,5-d]-1,3-dithiol-2-ylidene)-, dimethyl ester	CH_2Cl_2	238(4.25),260(4.11), 295(4.30)	77-0516-79
	70% $HClO_4$	225(4.20),310(3.18), 505(3.76)	77-0516-79
$C_{11}H_7BrN_4$			
4-Pyridazinecarbonitrile, 3-amino-5-(4-bromophenyl)-	DMF	288(3.95),337(3.69)	48-0071-79
$C_{11}H_7ClN_4O$			
2H-Tetrazole, 2-(4-chlorophenyl)-5-(2-furanyl)-	EtOH	252(4.38),300(4.27)	4-0123-79
$C_{11}H_7ClO_5$			
2H-1-Benzopyran-4-acetic acid, 6-chloro-7-hydroxy-2-oxo-	MeOH	333(4.15)	73-2211-79
	NH_3	371(4.31)	73-2211-79
$C_{11}H_7NOS$			
Thieno[3,2-d]oxazole, 2-phenyl-	EtOH	225(4.15),277s(3.60), 295s(3.57)	103-0384-79
$C_{11}H_7NO_2$			
4H-1-Benzopyran-3-carbonitrile, 2-methyl-4-oxo-	MeOH	234(4.29),294(3.76)	56-0229-79
3-Furancarbonitrile, 2,5-dihydro-2-oxo-4-phenyl-	EtOH	296(4.27)	152-0047-79
$C_{11}H_7NO_3$			
2H-1-Benzopyran-3-carbonitrile, 7-hydroxy-4-methyl-2-oxo-	pH 2	350(4.4),365s(4.3)	46-0810-79
	pH 12	410(4.6)	46-0810-79
$C_{11}H_7NO_3S$			
2H,5H-[1]Benzothiopyrano[4,3-b]-1,4-oxazine-3,5(4H)-dione	MeOH	230(4.5),280(4.23) 345(4.02)	25-0058-79
$C_{11}H_7NO_4$			
2H,5H-[1]Benzopyrano[4,3-b]-1,4-oxazine-3,5(4H)-dione	MeOH	210(4.23),250(3.82), 330(3.76)	25-0058-79
$C_{11}H_7NS_2$			
Thieno[3,2-d]thiazole, 2-phenyl-	EtOH	240(4.21),317(4.00)	103-0384-79
$C_{11}H_7N_3$			
[2,4'-Bipyridine]-2'-carbonitrile	EtOH	219(4.32),249(4.01), 278(4.15)	44-0041-79
Pyrido[3,2-f]quinoxaline	EtOH	222(4.62),276(4.48), 329(3.43),344(3.41)	94-2596-79
Pyrido[3,4-f]quinoxaline	EtOH	228(4.60),260(4.14), 281s(3.86),320s(3.70), 336(3.92),352(3.89)	94-2596-79
Pyrido[4,3-f]quinoxaline	EtOH	220s(4.66),224(4.70), 270(4.30),343(3.30), 358(3.25)	94-2596-79
$C_{11}H_7N_3OS$			
Isothiazolo[4,5-d]pyrimidin-7(4H)-one,	DMF	316s(4.01),324(4.04)	5-1534-79

Compound	Solvent	λmax(log ε)	Ref.
3-phenyl- (cont.)			5-1534-79
$C_{11}H_7N_3O_2$			
3(2H)-Furazanone, 4-(1-isoquinolinyl)-	EtOH	223(4.51),331(3.83)	4-0689-79
3(2H)-Furazanone, 4-(2-quinolinyl)-	EtOH	243(4.46),254s(4.30), 304(3.91),320s(3.81), 333(3.62)	4-0689-79
1,2,4-Oxadiazol-5(2H)-one, 3-(1-iso-quinolinyl)-	EtOH	224(4.62),284(3.67), 327(3.79)	4-0689-79
1,2,4-Oxadiazol-5(2H)-one, 3-(2-quino-linyl)-	EtOH	243(4.35),293(3.64), 322(3.43),335(3.28)	4-0689-79
$C_{11}H_7N_5O_2$			
2-Butenedinitrile, 2-amino-3-[[(4-ni-trophenyl)methylene]-	EtOH	266(4.05),398(4.35)	44-0827-79
$C_{11}H_7N_5O_4$			
1H-Pyrazole-5-carbonitrile, 3-methyl-4-nitro-1-(4-nitrophenyl)-	EtOH	307(4.30)	78-1331-79
$C_{11}H_7N_5S$			
1,2,3,4-Thiatriazolium, 5-(dicyanometh-yl)-3-(4-methylphenyl)-, hydroxide, inner salt	n.s.g.	239(3.74),293(4.41), 305s(4.39),461(3.56)	39-0744-79C
$C_{11}H_8ClNO_2S$			
2-Thiophenecarboxamide, N-(4-chloro-phenyl)-N-hydroxy-	EtOH	254(4.06),295(4.23)	34-0072-79
$C_{11}H_8ClNO_3$			
1,4-Naphthalenedione, 5-amino-2-chloro-3-methoxy-	C_6H_{12}	482(3.79)	39-0696-79C
1,4-Naphthalenedione, 5-amino-3-chloro-2-methoxy-	C_6H_{12}	487(3.73)	39-0696-79C
$C_{11}H_8ClN_3S$			
Pyrido[3',2':4,5]thieno[3,2-d]pyrimi-dine, 4-chloro-7,9-dimethyl-	EtOH	237(4.44),264(4.12), 290(4.27),317(3.62), 329(3.65)	103-1078-79
$C_{11}H_8Cl_2N_2$			
Pyrazine, 2,5-dichloro-3-methyl-6-phen-yl-	EtOH	250s(4.04),255(4.05), 310(4.08)	94-2027-79
$C_{11}H_8Cl_3N_3O_2$			
5(4H)-Isoxazolone, 3,4-dimethyl-4-[(2,3,4-trichlorophenyl)azo]-	MeOH	236(4.18),295(4.04)	33-1571-79
5(4H)-Isoxazolone, 3,4-dimethyl-4-[(2,3,5-trichlorophenyl)azo]-	MeOH	226(4.34),285(3.93)	33-1571-79
$C_{11}H_8F_3N_3OS$			
Urea, N-2-thiazolyl-N'-[2-(trifluoro-methyl)phenyl]-	n.s.g.	237(3.89),266(4.24)	87-0028-79
$C_{11}H_8N_2O$			
Benzonitrile, 4-(2-cyano-1-methoxyeth-enyl)-, (E)-	C_6H_{12}	275(3.94)	56-0839-79
	EtOH	275(4.02)	56-2251-79
(Z)-	C_6H_{12}	229(4.09),237(4.06)	56-0839-79
	EtOH	229(4.18),237(4.11)	56-0839-79 +56-2251-79
Benzonitrile, 3-(2-methyl-5-oxazolyl)-	EtOH	274(4.29)	18-3597-79

Compound	Solvent	$\lambda_{max}(\log \epsilon)$	Ref.
Imidazo[5,1-a]isoquinolin-3(2H)-one	EtOH	210(4.50),259(4.50), 268(4.63),339(3.79)	4-0689-79
Imidazo[1,5-a]quinolin-1(2H)-one	EtOH	209(4.59),257(4.36), 265(4.40),360(3.70)	4-0689-79
Pyrido[1,2-a]benzimidazol-8-ol	EtOH	248(4.5),300(3.76), 360(3.78)	18-3096-79
	EtOH-acid	238(4.17),292(3.71), 358(3.94)	18-3096-79
	EtOH-base	242(4.36),269(4.49), 405(3.87)	18-3096-79
$C_{11}H_8N_2OS$			
2H-Naphtho[1,8-bc]thiophen-2-one, 3-hydroxy-, hydrazone	MeOH	207(4.6),236(4.6), 255(4.6),278(4.4), 296(4.3),345(4.3), 404(4.4),421(4.4)	5-1789-79
$C_{11}H_8N_2O_2$			
Pyrano[3,2-e]benzimidazol-7(1H)-one, 9-methyl- (or isomer)	EtOH	234(4.24),241(4.25), 257(4.07),280(3.83), 314(3.82)	95-0813-79
$C_{11}H_8N_2O_4$			
4-Pyrimidinecarboxylic acid, 5,6-di-hydroxy-2-phenyl-	MeOH	277(4.00),314(4.00)	4-1423-79
$C_{11}H_8N_2S$			
Naphtho[1,2-d]thiazol-2-amine	MeOH	244(4.75),307(3.90)	83-0619-79
$C_{11}H_8N_4$			
2-Butenedinitrile, 2-amino-3-[(phenyl-methylene)amino]-	EtOH	259(4.17),366(4.44)	44-0827-79
4-Pyridazinecarbonitrile, 3-amino-5-phenyl-	DMF	281(3.84),353(3.68)	48-0071-79
$C_{11}H_8N_4O$			
Furazanamine, 4-(2-quinolinyl)-	EtOH	245(4.57),309(3.96), 322(3.94),336(3.82)	4-0689-79
1-Isoquinolineacetyl azide	EtOH	217(4.55),259(4.14), 267(4.26),291s(3.82), 299(3.93),324(3.68), 385(3.81),405(4.05), 428(4.05)	4-0689-79
7H-Pyrazolo[4,3-d]pyrimidin-7-one, 1,4-dihydro-3-phenyl-	pH 1	232(4.06)	18-0208-79
	pH 11	248(4.13)	18-0208-79
	EtOH	214s(4.03),231(4.08)	18-0208-79
2-Quinolineacetyl azide	EtOH	212(4.50),232s(4.20), 260(3.95),269(3.97), 290s(4.16),298(4.18), 312(4.04),390(3.90), 410(3.93),433(3.68)	4-0689-79
2H-Tetrazole, 5-(2-furanyl)-2-phenyl-	EtOH	250(4.31),285(4.28)	4-0123-79
$C_{11}H_8N_4OS$			
Urea, N-(4-cyanophenyl)-N'-2-thiazolyl-	n.s.g.	255(4.00),283(4.59), 314(3.39)	87-0028-79
$C_{11}H_8N_4O_2$			
Benzo[g]pteridine-2,4(1H,3H)-dione, 6-methyl-	MeOH	335(3.98),375(3.76)	88-4117-79

Compound	Solvent	λ_{max}(log ε)	Ref.
1H-Imidazole-4-carbonitrile, 2-methyl-1-(4-nitrophenyl)-	EtOH	299(4.08)	78-1331-79
1H-Pyrazole-4-carbonitrile, 3-methyl-1-(4-nitrophenyl)-	EtOH	313(4.36)	78-1331-79
$C_{11}H_8N_4S$			
Isothiazolo[3,4-c]pyridazin-3-amine, 4-phenyl-	DMF	463(3.42)	48-0071-79
2H-Tetrazole, 2-phenyl-5-(2-thienyl)-	EtOH	250(4.13),285(4.30)	4-0123-79
$C_{11}H_8N_6$			
Pyridine, 3-[5-(4-pyridinyl)-2H-tetrazol-2-yl]-	EtOH	272(4.42)	4-0123-79
Pyridine, 3,3'-(2H-tetrazole-2,5-diyl)-bis-	EtOH	268(4.25),279(4.26)	4-0123-79
$C_{11}H_8OS_3$			
4H-Dithieno[2,3-b:3',2'-e]thiopyran-4-one, 2-ethyl-	MeOH	266(4.49),304(3.90), 335(3.90)	73-2997-79
$C_{11}H_8O_2$			
1,4-Naphthalenedione, 2-methyl-	DMF	412(3.77)	104-1621-79
$C_{11}H_8O_2S_2$			
Methanone, 2-thienyl[3-(2-thienyl)oxiranyl]-, trans	EtOH	262(4.38)	104-2174-79
$C_{11}H_8O_3$			
1,2-Naphthalenedione, 4-methoxy-	n.s.g.	208(4.20),250(4.36), 276(3.95),404(3.32)	12-1749-79
$C_{11}H_8O_5$			
2H-1-Benzopyran-4-acetic acid, 7-hydroxy-2-oxo-	MeOH	327(4.17)	73-2211-79
	NH_3	368(4.28)	73-2211-79
$C_{11}H_8S$			
2H-Naphtho[1,8-bc]thiophene	MeOH	213(4.4),241(4.3), 319(3.9),333(3.8)	24-0349-79
$C_{11}H_9BrCl_3NO_3$			
4-Morpholinecarboxylic acid, 2-bromo-3,4,6-trichlorophenyl ester	MeOH	210(4.77)	73-0918-79
$C_{11}H_9BrO_3$			
2H-1-Benzopyran-2-one, 4-(2-bromoethoxy)-	MeOH	260s(3.91),267(4.02), 278(4.00),306(3.79), 315s(3.66)	150-0110-79S
$C_{11}H_9ClN_2$			
Pyrazine, 3-chloro-2-methyl-5-phenyl-	EtOH	254(4.30),291(4.10), 314(4.23)	94-2027-79
Pyrazine, 3-chloro-5-methyl-2-phenyl-	EtOH	244(4.01),290(3.89), 303(3.89)	94-2027-79
$C_{11}H_9ClN_2O$			
Pyrazine, 3-chloro-2-methyl-5-phenyl-, 1-oxide	EtOH	266(4.43),329(3.69)	94-2027-79
Pyrazine, 3-chloro-5-methyl-2-phenyl-, 1-oxide	EtOH	235(4.21),250(4.17), 313(3.53)	94-2027-79
Pyrazine, 3-chloro-5-methyl-2-phenyl-, 4-oxide	EtOH	266(4.31),328(3.55)	94-2027-79

Compound	Solvent	λ_{max}(log ϵ)	Ref.
$C_{11}H_9ClN_2O_2$			
1,4-Naphthalenedione, 5-amino-2-chloro-3-(methylamino)-	C_6H_{12}	448(3.85),490s(3.67)	39-0696-79C
1,4-Naphthalenedione, 5-amino-3-chloro-2-(methylamino)-	C_6H_{12}	454(3.56),500(3.64)	39-0696-79C
Pyrazine, 3-chloro-5-methyl-2-phenyl-, 1,4-dioxide	EtOH	259(4.31),278(4.14), 316(4.31)	94-2027-79
$C_{11}H_9ClN_4O$			
5H-1,2,4-Triazolo[4,3-d][1,4]benzodiazepin-6(7H)-one, 10-chloro-7-methyl-	MeOH	231(4.55),250(4.10), 298(3.28)	44-0088-79
$C_{11}H_9ClN_4O_2$			
3H-1,2,4-Triazolo[4,3-d][1,4]benzodiazepine-3,6(5H)-dione, 10-chloro-2,7-dihydro-7-methyl-	MeOH	251(4.25),300(3.57)	44-0088-79
$C_{11}H_9ClO_2$			
1H-Inden-1-one, 4-chloro-7-hydroxy-2,3-dimethyl-	EtOH	237(4.50),380(3.65)	107-0129-79
$C_{11}H_9Cl_2N_3O_2$			
5(4H)-Isoxazolone, 4-[(2,4-dichlorophenyl)azo]-3,4-dimethyl-	MeOH	233(4.00),291(4.09)	33-1571-79
$C_{11}H_9Cl_3INO_3$			
4-Morpholinecarboxylic acid, 3,4,6-trichloro-2-iodophenyl ester	MeOH	218(4.56)	73-0918-79
$C_{11}H_9Cl_3N_2O_2$			
1H-Indole-3-carboxamide, 3,5,7-trichloro-2,3-dihydro-N,N-dimethyl-2-oxo-	90% MeOH	228(4.36),266(3.67), 324(3.08)	39-0595-79C
$C_{11}H_9Cl_3N_2O_4S$			
4-Morpholinecarbothioic acid, O-(3,4,6-trichloro-2-nitrophenyl) ester	MeOH	209(4.515),256(4.184)	73-0918-79
$C_{11}H_9Cl_3N_2O_5$			
4-Morpholinecarboxylic acid, 3,4,6-trichloro-2-nitrophenyl ester	MeOH	209(4.50),292(3.12)	73-0918-79
$C_{11}H_9IO$			
1,4-Methanonaphthalen-2(1H)-one, 3,4-dihydro-6-iodo-	isooctane	238(4.32),244(4.25), 300(3.27),311(3.23), 323(2.76)	35-5972-79
1,4-Methanonaphthalen-2(1H)-one, 3,4-dihydro-7-iodo-	isooctane	240(4.26),246(4.32), 298(3.27),309(3.23), 322(2.75)	35-5972-79
$C_{11}H_9N$			
Cyclobuta[g]quinoline, 6,7-dihydro-	EtOH	291(3.58),298(3.57), 304(3.71),311(3.67), 318(3.92)	44-3261-79
$C_{11}H_9NO$			
1H-Pyrrole-2-carboxaldehyde, 3-phenyl-	H_2O	299(4.11)	152-0115-79
$C_{11}H_9NO_2$			
Methanone, (5-methyl-3-isoxazolyl)-phenyl-	EtOH	261(4.09)	103-0966-79

Compound	Solvent	λ max(log ε)	Ref.
1,4-Naphthalenedione, 5-(methylamino)-	C_6H_{12}	529(3.76)	39-0702-79C
2-Propenoic acid, 3-(4-cyanophenyl)-, methyl ester, (E)-	MeCN	283(4.49)	88-0863-79
(Z)-	MeCN	271(4.19)	88-0863-79
2,4-Pyrrolidinedione, 5-(phenylmethylene)-	aq NaOH	219(4.41),313(4.51)	142-0477-79B
3-Quinolinecarboxaldehyde, 1,2-dihydro-1-methyl-4-oxo-	EtOH	217(4.43),234(4.37), 265(3.91),324(4.21)	4-0177-79
$C_{11}H_9NO_2S$			
Phenol, 3-methyl-4-nitroso-5-(2-thienyl)-	DMF	695(1.36)	104-0311-79
$C_{11}H_9NO_2S_2$			
3H-1,2-Dithiole, 4-methyl-3-(nitromethylene)-5-phenyl-	MeOH	228s(4.31),268s(3.94), 290(3.89),450(4.58)	104-0955-79
$C_{11}H_9NO_3$			
2,4(3H,5H)-Furandione, 3-[(phenylamino)methylene]-	hexane	220s(4.45),252s(3.70), 346(4.40)	131-0077-79D
	EtOH	340(4.37)	131-0077-79D
1H-Indole-4-carboxylic acid, 1-formyl-, methyl ester	MeOH	248(4.25),287(4.15)	94-0946-79
Phenol, 2-(3-isoxazolyl)-, acetate	EtOH	211(4.01),237(4.04)	56-0229-79
Phenol, 2-(5-isoxazolyl)-, acetate	MeOH	214(4.07),259(4.21)	56-0229-79
2-Quinolinecarboxylic acid, 4-hydroxy-, methyl ester	pH -0.13	310(3.92)	149-0251-79B
	pH 7	342(3.97)	149-0251-79B
	pH 11.3	340(3.83)	149-0251-79B
$C_{11}H_9NO_4$			
Benzoic acid, 3-(2,5-dioxo-3-pyrrolidinyl)-	EtOH	252(4.24),303(3.72)	100-0615-79
1(4H)-Pyridineacetic acid, 4-ethynyl-3,5-diformyl-	EtOH	206s(3.98),231(4.26), 252(4.03),368(3.91)	49-0613-79
$C_{11}H_9NO_5$			
Acetic acid, hydroxy(2-oxofuro[3,2-b]pyridin-3(2H)-ylidene)-	$CHCl_3$	285(4.08),375(4.17)	39-0399-79C
7H-1,3-Dioxolo[4,5-f][3,1]benzoxazine-7,9(6H)-dione, 6-ethyl-	MeCN	242(4.38),260(3.95), 363(3.79)	87-1354-79
2H-Pyrano[4,3-b]pyridine-3-carboxylic acid, 1,5-dihydro-1-methyl-2,5-dioxo-, methyl ester	EtOH and EtOH-HCl	220(4.40),260(4.02), 266s(4.01),286(3.75), 297(3.68),356(4.03)	39-0686-79C
$C_{11}H_9N_3$			
Propanedinitrile, [1-(phenylamino)ethylidene]-	EtOH	289(4.22)	131-0077-79D
	hexane	288(--)	131-0077-79D
Pyrazine, [2-(2-pyridinyl)ethenyl]-	EtOH	260(4.14),321(4.35)	94-2596-79
Pyrazine, [2-(3-pyridinyl)ethenyl]-	EtOH	267(4.08),319(4.20)	94-2596-79
Pyrazine, [2-(4-pyridinyl)ethenyl]-	EtOH	270(4.34),315(4.52)	94-2596-79
$C_{11}H_9N_3OS$			
Pyrido[3',2':4,5]thieno[3,2-d]pyrimidin-4(1H)-one, 7,9-dimethyl-	EtOH	247(4.50),286(3.98), 295(4.10),323(3.85)	103-1078-79
$C_{11}H_9N_3OS_2$			
Thieno[3',4':4,5]imidazo[1,2-a]pyridine-3-carboxamide, 1-(methylthio)-	EtOH	260(4.21),294(4.23), 412(4.00)	95-1081-79

Compound	Solvent	λ_{max}(log ε)	Ref.
$C_{11}H_9N_3O_2$			
Pyrazine, [2-(2-pyridinyl)ethenyl]-, 1,4-dioxide	EtOH	224(4.01),267(4.13), 315(4.63),336(4.37), 350s(4.22)	94-2596-79
Pyrazine, [2-(3-pyridinyl)ethenyl]-, 1,4-dioxide	EtOH	272(3.97),312(4.51), 337s(4.23)	94-2596-79
Pyrazine, [2-(4-pyridinyl)ethenyl]-, 1,4-dioxide	EtOH	271s(4.26),305(4.44), 329(4.37)	94-2596-79
$C_{11}H_9N_3O_2S$			
3-Isothiazolecarboxamide, 4-amino-5-benzoyl-	MeCN	251(4.07),389(4.10)	5-1534-79
$C_{11}H_9N_3O_3$			
Acetamide, N-(8-nitro-3-quinolinyl)-	EtOH	254(4.25),285(3.62), 330(3.40)	94-2627-79
1H-Pyrazole-4-carboxaldehyde, 3-methyl-1-(4-nitrophenyl)-	EtOH	320(4.32)	78-1331-79
2(1H)-Pyridinone, 3-(2-aminophenyl)-5-nitro-	EtOH	312(4.02)	39-2902-79C
4(1H)-Pyridinone, 3-(2-aminophenyl)-5-nitro-	EtOH	234(4.10),334(3.47)	39-2902-79C
$C_{11}H_9N_3O_3S$			
Benzoic acid, 4-[[(2-thiazolylamino)-carbonyl]amino]-	n.s.g.	285(4.62)	87-0028-79
$C_{11}H_9N_3O_4$			
1H-Imidazole-4-carboxylic acid, 5-nitro-1-(phenylmethyl)-	MeOH	290(3.64)	35-6127-79
1H-Pyrazole-3-carboxylic acid, 1-(4-nitrophenyl)-, methyl ester	CH_2Cl_2	308(4.30)	24-1193-79
$C_{11}H_9N_3O_4S$			
2-Thiophenamine, N-(2-methylphenyl)-3,5-dinitro-	MeOH	404(4.20)	39-0219-79B
$C_{11}H_9N_3O_5S$			
2-Thiophenamine, N-(2-methoxyphenyl)-3,5-dinitro-	MeOH	402(4.30)	39-0219-79B
$C_{11}H_9N_3S_2$			
Pyrido[3',2':4,5]thieno[3,2-d]pyrimidine-4(1H)-thione, 7,9-dimethyl-	EtOH	227(4.43),279(4.08), 300(4.11),322(3.98), 377(4.00)	103-1078-79
$C_{11}H_9N_5O_3$			
2-Propenamide, 2-amino-3-cyano-3-[[(4-nitrophenyl)methylene]amino]-	EtOH	258(3.41),389(3.70)	44-0827-79
$C_{11}H_9N_5O_4$			
Benzoic acid, 2-(6-methyl-1,2,4,5-tetrazin-3-yl)-3-nitro-, methyl ester	MeOH	251s(3.81),277s(3.57), 520(2.63)	24-1981-79
$C_{11}H_9N_5O_5$			
1H-Pyrazole-5-carboxamide, 3-methyl-4-nitro-1-(4-nitrophenyl)-	EtOH	302(4.34)	78-1331-79
$C_{11}H_{10}ClNO$			
2(1H)-Quinolinone, 3-chloro-1,7-dimethyl-	EtOH	335(4.03)	4-0065-79

Compound	Solvent	$\lambda_{max}(\log \epsilon)$	Ref.
2(1H)-Quinolinone, 3-chloro-1-ethyl-	EtOH	334(3.93)	4-0065-79
$C_{11}H_{10}ClNO_3$			
Butanoic acid, 4-chloro-3-oxo-2-[(phenylamino)methylene]-, (E)-	MeOH	333(4.35)	49-1387-79
$C_{11}H_{10}ClN_3O$			
1H-1,2,4-Triazole, 1-acetyl-3-(4-chlorophenyl)-5-methyl-	MeOH	251(4.23)	44-0084-79
$C_{11}H_{10}Cl_4O_5$			
4-Cyclopentene-1,3-dione, 4,5-dichloro-2-(2,3-dichloro-1,1,3-trimethoxy-2-propenyl)-	hexane	219(4.13),285(4.06)	18-0811-79
$C_{11}H_{10}F_6N_2O_4$			
Uridine, 2',5'-dideoxy-5'-fluoro-5-(pentafluoroethyl)-	pH 1	269(--)	48-0449-79
	pH 14	270(3.74)	48-0449-79
$C_{11}H_{10}F_6N_2O_5$			
Uridine, 5'-deoxy-5'-fluoro-5-(pentafluoroethyl)-	pH 1	263(--)	48-0449-79
	pH 14	261(3.93)	48-0449-79
$C_{11}H_{10}F_7O_3P$			
Phosphonic acid, [2,3,5,6-tetrafluoro-4-(trifluoromethyl)phenyl]-, diethyl ester	EtOH	218(3.95),288(3.39)	65-0464-79
$C_{11}H_{10}N$			
Pyridinium, 1-phenyl-, chloride	n.s.g.	263(3.91)	39-1402-79B
$C_{11}H_{10}N_2$			
Pyrazine, 2-methyl-5-phenyl-	EtOH	249(4.13),290(3.96)	94-2027-79
2-Pyridinamine, 3-phenyl-	CH_2Cl_2	253(3.78),308(3.85)	118-0376-79
3-Quinolinecarbonitrile, 1,4-dihydro-1-methyl-	MeOH	333(4.02)	73-2238-79
$C_{11}H_{10}N_2O$			
Ethanone, 2-diazo-1-tricyclo[5.2.0.-$0^{2,9}$]nona-3,5-dien-8-yl-	C_6H_{12}	250(4.04),275(3.98),380(1.43)	88-0151-79
Pyrazine, 2-methyl-5-phenyl-, 1-oxide	EtOH	262(4.42),319(3.61)	94-2027-79
Pyrazine, 2-methyl-5-phenyl-, 4-oxide	EtOH	253(4.47),280(4.00),320(3.60)	94-2027-79
2(1H)-Pyrazinone, 6-methyl-3-phenyl-	EtOH	230(3.78),253(3.87),353(4.07)	94-2027-79
Pyrimidine, 4-(4-methoxyphenyl)-	EtOH	300(4.32)	24-0001-79
$C_{11}H_{10}N_2OS$			
1H-Imidazole-4-carboxaldehyde, 5-(methylthio)-1-phenyl-	EtOH	252(4.1),294s(3.7)	103-0544-79
	$CHCl_3$	253(4.0),290(3.9)	103-0544-79
1H-Imidazolium, 4-formyl-5-mercapto-3-methyl-1-phenyl-, hydroxide, inner salt	EtOH	272(3.9),302(3.6)	103-0544-79
	$CHCl_3$	315(3.8),382(3.9)	103-0544-79
$C_{11}H_{10}N_2O_2$			
1H-Imidazole-4-carboxaldehyde, 5-methoxy-1-phenyl-	EtOH	226(4.0),275(4.1)	103-0544-79
	$CHCl_3$	277(4.1)	103-0544-79
1H-Imidazolium, 4-formyl-5-hydroxy-3-methyl-1-phenyl-, hydroxide, inner salt	EtOH	228(3.9),313(3.6)	103-0544-79
	$CHCl_3$	330(3.5)	103-0544-79

Compound	Solvent	λ_{max}(log ε)	Ref.
1H-Indole-6-carbonitrile, 2,3-dihydro-1-hydroxy-3,3-dimethyl-2-oxo-	C_6H_{12}	225(4.6),263(3.8), 303(3.4)	5-0554-79
	pH 13	290(4.0)	5-0554-79
2-Propenoic acid, 2-cyano-3-(phenylamino)-, methyl ester	MeCN	320(4.51)	80-1143-79
Pyrazine, 2-methyl-5-phenyl-, 1,4-dioxide	EtOH	260(4.26),279(4.11), 317(4.25)	94-2027-79
2(1H)-Pyrazinone, 3-(4-hydroxyphenyl)-6-methyl-	pH 12	226(4.03),263(3.90), 359(4.18)	83-1054-79
2(1H)-Pyrazinone, 3-methyl-6-phenyl-, 4-oxide	EtOH	250(4.41),342(4.04)	94-2027-79
2(1H)-Pyrazinone, 6-methyl-3-phenyl-, 1-oxide	EtOH	250(4.29),341(3.98)	94-2027-79
2(1H)-Pyrazinone, 6-methyl-3-phenyl-, 4-oxide	EtOH	241(4.21),292(3.62), 353(3.93)	94-2027-79
Pyrimidine, 5-methoxy-4-phenyl-, 3-oxide	EtOH	205(4.05),232(4.18), 251(4.25),319s(3.71)	103-0677-79
$C_{11}H_{10}N_2O_2S$			
2,4(1H,3H)-Pyrimidinedione, 5-[(4-methylphenyl)thio]-	MeOH	245(4.06),275(3.81), 300(3.54)	4-0567-79
$C_{11}H_{10}N_2O_2S_2$			
2,4(1H,3H)-Pyrimidinedione, 5-[(phenylmethyl)dithio]-	MeOH	265(3.96)	4-0567-79
$C_{11}H_{10}N_2O_3$			
1,3-Dioxolo[4,5-g]quinazolin-8(5H)-one, 5,6-dimethyl-	80% EtOH	243(4.06),319(3.66), 332(3.66)	42-0708-79
$C_{11}H_{10}N_2O_3S$			
Benzo[b]thiophen-3(2H)-one, 2-(2-imidazolidinylidene)-, 1,1-dioxide	EtOH	247(4.05),267(4.21)	95-0038-79
$C_{11}H_{10}N_2O_4$			
2H-1-Benzopyran-4-acetic acid, 7-hydroxy-2-oxo-, hydrazide	MeOH	325(4.16)	73-2211-79
	NH_3	371(4.28)	73-2211-79
Sydnone, 4-acetyl-3-(3-methoxyphenyl)-	CH_2Cl_2	324(3.97)	5-0063-79
Sydnone, 4-acetyl-3-(4-methoxyphenyl)-	benzene	324(3.98)	5-0063-79
	MeOH	319(4.01)	5-0063-79
	CH_2Cl_2	229(4.23),321(4.03)	5-0063-79
	MeCN	320(4.00)	5-0063-79
$C_{11}H_{10}N_4$			
1H-Pyrazole-4-carbonitrile, 1-(4-aminophenyl)-3-methyl-	EtOH	288(4.32)	78-1331-79
1H-Pyrrole-3-carbonitrile, 1,2-diamino-4-phenyl-	EtOH	299(3.93)	48-0071-79
$C_{11}H_{10}N_4O$			
2-Propenamide, 2-amino-3-cyano-3-[(phenylmethylene)amino]-	EtOH	247(4.29),360(4.49)	44-0827-79
$C_{11}H_{10}N_4O_2$			
Benzoic acid, 2-(6-methyl-1,2,4,5-tetrazin-3-yl)-, methyl ester	MeOH	235(3.98),245(3.97), 524(2.65)	24-1981-79
Butanenitrile, 4-(5-azido-2-formylphenoxy)-	90% MeCN	292(4.20),325(4.02)	69-1288-79

Compound	Solvent	$\lambda_{max}(\log \epsilon)$	Ref.
$C_{11}H_{10}N_4O_2S$			
Imidazo[4,5-e]-1,2,4-thiadiazine, 2,5-dihydro-5-(phenylmethyl)-, 1,1-dioxide	pH 13	273(3.83)	44-4046-79
	MeOH	271(3.72)	44-4046-79
Imidazo[4,5-e]-1,2,4-thiadiazine, 2,7-dihydro-7-(phenylmethyl)-, 1,1-dioxide	pH 1	232(3.56),260(3.43)	44-4046-79
	pH 13	250(3.63),267(3.60)	44-4046-79
Isothiazolo[4,5-b]pyridine-3-carboxylic acid, 5-amino-6-cyano-7-methyl-, ethyl ester	DMF	289(3.81),295s(3.80), 392(3.76)	5-1534-79
Isothiazolo[5,1-e][1,2,3]thiadiazole-7-S^{IV}, 1,6-dihydro-6-methyl-1-(4-nitrophenyl)-	C_6H_{12}	236(3.99),344(3.78), 456(4.55)	39-2340-79C
$C_{11}H_{10}N_4O_3$			
1H-Pyrazole-4-carboxamide, 3-methyl-1-(4-nitrophenyl)-	EtOH	322(4.45)	78-1331-79
$C_{11}H_{10}N_4O_4$			
5(4H)-Isoxazolone, 3,4-dimethyl-4-[(4-nitrophenyl)azo]-	MeOH	283(4.20)	33-1570-79
$C_{11}H_{10}N_4O_4S$			
Isothiazolo[3,4-d]pyrimidine-3-acetic acid, α-cyano-4,5,6,7-tetrahydro-5,7-dimethyl-4,6-dioxo-, methyl ester	EtOH	215(4.50),235(4.41), 294(3.90),354(4.46)	95-0989-79 +142-0485-79
$C_{11}H_{10}N_4S$			
Propanedinitrile, [[(1-methyl-2(1H)-pyridinylidene)amino](methylthio)-methylene]-	EtOH	220(3.85),243(3.87), 308(4.08),376(4.24)	94-2879-79
4-Pyridazinecarbothioamide, 3-amino-5-phenyl-	DMF	347(3.62)	48-0071-79
$C_{11}H_{10}O$			
1,4-Etheno-1H-inden-7(4H)-one, 3a,7a-dihydro-	C_6H_{12}	221(3.72),271(3.13)	88-0151-79
1H-Indene, 1-(methoxymethylene)-	MeCN	226s(4.37),270(4.39), 310s(3.94),320(3.99), 335s(3.87)	33-0718-79
1,5,6-Methenocycloprop[cd]azulen-2(1H)-one, 2a,2b,5,6,6a,6b-hexahydro-	C_6H_{12}	225(3.35)	88-0151-79
Pentacyclo[4.4.1.$0^{2,4}$.$0^{3,10}$.$0^{5,7}$]undec-8-en-11-one	C_6H_{12}	250(2.94)	88-0151-79
$C_{11}H_{10}O_2$			
5H-Benzocycloheptene-5,9(6H)-dione, 7,8-dihydro-	isooctane	248(3.94),291(3.18)	56-1751-79
$(C_{11}H_{10}O_2)_n$			
2-Propen-1-one, 1-(4-acetylphenyl)-, polymer	$CHCl_3$	278(3.1),339s(2.43)	47-2893-79
$C_{11}H_{10}O_2S$			
2H-1-Benzopyran-2-thione, 4-methoxy-3-methyl-	hexane	244(3.70),276(3.92), 305(3.26),360s(4.03), 370(4.07),384s(3.96)	39-1166-79C
$C_{11}H_{10}O_2S_3$			
3-Thiophenecarboxylic acid, 5-ethyl-2-(2-thienylthio)-	MeOH	228(4.33),245s(4.10), 304(3.88)	73-2997-79

Compound	Solvent	λ_{max}(log ε)	Ref.
$C_{11}H_{10}O_3$			
1H-2-Benzopyran-1-one, 8-methoxy-3-methyl-	MeOH	220(4.53),270(4.12),346(3.5)	2-0430-79A
2H-Furo[2,3-h]-1-benzopyran-3-ol, 3,4-dihydro-	EtOH	218(4.44),250(4.14),257(4.18),285(3.42),295(3.36)	2-0011-79B
$C_{11}H_{10}S$			
Benzo[b]thiophene, 3-ethenyl-2-methyl-	EtOH	215(4.40),235(4.45),264s(3.90),273(3.95),282s(3.90),293s(3.74),304(3.70)	12-0133-79
Benzo[b]thiophene, 3-(1-methylethenyl)-	EtOH	217(4.18),225(4.30),233(4.35),255(3.80),277(3.75),288s(3.70),302(3.75),310s(3.52)	12-0133-79
Benzo[b]thiophene, 3-(1-propenyl)-, (E)-	EtOH	217s(4.32),226(4.40),233(4.40),256s(3.79),275(3.78),282s(3.78),302(3.79)	12-0133-79
$C_{11}H_{10}S_2$			
Thiophene, 2-(methylthio)-3-phenyl-	EtOH	233(4.12)	88-2493-79
Thiophene, 2-(methylthio)-4-phenyl-	EtOH	252(4.33)	88-2493-79
$C_{11}H_{11}BrCl_3NO_2$			
Carbamic acid, diethyl-, 2-bromo-3,4,6-trichlorophenyl ester	MeOH	210.0(4.75)	73-0918-79
$C_{11}H_{11}BrN_4O$			
Isoxazole, 5-[3-(4-bromophenyl)-1-triazenyl]-3,4-dimethyl-	MeOH	236(3.88),303(3.68),373(4.23)	33-1570-79
$C_{11}H_{11}BrO_2$			
1,2-Propanedione, 1-[2-(1-bromoethyl)-phenyl]-	CCl_4	413(1.58)	39-0508-79C
$C_{11}H_{11}ClN_2O_3$			
Benzeneacetaldehyde, 4-chloro-α-(dimethylamino)methylene]-2-nitro-	isoPrOH	287(4.44)	44-3748-79
$C_{11}H_{11}ClN_4O$			
Isoxazole, 5-[3-(4-chlorophenyl)-1-triazenyl]-3,4-dimethyl-	MeOH	238(3.94),302(3.72),372(4.25)	33-1570-79
$C_{11}H_{11}Cl_3INO_2$			
Carbamic acid, diethyl-, 3,4,6-trichloro-2-iodophenyl ester	MeOH	217.5(4.57)	73-0918-79
$C_{11}H_{11}Cl_3N_2O_4$			
Carbamic acid, diethyl-, 3,4,6-trichloro-2-nitrophenyl ester	MeOH	209(4.45),292(3.48)	73-0918-79
$C_{11}H_{11}FN_2O_3S_3$			
1,2,3-Thiadiazolium, 5-[2-(methylthio)-ethenyl]-2-phenyl-, fluorosulfonate	MeOH	448(4.46)	39-0926-79C
$C_{11}H_{11}FN_2O_5$			
2,2'-Anhydro-1-(3-acetoxy-5-deoxy-β-D-arabinofuranosyl)-5-fluorouracil	MeOH	228(3.86),252(3.94)	87-1330-79

Compound	Solvent	λ_{max}(log ϵ)	Ref.
$C_{11}H_{11}FN_4O$			
Isoxazole, 5-[3-(4-fluorophenyl)-1-triazenyl]-3,4-dimethyl-	MeOH	230(3.98),299(3.80), 367(4.20)	33-1570-79
$C_{11}H_{11}FN_4O_5S_3$			
Isothiazolium, 2-methyl-5-(4-nitrophenylhydrazonomethyl)-, fluorosulfonate	MeOH-$HClO_4$	245(4.03),322(3.88), 432(4.59)	39-2340-79C
$C_{11}H_{11}F_3N_2O_4S$			
5-Thia-1-azabicyclo[4.2.0]oct-2-ene-2-carboxylic acid, 3-methyl-8-oxo-7-[(trifluoroacetyl)amino]-, methyl ester, (6R-trans)-	EtOH	257(3.72)	39-1629-79C
$C_{11}H_{11}IN_4O$			
2H-Furo[2,3-b]indole, 3a-azido-3,3a,8,8a-tetrahydro-5(or 6)-iodo-8a-methyl-	EtOH	256(4.26),318(3.38)	39-3061-79C
$C_{11}H_{11}IO_8P_2$			
1,4-Naphthalenediol, 6-iodo-2-methyl-, bis(dihydrogen phosphate)-, tetraammonium salt	pH 2	230(4.55),247(4.60), 290(3.72)	77-0659-79
$C_{11}H_{11}NO$			
2-Propenenitrile, 3-methoxy-3-(4-methylphenyl)-, (E)-	C_6H_{12}	266(4.07)	56-0839-79
	EtOH	266(4.06)	56-2251-79
(Z)-	C_6H_{12}	274(4.22)	56-0839-79
	C_6H_{12}	274(4.19)	56-2251-79
	EtOH	274(4.39)	56-0839-79
$C_{11}H_{11}NOS$			
4H-1,4-Benzothiazine, 4-acetyl-3,4-dihydro-3-methylene-	EtOH	205(4.20),229(4.23), 255(3.99),290(3.18), 300(3.04)	94-1982-79
2(1H)-Quinolinone, 1-methyl-3-(methylthio)-	EtOH	336(3.89)	4-0065-79
$C_{11}H_{11}NOS_2$			
4H-1,3-Thiazin-4-one, tetrahydro-6-(4-methylphenyl)-2-thioxo-	EtOH	222(4.18),260(4.11), 311(4.21)	150-0212-79S
$C_{11}H_{11}NO_2$			
Ethanedione, cyclopropylphenyl-, 2-oxime, (E)-	EtOH	222(4.23),255s(3.73)	39-0156-79B
	EtOH-NaOH	290(4.17),394(1.93)	39-0156-79B
1(2H)-Isoquinolinone, 2-(2-hydroxyethyl)-	EtOH	209(4.47),224(4.27), 279(3.96),286(3.96), 325(3.78)	44-0285-79
4(5H)-Isoxazolone, 5,5-dimethyl-3-phenyl-	n.s.g.	230(4.08),302(3.82)	104-2204-79
Oxazole, 5-(4-methoxyphenyl)-2-methyl-	EtOH	275(4.32)	18-3597-79
2-Propenenitrile, 3-methoxy-3-(4-methoxyphenyl)-, (E)-	C_6H_{12}	279(4.20)	56-0839-79
	EtOH	279(4.16)	56-2251-79
(Z)-	C_6H_{12}	283(4.30)	56-0839-79
	EtOH	289(4.33)	56-0839-79
3,5-Pyridinedicarboxaldehyde, 1-ethyl-4-ethynyl-1,4-dihydro-	EtOH	207(4.02),233(4.32), 253(3.88),377(4.01)	49-0613-79
Quinoline, 4-methoxy-2-methyl-, 1-oxide	MeOH	223(4.52),245(4.28), 332(3.86)	94-1813-79

Compound	Solvent	λmax(log ε)	Ref.
2(1H)-Quinolinone, 3-methoxy-1-methyl-	EtOH	318(4.13)	4-0065-79
2(1H)-Quinolinone, 4-methoxy-1-methyl-	MeOH	229(4.71),269(3.85), 279(3.85),319(3.76)	94-1813-79
2(1H)-Quinolinone, 4-methoxy-3-methyl-	MeOH	228(4.61),269(3.88), 278(3.83),322(3.88)	94-1813-79
$C_{11}H_{11}NO_2S_3$			
2-Azetidinone, 4-[[1-(methylthio)-3-oxo-3-(2-thienyl)-1-propenyl]thio]-, (E)-	dioxan	274(4.10),350(4.39)	142-1315-79
(Z)-	dioxan	275(3.98),345(4.35)	142-1315-79
2-Propenenitrile, 3,3-bis(methylthio)-2-(phenylsulfonyl)-	EtOH	334(4.16)	95-0540-79
$C_{11}H_{11}NO_3$			
2H-1-Benzopyran-2-one, 7-(aminooxy)-4,8-dimethyl-	EtOH	247(3.57),256(3.57), 324(4.21)	44-2176-79
4,7-Methano-1H-isoindole-1,3,8(2H)-trione, 2-ethyl-3a,4,7,7a-tetrahydro-	MeCN	250(2.26),270s(1.54)	44-0604-79
1,2-Propanedione, 1-phenyl-, 1-(acetoxyoxime), (E)-	EtOH	260(3.43)	39-0156-79B
(Z)-	EtOH	255(4.05)	39-0156-79B
1,2-Propanedione, 1-phenyl-, 2-(acetoxyoxime), (E)-	EtOH	259(3.95),335s(1.98)	39-0156-79B
$C_{11}H_{11}NO_4$			
Acetamide, N-(2-acetoxy-6-formylphenyl)-	EtOH	224(4.07),251(3.77), 300(3.17)	33-0271-79
Acetamide, N-(4-acetoxy-2-formylphenyl)-	EtOH	261(4.01),268(3.97), 333(3.57)	33-0234-79
	EtOH	233(4.49),259(4.01), 266s(3.93),335(3.59)	33-0271-79
Carbamic acid, (2,3-dihydro-2-oxo-3-benzofuranyl)-, ethyl ester	MeOH	272(3.1),278(3.06)	39-1634-79C
1H-Indole-4-carboxylic acid, 1-formyl-2,3-dihydro-2-hydroxy-, methyl ester	MeOH	227(4.48),308(3.56)	94-0946-79
1H-Indole-6-carboxylic acid, 2,3-dihydro-1-hydroxy-3,3-dimethyl-2-oxo-	C_6H_{12}	224(4.45),306(3.3)	5-0554-79
	pH 13	285(4.0)	5-0554-79
$C_{11}H_{11}NS$			
Cyclohepta[c]pyrrole-6(2H)-thione, 1,3-dimethyl-	CH_2Cl_2	304(3.99),404(4.26)	24-2087-79
$C_{11}H_{11}NSe$			
3-Indolizinecarboselenoaldehyde, 1,2-dimethyl-	C_6H_{12}	238(4.32),268(3.98), 277(4.08),325s(4.02), 338(4.09),364(3.64), 375s(3.50),386(3.40), 478(4.49),489(4.57), 638(2.42),691(2.71)	39-2334-79C
3-Indolizinecarboselenoaldehyde, 2,7-dimethyl-	C_6H_{12}	237(4.25),241(4.34), 263(3.89),272(3.95), 328(4.00),351(3.61), 370(3.53),470(4.56), 477(4.56),631(2.55), 683(2.71)	39-2334-79C
3-Indolizinecarboselenoaldehyde, 2,8-dimethyl-	C_6H_{12}	233s(4.30),239(4.31), 252s(3.95),263(4.01), 271(4.11),314s(3.88), 326(4.08),351(3.77),	39-2334-79C

Compound	Solvent	$\lambda_{max}(\log \epsilon)$	Ref.
(cont.)		360(3.72),468(4.51), 476(4.51),643(2.38), 697(2.65)	39-2334-79C
$C_{11}H_{11}N_2S_2$			
Benzo[1,2-d:5,4-d']bisthiazolium, 2,3,6-trimethyl-, iodide	DMF	268(4.40),315s(3.81), 367(3.89),575(3.46)	126-1441-79
perchlorate	DMF	268(4.36),319(3.75), 365(3.81),544s(3.37), 575(3.71)	126-1441-79
$C_{11}H_{11}N_3$			
Acetonitrile, (1,3-dihydro-1,3-dimethyl-2H-benzimidazol-2-ylidene)-	50% EtOH	230(4.3),258(4.2), 324(4.63)	104-0178-79
	0.01N H_2SO_4	273(4.02),280(3.98)	104-0178-79
Propanedinitrile, (hexahydro-2,6-methano-1H-pyrrolizin-1-ylidene)-	hexane	237(4.01),290(2.38)	142-0343-79
Propanedinitrile, (hexahydro-2,6-methano-1H-pyrrolizin-8-ylidene)-	hexane	227(4.01),285(3.80)	142-0343-79
$C_{11}H_{11}N_3OS$			
2-Oxazolamine, 4,5-dihydro-N-(3-methyl-2(3H)-benzothiazolylidene)-, monohydriodide	EtOH	220(4.52),257(3.90), 304(4.17)	94-2879-79
1,3,4-Thiadiazolo[3,2-a]benzimidazol-6-ol, 2-(1-methylethyl)-	pH 1	315(3.73),375(3.52)	18-2033-79
	pH 13	307(3.81),435(3.54)	18-2033-79
	EtOH	235(4.15),315(3.83), 359(3.97)	18-2033-79
1,3,4-Thiadiazolo[3,2-a]benzimidazol-6-ol, 2-propyl-	pH 1	325(3.84),380(3.77)	18-2033-79
	pH 13	322(3.61),450(3.72)	18-2033-79
	EtOH	228(4.12),259(3.93), 360(3.67)	18-2033-79
Urea, N-(4-methylphenyl)-N'-2-thiazolyl-	n.s.g.	238(3.98),268(4.41)	87-0028-79
$C_{11}H_{11}N_3O_2$			
Acetic acid, cyano(phenylhydrazono)-, ethyl ester, (E)-	MeOH	240(3.91),354(4.37)	80-1061-79
	MeOH-NaOH	240(4.15),380(4.38)	80-1061-79
	MeOH-HOAc	240(3.84),360(4.39)	80-1061-79
	CCl_4	350(4.36)	80-1061-79
(Z)-	MeOH	240(3.91),350(4.37)	80-1061-79
	MeOH-NaOH	240(4.06),384(4.40)	80-1061-79
	MeOH-HOAc	240(4.36),356(4.36)	80-1061-79
	CCl_4	355(4.35)	80-1061-79
$C_{11}H_{11}N_3O_2S$			
2-Propenamide, N-[[aminocarbonyl)amino]thioxomethyl]-3-phenyl-	dioxan	232(4.44),288(4.36)	18-3728-79
$C_{11}H_{11}N_3O_3$			
1H-Imidazole-4-methanol, 2-methyl-1-(4-nitrophenyl)-	EtOH	275(3.98)	78-1331-79
$C_{11}H_{11}N_3O_3S$			
Urea, N-(4-methylbenzenesulfonyl)-N'-2-thiazolyl-	n.s.g.	264(4.23)	87-0028-79
$C_{11}H_{11}N_3O_4$			
Benzenamine, N-(1-ethyl-2-propynyl)-2,4-dinitro-, (R)-	C_6H_{12}	262(3.99),327(4.23), 388(3.71)	78-2413-79

Compound	Solvent	λ_{max}(log ϵ)	Ref.
(cont.)	MeOH	264(3.99),343(4.22), 395s(3.80)	78-2413-79
2,4-Pentanedione, 3-[(2-nitrophenyl)-azo]-	EtOH	390(3.74)	2-0502-79A'
	acetone	390(4.176)	2-0502-79A'
	dioxan	385(4.231)	2-0502-79A'
	$CHCl_3$	390(4.25)	2-0502-79A'
	CCl_4	385(4.28)	2-0502-79A'
$C_{11}H_{11}N_3O_5$			
Pyrido[3,2-d]pyrimidine-6-carboxylic acid, 5,8-dihydro-2,4-dimethoxy-8-oxo-, methyl ester	pH 1	246(4.38),261(4.14), 341(3.78)	44-0435-79
	pH 7	255(4.44),258(4.44), 325(3.86),335(3.90)	44-0435-79
	pH 11	257(4.46),333(3.95)	44-0435-79
1H-Pyrrolo[3,2-d]pyrimidine-7-carboxylic acid, 6-formyl-2,3,4,5-tetrahydro-1,3-dimethyl-2,4-dioxo-, methyl ester	EtOH	230(4.10),277(3.65), 335(3.35)	44-3830-79
$C_{11}H_{11}N_3O_8$			
1,4-Dioxaspiro[4.5]deca-6,9-diene, 6,10-dinitro-8-(2-propenyl-aci-nitro)-	MeOH	222(4.08),365(4.38)	104-0487-79
$C_{11}H_{11}N_3S$			
Isothiazolo[5,1-e][1,2,3]thiadiazole-7-S^{IV}, 1,6-dihydro-6-methyl-1-phenyl-	C_6H_{12}	239(4.10),250s(3.78), 277(3.79),430(4.33)	39-0926-79C
$C_{11}H_{11}N_3S_2$			
Thiourea, N-methyl-N'-(4-phenyl-2-thiazolyl)-	EtOH	229(4.04),262(4.12), 275(4.12),281(4.12)	2-0082-79B
$C_{11}H_{11}N_5O$			
Imidazo[1,2-c]pteridine, 6-methoxy-2,3-dimethyl-	pH -3.5	218(4.24),255(3.74), 277s(3.44),360(4.05), 365s(4.04)	18-0867-79
	pH 0.5	213(4.28),235s(3.89), 265(3.60),273s(3.51), 332(3.98),346(3.95)	18-0867-79
	pH 5.0	223(4.24),243s(3.74), 286(3.38),343(3.98)	18-0867-79
$C_{11}H_{11}N_5S$			
Imidazo[1,2-c]pteridine, 2,3-dimethyl-6-(methylthio)-	pH -3.5	242(4.28),265s(3.97), 297s(3.98),310(4.03), 384(4.20)	18-0867-79
	pH 0.5	226(4.25),248(4.24), 288s(4.05),296(4.07), 342(4.17),353(4.14)	18-0867-79
	pH 5.0	232(4.38),252(4.24), 294s(3.81),304(3.82), 351(4.19)	18-0867-79
$C_{11}H_{12}BrN_3OS$			
1,3,4-Thiadiazolo[3,2-a]benzimidazolium, 9-ethyl-6-hydroxy-2-methyl-, bromide	EtOH	257(3.92),512(3.95)	18-2033-79
$C_{11}H_{12}ClN_3O$			
Acetamide, N-[1-(4-chlorophenyl)-4,5-dihydro-1H-pyrazol-3-yl]-	EtOH	255s(3.78),303(4.28)	150-0801-79

Compound	Solvent	λmax(log ε)	Ref.
Benzamide, 2-chloro-N-(4,5-dihydro-1-methyl-1H-pyrazol-3-yl)-	EtOH	274(3.93)	150-0801-79
Benzamide, 3-chloro-N-(4,5-dihydro-1-methyl-1H-pyrazol-3-yl)-	EtOH	232(3.93),287(3.86)	150-0801-79
Benzamide, 4-chloro-N-(4,5-dihydro-1-methyl-1H-pyrazol-3-yl)-	EtOH	238(4.06),283(3.86)	150-0801-79
1,2,4-Oxadiazole-3-ethanamine, 5-(4-chlorophenyl)-N-methyl-, hydrochloride	EtOH	260(4.28)	150-0801-79
$C_{11}H_{12}ClN_5O_3$			
7H-Purine-7-acetic acid, α-(acetylamino)-6-chloro-, ethyl ester	pH 1	268(3.90)	44-2019-79
	pH 12	272(3.91)	44-2019-79
	MeOH	269(3.90)	44-2019-79
9H-Purine-9-acetic acid, α-(acetylamino)-6-chloro-, ethyl ester	MeOH	264(3.95)	44-2019-79
$C_{11}H_{12}FN_3O_3S_2$			
Isothiazolium, 2-methyl-5-(phenylhydrazonomethyl)-, fluorosulfonate	MeOH-$HClO_4$	244s(4.07),257(4.11), 444(4.41)	39-2340-79C
$C_{11}H_{12}F_3N_3O_6$			
Uridine, 2'-deoxy-2'-(trifluoroacetylamino)-	MeOH	259.5(3.97)	44-2039-79
$C_{11}H_{12}N_2$			
1H-Benzimidazole, 1-ethenyl-2-ethyl-	isooctane	242(4.29),281(3.71), 290(3.62)	65-1225-79
1H-Pyrazole, 3,5-dimethyl-4-phenyl-	EtOH	247(4.16)	103-0501-79
Pyrimidine, 1,4-dihydro-5-methyl-4-phenyl-	EtOH	269(3.06),284s(2.98)	39-1228-79C
$C_{11}H_{12}N_2O$			
Pyrimidine, 3,4-dihydro-4-(4-methoxyphenyl)-	EtOH	275(3.44),282(3.42), 294s(3.20)	24-0001-79
4(1H)-Quinazolinone, 2-ethyl-1-methyl-	80% EtOH	229(4.26),265-305(3.7-3.9)	42-0708-79
8-Quinolinol, 2-(dimethylamino)-	acid	245(4.08),269(4.44), 312(3.95)	123-0070-79
	neutral	250(4.23),271(4.39), 285(4.31),342(3.74)	123-0070-79
	base	237(4.19),281(4.51), 367(3.45)	123-0070-79
2(1H)-Quinolinone, 1-(dimethylamino)-	MeOH	228(4.56),270(3.90), 328(3.80)	64-0102-79B
$C_{11}H_{12}N_2OS$			
2,1-Benzisothiazole, 3-morpholino-	EtOH	234(4.35),288(3.19), 299(3.18),371(3.75)	33-0391-79
4-Imidazolidinone, 5,5-dimethyl-3-phenyl-2-thioxo-	n.s.g.	225s(3.99),266(4.26)	33-0160-79
2-Thiopheneacetonitrile, α-(4-morpholinylmethylene)-	MeOH	235(4.29),323(4.50)	83-0039-79
$C_{11}H_{12}N_2O_2$			
1,3-Benzenediol, 4-(1,4-dihydro-5-methyl-4-pyrimidinyl)-, monohydrochloride	EtOH	286.5(3.72)	24-0001-79
Benzonitrile, 4-(1,1-dimethylethyl)-3-nitro-	C_6H_{12}	274(2.7),324(2.3)	5-0554-79
	MeOH	224(2.3),273(2.9), 327(2.3)	5-0554-79

Compound	Solvent	λ_{max}(log ε)	Ref.
2(5H)-Furanone, 5-methyl-4-(2-phenylhydrazino)-	EtOH	256(4.28)	4-0505-79
2(5H)-Furanone, 4-[2-(phenylmethyl)hydrazino]-	EtOH	260(4.37)	4-0505-79
1H-Indazole-4,7-dione, 6-(1,1-dimethylethyl)-	n.s.g.	256(4.22)	70-1668-79
2,6-Methano-2H-1,3,5-benzoxadiazocin-9-ol, 3,6-dihydro-2-methyl-, hydrochloride	EtOH	277(3.22),284(3.20)	24-0001-79
1H-Pyrazole-3-methanol, 5-hydroxy-α-methyl-1-phenyl-	EtOH	247(4.18)	4-0505-79
1H-Pyrazole-3-methanol, 5-hydroxy-1-(phenylmethyl)-	EtOH	247(3.71)	4-0505-79
$C_{11}H_{12}N_2O_2S$			
2-Propenoic acid, 2-cyano-3-[(5-methyl-2-thienyl)amino]-, ethyl ester	EtOH	245(3.78),342(4.24)	49-1189-79
4-Thiazolidinone, 2-[(4-methoxyphenyl)imino]-3-methyl-	MeOH	252(4.31),284(3.91)	104-1344-79
	70% dioxan	285(3.90)	104-1344-79
4(5H)-Thiazolone, 2-[(4-methoxyphenyl)methylamino]-	MeOH	238s(4.26),252(4.31)	104-1344-79
	70% dioxan	254(4.29)	104-1344-79
$C_{11}H_{12}N_2O_3$			
8-Azabicyclo[3.2.1]oct-3-ene-6-carboxylic acid, 1-cyano-8-methyl-2-oxo-, methyl ester	EtOH	227(4.0)	39-2528-79C
Benzeneacetaldehyde, α-[(dimethylamino)methylene]-2-nitro-	EtOH	289(4.46)	44-3748-79
$C_{11}H_{12}N_2O_3S$			
2H-1,4-Benzothiazin-3(4H)-one, 2-[(dimethylamino)methylene]-, 1,1-dioxide	dioxan	270(4.0),304(4.38)	83-0302-79
Ethanone, 1-(2,5-dihydro-4-methyl-1,2,5-benzothiadiazepin-3-yl)-, S,S-dioxide	EtOH	234(4.01),298(3.95), 340(4.15)	4-0835-79
$C_{11}H_{12}N_2O_4$			
Pyrrolo[2,3-b]indole-2-carboxylic acid, 1,2,3,3a,8,8a-hexahydro-3a-hydroperoxy-	H_2O	235(3.80),295(3.30)	35-3136-79
$C_{11}H_{12}N_2O_4S$			
2H-1,2,6-Thiadiazin-3(6H)-one, 6-(4-methoxyphenyl)-5-methyl-, 1,1-dioxide	isoPrOH	228(4.21),293(3.99)	44-4191-79
$C_{11}H_{12}N_2O_5$			
4,11-Epoxy-7H-1,3-dioxolo[4,5-e]pyrimido[2,1-b][1,3]oxazepin-7-one, 3a,4-11,11a-tetrahydro-2,2-dimethyl-, [3aS-(3aα,4β,11β,11aα)]-	MeOH	231(4.11),248s(3.90)	44-4713-79
$C_{11}H_{12}N_2S_2$			
2H-1,3,4-Thiadiazine-2-thione, 3,4-dihydro-5,6-dimethyl-4-phenyl-	EtOH	233(4.090),326(4.120)	48-0959-79
$C_{11}H_{12}N_2S_9$			
Thiourea, bis[4,5-bis(methylthio)-1,3-dithiol-2-ylidene]-	MeCN	266(4.37),473(4.57)	48-0827-79

Compound	Solvent	λ_{max}(log ϵ)	Ref.
$C_{11}H_{12}N_3OS$			
1,3,4-Thiadiazolo[3,2-a]benzimidazol-ium, 9-ethyl-6-hydroxy-2-methyl-, bromide	EtOH	257(3.92),512(3.95)	18-2033-79
$C_{11}H_{12}N_3OS_2$			
Pyridinium, 1-[4-amino-5-(aminocarbo-nyl)-2-(methylthio)-3-thienyl]-, iodide	EtOH	221(4.47),268(4.03), 282(3.96),327(4.03)	95-1081-79
$C_{11}H_{12}N_4O$			
2H-Furo[2,3-b]indole, 3a-azido-3,3a,8,8a-tetrahydro-8a-methyl-	EtOH	245(3.77),308(3.21)	39-3061-79C
1H-Imidazole, 2-[(4-methoxyphenyl)-azo]-1-methyl-	MeOH	250(3.89),374(4.35), 385(4.35),418s(4.00)	19-0249-79
1H-Indole-3-ethanol, 2-(azidomethyl)-	EtOH	228(4.32),282(3.77), 288(3.80),296(3.72)	39-3061-79C
Isoxazole, 3,4-dimethyl-5-(3-phenyl-1-triazenyl)-	MeOH	237(4.08),297(3.73), 369(4.43)	33-1570-79
$C_{11}H_{12}N_4OS$			
1H-1,2,4-Triazolium, 4-(acetylamino)-2,3-dihydro-5-methyl-1-phenyl-3-thioxo-, hydroxide, inner salt	EtOH	248(4.28),285(3.46)	94-1683-79
$C_{11}H_{12}N_4O_2$			
Benzenamine, 4-(3,5-dimethyl-4-nitro-1H-pyrazol-1-yl)-	EtOH	255(4.16)	78-1331-79
$C_{11}H_{12}N_4O_3$			
1,2,4-Oxadiazol-3-ethenamine, 5-methyl-N-(4-nitrophenyl)-	EtOH	227(3.87),380(4.17)	150-0801-79
$C_{11}H_{12}N_4O_5$			
2,4(1H,3H)-Pyrimidinedione, 1,1'-(2-hy-droxy-1,3-propanediyl)bis-	H_2O	266.5(4.29)	126-2303-79
$C_{11}H_{12}N_4O_6$			
D-Arabinitol, 1,4-anhydro-1-C-(6-nitro-[1,2,4]triazolo[1,5-a]pyridin-2-yl)-, (R)-	H_2O	247(4.17),320(3.76)	111-0375-79
D-Arabinitol, 1,4-anhydro-1-C-(8-nitro-[1,2,4]triazolo[1,5-a]pyridin-2-yl)-, (R)-	H_2O	230(4.14),330(3.74)	111-0375-79
$C_{11}H_{12}N_4O_7$			
1H-Purine-8-carboxylic acid, 6,9-dihy-dro-6-oxo-9-β-D-ribofuranosyl-	H_2O	264.5(4.01)	88-2385-79
$C_{11}H_{12}N_4S$			
1H-Imidazol-2-amine, 4,5-dihydro-N-(3-methyl-2(3H)-benzothiazolylidene)-, monohydriodide	EtOH	220(4.56),310(4.40)	94-2879-79
$C_{11}H_{12}N_6$			
Imidazo[1,2-c]pteridin-6-amine, N,2,3-trimethyl-	pH -2.5	227(4.44),280s(4.10), 296(4.12),406(4.28)	18-0867-79
	pH 1.5	220(4.40),254(4.16), 279(4.15),286(4.15), 365(4.11)	18-0867-79

Compound	Solvent	λ_{max}(log ε)	Ref.
Imidazo[1,2-c]pteridin-6-amine, N,2,3-trimethyl- (cont.)	pH 5.5	227(4.55),257(4.01), 284(3.88),362(4.23)	18-0867-79
$C_{11}H_{12}N_6O_3$			
Benzoic acid, 4-[[(1H-tetrazol-5-ylamino)carbonyl]amino]-, ethyl ester	n.s.g.	276(4.49)	87-0028-79
1H-Imidazo[4,5-c]pyrimido[5,4-e]pyridazine-2,7,9(8H)-trione, 3,6-dihydro-1,3,6,8-tetramethyl-	$CHCl_3$	244(4.39),292(4.15), 302(4.14),358(4.03)	94-2143-79
$C_{11}H_{12}O$			
5H-Benzocyclohepten-5-ol, 4a,9a-dihydro-	MeOH	234(3.88),261s(3.65), 270(3.56),282s(3.27)	88-1051-79
stereoisomer	MeOH	238(3.89),265s(3.37)	88-1051-79
5H-Benzocyclohepten-5-one, 6,7,8,9-tetrahydro-	isooctane	240(4.00),284(3.08), 295s(2.85)	56-1751-79
Bicyclo[4.4.1]undeca-2,4,7,9-tetraen-11-ol	MeOH	215s(3.96),224(4.10), 231(4.08),242(3.54), 250(3.45),260(3.29)	88-1051-79
1H-Inden-1-one, 2,3-dihydro-3,4-dimethyl-	EtOH	250(4.40),290(3.29)	117-0255-79
2H-Inden-2-one, 1,3-dihydro-1,1-dimethyl-	EtOH	261(2.86),267(3.02), 274(3.06)	35-3277-79
Phenol, 2-(1-cyclopenten-1-yl)-	EtOH	232(3.86),257(3.90), 295(3.44)	39-2027-79C
Tetracyclo[5.3.1.$0^{2,4}$.$0^{8,10}$]undec-5-en-11-one, exo,exo-	EtOH	198(3.75),232s(2.72), 293(1.95)	44-1294-79
Tetracyclo[6.2.1.$0^{2,4}$.$0^{5,7}$]undec-9-en-11-one	EtOH	197(3.44)	44-1294-79
$C_{11}H_{12}O_2$			
Acetic acid, (2,4,6-cyclooctatrien-1-ylidene)-, methyl ester	$CHCl_3$	247(4.22),320(3.98)	24-0175-79
Benzenepropanal, α,α-dimethyl-β-oxo-	MeOH	209(3.92),239(3.92), 270-295s(2.9-2.6)	5-0617-79
Bicyclo[6.1.0]nona-2,4,6-triene-9-carboxylic acid, methyl ester, (1α,8α,9α)-	EtOH	239(3.57)	24-0175-79
1,3,5,7-Cyclooctatetraen-1-acetic acid, methyl ester	$CHCl_3$	283s(2.57)	24-0175-79
2-Propenoic acid, 3-(4-methylphenyl)-, methyl ester, (E)-	MeCN	286(4.37)	88-0863-79
Spiro[4.5]deca-6,9-diene-2,8-dione, 4-methyl-	MeOH	243(4.38)	31-1543-79
Spiro[3.5]nona-5,8-diene-2,7-dione, 5,9-dimethyl-	MeOH	246(4.54)	107-0077-79
Tricyclo[5.2.0.$0^{2,9}$]nona-3,5-diene-8-acetic acid, (1α,2α,7α,8β,9α)-	EtOH	276(3.30)	88-0155-79
$C_{11}H_{12}O_2S$			
1,3-Butadiene, 1-[(phenylmethyl)sulfonyl]-, (Z)-	EtOH	238(4.40)	70-0594-79
$C_{11}H_{12}O_2S_3$			
Benzeneacetic acid, α-[[(ethylthio)thioxomethyl]thio]-	CH_2Cl_2	305(4.19),428(1.77)	24-1650-79
$C_{11}H_{12}O_2S_4$			
1,3-Dithiole-4-carboxylic acid, 5-methyl-2-(4-methyl-1,3-dithiol-2-ylidene)-, ethyl ester	MeCN	212(3.99),289(3.95), 310(3.96),319(3.98), 415(3.11)	44-1476-79

Compound	Solvent	$\lambda_{max}(\log \epsilon)$	Ref.
$C_{11}H_{12}O_3$			
5-Benzofuranpropanol, 4-hydroxy-	EtOH	214(4.47),248(3.98), 255(3.99),285(3.40)	2-0011-79B
9,11-Dioxatetracyclo[4.3.1.1^{2,5}.0^{7,9}]-undec-3-en-10-one, 1,6-dimethyl-	EtOH	277(1.49)	35-7521-79
Ethanone, 1,1'-(4-hydroxy-6-methyl-1,3-phenylene)bis-	EtOH	210(3.80),244(4.49), 262s(4.00),320(3.44)	39-0464-79C
1,4-Pentanedione, 5-hydroxy-1-phenyl-	EtOH	242(4.12)	136-0055-79B
2-Propenoic acid, 3-(3-methoxyphenyl)-, methyl ester	MeOH	231(4.11),277(4.19), 318(3.54)	13-0361-79A
2-Propenoic acid, 3-(4-methoxyphenyl)-, methyl ester, (E)-	MeCN	309(4.37)	88-0863-79
(Z)-	MeCN	301(4.12)	88-0863-79
$C_{11}H_{12}O_4$			
2H-1,5-Benzodioxepin-6,9-dione, 3,4-dihydro-7,8-dimethyl-	MeCN	281(4.14),422(2.63)	64-0624-79B
1-Isobenzofurancarboxylic acid, 1,3,3a,7a-tetrahydro-1,5-dimethyl-3-oxo-	MeOH	260(3.56),270(3.52)	23-2853-79
1,2-Propanediol, 3-(4-hydroxy-5-benzofuranyl)-	EtOH	217(4.46),248(4.02), 255(4.03),286(3.36)	2-0011-79B
$C_{11}H_{12}O_5$			
1,2-Benzenedicarboxaldehyde, 3,4,5-trimethoxy-	EtOH	240s(4.16),247(4.18), 302(3.72)	20-0883-79
1,3-Benzenedicarboxylic acid, 4-hydroxy-6-methyl-, dimethyl ester	EtOH	230(4.33),250(4.05), 303(3.49)	39-0464-79C
1,3-Benzenedicarboxylic acid, 4-hydroxy-6-methyl-, 1-ethyl ester	EtOH	229(4.28),255(4.00), 300(3.45)	39-0464-79C
Benzoic acid, 3-acetoxy-5-methoxy-, methyl ester	EtOH	240(3.72),297(3.50)	150-0301-79
Benzoic acid, 2-hydroxy-4-methoxy-6-(2-oxopropyl)-	MeOH	265(4.02),301(3.76)	39-0337-79C
$C_{11}H_{12}O_6$			
Benzeneacetic acid, 3-methoxy-5-[(methoxycarbonyl)oxy]-	EtOH	211(3.84),219(3.84), 272(3.20),279(3.20)	150-0301-79
$C_{11}H_{12}O_7$			
Butanedioic acid, 2-[(3,4-dihydroxyphenyl)methyl]-2-hydroxy-, (R)-	MeOH	283(3.51)	102-1211-79
3-Furanpentanoic acid, 5-(carboxymethylene)-2,5-dihydro-4-hydroxy-2-oxo-, (E)- (multicolosic acid)	EtOH	262(4.18),295(3.90)	130-0311-79
$C_{11}H_{13}$			
Cycloheptatrienylium, 1-cyclopropyl-2-methyl-, perchlorate	10% HCl	252(4.43),333(3.90)	39-1005-79B
$C_{11}H_{13}Br$			
Bicyclo[4.3.1]deca-2,4,7-triene, 9-bromo-6(and 1)-methyl-	C_6H_{12}	247(3.85),254s(3.84), 263(3.71)	5-0533-79
$C_{11}H_{13}BrN_2O_5$			
Uridine, 5-(2-bromoethenyl)-2'-deoxy-	EtOH	252(4.14),296(4.07)	88-4415-79
$C_{11}H_{13}BrN_2O_6$			
Propanedioic acid, (5-bromo-3,4-dihydro-2,4-dioxo-1(2H)-pyrimidinyl)-, diethyl ester	MeOH	276(3.96)	44-1737-79

Compound	Solvent	λ_{max}(log ε)	Ref.
Uridine, 5-(bromoacetyl)-2'-deoxy-	pH 2	290(4.13)	87-1541-79
	H_2O	290(4.13)	87-1541-79
	pH 11.5	290(4.01)	87-1541-79
$C_{11}H_{13}BrO$			
Bicyclo[4.3.1]deca-2,4,7-triene, 5(and 7)-bromo-9-methoxy-	C_6H_{12}	265(3.81)	5-0533-79
Bicyclo[4.3.1]deca-2,4,7-triene, 6-bromo-9-methoxy-	C_6H_{12}	232(3.89)	5-0533-79
$C_{11}H_{13}Br_3O_2$			
1,3-Benzenediol-1-^{14}C, 2,4,6-tribromo-5-pentyl-	EtOH	213(4.11)	130-0311-79
$C_{11}H_{13}ClN_2O$			
2-Pentanone, 4-[(3-amino-4-chlorophenyl)imino]-	heptane	324(4.24)	40-1437-79
	EtOH	331(4.26)	40-1437-79
	dioxan	325(4.30)	40-1437-79
	$CHCl_3$	328(4.27)	40-1437-79
$C_{11}H_{13}ClN_2O_3$			
Ethenamine, 2-(4-chloro-5-methoxy-2-nitrophenyl)-N,N-dimethyl-	EtOH	326(4.12),462(3.65)	87-0063-79
$C_{11}H_{13}ClN_2O_5$			
Uridine, 5-(2-chloroethenyl)-2'-deoxy-	EtOH	250(4.20),293(4.07)	88-4415-79
$C_{11}H_{13}ClN_2Te$			
3-Pyrazolidinetellone, 5-(4-chlorophenyl)-1,2-dimethyl-	CCl_4	370(4.10),465(3.27)	77-1102-79
$C_{11}H_{13}ClN_4O_3$			
9H-Purine, 6-chloro-9-(2-ethoxy-1,3-dioxan-5-yl)-, cis	EtOH	205(4.12)	103-0798-79
trans	EtOH	205(4.16)	103-0798-79
$C_{11}H_{13}ClN_6$			
1H-Pyrazol-5-amine, 4-[(2-chloro-3-pyridinyl)azo]-1-ethyl-3-methyl-	n.s.g.	390(3.15),415(4.16)	103-0572-79
$C_{11}H_{13}Cl_2N_3O_4$			
Carbamic acid, (2-chloroethyl)-, 1-[[(2-chloroethyl)amino]carbonyl]-1,2-dihydro-2-oxo-3-pyridinyl ester	EtOH	226s(--),305(3.83)	36-0816-79
$C_{11}H_{13}CrNO_3$			
Chromium, tricarbonyl[(1,2,3,4,5,6-η)-3-ethyl-1,2-dihydro-1-methylpyridine]-	EtOH	403(3.64)	23-0300-79
Chromium, tricarbonyl[(1,2,3,4,5,6-η)-5-ethyl-1,2-dihydro-1-methylpyridine]-	EtOH	399(3.67)	23-0300-79
$C_{11}H_{13}FN_2O_5$			
2-Furancarboxylic acid, 5-(5-fluoro-3,4-dihydro-2,4-dioxo-1(2H)-pyrimidinyl)tetrahydro-, ethyl ester	pH 2	271(3.89)	103-0926-79
	pH 7	270(3.95)	103-0926-79
	pH 10	272(3.86)	103-0926-79
$C_{11}H_{13}IN_2O_5$			
Uridine, 2'-deoxy-5-(2-iodoethenyl)-, (E)-	EtOH	251(4.14),298(4.07)	88-4415-79

Compound	Solvent	λmax(log ε)	Ref.
$C_{11}H_{13}N$			
1H-Indole, 3-propyl-	C_6H_{12} -1% EtOH	221(4.50),273(3.76), 279(3.79),282s(3.77), 290(3.71)	35-0996-79
	EtOH	222(4.50),275s(3.74), 282(3.77),290(3.69)	35-0996-79
$C_{11}H_{13}NO_2$			
Acetamide, N-(2-acetyl-4-methylphenyl)-	EtOH	234(4.16),259(4.08), 267(4.00),333(3.67)	33-0271-79
Acetamide, N-(2-acetylphenyl)-N-methyl-	EtOH	227(3.92),285(3.05)	35-7332-79
Acetamide, N-(2-formyl-4,5-dimethyl-phenyl)-	EtOH	269(4.06),277(4.08), 335(3.68)	33-0234-79
Alanine, N-(phenylmethylene)-, methyl ester	EtOH	248(4.21),278s(--), 286s(--)	44-2732-79
Benzoic acid, 4-(dimethylamino)-, ethen-yl ester	C_6H_{12}	314(4.57)	65-0479-79
Isoquinoline, 3,4-dihydro-6,7-dimeth-oxy-	EtOH	245(4.15),308(3.88), 360(3.80)	39-0283-79C
	EtOH-NaOH	230(4.34),277(3.79), 308(3.73)	39-0283-79C
6-Isoquinolinol, 3,4-dihydro-7-methoxy-1-methyl-	pH 6.0	375(3.90)	39-2744-79C
1,2-Propanedione, phenyl-, 2-(ethoxy-oxime), (E)-	C_6H_{12}	251(4.09),341(2.02)	39-0151-79B
(Z)-	C_6H_{12}	246(4.04),341(1.88)	39-0151-79B
$C_{11}H_{13}NO_2S$			
Acetic acid, [[(4-methylphenyl)thio]-imino]-, ethyl ester	hexane	225(3.97),347(3.80)	44-1218-79
Propanoic acid, 2-[[(4-methylphenyl)-thio]imino]-, methyl ester	hexane	230(3.97),323(3.94)	44-1218-79
$C_{11}H_{13}NO_3$			
Acetamide, N-(2-formyl-4-methoxy-3-methylphenyl)-	EtOH	244(4.35),270s(--), 374(3.63)	33-0234-79
Acetamide, N-(2-formyl-4-methoxy-5-methylphenyl)-	EtOH	273(3.95),352(3.67), 382s(--)	33-0234-79
Acetamide, N-(2-formyl-4-methoxy-6-methylphenyl)-	EtOH	263(3.75),326(3.35)	33-0234-79
Butanoic acid, 2-[[(2-hydroxyphenyl)-methylene]amino]-, monopotassium salt	MeOH	257(4.20),281s(3.92) 403(3.88)(calcd.)	137-0118-79
Formamide, N-[2-(3,4-dimethoxyphenyl)-ethenyl]-, (Z)-	EtOH	212(4.08),225(4.10), 278(4.18),292s(4.06)	39-0652-79C
1H-Indole-2-carboxylic acid, 4,5,6,7-tetrahydro-1-methyl-4-oxo-, methyl ester	MeOH	226(4.20),245(3.92), 283(3.99)	64-0102-79B
1H-Indole-2-carboxylic acid, 4,5,6,7-tetrahydro-6-methyl-4-oxo-, methyl ester	MeOH	219(4.23),247(4.03), 284(4.17)	64-0102-79B
2H-Indol-2-one, 1,3-dihydro-1-hydroxy-6-methoxy-3,3-dimethyl-	C_6H_{12}	217(5.1),266(3.3), 287(3.4),294(3.3)	5-0554-79
	pH 13	297(3.4)	5-0554-79
Phenol, 3-acetyl-4-amino-5-methyl-, acetate	EtOH	229(4.39),254(3.83), 369(3.37)	33-0271-79
$C_{11}H_{13}NO_4$			
Benzoic acid, 4-(1,1-dimethylethyl)-3-nitro-	C_6H_{12}	234(4.2),276(3.0), 286s(2.9),330(2.3)	5-0554-79
	MeOH	224(4.2),280s(2.9), 330(2.4)	5-0554-79

Compound	Solvent	λ_{max}(log ε)	Ref.
Benzoic acid, 4-(1,1-dimethylethyl)-3-nitro- (cont.)	MeOH-NaOH	225(4.2),280s(3.2), 340s(2.6)	5-0554-79
3-Pyridinecarboxylic acid, 5-acetyl-1,2-dihydro-1,6-dimethyl-2-oxo-, methyl ester (same in acid or base)	EtOH	213(4.16),277(4.13), 340(3.92)	39-0686-79C
$C_{11}H_{13}NO_5$			
3,5-Pyridinedicarboxylic acid, 1,2-dihydro-1,6-dimethyl-2-oxo-, dimethyl ester	EtOH	209(4.28),262(4.17), 333(3.93)	39-0686-79C
	EtOH-HCl	210(4.30),262(4.18), 332(3.95)	39-0686-79C
	EtOH-NaOH	262(4.17),332(3.96)	39-0686-79C
$C_{11}H_{13}N_2O_6P$			
Phosphonic acid, [1-cyano-2-(5-nitro-2-furanyl)ethenyl]-, diethyl ester	EtOH	203s(3.69),241(4.04), 339(4.34)	48-0353-79
$C_{11}H_{13}N_2S_3$			
Benzothiazolium, 2-[[bis(methylthio)-methylene]amino]-3-methyl-, iodide	EtOH	220(4.61),280(3.90), 288(3.92),306(4.05), 320(3.74),370(3.86)	94-2879-79
$C_{11}H_{13}N_3O$			
Acetamide, N-(4,5-dihydro-1-phenyl-1H-pyrazol-3-yl)-	EtOH	250s(3.75),300(4.19)	150-0801-79
Benzamide, N-(4,5-dihydro-1-methyl-1H-pyrazol-3-yl)-	EtOH	230(3.98),283(3.89)	150-0801-79
1,2,4-Oxadiazole-3-ethanamine, N-methyl-5-phenyl-, hydrochloride	EtOH	254(4.26)	150-0801-79
1-Pentanone, 5-azido-1-phenyl-	heptane	238(4.20),276(3.04), 325(1.74)	35-0378-79
1H-Pyrazol-5-ol, 3-(aminomethyl)-1-(phenylmethyl)-, dihydrochloride	MeOH	211(4.16),248(3.73)	1-0294-79
$C_{11}H_{13}N_3OS$			
4(5H)-Thiazolone, 2-[[4-(dimethylamino)phenyl]amino]-	H_2O	225(4.23),258(4.18), 291(4.08)	104-1344-79
	MeOH	257(4.14),308(4.14)	104-1344-79
	dioxan	276s(4.00),305(4.11)	104-1344-79
	70% dioxan	256(4.09),307(4.13)	104-1344-79
$C_{11}H_{13}N_3O_2$			
2-Propenamide, 3-[4-(aminoiminomethyl)-phenyl]-2-methoxy-, monohydrochloride	n.s.g.	296(4.240)	106-0008-79
$C_{11}H_{13}N_3O_2S$			
Pyrrolidine, 1-[[4-(diazomethyl)phenyl]-sulfonyl]-	EtOH	228(4.02),310(4.47), 468(1.60)	118-0531-79
Sydnone, 3-[4-(dimethylamino)phenyl]-4-(methylthio)-	CH_2Cl_2	258(4.16),330(4.06)	5-0063-79
$C_{11}H_{13}N_3O_2S_2$			
1H-Pyrazol-3-amine, 4-[(4-methylphenyl)sulfonyl]-5-(methylthio)-	EtOH	256(4.03)	95-0038-79
$C_{11}H_{13}N_3O_2S_3$			
Sulfilimine, S,S-dimethyl-N-[4-[(2-thiazolylamino)sulfonyl]phenyl]-	EtOH	293(4.37)	139-0195-79

Compound	Solvent	λ_{max}(log ϵ)	Ref.
$C_{11}H_{13}N_3O_3S$			
2H-1,2,6-Thiadiazin-5-amine, 2-(4-methoxyphenyl)-3-methyl-, 1,1-dioxide	isoPrOH	230(4.10),288(4.11)	44-4191-79
$C_{11}H_{13}N_3O_4$			
D-Arabinitol, 1,4-anhydro-1-C-1,2,4-triazolo[4,3-a]pyridin-3-yl-, (R)-	H_2O	260(3.65),270(3.70), 280(3.62)	111-0375-79
Benzenamine, N-(1-ethyl-2-propenyl)-2,4-dinitro-, (R)-	C_6H_{12}	262(3.98),332(4.26), 400(3.73)	78-2413-79
	MeOH	266(3.97),350(4.24), 405s(3.80)	78-2413-79
(S)-	C_6H_{12}	257(3.98),330(4.27), 397(3.73)	78-2413-79
	MeOH	266(3.96),348(4.23), 400s(3.81)	78-2413-79
Pyrido[3,2-c]pyridazine-1,2-dicarboxylic acid, 3,4-dihydro-, dimethyl ester	MeOH	242(3.99),277(3.67)	103-0518-79
1H-Pyrrolo[3,2-d]pyrimidine-7-carboxylic acid, 2,3,4,5-tetrahydro-1,3,5-trimethyl-2,4-dioxo-, methyl ester	EtOH	234(4.23),272(3.50)	44-3830-79
1H-Pyrrolo[3,2-d]pyrimidine-7-carboxylic acid, 2,3,4,5-tetrahydro-1,3,6-trimethyl-2,4-dioxo-, methyl ester	EtOH	233(4.24),275(3.73)	44-3830-79
$C_{11}H_{13}N_3O_4S$			
Sulfamide, N-(4-methoxyphenyl)-N'-(3-methyl-5-isoxazolyl)-	isoPrOH	231(4.31),281(3.17)	44-4191-79
Sulfamide, N-(4-methoxyphenyl)-N'-(5-methyl-3-isoxazolyl)-	isoPrOH	229(4.17),281(3.16)	44-4191-79
$C_{11}H_{13}N_3O_5$			
Aspartic acid, N-[[(4-aminophenyl)-amino]carbonyl]-	pH 13	247(4.20),290s(3.20)	87-0874-79
4H-Pyrrolo[2,3-d]pyrimidin-4-one, 7-α-D-arabinofuranosyl-1,7-dihydro-	MeOH	217(4.09),259(3.81), 270s(3.71)	24-3432-79
4H-Pyrrolo[2,3-d]pyrimidin-4-one, 7-β-D-arabinofuranosyl-1,7-dihydro-	MeOH	216(4.23),259(3.91), 270s(3.84)	24-3432-79
4H-Pyrrolo[2,3-d]pyrimidin-4-one, 3,7-dihydro-3-β-D-ribofuranosyl-	MeOH	261(3.91),270s(3.84)	24-3526-79
$C_{11}H_{13}N_3O_8$			
1,4-Dioxaspiro[4.5]deca-6,9-diene, 6,10-dinitro-8-(propyl-aci-nitro)-	MeOH	223(4.04),368(4.32)	104-0487-79
1,4-Dioxaspiro[4.5]deca-6,9-diene, 8-[(1-methylethyl)-aci-nitro]-6,10-dinitro-	MeOH	230(3.96),365(4.40)	104-0487-79
$C_{11}H_{13}N_5$			
Benzenamine, N,N-dimethyl-4-(1H-pyrazol-3-ylazo)-	EtOH	402(4.43)	104-1396-79
$C_{11}H_{13}N_5O_3$			
D-Alanine, N-(1,4-dihydro-6,7-dimethyl-4-oxo-2-pteridinyl)-	pH -4.0	221(4.11),253(4.08), 286(3.72),336(3.85), 392(3.46)	18-2933-79
	pH -0.75	218(4.06),261(4.03), 285(4.00),324(3.61), 390(3.84)	18-2933-79

Compound	Solvent	λ_{max}(log ε)	Ref.
D-Alanine, N-(1,4-dihydro-6,7-dimethyl-4-oxo-2-pteridinyl)- (cont.)	pH 2.5	221(4.16),276(4.15), 344(3.80)	18-2933-79
	pH 6.0	224(4.18),278(4.23), 350(3.84)	18-2933-79
	pH 11.0	259(4.32),364(3.91)	18-2933-79
L-Alanine, N-(1,4-dihydro-6,7-dimethyl-4-oxo-2-pteridinyl)-	pH -4.0	222(4.13),253(4.11), 286(3.76),336(3.88), 393(3.53)	18-2933-79
	pH -0.75	218(4.09),261(4.07), 285(4.04),324(3.66), 389(3.88)	18-2933-79
	pH 2.5	220(4.21),276(4.18), 344(3.84)	18-2933-79
	pH 6.0	224(4.20),279(4.25), 350(3.87)	18-2933-79
	pH 11.0	259(4.34),364(3.93)	18-2933-79
β-Alanine, N-(1,4-dihydro-6,7-dimethyl-4-oxo-2-pteridinyl)-	pH -4.0	220(4.18),253(4.10), 338(3.95),398(3.76)	18-2933-79
	pH -0.25	218(4.26),253(4.05), 290(3.77),323(3.91), 395(3.42)	18-2933-79
	pH 5.5	224(4.21),278(4.24), 349(3.86)	18-2933-79
	pH 11.0	259(4.34),364(3.93)	18-2933-79
1H-Imidazo[1,2-f]purine-2,4(3H,6H)-dione, 8-acetyl-7,8-dihydro-1,3-dimethyl-	EtOH	292(4.05)	118-0581-79
9H-Purin-6-amine, 9-(5,6-dideoxy-β-D-erythro-hex-4-enofuranosyl)-, (E)-	H_2O	260(4.13)	44-4359-79
(Z)-	H_2O	260(4.13)	44-4359-79
$C_{11}H_{13}N_5O_6$			
Glycine, N-[1,4-dihydro-4-oxo-6-(1,2,3-trihydroxypropyl)-2-pteridinyl]-, (R*,S*)-	pH -4.0	210(4.11),251(4.09), 285(3.77),323(3.80), 394(3.46)	18-2933-79
	pH -0.5	211(4.14),239(4.12), 282(4.19),322(3.74), 389(3.35)	18-2933-79
	pH 2.0	213(4.11),239(4.08), 277(4.21),347(3.79)	18-2933-79
	pH 5.0	225(4.05),240(4.04), 280(4.29),332(3.79)	18-2933-79
	pH 10.0	218(4.00),266(4.37), 369(3.87)	18-2933-79
9H-Purine-8-carboxylic acid, 6-amino-9-β-D-ribofuranosyl-	H_2O	275(4.08)	88-2385-79
sodium salt	0.05M HCl	275(4.12)	94-0183-79
	H_2O	275(4.03)	94-0183-79
$C_{11}H_{13}N_5O_7$			
1H-Purine-8-carboxylic acid, 2-amino-6,9-dihydro-6-oxo-9-β-D-ribofuranosyl-	H_2O	273(4.10)	88-2385-79
$C_{11}H_{13}N_9$			
3,5'-Bi-2H-tetrazolium, 2-[4-(dimethylamino)phenyl]-5-methyl-, hydroxide, inner salt	EtOH	265(4.22),450(3.98)	104-1793-79
$C_{11}H_{14}$			
Benzene, 1-methyl-4-(2-methyl-1-propenyl)-	MeOH	247(4.19)	44-1458-79

Compound	Solvent	$\lambda_{max}(\log \epsilon)$	Ref.
1,3-Cyclopentadiene, 5-(1-methyl-4-pentenylidene)-	EtOH	271(4.26),356(2.56)	1-0256-79
1H-Indene, 2,3-dihydro-1,7-dimethyl-	EtOH	265(2.69),273(2.69)	117-0255-79
$C_{11}H_{14}BrN_3O_4$			
Cytidine, 5-(2-bromoethenyl)-2'-deoxy-, (E)-	EtOH	254(4.20),312(3.82)	88-4415-79
$C_{11}H_{14}ClNO$			
2(1H)-Quinolinone, 3-chloro-4a,5,6,7-tetrahydro-1,4a-dimethyl-	EtOH	298(3.30)	4-0065-79
$C_{11}H_{14}FN_3O_5$			
1(2H)-Pyrimidineacetic acid, α-(acetyl-amino)-5-fluoro-3,4-dihydro-α-methyl-2,4-dioxo-, ethyl ester	MeOH	266(3.93)	44-2019-79
$C_{11}H_{14}F_3NOSi$			
Acetamide, 2,2,2-trifluoro-N-[4-(tri-methylsilyl)phenyl]-	C_6H_{12}	250(4.22)	12-1521-79
$C_{11}H_{14}F_4O_5Si$			
Silane, trimethoxy[(tetrafluoromethoxy-phenoxy)methyl]-	heptane	213(4.03),263s(2.60)	70-2602-79
$C_{11}H_{14}IN_3O_4$			
Cytidine, 2'-deoxy-5-(2-iodoethenyl)-, (E)-	EtOH	256(4.18),315(3.79)	88-4415-79
$C_{11}H_{14}NO_4P$			
Phosphonic acid, [1-cyano-2-(2-furan-yl)ethenyl]-, diethyl ester	EtOH	205(3.77),234s(3.53), 327(4.52)	48-0353-79
$C_{11}H_{14}N_2$			
1H-Benzimidazole, 2-butyl-	EtOH	207(4.68),245(3.99), 274(3.99),281(4.06)	39-2289-79C
1H-Benzimidazole, 1,2-diethyl-	isooctane	245(4.09),278(3.67), 285(3.63)	65-1225-79
1H-Benzimidazole, 2-(1-methylpropyl)-	EtOH	207(4.69),244(3.95), 274(3.95),281(4.02)	39-2289-79C
1H-Imidazole, 4,5-dihydro-4,4-dimethyl-2-phenyl-	EtOH	224(4.28),265(3.78)	39-2289-79C
$C_{11}H_{14}N_2O$			
2(1H)-Quinolinone, 1-(dimethylamino)-7,8-dihydro-	MeOH	207(3.81),230(3.76), 279(4.09),290(3.96), 343(3.53)	64-0102-79B
$C_{11}H_{14}N_2OS$			
4(1H)-Pyrimidinone, 5-cyclopropyl-6-(cyclopropylmethyl)-2,3-dihydro-2-thioxo-	MeOH	220(4.13),280(4.27)	73-2426-79
$C_{11}H_{14}N_2OS_3$			
4-Thiazolidinone, 3-ethyl-5-(3-ethyl-4-methyl-2(3H)-thiazolylidene)-2-thioxo-	EtOH	414s(4.51),431(4.58)	73-1413-79
$C_{11}H_{14}N_2O_2$			
1H-1,2-Benzodiazepine-3,6(2H,7H)-dione, 8,9-dihydro-1,2-dimethyl-	MeOH	207(4.07),258(3.92), 341(3.97)	24-3237-79

Compound	Solvent	λ_{max}(log ε)	Ref.
3,5-Cinnolinedione, 1,2,4,6,7,8-hexahydro-1,2-dimethyl-4-methylene-	MeOH	206(3.78),246(3.94), 333(4.22)	24-3237-79
1H-Cyclopenta[b]quinoxaline, 2,3,5,6,7-8-hexahydro-, 4,9-dioxide	EtOH	242(4.49),303(4.33)	70-0848-79
1H-Indazole-4,7-diol, 6-(1,1-dimethylethyl)-, hydrochloride	n.s.g.	222(4.71)	70-1668-79
2,4(1H,3H)-Pyrimidinedione, 5-cyclopropyl-6-(cyclopropylmethyl)-	MeOH	272.0(4.06)	73-2426-79
2,5(1H,6H)-Quinolinedione, 1-(dimethylamino)-7,8-dihydro-	MeOH	206(3.93),281(4.24)	64-0102-79B
$C_{11}H_{14}N_2O_3$			
2-Butanone, 3-methyl-, O-(4-nitrophenyl)oxime, (E)-	hexane	302(4.23)	12-2413-79
(Z)-	hexane	300(4.23)	12-2413-79
Phenol, 5-nitro-2-(1-piperidinyl)-	8M H_2SO_4	228(3.96),266(3.82), 322(3.36)	77-0428-79
2-Piperidinecarboxylic acid, 1-(2-pyridinyl)-, N-oxide, (S)-	MeOH	325(3.53)	4-0591-79
3-Piperidinecarboxylic acid, 1-(2-pyridinyl)-, N-oxide, (R)-	MeOH	325(3.53)	4-0591-79
3-Pyridinecarboxylic acid, 5-cyano-1,4,5,6-tetrahydro-2,5-dimethyl-6-oxo-, ethyl ester	EtOH	277(4.09)	56-1913-79
$C_{11}H_{14}N_2O_4$			
Benzene, 1-(1,2-dimethyl-1-nitropropyl)-4-nitro-	hexane	260(4.05)	12-2413-79
Benzene, 1-(2,2-dimethyl-1-nitropropyl)-4-nitro-	MeOH	261(4.10)	12-1487-79
8-Quinazolinol, 5,6,7,8-tetrahydro-2-methyl-, acetate, 1,3-dioxide	EtOH	264(4.47),287(4.09), 354(3.26)	103-1025-79
$C_{11}H_{14}N_2O_4S$			
Cysteine, S-(5-acetylamino-2-hydroxyphenyl)-	H_2O	208(3.86),245(3.61), 296(3.00)	12-1307-79
5-Thia-1-azabicyclo[4.2.0]oct-2-ene-2-carboxylic acid, 7-acetylamino-3-methyl-8-oxo-, methyl ester, (6R-trans)-	EtOH	261(3.88)	39-1629-79C
Thiophene, 2-(1-methyl-1-nitroethyl)-5-(2-methyl-1-propenyl)-3-nitro-	MeOH	271(4.05)	12-1709-79
$C_{11}H_{14}N_2O_5$			
2-Furancarboxylic acid, 5-(3,4-dihydro-2,4-dioxo-1(2H)-pyrimidinyl)tetrahydro-, ethyl ester	pH 2	262(4.01)	103-0926-79
	pH 7	263(4.04)	103-0926-79
	pH 10	263(3.92)	103-0926-79
2-Furancarboxylic acid, 5-(3,4-dihydro-5-methyl-2,4-dioxo-1(2H)-pyrimidinyl)tetrahydro-, methyl ester	pH 2	266(3.99)	103-0926-79
	pH 7	266(3.97)	103-0926-79
	pH 10	266(3.86)	103-0926-79
$C_{11}H_{14}N_2O_5S$			
Butanamide, N-[2-(aminosulfonyl)-5-methoxyphenyl]-3-oxo-	EtOH	227(4.42),250(4.11), 316(3.18)	104-1495-79
$C_{11}H_{14}N_2O_6$			
Butanedioic acid, [(3,4-dihydro-2,4-dioxo-1(2H)-pyrimidinyl)methyl]-, dimethyl ester	MeOH	264(4.01)	126-2323-79

Compound	Solvent	λ$_{max}$(log ε)	Ref.
$C_{11}H_{14}N_2O_7$			
Uridine, 5'-acetate	EtOH	261(3.96)	39-2088-79C
Uridine, 5-acetyl-	pH 1	230(3.99),284(4.06)	78-1125-79
	pH 13	287(3.94)	78-1125-79
$C_{11}H_{14}N_2S$			
2,1-Benzisothiazol-3-amine, N,N-diethyl-	EtOH	234(4.36),277(3.31), 285s(3.3),298s(3.04), 385(3.75)	33-0391-79
$C_{11}H_{14}N_3O_8P$			
6H-Furo[2',3':4,5]oxazolo[3,2-a]pyrimi-dine-2-methanol, 3-acetoxy-2,3,3a,9a-tetrahydro-6-imino-, dihydrogen phosphate	MeOH	235(3.91),264(3.96)	87-0639-79
$C_{11}H_{14}N_4$			
1H-Pyrrolo[2,3-d]pyrimidin-4-amine, N-cyclobutyl-2-methyl-	pH 1	282(4.16)	102-0217-79
	H_2O	281(4.17)	102-0217-79
	pH 13	279(4.20)	102-0217-79
$C_{11}H_{14}N_4O$			
4H-Pyrazolo[3,4-d]pyrimidin-4-one, 1-cyclopentyl-1,5-dihydro-5-methyl-	MeOH	211(4.46),255(3.80)	83-0586-79
$C_{11}H_{14}N_4OS$			
4H-Pyrazolo[3,4-d]pyrimidin-4-one, 1-cyclopentyl-1,5-dihydro-3-(meth-ylthio)-	MeOH	231(4.19),250(3.97)	83-0586-79
$C_{11}H_{14}N_4O_2S$			
Isothiazolo[3,4-d]pyrimidine-4,6(5H,7H)-dione, 5,7-dimethyl-3-pyrrolidino-	EtOH	211(3.98),238(4.29), 277(4.00),310(4.10)	95-0989-79
$C_{11}H_{14}N_4O_3S$			
Isothiazolo[3,4-d]pyrimidine-4,6(5H,7H)-dione, 5,7-dimethyl-3-morpholino-	EtOH	212(4.42),232(4.24), 281(4.16)	95-0989-79
$C_{11}H_{14}N_4O_4$			
D-Arabinitol, 1-C-(6-amino-1,2,4-tria-zolo[1,5-a]pyridin-2-yl)-1,4-anhy-dro-, (R)-	H_2O	227(4.44),310(3.23)	111-0375-79
D-Arabinitol, 1-C-(8-amino-1,2,4-tria-zolo[1,5-a]pyridin-2-yl)-1,4-anhy-dro-, (R)-	H_2O	272(3.95),295(3.79)	111-0375-79
$C_{11}H_{14}N_4O_4S$			
β-D-arabino-Hexopyranoside, 1H-purin-6-yl 2-deoxy-1-thio-	MeOH	285(3.97)	136-0089-79B
D-Ribitol, 1,4-anhydro-1-C-[4-(methyl-thio)pyrazolo[1,5-a]-1,3,5-triazin-8-yl]-, (S)-	pH 0-10	257(4.08),314(3.58)	44-4547-79
$C_{11}H_{14}N_4O_5$			
3-Deazaguanine, 7-α-D-arabino-furanosyl-	pH 1	207(4.28),277(3.99), 318(3.74)	87-0958-79
	pH 7	217(4.34),258(3.75), 318(3.74)	87-0958-79
	pH 11	217(4.35),259(3.72), 316(3.78)	87-0958-79

Compound	Solvent	λ_{max}(log ε)	Ref.
3-Deazaguanine, 7-β-D-arabinofuranosyl-	pH 1	207(4.32),278(4.04), 317(3.75)	87-0958-79
	pH 7	216(4.38),260(3.76), 319(3.84)	87-0958-79
	pH 11	217(4.39),260(3.75), 315(3.75)	87-0958-79
3-Deazaguanine, 9-α-D-arabinofuranosyl-	pH 1	207(4.30),286(4.09), 310(3.83)	87-0958-79
	pH 7	205(4.43),272(4.07), 300(3.94)	87-0958-79
	pH 11	206(4.41),273(4.06), 300(3.91)	87-0958-79
$C_{11}H_{14}N_4O_5S$			
Inosine, 4'-C-(hydroxymethyl)-6-thio-	pH 13	232(4.15),310(4.37)	44-1301-79
$C_{11}H_{14}N_4O_6$			
Xanthosine, 8-methyl-	H_2O	272(3.91)	88-2385-79
$C_{11}H_{14}N_5O_7P$			
Guanosine, cyclic 3',5'-(methyl phosphate)	MeOH	256(4.39)	130-0009-79
$C_{11}H_{14}N_6O_4$			
Cytidine, N-acetyl-5'-azido-2',5'-dideoxy-	EtOH	249(4.17),302(3.87)	39-1389-79C
$C_{11}H_{14}N_6O_4S$			
Adenosine, 8-(aminothioxomethyl)-	pH 1	275(4.18)	94-0183-79
	H_2O	227(4.15),281(4.01)	94-0183-79
	pH 13	268(4.23)	94-0183-79
$C_{11}H_{14}N_6O_5$			
Adenosine, 2-(aminocarbonyl)-	0.5M HCl	267(4.14),287(3.81)	94-0183-79
	H_2O	263s(4.06),266(4.07), 291(3.83)	94-0183-79
Adenosine, 8-(aminocarbonyl)-	pH 1	274(4.15)	94-0183-79
	H_2O	222(4.26),287(4.03)	94-0183-79
	pH 13	281(4.02)	94-0183-79
$C_{11}H_{14}N_8O_5S$			
9H-Purin-6-amine, 9-[3-azido-3-deoxy-2-O-(methylsulfonyl)-β-D-xylofuranosyl]-	MeOH	259(4.17)	44-1317-79
$C_{11}H_{14}O$			
5(1H)-Azulenone, 2,3,6,7-tetrahydro-8-methyl-	EtOH	240s(3.82),303(4.21)	88-0565-79
Benzene, 1-methoxy-4-(2-methyl-1-propenyl)-	MeOH	251(4.25)	44-1458-79
Bicyclo[4.3.1]deca-2,4,8-trien-7-ol, 2-methyl-	C_6H_{12}	251s(3.83),255(3.84), 264(3.69)	5-0533-79
2(3H)-Naphthalenone, 4,4a,5,6-tetrahydro-7-methyl-	EtOH	289(4.36)	22-0627-79
4-Penten-1-ol, 4-phenyl-	C_6H_{12}	238(3.99)	35-7367-79
1-Propanone, 2-methyl-1-(2-methylphenyl)-	EtOH	243(3.81)	78-2655-79
$C_{11}H_{14}O_2$			
2,4,6-Cycloheptatriene-1-carboxylic acid, 1,2-dimethyl-, methyl ester	C_6H_{12}	270(3.60)	24-1168-79

Compound	Solvent	λ max(log ε)	Ref.
2,4,6-Cycloheptatriene-1-carboxylic acid, 1,4-dimethyl-, methyl ester	C_6H_{12}	273(3.45)	24-1168-79
Propanoic acid, 2,2-dimethyl-, phenyl ester	EtOH	260(2.38),266(2.26)	22-0373-79
1-Propanone, 1-(4-hydroxyphenyl)-2,2-dimethyl-	EtOH	220(3.97),273(4.10)	22-0373-79
[4.3.2]Propellane-7,10-dione	MeOH	289(1.78)	44-4557-79
$C_{11}H_{14}O_2S$			
1,4-Benzoxathiin, 2-ethoxy-2,3-dihydro-6-methyl-	hexane	215(4.60),242(3.92), 252(3.88),290(3.58), 299(3.54)	44-1977-79
1,3-Benzoxathiole, 2-ethoxy-2,5-dimethyl-	hexane	209(4.38),241(3.81), 293(3.67),301(3.61)	44-1977-79
$C_{11}H_{14}O_3$			
Bicyclo[2.2.2]octane-exo-2-carboxylic acid, 6-hydroxy-4,6-dimethyl-5-oxo-, lactone, exo-	MeOH	306(1.54)	23-2853-79
1,3-Dioxolane, 2-methoxy-2-(4-methylphenyl)-	n.s.g.	230s(3.9)	44-1855-79
$C_{11}H_{14}O_3Si$			
Acetic acid, (dimethylphenylsilyl)-oxo-, methyl ester	C_6H_{12}	279(2.79),455(2.33)	88-0871-79
$C_{11}H_{14}O_4$			
1,3-Dioxane-4,6-dione, 2,2-dimethyl-5-(3-methyl-2-butenylidene)-	C_6H_{12}	307(4.27)	24-3293-79
3-Heptene-2,6-dione, 3,5-diacetyl-	$CHCl_3$	277(4.05),334(3.80)	39-0464-79C
$C_{11}H_{14}O_6$			
Acetic acid, [3-hydroxy-4-(5-hydroxypentyl)-5-oxo-2(5H)-furanylidene]-, (E)-	EtOH	263(4.18),295(3.90)	130-0311-79
2-Pentenedioic acid, 2,4-diacetyl-, dimethyl ester	$CHCl_3$	250(3.91),315(3.86)	39-0464-79C
$C_{11}H_{14}S_2$			
1,3-Dithiane, 2-(phenylmethyl)-	EtOH	209(4.04),250(2.79)	150-0301-79
$C_{11}H_{14}S_3$			
Benzenecarbo(dithioperoxo)thioic acid, 1,1-dimethylethyl ester	EtOH	230s(--),295(4.0), 530(2.0)	44-0569-79
$C_{11}H_{15}$			
Cycloheptatrienylium, 1-methyl-2-(1-methylethyl)-, perchlorate	10% HCl	235(4.58),282s(--), 300(3.73),310s(--)	39-1005-79B
Cycloheptatrienylium, 1,2,3,4-tetramethyl-, perchlorate	10% HCl	246(4.74),298(3.75), 304s(--)	78-0949-79
Cycloheptatrienylium, 1,2,3,5-tetramethyl-, perchlorate	10% HCl	243(4.77),303(3.77), 307s(--)	78-0949-79
Cycloheptatrienylium, 1,2,4,5-tetramethyl-, perchlorate	10% HCl	240(4.82),301s(--), 308(3.87)	78-0949-79
Cycloheptatrienylium, 1,2,4,6-tetramethyl-, perchlorate	10% HCl	242(4.85),298(3.88), 310s(--)	78-0949-79
$C_{11}H_{15}BrN_2O$			
Pentanal, 5-hydroxy-, (4-bromophenyl)-hydrazone	EtOH	282(4.29)	104-1237-79

Compound	Solvent	λmax(log ε)	Ref.
$C_{11}H_{15}BrO$			
2,4-Cyclohexadien-1-one, 3-bromo-2,4,5,6,6-pentamethyl-	EtOH	328(3.59)	104-1703-79
2,4-Cyclohexadien-1-one, 4-bromo-2,3,5,6,6-pentamethyl-	EtOH	320(3.54)	104-1703-79
$C_{11}H_{15}ClO$			
2,4-Cyclohexadien-1-one, 4-chloro-2,3,5,6,6-pentamethyl-	EtOH	324(3.66)	104-1703-79
$C_{11}H_{15}ClO_4$			
5-α-D-xylo-Octeno-1,4-furanos-7-ulose, 3-chloro-3,5,6,8-tetradeoxy-1,2-O-(1-methylethylidene)-	hexane	219(3.92)	33-2091-79
	EtOH	219(4.09)	33-2091-79
$C_{11}H_{15}FN_2O_6$			
2,4(1H,3H)-Pyrimidinedione, 1-(4-deoxy-4-fluoro-β-D-glucopyranosyl)-5-methyl-	H_2O	265(3.95)	97-0106-79
	pH 13	264(3.80)	97-0106-79
$C_{11}H_{15}FN_2O_9S_2$			
Uridine, 5'-deoxy-5-fluoro-, 2',3'-dimethanesulfonate	MeOH	264(3.92)	87-1330-79
$C_{11}H_{15}FO$			
Bicyclo[3.3.1]non-3-en-2-one, 6-fluoro-1,4-dimethyl-	EtOH	240(3.93)	70-1636-79
2,4-Cyclohexadien-1-one, 4-fluoro-2,3,5,6,6-pentamethyl-	EtOH	321(3.78)	104-1703-79
$C_{11}H_{15}N$			
Benzenamine, 2-(2-butenyl)-N-methyl-	MeOH	242(3.99),291(3.43)	33-2581-79
Benzenamine, 2,6-dimethyl-N-2-propenyl-	MeOH	239(3.95),289(3.31)	33-2613-79
Benzenamine, 2-(1-methyl-2-butenyl)-, (E)-	hexane	235(3.88),286(3.42)	33-2581-79
Benzenamine, N-methyl-N-(1-methyl-2-propenyl)-	C_6H_{12}	244(4.00),294(3.45)	33-2581-79
	MeOH	243(3.95),292(3.39)	33-2581-79
1H-Indole, 3-ethyl-2,3-dihydro-2-methyl-, cis	MeOH	238(3.90),286(3.38)	33-2581-79
$C_{11}H_{15}NO$			
Phenol, 2-[(butylimino)methyl]-	MeOH	211(4.38),253(4.07), 280(3.59),314(3.65)	150-3801-79
Phenol, 2-[[(1-methylpropyl)imino]methyl]-	MeOH	254(4.18),278s(4.12), 401(3.81)(calcd.)	137-0118-79
	CCl_4	320(3.67)	137-0118-79
2-Propanone, 1-[2-(dimethylamino)phenyl]-	EtOH	245(3.72),346(2.53)	39-0376-79C
$C_{11}H_{15}NOS$			
1-Propanesulfenamide, 2,2-dimethyl-N-(4-oxo-2,5-cyclohexadien-1-ylidene)-	hexane	402(4.43)	138-1077-79
2-Propanesulfenamide, 2-methyl-N-(2-methyl-4-oxo-2,5-cyclohexadien-1-ylidene)-	hexane	399(4.32)	138-1077-79
$C_{11}H_{15}NO_2$			
7-Azaspiro[3.5]nona-5,8-diene-7-carboxylic acid, ethyl ester	isooctane	233(4.04)	44-2522-79
Benzaldehyde, 2-methoxy-3,5-dimethyl-6-(methylamino)-	EtOH	278(3.79),382(3.50)	33-0234-79

Compound	Solvent	$\lambda_{max}(\log \epsilon)$	Ref.
Benzaldehyde, 2-(methylamino)-5-(1-methylethoxy)-	EtOH	263s(--),405(3.69)	33-0234-79
Benzene, 2-butyl-4-methoxy-1-nitroso-	$CHCl_3$	745(1.45)	44-2087-79
Phenol, 2-[[[1-(hydroxymethyl)propyl]-imino]methyl]-	MeOH	255(4.18),279s(4.18), 402(3.79)(calcd.)	137-0118-79
	CCl_4	321(3.67)	137-0118-79
Pyridinium, 1-(carboxymethyl)-2-ethyl-3,5-dimethyl-, hydroxide, inner salt	MeOH	280(3.87)	44-1417-79
$C_{11}H_{15}NO_3$			
Benzene, 1-(1,1-dimethylethyl)-4-methyl-2-nitro-	C_6H_{12}	259(3.1),274(3.1), 283(3.1),296s(3.0)	5-0554-79
	MeOH	220(4.1),243s(3.3), 273(3.1),281s(3.0), 315s(2.8)	5-0554-79
Benzene, 2-(1,1-dimethylethyl)-4-methoxy-1-nitro-	C_6H_{12}	235s(3.7),271(3.6), 340(3.0)	5-0554-79
	MeOH	245s(3.5),273(3.5), 278s(3.5),346(3.1)	5-0554-79
1,4-Benzoxazine, 2,3-dihydro-3-hydroxy-2-methoxy-1,3-dimethyl-	EtOH	243(3.95),292(3.18)	35-7332-79
1-Propanol, 2,2-dimethyl-1-(4-nitrophenyl)-	hexane	263(4.05)	12-1487-79
$C_{11}H_{15}NO_3S$			
4-Thia-1-azabicyclo[3.2.0]hept-2-ene-2-carboxylic acid, 7-oxo-3-pentyl-	EtOH	257(3.57),307(3.73)	35-6296-79
$C_{11}H_{15}NO_4S$			
Benzenesulfonamide, 4-(acetoxymethyl)-N,N-dimethyl-	EtOH	230(4.06),274(2.87)	118-0531-79
$C_{11}H_{15}NO_6S$			
2-Thiazoleacetic acid, 5-β-D-ribofuranosyl-, methyl ester	acid	251(3.79)	44-4351-79
	pH 7	246(3.80)	44-4351-79
	base	247(3.87)	44-4351-79
$C_{11}H_{15}NS_2$			
1,3,2-Benzodithiazole, 2-(1,1-dimethylethyl)-5-methyl-	CH_2Cl_2	246(4.35)	4-0183-79
$C_{11}H_{15}N_3$			
5,8-Methano-1,2,3-benzotriazine, 5,6,7,8-tetrahydro-8,9,9-trimethyl-, (5S)-	EtOH	223(3.46),295(2.45)	95-0699-79
$C_{11}H_{15}N_3OS_2$			
4-Imidazolidinone, 5-(3-ethyl-4-methyl-2(3H)-thiazolylidene)-1,3-dimethyl-2-thioxo-	EtOH	429(4.03)	73-1413-79
$C_{11}H_{15}N_3O_2$			
Pyrimidinium, 5-methyl-4-(2-pyrrolyl)-3,4-dihydro-, acetate	EtOH	277(3.56)	24-0001-79
$C_{11}H_{15}N_3O_3$			
Carbamic acid, [[nitroso(phenylmethyl)-amino]methyl]-, ethyl ester	EtOH	237(3.83),366(1.79)	94-0682-79
Pentanal, 5-hydroxy-, (4-nitrophenyl)-hydrazone	EtOH	388(4.38)	104-1237-79

Compound	Solvent	λ_{max}(log ε)	Ref.
L-Valine, N-(pyrazinylcarbonyl)-, methyl ester	isooctane	208(4.04),267(3.89), 335f(2.78)	39-2881-79C
	EtOH	211(4.02),270(3.90), 320(2.78)	39-2881-79C
	MeCN	209(4.03),268(3.93), 321(2.78)	39-2881-79C
$C_{11}H_{15}N_3O_4$			
1H-Pyrazole-3-carboxylic acid, 1-acetyl-4-(acetylamino)-5-methyl-, ethyl ester	pH 1	221(3.91),265(3.57)	18-0208-79
	pH 11	257(3.92)	18-0208-79
	EtOH	221(3.94),265(3.58)	18-0208-79
$C_{11}H_{15}N_3O_5$			
Cytidine, 2'-deoxy-, 3'-acetate	EtOH	273(3.92)	39-2088-79C
Cytidine, 2'-deoxy-, 5'-acetate	EtOH	273(3.90)	39-2088-79C
1(2H)-Pyrimidineacetic acid, α-(acetylamino)-3,4-dihydro-α-methyl-2,4-dioxo-, ethyl ester	pH 1	259(4.01)	44-2019-79
	pH 12	260(3.85)	44-2019-79
	MeOH	259(4.00)	44-2019-79
1(2H)-Pyrimidineacetic acid, α-(acetylamino)-3,4-dihydro-5-methyl-2,4-dioxo-, ethyl ester	MeOH	264(3.98)	44-2019-79
$C_{11}H_{15}N_3O_6$			
Uridine, 5-(acetylamino)-2'-deoxy-	pH 1	277(3.88)	87-0621-79
	pH 12	273(3.78)	87-0621-79
$C_{11}H_{15}N_3O_7$			
2(1H)-Pyrimidinone, 4-amino-1-[5-O-(carboxymethyl)-β-D-arabinofuranosyl]-	pH 1	282(4.05)	73-3023-79
	pH 7-10.5	272(3.88)	73-3023-79
	pH 12	272(3.88)	73-3023-79
$C_{11}H_{15}N_3O_8$			
β-D-Allofuranuronic acid, 5-amino-1,5-dideoxy-1-[3,4-dihydro-5-(hydroxymethyl)-2,4-dioxo-1(2H)-pyrimidinyl]-	0.05M HCl	262(3.97)	142-0333-79B
	0.05M NaOH	264(3.87)	142-0333-79B
$C_{11}H_{15}N_3S$			
6H-Pyrimido[1,2-c]quinazoline-6-thione, 2,3,4,7,8,9,10,11-octahydro-	HCl	244(3.93),285(4.11)	103-0390-79
	NaOH	270(4.17),333(4.04)	103-0390-79
	EtOH	280(4.24),340(4.06)	103-0390-79
$C_{11}H_{15}N_5$			
1,2,4-Triazolo[4,3-a]pyrazin-8-amine, 3-methyl-N-(3-methyl-2-butenyl)-	EtOH	237(4.14),296(3.97)	44-1028-79
$C_{11}H_{15}N_5O_2$			
1H-[1,3]Diazepino[2,1-f]purine-2,4-(3H,6H)-dione, 7,8,9,10-tetrahydro-1,3-dimethyl-	EtOH	292(4.06)	118-0581-79
Propanoic acid, 2-methyl-, 2-(6-amino-9H-purin-9-yl)ethyl ester	DMSO	264.0(4.11)	47-0905-79
$C_{11}H_{15}N_5O_3$			
Adenosine, 2'-deoxy-3'-O-methyl-	H_2O	260(4.19)	23-0274-79
9H-Purin-6-amine, 9-(2-ethoxy-1,3-dioxan-5-yl)-, cis	EtOH	215(3.95)	103-0798-79
trans	EtOH	215(4.10)	103-0798-79
$C_{11}H_{15}N_5O_3S$			
Acetamide, N-(6,8-diethyl-5,6,7,8-tetrahydro-5,7-dioxo-1H-pyrimido[4,5-e]-	MeOH	252(4.25),280(3.90), 370(3.08)	94-1965-79

Compound	Solvent	$\lambda_{max}(\log \epsilon)$	Ref.
[1,3,4]thiadiazin-3-yl)- (cont.)			94-1965-79
Guanosine, 2',3'-dideoxy-3'-(hydroxymethyl)-6-thio-	pH 13	252(4.14),270(3.85), 319(4.30)	87-0518-79
9H-Purin-6-amine, 9-(2-S-methyl-2-thio-β-D-arabinofuranosyl)-	pH 1	259(4.16)	4-0353-79
	pH 13	260(4.19)	4-0353-79
6H-Purine-6-thione, 2-amino-9-(2,3-dideoxy-3-(hydroxymethyl)-α-D-erythro-pentofuranosyl]-1,9-dihydro-	pH 7	226(4.18),257(3.92), 341(4.36)	87-0518-79
	pH 13	252(4.12),270(3.84), 319(4.29)	87-0518-79
$C_{11}H_{15}N_5O_4$			
Adenosine, 1-methyl-	pH 4.0	257(4.11)	5-1872-79
	pH 12.0	258(4.15),264s(4.10), 295s(3.54)	5-1872-79
Adenosine, 3-methyl- (p-toluenesulfonate)	pH 7	270(4.24)	77-0135-79
	EtOH	272(4.22)	77-0135-79
Adenosine, 6-N-methyl-	pH 1.0	262(4.25)	5-1872-79
	pH 6.0	265(4.22)	5-1872-79
Adenosine, 8-methyl-	H_2O	260.5(4.19)	88-2385-79 +88-3159-79
9H-Purin-6-amine, 9-(2-O-methyl-β-D-arabinofuranosyl)-	pH 1	257(4.17)	4-0353-79
	pH 7	258(4.18)	4-0353-79
	pH 13	258(4.18)	4-0353-79
9H-Purin-6-amine, 9-(3-C-methyl-β-D-xylofuranosyl)-	EtOH	258(4.15)	33-0689-79
$C_{11}H_{15}N_5O_5$			
Adenosine, 4'-C-(hydroxymethyl)-	pH 2	256(4.16)	44-1301-79
	pH 13	260(4.04)	44-1301-79
Cytidine, 3'-deoxy-3'-[[(methylamino)-carbonyl]amino]-	pH 1	280(4.14)	87-1109-79
	pH 7 and 13	272(3.97)	87-1109-79
9H-Purin-6-amine, 9-[3-C-(hydroxymethyl)-β-D-xylofuranosyl]-	H_2O	258(4.15)	33-0689-79
$C_{11}H_{15}N_5O_7$			
Uridine, 3'-deoxy-3'-[[(methylnitrosoamino)carbonyl]amino]-	pH 1	261(4.15)	87-1109-79
	pH 7	260(4.14)	87-1109-79
Uridine, 5'-deoxy-5'-[[(methylnitrosoamino)carbonyl]amino]-	pH 1 and 7	257(4.12)	87-1109-79
	pH 13	262(3.89)	87-1109-79
$C_{11}H_{15}N_7$			
Propanedinitrile, [4,6-bis(dimethylamino)-2-methyl-1,2,3-triazin-5(2H)-ylidene]-	CH_2Cl_2	484(4.20)	24-1535-79
$C_{11}H_{15}N_9$			
Benzenamine, N,N-dimethyl-4-[3-methyl-5-(1H-tetrazol-5-yl)-1-formazano]-	EtOH	255(4.24),320(4.01), 445(4.68)	104-1793-79
$C_{11}H_{16}BrN_5O_2$			
1H-Purine-2,6-dione, 7-(4-aminobutyl)-8-bromo-3,7-dihydro-1,3-dimethyl-, monohydrobromide	EtOH	279(3.92)	118-0581-79
$C_{11}H_{16}ClN_5$			
1,2,3-Triazine, 5-chloro-4,6-di-1-pyrrolidinyl-	CH_2Cl_2	267(4.50),320s(--)	24-1529-79
$C_{11}H_{16}Cl_2N_4O_2$			
1,3,5-Triazin-2-amine, 4,6-dichloro-N-(5-ethyl-2,2-dimethyl-1,3-dioxan-5-yl)-	EtOH	236(4.35)	104-1144-79

Compound	Solvent	λ_{max}(log ε)	Ref.
$C_{11}H_{16}FN_3O_8S_2$			
2,2'-Anhydro-1-(5-deoxy-3-O-methylsulfonyl-β-D-arabinofuranosyl)-5-fluorocytosine methanesulfonate	MeOH	232(3.95),268(4.10)	87-1330-79
$C_{11}H_{16}N_2O$			
Pentanal, 5-hydroxy-, phenylhydrazone	EtOH	276(4.23)	104-1237-79
Pyridine, 2-(2-methyl-1-piperidinyl)-, 1-oxide, (R)-	MeOH	327(3.49)	4-0591-79
Pyridine, 2-(3-methyl-1-piperidinyl)-, 1-oxide, (R)-	MeOH	328(3.50)	4-0591-79
$C_{11}H_{16}N_2O_2$			
5H-Cycloheptapyrazine, 6,7,8,9-tetrahydro-2,3-dimethyl-, 1,4-dioxide	EtOH	240(4.46),303(4.30)	70-0848-79
2-Propenoic acid, 2-cyano-3-(cyclohexylamino)-, methyl ester	MeCN	292(4.45)	80-1143-79
2(1H)-Quinolinone, 1-(dimethylamino)-5,6,7,8-tetrahydro-5-hydroxy-	MeOH	205(3.86),235(3.91), 313(3.83)	64-0102-79B
$C_{11}H_{16}N_2O_3$			
7H-Pyrazolo[1,5-c][1,3]oxazine-3-carboxylic acid, 4,5-dihydro-2,5-dimethyl-, ethyl ester	EtOH	231(3.95)	118-0440-79
$C_{11}H_{16}N_2O_4$			
Isoxazolo[3,4-c]pyridine-6(7H)-carboxylic acid, 4,5-dihydro-3-hydroxy-, 1,1-dimethylethyl ester	MeOH	260(3.86)	111-0157-79
2,4(1H,3H)-Pyrimidinedione, 1-[(2,2-dimethyl-1,3-dioxolan-4-yl)methyl]-5-methyl-	n.s.g.	269(3.92)	128-0281-79
$C_{11}H_{16}N_2O_5$			
1(2H)-Pyrimidinebutanoic acid, 3,4-dihydro-β-hydroxy-5-methyl-2,4-dioxo-, ethyl ester	EtOH	271(3.90)	128-0051-79
2,4(1H,3H)-Pyrimidinedione, 1-(4-acetoxy-2-hydroxybutyl)-5-methyl-	EtOH	269(4.00)	128-0051-79
Uridine, 2'-deoxy-3-ethyl-	H_2O	263(3.9)	87-0621-79
$C_{11}H_{16}N_2O_6$			
2,4(1H,3H)-Pyrimidinedione, 1-α-D-arabinofuranosyl-5-ethyl-	pH 7	268(4.03)	87-0647-79
	pH 12	268(3.92)	87-0647-79
	pH 14	270(3.93)	87-0647-79
2,4(1H,3H)-Pyrimidinedione, 1-β-D-arabinofuranosyl-5-ethyl-	pH 7	268(4.02)	87-0647-79
	pH 12	268(3.92)	87-0647-79
	pH 14	270(3.92)	87-0647-79
Thymidine, 4'-C-(hydroxymethyl)-	MeOH	267(3.97)	44-1309-79
$C_{11}H_{16}N_2O_7$			
Uridine, 5-(1-hydroxyethyl)-	pH 1	266(3.88)	78-1125-79
	pH 13	266(3.74)	78-1125-79
$C_{11}H_{16}N_3O_9P$			
5'-Uridylic acid, 5-(acetylamino)-2'-deoxy-, disodium salt	pH 1	273(3.92)	87-0621-79
	pH 12	270(3.84)	87-0621-79
$C_{11}H_{16}N_4$			
1H-Pyrrolo[2,3-d]pyrimidin-4-amine, 2-methyl-N-(1-methylpropyl)-, picrate	pH 1	274(4.23),354(4.11)	102-0217-79
	H_2O	274(4.21),355(4.14)	102-0217-79

Compound	Solvent	λ_{max}(log ϵ)	Ref.
(cont.)	pH 13	275(4.26),356(4.15)	102-0217-79
Pyrrolo[2,3-d]pyrimidine, 2-methyl-N-(2-methylpropyl)-	pH 1	278(4.15)	102-0217-79
	H_2O	278(4.11)	102-0217-79
	pH 13	274(4.31)	102-0217-79
$C_{11}H_{16}N_4O$			
1-Propanol, 2-methyl-2-[(2-methyl-1H-pyrrolo[2,3-d]pyrimidin-4-yl)amino]-	pH 1	278(4.18)	102-0217-79
	H_2O	278(4.18)	102-0217-79
	pH 13	277(4.22)	102-0217-79
$C_{11}H_{16}N_4O_2$			
4H-Pyrimido[4,5-b][1,4]oxazin-4-one, 2-amino-5-pentyl-	2M HCl	264(3.96),350(3.72)	87-0797-79
	2M NaOH	277(4.02),323(4.00)	87-0797-79
$C_{11}H_{16}N_4O_3S$			
Morpholine, 4-[(6-amino-1,2,3,4-tetrahydro-1,3-dimethyl-2,4-dioxo-5-pyrimidinyl)thioxomethyl]-	EtOH	282(4.23)	95-0515-79
$C_{11}H_{16}N_4O_4$			
Cytidine, N-acetyl-5'-amino-2',5'-dideoxy-, monohydrochloride	pH 1	244(4.00),308(4.08)	39-1389-79C
$C_{11}H_{16}N_4O_5$			
L-Alanine, N-[3-(3,4-dihydro-2,4-dioxo-1(2H)-pyrimidinyl)alanyl]-, methyl ester, hydrochloride	EtOH	263(3.95)	65-0994-79
β-D-Ribofuranose, 5-[4-(aminocarbonyl)-1H-1,2,3-triazol-1-yl]-5-deoxy-2,3-O-(1-methylethylidene)-	MeOH	211(4.15)	44-1424-79
$C_{11}H_{16}N_4O_6$			
L-Serine, N-[3-(3,4-dihydro-2,4-dioxo-1(2H)-pyrimidinyl)alanyl]-, methyl ester, monohydrochloride	EtOH	263(3.95)	65-0994-79
Uridine, 3'-deoxy-3'-[[(methylamino)-carbonyl]amino]-	pH 1 and 7	263(4.03)	87-1109-79
	pH 13	263(3.91)	87-1109-79
Uridine, 5'-deoxy-5'-[[(methylamino)-carbonyl]amino]-	pH 1 and 7	262(4.00)	87-1109-79
	pH 13	262(3.87)	87-1109-79
$C_{11}H_{16}N_5$			
Pyrido[1,2-a]-1,3,5-triazin-5-ium, 2,4-bis(dimethylamino)-, perchlorate	EtOH	240(4.41),266(4.47), 340(3.97)	114-0029-79A
$C_{11}H_{16}N_6O_5S$			
9H-Purin-6-amine, 9-[3-amino-3-deoxy-2-O-(methylsulfonyl)-β-D-arabinofuranosyl]-	H_2O	260(4.18)	44-1317-79
$C_{11}H_{16}N_6O_6$			
Cytidine, 3'-deoxy-3'-[[(methylnitrosoamino)carbonyl]amino]-	pH 1	278(4.27)	87-1109-79
	pH 7	268(4.09)	87-1109-79
	pH 13	270(3.97)	87-1109-79
$C_{11}H_{16}O$			
4(1H)-Azuleneone, 2,3,3a,5,6,7-hexahydro-8-methyl-	isooctane	246(3.01),276(2.12), 286(2.11),294(2.06), 304(1.96),315(1.66)	35-3261-79
4(1H)-Azulenone, 2,3,5,6,7,8-hexahydro-8-methyl-	isooctane	245(4.02),300(1.88)	35-3261-79

Compound	Solvent	λ_{max}(log ε)	Ref.
2H-Benzocyclohepten-2-one, 3,4,4a,5,6-7,8,9-octahydro-	MeOH	241(4.12)	44-3959-79
Bicyclo[4.1.0]hept-4-en-2-one, 3,3,7,7-tetramethyl-	C_6H_{12}	292(2.39)	44-4254-79
Bicyclo[5.1.0]oct-3-en-2-one, 4,8,8-trimethyl-	EtOH	242(4.02)	44-4481-79
2-Buten-1-one, 1-(2-methyl-2-cyclohexen-1-yl)-	hexane	222(3.85)	35-5660-79
3,5-Cycloheptadien-1-one, 2,2,7,7-tetramethyl-	MeOH	243(3.67),290(2.80)	44-4254-79
2,5-Cyclohexadien-1-one, 4-methyl-4-(1-methylpropyl)-	H_2O	245.5(4.15)	39-1089-79C
	EtOH	240(4.17)	39-1089-79C
2-Cyclohexen-1-one, 6-(3-methyl-2-butenyl)-	hexane	224(4.14)	39-1837-79C
Cyclopentanone, 2-(1-cyclopenten-1-yl)-2-methyl-	isooctane	258(2.53),287(2.02), 302(2.11),308(2.05), 311(2.08),313(2.08), 323(1.80)	35-3261-79
4-Hexen-3-one, 2-(1-cyclopenten-1-yl)-, (E)-	hexane	225(4.02)	35-5660-79
2(3H)-Naphthalenone, hexahydro-3-methyl-, cis-(±)-	EtOH	238(4.13)	78-0961-79
trans	EtOH	238(4.18)	78-0961-79
[4.3.2]Propellan-10-one	MeOH	298(1.61)	44-4557-79
Tricyclo[5.3.0.0^{1,6}]decan-2-one, 6-methyl-	isooctane	278(1.42)	35-3261-79
$C_{11}H_{16}O_2$			
3H-2-Benzopyran-3-one, 4-ethyl-6,7,8,8a-tetrahydro-	MeOH	234(3.98)	146-0031-79
Ethanone, 1-(2,2,3,6-tetramethyl-2H-pyran-5-yl)-	EtOH	218(4.05),254(3.88), 325(3.53)	70-0758-79
$C_{11}H_{16}O_3$			
2H-Pyran-5-carboxylic acid, 2,2,3,6-tetramethyl-, methyl ester	EtOH	205(4.08),235(3.79), 300(3.55)	70-0758-79
$C_{11}H_{16}O_4$			
1,2-Benzenedimethanol, 4,5-dimethoxy--methyl-	MeOH	290(3.5)	63-0721-79
1,3-Dioxane-4,6-dione, 5-(2,2-dimethylcyclopropyl)-2,2-dimethyl-	C_6H_{12}	<220(>3.2)	24-3293-79
Ethanone, 1-(2,2,7-trimethyl-1,3,6-trioxaspiro[4.4]non-7-en-8-yl)-, (±)-	EtOH	271(5.02)	136-0055-79B
D-arabino-Oct-3-en-2-ulose, 5,8-anhydro 1,3,4-trideoxy-6,7-O-(1-methylethylidene)-, (E)-	EtOH	220(4.02)	33-2091-79
(Z)-	hexane	219(3.73)	33-2091-79
Propanedioic acid, (2,3-dimethyl-2-buten-1-ylidene)-, dimethyl ester	EtOH	289(4.28)	70-0758-79
$C_{11}H_{16}O_5$			
Propanedioic acid, (3-ethoxy-2-methyl-2-propenylidene)-, dimethyl ester	EtOH	310(4.37)	70-0758-79
1,3,6-Trioxaspiro[4.4]non-7-ene-8-carboxylic acid, 2,2,7-trimethyl-, methyl ester, (±)-	EtOH	248(4.03)	136-0055-79B
$C_{11}H_{16}O_6$			
2-Furanacetic acid, 2,5-dihydro-3-hydroxy-4-(5-hydroxypentyl)-5-oxo-	EtOH	234(3.84)	130-0311-79
	EtOH-NaOH	262(4.09)	130-0311-79

Compound	Solvent	λ_{max}(log ϵ)	Ref.
Propanedioic acid, [(2,2-dimethyl-1,3-dioxolan-4-yl)methylene]-, dimethyl ester	EtOH	224(4.23)	136-0055-79B
$C_{11}H_{16}S_2$			
Benzo[c]thiophene, 4,5,6,7-tetrahydro-4,4-dimethyl-1-(methylthio)-	EtOH	230(3.85)	88-2493-79
$C_{11}H_{17}ClO$			
2-Buten-1-one, 3-chloro-1-(2-methylcyclohexyl)-	hexane	243(3.85)	35-5660-79
stereoisomer	hexane	243(4.24)	35-5660-79
$C_{11}H_{17}FO$			
2-Buten-1-one, 1-(2-fluoro-6-methylcyclohexyl)-	hexane	222(4.09)	35-5660-79
2-Buten-1-one, 3-fluoro-1-(2-methylcyclohexyl)-	hexane	230(4.07)	35-5660-79
isomer	hexane	229(3.93)	35-5660-79
$C_{11}H_{17}N$			
Benzenamine, 2,6-dimethyl-4-propyl-	MeOH	236(3.95),288(3.31)	33-2613-79
1H-Pyrrole, 1-ethenyl-3-ethyl-2-propyl-	C_6H_{12}	201(4.05),254(4.07)	104-0535-79
$C_{11}H_{17}NO$			
Ethanone, 1-(9-methyl-9-azabicyclo[3.3.1]non-2-en-2-yl)-	EtOH	224(3.99)	56-0027-79
Phenol, 2-[(butylamino)methyl]-, hydrochloride	EtOH	216(4.14),277(3.84)	150-3801-79
5H-Pyrrolo[1,2-a]azepin-5-one, 1,2,3,6-7,8-hexahydro-6,6-dimethyl-	ether	244(3.83)	24-0734-79
$C_{11}H_{17}NO_2$			
Benzenemethanol, 2-[(4-hydroxybutyl)-amino]-	EtOH	248(3.91),296(3.31)	100-0615-79
$C_{11}H_{17}NO_3$			
1,3-Cyclohexadiene, 5-butyl-1-methoxy-4-nitro-	hexane	362(3.96)	44-2087-79
Pyrano[3,4-c]pyridine-4-carboxylic acid, 4a,5,6,7,8,8a-hexahydro-1-methyl-, methyl ester	MeOH	243(3.93)	35-6742-79
$C_{11}H_{17}NO_4$			
Butanoic acid, 2-(4-morpholinomethylene)-3-oxo-, ethyl ester	hexane	238(3.82),302(4.10)	131-0077-79D
	EtOH	312(--)	131-0077-79D
$C_{11}H_{17}NS_2$			
Cyclooctathiazole, 2-(ethylthio)-4,5,6,7,8,9-hexahydro-	EtOH	289(3.860)	48-0249-79
$C_{11}H_{17}N_2O_2$			
Pyridinium, 1-(5-amino-5-carboxypentyl)-	2M NH_3	257(3.62)	39-2282-79C
$C_{11}H_{17}N_3$			
Ethanehydrazonamide, N,N,N'-trimethyl-N'-phenyl-, monohydrochloride	H_2O	235(4.14),275s(3.37)	104-2066-79
	pH 13	222(4.24),260(4.16)	104-2066-79
$C_{11}H_{17}N_3O_2$			
1H-Pyrrole-2-carboxylic acid, 3-[[(di-	pH 7	275(4.22)	44-3826-79

Compound	Solvent	λ_{max}(log ε)	Ref.
methylamino)methylene]amino]-4-methyl-, ethyl ester (cont.)			44-3826-79
$C_{11}H_{17}N_3O_2S$			
1H-Pyrazole-4-carboxylic acid, 5-amino-1-cyclopentyl-3-(methylthio)-, methyl ester	MeOH	216(4.36),250(4.02)	83-0586-79
$C_{11}H_{17}N_3O_4$			
Cytidine, 2'-deoxy-N-ethyl-	pH 1	278(4.20)	87-0621-79
	pH 12	272(4.14)	87-0621-79
$C_{11}H_{17}N_3O_4S$			
Butanimidamide, 3-hydroxy-N-[[(4-methoxyphenyl)amino]sulfonyl]-	isoPrOH	229(4.17),281(3.62)	44-4191-79
$C_{11}H_{17}N_3O_5$			
2(1H)-Pyrimidinone, 4-amino-1-α-D-arabinofuranosyl-5-ethyl-	pH 1	288(4.06)	87-0647-79
	pH 12	278(3.88)	87-0647-79
	pH 14	280(3.90)	87-0647-79
β-	pH 1	290(4.09)	87-0647-79
	pH 12	278(3.93)	87-0647-79
	pH 14	282(3.96)	87-0647-79
Uridine, 2'-deoxy-5-(ethylamino)-	pH 1	267(3.97)	87-0621-79
	pH 12	292(3.74)	87-0621-79
$C_{11}H_{17}N_5$			
Imidazo[5,1-f][1,2,4]triazin-2-amine, N-ethyl-5-methyl-7-propyl-	n.s.g.	215(4.25),244(4.42), 323(3.71)	39-1120-79C
$C_{11}H_{17}N_5O_2$			
2H-Pyrazolo[3,4-d]pyrimidine-4,6(5H,7H)-dione, 3-(dimethylamino)-5,7-diethyl-	MeOH	220(4.29),253(3.81), 284(3.83)	94-1328-79
$C_{11}H_{17}N_5O_2S$			
1H-Pyrimido[4,5-e][1,3,4]thiadiazine-5,7(6H,8H)-dione, 6,8-diethyl-3-(ethylamino)-	MeOH	258(4.11),290(3.59), 358(3.50)	94-1965-79
1H-Pyrimido[4,5-e][1,3,4]thiadiazine-5,7(6H,8H)-dione, 6,8-diethyl-1-methyl-3-(methylamino)-	MeOH	226(4.08),251s(3.92), 342(3.52)	94-1965-79
$C_{11}H_{17}OPS$			
Phosphine sulfide, diethyl(4-methoxyphenyl)-	C_6H_{12} or dioxan	234(4.28)	65-0068-79
$C_{11}H_{17}O_2P$			
Phosphine oxide, diethyl(4-methoxyphenyl)-	C_6H_{12} or dioxan	233.5(4.28)	65-0068-79
$C_{11}H_{17}P$			
Phosphine, (1,1-dimethylethyl)(2-methylphenyl)-	C_6H_{12}	216s(4.15),225s(3.96), 253(3.58),272f(3.40)	39-0501-79B
Phosphine, (1,1-dimethylethyl)(3-methylphenyl)-	C_6H_{12}	216s(4.20),227s(3.95), 252(3.60),272f(3.41)	39-0501-79B
Phosphine, (1,1-dimethylethyl)(4-methylphenyl)-	C_6H_{12}	213s(3.86),225s(3.79), 247(3.56),272f(3.18)	39-0501-79B
Phosphine, dimethyl(2,4,6-trimethylphenyl)-	C_6H_{12}	206(4.76),230(4.15), 265(3.36),275f(3.32)	39-0501-79B
	12M HCl	206(4.67),235(4.04), 278f(3.26)	39-0501-79B

Compound	Solvent	λ_{max}(log ε)	Ref.
$C_{11}H_{18}$			
1,3-Cycloundecadiene, (E,Z)-	isooctane	227(3.93)	88-3401-79
	EtOH	226(3.79)	88-3401-79
$C_{11}H_{18}IN_2O_2$			
1-Imidazolidinyloxy, 4-(3-iodo-2-oxo-propylidenyl)-2,2,3,5,5-pentamethyl-	EtOH	322(4.25)	70-0872-79
$C_{11}H_{18}N_2O$			
4-Piperidinone, 1-methyl-3-(1-pyrrolidinylmethylene)-	EtOH	335(4.29)	4-0177-79
$C_{11}H_{18}N_2OS$			
4(1H)-Pyrimidinone, 2,3-dihydro-5-(1-methylethyl)-6-(2-methylpropyl)-2-thioxo-	MeOH	220(4.16),281(4.30)	73-2426-79
$C_{11}H_{18}N_2O_2$			
4H-Pyrazol-4-one, 3,5-bis(1,1-dimethylethyl)-, 1-oxide	isooctane	237(3.72),395(3.27)	44-3211-79
2,4(1H,3H)-Pyrimidinedione, 5-(1-methylethyl)-6-(2-methylpropyl)-	MeOH	268.0(3.99)	73-2426-79
$C_{11}H_{18}N_2O_2S$			
1-Thia-5,6-diazaspiro[2.4]hept-5-ene-2-carboxylic acid, 4,4,7,7-tetramethyl-, ethyl ester	EtOH	330(2.12)	39-2401-79C
$C_{11}H_{18}N_2O_3$			
4H-Pyrazol-4-one, 3,5-bis(1,1-dimethylethyl)-, 1,2-dioxide	isooctane	283(3.90),372(2.34)	44-3211-79
4a(5H)-Quinoxalinol, 6,7,8,8a-tetrahydro-2,3,3a-trimethyl-, 1,4-dioxide	EtOH	348(4.05)	70-0848-79
$C_{11}H_{18}N_2S$			
Cyclooctathiazolamine, 4,5,6,7,8,9-hexahydro-N,N-dimethyl-	EtOH	272(3.924)	48-0249-79
$C_{11}H_{18}N_3$			
Hydrazinium, 1-[(dimethylamino)methylene]-1,2-dimethyl-2-phenyl-, iodide	H_2O	229(4.44),273(3.57)	104-2073-79
Hydrazinium, 2-[(dimethylamino)methylene]-1,1-dimethyl-1-phenyl-, iodide	H_2O	228(4.43)	104-2073-79
$C_{11}H_{18}N_3O_8P$			
5'-Uridylic acid, 2'-deoxy-5-(ethylamino)-, disodium salt	pH 1	267(3.97)	87-0621-79
	pH 12	293(3.75)	87-0621-79
$C_{11}H_{18}N_3O_{15}P_3$			
Uridine, 5-(acetylamino)-2'-deoxy-, 5'-(tetrahydrogen triphosphate), tetrasodium salt	pH 1	272(3.92)	87-0621-79
	pH 12	269(3.85)	87-0621-79
$C_{11}H_{18}N_4O_2$			
4-Morpholineacetonitrile, α-(amino-4-morpholinylmethylene)-	EtOH	273(4.19)	39-2708-79C
$C_{11}H_{18}N_4O_7$			
1,2,4-Triazine-3,5(2H,4H)-dione, 6-(dimethylamino)-2-β-D-glucopyranosyl-	pH 1-7	314(3.65)	124-0048-79
	pH 13	301(3.60)	124-0048-79

Compound	Solvent	λ_{max}(log ε)	Ref.
$C_{11}H_{18}N_5O_{13}P_3S$			
Adenosine 5'-(tetrahydrogen triphosphate), 8-(methylthio)-, tetrasodium salt	pH 7	281(4.27)	87-1529-79
$C_{11}H_{18}N_6O_2$			
1,3-Propanediol, 2-[[4,6-bis(1-aziridinyl)-1,3,5-triazin-2-yl]amino]-2-methyl-	EtOH	222(4.62)	104-1144-79
1H-Pyrazole-4-carboxamide, 3-(3,3-dimethyl-1-triazenyl)-1-(tetrahydro-2H-pyran-2-yl)-	pH 1	309(4.14)	87-1422-79
	pH 11	236(4.11),307(4.16)	87-1422-79
	MeOH	303.5(4.13)	87-1422-79
1H-Pyrazole-4-carboxamide, 5-(3,3-dimethyl-1-triazenyl)-1-(tetrahydro-2H-pyran-2-yl)-	pH 1	316(4.19)	87-1422-79
	pH 11	232(4.23),320(3.76)	87-1422-79
	MeOH	322.0(4.10)	87-1422-79
$C_{11}H_{18}N_6O_3$			
1,3-Propanediol, 2-[[4,6-bis(1-aziridinyl)-1,3,5-triazin-2-yl]amino]-2-(hydroxymethyl)-	EtOH	223(4.69)	104-1144-79
$C_{11}H_{18}O$			
2-Cyclohepten-1-one, 4-(1,1-dimethylethyl)-	EtOH	230(4.03),315(1.73)	44-4481-79
2-Cyclohepten-1-one, 5-(1,1-dimethylethyl)-	EtOH	229(4.01)	44-4481-79
2-Cyclohepten-1-one, 6-(1,1-dimethylethyl)-	EtOH	229(4.01)	44-4481-79
2-Cyclohexen-1-one, 6-butyl-3-methyl-	hexane	224(4.18)	39-1837-79C
2-Cyclopenten-1-one, 3-methyl-2-pentyl-	MeOH	238(4.04)	146-0100-79
Ethanone, 1-[4-(1,1-dimethylethyl)-1-cyclopenten-1-yl]-	EtOH	249(4.04),318(1.81)	44-3031-79
$C_{11}H_{18}OS_2$			
Spiro[2H-1,5-benzodithiepin-3(4H),3'-oxetane], hexahydro-, cis	EtOH	212(3.00)	49-0279-79
trans	EtOH	210(2.93)	49-0279-79
$C_{11}H_{18}OSi$			
2-Propyn-1-one, 1-cyclopentyl-3-(trimethylsilyl)-	EtOH	220s(3.70),226(3.83), 234(3.78)	33-0852-79
$C_{11}H_{18}O_2$			
Cyclobutanecarboxylic acid, 2,2-dimethyl-4-(2-methyl-1-propenyl)-	MeOH	198(3.97),265(1.71), 273(1.65),280(1.53)	78-0025-79
Cyclobutanecarboxylic acid, 3,3-dimethyl-2-(2-methyl-1-propenyl)-	MeOH	197(4.20),280(0.95)	78-0025-79
$C_{11}H_{18}O_2Si$			
Silane, (2-methoxyethoxy)dimethylphenyl-	EtOH	264f(2.43)	3-0007-79
$C_{11}H_{18}O_3$			
2-Heptenoic acid, 2-ethyl-7-oxo-, ethyl ester, (E)-	n.s.g.	217(3.97),290s(--)	118-0279-79
(Z)-	n.s.g.	217(3.91),290s(--)	118-0279-79
2-Hexenoic acid, 6-oxo-2-propyl-, ethyl ester, (E)-	n.s.g.	217(4.08),290(1.70)	118-0279-79
(Z)-	n.s.g.	216(3.98),290(1.82)	118-0279-79

Compound	Solvent	$\lambda_{max}(\log \epsilon)$	Ref.
$C_{11}H_{18}O_4S$			
2-Cyclobuten-1-one, 3,4,4-triethoxy-2-(methylthio)-	EtOH	264(3.82)	44-1208-79
$C_{11}H_{18}S_2$			
Spiro[2H-1,5-benzodithiepin-3(4H),1'-cyclopropane], hexahydro-, trans	dioxan	226(2.79)	48-0437-79
Spiro[cyclobutane-1,3'(4'H)-[2H,6H]-cyclopenta[b][1,4]dithiepin], tetrahydro-, trans	EtOH	213(3.01)	49-0279-79
$C_{11}H_{18}S_2Si$			
Silane, bis(ethylthio)methylphenyl-	hexane	216(3.91),238s(3.24), 265(2.59),272(2.44)	114-0195-79D
$C_{11}H_{19}N$			
Piperidine, 1-(2,4-hexadienyl)-	EtOH	228(4.55)	104-1041-79
1H-Pyrrole, 2-butyl-3-propyl-	C_6H_{12}	222(3.90)	104-0535-79
$C_{11}H_{19}NO$			
Morpholine, 4-(1-cyclohepten-1-yl)-	MeCN	229(3.6)	24-2997-79
6-Oxa-1-azabicyclo[3.1.0]hex-3-ene, 5-(1,1-dimethylethyl)-2,2,4-trimethyl-	EtOH	217(3.23)	12-2041-79
2H-Pyrrole, 5-(1,1-dimethylethyl)-2,2,4-trimethyl-, 1-oxide	EtOH	300(3.71)	12-2025-79
$C_{11}H_{19}NO_2$			
2H-Pyrrole-5-butanoic acid, 3,4-dihydro-3,3-dimethyl-, dimethyl ester	MeOH	203(3.02),305(3.07)	83-0498-79
$C_{11}H_{19}N_2O_2$			
1,4-Dioxaspiro[4.5]dec-3-en-1-yloxy, 2,2,3-trimethyl-, 4-oxide	EtOH	232(4.00)	103-0092-79
1-Imidazolidinyloxy, 2,2,3,5,5-pentamethyl-4-(2-oxopropylidene)-	EtOH	305(4.34)	104-0364-79
$C_{11}H_{19}N_2O_4$			
1H-Imidazol-1-yloxy, 4-(1-acetoxyethyl)-2,5-dihydro-2,2,5,5-tetramethyl-, 3-oxide	EtOH	236(4.11)	70-2521-79
$C_{11}H_{19}N_2O_4PS$			
Phosphonothioic acid, ethyl-, O-(5-ethoxy-1,6-dihydro-1-methyl-6-oxo-4-pyridazinyl) O-ethyl ester	MeOH	213(4.32),288(3.68)	73-1761-79
$C_{11}H_{19}N_2O_4PS_2$			
Phosphorothioic acid, O-[1,6-dihydro-1-methyl-5-(methylthio)-6-oxo-4-pyridazinyl] O-ethyl O-(1-methylethyl) ester	MeOH	210(4.19),237(3.76), 320(3.80)	73-1761-79
$C_{11}H_{19}N_2O_5PS$			
Phosphorothioic acid, O-(5-ethoxy-1,6-dihydro-1-methyl-6-oxo-4-pyridazinyl) O,O-diethyl ester	MeOH	213(4.28),286(3.70)	73-1761-79
$C_{11}H_{19}N_2O_6P$			
Phosphoric acid, 5-ethoxy-1,6-dihydro-1-methyl-6-oxo-4-pyridazinyl diethyl ester	MeOH	212(4.31),286(3.73)	73-1761-79

Compound	Solvent	$\lambda_{max}(\log \epsilon)$	Ref.
$C_{11}H_{19}N_3O$			
Acetamide, N-(1-cyclohexyl-4,5-dihydro-1H-pyrazol-3-yl)-	EtOH	263(3.96)	150-0801-79
$C_{11}H_{19}N_3O_2$			
1,4-Diazaspiro[4.5]dec-1-ene, 2,3,3-trimethyl-4-nitroso-, 1-oxide	EtOH	234(4.26)	103-0092-79
$C_{11}H_{19}N_3O_3$			
Carbamic acid, [3-(2-hydroxy-2-methylpropyl)-5-methyl-1H-pyrazol-4-yl]-, ethyl ester	EtOH	220(3.62)	118-0584-79
$C_{11}H_{19}N_3O_3S$			
4(1H)-Pyrimidinone, 6-amino-5-(2,2-diethoxy-1-methylethyl)-2,3-dihydro-2-thioxo-	MeOH	240s(3.88),287(4.29)	24-0799-79
$C_{11}H_{19}N_5$			
Imidazo[5,1-f][1,2,4]triazin-2-amine, N-ethyl-1,4-dihydro-5-methyl-7-propyl- (maleate)	EtOH	256(4.07)	39-1120-79C
$C_{11}H_{20}Br_2N_6O_3$			
1,3-Propanediol, 2-[[4,6-bis[(2-bromoethyl)amino]-1,3,5-triazin-2-yl]amino]-2-(hydroxymethyl)-	EtOH	224(4.34)	104-1144-79
$C_{11}H_{20}NOS$			
Sulfonium, dimethyl[2-(4-morpholinyl)-1-cyclopenten-1-yl]-, fluorosulfate	MeCN	217(3.7),277(4.2)	24-2997-79
$C_{11}H_{20}N_2$			
1H-Benzimidazole, 3a,4,5,6,7,7a-hexahydro-2-(1-methylpropyl)-	EtOH	219(3.54)	39-2289-79C
$C_{11}H_{20}N_2O$			
4-Piperidinone, 3-[(diethylamino)methylene]-1-methyl-	EtOH	328.5(4.26)	4-0177-79
1,4-Diazaspiro[4.5]dec-1-ene, 2,3,3-trimethyl-, 1-oxide	EtOH	231(4.03)	103-0092-79
$C_{11}H_{20}N_2O_2$			
1-Cyclohepten-1-amine, N-(1,1-dimethylethyl)-2-nitro-	EtOH	245s(--),370(4.19)	44-3410-79
$C_{11}H_{20}N_2O_4$			
Butanedioic acid, (methylhydrazono)-, bis(1-methylethyl) ester. (E)-	MeOH	280(4.15)	5-1696-79
2-Butenedioic acid, 2-(1-methylhydrazino)-, bis(1-methylethyl) ester, (E)-	MeOH	280(4.33)	5-1696-79
$C_{11}H_{20}N_3O_3P$			
Carbamic acid, [bis(1-aziridinyl)phosphinyl]-, cyclohexyl ester	EtOH	208(3.30),243(3.34)	118-0269-79
$C_{11}H_{20}N_3O_4PS$			
Phosphoramidothioic acid, (1-methylethyl)-, O-(5-ethoxy-1,6-dihydro-1-methyl-6-oxo-4-pyridazinyl) O-methyl ester	MeOH	213(4.43),288(3.66)	73-1761-79

Compound	Solvent	λ_{max}(log ε)	Ref.
$C_{11}H_{20}N_3O_{14}P_3$			
Uridine 5'-(tetrahydrogen triphosphate), 2'-deoxy-5-(ethylamino)-	pH 1	267(3.97)	87-0621-79
	pH 12	293(3.74)	87-0621-79
$C_{11}H_{20}O_2$			
4,8-Undecanedione	hexane	278(1.70)	126-0079-79
$C_{11}H_{20}O_2Si$			
2-Cyclopenten-1-one, 4-[[(1,1-dimethylethyl)dimethylsilyl]oxy]-	MeOH	320(1.98)	44-3755-79
$C_{11}H_{20}O_6S_2$			
α-D-Glucopyranoside, methyl 2,3-di-O-methyl-4,6-O-[(methylthio)thiocarbonyl]-	MeOH	228(3.33),277(3.90)	136-0127-79G
$C_{11}H_{21}NO_2$			
3,4-Heptanedione, 2,6-dimethyl-, 4-(O-ethyloxime)-, (E)-	C_6H_{12}	238(4.04),328(1.51)	39-0151-79B
(Z)-	C_6H_{12}	242(3.32),322(1.66)	39-0151-79B
2H-Pyrrol-4-ol, 5-(1,1-dimethylethyl)-3,4-dihydro-2,2,4-trimethyl-, 1-oxide	EtOH	237(4.00)	12-2025-79
$C_{11}H_{21}N_2S_3$			
Cyclobutenylium, 1,3-bis(dimethylamino)-2,4,4-tris(methylthio)-, perchlorate	CH_2Cl_2	244(3.96),298(4.30)	5-0595-79
$C_{11}H_{21}N_3$			
2-Hexenenitrile, 3-[(2-amino-2-methylpropyl)amino]-4-methyl-	EtOH	260(4.26)	39-2289-79C
$C_{11}H_{22}N_2$			
Carbodiimide, N,N'-dineopentyl-	C_6H_{12}	209(3.07)(end abs.)	56-0631-79
$C_{11}H_{22}N_4O_3S$			
3-Pyrazolecarbonitrile, 4-amino-, p-toluenesulfonate	MeOH	219(4.11),272(3.29)	4-1113-79
$C_{11}H_{22}N_6O_2$			
1,3-Propanediol, 2-[[4,6-bis(dimethylamino)-1,3,5-triazin-2-yl]amino]-2-methyl-	EtOH	223(4.77)	104-1144-79
$C_{11}H_{23}N$			
2-Propanamine, 2-methyl-N-(1,3,3-trimethylbutylidene)-	hexane	235(2.432)	5-0083-79
$C_{11}H_{30}OSi_4$			
Trisilane, 2-acetyl-1,1,1,3,3,3-hexamethyl-2-(trimethylsilyl)-	C_6H_{12}	329(1.52),342(1.79), 356(2.00),368(2.10), 382(2.02)	35-0083-79

Compound	Solvent	λmax(log ε)	Ref.
$C_{12}ClF_9O_2$			
2,4-Cyclohexadien-1-one, 6-chloro-2,4,5,6-tetrafluoro-3-(pentafluorophenoxy)-	heptane	236(4.24),334(3.81)	104-1934-79
$C_{12}F_{10}N_2S$			
Sulfur diimide, bis(pentafluorophenyl)-	pentane	250(3.76),390(3.76)	70-2352-79
$C_{12}F_{18}O$			
2-Oxete, 2,3,4-tris(trifluoromethyl)-2-[1,2,3-tris(trifluoromethyl)-2-cyclopropen-1-yl]-	hexane	207(3.45)	35-6445-79
$C_{12}HClF_9NO$			
2,4-Cyclohexadien-1-one. 6-chloro-2,4,5,6-tetrafluoro-3-[(pentafluorophenyl)amino]-	heptane	236(4.08),247(4.08), 370s(3.85)	104-1934-79
$C_{12}H_2F_2N_4$			
Propanedinitrile, 2,2'-(2,5-difluoro-2,5-cyclohexadiene-1,4-diylidene)bis-	MeCN	372(4.43),392(4.61)	77-1027-79
$C_{12}H_3Mn_3O_{12}$			
Manganese, dodecacarbonyltri-α-hydrotri-, triangulo	isooctane	270(3.80),352(3.42), 407(3.32),487(3.62)	35-3847-79
$C_{12}H_3O_{12}Re_3$			
Rhenium, dodecacarbonyltri-α-hydrotri-, triangulo	isooctane	255(3.97),303(3.81), 342(3.80)	35-3847-79
$C_{12}H_4BrF_5N_2S$			
Sulfur diimide, (4-bromophenyl)(pentafluorophenyl)-	pentane	414(4.09)	70-2352-79
$C_{12}H_4ClF_5N_2S$			
Sulfur diimide, (4-chlorophenyl)(pentafluorophenyl)-	pentane	413(4.16)	70-2352-79
$C_{12}H_4F_5IN_2S$			
Sulfur diimide, (4-iodophenyl)(pentafluorophenyl)-	pentane	414(4.16)	70-2352-79
$C_{12}H_4F_5N_3O_2S$			
Sulfur diimide, (4-nitrophenyl)(pentafluorophenyl)-	pentane	414(4.07)	70-2352-79
$C_{12}H_4F_6N_2S$			
Sulfur diimide, (4-fluorophenyl)(pentafluorophenyl)-	pentane	408(4.11)	70-2352-79
$C_{12}H_4N_2O_2$			
Propanedinitrile, (1,3-dihydro-1,3-dioxo-2H-inden-2-ylidene)-	dioxan	243s(4.10),272(4.45), 281(4.46),340(3.85)	32-0329-79
$C_{12}H_4N_4O_4$			
Benzo[1,2-b:4,5-b']difuran-3,7-dicarbonitrile, 2,6-diamino-4,8-dihydro-4,8-dioxo-	DMF	273(4.31),426(3.85), 634(3.35)	49-0739-79
	DMSO	272(4.43),434(3.91), 644(3.47)	49-0739-79

Compound	Solvent	λ_{max}(log ε)	Ref.
$C_{12}H_5ClF_4O_2$			
2,4-Cyclohexadien-1-one, 6-chloro-2,4,5,6-tetrafluoro-3-phenoxy-	heptane	229s(3.78),330(3.20)	104-1934-79
$C_{12}H_5Cl_3O_3$			
1-Naphthaleneacetic acid, 2,3,4-trichloro-α-oxo-	MeOH	234(4.79),284(3.65),293(3.69),305s(--)	44-2391-79
$C_{12}H_5F_5N_2S$			
Sulfur diimide, (pentafluorophenyl)-phenyl-	pentane	406(3.97)	70-2352-79
$C_{12}H_6Br_2N_2$			
Phenazine, 2,7-dibromo-	EtOH	260(5.20),365(4.17),378(4.19)	94-2316-79
$C_{12}H_6Cl_4O_2S$			
Phenol, 2,2'-thiobis[4,6-dichloro-	pH 7.4	320(3.75)	149-0531-79A
$C_{12}H_6N_3O_8$			
Spiro[2,4-cyclohexadiene-1,3'-[2,4]dioxabicyclo[3.2.2]nona[5,7,8]triene], 2,4,6-trinitro-, potassium salt	MeCN	398(4.51),476(4.32)	104-0487-79
silver salt	MeOH	398(4.40),476(4.23)	104-0487-79
$C_{12}H_6N_4O_4$			
Phenazine, 2,7-dinitro-	EtOH	227(4.45),283(4.73),365(4.20)	94-2316-79
$C_{12}H_6O_2$			
Cyclobuta[b]naphthalene-1,2-dione	$CHCl_3$	257(4.18),268(4.84),323(3.29),348(3.65),353(3.87),367(3.46)	44-3790-79
$C_{12}H_7Br_2N_3$			
2H-Benzotriazole, 4,6-dibromo-2-phenyl-	EtOH	209(4.42),224(4.27),249(4.02),253(4.02),264s(3.82),320(4.31),329s(4.26),347s(3.83)	12-0643-79
$C_{12}H_7ClN_4$			
Pyridazino[4,5-d]pyridazine, 1-chloro-4-phenyl-	MeOH	297(4.02)	39-2215-79C
$C_{12}H_7Cl_3O_2$			
1-Naphthalenecarboxylic acid, 2,3,4-trichloro-, methyl ester	MeOH	236(4.86),283(3.71),294(3.84),304(3.70)	44-2391-79
$C_{12}H_7FOS_2$			
Thieno[2,3-b][1]benzothiepin-4(5H)-one, 8-fluoro-	MeOH	257(4.01),312(3.66)	73-2997-79
$C_{12}H_7NOS_2$			
Thieno[3,2-d]thiazole-5-carboxaldehyde, 2-phenyl-	EtOH	225(3.94),275(4.53),320(4.31)	103-0384-79
$C_{12}H_7NO_2S_2$			
5(4H)-Oxazolone, 2-(2-thienyl)-4-(2-thienylmethylene)-	toluene	290(3.93),405(4.52)	103-1303-79
Thieno[3,2-d]thiazole-5-carboxylic acid, 2-phenyl-	EtOH	264(4.67),316(4.51)	103-0384-79

Compound	Solvent	λ_{max}(log ε)	Ref.
$C_{12}H_7NO_3$			
2H-Pyrano[3,2-c]quinoline-2,5(6H)-dione	MeOH	313s(4.03),325(4.05), 352(4.05)	118-0903-79
$C_{12}H_7NO_3S$			
Thieno[3,2-d]oxazole-5-carboxylic acid, 2-phenyl-	EtOH	240(4.15),310(4.35)	103-0384-79
$C_{12}H_7NO_4$			
5(4H)-Oxazolone, 2-(2-furanyl)-4-(2-furanylmethylene)-	toluene	395(4.87),415(4.85)	103-1303-79
$C_{12}H_7N_3$			
5H-Indeno[1,2-b]pyridine, 5-diazo-	EtOH	218(4.64),254(4.30), 286(4.36),356(3.38)	103-0777-79
$C_{12}H_7N_3O$			
2-Propenenitrile, 3-(3-formyl-2-quinoxalinyl)-	C_6H_{12}	233(4.09),278(4.51), 355(3.70)	32-0175-79
$C_{12}H_7N_3O_2$			
Pyrrolo[1,2-a]quinoxaline-4-carboxaldehyde, 1-nitroso-	C_6H_{12}	235(4.03),266(4.02), 308(4.22),346(3.96), 424(4.05),448(4.00)	32-0175-79
$C_{12}H_7N_3O_3$			
1H-Benz[f]indazole-3-carboxamide, 4,9-dihydro-4,9-dioxo-	DMSO	271(3.96)	111-0151-79
$C_{12}H_7N_3O_4$			
9H-Carbazole, 1,3-dinitro-	hexane	212(4.5),250(4.2), 290(4.4),370(3.8)	110-0188-79
$C_{12}H_7N_3S$			
[1]Benzothieno[2,3-b]pyridine-3-carbonitrile, 4-amino-	DMF	284s(4.02),394(3.88), 325(3.82),338(3.94)	49-1189-79
Propanedinitrile, [(benzo[b]thien-2-ylamino)methylene]-	DMF	356(4.33)	49-1189-79
$C_{12}H_7N_5$			
Phenazine, 2-azido-	C_6H_{12}	367(4.08),387(4.10), 399(3.97),407(3.96), 424(3.03),448(2.08)	32-0175-79
$C_{12}H_7N_5O_8$			
Benzenamine, N-(2,4-dinitrophenyl)-2,4-dinitro-	EtOH	361(4.35)	73-1613-79
$C_{12}H_8As_2Cl_2$			
Arsanthrene, 5,10-dichloro-5,10-dihydro-	C_6H_{12}	230(4.57),274(3.83)	78-0155-79
$C_{12}H_8As_2O$			
5,10-Epoxyarsanthrene	C_6H_{12}	239s(3.98),278(2.87)	78-0155-79
$C_{12}H_8As_2S$			
5,10-Epithioarsanthrene	C_6H_{12}	222(4.40),279(3.25), 288(3.16)	78-0155-79
$C_{12}H_8BrCl_2N_3O_5S$			
Hydrazine, (4-bromophenyl)[(dichloromethyl)sulfonyl](5-nitro-2-furanyl)-	MeOH	208s(4.05),245(4.15) 320(4.26),415(4.10)	73-2507-79

Compound	Solvent	λ_{max}(log ε)	Ref.
methylene]- (cont.)			73-2507-79
$C_{12}H_8BrN_5$			
Pyridine, 3-[5-(4-bromophenyl)-2H-tetrazol-2-yl]-	EtOH	252(4.30),276(4.37), 291(4.24)	4-0123-79
$C_{12}H_8Br_2O_3$			
2,4-Pentadienal, 5-(benzoyloxy)-2,4-dibromo-	EtOH	240(4.03),311(4.18), 378(3.05)	78-1523-79
$C_{12}H_8ClF_3N_4O$			
5H-1,2,4-Triazolo[4,3-d][1,4]benzodiazepin-6(7H)-one, 10-chloro-7-methyl-3-(trifluoromethyl)-	MeOH	230(4.59),252(4.08), 300(3.35)	44-0088-79
$C_{12}H_8ClNO_3$			
4H-[1]Benzopyrano[3,4-d]oxazol-4-one, 2-(chloromethyl)-6-methyl-	EtOH	276(4.12),285(4.14), 305(3.97)	25-0478-79
$C_{12}H_8ClNS$			
10H-Phenothiazine, 2-chloro-	MeOH	256(4.67),325(3.65)	133-0197-79
$C_{12}H_8ClN_3$			
1H-Benzimidazole, 4-chloro-2-(2-pyridinyl)-	anion	307(4.25)	94-1235-79
1H-Benzimidazole, 5-chloro-2-(2-pyridinyl)-	anion	313(4.38)	94-1235-79
$C_{12}H_8ClN_5$			
Pyridine, 3-[5-(4-chlorophenyl)-2H-tetrazol-2-yl]-	EtOH	247(4.21),276(4.30), 291(4.23)	4-0123-79
Pyridine, 4-[2-(4-chlorophenyl)-2H-tetrazol-5-yl]-	EtOH	277(4.66)	4-0123-79
$C_{12}H_8Cl_2N_2O$			
Diazene, bis(3-chlorophenyl)-, 1-oxide	heptane	322.8(4.19)	18-1588-79
Diazene, bis(4-chlorophenyl)-, 1-oxide	heptane	333.2(4.33)	18-1588-79
$C_{12}H_8Cl_2N_4O_7S$			
Hydrazine, [[(dichloromethyl)sulfonyl]-(5-nitro-2-furanyl)methylene](3-nitrophenyl)-	MeOH	210s(4.16),244s(4.25), 305(4.33),395(4.11)	73-2507-79
Hydrazine, [[(dichloromethyl)sulfonyl]-(5-nitro-2-furanyl)methylene](4-nitrophenyl)-	MeOH	208s(4.02),242s(4.03), 345(4.11),410(4.23)	73-2507-79
$C_{12}H_8Cl_2O_2S$			
Benzene, 1,1'-sulfonylbis[4-chloro-	C_6H_{12}	250(4.39)	39-0007-79B
$C_{12}H_8Cl_2O_3$			
2,4-Pentadienal, 5-(benzoyloxy)-2,4-dichloro-, (Z,Z)-	EtOH	238(3.98),305(4.28), 380(3.73)	78-1523-79
$C_{12}H_8Cl_3N_3O_5S$			
Hydrazine, (4-chlorophenyl)[[(dichloromethyl)sulfonyl](5-nitro-2-furanyl)-methylene]-	MeOH	209s(4.03),244(4.15), 319(4.05),413(4.09)	73-2507-79
$C_{12}H_8N_2$			
Tricyclo[3.3.2.0^{2,8}]deca-3,6,9-triene-dicarbonitrile	MeOH	245(3.80),255s(3.75)	89-0311-79

Compound	Solvent	λ_{max}(log ε)	Ref.
$C_{12}H_8N_2O$			
2-Phenazinol	neutral	400(3.81),520(2.98)	59-0421-79
	cation	450(3.81)	59-0421-79
	anion	474(3.84)	59-0421-79
$C_{12}H_8N_2O_2$			
2,8-Phenazinediol	neutral	395(3.86),510(3.31)	59-0421-79
	cation	427(4.25)	59-0421-79
	anion	494(4.20)	59-0421-79
	dianion	443(4.22)	59-0421-79
10H-Pyrano[3,2-f]quinoxalin-10-one, 8-methyl-	EtOH	248(4.22),254(4.22), 292(3.69),318(3.91), 330(3.94)	95-0813-79
$C_{12}H_8N_2O_3$			
3,1-Benzoxazepine-6-carboxylic acid, 2-cyano-, methyl ester	MeCN	248(4.36),321(3.43)	94-0946-79
Carbamocyanidimidic acid, (1-oxo-1H-2-benzopyran-5-yl)-, methyl ester	MeOH	224(4.27),238s(4.26), 251(4.29),320(3.71)	94-0946-79
4H-Furo[3,2-b]pyrrole, 2-(2-nitrophen-yl)-	MeOH	332(4.67)	73-1805-79
1H-Indole-4-carboxylic acid, 2-cyano-3-formyl-, methyl ester	MeOH	224(4.61),255(3.87), 316(4.20)	94-0946-79
4-Pyridazinecarboxylic acid, 5-benzoyl-	MeOH	251(4.08)	39-2215-79C
5-Quinolinecarboxylic acid, 2-cyano-, methyl ester, 1-oxide	MeOH	243(4.64),273(4.19), 335(3.66),378(3.70)	94-0946-79
$C_{12}H_8N_2O_3S$			
Acetic acid, (3-oxothiazolo[3,2-a]benz-imidazo-2(3H)-ylidene)-, methyl ester	EtOH	270(4.22),334(3.48)	88-0053-79
4H-[1,3]Thiazino[3,2-a]benzimidazole-2-carboxylic acid, 4-oxo-, methyl	EtOH	255(4.42),268s(4.32), 298(--),315(3.52), 360s(3.25)	88-0053-79
$C_{12}H_8N_2O_4$			
1H,7H-Benzo[ij]quinolizine-1,7-dione, 2,3-dihydro-9-nitro-	EtOH	232(4.34),267(4.10), 340(3.85),382(3.97)	103-1120-79
Propanediamide, 2-(1,3-dihydro-1,3-di-oxo-2H-inden-2-ylidene)-	dioxan	244(4.28),307(3.66), 320(3.72)	32-0329-79
$C_{12}H_8N_2O_4Te_2$			
Ditelluride, bis(2-nitrophenyl)	EtOH	210(4.54),245(4.21)	44-3957-79
$C_{12}H_8N_4$			
1(4H)-Pyridinecarbonitrile, 4-(1-cyano-4(1H)-pyridinylidene)-	MeCN	355(4.46),371(4.58)	5-0727-79
Pyridazino[4,5-d]pyridazine, 1-phenyl-	MeOH	284(3.96)	39-2215-79C
$C_{12}H_8N_4O$			
Pyridazino[4,5-d]pyridazin-1(2H)-one, 4-phenyl-	MeOH	225s(4.08),245s(3.94), 298(3.83)	39-2215-79C
$C_{12}H_8N_4O_2$			
1H-Benzimidazole, 4-nitro-2-(2-pyridin-yl)-	anion	288(4.16)	94-1235-79
1H-Benzimidazole, 5-nitro-2-(2-pyridin-yl)-	anion	303(4.07)	94-1235-79
1H-1,2,3-Triazole, 4-(1-naphthalenyl)-5-nitro-	EtOH	234(4.13),280(3.91)	104-1168-79

Compound	Solvent	$\lambda_{max}(\log \epsilon)$	Ref.
$C_{12}H_8N_4O_2S$			
Benzoic acid, 4-[5-(2-thienyl)-2H-tetrazol-2-yl]-	EtOH	250(4.23),302(4.56)	4-0123-79
$C_{12}H_8N_4O_3$			
Benzoic acid, 4-[5-(2-furanyl)-2H-tetrazol-2-yl]-	EtOH	250(4.32),295(4.37)	4-0123-79
Sydnone, 3-phenyl-4-(1H-pyrazol-3-ylcarbonyl)-	n.s.g.	273(3.78),357(3.87)	103-1153-79
$C_{12}H_8N_4O_5$			
Diazene, bis(3-nitrophenyl)-, 1-oxide	heptane	316.4(4.19)	18-1588-79
$C_{12}H_8N_4S$			
Pyridazino[4,5-d]pyridazine-1(2H)-thione, 4-phenyl-	MeOH	253(4.15),265s(4.08), 370(4.09)	39-2215-79C
$C_{12}H_8N_6O_2$			
Pyridine, 3-[2-(4-nitrophenyl)-2H-tetrazol-5-yl]-	EtOH	237(4.10),295(4.36)	4-0123-79
Pyridine, 4-[2-(4-nitrophenyl)-2H-tetrazol-5-yl]-	EtOH	290(4.38)	4-0123-79
$C_{12}H_8O_2S$			
2H-Naphtho[1,8-bc]thiophen-2-one, 3-methoxy-	MeOH	237(4.4),266(4.5), 289(4.2),343(4.4), 375(4.2)	5-0965-79
$C_{12}H_8O_3$			
Benzo[1,2-b:5,4-b']difuran-2-carboxaldehyde, 6-methyl-	EtOH	315(4.3)	149-0645-79B
2H-1-Benzopyran-2-one, 4-(2-propynyloxy)-	MeOH	260s(3.91),267(4.02), 277(4.00),306(3.80), 314s(3.67)	150-0110-79S
Furo[3,2-g][1]benzopyran-6-carboxaldehyde	EtOH	312(4.2),380(3.8)	149-0645-79B
1,4-Naphthalenedione, 6-acetyl-	MeOH	211(4.36),252(4.39), 337(3.50)	12-0575-79
$C_{12}H_8O_3S$			
7H-Furo[3,2-g][1]benzopyran-7-thione, 4-methoxy-	n.s.g.	235(4.06),270(3.5), 380(3.8)	102-0139-79
4H,8H-Thieno[3,4-f]isobenzofuran-4,8-dione, 5,7-dimethyl-	CH_2Cl_2	257(4.51),308(3.66), 332(3.76)	150-3518-79
$C_{12}H_8O_4$			
7H-Furo[3,2-g][1]benzopyran-7-one, 4-methoxy-	EtOH	260s(4.2),297(4.1)	149-0645-79B
Tetracyclo[4.4.2.0^{2,5}.0^{7,10}]dodec-11-ene-3,4,8,9-tetrone	MeCN	250(3.32),494(1.81), 540(2.42)	88-2347-79
$C_{12}H_8O_5$			
Psoralen, 8-hydroxy-5-methoxy-	MeOH	275(4.4),320(4.1)	102-0352-79
$C_{12}H_9BrN_4O$			
Imidazo[1,2-b][1,2,4]triazin-3(4H)-one, 6-(4-bromophenyl)-2-methyl-	dioxan	276(4.35),347(3.96)	104-1798-79
$C_{12}H_9BrN_4OS$			
4H-Pyrimido[4,5-b][1,4]thiazin-4-one, 2-amino-6-(4-bromophenyl)-1,7-dihydro-	MeOH	243(4.179),271(4.276), 385(4.137)	83-0076-79

Compound	Solvent	λ_{max}(log ε)	Ref.
$C_{12}H_9BrO_2$			
1,4-Naphthalenedione, 2-bromo-5,8-dimethyl-	MeOH	214(4.32),229s(4.19), 241s(4.15),279(4.01), 345(3.50),356(3.54)	12-0575-79
$C_{12}H_9Br_2NO_2$			
Naphthalene, 1-(1,2-dibromo-2-nitroethyl)-	EtOH	274(3.89),368(3.80)	104-1168-79
$C_{12}H_9Br_4NO_3$			
1H-Indole-3-carboxylic acid, 4,5,6,7-tetrabromo-2,3-dihydro-3-methyl-2-oxo-, ethyl ester	MeOH	230(4.50),262(3.94), 315(3.50)	39-0595-79C
	MeOH-base	234(4.39),288(4.15), 335s(3.50)	39-0595-79C
$C_{12}H_9ClN_2$			
Pyrido[1,2-a]benzimidazole, 9-chloro-7-methyl-	MeOH	242(4.7),248(4.7), 259(4.2),268(4.2)	95-0880-79
$C_{12}H_9ClN_4O$			
Imidazo[1,2-b][1,2,4]triazin-3(4H)-one, 6-(4-chlorophenyl)-2-methyl-	dioxan	275(4.32),346(3.90)	104-1798-79
$C_{12}H_9ClN_4O_3$			
1,2,4-Triazino[4,3-d][1,4]benzodiazepine-3,4,7(6H)-trione, 11-chloro-2,8-dihydro-8-methyl-	MeOH	254(4.18),272(4.11), 310(3.98)	44-0088-79
$C_{12}H_9ClO_3$			
2,4-Pentadienal, 5-(benzoyloxy)-2-chloro-, (Z,E)-	EtOH	239(3.93),299(4.51), 369(3.18)	78-1523-79
$C_{12}H_9ClO_5$			
2H-1-Benzopyran-4-acetic acid, 6-chloro-7-hydroxy-2-oxo-, methyl ester	MeOH	331(4.15)	73-2211-79
$C_{12}H_9Cl_2N_3O_5S$			
Hydrazine, [[(dichloromethyl)sulfonyl]-(5-nitro-2-furanyl)methylene]phenyl-	MeOH	214s(4.09),239(4.19), 316(4.33),417(4.12)	73-2507-79
$C_{12}H_9Cl_3O_2$			
1-Naphthalenemethanol, 2-hydroxy-α-(trichloromethyl)-	EtOH	239(4.18),281(3.72), 336(3.50)	118-0824-79
$C_{12}H_9HgNO_2S$			
Mercury, (4-nitrobenzenethiolato-S)-phenyl-	benzene	346(4.1)	70-1585-79
$C_{12}H_9IO_3$			
2,4-Pentadienal, 5-(benzoyloxy)-2-iodo-, (Z,E)-	EtOH	250(4.15),317(4.35)	78-1523-79
$C_{12}H_9N$			
9H-Carbazole	EtOH	233(4.5),257(4.18), 293(4.10)	42-0328-79
$C_{12}H_9NO$			
Benzonorbornen-2-one, 6-cyano-	isooctane	241(4.05),249(4.05), 299(2.92),310(2.88), 322(2.66)	35-5972-79

Compound	Solvent	λ_{max}(log ε)	Ref.
Benzonorbornen-2-one, 7-cyano-	isooctane	242(4.14),248(4.15) 300(3.08),311(2.96), 323(2.48)	35-5972-79
$C_{12}H_9NO_2$			
Acetic acid, cyano(2,3-dihydro-1H-inden-1-ylidene)-	$CHCl_3$	305(4.24),328(4.34)	80-1485-79
$C_{12}H_9NO_2S_2$			
Acetic acid, 3H-1,2-benzodithiol-2-ylidenecyano-, ethyl ester	EtOH	270(4.05),440(4.29)	2-0131-79B
$C_{12}H_9NO_3$			
Benzoic acid, 2-(1H-pyrrol-2-ylcarbonyl)-	EtOH	203(4.27),295(4.05)	103-0747-79
Benzoic acid, 2-(1H-pyrrol-3-ylcarbonyl)-	EtOH	206(4.21),250s(4.02), 290s(3.72)	103-0747-79
Furan, 2-nitro-5-(2-phenylethenyl)-, (E)-	MeOH	221(4.11),243(4.00), 286(4.23),406(4.38)	73-2096-79
2(1H)-Pyridinone, 3-(benzoyloxy)-	EtOH	228(4.26),297(3.92)	36-0816-79
$C_{12}H_9NO_3S$			
4-Thia-1-azabicyclo[3.2.0]hept-2-ene-2-carboxylic acid, 7-oxo-3-phenyl-	EtOH	235(4.02),246s(3.98), 323(3.86)	35-6296-79
$C_{12}H_9NO_4$			
1H-Isoindole-1,3(2H)-dione, 2-(tetrahydro-2-oxo-3-furanyl)-	MeOH	241(3.97),294(3.30)	24-3072-79
Phenol, 4-[2-(5-nitro-2-furanyl)ethenyl]-, (E)-	MeOH	222(4.03),244(3.91), 296(4.14),423(4.31)	73-2096-79
1H-Pyrrole-2,5-dione, 3-acetyl-4-hydroxy-1-phenyl-	EtOH	260(4.47),345(3.47)	94-1792-79
$C_{12}H_9NS$			
Phenothiazine	MeOH	253(4.70),317(3.66)	133-0197-79
cation radical	MeCN	405s(--),438(3.64), 480s(--),497s(--), 516(3.84),735(3.01)	88-2389-79
$C_{12}H_9N_3$			
1H-Benzimidazole, 2-(2-pyridinyl)-	anion	240(4.22)	94-1255-79
1H-Benzimidazole, 2-(3-pyridinyl)-	anion	242(4.08)	94-1255-79
1H-Benzimidazole, 2-(4-pyridinyl)-	anion	243(3.88)	94-1255-79
2-Phenazinamine	neutral	488(3.80)	59-0421-79
	cation	517(3.99)	59-0421-79
3-Pyridinecarbonitrile, 2-amino-4-phenyl-	CH_2Cl_2	271(3.83),329(3.81)	118-0376-79
3-Pyridinecarbonitrile, 2-amino-6-phenyl-	CH_2Cl_2	259(4.29),341(4.27)	118-0376-79
$C_{12}H_9N_3O$			
2-Phenazinol, 8-amino-	cation	430(4.16),488(4.23)	39-0304-79B
	neutral	406(4.09),494(4.10)	39-0304-79B
	neutral	406(4.09),495(4.17)	59-0421-79
	anion	437(4.27)	39-0304-79B +59-0421-79
$C_{12}H_9N_3O_2$			
Imidazo[1,2-a]pyridine, 2-(5-methyl-2-furanyl)-3-nitroso-	dioxan	242(3.83),309(4.36), 321(4.32),400(4.25)	104-2292-79

Compound	Solvent	λ_{max}(log ϵ)	Ref.
2-Naphthalenecarbonitrile, 5-amino-1,4-dihydro-3-(methylamino)-1,4-dioxo-	C_6H_{12}	441(3.88),482(3.88)	39-0696-79C
2-Naphthalenecarbonitrile, 8-amino-1,4-dihydro-3-(methylamino)-1,4-dioxo-	C_6H_{12}	445(3.65),504(3.81)	39-0696-79C
1H-Pyrrolo[2,3-g]quinoline, 2-methyl-7-nitro-	EtOH	227(4.27),244(4.33), 316(4.24),360s(3.72), 452(3.76)	103-1113-79
3H-Pyrrolo[3,2-f]quinoline, 2-methyl-8-nitro-	EtOH	219(4.16),253(4.34), 310(3.82),369(3.50), 435(3.62)	103-1113-79
Quinoline, 2-(4-methoxy-3-furazanyl)-	EtOH	241(4.00),250(3.96), 300(3.52)	4-0689-79
$C_{12}H_9N_3O_4$			
Benzenamine, 2,4-dinitro-N-phenyl-	EtOH	232(4.15),261s(4.04), 355(3.94)	73-1613-79
Benzenamine, 2,6-dinitro-N-phenyl-	EtOH	255(3.69),426(3.11)	73-1613-79
Pyridine, 2-[(2,4-dinitrophenyl)methyl]-	EtOH at -75°	567(4.63)	104-1926-79
$C_{12}H_9N_3O_5$			
[1,1'-Biphenyl]-2-ol, 2'-amino-3,5-dinitro-, monopotassium salt	EtOH	364(4.10)	39-2902-79C
$C_{12}H_9N_3S$			
1,3-Indolizinedicarbonitrile, 8-methyl-2-(methylthio)-	EtOH	230(4.43),265(4.66), 326(4.06)	95-0540-79
$C_{12}H_9N_5$			
Pyridine, 3-(2-phenyl-2H-tetrazol-5-yl)-	EtOH	267(4.33),277(4.32)	4-0123-79
Pyridine, 3-(5-phenyl-2H-tetrazol-2-yl)-	EtOH	235(4.21),277(4.20), 286(4.19)	4-0123-79
Pyridine, 4-(2-phenyl-2H-tetrazol-5-yl)-	EtOH	270(4.39)	4-0123-79
$C_{12}H_9N_5O$			
Phenol, 4-[2-(3-pyridinyl)-2H-tetrazol-5-yl]-	EtOH	251(4.61),280(4.52), 302(4.39)	4-0123-79
$C_{12}H_9N_5O_2$			
2-Butenedinitrile, 2-amino-3-[[1-(4-nitrophenyl)ethylidene]amino]-, (Z,?)-	EtOH	267(4.25),294(4.26), 398(4.22)	44-0827-79
$C_{12}H_9N_5O_3S$			
4H-Pyrazolo[3,4-d]pyrimidin-4-one, 1,5-dihydro-3-(methylthio)-1-(4-nitrophenyl)-	MeOH	228(4.37),255(4.08), 340(4.22)	83-0586-79
$C_{12}H_9N_5O_4$			
Benzo[g]pteridine-2,4(3H,10H)-dione, 3,10-dimethyl-7-nitro-	MeCN	293(4.49),330s(--), 408s(--),427(4.06), 454s(--)	5-1067-79
$C_{12}H_9N_7O_3$			
4H-Imidazo[4,5-d]-1,2,3-triazin-4-one, 3-[[(1-nitrophenyl)ethylidene]amino]-	EtOH	202(4.41),270(4.16), 310(3.92)	103-0805-79
$C_{12}H_{10}$			
1,1'-Biphenyl	n.s.g.	200(4.58),247(4.26)	73-0873-79

Compound	Solvent	λmax(log ε)	Ref.
$C_{12}H_{10}ClN$			
[1,1'-Biphenyl]-2-amine, 4-chloro-	EtOH	226(4.45),306(3.65)	33-2129-79
[1,1'-Biphenyl]-2-amine, 5-chloro-	EtOH	227(4.42),312(3.63)	33-2129-79
$C_{12}H_{10}ClN_3$			
2-Pyridinecarboximidamide, N-(2-chloro-phenyl)-	anion	272(4.00)	94-1255-79
2-Pyridinecarboximidamide, N-(3-chloro-phenyl)-	anion	272(4.01)	94-1255-79
2-Pyridinecarboximidamide, N-(4-chloro-phenyl)-	anion	272(4.16)	94-1255-79
$C_{12}H_{10}ClN_5O_2$			
5H-1,2,4-Triazolo[4,3-d][1,4]benzodi-azepine-3-carboxamide, 10-chloro-6,7-dihydro-7-methyl-6-oxo-	MeOH	236(4.55),300(3.40)	44-0088-79
$C_{12}H_{10}ClOP$			
Phosphinic chloride, diphenyl-	MeCN	226(4.25),260(3.11), 266(3.26),273(3.18)	65-0275-79
	$C_2H_4Cl_2$	227(4.24),261(3.15), 266(3.28),274(3.18)	65-0275-79
$C_{12}H_{10}ClP$			
Phosphinous chloride, diphenyl-	hexane	267(3.28),274(3.28), 285(3.17)	22-0241-79I
$C_{12}H_{10}Cl_2N_4O$			
5H-1,2,4-Triazolo[4,3-d][1,4]benzodi-azepin-6(7H)-one, 10-chloro-3-(chlo-romethyl)-7-methyl-	MeOH	233(4.58),256(4.10), 300(3.48)	44-0088-79
$C_{12}H_{10}Cl_2P$			
Phosphorus(1+), dichlorodiphenyl-, hexachlorophosphate	MeCN	240(4.34),260(3.96), 345(2.00)	65-0275-79
	$MeNO_2$	241(4.35),268(3.94), 345(2.00)	65-0275-79
	$C_2H_4Cl_2$	244(4.34),271(3.97), 345(2.00)	65-0275-79
tetrachloroaluminate	MeCN	201(4.46),240(4.31), 275(3.59)	65-0275-79
$C_{12}H_{10}Cl_3F_3N_2O_4S$			
5-Thia-1-azabicyclo[4.2.0]oct-2-ene-2-carboxylic acid, 3-methyl-8-oxo-7-[(trifluoroacetyl)amino]-, 2,2,2-trichloroethyl ester, (6R-trans)-	EtOH	262(3.75)	39-1629-79C
$C_{12}H_{10}Cl_3N_3O_2$			
Acetamide, 2,2,2-trichloro-N-(4,5-di-hydro-3-methyl-5-oxo-1-phenyl-1H-pyrazol-4-yl)-	EtOH	245(4.13),269(3.95)	48-0495-79
$C_{12}H_{10}Cl_3P$			
Phosphorane, trichlorodiphenyl-	C_6H_{12}	229(4.27),270s(3.30)	65-0275-79
	MeCN	204(4.38),231s(4.22), 239(4.23),273(3.48)	65-0275-79
	$C_2H_4Cl_2$	230(4.24),272s(3.43)	65-0275-79

Compound	Solvent	λ max (log ε)	Ref.
$C_{12}H_{10}INO$			
1H-Carbazol-1-one, 2,3,4,9-tetrahydro-6-iodo-	EtOH	215(4.47),239(4.42), 313(4.44),346s(3.69)	39-2154-79C
$C_{12}H_{10}N_2$			
Pyrido[1,2-a]benzimidazole, 7-methyl-	MeOH	240(4.7),245(4.7), 258(4.2),266(4.1)	95-0880-79
Pyrimidine, 1,4-dihydro-4-(phenylethynyl)-	EtOH	242(4.03),285s(3.48)	39-1228-79C
$C_{12}H_{10}N_2O$			
Acetamide, 2-cyano-2-(2,3-dihydro-1H-inden-1-ylidene)-	$CHCl_3$	310s(4.29),328(4.39)	80-1485-79
Diazene, diphenyl-, 1-oxide	heptane	321.5(4.21)	18-1588-79
Imidazo[1,2-a]pyridine, 2-(5-methyl-2-furanyl)-	EtOH	255(4.60),260(4.60), 336(4.10)	104-2292-79
Pyrido[1,2-a]benzimidazol-9(5H)-one, 7-methyl-	MeOH	216(4.6),238(4.3), 261(4.0)	95-0880-79
$C_{12}H_{10}N_2O_2$			
Benzenamine, 4-nitro-N-phenyl-	MeOH	257(4.01),390(4.33)	83-0515-79
2,5-Cyclohexadien-1-one, 3-amino-4-[(4-hydroxyphenyl)imino]-	H_2O	470(3.90)	39-0304-79B
	anion	572(4.24)	39-0304-79B
$C_{12}H_{10}N_2O_2S_2$			
Propanedinitrile, [1-(methylthio)-2-(phenylsulfonyl)ethylidene]-	EtOH	218(4.06),269(3.61), 276(3.59),332(4.12)	95-1234-79
$C_{12}H_{10}N_2O_3$			
Isoxazole, 3-methyl-4-nitro-5-(2-phenylethenyl)-	C_6H_{12}	245(4.1),260(4.1), 347(4.3)	4-0253-79
1H-Pyrrole-2,5-dione, 3-acetyl-4-(phenylamino)-	EtOH	283(4.20),336(3.99)	95-0818-79
$C_{12}H_{10}N_2O_4$			
1H-Pyrazole-4-carboxylic acid, 3-(4-methoxybenzoyl)-	EtOH	224s(4.01),294(4.14), 328s(3.89)	73-0781-79
	ether	223(3.88),308(4.15)	73-0781-79
4-Pyrimidinecarboxylic acid, 5,6-dihydroxy-2-phenyl-, methyl ester	MeOH	318(4.05)	4-1423-79
4-Pyrimidinecarboxylic acid, 1,2,3,6-tetrahydro-2,6-dioxo-1-(phenylmethyl)-	pH 1	284(3.80)	44-0970-79
	pH 13	300(3.84)	44-0970-79
$C_{12}H_{10}N_2O_4S_2$			
Thiophene, 2,2'-(1,2-dimethyl-1,2-ethenediyl)bis[5-nitro-	MeOH	236(4.03),341(4.13)	12-2647-79
$C_{12}H_{10}N_2S$			
Quinazoline, 3,4-dihydro-4-(2-thienyl)-, monohydrochloride	EtOH	235(3.82),280s(3.39)	24-1348-79
Thieno[3,4-g]phthalazine, 6,8-dimethyl-	CH_2Cl_2	268(4.55),485(3.29), 497s(3.26)	150-3518-79
$C_{12}H_{10}N_4$			
2-Butenedinitrile, 2-amino-3-[[(4-methylphenyl)methylene]amino]-	EtOH	247(4.01),264(4.21), 364(4.01)	44-0827-79
2,8-Phenazinediamine	neutral	450(4.21)	59-0421-79
	cation	510(4.12)	59-0421-79

Compound	Solvent	λ max(log ε)	Ref.
$C_{12}H_{10}N_4O$			
2-Butenedinitrile, 2-amino-3-[[(4-methoxyphenyl)methylene]amino]-	EtOH	275(4.08),375(4.45)	44-0827-79
Formamide, N-[4-(4-cyano-3-methyl-1H-pyrazol-1-yl)phenyl]-	EtOH	285(4.48)	78-1331-79
Imidazo[1,2-b][1,2,3]triazin-3(4H)-one, 2-methyl-6-phenyl-	dioxan	272(4.21),345(3.86)	104-1798-79
4-Pyridazinecarbonitrile, 3-amino-5-(4-methoxyphenyl)-	DMF	316(3.88),351(3.81)	48-0071-79
2H-Tetrazole, 5-(2-furanyl)-2-(4-methylphenyl)-	EtOH	252(4.27),287(4.29)	4-0123-79
$C_{12}H_{10}N_4O_2$			
Benzo[g]pteridine-2,4(1H,3H)-dione, 3,9-dimethyl-	MeOH	336(3.81),382(3.76)	88-4117-79
Benzo[g]pteridine-2,4(3H,10H)-dione, 3,10-dimethyl-	H_2O	264(4.57),342(3.89), 435(3.98)	33-0593-79
	MeCN	267(4.53),328(3.85), 437(3.96)	33-0593-79
1H-Pyrazole-4-carbonitrile, 3,5-dimethyl-1-(4-nitrophenyl)-	EtOH	298(4.26)	78-1331-79
2-Pyridinecarboximidamide, N-(2-nitrophenyl)-	anion	270(3.96)	94-1255-79
2-Pyridinecarboximidamide, N-(3-nitrophenyl)-	anion	273(4.22)	94-1255-79
2-Pyridinecarboximidamide, N-(4-nitrophenyl)-	anion	303(4.03)	94-1255-79
4,6(1H,5H)-Pyrimidinedione, 5-(1,4-dihydro-4-quinazolinyl)-, hydrochloride	EtOH	255s(3.88),267s(3.93), 279(3.97)	24-1348-79
2H-Tetrazole, 5-(2-furanyl)-2-(4-methoxyphenyl)-	EtOH	257(4.21),293(4.35)	4-0123-79
$C_{12}H_{10}N_4O_4$			
1,2-Benzenediamine, N-(2,4-dinitrophenyl)-	n.s.g.	348(4.25)	73-1613-79
$C_{12}H_{10}N_4O_5$			
Ethanone, 2-nitro-1-[5-nitro-1-(phenylmethyl)-1H-imidazol-4-yl]-	MeOH	298(3.69)	35-6127-79
$C_{12}H_{10}N_4S$			
2H-Tetrazole, 2-(4-methylphenyl)-5-(2-thienyl)-	EtOH	250(4.13),290(4.32)	4-0123-79
1,2,4-Triazolo[4,3-a]pyrazine, 8-(benzylthio)-	EtOH	257(3.98),312(4.07)	44-1028-79
$C_{12}H_{10}N_6$			
Pyridazino[4,5-d]pyridazin-1(2H)-one, 4-phenyl-, hydrazone	MeOH	270(4.12),355(3.72)	39-2215-79C
$C_{12}H_{10}N_6O$			
4H-Imidazo[4,5-d]-1,2,3-triazin-4-one, 3,5-dihydro-3-[(1-phenylethylidene)amino]-	EtOH	205(4.54),300(3.91)	103-0805-79
$C_{12}H_{10}N_6O_2$			
Naphthalene, 2,3-diazido-1,4-dimethoxy-	MeOH	260(4.69),300s(--)	18-0789-79
$C_{12}H_{10}O$			
Benzene, 1,1'-oxybis-	pentane	270(3.43),280(3.30)	65-0672-79

Compound	Solvent	λ_{max}(log ε)	Ref.
$C_{12}H_{10}O_2$			
2(1H)-Dibenzofuranone, 3,4-dihydro-	EtOH	202(4.42),247(4.05), 275(3.60),283(3.53)	118-0122-79
1H-Indene-1,3(2H)-dione, 2-(1-methyl-ethylidene)-	dioxan	241s(4.44),253(4.52), 298(3.81),310(3.62)	32-0329-79
$C_{12}H_{10}O_2S$			
Benzene, 1,1'-sulfonylbis-	C_6H_{12}	236(4.17)	39-0007-79B
Benzo[c]thiophene-5,6-dicarboxaldehyde, 1,3-dimethyl-	CH_2Cl_2	286(4.87),376(3.96)	150-3518-79
$C_{12}H_{10}O_3$			
2H-1-Benzopyran-2-one, 4-hydroxy-3-(2-propenyl)-	n.s.g.	306(4.69)	2-0638-79A
2H-1-Benzopyran-2-one, 4-(2-propenyl-oxy)-	n.s.g.	265(3.99),275(3.99), 302(3.79)	2-0638-79A
3(2H)-Dibenzofuranone, 1,4-dihydro-8-hydroxy-	MeOH	204(4.71),253(4.29), 290(3.92)	24-2640-79
1-Naphthalenecarboxaldehyde, 4-hydroxy-8-methoxy-	HCl	232(4.28),251(4.20), 348(3.78)	44-2153-79
	NaOH	257(4.19),332(3.35), 394(4.26)	44-2153-79
1-Naphthalenecarboxaldehyde, 8-hydroxy-4-methoxy-	HCl	234(4.01),263(4.03), 365(3.87)	44-2153-79
	NaOH	216(4.43),269(4.21), 344(3.94)	44-2153-79
$C_{12}H_{10}O_4$			
2H-1-Benzopyran-2-one, 7-acetoxy-4-methyl-	MeOH	280(4.00),314(3.96)	73-2211-79
1,4-Naphthalenedione, 2,5-dimethoxy-	MeOH	220(4.06),243(4.10), 280(4.06),395(3.57)	12-0575-79
1,4-Naphthalenedione, 2,8-dimethoxy-	MeOH	224(4.11),237(4.08), 278(4.05),348s(3.47), 370s(3.50),394(3.51)	12-0575-79
$C_{12}H_{10}O_4S_2$			
1,4-Benzodithiin-2,3-dicarboxylic acid, dimethyl ester	C_6H_{12}	229s(--),237(4.03) 241s(--),273(3.97), 355(2.95)	44-1977-79
$C_{12}H_{10}O_4S_3$			
1,3-Dithiole-4,5-dicarboxylic acid, 4-(4H-thiopyran-4-ylidene)-, dimethyl ester	MeCN	323(4.21),337(4.44), 352(4.56),376s(3.91), 482(3.01)	44-0880-79
$C_{12}H_{10}O_5$			
2H-1-Benzopyran-4-acetic acid, 7-hy-droxy-2-oxo-, methyl ester	MeOH	327(4.16)	73-2211-79
$C_{12}H_{10}O_6$			
[2,2'-Bifuran]-3,4-dicarboxylic acid, dimethyl ester	$CHCl_3$	250(3.914),275(3.102), 364(2.870)	104-0541-79
$C_{12}H_{10}S$			
Benzene, 1,1'-thiobis-	pentane	250(4.09),277(3.76)	65-0672-79
$C_{12}H_{11}AsO$			
4-Arsenincarboxaldehyde, 1,2-dihydro-1-phenyl-	EtOH	230(4.08),290(3.42)	88-3141-79

Compound	Solvent	$\lambda_{max}(\log \epsilon)$	Ref.
$C_{12}H_{11}BrCl_3NOS$			
1-Piperidinecarbothioic acid, O-(2-bromo-3,4,6-trichlorophenyl) ester	MeOH	212(4.723),245(4.198)	73-0918-79
$C_{12}H_{11}BrO_4$			
Furo[2,3-b]benzofuran-2-ol, 3-bromo-2,3,3a,8a-tetrahydro-, acetate, trans	CH_2Cl_2	233(4.19),281(3.52), 287(3.46)	39-2664-79C
$C_{12}H_{11}Br_2NO$			
2H-Pyrrole, 3,4-dibromo-2,2-dimethyl-5-phenyl-, 1-oxide	EtOH	251(4.28),332(3.69)	12-1795-79
$C_{12}H_{11}Br_2NO_2$			
Furo[2,3-b]indol-2-one, 5,7-dibromo-3a,8-dimethyl-3,3a,8,8a-tetrahydro-	MeOH	260(4.05),315(3.27)	5-0927-79
3H-Pyrrol-3-one, 4,4-dibromo-4,5-dihydro-5,5-dimethyl-2-phenyl-, 1-oxide	EtOH	263(4.18),329(3.86)	12-1795-79
$C_{12}H_{11}Br_2N_3O_4$			
5-Oxa-9-azatricyclo[5.2.1.0^{4,8}]decan-2-one, 3,3-dibromo-9-(5-nitro-2-pyridinyl)-	$CHCl_3$	355(4.31)	39-1525-79C
$C_{12}H_{11}ClN_2O_2$			
8-Azabicyclo[3.2.1]oct-3-ene-6-carbonitrile, 6-chloro-2-oxo-8-(3-oxo-1-butenyl)-	EtOH	290(4.38)	56-0057-79
3H-Pyrrolizine-1,5-dicarboxaldehyde, 7-chloro-3-[(dimethylamino)methylene]-	EtOH	224(4.05),265(4.09), 320(4.32),385(4.32), 446(4.32)	24-2465-79
$C_{12}H_{11}ClN_2O_3$			
3H-Indole, 6-chloro-5-methoxy-3-(2-aci-nitropropylidene)-	MeOH	222(4.44),291(4.00), 395(4.21)	87-0063-79
$C_{12}H_{11}ClN_4O$			
5H-1,2,4-Triazolo[4,3-d][1,4]benzodiazepin-6(7H)-one, 10-chloro-3,7-dimethyl-	MeOH	234(3.54),255(4.10), 298(3.30)	44-0088-79
$C_{12}H_{11}ClN_4O_2$			
3H-1,2,4-Triazolo[4,3-d][1,4]benzodiazepine-3,6(5H)-dione, 10-chloro-2,7-dihydro-2,7-dimethyl-	MeOH	252(4.25),279s(3.89), 300s(3.59)	44-0088-79
$C_{12}H_{11}Cl_2NO_3$			
1H-Indole-3-carboxylic acid, 5,7-dichloro-2,3-dihydro-3-methyl-2-oxo-, ethyl ester	MeOH	257(4.07),300(3.26)	39-0595-79C
	MeOH-base	279(4.16),315s(3.33)	39-0595-79C
$C_{12}H_{11}Cl_3INOS$			
1-Piperidinecarbothioic acid, O-(2-iodo-3,4,6-trichlorophenyl) ester	MeOH	217(4.559),245(4.231)	73-0918-79
$C_{12}H_{11}Cl_3N_2O_3S$			
1-Piperidinecarbothioic acid, O-(3,4,6-trichloro-2-nitrophenyl) ester	MeOH	209(4.559),255(4.196)	73-0918-79
$C_{12}H_{11}F_3N_2O_5S$			
5-Thia-1-azabicyclo[4.2.0]oct-2-ene-2-carboxylic acid, 4-acetyl-3-methyl-	EtOH	263(3.78)	39-1629-79C

Compound	Solvent	λmax(log ε)	Ref.
8-oxo-7-[(trifluoroacetyl)amino]-, (4S-(4α,6α,7β)]- (cont.)			39-1629-79C
$C_{12}H_{11}F_3N_4O_5$			
Propanamide, 2-diazo-3,3,3-trifluoro-N-[2-hydroxy-1-(hydroxymethyl)-2-(4-nitrophenyl)ethyl]-, [R-(R*,R*)]-	n.s.g.	238(3.89),272(4.08)	63-0721-79
$C_{12}H_{11}N$			
Benzenamine, N-phenyl-	EtOH	240(3.90),286(4.22)	42-0328-79
	MeOH	284(4.32)	133-0197-79
6H-Cyclopenta[g]quinoline, 7,8-dihydro-	EtOH	307(3.78),310(3.70), 320(3.95)	44-3261-79
$C_{12}H_{11}NO$			
6,9-Etheno-5H-pyrrolo[1,2-a]azepin-5-one, 6,9-dihydro-7-methyl-	C_6H_{12}	210(3.66),230(3.53), 247(3.76),253(3.76)	88-4529-79
Pyrrolo[1,2-a]quinolin-5(1H)-one,	MeOH	320(4.1),334(4.1)	83-0219-79
2,3-dihydro-	MeOH-acid	300(4.0),320(3.7)	83-0219-79
$C_{12}H_{11}NO_2$			
1,3-Cyclopentanedione, 2-[(phenylamino)methylene]-	hexane	231(4.21),354(4.38)	131-0077-79D
	EtOH	353(4.35)	131-0077-79D
1H-Pyrrole-2-carboxaldehyde, 3-(phenylmethoxy)-	H_2O	292.5(4.31)	152-0115-79
$C_{12}H_{11}NO_3$			
1,4-Naphthalenedione, 5-methoxy-8-(methylamino)-	C_6H_{12}	556(3.72)	39-0702-79C
1,4-Naphthalenedione, 8-methoxy-2-(methylamino)-	MeOH	209(4.25),231(4.33), 268(4.22),293s(4.04), 395(3.77),440s(3.58)	12-0575-79
4(1H)-Pyridinone, 5-hydroxy-2-(hydroxymethyl)-1-phenyl-	MeOH	292(4.24)	18-0107-79
	acid	284(3.92)	18-0107-79
	neutral	290(4.24)	18-0107-79
	base	316(4.10)	18-0107-79
1H-Pyrrole-2-carboxylic acid, 3-hydroxy-, phenylmethyl ester	EtOH	265(4.29)	94-1448-79
2-Quinolinecarboxylic acid, 4-methoxy-,	pH 1	312(4.35)	149-0251-79B
methyl ester	pH 7.5	295(4.26)	149-0251-79B
5,6-Quinolinedione, 8-methoxy-2,4-dimethyl-	$CHCl_3$	251s(--),257(4.53), 272s(--),385(3.15)	83-0971-79
$C_{12}H_{11}NO_3S$			
2-Pyridinol, 4-methylbenzenesulfonate	EtOH	228(4.24),258(3.57)	150-1579-79
$C_{12}H_{11}NO_4$			
1,4-Naphthalenedione, 5-amino-2,3-dimethoxy-	C_6H_{12}	410s(3.34),471(3.72)	39-0696-79C
3-Pyrrolidinecarboxylic acid, 2,4-dioxo-5-phenyl-, methyl ester	MeOH	230(4.12),261(3.93)	142-0477-79B
$C_{12}H_{11}NO_4S$			
Thiophene, 2,5-dihydro-3-methyl-4-nitro-2-(phenylmethylene)-, 1,1-dioxide	HOAc	350(4.3)	104-0164-79
$C_{12}H_{11}NO_5$			
3-Benzofurancarboxylic acid, 2-methyl-5-nitro-, ethyl ester	EtOH	242(4.29),282(3.65)	103-0842-79

Compound	Solvent	λ_{max}(log ε)	Ref.
$C_{12}H_{11}N_3$			
Benzenamine, 4-(phenylazo)-	MeOH	385(4.40)	56-0989-79
1H-Imidazole-4-acetonitrile, α-methyl-2-phenyl-	EtOH	270(4.09)	44-0041-79
2H-Imidazole-2-acetonitrile, α-methyl-2-phenyl-	EtOH	240(3.06),259s(2.81),265s(2.77),269s(2.71)	44-0041-79
2-Pyridinecarboximidamide, N-phenyl-	anion	272(3.98)	94-1255-79
Pyrido[1,2-a]benzimidazol-9(5H)-imine, 7-methyl-	pH 1	218(4.5),225(4.5),238(4.4)	95-0880-79
	MeOH	225s(4.4),232(4.4),249(4.4)	95-0880-79
$C_{12}H_{11}N_3O$			
Aziridine, 2-methyl-1-(2-quinoxalinyl-carbonyl)-, (S)-	isooctane	203(4.56),242(4.67),244(4.66),305(3.82),317(3.86),328(3.79)	39-2881-79C
	EtOH	203(4.44),245(4.55),318(3.85)	39-2881-79C
	MeCN	203(4.51),243(4.61),317(3.90),328s(3.84)	39-2881-79C
[1,1'(4H,4'H)-Bipyridine]-4-carbonitrile, 2-methyl-4'-oxo-	EtOH	262.5(4.24)	39-1698-79C
[1,1'(4H,4'H)-Bipyridine]-4-carbonitrile, 4-methyl-4'-oxo-	EtOH	263.5(4.33)	39-1698-79C
1,3,6-Cycloheptatriene-1-carbonitrile, 6-[(2-cyanoethyl)methylamino]-5-oxo-	EtOH	210(3.98),265(4.08),280(4.00),352(3.86),432(3.75)	39-2528-79C
2,4-Hexadienenitrile, 4-methyl-6-[(4-oxo-1(4H)-pyridinyl)imino]-	EtOH	263(4.23),344(4.34)	39-1698-79C
Phenol, 4-[(2-amino-4-imino-2,5-cyclohexadien-1-ylidene)amino]-, zwitterion	H_2O	628(4.46)	39-0304-79B
cation	H_2O	490(4.12)	39-0304-79B
anion	H_2O	510(4.14)	39-0304-79B
$C_{12}H_{11}N_3OS$			
Pyrido[3',2':4,5]thieno[3,2-d]pyrimidine, 4-methoxy-7,9-dimethyl-	EtOH	237(4.52),260(4.21),286(4.21),312(3.64),323(3.66)	103-1078-79
$C_{12}H_{11}N_3O_2$			
Azepino[4,5-b]indole-4,5-dione, 1,2,3,6-tetrahydro-, 5-oxime	EtOH	318(4.21)	103-0780-79
4-Pyridinecarboxylic acid, [1-(2-furanyl)ethylidene]hydrazone	pH 1	273(4.2),340s(2.0)	106-0027-79
	pH 13	274(--),324(--),346s(--)	106-0027-79
	MeOH	272s(--),310(4.2),345s(--),400s(--)	106-0027-79
	$CHCl_3$	283(4.1),304s(4.0),392(3.3)	106-0027-79
1H-Pyrimido[4,5-b]indole-2,4(3H,9H)-dione, 3-ethyl-	$CHCl_3$	272(4.21)	103-0179-79
[1,2,4]Triazino[4,5-a]indole-1,4-dione, 2,3-dihydro-2,3-dimethyl-	dioxan	250(4.19),288(4.18),290(4.17)	4-1217-79
[1,2,4]Triazino[4,5-a]indol-4(3H)-one, 1-methoxy-3-methyl-	dioxan	250(4.28),300(4.14),313(4.15),329(4.11)	4-1217-79
$C_{12}H_{11}N_3O_2S$			
2-Thiazolamine, 4,5-dimethyl-N-[(4-nitrophenyl)methylene]-	EtOH	275(4.136),389(4.084)	48-0249-79

Compound	Solvent	λ_{max}(log ϵ)	Ref.
$C_{12}H_{11}N_3O_3$			
2-Propenal, 3-[(2-methyl-1H-indol-5-yl)-amino]-2-nitro-	EtOH	218(4.31),288(4.17), 382(4.24)	103-1113-79
1H-Pyrazole-4-carboxaldehyde, 3,5-di-methyl-1-(4-nitrophenyl)-	EtOH	247(4.08),300(4.22)	78-1331-79
1H-Pyrazole-3-carboxylic acid, 4-nitro-so-5-phenyl-, ethyl ester	pH 1	237(4.10),332(3.61)	18-0208-79
	pH 11	229(4.14),341(3.90)	18-0208-79
	EtOH	237(4.10),332(3.64)	18-0208-79
$C_{12}H_{11}N_3O_3S$			
Pyrido[2,3-d]pyrimidine-6-carboxalde-hyde, 7,8-dihydro-5-hydroxy-2-(meth-ylthio)-7-oxo-8-(2-propenyl)-	EtOH	238(4.30),274(4.13), 328s(4.16),346(4.19), 366(4.12)	4-1169-79
$C_{12}H_{11}N_3O_4S$			
Carbamic acid, (8-thioxo-1,3-dioxolo-[4,5-g]quinazolin-7(8H)-yl)-, ethyl ester	EtOH	226s(4.25),231(2.48), 255s(3.91),273(4.03), 330s(3.52),346s(3.87), 355s(3.96),363(4.06), 372s(3.99),379(4.00)	1-0079-79
2-Thiophenamine, N-(2-ethylphenyl)-3,5-dinitro-	MeOH	405(4.22)	39-0219-79B
$C_{12}H_{11}N_3O_6$			
2H-Furo[2,3-b]indol-2-one, 3,3a,8,8a-tetrahydro-3a,8-dimethyl-5,7-dinitro-	MeOH	357(4.11)	5-0927-79
$C_{12}H_{11}N_3S$			
[1]Benzothieno[2,3-b]pyridine-3-carbo-nitrile, 4-amino-5,6,7,8-tetrahydro-	DMF	292(3.70),327(3.73), 333s(3.71)	49-1189-79
Propanedinitrile, [[(4,5,6,7-tetrahy-drobenzo[b]thien-2-yl)amino]meth-ylene]-	EtOH	260(3.91),346(4.22)	49-1189-79
$C_{12}H_{11}N_5O_3$			
2-Propenamide, 2-amino-3-cyano-3-[[1-(4-nitrophenyl)ethylidene]amino]-	EtOH	262(3.83),285(3.81), 401(3.75)	44-0827-79
$C_{12}H_{11}P$			
Phosphine, diphenyl-	hexane	264(3.27)	22-0241-79I
lithium salt	DME	425(4.1)	65-2127-79
potassium salt	DMSO	470(4.2)	65-2127-79
$C_{12}H_{12}$			
Naphthalene, 2,7-dimethyl-	hexane	270(3.65),276(3.67), 307(2.56),317(2.39), 321(2.36)	39-1837-79C
Tetracyclo[8.2.0.0^{2,5}.0^{6,9}]dodeca-1,5,9-triene	isooctane	201(4.41),222(3.75), 247s(2.18),251s(2.23), 254(2.29),258(2.29), 262(2.32),265s(2.28), 269(2.23)	35-0770-79
$C_{12}H_{12}BrNO$			
Benzeamine, 4-bromo-N-[(3,4-dihydro-2H-pyran-2-yl)methylene]-	EtOH	252(4.22),297(3.46)	103-0488-79
dimer	EtOH	256(4.39),299(3.82)	103-0488-79
1H-Indole, 1-acetyl-2-(bromomethyl)-3-methyl-	CH_2Cl_2	290(4.06)	142-1141-79

Compound	Solvent	λ_{max}(log ε)	Ref.
$C_{12}H_{12}BrNO_2$			
1H-Indole-2-carboxylic acid, 4-bromo-3-methyl-, ethyl ester	MeOH and MeOH-base	234(4.54),299(4.35), 328s(3.93)	39-0595-79C
1H-Indole-2-carboxylic acid, 5-bromo-3-methyl-, ethyl ester	MeOH and MeOH-base	234(4.45),240s(4.42), 300(4.27)	39-0595-79C
1H-Indole-2-carboxylic acid, 6-bromo-3-methyl-, ethyl ester	MeOH and	231(4.46),307(4.31)	39-0595-79C
3H-Pyrrol-3-one, 4-bromo-4,5-dihydro-5,5-dimethyl-2-phenyl-, 1-oxide	EtOH	251(4.20),315(3.99)	12-1795-79
$C_{12}H_{12}BrNO_3$			
1H-Indole-3-carboxylic acid, 5-bromo-2,3-dihydro-3-methyl-2-oxo-, ethyl ester	MeOH	247(4.14),296(3.15)	39-0595-79C
	MeOH-base	267(4.08),276(4.03)	39-0595-79C
$C_{12}H_{12}Br_2O_3$			
Benzenebutanoic acid, α,β-dibromo-4-ethyl-γ-oxo-	MeOH	269(4.1740)	73-1318-79
$C_{12}H_{12}F_3N_5O_3$			
[1,2'-Bi-1H-imidazole]-4'-propanoic acid, α-[(trifluoroacetyl)amino]-, methyl ester, (S)-	EtOH	248(3.88)	44-4243-79
$C_{12}H_{12}N_2$			
1,4-Benzenediamine, N-phenyl-	EtOH	244(7.80)[sic],285(4.45)	42-1217-79
Propanedinitrile, (octahydro-2,5-methanopentalen-7-ylidene)-	hexane	239(4.22)	142-0343-79
1H-Pyrazole, 3-ethenyl-5-methyl-1-phenyl-	EtOH	212(4.01),258(4.18)	4-0657-79
$C_{12}H_{12}N_2O$			
1H-Benzimidazole, 1-ethenyl-2-[(ethenyloxy)methyl]-	EtOH	231(4.26),260(4.01), 282(3.81),291(3.39)	70-1931-79
5H-Cyclopenta[b][1,8]naphthyridin-5-one, 1,6,7,8-tetrahydro-2-methyl-	EtOH	248(4.40),278(3.65), 290(3.71),328(4.01)	4-0137-79
Cyclopenta[d]pyrido[1,2-a]pyrimidin-10(1H)-one, 2,3-dihydro-8-methyl-	EtOH	253(4.12),260(4.07), 327(3.81),357(3.95)	4-0137-79
Ethanone, 1-(4-amino-2-methyl-3-quinolinyl)-	DMF	276(4.17),306s(3.81), 313(3.82),343s(3.61)	48-0695-79
1H-Indole-2-acetonitrile, 3-(2-hydroxyethyl)-	EtOH	220(4.58),272(3.89), 279(3.90),289(3.79)	23-0289-79
1-Naphthalenol, 2-methyl-4-(methylazo)- (at 0°)	benzene	413(4.07)	24-2913-79
	acetone	420(3.93)	24-2913-79
	dioxan	416(3.66)	24-2913-79
	$CHCl_3$	420(4.17)	24-2913-79
	CCl_4	407(3.89)	24-2913-79
4H-Pyrido[1,2-a]pyrimidin-4-one, 2,3-tetramethylene-	n.s.g.	239(3.08),246(3.10), 253(4.04),331(4.01)	4-0137-79
Pyrimidine, 4-(4-methoxyphenyl)-5-methyl-	EtOH	289(4.13)	24-0001-79
2H-Pyrrol-2-one, 1,5-dihydro-3,4-dimethyl-, (Z)-	EtOH	246(4.29),334(3.54)	88-1303-79
$C_{12}H_{12}N_2OS$			
Acetamide, N-(3-methyl-4-phenyl-2(3H)-thiazolylidene)-	EtOH	218(4.14),260(3.45), 300(4.18)	78-1199-79
$C_{12}H_{12}N_2OS_2$			
Methanone, [3,4-diamino-5-(methylthio)-2-thienyl]phenyl-	EtOH	248(3.98),345(4.17)	95-1081-79

Compound	Solvent	λ_{max}(log ε)	Ref.
$C_{12}H_{12}N_2O_2$			
1H-Indole, 2,3-dimethyl-5-(2-nitroethenyl)-	MeOH	237(4.44),285(4.20), 380(4.36)	103-0276-79
Methanone, (4-methoxyphenyl)(1-methyl-1H-pyrazol-4-yl)-	EtOH	225(4.00),285(4.26)	73-0781-79
	ether	217(4.12),273(4.31)	73-0781-79
2-Propenoic acid, 2-cyano-3-(phenylamino)-, ethyl ester	hexane	228(3.85),321(4.35)	131-0077-79D
	EtOH	322(4.43)	131-0077-79D
$C_{12}H_{12}N_2O_2S$			
Cyclopentanone, 2-(2-benzoxazolylthio)-, oxime	EtOH	244(4.05),279(4.12), 286(4.13)	48-0249-79
1H-Pyrazole-3-carboxylic acid, 5-(methylthio)-1-phenyl-, methyl ester	CH_2Cl_2	233(4.15),256s(4.03)	24-1193-79
1H-Pyrazole-4-carboxylic acid, 5-(methylthio)-1-phenyl-, methyl ester	CH_2Cl_2	251(4.07)	24-1193-79
1H-Pyrazole-5-carboxylic acid, 3-(methylthio)-1-phenyl-, methyl ester	CH_2Cl_2	295(3.70)	24-1206-79
2-Thiophenemethanamine, α-methyl-N-(4-nitrophenyl)-, (R)-	MeOH	233(4.18),298s(3.20), 310s(3.34),382(4.28)	35-5186-79
$C_{12}H_{12}N_2O_2S_2$			
Pyridinium, 1-[4-amino-5-(ethoxycarbonyl)-2-mercapto-3-thienyl]-, hydroxide, inner salt	EtOH	250(4.10),296(4.03), 355(4.28)	95-1081-79
Pyridinium, 1-[1-cyano-2-[(2-ethoxy-2-oxoethyl)thio]-2-mercaptoethenyl]-, hydroxide, inner salt	EtOH	259(3.98),318(4.29), 430(3.46)	95-1081-79
$C_{12}H_{12}N_2O_3$			
2-Furanmethanamine, α-methyl-N-(4-nitrophenyl)-, (S)-	MeOH	213s(4.15),298s(3.32), 380(4.23)	35-5186-79
1,4-Naphthalenedione, 5-amino-2-methoxy-3-(methylamino)-	C_6H_{12}	446(3.89),490s(3.67)	39-0696-79C
1,4-Naphthalenedione, 5-amino-3-methoxy-2-(methylamino)-	C_6H_{12}	452(3.61),504(3.67)	39-0696-79C
Spiro[cyclopentane-1,4'(1'H)-[2,7]naphthyridine]-1',3'(2'H)-dione, 3-hydroxy- (sesbanine)	MeOH	228(4.02)	35-2784-79
$C_{12}H_{12}N_2O_3S$			
Acetonitrile, [(4-methylphenyl)sulfonyl]-2-oxazolidinylidene-	EtOH	225(4.22),263(4.24)	95-0038-79
1H-Pyrazole-3-carboxylic acid, 5-(methylsulfinyl)-1-phenyl-, methyl ester	CH_2Cl_2	254(4.04)	24-1193-79
1H-Pyrazole-4-carboxylic acid, 5-(methylsulfinyl)-1-phenyl-, methyl ester	CH_2Cl_2	250(3.99)	24-1193-79
$C_{12}H_{12}N_2O_4$			
Carbamic acid, [(4,5-dihydro-5-oxo-3-isoxazolyl)methyl]-, phenylmethyl ester	MeOH	251(3.77)	1-0294-79
$C_{12}H_{12}N_2O_4S$			
Thieno[2,3-b]pyridine-2,4-dicarboxylic acid, 3-amino-6-methyl-, 4-ethyl ester	EtOH	235(3.96),294(4.32), 390(3.47)	103-1070-79
Thieno[2,3-b]pyridine-2,6-dicarboxylic acid, 3-amino-4-methyl-, 6-ethyl ester	EtOH	250(3.97),287(4.37), 387(3.66)	103-1070-79

Compound	Solvent	λ_{max}(log ε)	Ref.
$C_{12}H_{12}N_2O_4S_2$			
1H-Pyrrole-2,5-dione, 3-[(4-methylphenyl)sulfonyl]-4-(methylthio)-, 5-oxime	EtOH	250(3.92),360(4.22)	95-1234-79
$C_{12}H_{12}N_2O_5$			
2,3,4(5H)-Furantrione, 5-(1,2-dihydroxyethyl)-, 3-(phenylhydrazone), [R-(R*,R*)]-	EtOH	208s(3.81),235(3.99), 354s(3.85),395(4.21)	136-0087-79A
$C_{12}H_{12}N_2O_8$			
Pyrazinetetracarboxylic acid, tetramethyl ester	MeOH	277(3.60)	39-2411-79C
$C_{12}H_{12}N_2S_2$			
Cyclopenta[1,3,4]thiadiazine-3(2H)-thione, 1,5,6,7-tetrahydro-1-phenyl-	EtOH	232(4.097),333(4.136)	48-0959-79
$C_{12}H_{12}N_4$			
Diimidazo[1,2-a:1',2'-c]quinazoline, 2,3,6,7-tetrahydro-	EtOH	220(4.36),237(4.46), 272(4.09),343(3.58)	106-0844-79
1H-Pyrazole-4-carbonitrile, 1-(4-aminophenyl)-3,5-dimethyl-	EtOH	276(4.43)	78-1331-79
$C_{12}H_{12}N_4O$			
2-Propenamide, 2-amino-3-cyano-3-[[(4-methylphenyl)methylene]amino]-, (Z,?)-	EtOH	245(4.11),258(4.12), 356(4.36)	44-0827-79
4-Pyridazinecarboxaldehyde, 5-(hydroxyphenylmethyl)-, hydrazone	MeOH	235s(3.85),321(4.15)	39-2215-79C
$C_{12}H_{12}N_4OS$			
Pyrido[3',2':4,5]thieno[3,2-d]pyrimidin-4(3H)-one, 3-amino-2,7,9-trimethyl-	EtOH	248(4.54),285(3.96), 294(4.10),327(3.81), 339s(3.68)	103-1074-79
$C_{12}H_{12}N_4O_2$			
2-Propenamide, 2-amino-3-cyano-3-[[(4-methoxyphenyl)methylene]amino]-, (Z,?)-	EtOH	271(4.10),360(4.40)	44-0827-79
$C_{12}H_{12}N_4O_3$			
Formamide, N-[4-(3,5-dimethyl-4-nitro-1H-pyrazol-1-yl)phenyl]-	EtOH	253(4.16)	78-1331-79
1H-Pyrazole-4-carboxamide, 3,5-dimethyl-1-(4-nitrophenyl)-	EtOH	310(4.30)	78-1331-79
$C_{12}H_{12}N_4O_3S$			
Benzoic acid, 4-[[(1,3,4-thiadiazol-2-ylamino)carbonyl]amino]-, ethyl ester	n.s.g.	277(4.55),310(3.75)	87-0028-79
$C_{12}H_{12}N_4O_4$			
Pyrazolo[1,5-a]pyrimidine-7-carboxylic acid, 6-acetyl-3-(aminocarbonyl)-, ethyl ester	EtOH	257(4.40),312(3.90)	142-0397-79
$C_{12}H_{12}N_6$			
Triimidazo[1,2-a:1',2'-c:1",2"-e]-[1,3,5]triazine, 2,6,10-trimethyl-	EtOH	234(4.64),241(4.62), 260(3.94)	44-4243-79
$C_{12}H_{12}N_6O_3$			
1H-Imidazole-4-carboxylic acid, 5-ami-	EtOH	230(4.05),280(4.15),	103-0805-79

Compound	Solvent	λ_{max}(log ε)	Ref.
no-, [1-(4-nitrophenyl)ethylidene]hydrazide (cont.)		350(4.24)	103-0805-79
$C_{12}H_{12}N_6O_4$			
Dipyrimido[4,5-c:5',4'-e]pyridazine-1,3,8,10(2H,9H)-tetrone, 4,7-dihydro-2,4,7,9-tetramethyl-	$CHCl_3$	258(4.56),423(3.58), 446(3.51)	94-2143-79
$C_{12}H_{12}O$			
3H-Biphenyleno[1,8b-b]oxirene, 1a,2,4,4a-tetrahydro-	MeOH	264(3.20),270(3.37), 277(3.33)	111-0543-79
2-Cyclohexen-1-one, 3-phenyl-	H_2SO_4	366(4.27)	124-1093-79
2,4-Hexadien-1-one, 1-phenyl-	EtOH	297(4.32)	32-0195-79
3,5-Hexadien-2-one, 6-phenyl-	EtOH	233(3.77),319(4.52)	12-2523-79
1(4H)-Naphthalenone, 4,4-dimethyl-	EtOH	244(4.04)	12-0179-79
$C_{12}H_{12}OS_2$			
Thiophene, 3-methoxy-2-(methylthio)-4-phenyl-	EtOH	235(4.27)	88-2493-79
Thiophene, 3-methoxy-5-(methylthio)-4-phenyl-	EtOH	250(4.10)	88-2493-79
Thiophene, 4-(4-methoxyphenyl)-2-(methylthio)-	EtOH	259(4.39)	88-2493-79
$C_{12}H_{12}OS_3$			
1H-2-Benzothiopyran-4(3H)-one, 3-[bis(methylthio)methylene]-	$CHCl_3$	285(3.90),420(3.89)	1-0460-79
$C_{12}H_{12}O_2$			
2-Cyclopenten-1-one, 5-hydroxy-3-methyl-4-phenyl-, cis	n.s.g.	218(4.09)	39-0274-79C
trans	n.s.g.	230(4.02)	39-0274-79C
2-Cyclopenten-1-one, 5-hydroxy-4-methyl-3-phenyl-, cis	n.s.g.	224(3.60),287(3.96)	39-0274-79C
trans	n.s.g.	218(3.94),283(4.27)	39-0274-79C
Ethanone, 2-(dihydro-2(3H)-furanylidene)-1-phenyl-, (E)-	EtOH	248(3.95),289(4.28)	44-2073-79
2,4-Pentadienal, 5-(4-methoxyphenyl)-, (E,E)-	EtOH	358(4.49)	104-1669-79
$C_{12}H_{12}O_3$			
2H-1-Benzopyran-2-one, 4-(1-methylethoxy)-	MeOH	260s(3.85),268(4.00), 279(3.99),306(3.80), 315s(3.66)	150-0110-79S
2-Propenoic acid, 3-(4-acetylphenyl)-, methyl ester, (E)-	MeCN	291(4.48)	88-0863-79
(Z)-	MeCN	281(4.24)	88-0863-79
$C_{12}H_{12}O_4$			
1H-Indene-4-carboxylic acid, 2,3-dihydro-5-methoxy-1-oxo-, methyl ester	MeOH	224(4.48),253s(3.92), 303(3.30)	18-2023-79
3aH-Indene-3a-carboxylic acid, 3,7a-dihydro-4-methoxy-3-oxo-, methyl ester	MeOH	210(4.10),279(3.63), 344(2.69)	18-2023-79
1-Isobenzofurancarboxylic acid, 1,3-dihydro-1,5-dimethyl-3-oxo-, methyl ester	MeOH	230(3.98),280(3.26), 290(3.27)	23-2853-79
Siderin	EtOH	288(4.07),307(4.17), 314(4.10)	39-2113-79C
Tricyclo[4.4.1.1^{3,8}]dodecane-4,5,9,10-tetrone	$CHCl_3$	408(1.79)	88-2347-79

Compound	Solvent	λ_{max}(log ε)	Ref.
$C_{12}H_{12}O_4S_4$			
1,3-Dithiole-4,5-dicarboxylic acid, 2-(1,3-dithiol-2-ylidene)-, diethyl ester	MeCN	292(4.25),302(4.27), 314(4.29),460(3.03)	44-1476-79
$C_{12}H_{12}O_5$			
1,4-Epoxynaphthalene-5,8-dione, 1,4,4a,8a-tetrahydro-2,3-dimethoxy-	EtOH	220(3.99),370(2.08)	33-2211-79
4,7-Ethanoisobenzofuran-1,3,8-trione, 3a,4,7,7a-tetrahydro-9-hydroxy-7,9-dimethyl-, (3aα,4α,7α,7aα,9S*)-	MeOH	312(1.98)	23-2853-79
$C_{12}H_{12}O_6$			
Benzoic acid, 2-(1,2-dioxopropyl)-4,6-dimethoxy-	MeOH	259(4.16),296(3.85)	39-0337-79C
sodium salt	H_2O	285(--),350(--)	39-0337-79C
2-Oxaspiro[4.5]deca-6,9-diene-3-carboxylic acid, 3-methoxy-1,8-dioxo-, methyl ester	EtOH	238(4.16),285s(1.77)	35-7013-79
$C_{12}H_{12}S$			
Benzo[b]thiophene, 2-methyl-3-(1-methylethenyl)-	EtOH	233(4.46),262(3.85), 271(3.85),291(3.52), 301(3.45)	12-0133-79
$C_{12}H_{12}S_2$			
Cycloocta[1,2-c:5,6-c']dithiophene, 4,5,9,10-tetrahydro-	EtOH	237(4.03),243(4.06), 249s(3.95)	44-2667-79
$C_{12}H_{12}S_3$			
2,4-Cyclohexadiene-1-thione, 6-(tetrahydro-4H-cyclopenta-1,3-dithiol-2-ylidene)-	CH_2Cl_2	267(3.87),350(3.34), 585(3.14)	18-0496-79
$C_{12}H_{13}BrO$			
1(2H)-Naphthalenone, 2-bromo-3,4-dihydro-4,4-dimethyl-	EtOH	253(4.05),294(3.29)	12-0179-79
$C_{12}H_{13}BrO_3$			
Furo[2,3-b]benzofuran, 3-bromo-2-ethoxy-2,3,3a,8a-tetrahydro-, trans	CH_2Cl_2	233(3.95),282(3.49), 290(3.44)	39-2664-79C
$C_{12}H_{13}ClN_4O_4$			
10H-Furo[2',3':4,5]oxazolo[3,2-a]pyrido[2,3-d]pyrimidine-2-methanol, 9-amino-8-chloro-2,3,3a,11a-tetrahydro-3-hydroxy-	H_2O	332(3.94)	103-0226-79
Furo[2',3':4,5]oxazolo[3,2-a]pyrrolo-[2,3-d]pyrimidine-7-carbonitrile, 8a-chloro-2,3,3a,7,8,8a,9,10-octahydro-3-hydroxy-2-(hydroxymethyl)-	H_2O	250(4.08)	103-0226-79
$C_{12}H_{13}ClO_3$			
Furo[2,3-b]benzofuran, 3-chloro-2-ethoxy-2,3,3a,8a-tetrahydro-, (2α,3α,3aα-8aα)-	CH_2Cl_2	231(3.17),282(3.48), 288(3.42)	39-2664-79C
(2α,3β,3aβ,8aβ)-	CH_2Cl_2	230(3.16),282(3.48), 287(3.42)	39-2664-79C

Compound	Solvent	λ_{max}(log ϵ)	Ref.
$C_{12}H_{13}FN_2O_5$			
Uridine, 4',5'-didehydro-5'-deoxy-5-fluoro-2',3'-O-(1-methylethylidene)-	MeOH	267(3.95)	87-1330-79
$C_{12}H_{13}FO_6Pb$			
Plumbane, triacetoxy(3-fluorophenyl)-	dioxane	260(3.67),271(3.59)	12-1521-79
Plumbane, triacetoxy(4-fluorophenyl)-	dioxane	259(3.62),266(3.53)	12-1521-79
$C_{12}H_{13}Fe$			
Ethylium, 1-ferrocenyl-	$C_2H_4Cl_2$	260(4.00),380(2.63)	32-0013-79
$C_{12}H_{13}GeN$			
9H-Pyrrolo[1,2-a]benzazagermole, 9,9-dimethyl-	EtOH	221(4.35),256(4.11), 278(4.14)	101-0139-79C
$C_{12}H_{13}IO_4$			
2,5-Cyclohexadiene-1,4-dione, 3-acetoxy-5-(1,1-dimethylethyl)-2-iodo-	EtOH	248(3.86),277(3.89), 378(3.11)	44-0428-79
$C_{12}H_{13}N$			
Indole, 2-ethenyl-1,3-dimethyl-	EtOH	235(4.42),305(4.21)	39-2154-79C
Pyrrolo[3,2,1-hi]indole, 1,2-dihydro-4,5-dimethyl-	EtOH	207(4.30),233(4.49), 292(3.90)	39-2387-79C
$C_{12}H_{13}NO$			
Benzenamine, N-[(3,4-dihydro-2H-pyran-2-yl)methylene]-	EtOH	242(4.01),285(3.44)	103-0488-79
dimer	EtOH	248(4.28),289(3.85)	103-0488-79
2H-Pyrrol-2-one, 1,5-dihydro-5,5-dimethyl-4-phenyl-	EtOH	215(4.06),221s(4.00), 267(4.04)	12-2035-79
6H-Pyrrolo[3,2,1-ij]quinolin-6-one, 1,2,4,5-tetrahydro-4-methyl-	MeOH	240(4.20),256s(3.80), 380(3.60)	4-0949-79
6(2H)-Quinolinone, 2,2,4-trimethyl-	MeOH	243(4.00),253(3.99), 281(4.09),366(3.62)	39-0488-79C
$C_{12}H_{13}NO_2$			
8-Azaspiro[4.5]deca-1,3,6,9-tetraene-8-carboxylic acid, ethyl ester	isooctane	225(4.42)	44-2522-79
1H-Indole-2-carboxylic acid, 3-methyl-, ethyl ester	MeOH and MeOH-NaOH	229(4.39),296(4.33)	39-0595-79C
Oxazole, 2-ethyl-5-(4-methoxyphenyl)-	EtOH	275(4.36)	18-3597-79
2,4-Pentanedione, 3-[(phenylamino)methylene]-	hexane	229(4.18),250(4.16), 333(4.37)	131-0077-79D
	EtOH	335(4.38)	131-0077-79D
$C_{12}H_{13}NO_2S_3$			
2-Propenenitrile, 2-[(4-methylphenyl)-sulfonyl]-3,3-bis(methylthio)-	EtOH	334(4.16)	95-0038-79
$C_{12}H_{13}NO_3$			
1H-Indole-3-carboxylic acid, 2,3-dihydro-3-methyl-2-oxo-, ethyl ester	MeOH	252(3.81)	39-0595-79C
$C_{12}H_{13}NO_4$			
Acetamide, N-(4-acetoxy-2-acetylphenyl)-	EtOH	257(4.06),263s(3.90), 330(3.62)	33-0271-79
Acetamide, N-(4-acetoxy-2-formyl-3-methylphenyl)-	EtOH	265(3.89),276s(--), 343(3.63)	33-0234-79
3-Butenoic acid, 4-hydroxy-2-oxo-4-(phenylamino)-, ethyl ester	EtOH	312(3.98)	94-1792-79

Compound	Solvent	λ max(log ε)	Ref.
1H-Indole-3-carboxylic acid, 2,3-dihydro-1-hydroxy-3-methyl-2-oxo-, ethyl ester	MeOH	262(3.79),285(3.66)	39-0595-79C
	MeOH-base	289(4.01)	39-0595-79C
1,2-Propanedione, 1-(2-methoxyphenyl)-, 1-(acetoxyoxime), (E)-	EtOH	210(4.24),244(3.62), 298(3.32)	39-0156-79B
$(C_{12}H_{13}NO_4)_n$			
1,2-Benzenedicarboxylic acid, 3-amino-6-ethenyl-, dimethyl ester, homopolymer	dioxane	260(3.6),350(3.6)	5-1085-79
$C_{12}H_{13}NO_4S$			
Butanedioic acid, 2-(1,2-dihydro-1-methyl-2-pyridinylidene)-3-thioxo-, dimethyl ester	EtOH	220(3.82),264(3.81), 332(4.26)	94-2879-79
$C_{12}H_{13}NO_5S$			
3-Penten-2-one, 3-methyl-5-[(2-nitrophenyl)sulfonyl]-	H_2O	230(3.963)	104-0578-79
$C_{12}H_{13}NS$			
Cyclohepta[c]pyrrole, 1,3-dimethyl-6-(methylthio)-	CH_2Cl_2	256(4.06),334(4.72), 373(3.76),392(3.91), 672(2.70)	24-2087-79
$C_{12}H_{13}N_2OS$			
Thiazolo[3,2-a]benzimidazolium, 9-ethyl-6-hydroxy-2-methyl-, bromide	EtOH	253(3.50),530(3.64)	18-3096-79
Thiazolo[3,2-a]benzimidazolium, 9-ethyl-6-hydroxy-3-methyl-, bromide	EtOH	265(3.65),525(3.90)	18-3096-79
$C_{12}H_{13}N_3$			
1H-Benzotriazole, 1-(1-cyclohexen-1-yl)-	EtOH	263(3.72),291(3.70)	33-2129-79
2-Propenenitrile, 3-(2-pyridinyl)-3-(1-pyrrolidinyl)-	ether	246(4.20),314(3.89)	22-0559-79
$C_{12}H_{13}N_3O$			
8-Azabicyclo[3.2.1]oct-2-ene-8-propanenitrile, 7-cyano-1-methyl-4-oxo-	$CHCl_3$	260(2.70)	39-2528-79C
Azepino[4,5-b]indol-4(1H)-one, 5-amino-2,3,5,6-tetrahydro-	EtOH	285(3.68)	103-0780-79
4H-Imidazol-4-one, 5-[(dimethylamino)-methylene]-3,5-dihydro-3-phenyl-	EtOH	230(3.9),260(4.1), 336(4.4)	103-0544-79
	$CHCl_3$	260(4.1),340(4.3)	103-0544-79
1H-Pyrrole-2-acetonitrile, α-(3,4-dimethyl-5-oxo-2-pyrrolidinylidene)-, (2E,3α,4β)-	EtOH	311(4.18)	49-0201-79
$C_{12}H_{13}N_3OS$			
Isothiazolo[4,5-b]quinoline-3-carboxamide, 5,6,7,8-tetrahydro-9-methyl-	DMF	280(3.73),310(3.69)	5-1534-79
Morpholine, 4-[[[2-cyano-2-(2-thienyl)-ethenyl]imino]methyl]-	MeOH	247(4.19),350(4.48)	83-0039-79
1,3,4-Thiadiazolo[3,2-a]benzimidazol-6-ol, 2-butyl-	pH 1	328(3.67),385(3.74)	18-2033-79
	pH 13	325(3.74),459(3.81)	18-2033-79
	EtOH	247(4.25),263(4.10), 375(3.78)	18-2033-79
1,3,4-Thiadiazolo[3,2-a]benzimidazol-6-ol, 2-(2-methylpropyl)-	pH 1	345(3.81),397(3.72)	18-2033-79
	pH 13	351(3.57),475(3.74)	18-2033-79
	EtOH	271(4.07),310(4.29), 364(4.31)	18-2033-79

Compound	Solvent	$\lambda_{max}(\log \epsilon)$	Ref.
$C_{12}H_{13}N_3O_2$			
Acetamide, N-[2-(5-phenyl-1,2,4-oxadiazol-3-yl)ethyl]-	EtOH	252(4.24)	150-0801-79
1H-Azepine-2,3,4(5H)-trione, dihydro-, 3-(phenylhydrazone)	EtOH	242(4.03),370(4.26)	103-0780-79
1H-Pyrazole-3-carboxylic acid, 4-amino-5-phenyl-, ethyl ester	pH 1	223(4.28)	18-0208-79
	pH 11	255(4.36),288s(4.01)	18-0208-79
	EtOH	228(4.32),309(3.97)	18-0208-79
$C_{12}H_{13}N_3O_2S$			
Acetonitrile, 2-imidazolidinylidene-[(4-methylphenyl)sulfonyl]-	EtOH	223(4.34),265(4.20)	95-0038-79
2-Propenoic acid, 2-cyano-3-[(1-methyl-2(1H)-pyridinylidene)amino]-3-(methylthio)-, methyl ester	EtOH	220(4.14),259(4.04), 310(4.19),374(4.30)	94-2879-79
$C_{12}H_{13}N_3O_3S$			
Sydnone, 3-morpholino-4-(phenylthio)-	CH_2Cl_2	315(3.86)	5-0063-79
$C_{12}H_{13}N_3O_4$			
Benzenamine, N-(1-ethyl-1-methyl-2-propynyl)-2,4-dinitro-, (R)-	C_6H_{12}	264(4.00),329(4.24), 396(3.71)	78-2413-79
	MeOH	265(4.00),343(4.23), 395s(3.80)	78-2413-79
Benzenamine, N-(1-ethynylbutyl)-2,4-dinitro-, (S)-	C_6H_{12}	262(4.01),327(4.25), 387(3.72)	78-2413-79
	MeOH	263(3.99),343(4.23), 395s(3.79)	78-2413-79
$C_{12}H_{13}N_3O_4S$			
1,2,3-Thiadiazolium, 5-[(ethoxycarbonyl)amino]-4-hydroxy-3-(4-methoxyphenyl)-, hydroxide, inner salt	EtOH	226(4.13),315(3.79), 386(3.94)	39-2349-79C
Thieno[2,3-b]pyridine-2-carboxylic acid, 4,6-dimethyl-3-(nitroamino)-, ethyl ester	EtOH	238(4.25),298(4.18)	103-1074-79
$C_{12}H_{13}N_3O_5$			
D-erythro-2,3-Hexodiulosonic acid, γ-lactone, 2-(phenylhydrazone), 3-oxime	EtOH	226(4.18),284(3.84), 386(4.36)	136-0087-79A
1H-Pyrrolo[3,2-d]pyrimidine-7-carboxylic acid, 6-formyl-2,3,4,5-tetrahydro-1,3,5-trimethyl-2,4-dioxo-, methyl ester	EtOH	235(4.14),283(3.68), 335(3.10)	44-3830-79
$C_{12}H_{13}N_3O_6$			
1H-Pyrrolo[3,2-d]pyrimidine-6,7-dicarboxylic acid, tetrahydro-1,3-dimethyl-2,4-dioxo-, dimethyl ester	EtOH	230(4.57),273(4.28), 307(4.22)	44-3830-79
$C_{12}H_{13}N_3S$			
4H-Imidazole-4-thione, 5-[(dimethylamino)methylene]-3,5-dihydro-3-phenyl-	EtOH	277(4.2),407(4.1)	103-0544-79
	$CHCl_3$	280(4.3),420(4.2)	103-0544-79
$C_{12}H_{13}N_5O$			
1H-Imidazole-4-carboxylic acid, 5-amino-, (1-phenylethylidene)hydrazide	EtOH	218(4.12),310(4.45)	103-0805-79
Imidazo[1,2-c]pteridine, 6-ethoxy-2,3-dimethyl-	pH -3.4	220(4.36),258(3.86), 277s(3.57),360s(4.16), 369(4.17)	18-0867-79

Compound	Solvent	λmax(log ε)	Ref.
Imidazo[1,2-c]pteridine, 6-ethoxy-2,3-dimethyl- (cont.)	pH 0.5	213(4.42),235s(4.03), 265(3.74),273s(3.66), 333(4.12),347(4.08)	18-0867-79
	pH 5.0	223(4.37),245s(3.87), 279(3.51),287(3.51), 344(4.12)	18-0867-79
Pyrrolo[2,3-b]indole, 1-acetyl-3a-azido-1,2,3,3a,8,8a-hexahydro-	EtOH	241(3.08),302(3.20)	39-3061-79C
$C_{12}H_{13}N_5O_2$			
Isoquinoline, 1,2,3,4-tetrahydro-2-(1-methyl-4-nitro-1H-1,2,3-triazol-5-yl)-	EtOH	234(4.11),348(3.36)	39-2361-79C
$C_{12}H_{13}N_5O_3$			
Adenosine, 2',3'-didehydro-2',3'-dideoxy-, 5'-acetate	MeOH	260(4.19)	44-1404-79
$C_{12}H_{13}O_2S$			
1-Benzothiopyrylium, 2,7-dimethoxy-4-methyl-, perchlorate	acetone	386(4.04)	18-0160-79
$C_{12}H_{14}$			
Benzene, 1-cyclohexen-1-yl-, cis	MeOH	248(4.08)	35-6383-79
$C_{12}H_{14}BrCl_3O$			
Bicyclo[3.1.0]hex-3-en-2-one, 6-bromo-1,4,5,6-tetramethyl-3-(2,2,2-trichloroethyl)-, endo	hexane	220(3.85),255(3.81)	44-2381-79
exo	hexane	215(3.95),235s(3.85), 258s(3.78)	44-2381-79
$C_{12}H_{14}BrNO$			
Pyrrolo[2,1-b]oxazole, 7a-(4-bromophenyl)hexahydro-	EtOH	258(3.26)	145-0983-79
$C_{12}H_{14}BrN_{11}$			
1H-Pyrazol-3-amine, 4-[[4-[(4-bromo-5-methyl-1H-pyrazol-3-yl)azo]-5-methyl-1H-pyrazol-3-yl]azo]-5-methyl-	MeOH	340(4.14),465(4.04)	103-0657-79
$C_{12}H_{14}BrOS$			
Thiophenium, 1-[2-(4-bromophenyl)-2-oxoethyl]tetrahydro-, tetrafluoroborate	MeOH	270(4.18),310(3.65), 360(2.54)	47-2877-79
$C_{12}H_{14}ClNO_5$			
α-D-Xylofuranose, 3-chloro-3,5-dideoxy-5-(2,5-dioxo-3-pyrrolidinylidene)-1,2-O-(1-methylethylidene)-, (E)-	EtOH	221(4.10)	33-0977-79
$C_{12}H_{14}ClN_5O_3$			
9H-Purine-9-acetic acid, α-(acetylamino)-6-chloro-α-methyl-, ethyl ester	MeOH	265(3.96)	44-2019-79
$C_{12}H_{14}Cl_3NO_3$			
2-Azabicyclo[2.2.2]oct-5-ene-2-carboxylic acid, 7-acetyl-, 2,2,2-trichloroethyl ester	MeCN	206(3.48)	44-0124-79
Carbamic acid, [(5-acetyl-2,4-cyclohexadien-1-yl)methyl]-, 2,2,2-tri-	MeCN	298(3.94)	44-0124-79

Compound	Solvent	λ_{max}(log ε)	Ref.
chloroethyl ester (cont.)			44-0124-79
$C_{12}H_{14}Cl_4O$			
Bicyclo[3.1.0]hex-3-en-2-one, 6-chloro-1,4,5,6-tetramethyl-3-(2,2,2-trichloroethyl)-, endo	hexane	230(3.78),255(3.74)	44-2381-79
exo	hexane	233(3.78),258s(3.74)	44-2381-79
$C_{12}H_{14}FNO$			
Pyrrolo[2,1-b]oxazole, 7a-(4-fluorophenyl)hexahydro-	EtOH	243(3.45)	145-0983-79
$C_{12}H_{14}INS$			
Cyclohepta[c]pyrrole, 1,3-dimethyl-6-(methylthio)-, hydriodide	MeCN	332(4.52),403(4.43), 605(3.18)	24-2087-79
$C_{12}H_{14}IN_5O_5$			
Guanosine, N-acetyl-5'-deoxy-5'-iodo-	MeOH-HCl	264(4.22)	44-0400-79
	MeOH-NaOH	267(4.14)	44-0400-79
$C_{12}H_{14}NO$			
Isoquinolinium, 1,4-dihydro-4-(methoxymethylene)-2-methyl-, tetrafluoroborate	EtOH	235(3.79),284(3.94), 345(3.82)	78-1861-79
$C_{12}H_{14}NO_3S$			
Thiophenium, tetrahydro-1-[2-(4-nitrophenyl)-2-oxoethyl]-, tetrafluoroborate	MeOH	263(4.20),355(3.58), 360(3.58)	47-2877-79
$C_{12}H_{14}N_2$			
1H-Benzimidazole, 1-ethenyl-2-propyl-	isooctane	243(4.28),281(3.70), 290(3.61)	65-1225-79
	pH 1	212(4.24),256(3.86), 264(3.90),270(3.98), 277(3.96)	65-1225-79
	H_2O	228(4.10),251(3.90), 275(3.73),280(3.66)	65-1225-79
	EtOH	234(4.17),250(3.99), 277(3.72),285(3.59)	65-1225-79
$C_{12}H_{14}N_2O$			
1H-Benzimidazole, 2-[(ethenyloxy)methyl]-1-ethyl-	EtOH	250(3.89),256(3.90), 277(3.83),283(3.77), 286(3.66)	70-1931-79
Benzonitrile, 4-[[(1,2-dimethylpropylidene)amino]oxy]-	hexane	250(4.49),272(3.47), 283(3.10)	12-2413-79
1H-Pyrazole-3-propanol, 5-phenyl-	MeOH	249(4.57),335(2.11)	44-2073-79
1H-Pyrazolium, 4-hydroxy-1,2,3-trimethyl-5-phenyl-, hydroxide, inner salt	H_2O	311(3.96)	23-0904-79
1H-Pyrazolium, 4-hydroxy-1,3,5-trimethyl-2-phenyl-, hydroxide, inner salt	H_2O	297(3.88)	23-0904-79
Pyrimidine, 1,4-dihydro-4-(4-methoxyphenyl)-5-methyl-	EtOH	276(3.44),282(3.43), 291s(3.26)	24-0001-79
hydrochloride	EtOH	246(3.82),273(3.70), 280s(3.66)	24-0001-79
2(1H)-Quinolinone, 1-(dimethylamino)-7-methyl-	MeOH	219(4.45),269(3.88), 318(3.83)	64-0102-79B

Compound	Solvent	λmax(log ε)	Ref.
$C_{12}H_{14}N_2OS$			
Acetamide, N-(2,3,6-trimethylthieno-[2,3-b]pyridin-4-yl)-	DMF	292(3.92)	49-1189-79
3-Thiophenecarbonitrile, 4,5-dimethyl-2-[(1-methyl-3-oxo-1-butenyl)amino]-	EtOH	228s(3.97),253(3.88), 367(4.03)	49-1189-79
$C_{12}H_{14}N_2OS_2$			
4-Thiazolidinone, 3-ethyl-5-(1-ethyl-2(1H)-pyridinylidene)-2-thioxo-	EtOH	463(4.55)	73-1413-79
4-Thiazolidinone, 3-ethyl-5-(1-ethyl-4(1H)-pyridinylidene)-2-thioxo-	EtOH	420s(4.30),444(4.70), 464(4.94)	73-1413-79
$C_{12}H_{14}N_2O_2$			
2(5H)-Furanone, 5,5-dimethyl-4-(2-phen-ylhydrazino)-	EtOH	256(4.32)	4-0505-79
2(5H)-Furanone, 5-methyl-4-[2-(phenyl-methyl)hydrazino]-	EtOH	258(4.31)	4-0505-79
1H-Indazole-4,7-dione, 6-(1,1-dimethyl-ethyl)-3-methyl-	n.s.g.	260(3.47)	70-1668-79
1H-Indole-3-acetamide, α-hydroxy-N,N-dimethyl-	EtOH	272(3.80),278(3.81), 288(3.73)	56-0073-79
2,6-Methano-2H-1,3,5-benzoxadiazocin-9-ol, 3,6-dihydro-2,4-dimethyl-, hydrochloride	EtOH	277(3.28),283(3.25)	24-0001-79
2(5H)-Oxazolone, 4-(dimethylamino)-5-methyl-5-phenyl-	EtOH	235(4.23)	33-1236-79
1H-Pyrazole-3-methanol, 5-hydroxy-α,α-dimethyl-1-phenyl-	EtOH	247(4.26)	4-0505-79
1H-Pyrazole-3-methanol, 5-hydroxy-α-methyl-1-(phenylmethyl)-	EtOH	254(3.69)	4-0505-79
Pyrrolo[2,3-b]indol-2(1H)-one, 3,3a,8-8a-tetrahydro-1-hydroxy-3a,8-dimeth-yl-	MeOH	252(3.94),302(3.41)	5-0927-79
Serotonin, N-acetyl-	EtOH	223(4.34),278(3.79), 298s(3.66),312s(3.54)	87-0063-79
Tryptophan, 6-methyl-, (R)-	EtOH	275(3.75),282(3.76), 292(3.69)	44-3741-79
$C_{12}H_{14}N_2O_2S$			
4-Oxazolidinone, 3-ethyl-5-(1-ethyl-4(1H)-pyridinylidene)-2-thioxo-	EtOH	400s(4.45),417(4.71), 440(4.88)	73-1413-79
Thieno[2,3-b]pyridine-2-carboxylic acid, 3-amino-4,6-dimethyl-, ethyl ester	EtOH	240(4.10),283(4.56), 360(3.71)	103-1070-79
$C_{12}H_{14}N_2O_2S_2$			
1H-Pyrazole, 3-methyl-4-[(4-methylphen-yl)sulfonyl]-5-(methylthio)-	EtOH	237(4.20)	95-0038-79
$C_{12}H_{14}N_2O_3$			
Benzeneacetaldehyde, α-[(dimethylamino)-methylene]-4-methyl-2-nitro-	EtOH	288(4.45)	44-3748-79
Benzoxazole, 7-(1,1-dimethylethyl)-4-methyl-5-nitro-	hexane	229(4.27),234s(4.25), 269(3.70),350s(2.55)	24-3956-79
2,4-Pentanedione, 3-[(4-methoxyphenyl)-azo]-	EtOH	400(4.328)	2-0502-79A'
	acetone	400(4.279)	2-0502-79A'
	dioxan	390(4.415)	2-0502-79A'
	$CHCl_3$	402(4.30)	2-0502-79A'
	CCl_4	395(4.255)	2-0502-79A'
2-Propenoic acid, 3-[4-(aminoiminometh-yl)phenyl]-2-methoxy-, methyl ester, monohydrochloride	n.s.g.	300(4.271)	106-0008-79

Compound	Solvent	$\lambda_{max}(\log \epsilon)$	Ref.
$C_{12}H_{14}N_2O_3S$			
2H-1,4-Benzothiazin-3(4H)-one, 2-[(dimethylamino)methylene]-4-methyl-, 1,1-dioxide	dioxane	270(4.1),308(4.3)	83-0302-79
$C_{12}H_{14}N_2O_4$			
2,1-Benzisoxazole, 6-(1,1-dimethylethyl)-5-methoxy-4-nitro-	hexane	205(4.17),367s(3.81), 382(3.86),400s(3.68)	24-3946-79
	MeOH	385(4.06)	24-3946-79
Benzonitrile, 2-(β-D-ribopyranosylamino)-	MeOH	219(4.35),248(4.01), 320(3.64)	44-0173-79
$C_{12}H_{14}N_2O_4S_2$			
Isothiazolium, 5-(hydroxyiminomethyl)-2-methyl-, p-toluenesulfonate	MeOH	218(4.24),253(3.25), 334(3.89)	39-2340-79C
	MeOH-$HClO_4$	210s(4.02),219(4.15), 263s(3.56),302(3.96), 333s(3.47)	39-2340-79C
$C_{12}H_{14}N_2O_5$			
2,4(1H,3H)-Pyrimidinedione, 1-(5-O-propanoyl-2,3-dideoxy-β-D-glycero-pent-2-enofuranosyl)-	MeOH	260(3.98)	44-1404-79
$C_{12}H_{14}N_2O_7$			
2,4(1H,3H)-Pyrimidinedione, 1-β-D-arabinofuranosyl-5-(2-propynyloxy)-	H_2O	277(3.95)	87-0316-79
$C_{12}H_{14}N_2O_{10}$			
β-D-Glucopyranoside, 3,4-dinitrophenyl	pH 5	282(3.8)	130-0147-79
$C_{12}H_{14}N_2S$			
Benzenamine, N-(4,4-dimethyl-5-methylene-2-thiazolidinylidene)-	EtOH	203(3.07),256(3.00)	103-0611-79
2,1-Benzisothiazole, 3-piperidino-	EtOH	234(4.43),287(3.23), 300(3.22),371(3.82)	33-0391-79
[1]Benzothieno[2,3-b]pyridin-4-amine, 5,6,7,8-tetrahydro-2-methyl-	DMF	275(4.11),282(4.14), 304(3.97),313(3.97)	49-1189-79
$C_{12}H_{14}N_2S_2$			
Benzo[1,2-d:5,4-d']bisthiazolium, 2,3,5,6-tetramethyl-, diperchlorate	DMF	262(4.02),367(3.72), 603(3.31)	126-1465-79
$C_{12}H_{14}N_3OS$			
1,3,4-Thiadiazolo[3,2-a]benzimidazolium, 2,9-diethyl-6-hydroxy-, bromide	EtOH	263(3.84),521(4.01)	18-2033-79
$C_{12}H_{14}N_4$			
2,2a,4,5-Tetraazabenz[cd]azulene, 3,4-dihydro-1,3,3-trimethyl-	MeOH	222(4.48),293(3.68), 350(4.01)	18-1972-79
$C_{12}H_{14}N_4O$			
Ethanol, 2-[(2,3-dihydroimidazo[1,2-c]quinazolin-5-yl)amino]-	EtOH	222(4.54),255(3.88), 266(3.94),284(4.00), 296(3.94),324(3.58), 340(3.74)	106-0844-79
Ethanone, 2-amino-1-[5-amino-1-(phenylmethyl)-1H-imidazol-4-yl]-, dihydrochloride	H_2O	303(4.12)	35-6127-79
Isoxazole, 3,4-dimethyl-5-[3-(4-methylphenyl)-1-triazenyl]-	MeOH	236(4.28),300(3.97), 375(4.61)	33-1570-79

Compound	Solvent	λmax(log ε)	Ref.
$C_{12}H_{14}N_4O_2S$			
1H-1,2,4-Triazolium, 4-[(ethoxycarbonyl)amino]-2,3-dihydro-1-methyl-5-phenyl-3-thioxo-, hydroxide, inner salt	EtOH	247(4.27),309(3.59)	94-1683-79
1H-1,2,4-Triazolium, 4-[(ethoxycarbonyl)amino]-2,3-dihydro-5-methyl-1-phenyl-3-thioxo-, hydroxide, inner salt	EtOH	248(4.29)	94-1683-79
$C_{12}H_{14}N_4O_2S_2$			
Sulfilimine, S,S-dimethyl-N-[4-[(2-pyrimidinylamino)sulfonyl]phenyl]-	70% EtOH	202(4.53),303(4.26)	139-0195-79
sodium salt	70% EtOH	285(4.24)	139-0195-79
$C_{12}H_{14}N_4O_6$			
Butanedioic acid, [(1,2,3,6-tetrahydro-1,3-dimethyl-2,6-dioxo-7H-purin-7-yl)methyl]-	H_2O	273(3.93)	126-0325-79
Inosine, 5'-acetate	EtOH	244(4.03),249(4.03), 274s(3.59)	39-2088-79C
$C_{12}H_{14}N_4S$			
Pyrido[2,3-d]pyrimidin-4-amine, N-cyclobutyl-2-(methylthio)-	0.2M HCl	230(4.17),261(4.08), 294(4.08),294(4.06), 329(4.14),324(4.13)	102-1265-79
	H_2O	225(4.21),270(4.30), 344(4.02)	102-1265-79
	0.2M NaOH	246(4.59),308(4.23)	102-1265-79
$C_{12}H_{14}N_6$			
Imidazo[1,2-c]pteridin-6-amine, N-ethyl-2,3-dimethyl-	pH -3.0	226(4.37),280(4.06), 296(4.08),407(4.22)	18-0867-79
	pH 1.5	219(4.39),255(4.14), 279(4.14),286(4.15), 367(4.07)	18-0867-79
	pH 5.5	227(4.51),257(3.99), 283(3.87),290s(3.86), 363(4.20)	18-0867-79
3H-1,3,4,6-Tetraazacyclopent[e]azulene, 2-amino-3,9-dimethyl-5-(methylamino)-	MeOH	224(4.12),256(4.03), 300(4.65),310s(4.59), 371(4.00),409(4.07)	23-1707-79
	MeOH-acid	221(4.09),247(3.96), 302(4.72),363(3.85), 407(4.24)	23-1707-79
$C_{12}H_{14}N_6O$			
Ethanol, 2-[(2,3-dimethylimidazo[1,2-c]pteridin-6-yl)amino]-	pH -2.5	228(4.43),279(4.10), 297(4.11),404(4.27)	18-0867-79
	pH 1.5	220(4.38),255(4.16), 279(4.15),286(4.14), 364(4.10)	18-0867-79
	pH 5.5	228(4.53),257(4.01), 284(3.89),290s(3.87), 362(4.21)	18-0867-79
$C_{12}H_{14}O$			
6(1H)-Azulenone, 2,3-dihydro-1,4-dimethyl-	EtOH	225s(--),235(4.47), 324(4.205)	102-0279-79
1,4:5,8-Dimethanonaphthalen-2(1H)-one, 3,4,4a,5,8,8a-hexahydro-, endo,exo	isooctane	295(1.60),305(1.58), 316s(--)	44-3908-79

Compound	Solvent	$\lambda_{max}(\log \epsilon)$	Ref.
(cont.)	EtOH	292.5(1.76)	44-3908-79
1,4:5,8-Dimethanonaphthalen-9-one,	isooctane	193(3.80),288(1.62)	44-3908-79
1,4,4a,5,6,7,8,8a-octahydro-, endo,exo-	EtOH	195(3.71),282(1.71)	44-3908-79
3,5-Hexadien-2-ol, 6-phenyl-	EtOH	285(4.36)	12-2523-79
1H-Inden-1-ol, 1-ethenyl-2,3-dihydro-3-methyl-	MeOH	211(3.88),242(3.02), 246(3.02),252(2.93), 260(2.91),267(2.86)	2-0324-79A
1(2H)-Naphthalenone, 3,4-dihydro-4,4-dimethyl-	EtOH	250(4.06),292(3.20)	12-0179-79
$C_{12}H_{14}O_2$			
Benzene, 4-(1,3-butadienyl)-1,2-dimethoxy-	MeOH	233(4.04),272(4.10), 288s(4.07)	12-0071-79
[Bi-1-cyclohexen-1-yl]-3,3'-dione	EtOH	284(4.10)	94-0676-79
Bullvalenedimethanol	MeOH	230(3.51)	89-0311-79
2,4-Cyclopentadiene-1-carboxylic acid, 1-(2-propenyl)-, 2-propenyl ester	EtOH	254(3.06)	1-0256-79
5,9-Epoxy-5H-benzocyclohepten-5-ol, 6,7,8,9-tetrahydro-9-methyl-	hexane	251s(2.48),256(2.67), 262(2.85),268(2.88)	56-1751-79
2,4-Pentanedione, 3-(4-methylphenyl)-	EtOH	288(3.98)	12-1561-79
Tricyclo[4.3.1.0^{7,9}]deca-2,4-dien-10-one, ethylene acetal, exo	EtOH	198(3.45),260s(3.45), 266(3.52),276(3.49), 287(3.19)	44-1294-79
$C_{12}H_{14}O_2S$			
Benzene, [[(2-methyl-1,3-butadienyl)-sulfonyl]methyl]-, (Z)-	EtOH	243(4.33)	70-0594-79
$C_{12}H_{14}O_3$			
Benzenepropanal, 3-methoxy-α,α-dimethyl-β-oxo-	MeOH	216(4.28),245(3.69), 292(3.26)	5-0617-79
2,4-Pentanedione, 3-(4-methoxyphenyl)-	EtOH	232(3.98),286(4.04)	12-1561-79
Tricyclo[4.4.1.1^{3,8}]dodecane-4,5,10-trione	$CHCl_3$	418(1.36)	88-2347-79
$C_{12}H_{14}O_3S$			
3-Penten-2-one, 3-methyl-5-(phenylsulfonyl)-	H_2O	227(4.037)	104-0578-79
$C_{12}H_{14}O_3S_3$			
3-Buten-2-one, 4,4-bis(methylthio)-3-(phenylsulfonyl)-	EtOH	305(3.99)	95-0038-79
$C_{12}H_{14}O_4$			
1,6-Benzodioxocin-7,10-dione, 2,3,4,5-tetrahydro-8,9-dimethyl-	MeCN	272(4.17),403(2.71)	64-0624-79B
Bicyclo[2.2.2]octa-2,7-diene-2-carboxylic acid, 6-hydroxy-4,6-dimethyl-5-oxo-, methyl ester, exo	MeOH	236(3.64),312(2.56)	23-2853-79
Furo[2,3-b]benzofuran-3-ol, 2-ethoxy-2,3,3a,8a-tetrahydro-, cis	CH_2Cl_2	233(3.15),281(3.46), 288(3.43)	39-2664-79C
trans	CH_2Cl_2	233(3.15),281(3.47), 288(3.42)	39-2664-79C
1-Isobenzofurancarboxylic acid, 1,3,3a-7a-tetrahydro-1,5-dimethyl-3-oxo-, methyl ester	MeOH	260(3.59),270(3.56)	23-2853-79
2-Propenal, 3-(3,4,5-trimethoxyphenyl)-	n.s.g.	239(5.22),326(4.30)	12-0653-79
$C_{12}H_{14}O_4S$			
2-Cyclohexen-1-one, 3-(1-oxo-2-cyclo-	EtOH	236(4.17),284(3.63)	94-0676-79

Compound	Solvent	λmax(log ε)	Ref.
hexen-3-yl)sulfonyl- (cont.)			94-0676-79
$C_{12}H_{14}O_5$			
Benzenebutanoic acid, 2-hydroxy-6-meth-oxy-α-methyl-γ-oxo-	EtOH	271(3.81),338(3.28)	102-0311-79
Benzoic acid, 2,4-dimethoxy-6-(2-oxo-propyl)-	MeOH	261(3.94),290(3.67)	39-0337-79C
Carbonic acid, 3-methoxy-5-(2-oxoprop-yl)phenyl methyl ester	EtOH	205(4.33),223s(3.99), 279(3.20)	150-0301-79
2-Oxaspiro[4.5]dec-3-ene-3-carboxylic acid, 1,8-dioxo-, ethyl ester	MeOH	239(3.9)	24-1550-79
$C_{12}H_{14}O_6$			
Benzoic acid, 2-hydroxy-6-(1-hydroxy-2-oxopropyl)-4-methoxy-, methyl ester	MeOH	262(4.19),302(3.88)	39-0337-79C
$C_{12}H_{15}$			
Cycloheptatrienylium, 2-cyclopropyl-1,3-dimethyl-, perchlorate	10% HCl	243(4.61),298(3.64)	39-1005-79B
$C_{12}H_{15}BrN_2O_4$			
2,4(1H,3H)-Pyrimidinedione, 5-bromo-1,3-bis(tetrahydro-2-furanyl)-	pH 1 and 7 (10% EtOH)	285(3.94)	94-0899-79
$C_{12}H_{15}BrN_2O_4S$			
Butanoic acid, 3-[[2-(aminosulfonyl)-5-bromophenyl]imino]-, ethyl ester	pH 1.5	221(4.49),255(3.93), 319(3.50)	104-0121-79
	pH 7	221(4.56),256(4.06), 320(3.69)	104-0121-79
$C_{12}H_{15}BrO$			
Benzene, 1-bromo-4(and 3)-[[(1,1-di-methylethoxy)ethenyl]-, (E)- (4:1 ratio of isomers)	C_6H_{12}	269(4.12)	12-2689-79
$C_{12}H_{15}ClN_2O$			
1H-Indole-3-ethanamine, 6-chloro-5-methoxy-α-methyl-	EtOH	225(4.36),298(3.81), 301(3.81),313s(3.60)	87-0063-79
2,6-Methano-2H-1,3,5-benzoxadiazocin-9-ol, 3,6-dihydro-2,4-dimethyl-, hydrochloride	EtOH	277(3.28),283(3.25)	24-0001-79
Pyrimidine, 4-(4-methoxyphenyl)-5-meth-yl-3,4-dihydro-, hydrochloride	EtOH	246(3.82),273(3.70), 280s(3.66)	24-0001-79
$C_{12}H_{15}ClN_2O_3$			
Hydrazinecarboxylic acid, [(4-chloro-phenyl)ethoxymethylene]-, ethyl ester	EtOH	275(4.30)	4-0403-79
2-Propenoic acid, 3-[4-(aminoiminometh-yl)phenyl]-2-methoxy-, methyl ester, monohydrochloride	n.s.g.	300(4.271)	106-0008-79
$C_{12}H_{15}ClN_2O_4$			
2,4(1H,3H)-Pyrimidinedione, 5-chloro-1,3-bis(tetrahydro-2-furanyl)- (spectra in 10% EtOH)	pH 1	283.5(3.94)	94-0899-79
	pH 7	283.5(3.94)	94-0899-79
	pH 12	283.5(3.71)	94-0899-79
$C_{12}H_{15}ClN_2O_4S$			
Butanoic acid, 3-[[2-(aminosulfonyl)-5-chlorophenyl]imino]-, ethyl ester	pH 1.5	216(4.78),250(4.25), 313(3.93)	104-0121-79
	pH 7	218(4.84),253(4.31), 317(3.83)	104-0121-79

Compound	Solvent	λmax(log ε)	Ref.
$C_{12}H_{15}ClN_8O_5$			
Adenosine, 2-chloro-3'-deoxy-3'-[[(methylnitrosoamino)carbonyl]amino]-	pH 1 and 7	264(4.25)	87-1109-79
	pH 13	261(4.18)	87-1109-79
$C_{12}H_{15}ClO$			
Benzene, 1-chloro-4-[2-(1,1-dimethylethoxy)ethenyl]-, (E)-	C_6H_{12}	270(4.23)	12-0849-79
(Z)-	C_6H_{12}	264(4.59)	12-0849-79
$C_{12}H_{15}Cl_3O_2$			
Benzenemethanol, 3-(1,1-dimethylethyl)-2-hydroxy-α-(trichloromethyl)-	EtOH	224(3.75),287(3.51)	118-0824-79
$C_{12}H_{15}D_3O$			
2(3H)-Naphthalenone, 4,4a,5,6,7,8-hexahydro-3-methyl-3-(methyl-d_3)-	EtOH	237(4.14)	78-0961-79
$C_{12}H_{15}FN_2O_4$			
2,4(1H,3H)-Pyrimidinedione, 5-fluoro-1,3-bis(tetrahydro-2-furanyl)-	pH 1	275(3.90)	94-0899-79
	pH 7	275(3.90)	94-0899-79
(spectra in 10% EtOH)	pH 12	272(3.81)	94-0899-79
$C_{12}H_{15}FN_2O_5$			
Uridine, 5'-deoxy-5-fluoro-2',3'-O-(1-methylethylidene)-	MeOH	204(4.04),267(3.94)	87-1330-79
2,4(1H,3H)-Pyrimidinedione, 1-(5-deoxy-2,3-O-(1-methylethylidene)-β-D-lyxofuranosyl)-5-fluoro-	MeOH	208(3.83),269(3.94)	87-1330-79
$C_{12}H_{15}F_2NO_2S$			
Homocysteine, 2-(difluoromethyl)-S-(phenylmethyl)-	EtOH	260(2.53),266(2.34)	44-2732-79
$C_{12}H_{15}F_2NO_4$			
Tyrosine, α-(difluoromethyl)-3-methoxy-O-methyl-	H_2O	229(3.90),277s(--)	44-2732-79
$C_{12}H_{15}N$			
1H-Indole, 2,3-dihydro-3,3-dimethyl-2-methylene-	pH 1	275(3.72)	88-4407-79
	H_2O	276(3.68)	88-4407-79
$C_{12}H_{15}NO$			
1H-Indole-2-ethanol, 1,3-dimethyl-	EtOH	230(4.48),275s(3.78),298(3.81)	39-2154-79C
5(6H)-Quinolinone, 7,8-dihydro-2,7,7-trimethyl-	pH 1	234(3.84),281(4.06)	39-1411-79C
	H_2O	238(3.95),285(3.90)	39-1411-79C
$C_{12}H_{15}NO_2$			
Acetamide, N-(2-acetyl-4,6-dimethylphenyl)-	EtOH	248s(3.71),296(3.17)	33-0271-79
Bellendine	EtOH	216(4.04),257(4.03)	12-1827-79
2H-Indol-2-one, 1,3-dihydro-3-(2-hydroxyethyl)-1,3-dimethyl-	EtOH	253(3.94),281s(3.22)	23-1694-79
Isobellendine	EtOH	212(4.02),259(4.03)	12-1827-79
2-Propenoic acid, 3-[4-(dimethylamino)phenyl]-, methyl ester, (E)-	MeCN	362(4.42)	88-0863-79
$C_{12}H_{15}NO_3$			
Acetamide, N-[4-(acetoxymethyl)-2-methyl]phenyl]-	EtOH	235(3.93)	33-0271-79

Compound	Solvent	λ max(log ε)	Ref.
Acetamide, N-(2-acetyl-4-methoxyphenyl)-N-methyl-	EtOH	235(3.85),295(3.02)	35-7332-79
Butanoic acid, 2-[[(2-hydroxyphenyl)-methylene]amino]-, methyl ester	MeOH	257(4.15),402(3.43) (calcd.)	137-0118-79
	CCl_4	325(3.67)	137-0118-79
10H-1,4-Dioxino[2,3-b][1,4]benzoxazine, 2,3,4a,10a-tetrahydro-4a,10-dimethyl-	EtOH	243(3.88),290(3.88)	35-7332-79
Ethanone, 1-[5-(acetoxymethyl)-2-amino-3-methylphenyl]-	EtOH	233(4.59),256(3.96), 364(3.82)	33-0271-79
1H-Indole-2-carboxylic acid, 4,5,6,7-tetrahydro-6,6-dimethyl-4-oxo-, methyl ester	MeOH	228(4.26),248(4.07), 285(4.19)	64-0102-79B
2-Pentanone, 4-methyl-3-(4-nitrophenyl)-	hexane	263(4.05)	12-1487-79
2(1H)-Quinolinone, 3,4-dihydro-4,4-dimethoxy-3-methyl-	MeOH	250(4.10),281(3.47), 291(3.37)	94-1813-79
$C_{12}H_{15}NO_4$			
1,2-Benzenedicarboxylic acid, 3-amino-6-ethyl-, dimethyl ester	dioxan	258(3.6),352(3.7)	5-1085-79
2H-Indol-2-one, 1,3-dihydro-3-hydroperoxy-3-(2-methoxyethyl)-1-methyl-	EtOH	258(3.82),286(3.15)	35-7332-79
$C_{12}H_{15}NO_5$			
D-Arabinitol, 2,5-anhydro-1-deoxy-1-(2,5-dioxo-3-pyrrolidinylidene)-3,4-O-(1-methylethylidene)-, (E)-	EtOH	219(4.04)	33-0977-79
Furo[3,4-c]pyridine-4-propanoic acid, 1,3-dihydro-7-hydroxy-1-methoxy-6-methyl-	MeOH	285(3.84)	88-2603-79
α-D-erythro-Pentofuranose, 3,5-dideoxy-5-(2,5-dioxo-3-pyrrolidinylidene)-1,2-O-(1-methylethylidene)-, (E)-	EtOH	223(4.12)	33-0977-79
β-L-threo-Pentofuranose, 3,5-dideoxy-5-(2,5-dioxo-3-pyrrolidinylidene)-1,2-O-(1-methylethylidene)-, (E)-	EtOH	224(4.15)	33-0977-79
$C_{12}H_{15}NS$			
2-Azetidinethione, 1,3,3-trimethyl-4-phenyl-	$CHCl_3$	217(4.16),238(4.03), 263(4.22),339s(1.75)	5-1702-79
$C_{12}H_{15}N_2O_2S$			
Thiazolo[3,4-a]pyridinium, 3-(dimethylamino)-1-(ethoxycarbonyl)-, bromide	n.s.g.	248(3.37),335(3.7), 435(3.47)	2-0486-79B
$C_{12}H_{15}N_2O_3$			
2H-Isoindol-2-yloxy, 1,3-dihydro-1,1,3-3-tetramethyl-5-nitro-	C_6H_{12}	262(4.00)	22-0048-79
	MeOH	215(3.82),265(3.76)	22-0048-79
$C_{12}H_{15}N_3$			
2-Pentenenitrile, 3-[(2-aminophenyl)-amino]-4-methyl-	EtOH	205(4.31),240(4.32), 265(4.26),295s(3.97)	39-2289-79C
Spiro[1,2,4-benzotriazine-3(4H),1'-cyclohexane]	pH 1	234(4.12),300s(3.30), 345(3.90),510(3.32)	4-1001-79
	EtOH	226(4.33),248s(4.02), 286(3.35),358(3.34), 454(3.04)	4-1001-79
$C_{12}H_{15}N_3O$			
Acetamide, N-[4,5-dihydro-1-(phenylmethyl)-1H-pyrazol-3-yl]-	EtOH	265(4.01)	150-0801-79

Compound	Solvent	λ_{max}(log ε)	Ref.
1-Hexanone, 6-azido-1-phenyl-	heptane	238(4.20),276(2.95), 325(1.70)	35-0378-79
1,2,4-Oxadiazole-3-ethanamine, 5-methyl-N-(4-methylphenyl)-	EtOH	282(4.22)	150-0801-79
1,2,4-Oxadiazole-3-ethanamine, 5-methyl-N-(phenylmethyl)-, monohydrochloride	EtOH	257(2.36)	150-0801-79
Pyrrolo[2,3-b]indol-2(1H)-one, 1-amino-3,3a,8,8a-tetrahydro-3a,8-dimethyl-	MeOH	252(3.89),302(3.37)	5-0927-79
$C_{12}H_{15}N_3OS$			
4-Imidazolidinone, 5-(1-ethyl-4(1H)-pyridinylidene)-1,3-dimethyl-2-thioxo-	EtOH	440s(4.67),457(4.68)	73-1413-79
4-Thiazolidinone, 2-[[4-(dimethylamino)phenyl]imino]-3-methyl-	H_2O	280(3.92)	104-1344-79
	MeOH	262(4.00),305(4.01)	104-1344-79
	dioxan	267(3.97),307(4.09)	104-1344-79
	70% dioxan	262(3.97),305(4.04)	104-1344-79
4(5H)-Thiazolone, 2-[[4-(dimethylamino)-phenyl]methylamino]-	H_2O	237(4.28),257(4.33)	104-1344-79
	MeOH	234(4.23),265(4.35)	104-1344-79
	dioxan	230(4.15),268(4.37)	104-1344-79
	70% dioxan	235(4.21),265(4.30)	104-1344-79
$C_{12}H_{15}N_3O_2$			
Acetamide, N-[4,5-dihydro-1-(4-methoxyphenyl)-1H-pyrazol-3-yl]-	EtOH	292.5(4.12)	150-0801-79
$C_{12}H_{15}N_3O_2S$			
1,2,3-Thiadiazolium, 5-[(dimethylamino)-methyl]-4-hydroxy-3-(4-methoxyphenyl)-, hydroxide, inner salt	EtOH	220(4.20),302(3.76), 385(4.08)	39-2349-79C
$C_{12}H_{15}N_3O_4$			
Benzenamine, N-cyclohexyl-2,4-dinitro-	EtOH	262(3.94),350(4.24), 405s(3.79)	73-1613-79
Benzenamine, N-cyclohexyl-2,6-dinitro-	EtOH	233(4.35),426(3.77)	73-1613-79
1,2-Hydrazinedicarboxylic acid, 1-[2-(2-pyridinyl)-2-propenyl]-, dimethyl ester	MeOH	253(1.77),280s(4.2), 286(4.12)	103-0518-79
Pyrido[3,2-c]pyridazine-1,2-dicarboxylic acid, 3,4-dihydro-6-methyl-, dimethyl ester	MeOH	232(4.05),282(3.71)	103-0518-79
Pyrido[3,2-c]pyridazine-1,2-dicarboxylic acid, 3,4-dihydro-7-methyl-, dimethyl ester	MeOH	234(3.96),283(3.68)	103-0518-79
Pyrido[3,2-c]pyridazine-1,2-dicarboxylic acid, 3,4-dihydro-8-methyl-, dimethyl ester	MeOH	238(3.92),278(3.65)	103-0518-79
Pyrido[3,2-c]pyridazine-1,2-dicarboxylic acid, 3,8a-dihydro-8a-methyl-, dimethyl ester	MeOH	266(3.57)	103-0518-79
1H-Pyrrolo[3,2-d]pyrimidine-7-carboxylic acid, 6-ethyl-2,3,4,5-tetrahydro-1,3-dimethyl-2,4-dioxo-, methyl ester	EtOH	234(4.23),275(3.60)	44-3830-79
1H-Pyrrolo[3,2-d]pyrimidine-7-carboxylic acid, 2,3,4,5-tetrahydro-1,3,5-6-tetramethyl-2,4-dioxo-, methyl ester	EtOH	237(4.34),275(3.90)	44-3830-79
$C_{12}H_{15}N_3O_5$			
4,12-Epoxy-5H-1,3-dioxolo[4,5-f]pyrimi-	MeOH	275(4.32)	44-1424-79

Compound	Solvent	λ_{max}(log ε)	Ref.
do[1,6-a][1,3]diazocine-8,10(6H,9H)-dione, 3a,4,12,12a-tetrahydro-2,2-dimethyl- (cont.)			44-1424-79
Glutamic acid, N-[[(4-aminophenyl)amino]carbonyl]-	pH 13	247(4.18),290s(3.20)	87-0874-79
7H-Pyrrolo[2,3-d]pyrimidine, 7-α-D-arabinofuranosyl-4-methoxy-	MeOH	217(4.31),262(3.88), 270s(3.86)	24-3432-79
β-	MeOH	217(4.30),262(3.87), 270s(3.86)	24-3432-79
$C_{12}H_{15}N_3O_6$			
2-Butenedioic acid, 2-[(2,4-dimethoxy-5-pyrimidinyl)amino]-, dimethyl ester, (Z)-	pH 1	245(3.86),315(3.97)	44-0435-79
	pH 7	235(3.90),321(4.08)	44-0435-79
	pH 11	240(3.79),299(4.06)	44-0435-79
$C_{12}H_{15}N_5O$			
1H-Azepine-2,3,4(5H)-trione, dihydro-, 3-hydrazone 4-(phenylhydrazone)	EtOH	260(4.21),355(4.04)	103-0780-79
1,2,4-Triazin-5(2H)-one, 3-amino-6-(1-aminoethyl)-2-(phenylmethyl)-	EtOH	214(4.36),263(3.85)	39-1120-79C
$C_{12}H_{15}N_5O_3$			
Butanoic acid, 4-[(1,4-dihydro-6,7-dimethyl-4-oxo-2-pteridinyl)amino]-	pH -4.0	219(4.22),253(4.14), 339(3.98)	18-2933-79
	pH 0.25	219(4.26),253(4.05), 293(3.73),323(3.93), 397(3.26)	18-2933-79
	pH 6.0	223(4.24),279(4.25), 350(3.86)	18-2933-79
	pH 11.0	259(4.34),365(3.94)	18-2933-79
$C_{12}H_{15}N_5O_3S$			
9H-Purine-9-acetic acid, α-(acetylamino)-1,6-dihydro-α-methyl-6-thioxo-, ethyl ester	MeOH	324(4.38)	44-2019-79
$C_{12}H_{15}N_5O_4$			
Adenosine, 2'-deoxy-, 3'-acetate	EtOH	260(4.16)	39-2088-79C
Adenosine, 2'-deoxy-, 5'-acetate	EtOH	260(4.18)	39-2088-79C
Butanedioic acid, [(6-amino-9H-purin-9-yl)methyl]-, dimethyl ester	MeOH	262(4.15)	126-2323-79
$C_{12}H_{15}N_5O_5$			
Guanosine, 2'-deoxy-, 3'-acetate	EtOH	254(4.14)	39-2088-79C
Guanosine, 2'-deoxy-, 5'-acetate	EtOH	260(4.00)	39-2088-79C
9H-Purin-6-amine, 9-(2-O-acetyl-β-D-arabinofuranosyl)-	MeOH	259(4.18)	87-0273-79
9H-Purin-6-amine, 9-(3-O-acetyl-β-D-arabinofuranosyl)-	MeOH	259(4.18)	87-0273-79
$C_{12}H_{15}N_5O_6$			
4,14-Epoxy-1,2,9-metheno-4H-1,3-dioxolo[4,5-j][1,2,3,6,8]pentaazacyclotridecine-6,8(5H,7H)-dione, 2-ethoxy-3a,13,14,14a-tetrahydro-	MeOH	none above 210 nm	44-1424-79
9H-Purine-2-carboxylic acid, 6-amino-9-β-D-ribofuranosyl-, methyl ester	H_2O	260s(3.99),264(4.00), 296(3.78)	94-0183-79
9H-Purine-8-carboxylic acid, 6-amino-9-β-D-ribofuranosyl-, methyl ester	0.5M HCl	244(3.61),279(4.17)	94-0183-79
	H_2O	227(4.23),298(4.06)	94-0183-79
Thymidine, 5'-azido-3'-O-(carboxymethyl)-5'-deoxy-	pH 5	267(3.99)	39-1389-79C
	pH 13	267(3.88)	39-1389-79C

Compound	Solvent	$\lambda_{max}(\log \epsilon)$	Ref.
$C_{12}H_{15}OS$			
Thiophenium, tetrahydro-1-(2-oxo-2-phenyl)-, tetrafluoroborate (and other anions)	MeOH	248(4.01),300(3.67)	47-2877-79
$C_{12}H_{16}$			
1,4:5,8-Dimethanonaphthalene, 1,2,3,4-4a,5,8,8a-octahydro-, endo,exo	isooctane	204.4(3.69)	44-3908-79
	EtOH	204.0(3.68)	44-3908-79
Naphthalene, 1,2,3,4-tetrahydro-2,7-dimethyl-	EtOH	264(2.75),270(2.92), 273(2.90),279(2.98)	39-1837-79C
$C_{12}H_{16}BrNO$			
2H-Pyrrolium, 3,4-dihydro-1-hydroxy-2,2-dimethyl-5-phenyl-, bromide	EtOH	225(3.88),293(4.15)	12-1795-79
$C_{12}H_{16}BrNO_2$			
1-Butanone, 1-(4-bromophenyl)-4-[(2-hydroxyethyl)amino]-, hydrochloride	EtOH	269(4.04)	145-0983-79
$C_{12}H_{16}BrN_3O_5$			
Hexanoic acid, 6-[[(5-bromo-3,4-dihydro-2,4-dioxo-1(2H)-pyrimidinyl)-acetyl]amino]-	H_2O	282(3.94)	73-1634-79
	pH 8.7	280(3.88)	73-1634-79
	pH 12	279(3.85)	73-1634-79
$C_{12}H_{16}ClNO$			
2(1H)-Quinolinone, 3-chloro-4a,5,6,7-tetrahydro-1,4a,8-trimethyl-	EtOH	283(3.46)	4-0065-79
$C_{12}H_{16}ClN_3O_5$			
Thymidine, 5'-[(chloroacetyl)amino]-5'-deoxy-	EtOH	267(3.97)	39-1389-79C
$C_{12}H_{16}Cl_2N_4O$			
Ethanone, 2-amino-1-[5-amino-1-(phenylmethyl)-1H-imidazol-4-yl]-, dihydrochloride	H_2O	303(4.12)	35-6127-79
$C_{12}H_{16}Cl_3N_3O_4$			
Morpholine, 4,4'-(3,4,4-trichloro-2-nitro-1,3-butadienylidene)bis-	MeOH	368(3.91)	104-0981-79
$C_{12}H_{16}FNO_2$			
1-Butanone, 1-(4-fluorophenyl)-4-[(2-hydroxyethyl)amino]-, oxalate	EtOH	259(3.97)	145-0983-79
$C_{12}H_{16}FN_3O_5$			
Hexanoic acid, 6-[[(5-fluoro-3,4-dihydro-2,4-dioxo-1(2H)-pyrimidinyl)acetyl]amino]-	H_2O	272(3.98)	73-1634-79
	pH 8.7	271(3.91)	73-1634-79
	pH 12	270(3.90)	73-1634-79
1(2H)-Pyrimidineacetic acid, 5-fluoro-3,4-dihydro-2,4-dioxo-α-[(1-oxobutyl)amino]-, ethyl ester	MeOH	266(3.94)	44-2019-79
$C_{12}H_{16}IN_3O_5$			
Hexanoic acid, 6-[[(3,4-dihydro-5-iodo-2,4-dioxo-1(2H)-pyrimidinyl)acetyl]-amino]-	H_2O	291(3.88)	73-1634-79
	pH 8.7	283(3.80)	73-1634-79
	pH 12	280(3.79)	73-1634-79
$C_{12}H_{16}NO$			
2H-Pyrrolium, 3,4-dihydro-1-hydroxy-2,2-dimethyl-5-phenyl-, bromide	EtOH	225(3.88),293(4.15)	12-1795-79

Compound	Solvent	λ max(log ε)	Ref.
$C_{12}H_{16}NO_2$			
Isoquinolinium, 3,4-dihydro-6,7-dimethoxy-2-methyl-, chloride	EtOH	210s(4.37),247(4.31), 308(4.06),360(4.06)	39-0283-79C
	EtOH-NaOH	282(3.60)	39-0283-79C
Pyridinium, 1-(4,4-dimethyl-3-oxo-1-pentenyl)-3-hydroxy-, chloride	EtOH	257(4.18),318(3.54), 375(3.18)	56-0057-79
$C_{12}H_{16}N_2$			
1H-Benzimidazole, 1-ethyl-2-propyl-	EtOH	249(3.81),253(3.81), 264(3.61),275(3.77), 282(3.80)	65-1225-79
$C_{12}H_{16}N_2O$			
1H-Indole-3-ethanamine, 5-methoxy-1-methyl-	EtOH	228(4.38),282(3.81), 305(3.70)	87-0063-79
2(1H)-Quinolinone, 1-(dimethylamino)-7,8-dihydro-7-methyl-	MeOH	205(3.86),231(3.79), 280(4.08)	64-0102-79B
$C_{12}H_{16}N_2O_2$			
Benzenemethanamine, N,N-diethyl-α-(nitromethylene)-, (Z)-	EtOH	208(4.00),241(3.68), 355(4.33)	28-0255-79B
Ethenamine, N,N-diethyl-2-nitro-2-phenyl-, (E)-	EtOH	210(4.16),364(4.24)	28-0255-79B
2-Pentanone, 4-[(3-amino-4-methoxyphenyl)imino]-	heptane	319(4.21)	40-1437-79
	EtOH	325(4.28)	40-1437-79
	dioxan	322(4.25)	40-1437-79
	70% dioxan	323(4.28)	40-1437-79
2-Propenoic acid, 3-(ethylamino)-3-(2-pyridinyl)-, ethyl ester	ether	250(3.93),313(3.98)	22-0559-79
2-Pyridinepropanamide, N,N-diethyl-β-oxo-	ether	313(4.23)	22-0559-79
2,5(1H,6H)-Quinolinedione, 1-(dimethylamino)-7,8-dihydro-7-methyl-	MeOH	207(3.96),282(4.28)	64-0102-79B
$C_{12}H_{16}N_2O_2S_2$			
Cyclobutenediylium, 1,3-dimercapto-2,4-dimorpholino-, dihydroxide, bis(inner salt)	CH_2Cl_2	242(4.29),282(3.93), 356(4.19),426(4.70), 488(2.53)	5-0595-79 +24-0990-79
$C_{12}H_{16}N_2O_3$			
Acetamide, N-[3-(1,1-dimethylethyl)-4-nitrophenyl]-	C_6H_{12}	238(4.1),270s(3.7), 335(3.0)	5-0554-79
	MeOH	241(4.1),280s(3.6), 345(3.2)	5-0554-79
Acetamide, N-[4-(1,1-dimethylethyl)-3-nitrophenyl]-	EtOH	243(4.3),300s(2.9)	5-0554-79
	ether	242(4.4),300s(2.9)	5-0554-79
2-Butanone, 3,3-dimethyl-, O-(4-nitrophenyl)oxime, (E)-	hexane	301(4.22)	12-2413-79
Hydrazinecarboxylic acid, (ethoxyphenylmethylene)-, ethyl ester	EtOH	265(4.29)	4-0403-79
1,8-Naphthyridine-3-carboxylic acid, 1,4,5,6,7,8-hexahydro-7-methyl-4-oxo-, ethyl ester	EtOH	266(3.96),327(4.16), 337(4.18),357(4.15)	142-1407-79
2-Pentanone, 4-methyl-3-(4-nitrophenyl)-, oxime	MeOH	273(4.05)	12-1487-79
$C_{12}H_{16}N_2O_4$			
Benzene, 1-[1-(1-methylethyl)-2-nitropropyl]-4-nitro-, (R*,R*)-	hexane	262(4.06)	12-1487-79
(R*,S*)-	hexane	262(4.08)	12-1487-79

Compound	Solvent	$\lambda_{max}(\log \epsilon)$	Ref.
Benzofuro[2,3-d]pyrimidine-2,4(3H,4aH)-dione, 4b,5,6,7,8,8a-hexahydro-4b-hydroxy-3,4a-dimethyl-	MeOH	260(4.20)	54-0341-79
4-Pyrimidinecarboxylic acid, 1-cyclohexyl-1,2,3,6-tetrahydro-3-methyl-2,6-dioxo-	pH 1	275(3.93)	44-0970-79
	pH 13	274(3.90)	44-0970-79
2,4(1H,3H)-Pyrimidinedione, 1,3-bis-(tetrahydro-2-furanyl)- (in 10% EtOH)	pH 1,7 and 12	269(3.92)	94-0899-79
$C_{12}H_{16}N_2O_4S$			
Butanoic acid, 3-[[2-(aminosulfonyl)-phenyl]imino]-, ethyl ester	pH 1.5	208(4.53),245(4.07), 307(3.64)	104-0120-79
	pH 7	210(4.58),249(4.15), 315(3.63)	104-0120-79
$C_{12}H_{16}N_2O_5$			
Benzene, 1-(1,1-dimethylethyl)-2-methoxy-4-methyl-3,5-dinitro-	hexane	210s(4.28),225s(4.07), 263(3.81),340s(2.88)	24-3946-79
	MeOH	222s(4.04),263(3.73), 354s(2.83)	24-3946-79
2-Furancarboxylic acid, 5-(3,4-dihydro-5-methyl-2,4-dioxo-1(2H)-pyrimidinyl)tetrahydro-, ethyl ester	pH 2	270(3.89)	103-0926-79
	pH 7	270(3.92)	103-0926-79
	pH 10	270(3.86)	103-0926-79
Hydroperoxide, 2,3-dihydro-2-methoxy-1,2,3-trimethyl-5-nitro-1H-indol-3-yl	EtOH	248(3.61),254(3.62), 260(3.54),379(4.05)	35-7332-79
$C_{12}H_{16}N_2O_6$			
Butanedioic acid, [(3,4-dihydro-5-methyl-2,4-dioxo-1(2H)-pyrimidinyl)methyl]-, dimethyl ester	MeOH	269(3.97)	126-0325-79
2,4(1H,3H)-Pyrimidinedione, 1-(2,3-diacetoxypropyl)-5-methyl-	n.s.g.	208(4.06),268(4.03)	128-0281-79
Thymidine, 3'-acetate	EtOH	265(3.98)	39-2088-79C
Thymidine, 5'-acetate	EtOH	266(4.02)	39-2088-79C
Uridine, 2',3'-O-(1-methylethylidene)-	MeOH	260(3.97)	44-4713-79
$C_{12}H_{16}N_2O_6S$			
Thymidine, 5'-(carboxymethyl)-5'-thio-	H_2O	267(3.98)	87-0621-79
$C_{12}H_{16}N_2S_2$			
Cyclobutenediylium, 1,3-dimercapto-2,4-dipyrrolidino-, dihydroxide, bis(inner salt)	CH_2Cl_2	230(4.30),276(4.01), 370(4.16),440(4.66), 490s(2.99)	5-0595-79 +24-0990-79
$C_{12}H_{16}N_4$			
1H-Pyrrolo[2,3-d]pyrimidin-4-amine, N-cyclopentyl-2-methyl-	pH 1	281(4.13)	102-0217-79
	H_2O	280(4.15)	102-0217-79
	pH 13	279(4.21)	102-0217-79
1H-Pyrrolo[2,3-d]pyrimidin-4-amine, 2-methyl-N-(3-methyl-2-butenyl)-	pH 1	280(4.16)	102-0217-79
	pH 13	279(4.17)	102-0217-79
2,4-Quinazolinediamine, N,N,N',N'-tetramethyl-	EtOH	238(4.41),270(4.30), 355(3.67)	114-0029-79A
$C_{12}H_{16}N_4OS$			
4H-Pyrazolo[3,4-d]pyrimidine, 1-cyclopentyl-1,5-dihydro-5-methyl-3-(methylthio)-	MeOH	230(4.11),250(3.95)	83-0586-79

Compound	Solvent	λmax(log ε)	Ref.
$C_{12}H_{16}N_4O_2S$			
Isothiazolo[3,4-d]pyrimidine-4,6(5H,7H)-dione, 5,7-dimethyl-3-piperidino-	EtOH	238(4.19),280(4.03), 315(3.97)	95-0989-79
$C_{12}H_{16}N_4O_2S_2$			
Cyclobuta[1,2-d:3,4-d']dipyrimidine-4,8(1H,4aH)-dione, 4b,5,8a,8b-tetrahydro-4b,8b-dimethyl-2,6-bis(methylthio)-	pH 13	237(3.80)	56-0529-79
$C_{12}H_{16}N_4O_5S$			
9H-Purine, 9-[4-C-(hydroxymethyl)-β-D-erythro-pentofuranosyl]-6-(methylthio)-	pH 13	223(4.07),287(4.27), 292(4.27)	44-1301-79
$C_{12}H_{16}N_4O_6$			
9H-Purine, 9-[4-C-(hydroxymethyl)-β-D-erythro-pentofuranosyl]-6-methoxy-	H_2O	250(4.00)	44-1301-79
	pH 13	250(4.01)	44-1301-79
$C_{12}H_{16}N_4O_9$			
Glucose, 2,4-dinitrophenylhydrazone	EtOH	347(4.16)	104-1237-79
$C_{12}H_{16}N_4S$			
Pyrido[2,3-d]pyrimidin-4-amine, N-butyl-2-(methylthio)-	0.2M HCl	225(4.25),265(4.97), 290(4.11),325(4.17), 339(4.15)	102-1265-79
	H_2O	224(4.18),268(4.30), 337(4.97)	102-1265-79
	0.2M NaOH	269(4.23),340(4.91)	102-1265-79
Pyrido[2,3-d]pyrimidin-4-amine, N-(1-methylpropyl)-2-(methylthio)-	0.2M HCl	226(4.13),265(4.10), 291(4.05),325(4.12), 339(4.10)	102-1265-79
	H_2O	225(4.17),268(4.28), 337(3.95)	102-1265-79
	0.2M NaOH	269(4.15),341(3.83)	102-1265-79
Pyrido[2,3-d]pyrimidin-4-amine, N-(2-methylpropyl)-2-(methylthio)-	0.2M HCl	226(4.20),265(4.14), 292(4.10),326(4.17), 339(4.14)	102-1265-79
	H_2O	225(4.19),268(4.30), 339(4.14)	102-1265-79
	0.2M NaOH	269(4.31),338(4.00)	102-1265-79
$C_{12}H_{16}N_5O_7P$			
Guanosine, 1-methyl-, cyclic 3',5'-(methyl phosphate)	H_2O	257(4.32)	130-0009-79
9H-Purin-2-amine, 6-methoxy-9-[3,5-O-(methoxyphosphinylidene)-β-D-ribofuranosyl]-	H_2O	246(4.23),279(4.14)	130-0009-79
$C_{12}H_{16}N_6O_3$			
9H-Purine-9-acetic acid, α-(acetylamino)-6-amino-α-methyl-, ethyl ester	pH 1	257(4.16)	44-2019-79
	pH 12	261(4.15)	44-2019-79
	MeOH	259(4.16)	44-2019-79
$C_{12}H_{16}N_6O_5$			
9H-Purine-2-methanimidic acid, 6-amino-9-β-D-ribofuranosyl-, methyl ester	H_2O	263s(4.02),267(4.03), 293(3.76)	94-0183-79
9H-Purine-8-methanimidic acid, 6-amino-9-β-D-ribofuranosyl-, methyl ester	H_2O	223(4.21),278s(4.00), 284(4.03)	94-0183-79

Compound	Solvent	λ_{max}(log ε)	Ref.
$C_{12}H_{16}N_8O_5$			
Adenosine, 5'-deoxy-5'-[[(methylnitrosoamino)carbonyl]amino]-	pH 1 and 7	226(4.24)	87-1109-79
	pH 13	258(4.17)	87-1109-79
$C_{12}H_{16}O$			
Bicyclo[4.3.1]deca-2,4,7-triene, 9-methoxy-5-methyl-	C_6H_{12}	253(3.85)	5-0533-79
Bicyclo[4.3.1]deca-2,4,7-triene, 9-methoxy-6-methyl-	C_6H_{12}	245s(3.76),253(3.81), 264(3.64)	5-0533-79
Bicyclo[4.3.1]deca-2,4,8-triene, 7-methoxy-6-methyl-	C_6H_{12}	253(3.78)	5-0533-79
1,4:5,8-Dimethanonaphthalen-2(1H)-one, octahydro-, endo,exo	isooctane	294(1.51),303(1.48), 317s(--)	44-3908-79
	EtOH	290.5(1.62)	44-3908-79
1,4:5,8-Dimethanonaphthalen-9-one, perhydro-, endo,exo	isooctane	184(3.40),296(1.32)	44-3908-79
	EtOH	293(1.42)	44-3908-79
5-Hexen-2-ol, 6-phenyl-	EtOH	251(4.22)	12-2523-79
$C_{12}H_{16}OS_3$			
Benzenecarbo(dithioperoxo)thioic acid, 4-methoxy-, 1,1-dimethylethyl ester	EtOH	245(3.90),341(4.34), 520(2.51),720(3.32)	44-0569-79
$C_{12}H_{16}O_2$			
2,6-Naphthalenedione, 1,3,4,7,8,8a-hexahydro-1,8a-dimethyl-	EtOH	234(3.98)	94-0331-79
Propanoic acid, 2,2-dimethyl-, 2-methylphenyl ester	EtOH	263(2.58),269(2.57)	22-0373-79
Propanoic acid, 2,2-dimethyl-, 3-methylphenyl ester	EtOH	263(2.49),269(2.41)	22-0373-79
Propanoic acid, 2,2-dimethyl-, 4-methylphenyl ester	EtOH	265(2.71),271(2.66)	22-0373-79
1-Propanone, 1-(2-hydroxy-4-methylphenyl)-2,2-dimethyl-	EtOH	263(4.24),327(3.54)	22-0373-79
1-Propanone, 1-(2-hydroxy-5-methylphenyl)-2,2-dimethyl-	EtOH	257(3.75),342(3.35)	22-0373-79
1-Propanone, 1-(4-hydroxy-3-methylphenyl)-2,2-dimethyl-	EtOH	225(4.00),277(4.05)	22-0373-79
[5.3.2]Propellane-8,11-dione	MeOH	296(1.71)	44-4557-79
Spiro[naphthalen-1(2H),2'-oxiran]-6(7H)-one, 3,4,8,8a-tetrahydro-8a-methyl-, cis	EtOH	236(4.22)	88-0565-79
$C_{12}H_{16}O_3$			
4-Azuleneacetic acid, 1,2,3,5,6,7,8,8a-octahydro-8-oxo-	ether	212(3.75),285(2.16)	35-3261-79
1H-2-Benzopyran-8-ol, 3,4-dihydro-6-methoxy-3,7-dimethyl-	MeOH	223s(4.43),285(3.89)	98-1347-79
4H-1-Benzopyran-4-one, 6-ethyl-5,6,7,8-tetrahydro-3-(hydroxymethyl)-	n.s.g.	219(3.72),258(3.73)	39-1481-79C
Butanoic acid, 3-hydroxy-3-(2-methylphenyl)-, methyl ester	EtOH	210(3.86)	117-0255-79
3-Buten-1-ol, 4-(3,4-dimethoxyphenyl)-, (E)-	MeOH	214(4.32),261(4.23), 300(3.74)	12-0071-79
Cyclopentaneacetic acid, 1-(1-cyclopenten-1-yl)-2-oxo-	ether	300(2.30)	35-3261-79
Tricyclo[5.3.0.0^{1,6}]decane-6-acetic acid, 2-oxo-	ether	284(1.57)	35-3261-79
$C_{12}H_{16}O_3S$			
1H-2-Benzothiopyran-7(3H)-one, 4β-acetoxy-4,4a,5,6-tetrahydro-4aβ-methyl-	EtOH	237(4.23)	39-0990-79C

Compound	Solvent	λ_{max}(log ϵ)	Ref.
$C_{12}H_{16}O_4$			
Benzene, 1,2,3-trimethoxy-5-(2-methoxy-ethenyl)-	EtOH	223(4.45),271(4.31)	150-0301-79
3,5-Cyclohexadiene-1,2-dione, 4,5-diPrO-	EtOH	290(4.15),415(2.73)	18-2169-79
11-Oxatricyclo[4.3.1.1^{2,5}]undec-3-en-10-one, 3,4-dimethoxy-, (1α,2β,5β,6α)-	ether	298(4.9),309(2.9)	33-2325-79
$C_{12}H_{16}S_3$			
Benzeneethane(dithioperoxo)thioic acid, 1,1-dimethylethyl ester	EtOH	258(3.89),315(4.04), 490(--)	44-0569-79
$C_{12}H_{17}$			
Cycloheptatrienylium, 1,3-dimethyl-2-(1-methylethyl)-	10% HCl	245(4.58),297(3.68)	39-1005-79B
Cycloheptatrienylium, 1,2,3,4,5-penta-methyl-, perchlorate	10% HCl	251(4.85),307(3.86)	78-0949-79
Cycloheptatrienylium, 1,2,3,4,6-penta-methyl-, perchlorate	10% HCl	248(4.83),304(3.81), 312s(--)	78-0949-79
Cycloheptatrienylium, 1,2,3,5,6-penta-methyl-, perchlorate	10% HCl	245(4.83),303(3.79), 312s(--)	78-0949-79
$C_{12}H_{17}BrN_2O_5$			
Glucose, (4-bromophenyl)hydrazone	EtOH	284(4.32)	104-1237-79
$C_{12}H_{17}BrO$			
2,5-Cyclohexadien-1-one, 4-(bromometh-yl)-2,3,4,5,6-pentamethyl-	heptane	240(4.12),266s(3.56)	104-1310-79
$C_{12}H_{17}BrO_5$			
α-D-xylo-Oct-5-enofuranos-7-ulose, 6-bromo-5,6,8-trideoxy-3-O-methyl-1,2-O-(1-methylethylidene)-, (Z)-	EtOH	245(3.83)	33-1303-79
$C_{12}H_{17}ClO$			
2,5-Cyclohexadien-1-one, 4-(chlorometh-yl)-2,3,4,5,6-pentamethyl-	heptane	239(4.11),262s(3.61)	104-1310-79
$C_{12}H_{17}FO$			
Bicyclo[3.3.1]non-3-en-2-one, 6-fluoro-1,3,4-trimethyl-	EtOH	248(4.10)	70-1636-79
$C_{12}H_{17}IN_2S$			
1H-Imidazolium, 4,5-dihydro-1,3-dimeth-yl-2-[2-(methylthio)phenyl]-, iodide	EtOH	217(4.52),247(4.21), 297s(3.29)	18-3640-79
$C_{12}H_{17}N$			
Benzenamine, 4-(2-butenyl)-2,6-dimeth-yl-	MeOH	238(3.98),288(3.33)	33-2613-79
Benzenamine, 2,6-dimethyl-4-(1-methyl-2-propenyl)-	hexane	239(4.04),286(3.39)	33-2613-79
	MeOH	238(4.04),287(3.35)	33-2613-79
$C_{12}H_{17}NO$			
Ethanone, 1-(1,2,4a,7,8,8a-hexahydro-2-methyl-4-isoquinolinyl)-, cis	EtOH	308(4.41)	44-0124-79
$C_{12}H_{17}NOS$			
2-Propanesulfenamide, N-(3,5-dimethyl-4-oxo-2,5-cyclohexadien-1-ylidene)-2-methyl-	hexane	405(4.38)	138-1077-79

Compound	Solvent	λ_{max}(log ε)	Ref.
$C_{12}H_{17}NO_2$			
Acetic acid, (hexahydro-2,6-methano-1H-pyrrolizin-1-ylidene)-, ethyl ester	hexane	216(4.14)	142-0343-79
Acetic acid, (hexahydro-2,6-methano-1H-pyrrolizin-1-ylidene)-, ethyl ester	hexane	208(4.04),260(3.71)	142-0343-79
9-Azabicyclo[3.3.1]non-2-ene, 2,9-diacetyl-	EtOH	226(4.02)	56-0027-79
8-Azaspiro[4.5]deca-6,9-diene-8-carboxylic acid, ethyl ester	isooctane	232(4.11)	44-2522-79
Bellendine, 2,3-dihydro-	EtOH	270(3.83)	12-1827-79
1,3-Dioxolan-2-amine, N,N-dimethyl-2-(4-methylphenyl)-	n.s.g.	221(3.8),240s(3.0)	44-1855-79
Isobellendine, 5,11-dihydro-	EtOH	266(3.83)	12-1827-79
5H-2-Pyrindine, 4-(dimethoxymethyl)-6,7-dihydro-7-methyl-, (R)-	EtOH	261(3.26),269(3.20)	106-0577-79
$C_{12}H_{17}NO_3$			
2-Azabicyclo[2.2.2]oct-5-ene-2-carboxylic acid, 7-acetyl-, ethyl ester	MeCN	199(3.60)	44-0124-79
2H-1,4-Benzoxazine, 3,4-dihydro-2,3-dimethoxy-2,4-dimethyl-	EtOH	241(3.57),285(3.20)	35-7332-79
Carbamic acid, [(5-acetyl-2,4-cyclohexadien-1-yl)methyl]-, ethyl ester	MeCN	299(3.98)	44-0124-79
2-Furancarbonitrile, tetrahydro-5-methoxy-3,3,5-trimethyl-2-(3-oxo-1-propenyl)-	MeOH	214(3.80)	107-0081-79
$C_{12}H_{17}NO_4$			
Propanoic acid, 2-amino-3-(3,4-dimethoxyphenyl)-, methyl ester, hydrochloride	EtOH	279(3.48)	44-2732-79
$C_{12}H_{17}NS_2$			
Spiro[2H-3,1-benzothiazine-2,1'-cyclopentane]-4(1H)-thione	EtOH	235s(3.44),341(3.62), 408(5.34)	150-1732-79
$C_{12}H_{17}N_2O_2$			
Benzeneethanaminium, N,N,N-trimethyl-β-methylene-4-nitro-, iodide	n.s.g.	295(4.11)	35-3097-79
$C_{12}H_{17}N_2S$			
1H-Imidazolium, 4,5-dihydro-1,3-dimethyl-2-[2-(methylthio)phenyl]-, iodide	EtOH	217(4.52),247(4.21), 297s(3.29)	18-3640-79
$C_{12}H_{17}N_3O_3$			
Benzofuro[2,3-d]pyrimidine-2,4(3H,4aH)-dione, 4b-amino-4b,5,6,7,8,8a-hexahydro-3,4a-dimethyl-, (4aα,4bβ,8aα)-	MeOH	260(4.17)	54-0341-79
Carbamic acid, [[nitroso(phenylmethyl)amino]methyl]-, 1-methylethyl ester	EtOH	234s(3.91),366(1.79)	94-0682-79
$C_{12}H_{17}N_3O_4$			
Benzenamine, 2,6-dinitro-N,N-dipropyl-	EtOH	292(3.22),332s(2.81)	73-1613-79
Benzenamine, N-(1-ethylbutyl)-2,4-dinitro-, (R)-	C_6H_{12}	255(4.00),335(4.26), 404(3.74)	78-2413-79
	MeOH	264(3.98),353(4.25), 410s(3.81)	78-2413-79
$C_{12}H_{17}N_3O_4S$			
1-Azabicyclo[3.2.0]hept-2-ene-2-carboxylic acid, 6-(1-hydroxyethyl)-3-[[2-	H_2O	299(3.99)	87-1435-79

Compound	Solvent	$\lambda_{max}(\log \epsilon)$	Ref.
(iminomethyl)amino]ethyl]thio]-7-oxo-			87-1435-79
$C_{12}H_{17}N_3O_5$			
1(2H)-Pyrimidineacetic acid, α-(acetyl-amino)-3,4-dihydro- ,5-dimethyl-2,4-dioxo-, ethyl ester	MeOH	264(4.00)	44-2019-79
1(2H)-Pyrimidineacetic acid, α-(acetyl-methylamino)-α-methyl-2,4-dioxo-, ethyl ester	MeOH	260(4.03)	44-2019-79
5-Pyrimidinepentanoic acid, 1,4-dihydro-6-hydroxy-4-oxo-2-[(1-oxopropyl)amino]-	H_2O	266(4.00)	73-1634-79
	pH 8.7	266(3.98)	73-1634-79
	pH 12	264(3.93)	73-1634-79
Thymidine, 5'-(acetylamino)-5'-deoxy-	H_2O	267(3.97)	87-0621-79
$C_{12}H_{17}N_3O_6$			
1(2H)-Pyrimidinepropanoic acid, α-[[(1,1-dimethylethoxy)carbonyl]-amino]-3,4-dihydro-2,4-dioxo-	n.s.g.	266(3.98)	65-0989-79
β-D-Ribofuranose, 5-deoxy-5-[4-(methoxycarbonyl)-1H-1,2,3-triazol-1-yl]-2,3-O-(1-methylethylidene)-	MeOH	214(3.94)	44-1424-79
Thymidine, 5'-amino-3'-O-(carboxymethyl)-5'-deoxy-	pH 5	267(3.97)	39-1389-79C
	pH 13	268(3.89)	39-1389-79C
Uridine, 5-(acetylaminomethyl)-2'-deoxy-	pH 1	267(4.00)	87-0621-79
	pH 12	267(3.87)	87-0621-79
$C_{12}H_{17}N_3O_7$			
Glucose, (4-nitrophenyl)hydrazone	EtOH	380(4.25)	104-1237-79
$C_{12}H_{17}N_4$			
Pyrido[1,2-a]pyrimidin-5-ium, 2,4-bis-(dimethylamino)-, perchlorate	EtOH	228(4.67),283(1.84)	114-0029-79A
$C_{12}H_{17}N_5O_2$			
3H-Pyrazolo[3',4':3,4]pyrrolo[2,3-d]-pyrimidine-7,9(3aH,8H)-dione, 4,5,5a,6-tetrahydro-6,8-dimethyl-5-(2-propenyl)-	EtOH	223(3.82)	4-0293-79
$C_{12}H_{17}N_7O_3$			
L-Alanine, N-[3-(6-amino-9H-purin-9-yl)alanyl]-, methyl ester, dihydrochloride	EtOH	260(4.12)	65-0994-79
$C_{12}H_{17}N_7O_4$			
Adenosine, 3'-deoxy-3'-[[(methylamino)-carbonyl]amino]-	pH 1	257(4.15)	87-1109-79
	pH 7	259(4.16)	87-1109-79
	pH 13	260(4.16)	87-1109-79
$C_{12}H_{17}OS_2$			
Sulfonium, dimethyl-, 1-(dimethylsulfonio)-2-oxo-2-phenylethylide, tetrafluoroborate	n.s.g.	220s(4.055),255(4.031)	104-0332-79
$C_{12}H_{17}O_2P$			
Benzoic acid, 4-(diethylphosphinyl)-, methyl ester	C_6H_{12}	284(3.70)	65-0479-79
$C_{12}H_{17}O_4PS_2$			
Benzeneethane(dithioic) acid, α-(di-	isooctane	244s(3.51),319(3.93),	5-1715-79

Compound	Solvent	λmax(log ε)	Ref.
methoxyphosphinyl)-α-methoxy-, dimethyl ester (cont.)		476(1.42)	5-1715-79
$C_{12}H_{17}O_7P$			
Benzoic acid, 2-(diethoxyphosphinyl)-3,6-dihydroxy-, methyl ester	EtOH	209(4.26),322(3.83)	33-2350-79
$C_{12}H_{18}$			
Cyclopropane, 1,1,2,2-tetramethyl-3-(3-methyl-1,2-butadienylidene)-	heptane	236s(3.59),264(4.03), 306s(2.18)	35-4772-79
$C_{12}H_{18}ClN_3O_2$			
4-Cyclopentene-1,3-dione, 2-[bis(dimethylamino)methylene]-4-chloro-5-(dimethylamino)-	isoPrOH	252(4.23),313(4.48)	104-0454-79
$C_{12}H_{18}CrNaO_8$			
Sodium bis(1-hydrocyclopentanecarboxylato)oxochromate monohydrate	H_2O	250(3.87),350(3.17), 519(2.36),750(1.63), 800(1.58)	35-3206-79
$C_{12}H_{18}N_2O$			
Benzenamine, N,N-diethyl-3,5-dimethyl-4-nitroso-	EtOH	416(4.53),695(1.88)	104-1437-79
Pentanal, 5-hydroxy-, methylphenylhydrazone	EtOH	278(4.29)	104-1237-79
Pentanal, 5-hydroxy-, (4-methylphenyl)-hydrazone	EtOH	278(4.24)	104-1237-79
Phenol, 2-(1,1-dimethylethyl)-6-methyl-4-(methylazo)-	C_6H_{12}	396(2.30)	24-2913-79
	acetone	394(2.37)	24-2913-79
2(1H)-Pyrazinone, 6-(2-methyl-1-propenyl)-3-(2-methylpropyl)-	EtOH	248(3.80),342(4.06)	94-1378-79
Pyridine, 2-(2-ethyl-1-piperidinyl)-, 1-oxide, (R)-	MeOH	332(3.53)	4-0591-79
Pyridine, 2-(3-ethyl-1-piperidinyl)-, 1-oxide, (R)-	MeOH	254(4.22),312(3.57)	4-0297-79
1H-Pyrrole-2-methanol, α-[(3,4-dihydro-3,3-dimethyl-2H-pyrrol-5-yl)methyl]-	MeOH	215(3.89),292(3.43), 330(3.27),395(2.79)	83-0498-79
$C_{12}H_{18}N_2O_2$			
Benzenamine, 4-nitro-N-(1,2,2-trimethylpropyl)-, (R)-	MeOH	234(3.90),265s(3.26), 300s(3.08),315s(3.20), 392(4.34)	35-5186-79
1H-Indole-3-carboxylic acid, 1-amino-4,5,6,7-tetrahydro-2-methyl-, ethyl ester	MeOH	219(4.15),231(4.04), 267(3.63)	88-2965-79
2-Pyridinepropanoic acid, β-(ethylamino)-, ethyl ester	ether	260(3.85)	22-0559-79
2(1H)-Quinolinone, 1-(dimethylamino)-5,6,7,8-tetrahydro-5-hydroxy-7-methyl-	MeOH	205(3.84),235(3.86), 313(3.80)	64-0102-79B
$C_{12}H_{18}N_2O_3$			
Ethanol, 2,2'-[(3,5-dimethyl-4-nitrosophenyl)imino]bis-	EtOH	415(4.65),706(1.85)	104-1437-79
2-Propenoic acid, 3-[1,2-dimethyl-2-(3-oxo-1-cyclohexen-1-yl)hydrazino]-, methyl ester, (E)-	MeOH	263(4.34),291(4.48)	24-3237-79
7H-Pyrazolo[1,5-c][1,3]oxazine-3-carboxylic acid, 4,5-dihydro-2,7,7-trimethyl-, ethyl ester	EtOH	233(3.96)	118-0440-79

Compound	Solvent	$\lambda_{max}(\log \epsilon)$	Ref.
$C_{12}H_{18}N_2O_4$			
1H-Benzimidazole, 4,5,6,7-tetrahydro-1-α-D-ribofuranosyl-	MeOH	225(3.41)	44-4378-79
$C_{12}H_{18}N_2O_4S$			
Thymidine, 3'-deoxy-3'-(ethylthio)-	H_2O	267(3.99)	87-0621-79
Thymidine, 5'-deoxy-5'-(ethylthio)-	H_2O	267(3.99)	87-0621-79
$C_{12}H_{18}N_2O_5$			
Glucose phenylhydrazone	EtOH	278(4.25)	104-1237-79
2,5,8,11,14-Pentaoxa-16,18-diazabicyclo[13.3.1]nonadeca-1(19),15,17-triene	EtOH	241(3.40),252(3.18)	44-3812-79
Uridine, 2'-deoxy-3-propyl-	H_2O	263(3.92)	87-0621-79
$C_{12}H_{18}N_2O_5S$			
Thymidine, 5'-deoxy-5'-(ethylsulfinyl)-	H_2O	267(3.98)	87-0621-79
Thymidine, 5'-S-(2-hydroxyethyl)-5'-thio-	H_2O	267(3.99)	87-0621-79
$C_{12}H_{18}N_2O_6$			
1,2,3,4-Butanetetrol, 1-[5-(3,4-dihydroxy-1-butenyl)pyrazinyl]-	H_2O	238(4.20),299(3.85)	136-0205-79J
$C_{12}H_{18}N_6O$			
9H-Purine-9-acetamide, 6-amino-N,N-diethyl-α-methyl-	pH 1	260(4.14)	121-0573-79
	H_2O	260(4.17)	121-0573-79
	pH 13	260(4.26)	121-0573-79
	EtOH	260(3.97)	121-0573-79
	CF_3CH_2OH	260(4.16)	121-0573-79
dimer	pH 1	260(4.18)	121-0573-79
	H_2O	260(4.14)	121-0573-79
	pH 13	260(4.17)	121-0573-79
	EtOH	260(3.91)	121-0573-79
	CF_3CH_2OH	260(4.12)	121-0573-79
9H-Purine-9-propanamide, 6-amino-N,N-diethyl-	pH 1	260(4.15)	47-1739-79
$C_{12}H_{18}N_6O_2S$			
2H-Pyrazolo[3,4-d]pyrimidine-2-carbothioamide, 5,7-diethyl-4,5,6,7-tetrahydro-N-methyl-3-(methylamino)-4,6-dioxo-	MeOH	258(4.41),278(4.38), 324(3.54)	94-1328-79
$C_{12}H_{18}N_6O_5$			
Urea, N-[5-[4-(aminocarbonyl)-1H-1,2,3-triazol-1-yl]-5-deoxy-2,3-O-(1-methylethylidene)-β-D-ribofuranosyl-	MeOH	210(4.14)	44-1424-79
$C_{12}H_{18}N_6O_6$			
Urea, [5-[4-(aminocarbonyl)-1H-1,2,3-triazol-1-yl]-5-deoxy-2,3-O-(ethoxymethylene)-β-D-ribofuranosyl-	MeOH	211(4.13)	44-1424-79
$C_{12}H_{18}O$			
6(1H)-Azulenone, 2,3,4,5,7,8-hexahydro-1,4-dimethyl-, (1R-cis)-	EtOH	215(4.42)	102-0279-79
Benzenepentanol, α-methyl-	EtOH	212(3.78)	12-2523-79
Bicyclo[2.2.2]oct-5-en-2-one, 5-methyl-7-(1-methylethyl)-, (1R,4R,7R)-(+)-	C_6H_{12}	287(2.18),296(2.27), 305(2.24),317(2.00)	33-2061-79

Compound	Solvent	λmax(log ε)	Ref.
Bicyclo[2.2.2]oct-5-en-2-one, 6-methyl-8-(1-methylethyl)-, (1S,4R,8R)-(-)-	C_6H_{12}	289(2.00),298(2.08), 308(2.05),313(1.81)	33-2061-79
1,3-Cyclohexadiene-1-carboxaldehyde, 5-ethyl-6-propyl-	EtOH	312(3.98)	32-0195-79
[5.3.2]Propellan-11-one	MeOH	302(1.51)	44-4557-79
$C_{12}H_{18}O_2$			
3H-2-Benzopyran-3-one, 1,5,6,7,8,8a-hexahydro-4-(1-methylethyl)-	MeOH	232(3.85)	146-0031-79
3H-2-Benzopyran-3-one, 1,5,6,7,8,8a-hexahydro-4-propyl-	MeOH	234(3.88)	146-0031-79
3-Butenoic acid, 4-cyclohexyl-2-methylene-, methyl ester	heptane	247(3.4)	24-3480-79
1-Cyclohexen-1-ol, 5-methyl-2-(1-methylethenyl)-, acetate, (R)-	EtOH	223(3.76)	18-3127-79
1-Cyclohexen-1-ol, 3-methyl-6-(1-methylethylidene)-, acetate, (R)-	EtOH	241(3.53)	18-3127-79 +18-3129-79
2-Cyclohexen-1-one, 4-hydroxy-3,5,5-trimethyl-4-(1-propenyl)-	MeOH	236(3.99)	107-0081-79
2-Cyclohexen-1-one, 6-hydroxy-3,5,5-trimethyl-6-(1-propenyl)-	MeOH	235(3.96)	107-0081-79
2,4-Hexadien-1-ol, 4-ethenyl-2,5-dimethyl-, acetate, (E)-	EtOH	239.5(4.14)	44-2441-79
1(7),5-p-Menthadien-2-ol, acetate, (2S,4R)-(-)-	EtOH	232(4.30)	33-2061-79
2,4-Pentadienoic acid, 5-cyclohexyl-2-methyl-	MeCN	263(4.39)	88-2317-79
$C_{12}H_{18}O_3$			
Benzenebutanol, 3,4-dimethoxy-	MeOH	229(3.92),280(3.48)	12-0071-79
1-Cyclononene-1-carboxylic acid, 9-oxo-, ethyl ester, (E)-	EtOH	220(3.79)	33-2630-79
Cyclopentaneacetic acid, 1-cyclopentyl-2-oxo-, (R)-	ether	294(1.58)	35-3261-79
2-Propenal, 3-(3-acetoxymethyl)-2,2-dimethylcyclopropyl]-2-methyl-, [1R-[1α(E),3β]]-	EtOH	246(4.23)	44-2441-79
2H-Pyran-2-one, 5,6-dihydro-6-(3-hydroxy-1-heptenyl)-	EtOH	205(1.025)	102-1215-79
$C_{12}H_{18}O_5$			
α-D-lyxo-Oct-5-enofuranosid-7-ulose, methyl 5,6,8-trideoxy-2,3-O-(1-methylethylidene)-, (E)-	EtOH	220(4.04)	33-2091-79
(Z)-	hexane	215(3.89)	33-2091-79
α-D-ribo-Oct-5-enofuranos-7-ulose, 5,6,8-trideoxy-3-O-methyl-1,2-O-(1-methylethylidene)-, (E)-	EtOH	224(4.05)	33-2091-79
α-D-xylo-Oct-5-enofuranos-7-ulose, 5,6,8-trideoxy-3-O-methyl-1,2-O-(1-methylethylidene)-, (E)-	EtOH	217(3.81)	33-2091-79
(Z)-	EtOH	212(3.79)	33-2091-79
1,3,6-Trioxaspiro[4.4]non-7-ene-8-carboxylic acid, 2,2,7-trimethyl-, ethyl ester, (±)-	EtOH	248(4.05)	136-0055-79B
$C_{12}H_{19}ClN_2O$			
Pyrazine, 3-chloro-2,5-bis(2-methylpropyl)-, 1-oxide	EtOH	237(4.27),275(4.13), 305(3.54),314(3.51)	94-1316-79
Pyrazine, 3-chloro-2,5-bis(2-methylpropyl)-, 4-oxide	EtOH	234(4.34),272(4.01), 304(3.50),314s(3.46)	94-1378-79

Compound	Solvent	$\lambda_{max}(\log \epsilon)$	Ref.
Pyrazinemethanol, 6-chloro- -(1-methylethyl)-5-(2-methylpropyl)-	EtOH	215(4.01),281(3.94), 302s(3.53)	94-1378-79
$C_{12}H_{19}ClN_2O_2$			
Pyrazine, 3-chloro-2,5-bis(2-methylpropyl)-, 1,4-dioxide	EtOH	247(4.43),313(4.29)	94-1316-79
Pyrazinemethanol, 3-chloro-α-(1-methylethyl)-5-(2-methylpropyl)-, 1-oxide	EtOH	210(4.16),236(4.23), 276(3.99)	94-1316-79
$C_{12}H_{19}N$			
Benzenamine, 4-butyl-2,6-dimethyl-	MeOH	238(3.98),288(3.32)	33-2613-79
Benzenamine, 2,6-dimethyl-4-(1-methylpropyl)-	hexane	236(4.02),287(3.38)	33-2613-79
$C_{12}H_{19}NO$			
Acetamide, N-1,3-butadienyl-N-cyclohexyl-	MeOH	256(3.97)	88-0981-79
4(1H)-Pyridinone, 1-cyclohexyl-2,3-dihydro-6-methyl-	MeOH	328(4.26)	78-1899-79
5(1H)-Quinolinone, 2,3,4,6,7,8-hexahydro-2,7,7-trimethyl-	pH 1	292(4.28)	39-1411-79C
	H_2O	307(4.38)	39-1411-79C
$C_{12}H_{19}NO_2$			
Bicyclo[2.2.1]heptane-2,3-dione, 1,7,7-trimethyl-, 3-(O-ethyloxime), (E)-	C_6H_{12}	246(4.03),347(1.49)	39-0151-79B
(Z)-	C_6H_{12}	265(3.89),376(2.00), 396(2.03)	39-0151-79B
Carbamic acid, 1,3-butadienylcyclohexyl-, methyl ester	MeOH	257(4.50)	88-0981-79
Carbamic acid, 1,3-butadienyl-4-hexenyl-, methyl ester	MeOH	258(4.43)	88-0981-79
$C_{12}H_{19}NO_4$			
4-Pyridinecarboxylic acid, 1,2,3,6-tetrahydro-1-(tert-butoxycarbonyl)-, methyl ester	MeOH	222(3.90)	111-0157-79
3-Pyrrolidinecarboxylic acid, 5-hexyl-2,4-dioxo-, methyl ester	MeOH	230(4.07),257(3.85)	142-0477-79B
$C_{12}H_{19}NO_5$			
Propanedioic acid, (4-morpholinylmethylene)-, diethyl ester	hexane	220(3.70),240s(--), 283(4.27)	131-0077-79D
	EtOH	288(--)	131-0077-79D
$C_{12}H_{19}N_3O_3$			
1(2H)-Pyrimidineacetamide, N,N-diethyl-3,4-dihydro-α,5-dimethyl-2,4-dioxo-	pH 1	270(4.01)	121-0573-79
	H_2O	270(4.01)	121-0573-79
	pH 13	265(3.93)	121-0573-79
	EtOH	270(3.79)	121-0573-79
	CF_3CH_2OH	270(3.94)	121-0573-79
dimer	pH 1	270(3.94)	121-0573-79
	H_2O	270(3.97)	121-0573-79
	pH 13	265(3.91)	121-0573-79
	EtOH	270(3.76)	121-0573-79
	CF_3CH_2OH	270(3.94)	121-0573-79
$C_{12}H_{19}N_3O_4$			
Thymidine, 5'-deoxy-5'-(ethylamino)-	pH 1	267(3.97)	87-0621-79
$C_{12}H_{19}N_3O_6$			
Uridine, 3-(3-aminopropyl)-, HCl salt	MeOH	264(3.90)	24-0700-79

Compound	Solvent	λ_{max}(log ε)	Ref.
$C_{12}H_{19}N_5O_5$			
1(2H)-Pyrimidinepropanoic acid, α-[[(1,1-dimethylethoxy)carbonyl]-amino]-3,4-dihydro-2,4-dioxo-, hydrazide	pH 12	264(3.87)	65-0989-79
$C_{12}H_{19}N_7O_5$			
Urea, [5-deoxy-5-[4-(hydrazinocarbonyl)-1H-1,2,3-triazol-1-yl]-2,3-O-(1-methylethylidene)-β-D-ribofuranosyl]-	MeOH	210(4.03)	44-1424-79
$C_{12}H_{19}P$			
Phosphine, bis(1-methylethyl)diphenyl-	C_6H_{12}	210s(4.03),219s(3.86), 254(3.28),266f(3.26)	39-0501-79B
	12M HCl	219(3.98),266f(2.90)	39-0501-79B
$C_{12}H_{20}Cl_3N_3O_2$			
1,3-Butadiene-1,1-diamine, 3,4,4-trichloro-N,N'-bis(1,1-dimethylethyl)-2-nitro-	EtOH	225(4.08),342(3.95)	104-0039-79
1,3-Butadiene-1,1-diamine, 3,4,4-trichloro-N,N,N',N'-tetraethyl-2-nitro-	MeOH	365(4.14)	104-0981-79
$C_{12}H_{20}CrNaO_7$			
Sodium bis(2-ethyl-2-hydroxybutyrato)-oxochromate (monohydrate)	H_2O	250(3.81),350(3.08), 510(2.23),740(1.61), 750(1.61),800(1.60)	35-3206-79
$C_{12}H_{20}N_2$			
Pyrazine, 2,3,5,6-tetraethyl-	EtOH	282(3.891),301s(3.373)	12-1281-79
$C_{12}H_{20}N_2O$			
4-Piperidinone, 1-methyl-3-[(1-piperidinyl)methylene]-	EtOH	329(4.23)	4-0177-79
$C_{12}H_{20}N_2O_2$			
Pyrazinemethanol, α-(1-methylethyl)-5-(2-methylpropyl)-, 1-oxide	EtOH	229(4.22),270(4.02)	94-1316-79
$C_{12}H_{20}N_2O_3$			
2(1H)-Pyrazinone, 1-hydroxy-6-(1-hydroxy-2-methylpropyl)-3-(2-methylpropyl)-, (±)-	EtOH	238(3.95),345(3.63)	94-1316-79
$C_{12}H_{20}N_2O_4$			
2(1H)-Pyrazinone, 1-hydroxy-6-(1-hydroxy-2-methylpropyl)-3-(2-methylpropyl)-, 4-oxide	EtOH	230(4.18),259(4.09), 296(3.85),362(3.96)	94-1316-79
$C_{12}H_{20}N_2O_7$			
1,2,3,4-Butanetetrol, 1-[[5-(2,3,4-trihydroxybutyl)pyrazinyl]-	H_2O	273(4.21)	136-0205-79J
isomer 5b	H_2O	274(4.8)	136-0205-79J
isomer 6b	H_2O	274(4.4)	136-0205-79J
$C_{12}H_{20}N_3$			
Hydrazinium, 2-[(dimethylamino)methylene]-1-ethyl-1-methyl-1-phenyl-, iodide	H_2O	228(4.40)	104-2073-79

Compound	Solvent	$\lambda_{max}(\log \epsilon)$	Ref.
$C_{12}H_{20}N_5O_{13}P_3S$			
Adenosine, 5'-(tetrahydrogen triphosphate), 8-ethoxy-, tetrasodium salt	pH 7	281(4.27)	87-1529-79
$C_{12}H_{20}N_6O_2$			
1,3-Propanediol, 2-[[4,6-bis(1-aziridinyl)-1,3,5-triazin-2-yl]amino]-2-ethyl-	EtOH	222(4.92)	104-1144-79
$C_{12}H_{20}O$			
2-Cyclohexen-1-one, 3-methyl-4-(3-methylbutyl)-	hexane	226(4.15)	39-1837-79C
2-Cyclohexen-1-one, 3-methyl-4-pentyl-	hexane	226(4.19)	39-1837-79C
2-Cyclopenten-1-one, 2-hexyl-3-methyl-	MeOH	239(4.04)	146-0100-79
$C_{12}H_{20}OSi$			
1(3aH)-Pentalenone, 4,5,6,6a-tetrahydro-6a-methyl-2-(trimethylsilyl)-	EtOH	228(3.88)	33-0852-79
2-Propyn-1-one, 1-cyclohexyl-3-(trimethylsilyl)-	EtOH	218s(3.74),226(3.86), 235(3.80)	33-0852-79
2-Propyn-1-one, 1-(1-methylcyclopentyl)-3-(trimethylsilyl)-	EtOH	221s(3.69),226(3.81), 235(3.74)	33-0852-79
Spiro[4.4]non-2-en-1-one, 2-(trimethylsilyl)-	EtOH	226(3.86)	33-0852-79
$C_{12}H_{20}O_2$			
2(5H)-Furanone, 5-octyl-	MeOH	217(4.16)	35-1544-79
$C_{12}H_{20}O_2S_2$			
7H-1,4-Dithiepin-7-one, 2,3-dihydro-5-(6-hydroxyheptyl)-	MeOH	226(3.74),237(3.67), 262(3.44),312(3.40)	39-0323-79C
$C_{12}H_{20}O_3$			
2-Heptenoic acid, 7-oxo-2-propyl-, ethyl ester, (E)-	n.s.g.	217(3.98),290s(--)	118-0279-79
(Z)-	n.s.g.	217(3.93),290s(--)	118-0279-79
2-Hexenoic acid, 2-(2-methylpropyl)-6-oxo-, ethyl ester, (E)-	n.s.g.	217(4.06),290(1.64)	118-0279-79
(Z)-	n.s.g.	217(3.95),290(1.67)	118-0279-79
$C_{12}H_{20}O_3S$			
7H-1,4-Oxathiepin-7-one, 2,3-dihydro-5-(6-hydroxyheptyl)-	MeOH	257(4.03)	39-0323-79C
$C_{12}H_{20}O_5$			
2-Cyclobuten-1-one, 2,3,4,4-tetraethoxy-	EtOH	251(4.09),296s(2.42)	44-1208-79
2H-Pyran-2-one, 5,6-dihydro-6-(1,2,3-trihydroxyheptyl)-	EtOH	205(0.977)	102-1215-79
$C_{12}H_{20}S_2$			
Spiro[2H-1,5-benzodithiepin-3(4H),1'-cyclobutane], hexahydro-, cis	EtOH	214(3.06)	49-0279-79
trans	EtOH	212(2.96)	49-0279-79
Spiro[2H,6H-cyclopenta[b][1,4]dithiepin-3(4H),1'-cyclopentane], tetrahydro-, trans	EtOH	212(3.21)	49-0279-79
$C_{12}H_{20}S_3Si$			
Silane, tris(ethylthio)phenyl-	hexane	218s(--),240s(3.43), 266(2.84),273(2.70)	114-0195-79D

Compound	Solvent	λmax(log ε)	Ref.
$C_{12}H_{21}N$			
1H-Azepine, 1-(2,4-hexadienyl)hexahydro-	EtOH	228(4.48)	104-1041-79
$C_{12}H_{21}NO$			
Morpholine, 4-(1-cycloocten-1-yl)-	MeCN	230(3.6)	24-2997-79
6-Oxa-1-azabicyclo[3.1.0]hexane, 5-(1,1-dimethylethyl)-4-ethylidene-2,2-dimethyl-	EtOH	209(3.61)	12-2041-79
2H-Pyrrole, 5-(1,1-dimethylethyl)-4-ethylidene-3,4-dihydro-2,2-dimethyl-, 1-oxide	EtOH	280(4.27)	12-2025-79
$C_{12}H_{21}NO_2$			
2H-Pyrrole, 5-(1,1-dimethylethyl)-4-ethenyl-3,4-dihydro-4-hydroxy-2,2-dimethyl-, 1-oxide	EtOH	239(4.00)	12-2025-79
$C_{12}H_{21}NO_3$			
2H-Pyrrole-5-propanoic acid, 3,4-dihydro-α-hydroxy-α,3,3-trimethyl-, ethyl ester	MeOH	203(3.05),220s(2.79)	83-0498-79
$C_{12}H_{21}N_2O_5PS$			
Phosphorothioic acid, O-(5-ethoxy-1,6-dihydro-1-methyl-6-oxo-4-pyridazinyl) O-ethyl O-(1-methylethyl) ester	MeOH	212(4.35),287(3.73)	73-1761-79
$C_{12}H_{22}NOS$			
Sulfonium, dimethyl[2-(4-morpholinyl)-1-cyclohexen-1-yl]-, chloride	MeCN	211(3.5),285(3.1)	24-2997-79
fluorosulfate	MeCN	212(3.5),287(3.2)	24-2997-79
$C_{12}H_{22}N_2$			
1H-Benzimidazole, 2-(1-ethylpropyl)-3a,4,5,6,7,7a-hexahydro-	EtOH	221(3.61)	39-2289-79C
$C_{12}H_{22}N_2O_3$			
Propanamide, 2-(methoxymethylene)-N-(diisopropylaminocarbonyl)-	MeOH	251.0(4.114)	73-0269-79
$C_{12}H_{22}N_4$			
Butanedinitrile, 2,3-bis[(1,1-dimethylethyl)amino]-	hexane	215(3.03)	44-1273-79
$C_{12}H_{22}O_5S_3$			
α-D-Galactopyranoside, methyl 6-O,4-S-[bis(methylthio)methylene]-2,3-di-O-methyl-4-thio-	MeOH	205(3.00)	136-0127-79G
α-D-Glucopyranoside, methyl 4-O,6-S-[bis(methylthio)methylene]-2,3-di-O-methyl-6-thio-	MeOH	206(2.98)	136-0127-79G
$C_{12}H_{23}NO_2$			
2H-Pyrrol-4-ol, 5-(1,1-dimethylethyl)-4-ethyl-3,4-dihydro-2,2-dimethyl-, 1-oxide	EtOH	238(4.00)	12-2025-79
$C_{12}H_{23}N_3$			
2-Hexenenitrile, 3-[(2-amino-2-methylpropyl)amino]-4-ethyl-	EtOH	260(4.20)	39-2289-79C

Compound	Solvent	λ_{max}(log ε)	Ref.
$C_{12}H_{23}N_3O$			
1H-Imidazole, 4-[[(1,1-dimethylethyl)-imino]methyl]-2,5-dihydro-2,2,5,5-tetramethyl-, 3-oxide	EtOH	286(4.15)	103-0092-79
$C_{12}H_{24}N_2$			
1,6-Diazabicyclo[4.4.4]tetradecane	isooctane	233(3.91),261s(3.58)	35-3651-79
$C_{12}H_{24}N_6O_2$			
1,3-Propanediol, 2-[[4,6-bis(dimethyl-amino)-1,3,5-triazin-2-yl]amino]-2-ethyl-	EtOH	222(4.93)	104-1144-79
$C_{12}H_{26}GeS$			
Germane, [(3,3-dimethyl-1-butenyl)-thio]triethyl-, (E)-	hexane	238(3.96)	70-1479-79
$C_{12}H_{26}N_2O_2$			
5-Isoxazolidinamine, N,2,4-triethyl-N-hydroxy-3-propyl-	EtOH	231(3.20)	73-2221-79
$C_{12}H_{26}SSi$			
Silane, [(3,3-dimethyl-1-butenyl)thio]-triethyl-, trans	hexane	233(3.88)	70-1479-79
$C_{12}H_{27}PS_3$			
Phosphorotrithious acid, tributyl ester	hexane	202(4.32),228s(3.93), 278s(3.18)	65-1760-79
$C_{12}H_{30}N_2P_2$			
Hypophosphonous diamide, hexaethyl-	hexane	262(2.26)	22-0241-79I
$C_{12}H_{30}OSi_2$			
Disiloxane, hexaethyl-	heptane	188(3.59),200s(--)	65-1333-79
	MeCN	188(3.72),198s(--)	65-1333-79
$C_{12}H_{36}Ge_4N_4$			
2-Tetrazene, 1,1,4,4-tetrakis(trimeth-ylgermyl)-, (E)-	pentane	254(3.26),298(3.49)	24-2718-79
$C_{12}H_{36}N_4Si_4$			
2-Tetrazene, 1,1,4,4-tetrakis(trimeth-ylsilyl)-	pentane	239(3.74),254(3.99)	24-2718-79
$C_{12}H_{36}N_4Sn_4$			
2-Tetrazene, 1,1,4,4-tetrakis(trimeth-ylstannyl)-, (E)-	pentane	262(3.52),314(4.24)	24-2718-79
$C_{12}H_{36}O_6Si_6$			
Cyclohexasiloxane, dodecamethyl-	heptane	186(2.54),198s(--)	65-1333-79

Compound	Solvent	λ_{max}(log ε)	Ref.
$C_{13}H_2F_{10}S$			
Benzene, [[(pentafluorophenyl)methyl]-thio]-	n.s.g.	217(4.11),270(3.62)	70-0315-79
$C_{13}H_4Cl_4O_2S_2$			
Spiro[1,3-benzodioxole-2,3'-[3H-1,2]-benzodithiole], 4,5,6,7-tetrahydro-	C_6H_{12}	302(3.71)	2-0131-79B
$C_{13}H_5ClO_4$			
6H-Dibenzo[b,d]pyran-6,7,10-trione, 2-chloro-	EtOH	218(4.64),277(4.10), 375(3.84),393(3.83)	33-2833-79
6H-Dibenzo[b,d]pyran-6,7,10-trione, 3-chloro-	EtOH	205(4.40),233(4.07), 275(3.83),392(3.66)	33-2833-79
6H-Dibenzo[b,d]pyran-6,7,10-trione, 4-chloro-	EtOH	216(4.40),375(3.69), 392(3.69)	33-2833-79
$C_{13}H_5Cl_3O$			
9H-Fluoren-9-one, 1,2,3-trichloro-	MeOH	215(4.45),259(4.65), 268(4.89),292(3.45), 303(3.49),311s(--), 318(3.28),335(3.08)	44-2391-79
$C_{13}H_5F_4NO$			
Benzoxazole, 4,5,6,7-tetrafluoro-2-phenyl-	EtOH	236(3.99),283(4.40), 288(4.40),293(4.40)	18-0516-79
$C_{13}H_5F_4NS$			
Benzothiazole, 4,5,6,7-tetrafluoro-2-phenyl-	EtOH	253(4.08),295(4.30)	18-0516-79
$C_{13}H_6BrN$			
1-Acenaphthylenecarbonitrile, 2-bromo-	CH_2Cl_2	332(4.03)	44-1359-79
$C_{13}H_6ClN_5O_3$			
1H-Pyrido[2',3':5,6][1,4]oxazino[2,3-b]quinoxaline, 9-chloro-8-nitro-	MeOH	275(4.31),335(4.01)	4-1025-79
$C_{13}H_6F_2O$			
9H-Fluoren-9-one, 2,7-difluoro-	dioxan	249(4.66),257(4.80), 279s(3.60),290(3.59), 302(3.43),318s(2.94), 338s(2.59),398(2.38)	24-3490-79
$C_{13}H_6F_4N_2$			
1H-Benzimidazole, 4,5,6,7-tetrafluoro-2-phenyl-	EtOH	242(4.14),288(4.24), 293(4.25)	18-0516-79
$C_{13}H_6N_2O_2S$			
Thiazolo[3,2-a]perimidine-9,10-dione	EtOH	231(4.60),280(4.42), 320(4.08)	83-0776-79
$C_{13}H_6N_6$			
Acenaphtheno[1,2-e]tetrazolo[1,5-b]-[1,2,4]triazine	MeOH	233(4.88),293(4.45), 310s(4.37)	83-0147-79
$C_{13}H_7ClN_4O$			
1H-Pyrido[2',3':5,6][1,4]oxazino[2,3-b]quinoxaline, 9-chloro-	MeOH	230(4.45),272(3.53), 378(3.91)	4-1025-79

Compound	Solvent	λ_{max}(log ε)	Ref.
$C_{13}H_7ClO_4$			
6H-Dibenzo[b,d]pyran-6-one, 2-chloro-7,10-dihydroxy-	EtOH	215(4.53),232(4.52),264(3.90),274(3.94),373(4.09)	33-2833-79
6H-Dibenzo[b,d]pyran-6-one, 3-chloro-7,10-dihydroxy-	EtOH	211(4.71),237(4.80),275(4.26),375(4.37)	33-2833-79
6H-Dibenzo[b,d]pyran-6-one, 4-chloro-7,10-dihydroxy-	EtOH	215(4.49),238(4.48),270(3.99),375(4.06)	33-2833-79
$C_{13}H_7Cl_3O_3$			
1-Naphthaleneacetic acid, 2,3,4-trichloro-α-oxo-, methyl ester	n.s.g.	234(4.83),282(3.64),293(3.65),305s(--)	44-2391-79
$C_{13}H_7F_5N_2OS$			
Sulfur diimide, (4-methoxyphenyl)(pentafluorophenyl)-	pentane	417(4.30)	70-2352-79
$C_{13}H_7F_5N_2S$			
Sulfur diimide, (4-methylphenyl)(pentafluorophenyl)-	pentane	413(4.11)	70-2352-79
$C_{13}H_7N_3O$			
Acenaphtho[1,2-e][1,2,4]triazin-9(8H)-one	MeOH	216(4.57),232(4.70),304(4.41),315(4.38)	83-0147-79
$C_{13}H_7N_3O_2$			
Furo[3,2-d]pyrimidine-7-carbonitrile, 6,7-dihydro-6-oxo-4-phenyl-	EtOH	212(4.31),234(4.26),265(4.29),345(4.24)	103-0677-79
$C_{13}H_7N_3S$			
Acenaphtho[1,2-e][1,2,4]triazine-9(8H)-thione	MeOH	218(4.46),283(4.38),335(4.26)	83-0147-79
$C_{13}H_8BrNO$			
1-Acenaphthylenecarboxamide, 2-bromo-	CH_2Cl_2	328(4.10)	44-1359-79
2,1-Benzisoxazole, 5-bromo-3-phenyl-	EtOH	218(4.30),257(4.17),352(3.99)	4-0033-79
Benzo[b]cyclohept[e][1,4]oxazine, 6-bromo-	MeOH	208(4.30),227(4.31),262(4.43),268(4.48),410(4.08)	18-1156-79
Benzoxazole, 5-bromo-2-phenyl-	EtOH	304(4.37)	4-0033-79
$C_{13}H_8BrN_3$			
1,2,4-Benzotriazine, 6-bromo-3-phenyl-	EtOH	214(4.40),266(4.54),352(3.81)	4-0033-79
$C_{13}H_8Br_3NO_2$			
Salicylanilide, tribromo-	pH 7.4	360(3.90)	149-0531-79A
$C_{13}H_8ClNO$			
6H-Azepino[1,2-a]indol-6-one, 11-chloro-	EtOH	275(4.50),284(4.56),430(3.67)	78-1273-79
Dibenz[c,f][1,2]oxazepine, 11-chloro-	EtOH	216(4.43),410(3.71)	78-1273-79
Oxepino[2,3-b]quinoline, 6-chloro-	EtOH	226(4.69),320(4.09)	78-1273-79
$C_{13}H_8Cl_2N_4O$			
1H-Tetrazolium, 1,3-bis(4-chlorophenyl)-4,5-dihydro-5-oxo-, hydroxide, inner salt	n.s.g.	228(4.36),269(4.27),333(4.38)	39-0736-79C

Compound	Solvent	λ_{max}(log ε)	Ref.
$C_{13}H_8Cl_2N_4S$			
1H-Tetrazolium, 1,3-bis(4-chlorophenyl)-2,5-dihydro-5-thioxo-, hydroxide, inner salt	n.s.g.	217(4.25),276(4.47), 392(3.43)	39-0741-79C
$C_{13}H_8N_2OS$			
Thiazolo[3,2-a]perimidin-10(9H)-one	EtOH	214(4.36),233(4.45), 337(4.02)	83-0776-79
$C_{13}H_8N_2OS_2$			
Thiazolo[3,2-a]benzimidazol-6-ol, 3-(2-thienyl)-	pH 1	334(3.84),387(3.61)	18-3096-79
	pH 13	325(3.63),453(3.57)	18-3096-79
	EtOH	251(4.31),277(4.13), 368(3.61)	18-3096-79
$C_{13}H_8N_2O_4$			
4H-Furo[3,2-b]pyrrole-5-carboxaldehyde, 2-(2-nitrophenyl)-	MeOH	357(4.5)	73-1805-79
$C_{13}H_8N_4O$			
1H-Pyrido[2',3':5,6][1,4]oxazino[2,3-b]quinoxaline	MeOH	255(4.66),300(4.25), 348(4.45)	4-1025-79
$C_{13}H_8N_4O_3S$			
Thiazolo[3,2-a]pyridinium, 3-hydroxy-2-[(4-nitrophenyl)azo]-, hydroxide, inner salt	MeCN	510(4.44)	103-1081-79
$C_{13}H_8O$			
9H-Fluoren-9-one	C_6H_{12}	281(3.49),292(3.62), 305(3.32),312(2.85), 318(2.70),370(2.60)	39-0393-79B
	CF_3COOH	290s(3.26),302(3.43), 320s(3.36),333(4.40), 395(2.30)	39-0393-79B
$C_{13}H_8OS$			
9H-Xanthene-9-thione	n.s.g.	405(4.17)	151-0205-79A
$C_{13}H_8O_2S$			
Methanone, 2-benzofuranyl-2-thienyl-	EtOH	335(4.25)	104-2174-79
$C_{13}H_8O_3$			
Methanone, 2-benzofuranyl-2-furanyl-	EtOH	334(4.45)	104-2174-79
9H-Xanthen-9-one, 2-hydroxy-	MeOH	237(4.46),247s(4.38), 299(3.48),357(3.66)	142-0269-79
	MeOH-NaOH	252(--),275s(--), 310(--)	142-0269-79
9H-Xanthen-9-one, 4-hydroxy-	EtOH	235s(4.45),250(4.59), 282(3.80),290(3.73), 353(3.66)	142-0269-79
	EtOH-NaOH	235(4.44),269(4.51), 301(3.94),311(3.94), 402(3.51)	142-0269-79
	EtOH-NaOAc	234(4.47),251(4.50), 267(4.11),293(3.71), 350(3.64)	142-0269-79
$C_{13}H_8O_4$			
9H-Xanthen-9-one, 1,5-dihydroxy-	EtOH	252(4.62),318(3.92), 378(3.73)	142-0269-79

Compound	Solvent	λ max(log ε)	Ref.
9H-Xanthen-9-one, 1,5-dihydroxy- (cont.)	EtOH-NaOH	252(4.62),318(3.82), 358(3.93),416(3.86)	142-0269-79
9H-Xanthen-9-one, 1,7-dihydroxy-	EtOH	231(4.47),280(4.56), 287(3.83),385(3.88)	142-0269-79
	EtOH-$AlCl_3$	236(4.63),277(4.52)	142-0269-79
$C_{13}H_8O_5$			
9H-Xanthen-9-one, 1,3,5-trihydroxy-	EtOH	220s(4.20),247(4.53), 313(4.21),360s(3.62)	142-0269-79
	EtOH-NaOH	257(4.34),291(4.13), 348(4.27)	142-0269-79
	EtOH-NaOAc	244(4.41),265s(4.14), 341(4.09)	142-0269-79
	EtOH-$AlCl_3$	246(4.14),267(4.34), 335(4.17)	142-0269-79
9H-Xanthen-9-one, 1,3,7-trihydroxy- (gentisein)	MeOH	205(3.95),237(4.29), 260(4.39),310(3.88), 374(3.39)	106-0447B-79
9H-Xanthen-9-one, 1,5,6-trihydroxy-	EtOH	251(4.58),315(3.81), 332(4.18)	142-0269-79
9H-Xanthen-9-one, 1,6,7-trihydroxy-	n.s.g.	251(4.34),268s(3.96), 296(3.93),313s(3.84), 360(4.00)	142-0269-79
$C_{13}H_8O_6$			
9H-Xanthen-9-one, 1,3,6,7-tetrahydroxy-	MeOH	237(4.40),254(4.55), 312(4.24),361(4.12)	142-0269-79
$C_{13}H_9BrClNO_2$			
Benzamide, 2-bromo-N-(4-chlorophenyl)- N-hydroxy-	EtOH	264(4.11)	34-0072-79
Benzamide, 4-bromo-N-(4-chlorophenyl)- N-hydroxy-	EtOH	238(4.11),275(4.10)	34-0072-79
$C_{13}H_9ClN_2$			
1H-Benzimidazole, 4-chloro-2-phenyl-	anion	246(4.25)	94-1255-79
1H-Benzimidazole, 5-chloro-2-phenyl-	anion	307(4.34)	94-1255-79
$C_{13}H_9ClN_2O_4$			
Benzamide, N-(4-chlorophenyl)-N-hydroxy- 2-nitro-	EtOH	259(4.28)	34-0072-79
$C_{13}H_9ClN_4O$			
1,2,3,4-Oxatriazolium, 5-[(4-chloro- phenyl)amino]-3-phenyl-, hydroxide, inner salt	n.s.g.	269(4.64),402(3.52)	39-0736-79C
1,2,3,4-Oxatriazolium, 3-(4-chlorophen- yl)-5-(phenylamino)-, hydroxide, inner salt	n.s.g.	270(4.46),416(3.38)	39-0736-79C
1H-Tetrazolium, 1-(4-chlorophenyl)-2,5- dihydro-5-oxo-3-phenyl-, hydroxide, inner salt	n.s.g.	227(4.70),263(4.57), 328(4.71)	39-0736-79C
1H-Tetrazolium, 3-(4-chlorophenyl)-2,5- dihydro-5-oxo-1-phenyl-, hydroxide, inner salt	n.s.g.	228(4.88),267(4.79), 330(4.86)	39-0736-79C
$C_{13}H_9ClN_4S$			
1H-Tetrazolium, 1-(4-chlorophenyl)-2,5- dihydro-3-phenyl-5-thioxo-, hydrox- ide, inner salt	n.s.g.	216(4.22),272(4.40), 389(3.46)	39-0741-79C

Compound	Solvent	$\lambda_{max}(\log \epsilon)$	Ref.
1H-Tetrazolium, 3-(4-chlorophenyl)-2,5-dihydro-1-phenyl-5-thioxo-, hydroxide, inner salt	n.s.g.	218(4.12),274(4.46), 388(3.37)	39-0741-79C
1,2,3,4-Thiatriazolium, 5-[(4-chlorophenyl)amino]-3-phenyl-, hydroxide, inner salt	n.s.g.	284(4.41),442(3.26)	39-0741-79C
1,2,3,4-Thiatriazolium, 3-(4-chlorophenyl)-5-(phenylamino)-, hydroxide, inner salt	n.s.g.	235s(4.21),285(4.65), 448(3.35)	39-0741-79C
$C_{13}H_9ClO_2S$			
Benzoic acid, 2-chloro-5-(phenylthio)-	MeOH	257(4.11),277s(3.92)	73-2124-79
$C_{13}H_9Cl_2N_3O$			
2H-Imidazo[4,5-b]pyridin-2-one, 4-[(2,6-dichlorophenyl)methyl]-1,4-dihydro-	CH_2Cl_2	332(3.5),345s(3.3)	64-1473-79B
$C_{13}H_9Cl_2N_3O_7S$			
Benzoic acid, 4-[[[(dichloromethyl)sulfonyl](5-nitro-2-furanyl)methylene]hydrazino]-	MeOH	218(4.09),259(4.07), 320(4.29),412(4.13)	73-2507-79
$C_{13}H_9I_2N_3$			
3,6-Acridinediamine, 4,5-diiodo- (spectra in 25% EtOH)	HCl	276(4.73),462(4.68)	12-2637-79
	NaOH	278(4.85),400(4.83)	12-2637-79
$C_{13}H_9NO$			
9(10H)-Acridinone	EtOH	251(4.76),254(4.78), 295(3.33),308(3.05), 370(3.63),381(3.93), 400(3.95)	42-0328-79
6H-Azepino[1,2-a]indol-6-one	EtOH	283(4.7),345s(--), 510(2.9)	138-0807-79
Benzeneacetonitrile, α-(2-furanylmethylene)-, cis	EtOH	235(3.95),320(4.25)	44-2896-79
Dibenz[b,f][1,4]oxazepine	MeOH	227(4.09),268(3.75), 330s(3.43)	118-0589-79
1H-Phenalen-1-one, 6-amino-	EtOH	206(3.99),258(4.01), 281(4.31),530(4.17)	104-0395-79
6(5H)-Phenanthridinone	CH_2Cl_2	231(4.47),236(4.41), 251(4.13),260(4.21), 272(3.99),308(3.81), 321(3.94),336(3.86)	24-1635-79
$C_{13}H_9NOS$			
5H-Thiazolo[3,2-a]pyridinium, 3-hydroxy-2-phenyl-, hydroxide, inner salt	MeOH	235(4.20),283(3.98), 435(4.18)	103-0872-79
$C_{13}H_9NO_2$			
Benzo[b]cyclohept[e][1,4]oxazin-6(11H)-one	MeOH	207(4.28),227(4.43), 275(3.88),310(3.48), 435(3.74)	18-1156-79
6(5H)-Phenanthridinone, 3-hydroxy-	EtOH	216(4.39),240(4.19), 250(4.10),264(4.60), 305(3.72),314(3.69), 330(3.70),342(3.62)	2-0503-79A
	EtOH-NaOH	226(4.62),247s(4.29), 262(4.28),277(4.26),	2-0503-79A

Compound	Solvent	λ_{max}(log ε)	Ref.
6(5H)-Phenanthridinone, 3-hydroxy- (cont.)		324(4.16),344s(4.02), 355s(3.95)	2-0503-79A
6(5H)-Phenanthridinone, 8-hydroxy-	EtOH	225(4.54),254(4.24), 263(4.29),282s(3.85), 309(3.97),332(3.94), 347(3.82)	2-0503-79A
	EtOH-NaOH	223(4.66),245(4.55), 256(4.50),268(4.44), 291(4.19),324(4.32), 364(3.90)	2-0503-79A
$C_{13}H_9NO_2S$			
Thiazolo[2,3-a]isoquinolinium, 2-acetyl-3-hydroxy-, hydroxide, inner salt	EtOH	237(3.66),315(3.89), 425(4.19)	150-2935-79
$C_{13}H_9NO_3$			
1H-Carbazole-1,4(9H)-dione, 6-hydroxy-9-methyl-	MeOH	227(4.54),261(4.43), 300s(3.40),465(3.84)	49-0051-79
	2M HCl	227(--),263(--), 300s(--),470(--)	49-0051-79
2H-Pyrano[3,2-c]quinolin-2-one, 5-methoxy-	MeOH	259(4.22),269(4.17), 315(4.02)	118-0903-79
$C_{13}H_9NO_3S$			
Thieno[3,2-d]oxazole-5-carboxylic acid, 2-phenyl-, methyl ester	EtOH	243(4.02),300(3.56)	103-0384-79
$C_{13}H_9NO_4S$			
Benzoic acid, 2-nitro-5-(phenylthio)-	MeOH	210(4.42),250s(3.92), 335(3.99)	73-2124-79
Methanone, [3-(4-nitrophenyl)oxiranyl]-2-thienyl-	EtOH	265(4.46)	104-2174-79
$C_{13}H_9NS$			
Benzeneacetonitrile, α-(2-thienylmethylene)-, cis	EtOH	245(3.73),320(4.28)	44-2896-79
Dibenzo[b,f][1,4]thiazepine	MeOH	217(4.14),250(4.18), 300s(3.39),356s(2.60)	118-0589-79
$C_{13}H_9NS_2$			
1,2-Benzisothiazole-3(2H)-thione, 2-phenyl-	EtOH	240(4.31),360(3.72)	2-0131-79B
$C_{13}H_9NSe$			
Benzeneacetonitrile, α-(selenophene-2-ylmethylene)-, (E)-	EtOH	244(3.75),299(4.24)	44-2896-79
$C_{13}H_9N_2$			
9H-Fluorene-2-diazonium tetrachlorozincate	5% H_2SO_4	365(4.43)	104-0733-79
$C_{13}H_9N_3$			
1,2,4-Benzotriazine, 3-phenyl-	EtOH	259(4.26),272s(4.11), 325(3.94),440(2.53)	4-1005-79
$C_{13}H_9N_3O$			
1,2,4-Benzenetricarbonitrile, 5-(tetrahydro-2-furanyl)-	MeOH	247(4.20),297(3.53), 308(3.59)	39-1147-79C

Compound	Solvent	λ_{max}(log ε)	Ref.
$C_{13}H_9N_3O_2$			
3,5-Pyridinedicarboxaldehyde, 4-ethynyl-1,4-dihydro-1-(2-pyrimidinyl)-	EtOH	228(4.11),275s(4.39), 288(4.47),346(3.78)	49-0613-79
$C_{13}H_9N_3O_3$			
Furazanol, 4-(2-quinolinyl)-, acetate	EtOH	245(4.48),292(3.87), 319s(3.61),332s(3.42)	4-0689-79
$C_{13}H_9N_3O_4S$			
10H-Phenothiazine, 10-methyl-1,3-dinitro-	dioxan	239(4.44),274(4.08), 299(4.15),438(3.74)	104-2316-79
10H-Phenothiazine, 10-methyl-2,4-dinitro-	dioxan	239(4.58),295(4.21), 470(3.56)	104-2316-79
$C_{13}H_9N_3O_8$			
Spiro[2,5-cyclohexadiene-1,3'-[2,4]dioxabicyclo[3.2.2]nona[5,7,8]triene], 4-(methyl-aci-nitro)-2,6-dinitro-	MeOH	267(4.33),374(4.39)	104-0487-79
$C_{13}H_9N_5O_2$			
Benzoic acid, 4-[5-(3-pyridinyl)-2H-tetrazol-2-yl]-	EtOH	272(4.26),283(4.29)	4-0123-79
$C_{13}H_{10}BrNO$			
2(1H)-Pyridinone, 1-(2-bromo-1-phenylethenyl)-, (Z)-	MeOH	230(4.09),257(4.24), 296(3.72),303(3.72)	1-0365-79
$C_{13}H_{10}BrNO_2$			
2,4,6-Cycloheptatrien-1-one, 2-bromo-7-[(2-hydroxyphenyl)amino]-	MeOH	205(4.52),250s(4.38), 260(4.39),346(3.98), 418(4.20)	18-1156-79
	MeOH-NaOH	240(4.72),346(3.98), 423(4.20)	18-1156-79
$C_{13}H_{10}Br_3N_3O_4$			
3,5-Methanofuro[3,2-b]pyridin-6(2H)-one, 7,7-dibromo-4-(3-bromo-5-nitro-2-pyridinyl)hexahydro-	$CHCl_3$	355(4.11)	39-1525-79C
$C_{13}H_{10}ClNO_2$			
[1,1'-Biphenyl]-3-ol, 4'-chloro-5-methyl-6-nitroso-	DMF	730(1.23)	104-0311-79
$C_{13}H_{10}ClN_3S_2$			
2-Thiophenecarbonitrile, 3-amino-4-[[(4-chlorophenyl)methylene]amino]-5-(methylthio)-	EtOH	273(4.40),356(4.07)	95-1081-79
$C_{13}H_{10}ClN_4S$			
1,2,3,4-Thiatriazolium, 5-[(4-chlorophenyl)amino]-3-phenyl-, tetrafluoroborate	n.s.g.	241s(4.21),282(4.61), 398s(3.56)	39-0741-79C
1,2,3,4-Thiatriazolium, 3-(4-chlorophenyl)-5-(phenylamino)-, tetrafluoroborate	n.s.g.	247s(4.08),283(4.24), 388s(3.33)	39-0741-79C
$C_{13}H_{10}ClN_5O$			
5H-1,2,4-Triazolo[4,3-d][1,4]benzodiazepine-3-acetonitrile, 10-chloro-6,7-dihydro-7-methyl-6-oxo-	MeOH	233(4.56),256(4.08), 300(3.29)	44-0088-79

Compound	Solvent	λ_{max}(log ε)	Ref.
$C_{13}H_{10}Cl_2Fe_2N_2O_6$			
Iron, hexacarbonyl[μ-(6,7-dichloro-4,4-dimethyl-2,3-diazabicyclo[3.2.0]hept-2-ene-$N^2,N^3:N^2,N^3$)]di-, (Fe-Fe)	hexane	300(4.40),350s(3.40), 413s(3.20)	5-1890-79
$C_{13}H_{10}Cl_2N_2O$			
2(1H)-Pyridinone, 3-[[[(2,6-dichlorophenyl)methyl]imino]methyl]-	CH_2Cl_2	310(3.8),345s(3.3)	64-1473-79B
$C_{13}H_{10}F_{10}N_2O_4$			
Uridine, 2',5'-dideoxy-5'-fluoro-5-(nonafluorobutyl)-	pH 1	268(--)	48-0449-79
	pH 14	268(3.79)	48-0449-79
$C_{13}H_{10}F_{10}N_2O_5$			
Uridine, 5'-deoxy-5'-fluoro-5-(nonafluorobutyl)-	pH 1	262(--)	48-0449-79
	pH 14	260.5(3.94)	48-0449-79
$C_{13}H_{10}Fe_2N_2O_6$			
Iron, hexacarbonyl[μ-(3,3-dimethyl-2,3-diazabicyclo[3.2.0]hepta-2,6-diene-$N^2,N^3:N^2,N^3$)]di-, (Fe-Fe)	hexane	296(4.47),351(3.47), 402s(3.29)	5-1890-79
$C_{13}H_{10}N_2$			
1H-Benzimidazole, 2-phenyl-	anion	241(4.21)	94-1255-79
5H-Dibenzo[b,e][1,4]diazepine	MeOH	210s(3.91),243(4.12), 272s(3.69),280(3.62)	118-0589-79
$C_{13}H_{10}N_2O$			
Benzoxazole, 2-(4-methyl-3-pyridinyl)-	EtOH	290(3.30),299(4.28)	4-1579-79
Benzoxazole, 2-(6-methyl-3-pyridinyl)-	EtOH	296(4.38),302(4.39)	4-1579-79
Phenazine, 2-methoxy-	neutral	390(3.90)	59-0421-79
	cation	438(3.53)	59-0421-79
2-Phenazinol, 3-methyl-	neutral	410(3.61),510(3.22)	59-0421-79
	cation	445(3.71)	59-0421-79
	anion	472(3.83)	59-0421-79
$C_{13}H_{10}N_2O_2$			
Benzenamine, N-[(4-nitrophenyl)methylene]-	EtOH	210(3.26),220s(--), 290(3.10),340(2.98)	2-0338-79B
	H_2SO_4	275(3.30),372(3.45)	2-0338-79B
2,8-Phenazinediol, 3-methyl-	neutral	398(3.63)	59-0421-79
	cation	428(3.97)	59-0421-79
	anion	498(4.15)	59-0421-79
	dianion	444(4.18)	59-0421-79
$C_{13}H_{10}N_2O_3$			
Carbonocyanidimidic acid, (1-oxo-1H-2-benzopyran-5-yl)-, ethyl ester	MeOH	224(4.26),237s(4.25), 245(4.29),251(4.29), 320(3.70)	94-0946-79
4-Pyridazinecarboxylic acid, 5-benzoyl-, methyl ester	MeOH	252(4.06)	39-2215-79C
$C_{13}H_{10}N_2O_3S$			
Benzenesulfenamide, N-(2-methyl-4-oxo-2,5-cyclohexadien-1-ylidene)-2-nitro-	EtOH	254(4.24),430(4.39)	94-2316-79
Benzenesulfenamide, N-(3-methyl-4-oxo-2,5-cyclohexadien-1-ylidene)-2-nitro- (contains isomer)	EtOH	251(4.13),434(4.37)	94-2316-79
2H-1,2,4-Benzothiadiazin-3(4H)-one, 4-phenyl-, 1,1-dioxide	EtOH	216(4.26),245(4.07), 291(3.41)	39-1043-79C

Compound	Solvent	$\lambda_{max}(\log \epsilon)$	Ref.
Thiazolo[3,2-c]quinazolin-4-ium, 2-(ethoxycarbonyl)-3-hydroxy-, hydroxide, inner salt	EtOH	280(3.23),320(3.34)	150-2935-79
$C_{13}H_{10}N_2O_4S$			
Benzenesulfenamide, N-(2-methoxy-4-oxo-2,5-cyclohexadien-1-ylidene)-2-nitro-(plus isomer)	EtOH	248(4.08),418(4.36)	94-2316-79
$C_{13}H_{10}N_2O_5S_2$			
Cyclohexanone, 2-(4,6-dinitro-1,3-benzodithiol-2-ylidene)-	$CHCl_3$	261(3.96),319s(4.04), 334(4.13),345(4.12)	150-1732-79
$C_{13}H_{10}N_2S$			
Benzothiazole, 2-(4-methyl-3-pyridinyl)-	EtOH	287(4.15)	4-1579-79
Benzothiazole, 2-(6-methyl-3-pyridinyl)-	EtOH	301(4.31)	4-1579-79
Thiazolo[3,2-a]perimidine, 9,10-dihydro-	EtOH	214(4.40),233(4.61), 326(4.17)	83-0776-79
$C_{13}H_{10}N_4O$			
1,2,3,4-Oxatriazolium, 3-phenyl-5-(phenylamino)-, hydroxide, inner salt	n.s.g.	265(4.49),410(3.41)	39-0736-79C
Pyridazino[4,5-d]pyridazin-1(2H)-one, 2-methyl-4-phenyl-	MeOH	235s(4.02),304(3.87)	39-2215-79C
1H-Tetrazolium, 5-hydroxy-1,3-diphenyl-, hydroxide, inner salt	n.s.g.	225(4.55),263(4.40), 326(4.51)	39-0736-79C
2H-Tetrazolium, 2,5-dihydro-5-oxo-2,3-diphenyl-, hydroxide, inner salt	n.s.g.	233(4.05),331(3.70)	39-0744-79C
$C_{13}H_{10}N_4O_2S_2$			
2-Thiophenecarbonitrile, 3-amino-5-(methylthio)-4-[[(2-nitrophenyl)-methylene]amino]-	EtOH	287(4.35),376(3.95)	95-1081-79
2-Thiophenecarbonitrile, 3-amino-5-(methylthio)-4-[[(3-nitrophenyl)-methylene]amino]-	EtOH	230(4.29),258(4.38), 285(4.35),362(4.01)	95-1081-79
2-Thiophenecarbonitrile, 3-amino-5-(methylthio)-4-[[(4-nitrophenyl)-methylene]amino]-	EtOH	282(4.32),300(4.34), 390(4.07)	95-1081-79
$C_{13}H_{10}N_4O_4$			
4H-Furo[3,2-b]pyrrole-5-carboxylic acid, 2-(2-nitrophenyl)-, hydrazide	MeOH	325(4.40)	73-1805-79
$C_{13}H_{10}N_4O_5$			
Benzamide, 4-amino-N-(2,4-dinitrophenyl)-	EtOH	270(4.09),340(4.10)	104-1730-79
Benzamide, N-(2-amino-4-nitrophenyl)-4-nitro-	EtOH	255(4.19),295(4.05)	104-1730-79
Benzamide, N-(4-amino-2-nitrophenyl)-4-nitro-	EtOH	255(4.33)	104-1730-79
$C_{13}H_{10}N_4O_6$			
Benzamide, N-[2-(hydroxyamino)-4-nitrophenyl]-4-nitro-	EtOH	250(4.04),355(4.08)	104-1730-79
$C_{13}H_{10}N_4S$			
1H-Tetrazolium, 2,5-dihydro-1,3-diphenyl-5-thioxo-, hydroxide, inner salt	n.s.g.	222s(3.92),270(4.25), 386(3.17)	39-0741-79C

Compound	Solvent	λmax(log ε)	Ref.
2H-Tetrazolium, 1,5-dihydro-2,3-diphenyl-5-thioxo-, hydroxide, inner salt	n.s.g.	255(4.38),414(4.05)	39-0744-79C
1,2,3,4-Thiatriazolium, 3-phenyl-5-(phenylamino)-, hydroxide, inner salt	n.s.g.	279(4.47),411(3.26)	39-0741-79C
$C_{13}H_{10}O$			
1H-Phenalen-2(3H)-one	MeOH	227(4.81),267s(--), 277(3.74),287(3.81), 296(3.70)	88-2867-79
$C_{13}H_{10}OS_2$			
2H-Naphtho[1,8-bc]thiophene-2-thione, 3-ethoxy-	MeOH	214(4.6),267(4.5), 277(4.5),287(4.5), 328(4.3),357(4.3), 375(4.4),449(4.4), 469(4.3)	5-0965-79
$C_{13}H_{10}O_2$			
2-Propenal, 3-(2-hydroxy-1-naphthalenyl)-	MeOH	277(3.80),297(3.83), 310(3.83),334(3.67), 346(3.66),373(3.32)	104-1715-79
	MeCN	297(4.06),311(3.85), 330(3.81),350(3.83)	104-1715-79
	CCl_4	287(3.57),300(3.69), 315(3.78),336(3.62), 352(3.77)	104-1715-79
	DMSO	315(3.85),329(3.94), 372(4.00),472(3.11)	104-1715-79
$C_{13}H_{10}O_2S$			
2H-Naphtho[1,8-bc]thiophen-2-one, 3-ethoxy-	MeOH	238(4.5),267(4.5), 289(4.2),343(4.4), 378(4.2)	5-0965-79
Oxirane, 2-benzoyl-3-(2-thienyl)-, trans	EtOH	248(4.28)	104-2174-79
$C_{13}H_{10}O_2Se$			
Oxirane, 2-benzoyl-3-(2-selenopheneyl)-, trans	EtOH	252(4.31)	104-2174-79
$C_{13}H_{10}O_3$			
Benzoic acid, 2-hydroxy-, phenyl ester	EtOH	242(4.09),312(3.69)	49-1057-79
7H-Furo[3,2-g][1]benzopyran-6-one, 7-methyl-	EtOH	311(4.0),380(3.6)	149-0645-79B
7H-Furo[3,2-g][1]benzopyran-6-one, 9-methyl-	EtOH	320(3.9),382(3.5)	149-0645-79B
Methanone, [3-(2-furanyl)oxiranyl]phenyl-	EtOH	251(4.23)	104-2174-79
4H-Pyran-3,5-dicarboxaldehyde, 4-phenyl-	EtOH	205(4.47),233(3.97), 292(3.95)	49-0613-79
$C_{13}H_{10}O_5$			
Psoralen, 5,8-dimethoxy-	MeOH	240(3.9),265(4.1), 310(3.9)	102-0352-79
$C_{13}H_{10}O_6$			
2H-1-Benzopyran-4-acetic acid, 7-acetoxy-2-oxo-	MeOH	280(3.99),313(3.95)	73-2211-79

Compound	Solvent	λ_{max}(log ε)	Ref.
$C_{13}H_{11}$			
Cycloheptatrienylium, phenyl-, tetrafluoroborate	10% HCl	226(4.58),271(4.17), 368(4.21)	39-1005-79B
Methylium, diphenyl-	H_2SO_4	443(4.63)	39-1395-79B
$C_{13}H_{11}BrCl_3NO_2$			
Carbamic acid, di-2-propenyl-, 2-bromo-3,4,6-trichlorophenyl ester	MeOH	210(4.77)	73-0918-79
$C_{13}H_{11}BrN_2O$			
Benzamide, 2-amino-N-(4-bromophenyl)-	EtOH	216(4.09),266(3.77), 340(2.85)	2-0593-79A
$C_{13}H_{11}BrN_2O_4$			
1H-Pyrazole-5-carboxylic acid, 3-bromo-4-(4-methoxybenzoyl)-1-methyl-	EtOH	233(4.23),277(4.22)	73-0781-79
	ether	231(4.13),268(4.15), 288(4.13),298(4.06), 308s(3.99)	73-0781-79
$C_{13}H_{11}BrN_4O_2$			
Benzenecarboximidic acid, 4-bromo-, 2-(4-nitrophenyl)hydrazide, hydrochloride	EtOH	245(4.23),332(4.12)	65-2056-79
	$EtOH-NH_3$	234(4.18),305(3.71), 431(4.36)	65-2056-79
Benzenecarboximidic acid, 4-nitro-, 2-(4-bromophenyl)hydrazide, hydrochloride	EtOH	249(4.30)	65-2056-79
	$EtOH-NH_3$	278(4.24)	65-2056-79
$C_{13}H_{11}Cl$			
1,3,5-Cycloheptatriene, 1-(4-chlorophenyl)-	EtOH	303(3.88)	48-0117-79
1,3,5-Cycloheptatriene, 2-(4-chlorophenyl)-	hexane	247(4.31)	48-0117-79
1,3,5-Cycloheptatriene, 3-(4-chlorophenyl)-	EtOH	285(3.90)	48-0117-79
1,3,5-Cycloheptatriene, 7-(4-chlorophenyl)-	hexane	265(3.52)	48-0117-79
$C_{13}H_{11}ClN_2$			
1H-Pyrido[2,3-b]indole, 2-chloro-1,3-dimethyl-	pH 1	250(4.20),265s(4.02), 319(4.16),355(3.91)	103-0879-79
	pH 13	262s(4.20),279(4.27), 325(4.17),400(3.63)	103-0879-79
$C_{13}H_{11}ClN_2O$			
Benzamide, 2-amino-N-(3-chlorophenyl)-	EtOH	220(4.04),260(3.76), 340(2.30)	2-0593-79A
Benzamide, 2-amino-N-(4-chlorophenyl)-	EtOH	222(4.13),262(3.79), 340(3.15)	2-0593-79A
$C_{13}H_{11}ClN_2OS$			
1H-Pyrrole-3-carboxaldehyde, 2-chloro-4,5-dihydro-1-methyl-4-[(phenylamino)methylene]-5-thioxo-, potassium salt	EtOH	330(4.22),410(4.17)	65-0365-79
$C_{13}H_{11}ClN_2OSe$			
1H-Pyrrole-3-carboxaldehyde, 2-chloro-4,5-dihydro-1-methyl-4-[(phenylamino)methylene]-5-selenoxo-, potassium salt	EtOH	345(4.12),410(4.24)	65-0365-79

Compound	Solvent	λmax(log ε)	Ref.
$C_{13}H_{11}ClN_2O_2$			
1H-Pyrrole-3-carboxaldehyde, 2-chloro-4,5-dihydro-1-methyl-5-oxo-4-[(phenylamino)methylene]-	EtOH-DMF	250(4.05),330(3.96), 430(4.22)	65-0365-79
sodium deriv.	EtOH	245(4.27),290(4.06), 400(4.64)	65-0365-79
$C_{13}H_{11}ClN_4O_3$			
[1,2,4]Triazino[4,3-d][1,4]benzodiazepine-3,4,7(6H)-trione, 11-chloro-2,8-dihydro-2,8-dimethyl-	MeOH	255(4.18),278(4.10), 308s(3.99)	44-0088-79
$C_{13}H_{11}ClO_5$			
1,4-Naphthalenedione, 2-chloro-3,5,8-trimethoxy-	C_6H_{12}	360(3.63),400s(3.34)	39-0696-79C
$C_{13}H_{11}Cl_2NO_4$			
1,4-Naphthalenedione, 6,7-dichloro-5,8-dimethoxy-2-(methylamino)-	C_6H_{12}	370(3.76),415s(3.43)	39-0696-79C
$C_{13}H_{11}Cl_2N_3$			
2-Pyridinamine, 3-[[[(2,6-dichlorophenyl)methyl]imino]methyl]-	CH_2Cl_2	262(3.4),338(3.6)	64-1019-79B
$C_{13}H_{11}Cl_2N_3O_5S$			
Hydrazine, [[(dichloromethyl)sulfonyl]-(5-nitro-2-furanyl)methylene](4-methylphenyl)-	MeOH	213s(4.01),242(4.13), 323(4.25),426(4.06)	73-2507-79
$C_{13}H_{11}Cl_2N_3O_6S$			
Hydrazine, [[(dichloromethyl)sulfonyl]-(5-nitro-2-furanyl)methylene]-(4-methoxyphenyl)-	MeOH	213s(4.03),245(4.13), 333(4.19),441(4.03)	73-2507-79
$C_{13}H_{11}Cl_3INO_2$			
Carbamic acid, di-2-propenyl-, 3,4,6-trichloro-2-iodophenyl ester	MeOH	217(4.56)	73-0918-79
$C_{13}H_{11}Cl_3N_2O_3S$			
Carbamothioic acid, di-2-propenyl-, 3,4,6-trichloro-2-nitrophenyl ester	MeOH	209(4.53),251(4.16)	73-0918-79
$C_{13}H_{11}Cl_3N_2O_4$			
Carbamic acid, di-2-propenyl-, 3,4,6-trichloro-2-nitrophenyl ester	MeOH	210(4.56),291(3.48)	73-0918-79
$C_{13}H_{11}DO_2$			
1H-Indene-1,2-dicarboxaldehyde-1-d, 1,3-dimethyl-, (-)-	EtOH	236(3.90),308(4.19)	39-1273-79C
$C_{13}H_{11}D_6N_3O_2$			
1H-Imidazole, 2,5-dihydro-5,5-dimethyl-2,2-di(methyl-d_3)-1-nitroso-4-phenyl-, 3-oxide	EtOH	228(4.16),286(3.96)	103-0092-79
$C_{13}H_{11}F$			
1,1'-Biphenyl, 4-fluoro-4'-methyl-	C_6H_{12}	250(4.24)	12-1531-79
1,1'-Biphenyl, 4'-fluoro-2-methyl-	C_6H_{12}	235(3.99)	12-1531-79
1,1'-Biphenyl, 4'-fluoro-3-methyl-	C_6H_{12}	248(4.18)	12-1531-79

Compound	Solvent	λ_{max}(log ε)	Ref.
$C_{13}H_{11}F_2N$			
[1,1'-Biphenyl]-2-amine, 2',5'-difluoro-N-methyl-	EtOH	211(3.53),226(4.26)	33-2129-79
$C_{13}H_{11}N$			
Benzenamine, N-(phenylmethylene)-	EtOH	218(3.23),232s(--), 262(3.25),312s(2.96)	2-0338-79B
	H_2SO_4	220(--),275(2.90), 340(3.42)	2-0338-79B
Benzo[a]cyclopropa[cd]pentalene-6c(2H)-carbonitrile, 1,2a,2b,6b-tetrahydro-	C_6H_{12}	220s(3.61),257s(2.42), 262(2.64),267s(2.78), 268(2.83),276(2.92)	23-2804-79
1,4-Ethanonaphthalene-2-carbonitrile, 1,4-dihydro-	C_6H_{12}	222s(3.79),238s(3.05), 253s(2.86),260(2.73), 267(2.52),269(2.45)	23-2804-79
$C_{13}H_{11}NO$			
Azepino[4,5-b]indol-2(3H)-one, 4,5-dihydro-	EtOH	260(4.5),330(3.9), 380s(--)	138-0807-79
Benzamide, N-phenyl-	H_2O	260(4.11)	104-0101-79
	acid	270(4.09)	104-0101-79
Methanone, (2-aminophenyl)phenyl-	EtOH	234(4.37)	42-0328-79
Phenol, 2-[(phenylimino)methyl]-	MeOH	208(4.11),222(4.14), 300(3.89),321(3.89), 338(3.92)	150-3801-79
$C_{13}H_{11}NOS$			
Benzene, 2-methyl-1-nitroso-4-(phenylthio)-	$CHCl_3$	770(1.53)	44-2087-79
Benzenesulfenamide, 4-methyl-N-(4-oxo-2,5-cyclohexadien-1-ylidene)-	hexane	438(4.23)	138-1077-79
Benzothiazole, 2-ethyl-6-(2-furanyl)-	EtOH	205(4.23),216(4.20), 232s(4.05),254(3.96), 247(3.98),305(4.21), 320s(4.06)	33-0021-79
	$CHCl_3$	249(3.99),255(3.96), 298(4.19),307(4.24), 321s(4.08)	33-0021-79
$C_{13}H_{11}NO_2$			
Benzamide, N-hydroxy-N-phenyl-	80% MeOH	263(3.89)	140-1562-79
	ion	303(3.69)	140-1562-79
	pH 12	300(3.68)	140-1436-79
	9M KOH	318(3.69)	140-1436-79
Benzene, 2-methyl-1-nitroso-4-phenoxy-	$CHCl_3$	750(1.67)	44-2087-79
[1,1'-Biphenyl]-3-ol, 5-methyl-6-nitroso-	DMF	740(1.20)	104-0311-79
1(3H)-Isobenzofuranone, 3-(1-methyl-1H-pyrrol-2-yl)-	EtOH	204(4.24),226(4.30)	103-0747-79
3,5-Pyridinedicarboxaldehyde, 1,4-dihydro-4-phenyl-	EtOH	208(4.20),229(4.23), 256(3.79),372(3.99)	49-0613-79
Quinoline, 2-methyl-4-(2-propynyloxy)-, 1-oxide	MeOH	223(4.57),244(4.37), 332(3.93)	94-1813-79
$C_{13}H_{11}NO_2S$			
Benzoic acid, 2-amino-5-(phenylthio)-	MeOH	222(4.50),268(4.28), 341(3.61)	73-2124-79
$C_{13}H_{11}NO_2Te$			
Benzene, 1-nitro-2-[(phenylmethyl)telluro]-	EtOH	210(4.23),222(4.23), 266(3.97)	44-3957-79

Compound	Solvent	λ_{max}(log ε)	Ref.
$C_{13}H_{11}NO_3$			
Benzoic acid, 2-(1-methyl-1H-pyrrol-2-yl)carbonyl]-	EtOH	203(4.32),296(4.21)	103-0747-79
Furan, 2-[2-(4-methylphenyl)ethenyl]-5-nitro-, (E)-	MeOH	220(4.03),243(3.89), 280(4.08),395(4.23)	73-2096-79
2H-Pyran-2,4(3H)-dione, 6-methyl-3-[(phenylamino)methylene]-	hexane	223s(4.38),236s(4.28), 362(4.47)	131-0077-79D
	EtOH	359(4.44)	131-0077-79D
$C_{13}H_{11}NO_4$			
Furan, 2-[2-(4-methoxyphenyl)ethenyl]-5-nitro-, (E)-	MeOH	222(4.15),244(4.08), 296(4.29),418(4.47)	73-2096-79
2,4(3H,5H)-Furandione, 3-(1-hydroxyethylidene)-5-[(phenylamino)methylene]-	EtOH	242(4.13),273(3.91), 363(4.51)	4-1335-79
Furo[2,3-b]quinolin-8-ol, 4,7-dimethoxy-	EtOH	212(4.14),239(4.37), 260(4.67),330(4.01)	105-0656-79
3-Pyrrolidinecarboxylic acid, 2,4-dioxo-5-(phenylmethylene)-, methyl ester	MeOH	233(4.12),328(4.39)	142-0477-79B
9H-Pyrrolo[1,2-a]indole-1,5,8-trione, 2,3,5,8-tetrahydro-7-methoxy-8-methyl-	MeOH	289(4.28)	142-0411-79B
$C_{13}H_{11}NO_5$			
1,3-Dioxolo[4,5-f]quinoline-8-carboxylic acid, 6-ethyl-6,9-dihydro-9-oxo-	1% KOH	249(4.48),318(3.94), 364(3.93)	87-1354-79
1,3-Dioxolo[4,5-h]quinoline-7-carboxylic acid, 9-ethyl-6,9-dihydro-6-oxo-	1% KOH	233(4.37),280(4.40), 324(3.92)	87-1354-79
$C_{13}H_{11}NS_2$			
1,3,2-Benzodithiazole, 5-methyl-2-phenyl-	CH_2Cl_2	248(4.33)	4-0183-79
Cyclopenta[d][1,3]thiazine-4(5H)-thione, 6,7-dihydro-2-phenyl-	EtOH	258(4.05),320(3.76), 438(3.50)	150-1732-79
$C_{13}H_{11}N_3$			
1H-Benzimidazole, 2-(4-methyl-3-pyridinyl)-	EtOH	290(4.20)	4-1579-79
1H-Benzimidazole, 2-(6-methyl-3-pyridinyl)-	EtOH	307(4.38)	4-1579-79
1H-Benzimidazole, 4-methyl-2-(2-pyridinyl)-	anion	308(4.34)	94-1235-79
1H-Benzimidazole, 5-methyl-2-(2-pyridinyl)-	anion	313(4.40)	94-1235-79
1H-Benzotriazole, 1-(phenylmethyl)-	EtOH	255(3.85),279(3.64)	33-2129-79
2-Phenazinamine, 3-methyl-	neutral	450(3.75)	59-0421-79
	cation	514(3.98)	59-0421-79
3-Pyridinecarbonitrile, 2-amino-5-methyl-4-phenyl-	CH_2Cl_2	263(3.85),334(3.86)	118-0376-79
3-Pyridinecarbonitrile, 2-amino-6-(4-methylphenyl)-	CH_2Cl_2	275(4.22),343(4.28)	118-0376-79
3-Pyridinecarbonitrile, 2-amino-4-(phenylmethyl)-	CH_2Cl_2	321(3.80)	118-0376-79
$C_{13}H_{11}N_3O$			
1,2,4-Benzenetricarbonitrile, 5-(1-ethoxyethyl)-	MeOH	248(4.26),295(3.49), 306(3.58)	39-1147-79C
1H-Benzimidazole, 4-methoxy-2-(2-pyridinyl)-	anion	310(4.03)	94-1235-79
1H-Benzimidazole, 5-methoxy-2-(2-pyridinyl)-	anion	322(4.36)	94-1235-79

Compound	Solvent	λ max(log ε)	Ref.
2H-Imidazo[4,5-b]pyridin-2-one, 1,4-dihydro-4-(phenylmethyl)-	CH_2Cl_2	332(4.1),345s(3.9)	64-1473-79B
2-Phenazinol, 8-amino-7-methyl-	neutral	409(4.09),494(4.10)	39-0304-79B
	cation	435(4.20),483(4.20)	59-0421-79
	anion	437(4.29)	39-0304-79B
Propanedinitrile, [1-amino-3-(2-methoxyphenyl)-2-propenylidene]-	EtOH	353(4.27)	64-1580-79B
$C_{13}H_{11}N_3OS_2$			
Benzamide, N-[4-amino-5-cyano-2-(methylthio)-3-thienyl]-	EtOH	226(4.28),293(4.10), 320(3.99)	95-1081-79
Thieno[3,2-d]pyrimidin-4(1H)-one, 7-amino-6-(methylthio)-2-phenyl-, monohydrochloride	EtOH	276(4.32),352(4.07)	95-1081-79
$C_{13}H_{11}N_3O_2$			
Carbamic acid, 1H-perimidin-2-yl-, methyl ester	n.s.g.	231(4.77),256(4.48), 310(4.09)	135-1183-79
1H-Pyrrolo[2,3-f]quinoline, 2,3-dimethyl-8-nitro-	EtOH	210(4.30),253(4.19), 317(4.06),394(3.62)	103-1113-79
1H-Pyrrolo[2,3-g]quinoline, 2,3-dimethyl-7-nitro-	EtOH	233(4.22),248(4.37), 323(4.23),365s(4.74), 473(3.76)	103-1113-79
1H-Pyrrolo[3,2-g]quinoline, 2,3-dimethyl-6-nitro-	EtOH	229(4.32),250(4.19), 325(4.41),370s(3.75), 424(3.29)	103-1113-79
3H-Pyrrolo[3,2-f]quinoline, 1,2-dimethyl-8-nitro-	EtOH	225(4.16),256(4.34), 319(3.85),380(3.53), 447(3.76)	103-1113-79
$C_{13}H_{11}N_3O_2S_2$			
Isothiazolo[3,4-d]pyrimidine-4,6(5H,7H)-dione, 5-methyl-3-(methylthio)-7-phenyl-	EtOH	293(4.32)	95-0989-79 +142-0485-79
$C_{13}H_{11}N_3O_3$			
1H-Isoindole-1,3(2H)-dione, 2-[(5-hydroxy-1-methyl-1H-pyrazol-3-yl)-methyl]-	MeOH	220(4.74),140s(--)[sic]	1-0294-79
1H-Naphth[2,3-d]imidazole-4,9-dione, 5-amino-8-hydroxy-1,2-dimethyl-	C_6H_{12}	487(--),521(3.68), 562(--)	39-0702-79C
1H-Naphth[2,3-d]imidazole-4,9-dione, 8-amino-5-hydroxy-1,2-dimethyl-	C_6H_{12}	486(--),520(3.85), 560(--)	39-0702-79C
$C_{13}H_{11}N_3O_3S$			
Pyrido[1,2-b][1,2,4,6]thiatriazinium, 2,3-dihydro-3-oxo-4-(phenylmethyl)-, hydroxide, inner salt, 1,1-dioxide	MeCN	312(3.96)	142-0815-79
$C_{13}H_{11}N_3O_4$			
Acetamide, N-[2-(1,4-dihydro-5-nitro-4-oxo-3-pyridinyl)phenyl]-	EtOH	233(4.15),338(3.68)	39-2902-79C
Benzenamine, N-methyl-2,4-dinitro-N-phenyl-	EtOH	246(4.19)	73-1613-79
$C_{13}H_{11}N_3O_4S_2$			
Cyclohexanimine, 2-(4,6-dinitro-1,3-benzodithiol-2-ylidene)-	$CHCl_3$	270(4.04),323(4.25), 484(3.75)	150-1732-79
$C_{13}H_{11}N_3O_6$			
1H-Pyrazole-3,4-dicarboxylic acid,	CH_2Cl_2	301(4.32)	24-1193-79

Compound	Solvent	λ_{max}(log ε)	Ref.
1-(4-nitrophenyl)-, dimethyl ester (cont.)			24-1193-79
$C_{13}H_{11}N_3S$			
3-Pyridinecarbonitrile, 2-amino-6-(methylthio)-4-phenyl-	CH_2Cl_2	253(4.12),344(3.76)	118-0376-79
$C_{13}H_{11}N_3S_2$			
5,11-Imino-5H,11H-[1,5]dithiocino[2,3-b:6,7-b']dipyridine, 13-methyl-	EtOH	207(4.36),245(4.28), 303(3.85)	78-0869-79
2(1H)-Pyrimidinethione, 4-[3-(methylamino)benzo[b]thien-2-yl]-	$CHCl_3$	308(4.12),337(3.82), 426(4.24)	118-0442-79
2-Thiophenecarbonitrile, 3-amino-5-(methylthio)-4-[(phenylmethylene)-amino]-	EtOH	266(4.31),290(4.33), 350(4.02)	95-1081-79
$C_{13}H_{11}N_4O_2$			
4H-Benz[g]imidazo[1,2,3-ij]pteridin-3-ium, 1,2,5,6-tetrahydro-5-methyl-4,6-dioxo-, perchlorate	H_2O	366(4.02),408(3.79)	33-0593-79
	MeCN	253(4.45),358(4.08), 407(3.91)	33-0593-79
$C_{13}H_{11}N_4S$			
1,2,3,4-Thiatriazolium, 3-phenyl-5-(phenylamino)-, tetrafluoroborate	n.s.g.	240s(4.04),278(4.34), 390(3.38)	39-0741-79C
$C_{13}H_{11}N_5$			
Pyridine, 3-[2-(4-methylphenyl)-2H-tetrazol-5-yl]-	EtOH	270(4.33),280(4.33)	4-0123-79
Pyridine, 3-[5-(4-methylphenyl)-2H-tetrazol-2-yl]-	EtOH	240(4.31),276(4.24), 290(4.21)	4-0123-79
Pyridine, 4-[2-(4-methylphenyl)-2H-tetrazol-5-yl]-	EtOH	275(4.21)	4-0123-79
$C_{13}H_{11}N_5O$			
Pyridine, 3-[5-(4-methoxyphenyl)-2H-tetrazol-2-yl]-	EtOH	251(4.36),281(4.32), 300(4.21)	4-0123-79
Pyridine, 4-[2-(4-methoxyphenyl)-2H-tetrazol-5-yl]-	EtOH	290(4.66)	4-0123-79
$C_{13}H_{11}N_5O_4$			
Benzo[g]pteridine-2,4(3H,10H)-dione, 3,7,10-trimethyl-6-nitro-	MeCN	327(3.83),428s(--), 446(4.02),470s(--)	5-1067-79
Benzo[g]pteridine-2,4(3H,10H)-dione, 3,7,10-trimethyl-8-nitro-	MeCN	330(4.08),452(4.17)	5-1067-79
$C_{13}H_{11}N_5O_4S_3$			
5-Thia-1-azabicyclo[4.2.0]oct-2-ene-2-carboxylic acid, 7-[(cyanoacetyl)amino]-8-oxo-3-[(1,2,3-thiadiazol-5-ylthio)methyl]-, monosodium salt, (6R-trans)-	H_2O	259(3.83)	87-1214-79
$C_{13}H_{11}S$			
Dibenzothiophenium, 5-methyl-, tetrafluoroborate	CH_2Cl_2	232(4.41),239(4.42), 272(4.00),380(3.16)	4-0471-79
Naphtho[2,1-b]thiophenium, 3-methyl-, tetrafluoroborate	CH_2Cl_2	254(4.56),292(4.20), 303(4.20),315s(3.67), 329(3.38)	4-0471-79
Naphtho[2,3-b]thiophenium, 1-methyl-, tetrafluoroborate	CH_2Cl_2	240(4.36),263(4.49), 298(4.00),310(4.00), 348(3.59),363(3.63)	4-0471-79

Compound	Solvent	$\lambda_{max}(\log \epsilon)$	Ref.
$C_{13}H_{12}BrN$			
[1,1'-Biphenyl]-2-amine, 2'-bromo-N-methyl-	EtOH	233(4.37),315(3.49)	33-2129-79
[1,1'-Biphenyl]-2-amine, 4'-bromo-N-methyl-	EtOH	208(4.51),306(3.38)	33-2129-79
$C_{13}H_{12}BrN_3$			
Benzenecarboximidic acid, 2-(4-bromophenyl)hydrazide	EtOH	238(4.36),270s(3.56)	65-2056-79
	$EtOH-NH_3$	219(4.08),259(4.01),319(4.09)	65-2056-79
Benzenecarboximidic acid, 4-bromo-, 2-phenylhydrazide	EtOH	240(4.31)	65-2056-79
	$EtOH-NH_3$	234(4.17),251s(4.12),339(4.03)	65-2056-79
$C_{13}H_{12}ClN$			
[1,1'-Biphenyl]-2-amine, 2'-chloro-N-methyl-	EtOH	232(4.40),314(3.55)	33-2129-79
[1,1'-Biphenyl]-2-amine, 4-chloro-N-methyl-	EtOH	227(4.42),315(3.79)	33-2129-79
[1,1'-Biphenyl]-2-amine, 4'-chloro-N-methyl-	EtOH	210(4.49),305(3.46)	33-2129-79
[1,1'-Biphenyl]-2-amine, 5-chloro-N-methyl-	EtOH	227(4.42),324(3.54)	33-2129-79
$C_{13}H_{12}ClNO$			
Furo[3,4-b]quinoline, 9-chloro-1,3-dihydro-3,3-dimethyl-	n.s.g.	225(4.50),294(3.68),306(3.70),320(3.80)	23-3296-79
$C_{13}H_{12}ClNO_2$			
2H-Pyran-2-one, 3-chloro-4-(dimethylamino)-6-phenyl-	EtOH	229(3.98),261(4.46),300(4.18),346(3.99)	4-0093-79
$C_{13}H_{12}ClNO_2S_2$			
2-Azetidinone, 4-[[3-(4-chlorophenyl)-1-(methylthio)-3-oxo-1-propenyl]thio]-, (E)-	dioxan	270(4.15),342(4.30)	142-1315-79
(Z)-	dioxan	270(4.07),337(4.31)	142-1315-79
$C_{13}H_{12}ClNO_4$			
1,4-Naphthalenedione, 2-chloro-5,8-dimethoxy-3-(methylamino)-	C_6H_{12}	414(3.84),460s(3.62)	39-0696-79C
$C_{13}H_{12}ClN_3$			
Propanedinitrile, [[4-(2-chloroethyl)methylamino]phenyl]methylene]-	EtOH	425(4.69)	110-1769-79
	EtOH-KOH	338(--)	110-1769-79
	CCl_4	414(--)	110-1769-79
	KBr	428(--)	110-1769-79
$C_{13}H_{12}Cl_2O_4$			
Acetic acid, [2,3-dichloro-4-(2-methylene-1-oxobutyl)phenoxy]-	H_2SO_4	270(3.7),330(3.7),345(3.7),370(3.8)	83-1037-79
after standing	H_2SO_4	320(4.3)	83-1037-79
$C_{13}H_{12}D_2O_2$			
1H-Indene-2-carboxaldehyde, 1-(hydroxymethyl-d_2)-1,3-dimethyl-, (+)-	EtOH	234(3.79),307(4.05)	39-1273-79C
$C_{13}H_{12}D_6N_2O$			
1H-Imidazole, 2,5-dihydro-5,5-dimethyl-2,2-di(methyl-d_3)-4-phenyl-, 3-oxide	EtOH	220(3.90),285(4.00)	103-0092-79

Compound	Solvent	$\lambda_{max}(\log \epsilon)$	Ref.
$C_{13}H_{12}FN$			
[1,1'-Biphenyl]-2-amine, 2'-fluoro-N-methyl-	EtOH	222(4.33),305(3.65)	33-2129-79
[1,1'-Biphenyl]-2-amine, 4'-fluoro-N-methyl-	EtOH	225(4.38),307(3.66)	33-2129-79
$C_{13}H_{12}K$			
Potassium, (diphenylmethyl)-	ether	432(4.60)	23-0999-79
	THF	440(4.63)	23-0999-79
	$MeOCH_2CH_2OMe$	441(4.64)	23-0999-79
$C_{13}H_{12}N_2$			
Benzenemethanamine, N-(3-pyridinyl-methylene)-	EtOH	257(3.14),261(3.16), 269(3.04)	44-4332-79
$C_{13}H_{12}N_2O$			
Acetamide, 2-cyano-2-(2,3-dihydro-1H-inden-1-ylidene)-N-methyl-	$CHCl_3$	300s(4.28),328(4.38)	80-1485-79
Benzamide, N-(2-aminophenyl)-	H_2O	228(4.30),288(3.59)	104-0101-79
	acid	240(4.13)	104-0101-79
Benzamide, N-(4-aminophenyl)-	H_2O	230(4.07),280(3.93)	104-0101-79
	acid	260(4.13)	104-0101-79
Benzamide, 2-amino-N-phenyl-	EtOH	218(4.16),256(3.84), 338(3.20)	2-0593-79A
	H_2O	250(4.06),315(3.64)	104-0101-79
	acid	262(3.94)	104-0101-79
Benzamide, 4-amino-N-phenyl-	H_2O	295(4.32)	104-0101-79
	acid	260(4.00)	104-0101-79
3-Buten-2-one, 4-(1H-imidazol-1-yl)-4-phenyl-	MeOH	209(4.17),228s(3.94), 277(4.14)	39-0584-79C
	$MeOH-HClO_4$	209(4.17),225s(4.03), 257(3.91)	39-0584-79C
2,4,6-Cycloheptatrien-1-one, 2-(2-phenylhydrazino)-	MeOH	249(4.48),338(4.01), 404(4.07)	18-2447-79
6-Oxa-1-azabicyclo[3.1.0]hex-3-ene-5-carbonitrile, 2,2-dimethyl-3-phenyl-	EtOH	215(3.89),269(3.95)	12-2035-79
Pyrido[1,2-a]benzimidazole, 9-methoxy-7-methyl-	MeOH	233(4.6),238(4.6), 247(4.5)	95-0880-79
Pyrido[1,2-a]benzimidazol-9(5H)-one, 5,7-dimethyl-	MeOH	217(4.6),239(4.3), 265(4.0)	95-0880-79
2H-Pyrrole-5-carbonitrile, 2,2-dimethyl-3-phenyl-, 1-oxide	EtOH	211(3.93),256(4.07), 362(3.95)	12-1785-79
$C_{13}H_{12}N_2OS_3$			
4-Thiazolidinone, 3-ethyl-5-(3-methyl-2(3H)-benzothiazolylidene)-2-thioxo-	EtOH	410s(4.32),428(4.52)	73-1413-79
$C_{13}H_{12}N_2O_2$			
2,5-Cyclohexadien-1-one, 5-amino-4-[(4-hydroxyphenyl)imino]-2-methyl-	neutral	464(3.88)	39-0304-79B
	anion	556(4.22)	39-0304-79B
Pyrazinemethanol, 5-phenyl-, acetate	EtOH	251(4.14),291(4.08)	94-2027-79
$C_{13}H_{12}N_2O_3$			
2,4(3H,5H)-Furandione, 3-(1-aminoethylidene)-5-[(phenylamino)methylene]-	EtOH	246(4.16),292(4.22), 376(4.52)	4-1335-79
1H-Pyrazole-3-carboxylic acid, 5-acetyl-1-phenyl-, methyl ester	CH_2Cl_2	end absorption	24-1193-79
1H-Pyrazole-4-carboxylic acid, 5-acetyl-1-phenyl-, methyl ester	CH_2Cl_2	254(4.01)	24-1193-79
1H-Pyrrole-2,5-dione, 3-acetyl-4-[(4-methylphenyl)amino]-	EtOH	283(4.24),337(4.03)	95-0818-79

Compound	Solvent	$\lambda_{max}(\log \epsilon)$	Ref.
$C_{13}H_{12}N_2O_3S$			
3-Isothiazolecarboxylic acid, 4-amino-5-benzoyl-, ethyl ester	MeCN	256(3.92),390(4.09)	5-1534-79
Thiazolo[3,2-a]benzimidazole-2-carboxylic acid, 6-hydroxy-3-methyl-, ethyl ester	pH 1	313(3.41),372(3.35)	18-3096-79
	pH 13	308(3.51),415(3.29)	18-3096-79
	EtOH	240(3.98),255(3.90), 361(3.78)	18-3096-79
$C_{13}H_{12}N_2O_4$			
1H-Pyrazole-4-carboxylic acid, 5-(4-methoxybenzoyl)-, methyl ester	EtOH	221(4.16),292(4.24)	73-0781-79
	ether	218(4.20),283(4.21)	73-0781-79
1H-Pyrazole-4-carboxylic acid, 5-(4-methoxybenzoyl)-, methyl ester	EtOH	230(4.17),297(4.27)	73-0781-79
	ether	221(4.19),290(4.24)	73-0781-79
1H-Pyrazole-5-carboxylic acid, 4-(4-methoxybenzoyl)-1-methyl-	EtOH	220(4.11),287(4.24)	73-0781-79
	ether	215(4.07),285(4.14), 305(4.22)	73-0781-79
5-Pyrimidinecarboxylic acid, 2-(2-ethoxyphenyl)-1,4-dihydro-4-oxo-	EtOH	208(4.19),228(4.01), 263(3.89),323(3.99)	87-0263-79
$C_{13}H_{12}N_2S$			
Diazene, (3-methylphenyl)(phenylthio)-	toluene	330(4.0)	126-1651-79
$C_{13}H_{12}N_4$			
2,8-Phenazinediamine, 3-methyl-	neutral	438(4.13)	59-0421-79
	cation	506(4.30)	59-0421-79
$C_{13}H_{12}N_4O$			
Acetamide, N-[4-(4-cyano-3-methyl-1H-pyrazol-1-yl)phenyl]-	EtOH	283(4.45)	78-1331-79
Formamide, N-[4-(4-cyano-3,5-dimethyl-1H-pyrazol-1-yl)phenyl]-	EtOH	273(4.43)	78-1331-79
Imidazo[1,2-b][1,2,4]triazine, 3-methoxy-2-methyl-6-phenyl-	dioxan	246s(4.44),270s(4.23)	104-1798-79
Imidazo[1,2-b][1,2,4]triazin-3(4H)-one, 2,4-dimethyl-6-phenyl-	dioxan	271(4.23),350(3.91)	104-1798-79
$C_{13}H_{12}N_4OS$			
4H-Pyrimido[4,5-b][1,4]thiazin-4-one, 2-amino-1,7-dihydro-7-methyl-6-phenyl-	MeOH	235(4.170),266(4.258), 378(4.127)	83-0076-79
$C_{13}H_{12}N_4O_2$			
Benzo[g]pteridine-2,4(3H,10H)-dione, 3,6,10-trimethyl-	H_2O	266(4.57),370(4.01), 439(3.93)	33-0593-79
	MeCN	270(4.55),344(3.94), 441(3.93)	33-0593-79
Benzo[g]pteridine-2,4(3H,10H)-dione, 3,7,10-trimethyl-	H_2O	268(4.62),346(3.91), 446(3.99)	33-0593-79
	MeCN	270(4.55),330(3.86), 446(3.97)	33-0593-79
Benzo[g]pteridine-2,4(3H,10H)-dione, 3,8,10-trimethyl-	H_2O	264(4.40),365(3.94), 433(4.06)	33-0593-79
	MeCN	267(4.52),340(3.89), 435(4.04)	33-0593-79
Benzo[g]pteridine-2,4(3H,10H)-dione, 3,9,10-trimethyl-	H_2O	266(4.64),370(4.08), 439(3.98)	33-0593-79
	MeCN	268(4.60),344(3.97), 439(3.97)	33-0593-79
Carbamic acid, [4-(4-cyano-3-methyl-1H-pyrazol-1-yl)phenyl]-, methyl ester	EtOH	283(4.49)	78-1331-79
4H-Pyrimido[4,5-b][1,4]oxazin-4-one, 2-amino-6-(phenylmethyl)-	2M HCl	257(3.99),349(3.73)	87-0797-79
	2M NaOH	276(3.98),326(3.91)	87-0797-79

Compound	Solvent	λ_{max}(log ε)	Ref.
$C_{13}H_{12}N_4O_3$			
Benzamide, 4-amino-N-(2-amino-4-nitrophenyl)-	EtOH	300(4.14),290-300[sic] (4.32)	104-1730-79
Benzamide, 4-amino-N-(4-amino-2-nitrophenyl)-	EtOH	240(4.09)	104-1730-79
Benzo[g]pteridine-2,4(3H,10H)-dione, 10-(2-hydroxyethyl)-3-methyl-	EtOH	265(4.35),332(3.84), 421s(3.82),437(3.86), 456s(3.76)	4-1365-79
$C_{13}H_{12}N_4S$			
1,2,4-Triazolo[4,3-a]pyrazine, 3-methyl-8-[(phenylmethyl)thio]-	EtOH	258(4.01),315(3.94)	44-1028-79
$C_{13}H_{12}N_4S_2$			
Thiazolo[5,4-d]pyrimidin-7-amine, 2-(methylthio)-N-(phenylmethyl)-	EtOH	248(4.39),288(4.23), 308(4.08),320(4.01)	2-0307-79B
$C_{13}H_{12}N_4S_3$			
Thiourea, N-[4-amino-5-cyano-2-(methylthio)-3-thienyl]-N'-phenyl-	EtOH	280(4.40)	95-1081-79
$C_{13}H_{12}N_8O_4S_3$			
5-Thia-1-azabicyclo[4.2.0]oct-2-ene-2-carboxylic acid, 8-oxo-7-[(1H-tetrazol-1-ylacetyl)amino]-3-[(1,2,3-thiadiazol-5-ylthio)methyl]-	MeOH	262(3.89),309(3.60)	87-1214-79
$C_{13}H_{12}O$			
1,3-Cyclohexadiene-1-carboxaldehyde, 6-phenyl-	EtOH	301(4.10)	32-0195-79
4H-Fluoren-4-one, 1,4a,9,9a-tetrahydro-	EtOH	227(3.95),267(3.06), 274(3.04),334(2.08)	118-0987-79
4H-Fluoren-4-one, 3,4a,9,9a-tetrahydro-	EtOH	254s(2.56),261(2.79), 266(2.97),273(3.00)	118-0987-79
$C_{13}H_{12}O_2$			
Benzeneacetic acid, α-cyclopentadienyl-	EtOH	247(3.49)	1-0307-79
5H-Benzocycloheptene-5-carboxylic acid, methyl ester	EtOH	273(3.90)	88-0867-79
$C_{13}H_{12}O_3$			
Ethanone, 1-(1-hydroxy-5-methyl-2-naphthalenyl)-	MeCN	255(4.54),285(3.67), 295(3.61),309(3.54)	107-0877-79
Ethanone, 1-[6-hydroxy-2-(1-methylethenyl)-5-benzofuranyl]- (euparin)	$CHCl_3$	240(4.32),266(4.48), 293(4.11),304(4.04)	44-1429-79
2H-Pyran-2-one, 6-methyl-4-(phenylmethoxy)-	MeOH	284(3.82)	150-0110-79S
$C_{13}H_{12}O_3S_4$			
4H-Thiopyran-4-one, 2,6-bis(methylthio)-3-(phenylsulfonyl)-	EtOH	277(4.25)	95-0038-79
$C_{13}H_{12}O_4$			
1,4-Naphthalenedione, 6-ethyl-5-hydroxy-7-methoxy-	MeOH	220(4.83),262(4.56), 268s(4.56),426(4.01)	150-2685-79
$C_{13}H_{12}O_5$			
4H-1-Benzopyran-3-acetic acid, 2-ethyl-5-hydroxy-4-oxo-	EtOH	237(4.46),258s(4.19), 326(3.86)	102-0311-79
2,4-Pentadienoic acid, 5-(6-methoxy-1,3-benzodioxol-5-yl)-, (Z,E)-	MeOH	220(4.15),250(4.05), 260(4.06),300(4.01),	78-0385-79

Compound	Solvent	λ_{max}(log ϵ)	Ref.
(cont.)		362(4.17)	78-0385-79
2,4-Pentadienoic acid, 5-(6-methoxy-1,3-benzodioxol-5-yl)-, (Z,Z)-	MeOH	220(4.23),345(4.07), 260(4.07),300(4.05), 362(4.13)	78-0385-79
$C_{13}H_{12}O_6$			
1H-2-Benzopyran-3-carboxaldehyde, 5,6,7-trimethoxy-1-oxo-	MeOH	247(4.2),270(3.7), 338(3.5)	2-0642-79A
$C_{13}H_{12}O_7$			
1H-2-Benzopyran-3-carboxylic acid, 5,6,7-trimethoxy-1-oxo-	MeOH	252(4.21),288(3.71), 300(3.72),334(3.53)	2-0642-79A
$C_{13}H_{13}BrN_2O$			
2H-Pyrrole-5-carbonitrile, 4-bromo-3,4-dihydro-2,2-dimethyl-3-phenyl-, 1-oxide	EtOH	212(3.93),276(4.09)	12-1785-79
$C_{13}H_{13}BrN_4O_4$			
1H-Purine-2,6-dione, 7-(4-bromo-3,6-dihydro-6-methyl-3-oxo-2H-pyran-2-yl)-3,7-dihydro-1,3-dimethyl-, (2R-trans)-	MeOH	267(4.05)	39-2682-79C
$C_{13}H_{13}BrO_4$			
Propanedioic acid, [[2-(bromomethyl)-phenyl]methylene]-, dimethyl ester	DMSO	284(4.1)	1-0138-79
$C_{13}H_{13}Cl$			
Bicyclo[2.2.1]hept-2-ene, 7-(4-chloro-phenyl), syn	hexane	255(--),261(2.96)	44-4899-79
$C_{13}H_{13}ClN_4O_4$			
1H-Purine-2,6-dione, 7-(4-chloro-3,6-dihydro-6-methyl-3-oxo-2H-pyran-2-yl)-3,7-dihydro-1,3-dimethyl-, (2R-trans)-	MeOH	255(3.96),272(3.93)	39-2682-79C
$C_{13}H_{13}ClN_4O_5$			
9H-Purine, 2-chloro-6-methoxy-9-(6,6,7,7-tetradehydro-6,7-dideoxy-α-L-idoheptofuranosyl)-	pH 1	258(3.99)	136-0141-79H
	pH 7	257(3.93)	136-0141-79H
	pH 12	257(3.97)	136-0141-79H
	MeOH	257(4.11)	136-0141-79H
$C_{13}H_{13}ClO_2$			
Naphthalene, 6-(chloromethyl)-2,3-di-methoxy-	MeOH	238(4.80),268(3.84), 297(4.81),313(3.34), 320(3.21),325(3.35)	5-1212-79
$C_{13}H_{13}Cl_4NO_6S$			
Pyrrolo[2,1-b]thiazole-3,6-dicarboxylic acid, 6-chlorohexahydro-2,2-dimethyl-5,7-dioxo-, 6-methyl 3-(2,2,2-tri-chloroethyl) ester	n.s.g.	255(3.74),270(3.70)	142-0227-79B
$C_{13}H_{13}FN_2O$			
Benzeneacetonitrile, 4-fluoro-α-(4- mor-pholinylmethylene)-	MeOH	217(4.08),293(4.35)	83-0039-79
$C_{13}H_{13}N$			
Benzenamine, 4-methyl-N-phenyl-	EtOH	207(4.42),287(4.32)	4-0257-79

Compound	Solvent	$\lambda_{max}(\log \epsilon)$	Ref.
[1,1'-Biphenyl]-2-amine, N-methyl-	EtOH	226(4.33),258(3.91)	33-2129-79
1H-Pyrrolizine, 2,3-dihydro-6-phenyl-	MeOH	210(4.16),234(4.01), 277(4.03)	83-0896-79
Pyrrolo[2,1-a]isoquinoline, 5,6-dihydro-2-methyl-	MeOH	213(4.00),317(4.08)	83-0896-79
$C_{13}H_{13}NO$			
Indeno[1,2-d]azepin-4(1H)-one, 2,3,5,10-tetrahydro-	EtOH	207(4.28),260(4.01)	138-0807-79
Phenol, 2-[(phenylamino)methyl]-, monohydrochloride	EtOH	208(4.18),223s(3.88), 246(3.83),278(3.58), 305(2.95)	150-3801-79
$C_{13}H_{13}NO_2$			
1,3-Cyclopentanedione, 2-[1-(phenyl-	hexane	234(4.23),321(4.31)	131-0077-79D
amino)ethylidene]-	EtOH	314(4.32)	131-0077-79D
Furo[3,4-b]quinolin-9(3H)-one, 1,4-dihydro-3,3-dimethyl-	n.s.g.	239(4.52),314(4.11), 326(4.15)	23-3296-79
Quinoline, 2-methyl-4-(2-propenyloxy)-, 1-oxide	MeOH	223(4.56),245(4.34), 333(3.94)	94-1813-79
Salicylaldimine, N-[1-(2-furanyl)ethyl]-, (S)-	hexane	216(4.46),256(4.15), 260s(4.11),320(3.67)	35-5186-79
	MeOH	216(4.43),256(4.11), 314(3.61)	35-5186-79
$C_{13}H_{13}NO_2S_2$			
2-Azetidinone, 4-[[1-(methylthio)-3-oxo-3-phenyl-1-propenyl]thio]-, (E)-	dioxan	268(3.97),338(4.23)	142-1315-79
(Z)-	dioxan	262(3.93),275(3.90), 331(4.27)	142-1315-79
$C_{13}H_{13}NO_3$			
9H-Carbazole-1,4-dione, 1,4,5,6,7,8-hexahydro-3-hydroxy-2-methyl-	pH 1	237(4.31),293(4.28), 370(3.64),510(3.14)	142-0411-79B
	pH 13	246(4.39),306(4.10), 365(3.67),595(3.21)	142-0411-79B
2-Cyclopenten-1-one, 2,4-dimethyl-5-(4-nitrophenyl)-	EtOH	219(4.11),275(4.00)	88-3457-79
2-Cyclopenten-1-one, 3,5-dimethyl-2-(4-nitrophenyl)-	EtOH	237(4.00),288(4.11)	88-3457-79
Ethanedione, cyclopropylphenyl-, 2-(O-acetyloxime), (Z)-	C_6H_{12}	255(4.07)	39-0156-79B
2,4(3H,5H)-Furandione, 3-[1-(phenyl-	hexane	223(3.84),306(4.30)	131-0077-79D
amino)propylidene]-	EtOH	300(4.30)	131-0077-79D
1H-Indole-1-butanoic acid, 3-methyl-γ-oxo-	MeOH	239(4.33),292(3.87), 301(3.91)	44-3994-79
1(2H)-Isoquinolinone, N-(2-acetoxyethyl)-	EtOH	209(4.41),224(4.24), 279(3.90),286(3.90), 325(3.64)	44-0285-79
1,4-Naphthalenedione, 2-(dimethylamino)-5-methoxy-	$CHCl_3$	273(4.19),385(3.54), 464(3.59)	12-0575-79
1,4-Naphthalenedione, 2-(dimethylamino)-8-methoxy-	MeOH	217s(4.19),238(4.31), 268(4.04),282s(3.94), 346s(3.47),370s(3.54), 394(3.57),450s(3.34)	12-0575-79
2-Propenoic acid, 2-cyano-3-(4-methoxyphenyl)-, ethyl ester	n.s.g.	240(4.07)	2-0541-79A
1H-Pyrrole-2-carboxylic acid, 3-hydroxy-1-methyl-, phenylmethyl ester	EtOH	265(4.32)	94-1448-79
1H-Pyrrole-2-carboxylic acid, 3-hydroxy-4-methyl-, phenylmethyl ester	EtOH	269(4.20)	94-1448-79

Compound	Solvent	λ_{max}(log ε)	Ref.
1H-Pyrrole-2-carboxylic acid, 3-hydroxy-5-methyl-, phenylmethyl ester	EtOH	274(4.33)	94-1448-79
1H-Pyrrole-3-carboxylic acid, 4-hydroxy-1-phenyl-, ethyl ester	MeOH	261(4.19),300(3.30), 356(3.40)	49-1387-79
$C_{13}H_{13}NO_4$			
1,3-Dioxane-4,6-dione, 2,2-dimethyl-5-[(phenylamino)methylene]-	hexane	222(4.16),327(4.41)	131-0077-79D
	EtOH	326(4.39)	131-0077-79D
3-Quinolinepropanoic acid, 4-hydroxy-2-methoxy-	MeOH	230(4.31),249s(3.71), 259s(3.63),270(3.67), 282s(3.62),291s(3.46), 303(3.48),315(3.51)	118-0903-79
	MeOH-acid	221(4.28),251(4.31), 302(3.77)	118-0903-79
$C_{13}H_{13}NO_4S$			
2H-1,4-Benzothiazine-2-acetic acid, 3,4-dihydro-4-methyl-α,3-dioxo-, ethyl ester	dioxan	380(3.7)	83-0302-79
1H-Pyrrole-3-carboxylic acid, 5-[(4-methylphenyl)sulfonyl]-, methyl ester	EtOH	260(4.26)	94-2857-79
$C_{13}H_{13}NO_5$			
Benzenepropanal, 2-acetoxy-β-oxo-, α-(O-acetyloxime)-, (Z)-	MeOH	218(4.06),302(4.07)	56-0229-79
1H-Indole-3-acetic acid, α-hydroxy-1-(methoxycarbonyl)-, methyl ester	MeOH	282(3.62)	142-0187-79B
1H-Indole-3-carboxylic acid, 4,7-dihydro-5-hydroxy-2,6-dimethyl-4,7-dioxo-	MeOH	220(4.32),241(4.18), 291(4.16),330(3.84), 450(2.73)	142-0411-79B
3-Quinolinecarboxylic acid, 1-ethyl-1,4-dihydro-6-hydroxy-7-methoxy-4-oxo-	MeOH	255(4.8),331(4.2), 341(4.2)	4-1353-79
$C_{13}H_{13}NO_5S$			
Thiophene, 2,5-dihydro-2-[(4-methoxyphenyl)methylene]-3-methyl-4-nitro-, 1,1-dioxide	HOAc	390(4.3)	104-0164-79
$C_{13}H_{13}NO_6S$			
Phenol, 2-methoxy-4-[(3-methyl-4-nitro-2(5H)-thienylidene)methyl]-, S,S-dioxide	HOAc	406(4.4)	104-0164-79
$C_{13}H_{13}N_3$			
Benzaldehyde, (2-aminophenyl)hydrazone	EtOH	243s(4.14),298(3.87), 353(4.24)	4-1005-79
Benzenamine, N-methyl-2-(phenylazo)-	EtOH	207(4.16),242(4.06), 317(4.04),455(3.81)	7-0563-79
Benzenamine, N-methyl-4-(phenylazo)-	MeOH	405(4.45)	56-0989-79
Benzenecarboximidic acid, 2-phenylhydrazide	EtOH-NH_3	217s(4.11),251(4.03), 313(3.98)	65-2056-79
hydrochloride	EtOH	233(4.31),274(3.53)	65-2056-79
1H-Pyrazol-3-amine, 4,5-dihydro-1-(2-naphthalenyl)-	EtOH	259(4.32),304(4.16), 350s(3.43)	150-0801-79
2-Pyridinamine, 3-[[(phenylmethyl)imino]methyl]-	CH_2Cl_2	262(3.4),338(3.6)	64-1019-79B
2-Pyridinecarboximidamide, N-(2-methylphenyl)-	anion	271(4.03)	94-1255-79
2-Pyridinecarboximidamide, N-(3-methylphenyl)-	anion	272(3.95)	94-1255-79

Compound	Solvent	λ_{max}(log ε)	Ref.
2-Pyridinecarboximidamide, N-(4-methyl-phenyl)-	anion	272(3.99)	94-1255-79
Pyrido[1,2-a]benzimidazol-9(5H)-imine, 5,7-dimethyl-	pH 1	219(4.5),226(4.5), 241(4.5)	95-0880-79
	MeOH	220(4.5),228s(4.4), 244(4.4)	95-0880-79
$C_{13}H_{13}N_3O$			
Benzamide, 2-amino-N-(2-aminophenyl)-	H_2O	305(3.69)	104-0101-79
	acid	232(4.04)	104-0101-79
Benzamide, 3-amino-N-(2-aminophenyl)-	H_2O	294(3.70)	104-0101-79
	acid	232(4.10)	104-0101-79
Benzamide, 3-amino-N-(4-aminophenyl)-	H_2O	288(4.25)	104-0101-79
	acid	232(4.09)	104-0101-79
Benzamide, 4-amino-N-(4-aminophenyl)-	H_2O	290(4.32)	104-0101-79
	acid	260(4.07)	104-0101-79
Benzamide, N-(2,4-diaminophenyl)-	H_2O	294(3.70)	104-0101-79
	acid	245(4.20)	104-0101-79
[1,1'(4H,4'H)-Bipyridine]-4-carbo-nitrile, 2',6'-dimethyl-4'-oxo-	EtOH	261.5(4.29)	39-1698-79C
Phenol, 4-[(2-amino-4-imino-5-methyl-2,5-cyclohexadien-1-yliden)amino]-, zwitterion	H_2O	624(4.36)	39-0304-79B
	cation	492(4.07)	39-0304-79B
	anion	504(4.07)	39-0304-79B
Pyrazinecarboxamide, N-(1-phenylethyl)-, (S)-	isooctane	207(4.25),266(3.89), 333f(2.70)	39-2881-79C
	EtOH	207(4.24),270(3.92), 323(2.78)	39-2881-79C
	MeCN	207(4.27),268(3.94), 322(2.78)	39-2881-79C
2-Pyridinecarboximidamide, N-(3-meth-oxyphenyl)-	anion	274(3.96)	94-1255-79
2-Pyridinecarboximidamide, N-(4-meth-oxyphenyl)-	anion	272(3.99)	94-1255-79
$C_{13}H_{13}N_3O_2$			
Acetamide, N,N'-3,5-quinolinediylbis-	EtOH	231(3.74),255(4.26), 325(3.41)	94-2627-79
Acetamide, N,N'-3,8-quinolinediylbis-	EtOH	235(3.87),263(4.17)	94-2627-79
Formamide, N-(1,2,3,4,5,6-hexahydro-4-oxoazepino[4,5-b]indol-5-yl)-	EtOH	222(4.50),283(3.93)	103-0780-79
$C_{13}H_{13}N_3O_2S_2$			
Benzoic acid, 4-[[(2-thiazolylamino)-thioxomethyl]amino]-, ethyl ester	n.s.g.	317(4.44)	87-0028-79
5-Pyrimidinecarbodithioic acid, 6-ami-no-1,2,3,4-tetrahydro-3-methyl-2,4-dioxo-1-phenyl-, methyl ester	EtOH	238(3.93),262(4.11), 346(4.41)	95-0515-79 +142-0485-79
$C_{13}H_{13}N_3O_2S_3$			
Benzenesulfonamide, N-[4-amino-5-cyano-2-(methylthio)-3-thienyl]-4-methyl-	EtOH	227(4.35),298(4.06), 320(3.99)	95-1081-79
$C_{13}H_{13}N_3O_3$			
2-Propenal, 3-[(2,3-dimethyl-1H-indol-5-yl)amino]-2-nitro-	EtOH	228(4.29),285(4.14), 382(4.18)	103-1113-79
2-Propenal, 3-[(2,3-dimethyl-1H-indol-6-yl)amino]-2-nitro-	EtOH	227(4.29),288(3.93), 407(4.16)	103-1113-79

Compound	Solvent	λ_{max}(log ε)	Ref.
$C_{13}H_{13}N_3O_3S$			
Benzoic acid, 4-[[(2-thienylamino)carbonyl]amino]-, ethyl ester	n.s.g.	290(4.45)	87-0028-79
$C_{13}H_{13}N_3O_3S_2$			
Acetic acid, [6-cyano-4,5-dihydro-8-(methylthio)-4-oxo-1H-thieno[3,4-b]-[1,4]diazepin-2(3H)-ylidene]-, ethyl ester	EtOH	230(4.14),294(4.44), 350(4.15)	142-0401-79
$C_{13}H_{13}N_3O_4$			
L-Alanine, N-(2-quinoxalinylcarbonyl)-, methyl ester, N-oxide	C_6H_{12}	250(4.5),340(3.7), 358(3.7)	78-2571-79
	EtOH	250(4.6),340(3.7), 358(3.7)	78-2571-79
3,5-Methanofuro[3,2-b]pyridin-6(2H)-one, hexahydro-4-(5-nitro-2-pyridinyl)-	$CHCl_3$	355(3.68)	39-1525-79C
2,4(1H,3H)-Pyrimidinedione, 6-amino-5-(benzoyloxy)-1,3-dimethyl-	$CHCl_3$	242(4.18),272(4.20)	94-2143-79
2H-Pyrrole-5-carbonitrile, 3,4-dihydro-2,3-dimethyl-4-(nitrooxy)-3-phenyl-, 1-oxide	EtOH	270(4.08)	12-1785-79
$C_{13}H_{13}N_3O_4S$			
Carbamic acid, [6-methyl-8-thioxo-1,3-dioxolo[4,5-g]quinazolin-7(8H)-yl-, ethyl ester	EtOH	205(4.16),227s(4.45), 231(4.46),256s(4.24), 274(4.25),352s(3.98), 366(4.21),377(4.11), 386(4.18)	1-0079-79
$C_{13}H_{13}N_3O_4S_2$			
Cyclohexanecarbodithioic acid, 2-imino-, 2,4-dinitrophenyl ester	EtOH	258(4.12),307(3.84), 384(3.96)	150-1732-79
$C_{13}H_{13}N_3O_7$			
1H-Pyrrolo[3,2-d]pyrimidine-6-acetic acid, 2,3,4,5-tetrahydro-7-(methoxycarbonyl)-1,3-dimethyl-α,2,4-trioxo-, methyl ester	EtOH	228(4.27),255(3.84), 347(3.66)	44-3830-79
$C_{13}H_{13}N_3S_2$			
2-Thiophenecarbonitrile, 3-amino-5-(methylthio)-4-[(phenylmethyl)amino]-	EtOH	306(4.03)	95-1081-79
$C_{13}H_{13}N_5OS$			
Hydrazinecarbothioamide, 2-(1,3,4,6-tetrahydro-4-oxoazepino[4,5-b]indol-5(2H)-ylidene)-	EtOH	220(4.47),390(4.40)	103-0780-79
3H-Pyrazol-3-one, 2,4-dihydro-5-methyl-4-[(5-methyl-1H-1,2,4-triazol-3-yl)-thio]-2-phenyl-	EtOH	204(4.33),244(4.13)	48-0495-79
$C_{13}H_{13}N_7O_4$			
1H-Purine-2,6-dione, 3,7-dihydro-1,3-dimethyl-7-(1,4,6,7-tetrahydro-4-methyl-7-oxopyrano[3,4-d]-1,2,3-triazol-6-yl)-, (4R-trans)-	MeOH	252(4.03),274(4.01)	39-2682-79C

Compound	Solvent	λ_{max}(log ε)	Ref.
$C_{13}H_{13}N_7O_6$			
α-D-Arabinofuranoside, methyl 2,5-diazido-2,5-dideoxy-, 3-(4-nitrobenzoate)	MeOH	258(4.12)	136-0071-79B
α-D-Arabinofuranoside, methyl 3,5-diazido-3,5-dideoxy-, 2-(4-nitrobenzoate)	MeOH	258(4.15)	136-0071-79B
$C_{13}H_{14}$			
Bicyclo[2.2.1]hept-2-ene, 7-phenyl-, syn-	hexane	243(--),248(2.88)	44-4899-79
$C_{13}H_{14}BrNO_4S$			
Pyridinium, 2-bromo-3-hydroxy-1-methyl-, p-toluenesulfonate	EtOH	225(3.84),265(3.51), 322(3.79),347(3.54)	39-2528-79C
$C_{13}H_{14}BrN_3O$			
1H-1,2,3-Triazole, 1-(4-bromophenyl)-5-(3,4-dihydro-2H-pyran-2-yl)-4,5-dihydro-	EtOH	229(4.17),293s(3.94), 313(4.02)	103-0488-79
$C_{13}H_{14}ClNO_2$			
1H-Indole-2-carboxylic acid, 3-(2-chloroethyl)-, ethyl ester	EtOH	229(4.40),296(4.27)	23-0289-79
$C_{13}H_{14}ClNO_3S$			
Pyridinium, 2-chloro-3-hydroxy-1-methyl-, p-toluenesulfonate	EtOH	225(4.54),265(3.88), 345(3.88)	39-2528-79C
$C_{13}H_{14}ClN_3O_2$			
Acetamide, N-[2-[5-(3-chlorophenyl)-1,2,4-oxadiazol-3-yl]ethyl]-N-methyl-	EtOH	253(4.21),286(3.20), 295(3.07)	150-0801-79
Acetamide, N-[2-[5-(4-chlorophenyl)-1,2,4-oxadiazol-3-yl]ethyl]-N-methyl-	EtOH	260(4.35)	150-0801-79
$C_{13}H_{14}F_3NO_5S$			
1H-Pyrrole-3,4-dicarboxylic acid, 2-(ethylthio)-1-methyl-5-(trifluoroacetyl)-, dimethyl ester	CH_2Cl_2	325(3.97)	5-0650-79
$C_{13}H_{14}F_3N_3O_4$			
2H-2,6-Methanobenz[g][1,3,5]oxadiazocin-9-ol, 4-amino-2-methyl-3,6-dihydro-, hydrotrifluoroacetate	EtOH	277(3.39),281s(3.33)	24-0001-79
$C_{13}H_{14}F_7O_4P$			
Phosphonic acid, [2,3,5,6-tetrafluoro-4-(trifluoromethyl)phenyl]-, 1-ethoxyethyl ethyl ester	EtOH	218(3.94),278(3.36)	65-0464-79
$C_{13}H_{14}N_2$			
3,4-Diazabicyclo[4.1.0]hepta-2,4-diene, 7,7-dimethyl-2-phenyl-	$CHCl_3$	303(3.69)	20-0905-79
1H-Pyrazole, 5-methyl-1-phenyl-3-propenyl-	EtOH	212(3.96),263(4.16)	4-0657-79
1H-Pyrazole, 5-methyl-1-phenyl-3-(1-propenyl)-, (E)-	EtOH	212(4.02),257(4.26)	4-0657-79
$C_{13}H_{14}N_2O$			
Azetidine, 1-(cyanocarbonyl)-2,2-dimethyl-3-phenyl-	EtOH	217(4.00),230(3.90)	12-1775-79
Benzo[b][1,8]naphthyridin-5(1H)-one, 6,7,8,9-tetrahydro-2-methyl-	EtOH	249(4.48),279(3.66), 289(3.64),343(3.99)	4-0137-79

Compound	Solvent	$\lambda_{max}(\log \epsilon)$	Ref.
5H-Cyclopenta[b][1,8]naphthyridin-5-one, 1,6,7,8-tetrahydro-2,4-dimethyl-	EtOH	250(4.18),276(3.20), 324(3.88)	4-0137-79
5H-Cyclopenta[b][1,8]naphthyridin-5-one, 1,6,7,8-tetrahydro-2,8-dimethyl-	EtOH	247(4.38),289(3.68), 328(3.98)	4-0137-79
Cyclopenta[d]pyrido[1,2-a]pyrimidin-10(1H)-one, 2,3-dihydro-3,8-dimethyl-	EtOH	252(4.06),357(3.93)	4-0137-79
Cyclopenta[d]pyrido[1,2-a]pyrimidin-10(1H)-one, 2,3-dihydro-6,8-dimethyl-	EtOH	249(4.14),350(4.13)	4-0137-79
6-Oxa-1-azabicyclo[3.1.0]hexane-5-carbonitrile, 2,2-dimethyl-3-phenyl-	EtOH	222(2.92),248(2.04), 253(2.18),259(2.28), 266(2.18)	12-1775-79
11H-Pyrido[2,1-b]quinazolin-11-one, 1,2,3,4-tetrahydro-9-methyl-	EtOH	251(4.12),259(4.07), 355(3.92)	4-0137-79
2H-Pyrrole-5-carbonitrile, 3,4-dihydro-2,2-dimethyl-3-phenyl-, 1-oxide	EtOH	273(3.98)	12-1775-79
2H-Pyrrol-2-one, 1,5-dihydro-3,4-dimethyl-5-[(4-methylphenyl)imino]-, (Z)-	EtOH	246(4.31),345(3.66)	88-1303-79
2H-Pyrrol-2-one, 1,5-dihydro-1,3,4-trimethyl-5-(phenylimino)-	EtOH	247(4.42),356(3.30)	88-1303-79
$C_{13}H_{14}N_2O_2$			
1H-1,3-Benzodiazepine-1-carboxylic acid, 2-methyl-, ethyl ester	EtOH	240(3.95),285(3.72)	77-0534-79
1H-Indole, 2,3-dimethyl-5-(2-nitro-1-propenyl)-	MeOH	237(4.46),287(4.14), 370(4.11)	103-0276-79
4H-Pyrazol-4-one, 3-(1,1-dimethylethyl)-5-phenyl-, 2-oxide	isooctane	319(3.95),433(3.16)	44-3211-79
8-Quinolinol, 2-morpholino-	neutral	268(4.51),347(3.55)	123-0070-79
	acid	247(4.12),273(4.47), 322(3.98)	123-0070-79
	base	278(4.49),358(3.39)	123-0070-79
$C_{13}H_{14}N_2O_3$			
7H-Indazol-7-one, 4-acetyl-6-(1,1-dimethylethyl)-	n.s.g.	249(4.48)	70-1668-79
1H-Indole, 7-methoxy-2,3-dimethyl-6-(2-nitroethenyl)-	MeOH	233(4.46),275(4.14), 457(4.20)	103-0276-79
1H-Pyrazole-3-carboxylic acid, 5-hydroxy-1-(phenylmethyl)-, ethyl ester	MeOH	223(4.11),253s(3.53)	24-1712-79
4H-Pyrazol-4-one, 3-(1,1-dimethylethyl)-5-phenyl-, 1,2-dioxide	isooctane	258(4.14),285(4.04), 418(3.27)	44-3211-79
4-Pyridazinecarboxylic acid, 2,5-dihydro-5-(hydroxyphenylmethyl)-, methyl ester	MeOH	220s(3.86),323(3.6)	39-2215-79C
$C_{13}H_{14}N_2O_3S$			
[1]Benzothieno[2,3-d]pyrimidine-2-carboxylic acid, 1,4,5,6,7,8-hexahydro-4-oxo-, ethyl ester	pH 1	255(3.83),348(4.25)	87-0505-79
	pH 13	275(4.01),310(4.14)	87-0505-79
4-Pyrimidinol, 2,6-dimethyl-, 4-methylbenzenesulfonate	EtOH	233(3.95),245s(3.83)	150-1579-79
$C_{13}H_{14}N_2O_3S_2$			
4-Pyrimidinol, 6-methyl-2-(methylthio)-, 4-methylbenzenesulfonate	EtOH	231(4.14),245(4.16)	150-1579-79
$C_{13}H_{14}N_2O_4$			
Quinolinium, 4-amino-3-carboxy-1-ethyl-6-hydroxy-7-methoxy-, hydroxide, inner salt	MeOH	265(4.5),275(4.5), 338(4.0),350(4.0)	4-1353-79

Compound	Solvent	λmax(log ε)	Ref.
$C_{13}H_{14}N_2O_4S$			
Benzenamine, N,N-dimethyl-4-[(4-nitro-2-(5H)-thienylidene)methyl]-, S,S-dioxide	HOAc	502(4.6)	104-0164-79
$C_{13}H_{14}N_2O_5$			
Phenol, 2-[5-(acetoxyamino)-4,5-dihydro-3-isoxazolyl]-, acetate	EtOH	215(4.21),260(3.97), 270(3.78),308(3.63)	56-0229-79
2H-Pyrrol-2-one, 1-[[1,5-dihydro-4-(hydroxymethyl)-1-methyl-5-oxo-2H-pyrrol-2-ylidene]acetyl]-1,5-dihydro-4-methoxy (pukeleimide A and B)	MeOH	207(4.20),227(4.14), 291(4.45),330s(4.19)	88-2007-79
$C_{13}H_{14}N_2O_6$			
1H-Indole, 1-α-L-arabinopyranosyl-5-nitro-	EtOH	267(4.15),317(3.76)	103-0188-79
1H-Indole, 1-α-L-arabinopyranosyl-6-nitro-	EtOH	247(4.28),320(3.96), 355(3.90)	103-0188-79
$C_{13}H_{14}N_2S$			
2-Pyridinamine, N-[[(4-methylphenyl)-thio]methyl]-	EtOH	249(4.28),299(3.74)	130-0339-79
$C_{13}H_{14}N_4$			
6H-Imidazo[1,2-c]pyrimido[1,2-a]quinazoline, 2,3,7,8-tetrahydro-	EtOH	220(4.40),231(4.43), 237(4.45),262(3.97), 271(3.92),325(3.58), 341(3.48)	106-0844-79
$C_{13}H_{14}N_4O$			
Benzamide, 4-amino-N-(2,4-diaminophenyl)-	H_2O	285(4.26)	104-0101-79
	acid	242(4.14)	104-0101-79
$C_{13}H_{14}N_4O_2S$			
Isothiazolo[5,1-e][1,2,3]thiadiazole-7-S^{IV}, 1,6-dihydro-3,4,6-trimethyl-1-(4-nitrophenyl)-	C_6H_{12}	239(4.05),285(3.64), 355(3.79),475(4.63)	39-0926-79C
5-Pyrimidinecarbothioamide, 6-amino-1,2,3,4-tetrahydro-N,3-dimethyl-1-phenyl-	EtOH	260(4.40),298(4.20)	95-0515-79
1H-1,2,4-Triazolium, 4-(diacetylamino)-2,3-dihydro-5-methyl-1-phenyl-3-thioxo-, hydroxide, inner salt	EtOH	250(4.31),290(3.43)	94-1683-79
$C_{13}H_{14}N_4O_4$			
Carbamic acid, 4-(3,5-dimethyl-4-nitro-1H-pyrazol-1-yl)phenyl]-, methyl ester	EtOH	247(4.42),287(4.22)	78-1331-79
6aH-Cyclopropa[e]pyrazolo[1,5-a]pyrimidine-6a-carboxylic acid, 5a-acetyl-3-(aminocarbonyl)-5a,6-dihydro-, ethyl ester	EtOH	284(3.95)	142-0397-79
$C_{13}H_{14}N_4O_6$			
2H-Pyrrole-5-carboxaldehyde, 3,4-dihydro-3,3-dimethyl-, O-(2,4-dinitrophenyl)oxime, 1-oxide	EtOH	215(4.15),324(4.44)	12-1775-79
$C_{13}H_{14}N_8O_7$			
1,2,3-Triazin-5(2H)-one, 4,6-bis(dimethylamino)-2-(2,4,6-trinitrophenyl)-	CH_2Cl_2	546(4.26)	24-1535-79

Compound	Solvent	λmax(log ε)	Ref.
$C_{13}H_{14}O$			
Benzo[3',4']cyclobuta[1',2':1,7]cyclohept[1,2-b]oxirene, 1a,2,3,4,5,5a-hexahydro-	MeOH	264(3.21),270(3.39), 277(3.36)	111-0543-79
6,8-Ethano-7H-benzocyclohepten-7-one, 5,6,8,9-tetrahydro-	EtOH	212(4.0),255(2.20), 262(2.28),268(2.21), 271(2.06)	56-1221-79
$C_{13}H_{14}O_2$			
1H-Cyclopropa[a]naphthalene-1-carboxylic acid, 1a,2,3,7b-tetrahydro-, methyl ester, endo	EtOH	270(2.78),277(2.74)	88-0867-79
exo	EtOH	229(4.02),268(2.75), 277(2.65)	88-0867-79
Ethanone, 2-(dihydro-2(3H)-furanylidene)-1-(4-methylphenyl)-	EtOH	261s(4.08),289(4.38)	44-2073-79
Ethanone, 1-(2,3-dihydro-2-(1-methylethenyl)-5-benzofuranyl]- (tremetone)	EtOH	226(3.94),279(3.90), 286(3.90)	100-0203-79
3-Pentenoic acid, 2-methylene-5-phenyl-, methyl ester, (Z)-	heptane	249(3.6),306(2.7)	24-3480-79
$C_{13}H_{14}O_2S_3$			
3-Thiophenecarboxylic acid, 5-ethyl-2-(2-thienylthio)-, ethyl ester	MeOH	229(4.39),250(4.10), 310(3.93)	73-2997-79
$C_{13}H_{14}O_3$			
2H-1-Benzopyran-2-one, 4-butoxy-	MeOH	264s(3.88),268(4.00), 278(3.89),305(3.79), 315(3.65)	150-0110-79S
2H-1-Benzopyran-2-one, 4-(1,1-dimethylethoxy)-	MeOH	260s(3.88),268(4.00), 279(4.00),305(3.82), 314s(3.69)	150-0110-79S
1,3-Cyclopentanedione, 2-(4-methoxyphenyl)-2-methyl-	EtOH	220s(3.88),251(3.59), 273(3.43),282(3.38), 292(3.08)	12-1561-79
2-Naphthalenol, 5,7-dimethoxy-4-methyl-	EtOH	242(4.51),247s(4.39), 250(3.39)	150-0301-79
$C_{13}H_{14}O_4$			
Ethanone, 1-(7,8-dihydroxy-2,2-dimethyl-2H-1-benzopyran-6-yl)-	MeOH	230(4.2),246(3.9), 270(3.1)	18-1203-79
$C_{13}H_{14}O_4S_4$			
1,3-Dithiole-4,5-dicarboxylic acid, 2-(4-methyl-1,3-dithiol-2-ylidene)-, diethyl ester	MeCN	293(4.14),316(4.14), 447(3.16)	44-1476-79
$C_{13}H_{14}O_5$			
1,4-Epoxynaphthalene-5,8-dione, 1,4,4a-8a-tetrahydro-2,3-dimethoxy-6-methyl-, (1α,4α,4aα,8aα)-	EtOH	232(4.12),345(2.34)	33-2211-79
1(3H)-Isobenzofuranone, 3-acetyl-5,7-dimethoxy-3-methyl-	MeOH	259(4.13),295(3.75)	39-0337-79C
1(3H)-Isobenzofuranone, 5,7-dimethoxy-3-(2-methyloxiranyl)-	MeOH	258(4.27),293(3.83)	39-0337-79C
$C_{13}H_{14}O_5S_2$			
1,3-Dithiole-4,5-dicarboxylic acid, 2-(4-oxocyclohexylidene)-, dimethyl ester	CH_2Cl_2	257(4.10),328(3.11), 400(3.35)	44-0930-79

Compound	Solvent	$\lambda_{max}(\log \epsilon)$	Ref.
$C_{13}H_{14}S_2$			
Thiophene, 3-ethyl-2-(methylthio)-4-phenyl-	EtOH	233(4.20)	88-2493-79
$C_{13}H_{14}S_3$			
2,4-Cyclohexadiene-1-thione, 6-(hexahydro-1,3-benzodithiol-2-ylidene)-	C_6H_{12}	262(3.70),355(2.85), 580(--)	18-0496-79
	benzene	354(3.16),585(2.96)	18-0496-79
	EtOH	264(3.79),350(3.29), 580(3.07)	18-0496-79
	CH_2Cl_2	269(4.04),351(3.61), 584(3.42)	18-0496-79
$C_{13}H_{15}AsO_4$			
Propanedioic acid, (4-arseninylmethylene)-, diethyl ester	EtOH	230(4.06),325(4.37)	88-3141-79
$C_{13}H_{15}BrCl_3NO_2$			
Carbamic acid, bis(1-methylethyl)-, 2-bromo-3,4,6-trichlorophenyl ester	MeOH	210.5(4.77)	73-0918-79
$C_{13}H_{15}BrN_2O_7$			
Uridine, 2'-bromo-2'-deoxy-, 3',5'-diacetate	EtOH	257(3.94)	73-0439-79
Uridine, 5-bromo-2'-deoxy-, 3',5'-diacetate	EtOH	278(3.92)	73-0439-79
$C_{13}H_{15}BrN_4$			
1H-Imidazole, 2-[(4-bromophenyl)azo]-4,5-diethyl-	MeOH	247(--),287(--), 407(4.45)	56-2340-79
$C_{13}H_{15}BrN_4O_4$			
1H-Purine-2,6-dione, 7-(4-bromo-3,6-dihydro-3-hydroxy-6-methyl-2H-pyran-2-yl)-3,7-dihydro-1,3-dimethyl-	MeOH	274(3.93)	39-2682-79C
$C_{13}H_{15}BrO_4$			
2-Propenoic acid, 3-(3-bromo-4-hydroxyphenyl)-2-ethoxy-, ethyl ester, (Z)-	MeOH	287(4.36)	24-1571-79
$C_{13}H_{15}ClN_2S$			
Benzenamine, 4-chloro-N-(4-ethyl-4-methyl-5-methylene-2-thiazolidinylidene)-	EtOH	203(3.46),263(3.42)	103-0611-79
$C_{13}H_{15}Cl_3INO_2$			
Carbamic acid, bis(1-methylethyl)-, 3,4,6-trichloro-2-iodophenyl ester	MeOH	218(4.55),295(3.11)	73-0918-79
$C_{13}H_{15}Cl_3N_2O_4$			
Carbamic acid, bis(1-methylethyl)-, 3,4,6-trichloro-2-nitrophenyl ester	MeOH	211(4.45),292(3.12)	73-0918-79
$C_{13}H_{15}FN_2O_2S_3$			
1,2,3-Thiadiazolium, 4-methyl-5-(1-methyl-2-methylthiovinyl)-2-phenyl-, fluorosulfate	MeOH	226s(3.91),323(3.51), 460(4.45)	39-0926-79C
$C_{13}H_{15}FN_2O_7$			
Uridine, 2'-deoxy-5-fluoro-, 3',5'-diacetate	MeOH	269(3.97)	73-0439-79

Compound	Solvent	λ_{max}(log ϵ)	Ref.
$C_{13}H_{15}N$			
1H-Indole, 1,3-dimethyl-2-(1-methyl-ethenyl)-	EtOH	229(4.48),292(3.97)	39-2154-79C
$C_{13}H_{15}NO$			
6-Oxa-1-azabicyclo[3.1.0]hex-3-ene, 2,2,4-trimethyl-5-phenyl-	EtOH	217(3.77)	12-2041-79
2H-Pyrrole, 2,2,4-trimethyl-5-phenyl-, 1-oxide	EtOH	241(4.24),316(3.70)	12-2025-79
2-Pyrrolidinone, 5,5-dimethyl-3-(phen-ylmethylene)-, (E)-	EtOH	218(4.04),224(3.97), 278(3.31)	12-2041-79
(Z)-	EtOH	220(3.96),225(3.93), 283(4.20)	12-2041-79
$C_{13}H_{15}NOS$			
Morpholine, 4-(5-methylbenzo[b]thien-2-yl)-	MeOH	233(4.40),287(4.27)	73-2677-79
$C_{13}H_{15}NO_2$			
1,8(2H,5H)-Acridinedione, 3,4,6,7,9,10-hexahydro-	H_2O	249(4.32),395(3.91)	39-1593-79C
2-Propen-1-one, 3-(4-morpholinyl)-1-phenyl-	EtOH	247(4.06),343(4.38)	4-0217-79
3,5-Pyridinedicarbonitrile, 1-(1,1-di-methylethyl)-4-ethynyl-1,4-dihydro-	EtOH	233(4.35),253(3.95), 373(4.01)	49-0613-79
$C_{13}H_{15}NO_3$			
Butanoic acid, 3-oxo-2-[(phenylamino)-methylene]-, ethyl ester	hexane	228(4.10),239s(3.98), 334(4.34)	131-0077-79D
	EtOH	334(4.38)	131-0077-79D
2H-Furo[2,3-b]indol-2-one, 3,3a,8,8a-tetrahydro-5-methoxy-3a,8-dimethyl-	pH 2	244(3.78),317(3.79)	5-0927-79
	MeOH-H_2O	246(3.99),315(3.55)	5-0927-79
$C_{13}H_{15}NO_4$			
Acetamide, N-[4-(acetoxymethyl)-2-acet-ylphenyl]-	EtOH	234(4.45),258(4.12), 267(4.05),325(3.66)	33-0271-79
Acetamide, N-(4-acetoxy-2-acetyl-3-methylphenyl)-	EtOH	240s(3.77),286(2.99)	33-0271-79
Acetamide, N-(4-acetoxy-2-acetyl-6-methylphenyl)-	EtOH	240s(3.78),292(3.15)	33-0271-79
2-Butenedioic acid, 2-[(phenylmethyl)-amino]-, dimethyl ester	MeOH	210(3.98),285(4.41)	39-0591-79C
Carbamic acid, (2,3-dihydro-2-oxo-3-benzofuranyl)-, 1,1-dimethylethyl ester	MeOH	272(3.1),278s(3.05)	39-1634-79C
$C_{13}H_{15}NO_4S$			
Butanedioic acid, (1,3-dimethyl-2(1H)-pyridinylidene)thioxo-, dimethyl ester	EtOH	220(3.94),272(3.89), 334(4.33)	94-2879-79
Butanedioic acid, (1,5-dimethyl-2(1H)-pyridinylidene)thioxo-, dimethyl ester	EtOH	220(4.03),272(3.87), 332(4.28)	94-2879-79
Butanedioic acid, (1,6-dimethyl-2(1H)-pyridinylidene)thioxo-, dimethyl ester	EtOH	220(3.80),272(3.92), 330(4.28)	94-2879-79
2-Propanone, 1-[(4-methylphenyl)sulfon-yl]-1-(2-oxazolidinylidene)-	EtOH	263(4.26)	95-0038-79
$C_{13}H_{15}NS$			
24,4H-1,3-Thiazeto[2,3-a]isoquinoline,	CH_2Cl_2	279(4.22),330s(2.8)	5-1702-79

Compound	Solvent	$\lambda_{max}(\log \epsilon)$	Ref.
5,9b-dihydro-2-(1-methylethylidene)-			5-1702-79
$C_{13}H_{15}NS_2$			
Cyclohexanecarbodithioic acid, 2-(phenylimino)-	EtOH	240s(3.39),262(3.69), 380(4.30)	150-1732-79
$C_{13}H_{15}N_2O_2S_2$			
Pyridinium, 1-[4-amino-5-(ethoxycarbonyl)-2-(methylthio)-3-thienyl]-, iodide	EtOH	221(4.38),270(4.00), 288(4.05),328(4.06)	95-1081-79
$C_{13}H_{15}N_3O$			
1H-1,2,3-Triazole, 5-(3,4-dihydro-2H-pyran-2-yl)-4,5-dihydro-1-phenyl-	EtOH	217s(4.22),234s(4.01), 286(4.14),302(4.08)	103-0488-79
$C_{13}H_{15}N_3OS$			
1,3,4-Thiadiazolo[3,2-a]benzimidazol-6-ol, 2-pentyl-	pH 1	330(3.62),359(3.71)	18-2033-79
	pH 13	323(3.04),445(3.34)	18-2033-79
	EtOH	258(4.35),302(3.97), 352(4.12)	18-2033-79
$C_{13}H_{15}N_3O_2$			
Acetamide, N-[[5-hydroxy-1-(phenylmethyl)-1H-pyrazol-3-yl]methyl]-	MeOH	252(3.36)	1-0294-79
Acetamide, N-methyl-N-[2-(5-phenyl-1,2,4-oxadiazol-3-yl)ethyl]-	EtOH	251(4.21)	150-0801-79
$C_{13}H_{15}N_3O_2S$			
4-Morpholinecarboxamide, N-(3-methyl-2(3H)-benzothiazolylidene)-	EtOH	279(4.08),305(4.45), 310(4.57)	94-2879-79
Sydnone, 4-(phenylthio)-3-piperidino-	CH_2Cl_2	315(3.86)	5-0063-79
$C_{13}H_{15}N_3O_3S$			
Benzoic acid, 4-[[[(4,5-dihydro-2-thiazolyl)amino]carbonyl]amino]-, ethyl ester	n.s.g.	242(3.92),294(4.64)	87-0028-79
$C_{13}H_{15}N_3O_4$			
5-Pyrimidinecarbonitrile, 1,2,3,4-tetrahydro-2,4-dioxo-1,3-bis(tetrahydro-2-furanyl)-	pH 1	283(4.08)	94-0899-79
	pH 7	283(4.08)	94-0899-79
$C_{13}H_{15}N_3O_4S$			
2(1H)-Quinazolinethione, 4-amino-1-β-D-ribopyranosyl-	MeOH	222(4.23),234(4.16), 289(4.54)	44-0173-79
1,2,3-Thiadiazolium, 5-[(ethoxycarbonyl)amino]-4-methoxy-3-(4-methoxyphenyl)-, hydroxide, inner salt	EtOH	221(4.19),242(4.08), 292(3.84),365(3.99)	39-2349-79C
1,2,3-Thiadiazolium, 5-[(ethoxycarbonyl)methylamino]-4-hydroxy-3-(4-methoxyphenyl)-, hydroxide, inner salt	EtOH	322(3.38),400(4.02)	39-2349-79C
$C_{13}H_{15}N_3O_5$			
Cytosine, 1-(5-O-acetyl-2,3-dideoxy-β-D-glycero-pent-2-enofuranosyl)-N-acetyl-	MeOH	249(4.16),299(3.75)	44-1404-79
$C_{13}H_{15}N_3O_6$			
1H-Pyrrolo[2,3-d]pyrimidine-6,7-dicarboxylic acid, 2,3,4,5-tetrahydro-1,3,5-	EtOH	230(4.51),275(4.21), 310(3.97)	44-3830-79

Compound	Solvent	λ_{max}(log ε)	Ref.
trimethyl-2,4-dioxo-, dimethyl ester			44-3830-79
$C_{13}H_{15}N_3S$			
Isothiazolo[5,1-e][1,2,3]thiadiazole-7-S^{IV}, 1,6-dihydro-3,4,6-trimethyl-1-phenyl-	C_6H_{12}	242(4.12),285(3.90), 447(4.36)	39-0926-79C
Piperidine, 1-[[[2-cyano-2-(2-thienyl)-ethenyl]imino]methyl]-	MeOH	246(4.29),351(4.50)	83-0039-79
$C_{13}H_{15}N_5O$			
Acetamide, N-[2-[2-(azidomethyl)-1H-indol-3-yl]ethyl]-	EtOH	223(4.40),278(3.81), 284(3.86),292(3.75)	39-3061-79C
Pyrrolo[2,3-b]indole, 1-acetyl-3a-azido-1,2,3,3a,8,8a-hexahydro-8a-methyl-	EtOH	241(3.81),299(3.27)	39-3061-79C
$C_{13}H_{15}N_5O_4S_2$			
1H-Pyrazolo[3,4-d]pyrimidine-3-carbonitrile, 4,6-bis(methylthio)-1-β-D-ribofuranosyl-	EtOH	203(4.19),253(4.32), 293(4.07),315(3.89)	103-1361-79
$C_{13}H_{16}$			
6,9-Methanobenzocyclooctene, 5,6,7,8-9,10-hexahydro-	EtOH	212(3.93),256(2.25), 263(2.33),267(2.24), 273(2.22)	56-1221-79
$C_{13}H_{16}BrNO_2$			
Acetamide, 2-bromo-N-(4-oxo-5-phenyl-pentyl)-	MeOH	209(4.03)	83-0896-79
$C_{13}H_{16}ClNO_5$			
Benzeneacetic acid, 5-chloro-α-[[(1,1-dimethylethoxy)carbonyl]amino]-2-hydroxy-	MeOH	283(3.3)	39-1634-79C
$C_{13}H_{16}Cl_4$			
Benzene, 1-(chloromethyl)-2,3,4,5-tetramethyl-6-(2,2,2-trichloroethyl)-	hexane	221(4.30),278(3.30)	44-2381-79
$C_{13}H_{16}FN_3O_5$			
1(2H)-Pyrimidineacetic acid, α-(acetyl-amino)-5-fluoro-3,4-dihydro-2,4-dioxo-α-2-propenyl-, ethyl ester	MeOH	266(3.93)	44-2019-79
$C_{13}H_{16}IN_5O_4$			
Guanosine, 5'-deoxy-5'-iodo-2',3'-O-(1-methylethylidene)-	MeOH-HCl	261(4.14)	44-0400-79
	MeOH-NaOH	265(4.10)	44-0400-79
$C_{13}H_{16}NO_2$			
Pyridinium, 1-(5,5-dimethyl-3-oxo-1-cyclohexen-1-yl)-3-hydroxy-, chloride	EtOH	225(4.08),300(3.47)	56-0057-79
$C_{13}H_{16}N_2$			
Indolizine, 3-(1-piperidinyl)-	EtOH	241(4.58)	138-0241-79
1H-Pyrazole, 3,5-diethyl-4-phenyl-	EtOH	237(3.98)	103-0501-79
$C_{13}H_{16}N_2O$			
2,3-Diazabicyclo[2.2.1]hept-2-ene, 7-[(phenylmethoxy)methyl]-, anti	MeOH	344(1.94)	35-3315-79
syn	MeOH	344(1.99)	35-3315-79
1H-Pyrazole-3-propanol, 5-(4-methyl-phenyl)-	MeOH	252(4.60),320(1.70)	44-2073-79

Compound	Solvent	λ_{max}(log ε)	Ref.
8-Quinolinol, 2-(butylamino)-	neutral	246(4.18),266(4.28), 283(4.35),332(3.68)	123-0070-79
	acid	242(4.14),267(4.46), 309(3.92)	123-0070-79
	base	234(4.17),277(4.51), 360(3.38)	123-0070-79
8-Quinolinol, 2-(diethylamino)-	neutral	250(4.18),274(4.36), 287(4.40),341(3.79)	123-0070-79
	acid	247(4.19),270(4.46), 313(3.95),350(3.74)	123-0070-79
	base	240(4.17),253(4.18), 284(4.52),370(3.53)	123-0070-79
2H-Pyrrol-2-one, 5-[(4-ethyl-3,5-dimethyl-1H-pyrrol-2-yl)methylene]-1,5-dihydro-	MeOH	430(4.59)	78-0463-79
	$CHCl_3$	424(4.53)	78-0463-79
$C_{13}H_{16}N_2O_2$			
Acetic acid, cyano(hexahydro-2,6-methano-1H-pyrrolizin-8-ylidene)-, ethyl ester	hexane	224(3.95),298(3.78)	142-0343-79
2(5H)-Furanone, 5,5-dimethyl-4-[2-(phenylmethyl)hydrazino]-	EtOH	259(4.34)	4-0505-79
1H-Indole-2-carboxamide, 3-(2-hydroxyethyl)-N,N-dimethyl-	EtOH	218(4.75),289(4.31)	23-0289-79
Piperidine, 1-[1,3-dioxo-3-(2-pyridinyl)propyl]-	ether	230(3.81),304(3.94)	22-0559-79
2-Propenoic acid, 3-(2-propenylamino)-3-(2-pyridinyl)-, ethyl ester, (E)-	ether	216(3.94),245(3.89), 312(3.95)	22-0559-79
1H-Pyrazole-3-methanol, 5-hydroxy-α,α-dimethyl-1-(phenylmethyl)-	EtOH	254(3.71)	4-0505-79
Pyrimidine, 4-(2,4-dimethoxyphenyl)-1,4-dihydro-5-methyl-, hydrochloride	EtOH	280(3.78)	24-0001-79
$C_{13}H_{16}N_2O_3$			
1H-Indazole-4,7-diol, 1-acetyl-1-(1,1-dimethylethyl)-	n.s.g.	222(4.66)	70-1668-79
2-Propenoic acid, 3-(4-morpholinyl)-3-(2-pyridinyl)-, methyl ester	ether	276(4.31)	22-0559-79
$C_{13}H_{16}N_2O_3S$			
2-Propanone, 1-(2-imidazolidinylidene)-1-[(4-methylphenyl)sulfonyl]-	EtOH	265(4.28)	95-0038-79
$C_{13}H_{16}N_2O_4$			
Acetic acid, (2,3,5,6,7,8-hexahydro-1,2-dimethyl-3,5-dioxo-4(1H)-cinnolinylidene)-, methyl ester, (E)-	MeOH	221(4.09),260(3.89), 340(4.14)	24-3237-79
Benzene, 1-(1-methyl-1-nitroethyl)-2-(2-methyl-1-propenyl)-4-nitro-	MeOH	255(4.06)	12-1949-79
Benzene, 1-(1-methyl-1-nitroethyl)-4-(2-methyl-1-propenyl)-2-nitro-	MeOH	253(4.21),315s(3.18)	12-1949-79
1H-1,2-Benzodiazepine-5-carboxylic acid, 2,3,6,7,8,9-hexahydro-1,2-dimethyl-3,6-dioxo-, methyl ester	MeOH	207(4.17),257(4.08), 358(3.86)	24-3237-79
4H-Pyrido[1,2-a]pyrimidine-3-carboxylic acid, 9-formyl-1,6,7,8-tetrahydro-6-methyl-4-oxo-, ethyl ester	EtOH	223(4.20),265(3.49), 315s(3.86),358(4.34)	88-2537-79
$C_{13}H_{16}N_2O_5$			
1-Butanone, 2,2,3-trimethyl-3-nitro-1-(4-nitrophenyl)-	MeOH	262(4.05)	12-1487-79

Compound	Solvent	λ_{max}(log ε)	Ref.
$C_{13}H_{16}N_2O_6$			
1H-Indole, 1-α-L-arabinopyranosyl-2,3-dihydro-6-nitro-	EtOH	254(4.08)	103-0188-79
2H-Pyrrol-2-one, 1,5-dihydro-1-[[4-hydroxy-4-(hydroxymethyl)-1-methyl-5-oxo-2-pyrrolidinylidene]acetyl]-4-methoxy-, (E)-	MeOH	205(4.04),224(4.07), 286(4.40)	88-2007-79
$C_{13}H_{16}N_2O_7$			
2,4(1H,3H)-Pyrimidinedione, 1-[4(R)-acetoxy-2,3-O-(1-methylethylidene)-β-D-erythro-furanosyl]-	MeOH	258(4.03)	44-4713-79
(S)-	MeOH	258(4.03)	44-4713-79
$C_{13}H_{16}N_2O_8$			
Uridine, 3',5'-diacetate	EtOH	259(3.98)	39-2088-79C
$C_{13}H_{16}N_2S$			
Benzenamine, N-(4-ethyl-4-methyl-5-methylene-2-thiazolidinylidene)-	EtOH	206(3.26),236(3.08)	103-0611-79
Benzenamine, N-(3,4,4-trimethyl-5-methylene-2-thiazolidinylidene)-	EtOH	204(3.27),238(3.11)	103-0611-79
Benzenemethanamine, N-(4,4-dimethyl-5-methyl-2-thiazolidinylidene)-	EtOH	208(3.29)	103-0611-79
Ethanethione, 2-(1,3-dimethyl-2-imidazolidinylidene)-1-phenyl-	EtOH	235(3.98),351(4.36)	18-3640-79
2-Thiazolamine, 4,5-dihydro-4,4-dimethyl-5-methylene-N-(phenylmethyl)-	C_6H_{12}	204(3.27),228(2.98), 269(2.44)	103-0611-79
$C_{13}H_{16}N_2S_2$			
Cyclohexanecarbodithioic acid, 2-[(4-aminophenyl)imino]-	EtOH	253(3.95),308(3.73), 400(4.20)	150-1732-79
$C_{13}H_{16}N_3OS$			
Isoxazolium, 2-ethyl-3-methyl-5-(methylthio)-4-(phenylazo)-, tetrafluoroborate	HOAc	292(4.18),351(4.09), 363s(4.05),417s(3.06)	97-0446-79
1,3,4-Thiadiazolo[3,2-a]benzimidazolium, 9-ethyl-6-hydroxy-2-(1-methylethyl)-, bromide	EtOH	258(3.62),485(3.91)	18-2033-79
1,3,4-Thiadiazolo[3,2-a]benzimidazolium, 9-ethyl-6-hydroxy-2-propyl-, bromide	EtOH	276(3.51),515(3.84)	18-2033-79
$C_{13}H_{16}N_4$			
1H-Imidazole, 4,5-diethyl-2-(phenylazo)-	MeOH	235(--),280(--), 399(4.39)	56-2340-79
$C_{13}H_{16}N_4O$			
1-Propanol, 3-[(2,3-dihydroimidazo-[1,2-c]quinazolin-5-yl)amino]-	EtOH	222(5.47),255(3.81), 267(3.87),283(3.94), 296(3.86),325(3.51), 340(3.66)	106-0844-79
$C_{13}H_{16}N_4O_2S$			
1H-1,2,4-Triazolium, 4-[(ethoxycarbonyl)amino]-1-methyl-3-(methylthio)-5-phenyl-, hydroxide, inner salt	EtOH	228(4.18),254(3.98)	94-1683-79
$C_{13}H_{16}N_4O_2S_2$			
Sulfilimine, S,S-dimethyl-N-[4-[[(4-methyl-2-pyrimidinyl)amino]sulfonyl]-	EtOH	296(4.34)	139-0195-79

Compound	Solvent	λ max (log ε)	Ref.
phenyl]-, sodium salt (cont.)			139-0195-79
$C_{13}H_{16}N_4O_4$			
3,5-Methanofuro[2,3-b]pyridin-6(2H)-one, 4-(4,6-dimethoxy-1,3,5-triazin-2-yl)-hexahydro-	$CHCl_3$	247(3.88)	39-1525-79C
$C_{13}H_{16}N_4O_4S$			
6H-Purine-6-thione, 3,7-dihydro-3-[2,3-O-(1-methylethylidene)-β-D-ribofuranosyl]-	pH 1	322(4.25)	136-0234-79J
	pH 7	341(4.34)	136-0234-79J
	pH 11	339(4.20)	136-0234-79J
$C_{13}H_{16}N_4O_5$			
1H-Purine-2,6-dione, 7-(3,4-anhydro-6-deoxy-α-L-talopyranosyl)-3,7-dihydro-1,3-dimethyl-	MeOH	275(3.90)	39-2682-79C
6H-Purin-6-one, 3,7-dihydro-3-[2,3-O-(1-methylethylidene)-β-D-ribofuranosyl]-	pH 1	254(4.05)	136-0234-79J
	pH 7	263(4.09)	136-0234-79J
	pH 11	276(4.04)	136-0234-79J
9H-Pyrrolo[1,2-a]purin-6-one, 3,5,6,7-tetrahydro-3-β-D-ribofuranosyl-	pH -1.0	254(4.00)	5-1872-79
	pH 5.0	243s(3.96),250(4.04), 275s(3.44)	5-1872-79
$C_{13}H_{16}N_4S$			
Pyrido[2,3-d]pyrimidin-4-amine, N-cyclopentyl-	H_2O	226(4.09),269(4.29), 339(4.00)	102-1265-79
	0.2M HCl	227(4.19),265(4.12), 293(4.10),327(4.19), 340(4.15)	102-1265-79
	0.2M NaOH	270(4.29),338(4.00)	102-1265-79
$C_{13}H_{16}N_6$			
3H-1,3,4,6-Tetraazacyclopent[e]azulene, 2-amino-3,9-dimethyl-5-(dimethylamino)-	MeOH	226(4.02),261(4.02), 306(4.59),317s(4.49), 377(4.00),416(4.18)	23-1707-79
	MeOH-acid	241(4.02),249(4.07), 298(4.61),359(3.74), 414(4.32)	23-1707-79
$C_{13}H_{16}N_6OS$			
Hydrazinecarbothioamide, 2-[hexahydro-2-oxo-3-(phenylhydrazono)-4H-azepin-4-ylidene]-	EtOH	246(4.34),406(4.12)	103-0780-79
Hydrazinecarbothioamide, 2-[hexahydro-2-oxo-4-(phenylhydrazono)-3H-azepin-3-ylidene]-	EtOH	261(4.36),406(4.07)	103-0780-79
$C_{13}H_{16}N_6O_2$			
1,2,4-Triazine-6-acetic acid, 2,5-dihydro-α-methyl-5-oxo-2-(phenylmethyl)-, hydrazide	EtOH-HCl	213(4.40),263(3.88)	39-1120-79C
$C_{13}H_{16}O$			
Benzocyclooctene, 5,6,7,8-tetrahydro-10-methoxy-	C_6H_{12}	250(3.64)	39-1395-79C
Biphenylene, 1,2,3,4,4a,8b-hexahydro-4a-methoxy-, cis	MeOH	261(3.06),267(3.23), 274(3.22)	39-1395-79C
1H-Cyclobuta[de]benzocycloocten-9a-ol, 5,6,7,8,9,9a-hexahydro-	MeOH	261(2.73),266(2.86), 273(2.89)	39-1395-79C

Compound	Solvent	λ max(log ε)	Ref.
6,9-Methanobenzocycloocten-11-ol, 5,6,7,8,9,10-hexahydro-	EtOH	212(3.97),256(2.33), 263(2.43),267(2.33), 272(2.41)	56-1221-79
Tricyclo[6.3.1.0^{3,8}]dodeca-3,6-dien-5-one, 1 -methyl-	EtOH	246(4.16)	39-2914-79C
$C_{13}H_{16}O_2$			
Benzenepropanal, α,α-diethyl-β-oxo-	MeOH	208(3.99),245(3.98), 275-295s(3.04-2.65)	5-0617-79
5,9-Epoxy-5H-benzocycloheptene, 6,7,8,9-tetrahydro-5-methoxy-9-methyl-	isooctane	251s(2.52),257(2.71), 263(2.89),270(2.89)	56-1751-79
5,9-Epoxy-5H-benzocyclohepten-5-ol, 9-ethyl-6,7,8,9-tetrahydro-	hexane	251s(2.45),256(2.67), 263(2.86),269(2.88)	56-1751-79
4H-1,4-Epoxy-4a,8-methanobenzocyclo-octen-10(5H)-one, 1,6,7,8,9,10a-hexahydro-	EtOH	214(2.58)(end abs.)	44-3793-79
isomer 9	EtOH	285(1.26)	44-3793-79
1H-Inden-1-ol, 1-ethenyl-2,3-dihydro-5-methoxy-3-methyl-	MeOH	226(3.95),277(3.42), 284(3.33)	2-0324-79A
2-Propenoic acid, 3-[4-(1-methylethyl)-phenyl]-, methyl ester, (E)-	MeCN	286(4.39)	88-0863-79
(Z)-	MeCN	283(4.05)	88-0863-79
Spiro[1,3-dioxolane-2,11'-tetracyclo-[5.3.1.0^{2,4}.0^{8,10}]indec[5]ene	EtOH	198(3.89)	44-1294-79
$C_{13}H_{16}O_3$			
Benzaldehyde, 3-methoxy-5-[(3-methyl-2-butenyl)oxy]-	EtOH	216(4.36),270(3.79), 325(3.38)	150-0301-79
2H-1-Benzopyran, 2,2-diethoxy-	pH 11	255(4.0),262s(3.9), 291(3.0)	23-2260-79
$C_{13}H_{16}O_3S$			
3-Penten-2-one, 3-methyl-5-[(4-methyl-phenyl)sulfonyl]-	H_2O	231(3.959)	104-0578-79
$C_{13}H_{16}O_3S_3$			
Ethanone, 2-[[1-methyl-2,2-bis(methyl-thio)ethenyl]sulfonyl]-1-phenyl-	EtOH	241(3.96),306(3.96)	95-0038-79
$C_{13}H_{16}O_4$			
2H-1,7-Benzodioxonin-8,11-dione, 3,4,5,6-tetrahydro-9,10-dimethyl-	MeCN	274(4.18),413(2.75)	64-0624-79B
4H-1-Benzopyran-4-one, 2-ethyl-2,3-di-hydro-5,7-dimethoxy-	MeOH	284(4.41)	94-2874-79
Bicyclo[2.2.2]octa-2,5-diene-2-carbox-ylic acid, 7-hydroxy-4,7-dimethyl-8-oxo-, ethyl ester, (1α,4α,7S*)-	MeOH	312(2.57),325(3.66)	23-2853-79
2-Buten-1-one, 1-(2,4,6-trimethoxy-phenyl)-	MeOH	224(4.29),302(3.49)	94-2874-79
2-Propenoic acid, 2-ethoxy-3-(4-hydroxy-phenyl)-, ethyl ester, (Z)-	MeOH	285(4.34)	24-1571-79
$C_{13}H_{16}O_4S_2$			
1,3-Dithiole-4,5-dicarboxylic acid, 2-cyclohexylidene-, dimethyl ester	CH_2Cl_2	254(4.07),326(2.99), 406(3.26)	44-0930-79
$C_{13}H_{16}O_5$			
Dispiro[1,3-dioxolane-2,1'-[1H]indene-3'(2'H),2"-[1,3]dioxolan]-5'(4'H)-one, 3'a,7'a-dihydro-, trans	EtOH	222(3.99)	88-1223-79

Compound	Solvent	λ_{max}(log ε)	Ref.
Dispiro[1,3-dioxolane-2,1'(2'H)-pentalene-3'(3'aH),2"-[1,3]dioxolane]-4'-carboxaldehyde, 6',6'a-dihydro-, cis	EtOH	232.5(3.86)	88-1223-79
Parvulenone	MeOH	224(3.99),287(3.97), 330s(3.39)	150-2685-79
$C_{13}H_{16}O_6$			
1,2-Benzenedicarboxylic acid, 3-butyl-6-hydroxy-4-methoxy-	MeOH	258(3.78),307(3.60)	39-0807-79C
1,2-Benzenedicarboxylic acid, 3,4-dimethoxy-, 1-ethyl 2-methyl ester	EtOH	258(3.82),288(3.62)	44-4337-79
Bicyclo[2.2.2]oct-5-ene-2,3-dicarboxylic acid, 8-hydroxy-1,8-dimethyl-7-oxo-, 2-methyl ester, monosodium salt, (1α,2α,3α,4α,8R*)-	MeOH	308(2.00)	23-2853-79
$C_{13}H_{16}O_7$			
Butanedioic acid, 2-[(3,4-dihydroxyphenyl)methyl]-2-hydroxy-, dimethyl ester, (R)-	MeOH	283(3.56)	102-1211-79
$C_{13}H_{16}O_7Pb$			
Plumbane, triacetoxy(3-methoxyphenyl)-	n.s.g.	271(3.45),277(3.46)	12-1521-79
$C_{13}H_{16}S_3$			
2,4-Cyclohexadiene-1-thione, 6-(4,4,5,5-tetramethyl-1,3-dithiolan-2-ylidene)-	CH_2Cl_2	269(4.37),351(4.02), 585(3.82)	18-0496-79
$C_{13}H_{17}ClN_4O_5$			
Cytidine, N-acetyl-5'-[(chloroacetyl)amino]-2',5'-dideoxy-	EtOH	249(4.20),302(3.91)	39-1389-79C
$C_{13}H_{17}ClO_2$			
2-Cyclohexen-1-one, 6-chloro-2,4,4-trimethyl-3-(3-oxo-1-butenyl)-, (E)-	pentane	271(3.96),340s(2.30)	33-0553-79
$C_{13}H_{17}ClO_3$			
2-Propenoic acid, 3-(4-chloro-2,6,6-trimethyl-3-oxo-1-cyclohexen-1-yl)-, methyl ester	pentane	267(4.00),351s(1.85)	33-0553-79
$C_{13}H_{17}Cl_2F_3OSi$			
Silane, [(dichlorotrifluorophenoxy)-methyl]triethyl-	heptane	197(4.92),219(4.21), 275(2.89)	70-2602-79
$C_{13}H_{17}Cl_3O_2$			
Benzenemethanol, 3-(1,1-dimethylethyl)-2-hydroxy-5-methyl-α-(trichloromethyl)-	EtOH	219(3.88),292(3.53)	118-0824-79
$C_{13}H_{17}F_5OSi$			
Silane, triethyl[(pentafluorophenoxy)-methyl]-	heptane	209(3.83),233s(3.07), 256s(2.59)	70-2602-79
$C_{13}H_{17}N$			
Benzenamine, 2-(2-cyclohexen-1-yl)-N-methyl-	MeOH	245(3.99),293(3.40)	33-2581-79
1H-Indole, 1,3-dimethyl-2-(1-methylethyl)-	EtOH	230(4.61),281s(3.90), 286(3.95),293(3.94)	23-0558-79

Compound	Solvent	$\lambda_{max}(\log \epsilon)$	Ref.
$C_{13}H_{17}NO_2$			
Darlingine	EtOH	217(4.01),258(4.03)	12-2523-79
1H-Indole-3-acetic acid, 2,3-dihydro-1,2,3-trimethyl-, trans	MeOH	253(4.00),298(3.46)	5-0927-79
3-Piperidinol, 1-methyl-, benzoate	MeOH	270(3.30),280(3.18), 282(3.11)	4-0625-79
4-Piperidinol, 1-methyl-, benzoate	MeOH	274(3.00),282(2.90)	4-0625-79
2H-Pyrrol-4-ol, 3,4-dihydro-2,2,4-trimethyl-5-phenyl-, 1-oxide	EtOH	214(3.86),284(4.05)	12-2025-79
$C_{13}H_{17}NO_3$			
Acetamide, N-[2-(3-methoxy-1-oxopropyl)phenyl]-N-methyl-	EtOH	223(3.90),253(3.46), 280(3.11)	35-7332-79
2H-Furo[3,2-b][1,4]benzoxazine, 3,3a,9,9a-tetrahydro-3a-methoxy-9,9a-dimethyl-	EtOH	249(3.97),275(3.50)	35-7332-79
2-Pentanone, 4,4-dimethyl-3-(4-nitrophenyl)-	hexane	266(4.04)	12-1487-79
$C_{13}H_{17}NO_4$			
2-Azabicyclo[2.2.2]oct-5-ene-2-carboxylic acid, 7-(3-methoxy-3-oxo-1-propenyl)-, methyl ester	EtOH	221(3.81)	88-2485-79
4H-Azepine-3,6-dicarboxylic acid, 2,4,7-trimethyl-, dimethyl ester	n.s.g.	213(3.91),295(3.85)	23-0044-79
2,5(1H)-Isoquinolinedicarboxylic acid, 4a,5,8,8a-tetrahydro-, dimethyl ester, (4aα,5β,8aα)-	CCl_4	265(2.98)	88-2485-79
$C_{13}H_{17}NO_5$			
Acetic acid, 2-(tert-butoxycarbamoyl)-2-(2-hydroxyphenyl)-	MeOH	274(3.5),278s(3.4)	39-1634-79C
1H-Pyrrole-3-propanoic acid, 2-formyl-4-(2-methoxy-2-oxoethyl)-5-methyl-, methyl ester	n.s.g.	268(3.66),309(4.14)	39-1927-79C
$C_{13}H_{17}NO_6$			
α-D-Lyxofuranoside, methyl 5-deoxy-5-(2,5-dioxo-3-pyrrolidinylidene)-2,3-O-(1-methylethylidene)-, (E)-	EtOH	221(4.18)	33-0977-79
1H-Pyrrole-3-propanoic acid, 2-carboxy-4-(2-methoxy-2-oxoethyl)-5-methyl-, methyl ester	n.s.g.	278(4.08)	39-1927-79C
α-D-Ribofuranose , 5-deoxy-5-(2,5-dioxo-3-pyrrolidinylidene)-3-O-methyl-1,2-O-(1-methylethylidene)-, (E)-	EtOH	224(4.13)	33-0977-79
α-D-Xylofuranose, 5-deoxy-5-(2,5-dioxo-3-pyrrolidinylidene)-3-O-methyl-1,2-O-(1-methylethylidene)-, (E)-	EtOH	232(4.21)	33-0977-79
$C_{13}H_{17}N_3$			
2-Heptenenitrile, 3-[(2-aminophenyl)-amino]-	EtOH	205(4.28),240(4.31), 265(4.24),295s(3.96)	39-2289-79C
2-Hexenenitrile, 3-[(2-aminophenyl)-amino]-4-methyl-	EtOH	205(4.29),240(4.32), 267(4.26),295s(3.90)	39-2289-79C
2-Propenenitrile, 3-[(2-amino-2-methylpropyl)amino]-3-phenyl-	EtOH	223(4.40),278(4.11)	39-2289-79C
$C_{13}H_{17}N_3O_2$			
1H-Imidazole, 2,5-dihydro-2,2,5,5-tetramethyl-1-nitroso-4-phenyl-, 3-oxide	EtOH	228(4.16),286(3.96)	103-0092-79

Compound	Solvent	λ_{max}(log ϵ)	Ref.
$C_{13}H_{17}N_3O_4$			
Pyrido[3,2-c]pyridazine-1,2-dicarboxylic acid, 3,4-dihydro-, diethyl ester	EtOH	233(3.90),269(3.58)	78-2027-79
Pyrido[3,2-c]pyridazine-1,2-dicarboxylic acid, 7-ethyl-3,4-dihydro-, dimethyl ester	MeOH	232(3.93),283(3.66)	103-0518-79
Pyrido[3,4-c]pyridazine-1,2-dicarboxylic acid, 3,4-dihydro-, diethyl ester	EtOH	233(4.19),277(3.74)	78-2027-79
3H-Pyrido[1,2-c][1,2,3]triazine-1,2(3H)-dicarboxylic acid, diethyl ester	EtOH	258(3.49),260(3.50), 267(3.44)	78-2027-79
1H-Pyrrolo[3,2-d]pyrimidine-7-carboxylic acid, 6-ethyl-2,3,4,5-tetrahydro-1,3,5-trimethyl-2,4-dioxo-, methyl ester	EtOH	237(4.38),275(3.74)	44-3830-79
$C_{13}H_{17}N_3O_5$			
L-Aspartic acid, N-[[(4-aminophenyl)-amino]carbonyl]-, dimethyl ester	EtOH	253(4.32),300(3.32)	87-0874-79
4,12-Epoxy-5H-1,3-dioxolo[4,5-f]pyrimido[1,6-a][1,3]diazocine-8,10(6H,9H)-dione, 3a,4,12,12a-tetrahydro-2,2,9-trimethyl-	MeOH	275(4.29)	44-1424-79
5-Pyrimidinecarboxamide, 1,2,3,4-tetrahydro-2,4-dioxo-1,3-bis(tetrahydro-2-furanyl)- (spectra in 10% EtOH)	pH 1	280(4.08)	94-0899-79
	pH 7	280(4.08)	94-0899-79
	pH 12	282(4.10)	94-0899-79
$C_{13}H_{17}N_3O_5S$			
1H-Pyrrolo[2,3-d]pyrimidine, 5-methyl-2-(methylthio)-4-(β-D-ribofuranosyloxy)-	MeOH	243(4.31),284(3.98)	24-0799-79
$C_{13}H_{17}N_3O_8$			
1,2,4-Triazine-3,5(2H,4H)-dione, 2-[2,3-O-(3-carboxy-1-methylpropylidene)-β-D-ribofuranosyl]-, (R)-	MeOH	264(3.65)	87-1545-79
$C_{13}H_{17}N_3O_8S$			
2-Thiophenemethanol, α,5-bis(1-methyl-1-nitroethyl)-4-nitro-, acetate	MeOH	272(3.83)	12-1709-79
$C_{13}H_{17}N_3S$			
1H-Imidazolium, 4-(dimethylamino)-2,5-dihydro-5,5-dimethyl-3-phenyl-2-thioxo-, hydroxide, inner salt	n.s.g.	230(4.11),259(4.12), 298(3.57)	33-0160-79
$C_{13}H_{17}N_5O$			
1H-Pyrazole, 1-acetyl-3-[[4-(dimethylamino)phenyl]azo]-4,5-dihydro-	EtOH	473(4.63)	104-1396-79
$C_{13}H_{17}N_5O_3$			
1H-[1,3]Diazepino[2,1-f]purine-2,4(3H,6H)-dione, 10-acetyl-7,8,9,10-tetrahydro-1,3-dimethyl-	EtOH	281(3.97)	118-0581-79
$C_{13}H_{17}N_5O_3S$			
3-Thiophenecarboxylic acid, 2-[(3-amino-1,5-dihydro-1-methyl-5-oxo-4H-pyrazol-4-ylidene)hydrazino]-5-ethyl-, ethyl ester	MeOH	260(4.00),335(3.55), 448(4.32)	83-0726-79

Compound	Solvent	λ_{max}(log ε)	Ref.
$C_{13}H_{17}N_5O_4$			
9H-Pyrrolo[1,2-a]purin-9-imine, 3,5,6,7-tetrahydro-3-β-D-ribofuranosyl-	pH 6.0	259(4.13)	5-1872-79
	pH 11.0	260(4.16),264s(4.14), 290s(3.60)	5-1872-79
$C_{13}H_{17}N_5O_5$			
Adenosine, 2'-O-methyl-, 5'-acetate	EtOH	260(4.15)	39-2088-79C
Adenosine, 3'-O-methyl-, 2'-acetate	MeOH	259(4.16)	23-0274-79
Adenosine, 3'-O-methyl-, 5'-acetate	EtOH	259(4.13)	39-2088-79C
4,14-Epoxy-12,9-metheno-4H-1,3-dioxolo-[4,5-j][1,2,3,6,8]pentaazacyclotridecine-6,8(5H,7H)-dione, 3a,13,14,14a-tetrahydro-2,2,7-trimethyl-	MeOH	215(4.00)	44-1424-79
9H-Purin-6-amine, 9-[2-O-(1-oxopropyl)-β-D-arabinofuranosyl]-	MeOH	259(4.17)	87-0273-79
9H-Purin-6-amine, 9-[3-O-(1-oxopropyl)-β-D-arabinofuranosyl]-	MeOH	259(4.17)	87-0273-79
Uridine, 5'-azido-5'-deoxy-3-methyl-2',3'-O-(1-methylethylidene)-	MeOH	256(4.04)	44-1424-79
$C_{13}H_{17}N_5O_6$			
Guanosine, 2',3'-O-(1-methoxyethylidene)-	MeOH	254(4.14),270s(4.01)	24-0625-79
$C_{13}H_{17}OS$			
2H-Thiopyranium, tetrahydro-1-(2-oxo-2-phenylethyl)-, hexafluoroarsenate	MeOH	250(4.05),293(3.63)	47-2877-79
$C_{13}H_{18}BrNO_4$			
3,5-Pyridinedicarboxylic acid, 4-(1-bromoethyl)-1,4-dihydro-2,6-dimethyl-, dimethyl ester	n.s.g.	233(4.16),333(3.85)	23-0044-79
$C_{13}H_{18}ClNO_4$			
3,5-Pyridinedicarboxylic acid, 4-(1-chloroethyl)-1,4-dihydro-2,6-dimethyl-, dimethyl ester	n.s.g.	232(4.23),339(3.86)	23-0044-79
$C_{13}H_{18}NO_8P$			
2-Propenoic acid, 2-(diethoxyphosphinyl)-3-(5-nitro-2-furanyl)-, ethyl ester	EtOH	203s(3.78),233(4.15), 339(4.26)	48-0353-79
$C_{13}H_{18}N_2$			
Benzenemethanamine, N-[(1,1-dimethylethyl)carbonimidoyl]-α-methyl-, (S)-	C_6H_{12}	203s(3.61),209(3.66), 248(2.35),253(2.33), 253(2.33),259(2.34), 265(2.20),269s(2.00)	56-0631-79
$C_{13}H_{18}N_2O$			
1H-Imidazole, 2,5-dihydro-2,2,5,5-tetramethyl-4-phenyl-, 3-oxide	EtOH	220(3.90),285(4.00)	103-0092-79
1H-Indole-3-ethanol, 2-[(dimethylamino)methyl]-	EtOH	222(4.61),274(3.91), 281(3.95),290(3.88)	23-0289-79
$C_{13}H_{18}N_2O_2$			
1H-Cyclohepta[b]quinoxaline, 2,3,4,6-7,8,9,10-octahydro-, 5,11-dioxide	EtOH	245(4.40),307(4.20)	70-0848-79
2-Cyclohexen-1-one, 2,2'-methylenebis-[3-amino-	pH 1	275(4.56)	39-1593-79C
	H_2O	280(4.63)	39-1593-79C

Compound	Solvent	λ_{max}(log ε)	Ref.
4(5H)-Isoxazolone, 5,5-dimethyl-3-(4-pyrrolidino-1,3-butadienyl)-	ether	313(4.34),413(4.12)	78-0341-79
Piperidine, 1-(3,5-dimethyl-4-nitrophenyl)-	EtOH	263(4.00),305(3.51),391(3.76)	103-0087-79
2-Propenoic acid, 3-(diethylamino)-3-(2-pyridinyl)-, methyl ester	ether	280(4.19)	22-0559-79
2-Propenoic acid, 3-[(1-methylethyl)-amino]-3-(2-pyridinyl)-, ethyl ester, (E)-	ether	246(3.90),306(3.92)	22-0559-79
2,5(1H,6H)-Quinolinedione, 1-(dimethylamino)-7,8-dihydro-7,7-dimethyl-	MeOH	207(3.97),284(4.27)	64-0102-79B
$C_{13}H_{18}N_2O_3$			
Hydrazinecarboxylic acid, [ethoxy(4-methylphenyl)methylene]-, ethyl ester	EtOH	270(4.20)	4-0403-79
2-Pentanone, 4,4-dimethyl-3-(4-nitrophenyl)-, oxime	hexane	266(4.03)	12-1487-79
3-Pentanone, 2,4-dimethyl-, O-(4-nitrophenyl)oxime	hexane	302(4.21)	12-2413-79
3-Piperidinecarboxylic acid, 1-(2-pyridinyl)-, ethyl ester, N-oxide, (R)-	MeOH	323(3.51)	4-0591-79
$C_{13}H_{18}N_2O_4$			
Benzene, 1-[2,2-dimethyl-1-(1-nitroethyl)propyl]-4-nitro-, (R*,S*)-(±)-	hexane	261(4.08)	12-1487-79
Benzene, 1-[2-methyl-1-(1-methylethyl)-2-nitropropyl]-4-nitro-	hexane	263(4.11)	12-1487-79
Benzene, 1-nitro-4-(1,3,3-trimethyl-1-nitrobutyl)-	hexane	255(4.08)	12-2413-79
2H-Cyclohepta[4,5]furo[2,3-d]pyrimidine-2,4(3H)-dione, 4a-ethyl-4a,4b,5,6,7-8,9,9a-octahydro-4b-hydroxy-	MeOH	260(4.20)	54-0341-79
Ethanaminium, N-[(2,6-dicarboxy-2,3-dihydro-4(1H)-pyridinylidene)ethylidene]-N-ethyl-, hydroxide, inner salt, [S-(E)]-	H_2O	465s(--),475(4.61)	33-1330-79
Hydrazinecarboxylic acid, [ethoxy(4-methoxyphenyl)methylene]-, ethyl ester	EtOH	275(4.34)	4-0403-79
2,4(1H,3H)-Pyrimidinedione, 5-methyl-1,3-bis(tetrahydro-2-furanyl)-	pH 1	273.5(3.96)	94-0899-79
	pH 7	273.5(3.97)	94-0899-79
	pH 12	273.5(3.97)	94-0899-79
$C_{13}H_{18}N_2O_4S$			
Butanoic acid, 3-[[2-(aminosulfonyl)-5-methylphenyl]imino]-, ethyl ester	pH 1.5	213(4.56),247(3.96),307(3.54)	104-0120-79
	pH 7	213(4.48),251(3.98),313(3.53)	104-0120-79
$C_{13}H_{18}N_2O_6$			
1(2H)-Pyrimidinebutanoic acid, β-acetoxy-3,4-dihydro-5-methyl-2,4-dioxo-, ethyl ester	EtOH	269(3.96)	128-0051-79
2,4(1H,3H)-Pyrimidinedione, 1-(2,4-diacetoxybutyl)-5-methyl-	EtOH	267(3.99)	128-0051-79
2,4(1H,3H)-Pyrimidinedione, 5-[4-C-methyl-2,3-O-(1-methylethylidene)-β-D-ribofuranosyl]-	pH 13	285(3.88)	88-2897-79
	MeOH	266(3.86)	88-2897-79
$C_{13}H_{18}N_2O_6S$			
Thymidine, 5'-S-(2-carboxyethyl)-5'-thio-	H_2O	267(3.98)	87-0621-79

Compound	Solvent	$\lambda_{max}(\log \epsilon)$	Ref.
$C_{13}H_{18}N_2O_7S$			
Thymidine, 5'-[(2-carboxyethyl)sulfinyl]-5'-deoxy-	H_2O	267(3.98)	87-0621-79
$C_{13}H_{18}N_2O_8$			
1H-Pyrazole-3,4,5-tricarboxylic acid, 4,5-dihydro-5-(2-methoxy-2-oxoethyl)-1-methyl-, trimethyl ester, cis	MeOH	306(4.18)	24-1719-79
trans	MeOH	306(4.22)	24-1719-79
1(2H)-Pyrimidinebutanoic acid, 3,6-dihydro-2,6-dioxo-3-β-D-ribofuranosyl-	H_2O	262(3.95)	24-0700-79
$C_{13}H_{18}N_2S$			
2-Cyclododecathiazolamine, 4,5,8,9,12-13-hexahydro-, (E,Z)-	EtOH	263(3.772)	48-0249-79
2,4-Cyclohexadiene-1-thione, 6-(1,3-dimethyl-2-imidazolidinylidene)-	benzene	307(4.27)	18-3640-79
	H_2O	252(4.00)	18-3640-79
	EtOH	278(4.18)	18-3640-79
	HOAc	263(3.57)	18-3640-79
	MeCN	299(4.26)	18-3640-79
	DMF	303(4.18)	18-3640-79
	CH_2Cl_2	299(4.06)	18-3640-79
$C_{13}H_{18}N_4$			
4H-Imidazole, 5-(dimethylamino)-4,4-dimethyl-2-(2-aminophenyl)-	EtOH	260(4.00),291(3.83), 337(3.68),405s(2.54)	33-0768-79
1H-Pyrrolo[2,3-d]pyrimidin-4-amine, N-cyclohexyl-	pH 1	278(4.20)	102-0217-79
	H_2O	278(4.20)	102-0217-79
	pH 13	277(4.25)	102-0217-79
2,4-Quinazolinediamine, N,N,N',N',7-pentamethyl-	EtOH	250(4.85),270(4.70), 355(3.94)	114-0029-79A
$C_{13}H_{18}N_4O$			
2,4-Quinazolinediamine, 7-methoxy-N,N,N',N'-tetramethyl-	EtOH	252(4.78),343(3.89)	114-0029-79A
$C_{13}H_{18}N_4O_2S$			
Isothiazolo[3,4-d]pyrimidine-4,6(5H,7H)-dione, 3-(cyclohexylamino)-5,7-dimethyl-	EtOH	236(4.38),272(4.13), 298(3.96)	95-0989-79
$C_{13}H_{18}N_4O_6$			
Inosine, 8-(1-hydroxy-1-methylethyl)-	H_2O	251(4.08)	88-2385-79
1H-Purine-2,6-dione, 9-(2-deoxy-β-D-arabino-hexopyranosyl)-3,9-dihydro-1,3-dimethyl-	pH 1	274(3.97)	136-0061-79A
	pH 13	274(3.99)	136-0061-79A
	MeOH	274(3.96)	136-0061-79A
β-D-Ribofuranose, 5-[4-(aminocarbonyl)-1H-1,2,3-triazol-1-yl]-5-deoxy-2,3-O-(1-methylethylidene)-, 1-acetate	MeOH	210(4.18)	44-1424-79
$C_{13}H_{18}N_4S$			
Pyrido[2,3-d]pyrimidin-4-amine, 2-(methylthio)-N-pentyl-	H_2O	225(4.27),268(4.39), 338(4.08)	102-1265-79
	0.2M HCl	226(4.30),265(4.26), 291(4.21),326(4.27), 339(4.06)	102-1265-79
	0.2M NaOH	269(4.38),339(4.06)	102-1265-79
$C_{13}H_{18}N_6O_4$			
9H-Purine-9-propanoic acid, 6-amino-α-[[(1,1-dimethylethoxy)carbonyl]amino]-	n.s.g.	260(4.14)	65-0989-79

Compound	Solvent	λmax(log ε)	Ref.
$C_{13}H_{18}O$			
Bicyclo[4.3.1]deca-2,4,7-triene, 9-methoxy-2,5-dimethyl-	C_6H_{12}	262(4.00),254s(3.98), 270(3.88)	5-0533-79
$C_{13}H_{18}O_2$			
Acetic acid, (octahydro-2,5-methano-pentalen-7-ylidene)-, ethyl ester	hexane	224(4.31)	142-0343-79
Bicyclo[2.2.1]hept-2-ene, 7-(1-ethoxy-ethoxy)-5,6-bis(methylene)-, syn	isooctane	243(3.96)	33-0511-79
	EtOH	243(3.97)	33-0511-79
Dispiro[oxirane-2,1'(2'H)-naphthalen-6'(5'H),2"-oxirane], 3',7',8',8'a-tetrahydro-8'a-methyl-	EtOH	206(4.07)	88-0565-79
3a,9a-Ethano-1H-cyclopentacyclooctene-1,11-dione, octahydro-	MeOH	291(1.75)	44-4557-79
1-Pentanone, 1-(5-methoxy-2-methyl-phenyl)-	ether	217(4.29)	78-2655-79
1-Propanone, 1-(2-hydroxy-3,4-dimethyl-phenyl)-2,2-dimethyl-	EtOH	268(4.11),336(3.58)	22-0373-79
1-Propanone, 1-(2-hydroxy-3,5-dimethyl-phenyl)-2,2-dimethyl-	EtOH	261(3.94),344(3.52)	22-0373-79
1-Propanone, 1-(2-hydroxy-4,5-dimethyl-phenyl)-2,2-dimethyl-	EtOH	264(4.02),339(3.55)	22-0373-79
1-Propanone, 1-(4-hydroxy-3,5-dimethyl-phenyl)-2,2-dimethyl-	EtOH	226(4.03),280(4.02)	22-0373-79
Propanoic acid, 2,2-dimethyl-, 2,3-di-methylphenyl ester	EtOH	262(2.37),268(2.34)	22-0373-79
Propanoic acid, 2,2-dimethyl-, 2,4-di-methylphenyl ester	EtOH	267(2.77),273(2.80)	22-0373-79
$C_{13}H_{18}O_3$			
Benzenemethanol, 3-methoxy-5-[(3-meth-yl-2-butenyl)oxy]-	EtOH	213(4.03),225s(3.91), 275(3.30),280(3.30)	150-0301-79
Benzoic acid, 3,5-diethyl-2-hydroxy-, ethyl ester	MeOH	209(4.32),242(3.97), 314(3.52)	44-0964-79
Bicyclo[2.1.1]hexan-5-one, 6-hydroxy-2,2,6-trimethyl-1-(3-oxo-1-butenyl)-	pentane	220s(3.46)	33-0553-79
	MeCN	290(1.80)	33-0553-79
Cyclopentanone, 2-acetyl-3,3-dimethyl-2-(3-oxo-1-butenyl)-, (E)-	pentane	232(3.95),290(2.54), 296s(2.53),305s(2.49)	33-0553-79
(Z)-	pentane	240s(4.41),313s(2.31), 325s(2.14)	33-0553-79
2,11-Dioxabicyclo[4.4.1]undeca-3,5-di-en-10-one, 1,3,7,7-tetramethyl-	pentane	252(4.00)	33-0553-79
2,3-Heptanedione, 6-methyl-6-(5-methyl-2-furanyl)-	pentane	218(4.01),267(2.77), 423(1.36)	33-0553-79
7-Oxabicyclo[4.1.0]heptan-2-one, 1,5,5-trimethyl-6-(3-oxo-1-butenyl)-, (E)-	pentane	230(4.09),304(2.25)	33-0553-79
(Z)-	pentane	217(3.92),304(2.07)	33-0553-79
2-Pentene-1,4-dione, 1-(1,2,2-trimeth-yl-5-oxocyclopentyl)-, (Z)-	pentane	223(3.78)	33-0553-79
1-Propanone, 1-(2,4-dimethoxyphenyl)-2,2-dimethyl-	EtOH	267(3.53),278(3.53), 281(3.52)	22-0373-79
2-Propenoic acid, 3-(2,6,6-trimethyl-3-oxo-1-cyclohexen-1-yl)-, methyl ester, (E)-	pentane	270(4.07),318s(2.18), 338s(1.80)	33-0553-79
$C_{13}H_{18}O_4$			
2-Butenoic acid, 4-oxo-4-(1,2,2-tri-methyl-5-oxocyclopentyl)-, methyl ester, (E)-	pentane	228(4.17),348s(1.78)	33-0553-79
(Z)-	pentane	307(2.24),319(2.21), 331s(2.11)	33-0553-79

Compound	Solvent	λmax(log ε)	Ref.
2-Propenoic acid, 3-(2,2,6-trimethyl-5-oxo-1,6-epoxy-1-cyclohexyl)-, methyl ester, (E)-	pentane	214(4.18),298s(2.02), 304(2.06),317s(2.01), 324s(1.83),337s(1.34)	33-0553-79
(Z)-	pentane	300s(1.60),313(1.56), 325(1.38)	33-0553-79
$C_{13}H_{18}O_5$			
Acetic acid, (3-methoxy-5-oxo-4-pentyl-2(5H)-furanylidene)-, methyl ester	EtOH	256(4.10)	130-0311-79
(E)-	$CHCl_3$	270(4.21)	39-0089-79C
(Z)-	$CHCl_3$	271(4.21)	39-0089-79C
4-Cyclohexene-1,3-dicarboxylic acid, 4-methyl-6-oxo-, diethyl ester	EtOH	230(4.15)	39-1837-79C
$C_{13}H_{18}O_6$			
Acetic acid, [4-(5-hydroxypentyl)-3-methoxy-5-oxo-2(5H)-furanylidene]-, methyl ester, (E)-	EtOH	266(4.07)	130-0311-79
2-Pentenedioic acid, 2,4-diacetyl-, diethyl ester	EtOH	209(3.99),250(3.92), 311(3.83),388(3.68)	39-0464-79C
	EtOH-HCl	208(3.98),248(4.00), 314(3.90)	39-0464-79C
	EtOH-KOH	212(4.29),272(4.04), 389(4.37)	39-0464-79C
$C_{13}H_{19}$			
Cycloheptatrienylium, 1,2,3,4,5,6-hexamethyl-, perchlorate	10% HCl	253(4.80),311(3.76)	78-0949-79
$C_{13}H_{19}BrO_6$			
α-D-xylo-Hept-5-enofuranuronic acid, 6-bromo-5,6-dideoxy-3-O-methyl-1,2-O-(1-methylethylidene)-, ethyl ester, (Z)-	EtOH	234(3.48)	33-1303-79
$C_{13}H_{19}N$			
Benzenamine, 4-(1,1-dimethyl-2-propenyl)-2,6-dimethyl-	MeOH	237(3.94),286(3.24)	33-2613-79
Benzenamine, N,N,2,6-tetramethyl-4-(2-propenyl)-	MeOH	215s(4.13),262(3.45)	33-2613-79
Benzenamine, N,3,5-trimethyl-2-(1-methyl-2-propenyl)-	MeOH	214(4.44),249(3.91), 296(3.42)	33-2581-79
$C_{13}H_{19}NO_2$			
3-Azaspiro[5.5]undeca-1,4-diene-3-carboxylic acid, ethyl ester	isooctane	230(4.24)	44-2522-79
Darlingine, 2,3-dihydro-	EtOH	270(3.83)	12-1827-79
Darlingine, 5,11-dihydro-	EtOH	271(3.83)	12-2523-79
Phenylalanine, N-methyl-, propyl ester, (S)-(+)-	MeOH	217s(3.64),247(2.18), 253(2.22),259(2.29), 265(2.17),268(1.97)	83-0273-79
$C_{13}H_{19}NO_4$			
1-Isoquinolinemethanol, 1,2,3,4-tetrahydro-5-hydroxy-6,7-dimethoxy-2-methyl-, hydrochloride	H_2O	215s(3.15),268(2.16)	100-0197-79
$C_{13}H_{19}NO_4S$			
8-Thia-2-azabicyclo[3.2.1]oct-3-ene-4,7-dicarboxylic acid, 1,3,6-trimethyl-, dimethyl ester, endo,endo	n.s.g.	231(3.45),291(4.11)	23-0044-79

Compound	Solvent	$\lambda_{max}(\log \epsilon)$	Ref.
8-Thia-2-azabicyclo[3.2.1]oct-3-ene-4,7-dicarboxylic acid, 1,3,6-trimethyl-, dimethyl ester, endo,exo	n.s.g.	293.5(4.13)	23-0044-79
$C_{13}H_{19}NO_5$			
8-Oxa-2-azabicyclo[3.2.1]oct-3-ene-4,7-dicarboxylic acid, 1,3,6-trimethyl-, dimethyl ester, exo,endo	n.s.g.	288(4.18)	23-0044-79
1H-Pyrano[3,4-c]pyridine-4,7(4aH)-dicarboxylic acid, 5,6,8,8a-tetrahydro-1-methyl-, dimethyl ester	MeOH	240(4.03)	35-6742-79
$C_{13}H_{19}N_3O_2$			
1H-Pyrazol-3-amine, 1-[2-(3,4-dimethoxyphenyl)ethyl]-4,5-dihydro-, monohydrochloride	EtOH	230(3.85),278(3.43)	150-0801-79
$C_{13}H_{19}N_3O_3$			
2H-Cyclohepta[4,5]furo[2,3-d]pyrimidine-2,4(3H)-dione, 4b-amino-4a-ethyl-4a,4b,5,6,7,8,9,9a-octahydro-	MeOH	260(4.20)	54-0341-79
$C_{13}H_{19}N_3O_4S$			
1-Azabicyclo[3.2.0]hept-2-ene-2-carboxylic acid, 6-(1-hydroxyethyl)-3-[[2-[(1-iminoethyl)amino]ethyl]thio]-7-oxo-	H_2O	298(3.92)	87-1435-79
$C_{13}H_{19}N_3O_6$			
Cytidine, 5-(hydroxymethyl)-2',3'-O-(1-methylethylidene)-	pH 1	286(4.06)	150-2567-79
	EtOH	240(3.83),270(3.83)	150-2567-79
Cytidine, 6-(hydroxymethyl)-2',3'-O-(1-methylethylidene)-	EtOH	242(3.91),272(3.82), 282(4.06)	150-2567-79
2,4(1H,3H)-Pyrimidinedione, 1-[6-(acetylamino)-2,6-dideoxy-β-D-ribohexofuranosyl]-5-methyl-	H_2O	267(3.98)	87-0621-79
less polar epimer	H_2O	267(3.98)	87-0621-79
$C_{13}H_{19}N_3S$			
2-Imidazolidinethione, 5-(dimethylamino)-4,4-dimethyl-1-phenyl-	n.s.g.	240(3.93),267(3.96)	33-0160-79
$C_{13}H_{19}N_5O_3$			
2H-Pyrazolo[3,4-d]pyrimidine-4,6(5H,7H)-dione, 2-acetyl-5,7-diethyl-3-(ethylamino)-	MeOH	244(4.32),262(4.17), 314(3.67)	94-1328-79
$C_{13}H_{19}N_5O_6$			
Urea, N-[5-deoxy-5-[4-(methoxycarbonyl)-1H-1,2,3-triazol-1-yl]-2,3-O-(1-methylethylidene)-β-D-ribofuranosyl-	MeOH	214(4.00)	44-1424-79
$C_{13}H_{19}N_5O_7$			
Urea, [5-deoxy-2,3-O-(ethoxymethylene)-5-[4-(methoxycarbonyl)-1H-1,2,3-triazol-1-yl]-β-D-ribofuranosyl]-	MeOH	213(4.15)	44-1424-79
$C_{13}H_{19}N_7O_3$			
Alanine, N-L-alanyl-3-(6-amino-9H-purin-9-yl)-, ethyl ester, dihydrochloride	EtOH	260(4.12)	65-0994-79

Compound	Solvent	λ_{max}(log ε)	Ref.
$C_{13}H_{19}O_4PS_2$			
Benzeneethane(dithioic) acid, α-(dimethoxyphosphinyl)-α-ethoxy-, methyl ester	isooctane	214s(--),245s(--), 318(3.94),475(1.45)	5-1715-79
$C_{13}H_{19}O_6P$			
2-Propenoic acid, 2-(diethoxyphosphinyl)-3-(2-furanyl)-, ethyl ester	EtOH	205(3.65),231s(3.54), 295(4.34)	48-0353-79
$C_{13}H_{20}N_2O_2$			
4-Isoxazolol, 4,5-dihydro-5,5-dimethyl-3-(4-pyrrolidino-1,3-butadienyl)-, (E,E)-	MeOH	354(4.68)	78-0341-79
4(5H)-Isoxazolone, 3-[4-(diethylamino)-1,3-butadienyl]-5,5-dimethyl-	ether	312(4.37),413(4.15)	78-0341-79
2-Pentenoic acid, 4-(6,6-dimethyl-2,3-diazabicyclo[3.1.0]hex-2-en-4-yl)-4-methyl-, methyl ester	MeOH	215(3.40)	44-1202-79
$C_{13}H_{20}N_2O_3$			
4a(2H)-Phenazinol, 1,3,4,6,7,8,9,10a-octahydro-10a-methyl-, 5,10-dioxide	EtOH	350(4.17)	70-0848-79
Pyrazine, 5-(3,3-dimethyloxiranyl)-3-methoxy-2-(2-methylpropyl)-, 1-oxide	EtOH	231(4.31),269(3.98), 313(3.81)	94-1378-79
7H-Pyrazolo[1,5-c][1,3]oxazine-3-carboxylic acid, 4,5-dihydro-2,5,7,7-tetramethyl-, ethyl ester	EtOH	233(3.98)	118-0440-79
$C_{13}H_{20}N_2O_5$			
Glucose, methylphenylhydrazone	EtOH	279(4.31)	104-1237-79
Glucose, (4-methylphenyl)hydrazone	EtOH	281(4.26)	104-1237-79
Thymidine, 3-propyl-	H_2O	267(3.96)	87-0621-79
$C_{13}H_{20}N_2O_8S$			
2H-Imidazole-2-thione, 1,3-dihydro-1,3-di-β-D-ribofuranosyl-	pH 1	269(4.13)	4-1185-79
	H_2O	228(3.73),269(4.10)	4-1185-79
	pH 12	268(4.11)	4-1185-79
	MeOH	226(3.59),269(4.12)	4-1185-79
$C_{13}H_{20}N_2S_2$			
2,1-Benzisothiazole-3(1H)-thione, 1-(1-aminocyclohexyl)-4,5,6,7-tetrahydro-(inner salt)	EtOH	253(3.73),318(4.06)	150-0410-79S
aniline salt	EtOH	251(3.67),257s(3.62), 319(4.02)	150-0410-79S
$C_{13}H_{20}N_4O_2S$			
5-Pyrimidinecarbothioamide, 6-amino-N-cyclohexyl-1,2,3,4-tetrahydro-1,3-dimethyl-2,4-dioxo-	EtOH	260(4.31),398(4.20)	95-0515-79
$C_{13}H_{20}N_4O_5$			
1H-Imidazole-4-carboxamide, 5-(methylamino)-1-[2,3-O-(1-methylethylidene)-β-D-ribofuranosyl]-	EtOH	265(3.95)	130-0339-79
$C_{13}H_{20}N_6$			
3H-Purine-3-propanamine, 6-[(3-methyl-2-butenyl)amino]-	MeOH	220(4.19),293(4.20)	24-3072-79

Compound	Solvent	$\lambda_{max}(\log \epsilon)$	Ref.
$C_{13}H_{20}N_6O_2$			
1,3,5-Triazin-2-amine, 4,6-bis(1-aziri-dinyl)-N-(2,2-dimethyl-1,3-dioxan-5-yl)-	EtOH	223(4.65)	104-1144-79
$C_{13}H_{20}N_8O_3$			
9H-Purine-9-propanoic acid, 6-amino-α-[[(1,1-dimethylethoxy)carbonyl]-amino]-, hydrazide	pH 12	261(4.10)	65-0989-79
$C_{13}H_{20}O$			
3-Buten-2-one, 4-(2,6,6-trimethyl-2-cy-clohexen-1-yl)- [(+)-(R)-α-ionone]	EtOH	226(4.18)	33-2534-79
3a,9a-Ethano-1H-cyclopentacycloocten-1-one, octahydro-	MeOH	304(1.53)	44-4557-79
$C_{13}H_{20}O_2$			
3H-2-Benzopyran-3-one, 4-butyl-1,5,6,7,8,8a-hexahydro-	MeOH	235(3.84)	146-0031-79
$C_{13}H_{20}O_3$			
3-Buten-2-ol, 4-(2,6,6-trimethyl-5-oxo-1,6-epoxy-1-cyclohexyl)-, (E)-	n.s.g.	302(1.86),310s(1.84), 320s(1.69)	33-1645-79
3-Buten-2-one, 4-(5-hydroxy-2,2,6-tri-methyl-1,6-epoxy-1-cyclohexyl)-, (E)-	pentane	226(4.06),325s(1.66)	33-0553-79
2-Cyclohexen-1-one, 4-hydroxy-4-(3-hy-droxy-1-butenyl)-3,5,5-trimethyl-	MeOH	236(3.98)	107-0081-79
2-Cyclohexen-1-one, 6-hydroxy-6-(3-hy-droxy-1-butenyl)-3,5,5-trimethyl-	MeOH	235(3.96)	107-0081-79
2,11-Dioxabicyclo[4.4.1]undeca-3,5-dien-10-ol, 1,3,7,7-tetramethyl-, (+)-	n.s.g.	247(3.90)	33-1668-79
2,4-Hexadienoic acid, 2-acetyl-5-meth-yl-, 1,1-dimethylethyl ester	EtOH	220(4.61),290(4.38)	70-0758-79
7-Oxabicyclo[4.1.0]heptan-2-one, 1,5,5-trimethyl-6-(3-oxobutyl)-	pentane	291(1.62)	33-0553-79
2-Propenoic acid, 3-(3-hydroxy-2,6,6-trimethyl-1-cyclohexen-1-yl)-, methyl ester, (E)-	pentane	268(3.99),309s(2.13)	33-0553-79
2H-Pyran-5-carboxylic acid, 2,2,6-tri-methyl-, 1,1-dimethylethyl ester	EtOH	205(4.07),232(3.82), 291(3.93)	70-0758-79
4H-Pyran-4-one, 2,3-dihydro-2,3,5-tri-methyl-6-(1-methyl-2-oxobutyl)-	EtOH	273(4.04)	88-2401-79
$C_{13}H_{20}O_4$			
1-Cyclohexene-1-carboxylic acid, 3,5-diethyl-3-hydroxy-6-oxo-, ethyl ester	$CHCl_3$	239(3.85)	44-0964-79
Cyclopentanepropanoic acid, 1-acetyl-2,2-dimethyl-5-oxo-, methyl ester	pentane	286(1.81)	33-0553-79
2-Decenoic acid, 5,5-dimethyl-4,9-di-oxo-, methyl ester, (E)-	pentane	226(4.10),347(1.58)	33-0553-79
Propanoic acid, 3-(5-hydroxy-2,2,6-tri-methyl-1,6-epoxy-1-cyclohexyl)-, methyl ester, (E)-	pentane	217(4.13)	33-0553-79
Propanoic acid, 3-(2,2,6-trimethyl-5-oxo-1,6-epoxy-1-cyclohexyl)-, methyl ester	pentane	300(1.56)	33-0553-79
$C_{13}H_{20}O_6$			
2-Furanacetic acid, 2,5-dihydro-4-(5-hydroxypentyl)-3-methoxy-5-oxo-, methyl ester	EtOH	227(3.86)	130-0311-79

Compound	Solvent	λmax(log ε)	Ref.
α-D-xylo-Hept-5-enofuranuronic acid, 5,6-dideoxy-3-O-methyl-1,2-O-(1-methylethylidene)-, ethyl ester, (E)-	EtOH	223(3.95)	33-2091-79
(Z)-	hexane	226(3.76)	33-2091-79
$C_{13}H_{21}N$			
Benzenamine, 4-(1,1-dimethylpropyl)-2,6-dimethyl-	MeOH	235(3.92),286(3.22)	33-2613-79
1H-Pyrrole, 2-butyl-1-ethenyl-3-propyl-	C_6H_{12}	201(4.08),254(4.08)	104-0535-79
$C_{13}H_{21}NO_6$			
Propanedioic acid, [3-(dimethylamino)-4,4-dimethoxy-2-butenylidene]-, dimethyl ester	EtOH	390(4.6)	88-0921-79
$C_{13}H_{21}NS_2$			
2(3H)-Cyclododecathiazolethione, 4,5,6,7,8,9,10,11,12,13-decahydro-	EtOH	326(3.889)	48-0249-79
$C_{13}H_{21}N_2O_5PS$			
Phosphorothioic acid, O-(1-cyclohexyl-1,6-dihydro-5-methoxy-6-oxo-4-pyridazinyl) O,O-dimethyl ester	MeOH	214(4.32),288(3.74)	73-1761-79
$C_{13}H_{21}N_2O_6$			
1H-Imidazol-1-yloxy, 2,5-dihydro-4-[3-methoxy-2-(methoxycarbonyl)-3-oxopropyl]-2,2,5,5-tetramethyl-, 3-oxide	EtOH	238(4.08)	70-2521-79
$C_{13}H_{21}N_3O_6$			
Cytidine, 5,6-dihydro-6-(hydroxymethyl)-2',3'-O-(1-methylethylidene)-	EtOH	221(3.98),245(3.98)	150-2567-79
$C_{13}H_{22}N_2$			
5,8-Ethano-1H-pyrazolo[1,2-a]pyridazine, 2,2-diethyl-2,3,5,8-tetrahydro-	hexane	300(2.85)	35-7347-79
$C_{13}H_{22}N_2O_2$			
Pyrazineethanol, 6-methoxy-α,α-dimethyl-5-(2-methylpropyl)-	EtOH	218(4.01),279s(3.82), 298(3.96)	94-1378-79
Pyrazinemethanol, 6-methoxy-α-(1-methyl)-5-(2-methylpropyl)-	EtOH	216(3.87),280s(3.70), 297(3.78)	94-1378-79
$C_{13}H_{22}N_2O_3$			
Pyrazineethanol, 6-methoxy-α,α-dimethyl-5-(2-methylpropyl)-, 4-oxide	EtOH	222s(4.21),227(4.23), 268(3.93),308s(3.79), 312(3.80)	94-1378-79
$C_{13}H_{22}N_2S$			
2-Cyclododecathiazolamine, 4,5,6,7,8-9,10,11,12,13-decahydro-	EtOH	262(3.858)	48-0249-79
$C_{13}H_{22}N_4O_4S$			
5-Pyrimidinecarbothioamide, 6-amino-N-(2,3-diethoxyethyl)-1,2,3,4-tetrahydro-1,3-dimethyl-2,4-dioxo-	EtOH	259(4.28),302(4.18)	95-0515-79
$C_{13}H_{22}N_5O_{13}P_3S$			
Adenosine, 5'-(tetrahydrogen triphosphate), 8-(propylthio)-, tetrasodium salt	pH 7	281(4.27)	87-1529-79

Compound	Solvent	$\lambda_{max}(\log \epsilon)$	Ref.
$C_{13}H_{22}O$			
3-Cyclohexene-1-propanol, α,6,6-trimethyl-2-methylene-	EtOH	233(4.39)	142-0191-79B
$C_{13}H_{22}O_2$			
2-Butanone, 4-(2,2,6-trimethyl-1,6-epoxy-1-cyclohexyl)-	pentane	280(1.28)	33-0553-79
3-Buten-2-one, 4-(2-hydroxy-2,6,6-trimethyl-1-cyclohexyl)-, (E)-	MeCN	230(4.22),317(1.76)	33-0553-79
$C_{13}H_{22}O_3$			
3-Buten-2-one, 4-(1,2-dihydroxy-2,6,6-trimethylcyclohexyl)-	EtOH	235(4.08)	94-2807-79
2,11-Dioxabicyclo[4.4.1]undecan-10-one, 1,3,7,7-tetramethyl-	pentane	301(1.76)	33-0553-79
2-Heptenoic acid, 2-(2-methylpropyl)-7-oxo-, ethyl ester, (E)-	n.s.g.	217(3.94),290s(--)	118-0279-79
(Z)-	n.s.g.	217(3.86),290s(--)	118-0279-79
$C_{13}H_{22}O_6S_4$			
α-D-Glucopyranoside, methyl 2,3-di-O-methyl-, bis(S-methyl carbonodithioate)	MeOH	228(3.71),278(4.30)	136-0127-79G
$C_{13}H_{22}S_2$			
Spiro[2H-1,5-benzodithiepin-3(4H),1'-cyclopentane], tetrahydro-, cis	EtOH	213(3.21)	49-0279-79
trans	EtOH	212(3.19)	49-0279-79
Spiro[cyclohexane-1,3'(4'H)-[2H,6H]cyclopenta[b][1,4]dithiepin], tetrahydro-, trans	EtOH	212(3.21)	49-0279-79
$C_{13}H_{23}NO$			
6-Oxa-1-azabicyclo[3.1.0]hexane, 5-(1,1-dimethylethyl)-2,2-dimethyl-4-propylidene-	EtOH	209(3.73)	12-2041-79
6-Oxa-1-azabicyclo[3.1.0]hex-3-ene, 5-(1,1-dimethylethyl)-2,2-dimethyl-4-(1-methylethyl)-	EtOH	220(3.51)	12-2041-79
$C_{13}H_{23}NO_2$			
2H-Pyrrol-4-ol, 5-(1,1-dimethylethyl)-3,4-dihydro-2,2-dimethyl-4-(2-propenyl)-, 1-oxide	EtOH	291(4.01)	12-2025-79
$C_{13}H_{23}NO_3Si_2$			
6H-[1,2,5]Oxadisilolo[3,4-d]azepine-6-carboxylic acid, 1,3,3a,8a-tetrahydro-1,1,3,3-tetramethyl-, ethyl ester, trans	EtOH	238(4.2)	142-0263-79
$C_{13}H_{23}N_5O_3$			
1,2,3-Triazine-2-carboxylic acid, 4-[bis(1-methylethyl)amino]-6-(dimethylamino)-5-oxo-, methyl ester	CH_2Cl_2	433(3.92)	24-1535-79
$C_{13}H_{24}NOS$			
Sulfonium, dimethyl[2-(4-morpholinyl)-1-cyclohexen-1-yl]-, fluorosulfate	MeCN	215(3.6),295(3.6)	24-2997-79
Sulfonium, dimethyl[2-(4-morpholinyl)-2-cyclohexen-1-yl]-, chloride	MeCN	210(3.6),250(3.5)	24-2997-79
fluorosulfate	MeCN	214(3.5),249(3.5)	24-2997-79

Compound	Solvent	λ_{max}(log ε)	Ref.
$C_{13}H_{24}N_2O_3$			
Pentanediamide, N,N'-bis(1,1-dimethylethyl)-3-oxo-	MeOH-NaOH	273(3.97)	35-2171-79
$C_{13}H_{24}N_2O_4$			
2-Pentenedioic acid, 2-(1-methylhydrazino)-, bis(1,1-dimethylethyl) ester, (E)-	MeOH	280(4.31)	5-1696-79
2-Pentenedioic acid, 2-(2-methylhydrazino)-, bis(1,1-dimethylethyl) ester, (Z)-	MeOH	280(4.10)	5-1696-79
$C_{13}H_{24}N_6O_2$			
1,3,5-Triazine-2,4,6-triamine, N"-(2,2-dimethyl-1,3-dioxan-5-yl)-N,N,N',N'-tetramethyl-	EtOH	223(4.97)	104-1144-79
$C_{13}H_{25}NO_2$			
2H-Pyrrol-4-ol, 5-(1,1-dimethylethyl)-3,4-dihydro-2,2-dimethyl-4-(1-methylethyl)-, 1-oxide	EtOH	238(3.99)	12-2025-79
2H-Pyrrol-4-ol, 5-(1,1-dimethylethyl)-3,4-dihydro-2,2-dimethyl-4-propyl-, 1-oxide	EtOH	239(4.02)	12-2025-79
$C_{13}H_{25}NO_4Si_2$			
1H-Azepine-1-carboxylic acid, 4,5-dihydro-4,5-bis(hydroxydimethylsilyl)-, ethyl ester, trans	EtOH	240(4.1)	142-0263-79
$C_{13}H_{26}N_2$			
2-Butanamine, N,N'-methanetetraylbis-[3,3-dimethyl-	C_6H_{12}	215(2.97)	56-0631-79
$C_{13}H_{28}N_2S$			
Thiourea, N,N'-bis(1,2,2-trimethylpropyl)-	MeOH	215(4.17),241(4.20)	56-0631-79

Compound	Solvent	λ_{max}(log ε)	Ref.
$C_{14}H_4Cl_4O_2$			
1,4-Anthracenedione, 2,3,9,10-tetra-chloro-	MeOH	238(4.69),286(4.32), 300s(4.20),333s(3.70), 411(3.71)	104-0139-79
1,10-Anthracenedione, 2,3,4,9-tetra-chloro-	benzene	489(4.04)	104-0139-79
$C_{14}H_5Cl_3O_2$			
1,10-Anthracenedione, 2,4,9-trichloro-	benzene	484(4.06)	104-0139-79
$C_{14}H_6Cl_2O_2$			
9,10-Anthracenedione, 1,4-dichloro- (also spectrum at 77° K)	C_6H_{12}	337s(--),348(3.62), 362s(--)	18-0329-79
9,10-Anthracenedione, 1,5-dichloro-	C_6H_{12}	340(3.80),351s(--)	18-0329-79
$C_{14}H_6Cl_2O_3$			
1,4-Anthracenedione, 2,3-dichloro-9-hydroxy-	$CHCl_3$	247(4.73),290(4.24), 475(3.99)	107-0129-79
4-Cyclopentene-1,3-dione, 4,5-dichloro-2-(6H-cyclohepta[c]furan-6-ylidene)-	CH_2Cl_2	238(4.17),256(4.27), 281(4.21),292(4.15), 404s(4.38),418(4.40), 442s(4.32)	83-0120-79
$C_{14}H_6Cl_2O_4S$			
1,1'-Spirobi[3H-2,1-benzoxathiole]-3,3'-dione, 5,5'-dichloro-	dioxan	242s(4.35),287(3.54)	78-1869-79
1,1'-Spirobi[3H-2,1-benzoxathiole]-3,3'-dione, 5,7-dichloro-	dioxan	248s(4.13),301s(3.27)	78-1869-79
$C_{14}H_6Cl_4$			
Benzo[3',4']cyclobuta[1',2':3,4]cyclo-buta[1,2]benzene, 1,2,3,4-tetrachlo-ro-4b,8b-dihydro-	hexane	239s(4.32),260(3.08), 275(3.49),285(3.32), 296(3.38),312s(3.26)	88-4545-79
$C_{14}H_6Cl_4N_2$			
15,16-Diazatricyclo[9.3.1.1^{4,8}]hexa-deca-1(15),2,4,6,8(16),9,11,13-octaene, 2,3,9,10-tetrachloro-	C_6H_{12}	277(4.27),301(4.36), 313(4.31),350(3.05)	12-1241-79
$C_{14}H_6CrN_4O_4$			
Chromium, tetracarbonyl(pyrazino[2,3-f]quinoxaline-N^1,N^{10})-, (OC-6-22)-	MeOH	284(4.3),568(3.5)	101-0177-79E
$C_{14}H_6MoN_4O_4$			
Molybdenum, tetracarbonyl(pyrazino[2,3-f]quinoxaline-N^1,N^{10})-, (OC-6-22)-	MeOH	258(4.3),284(4.4), 527(3.7)	101-0177-79E
$C_{14}H_6N_2$			
1,2-Acenaphthylenedicarbonitrile	CH_2Cl_2	345(4.08)	44-1359-79
$C_{14}H_6N_2O_8S$			
1,1'-Spirobi[3H-2,1-benzoxathiole]-3,3'-dione, 5,5'-dinitro-	dioxan	257(4.31),340s(2.71)	78-1869-79
1,1'-Spirobi[3H-2,1-benzoxathiole]-3,3'-dione, 5,7-dinitro-	dioxan	246(4.25),308s(3.42)	78-1869-79
$C_{14}H_6N_4$			
Benzo[3,4]cyclobuta[1,2-b]pyrazine-2-carbonitrile, 3-(2-cyanoethenyl)-, (Z)-	EtOH	267(4.58),380(3.93), 393(3.95)	78-0241-79

Compound	Solvent	$\lambda_{max}(\log \epsilon)$	Ref.
$C_{14}H_6N_4O$			
Benzo[3,4]cyclobut[1,2-b][1,2,5]oxadiazolo[3,4-f]quinoxaline	EtOH	283(4.54),300s(4.24), 363s(4.09),375(4.23), 394(4.24)	78-0241-79
$C_{14}H_6N_4O_4W$			
Tungsten, tetracarbonyl(pyrazino[2,3-f]-quinoxaline-N^1,N^{10})-, (OC-6-22)-	MeOH	252(4.5),284(4.4), 548(3.8)	101-0177-79E
$C_{14}H_6O_3$			
Acenaphtho[1,2-c]furan-7,9-dione	CH_2Cl_2	350(4.04)	44-1359-79
$C_{14}H_7ClN_2O_2$			
Anthra[1,9-cd]isoxazol-6-one, 3-amino-5-chloro-	dioxan	459(4.23),478(4.28)	104-0510-79
$C_{14}H_7ClO_4S$			
1,1'-Spirobi[3H-2,1-benzoxathiole]-3,3'-dione, 5-chloro-	dioxan	237s(4.31),284(3.48)	78-1869-79
$C_{14}H_7Cl_2NO_2$			
9(10H)-Anthracenone, 1,3-dichloro-4-hydroxy-10-imino-	benzene	417(3.53),530f(3.63)	104-0147-79
	EtOH	514f(3.97)	104-0147-79
	dioxan	417s(3.30),521(3.84)	104-0147-79
$C_{14}H_7Cl_3N_4$			
4,5'-Bipyrimidine, 2,2',4'-trichloro-6-phenyl-	EtOH	210(4.40),252(4.30), 303(4.26)	103-0671-79
$C_{14}H_7Cl_3O_3$			
[1,1'-Biphenyl]-2-acetic acid, 3,4,5-trichloro-α-oxo-	MeOH	207(4.59),245(4.26)	44-2391-79
[1,1'-Biphenyl]-3-acetic acid, 4,5,6-trichloro-α-oxo-	MeOH	207(4.59)	44-2391-79
$C_{14}H_7F_5N_2OS$			
Sulfur diimide, (4-acetylphenyl)(pentafluorophenyl)-	pentane	413(4.03)	70-2352-79
$C_{14}H_7NO_3$			
8H-Acenaphtho[1,2-d][1,3]oxazine-8,10(7H)-dione	CH_2Cl_2	334(3.91)	44-1359-79
$C_{14}H_7NO_6S$			
1,1'-Spirobi[3H-2,1-benzoxathiole]-3,3'-dione, 5-nitro-	dioxan	259(4.06),335s(2.78)	78-1869-79
$C_{14}H_7N_5$			
Acenaphtho[1,2-e][1,2,4]triazolo[4,3-b][1,2,4]triazine	MeOH	218(4.53),234(4.86), 293(4.49),320s(4.27)	83-0147-79
$C_{14}H_8Br_2N_2O_2$			
9,10-Anthracenedione, 1,4-diamino-2,3-dibromo-	benzene	554(3.97),592(3.91)	153-0033-79
$C_{14}H_8ClFOS$			
Dibenzo[b,f]thiepin-10(11H)-one, 2-chloro-6-fluoro-	MeOH	229(4.35),257s(4.05), 330(3.68)	73-2139-79
Dibenzo[b,f]thiepin-10(11H)-one, 8-chloro-6-fluoro-	MeOH	240(4.30),260(4.09), 340(3.72)	73-2139-79

Compound	Solvent	λ_{max}(log ε)	Ref.
$C_{14}H_8ClFS$			
Dibenzo[b,f]thiepin, 2-chloro-6-fluoro-	MeOH	259(4.37),299(3.55)	73-2139-79
$C_{14}H_8ClNOS$			
Methanone, (5-chloro-2-isothiocyanato-phenyl)phenyl-	hexane	228(4.51),257(4.25), 288(4.12)	106-0663-79
$C_{14}H_8Cl_2N_2O_2$			
9,10-Anthracenedione, 1,4-diamino-2,3-dichloro-	benzene	555(4.01),592(3.95)	153-0033-79
$C_{14}H_8Cl_2O$			
Cyclobut[a]acenaphthylen-7(6aH)-one, 8,8-dichloro-8,8a-dihydro-	EtOH	280(3.83),290(3.89), 301s(3.75)	39-2995-79C
$C_{14}H_8Cl_2O_5S$			
Benzoic acid, 2-[(2-carboxyphenyl)sulfinyl]-3,5-dichloro-	dioxan	234s(4.35),287s(3.55)	78-1875-79
Benzoic acid, 2,2'-sulfinylbis[5-chloro-	dioxan	235(4.29),248s(4.19), 294(3.54)	78-1875-79
$C_{14}H_8F_6N_2O_2$			
Pyridine, 1,4-dihydro-1-(trifluoroacetyl)-4-[1-(trifluoroacetyl)-4(1H)-pyridinylidene]-	MeCN	423(--),440(--)(changing)	5-0727-79
$C_{14}H_8N_2O$			
Dibenz[c,f][1,2]oxazepine-11-carbonitrile	C_6H_{12}	224(4.50),400(3.68)	78-1273-79
$C_{14}H_8N_2OS$			
9H-Naphtho[1',2':4,5]thiazolo[3,2-a]-pyrimidin-9-one	MeOH	247(4.60),298(4.10), 311(4.08),327(3.94), 340(4.01)	83-0619-79
$C_{14}H_8N_2O_2$			
6H-Anthra[1,9-cd]isoxazol-6-one, 5-amino-	dioxan	468(4.06),503(4.07)	104-0510-79
$C_{14}H_8N_2O_4$			
1,9-Phenazinedicarboxylic acid	EtOH	205(4.49),250(4.77), 352s(4.02),370(4.24)	87-0918-79
$C_{14}H_8N_2O_9S$			
Benzoic acid, 2,2'-sulfinylbis[5-nitro-	dioxan	256(4.20),333s(3.13)	78-1875-79
$C_{14}H_8N_4O$			
Benzonitrile, 3,3'-azoxybis-, (Z)-	MeCN	320.4(4.22)	18-1588-79
Benzonitrile, 4,4'-azoxybis-, (Z)-	MeCN	334.8(4.26)	18-1588-79
$C_{14}H_8N_4O_2S_2$			
Bisthiazolo[3,2-a:3',2'-a']benzo[1,2-d:4,5-d']diimidazole-5,11-dione, 2,8-dimethyl-	EtOH	285(4.39),320(4.32), 451(4.10)	2-0523-79A
Bisthiazolo[3,2-a:3',2'-a']benzo[1,2-d:4,5-d']diimidazole-5,11-dione, 3,9-dimethyl-	EtOH	294(4.40),315(4.37), 456(4.15)	2-0523-79A
Bisthiazolo[3,2-a:3',2'-a']benzo[1,2-d:5,4-d']diimidazole-5,11-dione, 2,8-dimethyl-	EtOH	260(4.25),310(4.13), 440(3.85)	2-0523-79A

Compound	Solvent	λ_{max}(log ε)	Ref.
Bisthiazolo[3,2-a:3',2'-a']benzo[1,2-d:5,4-d']diimidazole-5,11-dione, 3,9-dimethyl-	EtOH	279(4.23),308(4.03), 445(3.91)	2-0523-79A
$C_{14}H_8N_4O_6$			
Sydnone, 3-(2,4-dinitrophenyl)-4-phenyl-	CH_2Cl_2	238(4.33),329(3.95), 410s(2.96)	5-0063-79
$C_{14}H_8OS$			
9(10H)-Anthracenone, 10-thioxo-	MeCN	224(4.38),267(4.41), 334(4.14),690(1.69)	44-0632-79
	$CHCl_3$	270(4.42),334(4.16), 697(1.67)	44-0632-79
$C_{14}H_8O_2$			
9,10-Anthracenedione	C_6H_{12}	308(--),320(3.69), 333(3.57)	18-0329-79
Cyclohepta[de]naphthalene-7,10-dione	MeOH	241(4.11),350(3.89)	39-2995-79C
$C_{14}H_8O_2S$			
1,4-Naphthalenedione, 2-(2-thienyl)-	MeOH	205(4.33),217(4.24), 260(4.17),431(3.62)	2-0079-79A
$C_{14}H_8O_4$			
1,2-Acenaphthylenedicarboxylic acid	CH_2Cl_2	355(4.14)	44-1359-79
6H-Dibenzo[b,d]pyran-6,7,10-trione, 2-methyl-	EtOH	216(4.33),390(3.55)	33-2833-79
6H-Dibenzo[b,d]pyran-6,7,10-trione, 3-methyl-	EtOH	209(4.51),423(3.74)	33-2833-79
9H-Xanthen-9-one, 1,2-(methylenedioxy)-	EtOH	246(4.66),270s(4.03), 308(4.26),353(4.15)	142-0269-79
$C_{14}H_8O_5$			
6H-Dibenzo[b,d]pyran-6,7,10-trione, 3-methoxy-	$CHCl_3$	255(4.15),294(3.95), 475(3.94)	33-2833-79
9H-Xanthen-9-one, 4-hydroxy-2,3-(methylenedioxy)-	EtOH	244(4.53),287(3.82), 322(4.11)	142-0269-79
	EtOH-NaOH	242(4.50),275(4.34), 349(4.08)	142-0269-79
	EtOH-NaOAc	241(4.54),275(4.31), 348(4.07)	142-0269-79
$C_{14}H_8O_5S$			
1-Anthracenesulfonic acid, 9,10-dihydro-9,10-dioxo-	H_2O	257(4.67),280s(4.10), 332(3.67)	78-2255-79
2-Anthracenesulfonic acid, 9,10-dihydro-9,10-dioxo-	H_2O	257(4.69),275s(4.19), 332(3.69)	78-2255-79
$C_{14}H_8O_6$			
9,10-Anthracenedione, 1,3,5,8-tetrahydroxy-	MeOH	227(4.57),252(4.24), 278(4.28),484(4.14), 502(4.06),517(3.65)	24-2640-79
$C_{14}H_9Br$			
Anthracene, 9-bromo-	CCl_4	336(3.47),353(3.79), 372(3.96),392(3.92)	78-2131-79
$C_{14}H_9BrN_4O_2$			
Benzoic acid, 4-[5-(4-bromophenyl)-2H-tetrazol-2-yl]-	EtOH	247(4.34),278(4.48), 293(4.46)	4-0123-79

Compound	Solvent	λmax(log ε)	Ref.
$C_{14}H_9BrN_8$			
2,5'-Bi-2H-tetrazolium, 3-(2-bromophenyl)-5-phenyl-, hydroxide, inner salt	EtOH	250(4.33)	104-0558-79
$C_{14}H_9ClN_2S$			
2(1H)-Quinazolinethione, 6-chloro-4-phenyl-	EtOH	304(4.53),421(3.65)	118-0120-79
$C_{14}H_9ClN_4O_2$			
Benzoic acid, 4-[5-(4-chlorophenyl)-2H-tetrazol-2-yl]-	EtOH	243(4.27),278(4.39), 292(4.37)	4-0123-79
$C_{14}H_9ClN_8$			
2,5'-Bi-2H-tetrazolium, 3-(2-chlorophenyl)-5-phenyl-, hydroxide, inner salt	EtOH	249(4.36)	104-0558-79
$C_{14}H_9ClO_2S$			
Dibenzo[b,f]thiepin-10(11H)-one, 8-chloro-3-hydroxy-	MeOH	235(4.38),262(4.07), 293(3.55),340(3.60)	73-3617-79
$C_{14}H_9ClO_5S$			
Benzoic acid, 2-[(2-carboxyphenyl)sulfinyl]-5-chloro-	dioxan	231(4.23),285(3.43)	78-1875-79
$C_{14}H_9Cl_2NO_4$			
Benzene, 1,1'-[(nitroethenylidene)-bis(oxy)]bis[2-chloro-	EtOH	209(4.31),238(3.65), 286(4.05)	104-1315-79
$C_{14}H_9Cl_3O_2$			
[1,1'-Biphenyl]-2-carboxylic acid, 3,4,5-trichloro-, methyl ester	MeOH	208(4.61),255s(--)	44-2391-79
[1,1'-Biphenyl]-3-carboxylic acid, 4,5,6-trichloro-, methyl ester	MeOH	209(4.58),298(3.11)	44-2391-79
$C_{14}H_9Cl_3O_2S$			
Benzeneacetic acid, 2,5-dichloro-α-[(4-chlorophenyl)thio]-	EtOH	202(4.57),220(4.35), 265(3.35)	80-0137-79
Benzeneacetic acid, 3,4-dichloro-α-[(4-chlorophenyl)thio]-	EtOH	204(4.79),239(4.33), 273(3.23),281(3.26), 290(3.17)	80-0137-79
$C_{14}H_9Cl_3O_3$			
1-Naphthaleneacetic acid, 2,3,4-trichloro- -oxo-, ethyl ester	MeOH	234(4.82),283(3.64), 293(3.65)	44-2391-79
$C_{14}H_9FOS$			
Dibenzo[b,f]thiepin-10(11H)-one, 3-fluoro-	MeOH	238(4.27),265s(3.96), 325(3.73)	73-2108-79
Dibenzo[b,f]thiepin-10(11H)-one, 6-fluoro-	MeOH	252(4.09),330(3.71)	73-2139-79
$C_{14}H_9FS$			
Dibenzo[b,f]thiepin, 3-fluoro-	MeOH	261(4.39),293(3.66)	73-2108-79
$C_{14}H_9IN_2O$			
1H-Benzimidazole, 1-(2-iodobenzoyl)-	MeOH	236s(--),266(3.71), 268(4.10),274(3.33), 280(3.44)	4-1235-79

Compound	Solvent	λmax(log ε)	Ref.
$C_{14}H_9IN_8$			
2,5'-Bi-2H-tetrazolium, 3-(2-iodophenyl)-5-phenyl-, hydroxide, inner salt	EtOH	244(4.46)	104-0558-79
$C_{14}H_9N$			
Pyrrolo[3,2,1-jk]carbazole	EtOH	234s(4.56),256s(4.60), 267(4.79),273(4.80), 278(4.78),303s(3.97), 314s(4.16),326s(4.23), 333(4.28)	39-2387-79C
$C_{14}H_9NO_2$			
Benzonitrile, 3-bromo-2-hydroxy-	EtOH	241(4.45),336(3.88)	56-0533-79
$C_{14}H_9NO_2S$			
5(4H)-Oxazolone, 4-(phenylmethylene)-2-(2-thienyl)-	toluene	380(4.57)	103-1303-79
5(4H)-Oxazolone, 2-phenyl-4-(2-thienylmethylene)-	toluene	300s(--),395(4.55)	103-1303-79
$C_{14}H_9NO_3$			
1-Acenaphthylenecarboxylic acid, 2-(aminocarbonyl)-	CH_2Cl_2	339(4.30)	44-1359-79
5(4H)-Oxazolone, 4-(2-furanylmethylene)-2-phenyl-	toluene	390(4.65),410(4.60)	103-1303-79
5(4H)-Oxazolone, 2-(2-furanyl)-4-(phenylmethylene)-	toluene	370(4.64),395(4.53)	103-1303-79
$C_{14}H_9NO_4$			
Acetic acid, cyano(1,3-dihydro-1,3-dioxo-2H-inden-2-ylidene)-, ethyl ester	dioxan	234s(4.24),269(4.45), 327(3.81)	32-0329-79
$C_{14}H_9NO_7S$			
Benzoic acid, 2-[(2-carboxyphenyl)sulfinyl]-5-nitro-, (ethanolate)	dioxan	264(4.01),333s(3.22)	78-1875-79
$C_{14}H_9N_3$			
Phenanthrene, 9-azido-	$CHCl_3$	246s(4.54),256s(4.59), 262(4.61),272s(4.41), 279s(4.24),298s(4.05), 310(4.10),318(4.03)	78-2901-79
$C_{14}H_9N_3O$			
Acenaphtho[1,2-e][1,2,4]triazin-9(8H)-one, 8-methyl-	MeOH	220(4.59),232(4.68), 306(4.46),317(4.49)	83-0147-79
$C_{14}H_9N_3OS$			
1,2,4-Thiadiazolo[4,5-a]benzimidazol-3(2H)-one, 2-phenyl-	EtOH	227(4.54),281(4.43), 290(4.34),301(4.29)	39-2909-79C
$C_{14}H_9N_3O_2S_2$			
4,8-Epithio-4H-pyrrolo[3,4-f]-2,1,3-benzothiadiazole-5,7(4aH,6H)-dione, 7a,8-dihydro-6-phenyl-	MeOH	298(3.94)	88-4493-79
$C_{14}H_9N_3O_4$			
Sydnone, 3-(4-nitrophenyl)-4-phenyl-	CH_2Cl_2	246(4.28),309(3.94), 360s(--)	5-0063-79
$C_{14}H_9N_3O_4S$			
Benzothiazole, 2-[(2,4-dinitrophenyl)-	EtOH at -75°	526(4.68)	104-1926-79

Compound	Solvent	$\lambda_{max}(\log \epsilon)$	Ref.
methyl]- (cont.)			104-1926-79
anion	50% EtOH	512(4.54),630s(4.10)	104-1926-79
$C_{14}H_9N_3O_5$			
Benzoxazole, 2-[(2,4-dinitrophenyl)-methyl]-	EtOH at -75°	500(4.68)	104-1926-79
anion	50% EtOH	503(4.55),620s(4.11)	104-1926-79
$C_{14}H_9N_3S$			
Acenaphtho[1,2-e][1,2,4]triazine, 9-(methylthio)-	MeOH	232(4.64),280(4.18) 324(3.4.52)[sic]	83-0147-79
Propanedinitrile, [[(4-phenyl-2-thienyl)amino]methylene]-	EtOH	272(4.25),337(4.20)	49-1189-79
Propanedinitrile, [[(5-phenyl-2-thienyl)amino]methylene]-	DMF	371(4.35)	49-1189-79
Thieno[2,3-b]pyridine-5-carbonitrile, 4-amino-2-phenyl-	DMF	318(4.20),340(4.18), 348(4.15)	49-1189-79
$C_{14}H_9N_3S_2$			
Benzenamine, N-3H-1,2,4-dithiazolo-[4,3-a]benzimidazol-2-ylidene-	CH_2Cl_2	244(4.40),250(4.40), 274(4.19)	39-2909-79C
1,2,4-Thiadiazolo[4,5-a]benzimidazole-3(2H)-thione, 2-phenyl-	EtOH	278(4.39),285(4.39), 317(4.22),325(4.19)	39-2909-79C
$C_{14}H_9N_5O_4$			
Benzoic acid, 4-[5-(3-nitrophenyl)-2H-tetrazol-2-yl]-	EtOH	233(4.35),275(4.50)	4-0123-79
Benzoic acid, 4-[5-(4-nitrophenyl)-2H-tetrazol-2-yl]-	EtOH	295(4.46)	4-0123-79
$C_{14}H_{10}$			
Anthracene	pH 7.4	400(3.52)	149-0531-79A
	CCl_4	326(3.46),342(3.75), 358(3.90),378(3.88)	78-2131-79
Cyclohepta[de]naphthalene	ether	229(4.50),238(4.45), 246(4.45)M272s(3.44), 284(3.56),297(3.61), 310s(3.60),328(3.75), 340(3.84),352(3.72), 360(3.59),367(3.10), 420(2.48),447(2.53), 477(2.49),511(2.31), 553(1.91)	39-2995-79C
$C_{14}H_{10}ClFOS$			
Ethanone, 1-[5-chloro-2-[(2-fluorophenyl)thio]phenyl]-	MeOH	234(4.06),268(3.95), 343(3.59)	73-2139-79
$C_{14}H_{10}ClNO_4$			
Pyrido[2,1,5-cd]indolizine-5,6-dicarboxylic acid, 3-chloro-, dimethyl ester	EtOH	218(4.09),265(4.57), 415(3.42)	24-2465-79
$C_{14}H_{10}ClN_3$			
Pyridazine, 3-(4-chlorophenyl)-6-(1H-pyrrol-1-yl)-	EtOH	274(4.32)	80-0453-79
$C_{14}H_{10}ClN_3S$			
2H-1,3,4-Benzotriazepine-2-thione, 7-chloro-1,3-dihydro-5-phenyl-	MeOH	239(4.38),296(4.00), 333(3.99)	106-0847-79

Compound	Solvent	$\lambda_{max}(\log \epsilon)$	Ref.
Diazirino[1,3-c]quinazoline-3(1H)-thione, 7-chloro-4,8b-dihydro-8b-phenyl-	MeOH	289(4.33)	106-0663-79
$C_{14}H_{10}Cl_2N_4O_2S_2$			
2,5-Cyclohexadiene-1,4-dione, 2,5-dichloro-3,6-bis[(4-methyl-2-thiazolyl)amino]-	EtOH	243(3.65),349(3.91), 551(4.15)	2-0523-79A
2,5-Cyclohexadiene-1,4-dione, 2,5-dichloro-3,6-bis[(5-methyl-2-thiazolyl)amino]-	EtOH	251(3.91),341(3.50), 533(4.19)	2-0523-79A
$C_{14}H_{10}Cl_2O_2S$			
Benzeneacetic acid, 4-chloro-α-[(4-chlorophenyl)thio]-	EtOH	226(4.20),260(3.83)	80-0137-79
Benzeneacetic acid, 2,5-dichloro-α-(phenylthio)-	EtOH	220(4.32),270(3.58)	80-0137-79
Benzeneacetic acid, 3,4-dichloro-α-(phenylthio)-	EtOH	208(4.57),239(4.36), 272(3.22),281(3.25), 290(3.14)	80-0137-79
$C_{14}H_{10}N_2$			
Pyrrolo[2,3-a]carbazole, 1,10-dihydro-	EtOH	207(4.23),250(4.86), 270(4.21),308(4.29)	103-1097-79
Pyrrolo[2,3-c]carbazole, 3,6-dihydro-	EtOH	234(4.47),262(4.22), 271(4.10),285(3.57), 317(4.30),353(3.75)	103-0642-79
$C_{14}H_{10}N_2O$			
1,2,4-Oxadiazole, 3,5-diphenyl-	EtOH	244(4.51)	40-0389-79
8-Quinolinol, 2-(2-pyridinyl)-	pH 2	296(4.51)	86-0297-79
	pH 7	263(4.49),280(4.48)	86-0297-79
	pH 13	295(4.52)	86-0297-79
$C_{14}H_{10}N_2OS$			
1,2,3-Oxadiazolium, 5-mercapto-3,4-diphenyl-, hydroxide, inner salt	EtOH	238(4.05),290s(3.77), 370(3.50),480(3.24)	39-0956-79C
1,2,3-Thiadiazolium, 5-hydroxy-3,4-diphenyl-, hydroxide, inner salt	EtOH	242(4.01),353(3.81)	39-0956-79C
$C_{14}H_{10}N_2O_2$			
9,10-Anthracenedione, 1,2-diamino-	benzene	465s(3.76),488(3.79)	153-0033-79
5H-Dibenz[b,e]azepine-6,11-dione, 1-amino-	dioxan	300(3.9),390(3.6)	83-0662-79
5H-Dibenz[b,e]azepine-6,11-dione, 10-amino-	dioxan	323(3.5),393(3.6)	83-0662-79
$C_{14}H_{10}N_2O_2S$			
Sydnone, 3-phenyl-4-(phenylthio)-	CH_2Cl_2	230(4.16),321(3.85)	5-0063-79
$C_{14}H_{10}N_2O_2S_2$			
Thiazolo[3,2-a]pyridinium, 3-hydroxy-2-[(2-pyridinylthio)acetyl]-, hydroxide, inner salt	MeOH	250(3.50),284(3.42), 416(3.55)	103-0872-79
	benzene	443(--)	103-0872-79
	MeOH-CF_3COOH	282(3.39),316(3.38), 416(3.53)	103-0872-79 +103-1081-79
$C_{14}H_{10}N_2O_4$			
[4,5'-Bioxazole]-4'-carboxylic acid, 5-phenyl-, methyl ester	MeOH	228(4.22),284(4.04)	5-1370-79

Compound	Solvent	$\lambda_{max}(\log \epsilon)$	Ref.
$C_{14}H_{10}N_2O_4S$			
Thiazolo[3,2-a]pyridinium, 3-hydroxy-2-[hydroxy(4-nitrophenyl)methyl]-, hydroxide, inner salt	MeCN	430(4.03)	103-1081-79
$C_{14}H_{10}N_2O_5$			
2H-Pyran-3-carboxylic acid, 2-(3,3-dicyano-2-propenylidene)-5,6-dihydro-5-(1-hydroxyethylidene)-6-oxo-, methyl ester, (?,Z)-	EtOH and EtOH-KOH	236(3.64),247(3.72), 295(3.81),326(3.96), 358(4.04),493s(4.72), 521(4.95)	77-0666-79
	$CHCl_3$	431(4.66)	77-0666-79
$C_{14}H_{10}N_2O_6$			
2H-Pyran-3,5-dicarboxylic acid, 6-(3,3-dicyano-2-propenyl)-2-oxo-, dimethyl ester	EtOH-HCl or EtOH-KOH	229(4.03),247(4.09), 317(3.85),352(4.01), 507(4.90)	77-0666-79
	$CHCl_3$-CF_3COOH	317(3.90),460(3.20)	77-0666-79
$C_{14}H_{10}N_2S$			
2(1H)-Quinazolinethione, 4-phenyl-	EtOH	297(4.52),417(3.76)	118-0120-79
1,2,4-Thiadiazole, 3,5-diphenyl-	EtOH	255(4.54)	40-0389-79
1,2,5-Thiadiazole, 3,4-diphenyl-	EtOH	258(3.96),305(4.05)	4-1009-79
$C_{14}H_{10}N_2S_2$			
Compd. from diphenylethyne and N_2S_2	EtOH	280(4.30),457(3.42)	4-1009-79
$C_{14}H_{10}N_2S_3$			
1,3,2-Benzodithiazole, 2-(2-benzothiazolyl)-5-methyl-	THF	224(4.42)	4-0183-79
$C_{14}H_{10}N_4$			
Pyrimido[1',6':1,5]pyrrolo[2,3-b]quinoxaline, 1-methyl-	EtOH	254s(3.98),264(4.11), 272s(4.07),278s(4.02), 327s(3.53),339(3.70), 353(3.75),396s(3.51), 408(3.53),430(3.38)	78-2463-79
$C_{14}H_{10}N_4O$			
Naphtho[2,1-e]pyrazolo[5,1-c][1,2,4]triazin-5-ol, 2-methyl-	MeOH	306(4.08),410(3.62), 442(3.87)	103-0657-79
	HOAc	295(4.06),316s(4.02)	103-0657-79
$C_{14}H_{10}N_4O_2$			
Benzoic acid, 4-(5-phenyl-2H-tetrazol-2-yl)-	EtOH	233(3.97),279(4.04), 288(4.05)	4-0123-79
$C_{14}H_{10}N_4O_3$			
Benzoic acid, 4-[5-(4-hydroxyphenyl)-2H-tetrazol-2-yl]-	EtOH	253(4.19),279(4.10), 304(4.05)	4-0123-79
$C_{14}H_{10}N_4O_4$			
1H-Benzimidazole, 2-[(2,4-dinitrophenyl)methyl]-	EtOH at -75°	515(4.54)	104-1926-79
anion	50% EtOH	480(4.45),645s(3.97)	104-1926-79
$C_{14}H_{10}N_6O_6$			
Benzamide, 2,2'-azobis[4-nitro-	MeOH	329(4.25)	94-2775-79
Benzamide, 3,3'-azobis[6-nitro-	MeOH	262(4.32),310(4.21)	94-2775-79

Compound	Solvent	$\lambda_{max}(\log \epsilon)$	Ref.
$C_{14}H_{10}N_8O$			
2,5'-Bi-2H-tetrazolium, 3-(2-hydroxy-phenyl)-5-phenyl-, hydroxide, inner salt	pH 13	240(4.40),330s(--), 468(3.10)	104-0558-79
	EtOH	241(4.28)	104-0558-79
	EtOH-NaOH	240(4.40),288(3.92), 490(3.20)	104-0558-79
$C_{14}H_{10}O$			
Cyclobut[a]acenaphthylen-7(6bH)-one, 8,8a-dihydro-	EtOH	281(3.76),291(3.83), 303s(3.65),323(3.15)	39-2995-79C
Cyclohepta[de]naphthalen-7(8H)-one	EtOH	246(4.15),308(3.72), 333(3.67),349(3.63)	39-2995-79C
Ethanone, 1-(5-acenaphthylenyl)-	C_6H_{12}	205(4.40),232(4.45), 268(3.55),278(3.34), 334(4.01),353(3.68)	44-0514-79
$C_{14}H_{10}OS$			
Thiirene, diphenyl-, 1-oxide	EtOH	220(4.41),228(4.40), 293s(4.40),299(4.45), 310s(4.38)	35-0390-79
$C_{14}H_{10}O_2$			
Anthra[4a,10-b:9,9a-b']bisoxirene, 6a,10b-dihydro-	ether	273(3.48),279(3.51), 285(3.49)	89-0413-79
Cyclohepta[de]naphthalene-7,10-dione, 8,9-dihydro-	M NaOH	264s(3.57),275s(3.77), 286(3.85),295(3.72), 302(3.47),312(3.11), 317(3.03)	39-2995-79C
	MeOH	318(3.90)	39-2995-79C
6,11-Epoxydibenz[b,e]oxepin, 6,11-di-hydro-	ether	278(3.48),286(3.52)	89-0413-79
1,6-Heptalenedicarboxaldehyde	EtOH	290(4.20),362(3.71), 485(2.93)	89-0545-79
9H-Xanthen-9-one, 2-methyl-	EtOH	244(4.21),262(4.10), 288(3.64),293(3.64), 344(3.86)	35-0665-79
$C_{14}H_{10}O_3$			
1,8,9-Anthracenetriol	$CHCl_3$	356(4.01)	36-0388-79
9(10H)-Anthracenone, 1,8-dihydroxy-	$CHCl_3$	432(4.08)	36-0388-79
Anthra[2,3-b]oxiren-2(1aH)-one, 9,9a-dihydro-9-hydroxy-, (1aα,9α,9aα)-	EtOH	248(4.61),257(4.67), 280s(3.83),290(3.97), 300(3.90),340(3.34), 350s(3.33)	22-0110-79
(1aα,9β,9aα)-	EtOH	247(4.57),255(4.63), 260s(4.15),278s(3.72), 290(3.86),300s(3.76), 336s(3.20),345(3.21)	22-0110-79
Naphtho[2,3-c]furan-4,9-dione, 5,8-di-methyl-	CH_2Cl_2	244(4.15),294(3.46), 344(3.50)	150-3518-79
9H-Xanthen-9-one, 2-methoxy-	MeOH	236(4.59),248(4.52), 297(3.68),302(3.66), 359(3.88)	142-0269-79
$C_{14}H_{10}O_4$			
6H-Dibenzo[b,d]pyran-6-one, 7,10-di-hydroxy-2-methyl-	EtOH	210(4.51),235(4.62), 270(4.05),374(4.15)	33-2833-79
6H-Dibenzo[b,d]pyran-6-one, 7,10-di-hydroxy-3-methyl-	EtOH	208(4.60),237(4.61), 273(4.05),373(4.10)	33-2833-79
1H-Indene-1,3(2H)-dione, 2-(1-acetyl-2-oxopropylidene)-	dioxan	251(4.50),305(3.60), 317(3.60)	32-0329-79

Compound	Solvent	λ max (log ε)	Ref.
9H-Xanthen-9-one, 1-hydroxy-5-methoxy-	MeOH	251(4.62),311(3.89), 375(3.70)	142-0269-79
9H-Xanthen-9-one, 1-hydroxy-7-methoxy-	EtOH	234(4.31),260(4.40), 286(3.63),380(3.68)	142-0269-79
	EtOH-AlCl$_3$	234(4.66),277(4.66), 307(4.13),330(3.48)	142-0269-79
9H-Xanthen-9-one, 2-hydroxy-1-methoxy-	EtOH	239(4.48),254(4.43), 275s(4.00),369(3.72)	142-0269-79
	EtOH-NaOH	225(4.47),275(4.39)	142-0269-79
9H-Xanthen-9-one, 2-hydroxy-5-methoxy-	MeOH	245s(4.37),256(4.43), 285s(3.20),372(3.55)	100-0301-79
	MeOH-NaOMe	255(--),416(--)	100-0301-79
9H-Xanthen-9-one, 3-hydroxy-2-methoxy-	EtOH	240(4.51),273(3.85), 309(4.06),349(4.00)	142-0269-79
	EtOH-NaOH	231(4.58),267(4.03), 277(3.92),360(4.39)	142-0269-79
	EtOH-NaOAc	231(4.57),267s(3.93), 277s(3.81),360(4.33)	142-0269-79
9H-Xanthen-9-one, 3-hydroxy-4-methoxy-	EtOH	235(4.47),282(3.97), 337(4.19),370(4.11)	142-0269-79
	EtOH-NaOAc	235(4.48),292(3.98), 335(4.19),370(3.71)	142-0269-79
9H-Xanthen-9-one, 5-hydroxy-1-methoxy-	EtOH	236(4.37),245(4.63), 304(4.48),351(3.81)	142-0269-79
$C_{14}H_{10}O_4S$			
1,4-Cyclohexadiene-1-carboxylic acid, 3,6-dioxo-2-(phenylthio)-, methyl ester	EtOH	209(4.18),220(4.14), 244(4.01),420(3.14)	33-2350-79
$C_{14}H_{10}O_5$			
6H-Dibenzo[b,d]pyran-6-one, 7,10-dihydroxy-3-methoxy-	EtOH	212(4.38),241(4.49), 280(4.02),292(4.01), 380(4.06),393(4.03)	33-2833-79
Rubrofusarin	EtOH	224(4.41),280(4.72), 325(4.34),395(4.37)	98-1347-79
9H-Xanthen-9-one, 1,3-dihydroxy-5-methoxy-	MeOH	240(4.54),312(4.18), 350(3.83)	142-0269-79
9H-Xanthen-9-one, 1,5-dihydroxy-3-methoxy-	EtOH	250(4.43),274s(3.80), 310(4.09),355(3.4)	142-0269-79
	EtOH-NaOH	240s(4.36),263(4.54), 278s(4.08),344(4.14)	142-0269-79
	EtOH-NaOAc	253(4.42),287(4.15), 314(4.08)	142-0269-79
	EtOH-AlCl$_3$	240(4.23),267(4.46), 335(4.20)	142-0269-79
9H-Xanthen-9-one, 1,6-dihydroxy-5-methoxy-	EtOH	243(4.59),267(4.02), 313(4.12),357(3.95)	142-0269-79
9H-Xanthen-9-one, 2,3-dihydroxy-1-methoxy-	EtOH	239(4.47),255s(4.31), 313(4.16),355(3.79)	142-0269-79
	EtOH-NaOH	231(4.47),275(4.05), 354(4.21)	142-0269-79
	EtOH-NaOAc	235(4.54),270s(4.09), 364(4.29)	142-0269-79
	EtOH-AlCl$_3$	235(4.39),260(4.26), 330(4.25)	142-0269-79
	EtOH-NaOAc-H_3BO_3	237(4.47),315(4.10), 355(3.88)	142-0269-79
9H-Xanthen-9-one, 2,8-dihydroxy-1-methoxy-	EtOH	238(4.43),262(4.52), 290(3.72),322(3.64)	142-0269-79

Compound	Solvent	λ_{max}(log ε)	Ref.
9H-Xanthen-9-one, 2,8-dihydroxy-1-methoxy- (cont.)	EtOH-NaOH	254(4.50),275(4.40), 350(3.60)	142-0269-79
	EtOH-AlCl$_3$	238(4.46),277(4.46), 311(3.79),350(3.60)	142-0269-79
9H-Xanthen-9-one, 3,4-dihydroxy-2-methoxy-	EtOH	240(4.48),258(4.45), 286(3.79),337(4.11)	142-0269-79
	EtOH-NaOAc	232(4.42),276(4.16), 364(4.10)	142-0269-79
$C_{14}H_{10}O_5S$			
Benzoic acid, 2,2'-sulfinylbis-	dioxan	225s(4.27),281(3.41)	78-1875-79
$C_{14}H_{10}O_6$			
1H-Naphtho[2,3-c]pyran-1,6,9-trione, 3,4-dihydro-7,10-dihydroxy-3-methyl-	MeOH	233(4.09),274(4.24), 378(3.45),490(3.32)	24-0957-79
	MeOH-HCl	225(4.32),289(3.85), 390s(--),418(3.48)	24-0957-79
	MeOH-NaOH	245s(--),269(4.18), 300s(--),390(3.26), 450(3.28),525(3.36)	24-0957-79
Psoralen, 8-acetoxy-5-methoxy-	MeOH	245(4.3),260(4.5), 310(4.1)	102-0352-79
$C_{14}H_{11}BrN_8$			
5H-Tetrazol-5-one, 1,2-dihydro-, [[(2-bromophenyl)azo]phenylmethylene]hydrazone	pH 13	482(4.68)	104-0558-79
	EtOH	280(4.30),460(4.04)	104-0558-79
	dioxan	280(4.25),450(4.00)	104-0558-79
	CHCl$_3$	275(4.37),325(4.22), 440(4.21)	104-0558-79
5H-Tetrazol-5-one, 1,2-dihydro-, [[(4-bromophenyl)azo]phenylmethylene]hydrazone	pH 13	498(4.69)	104-0558-79
	EtOH	295(4.38),480(4.19)	104-0558-79
	dioxan	250(4.19),280(4.20), 330(4.18),380(4.14), 420s(4.09)	104-0558-79
	CHCl$_3$	275(4.08),340(4.17), 420(4.00)	104-0558-79
$C_{14}H_{11}BrO_2S$			
Ethanone, 1-(4-bromophenyl)-2-(phenylsulfinyl)-	C$_6$H$_{12}$	218(4.23),266(4.34)	2-0480-79B'
	pH 2-3	262(4.34)	2-0480-79B'
	pH 11-12	310(3.99)	2-0480-79B'
	EtOH	215(4.31),264(4.38)	2-0480-79B'
	CHCl$_3$	269(4.39)	2-0480-79B'
	CCl$_4$	268(4.38)	2-0480-79B'
$C_{14}H_{11}ClN_8$			
5H-Tetrazol-5-one, 1,2-dihydro-, [[(2-chlorophenyl)azo]phenylmethylene]-hydrazone]	pH 13	488(4.64)	104-0558-79
	EtOH	280(4.30),460(4.04)	104-0558-79
	dioxan	280(4.37),442(4.08)	104-0558-79
	CHCl$_3$	280(4.37),325(4.17), 440(4.16)	104-0558-79
5H-Tetrazol-5-one, 1,2-dihydro-, [[(4-chlorophenyl)azo]phenylmethylene]-hydrazone]	pH 13	490(4.57)	104-0558-79
	EtOH	240(3.92),290(3.99), 470(3.78)	104-0558-79
	dioxan	245(4.15),280(4.16), 325s(4.10),380(4.09), 420s(4.04)	104-0558-79
	CHCl$_3$	280(4.25),335(4.27), 420(4.10)	104-0558-79

Compound	Solvent	λmax(log ε)	Ref.
$C_{14}H_{11}ClO_2S$			
Benzeneacetic acid, 4-chloro-α-(phenylthio)-	EtOH	228(4.19),270(3.52)	80-0137-79
$C_{14}H_{11}ClO_3$			
1(2H)-Anthracenone, 2-chloro-3,4-dihydro-3,4-dihydroxy-, (2α,3β,4α)-	ether	223s(4.27),234s(4.35), 247(4.61),254(4.66), 272s(3.46),282s(3.70), 294(3.90),306(3.89), 326s(3.06),342(3.25), 356(3.25)	22-0110-79
(2α,3β,4β)-	ether	230(4.35),247s(4.59), 253(4.66),259s(4.49), 282s(3.75),294(3.95), 305(3.94),335s(3.21), 350(3.29)	22-0110-79
$C_{14}H_{11}ClO_5$			
3,4-Furandicarboxylic acid, 2-(4-chlorophenyl)-, dimethyl ester	MeOH	278(4.24)	44-0626-79
$C_{14}H_{11}ClO_6$			
2H-1-Benzopyran-4-acetic acid, 7-acetoxy-6-chloro-2-oxo-, methyl ester	MeOH	274(3.97),323(3.85)	73-2211-79
$C_{14}H_{11}Cl_2NO_3$			
Acetohydroxamic acid, N-(4-chlorophenyl)(4-chlorophenoxy)-	EtOH	228(4.15),260(4.27)	34-0072-79
$C_{14}H_{11}IN_8$			
5H-Tetrazol-5-one, 1,2-dihydro-, [[(2-iodophenyl)azo]phenylmethylene]-hydrazone	pH 13	488(4.84)	104-0558-79
	EtOH	280(4.28),460(4.00)	104-0558-79
	dioxan	280(3.96),440(3.72)	104-0558-79
	$CHCl_3$	275(4.15),327(3.86), 440(3.88)	104-0558-79
5H-Tetrazol-5-one, 1,2-dihydro-, [[(4-iodophenyl)azo]phenylmethylene]-hydrazone	pH 13	494(4.66)	104-0558-79
	EtOH	290(4.18),460(3.96)	104-0558-79
	dioxan	240(4.32),350(4.27), 420s(4.15)	104-0558-79
	$CHCl_3$	250(4.09),355(4.06), 420(3.84)	104-0558-79
$C_{14}H_{11}N$			
5H-Dibenz[b,f]azepine	EtOH	210(4.34),260(4.62)	4-0257-79
1H-Phenanthro[9,10b]azirine, 1a,9b-dihydro-	$CHCl_3$	272s(4.25),278s(4.28), 282(4.31),288s(4.17), 294s(4.05),305(3.74)	78-2901-79
Pyrrolo[3,2,1-jk]carbazole, dihydro-	EtOH	238(4.71),262(4.40), 281s(3.99),286s(4.04), 296(4.29),339(3.67), 355(3.60)	39-2387-79C
$C_{14}H_{11}NO$			
Acridine. 9-methoxy-	EtOH	215(4.51),234s(4.43), 256(4.89),265s(4.81), 294(3.30),307s(2.95), 367s(3.53),385(3.83), 403(3.90)	118-0177-79
9(10H)-Acridinone, 10-methyl-	CH_2Cl_2-DMF	380(3.93),400(4.07)	36-0036-79
Indeno[1,2-d]azepin-4(3H)-one, 3-methyl-	EtOH	275(4.2),330s(--), 550(2.9)	138-0807-79

Compound	Solvent	$\lambda_{max}(\log \epsilon)$	Ref.
1H-Phenalen-1-one, 9-(methylamino)-	n.s.g.	254(4.55),349(4.55), 474(4.32)	44-1704-79
$C_{14}H_{11}NOS$			
Thiazolo[3,2-a]pyridinium, 3-hydroxy-5-methyl-2-phenyl-, hydroxide, inner salt	MeOH	235(4.20),290(4.0), 451(4.16)	103-0872-79
$C_{14}H_{11}NO_2$			
Ethanedione, diphenyl-, monooxime, (E)-	EtOH	249(4.15),340s(2.04)	39-0156-79B
	EtOH-NaOH	247(4.04),310(3.99), 420s(1.95)	39-0156-79B
(Z)-	EtOH	251(4.26)	39-0156-79B
	EtOH-NaOH	252(4.24),281(4.17)	39-0156-79B
1H-Isoindole-1,3(2H)-dione, 3a,7a-dihydro-2-phenyl-	MeCN	262(3.59),272(3.54)	44-0604-79
1H-Pyrano[3,2-f]quinolin-1-one, 3,8-dimethyl-	EtOH	252(4.34),291(3.98), 305(3.62),318(3.82), 325(3.69),332(3.85)	95-0813-79
$C_{14}H_{11}NO_3S$			
Acetic acid, (9-methyl-3-oxothiazolo-[3,2-a]indol-2(3H)-ylidene)-, methyl ester, (Z)-	$CHCl_3$	287(4.41),436(3.85)	44-3994-79
Thiazolo[2,3-a]isoquinolinium, 2-(ethoxycarbonyl)-3-hydroxy-, hydroxide, inner salt	EtOH	305(3.41),315(3.54), 445(3.80)	150-2935-79
$C_{14}H_{11}NO_4S$			
Ethanone, 1-(4-nitrophenyl)-2-(phenylsulfinyl)-	C_6H_{12}	215(4.25),262(4.34)	2-0480-79B'
	pH 2-3	263(4.22)	2-0480-79B'
	pH 11-12	360(3.76)	2-0480-79B'
	EtOH	211(4.22),264(4.30)	2-0480-79B'
	$CHCl_3$	266(4.34)	2-0480-79B'
	CCl_4	264(4.37)	2-0480-79B'
$C_{14}H_{11}NO_4S_2$			
1H-Indeno[1,2-b]pyridine-2,5-dione, 3-(methylsulfonyl)-4-(methylthio)-	EtOH	242(4.52),271(4.25), 313(4.35),358(4.15)	95-1234-79
$C_{14}H_{11}NO_5$			
Propanoic acid, 3-amino-2-(1,3-dihydro-1,3-dioxo-2H-inden-2-ylidene)-3-oxo-, ethyl ester	dioxan	256(4.50),305(3.90), 318(3.86)	32-0329-79
$C_{14}H_{11}NS$			
9(10H)-Acridinethione, 10-methyl-	CH_2Cl_2-MeCONMe	461(4.25),491(4.52)	36-0036-79
Benzonitrile, 5-methyl-2-(phenylthio)-	MeOH	225(4.11),255(3.94), 280s(3.62),318(3.52)	73-2677-79
$C_{14}H_{11}NS_2$			
1,2-Benzisothiazole-3(2H)-thione, 2-(phenylmethyl)-	EtOH	250(4.17),365(3.81)	2-0131-79B
$C_{14}H_{11}N_3$			
Benzenecarboximidamide, N-cyano-N'-phenyl-	n.s.g.	231(3.64),245(3.47), 289(4.09)	39-0724-79C
1,2,4-Benzotriazine, 3-(phenylmethyl)-	EtOH	235(4.42),305(3.67), 327s(3.51),440(2.51)	4-1005-79

Compound	Solvent	λ_{max}(log ε)	Ref.
Pyridazine, 3-phenyl-6-(1H-pyrrol-1-yl)-	EtOH	286(4.27)	80-0453-79
1H-1,2,4-Triazole, 3,5-diphenyl-	EtOH	255(4.30)	40-0389-79
$C_{14}H_{11}N_3O$			
8-Quinolinol, 2-(2-pyridinylamino)-	neutral	282(4.26),310(4.47), 338(4.02),352(4.03)	123-0070-79
	acid	254(4.19),272(4.32), 293(4.32),336(4.11)	123-0070-79
	base	295(4.35)	123-0070-79
$C_{14}H_{11}N_3OS$			
Benzothiazole, 2-[(4-methoxyphenyl)azo]-	EtOH	400(3.26)	103-1185-79
2,5-Cyclohexadiene-1,4-dione, mono-[(3-methyl-2(3H)-benzothiazolylidene)hydrazone]	EtOH	514(3.59)	103-1185-79
$C_{14}H_{11}N_3O_2S_2$			
2-Thiophenecarbonitrile, 3-amino-4-[(1,3-benzodioxol-5-ylmethylene)-amino]-5-(methylthio)-	EtOH	233(4.19),286(4.30), 354(4.20)	95-1081-79
$C_{14}H_{11}N_3O_3$			
Imidazo[1,5-b]pyridazine-5,7(3H,6H)-dione, 4-acetyl-2-phenyl-	pH 13	260s(3.60)	4-1105-79
	50% EtOH	220(3.74),270(3.91), 300s(3.71)	4-1105-79
3-Pyridinecarboxylic acid, 5-cyano-1,4,5,6-tetrahydro-2-methyl-6-oxo-4-(3-pyridinyl)-, methyl ester	n.s.g.	340(3.94)	56-2121-79
3-Pyridinecarboxylic acid, 5-cyano-1,4,5,6-tetrahydro-2-methyl-6-oxo-4-(4-pyridinyl)-, methyl ester	n.s.g.	340(3.92)	56-2121-79
$C_{14}H_{11}N_3O_4$			
3H-Benz[e]indole, 1,2-dimethyl-7,9-dinitro-	EtOH	240(3.70),325(3.81), 440(3.00)	103-0883-79
1H-Pyrazol-3-ol, 1(or 2)-acetyl-5-[(1,3-dihydro-1,3-dioxo-2H-isoindol-2-yl)-methyl]-	MeOH	216(4.67),236s(--), 271(4.12)	1-0294-79
$C_{14}H_{11}N_3S$			
2(1H)-Quinazolinethione, 3,4-dihydro-4-imino-3-phenyl-	MeOH	207(4.63),222(4.35), 240(4.28),291(4.44)	44-0173-79
$C_{14}H_{11}N_5O_4$			
1H-Benzimidazole, 2-[(3,5-dinitro-2-pyridinyl)methyl]-1-methyl-	0.01N H_2SO_4	272(4.17),279(4.16)	104-0178-79
	pH 12	335(3.93),480(4.31)	104-0178-79
	EtOH	335(4.00),480(4.2)	104-0178-79
$C_{14}H_{11}N_9$			
2H-Tetrazolium, 2-(3-aminophenyl)-5-phenyl-3-(1H-tetrazol-5-yl)-, hydroxide, inner salt	EtOH	255(4.54),320s(--)	104-1793-79
$C_{14}H_{11}S_4$			
1,2-Dithiol-1-ium, 4-methyl-3-phenyl-5-(2-thienylthio)-, triiodide	MeCN	223(4.46),292(4.76), 365(4.09)	104-0955-79
$C_{14}H_{12}$			
1,1'-Biphenyl, 2-ethenyl-	EtOH	232(4.32),253(4.19)	44-2300-79

Compound	Solvent	λ_{max}(log ε)	Ref.
$C_{14}H_{12}BrNO_2$			
2,4,6-Cycloheptatrien-1-one, 2-bromo-7-[(2-methoxyphenyl)amino]-	MeOH	205(4.46),244(4.33), 260(4.34),348(4.10), 420(4.31)	18-1156-79
$C_{14}H_{12}BrN_3O_3$			
7-Azabicyclo[4.3.1]deca-3,8-dien-10-one, 9-bromo-7-(5-nitro-2-pyridinyl)-	$CHCl_3$	350(3.92)	39-1525-79C
$C_{14}H_{12}ClNO$			
Benzene, 4-chloro-1-nitroso-2-(2-phenylethyl)-	$CHCl_3$	775(1.40)	44-2087-79
$C_{14}H_{12}ClNOS$			
Benzenecarbothioamide, 3-chloro-N-methyl-N-phenyl-, S-oxide	MeOH	362.5(3.81)	5-0248-79
Benzenecarbothioamide, N-(3-chlorophenyl)-N-methyl-, S-oxide	MeOH	361(3.93)	5-0248-79
Benzenecarbothioamide, N-(4-chlorophenyl)-N-methyl-, S-oxide	MeOH	361(3.95)	5-0248-79
$C_{14}H_{12}ClNO_2$			
[1,1'-Biphenyl]-3-ol, 4'-chloro-2,5-dimethyl-6-nitroso-	DMF	625(1.15)	104-0311-79
$C_{14}H_{12}ClN_3$			
Pyrazolo[3,4-b]pyridine, 4-chloro-6-methyl-1-(phenylmethyl)-	MeOH	218(4.75),268(4.09), 297(3.98)	48-0881-79
Pyrazolo[3,4-b]pyridine, 6-chloro-4-methyl-2-(phenylmethyl)-	MeOH	216(4.56),286(3.97), 302s(3.88)	48-0881-79
1H-Pyrazolo[3,4-b]pyridine, 6-chloro-4-methyl-1-(phenylmethyl)-	MeOH	219(4.51),269(3.73), 299(3.78)	48-0881-79
$C_{14}H_{12}ClN_3O$			
3(2H)-Pyridazinone, 6-(4-chlorophenyl)-4,5-dihydro-6-(4-chlorophenyl)-4-(1H-pyrrol-1-yl)-	EtOH	264(4.23)	80-0453-79
$C_{14}H_{12}ClN_3OS$			
2(1H)-Quinazolinethione, 3-amino-6-chloro-3,4-dihydro-4-hydroxy-4-phenyl-	MeOH	287(4.44)	106-0663-79
$C_{14}H_{12}ClN_3O_2$			
Pyrimido[4,5-b]quinoline-2,4(3H,10H)-dione, 6-chloro-3,7,10-trimethyl-	6M HCl	266(4.29),347(4.11)	5-1802-79
	MeOH	225(4.51),264(4.58), 337(3.94),410(4.03), 430s(--)	5-1802-79
Pyrimido[4,5-b]quinoline-2,4(3H,10H)-dione, 8-chloro-3,7,10-trimethyl-	6M HCl	258(4.48),345s(--), 355(4.14)	5-1802-79
	MeOH	224(4.60),261(4.60), 322(4.01),403(4.08), 420s(--)	5-1802-79
$C_{14}H_{12}F_3N_3O$			
Propanedinitrile, [[4-(dimethylamino)-phenyl](2,2,2-trifluoroethoxy)methylene]-	MeCN	401(4.36)	35-2682-79
$C_{14}H_{12}NOS$			
Thiazolo[3,2-a]pyridinium, 3-methoxy-	MeOH	225(4.28),256(3.88),	103-0872-79

Compound	Solvent	$\lambda_{max}(\log \epsilon)$	Ref.
2-phenyl-, perchlorate (cont.)		330(4.29)	103-0872-79
$C_{14}H_{12}NS_2$			
Benzothiazolium, 3-methyl-2-[2-(2-thienyl)ethenyl]-, iodide	DMF	301(3.08),409(4.41)	126-1441-79
	KBr	420(--)	126-1441-79
perchlorate	DMF	301(3.79),409(4.43)	126-1441-79
	KBr	415(--)	126-1441-79
$C_{14}H_{12}N_2$			
1H-Benzimidazole, 4-methyl-2-phenyl-	anion	242(4.32)	94-1255-79
1H-Benzimidazole, 5-methyl-2-phenyl-	anion	251(4.06)	94-1255-79
Benzo[g]phthalazine, 6,9-dimethyl-	CH_2Cl_2	261(4.34),361(3.49), 382s(3.33)	150-3518-79
[1,1'-Biphenyl]-4-carbonitrile, 2'-(methylamino)-	EtOH	243(4.43),345(3.61)	33-2129-79
$C_{14}H_{12}N_2O$			
1H-Indole-3-methanol, α-(4-pyridinyl)-	EtOH	220(4.32),265(3.72), 279(3.73),288(3.65)	39-3155-79C
3(2H)-Isoquinolinone, 1,4-dihydro-1-(3-pyridinyl)-	n.s.g.	256(3.53),260(3.54)	114-0305-79D
3(2H)-Isoquinolinone, 1,4-dihydro-1-(4-pyridinyl)-	n.s.g.	258(3.58),265(3.50)	114-0305-79D
Phenazine, 2-methoxy-7-methyl-	MeOH	258(4.99),352(3.92), 392(3.92),410(3.87)	94-0351-79
Phenol, 4-(1,4-dihydro-4-quinazolinyl)-, monohydrochloride	EtOH	279(3.84)	24-1348-79
$C_{14}H_{12}N_2OS$			
9H-[1,3]Thiazino[3,2-a]perimidin-10-ol, 10,11-dihydro-	EtOH	211(4.28),230(4.53), 323(4.00)	83-0776-79
$C_{14}H_{12}N_2O_2$			
Benzenamine, N-(2-nitro-2-phenylethenyl)-, (Z)-	EtOH	206(4.23),241(4.20), 265(4.11),394(4.31)	28-0255-79B
1,2-Benzenediol, 4-(1,4-dihydro-4-quinazolinyl)-, monohydrochloride	EtOH	286(3.82)	24-1348-79
1,3-Benzenediol, 4-(1,4-dihydro-4-quinazolinyl)-, monohydrochloride	EtOH	285(4.03)	24-1348-79
Benzenemethanamine, α-(nitromethylene)-N-phenyl-	EtOH	206(4.18),231(4.04), 295(3.76),370(4.29)	28-0255-79D
1H-Benz[g]indole, 2,3-dimethyl-6-nitro-	EtOH	257(4.48),280(4.30), 300(4.30),400(4.00)	103-0883-79
1H-Benz[g]indole, 2,3-dimethyl-9-nitro-	EtOH	258(4.65),315(4.08), 410(3.60),440(3.70)	103-0883-79
3H-Benz[e]indole, 1,2-dimethyl-6-nitro-	EtOH	245(4.30),305(3.66), 410(3.60),440(3.60)	103-0883-79
3H-Benz[e]indole, 1,2-dimethyl-7-nitro-	EtOH	220(4.08),320(4.00), 380(3.48)	103-0883-79
3H-Benz[e]indole, 1,2-dimethyl-9-nitro-	EtOH	235(4.73),325(4.14), 400(3.51),430(3.34)	103-0883-79
Oxazole, 5,5'-(1,4-phenylene)bis[2-methyl-	EtOH	298(4.61),310(4.70), 325(4.56)	18-3597-79
Phenazine, 2,8-dimethoxy-	neutral	394(3.87)	59-0421-79
	cation	426(4.00)	59-0421-79
1H-Pyrrolo[1,2-a]indole-9a(9H)-propanenitrile, 2,3-dihydro-3,9-dioxo-	EtOH	204(3.81),238(4.42), 260(4.17),312(3.56), 357(3.26)	103-0994-79

Compound	Solvent	$\lambda_{max}(\log \epsilon)$	Ref.
$C_{14}H_{12}N_2O_2S$			
1,2,5-Benzothiadiazepine, 2,5-dihydro-4-phenyl-, 1,1-dioxide	EtOH	254(3.65),300(3.13)	4-0835-79
Pyrrolo[1,2-c]pyrimidine, 3-[(4-methylphenyl)sulfonyl]-	EtOH	228(4.30),253(4.21), 298(3.89)	94-0793-79
$C_{14}H_{12}N_2O_3$			
1H-Carbazole-1,4(9H)-dione, 6-hydroxy-9-methyl-3-(methylamino)-	MeOH	229(4.40),273(4.28), 278s(4.26),303s(3.77), 347(4.11),436(3.75)	49-0051-79
	2M HCl	231(--),273(--), 319s(--),453(--)	49-0051-79
$C_{14}H_{12}N_2O_3S$			
Benzenecarbothioamide, N-methyl-3-nitro-N-phenyl-, S-oxide	MeOH	360(3.84)	5-0248-79
$C_{14}H_{12}N_2O_3S_2$			
3-Pyridinecarbonitrile, 1,2-dihydro-6-methyl-4-(methylthio)-2-oxo-5-(phenylsulfonyl)-	EtOH	220(4.28),259(4.25), 337(3.96)	95-1234-79
$C_{14}H_{12}N_2O_4$			
2-Naphthalenecarbonitrile, 1,4-dihydro-5,8-dimethoxy-3-(methylamino)-1,4-dioxo-	acetone	430(3.84)	39-0696-79C
$C_{14}H_{12}N_2O_4S_2$			
3-Pyridinecarbonitrile, 1,2-dihydro-6-hydroxy-5-[(4-methylphenyl)sulfonyl]-4-(methylthio)-2-oxo-	EtOH	227s(4.17),267(4.05), 349(4.35)	95-1234-79
Pyrrolo[1,2-b]isoquinoline-5,10-dione, 3-amino-2-(methylsulfonyl)-1-(methylthio)-	EtOH	238(4.49),284(3.98), 335(3.87),446(4.05)	95-1234-79
$C_{14}H_{12}N_2O_5$			
2,3,4(5H)-Furantrione, 5-(2-acetoxyethylidene)-, 2-(phenylhydrazone)	EtOH	232(4.01),270s(4.11), 405(4.30)	136-0087-79A
$C_{14}H_{12}N_2O_5S$			
4-Thia-1-azabicyclo[3.2.0]hept-2-ene-2-carboxylic acid, 3-methyl-7-oxo-, (4-nitrophenyl)methyl ester	EtOH	262(4.12),308(4.00)	35-6296-79
	EtOH	265(4.07),311(3.96)	77-0665-79
(R)-	EtOH	263(4.06),310(3.96)	35-6301-79
$C_{14}H_{12}N_2O_5S_2$			
4-Thia-1-azabicyclo[3.2.0]hept-2-ene-2-carboxylic acid, 3-(methylthio)-7-oxo-, (4-nitrophenyl)methyl ester	dioxan	268(4.23),317(4.04)	35-2210-79
5-Thia-1-azabicyclo[4.2.0]oct-2-ene-2-carboxylic acid, 3-methyl-4,8-dioxo-7-[(2-thienyl(acetyl)amino]-, (6R-trans)-	EtOH	314(3.76)	87-0743-79
$C_{14}H_{12}N_2S$			
Benzenamine, 4-(1,2-benzisothiazol-3-yl)-N-methyl-	5M HCl	265(4.12),338(3.83)	24-3286-79
	MeOH	333(4.16)	24-3286-79
Diazene, (3-ethenylphenyl)(phenylthio)-	toluene	336(4.0)	126-1651-79
9H-[1,3]Thiazino[3,2-a]perimidine, 10,11-dihydro-	EtOH	210(4.41),234(4.58), 330(4.21)	83-0776-79

Compound	Solvent	λ_{max}(log ϵ)	Ref.
$C_{14}H_{12}N_4$			
1H-1,2,4-Triazol-3-amine, 4,5-diphenyl-	H_2O	259(3.98)	118-0359-79
	acid	243(3.99)	118-0359-79
	base	259(3.98)	118-0359-79
$C_{14}H_{12}N_4O$			
1,2,3,4-Oxatriazolium, 3-(4-methylphenyl)-5-(phenylamino)-, hydroxide, inner salt	n.s.g.	235s(3.98),270(4.31), 406(3.56)	39-0736-79C
1,2,3,4-Oxatriazolium, 5-[(4-methylphenyl)amino]-3-phenyl-, hydroxide, inner salt	n.s.g.	267(4.63),422(3.37)	39-0736-79C
1H-Tetrazolium, 2,5-dihydro-1-(4-methylphenyl)-5-oxo-3-phenyl-, hydroxide, inner salt	n.s.g.	225(4.57),261(4.40), 330(4.54)	39-0736-79C
1H-Tetrazolium, 2,5-dihydro-3-(4-methylphenyl)-5-oxo-1-phenyl-, hydroxide, inner salt	n.s.g.	227(4.62),269(4.57), 326(4.63)	39-0736-79C
$C_{14}H_{12}N_4O_2$			
2,3-Naphthalenediol, 1-[(5-methyl-1H-pyrazol-3-yl)azo]-	DMF	305(3.85),450(4.06)	103-0657-79
$C_{14}H_{12}N_4O_4$			
Pyrimido[4,5-b]quinoline-2,4(3H,10H)-dione, 3,7,10-trimethyl-6-nitro-	6M HCl	246(4.54),325(4.00), 358(4.02),373s(--)	5-1802-79
	MeOH	217(4.49),264(4.68), 308(3.89),409(4.03), 430s(--)	5-1802-79
Pyrimido[4,5-b]quinoline-2,4(3H,10H)-dione, 3,7,10-trimethyl-8-nitro-	6M HCl	242(4.46),260s(--), 333(4.11),375s(--)	5-1802-79
	MeOH	221(4.48),261(4.60), 316(4.01),422(3.97)	5-1802-79
$C_{14}H_{12}N_4O_5$			
Sydnone, 4-[[4,5-dihydro-3-(methoxycarbonyl)-1H-pyrazol-5-yl]carbonyl]-3-phenyl-	n.s.g.	268(3.93),360(4.12)	103-1153-79
$C_{14}H_{12}N_4S$			
Pyrido[2,3-d]pyrimidin-4-amine, 2-(methylthio)-N-phenyl-, picrate	H_2O	239(4.51),352(4.44)	102-1265-79
	0.2M HCl	241(4.47),347(4.42)	102-1265-79
	0.2M NaOH	246(4.30),364(4.38)	102-1265-79
1,2,3,4-Thiatriazolium, 3-(4-methylphenyl)-5-(phenylamino)-, hydroxide, inner salt	n.s.g.	237(4.06),290(4.46), 440(3.35)	39-0741-79C
4H-1,2,4-Triazolium, 4-amino-2,3-dihydro-1,5-diphenyl-3-thioxo-, hydroxide inner salt	EtOH	247(4.45),318(3.57)	94-1683-79
	n.s.g.	248(4.36),323(3.50)	39-0724-79C
$C_{14}H_{12}N_5O_4$			
1H-1,2,3-Triazolium, 4,5-dihydro-1,3-bis(4-nitrophenyl)-, perchlorate	MeOH	392(4.37)	24-0445-79
$C_{14}H_{12}N_6O_4S_4$			
Isothiazolo[3,4-d]pyrimidine-4,6(5H,7H)-dione, 3,3'-dithiobis[5,7-dimethyl-	EtOH	282(4.67),330(4.59), 420(4.29)	95-0515-79
$C_{14}H_{12}N_6O_6$			
Benzo[g]pteridine-2,4(3H,10H)-dione, 3,7,8,10-tetramethyl-6,9-dinitro-	MeCN	324(3.77),441(3.99)	5-1067-79

Compound	Solvent	λ_{max}(log ε)	Ref.
$C_{14}H_{12}N_8$			
Formazan, 3,5-diphenyl-1-(1H-tetrazol-5-yl)-	pH 13	486(4.48)	104-0558-79
	EtOH	285(4.16),442(3.82)	104-0558-79
	dioxan	280(4.19),375(4.01), 410s(3.99)	104-0558-79
	$CHCl_3$	275(4.27),325(4.20), 415(4.08)	104-0558-79
$C_{14}H_{12}N_8O$			
Formazan, 5-(2-hydroxyphenyl)-3-phenyl-1-(1H-tetrazol-5-yl)-	pH 13	502(4.56)	104-0558-79
	EtOH	295(4.19),480(4.01)	104-0558-79
	dioxan	250(4.16),290(4.16), 408(4.09)	104-0558-79
	$CHCl_3$	255(4.02),335(4.06), 442(3.97)	104-0558-79
Formazan, 5-(4-hydroxyphenyl)-3-phenyl-1-(1H-tetrazol-5-yl)-	pH 13	472(4.66)	104-0558-79
	EtOH	299(4.10),350(3.88), 460(4.12)	104-0558-79
	dioxan	260(4.28),350(4.28), 410(4.25)	104-0558-79
$C_{14}H_{12}O$			
Cyclohepta[de]naphthalen-1-ol, 1,2-dihydro-	EtOH	231(4.26),243s(3.86), 253(3.68),296s(3.63), 309(3.76),323(3.63)	39-2995-79C
Cyclohepta[de]naphthalen-2-ol, 1,2-dihydro-	EtOH	231(4.28),243s(3.84), 253(3.66),296(3.64), 309(3.78),324(3.63)	39-2995-79C
$C_{14}H_{12}O_2$			
7,10-Epoxycyclohepta[de]naphthalen-7(8H)-ol, 9,10-dihydro-	H_2O	283(3.87)	39-2995-79C
	M NaOH	285(3.87)	39-2995-79C
3,8-Heptalenedione, 2,4-dimethyl-	MeOH or CH_2Cl_2	267(4.74),276(4.89), 295(4.14),350s(3.93), 368(4.01),385s(3.94), 407s(3.51)	138-0043-79
	H_2SO_4	282(4.66),296(4.89), 310(4.44),333(3.65), 351(3.87),360(3.78), 380(3.98),402(4.02)	138-0043-79
	CF_3COOH	272(4.82),306(4.54), 376(4.13),395s(4.10)	138-0043-79
Methanone, (2-hydroxy-5-methylphenyl)-phenyl- (also nickel chelate spectrum)	$CHCl_3$	438(3.9),550(3.0) (changing)	97-0226-79
Naphthalene, 1,8-diacetyl-	MeOH	295(3.81)	39-2995-79C
	MeOH-HOAc	265(3.53),275(3.68), 285(3.84),297(3.69)	39-2995-79C
2,3-Naphthalenedicarboxaldehyde, 5,8-dimethyl-	CH_2Cl_2	274(4.81),366(3.74), 381(3.82)	150-3518-79
1(2H)-Naphthalenone, 3-(2-furanyl)-3,4-dihydro-	EtOH	248(4.13),293(3.43)	78-1167-79
9,10-Phenanthrenedione, 1,2,3,4-tetrahydro-	EtOH	260(4.35),344(3.19), 425(3.02)	44-1502-79
1(2H)-Phenanthrenone, 3,4-dihydro-9-hydroxy-	MeOH	221(4.35),241(4.11), 263(4.41),281(3.61), 291(3.66),299(3.66), 310s(3.52),326(3.15), 366(3.62)	5-0297-79
1(2H)-Phenanthrenone, 3,4-dihydro-10-hydroxy-	EtOH	233(4.40),255(3.91), 264(3.83),291(4.00), 363(4.12)	44-1502-79

Compound	Solvent	λ_{max}(log ε)	Ref.
$C_{14}H_{12}O_2S$			
Ethanone, 1-phenyl-2-(phenylsulfinyl)-	C_6H_{12}	218(4.20),243(4.26)	2-0480-79B'
	pH 2-3	250(4.17)	2-0480-79B'
	pH 11-12	306(3.98)	2-0480-79B'
	EtOH	220(4.26),240(4.31)	2-0480-79B'
$C_{14}H_{12}O_2S_2$			
[2,3'-Bithiophen]-5'(2'H)-one, 3',4'-dihydro-5-(4-hydroxyphenyl)-	MeOH	304(4.22)	18-1126-79
$C_{14}H_{12}O_2S_5$			
Disulfide, (4-methylphenyl)sulfonyl (phenylthio)thioxomethyl	C_6H_{12}	249(4.23),304(3.91)	77-1135-79
$C_{14}H_{12}O_3$			
Benzoic acid, 2-methoxy-, phenyl ester	EtOH	239(4.02),300(3.62)	49-1057-79
Benzoic acid, 4-methoxy-, phenyl ester	EtOH	261(4.34)	49-1057-79
Benzoic acid, 2-(4-methylphenoxy)-	EtOH	231(4.06),287(3.57)	35-0665-79
2H-Furo[2,3-h]-1-benzopyran-2-one, 8-(1-methylethyl)-	EtOH	217(4.23),250(4.42), 300(4.08)	2-0113-79A
Methanone, (4-hydroxyphenyl)(2-methoxyphenyl)-	EtOH	224(4.14),294(4.24)	49-1057-79
Methanone, (4-hydroxyphenyl)(4-methoxyphenyl)-	EtOH	297(4.34)	49-1057-79
$C_{14}H_{12}O_4$			
2-Butenoic acid, 4-methyl-2-oxo-2H-1-benzopyran-7-yl ester	MeOH	279(4.04),313(4.00)	73-2211-79
2,5-Cyclohexadiene-1,4-dione, 5-(2,4-dihydroxyphenyl)-2,3-dimethyl-	EtOH	246(4.23),278(3.89), 318(3.48),450(3.35)	1-0271-79
	EtOH-Na_2CO_3	575(3.45)	1-0271-79
3(2H)-Dibenzofuranone, 8-acetoxy-1,4-dihydro-	MeOH	210s(4.58),248(4.12), 279(3.82),286(3.81)	24-2640-79
Propanedioic acid, 1,3-cyclopentadien-1-ylphenyl-	EtOH	246(3.46)	1-0307-79
$C_{14}H_{12}O_4S_2$			
1,3-Dithiole-4,5-dicarboxylic acid, 2-(phenylmethylene)-, dimethyl ester	CH_2Cl_2	243(3.96),328(4.16)	44-0930-79
$C_{14}H_{12}O_5$			
3,4-Furandicarboxylic acid, 2-phenyl-, dimethyl ester	MeOH	259(3.34)	44-0626-79
$C_{14}H_{12}O_6$			
2,9,10(1H)-Anthracenetrione, 3,4,4a,9a-tetrahydro-4,5,8-trihydroxy-	MeOH	223(4.20),270(3.97), 393(3.51)	24-3453-79
$C_{14}H_{13}$			
Cycloheptatrienylium, 1-methyl-2-phenyl-, perchlorate	10% HCl	230(4.64),280(3.94), 354(3.70)	39-1005-79B
Cycloheptatrienylium, (3-methylphenyl)-	10% HCl	225(4.49),272(4.12), 375(4.14)	39-0262-79B
Ethylium, 1,1-diphenyl-	H_2SO_4	428(4.51)	39-1395-79B
$C_{14}H_{13}ClN_2$			
1H-Pyrido[2,3-b]indole, 2-chloro-3-ethyl-1-methyl-	pH 1	250(4.21),265s(4.01), 320(4.16),355(3.89)	103-0879-79
	pH 13	260s(4.20),280(4.27), 317s(4.13),400(3.60)	103-0879-79

Compound	Solvent	λ_{max}(log ε)	Ref.
1H-Pyrrolo[2,3-b]pyridine, 6-chloro-2,3-dihydro-4-methyl-1-phenyl-	n.s.g.	286(4.28),329(4.16)	103-0310-79
$C_{14}H_{13}ClN_2O$			
Ethanone, 2-[(4-chlorophenyl)amino]-1-phenyl-, oxime, (70% Z)	MeOH	254(4.43)	56-1147-79
$C_{14}H_{13}ClN_2O_2$			
4-Pyridazinecarboxylic acid, 5-chloro-6-methyl-3-phenyl-, ethyl ester	EtOH	227(4.00),242(4.11)	44-3053-79
$C_{14}H_{13}ClN_4O_3$			
5H-1,2,4-Triazolo[4,3-d][1,4]benzodiazepine-3-carboxylic acid, 10-chloro-6,7-dihydro-7-methyl-6-oxo-, ethyl ester	MeOH	237(4.56),303(3.45)	44-0088-79
$C_{14}H_{13}ClO$			
Phenol, 2-chloro-6-methyl-4-(phenyl-	EtOH	206.2(4.66),281.7(3.39)	106-0221-79
$C_{14}H_{13}ClO_3$			
2H-1-Benzopyran-2-one, 7-[(2-chloro-2-propenyl)oxy]-	EtOH	244(3.59),254(3.62), 319(4.16)	44-2176-79
$C_{14}H_{13}F$			
1,1'-Biphenyl, 4'-fluoro-2,3-dimethyl-	C_6H_{12}	236(3.94)	12-1531-79
1,1'-Biphenyl, 4'-fluoro-2,4-dimethyl-	C_6H_{12}	239(4.04)	12-1531-79
1,1'-Biphenyl, 4'-fluoro-2,5-dimethyl-	C_6H_{12}	237(3.97),270(3.25)	12-1531-79
1,1'-Biphenyl, 4'-fluoro-2,6-dimethyl-	C_6H_{12}	259(3.05),265(3.10), 271(3.01)	12-1531-79
1,1'-Biphenyl, 4'-fluoro-3,4-dimethyl-	C_6H_{12}	251(4.22)	12-1531-79
$C_{14}H_{13}NO$			
Benzenamine, N-[(4-methoxyphenyl)methylene]-	EtOH	224(3.21),288(3.23), 310s(3.21)	2-0338-79B
	H_2SO_4	369(--)(changing)	2-0338-79B
2-Naphthalenol, 1-[3-(methylimino)-1-propenyl]-	MeOH	310(3.83),330(3.76), 416(3.23),500(3.76)	104-1715-79
	dioxan	300(3.73),310(3.73), 340(3.52),350(3.54), 400(2.60),420(2.60)	104-1715-79
	DMSO	310(3.71),340(3.69), 350(3.69),420(3.00), 520(3.66)	104-1715-79
Phenol, 2-[[(phenylmethyl)imino]methyl]-	MeOH	216(4.46),253(4.26), 283(3.92),320(3.64)	150-3801-79
$C_{14}H_{13}NOS$			
4H-3,1-Benzoxazine-4-thione, 5,6,7,8-tetrahydro-2-phenyl-	EtOH	230(4.48),267(4.51), 296(4.29),306s(4.25), 374(4.33)	150-1732-79
$C_{14}H_{13}NOS_2$			
1,3,2-Benzodithiazole, 2-(4-methoxyphenyl)-5-methyl-	CH_2Cl_2	247(4.23)	4-0183-79
$C_{14}H_{13}NO_2$			
[1,1'-Biphenyl]-3-ol, 2,5-dimethyl-6-nitroso-	DMF	710(1.08)	104-0311-79
[1,1'-Biphenyl]-3-ol, 4',5-dimethyl-6-nitroso-	DMF	740(1.26)	104-0311-79

Compound	Solvent	λ_{max}(log ε)	Ref.
Cyclopenta[f]pyrrolo[3,2,1-ij]quinoline-1,8-dione, 2,3,5,6,9,10-hexahydro-	MeOH	240(4.10),256s(3.65), 380(3.49)	4-0949-79
$C_{14}H_{13}NO_2S$			
2-Propanone, 1,1'-(3-phenyl-1,3-thiazetidine-2,4-diylidene)bis-	EtOH	223(4.26),240(4.04), 288(3.93),351(4.65), 356(4.64)	103-1187-79
$C_{14}H_{13}NO_2S_2$			
2-Propanone, 1,1'-(4-phenyl-1,2,4-dithiazolidine-3,5-diylidene)di-	EtOH	343(4.80)	103-1187-79
$C_{14}H_{13}NO_3$			
Benzoic acid, 2-[(1-methyl-1H-pyrrol-2-yl)carbonyl]-, methyl ester	EtOH	206(4.18),298(4.18)	103-0747-79
[1,1'-Biphenyl]-3-ol, 4'-methoxy-5-methyl-6-nitroso-	DMF	730(1.23)	104-0311-79
1(3H)-Isobenzofuranone, 3-ethoxy-3-(1H-pyrrol-2-yl)-	EtOH	205(4.21),230(4.18)	103-0747-79
6-Oxa-1-azabicyclo[5.2.0]non-4-ene-3,9-dione, 4-methyl-5-phenyl-	EtOH	282(4.01)	88-0391-79
2H-Pyran-2,4(3H)-dione, 6-methyl-3-[1-(phenylamino)ethylidene]-	EtOH	324(4.27)	131-0077-79D
	hexane	239(--),329(--)	131-0077-79D
2(1H)-Pyridinone, 3-acetyl-6-hydroxy-4-methyl-1-phenyl-	50% HOAc	325(4.24)	5-0769-79
	aq base	341(4.35)	5-0769-79
$C_{14}H_{13}NO_3S$			
Benzothiazole, 2-(3a,6a-dihydro-2,2-dimethylfuro[2,3-d]-1,3-dioxol-5-yl)-, (3aR-cis)-	EtOH	224(3.72),248(3.34), 253(3.36),298s(4.26), 305(4.29),322s(4.10)	33-1298-79
$C_{14}H_{13}NO_4$			
2,4(3H,5H)-Furandione, 3-(1-hydroxyethylidene)-5-[(4-methylphenyl)amino]-methylene]-	EtOH	242(4.13),277s(3.95), 368(4.47)	4-1335-79
2,4(3H,5H)-Furandione, 3-(1-methoxyethylidene)-5-[(phenylamino)methylene]-	EtOH	243(3.85),408(4.68)	4-1335-79
Furo[2,3-b]quinoline, 4,6,7-trimethoxy-(kokusaginine)	EtOH	244(4.76),251(4.74), 307(3.69),320(3.70), 331(3.58)	2-0115-79B
2-Propenamide, N-[(7-hydroxy-2-oxo-2H-1-benzopyran-4-yl)methyl]-2-methyl-	MeOH	323(4.15)	73-2211-79
	NH_3	368(4.28)	73-2211-79
1H-Pyrrolo[1,2-a]indole-9a(9H)-propanoic acid, 2,3-dihydro-3,9-dioxo-	EtOH	206(3.93),238(4.38), 260(3.93),322(3.28)	103-0994-79
$C_{14}H_{13}NO_5$			
2,4(3H,5H)-Furandione, 3-(1-hydroxyethylidene)-5-[[(4-methoxyphenyl)amino]-methylene]-	EtOH	245(4.11),275s(3.87), 369(4.43)	4-1335-79
3,6-Quinolinedicarboxylic acid, 1,2-dihydro-5-methyl-2-oxo-, dimethyl ester	EtOH and EtOH-HCl	211(4.21),256(4.57), 306s(3.90),314(3.93), 358(3.73)	39-0686-79C
	EtOH-NaOH	258(4.65),290s(3.91), 300s(3.85),342(3.84)	39-0686-79C
$C_{14}H_{13}NO_6$			
3,6-Quinolinedicarboxylic acid, 1,2-dihydro-5-hydroxy-1-methyl-2-oxo-, dimethyl ester	EtOH	208(4.21),267(4.60), 282s(4.34),328(3.98)	39-0686-79C

Compound	Solvent	λ_{max}(log ϵ)	Ref.
3,6-Quinolinedicarboxylic acid, 1,2-dihydro-5-hydroxy-1-methyl-2-oxo-, dimethyl ester (cont.)	EtOH-HCl	208(4.25),267(4.62), 282s(4.36),327(4.02)	39-0686-79C
	EtOH-NaOH	235(4.51),262(4.42), 310(4.31),351(3.78), 422(4.10)	39-0686-79C
$C_{14}H_{13}NS$			
Benzothiazole, 2,3-dihydro-3-methyl-2-phenyl-	MeCN	314(3.62)	153-0199-79
$C_{14}H_{13}NS_2$			
1,3,2-Benzodithiazole, 5-methyl-2-(phenylmethyl)-	CH_2Cl_2	245(4.49)	4-0183-79
4H-3,1-Benzothiazine-4-thione, 5,6,7,8-tetrahydro-2-phenyl-	EtOH	257(3.99),315(3.63), 430(3.38)	150-1732-79
$C_{14}H_{13}NS_3$			
2H-3,1-Benzothiazine-2,4(1H)-dithione, 5,6,7,8-tetrahydro-1-phenyl-	EtOH	240s(4.27),306(4.34), 320s(4.26),414(3.93), 430s(3.79)	150-1732-79
$C_{14}H_{13}N_2O$			
Pyridinium, 3-(2-benzoxazolyl)-1,4-dimethyl-, iodide	EtOH	309(4.22)	4-1579-79
Pyridinium, 5-(2-benzoxazolyl)-1,2-dimethyl-, iodide	EtOH	310(4.26)	4-1579-79
$C_{14}H_{13}N_2S$			
Pyridinium, 3-(2-benzothiazolyl)-1,4-dimethyl-, iodide	EtOH	304(4.07)	4-1579-79
Pyridinium, 5-(2-benzothiazolyl)-1,2-dimethyl-, iodide	EtOH	315(4.22)	4-1579-79
$C_{14}H_{13}N_3$			
Propanedinitrile, [3-(dimethylamino)-1-phenyl-2-propenylidene]-	CH_2Cl_2	391(4.66)	118-0376-79
$C_{14}H_{13}N_3O$			
Acetamide, N-[2-(phenylazo)phenyl]-	EtOH	232(4.16),250s(4.10), 322(4.06),455s(2.85)	7-0563-79
Aziridine, 2-(phenylmethyl)-1-(pyrazinylcarbonyl)-, (S)-	isooctane	208(4.25),267(3.96), 333(2.78)	39-2881-79C
	EtOH	208(4.22),268(3.97), 324(3.90)	39-2881-79C
	MeCN	208(4.20),268(3.94), 326(2.95)	39-2881-79C
Debenzorutecarpine	EtOH	229(4.28),310(4.39)	114-0043-79A
2H-Indole-2,2-dipropanenitrile, 1,3-dihydro-3-oxo-	EtOH	203(4.35),307(4.05), 426(4.12)	103-0994-79
2(10H)-Phenazinone, 8-amino-7,10-dimethyl-	neutral	509(4.58)	59-0421-79
	cation	434(4.29),490(4.35)	59-0421-79
4H-Pyrazolo[3,4-b]pyridin-4-one, 1,7-dihydro-6-methyl-1-(phenylmethyl)-	MeOH	211(4.56),255(3.95), 285(4.14),294s(4.08)	48-0881-79
4H-Pyrazolo[3,4-b]pyridin-4-one, 2,7-dihydro-6-methyl-2-(phenylmethyl)-	MeOH	214(4.38),262(4.08), 311(4.17)	48-0881-79
6H-Pyrazolo[3,4-b]pyridin-6-one, 1,7-dihydro-4-methyl-1-(phenylmethyl)-	MeOH	210(4.39),299(4.00)	48-0881-79
6H-Pyrazolo[3,4-b]pyridin-6-one, 2,7-dihydro-4-methyl-2-(phenylmethyl)-	MeOH	207(4.38),306(4.25), 320s(4.02)	48-0881-79
1H-Pyrrolo[1,2-a]indole-9a(9H)-propanenitrile, 3-amino-9-oxo-, hydrochloride	EtOH	207(4.08),240(4.35), 261(3.92)	103-0994-79

Compound	Solvent	λ max(log ε)	Ref.
$C_{14}H_{13}N_3OS_2$			
2-Thiophenecarbonitrile, 3-amino-4-[[(4-methoxyphenyl)methylene]-amino]-5-(methylthio)-	EtOH	224(4.20),292(4.47), 348(4.19)	95-1081-79
$C_{14}H_{13}N_3O_2$			
Carbamic acid, 1H-perimidin-2-yl-, ethyl ester	n.s.g.	231(4.83),256(4.54), 318(4.14)	135-1183-79
1H-Naphth[2,3-d]imidazole-4,9-dione, 1,2-dimethyl-5-(methylamino)-	C_6H_{12}	513(3.61)	39-0702-79C
	EtOH	527(--)	39-0702-79C
	EtOH-HCl	553(--)	39-0702-79C
1H-Naphth[2,3-d]imidazole-4,9-dione, 1,2-dimethyl-8-(methylamino)-	C_6H_{12}	509(3.77)	39-0702-79C
	EtOH	527(--)	39-0702-79C
	EtOH-HCl	553(--)	39-0702-79C
1H-Pyrrolo[3,2-d]pyrimidine-2,4(3H,5H)-dione, 1,3-dimethyl-6-phenyl-	EtOH	242(3.50),310(3.76)	44-3830-79
$C_{14}H_{13}N_3O_2S$			
Benzenesulfonamide, 4-(diazomethyl)-N-methyl-N-phenyl-	EtOH	228(4.19),313(4.49), 463(1.58)	118-0531-79
$C_{14}H_{13}N_3O_3$			
7-Azabicyclo[4.3.1]deca-3,8-dien-10-one, 7-(5-nitro-2-pyridinyl)-	$CHCl_3$	386(4.52)	39-1525-79C
Benzeneacetic acid, α-[(pyrazinylcarbonyl)amino]-, methyl ester, (S)-	isooctane	207(4.27),267(3.94), 333f(2.78)	39-2881-79C
	EtOH	207(4.36),268(4.05), 322(2.78)	39-2881-79C
	MeCN	207(4.25),270(3.93), 324(2.78)	39-2881-79C
[3,4'-Bipyridine]-3'-carboxylic acid, 5'-cyano-1',4',5',6'-tetrahydro-2'-methyl-6'-oxo-, methyl ester	n.s.g.	269(3.88)	56-2121-79
[4,4'-Bipyridine]-3'-carboxylic acid, 5'-cyano-1',4',5',6'-tetrahydro-2'-methyl-6'-oxo-, methyl ester	n.s.g.	266(3.97),280(4.01)	56-2121-79
$C_{14}H_{13}N_3O_3S_3$			
4-Thiazolidinone, 3-ethyl-5-(3-ethyl-x-nitro-2(3H)-benzothiazolylidene)-2-thioxo-	EtOH	425s(4.36),444(4.49)	73-1413-79
$C_{14}H_{13}N_3O_5$			
Acetamide, N-[1-acetyl-8-acetoxy-1,2-dihydro-2-oxo-5-cycloheptimidazolyl]-	MeOH	245(4.17),327(3.79), 378(3.66),394(3.63)	138-0855-79
$C_{14}H_{13}N_3S$			
Benzo[b]thiophen-3-amine, N-ethyl-2-(4-pyrimidinyl)-	MeOH	267(3.97),298(4.10), 330(3.99),413(4.16)	118-0442-79
	MeOH-HCl	282(4.08),352(4.28), 491(4.41)	118-0442-79
	$CHCl_3$	266(3.96),302(4.11), 331(3.88),410(4.15)	118-0442-79
	CF_3COOH	366(4.43),482(3.52)	118-0442-79
$C_{14}H_{13}N_3S_2$			
2(1H)-Pyrimidinethione, 4-[3-(ethylamino)-benzo[b]thien-2-yl]-	$CHCl_3$	308(4.10),340(3.84), 426(4.20)	118-0442-79

Compound	Solvent	λ_{max}(log ε)	Ref.
$C_{14}H_{13}N_4O_2$			
4H-Benz[g]imidazo[1,2,3-ij]pteridin-3-ium, 1,2,5,6-tetrahydro-5,9-dimethyl-4,6-dioxo-, perchlorate	H_2O	370(4.00),429(3.70)	33-0593-79
	MeCN	262(4.49),364(4.05), 420(3.85)	33-0593-79
4H-Benz[g]imidazo[1,2,3-ij]pteridin-10-ium, 1,2,5,6-tetrahydro-5,10-dimethyl-4,6-dioxo-, perchlorate	H_2O	391(4.31)	33-0593-79
	MeCN	255(4.52),383(4.23)	33-0593-79
$C_{14}H_{13}N_4S$			
1,2,3,4-Thiatriazolium, 5-[(4-methylphenyl)amino]-3-phenyl-, tetrafluoroborate	n.s.g.	239s(4.03),280(4.37), 403(3.41)	39-0741-79C
1,2,3,4-Thiatriazolium, 3-(4-methylphenyl)-5-(phenylamino)-, tetrafluoroborate	n.s.g.	247s(4.05),267(4.15), 313(4.15),384s(3.37)	39-0741-79C
$C_{14}H_{13}N_5O_2S$			
Pyrimido[4,5-d]pyrimidine-2,4(1H,3H)-dione, 5-amino-3-methyl-7-(methylthio)-1-phenyl-	EtOH	240(4.54),283(4.23)	142-0503-79
$C_{14}H_{13}N_5O_4$			
Benzo[g]pteridine-2,4(3H,10H)-dione, 3,7,8,10-tetramethyl-6-nitro-	pH 7	335(3.90),444(4.10)	5-1067-79
Benzo[g]pteridine-2,4(3H,10H)-dione, 3,7,8,10-tetramethyl-9-nitro-	MeCN	327(3.91),439(4.08)	5-1067-79
$C_{14}H_{13}N_7O_4$			
Butanedioic acid, [(6-amino-9H-purin-9-yl)methyl]-, bis(cyanomethyl) ester	MeOH	262(4.16)	126-2323-79
$C_{14}H_{13}N_9$			
Benzenamine, 3-[3-phenyl-5-(1H-tetrazol-5-yl)-1-formazano]-	EtOH	290(4.37),474(4.25)	104-1793-79
$C_{14}H_{14}$			
Benzene, (1-cyclohexen-1-ylethynyl)-	hexane	274(4.31),291(4.25)	39-2429-79C
Bicyclo[2.2.1]hept-2-ene, 5-(phenylmethylene)-, (E)-	C_6H_{12}	255(4.33),296(2.77)	44-1604-79
(Z)-	C_6H_{12}	253s(4.35),261(4.36), 270(4.21),285(3.27)	44-1604-79
1,3,5-Cycloheptatriene, 1-(4-methylphenyl)-	EtOH	300(3.86)	48-0117-79
1,3,5-Cycloheptatriene, 2-(4-methylphenyl)-	EtOH	243(4.21)	48-0117-79
1,3,5-Cycloheptatriene, 3-(4-methylphenyl)-	EtOH	283(3.82)	48-0117-79
1,3,5-Cycloheptatriene, 7-(4-methylphenyl)-	EtOH	263(3.56)	48-0117-79
Naphthalene, 1,4-dihydro-5,8-dimethyl-	n.s.g.	2.4(7.076)[sic],237 (4.105),275(3.90)	77-0823-79
Phenanthrene, 1,2,3,4-tetrahydro-	EtOH	231(4.96),283(3.76), 316(2.75),324(2.75)	44-1502-79
Tricyclo[3.2.0.0^{2,7}]heptane, 3-(phenylmethylene)-, (E)-	C_6H_{12}	263(4.26),299s(3.06)	44-1604-79
(Z)-	C_6H_{12}	265(4.28),299s(3.15)	44-1604-79
$C_{14}H_{14}BrNO$			
Benzenemethanol, α-(aminomethyl)-2-bromo-α-phenyl-	EtOH	217(4.08),268(3.04)	39-0829-79C

Compound	Solvent	λ_{max}(log ε)	Ref.
$C_{14}H_{14}Br_3N_3O_2$			
3,5-Methanofuro[3,2-b]pyridin-6(2H)-one, 7,7-dibromo-4-(5-bromo-4,6-dimethyl-2-pyrimidinyl)-	$CHCl_3$	253(4.22)	39-1525-79C
$C_{14}H_{14}ClN_3O_2$			
Pyrimido[4,5-b]quinoline-2,4(1H,3H)-dione, 6-chloro-5,10-dihydro-3,7,10-trimethyl-	pH 11	242(4.28),269(4.34), 309(4.08)	5-1802-79
	MeOH	260s(4.13),314(4.13)	5-1802-79
Pyrimido[4,5-b]quinoline-2,4(1H,3H)-dione, 8-chloro-5,10-dihydro-3,7,10-trimethyl-	pH 11	241(4.24),261(4.33), 314(4.09)	5-1802-79
	MeOH	260s(4.15),318(4.05)	5-1802-79
$C_{14}H_{14}ClN_3O_2S$			
Pyrimido[4,5-b]quinoline-2,4(1H,3H)-dione, 8-chloro-5,10-dihydro-5-mercapto-3,7,10-trimethyl-	pH 8	303(4.08)	5-1802-79
$C_{14}H_{14}ClN_3O_6$			
2,4-Pentadienoic acid, 4-(4-chloro-2-nitrophenyl)-5-(dimethylamino)-2-nitro-, methyl ester, (E,Z)-	EtOH	219(4.27),250s(4.06), 436(4.60)	44-3748-79
$C_{14}H_{14}D_6S$			
1-Pentanethione-5,5,5-d_3, 2,7-dimethyl-4-(methyl-d_3)-1-phenyl-	C_6H_{12}	225(3.89),290(3.59), 558(2.00)	35-5725-79
$C_{14}H_{14}F_3NO$			
2-Propanone, 3-(1,3-dihydro-1,3,3-trimethyl-2H-indol-2-ylidene)-1,1,1-trifluoro-	pH 1	374(4.26)	88-4407-79
	H_2O	374(4.37)	88-4407-79
$C_{14}H_{14}FeO$			
Ferrocene, 1,1'-(1-oxo-1,4-butanediyl)-	H_2O	260s(--),275(3.70), 345(3.25),465(2.80)	44-2920-79
	70% H_2SO_4	260(3.96),350(3.5), 455(2.9)	44-2920-79
Ferrocene, 1,1'-(2-oxo-1,4-butanediyl)-	H_2O	260s(3.98),320(2.70), 430(2.15)	44-2920-79
	70% H_2SO_4	260(4.25),450(2.45)	44-2920-79
$C_{14}H_{14}N_2$			
Pyrrolo[1,2-b]pyridazine, 3,4-dihydro-7-methyl-2-phenyl-	C_6H_{12}	202(4.48),226(4.30), 307(4.39)	4-0839-79
$C_{14}H_{14}N_2O$			
Benzamide, 2-amino-N-(4-methylphenyl)-	EtOH	214(4.08),255(3.65), 330(2.48)	2-0593-79A
2,4,6-Cycloheptatrien-1-one, 4-methyl-2-(2-phenylhydrazino)-	MeOH	254(4.54),341(4.03), 403(4.08)	18-2447-79
2,4,6-Cycloheptatrien-1-one, 6-methyl-2-(2-phenylhydrazino)-	MeOH	252(4.55),341(4.01), 401(4.05)	18-2447-79
Diazene, bis(3-methylphenyl)-, 1-oxide	heptane	324.6(4.21)	18-1588-79
Diazene, bis(4-methylphenyl)-, 1-oxide	heptane	330.3(4.29)	18-1588-79
$C_{14}H_{14}N_2OS_3$			
4-Thiazolidinone, 3-ethyl-5-(3-ethyl-2(3H)-benzothiazolylidene)-2-thioxo-	EtOH	412s(4.65),429(4.78)	73-1413-79
$C_{14}H_{14}N_2O_2$			
Benzamide, 2-amino-N-(2-methoxyphenyl)-	EtOH	222(4.00),265(3.73),	2-0593-79A

Compound	Solvent	λ_{max}(log ε)	Ref.
(cont.)		340(2.48)	2-0593-79A
Benzamide, 2-amino-N-(4-methoxyphenyl)-	EtOH	218(4.00),258(3.73), 333(2.48)	2-0593-79A
Benzenemethanamine, α-methyl-N-(4-nitrophenyl)-	MeOH	230(3.92),257s(3.43), 297s(3.18),310(3.30), 384(4.30)	35-5186-79
Benzenepropanenitrile, α-(4-morpholinylmethylene)-β-oxo-	MeOH	242(4.02),312(4.27)	83-0039-79
$C_{14}H_{14}N_2O_2S$			
1,2,5-Benzothiadiazepine, 2,3,4,5-tetrahydro-4-phenyl-, 1,1-dioxide	EtOH	253(3.70),302(3.15)	4-0835-79
3-Pyridinol, 6-methyl-2-(2-methyl-1,3-oxathiolo[4,5-b]pyridin-5-yl)methyl]-	EtOH-HCl	305(4.00)	1-0299-79
	EtOH-NaOH	243(4.05),320(4.15)	1-0299-79
$C_{14}H_{14}N_2O_2S_2$			
4-Thiazolidinone, 3-ethyl-5-(3-ethyl-2(3H)-benzoxazolylidene)-2-thioxo-	EtOH	398s(4.63),410(4.69)	73-1413-79
$C_{14}H_{14}N_2O_3$			
1H-Benzimidazole, 2-(3a,6a-dihydro-2,2-dimethylfuro[2,3-d]-1,3-dioxol-5-yl)-, (3aR-cis)-	EtOH	207(3.89),238(3.83), 242(3.83),293s(4.23), 300(4.31),313s(4.20)	33-1298-79
Diazene, bis(3-methoxyphenyl)-, 1-oxide	heptane	320.0(4.15)	18-1588-79
Diazene, bis(4-methoxyphenyl)-, 1-oxide	heptane	345.4(4.38)	18-1588-79
2,4(3H,5H)-Furandione, 3-(1-aminoethylidene)-5-[[(4-methylphenyl)amino]-methylene]-	EtOH	245(4.25),292(4.29), 378(4.53)	4-1335-79
2H-Indazole-6-carboxylic acid, 3,3a,4-5,6,7-hexahydro-3-oxo-2-phenyl-	EtOH	249(4.18),266s(4.03)	39-2099-79C
Phenol, 2,6-dimethoxy-4-(phenylazo)-	C_6H_{12}	364(4.29)	78-2071-79
	benzene	370(4.27)	78-2071-79
	MeOH	370(4.27)	78-2071-79
	dioxan	374(4.27)	78-2071-79
	MeCN	369(4.27)	78-2071-79
	CH_2Cl_2	366(4.26)	78-2071-79
	$CHCl_3$	368(4.27)	78-2071-79
Phenol, 3,5-dimethoxy-4-(phenylazo)-	C_6H_{12}	400(4.59)	78-2071-79
	benzene	408(4.59)	78-2071-79
	MeOH	420(4.60)	78-2071-79
	dioxan	374(4.59)	78-2071-79
	MeCN	406(4.60)	78-2071-79
	CH_2Cl_2	411(4.62)	78-2071-79
	$CHCl_3$	409(4.61)	78-2071-79
2-Propenoic acid, 2-(acetylamino)-3-(6-methyl-1H-indol-3-yl)-, (Z)-	isoPrOH	333(4.23)	44-3741-79
2-Propenoic acid, 2-(formylamino)-3-(6-methyl-1H-indol-3-yl)-, methyl ester, (Z)-	isoPrOH	346(4.33)	44-3741-79
4-Pyridazinecarboxylic acid, 5-methoxy-6-methyl-3-phenyl-, methyl ester	EtOH	232(4.16)	44-3053-79
5-Pyrimidinecarboxylic acid, 1,6-dihydro-1-methyl-6-oxo-2-phenyl-, ethyl ester	EtOH	203(4.30),233(3.91), 312(4.03)	87-0263-79
$C_{14}H_{14}N_2O_3S$			
2,4-Thiazolidinedione, 3-ethyl-5-(3-ethyl-2(3H)-benzoxazolylidene)-	EtOH	372(4.72),383(4.70)	73-1413-79
$C_{14}H_{14}N_2O_4$			
2,4(3H,5H)-Furandione, 3-(1-aminoeth-	EtOH	246(4.17),294(4.20),	4-1335-79

Compound	Solvent	λ max (log ε)	Ref.
ylidene)-5-[[(4-methoxyphenyl)amino]-methylene]- (cont.)		384(4.49)	4-1335-79
1H-Pyrazole-4-carboxylic acid, 5-(4-methoxybenzoyl)-1-methyl-, methyl ester	EtOH	225(4.20),298(4.28)	73-0781-79
	ether	212(4.24),294(4.27)	73-0781-79
1H-Pyrazole-5-carboxylic acid, 4-(4-methoxybenzoyl)-1-methyl-, methyl ester	EtOH	225(4.14),291(4.28)	73-0781-79
	ether	219(4.24),276(4.27), 282(4.26)	73-0781-79
1H-Pyrazole-4,5-dicarboxylic acid, 3-methyl-1-phenyl-, dimethyl ester	CH_2Cl_2	260(4.11)	24-1206-79
4-Pyrimidinecarboxylic acid, 3,6-dihydro-5-methoxy-3-methyl-6-oxo-2-phenyl-, methyl ester	MeOH	237(3.81),298(3.89)	4-1423-79
4-Pyrimidinecarboxylic acid, 5,6-dimethoxy-2-phenyl-, methyl ester	MeOH	264(4.29)	4-1423-79
Pyrrolidine, 1-[1-(2-furanyl)-2-(5-nitro-2-furanyl)ethenyl]-	EtOH	490(3.90)	94-3078-79
$C_{14}H_{14}N_2O_4S$			
1H-Pyrazole-3,4-dicarboxylic acid, 5-(methylthio)-1-phenyl-, dimethyl ester	CH_2Cl_2	235(4.16)	24-1193-79
1H-Pyrazole-4,5-dicarboxylic acid, 3-(methylthio)-1-phenyl-, dimethyl ester	CH_2Cl_2	235(4.24),291(3.88)	24-1206-79
$C_{14}H_{14}N_2O_4Sn$			
Tin, dimethylbis(2-pyridinecarboxylato-N,O^2)-	$CHCl_3$	238s(3.61),264(4.01)	131-0165-79D
	MeCN	221(3.97),263(3.93)	131-0165-79D
$C_{14}H_{14}N_2O_5$			
Morpholine, 4-[1-(2-furanyl)-2-(5-nitro-2-furanyl)ethenyl]-	EtOH	445(4.29)	94-3078-79
$C_{14}H_{14}N_2O_5S$			
1H-Pyrazole-3,4-dicarboxylic acid, 5-(methylsulfinyl)-1-phenyl-, dimethyl ester	CH_2Cl_2	end absorption	24-1193-79
1H-Pyrazole-4,5-dicarboxylic acid, 3-(methylsulfinyl)-1-phenyl-, dimethyl ester	CH_2Cl_2	end absorption	24-1206-79
$C_{14}H_{14}N_3$			
Pyridinium, 3-(1H-benzimidazol-2-yl)-1,4-dimethyl-, iodide	EtOH	305(4.06)	7-1583-79
Pyridinium, 4-(1H-benzimidazol-2-yl)-1,2-dimethyl-, iodide	EtOH	362(4.38)	4-1583-79
Pyridinium, 5-(1H-benzimidazol-2-yl)-1,2-dimethyl-, iodide	EtOH	318(4.26)	4-1583-79
1H-1,2,3-Triazolium, 4,5-dihydro-1,3-diphenyl-, perchlorate	MeOH	234(3.98),245(3.94), 384(4.24)	24-0445-79
$C_{14}H_{14}N_3O$			
Phenazinium, 3-amino-7-hydroxy-2,5-dimethyl- (neutral)	H_2O	509(4.58)	39-0304-79B
cation	H_2O	434(4.29),490(4.35)	39-0304-79B
$C_{14}H_{14}N_4$			
Propanedinitrile, [1-amino-3-[4-(dimethylamino)phenyl]-2-propenylidene]-	EtOH	405(4.02)	64-1580-79B

Compound	Solvent	λ_{max}(log ε)	Ref.
$C_{14}H_{14}N_4O$			
1H-Benzimidazole-2-acetonitrile, α-(4-morpholinylmethylene)-	MeOH	211(4.48),264(4.32), 324(4.47)	83-0039-79
Compd. m. 215°	EtOH	252(4.13),260(4.20), 277(4.28)	18-0462-79
$C_{14}H_{14}N_4O_2$			
Benzo[g]pteridine-2,4(1H,3H)-dione, 1,3,7,8-tetramethyl-	H_2O	254(4.48),353(3.88), 388(3.75)	33-0593-79
	MeCN	251(4.47),333(3.76), 385(3.77)	33-0593-79
Benzo[g]pteridine-2,4(3H,10H)-dione, 3,6,7,10-tetramethyl-	H_2O	268(4.78),380(4.19), 450(4.02)	33-0593-79
	MeCN	270(4.73),350(4.08), 448(4.06)	33-0593-79
Benzo[g]pteridine-2,4(3H,10H)-dione, 3,7,8,10-tetramethyl-	H_2O	266(4.63),366(4.00), 444(4.09)	33-0593-79
	MeCN	269(4.59),340(3.94), 444(4.09)	33-0593-79
Carbamic acid, [4-[4-cyano-3,5-dimethyl-1H-pyrazol-1-yl)phenyl]-, methyl ester	EtOH	270(4.34)	78-1331-79
3-Pyridinecarboxamide, N-[[nitroso-(phenylmethyl)amino]methyl]-	EtOH	237s(4.03),368(1.79)	94-0682-79
4H-Pyrimido[4,5-b][1,4]oxazin-4-one, 2-amino-6-(2-phenylethyl)-	2M HCl	264(4.06),352(3.88)	87-0797-79
	2M NaOH	273(3.65),320(3.64)	87-0797-79
Pyrimido[4,5-b]quinoline-2,4(3H,10H)-dione, 8-amino-3,7,10-trimethyl-	12M HCl	255(4.51),329(4.10), 357(3.92)	5-1802-79
	M HCl	240(4.52),293(4.10), 421(4.46)	5-1802-79
	pH 6	245(4.62),265s(--), 293s(--),421(4.57)	5-1802-79
	MeOH	245(4.64),263s(--), 295s(--),425(4.63)	5-1802-79
$C_{14}H_{14}N_4O_2S$			
Isothiazolo[3,4-d]pyrimidine-4,6(5H,7H)-dione, 5,7-dimethyl-3-[(phenylmethyl)amino]-	EtOH	233(4.38),272(4.17), 294(3.96)	95-0989-79
$C_{14}H_{14}N_4O_3$			
Benzo[g]pteridine-2,4(3H,10H)-dione, 10-(3-hydroxypropyl)-3-methyl-	EtOH	264(4.40),331(3.92), 415s(4.01),437(3.95), 455s(3.87)	4-1365-79
$C_{14}H_{14}N_4O_4$			
Pyrimido[4,5-b]quinoline-2,4(1H,3H)-dione, 3,7,10-trimethyl-6-nitro-5,10-dihydro-	pH 11	240(4.38),261(4.42), 308(4.05)	5-1802-79
	MeOH	240s(4.26),315(4.11)	5-1802-79
Pyrimido[4,5-b]quinoline-2,4(1H,3H)-dione, 3,7,10-trimethyl-8-nitro-5,10-dihydro-	pH 11	258(4.38),314(4.00)	5-1802-79
	MeOH	231(4.60),312(4.11)	5-1802-79
$C_{14}H_{14}N_4O_4S_2$			
Benzenesulfonamide, 4-methyl-N-(4,5,6,7-tetrahydro-5,7-dimethyl-4,6-dioxoisothiazolo[3,4-d]pyrimidin-3-yl)-	EtOH	227(4.37),280(4.15), 320(4.10)	95-0989-79 +142-0485-79
$C_{14}H_{14}N_4O_5$			
8H-Imidazo[4,5-g]quinazolin-8-one, 3,5-dihydro-3-β-D-ribofuranosyl-	pH 7	298(3.75),313(3.80), 326(3.80)	44-2989-79

Compound	Solvent	λ_{max}(log ε)	Ref.
$C_{14}H_{14}N_4O_6$			
Inosine, 4',5'-didehydro-5'-deoxy-, 2',3'-diacetate	MeOH	243(4.05),248(4.03), 268s(3.69)	44-0400-79
	MeOH-NaOH	254(4.04)	44-0400-79
$C_{14}H_{14}N_4O_6S$			
Benzenesulfonamide, 4-(dimethylamino)-N-(2,4-dinitrophenyl)-	EtOH	283(4.47),368(3.72)	80-1027-79
Benzenesulfonamide, N-[4-(dimethylamino)phenyl]-2,4-dinitro-	EtOH	261(4.45),449(4.08)	80-1027-79 +80-1329-79
$C_{14}H_{14}O$			
[1,1'-Biphenyl]-3-ol, 4,5-dimethyl-	EtOH	204(4.61),220s(4.42), 259(4.18),285s(3.70)	104-1973-79
[1,1'-Biphenyl]-4-ol, 3,5-dimethyl-	EtOH	206(4.55),264(4.20)	104-1973-79
1,3,5-Cycloheptatriene, 1-(4-methoxyphenyl)-	EtOH	310(4.11)	48-0117-79
1,3,5-Cycloheptatriene, 2-(4-methoxyphenyl)-	EtOH	250(4.44)	48-0117-79
1,3,5-Cycloheptatriene, 3-(4-methoxyphenyl)-	EtOH	288(4.19)	48-0117-79
1,3,5-Cycloheptatriene, 7-(4-methoxyphenyl)-	EtOH	275(3.75)	48-0117-79
Dibenz[b,d]oxepin, 8,9,10,11-tetrahydro-	EtOH	242(4.33),269(3.41), 341(2.64),375(2.54), 396(2.45)	44-1502-79
1,4,6-Octatrien-3-one, 1-phenyl-	EtOH	230(4.11),328(4.44)	32-0195-79
2(3H)-Phenanthrenone, 4,4a,9,10-tetrahydro-	EtOH	236(4.24)	118-0374-79
$C_{14}H_{14}O_2$			
2,4-Cyclohexadien-1-one, 6-(4-methoxyphenyl)-6-methyl-	MeOH	227(4.15)	12-1551-79
2,4,6-Heptatrienal, 7-(4-methoxyphenyl)-, (E,E,E)-	EtOH	384(4.52)	104-1669-79
$C_{14}H_{14}O_2S$			
Benzene, 1,1'-sulfonylbis[4-methyl-	C_6H_{12}	244.5(4.27)	39-0007-79B
$C_{14}H_{14}O_3$			
2H-1-Benzopyran-2-one, 4-[(3-methyl-2-butenyl)oxy]-	n.s.g.	265(4.07),275(4.05), 300(3.89)	2-0638-79A
2,4-Cyclohexadien-1-one, 6-methoxy-6-(4-methoxyphenyl)-	MeOH	227(4.18)	12-1551-79
2-Cyclopenten-1-one, 5-acetoxy-3-methyl-4-phenyl-, trans	n.s.g.	229(4.7)	39-0274-79C
Ethanone, 1-(2,7-dimethoxy-1-naphthalenyl-)-	EtOH	239(4.59),329(3.49)	150-0301-79
4H-Furo[3,2-c][1]benzopyran-4-one, 2,3-dihydro-2,3,3-trimethyl-	n.s.g.	277(3.88),289(4.01), 312(4.03),326(3.87)	2-0638-79A
1(2H)-Phenanthrenone, 3,4,9,10-tetrahydro-9,10-dihydroxy-, cis	MeOH	208(3.93),217(3.87), 228(4.02),253(3.38), 298(4.12)	5-0297-79
$C_{14}H_{14}O_4$			
2H,6H-Benzo[1,2-b:5m4-b']dipyran-2-one, 7,8-dihydro-10-hydroxy-8,8-dimethyl-	MeOH	265(3.91),330(4.15)	102-1580-79
4a,10a-Epoxyphenanthren-1(2H)-one, 3,4,9,10-tetrahydro-9,10-dihydroxy-, cis	MeOH	256(2.58),261(2.59), 266(2.59),274s(2.49), 298(2.06)	5-0297-79

Compound	Solvent	$\lambda_{max}(\log \epsilon)$	Ref.
$C_{14}H_{14}O_4S$			
Benzene, 1,1'-sulfonylbis[4-methoxy-	C_6H_{12}	236(4.29)	39-0007-79B
$C_{14}H_{14}O_5$			
2-Benzoxepin-1,4-dicarboxylic acid, 1,3-dihydro-, dimethyl ester	EtOH	222(4.20),285(4.26)	88-4049-79
1H-Indene-1,7-dicarboxylic acid, 2,3-dihydro-1-methyl-3-oxo-, dimethyl ester	MeOH	219(4.51),241(4.01), 292(3.39),301(3.39)	18-2962-79
1,4-Naphthalenedione, 5-hydroxy-7-methoxy-6-(1-methoxyethyl)-	MeOH	217(4.21),260(3.83), 269s(3.79),424(3.58)	150-2685-79
Oxiraneacetic acid, 3-(methoxycarbonyl)-α-(phenylmethylene)-, methyl ester, [2α(E),3β]-	EtOH	274(4.22)	88-4049-79
$C_{14}H_{14}O_5S$			
2-Furancarboxylic acid, tetrahydro-2-methoxy-5-oxo-4-[(phenylthio)methylene]-, methyl ester	EtOH	205(4.12),256(3.78), 294(4.24)	35-7013-79
3,4-Furandicarboxylic acid, 2-(2-thienyl)-, diethyl ester	$CHCl_3$	250(3.778),320(3.479), 353(3.682)	104-0541-79
$C_{14}H_{14}O_5Se$			
3,4-Furandicarboxylic acid, 2-(selenophene-2-yl)-, diethyl ester	C_6H_{12}	280(3.870),307(3.70)	104-0541-79
$C_{14}H_{14}O_6$			
Butanedioic acid, (1,3-benzodioxol-5-ylmethylene)-, dimethyl ester	EtOH	235(4.09),290(4.01), 316(4.13)	2-0202-79
1,4-Naphthalenedione, 2,3,5,8-tetramethoxy-	C_6H_{12}	335(3.3),398(3.57)	39-0696-79C
$C_{14}H_{14}O_6S$			
2-Furancarboxylic acid, tetrahydro-2-methoxy-5-oxo-4-[(phenylsulfinyl)-methylene]-, methyl ester	EtOH	207(4.16),238(4.09), 292(3.21)	35-7013-79
$C_{14}H_{14}S_2Si$			
1,3-Dithia-2-silacyclopentane, 2,2-diphenyl-	hexane	197(4.83),221(4.20), 245s(3.55),267(3.05), 274(2.88)	114-0195-79D
$C_{14}H_{15}ClN_2O_2$			
Pyridine, 3-chloro-1,4-dihydro-4-(1-nitroethyl)-1-(phenylmethyl)-	DMSO	304(3.59),353(3.12)	44-1761-79
$C_{14}H_{15}ClN_4O_3$			
3H-1,2,4-Triazolo[4,3-d][1,4]benzodiazepine-3,6(5H)-dione, 10-chloro-2,7-dihydro-2-(3-hydroxypropyl)-7-methyl-	MeOH	252(4.26),277s(3.91), 303s(3.67)	44-0088-79
$C_{14}H_{15}ClO_4$			
1H,7H-Cyclopropa[c]benzofuran-4,7(3aH)-dione, 5-(1-chloro-1-propenyl)-1a,2-dihydro-3a-hydroxy-2,2-dimethyl-	EtOH	295(3.55)	33-1129-79
6H-Furo[3,2-h][1]benzopyran-5,7-diol, 3-chloro-7,8-dihydro-2,8,8-trimethyl- (mycorrhizinol)	EtOH	250(4.00),264(4.18), 269(3.48)	33-1129-79
2-Naphthalenol, 1-chloro-5,6,7-trimethoxy-4-methyl-	EtOH	224(4.89),280s(3.68), 291(3.77),304s(3.71),	150-0301-79

Compound	Solvent	$\lambda_{max}(\log \epsilon)$	Ref.
(cont.)		322s(3.35),337(3.31)	150-0301-79
$C_{14}H_{15}FN_2O_3S_3$			
1,2,3-Benzothiadiazolium, 4,5,6,7-tetrahydro-7-[(methylthio)methylene]-2-phenyl-, fluorosulfate	MeOH	339(3.63),475(4.30)	39-0926-79C
$C_{14}H_{15}F_3N_4O_4S_2$			
Sulfonium, S,S-dimethyl-N[4]-(N'-2-pyrimidinylsulfonamido)imino-, trifluoroacetate	70% EtOH	202(4.66),303(4.26)	139-0195-79
$C_{14}H_{15}IN_4O_6$			
Inosine, 5'-deoxy-5'-iodo-, 2',3'-diacetate	MeOH	244(4.02),249(4.01), 268s(3.65)	44-0400-79
	MeOH-NaOH	254(4.13)	44-0400-79
$C_{14}H_{15}N$			
Benzenamine, N-ethyl-N-phenyl-	hexane	297(4.18)	65-0672-79
[1,1'-Biphenyl]-2-amine, 4,5-dimethyl-	EtOH	225(4.44),303(3.66)	33-2129-79
Cyclohept[b]indole, 5,8,9,10-tetrahydro-5-methyl-	EtOH	207(4.24),231(4.39), 301s(4.08),308(4.09)	39-2154-79C
1H-Pyrrolizine, 2,3-dihydro-6-methyl-7-phenyl-	MeOH	208(4.21),268(4.04)	83-0896-79
9H-Pyrrolo[1,2-a]indole, 2,9,9-trimethyl-	MeOH	213(4.13),269(4.09)	83-0896-79
$C_{14}H_{15}NO$			
Benzenamine, 2-(2-methoxyphenyl)-N-methyl-	EtOH	278(3.73),300(3.67)	33-2129-79
Benzenamine, 2-(4-methoxyphenyl)-N-methyl-	EtOH	232(4.43),305(3.73)	33-2129-79
9H-Indeno[2,1-b]pyridine, 1,2,3,9a-tetrahydro-3-(hydroxymethylene)-1-methyl-, hydrochloride (isomer mixt.)	n.s.g.	233(--),238(4.00), 298(4.18),317(4.24)	44-1108-79
Phenol, 2-[[(phenylmethyl)amino]methyl]-, hydrochloride	EtOH	210(4.13),277(3.53)	150-3801-79
$C_{14}H_{15}NOS$			
1(4H)-Naphthalenone, 4-[[(1,1-dimethylethyl)thio]imino]-	hexane	418(4.28)	138-1077-79
1H-Phenothiazine, 10-acetyl-2,3,4,10-tetrahydro-	EtOH	213(4.14),254(3.93)	94-1982-79
2H-Phenothiazine, 10-acetyl-3,4,4a,10-tetrahydro-	EtOH	215(4.11),230(4.26), 255(3.15),290(3.15), 300(3.02)	94-1982-79
$C_{14}H_{15}NO_2$			
1-Oxa-2-azaspiro[4.5]dec-2-en-4-one, 3-phenyl-	n.s.g.	230(4.22),304(3.98)	104-2204-79
2H-Pyrrole-4-carboxylic acid, 2,2-dimethyl-3-phenyl-, methyl ester	MeOH	280(3.59)	88-2983-79
$C_{14}H_{15}NO_2S_2$			
2-Azetidinone, 4-[[3-(4-methylphenyl)-1-(methylthio)-3-oxo-1-propenyl]thio]-, (E)-	dioxan	271(4.03),337(4.21)	142-1315-79
(Z)-	dioxan	270(4.11),335(4.34)	142-1315-79

Compound	Solvent	λ_{max}(log ε)	Ref.
$C_{14}H_{15}NO_3$			
2H-1-Benzopyran-2-one, 4,8-dimethyl-7-[[(1-methylethylidene)amino]oxy]-	EtOH	248(3.77),257(3.77), 323(4.26)	44-2176-79
2-Naphthaleneacetonitrile, 1,2,3,4-tetrahydro-5,7-dimethoxy-4-oxo-	MeOH	219(4.19),228(4.24), 232s(4.23),275(4.23), 307(3.90)	35-2171-79
1H-Pyrrole-2-carboxylic acid, 3-(phenylmethoxy)-, ethyl ester	EtOH	266(4.28)	94-1448-79
Pyrrolo[1,2,3-ij]quinoline-2,6-dione, 7-methoxy-4,4-dimethyl-	MeOH	232(4.20),260(4.01), 345(3.73)	39-1751-79C
$C_{14}H_{15}NO_4$			
1,4-Naphthalenedione, 2-(butylamino)-5,8-dihydroxy-	benzene	474(3.89),500(3.93), 534(3.81)	138-0627-79
$C_{14}H_{15}NO_5$			
1,4-Naphthalenedione, 2,5,8-trimethoxy-3-(methylamino)-	C_6H_{12}	404(3.74),480s(3.42)	39-0696-79C
Pentanoic acid, 3-[hydroxy(phenylamino)methylene]-2,4-dioxo-, ethyl ester	EtOH	265(4.32)	94-1792-79
$C_{14}H_{15}NS_2$			
4H-3,1-Benzothiazine-4-thione, 1,2,5,6,7,8-hexahydro-2-phenyl-	EtOH	244s(3.56),343(3.53), 408(4.18)	150-1732-79
$C_{14}H_{15}N_3$			
Benzenamine, N,N-dimethyl-2-(phenylazo)-	EtOH	207(4.12),227(4.02), 440(3.46)	7-0563-79
Benzenamine, N,N-dimethyl-4-(phenylazo)-	MeOH	410(4.47)	56-0989-79
Benzenamine, N-ethyl-4-(phenylazo)-	MeOH	410(4.46)	56-0989-79
Benzenecarboximidic acid, 2-(4-methylphenyl)hydrazide	EtOH	234(4.33),278(3.48)	65-2056-79
	EtOH-NH_3	219(4.11),252(4.05), 315(3.95)	65-2056-79
Benzenecarboximidic acid, 4-methyl-, 2-phenylhydrazide	EtOH	236(4.30)	65-2056-79
	EtOH-NH_3	225(4.13),249(4.08), 308(4.02)	65-2056-79
1,4-Benzenediamine, N,N-dimethyl-N'-(2-pyridinylmethylene)-	EtOH	208(3.42),258(3.40), 305s(--),400(3.51)	2-0338-79B
1,4-Benzenediamine, N,N-dimethyl-N'-(4-pyridinylmethylene)-	EtOH	208(3.28),254(3.27), 295s(--),411(3.30)	2-0338-79B
Debenzorutecarpene	EtOH	240(4.18),310(4.24)	114-0043-79A
Pyrido[1,2-a]benzimidazol-9-amine, N,N,7-trimethyl-	pH 1	229(4.5),241(4.4)	95-0880-79
	MeOH	240(4.6),247(4.6)	95-0880-79
$C_{14}H_{15}N_3O$			
Aziridine, 2-(1-methylethyl)-1-(2-quinoxalinylcarbonyl)-, (S)-	isooctane	203(4.46),241(4.57), 244(4.56),307(3.79), 317(3.83),328(3.76)	39-2881-79C
	EtOH	203(4.41),245(4.50), 318(3.81)	39-2881-79C
	MeCN	203(4.46),243(4.58), 316(3.91),328s(3.85)	39-2881-79C
Benzenecarboximidic acid, 2-(4-methoxyphenyl)hydrazide	EtOH-HCl	235(4.32),298(3.57)	65-2056-79
	EtOH-NH_3	219s(4.06),248(4.04), 314(3.91)	65-2056-79
Benzenecarboximidic acid, 4-methoxy-, 2-phenylhydrazide	EtOH-HCl	228(4.06),262(4.15)	65-2056-79
	EtOH-NH_3	248(4.17),303(4.06)	65-2056-79
[1,1'(4H,4'H)-Bipyridine]-4-carbonitrile, 2,2',6'-trimethyl-4'-oxo-	EtOH	260.0(4.32)	39-1698-79C

Compound	Solvent	$\lambda_{max}(\log \epsilon)$	Ref.
[1,1'(4H,4'H)-Bipyridine]-4-carbonitrile, 2,4,6-trimethyl-4'-oxo-	EtOH	263.5(4.34)	39-1698-79C
[1,1'(4H,4'H)-Bipyridine]-4-carbonitrile, 2',3,6'-trimethyl-4'-oxo-	EtOH	261.5(4.30)	39-1698-79C
[1,1'(4H,4'H)-Bipyridine]-4-carbonitrile, 2',4,6'-trimethyl-4'-oxo-	EtOH	262.0(4.32)	39-1698-79C
Debenzorutecarpine, 3,14-dihydro-	EtOH	224(4.29),280(3.56), 290(3.49)	114-0043-79A
Phenol, 4-[[4-imino-5-methyl-2-(methylamino)-2,5-cyclohexadien-1-ylidene]-amino]-	H_2O	618(4.27)(zwitterion)	39-0304-79B
	cation	495(4.05)	39-0304-79B
	anion	494(4.13)	39-0304-79B
$C_{14}H_{15}N_3OS_2$			
4-Imidazolidinone, 5-(3-ethyl-2(3H)-benzothiazolylidene)-1,3-dimethyl-2-thioxo-	EtOH	425(4.54)	73-1413-79
$C_{14}H_{15}N_3O_2$			
Acetamide, N-(1,2,3,4,5,6-hexahydro-4-oxoazepino[4,5-b]indol-5-yl)-	EtOH	222(4.50),283(3.93)	103-0780-79
Pyrazinecarboxamide, N-[1-(hydroxymethyl)-2-phenylethyl]-, (S)-	EtOH	207(4.31),269(3.94), 323(2.95)	39-2881-79C
	MeCN	208(4.35),268(3.98), 322(3.00)	39-2881-79C
$C_{14}H_{15}N_3O_2S$			
4-Imidazolidinone, 5-(3-ethyl-2(3H)-benzoxazolylidene)-1,3-dimethyl-2-thioxo-	EtOH	380s(4.67),392(4.74)	73-1413-79
$C_{14}H_{15}N_3O_3$			
3,5-Methanofuro[3,2-b]pyridine-2,6-dione, 4-(4,6-dimethyl-2-pyrimidinyl)-dihydro-	$CHCl_3$	247(4.31),287(3.67)	39-1525-79C
1H-Pyrazole-3-carboxylic acid, 4-(acetylamino)-5-phenyl-, ethyl ester	pH 1	225(4.34)	18-0208-79
	pH 11	247(4.39)	18-0208-79
	EtOH	225(4.33)	18-0208-79
$C_{14}H_{15}N_3O_3S$			
Benzoic acid, 4-[[[(4-methyl-2-thiazolyl)amino]carbonyl]amino]-, ethyl ester	n.s.g.	290(4.61)	87-0028-79
1H-Indole-3-carbothioamide, N-acetyl-2-(ethoxycarbonylamino)-	$CHCl_3$	268(4.25),287(4.32), 393(4.23)	103-0179-79
$C_{14}H_{15}N_3O_4$			
Benzoic acid, 4-[(4,5-dihydro-3,4-dimethyl-5-oxo-4-isoxazolyl)azo]-, ethyl ester	MeOH	219(4.03),282(4.19)	33-1570-79
3-Pyridinepropanoic acid, α-acetyl-β-(2-amino-1-cyano-2-oxoethyl)-, methyl ester	n.s.g.	270(4.01),284(4.02)	56-2121-79
$C_{14}H_{15}N_3O_4S$			
Benzenesulfonamide, 4-(dimethylamino)-N-(2-nitrophenyl)-	EtOH	282(4.55),346(3.60)	80-1027-79
Benzenesulfonamide, 4-(dimethylamino)-N-(3-nitrophenyl)-	EtOH	282(4.52),356(3.26)	80-1027-79
Benzenesulfonamide, 4-(dimethylamino)-N-(4-nitrophenyl)-	EtOH	282(4.55),330(4.13)	80-1027-79

Compound	Solvent	$\lambda_{max}(\log \epsilon)$	Ref.
Benzenesulfonamide, N-[3-(dimethyl-amino)phenyl]-4-nitro-	EtOH	259(4.49),349(3.30)	80-1027-79
	EtOH	259(4.49),359(3.30)	80-1329-79
Benzenesulfonamide, N-[4-(dimethyl-amino)phenyl]-2-nitro-	EtOH	262(4.43),318(3.46)	80-1027-79 +80-1329-79
Benzenesulfonamide, N-[4-(dimethyl-amino)phenyl]-3-nitro-	EtOH	262(4.47),314(3.61)	80-1027-79
Benzenesulfonamide, N-[4-(dimethyl-amino)phenyl]-4-nitro-	EtOH	262(4.49),365(3.00)	80-1027-79
	EtOH	262(4.49),360(3.30)	80-1329-79
	pH 2	261(3.96),358(2.70)	80-1329-79
	pH 10	257(4.37),370s(3.44)	80-1329-79
$C_{14}H_{15}N_3O_6$			
2,4-Pentadienoic acid, 5-(dimethylami-no)-2-nitro-4-(2-nitrophenyl)-, methyl ester, (E,Z)-	EtOH	250(4.08),438(4.64)	44-3748-79
$C_{14}H_{15}N_3O_7$			
1H-Pyrrolo[3,2-d]pyrimidine-6-acetic acid, 2,3,4,5-tetrahydro-7-(methoxy-carbonyl)-1,3,5-trimethyl-α,2,4-tri-oxo-, methyl ester	EtOH	230(4.43),255(3.97), 295(3.83),350(3.43)	44-3830-79
$C_{14}H_{15}N_3S$			
2H-Isothiazolo[4,5,1-hi][1,2,3]benzo-thiadiazole-3-S^{IV}, 4,6,7,8-tetrahy-dro-4-methyl-2-phenyl-	C_6H_{12}	243(4.05),286(3.92), 458(4.33)	39-0926-79C
$C_{14}H_{15}N_4$			
Phenazinium, 3,7-diamino-2,5-dimethyl-	cation	511(4.37)	59-0421-79
$C_{14}H_{15}N_4O_2$			
Benzo[g]pteridinium, 3,4-dihydro-2-methoxy-3,7,10-trimethyl-4-oxo-, perchlorate	H_2O	373(4.02),426(3.92)	33-0593-79
	MeCN	267(4.57),369(3.97), 418(3.77)	33-0593-79
Benzo[g]pteridinium, 3,4-dihydro-2-methoxy-3,8,10-trimethyl-4-oxo-, perchlorate	H_2O	398(4.25)	33-0593-79
	MeCN	262(4.62),400(4.20)	33-0593-79
Benzo[g]pteridinium, 1,2,3,4-tetrahy-dro-1,3,7,10-tetramethyl-2,4-dioxo-, perchlorate	H_2O	372(3.83)	33-0593-79
	MeCN	268(4.32),365(3.96), 405(3.83)	33-0593-79
Benzo[g]pteridinium, 1,2,3,4-tetrahy-dro-1,3,8,10-tetramethyl-2,4-dioxo-, perchlorate	H_2O	398(4.28)	33-0593-79
	MeCN	265(4.46),392(4.30)	33-0593-79
$C_{14}H_{15}N_4O_8P$			
8H-Imidazo[4,5-g]quinazolin-8-one, 3,5-dihydro-3-(5-O-phosphono-β-D-ribo-furanosyl)-	pH 7.6	270(3.84),285(3.67), 321(3.80)	44-2989-79
$C_{14}H_{15}N_5O_2$			
Pyrido[2,3-d]pyrimidine-6-carbonitrile, 8-ethyl-7,8-dihydro-5-hydroxy-7-oxo-2-(1-pyrrolidinyl)-	EtOH	223(4.42),234s(4.37), 271(4.31),301(4.01), 341(4.19),366(4.11)	4-1169-79
$C_{14}H_{15}N_5O_5$			
8H-Imidazo[4,5-g]quinazolin-8-one, 6-amino-3,5-dihydro-3-β-D-ribo-furanosyl-	pH 8	277(3.71),288(3.61), 310s(--),323(3.75), 335s(--)	44-2989-79

Compound	Solvent	λ_{max}(log ϵ)	Ref.
$C_{14}H_{15}N_7O_5S$			
D-erythro-Pentitol, 1,4-anhydro-2-deoxy-1-C-[8-[(1-methyl-4-nitro-1H-imidazol-5-yl)thio]-1,2,4-triazolo[4,3-a]pyrazin-3-yl]-, (E)-	EtOH	236(4.23),298(4.13)	44-1028-79
$C_{14}H_{15}N_7O_6S$			
D-Ribitol, 1,4-anhydro-1-C-[8-[(1-methyl-4-nitro-1H-imidazol-5-yl)thio]-1,2,4-triazolo[4,3-a]pyrazin-3-yl]-	EtOH	242(4.21),300(4.11)	44-1028-79
$C_{14}H_{15}OP$			
Phosphinous acid, diphenyl-, ethyl ester	hexane	223(3.76),245s(3.50), 264s(3.18)	22-0241-79I
$C_{14}H_{15}P$			
Phosphine, ethyldiphenyl-	hexane	251.2(3.90)	22-0241-79I
$C_{14}H_{15}S_3$			
1,2-Dithiol-1-ium, 4-methyl-3-[(2-methyl-1-propenyl)thio]-5-phenyl-, bromide	MeCN	216(4.52),252s(3.85), 332(3.98),377(4.26)	104-0955-79
$C_{14}H_{16}$			
Benzo[3,4]cyclobuta[1,2]cyclooctene, 4b,5,6,7,8,9-hexahydro-	MeOH	223(3.89),248(4.21), 256(4.16),291(3.76), 299(3.80)	111-0543-79
$C_{14}H_{16}BrN_3O_2$			
3,5-Methanofuro[3,2-b]pyridin-6(2H)-one, 4-(5-bromo-4,6-dimethyl-2-pyrimidinyl)hexaxydro-	$CHCl_3$	257(4.38)	39-1525-79C
$C_{14}H_{16}FN_5O_4S_2$			
Ethanesulfonyl fluoride, 2-[ethyl[3-methyl-4-[(5-nitro-2-thiazolyl)azo]phenyl]amino]-	acetone	564(4.64)	44-3847-79
$C_{14}H_{16}FeO$			
Ferrocene, 1,1'-(1-hydroxy-1,4-butanediyl)-	H_2O	435(2.10)	44-2920-79
	70% H_2SO_4	255(3.94),410(2.68)	44-2920-79
Ferrocene, 1,1'-(2-hydroxy-1,4-butanediyl)-	H_2O	430(1.78)	44-2920-79
	70% H_2SO_4	252(3.7),430(2.0)	44-2920-79
$C_{14}H_{16}N_2$			
1-Cyclohexene-1-carbonitrile, 2-[(phenylmethyl)amino]-	MeOH	209(3.71),278(4.07)	44-4381-79
Isoquinoline, 4-(1-methyl-2-pyrrolidinyl)-	EtOH	219(4.68),262(3.36), 272(3.40),285(3.31), 310(3.38),318s(3.40), 323(3.52)	88-4527-79
$C_{14}H_{16}N_2O$			
5H-Cyclohepta[b][1,8]naphthyridin-5-one, 1,6,7,8,9,10-hexahydro-2-methyl-	EtOH	254(4.49),282(3.61), 293(3.59),335(4.01)	4-0137-79
Cyclohepta[d]pyrido[1,2-a]pyrimidin-11(6H)-one, 7,8,9,10-tetrahydro-1-methyl-	EtOH	245(4.05),254(4.10), 263(4.06),362(3.97)	4-0137-79
8-Quinolinol, 2-(1-piperidinyl)-	neutral	272(4.45),346(3.66)	123-0070-79
	acid	251(4.19),272(4.47), 317(3.95),354(3.79)	123-0070-79

Compound	Solvent	λ_{max}(log ε)	Ref.
(cont.)	base	279(4.47),360(3.40)	123-0070-79
$C_{14}H_{16}N_2OS$			
Acetamide, N-(5,6,7,8-tetrahydro-2-methyl-[1]benzothieno[2,3-b]pyridin-4-yl)-	DMF	293(3.93)	49-1189-79
Benzo[b]thiophene-3-carbonitrile, 4,5,6,7-tetrahydro-2-[(1-methyl-3-oxo-1-butenyl)amino]-	EtOH	253(3.95),321s(3.91), 369(4.07)	49-1189-79
$C_{14}H_{16}N_2O_3$			
1H-Indole, 7-methoxy-2,3-dimethyl-6-(2-nitro-1-propenyl)-	MeOH	231(4.55),272(4.11), 435(3.93)	103-0276-79
1,4-Naphthalenedione, 5-amino-x-(butylamino)-8-hydroxy-	benzene	526(3.95),558(3.86)	138-0627-79
$C_{14}H_{16}N_2O_3S$			
Thieno[2,3-b]pyridine-2-carboxylic acid, 3-(acetylamino)-4,6-dimethyl-, ethyl ester	EtOH	238(4.24),298(4.23)	103-1074-79
$C_{14}H_{16}N_2O_4S$			
Benzenamine, N,N-dimethyl-4-[(3-methyl-4-nitro-2(5H)-thienylidene)methyl]-	HOAc	490(4.6)	104-0164-79
$C_{14}H_{16}N_2O_6S$			
2,4(1H,3H)-Pyrimidinedione, 1-[2-hydroxy-3-[[(4-methylphenyl)sulfonyl]-oxy]propyl]-	n.s.g.	218(3.66),262(4.04)	128-0281-79
$C_{14}H_{16}N_4$			
2-Tetrazene, 1,4-dimethyl-1,4-diphenyl-	MeCN	345(4.43)	40-0915-79
$C_{14}H_{16}N_4O_2$			
Pyrimido[4,5-b]quinoline-2,4(1H,3H)-dione, 8-amino-5,10-dihydro-3,7,10-trimethyl-	pH 11	233(4.18),317(4.08)	5-1802-79
	MeOH	232(4.53),262s(4.16), 321(4.06)	5-1802-79
$C_{14}H_{16}N_4O_2S$			
5-Pyrimidinecarbothioamide, 6-amino-1,2,3,4-tetrahydro-1,3-dimethyl-2,4-dioxo-N-(phenylmethyl)-	EtOH	259(4.43),302(4.30)	95-0515-79
$C_{14}H_{16}N_4O_3$			
Pyrido[2,3-d]pyrimidine-6-carboxaldehyde, 8-ethyl-7,8-dihydro-5-hydroxy-7-oxo-2-(1-pyrrolidinyl)-	EtOH	238(4.40),281(4.26), 314s(4.13),330s(4.13), 348s(4.20),374(4.32)	4-1169-79
$C_{14}H_{16}N_4O_4$			
2,6(1H,3H)-Pyridinedione, 3-[1,6-dihydro-1-methyl-5-(methylamino)-2,6-dioxo-3(2H)-pyridinylidene]-1-methyl-5-(methylamino)-	$CHCl_3$	280(4.09),624(4.40)	118-0948-79
$C_{14}H_{16}N_4O_4S_2$			
5-Thiazolecarboxylic acid, 2,2'-azobis-[4-methyl-, diethyl ester	MeCN	217(3.84),298(3.59), 443(3.92)	4-0413-79
$C_{14}H_{16}N_4O_7$			
Inosine, 2',5'-diacetate	EtOH	244(4.03),250s(3.99), 274s(3.45)	39-2088-79C

Compound	Solvent	$\lambda_{max}(\log \epsilon)$	Ref.
$C_{14}H_{16}N_6O_5$			
1H-Purine-2,6-dione, 7-[3-(3,4-dihydro-2,4-dioxo-1(2H)-pyrimidinyl)-2-hydroxypropyl]-3,7-dihydro-1,3-dimethyl-	H_2O	270(4.13)	126-2303-79
$C_{14}H_{16}O$			
2H-Benz[e]inden-3-ol, 3,3a,4,5-tetrahydro-3a-methyl-, (3S-cis)-	EtOH	260(4.03),289(3.26), 300(3.15)	39-1322-79C
3H-Benzo[3',4']cyclobuta[1',2':1,8]cyclooct[1,2-b]oxirene, 1a,2,4,5,6,6a-hexahydro-, (1aα,6aβ,10bS*)-	MeOH	263(3.21),270(3.39), 276(3.37)	111-0543-79
2-Cyclohexen-1-one, 5,5-dimethyl-3-phenyl-	$CHCl_3$	220(3.92),282(4.19)	94-0676-79
Ethanone, 1-(6-phenyl-2-cyclohexen-1-yl)-	isooctane	248(2.35),253(2.42), 259(2.24),264(2.30), 268(2.18)	101-0027-79K
6,10-Methano-5H-benzocyclononen-12-one, 6,7,8,9,10,11-hexahydro-	EtOH	212(3.9),258(1.67), 264(1.77),272(1.8)	56-1221-79
9(1H)-Phenanthrenone, 2,3,4,4a,10,10a-hexahydro-	EtOH	250(3.98),292(3.22)	56-2021-79
$C_{14}H_{16}O_2$			
1,3-Cyclohexanedione, 2-methyl-2-(4-methylphenyl)-	MeOH	233(3.62),267(2.80), 275(2.75)	12-1561-79
1,2-Cyclopentanedione, 3,3,5-trimethyl-5-phenyl-	C_6H_{12}	495(1.75),505(1.76), 527(1.72)	137-0147-79
Methanone, (3,4-dihydro-2,5-dimethyl-2H-pyran-2-yl)phenyl-	C_6H_{12}	210(3.88),243(4.07), 275(3.08)	54-0346-79
$C_{14}H_{16}O_3$			
2H-1-Benzopyran-2-one, 7-hydroxy-8-(3-methylbutyl)-	EtOH	258(3.64),260(3.66), 320(4.19)	2-0113-79A
	EtOH-NaOH	257(3.68),327(4.20)	2-0113-79A
1,3-Cyclohexanedione, 2-(4-methoxyphenyl)-2-methyl-	MeOH	227(3.95),242(3.61), 278s(3.34),285(3.28)	12-1561-79
Ethanone, 1-(8-methoxy-2,2-dimethyl-2H-1-benzopyran-6-yl)-	MeOH	225(3.31),302(3.90)	18-1203-79
2H-Furo[2,3-h]-1-benzopyran-3-ol, 3,4-dihydro-8-(1-methylethyl)-	EtOH	219(4.45),254(4.25), 261(4.30),283(3.45), 293(3.38)	2-0011-79B
Naphthalene, 1,2,3-trimethoxy-8-methyl-	EtOH	236(4.78),282(3.34)	150-0301-79
Resorcinol, 5-benzyloxymethyldihydro-	EtOH	281.0(4.42)	83-0240-79
$C_{14}H_{16}O_3S$			
2-Cyclohexen-1-one, 5,5-dimethyl-3-(phenylsulfonyl)-	EtOH	238(4.08)	94-0676-79
$C_{14}H_{16}O_4$			
Ethanone, 1-(5-hydroxy-8-methoxy-2,2-dimethyl-2H-1-benzopyran-6-yl)-	MeOH	255(4.31),320(3.31), 340(3.74)	18-1203-79
Ethanone, 1-(7-hydroxy-8-methoxy-2,2-dimethyl-2H-1-benzopyran-6-yl)-	MeOH	242(3.2),292(3.1)	18-1203-79
Ethanone, 1-[2-hydroxy-5-methoxy-4-(1,1-dimethyl-2-propynyloxy)phenyl]-	MeOH	281(4.2),302(3.9)	18-1203-79
2-Naphthaleneacetaldehyde, 1,2,3,4-tetrahydro-5,7-dimethoxy-4-oxo-, (±)-	MeOH	218(4.21),227(4.26), 232s(4.24),274(4.22), 305(3.88)	35-2171-79
2-Naphthalenol, 5,6,7-trimethoxy-4-methyl-	EtOH	241(4.72),287(3.75), 338(3.31)	150-0301-79
3,4-Pentadien-2-one, 1-(3,4,5-trimethoxyphenyl)-	EtOH	212(4.39),222(4.23)	150-0301-79

Compound	Solvent	λ_{max}(log ε)	Ref.
$C_{14}H_{16}O_5$			
Benzenepropanoic acid, α-(3-hydroxy-2-oxopropyl)-β-oxo-, ethyl ester, (±)-	EtOH	210(4.24),249(4.28)	136-0055-79B
1,4-Epoxynaphthalene-5,8-dione, 1,4,4a,8a-tetrahydro-2,3-dimethoxy-6,7-dimethyl-, (1α,4α,4aβ,8aβ)-	EtOH	250(4.18),335(2.26)	33-2211-79
1,3-Isobenzofurandione, 4-butyl-5,7-dimethoxy-	MeOH	226(4.40),247(4.40), 346(3.90)	39-0807-79C
2-Naphthalenecarboxylic acid, 1,2,3,4-tetrahydro-5,7-dimethoxy-4-oxo-, methyl ester	MeOH	220(4.17),228(4.22), 233s(4.21),276(4.20), 308(3.87)	35-2171-79
$C_{14}H_{16}O_6$			
2-Oxaspiro[4.5]deca-6,9-diene-3-carboxylic acid, 3-ethoxy-1,8-dioxo-, ethyl ester	MeOH	229(3.9)	24-1571-79
$C_{14}H_{16}O_7$			
1,4-Epoxynaphthalene-5,8-dione, 1,2,3,4-tetrahydro-2,2,3,3-tetramethoxy-	EtOH	246(3.84),365(2.70)	33-2211-79
$C_{14}H_{16}O_9$			
Pyrano[3,2-c][2]benzopyran-6(2H)-one, 3,4,4a,10b-tetrahydro-3,4,8,10-tetrahydroxy-2-(hydroxymethyl)-9-methoxy-(bergenin)	EtOH	277(3.98)	39-2313-79C
$C_{14}H_{17}ClN_2S$			
Benzenamine, 4-chloro-N-(4-ethyl-3,4-dimethyl-5-methylene-2-thiazolidinylidene)-	EtOH	202(3.51),236(3.34)	103-0611-79
$C_{14}H_{17}NO$			
Benzamide, N-1,3-butadienyl-N-(1-methylethyl)-	MeOH	254(4.14)	88-0981-79
Cyclohept[b]indol-6-ol, 5,6,7,8,9,10-hexahydro-5-methyl-	EtOH	207(4.50),229(4.74), 282s(3.97),290(3.99), 294(3.99)	39-2154-79C
Ethanone, 2-(4,4-dimethyl-2-pyrrolidinylidene)-1-phenyl-, (Z)-	MeOH	204(4.12),242(3.95), 326(4.31)	83-0498-79
1H-Isoindol-1-one, 2,3-dihydro-4,5-dimethyl-3-(2-methylpropylidene)-	EtOH	224(4.36),230(4.39), 264(4.20),314(3.89), 323s(3.85)	33-1501-79
	EtOH	224(4.46),230(4.49), 264(4.34),313(4.04), 323s(4.00)	33-1525-79
1H-Isoindol-1-one, 2,3-dihydro-6,7-dimethyl-3-(2-methylpropylidene)-	EtOH	218(4.36),224(4.36), 230s(4.28),267(4.25), 320(4.09),330s(4.01)	33-1525-79
2-Propanone, 1-(1,3-dihydro-1,3,3-tri-	pH 1	287(3.72)	88-4407-79
methyl-2H-indol-2-ylidene)-	H_2O	360(4.42)	88-4407-79
2(1H)-Pyridinone, 5-ethyl-5,6-dihydro-1-(phenylmethyl)-	EtOH	253.5(3.49)	94-1847-79
$C_{14}H_{17}NO_2$			
Acetic acid, cyano(octahydro-2,5-methanopentalen-7-ylidene)-, ethyl ester	hexane	240(4.24)	142-0343-79
1,8(2H,5H)-Acridinedione, 3,4,6,7,9,10-hexahydro-9-methyl-	H_2O	251(4.39),381(3.99)	39-1593-79C
1,8(2H,5H)-Acridinedione, 3,4,6,7,9,10-hexahydro-10-methyl-	H_2O	254(4.31),274(4.06), 406(3.86)	39-1593-79C

Compound	Solvent	$\lambda_{max}(\log \epsilon)$	Ref.
6-Quinolinol, 1,2-dihydro-2,2,4-trimethyl-, acetate	n.s.g.	234(4.50),277(3.43), 352(3.44)	39-0488-79C
$C_{14}H_{17}NO_3$			
2H-Furo[2,3-b]indol-2-one, 5-ethoxy-3,3a,8,8a-tetrahydro-3a,8-dimethyl-	MeOH-HCl	247(3.78),322(3.80)	5-0927-79
	aq MeOH	246(4.00),315(3.52)	5-0927-79
Spiro[cyclohexane-1,3'(5'H)-quinoline]-2,5',6-trione, 1',2',4',6',7',8'-hexahydro-	pH 1	291(4.24)	39-1593-79C
	H_2O	299(4.37)	39-1593-79C
	pH 13	303(4.41)	39-1593-79C
$C_{14}H_{17}NO_4$			
Acetamide, N-[2-acetyl-4-(acetoxymethyl)-6-methylphenyl]-	EtOH	225(4.25),234s(3.77), 292(3.18)	33-0271-79
L-Glutamic acid, N-(phenylmethylene)-, dimethyl ester	EtOH	249(4.25),277s(--), 287s(--)	44-2732-79
Propanedioic acid, [(phenylamino)methylene]-, diethyl ester	hexane	217(3.69),320(4.41)	131-0077-79D
	EtOH	319(4.44)	131-0077-79D
$C_{14}H_{17}NO_5$			
1,3,6-Cycloheptatriene-1-carboxylic acid, 6-[(3-methoxy-3-oxopropyl)-methylamino]-5-oxo-, methyl ester	EtOH	210(4.00),265(4.00), 284(3.97),352(3.81), 445(3.71)	39-2528-79C
$C_{14}H_{17}NO_6$			
1,3-Benzenedicarboxylic acid, 2-hydroxy-4,6-dimethyl-5-nitroso-, diethyl ester	DMF	680(1.86)	104-0311-79
$C_{14}H_{17}NO_7$			
1H-Pyrrole-3-propanoic acid, 2-formyl-5-(methoxycarbonyl)-4-(2-methoxy-2-oxoethyl)-, methyl ester	n.s.g.	235(4.04),301(4.21)	39-1927-79C
$C_{14}H_{17}NS_2$			
Cyclohexanecarbodithioic acid, 2-[(4-methylphenyl)imino]-	EtOH	242(4.84),315(4.71), 398(5.04)	150-1732-79
$C_{14}H_{17}NSe$			
3-Indolizinecarboselenoaldehyde, 2-(1,1-dimethylethyl)-1-methyl-	C_6H_{12}	239(4.34),269s(3.94), 277(4.01),325s(3.90), 336(4.06),478s(4.51), 485(4.57),610s(2.07), 652(2.41),706(2.68)	39-2334-79C
3-Indolizinecarboselenoaldehyde, 2-(1,1-dimethylethyl)-7-methyl-	C_6H_{12}	237(4.40),263(3.89), 271(3.91),327(4.03), 350s(3.56),370(3.40), 471s(4.58),477(4.60), 637(2.46),691(2.71)	39-2334-79C
$C_{14}H_{17}N_2O_5PS$			
Phosphorothioic acid, O-[1,6-dihydro-5-methoxy-6-oxo-1-(phenylmethyl)-4-pyridazinyl] O,O-dimethyl ester	MeOH	213(4.37),288(3.80)	73-1761-79
$C_{14}H_{17}N_3$			
Pyrimido[1',2':1,2]pyrido[3,4-b]indole, 1,2,3,4,6,7,12,12b-octahydro-, (±)-	EtOH	229(4.43),282(3.85)	114-0043-79A
$C_{14}H_{17}N_3OS$			
2-Butanone, 1-[(3-amino-2-quinoxalinyl)-thio]-3,3-dimethyl-	EtOH	359(4.0),375s(3.9)	103-0102-79

Compound	Solvent	λ_{max}(log ε)	Ref.
$C_{14}H_{17}N_3O_2$			
8-Azabicyclo[3.2.1]oct-3-en-2-one, 8-(4,6-dimethyl-2-pyrimidinyl)-6-(hydroxymethyl)-, exo	$CHCl_3$	251(6.10),295(5.49)	39-1525-79C
3,5-Methanofuro[3,2-b]pyridin-6(2H)-one, 4-(4,6-dimethyl-2-pyrimidinyl)hexahydro-	$CHCl_3$	250(4.10),293(3.50)	39-1525-79C
Propanamide, N-methyl-N-[2-(5-phenyl-1,2,4-oxadiazol-3-yl)ethyl]-	EtOH	251(4.22)	150-0801-79
$C_{14}H_{17}N_3O_4S$			
2(1H)-Quinazolinethione, 3,4-dihydro-4-imino-3-methyl-1-β-D-ribopyranosyl-	MeOH	206(4.14),222(4.14), 241(4.17),281(4.34)	44-0173-79
3-Thiophenecarboxylic acid, 2-[(1-cyano-2-ethoxy-2-oxoethylidene)hydrazino]-5-ethyl-, ethyl ester	MeOH	209(4.28),238(3.94), 256(3.99),410(4.26)	83-0726-79
$C_{14}H_{17}N_3O_9$			
1H-Imidazole, 4-nitro-1-(2,3,5-tri-O-acetyl-β-D-ribofuranosyl)-	n.s.g.	283(3.89)	111-0123-79
1H-Imidazole, 5-nitro-1-(2,3,5-tri-O-acetyl-β-D-ribofuranosyl)-	n.s.g.	293(3.94)	111-0123-79
1H-Pyrazole, 3-nitro-1-(2,3,5-tri-O-acetyl-β-D-ribofuranosyl)-	n.s.g.	261(3.91)	111-0123-79
1H-Pyrazole, 5-nitro-1-(2,3,5-tri-O-acetyl-β-D-ribofuranosyl)-	n.s.g.	272(3.86)	111-0123-79
$C_{14}H_{17}N_5O_2$			
Pyrido[2,3-d]pyrimidine-6-carboxaldehyde, 7-amino-8-ethyl-5,8-dihydro-5-oxo-2-(1-pyrrolidinyl)-	EtOH	223(4.32),237(4.42), 283(4.41),296s(4.39), 315(4.41)	4-1169-79
$C_{14}H_{17}N_5O_6$			
Adenosine, 3',5'-diacetate	EtOH	259(4.13)	39-2088-79C
9H-Purin-6-amine, 9-(3,5-di-O-acetyl-β-D-arabinofuranosyl)-	MeOH	258(4.19)	87-0273-79
$C_{14}H_{17}N_5O_8$			
1(2H)-Pyrimidineacetic acid, 3-[5-azido-3-O-(carboxymethyl)-2,5-dideoxy-β-D-erythro-pentofuranosyl]-3,6-dihydro-5-methyl-2,6-dioxo-	pH 5	268(3.92)	39-1389-79C
	pH 13	268(3.92)	39-1389-79C
$C_{14}H_{18}$			
Bicyclo[2.2.1]heptane, 2-(2-methylphenyl)-	EtOH	210(3.85),260(2.85)	70-0854-79
Phenanthrene, 1,2,3,4,4a,9,10,10a-octahydro-, trans	EtOH	204(4.05),267(2.69), 274(2.71)	56-2021-79
Phenanthrene, 1,2,3,4,5,6,7,8-octahydro-	EtOH	206(4.42),270(2.59), 279(2.48)	56-2021-79
$C_{14}H_{18}BrNO_5$			
α-D-galacto-Oct-6-enopyranurononitrile, 7-bromo-6,7-dideoxy-1,2:3,4-bis-O-(1-methylethylidene)-	EtOH	224(3.83)	33-1632-79
$C_{14}H_{18}BrN_{11}$			
1H-Pyrazol-5-amine, 4-[(4-bromo-5-methyl-1H-pyrazol-3-yl)azo]-5-methyl-1H-pyrazol-3-yl]azo]-1-ethyl-3-methyl-	MeOH	340(4.09),470(4.06)	103-0657-79

Compound	Solvent	$\lambda_{max}(\log \epsilon)$	Ref.
$C_{14}H_{18}ClNO$			
9H-Pyrrolo[2,1-b][1,3]benzoxazine, 5-chloro-1,2,3,3a-tetrahydro-6,8,9-trimethyl-	EtOH	277(3.31),286(3.38)	44-4005-79
$C_{14}H_{18}N_2O$			
2,2'-Dipyrromethene, 5'-oxo-3',4'-diethyl-5-methyl-1',5'-dihydro-	MeOH	400(4.49)	78-0463-79
	$CHCl_3$	386(4.49)	78-0463-79
2,2'-Dipyrromethene, 5'-oxo-3'-ethyl-3,4',5-trimethyl-1',5'-dihydro-	MeOH	407(4.53)	78-0463-79
	$CHCl_3$	398(4.52)	78-0463-79
2,2'-Dipyrromethene, 5'-oxo-3'-ethyl-4,4',5-trimethyl-1',5'-dihydro-	MeOH	408(4.53)	78-0463-79
	$CHCl_3$	400(4.48)	78-0463-79
4-Piperidinone, 1-methyl-3-[(methylphenylamino)methylene]-	EtOH	235(3.61),332(4.14)	4-0177-79
$C_{14}H_{18}N_2O_2$			
Acetamide, N-[2-(5-methoxy-1-methyl-1H-indol-3-yl)ethyl]-	MeOH	226(4.42),282(3.81), 304(3.70),315s(3.60)	87-0063-79
2-Propenoic acid, 3-(1-piperidinyl)-3-(2-pyridinyl)-, methyl ester	ether	212(4.48),270(4.37)	22-0559-79
2-Propenoic acid, 3-(2-pyridinyl)-3-(1-pyrrolidinyl)-, ethyl ester	ether	265(4.12)	22-0559-79
Pyrrolo[2,3-b]indol-2(1H)-one, 3,3a,8,8a-tetrahydro-1-(2-hydroxyethyl)-3a,8-dimethyl-	MeOH	248(3.91),300(3.38)	5-0927-79
Pyrrolo[2.3-b]indol-2(1H)-one, 3,3a,8,8a-tetrahydro-5-methoxy-1,3a,8-trimethyl-	MeOH-H_2O	247(3.98),317(3.46)	5-0927-79
$C_{14}H_{18}N_2O_3$			
4,7-Methano-8H-pyrazolo[1,5-a]azepine-2-carboxylic acid, 4,5,6,7-tetrahydro-7,10,10-trimethyl-8-oxo-, (4S)-	EtOH	255(3.80)	95-0705-79
Quinoline, 6-ethoxy-1,2-dihydro-2,2,4-trimethyl-8-nitro-	MeOH	228(4.45),318(3.89), 494(4.09)	39-0488-79C
$C_{14}H_{18}N_2O_4$			
1H-Azepine-3,6-dicarboxylic acid, 4-cyano-4,5-dihydro-2,5,7-trimethyl-, dimethyl ester	n.s.g.	229(4.16),326(4.21)	23-0044-79
2,4(1H,3H)-Pyrimidinedione, 6-[2-(4,4-dimethyl-2,6-dioxocyclohexyl)ethyl]-	MeOH	265(4.30)	4-0239-79
$C_{14}H_{18}N_2O_4S$			
3,5-Pyridinedicarboxylic acid, 1,4-dihydro-2,6-dimethyl-4-(1-thiocyanatoethyl)-, dimethyl ester	n.s.g.	233(4.24),341(3.83)	23-0044-79
$C_{14}H_{18}N_2O_5$			
1,2-Hydrazinedicarboxylic acid, 1-(1,1-dimethyl-2-oxo-2-phenylethyl)-, dimethyl ester	n.s.g.	245(3.97),280(3.00), 312(2.04)	104-2203-79
2-Pentanone, 4-[[2-hydroxy-1-(hydroxymethyl)-2-(4-nitrophenyl)ethyl]imino]-, [R-(R*,R*)]-	MeOH	274(4.10),312(4.30)	94-1245-79
3,5-Pyridinedicarboxylic acid, 1,4-dihydro-4-(1-methyl-2-oxo-3-pyrrolidinyl)-, dimethyl ester	EtOH	279(4.22),285(3.67)	44-4332-79

Compound	Solvent	λmax(log ε)	Ref.
$C_{14}H_{18}N_2O_6$			
2H-Pyrrol-2-one, 1,5-dihydro-1-[[4-hydroxy-4-(methoxymethyl)-1-methyl-5-oxo-2-pyrrolidinylidene]acetyl]-4-methoxy-, (E)-(±)-	MeOH	224(4.05),287(4.40)	88-2003-79
$C_{14}H_{18}N_2O_7$			
Uridine, 5-acetyl-2',3'-O-(1-methylethylidene)-	EtOH-acid	227(4.01),285(4.07)	78-1125-79
	EtOH-base	285(3.99)	78-1125-79
$C_{14}H_{18}N_2O_7S$			
2H-Imidazole-2-thione, 1,3-dihydro-1-(2,3,5-tri-O-acetyl-β-D-ribofuranosyl)-	EtOH	266(4.19)	4-1185-79
	$CHCl_3$	276(4.07)	4-1185-79
$C_{14}H_{18}N_2S$			
Benzenamine, N-(4-ethyl-3,4-dimethyl-5-methylene-2-thiazolidinylidene)-	EtOH	206(3.60),240(3.20)	103-0611-79
Benzenamine, N-(4-ethyl-4-methyl-5-methylene-2-thiazolidinylidene)-4-methyl-	EtOH	205(3.38),235(3.28)	103-0611-79
Benzenemethanamine, N-(4-ethyl-4-methyl-5-methylene-2-thiazolidinylidene)-	EtOH	205(3.29)	103-0611-79
Benzenemethanamine, N-(3,4,4-trimethyl-5-methylene-2-thiazolidinylidene)-	EtOH	225(3.30)	103-0611-79
2-Thiazolamine, 4-ethyl-4,5-dihydro-4-methyl-5-methylene-N-(phenylmethyl)-	EtOH	204(3.40),228(3.20), 269(3.10)	103-0611-79
Thieno[2,3-b]quinolin-4-amine, 5,6,7,8-tetrahydro-N,N,2-trimethyl-	EtOH	230(4.29),250(4.31), 306(3.96)	1-0313-79
$C_{14}H_{18}N_2S_2$			
Cyclohexanimine, 2,2'-(1,3-dithietane-2,4-diylidene)bis-	EtOH	228s(3.83),262(3.74), 306(4.21),360(4.15), 470s(4.31),494(4.35)	150-1732-79
$C_{14}H_{18}N_2S_3$			
Cyclohexanimine, 2,2'-(1,2,4-trithiolane-3,5-diylidene)bis-	EtOH	235(3.85),272(3.80), 311(3.73),392(4.47)	150-1732-79
Isothiazolo[2,3,4-ij]quinazoline-2,6-dithione	EtOH	239(3.29),270s(3.37), 277(3.41),340(3.18), 406s(4.12),416(4.13)	150-0410-79S
$C_{14}H_{18}N_3$			
4,7-Methano-1H-benzotriazolium, 3a,4,5,6,7,7a-hexahydro-1-methyl-3-phenyl-, tetrafluoroborate	MeOH	332(4.02)	24-0445-79
$C_{14}H_{18}N_3OS$			
Isoxazolium, 2-ethyl-3-methyl-4-[(4-methylphenyl)azo]-5-(methylthio)-, tetrafluoroborate	HOAc	296(4.20),357(3.96), 372(3.94),427s(3.29)	97-0446-79
1,3,4-Thiadiazolo[2,3-b]benzimidazolium, 2-butyl-9-ethyl-6-hydroxy-, bromide	EtOH	270(3.83),495(3.95)	18-2033-79
1,3,4-Thiadiazolo[2,3-b]benzimidazolium, 9-ethyl-6-hydroxy-2-(2-methylpropyl)-, bromide	EtOH	265(3.93),525(3.97)	18-2033-79
$C_{14}H_{18}N_4O_3S$			
1H-Imidazole-4-carbonitrile, 5-amino-3-(1-methylethyl)-, tosylate	MeOH	223(4.19),264(3.99)	44-1273-79

Compound	Solvent	$\lambda_{max}(\log \epsilon)$	Ref.
1H-Imidazole-4-carbonitrile, 5-[(1-methylethyl)amino]-, tosylate	MeOH	223(4.16),255(4.02)	44-1273-79
$C_{14}H_{18}N_4O_6$			
Butanedioic acid, [(1,2,3,6-tetrahydro-1,3-dimethyl-2,6-dioxo-7H-purin-7-yl)methyl]-, dimethyl ester	MeOH	273(3.86)	126-0325-79
$C_{14}H_{18}N_4S$			
Pyrido[2,3-d]pyrimidin-4-amine, N-cyclohexyl-2-(methylthio)-	H_2O	225(4.21),269(4.29), 340(4.02)	102-1265-79
	0.2M HCl	227(4.23),265(4.14), 292(4.12),326(4.20), 340(4.18)	102-1265-79
	0.2M NaOH	269(4.30),339(4.01)	102-1265-79
$C_{14}H_{18}N_4S_2$			
1H-Indazole, 3,3'-dithiobis[4,5,6,7-tetrahydro-	EtOH	213(4.28),255(3.41)	150-1732-79
$C_{14}H_{18}N_6O_4S$			
Adenosine, 8-(aminothioxomethyl)-2',3'-O-(1-methylethylidene)-	H_2O	218(4.23),263s(4.05), 276(4.06),308s(4.03)	94-0183-79
$C_{14}H_{18}N_6O_5$			
Adenosine, 8-(aminocarbonyl)-2',3'-O-(1-methylethylidene)-	0.5M HCl	275(4.15)	94-0183-79
	H_2O	291(4.03)	94-0183-79
	0.5M NaOH	291(4.01)	94-0183-79
$C_{14}H_{18}O$			
1H-Benz[e]inden-3-ol, 2,3,3a,4,5,9b-hexahydro-3a-methyl-	EtOH	260(2.61),266(2.72), 273(2.69)	39-1322-79C
5H-Benzo[3,4]cyclobuta[1,2]cycloheptene, 4b,6,7,8,9,9a-hexahydro-4b-methoxy-, cis	MeOH	260(3.06),266(3.25), 273(3.22)	39-1395-79C
Benzo[3,4]cyclobuta[1,2]cycloocten-4b(5H)-ol, 6,7,8,9,10,10a-hexahydro-	MeOH	261(2.76),266(2.88), 273(2.86)	39-2542-79C
5H-Benzocyclononene, 6,7,8,9-tetrahydro-11-methoxy-	C_6H_{12}	240s(3.31)	39-1395-79C
6,10-Methano-5H-benzocyclononen-12-ol, 6,7,8,9,10,11-hexahydro-	MeOH	212(3.83),266(2.15), 274(2.17)	56-1221-79
1,10-Methanobenzocycloocten-10(5H)-ol, 6,7,8,9-tetrahydro-11-methyl-	MeOH	212(3.92),257(2.32), 261(2.38),263(2.42), 268(2.52),271(2.40)	56-1221-79
Phenol, 2-cyclooctenyl-	EtOH	220(3.72),252(3.53), 279(3.12)	39-2027-79C
$C_{14}H_{18}OS_2$			
2-Propanone, 1-[2-(phenylmethyl)-1,3-dithian-2-yl]-	EtOH	204(4.02)	150-0301-79
$C_{14}H_{18}O_2$			
2H-1-Benzopyran, 6-ethyl-7-methoxy-2,2-dimethyl-	$CHCl_3$	240(4.18),280s(3.82), 290(3.83),311(3.89), 324(3.85)	44-1429-79
Spiro[5.5]undeca-7,10-diene-2,9-dione, 1,5,5-trimethyl-, (±)-	EtOH	241(4.23)	94-0274-79
$C_{14}H_{18}O_3$			
Benzenepropanal, α,α-diethyl-3-methoxy-β-oxo-	MeOH	219(4.29),252(3.84), 305(3.36)	5-0617-79

Compound	Solvent	λ_{max}(log ε)	Ref.
5-Benzofuranpropanol, 4-hydroxy-2-(1-methylethyl)-	EtOH	219(4.45),251(4.18), 259(4.20),285(3.42)	2-0011-79B
Benzoic acid, 2,3-dimethyl-6-(3-methyl-1-oxobutyl)-	EtOH	213(4.33),238(3.91), 288(3.40),293(3.40)	33-1525-79
Benzoic acid, 3,4-dimethyl-2-(3-methyl-1-oxobutyl)-	EtOH	212(4.31),244(4.06), 277(3.92),286(3.88)	33-1525-79
2H-1-Benzopyran-6-methanol, 7-methoxy-α,2,2-trimethyl-	EtOH	225(4.42),250(3.73), 276(3.67),284(3.68), 308(3.72)	118-0708-79
7H-3,9a-Epoxy-1-benzoxepin-7-one, 2,3,4,5-tetrahydro-3,6,8,9-tetramethyl-, [3S-(3R*,9aS*)]-	EtOH	236(4.17),293(3.18)	35-6710-79
1H-Inden-1-one, 2,3-dihydro-6-(2-hydroxyethyl)-5-(hydroxymethyl)-2,7-dimethyl-, (S)- (pterosin P)	EtOH	218(4.46),258(4.31), 302(3.69)	94-0592-79
$C_{14}H_{18}O_3Se$			
Butanoic acid, 2-acetyl-2-(phenylseleno)-, ethyl ester	EtOH	229(3.27),300(2.83)	33-2630-79
$C_{14}H_{18}O_4$			
Benzeneethanol, 3,4,5-trimethoxy-α-2-propynyl-	EtOH	209(4.49),225s(3.91)	150-0301-79
Benzeneheptanoic acid, 4-methoxy-γ-oxo-	MeOH	224(4.03)	44-0168-79
2H,8H-Benzo[1,2-b:3,4-b']dipyran, 3,4,9,10-tetrahydro-3,9-dihydroxy-8,8-dimethyl-			
4,7-Benzofurandione, 2,3-dihydro-6-(2-hydroxypropyl)-2,2,3-trimethyl-, [R-(R*,R*)]-	EtOH	272(4.21)	33-1129-79
4-Benzofuranol, 5-(2,3-dihydroxypropyl)-2-(1-methylethyl)-	EtOH	218(4.45),252(4.53), 258(4.16),284(3.39), 292(3.32)	2-0011-79B
Benzoic acid, 3-methoxy-5-[(3-methyl-2-butenyl)oxy]-, methyl ester	EtOH	215(4.30),252(3.74), 306(3.47)	150-0301-79
3-Buten-1-ol, 4-(3,4-dimethoxyphenyl)-, acetate, (E)-	MeOH	220(4.45),264(4.40), 301(3.95)	12-0071-79
2,5-Cyclohexadiene-1,4-dione, 2,3-dimethoxy-5-methyl-6-(3-methyl-2-butenyl)-	DMF	422(3.92)	104-1621-79
2(1H)-Naphthalenone, 3,4-dihydro-5,6,7-trimethoxy-4-methyl-	EtOH	209(4.37),274(3.79)	150-0301-79
3-Penten-2-one, 1-(3,4,5-trimethoxyphenyl)-	EtOH	208(4.21),222s(4.01), 273(3.20)	150-0301-79
4-Penten-2-one, 1-(3,4,5-trimethoxyphenyl)-	EtOH	210(4.42),275(3.22)	150-0301-79
$C_{14}H_{18}O_5$			
Benzenepropanoic acid, 3-methoxy-2-(methoxycarbonyl)-β-methyl-, methyl ester	MeOH	280(3.43)	18-2962-79
1H,7H-Cyclopropa[c]benzofuran-4,7(3aH)-dione, 1a,2-dihydro-3a-hydroxy-5-(2-hydroxypropyl)-2,2-dimethyl- (gilmicolin)	EtOH	290(3.9)	33-1129-79
Parvulenone, O-methyl-	MeOH	223(4.09),286(4.02), 330s(3.51)	150-2685-79
2,3-Pentanedione, 1-(3,4,5-trimethoxyphenyl)-	EtOH	210(4.40),286(3.71)	150-0301-79
2,4-Pentanedione, 1-(3,4,5-trimethoxyphenyl)-	EtOH	210(4.33),277(3.96)	150-0301-79

Compound	Solvent	$\lambda_{max}(\log \epsilon)$	Ref.
$C_{14}H_{18}O_6$			
α-D-galacto-Octopyranos-6-ulose, 7,7,8,8-tetradehydro-7,8-dideoxy-1,2:3,4-bis-O-(1-methylethylidene)-	MeOH	212(3.69)	136-0151-79H
2-Oxaspiro[4.5]dec-6-ene-3-carboxylic acid, 3-ethoxy-1,8-dioxo-, ethyl ester, cis	MeOH	220(3.9)	24-1550-79
trans	MeOH	219(3.8),233s(3.1)	24-1550-79
$C_{14}H_{18}O_7$			
1,4-Epoxynaphthalene-5,8-diol, 1,2,3,4-tetrahydro-2,2,3,3-tetramethoxy-	ether	295(3.55)	33-2211-79
3-Furanpentanoic acid, 2,5-dihydro-4-methoxy-5-(2-methoxy-2-oxoethylidene)-2-oxo-, methyl ester, (E)-	EtOH	266(4.06)	130-0311-79
$C_{14}H_{19}IN_4O_7$			
Uridine, 2'-deoxy-5-[[3-[(iodoacetyl)-amino]-1-oxopropyl]amino]-	H_2O	278(3.91)	87-0621-79
$C_{14}H_{19}N$			
2H-Pyrrole, 4-butyl-3,4-dihydro-5-phenyl-	MeOH	207(4.14),241(4.08)	83-0498-79
2H-Pyrrole, 3,4-dihydro-3,3-dimethyl-5-(2-phenylethyl)-	MeOH	208(3.90)	83-0498-79
$C_{14}H_{19}NO$			
1H-Isoindol-1-one, 2,3-dihydro-4,5-dimethyl-3-(2-methylpropyl)-	EtOH	208(4.56),237(4.09), 275(3.25),284(3.17)	33-1501-79
	EtOH	214s(4.47),237(4.16), 275(3.38),284(3.30)	33-1525-79
1H-Isoindol-1-one, 2,3-dihydro-6,7-dimethyl-3-(2-methylpropyl)-	EtOH	214s(4.47),223(4.23), 232s(4.10),282(3.51), 290(3.51)	33-1525-79
2H-Pyrrole-5-ethanol, 3,4-dihydro-3,3-dimethyl-α-phenyl-	MeOH	206(3.99),282(3.60)	83-0498-79
Pyrrolo[2,1-b]oxazole, 7a-(2,5-dimethylphenyl)hexahydro-	EtOH	248(3.54)	145-0983-79
Pyrrolo[2,1-b]oxazole, 7a-(4-ethylphenyl)hexahydro-	EtOH	258(3.66)	145-0983-79
$C_{14}H_{19}NO_4S$			
D-Ribitol, 1,4-anhydro-2,3-O-(1-methylethylidene)-1-C-[2-(methylthio)-3-pyridinyl]-, α-	EtOH	249(3.85),290(3.57)	44-1892-79
β-	EtOH	250(3.90),292(3.57)	44-1892-79
D-Ribitol, 1,4-anhydro-2,3-O-(1-methylethylidene)-1-C-[4-(methylthio)-3-pyridinyl]-, β-	EtOH	264(4.04)	44-1892-79
D-Ribitol, 1,4-anhydro-2,3-O-(1-methylethylidene)-1-C-[6-(methylthio)-3-pyridinyl]-, α-	EtOH	254(3.96),295(3.58)	44-1892-79
β-	EtOH	254(3.95),296(3.58)	44-1892-79
$C_{14}H_{19}NO_5$			
2-Azabicyclo[2.2.2]oct-5-ene-2-carboxylic acid, 7-(1,3-dimethoxy-3-oxo-1-propenyl)-, methyl ester, [1α,4α-7R*(Z)]-	EtOH	245(3.93)	88-2485-79
2,5(1H)-Isoquinolinedicarboxylic acid, 4a,5,8,8a-tetrahydro-6-methoxy-, di-	CCl_4	266(3.11)	88-2485-79

Compound	Solvent	λ_{max}(log ε)	Ref.
methyl ester, (4aα,5β,8aα)- (cont.)			88-2485-79
α-D-galacto-Oct-6-enopyranurononitrile, 6,7-dideoxy-1,2:3,4-bis-O-(1-methylethylidene)-	EtOH	212(3.82)	33-1632-79
$C_{14}H_{19}NO_6$			
Propanedioic acid, 3-[(5-carboxy-1-methyl-1H-pyrrol-2-yl)propyl]-, 1,3-dimethyl ester	MeOH	226(4.11)	35-1259-79
$C_{14}H_{19}NO_8$			
Acetonitrile, [6-(β-D-glucopyranosyloxy)-4,5-dihydroxy-2-cyclohexen-1-ylidene)- (lithospermoside)	MeOH	259(4.18)	100-0500-79
Dasycarponin	MeOH	261(4.17)	100-0500-79
$C_{14}H_{19}NSi_2$			
Silanamine, 1-methyl-N-(methylphenylsilyl)-1-phenyl-	heptane	191.7(5.00)	65-1333-79
$C_{14}H_{19}N_3O_2$			
3,5-Methanofuro[3,2-b]pyridin-6-ol, 4-(4,6-dimethyl-2-pyrimidinyl)octahydro-	$CHCl_3$	256(4.08),306(3.52)	39-1525-79C
$C_{14}H_{19}N_3O_3$			
Tryptophan, N-acetyl-6-methyl-, ammonium salt, (R)-	EtOH	277(3.72),283(3.74), 294(3.68)	44-3741-79
$C_{14}H_{19}N_3O_4$			
Pyrido[2,3-c]pyridazine-1,2-dicarboxylic acid, 3,4-dihydro-7-methyl-, diethyl ester	EtOH	228(3.97),282(3.79)	78-2027-79
Pyrido[3,2-c]pyridazine-1,2-dicarboxylic acid, 3,4-dihydro-3-methyl-, diethyl ester	EtOH	233(4.04),280(3.67)	78-2027-79
Pyrido[4,3-c]pyridazine-1,2-dicarboxylic acid, 3,4-dihydro-7-methyl-, diethyl ester	EtOH	239(4.06),268(3.48), 277(3.38)	78-2027-79
$C_{14}H_{19}N_3O_5$			
DL-Glutamic acid, N-[[[4-(dimethylamino)phenyl]amino]carbonyl]-	pH 1	244(4.18),275s(2.89)	87-0869-79
L-isomer	EtOH	253(4.26),298(3.27)	87-0874-79
$C_{14}H_{19}N_3O_7$			
β-D-Ribofuranose, 5-deoxy-5-[4-(methoxycarbonyl)-1H-1,2,3-triazol-1-yl]-2,3-O-(1-methylethylidene)-, 1-acetate	MeOH	214(3.93)	44-1424-79
$C_{14}H_{19}N_5O_2$			
3H-Purine-3-butanoic acid, 6-[3-(3-methyl-2-butenyl)amino]-	50% MeOH	216(4.24),289(4.24)	24-3072-79
$C_{14}H_{19}N_5O_3$			
Hexanoic acid, 6-[(1,4-dihydro-6,7-dimethyl-4-oxo-2-pteridinyl)amino]-	pH -4.0	220(4.18),254(4.11), 340(3.94)	18-2933-79
	pH 0.25	219(4.29),253(4.06), 324(3.96),400(3.10)	18-2933-79
	pH 6.0	213(4.23),279(4.24), 350(3.85)	18-2933-79

Compound	Solvent	λmax(log ε)	Ref.
(cont.)	pH 10.5	260(4.31),366(3.91)	18-2933-79
$C_{14}H_{19}N_5O_4S$			
Adenosine, 2',3'-O-(1-methylethylidene)-8-(methylthio)-	M HCl	282(4.30)	94-0183-79
	H_2O	280(4.28)	94-0183-79
	M NaOH	279(4.28)	94-0183-79
$C_{14}H_{19}N_5O_5$			
9H-Purin-6-amine, 9-[3-O-(2-methyl-1-oxopropyl)-β-D-arabinofuranosyl]-	MeOH	258(4.15)	87-0273-79
$C_{14}H_{20}$			
Bicyclo[2.2.1]heptane, 2-(6-methylene-cyclohexen-1-yl)-	EtOH	240(2.92)	70-0854-79
Cyclopropane, [1-(2-propenyl)-2,4,6-octatrienyl]-	EtOH	261(4.49),269(4.57),279(4.45)	138-0931-79
$C_{14}H_{20}Cl_2N_2O_2$			
4-Cyclopentene-1,3-dione, 2-[bis(di-ethylamino)methylene]-4,5-dichloro-	isoPrOH	252(4.41),299(4.43)	104-0454-79
$C_{14}H_{20}Cl_3N_3O_2$			
Piperidine, 1,1'-(3,4,4-trichloro-2-nitro-1,3-butadienylidene)bis-	MeOH	365(4.00)	104-0981-79
$C_{14}H_{20}CrNaO_7$			
Sodium bis(1-hydroxycyclohexanecarbox-ylato)oxochromate	H_2O	250(3.78),350(3.11),520s(2.32),750(1.62),800(1.59)	35-3206-79
$C_{14}H_{20}NO_5P$			
Phosphoric acid, 3,6-dihydro-2-phenyl-2H-1,2-oxazin-4-yl diethyl ester	EtOH	240(3.90),282(2.93)	33-0442-79
$C_{14}H_{20}N_2O$			
Benzenamine, N-cyclohexyl-3,5-dimethyl-4-nitroso-	EtOH	407(4.57),685(1.81)	104-1437-79
Pyrrolo[2,3-b]indole, 1,2,3,3a,8,8a-hexahydro-5-methoxy-1,3a,8-trimethyl-	12M HCl	252(3.77),332(3.78)	5-0927-79
	MeOH	249(4.01),319(3.50)	5-0927-79
1H-Pyrrolo[2,3-b]quinoline, 2,3,3a,4-9,9a-hexahydro-6-methoxy-3a,9-di-methyl-, cis	EtOH	251(4.01),296(3.31)	39-2162-79C
	EtOH-HCl	230(4.90),235(3.87),286(3.85)	39-2162-79C
Quinoline, decahydro-1-(2-pyridinyl)-, N-oxide, monohydrochloride, (4aS-trans)-	MeOH	320(3.08)	4-0591-79
$C_{14}H_{20}N_2O_2$			
2-Cyclohexen-1-one, 3,3'-(dimethyl-hydrazo)bis-	MeOH	273(4.57),299(4.70)	24-3237-79
4(5H)-Isoxazolone, 5,5-dimethyl-3-(4-piperidino-1,3-butadienyl)-	ether	310(4.38),410(4.15)	78-0341-79
2-Pyridinepropanoic acid, β-1-pyrroli-dinyl-, ethyl ester	ether	260(3.81)	22-0559-79
$C_{14}H_{20}N_2O_4$			
1,4-Benzenedicarboxylic acid, 2,5-bis-(methylamino)-, diethyl ester	EtOH	478(3.77)	48-0905-79
	dioxan	487(3.76)	48-0905-79
	EtCOMe	481(3.70)	48-0905-79
	$CHCl_3$	485(3.78)	48-0905-79
	o-$C_6H_4Cl_2$	490(3.79)	48-0905-79

Compound	Solvent	λ_{max}(log ϵ)	Ref.
1,4-Benzenedicarboxylic acid, 2,5-bis-(methylamino)-, dimethyl ester (continued)	DMF	487(3.70)	48-0905-79
	DMSO	488(3.76+)	48-0905-79
	HCONMe2	478(--)	48-0905-79
$C_{14}H_{20}N_2O_5$			
2-Butenedioic acid, 2-[1,2-dimethyl-2-(3-oxo-1-cyclohexen-1-yl)hydrazino]-, dimethyl ester, (E)-	MeOH	291(4.54)	24-3237-79
$C_{14}H_{20}N_2O_6S$			
Thymidine, 5'-S-(3-carboxypropyl)-5'-thio-	H_2O	267(3.99)	87-0621-79
$C_{14}H_{20}N_2O_7S$			
Thymidine, 5'-[(3-carboxypropyl)sulfinyl]-5'-deoxy-	H_2O	267(3.99)	87-0621-79
$C_{14}H_{20}N_2O_8$			
1H-Imidazole-4-carboxylic acid, 2,3-dihydro-5-(hydroxymethyl)-1-[2,3-O-(1-methylethylidene)-β-D-ribofuranosyl]-2-oxo-, methyl ester	H_2O	270(4.08)	4-0411-79
$C_{14}H_{20}N_2S_2$			
Cyclobutenediylium, 1,3-dimercapto-2,4-di-1-piperidinyl-, dihydroxide, bis(inner salt)	CH_2Cl_2	284(3.96),350(4.20), 430(4.67),496s(2.57)	5-0595-79 24-0990-79
Spiro[cyclohexane-1,8'-[2H,8H]isothiazolo[4,3,2-ij]quinazolin]-2'-thione, 3',4',5',5'a,6',7'-hexahydro-	EtOH	263(4.02),366(4.58)	150-0410-79S
$C_{14}H_{20}N_3O_8P$			
Pentanoic acid, 2,3,3a,9a-tetrahydro-6-imino-2-[(phosphonooxy)methyl]-6H-furo[2',3':4,5]oxazolo[3,2-a]-pyrimidin-3-yl ester, [2R-(2α,3β,3aβ,9aβ)-	MeOH	235(3.85),264(3.89)	87-0639-79
$C_{14}H_{20}N_3S$			
4H-Imidazolium, 5-(dimethylamino)-4,4-dimethyl-2-(methylthio)-1-phenyl-, iodide	n.s.g.	242(4.39)	33-0160-79
$C_{14}H_{20}N_4$			
4,4'-Bipyridinium, 1,1'-bis(dimethylamino)-, diperchlorate	MeCN	258(4.32)	5-0727-79
$C_{14}H_{20}N_4O_2S_2$			
Cyclobuta[1,2-d:3,4-d']dipyrimidine-4,8(1H,4aH)-dione, 4b,8b-diethyl-4b,5,8a,8b-tetrahydro-2,6-bis-(methylthio)-	pH 13	242(4.04)	56-0529-79
$C_{14}H_{20}N_4O_4S$			
Uridine, 5'-[[2-amino-4-(methylthio)-1-oxo-2',3'-didehydro-2',3',5'-trideoxy-	H_2O	262(3.99)	136-0113-79F
$C_{14}H_{20}N_4O_7$			
Uridine, 5-[[3-(acetylamino)-1-oxopropyl]amino]-2'-deoxy-	n.s.g.	281(3.91)	87-1524-79

Compound	Solvent	λmax(log ε)	Ref.
$C_{14}H_{20}N_4O_8S$			
1H-Purine-2,6-dione, 7-(6-deoxy-4-O-(methylsulfonyl)-α-L-manno-pyranosyl]-3,7-dihydro-1,3-dimethyl-	MeOH	274(3.91)	39-2682-79C
$C_{14}H_{20}N_6O_2$			
Hexanamide, 6-[(1,4-dihydro-6,7-dimethyl-9-oxo-2-pteridinyl)amino]-	pH -4.0	220(4.21),254(4.13), 340(3.97)	18-2933-79
	pH 0.25	219(4.32),252(4.09), 324(3.98),400(3.13)	18-2933-79
	pH 6.0	223(4.26),279(4.26), 350(3.87)	18-2933-79
	pH 10.5	260(4.34),365(3.94)	18-2933-79
3H-Purine-3-butanoic acid, α-amino-6-[(3-methyl-2-butenyl)amino]-, (S)-	MeOH	293(4.20)	24-3072-79
$C_{14}H_{20}N_6O_4$			
9H-Purine-9-propanoic acid, 6-amino-α-[(1,1-dimethylethoxy)carbonyl]amino]-, methyl ester	n.s.g.	260(4.14)	65-0989-79
$C_{14}H_{20}O$			
5H-Inden-5-one, 4-(3-butenyl)-1,2,3,6,7,7a-hexahydro-7a-methyl-	EtOH	247(4.06)	33-1493-79
$C_{14}H_{20}OS_2$			
1,3-Dithiane-2-ethanol, α-methyl-2-(phenylmethyl)-	EtOH	205(3.98),250(2.91)	150-0301-79
$C_{14}H_{20}O_2$			
Bicyclo[5.1.0]octan-2-one, 8-acetyl-3,3,7-trimethyl-6-methylene-	n.s.g.	285(2.18)	33-1645-79
2,11-Dioxabicyclo[4.4.1]undeca-3,5-diene, 1,3,7,7-tetramethyl-10-methylene-	pentane	262(3.89)	33-0553-79
Ethanone, 1-(5,6,7,8-tetrahydro-2,8,8-trimethyl-4H-cyclohepta[b]furan-5-yl)-	n.s.g.	224(3.92),308(1.90)	33-1645-79
2-Heptanone, 6-(3-acetyl-1-cyclopropen-1-yl)-6-methyl-3-methylene-	n.s.g.	215(4.12)	33-1645-79
Isovalerophenone, 5-ethyl-2-methoxy-	EtOH	220(4.05),251(3.62), 315(3.30)	2-0180-79B
2-Propanone, 1-(4,5,6,7-tetrahydro-2,7,7-trimethyl-4-benzofuranyl)-	n.s.g.	219(3.99),284(1.74)	33-1645-79
Spiro[5.5]undeca-1,4-dien-3-one, 10-hydroxy-7,7,11-trimethyl-, cis	EtOH	248(4.18)	94-0274-79
3,4-Undecadiene-2,10-dione, 6,6-dimethyl-9-methylene-	n.s.g.	220(4.20)	33-1645-79
$C_{14}H_{20}O_3$			
Benzene, 1,2,3-trimethoxy-5-(1-pentenyl)-	EtOH	220(4.56),236(4.20)	150-0301-79
2,7-Oxepindione, 3,5-bis(1,1-dimethylethyl)-, cis,cis	hexane	248(3.75)	24-0389-79
Spiro[1,3-dioxolane-2,2'(1'H)-naphthalen]-6'-one, 1',3',4',7',8',8'a-hexahydro-1',8'a-dimethyl-	EtOH	236(4.03)	94-0331-79
3-Undecene-2,5,10-trione, 6,6-dimethyl-9-methylene-, (E)-	n.s.g.	222(4.32),340(2.06), 350s(2.02)	33-1645-79
(Z)-	n.s.g.	306(2.24)	33-1645-79

Compound	Solvent	λ_{max}(log ϵ)	Ref.
$C_{14}H_{20}O_3S_2$			
1,3-Dithiane, 2-[(3,4,5-trimethoxyphen-yl)methyl]-	EtOH	213(4.38),227s(3.96), 270(2.92)	150-0301-79
$C_{14}H_{20}O_4$			
Benzeneethanol, 3,4,5-trimethoxy- -2-propenyl-	EtOH	209(4.47),228s(3.95)	150-0301-79
2H-1-Benzopyran, 3,4-dihydro-2,2-dimethyl-3,5-dihydroxy-6-(3-hydroxy-propyl)-	EtOH	214(4.17),281(3.25), 285(3.25)	2-0011-79B
2,5-Cyclohexadiene-1,4-dione, 2-(3,4-dihydroxy-3-methylbutyl)-3,5,6-tri-methyl-, (S)-(+)-	EtOH	262(4.27),268(4.28), 346(2.53)	35-6710-79
3,5-Cyclohexadiene-1,2-dione, 4,5-bis-(2-methylpropoxy)-	EtOH	290(4.14),414(2.71)	18-2169-79
3,5-Cyclohexadiene-1,2-dione, 4,5-di-butoxy-	EtOH	291(4.11),414(2.69)	18-2169-79
3(2H)-Furanone, 4-hydroxy-2-(3-methyl-2-butenyl)-5-(3-methyl-1-oxobutyl)-	MeOH-HCl	265(3.99)	20-0087-79
	MeOH-NaOH	270(4.01)	20-0087-79
2-Naphthalenol, 1,2,3,4-tetrahydro-5,6,7-trimethoxy-4-methyl-	EtOH	209(4.21),226s(3.68), 273(3.73)	150-0301-79
2-Pentanone, 1-(3,4,5-trimethoxyphenyl)-	EtOH	228(4.44),275(3.25)	150-0301-79
2H-Pyran-2-one, 6-(3-acetoxy-1-hept-enyl)-5,6-dihydro-	EtOH	210(1.029)	102-1215-79
$C_{14}H_{20}O_5$			
2H-1-Benzopyran-3,5-diol, 6-(2,3-di-hydroxypropyl)-3,4-dihydro-2,2-di-methyl-	EtOH	213(4.22),281(3.14), 286(3.15)	2-0011-79B
2-Cyclohexen-1-one, 2,6-diacetoxy-3-methyl-6-(1-methylethyl)-	MeOH	242(3.91)	18-2372-79
$C_{14}H_{20}O_7$			
3-Furanpentanoic acid, 2,5-dihydro-4-methoxy-5-(2-methoxy-2-oxoethyl)-2-oxo-, methyl ester	EtOH	228(3.86)	130-0311-79
α-D-galacto-Oct-6-enopyranuronic acid, 6,7-dideoxy-1,2:3,4-bis-O-(1-methyl-ethylidene)-, (E)-	EtOH	214(3.62)	33-1632-79
$C_{14}H_{21}$			
Cycloheptatrienylium, heptamethyl-, perchlorate	10% HCl	260(4.69),345(3.80)	78-0949-79
$C_{14}H_{21}ClN_2O_2$			
Pyrazinemethanol, 3-chloro-α-(1-methyl-ethyl)-5-(2-methylpropyl)-, acetate	EtOH	216(4.03),281(3.94), 299s(3.59)	94-1316-79
Pyrazinemethanol, 6-chloro-α-(1-methyl-ethyl)-5-(2-methylpropyl)-, acetate	EtOH	214(4.00),281(3.91), 300s(3.55)	94-1316-79
$C_{14}H_{21}ClN_2O_3$			
Pyrazinemethanol, 6-chloro-α-(1-methyl-ethyl)-5-(2-methylpropyl)-, acetate, 1-oxide	EtOH	238(4.21),276(3.98), 303s(3.55),313(3.46)	94-1316-79
Pyrazinemethanol, 6-chloro-α-(1-methyl-ethyl)-5-(2-methylpropyl)-, acetate 4-oxide	EtOH	238(4.20),276(3.96)	94-1316-79
$C_{14}H_{21}ClN_2O_4$			
Pyrazinemethanol, 6-chloro-α-(1-methyl-	EtOH	247(4.37),315(4.27)	94-1316-79

Compound	Solvent	λ_{max}(log ϵ)	Ref.
ethyl)-5-(2-methylpropyl)-, acetate, 1,4-dioxide (cont.)			94-1316-79
$C_{14}H_{21}ClO$			
1(2H)-Naphthalenone, 7-(2-chloro-1-methylethyl)-3,4,5,6,7,8-hexahydro-4-methyl-	EtOH	247(4.3)	44-4042-79
$C_{14}H_{21}NOS_2$			
3H-1,2,3-Benzodithiazole, 4,6-bis(1,1-dimethylethyl)-, 2-oxide	hexane	284s(3.33),294s(3.19)	18-2002-79
$C_{14}H_{21}NO_2$			
3-Azaspiro[5.6]dodeca-1,4-diene-3-carboxylic acid, ethyl ester	isooctane	230(4.25)	44-2522-79
Benzene, 1,4-bis(1,1-dimethylethyl)-2-nitro-	hexane	233s(3.4),254s(3.1), 274s(2.9),330(2.4)	5-0554-79
	EtOH	233s(3.4),255s(3.2), 282s(3.0),332s(2.5)	5-0554-79
Benzeneacetamide, N-hydroxy-α,α-dipropyl-	EtOH	209(3.52)	32-0357-79
1-Butanone, 1-(2,5-dimethylphenyl)-4-[(2-hydroxyethyl)amino]-, hydrobromide	EtOH	269(3.61)	145-0983-79
1-Butanone, 1-(4-ethylphenyl)-4-[(2-hydroxyethyl)amino]-, mono(4-methylbenzenesulfonate)	EtOH	275(4.07)	145-0983-79
Pyridinium, 1-(carboxymethyl)-3,5-diethyl-2-propyl-, hydroxide, inner salt	MeOH	281(3.89)	44-1417-79
$C_{14}H_{21}NO_5$			
1H-Azepine-3,6-dicarboxylic acid, 4,5-dihydro-4-methoxy-2,5,7-trimethyl-, dimethyl ester	n.s.g.	231(4.11),325(4.19)	23-0044-79
DL-glycero-DL-allo-Octonic acid, 3,6-anhydro-2,8-dideoxy-2-[(dimethylamino)methylene]-4,5-O-(1-methylethylidene)-, ζ-lactone	MeOH	297(4.30)	88-2897-79
3,5-Pyridinedicarboxylic acid, 1,4-dihydro-4-(1-methoxyethyl)-2,6-dimethyl-, dimethyl ester	n.s.g.	234(4.15),347(3.83)	23-0044-79
$C_{14}H_{21}N_2O$			
1H-Indole-2-methanaminium, 3-(2-hydroxyethyl)-N,N,N-trimethyl-, iodide	EtOH	218(4.72),273(4.02), 286(3.93),296(3.68)	23-0289-79
$C_{14}H_{21}N_2O_2P$			
Phosphinic acid, di-1-pyrrolidinyl-, phenyl ester	EtOH	209(3.71),263(2.68), 268(2.55)	1-0319-79
$C_{14}H_{21}N_3OS$			
Carbamimidothioic acid, N-[2-(dimethylamino)-1,1-dimethyl-2-oxoethyl]-N'-phenyl-, methyl ester	n.s.g.	233(4.04),276s(3.71)	33-0160-79
$C_{14}H_{21}N_3O_4$			
Pyrrolidinium, 1-[2-[[2-methoxy-1-(methoxycarbonyl)-2-oxoethyl]azo]-cyclopentylidene]-, hydroxide, inner salt	$CHCl_3$	477(4.3)	89-0331-79

Compound	Solvent	$\lambda_{max}(\log \epsilon)$	Ref.
$C_{14}H_{21}N_3O_5$			
Thymidine, 5'-deoxy-5'-[(1-oxobutyl)-amino]-	H_2O	267(3.96)	87-0621-79
$C_{14}H_{21}N_3O_6$			
2,4(1H,3H)-Pyrimidinedione, 1-[2,6-di-deoxy-6-[(1-oxopropyl)amino]-β-D-ribo-hexofuranosyl]-5-methyl-	H_2O	267(3.98)	87-0621-79
less polar epimer	H_2O	267(3.97)	87-0621-79
1(2H)-Pyrimidinepropanoic acid, α-[[(1,1-dimethylethoxy)carbonyl]-amino]-3,4-dihydro-2,4-dioxo-, ethyl ester	n.s.g.	263(3.97)	65-0989-79
$C_{14}H_{21}N_3S$			
1H-Imidazol-5-amine, 4,5-dihydro-N,N,4,4-tetramethyl-2-(methylthio)-1-phenyl-	n.s.g.	263(3.98)	33-0160-79
$C_{14}H_{21}O_4PS_2$			
Benzeneethane(dithioic) acid, α-(di-ethoxyphosphinyl)-α-methoxy-, methyl ester	isooctane	243(3.50),318(3.92), 477(1.40)	5-1715-79
$C_{14}H_{22}$			
Anthracene, 1,2,3,4,4a,5,6,7,8,9,9a,10-dodecahydro-	hexane	214(3.39)	56-2385-79
$C_{14}H_{22}B_{10}Co_2$			
Cobalt, bis(η^5-2,4-cyclopentadien-1-yl)-[μ-[η^4,η^4-(2,4-dicarbaheptaboran(7)-3-yl)hexahydrodicarbaheptaborato-(4-)]]di- (also several isomers)	MeCN	237(4.20),284(4.23), 309s(4.1),360(3.45), 442(3.20),535s(2.51)	125-2165-79
$C_{14}H_{22}N_2$			
Borneno[2,3-b]pyrazine, 2,3-dihydro-	heptane and EtOH	210(3.44),235(3.37)	56-1729-79
$C_{14}H_{22}N_2O_2$			
2-Isoxazoline, 3-(4-piperidino-1,3-butadienyl)-4-hydroxy-5,5-dimethyl-	MeOH	348(4.59)	78-0341-79
$C_{14}H_{22}N_2O_3$			
Pyrazinemethanol, α-(1-methylethyl)-5-(2-methylpropyl)-, acetate, 1-oxide	EtOH	230(4.20),270(3.95)	94-1316-79
$C_{14}H_{22}N_2O_5S$			
4(1H)-Pyrimidinone, 2,3-dihydro-5-(1-C-pentyl-β-L-ribofuranosyl)-2-thioxo-	pH 1	213s(3.86),273(3.93), 295s(3.79)	88-2897-79
	pH 13	220s(3.97),262(3.97), 297s(3.66)	88-2897-79
$C_{14}H_{22}N_2O_6$			
2,5,8,11,14,17-Hexaoxa-19,21-diazabi-cyclo[16.3.1]docosa-1(22),18,20-tri-ene	EtOH	241(3.48),252(3.11)	44-3812-79
$C_{14}H_{22}N_2O_8$			
L-Threonine, N-[3-[(carboxymethyl)ami-no]-5-hydroxy-5-(hydroxymethyl)-2-methoxy-2-cyclohexen-1-ylidene]-, Na salt	H_2O	334(4.63)	138-0419-79

Compound	Solvent	$\lambda_{max}(\log \epsilon)$	Ref.
$C_{14}H_{22}N_2S_2$			
Cyclohexanamine, 1-[5,6-dihydro-3-(methylthio)-2,1-benzisothiazol-1(4H)-yl]-	EtOH	253(3.67),286(4.00)	150-0410-79S
monohydriodide	EtOH	218(4.19),251s(3.66), 286(3.87)	150-0410-79S
$C_{14}H_{22}N_4O_5$			
Thymidine, 5'-[[(2-acetylamino)ethyl]-5'-deoxy-	H_2O	267(3.98)	87-0621-79
$C_{14}H_{22}N_6O_2$			
1,3,5-Triazin-2-amine, 4,6-bis(1-aziridinyl)-N-(2,2,5-trimethyl-1,3-dioxan-5-yl)-	EtOH	223(4.70)	104-1144-79
$C_{14}H_{22}N_6O_3$			
1,3-Dioxane-5-methanol, 5-[[4,6-bis(1-aziridinyl)-1,3,5-triazin-2-yl]amino]-2,2-dimethyl-	EtOH	224(4.68)	104-1144-79
$C_{14}H_{22}O$			
Bicyclo[3.2.1]oct-6-ene-6-carboxaldehyde, 1,7-dimethyl-4-(1-methylethyl)-	n.s.g.	254(3.45)	12-0823-79
3-Buten-2-one, 4-(2,2,3-trimethyl-6-methylenecyclohexyl)-, trans-(±)-	EtOH	229.5(4.07)	22-0015-79
2-Cyclohexen-1-one, 2,4-dimethyl-3-(4-methyl-4-pentenyl)-	hexane	240(4.14),324(1.52)	35-7130-79
Cyclopenta[1,4]cyclobuta[1,2]benzen-5(6H)-one, octahydro-3a,4a,8-trimethyl-	hexane	283(1.50)	35-7130-79
$C_{14}H_{22}O_2$			
Bicyclo[3.2.1]oct-6-ene-6-carboxylic acid, 1,7-dimethyl-4-(1-methylethyl)-	n.s.g.	241(3.61)	12-0823-79
2-Naphthalenecarboxaldehyde, 3,4,4a,5-6,7,8,8a-octahydro-3-hydroxy-5,5,8a-trimethyl- (polygonal)	n.s.g.	223(4.14)	31-1420-79
4-Oxatricyclo[5.4.0.0^{1,3}]undec-5-en-8-ol, 3,5,9,9-tetramethyl-	n.s.g.	216(3.63)	33-1645-79
	n.s.g.	214(3.54)	33-1645-79
$C_{14}H_{22}O_2S$			
3-Thiabicyclo[3.2.0]hepta-1,4-diene, 6,7-bis(1,1-dimethylethyl)-, 3,3-dioxide, trans	EtOH	255(3.68),297(3.02)	44-2667-79
$C_{14}H_{22}O_3$			
1,2-Butanediol, 4-(3-hydroxy-2,4,5-trimethylphenyl)-2-methyl-, (S)-	EtOH	273(2.94),281(2.95)	35-6710-79
1-Cyclododecenecarboxylic acid, 12-oxo-, methyl ester	EtOH	222.5(3.81)	33-2630-79
geometric isomer (85%)	EtOH	225.5(3.68)	33-2630-79
Cycloheptanone, 5-acetyl-2,2-dimethyl-7-(2-oxopropyl)-	n.s.g.	286(1.74)	33-1645-79
isomer 13B	n.s.g.	286(1.88)	33-1645-79
2,6-Decadienoic acid, 3,7-dimethyl-10-oxo-, ethyl ester, (E,E)-	EtOH	206(3.72),208(3.72), 218(3.72)	70-0353-79
(E,Z)-	EtOH	205(3.90),218(3.94)	70-0353-79
(Z,E)-	EtOH	205(3.89),208(3.89), 218(3.87)	70-0353-79

Compound	Solvent	λ_{max}(log ε)	Ref.
(Z,Z)- (cont.)	EtOH	205(4.61),208(4.16), 217(4.11)	70-0353-79
Ethanone, 1-(1-hydroxy-2,2,6-trimethyl-5-methylene-9-oxabicyclo[4.2.1]non-7-yl)-	MeCN	282(1.48)	33-1645-79
4-Oxatricyclo[5.4.0.0^{1,3}]undecan-8-one, 5-hydroxy-3,5,9,9-tetramethyl-	MeCN	291(1.78)	33-1645-79
2,5,9-Undecanetrione, 6,6-dimethyl-9-methylene-	pentane	219(4.03),280(1.93)	33-0553-79
$C_{14}H_{22}O_4$			
Cyclohexanone, 5-hydroxy-2,2-dimethyl-5,6-bis(2-oxopropyl)-	MeCN	284(1.93)	33-1645-79
2-Furanacetic acid, 2,4-bis(1,1-dimethyl)-2,5-dihydro-5-oxo-	MeOH	208.5(4.06)	24-0389-79
$C_{14}H_{22}O_5$			
α-D-ribo-Oct-5-enofuranos-7-ulose, 5,6,8-trideoxy-3-C-ethyl-3-O-methyl-1,2-O-(1-methylethylidene)-, (E)-	EtOH	227(4.06)	33-2091-79
$C_{14}H_{22}S$			
3-Thiabicyclo[3.2.0]hepta-1,4-diene, 6,7-bis(1,1-dimethylethyl)-	EtOH	248(3.95)	44-2667-79
$C_{14}H_{23}FO$			
2-Buten-1-one, 1-[4-(1,1-dimethylethyl)cyclohexyl]-3-fluoro-	hexane	228(3.95)	35-5660-79
2-Buten-1-one, 1-[4-(1,1-dimethylethyl)-2-fluorocyclohexyl]-	hexane	223(4.06)	35-5660-79
$C_{14}H_{23}N$			
Pyrrolidine, 1-(1,7,7-trimethylbicyclo-[2.2.1]hept-2-en-2-yl)-	EtOH	213(3.18)	118-0830-79
$C_{14}H_{23}NO$			
Propanamide, N-(1,3-butadienyl)-N-cyclohexyl-2-methyl-	MeOH	265(4.45)	88-0981-79
Pyrrolidine, 1-(1,3,3-trimethyl-2-oxabicyclo[2.2.2]oct-5-en-6-yl)-	EtOH	212(2.70)	118-0830-79
$C_{14}H_{23}NO_3$			
2-Furanacetamide, 2,4-bis(1,1-dimethylethyl)-2,5-dihydro-5-oxo-	EtOH	206(4.40),280(3.02)	24-0389-79
$C_{14}H_{23}N_2O_5PS$			
Phosphorothioic acid, O-(1-cyclohexyl-1,6-dihydro-5-methoxy-6-oxo-4-pyridazinyl) O-ethyl O-methyl ester	MeOH	214(4.31),288(3.73)	73-1761-79
$C_{14}H_{23}N_2O_6$			
1H-Imidazol-1-yloxy, 2,5-dihydro-4-(3-methoxy-2-(methoxycarbonyl)-1-methyl-3-oxopropyl]-2,2,5,5-tetramethyl-, 3-oxide	EtOH	236(4.07)	70-2521-79
$C_{14}H_{23}N_3O_4$			
Thymidine, 5'-(butylamino)-5'-deoxy-	pH 1	267(3.98)	87-0621-79
$C_{14}H_{23}N_5O_4$			
1H-Purine-2,6-dione, 3,7-dihydro-8-(hy-	n.s.g.	211(4.43),234(3.73),	73-0424-79

Compound	Solvent	λ_{max}(log ϵ)	Ref.
droxymethyl)-7-[2-hydroxy-3-[(1-methylethyl)amino]propyl]-1,3-dimethyl-, monohydrochloride (cont.)		279(4.05)	73-0424-79
$C_{14}H_{23}N_5O_5$			
1H-Purine-2,6-dione, 3,7-dihydro-7-[2-hydroxy-3-[(2-hydroxyethyl)methylamino]propyl]-8-(hydroxymethyl)-1,3-dimethyl-, nicotinate	n.s.g.	211(4.57),275(4.11)	73-0424-79
$C_{14}H_{23}N_7$			
1H-Pyrazol-5-amine, 3-methyl-1-(1-methylethyl)-4-[[3-methyl-1-(1-methylethyl)-1H-pyrazol-5-yl]azo]-	MeOH	410(4.48)	103-0657-79
$C_{14}H_{24}Cl_4N_4Pd_2$			
Palladium, bis[2,3-bis(dimethylamino)-2-cyclopropen-1-ylidene]di-μ-chlorodichlorodi-	CH_2Cl_2	306s(3.00),366(3.49)	101-0199-79J
$C_{14}H_{24}N_2O_2S$			
2-Propenoic acid, 3-[(aminoiminomethyl)-thio]-5-methyl-2-(1-methylethyl)cyclohexyl ester, monohydrochloride, 1R-[[1α(Z),2β,5α]]-	EtOH	262(4.21)	35-6306-79
$C_{14}H_{24}N_2O_6$			
Morpholine, 4,4'-[1,2-ethanediylbis-[oxy(1-oxo-2,1-ethanediyl)]]bis-	H_2O	205(4.13)	33-0754-79
$C_{14}H_{24}N_3$			
1-Triazenium, 3-methyl-1,1-bis(1-methylethyl)-3-(4-methylphenyl)-, perchlorate	MeOH	213(3.53),254(3.57), 291(3.32)	24-0445-79
$C_{14}H_{24}N_3O_{15}P_3$			
2,4(1H,3H)-Pyrimidinedione, 1-(2,6-dideoxy-5-O-[hydroxy[[hydroxy(phosphonooxy)phosphinyl]oxy]phosphinyl]-6-[(1-oxopropyl)amino]-β-D-ribo-hexofuranosyl]-5-methyl-, tetrasodium salt	H_2O	266(3.98)	87-0621-79
$C_{14}H_{24}N_4S$			
11-Thia-2,3,8,9-tetraazadispiro-[4.0.4.1]undeca-2,8-diene, 1,1,4,4,7,7,10,10-octamethyl-	EtOH	323(2.45)	39-2401-79C
$C_{14}H_{24}N_5O_{13}P_3S$			
Adenosine 5'-(tetrahydrogen triphosphate), 8-(butylthio)-, tetrasodium salt	pH 7	281(4.28)	87-1529-79
$C_{14}H_{24}N_6OS$			
6-Thia-2,3,9,10,12,13-hexaazadispiro-[4.1.4.2]trideca-2,9,12-triene, 1,1,4,4,8,8,11,11-octamethyl-, 2-oxide	EtOH	301(3.14),331(2.98)	39-2401-79C

Compound	Solvent	λ_{max}(log ε)	Ref.
$C_{14}H_{24}N_6S$			
6-Thia-2,3,9,10,12,13-hexaazadispiro-[4.1.4.2]trideca-2,9,12-triene, 1,1,4,4,8,8,11,11-octamethyl-	EtOH	303(3.20),334(3.12)	39-2401-79C
$C_{14}H_{24}O$			
4(2H)-Azulenone, 2-(1,1-dimethylethyl)-octahydro-, cis	EtOH	285(1.42)	44-3031-79
trans	EtOH	282(1.57)	44-3031-79
$C_{14}H_{24}O_3$			
2-Dodecynoic acid, 4-hydroxy-, ethyl ester	MeOH	215(3.48)	35-1544-79
2,5,10-Undecanetrione, 6,6,9-trimethyl-	n.s.g.	285(1.98)	33-1645-79
$C_{14}H_{24}S_2$			
Spiro[2H-1,5-benzodithiepin-3(4H),1'-cyclohexane], hexahydro-, cis	EtOH	213(4.22)	49-0279-79
trans	EtOH	212(3.19)	49-0279-79
$C_{14}H_{25}NO$			
2,4-Decadienamide, N-(2-methylpropyl)-, (E,E)-	n.s.g.	258(4.67)	2-0538B-79A
Morpholine, 4-[4-methyl-1-(1-methylethyl)-2,4-hexadienyl]-	EtOH	238(4.04)	104-1041-79
2H-Pyrrole, 4,5-bis(1,1-dimethylethyl)-2,2-dimethyl-, 1-oxide	EtOH	299(3.65)	12-2025-79
$C_{14}H_{26}NOS$			
Sulfonium, dimethyl[2-(4-morpholinyl)-1-cycloocten-1-yl]-, chloride	MeCN	213(3.6),298(3.5)	24-2997-79
Sulfonium, dimethyl[2-(4-morpholinyl)-2-cycloocten-1-yl]-, chloride	MeCN	226(3.7)	24-2997-79
$C_{14}H_{26}N_2O_4$			
1,4-Dioxa-7,14-diazacyclohexadecane-6,15-dione, 7,14-dimethyl-	H_2O	203(4.19)	33-0754-79
$C_{14}H_{26}N_2S$			
2-Thiazolamine, 5-undecyl-	EtOH	262(3.894)	48-0249-79
$C_{14}H_{26}N_4O_4P$			
1-Piperidinyloxy, 4-[[[[bis(1-aziridinyl)phosphinyl]amino]carbonyl]oxy]-2,2,6,6-tetramethyl-	EtOH	208(3.32),243(3.34)	118-0269-79
$C_{14}H_{26}N_6O_2$			
1,3,5-Triazine-2,4,6-triamine, N,N,N'-N'-tetramethyl-N"-(2,2,5-trimethyl-1,3-dioxan-5-yl)-	EtOH	222(4.83)	104-1144-79
$C_{14}H_{26}N_6O_3$			
1,3,5-Triazine-2,4,6-triamine, N,N,N'-N'-tetramethyl-N"-[5-(hydroxymethyl)-2,2-dimethyl-1,3-dioxan-5-yl]-	EtOH	223(4.68)	104-1144-79
$C_{14}H_{26}N_6O_9$			
DL-Aspartic acid, N-[5-amino-1-β-D-ribofuranosylimidazole-4-carbonyl]-β-methyl-, threo-, diammonium salt	pH 3	270(3.84)	39-1415-79C
	pH 10	268(3.90)	39-1415-79C

Compound	Solvent	λ max (log ε)	Ref.
$C_{14}H_{26}O_2$			
2,10-Undecanedione, 3,6,6-trimethyl-	n.s.g.	285(1.70)	33-1645-79
$C_{14}H_{27}NO_2$			
Cyclohexaneacetamide, N-hydroxy-α,α-dipropyl-	EtOH	208(3.52)	32-0357-79
2H-Pyrrol-4-ol, 4,5-bis(1,1-dimethylethyl)-3,4-dihydro-2,2-dimethyl-, 1-oxide	EtOH	246(3.96)	12-2025-79
$C_{14}H_{28}$			
3-Hexene, 3-(1,1-dimethylethyl)-2,2,5,5-tetramethyl-	C_6H_{12}	194.5(4.12)	88-1305-79
$C_{14}H_{29}NO_2$			
Dodecanamide, N-hydroxy-2,2-dimethyl-	EtOH	208(3.55)	32-0357-79
Hexanamide, 2,2-dibutyl-N-hydroxy-	EtOH-heptane	204(3.62),215(3.33)	32-0357-79
$C_{14}H_{30}SSn$			
Stannane, tributyl(ethenylthio)-	hexane	237(3.88)	70-1479-79
$C_{14}H_{31}N_2P$			
Phosphonous diamide, P-cyclohexyl-N,N,N',N'-tetraethyl-	hexane	219(3.73)	22-0241-79I
$C_{14}H_{36}OSi_4$			
Trisilane, 2-(2,2-dimethyl-1-oxopropyl)-1,1,1,3,3,3-hexamethyl-2-(trimethylsilyl)-	C_6H_{12}	348(2.00),366(2.70), 380(1.99)	35-0083-79

Compound	Solvent	λ_{max}(log ε)	Ref.
$C_{15}F_{10}N_2O_3$			
Isoxazole, 4-nitro-3,5-bis(pentafluoro-phenyl)-	EtOH	217(4.24),270(3.87)	104-2179-79
$C_{15}H_2F_{10}N_2O_3$			
Isoxazole, 4,5-dihydro-4-nitro-3,5-bis-(pentafluorophenyl)-	EtOH	217(4.27),272(3.88),345(2.60)	104-2179-79
$C_{15}H_5F_5N_2O_2S$			
Isothiazole, 4-nitro-3-(pentafluoro-phenyl)-5-phenyl-	EtOH	232(4.20),297(3.89)	104-2179-79
$C_{15}H_5F_5N_2O_3$			
Isoxazole, 4-nitro-3-(pentafluorophen-yl)-5-phenyl-	EtOH	232(4.20),297(3.90)	104-2179-79
$C_{15}H_6BrF_5N_2O_3$			
Isoxazole, 4-bromo-4,5-dihydro-4-nitro-5-(pentafluorophenyl)-3-phenyl-	EtOH	210(4.17),232(4.20)	104-2179-79
Isoxazole, 5-bromo-4,5-dihydro-4-nitro-3-(pentafluorophenyl)-5-phenyl-	EtOH	211(4.18),251(4.08),342(3.20)	104-2179-79
$C_{15}H_6Br_4O_4$			
9,10-Anthracenedione, 1,3,6,8-tetra-bromo-4,5-dihydroxy-2-methyl-	hexane	244(4.44),264(4.25),335(3.92),430(3.60)	110-0097-79
	EtOH	250(4.40),275(4.39),325(3.92),450(3.60)	110-0097-79
	EtOH-H_2SO_4	246(4.20),500(3.70)	110-0097-79
	EtOH-NaOH	245(4.44),335(--),500(3.48)	110-0097-79
$C_{15}H_6F_5N_3O_5$			
Isoxazole, 4,5-dihydro-4-nitro-5-(4-ni-trophenyl)-3-(pentafluorophenyl)-	EtOH	213(4.19),266(4.25),345(3.62)	104-2179-79
$C_{15}H_6F_6N_2O_3$			
Isoxazole, 5-(3-fluorophenyl)-4,5-di-hydro-4-nitro-3-(pentafluorophenyl)-	EtOH	230(4.25),294(3.94)	104-2179-79
Isoxazole, 5-(4-fluorophenyl)-4,5-di-hydro-4-nitro-3-(pentafluorophenyl)-	EtOH	206(4.20),257(4.02),345(3.27)	104-2179-79
$C_{15}H_6O_5S_{10}$			
1,3-Dithiole-4,5-dicarboxylic acid, 2-[5-(5-oxo-[1,3]dithiolo[4,5-d]-1,3-dithiol-2-ylidene)[1,3]dithiolo[4,5-d]-1,3-dithiol-2-ylidene]-, dimethyl ester	CH_2Cl_2	239(4.22),280(4.20),310(4.29),440(3.14)	77-0516-79
	70% $HClO_4$	225(4.52),395(3.84),440(3.77),545(3.95),1050(4.00)	77-0516-79
$C_{15}H_7Br_3O_4$			
9,10-Anthracenedione, 1,3,8-tribromo-4,5-dihydroxy-2-methyl-	hexane	236(4.55),260(4.46),300s(3.80),440(3.24)	110-0097-79
	EtOH	238(4.54),260(4.42),305s(3.78),450(3.28)	110-0097-79
	EtOH-H_2SO_4	230(4.38),262(4.15),300s(3.72),440(3.68)	110-0097-79
	EtOH-NaOH	244(4.52),300s(3.74),365(3.58)	110-0097-79
$C_{15}H_7F_5N_2O_3$			
Isoxazole, 4,5-dihydro-4-nitro-3-(penta-fluorophenyl)-5-phenyl-	EtOH	215(4.23),250(4.00),345(3.83)	104-2179-79

Compound	Solvent	λ_{max}(log ε)	Ref.
Isoxazole, 4,5-dihydro-4-nitro-5-(pentafluorophenyl)-3-phenyl-	EtOH	211(4.18),251(4.08), 342(3.24)	104-2179-79
$C_{15}H_8Br_2O_3$			
9,10-Anthracenedione, 2,7-dibromo-1-hydroxy-3-methyl-	hexane	234(4.36),266(4.26), 290(4.12),300s(3.88), 440(3.85)	110-0097-79
	EtOH	236(4.40),268(4.36), 292(4.10),310s(3.80), 440(3.42)	110-0097-79
	EtOH-H_2SO_4	234(4.30),242(4.20), 290(4.10),300(3.70), 440(3.70)	110-0097-79
	EtOH-NaOH	244(4.42),292(3.84), 300s(3.72),525(3.29)	110-0097-79
$C_{15}H_8Br_2O_4$			
9,10-Anthracenedione, 1,3-dibromo-4,5-dihydroxy-2-methyl-	hexane	232(4.75),252(4.48), 290(4.15),322(3.88), 430(3.25)	110-0097-79
	EtOH	234(4.67),252(4.48), 292(4.15),325(3.80), 440(3.48)	110-0097-79
	EtOH-H_2SO_4	234(4.62),256(4.42), 290(4.12),420(3.10)	110-0097-79
	EtOH-NaOH	238(4.60),224(4.10), 325(3.84),510(3.03)	110-0097-79
$C_{15}H_8Cl_2O_3$			
2H-1-Benzopyran-2-one, 6-chloro-3-(4-chlorophenoxy)-	MeOH	210(4.553),280(4.175), 315(4.103)	2-0410-79
1(3H)-Isobenzofuranone, 3-[(3,5-dichloro-4-hydroxyphenyl)methylene]-, (E)-	EtOH	249(4.18),304(4.03), 329(4.06),410(3.32)	111-0411-79
(Z)-	EtOH	247(4.09),305(4.05), 315(4.06),350(4.19), 415(3.49)	111-0411-79
$C_{15}H_8Cl_4N_2O_2$			
1H-Isoindole-1,3(2H)-dione, 4,5,6,7-tetrachloro-2-(methylphenylamino)-	C_6H_{12}	412(1.81)	39-1103-79B
	benzene	408(1.79)	39-1103-79B
	EtOH	402(1.60)	39-1103-79B
$C_{15}H_8F_3N_3$			
Benzimidazo[1,2-c]quinazoline, 6-(trifluoromethyl)-	n.s.g.	268(4.58),282(4.60)	124-0225-79
$C_{15}H_8F_4O$			
Benzofuran, 4,5,6,7-tetrafluoro-2-methyl-3-phenyl-	C_6H_{12}	246(4.19)	18-2657-79
Benzofuran, 4,5,6,7-tetrafluoro-3-methyl-2-phenyl-	C_6H_{12}	285(4.40)	18-2657-79
$C_{15}H_8N_2O_4S$			
2,4,6(1H,3H,5H)-Pyrimidinetrione, 5-(3-hydroxy-2H-naphtho[1,8-bc]thien-2-ylidene)-	MeOH	218(4.7),246(4.6), 267(4.5),332(4.2), 358(4.4),388(4.4), 491(4.6)	5-1789-79

Compound	Solvent	λ_{max}(log ϵ)	Ref.
$C_{15}H_8N_4$			
1H-Benzo[3,4]cyclobut[1,2-b]imidazo-[4,5-g]quinoxaline	EtOH	261s(4.42),280(4.57), 301(4.28),366(4.04), 385(4.23),405(4.20)	78-0241-79
$C_{15}H_8O_3$			
4H-Fluorene[4,5-cde]oxepin-4,6(10H)-dione	C_6H_{12}	255(4.0),275s(3.4), 322s(3.42),336(3.53)	78-2237-79
$C_{15}H_9BrN_2OS$			
Thiazolo[3,2-a]benzimidazol-6-ol, 3-(4-bromophenyl)-	pH 1	319(3.38),384(3.40)	18-3096-79
	pH 13	312(3.43),449(3.61)	18-3096-79
	EtOH	245(3.69),267(4.35), 357(3.81)	18-3096-79
$C_{15}H_9BrO_2$			
9,10-Anthracenedione, 1-bromo-2-methyl-	isopentane-20% $C_6H_{11}Me$	257(4.65),274(4.16), 327s(3.53),335(2.59), 351s(3.49),395(--), 415s(--)	78-2255-79
	MeOH-EtOH	259(4.68),274(4.20), 340(3.72),416s(--)	78-2255-79
$C_{15}H_9BrO_4$			
9,10-Anthracenedione, 1-bromo-4,5-dihydroxy-2-methyl-	hexane	230(4.57),254(4.29), 274(4.05),288(4.00), 325(3.43),430(3.09)	110-0097-79
	EtOH	232(4.66),254(4.42), 284(4.12),330(3.56), 440(3.15)	110-0097-79
	EtOH-H_2SO_4	230(4.67),252(4.41), 284(3.82),315(3.28), 420(3.10)	110-0097-79
	EtOH-NaOH	236(4.62),320(3.78), 520(3.09)	110-0097-79
9,10-Anthracenedione, 2-bromo-1,8-dihydroxy-3-methyl-	hexane	230(4.47),260(4.31), 290(4.11),300s(3.97), 430(3.71)	110-0097-79
	EtOH	232(4.45),260(4.75), 290(4.47),305s(3.89), 435(3.97)	110-0097-79
	EtOH-H_2SO_4	230(4.38),262(4.28), 294(3.83),300s(3.87), 420(3.89)	110-0097-79
	EtOH-NaOH	240(4.49),254(4.45), 294(4.05),305s(3.97), 530(3.02)	110-0097-79
$C_{15}H_9BrO_5S$			
2-Anthracenemethanesulfonic acid, 1-bromo-9,10-dihydro-9,10-dioxo-, sodium salt	H_2O	262(4.61),277(4.08), 345(3.70)	78-2255-79
$C_{15}H_9ClN_2O_3$			
Benzamide, 2-chloro-N-(2,3-dihydro-1H-isoindol-4-yl)-	dioxan	226(4.77),261(4.32), 339(3.79)	4-0225-79
Benzamide, 3-chloro-N-(2,3-dihydro-1H-isoindol-4-yl)-	dioxan	225(4.79),270(4.47), 341(3.96)	4-0225-79
Benzamide, 4-chloro-N-(2,3-dihydro-1H-isoindol-4-yl)-	dioxan	230(4.65),272(4.45), 342(3.83)	4-0225-79

Compound	Solvent	$\lambda_{max}(\log \epsilon)$	Ref.
$C_{15}H_9ClO_2$			
9,10-Anthracenedione, 1-chloro-2-methyl-	isopentane-20% $C_6H_{11}Me$	255(4.66),272(4.17), 326s(3.58),334(3.77), 351s(3.5),395(--), 415(--)	78-2255-79
	MeOH-EtOH	257(4.68),272(4.19), 337(3.72),415s(2)	78-2255-79
$C_{15}H_9ClO_5S$			
2-Anthracenemethanesulfonic acid, 1-chloro-9,10-dihydro-9,10-dioxo-, sodium salt	H_2O	260(4.62),277s(4.08), 345(3.71)	78-2255-79
$C_{15}H_9ClS$			
2H-Cyclopenta[kl]thioxanthene, 3-chloro-	heptane	235(4.73),256(4.26), 264(4.32),277(4.33), 299(3.45),312(3.53), 342(3.47),356(3.64), 374(3.71)	73-2124-79
$C_{15}H_9Cl_2NO_2$			
9,10-Anthracenedione, x,y-dichloro-1-(methylamino)- (x,y=2,3,or 4)	benzene	502(3.65)	153-0033-79
$C_{15}H_9Cl_2NO_3$			
2-Propen-1-one, 2-chloro-3-(4-chlorophenyl)-1-(4-nitrophenyl)-	hexane	268(4.40),315(4.36)	97-0096-79
$C_{15}H_9Cl_3O$			
2-Propen-1-one, 2-chloro-1,3-bis(4-chlorophenyl)-, (E)-	EtOH	262(4.37)	97-0096-79
(Z)-	EtOH	310(4.33)	97-0096-79
$C_{15}H_9Cl_3O_3$			
[1,1'-Biphenyl]-2-acetic acid, 3,4,5-trichloro-α-oxo-, methyl ester	MeOH	204(4.63),247(4.26), 310s(--)	44-2391-79
[1,1'-Biphenyl]-3-acetic acid, 4,5,6-trichloro-α-oxo-, methyl ester	MeOH	205(4.67),247(4.08)	44-2391-79
$C_{15}H_9FN_2O_3$			
Benzamide, N-(2,3-dihydro-1,3-dioxo-1H-isoindol-4-yl)-2-fluoro-	dioxan	231(4.53),271(4.26), 338(3.71)	4-0225-79
Benzamide, N-(2,3-dihydro-1,3-dioxo-1H-isoindol-4-yl)-3-fluoro-	dioxan	232(4.51),271(4.26), 342(3.70)	4-0225-79
Benzamide, N-(2,3-dihydro-1,3-dioxo-1H-isoindol-4-yl)-4-fluoro-	dioxan	229(4.50),269(4.24), 343(3.69)	4-0225-79
$C_{15}H_9F_3O$			
9(10H)-Anthracenone, 3-(trifluoromethyl)-	CH_2Cl_2	265(4.22),302s(3.62), 310s(3.58),350s(2.04)	44-1941-79
$C_{15}H_9F_3O_3$			
Benzoic acid, 2-[3-(trifluoromethyl)-benzoyl]-	EtOH	239(4.16),280s(3.36), 330s(2.08)	44-1941-79
$C_{15}H_9IO_2$			
9,10-Anthracenedione, 1-iodo-2-methyl-	isopentane-$C_6H_{11}Me$	248(4.50),260(4.52), 320(3.44),335(3.46), 360(3.56),394(--), 415(--)	78-2255-79

Compound	Solvent	λ_{max}(log ε)	Ref.
(cont.)	MeOH-EtOH	252(4.53),262(4.55), 336s(3.56),360(3.62)	78-2255-79
$C_{15}H_9NO$			
Benzofuro[2,3-b]quinoline	EtOH	219(4.52),249s(4.51), 257(4.81),276(3.55), 318(4.24),330s(4.16)	4-0487-79
Benzofuro[3,2-c]quinoline	EtOH	212(4.42),228(4.42), 248(4.65),256(4.83), 282(4.24),290(4.26), 297s(4.17),317(3.32), 333(3.07)	4-0487-79
$C_{15}H_9NO_2$			
Benzofuro[2,3-b]quinoline, 6-oxide	EtOH	224(4.34),250s(4.34), 262(4.68),281s(4.22), 320(3.96),335(4.15), 351s(3.93),364(3.85)	4-0487-79
Benzofuro[3,2-c]quinoline, 7-oxide	EtOH	214(4.37),236(4.50), 248s(4.37),258s(4.34), 272(4.50),287s(4.36), 295(4.34),328(3.87), 342(3.89)	4-0487-79
4H-Cyclopenta[def]phenanthrene, 1-nitro-	C_6H_{12}	227(4.61),283(3.75), 296(3.65),343(3.82), 360(3.71),378(3.45)	44-1915-79
4H-Cyclopenta[def]phenanthrene, 2-nitro-	C_6H_{12}	273(4.44),283(4.53), 296(3.85),319(3.90), 332(3.83),358(3.25), 370(3.04)	44-1915-79
4H-Cyclopenta[def]phenanthrene, 3-nitro-	C_6H_{12}	228(4.48),249(4.44), 283(3.70),295(3.68), 326(3.87),341(3.98), 356(3.78),377(3.41)	44-1915-79
4H-Cyclopenta[def]phenanthrene, 8-nitro-	C_6H_{12}	228(4.58),278(3.98), 289(3.92),350(3.73)	44-1915-79
$C_{15}H_9N_2O_2S_2$			
Thiazolo[3,2-a]pyridinium, 2,3-dihydro-2-[(3-hydroxythiazolo[3,2-a]pyridinium-2-yl)methylene]-3-oxo-, hydroxide, inner salt perchlorate	MeCN	568(4.65),608(4.79)	103-1081-79
$C_{15}H_9N_3O$			
Benzimidazo[1,2-c]quinazoline-6-carboxaldehyde	n.s.g.	268(4.28),280(4.32)	124-0225-79
$C_{15}H_9N_3O_5$			
Benzamide, N-(2,3-dihydro-1,3-dioxo-1H-isoindol-4-yl)-2-nitro-	dioxan	227(4.60),255(4.39), 334(3.70)	4-0225-79
Benzamide, N-(2,3-dihydro-1,3-dioxo-1H-isoindol-4-yl)-3-nitro-	dioxan	225(4.67),264(4.36), 339(3.80)	4-0225-79
Benzamide, N-(2,3-dihydro-1,3-dioxo-1H-isoindol-4-yl)-4-nitro-	dioxan	229(4.54),290(4.16), 336(3.88)	4-0225-79
$C_{15}H_9N_3O_6$			
3,5-Pyridinedicarboxaldehyde, 1-(3,5-dinitrophenyl)-4-ethynyl-1,4-dihydro-	EtOH	227(4.45),237s(4.42), 271(4.42),342(4.02)	49-0613-79

Compound	Solvent	λ_{max}(log ε)	Ref.
$C_{15}H_9N_5$			
7H-Indolo[2',3':5,6][1,2,4]triazino-[2,3-a]benzimidazole	EtOH	232(4.06),272(4.39), 282(4.45),291(4.45), 365(3.93)	142-1001-79
$C_{15}H_{10}$			
4H-Cyclopenta[def]phenanthrene	C_6H_{12}	252(4.74),288(4.04), 299(4.12)	78-2237-79
$C_{15}H_{10}BrClO$			
2-Propen-1-one, 1-(4-bromophenyl)-2-chloro-3-phenyl-, (Z)-	hexane	301(4.40)	97-0096-79
2-Propen-1-one, 3-(4-bromophenyl)-2-chloro-1-phenyl-	hexane	256(3.98),305(4.34)	97-0096-79
$C_{15}H_{10}BrNO$			
Benzoxazole, 2-[2-(4-bromophenyl)ethenyl]-	EtOH	231(4.20),328(4.62)	56-1033-79
$C_{15}H_{10}BrN_3$			
Benzimidazo[1,2-c]quinazoline, 6-(bromomethyl)-	n.s.g.	274(4.42),282(4.41)	124-0225-79
$C_{15}H_{10}ClFN_2O$			
2H-1,4-Benzodiazepin-2-one, 7-chloro-5-(2-fluorophenyl)-1,3-dihydro-	pH 0	242(4.43),287(4.06), 382(3.54)	59-0603-79
	pH 7	231(4.55),250s(4.21), 330(3.18)	59-0603-79
	pH 14	237(4.43),275s(4.00), 354(3.18)	59-0603-79
$C_{15}H_{10}ClFN_2O_2$			
2H-1,4-Benzodiazepin-2-one, 7-chloro-5-(2-fluorophenyl)-1,3-dihydro-3-hydroxy-	pH 0	240(4.41),286(4.06), 370(3.54)	59-0603-79
	pH 7	231(4.58),250s(4.20), 321(3.23)	59-0603-79
	pH 14	238(4.49),270s(4.03), 350(3.43)	59-0603-79
$C_{15}H_{10}ClFO$			
2-Propen-1-one, 2-chloro-1-(4-fluorophenyl)-3-phenyl-	hexane	258(4.09),297(4.20)	97-0096-79
2-Propen-1-one, 2-chloro-3-(4-fluorophenyl)-1-phenyl-	hexane	256(4.02),298(4.24)	97-0096-79
$C_{15}H_{10}ClF_6NO$			
2(1H)-Naphthalenone, 1-chloro-1,3,5,6-7,8-hexafluoro-4-(1-piperidinyl)-	heptane	228(4.03),265(4.00), 313s(3.54),400(3.86)	104-1934-79
$C_{15}H_{10}ClN$			
Benzeneacetonitrile, α-[(4-chlorophenyl)methylene]-, cis	EtOH	228(4.22),298(4.19)	44-2896-79
Benzeneacetonitrile, 4-chloro-α-(phenylmethylene)-, cis	EtOH	234(4.39),295(4.20)	44-2896-79
$C_{15}H_{10}ClNO$			
Benzoxazole, 2-[2-(4-chlorophenyl)ethenyl]-	EtOH	226(4.17),324(4.31)	56-1033-79

Compound	Solvent	$\lambda_{max}(\log \epsilon)$	Ref.
$C_{15}H_{10}ClNO_2$			
4H-1-Benzopyran-4-one, 3-amino-2-(4-chlorophenyl)-	EtOH	249(4.33),301(4.13), 358(3.90)	5-0162-79
$C_{15}H_{10}ClNO_3$			
2-Propen-1-one, 2-chloro-1-(4-nitrophenyl)-3-phenyl-	hexane	264(4.26),312(4.21)	97-0096-79
2-Propen-1-one, 2-chloro-3-(4-nitrophenyl)-1-phenyl-, (Z)-	hexane	303(4.37)	97-0096-79
$C_{15}H_{10}ClN_3$			
Benzimidazo[1,2-c]quinazoline, 6-(chloromethyl)-	n.s.g.	272(4.36),283(4.35)	124-0225-79
1H-Pyrrolo[3,2-c]pyridine-7-carbonitrile, 6-chloro-1-(phenylmethyl)-	n.s.g.	241(4.47),302(3.55)	103-0310-79
$C_{15}H_{10}ClN_3OS$			
Benzenecarbothioic acid, 3-chloro-, (1,3-dihydro-3-oxo-2H-indol-2-ylidene)hydrazide	EtOH	242(4.35),303(4.03), 508(3.45)	104-0765-79
	$CHCl_3$	246(4.24),304(4.02), 377s(3.53),463s(3.3), 526(3.40)	104-0765-79
[1,3,4]Thiadiazino[5,6-b]indol-4a(9H)-ol, 3-(3-chlorophenyl)-	EtOH	240(4.21),257(4.19), 430(3.79)	104-0765-79
$C_{15}H_{10}Cl_2O$			
2-Propen-1-one, 2-chloro-1-(4-chlorophenyl)-3-phenyl-, (Z)-	hexane	300(4.37)	97-0096-79
2-Propen-1-one, 2-chloro-3-(4-chlorophenyl)-1-phenyl-	hexane	256(3.78),302(4.04)	97-0096-79
$C_{15}H_{10}F_{14}N_2O_5$			
2,4(1H,3H)-Pyrimidinedione, 1-(5-deoxy-5-fluoro-β-D-ribofuranosyl)-5-(tridecafluorohexyl)-	pH 1	262(--)	48-0449-79
	pH 14	261(3.93)	48-0449-79
$C_{15}H_{10}HgO_2S$			
Mercury, (2,3-dihydro-3-oxobenzo[b]thiophene-2-carboxaldehydato-O,O')phenyl-	benzene	318(4.04),385(3.54)	103-0056-79
	DMSO	297(4.06),400(3.93)	103-0056-79
$C_{15}H_{10}INO$			
Benzoxazole, 2-[2-(4-iodophenyl)ethenyl]-	EtOH	232(3.98),339(4.61)	56-1033-79
$C_{15}H_{10}N_2O$			
Indolo[7,6-g]indole-1-carboxaldehyde, 3,8-dihydro-	EtOH	204(4.16),233(4.23), 252(4.60),261(4.78), 282(4.44),338(3.75), 354(3.62)	103-0989-79
4H-Pyrazol-4-one, 3,5-diphenyl-	EtOH	253(4.11),433(2.95)	23-0904-79
Pyrrolo[2,3-c]carbazole-1-carboxaldehyde, 3,6-dihydro-	EtOH	218(4.76),256(4.32), 267(4.26),298(4.43)	103-0890-79
$C_{15}H_{10}N_2OS$			
Thiazolo[3,2-a]benzimidazol-6-ol, 3-phenyl-	pH 1	315(3.40),375(3.47)	18-3096-79
	pH 13	312(3.53),450(3.55)	18-3096-79
	EtOH	230(4.13),258(3.93), 350(3.39)	18-3096-79

Compound	Solvent	$\lambda_{max}(\log \epsilon)$	Ref.
$C_{15}H_{10}N_2O_2$			
6H-Anthra[1,9-cd]isoxazol-6-one, 3-(methylamino)-	dioxan	500(5.07)	104-0510-79
Benzeneacetonitrile, α-(nitrophenyl-methylene)-, (E)-	MeCN	277(4.00)	4-1611-79
(Z)-	MeCN	310(3.80)	4-1611-79
Benzeneacetonitrile, 4-nitro-α-(phenyl-methylene)-, cis	EtOH	264(4.19),308(4.05)	44-2896-79
Benzeneacetonitrile, α-[(4-nitrophen-yl)methylene]-, cis	EtOH	265(4.14),316(4.22)	44-2896-79
4H-Pyrazol-4-one, 3,5-diphenyl-, 1-oxide	isooctane	254(4.24),327(3.27), 508(3.30)	44-3211-79
Pyrrolo[2,3-a]carbazole-2-carboxylic acid, 1,10-dihydro-	EtOH	204(4.47),258(4.74), 277(4.73),322(4.48)	103-1097-79
Pyrrolo[2,3-c]carbazole-2-carboxylic acid, 3,6-dihydro-	EtOH	205(4.32),223(4.49), 248(4.35),273(4.09), 282(4.23),333(4.27), 346(4.25)	103-0642-79
$C_{15}H_{10}N_2O_2S$			
Quinoline, 2-[2-(4-nitro-2-thienyl)eth-enyl]-	EtOH	247(4.18),305(4.21)	103-0970-79
Quinoline, 2-[2-(5-nitro-2-thienyl)eth-enyl]-	EtOH	248(4.27),288(4.42), 332(4.45)	103-0970-79
Thiazolo[3,2-a]benzimidazol-6-ol, 3-(4-hydroxyphenyl)-	pH 1	315(3.46),377(3.38)	18-3096-79
	pH 13	308(3.28),438(3.72)	18-3096-79
	EtOH	248(4.01),272(4.41), 352(3.87)	18-3096-79
$C_{15}H_{10}N_2O_3$			
Benzamide, N-(2,3-dihydro-1,3-dioxo-1H-isoindol-4-yl)-	dioxan	230(4.51),271(4.25), 344(3.69)	4-0225-79
Benzoxazole, 2-[2-(4-nitrophenyl)ethen-yl]-	EtOH	273(3.99),345(4.37)	56-1033-79
4H-Pyrazol-4-one, 3,5-diphenyl-, 1,2-dioxide	isooctane	256(4.58),333(3.59), 455(3.19)	44-3211-79
$C_{15}H_{10}N_2O_3S$			
Furo[3',4':5,6]thiopyrano[2,3-c]pyraz-ole-5,7-dione, 1,7a-dihydro-3-methyl-1-phenyl-	EtOH	255(4.04)	103-0429-79
$C_{15}H_{10}N_2O_3Se$			
Furo[3',4':5,6]selenino[2,3-c]pyrazole-5,7-dione, 1,7a-dihydro-3-methyl-1-phenyl-	EtOH	258(3.75)	103-0429-79
$C_{15}H_{10}N_2O_4$			
2(3H)-Benzofuranone, 3-(aminophenyl-methylene)-5-nitro-	EtOH	249(4.42),342(4.26)	103-0842-79
1,9-Phenazinedicarboxylic acid, 4-meth-yl-	EtOH	207(4.58),254(4.83), 353s(4.04),369(4.28)	87-0918-79
3,5-Pyridinedicarboxaldehyde, 4-ethynyl-1-(2-nitrophenyl)-1,4-dihydro-	EtOH	228(4.46),257(4.24), 356(4.04)	49-0613-79
3,5-Pyridinedicarboxaldehyde, 4-ethynyl-1-(4-nitrophenyl)-1,4-dihydro-	EtOH	233(4.27),252s(4.11), 287s(4.05),347(4.24)	49-0613-79
$C_{15}H_{10}N_2S_2$			
Benzo[b]thiophen-3-amine, 2-(1,2-benz-isothiazol-3-yl)-	EtOH	250(4.30),273(4.34), 295(4.27),313(4.13), 327(4.13),385(4.32)	39-1665-79B

Compound	Solvent	λ_{max}(log ϵ)	Ref.
$C_{15}H_{10}N_4$			
1,2,4-Triazolo[3,4-a]phthalazine, 3-phenyl-	EtOH	262(4.53)	103-0443-79
	MeCN	265(4.53)	103-0443-79
$C_{15}H_{10}N_4O$			
1,4-Methanonaphthalene-6,6,7,7-tetracarbonitrile, 1,2,3,4,5,8-hexahydro-2-oxo-	EtOH	216(3.98)	33-2341-79
$C_{15}H_{10}N_4OS$			
[1,2,4]Triazolo[3,4-b][1,3,4]thiadiazolium, 5,6-dihydro-6-oxo-2,3-diphenyl-, hydroxide, inner salt	EtOH	280(4.15)	94-1688-79
$C_{15}H_{10}N_4O_5$			
4H-Pyran-3,5-dicarboxaldehyde, 4-[1-(4-nitrophenyl)-1H-1,2,3-triazol-4-yl]-	EtOH	213(4.41),291(4.36)	49-0613-79
$C_{15}H_{10}N_6OS$			
1,2,4-Triazolo[3,4-b][1,3,4]thiadiazolium, 6-(nitrosoamino)-2,3-diphenyl-, hydroxide, inner salt	EtOH	319(4.29)	94-1688-79
$C_{15}H_{10}N_6O_4$			
2-Pyridineacetonitrile, α-(1,3-dihydro-1-methyl-2H-benzimidazol-2-ylidene)-3,5-dinitro-	0.01N H_2SO_4	300(4.01),455(4.41)	104-0178-79
	pH 12	300(4.15),470(4.41)	104-0178-79
	EtOH	300(4.01),455(4.41)	104-0178-79
$C_{15}H_{10}OS_2$			
3H-1,2-Dithiol-3-one, 4,5-diphenyl-	EtOH	237s(4.06),283(3.83), 333(3.83)	33-1236-79
$C_{15}H_{10}O_2$			
9,10-Anthracenedione, 2-methyl-	hexane	254(4.61),273(4.18), 321(3.60),370-435 (2.3-1.6)	78-2255-79
	EtOH	255(4.76),275(4.39), 328(3.83),400-450 (2.3-1.8)	78-2255-79
1(3H)-Isobenzofuranone, 3-(phenylmethylene)-, (E)-	EtOH	232(3.98),291(3.94), 318(3.98)	111-0411-79
(Z)-	EtOH	231(4.12),238(4.12), 295(4.29),308(4.27), 338(4.30)	111-0411-79
Methanone, 2-benzofuranylphenyl-	EtOH	315(4.48)	104-2174-79
$C_{15}H_{10}O_2S$			
2H-1-Benzopyran-2-one, 3-(phenylthio)-	MeOH	230(4.65),275(4.01), 335(4.17)	25-0351-79
2H-1-Benzopyran-2-one, 4-(phenylthio)-	MeOH	225(4.04),271(3.8), 300(3.74)	25-0351-79
$C_{15}H_{10}O_3$			
4H-1-Benzopyran-4-one, 3-hydroxy-2-phenyl-	pH 12	235(4.26),275s(4.00), 320s(3.60),405(4.13)	114-0187-79D
	EtOH	216(4.28),243(4.18), 306(4.00),344(4.10)	114-0187-79D
Cyclohepta[de]naphthalene-8-carboxylic acid, 9,10-dihydro-10-oxo-	EtOH	225(4.5),243(4.4), 320(3.9)	18-0641-79
1H-Cyclopenta[b]naphtho[2,3-d]furan-5,10-dione, 3a,10b-dihydro-	n.s.g.	252(4.36),286(4.08), 338(3.41),391(3.05)	39-0719-79C

Compound	Solvent	λmax(log ε)	Ref.
4,7-Epoxy-4H-fluoreno[4,5-def][1,2]dioxocin, 7,11-dihydro-	C_6H_{12}	265(3.9),298(3.7) 307(3.95),335s(2.4)	78-2237-79
1(3H)-Isobenzofuranone, 3-[(4-hydroxyphenyl)methylene]-, (Z)-	EtOH	238(4.18),311(4.21), 324(4.22),360(4.36)	111-0411-79
$C_{15}H_{10}O_4$			
1,2-Acenaphthylenedicarboxylic acid, monomethyl ester	CH_2Cl_2	324(4.11)	44-1359-79
9,10-Anthracenedione, 3,8-dihydroxy-1-methyl-	MeOH	217(4.15),269s(4.09), 278(4.11),390s(3.55), 400(3.59),430s(3.53)	118-0148-79
4H-Difuro[3,2-c:3',2'-f][1]benzopyran-4-one, 2,9-dimethyl-	MeOH	326(4.50),342(4.41)	42-0056-79
$C_{15}H_{10}O_4S$			
Benzoic acid, 2-[(1,3-dihydro-3-oxoisobenzofuran-1-yl)thio]-	dioxan	220s(4.49),248s(3.96), 276(3.48),283(3.49), 305(3.45)	78-1875-79
2H-1-Benzopyran-2-one, 3-(phenylsulfonyl)-	MeOH	280(3.85),310(4.29)	25-0351-79
$C_{15}H_{10}O_5$			
9,10-Anthracenedione, 1,4-dihydroxy-5-methoxy-	MeOH	228(4.66),249(4.21), 265s(--),280s(--), 381s(--),373(4.01), 482s(--),522s(--)	24-3453-79
9,10-Anthracenedione, 1,4-dihydroxy-6-methoxy-	MeOH	221(4.50),268(4.47), 462(3.99),473(3.98), 508s(--)	24-3453-79
4H-1-Benzopyran-4-one, 5,7-dihydroxy-2-(4-hydroxyphenyl)-	EtOH	272(4.12),335(4.15)	105-0639-79
4H-1-Benzopyran-4-one, 5,7-dihydroxy-3-(2-hydroxyphenyl)-	MeOH	260(4.65),325(3.81)	102-0365-79
	$MeOH-AlCl_3$	270(--),370(--)	102-0365-79
	MeOH-NaOAc	273(--),375(--)	102-0365-79
9H-Xanthen-9-one, 4-methoxy-2,3-(methylenedioxy)-	EtOH	245(4.55),280(3.76), 310(4.08)	142-0269-79
$C_{15}H_{10}O_5S$			
1-Anthracenemethanesulfonic acid, 9,10-dihydro-9,10-dioxo-, sodium salt	H_2O	257(4.62),274(4.08), 336(3.68)	78-2255-79
2-Anthracenemethanesulfonic acid, 9,10-dihydro-9,10-dioxo-, sodium salt	H_2O	259(4.65),278s(4.12), 333(3.71)	78-2255-79
1,1'-Spirobi[3H-2,1-benzoxathiole]-3,3'-dione, 5-methoxy-	dioxan	244s(4.16),284(3.57)	78-1869-79
$C_{15}H_{10}O_5S_2$			
1,3-Dithiole-4,5-dicarboxylic acid, 2-(8-oxobicyclo[4.2.0]octa-1,3,5-trien-7-ylidene)-, dimethyl ester	CH_2Cl_2	243(4.08),329(4.06), 346(4.02),424(3.92)	44-0930-79
$C_{15}H_{10}O_6$			
4H-1-Benzopyran-4-one, 3,5,7-trihydroxy-2-(4-hydroxyphenyl)-	MeOH	215(4.06),268(4.00), 370(4.09)	36-0247-79
2,5-Cyclohexadiene-1,4-dione, 3,5-dihydroxy-2-[3-(4-hydroxyphenyl)-1-oxo-2-propenyl]-	EtOH	260(3.90),310(3.97), 412(4.41)	18-2596-79
9H-Xanthene-1-carboxylic acid, 2,8-dihydroxy-6-methyl-9-oxo- (pinselic acid)	$CHCl_3$	253(3.84),275(3.84), 297(3.38),326(3.35), 412(3.21)	44-4452-79

Compound	Solvent	λ_{max}(log ϵ)	Ref.
$C_{15}H_{10}O_7$			
7H-Furo[3,2-g][1]benzopyran-7-one, 4,9-diacetoxy-	MeOH	245(3.8),295(3.5), 350(2.9)	102-0352-79
$C_{15}H_{10}O_8S_2$			
2-Anthracenemethanesulfonic acid, 9,10-dihydro-9,10-dioxo-1-sulfo-, disodium salt	H_2O	266(4.59),242s(4.22), 325(3.55)	78-2255-79
$C_{15}H_{10}S$			
2H-Cyclopenta[kl]thioxanthene	MeOH	230(4.61),235s(4.55), 251(4.20),259(4.18), 273(4.20),353(3.55), 369(3.51)	73-2124-79
$C_{15}H_{11}Br$			
Anthracene, 9-bromo-10-methyl-	CCl_4	344(3.48),362(3.83), 380(4.05),403(4.02)	78-2131-79
$C_{15}H_{11}BrN_2O_2$			
9,10-Anthracenedione, 1-amino-2-bromo-4-(methylamino)-	benzene	585(3.86),628(3.85)	153-0033-79
$C_{15}H_{11}BrN_2O_3$			
Phenol, 2-[3-[(4-bromophenyl)imino]-1-propenyl]-4-nitro-, (?,E)-	MeOH	300(4.53),376(4.51), 420(4.37)	104-1715-79
	dioxan	293(4.47),348(4.41)	104-1715-79
	DMSO	300(4.41),410(4.31), 480(4.47)	104-1715-79
$C_{15}H_{11}ClN_2$			
Benzenamine, 4-chloro-N-(1H-indol-3-ylmethylene)-	EtOH	221(4.37),269(4.06), 330(4.30)	103-0741-79
Cinnoline, 6-chloro-3-methyl-4-phenyl-	EtOH	235(4.72),304(3.78), 331(3.70)	78-2463-79
$C_{15}H_{11}ClN_2O$			
4(1H)-Quinazolinone, 6-chloro-1-methyl-2-phenyl-	80% EtOH	232(4.67),290-315(4.3-4.0)	42-0708-79
4(1H)-Quinazolinone, 7-chloro-1-methyl-2-phenyl-	80% EtOH	240(4.56),280-298(3.9-4.0)	42-0708-79
$C_{15}H_{11}ClN_2O_4$			
4H-Furo[3,2-b]pyrrole-5-carbonyl chloride, 4-ethyl-2-(2-nitrophenyl)-	heptane	351(4.40)	73-1805-79
2-Propenamide, N-(4-chlorophenyl)-N-hydroxy-3-(4-nitrophenyl)-	EtOH	310(4.04)	34-0072-79
$C_{15}H_{11}ClN_4$			
1H-Pyrazole, 3-chloro-5-phenyl-4-(phenylazo)-	EtOH	230(4.71),336(4.82)	48-0127-79
$C_{15}H_{11}ClN_6$			
Pyrazolo[3,4-d]-1,2,3-triazole, 2-(2-chloro-3-pyridinyl)-2,4-dihydro-6-methyl-4-phenyl-	n.s.g.	425(3.19),490(2.86)	103-0572-79
$C_{15}H_{11}ClO$			
2-Propen-1-one, 2-chloro-1,3-diphenyl-	hexane	256(4.14),298(4.35)	97-0096-79

Compound	Solvent	$\lambda_{max}(\log \epsilon)$	Ref.
$C_{15}H_{11}ClOS$			
1H-Inden-1-one, 4-chloro-2,3-dihydro-7-(phenylthio)-	MeOH	214(4.34),234(4.34),240(4.34),266(3.88),275(3.94),341(3.83)	73-2124-79
$C_{15}H_{11}ClO_2$			
2-Propen-1-one, 1-(5-chloro-2-hydroxyphenyl)-3-phenyl-	EtOH	226(4.18),321(4.09),349(3.86)	78-2061-79
$C_{15}H_{11}Cl_2NO_2$			
2-Propenamide, N,3-bis(4-chlorophenyl)-N-hydroxy-	EtOH	239(4.43),295(4.80)	34-0072-79
$C_{15}H_{11}Cl_3N_2O_3S$			
Carbamothioic acid, N-ethyl-N-phenyl-, O-(3,4,6-trichloro-2-nitrophenyl) ester	MeOH	210(4.572),251(4.202)	73-0918-79
$C_{15}H_{11}F_3O_2$			
Benzoic acid, 2-[[3-(trifluoromethyl)-phenyl]methyl]-	EtOH	216(4.17),262s(3.11),273(3.20),275(3.24)	44-1941-79
$C_{15}H_{11}IN_2O$			
1H-Benzimidazole, 1-(2-iodobenzoyl)-2-methyl-	MeOH	208(4.26),235(3.75),265s(3.26),269s(3.38),274(3.51),280(3.58)	4-1235-79
$C_{15}H_{11}N$			
Benzeneacetonitrile, α-(phenylmethylene)-, cis	EtOH	224(4.36),295(4.22)	44-2896-79
Isoquinoline, 1-phenyl-	EtOH	219(4.624),245s(3.949),278(3.917),315(3.692),322(3.717)	12-0345-79
Isoquinoline, 3-phenyl-	EtOH	209(4.594),249(4.606),248s(4.202),293(4.230),306s(4.048),326(3.317),335s(3.173),342s(2.987)	12-0345-79
Isoquinoline, 4-phenyl-	EtOH	222(4.718),240s(4.056),279(3.845),313(3.680),324(3.751)	12-0345-79
Isoquinoline, 5-phenyl-	EtOH	220(4.554),239s(3.723),280(3.767),308(3.404),322(3.428)	12-0345-79
Isoquinoline, 6-phenyl-	EtOH	222(4.292),251(4.649),280(4.008),325s(3.117)	12-0345-79
Isoquinoline, 7-phenyl-	EtOH	212(4.586),247(4.577),279(4.126),327(3.057)	12-0345-79
Isoquinoline, 8-phenyl-	EtOH	222(4.653),242s(3.874),279(3.809),315(3.609),323(3.674)	12-0345-79
$C_{15}H_{11}NO$			
9-Acridinecarboxaldehyde, 2-methyl-	EtOH	230(4.39),256(5.05),362(3.93)	4-0257-79
	pH 1	217(4.21),263(5.00),346(3.94),362(4.25),413(3.59)	4-0257-79
Oxazole, 2,5-diphenyl-	EtOH	305(4.41),316(4.38)	18-3597-79
Pyrrolo[3,2,1-de]acridin-6-one, 1,2-dihydro-	EtOH	215(4.4),260(4.8),310(3.7),320(3.7),395(4.0),412(4.0)	103-1223-79

Compound	Solvent	λ_{max}(log ε)	Ref.
$C_{15}H_{11}NOS$			
Ethanone, 2-(1-isoquinolinyl)-1-(2-thienyl)-	MeCN	223(4.27),294(3.89)	103-1337-79
$C_{15}H_{11}NO_2$			
9,10-Anthracenedione, 1-(methylamino)-	C_6H_{12}	495(3.83)	39-0702-79C
Benz[g]isoquinoline-5,10-dione, 3,8-dimethyl-	EtOH	208(4.46),270(4.44), 294(4.22),340s(4.12), 398s(3.40)	103-0421-79
2(3H)-Benzofuranone, 3-(aminophenylmethylene)-	EtOH	252(4.20),348(4.09)	103-0842-79
4H-1-Benzopyran-4-one, 2-(2-aminophenyl)-	MeOH	203(4.55),239(4.44), 297(4.12),362(3.84)	83-0248-79
4H-1-Benzopyran-4-one, 3-amino-2-phenyl-	EtOH	243(4.31),305(3.75), 365(4.01)	5-0162-79
4H-Cyclopenta[def]phenanthrene, 8,9-dihydro-2-nitro-	C_6H_{12}	226(4.40),340(4.25), 358(3.96)	44-1915-79
Phenol, 4-[2-(1,2-benzisoxazol-3-yl)ethenyl]-, (E)-	EtOH	230(4.18),255(4.05), 285(4.12),322(4.47)	56-1033-79
Phenol, 4-[2-(2-benzoxazolyl)ethenyl]-	EtOH	223(4.18),340(4.20)	56-1033-79
3,5-Pyridinedicarboxaldehyde, 4-ethynyl-1,4-dihydro-1-phenyl-	EtOH	224(4.21),236(4.21), 277(4.33),375(3.95)	49-0613-79
2(1H)-Quinolinone, 3-(2-hydroxyphenyl)-	EtOH	220(4.50),267(3.61), 291(3.65),340(3.93)	4-0487-79
$C_{15}H_{11}NO_3$			
4,7-Methano-1H-isoindole-1,3,8(2H)-trione, 3a,4,7,7a-tetrahydro-2-phenyl-	MeCN	255(2.76),280s(1.90)	44-0604-79
$C_{15}H_{11}NO_4$			
Benzoic acid, 2-hydroxy-5-[2-(4-nitrophenyl)ethenyl]-, (E)-	EtOH	398(4.18)	103-0173-79
Methanone, [3-(4-nitrophenyl)oxiranyl]phenyl-	EtOH	256(4.76)	104-2174-79
$C_{15}H_{11}NS$			
1H-Indene-1-thione, 3-amino-2-phenyl-	$C_2H_4Cl_2$	299(4.35),312(4.24), 342(4.02),526(3.64)	99-0043-79
Quinoline, 2-[2-(2-thienyl)ethenyl]-, (E)-	EtOH	259(4.31),308(4.35)	103-0970-79
$C_{15}H_{11}NS_2$			
Benzothiazole, 2-(2,3-dihydrobenzo[b]thien-3-yl)-	MeOH	235(4.40),273(4.10), 325(3.82)	39-3207-79C
5aH-[1]Benzothieno[2,3-b][1,4]benzothiazine, 5a-methyl-	MeOH	215(4.38),250(4.39)	39-3207-79C
11aH-[1]Benzothieno[3,2-b][1,4]benzothiazine, 11a-methyl-	MeOH	223(4.52),255(4.29)	39-3207-79C
$C_{15}H_{11}N_2OS_2$			
Thiazolo[3,2-a]pyridinium, 2,3-dihydro-2-(3-methyl-2(3H)-benzothiazolylidene)-3-oxo-, perchlorate	MeCN	453(4.48),470(4.40)	103-1081-79
$C_{15}H_{11}N_2O_2S$			
Thiazolo[3,2-a]pyridinium, 2,3-dihydro-2-(3-methyl-2(3H)-benzoxazolylidene)-3-oxo-, perchlorate	MeCN	435(4.39)	103-1081-79
$C_{15}H_{11}N_3$			
Benzimidazo[1,2-c]quinazoline, 6-methyl-	n.s.g.	262(4.57),274(4.58)	124-0225-79

Compound	Solvent	$\lambda_{max}(\log \epsilon)$	Ref.
$C_{15}H_{11}N_3OS$			
Benzenecarbothioic acid, (1,3-dihydro-3-oxo-2H-indol-2-ylidene)hydrazide	$CHCl_3$	247(4.22),274(4.14), 348(4.04),425(3.60), 525(3.68)	104-0765-79
$C_{15}H_{11}N_3OS_2$			
1H-Thieno[3,4-b][1,4]diazepine-6-carbonitrile, 2,3-dihydro-8-(methylthio)-2-oxo-4-phenyl-	EtOH	224(4.30),275(4.35), 338(4.25)	142-0401-79
$C_{15}H_{11}N_3O_2$			
4H-1-Benzopyran-4-one, 3-azido-2,3-dihydro-2-phenyl-, trans	EtOH	254(3.88),322(3.47)	5-0162-79
1H-Imidazole, 1-(4-nitrophenyl)-4-phenyl-	EtOH	328(4.05)	78-1331-79
$C_{15}H_{11}N_3O_3$			
4H-Pyran-3,5-dicarboxaldehyde, 4-(1-phenyl-1H-1,2,3-triazol-4-yl)-	EtOH	227(4.12),249(4.05), 298(3.67),387(2.36)	49-0613-79
2(1H)-Quinolinone, 4-amino-3-(4-nitrophenyl)-	DMF	299(3.98),340s(3.76), 379(3.85)	48-0695-79
$C_{15}H_{11}N_3O_5$			
Phenol, 4-nitro-2-[3-[(4-nitrophenyl)-imino]-1-propenyl]-, (?,E)-	MeOH	308(4.16),360(4.12)	104-1715-79
	dioxan	310(4.45),335(4.45)	104-1715-79
	DMSO	314(4.33),345(4.31), 480(4.17)	104-1715-79
$C_{15}H_{12}$			
Anthracene, 9-methyl-	CCl_4	334(3.46),350(3.77), 368(3.98),388(3.96)	78-2131-79
$C_{15}H_{12}BrNO_2$			
4H-1-Benzopyran-4-one, 2-(4-bromophenyl)-2,3-dihydro-, oxime, (E)-	EtOH	223(4.44),255(4.03), 304(3.69),315(3.61)	56-1033-79
2-Propen-1-one, 3-(4-bromophenyl)-1-(2-hydroxyphenyl)-, oxime, (E,E)-	EtOH	222(4.22),297(4.30)	56-1033-79
$C_{15}H_{12}BrN_9O_2$			
5H-Tetrazol-5-one, 1,2-dihydro-1-methyl-, [[(2-bromo-4-nitrophenyl)azo]-phenylmethylene]hydrazone	pH 13	290(3.76),377(3.65), 520(4.36)	104-2000-79
	EtOH	280(3.37),385(3.16), 565(3.63)	104-2000-79
	dioxan	285(4.26),337(4.17), 505(4.30)	104-2000-79
$C_{15}H_{12}ClNO_2$			
2-Propenamide, 3-(4-chlorophenyl)-N-hydroxy-N-phenyl-	EtOH	222(4.11),288(4.34)	34-0072-79
2-Propen-1-one, 3-(4-chlorophenyl)-1-(2-hydroxyphenyl)-, oxime	EtOH	221(4.23),294(4.27)	56-1033-79
$C_{15}H_{12}ClNO_3$			
1H-Indole-2-carboxylic acid, 5-chloro-3-(2-furanyl)-, ethyl ester	EtOH	244(4.02),310(3.52)	77-0221-79
$C_{15}H_{12}ClN_3$			
1H-Pyrrolo[3,2-c]pyridine-7-carbonitrile, 6-chloro-2,3-dihydro-1-(phenylmethyl)-	n.s.g.	223(4.41),276(4.22), 331(3.74)	103-0310-79

Compound	Solvent	λ_{max}(log ε)	Ref.
$C_{15}H_{12}ClN_3O_2$			
Benzenepropanamide, α-[(4-chlorophenyl)-hydrazono]-β-oxo-	EtOH	250(4.30),370(4.59)	104-1324-79
$C_{15}H_{12}ClN_3S$			
2H-1,3,4-Benzotriazepine-2-thione, 7-chloro-1,3-dihydro-3-methyl-5-phenyl-	MeOH	237(4.33),270(4.31), 333(3.92)	106-0847-79
$C_{15}H_{12}ClN_5OS$			
Pyrido[3,2-d]pyrimidine-6-carboxamide, 4-amino-8-chloro-2-[(4-methylphenyl)-thio]-	pH 1	238(4.42),265(4.21), 328(4.14),342(4.11)	44-0435-79
	pH 7	242(3.92),292(3.71)	44-0435-79
	pH 11	242(3.85)	44-0435-79
$C_{15}H_{12}ClN_5O_2$			
Pyrido[3,2-d]pyrimidine-6-carboxamide, 4-amino-8-chloro-2-(phenylmethoxy)-	pH 1	225(4.55),237(4.49), 307(3.86),320(4.03), 333(3.99)	44-0435-79
	pH 7	247(4.41),304(3.75), 337(3.75)	44-0435-79
	pH 11	247(4.41),304(3.80), 337(3.81)	44-0435-79
$C_{15}H_{12}ClN_9O_2$			
5H-Tetrazol-5-one, 1,2-dihydro-1-methyl-, [[(4-chloro-2-nitrophenyl)azo]-phenylmethylene]hydrazone	pH 13	230(4.29),485(4.60)	104-2000-79
	EtOH	285(4.30),465(4.22)	104-2000-79
	dioxan	290(4.36),470(4.24)	104-2000-79
$C_{15}H_{12}Cl_2N_2S_2$			
Propanedithioamide, N,N'-bis(3-chlorophenyl)-	EtOH	230(2.15),290(2.11), 308(2.23),395(1.38)	48-0001-79
Propanedithioamide, N,N'-bis(4-chlorophenyl)-	EtOH	225(2.30),290(2.15), 308(2.23),395(1.38)	48-0001-79
$C_{15}H_{12}Cl_2O_2S$			
Benzeneacetic acid, 2,4-dichloro-α-[(4-methylphenyl)thio]-	EtOH	206(4.54),229(4.11), 273(3.11),281(3.05), 290(2.85)	80-0137-79
Benzeneacetic acid, 2,5-dichloro-α-[(4-methylphenyl)thio]-	EtOH	203(4.40),224(4.19), 268(2.78),276(2.89), 284(2.83)	80-0137-79
Benzeneacetic acid, 3,4-dichloro-α-[(4-methylphenyl)thio]-	MeOH	204(4.73),238(4.27), 273(3.29),280(3.27), 290(3.15)	80-0137-79
$C_{15}H_{12}INO_2$			
4H-1-Benzopyran-4-one, 2,3-dihydro-2-(4-iodophenyl)-, oxime, (E)-	EtOH	233(4.39),253(4.04), 303(3.64),315(3.52)	56-1033-79
2-Propen-1-one, 1-(2-hydroxyphenyl)-3-(4-iodophenyl)-, oxime, (E,E)-	EtOH	238(4.21),302(4.14)	56-1033-79
$C_{15}H_{12}N_2$			
Benz[f]imidazo[1,2-a]quinoline, 2,3-dihydro-	EtOH	212(4.00),246(4.57), 269(3.96)	4-0517-79
hydrobromide	EtOH	212(3.85),246(4.28)	4-0517-79
	EtOH-base	207(4.60),266(4.28)	4-0517-79
1H-Cyclopenta[b]phenazine, 2,3-dihydro-	MeOH	209(4.40),252(5.14), 370(4.38)	56-1221-79

Compound	Solvent	$\lambda_{max}(\log \epsilon)$	Ref.
$C_{15}H_{12}N_2O$			
1H-Cyclopenta[b]phenazine, 2,3-dihydro-, 5-oxide	EtOH	206(4.09),225(4.03), 272(4.94),369(3.90), 389(4.18),411(3.91)	56-1221-79
5-Isoxazolamine, 3,4-diphenyl-	MeOH	228(4.08),265(3.86)	4-1611-79
1H-Pyrazol-4-ol, 3,5-diphenyl-	EtOH	252(4.36),276s(4.23), 295s(4.00)	23-0904-79
Quinazoline, 4-(4-methoxyphenyl)-	EtOH	222(4.55),296(3.93), 327(4.10)	24-1348-79
4(1H)-Quinazolinone, 1-methyl-2-phenyl-	80% EtOH	231(4.56),280-305(4.0-3.7)	42-0708-79
4(1H)-Quinazolinone, 2-(phenylmethyl)- (glycosminine)	EtOH	225(4.44),265(3.95), 303(3.66),312(3.57)	142-0929-79
8-Quinolinol, 2-(phenylamino)-	neutral	283(4.48),349(3.78)	123-0070-79
	acid	272(4.36),323(3.99)	123-0070-79
	base	297(4.54)	123-0070-79
2(1H)-Quinolinone, 4-amino-3-phenyl-	DMF	316s(4.01),326(4.03), 333s(4.01)	48-0695-79
$C_{15}H_{12}N_2O_2$			
Acetamide, N-(6-oxo-5(6H)-phenanthridinyl)-	CH_2Cl_2	232(4.63),239(4.64), 251(4.13),260(4.20), 273s(3.93),303s(3.73), 321(3.87),334(3.80)	24-1635-79
9,10-Anthracenedione, 1-amino-2-(methylamino)-	benzene	494(3.87),528(3.80)	153-0033-79
9,10-Anthracenedione, 1-amino-4-(methylamino)-	benzene	573(4.07),617(4.08)	153-0033-79
1H-Cyclopenta[b]phenazine, 2,3-dihydro-	EtOH	206(4.07),228(4.19), 292(4.87),402(2.70), 424(3.96),438(4.13)	56-1221-79
Glycine, N-benzo[f]quinolin-3-yl-	EtOH	204(4.30),255(4.79), 296(4.24)	4-0517-79
1H-Isoindole-1,3(2H)-dione, 2-(methylphenylamino)-	C_6H_{12}	370(1.94)	39-1103-79B
	benzene	383(1.92)	39-1103-79B
	EtOH	378(1.93)	39-1103-79B
$C_{15}H_{12}N_2O_2S$			
2,5-Pyrrolidinedione, 1-phenyl-3-(2-pyridinylthio)-	EtOH	237(4.07),285(3.60)	104-1140-79
$C_{15}H_{12}N_2O_3$			
Phenol, 4-nitro-2-[3-(phenylimino)-1-propenyl]-	MeOH	292(4.20),380(4.09), 420(4.02)	104-1715-79
	dioxan	312(4.49),335(4.29)	104-1715-79
	DMSO	332(4.13),400(4.14), 468(4.48)	104-1715-79
Pyrrolo[2',3':4,5]furo[3,2-b]indole-2-carboxylic acid, 1,9-dihydro-, ethyl ester	MeOH	355(4.3)	73-1805-79
$C_{15}H_{12}N_2O_3S$			
2(1H)-Quinolinone, 4-amino-3-(phenylsulfonyl)-	DMF	278s(3.75),302(4.09), 332s(3.72),345s(3.65)	48-0695-79
$C_{15}H_{12}N_2O_4$			
Benzoic acid, 2-(2,3-dihydro-1H-indol-1-yl)-5-nitro-	EtOH	208(4.41),273(4.18), 417(3.88)	103-1223-79
4H-1-Benzopyran-4-one, 2,3-dihydro-2-(4-nitrophenyl)-, oxime, (E)-	EtOH	215(4.39),260(4.33), 303(3.90),315(3.71)	56-1033-79

Compound	Solvent	λ_{max}(log ϵ)	Ref.
2-Propenamide, N-hydroxy-3-(4-nitrophenyl)-N-phenyl-	EtOH	310(4.08)	34-0072-79
$C_{15}H_{12}N_2O_4S$			
Thiopyrano[2,3-c]pyrazole-5,6-dicarboxylic acid, 1,6-dihydro-3-methyl-1-phenyl-	EtOH	255(4.04)	103-0429-79
$C_{15}H_{12}N_2O_4Se$			
Selenino[2,3-c]pyrazole-5,6-dicarboxylic acid, 1,6-dihydro-3-methyl-1-phenyl-	EtOH	258(3.75)	103-0429-79
$C_{15}H_{12}N_2O_5$			
4H-Furo[3,2-b]pyrrole-5-carboxylic acid, 4-ethyl-2-(2-nitrophenyl)-	MeOH	328(4.44)	73-1805-79
$C_{15}H_{12}N_2O_6$			
Benzoic acid, 2-[(2-carboxy-5-methylphenyl)amino]-3-nitro-	MeOH	218(4.44),269(4.08), 332(3.95)	87-0918-79
$C_{15}H_{12}N_2O_6S$			
5-Thia-1-azabicyclo[4.2.0]oct-2-ene-2-carboxylic acid, 4,8-dioxo-7-[(phenoxyacetyl)amino]-, (6R-trans)-	pH 6.0	267(3.73),274(3.76), 296(3.81)	33-2681-79
$C_{15}H_{12}N_3O$			
9H-Fluorene-2-diazonium, 7-(acetylamino)-, tetrafluoroborate	EtOH-HBF_4	412(4.46)	104-0733-79
$C_{15}H_{12}N_4O_2$			
Benzoic acid, 4-[5-(4-methylphenyl)-2H-tetrazol-2-yl]-	EtOH	242(4.13),280(4.12), 293(4.15)	4-0123-79
3,5-Pyridinedicarboxaldehyde, 1,4-dihydro-4-(1-phenyl-1H-1,2,3-triazol-4-yl)-	EtOH	230(4.34),249s(4.12), 371(3.96)	49-0613-79
1H-Pyrido[3,2-c][1,2,4]triazolo[1,2-a]pyridazine-1,3(2H)-dione, 5,6-dihydro-2-phenyl-	EtOH	223(4.06),260(4.11), 292(3.66)	78-2027-79
$C_{15}H_{12}N_4O_3$			
Propanoic acid, 2-oxo-3-(phenylazo)-3-(phenylhydrazono)-	EtOH	254(3.94),261(3.87), 308(4.18),437(4.34)	24-1477-79
	dioxan	254(3.94),262(3.87), 305(4.18),439(4.33)	24-1477-79
Benzoic acid, 4-[5-(4-methoxyphenyl)-2H-tetrazol-2-yl]-	EtOH	252(4.46),281(4.40), 303(4.37)	4-0123-79
3H-Pyrazol-3-one, 2,4-dihydro-4,4-dihydroxy-2-phenyl-5-(phenylazo)-	dioxan	237(4.19),288(4.08), 390(4.26)	24-1477-79
$C_{15}H_{12}N_4O_4$			
Benzenepropanamide, α-[(4-nitrophenyl)hydrazono]-β-oxo-	EtOH	232(4.15),385(4.53)	104-1324-79
$C_{15}H_{12}N_4O_4S_2$			
Isothiazolo[3,4-d]pyrimidine-3-acetonitrile, 4,5,6,7-tetrahydro-5,7-dimethyl-4,6-dioxo-α-(phenylsulfonyl)-	EtOH	217(4.47),258(3.92), 297(3.72)	95-0989-79
	EtOH	213(4.52),235(4.44), 294(3.87)	142-0485-79

Compound	Solvent	$\lambda_{max}(\log \epsilon)$	Ref.
Propanedithioamide, N,N'-bis(3-nitrophenyl)-	EtOH	228(2.20),265(2.34), 326(2.40),345(1.20)	48-0001-79
$C_{15}H_{12}N_5S$			
1,2,4-Triazolo[3,4-b][1,3,4]thiadiazolium, 6-amino-2,3-diphenyl-, bromide	EtOH	274(4.31)	94-1688-79
$C_{15}H_{12}N_6O_5$			
Propanedial, [(4-nitrophenyl)hydrazono]-, mono[(4-nitrophenyl)hydrazone]	MeOH	450(4.44)	39-0603-79C
$C_{15}H_{12}N_8$			
2,5'-Bi-2H-tetrazolium, 3-(2-methylphenyl)-5-phenyl-, hydroxide, inner salt	EtOH	250(4.55)	104-0558-79
$C_{15}H_{12}O$			
Anthracene, 9-methoxy-	EtOH	249s(5.02),255(5.23), 318s(3.23),333(3.52), 350(3.78),368(3.95), 388(3.90)	118-0177-79
9(10H)-Anthracenone, 3-methyl-	EtOH	274(4.23)	44-1941-79
9H-Fluoren-9-one, 1,8-dimethyl-	dioxan	244s(4.43),253(4.77), 262(4.94),292(3.34), 304(3.47),321(3.45), 336(3.39),382(2.88), 400(2.84),421s(2.51)	24-3490-79
9H-Fluoren-9-one, 2,7-dimethyl-	dioxan	255(4.70),264(4.89), 283s(3.69),297(3.62), 310(3.45),327s(2.65), 336s(2.33),405(2.36)	24-3490-79
$C_{15}H_{12}OS$			
1H-Inden-1-one, 2,3-dihydro-4-(phenylthio)-	MeOH	242(4.44),260s(4.05), 317(3.43)	73-2124-79
1H-Inden-1-one, 2,3-dihydro-5-(phenylthio)-	MeOH	242(4.08),255s(3.83), 292s(4.08),313(4.29)	73-2124-79
$C_{15}H_{12}O_2$			
Benzaldehyde, 2-hydroxy-5-(2-phenylethenyl)-, (E)-	EtOH	309(4.37)	103-0173-79
Cyclohepta[de]naphthalen-7(8H)-one, 10-methoxy-	MeOH	310(3.74),330s(3.62), 353s(2.94)	39-2995-79C
Methanone, phenyl(3-phenyloxiranyl)-	EtOH	250(4.23)	104-2174-79
2-Propen-1-one, 1-(2-hydroxyphenyl)-3-phenyl-	EtOH	224(4.00),319(4.29), 350(4.05)	78-2061-79
$C_{15}H_{12}O_2S$			
Dibenzo[b,e]thiepin-11-carboxylic acid, 6,11-dihydro-	MeOH	260(3.92),288s(3.12), 297s(2.95)	73-2536-79
Dibenzo[b,f]thiepin-10(11H)-one, 3-methoxy-	MeOH	235(4.34),255(4.09), 290(3.52),327(3.60)	73-2108-79
$C_{15}H_{12}O_3$			
Benzoic acid, 2-(3-methylbenzoyl)-	EtOH	217(4.15),253(4.07), 280s(3.45)	44-1941-79
4H-1-Benzopyran-4-one, 2,3-dihydro-3-hydroxy-2-phenyl-	pH 12	235(4.26),275s(4.00), 320s(3.60),405(4.13)	114-0187-79D
	EtOH	216(4.46),252(3.94), 322(3.53)	114-0187-79D

Compound	Solvent	λ_{max}(log ε)	Ref.
9aH-Fluorene-9a-carboxylic acid, 3,9-dihydro-3-oxo-, methyl ester	dioxan	247(4.13),314(4.18)	44-2238-79
2-Propenal, 3-(2-acetoxy-1-naphthalenyl)-	dioxan	327(4.05)	104-1715-79
	DMSO	334(3.94)	104-1715-79
2-Propen-1-one, 1-(2,4-dihydroxyphenyl)-3-phenyl-	EtOH	260(4.23),320(4.14), 352(4.13)	78-2061-79
$C_{15}H_{12}O_3S$			
9H-Thioxanthen-9-one, 1,4-dimethoxy-	EtOH	208(4.39),255(4.58), 321(4.09),396(3.80)	33-2350-79
$C_{15}H_{12}O_4$			
9H-Xanthen-9-one, 2,3-dimethoxy-	EtOH	243(4.52),272(3.85), 307(4.06),349(3.98)	102-0182-79
$C_{15}H_{12}O_4S$			
1,4-Cyclohexadiene-1-carboxylic acid, 2-[(4-methylphenyl)thio]-3,6-dioxo-, methyl ester	EtOH	208(4.42),224(4.36), 245(4.22),312(3.57), 425(3.28)	33-2350-79
$C_{15}H_{12}O_5$			
2H-1-Benzopyran-2-one, 6-(2,5-dihydro-4-methyl-5-oxo-2-furanyl)-7-methoxy-	MeOH	221(4.22),245(3.62), 256(3.55),332(4.20)	100-0274-79
4H-1-Benzopyran-4-one, 2,3-dihydro-5,7-dihydroxy-2-(4-hydroxyphenyl)-	MeOH	230(3.83),290(3.69), 333(3.04)	36-0247-79
Butanoic acid, 2-(1,3-dihydro-1,3-dioxo-2H-inden-2-ylidene)-3-oxo-, ethyl ester	dioxan	255(4.47),304(3.63), 317(3.63)	32-0329-79
1,4-Cyclohexadiene-1-carboxylic acid, 2-(4-methylphenoxy)-3,6-dioxo-, methyl ester	EtOH	219(4.21),279(3.84), 341(3.28)	33-2350-79
1,3-Propanedione, 1-(2,6-dihydroxyphenyl)-3-(4-hydroxyphenyl)-	EtOH	255(3.98),270(3.97), 332(3.65)	22-0119-79
	EtOH-AlCl$_3$	255(--),275(--), 355(--)	22-0119-79
	EtOH-NaOH	275s(--),392(--)	22-0119-79
	EtOH-NaOAc	260(--),370(--)	22-0119-79
9H-Xanthen-9-one, 2-hydroxy-1,8-dimethoxy-	EtOH	242(4.48),257(4.49), 285(3.76),315(3.72)	142-0269-79
9H-Xanthen-9-one, 3-hydroxy-1,2-dimethoxy-	EtOH	241(4.55),280(3.94), 305(4.15),340s(3.85)	142-0269-79
	EtOH-NaOH	233(4.57),280s(3.82), 356(4.31)	142-0269-79
	EtOH-NaOAc	234(4.54),280s(3.82), 356(4.31)	142-0269-79
	EtOH-AlCl$_3$	241(4.56),280(3.95), 305(4.17),340s(3.83)	142-0269-79
9H-Xanthen-9-one, 3-hydroxy-2,4-dimethoxy-	EtOH	240(4.57),280(3.83), 313(4.13),350s(3.97), 380(3.20)	142-0269-79
9H-Xanthen-9-one, 3-hydroxy-2,5-dimethoxy-	MeOH	249(4.32),272s(3.80), 285s(3.62),315(3.58), 362(3.74)	100-0301-79
	MeOH-NaOMe	245(--),272s(--), 285s(--),373(3.96)	100-0301-79
	MeOH-NaOAc	245(--),272s(--), 285s(--),373(4.10)	100-0301-79
9H-Xanthen-9-one, 4-hydroxy-2,3-dimethoxy-	EtOH	237(4.42),256(4.52), 290s(3.96),307(4.00), 354(3.73)	142-0269-79

Compound	Solvent	λ_{max}(log ε)	Ref.
9H-Xanthen-9-one, 4-hydroxy-2,3-dimethoxy- (cont.)	EtOH-NaOH	213(4.69),235s(4.39), 275(4.36),298(4.00), 335(3.88),396(3.60)	142-0269-79
	EtOH-NaOAc	210(4.46),236(4.39), 255(4.39),295(4.13), 305(3.96),350(3.81)	142-0269-79
9H-Xanthen-9-one, 5-hydroxy-1,3-dimethoxy-	EtOH	248(4.62),304(4.26), 344(3.66)	142-0269-79
	EtOH-NaOH	241(4.57),265(4.43), 283(4.42),308(4.30)	142-0269-79
	EtOH-NaOAc	247(4.56),285(4.16), 303(4.22)	142-0269-79
9H-Xanthen-9-one, 8-hydroxy-1,2-dimethoxy-	EtOH	238(4.47),260(4.55), 290(3.75),322(3.70)	142-0269-79
	EtOH-NaOH	238(4.58),263(4.25), 326(3.85)	142-0269-79
	EtOH-$AlCl_3$	238(4.50),276(4.49), 310(3.83),351(3.64)	142-0269-79
$C_{15}H_{12}O_5S$			
Benzoic acid, 2-[[(2-carboxyphenyl)-methyl]sulfinyl]-	dioxan	227(4.15),287(3.50)	78-1875-79
$C_{15}H_{12}O_6$			
2H-1-Benzopyran-4-acetic acid, 7-[(2-methyl-1-oxo-2-propenyl)oxy]-2-oxo-	MeOH	281(4.05),313(4.01)	73-2211-79
4H-1-Benzopyran-4-one, 2,3-dihydro-3,5,7-trihydroxy-2-(4-hydroxyphenyl)-	MeOH	228(3.93),293(3.80)	36-0247-79
3,6-Dioxabicyclo[3.1.0]hexan-2-one, 4-(7-methoxy-2-oxo-2H-1-benzopyran-6-yl)-1-methyl- (micromelin)	MeOH	221(3.99),240(3.80), 250(3.55),292(3.99), 318(4.2)	100-0274-79
1H-Naphtho[2,3-c]pyran-1,6,9-trione, 3,4-dihydro-10-hydroxy-7-methoxy-3-methyl-	MeOH	226(4.47),287(3.93), 412(3.67)	24-0957-79
	MeOH-NaOH	228(4.48),287(4.10), 353(3.11),540(3.79)	24-0957-79
	dioxan	227(4.48),287(4.03), 415(3.70)	24-0957-79
1,3-Propanedione, 1-(2-hydroxyphenyl)-3-(2,4,6-trihydroxyphenyl)-	EtOH	250(3.80),290(4.15), 335s(--)	22-0119-79
	EtOH-NaOH	325(--),405(--)	22-0119-79
	EtOH-$AlCl_3$	250(--),302(--), 380s(--)	22-0119-79
$C_{15}H_{12}O_6S$			
Benzoic acid, 2-[(2-carboxyphenyl)sulfinyl]-5-methoxy-	dioxan	240s(4.17),293(3.58)	78-1875-79
$C_{15}H_{12}O_7$			
4H-1-Benzopyran-4-one, 2-(3,4-dihydroxyphenyl)-2,3-dihydro-3,5,7-trihydroxy-	MeOH	292(4.315),322s(--)	106-0841-79
$C_{15}H_{12}O_8$			
4H-1-Benzopyran-4-one, 2-(3,4-dihydroxyphenyl)-2,3-dihydro-2,3,5,7-tetrahydroxy-	EtOH	286(4.15),335s(--)	22-0125-79
$C_{15}H_{13}BrN_2O_2$			
1-Propanone, 1-[4-bromo-2-(phenyl-ONN-azoxy)phenyl]	EtOH	253(4.33),316(3.32)	104-0847-79

Compound	Solvent	$\lambda_{max}(\log \epsilon)$	Ref.
$C_{15}H_{13}BrO_3$			
2H-Naphtho[2,3-b]pyran-5,10-dione, 4-bromo-3,4-dihydro-2,2-dimethyl-	$CHCl_3$	253(4.12),282(4.06), 318(3.21),335(3.28)	2-0016-79B
$C_{15}H_{13}ClN_2O$			
1H-Imidazole, 1-(4-chlorophenyl)-2,5-dihydro-4-phenyl-, 3-oxide	MeOH	252(4.59),294(4.56)	56-1147-79
$C_{15}H_{13}ClN_2O_4S$			
Benzenepropanamide, N-[(2-aminosulfonyl)-5-chlorophenyl]-β-oxo-	EtOH	205(4.40),223(4.43), 250(4.29),317(3.97)	104-1495-79
$C_{15}H_{13}ClN_2S$			
Benzo[b]thiophen-3-amine, 6-chloro-N-ethyl-2-(4-pyridinyl)-	MeOH	265(4.24),313(3.89), 325(3.89),363(3.97)	118-0442-79
	MeOH-HCl	287(4.11),343(4.10), 444(4.13)	118-0442-79
	$CHCl_3$	264(4.21),315(3.89), 326(3.91),350(3.97), 430(--)	118-0442-79
	CF_3COOH	342(4.03)	118-0442-79
$C_{15}H_{13}ClN_3S$			
1H-1,2,4-Triazolium, 3-(chlorothio)-4-phenyl-1-(phenylmethyl)-, tetrafluoroborate	MeOH	250(3.95),297(3.05)	70-2526-79
$C_{15}H_{13}ClN_4O$			
Benzenamine, 4-[(5-chloro-1,2-benzisoxazol 3 yl)azo] N,N dimethyl	HOAc	280(3.89),301s(3.72), 458(4.44)	97-0452B-79
$C_{15}H_{13}ClN_6$			
1H-Pyrazol-5-amine, 4-[(2-chloro-3-pyridinyl)azo]-3-methyl-1-phenyl-	n.s.g.	390(4.14),420(4.21)	103-0572-79
$C_{15}H_{13}ClO_2S$			
Benzeneacetic acid, 4-chloro-α-[(4-methylphenyl)thio]-	EtOH	229(4.24),270(3.50)	80-0137-79
$C_{15}H_{13}Cl_2N_3O_2$			
1(2H)-Pyridineacetamide, 3-[[[(2,6-dichlorophenyl)methyl]imino]methyl]-2-oxo-	CH_2Cl_2	350(3.8)	64-1473-79B
$C_{15}H_{13}Cl_2N_3O_7S$			
Benzoic acid, 4-[[[(dichloromethyl)sulfonyl](5-nitro-2-furanyl)methylene]hydrazino]-, ethyl ester	MeOH	217(4.14),262(4.11), 319(4.34),407(4.19)	73-2507-79
$C_{15}H_{13}Cl_2N_3S$			
Sulfur, dichloro[4-phenyl-1-(phenylmethyl)-1H-1,2,4-triazolium-3-yl]-	MeOH	248(3.90),294(3.79)	70-2526-79
$C_{15}H_{13}Cl_2N_3Se$			
Selenium, dichloro[4-phenyl-1-(phenylmethyl)-1H-1,2,4-triazolium-3-yl]-	MeOH	264(3.68)	70-2526-79
$C_{15}H_{13}Cl_2N_4O$			
1H-Tetrazolium, 1,3-bis(4-chlorophenyl)-5-ethoxy-, tetrafluoroborate	n.s.g.	220(4.23),311(4.31)	39-0736-79C

Compound	Solvent	λ_{max}(log ϵ)	Ref.
$C_{15}H_{13}N$			
Acridine, 2,9-dimethyl-	pH 1	218(4.19),262(5.05), 341(3.92),358(4.24), 409(3.61)	4-0257-79
	EtOH	220(4.10),250(5.27), 359(3.94),383s(3.59)	4-0257-79
Benzenamine, N-(2,3-dihydro-1H-inden-1-ylidene)-	dioxan	286(3.83),311s(3.59)	24-3490-79
5H-Dibenz[b,f]azepine, 2-methyl-	EtOH	211(4.39),261(4.64)	4-0257-79
1H-Indole, 5-methyl-3-phenyl-	n.s.g.	212(4.27),277(4.38), 273(4.08)	2-0067-79A
$C_{15}H_{13}NO$			
Acridine, 2-methoxy-9-methyl-	EtOH	247s(4.80),256(5.51), 317s(3.35),333(3.70), 349(3.92),370(3.82), 390(3.73)	33-0304-79
Indeno[1,2-d]azepine, 4-ethoxy-	EtOH	288(4.5),345(3.6), 361(3.6),282(3.5), 544(2.6)	138-0807-79
1H-Indole, 3-(4-methoxyphenyl)-	n.s.g.	207(4.36),228(4.28), 268(4.06)	2-0067-79A
1H-Phenalen-1-one, 9-(dimethylamino)-	n.s.g.	280(4.24),357(4.13), 460(3.92)	44-1704-79
6H-Pyrrolo[3,2,1-de]acridin-6-ol, 1,2-dihydro-	EtOH	210(4.31),289(3.95)	103-1223-79
$C_{15}H_{13}NOS$			
Dibenzo[b,e]thiepin-11(6H)-one, 2-methyl-, oxime	MeOH	232(4.30),261(4.00), 320(3.41)	73-2689-79
$C_{15}H_{13}NO_2$			
Benzamide, N-benzoyl-N-methyl-	EtOH	231(4.06),242(4.06)	33-1236-79
Benzenamine, 2-(di-2-furanylmethyl)-	EtOH	226s(4.36),290(3.53)	39-0599-79C
Benzoic acid, 2-(2,3-dihydro-1H-indol-1-yl)-	EtOH	207(4.52),294(4.02)	103-1223-79
4H-1-Benzopyran-4-one, 3-amino-2,3-dihydro-2-phenyl-, hydrochloride	pH 12	245(4.30),305s(3.78), 360(3.95)	114-0187-79D
	EtOH	216(4.48),253(4.06), 320(3.62)	114-0187-79D
$C_{15}H_{13}NO_3$			
Benzamide, N-(2-acetylphenyl)-4-hydroxy-	EtOH	218(4.48),248(4.37), 279s(4.04),341(4.03)	120-0189-79
6(5H)-Phenanthridinone, 8,9-dimethoxy-	EtOH	222(4.17),250(4.25), 264s(4.07),279s(3.92), 290(3.90),305(3.80), 321(3.65),336(3.56)	2-0503-79A
$C_{15}H_{13}NO_4$			
2H-Azepine-4-carboxylic acid, 3-hydroxy-2-oxo-7-phenyl-, ethyl ester	dioxan	241(4.03),290s(3.95), 357(3.81)	142-1427-79
$C_{15}H_{13}NS$			
2-Azetidinethione, 1,4-diphenyl-	EtOH	307(4.31)	97-0109-79
$C_{15}H_{13}N_2OS_2$			
Thiazolo[3,2-a]benzimidazolium, 9-ethyl-6-hydroxy-3-(2-thienyl)-, bromide	EtOH	271(3.71),535(3.56)	18-3096-79

Compound	Solvent	λ_{max}(log ε)	Ref.
$C_{15}H_{13}N_3$			
Pyridazine, 3-(4-methylphenyl)-6-(1H-pyrrol-1-yl)-	EtOH	291(4.29)	80-0453-79
$C_{15}H_{13}N_3O$			
8-Quinolinol, 2-(methyl-2-pyridinyl-amino)-	neutral	282(4.33),346(3.94)	123-0070-79
	acid	246(4.18),253(4.18), 276(4.35),291(4.27), 338(4.07)	123-0070-79
	base	297(4.38)	123-0070-79
$C_{15}H_{13}N_3OS$			
Benzothiazole, 2-[(4-ethoxyphenyl)azo]-	EtOH	420(3.39)	103-1185-79
2,5-Cyclohexadiene-1,4-dione, mono[(3-ethyl-2(3H)-benzothiazolylidene)hy-drazone]	EtOH	500(3.54)	103-1185-79
$C_{15}H_{13}N_3O_2$			
Benzenepropanamide, β-oxo-α-(phenyl-hydrazono)-	EtOH	240(4.65),275(4.53), 365(4.78)	104-1324-79
4,4'-Bipyridinium, 1-cyano-2-ethoxy-2-oxoethylide	MeCN	231(4.35),253s(--), 434(4.41)	5-0727-79
3,5-Pyridinedicarboxaldehyde, 1-(4,6-dimethyl-2-pyrimidinyl)-4-ethynyl-1,4-dihydro-	EtOH	228(4.13),275s(4.41), 286(4.49),344(3.85)	49-0613-79
$C_{15}H_{13}N_3O_2S_2$			
5,11-Imino-5H,11H-[1,5]dithiocino[2,3-b:6,7-b']dipyridine-13-propanoic acid	EtOH	210(4.22),242(4.17), 298(3.81)	78-0869-79
$C_{15}H_{13}N_3O_3$			
[3,4'-Bipyridine]-3'-carboxylic acid, 5'-cyano-1',6'-dihydro-2'-methyl-6'-oxo-, ethyl ester	n.s.g.	335(3.96)	56-2121-79
[4,4'-Bipyridine]-3'-carboxylic acid, 5'-cyano-1',6'-dihydro-2'-methyl-6'-oxo-, ethyl ester	n.s.g.	257(3.83),336(3.93)	56-2121-79
Imidazo[1,5-b]pyridazine-5,7(3H,6H)-dione, 4-acetyl-6-methyl-2-phenyl-	50% EtOH	250(3.96),315s(3.54)	4-1105-79
$C_{15}H_{13}N_3O_4$			
4H-Furo[3,2-b]pyrrole-5-carboxamide, 4-ethyl-2-(2-nitrophenyl)-	MeOH	329(4.42)	73-1805-79
Imidazo[1,5-b]pyridazine-4-carboxylic acid, 3,5,6,7-tetrahydro-5,7-dioxo-2-phenyl-, ethyl ester	50% EtOH	220(3.93),273(4.10), 300s(3.80)	4-1105-79
	pH 13	260s(3.67)	4-1105-79
$C_{15}H_{13}N_3O_5$			
Ethenetricarbonitrile, (4-hydroxy-2,3,5,6-tetramethoxyphenyl)-	MeOH	412(3.96)	49-0737-79
	$MeOH-NH_3$	270(3.55),536(4.08)	49-0737-79
1H-Pyrazole-3,4-dicarboxylic acid, 5-cyano-1-(4-methoxyphenyl)-, dimethyl ester	CH_2Cl_2	288(3.96)	24-1193-79
$C_{15}H_{13}N_3O_8$			
1,4-Dioxaspiro[4.5]deca-6,9-diene, 6,10-dinitro-8-[(phenylmethyl)-aci-nitro]-	MeOH	237(4.07),370(4.31)	104-0487-79
	EtOH	292(4.26)	104-0586-79

Compound	Solvent	λmax(log ε)	Ref.
$C_{15}H_{13}N_3S$			
1,2,4-Thiadiazol-5(2H)-imine, 2-methyl-	MeOH	243(4.41),322(3.85)	24-0517-79
3,N-diphenyl-	dioxan	233(4.02),275(3.88)	24-0517-79
1H-1,2,4-Triazolium, 2,3-dihydro-4-	MeOH	250(3.73),294(3.04)	70-2526-79
phenyl-1-(phenylmethyl)-3-thioxo-,	MeCN	265(3.77),309(3.20)	70-2526-79
hydroxide, inner salt			
$C_{15}H_{13}N_3S_2$			
2-Thiophenecarbonitrile, 3-amino-5-(methylthio)-4-[(3-phenyl-2-propenylidene)amino]-	EtOH	227(4.16),299(4.58), 364(4.21)	95-1081-79
$C_{15}H_{13}N_3Se$			
1H-1,2,4-Triazolium, 2,3-dihydro-4-phenyl-1-(phenylmethyl)-3-selenoxo-, hydroxide, inner salt	MeCN	247(4.10),269(4.03), 328(3.23)	70-2526-79
$C_{15}H_{13}N_5O_3$			
Benzoic acid, 4-[[(2-amino-1,4-dihydro-4-oxopyrido[3,4-d]pyrimidin-6-yl)-methyl]amino]-	pH 13	226(4.32),277(4.40), 343(3.76)	4-0133-79
$C_{15}H_{13}N_5O_4$			
1H-Benzimidazole, 2-[(3,5-dinitro-2-	0.01N H_2SO_4	273(4.38),280(4.39)	104-0178-79
pyridinyl)methylene]-2,3-dihydro-	pH 12	330(4.16),515(4.66)	104-0178-79
1,3-dimethyl-	EtOH	330(4.09),515(4.57)	104-0178-79
$C_{15}H_{13}N_9O_2$			
5H-Tetrazol-5-one, 1,2-dihydro-1-meth-	pH 13	250(4.33),470(4.60)	104-2000-79
yl-, [[(3-nitrophenyl)azo]phenyl-	EtOH	255(4.32),430(3.93)	104-2000-79
methylene]hydrazone	dioxan	264(4.38),430(3.89)	104-2000-79
5H-Tetrazol-5-one, 1,2-dihydro-1-meth-yl-, [[(4-nitrophenyl)azo]phenyl-	pH 13	285(3.94),370(3.81), 542(4.58)	104-2000-79
methylene]hydrazone	EtOH	262(4.14),345(4.09), 535(4.24)	104-2000-79
	dioxan	290(4.19),532(4.13)	104-2000-79
5H-Tetrazol-5-one, 1,2-dihydro-2-meth-	pH 13	250(4.02),475(4.48)	104-2000-79
yl-, [[(3-nitrophenyl)azo]phenyl-	EtOH	265(4.39),455(4.00)	104-2000-79
methylene]hydrazone	dioxan	260(4.38),455(3.97)	104-2000-79
5H-Tetrazol-5-one, 1,2-dihydro-2-meth-yl-, [[(4-nitrophenyl)azo]phenyl-	pH 13	285(4.00),380(3.90), 530(4.77)	104-2000-79
methylene]hydrazone	EtOH	260(4.21),347(4.14), 490(4.35)	104-2000-79
	dioxan	262(4.25),340(4.13), 495(4.29)	104-2000-79
$C_{15}H_{14}ClN_3OS$			
Hydrazinecarbothioamide, N-(2-benzoyl-4-chlorophenyl)-1-methyl-	MeOH	246(4.37)	106-0847-79
2(1H)-Quinazolinethione, 3-amino-6-chloro-3,4-dihydro-4-methoxy-4-phenyl-	MeOH	287(4.47)	106-0663-79
$C_{15}H_{14}ClN_4O$			
1H-Tetrazolium, 1-(4-chlorophenyl)-5-ethoxy-3-phenyl-, tetrafluoroborate	n.s.g.	222(4.40),304(4.52)	39-0736-79C
1H-Tetrazolium, 3-(4-chlorophenyl)-5-ethoxy-1-phenyl-, tetrafluoroborate	n.s.g.	215s(4.10),228s(3.95), 308(4.35)	39-0736-79C
$C_{15}H_{14}IN_3O$			
3,9-Acridinediamine, 7-ethoxy-4-iodo-	25% EtOH-HCl	276(4.81),372(4.24)	12-2637-79
	+ NaOH	276(4.81),419(3.86)	12-2637-79

Compound	Solvent	λ max(log ε)	Ref.
$C_{15}H_{14}NOS$			
Thiazolo[3,2-a]pyridinium, 3-methoxy-5-methyl-2-phenyl-, perchlorate	MeOH	227(4.29),256(3.87), 340(4.29)	103-0872-79
$C_{15}H_{14}NO_2$			
Pyridinium, 3-hydroxy-1-(2-oxo-4-phenyl-3-butenyl)-, bromide	EtOH	225(4.59),300(4.69)	56-0057-79
$C_{15}H_{14}N_2$			
Benzenamine, N,N'-1,3-propanediylidenebis-, cis	$C_6H_{11}Me$	378(4.42)	24-0484-79
trans	EtOH	360(4.62)	24-0484-79
Benzenemethanamine, α-methyl-N-(phenylcarbonimidoyl)-	C_6H_{12}	209(4.45),251(4.16), 278(3.68),286(3.52)	56-0631-79
1,4-Methanobenzo[3,4]cyclobuta[1,2-b]quinoxaline, 1,2,3,4,4a,10b-hexahydro-	3-Mepentane	314(4.0),324(4.1), 357(3.7)	35-1820-79
$C_{15}H_{14}N_2O$			
Benz[f]imidazo[1,2-a]quinolin-11(1H)-one, 2,3,5,6-tetrahydro-, monohydriodide	MeOH	224(4.53),250(4.36), 268(4.29)	4-0517-79
7,10-Methanocycloocta[b]quinoxalin-13-one, 6,7,8,9,10,11-hexahydro-	EtOH	206(4.4),238(4.51), 318(3.91)	56-1221-79
Quinazoline, 3,4-dihydro-4-(4-methoxyphenyl)-	EtOH	279s(3.88),284(3.91), 290s(3.87)	24-1348-79
hydrochloride	EtOH	248(3.97),276(3.97)	24-1348-79
$C_{15}H_{14}N_2O_2$			
1,2-Benzenediol, 4-(1,4-dihydro-2-methyl-4-quinazolinyl)-, hydrochloride	EtOH	223(4.21),284(3.83)	24-1348-79
1-Propanone, 1-[2-(phenyl-NNO-azoxy)-phenyl]-	EtOH	249(4.19),323(3.35)	104-0847-79
$C_{15}H_{14}N_2O_3$			
3H-Pyrrolo[3,2-f]quinoline-8-carboxylic acid, 9-hydroxy-2-methyl-, ethyl ester	EtOH	222(4.55),255(4.10), 295(4.44),349(4.20)	103-0888-79
$C_{15}H_{14}N_2O_3S$			
Benzenesulfonic acid, 4-(4,5-dihydro-5-phenyl-1H-pyrazol-1-yl)-, sodium salt, (±)-	MeOH	290(4.25)	23-0360-79
$C_{15}H_{14}N_2O_3S_2$			
2-Azetidinone, 4,4'-[(3-oxo-3-phenyl-1-propenylidene)bis(thio)]bis-	dioxan	266(3.95),332(4.21)	142-1315-79
$C_{15}H_{14}N_2O_3S_4$			
Propanedinitrile, 3-(3-ethyl-4-oxo-2-thioxo-5-thiazolidinylidene)-3-(methylthio)-2-(phenylsulfonyl)-	EtOH	300(4.04),388(3.74), 473(4.51)	95-1234-79
$C_{15}H_{14}N_2O_4$			
1H-Naphtho[2,3-d]imidazole-4,9-dione, 5,8-dimethoxy-1,2-dimethyl-	C_6H_{12}	410(3.72)	39-0702-79C
	EtOH	440(--)	39-0702-79C
	EtOH-HCl	471(--)	39-0702-79C
$C_{15}H_{14}N_2O_4S$			
Benzenepropanamide, N-[2-(aminosulfonyl)phenyl]-β-oxo-	EtOH	206(4.48),247(4.26), 290(3.80),316(3.84)	104-1495-79

Compound	Solvent	λ_{max}(log ε)	Ref.
$C_{15}H_{14}N_2O_5$			
1-Propanone, 3-hydroxy-1-(2-hydroxy-phenyl)-3-(4-nitrophenyl)-, oxime	EtOH	262(4.21)	56-1033-79
1H-Pyrazole-3,4-dicarboxylic acid, 5-acetyl-1-phenyl-, dimethyl ester	CH_2Cl_2	end absorption	24-1193-79
1H-Pyrazole-4,5-dicarboxylic acid, 3-acetyl-1-phenyl-, dimethyl ester	CH_2Cl_2	end absorption	24-1206-79
$C_{15}H_{14}N_2O_5S$			
4-Thia-1-azabicyclo[3.2.0]hept-2-ene-2-carboxylic acid, 3-ethyl-7-oxo-, (4-nitrophenyl)methyl ester	EtOH	265(4.09),314(3.97)	77-0663-79
$C_{15}H_{14}N_2O_5S_2$			
Propanoic acid, 2-cyano-3-(3,4-dihydro-4-methyl-3-oxo-2H-1,4-benzothiazin-2-ylidene)-3-(methylthio)-, methyl ester, S,S-dioxide	dioxan	250(3.3),330(3.2)	83-0302-79
$C_{15}H_{14}N_2O_7$			
4H-Quinolizine-1,3,7-tricarboxylic acid, 6-amino-4-oxo-, trimethyl ester	EtOH	210(4.47),231s(4.06), 255(3.82),293(3.97), 338(3.77),365(3.97), 465(4.48)	39-0686-79C
	EtOH-HCl	210(4.43),231s(4.01), 255(3.75),293(3.94), 338s(3.72),365(3.96), 465(4.44)	39-0686-79C
	EtOH-NaOH	224(4.04),243(3.98), 266s(3.90),293(3.84), 338(4.16),435(4.26)	39-0686-79C
$C_{15}H_{14}N_2S$			
Benzenamine, 4-(1,2-benzisothiazol-3-yl)-N,N-dimethyl-	5M HCl	263(4.11),338(3.94)	24-3286-79
	MeOH	264(4.14),336(4.20)	24-3286-79
Benzo[b]thiophen-3-amine, N-ethyl-2-(2-pyridinyl)-	MeOH	276(4.14),323(4.03), 351(4.03)	118-0442-79
	MeOH-HCl	313(4.37)	118-0442-79
	$CHCl_3$	289(4.16),326(3.90), 372(4.05)	118-0442-79
	CF_3COOH	315(4.00)	118-0442-79
Benzo[b]thiophen-3-amine, N-ethyl-2-(4-pyridinyl)-	MeOH	261(4.16),310(3.89), 320(3.89),364(3.92)	118-0442-79
	MeOH-HCl	280(4.07),344(4.09), 446(4.09)	118-0442-79
	$CHCl_3$	262(4.11),310(3.84), 320(3.86),350(4.03), 433(3.32)	118-0442-79
	CF_3COOH	336(4.00)	118-0442-79
$C_{15}H_{14}N_2S_2$			
Propanedithioamide, N,N'-diphenyl-	EtOH	230(2.72),285(2.95), 302(3.00),380(1.38)	48-0001-79
$C_{15}H_{14}N_3$			
9H-Fluorene-2-diazonium, 7-(dimethyl-amino)-, tetrafluoroborate	EtOH-HBF_4	522(4.48)	104-0733-79
$C_{15}H_{14}N_3O$			
Pyridinium, 1-(4,5-dihydro-3-methyl-5-oxo-1-phenyl-1H-pyrazol-4-yl)-, bromide	EtOH	204(4.30),243(4.11), 332(4.30),417(4.36)	48-0495-79

Compound	Solvent	λ_{max}(log ε)	Ref.
$C_{15}H_{14}N_4$			
Propanedinitrile, [[4-[(2-cyanoethyl)-ethylamino]phenyl]methylene]-	EtOH	425(4.69)	110-1769-79
	EtOH-KOH	336(--)	110-1769-79
	CCl_4	412(--)	110-1769-79
	KBr	429(--)	110-1769-79
1H-Tetrazole, 1-(2,6-dimethylphenyl)-5-phenyl-	EtOH	241(4.10)	39-1871-79C
$C_{15}H_{14}N_4O$			
Benzenamine, 4-(1,2-benzisoxazol-3-yl-azo)-N,N-dimethyl-	HOAc	279(3.86),311s(3.62), 326s(3.47),449(4.44)	97-0452B-79
Mesoxaldehyde 1,2-bis(phenylhydrazone)	MeOH	415(4.30)	39-0603-79C
1H-Tetrazolium, 5-hydroxy-1,3-bis(4-methylphenyl)-, hydroxide, inner salt	n.s.g.	227(4.39),268(4.22), 331(4.43)	39-0736-79C
$C_{15}H_{14}N_4O_2$			
1H-Pyrazole, 1-acetyl-4,5-dihydro-3-[(2-hydroxy-1-naphthalenyl)azo]-	$CHCl_3$	480(4.28)	104-1396-79
1H-Tetrazole, 1-(2,6-dimethoxyphenyl)-5-phenyl-	EtOH	234s(4.17),277(3.63)	39-1871-79C
$C_{15}H_{14}N_4O_3S_2$			
Acetamide, N-[4-amino-5-cyano-2-(methylthio)-3-thienyl]-N-[(3-nitrophenyl)methyl]-	EtOH	289(4.19),320(4.00)	95-1081-79
$C_{15}H_{14}N_4O_4$			
Benzo[g]pteridine-2,4(3H,10H)-dione, 10-(2-acetoxyethyl)-3-methyl-	EtOH	264(4.40),334(3.82), 433s(3.87),436(3.91), 456s(3.80)	4-1365-79
$C_{15}H_{14}N_4O_5$			
Sydnone, 4-[[4,5-dihydro-5-(methoxycarbonyl)-5-methyl-3H-pyrazol-3-yl]-carbonyl]-3-phenyl-	n.s.g.	288(3.79),369(4.35)	103-1153-79
$C_{15}H_{14}N_4O_9S$			
Benzenesulfonamide, N,N-dimethyl-4-[(2,4,6-trinitrophenyl)methyl]-	EtOH	229(4.44),272s(4.03)	118-0531-79
$C_{15}H_{14}N_4S$			
Pyrido[2,3-d]pyrimidin-4-amine, 2-(methylthio)-N-(phenylmethyl)-, picrate	H_2O	265(4.36),340(4.37)	102-1265-79
	0.2M HCl	225(4.46),259(4.32), 291(4.21),327(4.36), 340(4.39)	102-1265-79
	0.2M NaOH	267(4.39),346(4.35)	102-1265-79
1H-Tetrazolium, 2,5-dihydro-1,3-bis(4-methylphenyl)-5-thioxo-, hydroxide, inner salt	n.s.g.	220(4.35),273(4.51), 382(3.48)	39-0741-79C
1,2,3,4-Thiatriazolium, 3-(4-methylphenyl)-5-[(4-methylphenyl)amino]-, hydroxide, inner salt	n.s.g.	235s(4.01),289(4.40), 448(3.26)	39-0741-79C
$C_{15}H_{14}N_6O_2$			
Benzenamine, N,N-dimethyl-4-[(5-nitro-1H-indazol-3-yl)azo]-	EtOH	285(4.2),468(4.38)	103-1231-79
Pyrido[3,2-d]pyrimidine-6-carboxamide, 2,4-diamino-8-(phenylmethoxy)-	pH 1	240(4.66),290(3.94), 315(3.93),328(3.79)	44-0435-79
	pH 7	245(4.53),316(4.08)	44-0435-79
	pH 11	245(4.51),316(4.09)	44-0435-79

Compound	Solvent	λ_{max}(log ε)	Ref.
$C_{15}H_{14}N_6O_3$			
Carbamic acid, [2-oxo-2-(1H-pyrazolo-[3,4-d]pyrimidin-4-ylamino)ethyl]-, phenylmethyl ester	EtOH	264(4.02)	39-2672-79C
	EtOH-HCl	263(4.02)	39-2672-79C
$C_{15}H_{14}N_6O_8S_2$			
Formazan, 3-[[(methylsulfonyl)methyl]-sulfonyl]-1,5-bis(4-nitrophenyl)-	EtOH	440(4.36)	104-0370-79
	$HOAc-H_2SO_4$	544(4.29)	104-0370-79
$C_{15}H_{14}N_8$			
Formazan, 1-(1-methyl-5-tetrazolyl)-3,5-diphenyl-	pH 13	450(4.49)	104-0558-79
	EtOH	270(4.19),410(3.90)	104-0558-79
	dioxan	277(4.24),312(4.02), 415(4.00)	104-0558-79
	$CHCl_3$	280(4.29),335(4.08), 422(4.09)	104-0558-79
Formazan, 1-(1-methyl-5-tetrazolyl)-3,5-diphenyl- (cont.)	pH 13	250(4.08),450(4.58)	104-2000-79
	EtOH	270(4.19),408(3.93)	104-2000-79
	dioxan	277(4.36),420(4.26)	104-2000-79
Formazan, 1-(2-methyl-2H-tetrazol-5-yl)-3,5-diphenyl-	pH 13	462(4.76)	104-0558-79
	pH 13	257(4.05),462(4.76)	104-2000-79
	EtOH	280(4.28),320s(4.05), 427(4.07)	104-0558-79
	dioxan	275(4.29),430(4.11)	104-0558-79
	$CHCl_3$	280(4.35),435(4.22)	104-0558-79
5H-Tetrazol-5-one, 1,2-dihydro-, [[(2-methylphenyl)azo]phenylmethylene]hydrazone	pH 13	480(4.69)	104-0558-79
	EtOH	290(4.29),420(4.05)	104-0558-79
	dioxan	280(4.24),380(4.08), 420(4.09)	104-0558-79
	$CHCl_3$	275(4.15),340(4.08), 420(3.99)	104-0558-79
5H-Tetrazol-5-one, 1,2-dihydro-, [[(4-methylphenyl)azo]phenylmethylene]hydrazone	pH 13	486(4.52)	104-0558-79
	EtOH	250(3.63),290(3.86), 445(4.00)	104-0558-79
	dioxan	250(4.02),280(4.01), 325(3.97),380s(--), 420s(3.94)	104-0558-79
	$CHCl_3$	275(4.03),340(4.04), 413(3.90)	104-0558-79
$C_{15}H_{14}N_8O$			
5H-Tetrazol-5-one, 1,2-dihydro-1-methyl-, [[(4-hydroxyphenyl)azo]phenylmethylene]hydrazone	pH 13	327(3.96),485(4.49)	104-2000-79
	EtOH	260(4.25),408(4.16)	104-2000-79
	dioxan	256(4.17),357(4.05), 420(4.10)	104-2000-79
5H-Tetrazol-5-one, 1,2-dihydro-2-methyl-, [[(4-hydroxyphenyl)azo]phenylmethylene]hydrazone	pH 13	245(4.41),482(4.29)	104-2000-79
	EtOH	257(4.37),367(4.23), 430(4.29)	104-2000-79
	dioxan	258(4.29),350(4.06), 430(4.15)	104-2000-79
$C_{15}H_{14}N_{10}O$			
Benzoyl azide, 4-[[(2,4-diamino-6-pteridinyl)methyl]methylamino]-	EtOH	318(4.63)	87-0869-79
$C_{15}H_{14}O$			
Benzenemethanol, 2-(1-phenylethenyl)-	hexane	257(3.96)	44-3698-79
1H-2-Benzopyran, 3,4-dihydro-3-phenyl-, (R)-(+)-	EtOH	223(3.18),251(2.52), 263(2.71),272(2.65)	83-0385-79
Bicyclo[3.2.2]nona-3,6-dien-2-one, 3-phenyl-	MeOH	224(4.07),275(3.56), 335s(2.05)	18-3355-79

Compound	Solvent	$\lambda_{max}(\log \epsilon)$	Ref.
$C_{15}H_{14}OS$			
Dibenzo[b,e]thiepin-11-methanol, 6,11-dihydro-	MeOH	212(4.39),262(3.92)	73-2536-79
Ethanone, 1-[5-methyl-2-(phenylthio)-phenyl]-	MeOH	211(4.33),235(4.34), 260s(3.89),342(3.59)	73-2677-79
$C_{15}H_{14}O_2$			
4H-Benzo[b]indeno[5,4-d]furan-4-one, 1,2,3,3a,5,10b-hexahydro-, cis	EtOH	207(4.33),248(4.05), 276(3.61),283(3.57)	118-0122-79
Benzoic acid, 2-[(3-methylphenyl)meth-yl]-	EtOH	279(3.18)	44-1941-79
1,4-Naphthalenedione, 2-(3-methyl-2-butenyl)- (deoxylapachol)	EtOH	252(4.29),265(4.16), 331(3.46)	95-0500-79
1-Naphthalenepropanal, α,α-dimethyl-β-oxo-	MeOH	221(4.87),270s(3.72), 281(3.81),290s(3.76)	5-0617-79
$C_{15}H_{14}O_2S$			
Ethanone, 1-(4-methylphenyl)-2-(phenyl-sulfinyl)-	C_6H_{12}	220(4.40),258(4.45)	2-0480-79B'
	pH 2-3	264(4.20)	2-0480-79B'
	pH 11-12	305(4.04)	2-0480-79B'
	EtOH	221(4.36),261(4.43)	2-0480-79B'
	$CHCl_3$	265(--)	2-0480-79B'
$C_{15}H_{14}O_2S_2$			
[2,3'-Bithiophen]-5'(2'H)-one, 3',4'-dihydro-5-(4-methoxyphenyl)-	MeOH	300(4.36)	18-1126-79
$C_{15}H_{14}O_3$			
Cannabispiradienone	EtOH	212(4.46),240(4.36), 277(3.49),285(3.48), 307s(2.78)	88-0661-79
9aH-Fluorene-9a-carboxylic acid, 1,2,3,9-tetrahydro-3-oxo-, methyl ester	dioxan	229(4.01),289(4.27), 307(4.19)	44-2238-79
Methanone, (2-hydroxy-5-methylphenyl)-(2-methoxyphenyl)-	EtOH	219(4.32),262(4.08), 347(3.71)	49-1057-79
Methanone, (2-hydroxy-5-methylphenyl)-(4-methoxyphenyl)-	EtOH	268(3.97),293(4.09), 345(3.76)	49-1057-79
Methanone, (4-hydroxy-3-methylphenyl)-(2-methoxyphenyl)-	EtOH	227(4.12),299(4.17)	49-1057-79
Methanone, (4-hydroxy-3-methylphenyl)-(4-methoxyphenyl)-	EtOH	302(4.32)	49-1057-79
2-Naphthalenecarboxylic acid, 3,4-di-hydro-3-(1-methylpropylidene)-4-oxo-	EtOH	245(4.62),294(3.58), 303s(--),343s(--), 349(3.65)	42-0068-79
1H-Naphtho[2,1-b]pyran-1-one, 2,3-di-hydro-6-hydroxy-3,3-dimethyl-	EtOH	255(4.37),318(4.07), 352s(4.11),366(4.16), 385(4.01)	80-0059-79
1H-Naphtho[2,1-b]pyran-1-one, 2,3-di-hydro-9-hydroxy-3,3-dimethyl-	EtOH	230(4.68),276(3.79), 362(3.97)	80-0059-79
$C_{15}H_{14}O_3S$			
Ethanone, 1-(4-methoxyphenyl)-2-(phen-ylsulfinyl)-	C_6H_{12}	223(4.39),284(4.45)	2-0480-79B'
	pH 2-3	240(4.15)	2-0480-79B'
	pH 11-12	285(4.22)	2-0480-79B'
	EtOH	222(4.41),288(4.49)	2-0480-79B'
	$CHCl_3$	290(4.43)	2-0480-79B'
	CCl_4	285(4.46)	2-0480-79B'
$C_{15}H_{14}O_4$			
Acetic acid, (2,3-dihydro-1,3-dioxo-1H-	dioxan	247(4.68),303(3.81),	32-0329-79

Compound	Solvent	$\lambda_{max}(\log \epsilon)$	Ref.
inden-2-ylidene)-, 1,1-dimethylethyl ester (cont.)		316(3.79)	32-0329-79
2H-1-Benzopyran-2-one, 7-methoxy-6-(3-methyl-2-oxo-3-butenyl)-	EtOH	223(4.46),256s(4.06), 285s(4.12),327(4.18)	102-1073-79
4H-Difuro[3,2-c:3',2'-f][1]benzopyran-4-one, 2,3,9,10-tetrahydro-2,9-dimethyl-	MeOH	269(4.13),307(4.05), 342(3.63)	42-0056-79
2(5H)-Furanone, 4-methoxy-5-(1-methoxy-3-phenyl-2-propenylidene)-, (E,E)-	MeOH	258(4.18),352(4.52)	64-1576-79B
(Z,Z)-	MeOH	258(4.06),354(4.67)	64-1576-79B
$C_{15}H_{14}O_4S$			
Benzoic acid, 3,6-dihydroxy-2-[(4-methylphenyl)thio]-, methyl ester	EtOH	209(4.46),243(4.12), 317(3.79)	33-2350-79
Benzoic acid, 3,6-dimethoxy-2-(phenylthio)-	EtOH	208(4.31),235(3.96), 279(3.52),306(3.62)	33-2350-79
Benzoic acid, 4-methoxy-2-[(4-methoxyphenyl)thio]-	MeOH	235(4.53),263s(4.17), 301s(3.64)	73-2987-79
$C_{15}H_{14}O_5$			
1H-Naphtho[2,3-c]pyran-1-one, 3,4-dihydro-9,10-dihydroxy-7-methoxy-3-methyl-	C_6H_{12}-5% dioxan	262(4.74),297s(--), 308(3.59),342s(--), 361(4.01),376(4.00)	24-0957-79
	MeOH	260(4.68),308(3.56), 371(4.00)	24-0957-79
	MeOH-NaOH	261(4.61),330(3.60), 376(4.09)	24-0957-79
4H-Pyrano[2,3-g][1]benzoxepin-4-one, 8,11-dihydro-5-hydroxy-9-(hydroxymethyl)-2-methyl- (eranthin)	MeOH	227(4.31),238s(4.19), 253(4.27),258(4.28), 292s(3.54),325(3.59)	102-2053-79
$C_{15}H_{14}O_6$			
2,9,10(1H)-Anthracenetrione, 3,4,4a,9a-tetrahydro-5,8-dihydroxy-4-methoxy-	MeOH	212(4.17),226(4.18), 257(3.96),395(3.89), 414s(--)	24-3453-79
$C_{15}H_{14}S$			
Azuleno[6,5-b]thiophene, 3,5,8-trimethyl-	hexane	235(4.24),259(4.46), 300s(4.18),321(4.37), 335(4.34),365(3.52), 383(3.58),403(3.12), 622(2.72),650s(2.67), 683(2.59),725s(2.28)	18-1549-79
$C_{15}H_{15}$			
Cycloheptatrienylium, 1,3-dimethyl-2-phenyl-, perchlorate	10% HCl	239(4.75),289(3.79), 328(3.10)	39-1005-79B
Cycloheptatrienylium, (3,5-dimethylphenyl)-, perchlorate	10% HCl	227(4.55),270(4.29), 381(4.15)	39-0262-79B
Propylium, 1,1-diphenyl-	H_2SO_4	430(4.49)	39-1395-79B
$C_{15}H_{15}Cl$			
1,1'-Biphenyl, 4'-chloro-2,4,6-trimethyl-	C_6H_{12}	220(4.38)	12-1531-79
$C_{15}H_{15}ClN_2$			
1,4-Benzenediamine, N'-[(4-chlorophenyl)methylene]-N,N-dimethyl-	EtOH	220s(--),264(4.38), 334s(2.88),388(3.29)	2-0338-79B
1H-Pyrido[2,3-b]indole, 2-chloro-1-methyl-3-propyl-	pH 1	250(4.24),265s(4.03), 318(4.17),355(3.88)	103-0879-79

Compound	Solvent	λ_{max}(log ε)	Ref.
1H-Pyrido[2,3-b]indole, 2-chloro-1-methyl-3-propyl- (cont.)	pH 13	260s(4.21),280(4.29), 325(4.17),400(3.62)	103-0879-79
$C_{15}H_{15}ClN_2O_2$			
1H-Indazole-5-carboxylic acid, 1-(4-chlorophenyl)-4,5,6,7-tetrahydro-, methyl ester	MeOH	256(4.19)	87-0048-79
2H-Indazole-5-carboxylic acid, 2-(4-chlorophenyl)-4,5,6,7-tetrahydro-, methyl ester	MeOH	274(4.37)	87-0048-79
$C_{15}H_{15}ClN_2O_2S$			
Acetamide, 2-amino-N-[3-(2-chlorobenzoyl)-5-ethyl-2-thienyl]-	MeOH	240(4.24),270(4.06), 351(3.95)	73-3604-79
$C_{15}H_{15}ClN_2O_3$			
2-Propenoic acid, 2-[(chloroacetyl)amino]-3-(6-methyl-1H-indol-3-yl)-, methyl ester, (E)-	isoPrOH	355(4.18)	44-3741-79
(Z)-	isoPrOH	346(4.32)	44-3741-79
1H-Pyrazole-3-carboxylic acid, 1-(4-chlorophenyl)-5-(3-hydroxy-1-propenyl)-, ethyl ester	EtOH	254(3.9)	77-0221-79
$C_{15}H_{15}Cl_2NO_2$			
1,3-Cyclohexanedione, 2-[(3,4-dichlorophenyl)amino]methylene]-5,5-dimethyl-	hexane	238(4.15),356(4.52)	131-0077-79D
	EtOH	352(4.41)	131-0077-79D
$C_{15}H_{15}F$			
1,1'-Biphenyl, 4'-fluoro-2,3,4-trimethyl-	C_6H_{12}	238(4.02)	12-1531-79
1,1'-Biphenyl, 4'-fluoro-2,4,6-trimethyl-	C_6H_{12}	266(3.11),272(3.02)	12-1531-79
$C_{15}H_{15}N$			
Benzenemethanamine, α-methyl-N-(phenylmethylene)-, (S)-	hexane	210s(4.43),240s(4.28), 247(4.34),255s(4.18), 277(3.15),287(3.00)	44-1690-79
	EtOH	240s(4.23),249(4.32), 278s(3.28),287s(3.04)	44-1690-79
$C_{15}H_{15}NO$			
9-Acridinemethanol, 9,10-dihydro-2-methyl-	pH 1	209(4.52),285(4.19)	4-0257-79
	EtOH	209(4.52),285(4.20)	4-0257-79
Cyclopenta[b]pyrido[1,2-a]indol-5(4H)-one, 1,2,3,12b-tetrahydro-	MeOH	245(3.92),302(3.30), 373(4.34)	5-1048-79
Ethanamine, α-phenyl-N-salicylidene-, (S)-	hexane	255(4.18),262s(4.11), 320(3.70)	44-1690-79
4H-Indol-4-one, 1,5,6,7-tetrahydro-2-methyl-1-phenyl-	EtOH	250(4.87),280s(4.70)	4-0913-79
4a,9a-Propano-9H-carbazol-2(1H)-one	MeOH	299(4.28),302(3.30), 355s(3.03)	5-1048-79
	dioxan	228(4.40),308(3.55)	5-1048-79
1H-Pyrrolizine-5-carboxaldehyde, 2,3-dihydro-6-methyl-7-phenyl-	MeOH	206(4.15),251(4.14), 315(4.24)	83-0896-79
$C_{15}H_{15}NOS$			
Benzenecarbothioamide, N,3-dimethyl-N-phenyl-, S-oxide	MeOH	358(3.91)	5-0248-79
Benzenecarbothioamide, N,4-dimethyl-N-phenyl-, S-oxide	MeOH	358(3.95)	5-0248-79

Compound	Solvent	λ_{max}(log ϵ)	Ref.
$C_{15}H_{15}NOS_2$			
2-Cyclohexen-1-one, 5,5-dimethyl-3-(2-benzothiazolylthio)-	EtOH	238(4.02),270(4.11), 295(4.03)	94-0676-79
$C_{15}H_{15}NO_2$			
Acetophenone, 2-amino-3-(4-methoxy-phenyl)-	EtOH	225(4.42),242(4.36), 277s(3.52),369(3.79)	33-0304-79
Acetophenone, 2-amino-5-(4-methoxy-phenyl)-	EtOH	247(4.50),284(4.37), 382(3.65)	33-0304-79
1,1'-Biphenyl, 2,4,6-trimethyl-4'-ni-tro-	C_6H_{12}	259(3.97)	12-1531-79
[1,1'-Biphenyl]-3-ol, 2,4',5-trimethyl-6-nitroso-	DMF	720(1.04)	104-0311-79
$C_{15}H_{15}NO_2S$			
Benzenecarbothioamide, 4-methoxy-N-(4-methoxyphenyl)-N-methyl-, S-oxide	MeOH	356(3.91)	5-0248-79
	CCl_4	380(3.89)	5-0248-79
$C_{15}H_{15}NO_3$			
[1,1'-Biphenyl]-3-ol, 4'-methoxy-2,5-dimethyl-6-nitroso-	DMF	710(1.08)	104-0311-79
$C_{15}H_{15}NO_3S_2$			
2-Cyclohexen-1-one, 5,5-dimethyl-3-(2-benzothiazolylsulfonyl)-	EtOH	246(4.09)	94-0676-79
$C_{15}H_{15}NO_4$			
1H-Azepine-4-carboxylic acid, 2,5-di-hydro-3-hydroxy-2-oxo-7-phenyl-, ethyl ester	dioxan	220(4.15),257(4.16)	142-1427-79
Benzoic acid, 3,6-dihydroxy-2-(methyl-phenylamino)-, methyl ester	EtOH	206(4.32),241(4.20), 298(3.71)	33-2350-79
6-Oxa-1-azabicyclo[5.2.0]nonane-3,5,9-trione, 2,2-dimethyl-4-phenyl-	EtOH	291(3.92)	88-0391-79
2-Propenoic acid, 3-(1,2-dihydro-1-methoxy-2-oxo-3-quinolinyl)-, ethyl ester	MeOH	253(3.88),306(4.32)	118-0903-79
$C_{15}H_{15}NO_4S_2$			
2-Hexenenitrile, 4-acetyl-3-(methyl-thio)-5-oxo-2-(phenylsulfonyl)-	EtOH	226s(3.97),309(4.24), 410(2.91)	95-1234-79
$C_{15}H_{15}NO_5$			
2,3-Indolizinedicarboxylic acid, 1-(1-oxopropyl)-, dimethyl ester	MeOH and MeOH-$HClO_4$	225(4.35),248(4.57), 279s(4.00),286(4.10), 320s(4.35),332(4.40), 347s(4.18)	39-0584-79C
1H-Indole-1-butanoic acid, 3-(2-meth-oxy-2-oxoethyl)-γ-oxo-	MeOH	238(4.26),291(3.80), 298(3.85)	44-3994-79
3,6-Quinolinedicarboxylic acid, 1,2-di-hydro-1,5-dimethyl-2-oxo-, dimethyl ester	EtOH	212(4.24),260(4.66), 303(3.83),359(3.73)	39-0686-79C
$C_{15}H_{15}NO_6S$			
1H-Pyrrole-3,4-dicarboxylic acid, 2-[(4-methylphenyl)sulfonyl]-, dimethyl ester	EtOH	262(4.21)	94-2857-79
$C_{15}H_{15}NO_6S_2$			
Propanedioic acid, [2-cyano-1-(methyl-thio)-2-(phenylsulfonyl)ethenyl]-,	EtOH	332(4.06),398(3.79)	95-1234-79

Compound	Solvent	λ_{max}(log ε)	Ref.
dimethyl ester (cont.)			95-1234-79
$C_{15}H_{15}N_2$			
1H-Imidazolium, 4,5-dihydro-1,3-diphenyl-, chloride	MeOH	313(4.12)	24-0445-79
$C_{15}H_{15}N_3$			
Propanedinitrile, [3-(dimethylamino)-2-methyl-1-phenyl-2-propenylidene]-	CH_2Cl_2	403(4.55)	118-0376-79
Propanedinitrile, [3-(dimethylamino)-1-(phenylmethyl)-2-propenylidene]-	CH_2Cl_2	392(4.64)	118-0376-79
$C_{15}H_{15}N_3O$			
Dehydrodebenzoevodiamine, hydrochloride	EtOH	242(4.06),326(4.16)	114-0127-79D
2H-Indole-2,2-dipropanenitrile, 1,3-dihydro-1-methyl-3-oxo-	EtOH	235(4.37),260(3.88), 425(3.68)	103-0994-79
1,2,4-Oxadiazol-3-ethanamine, 5-methyl-N-2-naphthalenyl-	EtOH	244(4.65),284(3.97), 348(2.13)	150-0801-79
Propanamide, N-phenyl-2-(phenylhydrazono)-	EtOH	207(4.10),222(4.08), 242(4.06),455(3.81)	7-0563-79
3(2H)-Pyridazinone, 4,5-dihydro-6-(4-methylphenyl)-4-(1H-pyrrol-1-yl)-	EtOH	271(4.21)	80-0453-79
$C_{15}H_{15}N_3OS$			
4H-Pyrrolo[2,3-d]pyrimidin-4-one, 1,7-dihydro-5-methyl-2-(methylthio)-	MeOH	227(4.31),275s(3.95), 295(3.98)	138-1283-79
7-(phenylmethyl)-	MeOH-KOH	227(4.31),283(4.01)	138-1283-79
$C_{15}H_{15}N_3OS_2$			
Acetamide, N-[4-amino-5-cyano-2-(methylthio)-3-thienyl]-N-(phenylmethyl)-	EtOH	293(4.10),321(3.97)	95-1081-79
$C_{15}H_{15}N_3OS_4$			
4-Thiazolidinone, 3-ethyl-5-[[(3-methyl-2(3H)-benzothiazolylidene)amino]-(methylthio)methylene]-2-thioxo-	EtOH	220(4.75),275(4.22), 291(4.22),413(4.47)	94-2879-79
$C_{15}H_{15}N_3O_2$			
1,4-Benzenediamine, N,N-dimethyl-N'-[(4-nitrophenyl)methylene]-	EtOH	209(3.19),280(3.14), 445(3.11)	2-0338-79B
3-Pyridinecarbonitrile, 1,4-dihydro-4-(1-nitroethyl)-1-(phenylmethyl)-	DMSO	325(3.79)	44-1761-79
Pyrimido[4,5-b]quinoline-2,4(3H,10H)-dione, 3,7,8,10-tetramethyl-	6M HCl	259(4.57),351(4.27)	5-1802-79
	MeOH	223(4.54),259(4.57), 329(4.00),401(4.08), 415s(--)	5-1802-79
$C_{15}H_{15}N_3O_2S$			
Benzenesulfonamide, 4-(diazomethyl)-N-methyl-N-(phenylmethyl)-	EtOH	228(4.07),310(4.48), 465(1.65)	118-0531-79
$C_{15}H_{15}N_3O_3$			
[3,4'-Bipyridine]-3'-carboxylic acid, 5'-cyano-1',4',5',6'-tetrahydro-2'-methyl-6'-oxo-, ethyl ester	n.s.g.	270(3.86)	56-2121-79
[4,4'-Bipyridine]-3'-carboxylic acid, 5'-cyano-1',4',5',6'-tetrahydro-2'-methyl-6'-oxo-, ethyl ester	n.s.g.	267(3.88),280(3.91)	56-2121-79
1H-Naphth[2,3-d]imidazole-4,9-dione, 5-methoxy-1,2-dimethyl-8-(methylamino)-	C_6H_{12}	535(3.90)	39-0702-79C
	EtOH	557(--)	39-0702-79C
	EtOH-HCl	582(--)	39-0702-79C

Compound	Solvent	λ_{max}(log ε)	Ref.
1H-Naphth[2,3-d]imidazole-4,9-dione, 8-methoxy-1,2-dimethyl-5-(methyl-amino)-	C_6H_{12}	539(3.84)	39-0702-79C
	EtOH	560(--)	39-0702-79C
	EtOH-HCl	582(--)	39-0702-79C
L-Phenylalanine, N-(pyrazinylcarbonyl)-, methyl ester	isooctane	207(4.31),267(3.96), 332f(2.78)	39-2881-79C
	EtOH	208(4.27),269(3.91), 322(2.85)	39-2881-79C
	MeCN	208(4.31),268(3.98), 312(2.70)	39-2881-79C
Propanedinitrile, [1-amino-3-(2,4,6-trimethoxyphenyl)-2-propenylidene]-	EtOH	322(4.09)	64-1580-79B
2,4,6-Triazatricyclo[5.2.1.$0^{2,6}$]dec-8-ene-3,5-dione, 10-(methoxymethyl)-4-phenyl-, anti	MeCN	230(3.82)	35-3315-79
syn	MeCN	229(3.51)	35-3315-79
$C_{15}H_{15}N_3O_5$			
8-Azabicyclo[3.2.1]oct-3-en-2-one, 6-(acetoxymethyl)-8-(5-nitro-2-pyridinyl)-, endo	$CHCl_3$	350(3.92)	39-1525-79C
$C_{15}H_{15}N_3S_2$			
Benzo[b]thiophen-3-amine, N-ethyl-2-[2-(methylthio)-4-pyrimidinyl]-	MeOH	258(4.33),299(4.13), 341(3.89),412(4.21)	118-0442-79
$C_{15}H_{15}N_4O$			
1H-Tetrazolium, 5-ethoxy-1,3-diphenyl-, tetrafluoroborate	n.s.g.	215s(3.77),233s(3.61), 296(4.02)	39-0736-79C
2H-Tetrazolium, 5-ethoxy-2,3-diphenyl-, tetrafluoroborate	n.s.g.	265(3.78),292(3.81)	39-0744-79C
$C_{15}H_{15}N_4O_2$			
4H-Benzo[g]imidazo[1,2,3-ij]pteridin-3-ium, 1,2,5,6-tetrahydro-5,8,9-tri-methyl-4,6-dioxo-, perchlorate	H_2O	385(4.27)	33-0593-79
	MeCN	265(4.48),382(4.26), 431(3.68)	33-0593-79
4H-Benzo[g]imidazo[1,2,3-ij]pteridin-3-ium, 1,2,5,6-tetrahydro-5,9,10-tri-methyl-4,6-dioxo-, perchlorate	H_2O	388(4.03)	33-0593-79
	MeCN	263(4.60),379(4.13)	33-0593-79
1H-1,2,3-Triazolium, 4,5-dihydro-1-(4-methylphenyl)-3-(4-nitrophenyl)-, perchlorate	MeOH	400(4.45)	24-0445-79
$C_{15}H_{15}N_4S$			
2H-Tetrazolium, 5-(ethylthio)-2,3-di-phenyl-, tetrafluoroborate	n.s.g.	231(4.39),257(3.83), 343(3.74)	39-0744-79C
1,2,3,4-Thiatriazolium, 3-(4-methyl-phenyl)-5-(4-methylphenyl)-, tetrafluoroborate	n.s.g.	247s(4.02),270(4.18), 315(4.12),398s(3.28)	39-0741-79C
$C_{15}H_{15}N_7O_2$			
Benzoic acid, 4-[[(2,4-diamino-6-pteri-dinyl)methyl]methylamino]-	pH 13	258(4.38),286(4.33), 371(3.85)	87-0869-79
$C_{15}H_{16}BrNOS_2$			
Cyclohexanecarbodithioic acid, 2-imino-, 2-(4-bromophenyl)-2-oxoethyl ester	EtOH	250(4.23),313(3.91), 387(4.32)	150-1732-79
$C_{15}H_{16}BrN_3O$			
7-Azabicyclo[4.3.1]deca-3,8-dien-10-one, 9-bromo-7-(4,6-dimethylpyrimi-din-2-yl)-	$CHCl_3$	287(4.24)	39-1525-79C

Compound	Solvent	λ_{max}(log ε)	Ref.
$C_{15}H_{16}ClNO_2$			
2H-Pyran-2-one, 3-chloro-4-(diethyl-amino)-6-phenyl-	EtOH	229(3.87),262(4.41), 303(4.09),341s(3.91)	4-0093-79
$C_{15}H_{16}ClN_3$			
Propanedinitrile, [[4-(2-chloroethyl)-ethylamino]-2-methylphenyl]methylene]-	EtOH	438(4.69)	110-1769-79
$C_{15}H_{16}ClN_3O_3$			
Pyrimido[4,5-b]quinoline-2,4(1H,3H)-di-one, 8-chloro-5,10-dihydro-5-methoxy-3,7,10-trimethyl-	MeOH	255(4.39),289(4.11)	5-1802-79
$C_{15}H_{16}FN_3$			
Piperidine, 1-[[[2-cyano-2-(4-fluoro-phenyl)ethenyl]imino]methyl]-	MeOH	231(4.06),336(4.53)	83-0039-79
$C_{15}H_{16}FeO$			
[4]Ferrocenophan-6-one, 9-methyl-	H_2O	268(3.74),344(2.83), 440(2.35)	44-2920-79
	70% H_2SO_4	262(3.94),350(2.87), 450(2.68)	44-2920-79
$(C_{15}H_{16}N)_n$			
Poly(vinylbenzyl 4-picolinium), chloride	MeOH	220s(4.47),257(3.89)	47-0777-79
$C_{15}H_{16}NO$			
Pyridinium, 1-ethyl-2-[2-(2-hydroxy-phenyl)ethenyl]-, iodide	EtOH	373(4.17),500(3.38)	80-1491-79
	$CHCl_3$	386(4.14),525(3.20)	80-1491-79
	CCl_4	380(4.19),520(3.18)	80-1491-79
Pyridinium, 1-ethyl-2-[2-(4-hydroxy-phenyl)ethenyl]-, iodide	EtOH	385(4.63),495(3.91)	80-1491-79
	$CHCl_3$	390(4.34),560(3.80)	80-1491-79
	CCl_4	390(4.34),546(3.49)	80-1491-79
$C_{15}H_{16}N_2$			
Benzenamine, N,N-dimethyl-4-[(phenyl-imino)methyl]-	EtOH	220(2.97),242(2.78), 315s(2.90),339(3.41)	2-0338-79B
1,4-Benzenediamine, N,N-dimethyl-N'-(phenylmethylene)-	EtOH	221(3.32),256(3.34), 328s(--),380(3.25)	2-0338-79B
5H-Cyclopenta[d]pyrimidine, 6,7-di-hydro-4,7-dimethyl-2-phenyl-	EtOH	258(4.38)	39-1871-79C
1H-Indole-2-acetonitrile, α-(2,2-di-methylpropylidene)-	EtOH	248(3.85),272(3.71), 317(4.22)	107-0505-79
7,10-Methanocycloocta[b]quinoxaline, 6,7,8,9,10,11-hexahydro-	EtOH	205(4.54),237(4.51), 318(3.92)	56-1221-79
$C_{15}H_{16}N_2O$			
Benzeneacetonitrile, α-(3,4-dimethyl-5-oxo-2-pyrrolidinylidene)-4-methyl-, (E)-	EtOH	278(4.25)	49-0201-79
Cyclopenta[5,6]pyrido[2,1-f][1,6]naph-thyridin-6(7H)-one, 4b,5,8,9,11,12-hexahydro-	EtOH	330(4.22)	4-0527-79
Ethanone, 2-[(4-methylphenyl)amino]-1-phenyl-, oxime, (70% Z)	MeOH	243(4.18)	56-1147-79
Indolo[2,3-a]quinolizin-7(6H)-one, 1,2,3,4,12,12b-hexahydro-	MeOH	243(4.22),262(4.07), 297(4.00)	5-1643-79
7,10-Methanocycloocta[b]quinoxalin-13-ol, 6,7,8,9,10,11-hexahydro-	EtOH	208(4.40),238(4.46), 320(3.94)	56-1221-79
Pyridine, 2-(2-phenyl-1-pyrrolidinyl)-, 1-oxide, (S)-	MeOH	335(3.61)	4-0591-79

Compound	Solvent	λ_{max}(log ε)	Ref.
Pyridine, 2-(3-phenyl-1-pyrrolidinyl)-, 1-oxide, (S)-(+)-	MeOH	337(3.63)	4-0591-79
$C_{15}H_{16}N_2OS_3$			
4-Thiazolidinone, 3-ethyl-5-(3-propyl-2(3H)-benzothiazolylidene)-2-thioxo-	EtOH	412s(4.48),429(4.65)	73-1413-79
$C_{15}H_{16}N_2OS_4$			
Urea, bis(4,5,6,7-tetrahydro-1,3-benzodithiol-2-ylidene)-	MeCN	229(4.40),409(4.84)	48-0827-79
$C_{15}H_{16}N_2O_2S$			
3-Indolizinecarboxylic acid, 1-cyano-6,8-dimethyl-2-(methylthio)-, ethyl ester	EtOH	236(4.37),273(4.48), 281(4.49),331(4.33)	95-0540-79
$C_{15}H_{16}N_2O_2S_2$			
2,4-Pentanedione, 3-[[(3-methyl-2(3H)-benzothiazolylidene)amino](methylthio)methylene]-	EtOH	220(4.52),264(4.19), 302(4.15),322(4.12)	94-2879-79
2-Thiophenecarboxylic acid, 3-amino-5-(methylthio)-4-[(phenylmethylene)-amino]-, ethyl ester	EtOH	266(4.23),303(4.35), 356(4.07)	95-1081-79
$C_{15}H_{16}N_2O_2S_3$			
4-Thiazolidinone, 3-ethyl-5-(3-ethyl-x-methoxy-2(3H)-benzothiazolylidene)-2-thioxo-	EtOH	420s(4.65),437(4.79)	73-1413-79
$C_{15}H_{16}N_2O_3$			
Methanone, (3,6-diethoxypyrazinyl)phenyl-	EtOH	207(4.08),220(4.04), 253(3.77),329(3.72)	39-1889-79C
2-Propenamide, 2-acetoxy-3-(4-cyanophenyl)-N-(1-methylethyl)-	n.s.g.	284(4.255)	106-0008-79
2-Propenoic acid, 2-(acetylamino)-3-(6-methyl-1H-indol-3-yl)-, methyl ester, (E)-	isoPrOH	346(4.15)	44-3741-79
(Z)-	isoPrOH	342(4.33)	44-3741-79
4-Pyridazinecarboxylic acid, 2,5-dihydro-2,6-dimethyl-5-oxo-3-phenyl-, ethyl ester	EtOH	210(3.95),233(3.74), 280(4.13)	44-3053-79
Pyridazinium, 4-(ethoxycarbonyl)-5-hydroxy-1,6-dimethyl-3-phenyl-, hydroxide, inner salt	EtOH	209(4.16),247(4.15), 332(3.82)	44-3053-79
$C_{15}H_{16}N_2O_3S_2$			
Acetic acid, [[3,4,5,6,7,8-hexahydro-4-oxo-3-(2-propenyl)[1]benzothieno-[2,3-d]pyrimidin-2-yl]thio]-	n.s.g.	245(4.18),275(3.83), 305(3.16),325(4.05)	124-0871-79
$C_{15}H_{16}N_2O_4$			
Piperidine, 1-[1-(2-furanyl)-2-(5-nitro-2-furanyl)ethenyl]-	EtOH	466(4.24)	94-3078-79
5-Pyrimidinecarboxylic acid, 2-(2-ethoxyphenyl)-1,4-dihydro-4-oxo-, ethyl ester	EtOH	205(4.25),228(4.03), 261s(3.81),331(4.14)	87-0263-79
$C_{15}H_{16}N_2O_5$			
1H-Pyrazole-4,5-dicarboxylic acid, 3-acetyl-4,5-dihydro-1-phenyl-, dimethyl ester	CH_2Cl_2	241(4.05),289(3.41), 299(3.41),361(4.27)	24-1206-79

Compound	Solvent	λ_{max}(log ε)	Ref.
$C_{15}H_{16}N_2O_5S$			
Benzoic acid, 3-hydroxy-5-methoxy-, 2-[(4-methylphenyl)sulfonyl]hydrazide	EtOH	209(4.47),250s(3.87), 301(3.19)	150-0301-79
$C_{15}H_{16}N_2O_7S_2$			
Ceph-3-em-4-carboxylic acid, 7-amino-3-methyl-2-oxo-, p-toluenesulfonate	EtOH	316(3.74)	87-0743-79
$C_{15}H_{16}N_2S$			
1(2H)-Naphthalenethione, 2-(1,3-dimethyl-2-imidazolidinylidene)-	EtOH	223(4.78),245s(4.44), 348(4.11)	18-3640-79
2(3H)-Naphthalenethione, 3-(1,3-dimethyl-2-imidazolidinylidene)-	EtOH	218(4.82),262(4.58), 314(4.31)	18-3640-79
$C_{15}H_{16}N_2S_2$			
Carbamodithioic acid, (1,5-dimethyl-2(1H)-pyridinylidene)-, phenylmethyl ester	EtOH	220(4.16),308(3.91), 370(4.06)	94-2879-79
$C_{15}H_{16}N_2S_5$			
Thiourea, bis(4,5,6,7-tetrahydro-1,3-benzodithiol-2-ylidene)-	MeCN	250(4.80),261(4.80), 403(4.85)	48-0827-79
$C_{15}H_{16}N_3$			
1H-Benzimidazolium, 1,3-dimethyl-2-(4-methyl-2-pyridinyl)-, iodide	EtOH	285(4.18)	4-1583-79
1H-Benzimidazolium, 1,3-dimethyl-2-(6-methyl-2-pyridinyl)-, iodide	EtOH	288(4.17)	4-1583-79
1H-1,2,3-Triazolium, 4,5-dihydro-1-(4-methylphenyl)-3-phenyl-, perchlorate	MeOH	243(4.10),248(4.07), 392(4.37)	24-0445-79
$C_{15}H_{16}N_3O$			
Pyrimido[1',2':1,2]pyrido[3,4-b]indolium, 2,3,4,6,7,12-hexahydro-1-methyl-4-oxo-, iodide	EtOH	242(4.06),328(4.16), 340(4.00)	114-0127-79D
$C_{15}H_{16}N_4$			
1H-Benzimidazole-2-acetonitrile, α-(1-piperidinylmethylene)-	MeOH	211(4.36),264(3.96), 325(4.47)	83-0039-79
$C_{15}H_{16}N_4O$			
Formazan, 3-ethoxy-1,5-diphenyl-	n.s.g.	258(4.19),295(3.92), 433(4.43)	39-0744-79C
$C_{15}H_{16}N_4O_2$			
Benzo[g]pteridine-2,4(1H,3H)-dione, 1,3,7,8,9-pentamethyl-	MeCN	254(4.44),352(3.86), 389(3.66)	33-0593-79
Benzo[g]pteridine-2,4(3H,10H)-dione, 3,7,8,9,10-pentamethyl-	H_2O	271(4.56),395(4.16), 452(3.95)	33-0593-79
	MeCN	271(4.53),370(4.01), 450(3.97)	33-0593-79
4H-Furo[3,2-b]pyrrole-5-carboxylic acid, 2-(2-aminophenyl)-4-ethyl-, hydrazide	MeOH	357(4.44)	73-1805-79
1H-Pyrazole-4-carbonitrile, 5-(1,1-dimethylethyl)-3-methyl-1-(4-nitrophenyl)-	EtOH	270(3.90)	78-1331-79
4H-Pyrimido[4,5-b][1,4]oxazin-4-one, 2-amino-6-(3-phenylpropyl)-	2M HCl	266(3.94),351(3.71)	87-0797-79
	2M NaOH	276(4.04),323(4.00)	87-0797-79
$C_{15}H_{16}N_4O_3$			
Pyrido[2,3-d]pyrimidine-6-carboxalde-	EtOH	237(4.31),281(4.07),	4-1169-79

Compound	Solvent	λ max(log ε)	Ref.
hyde, 7,8-dihydro-5-hydroxy-7-oxo-8-(2-propenyl)-2-(1-pyrrolidinyl)-		314s(3.96),330s(4.07), 344(4.11),374(4.16)	4-1169-79
$C_{15}H_{16}N_4O_4S$			
Formazan, 3-[[(methylsulfonyl)methyl]-sulfonyl]-1,5-diphenyl-	EtOH	434(4.31)	104-0370-79
	$HOAc-H_2SO_4$	580(4.48)	104-0370-79
$C_{15}H_{16}N_4O_6$			
2-Propenoic acid, 2-methyl-, 2-(3,4-dihydro-2,4-dioxo-1(2H)-pyrimidinyl)-1-[(3,4-dihydro-2,4-dioxo-1(2H)-pyrimidinyl)methyl]ethyl ester	H_2O	266(4.28)	126-2303-79
$C_{15}H_{16}N_4S$			
Formazan, 3-(ethylthio)-1,5-diphenyl-	n.s.g.	270(4.13),413(4.35), 535(3.64)	39-0744-79C
1,3,4-Thiadiazol-2-amine, N-butyl-5-(4-quinolinyl)-	EtOH	237(4.32),330s(--), 348(4.07)	106-0537-79
$C_{15}H_{16}N_6O_4S$			
9H-Purine-9-propanoic acid, 6-amino-α-[[(4-methylphenyl)sulfonyl]amino]-	n.s.g.	260(4.08)	65-0989-79
$C_{15}H_{16}N_8O_8$			
Imidazo[1,5-a]-1,3,5-triazin-4(3H)-one, 2-(dimethylamino)-6,8-dimethyl-, picrate	MeCN	257(4.21),374(4.25)	44-3835-79
$C_{15}H_{16}O$			
Ethanone, 1-(4,6,8-trimethyl-2-azulenyl)-	benzene	585(2.87)	70-0221-79
2-Propyn-1-one, 1-(1-methylcyclopentyl)-3-phenyl-	EtOH	216(4.02),226(3.79), 237s(3.78),250s(3.91), 273(4.16),281s(4.12)	33-0852-79
$C_{15}H_{16}O_2$			
2,4-Cyclohexadien-1-one, 6-(4-methoxyphenyl)-2,6-dimethyl-	MeOH	227(4.10)	12-1551-79
2,4-Cyclohexadien-1-one, 6-(4-methoxyphenyl)-4,6-dimethyl-	MeOH	228(4.11)	12-1551-79
1H-Fluorene-2-carboxylic acid, 2,3,4,9-tetrahydro-8-methyl-	EtOH	262(4.20)	44-4562-79
1,4-Naphthalenedione, 2,3-dihydro-2-(3-methyl-2-butenyl)-, (R)- (catalponone)	EtOH	225(4.56),253(4.10), 302(3.48)	95-0500-79
2(1H)-Phenanthrenone, 3,4,9,10-tetrahydro-7-methoxy-	EtOH	274(4.21)	118-0374-79
2(3H)-Phenanthrenone, 4,4a,9,10-tetrahydro-7-methoxy-	EtOH	232(4.28)	118-0374-79
$C_{15}H_{16}O_2S_2$			
Naphtho[2,1-b:6,5-b']dithiophene, 2,3,3a,9,10,10a-hexahydro-10a-methyl-, 1,1-dioxide	MeOH	227(4.32),259(3.79), 265(3.77),293(3.50), 303(3.51)	13-0729-79B
3,17-Dithia-A-norestra-1,5(10),8,14-tetraene, 2,4,5,9,10,10a-hexahydro-10a-methyl-, S,S-dioxide	MeOH	245(4.33),252(4.29), 313(4.22)	13-0729-79B
3-Thiophenecarboxylic acid, 5-ethyl-2-(phenylthio)-, ethyl ester	MeOH	223(4.29),245s(4.03), 314(3.87)	73-2997-79
$C_{15}H_{16}O_3$			
1H-Benzocycloheptene-9-carboxylic acid,	n.s.g.	265(4.10),400(4.37)	77-0528-79

Compound	Solvent	λ_{max}(log ϵ)	Ref.
9,9a-dihydro-9a-methyl-1-oxo-, ethyl ester, trans (cont.)			77-0528-79
1,2-Naphthalenedione, 3-(1-hydroxy-1-methylethyl)-5,8-dimethyl-	EtOH	225(4.23),255(4.32), 400(3.14)	39-0237-79C
Naphtho[2,3-b]furan-2,6(3H,4H)-dione, 3a,4,5,8a,9,9a-hexahydro-8a-methyl-3,5-bis(methylene)- (encelin)	MeOH	213(4.18),239(4.03)	102-1743-79
1(2H)-Phenanthrenone, 3,4,9,10-tetrahydro-9-hydroxy-10-methoxy-, cis	MeOH	211(3.93),218(3.89), 228(4.14),231(4.04), 249(3.35),299(4.11), 312s(3.98)	5-0297-79
$C_{15}H_{16}O_4$			
2H,6H-Benzo[1,2-b:5,4-b']dipyran-2-one, 7,8-dihydro-10-methoxy-8,8-dimethyl-	MeOH	260(3.55),325(3.99)	102-1580-79
2H-1-Benzopyran-2-one, 8-(2-formyl-2-methylpropyl)-7-methoxy-	EtOH	250(3.69),258(3.79), 322(4.17)	2-0113-79A
2H-1-Benzopyran-2-one, 7-hydroxy-5-methyl-6-(3-methyl-2-butenyl)-	MeOH	260(3.05),325(3.58)	102-1580-79
2H-1-Benzopyran-2-one, 6-(2-hydroxy-3-methyl-3-butenyl)-7-methoxy-	EtOH	225(3.98),245s(3.55), 254s(3.52),300s(3.85), 331(4.12)	102-1073-79
2H-1-Benzopyran-2-one, 7-methoxy-8-(3-methyl-2-oxobutyl)-	EtOH	248(3.52),255(3.57), 324(4.22)	2-0113-79A
Butanedioic acid, (1-methylpropylidene)(phenylmethylene)-	EtOH	262(4.07)	42-0068-79
$C_{15}H_{16}O_5$			
2H-1-Benzopyran-2-one, 8-hydroxy-6-methoxy-7-[(3-methyl-2-butenyl)oxy]-(capensin)	MeOH	214(4.57),232s(4.21), 254(3.72),312(4.10)	102-0688-79
1H-Indene-1,7-dicarboxylic acid, 2,3-dihydro-3-oxo-, diethyl ester	MeOH	218(4.70),240s(4.06), 265s(3.28),290(3.53), 299(3.55)	18-2962-79
1,4-Naphthalenedione, 6-(1-ethoxyethyl)-5-hydroxy-7-methoxy-	MeOH	223(3.90),262(3.47), 270s(3.70),426(3.13)	150-2685-79
1,3,6-Trioxaspiro[4.4]non-7-ene-8-carboxylic acid, 2,2-dimethyl-7-phenyl-, (±)-	EtOH	216(3.98),282(3.94)	136-0055-79B
$C_{15}H_{16}O_6$			
1H-Indene-1,7-dicarboxylic acid, 2,3-dihydro-6-methoxy-1-methyl-3-oxo-, dimethyl ester	MeOH	228(4.43),271(4.33), 295(4.13)	18-2962-79
$C_{15}H_{16}O_7$			
Bicyclo[3.2.2]nona-2,6,8-triene-6,7-dicarboxylic acid, 1,5-dimethoxy-4-oxo-, dimethyl ester	MeOH	214(3.90),285s(2.85), 360(1.91)	18-2023-79
1H-Indene-3a,7a-dicarboxylic acid, 4,7-dimethoxy-1-oxo-, dimethyl ester, cis	MeOH	217(4.00),290(3.73), 365(2.83)	18-2023-79
$C_{15}H_{16}O_9$			
4H-1-Benzopyran-4-one, 3-[(6-deoxy-α-L-mannopyranosyl)oxy]-5,7-dihydroxy-(eucryphin)	MeOH	252(4.351),260s(4.327), 298(3.898),328(3.66)	102-0867-79
$C_{15}H_{16}S_2Si$			
1,3-Dithia-2-silacyclohexane, 2,2-diphenyl-	hexane	194(4.73),220(4.15), 260s(2.94),266(2.91), 273(2.79)	114-0195-79D

Compound	Solvent	λmax(log ε)	Ref.
1,3-Dithia-2-silacyclopentane, 4-methyl-2,2-diphenyl-	hexane	223(4.27),245s(3.63), 273(2.86)	114-0195-79D
$C_{15}H_{16}Si$			
Silane, 1-acenaphthylenyltrimethyl-	C_6H_{12}	233(4.51),329(3.95)	44-4275-79
$C_{15}H_{17}BrO_2$			
1,2-Propanedione, 1-(8-bromo-5,6,7,8-tetrahydro-5,5-dimethyl-1-naphthalenyl)-	CCl_4	416(1.61)	39-0508-79C
$C_{15}H_{17}ClN_2O_2$			
8-Azabicyclo[3.2.1]oct-3-ene-6-carbonitrile, 6-chloro-8-(4,4-dimethyl-3-oxo-1-pentenyl)-2-oxo-	EtOH	225(3.15),300(4.34)	56-0057-79
2-Propenoic acid, 3-[4-[(2-chloroethyl)methylamino]phenyl]-2-cyano-, ethyl ester	EtOH	418(4.63)	110-1769-79
	EtOH-KOH	346(--)	110-1769-79
	CCl_4	405(--)	110-1769-79
	KBr	422(--)	110-1769-79
$C_{15}H_{17}Cl_2N_3O_6$			
Propanoic acid, 3-chloro-, 2-[(3-chloro-1-oxopropoxy)methyl]-2,3,3a,9a-tetrahydro-6-imino-6H-furo[2',3':4,5]-oxazolo[3,2-a]pyrimidin-3-yl ester, monotetrafluoroborate	MeOH	235(4.01),264(4.08)	87-0639-79
$C_{15}H_{17}Cl_3NO_4$			
1-Piperidinyloxy, 2,2,6,6-tetramethyl-4-[(2,4,5-trichloro-3,6-dioxo-1,4-cyclohexadien-1-yl)oxy]-	heptane	294(4.19),425(2.66)	70-1441-79
	EtOH	293(4.14),421(2.70)	70-1441-79
$C_{15}H_{17}F_2N_2S$			
Benzothiazolium, 2-[4-(dimethylamino)-1,3-difluoro-1,3-butadienyl]-3-ethyl-, perchlorate	EtOH	518(4.02)	124-0872-79
$C_{15}H_{17}N$			
Benzenamine, 4-(1,3,5-cycloheptatrien-1-yl)-N,N-dimethyl-	EtOH	342(4.30)	48-0117-79
Benzenamine, 4-(1,3,5-cycloheptatrien-2-yl)-N,N-dimethyl-	EtOH	276(4.41)	48-0117-79
Benzenamine, 4-(1,3,5-cycloheptatrien-3-yl)-N,N-dimethyl-	EtOH	313(4.27)	48-0117-79
Benzenamine, 4-(1,3,5-cycloheptatrien-7-yl)-N,N-dimethyl-	EtOH	253(4.34),300s(--)	48-0117-79
Benzenamine, N-methyl-2-(2,5-dimethylphenyl)-	EtOH	300(3.59)	33-2129-79
Benz[g]isoquinoline, 1,2,3,4-tetrahydro-2,3-dimethyl-	EtOH	228(5.08),256(3.48), 266(3.60),276(3.72), 285(3.70),296(3.50), 309(2.90),320(2.66), 324(2.86)	103-0421-79
Pyrido[1,2-a]indole, 6,7-dihydro-6,9,10-trimethyl-	EtOH	210(4.33),235s(4.19), 254s(3.98),263s(3.81), 307(4.19),319s(4.15), 336s(3.70)	23-0558-79
1H-Pyrrolizine, 2,3-dihydro-2,2-dimethyl-6-phenyl-	MeOH	210(4.21),234(4.08), 278(4.12)	83-0896-79

Compound	Solvent	λ_{max}(log ϵ)	Ref.
$C_{15}H_{17}NO$			
1H-Indeno[2,1-b]pyridine, 2,3,9,9a-tetrahydro-3-(methoxymethylene)-1-methyl-	n.s.g.	230(--),235(3.95), 295(4.24),314(4.34)	44-1108-79
4a,9a-Propano-9H-carbazol-2(1H)-one, 3,4-dihydro-	MeOH	248(3.91),303(3.48)	5-1048-79
	dioxan	249(4.07),307(3.52)	5-1048-79
$C_{15}H_{17}NOS$			
1H-Phenothiazine, 10-acetyl-2,3,4,10-tetrahydro-1-methyl-	EtOH	255(3.63)	94-1982-79
3H-Phenothiazine, 10-acetyl-2,4,4a,10-tetrahydro-1-methyl-	EtOH	233(4.01),255(3.66), 292(2.89),302(2.73)	94-1982-79
$C_{15}H_{17}NO_2$			
[1,1'-Biphenyl]-2-amine, 2',5'-dimethoxy-N-methyl-	EtOH	297(3.30)	33-2129-79
1H-Carbazole-2-carboxylic acid, 2,3,4,9-tetrahydro-3,4-dimethyl-	EtOH	228(4.57),275s(3.84), 283(3.88),290(3.83)	44-4402-79
1,3-Cyclohexanedione, 5,5-dimethyl-2-[(phenylamino)methylene]-	hexane	234(4.06),249(3.96), 351(4.38)	131-0077-79D
	EtOH	349(4.41)	131-0077-79D
3,5-Pyridinedicarboxaldehyde, 1-cyclohexyl-4-ethynyl-1,4-dihydro-	n.s.g.	207s(4.03),234(4.32), 256(3.97),377(3.99)	49-0613-79
1H-Pyrrolo[1,2-a]indole-9-carboxylic acid, 2,3-dihydro-7-methyl-, ethyl ester	EtOH	214(4.45),234(4.23), 283(4.02),291(4.01)	44-4742-79
Quinoline, 2-methyl-4-[(3-methyl-2-butenyl)oxy]-, 1-oxide	MeOH	223(--),246(--), 333(--)	94-1813-79
Spiro[piperidine-3,2'-[2H]pyran]-2-one, 3',4'-dihydro-6-phenyl-	EtOH	242(3.9)	24-0734-79
$C_{15}H_{17}NO_3$			
Benzoic acid, 4-hydroxy-, 8-azabicyclo-[3.2.1]oct-6-en-3-yl ester	EtOH	259(4.01)	12-2071-79
	EtOH-NaOH	302(4.15)	12-2071-79
Geibalansine	EtOH and EtOH-NaOH	230(4.54),237s(4.52), 257s(3.59),265(3.70), 275(3.74),287(3.68), 301s(3.47),313(3.71), 326(3.78)	102-1415-79
4(1H)-Pyridinone, 1-ethyl-2-(hydroxymethyl)-5-(phenylmethoxy)-	MeOH	225(4.35),286(4.16)	18-0107-79
1H-Pyrrole-3-carboxylic acid, 4,5-dihydro-2-methyl-5-oxo-4-(phenylmethyl)-, ethyl ester	EtOH	212(3.85),285(3.93)	44-0808-79
$C_{15}H_{17}NO_4$			
3-Quinolinepropanoic acid, 1,2-dihydro-4-methoxy-2-oxo-, ethyl ester	MeOH and MeOH-acid	226(4.42),245s(3.98), 261s(3.80),269(3.90), 275(3.82),312s(3.78), 322(3.88),333(7.74)	118-0903-79
$C_{15}H_{17}NO_4S$			
D-Ribitol, 1,4-anhydro-1-C-[5-(phenylmethyl)-2-thiazolyl]-, (R)-	acid	254(3.94)	44-4351-79
	pH 7	247(3.97)	44-4351-79
	base	248(4.02)	44-4351-79
$C_{15}H_{17}NO_5$			
Pentanoic acid, 3-[methoxy(phenylamino)-methylene]-2,4-dioxo-, ethyl ester	EtOH	286(4.35)	94-1792-79

Compound	Solvent	λ_{max}(log ϵ)	Ref.
$C_{15}H_{17}NO_6$			
Propanedioic acid, [(1,3-benzodioxol-4-ylamino)methylene]-, diethyl ester	EtOH	207(4.46),323(4.37)	87-1354-79
$C_{15}H_{17}N_2O_3S$			
Thiazolo[3.2-a]benzimidazolium, 2-(ethoxycarbonyl)-9-ethyl-6-hydroxy-3-methyl-, bromide	EtOH	257(3.45),515(3.85)	18-3096-79
$C_{15}H_{17}N_3O$			
7-Azabicyclo[4.3.1]deca-3,8-dien-10-one, 7-(4,6-dimethyl-2-pyrimidinyl)-	$CHCl_3$	277(4.50)	39-1525-79C
[1,1'(4H,4'H)-Bipyridine]-4-carbonitrile, 2,2',4,6'-tetramethyl-4'-oxo-	EtOH	263.0(4.37)	39-1698-79C
Debenzoevodiamine	EtOH	226(4.40),274(3.95), 282(3.96)	114-0127-79D
Pyridine, 2-[2-(3-pyridinyl)-1-piperidinyl]-, 1-oxide, (S)-	MeOH	315(3.44)	4-0591-79
$C_{15}H_{17}N_3O_2$			
β-Alanine, N-(4,9-dihydro-3H-pyrido-[3,4-b]indol-1-yl)-N-methyl-, monoammonium salt	EtOH	242(4.43),320(4.45)	114-0127-79D
1H-Pyrimido[4,5-b]indole-2,4(3H,9H)-dione, 3-pentyl-	$CHCl_3$	272(4.17)	103-0179-79
Pyrimido[4,5-b]quinoline-2,4(1H,3H)-dione, 5,10-dihydro-3,7,8,10-tetramethyl-	pH 11	244(4.25),262(4.27), 314(4.11)	5-1802-79
	MeOH	230(4.23),318(4.10)	5-1802-79
$C_{15}H_{17}N_3O_3$			
5,8-Methano-1H-[1,2,4]triazolo[1,2-a]-pyridazine-1,3(2H)-dione, tetrahydro-10-(methoxymethyl)-2-phenyl-, anti	MeCN	229(3.92)	35-3315-79
syn	MeCN	229(3.95)	35-3315-79
$C_{15}H_{17}N_3O_3S$			
Pyridinium, 4-(dimethylamino)-1-[[[(4-methylphenyl)sulfonyl]amino]carbonyl]-, hydroxide, inner salt	MeCN	302(4.3)	5-1388-79
$C_{15}H_{17}N_3O_4$			
3-Pyridinepropanoic acid, α-acetyl-β-(2-amino-1-cyano-2-oxoethyl)-, ethyl ester	n.s.g.	270(4.00),282(4.01)	56-2121-79
$C_{15}H_{17}N_3O_6$			
4,11-Epoxy-5H-1,3-dioxolo[4,5-e]imidazo[2,1-b][1,3]oxazocine-8-carboxylic acid, 9-(cyanomethyl)-3a,4,11,11a-tetrahydro-2,2-dimethyl-, methyl ester, [3aR-(3aα,4β,11β,11aα)]-	MeOH	243(3.96)	4-0411-79
2,4-Pentadienoic acid, 5-(dimethylamino)-4-(4-methyl-2-nitrophenyl)-2-nitro-, methyl ester. (E,Z)-	EtOH	252(4.07),439(4.63)	44-3748-79
$C_{15}H_{17}N_3O_7$			
Furo[2,3-d]-1,3-dioxol-6-ol, tetrahydro-2,2-dimethyl-6-[(4-nitrophenyl)-azo]-, acetate, [3aS-(3aα,6α,6aα)]-	EtOH	282(4.11)	136-0287-79B

Compound	Solvent	λmax(log ε)	Ref.
$C_{15}H_{17}N_4O_2$			
Benzo[g]pteridinium, 3,4-dihydro-2-methoxy-3,7,8,10-tetramethyl-4-oxo-, perchlorate	H_2O	394(4.23)	33-0593-79
	MeCN	263(4.52),389(4.11), 413(4.09)	33-0593-79
Benzo[g]pteridinium, 1,2,3,4-tetrahydro-1,3,7,8,10-pentamethyl-2,4-dioxo-, perchlorate	H_2O	398(4.23)	33-0593-79
	MeCN	394(4.23)	33-0593-79
$C_{15}H_{17}N_5O_5$			
N^2,5'-Cycloguanosine, N^3-acetyl-2',3'-O-(1-methylethylidene)-	MeOH-HCl	273(4.14)	44-0400-79
	MeOH-NaOH	223(4.13),245(4.23), 280(4.13)	44-0400-79
$C_{15}H_{18}$			
Naphthalene, 1,2-dihydro-2,2,3,4-tetramethyl-1-methylene-	hexane	239s(4.52),244(4.55), 283(3.89)	104-0685-79
$C_{15}H_{18}BrIO$			
2,5-Methano-1-benzoxepin, 7-bromo-2,3,4,5-tetrahydro-2-(iodomethyl)-5,8,10-trimethyl-	EtOH	237(3.89),288(3.34), 298(3.36)	35-6136-79
Phenol, 4-bromo-2-(1,2-dimethyl-3-methylenecyclopentyl)-3-iodo-5-methyl-	EtOH	287(3.68),292(3.33)	35-6136-79
$C_{15}H_{18}ClN_5O_2$			
3H-1,2,4-Triazolo[4,3-d][1,4]benzodiazepine-3,6(5H)-dione, 10-chloro-2-[2-(dimethylamino)ethyl]-2,7-dihydro-7-methyl-, hydrochloride	MeOH	253(4.25),275s(3.92), 302s(3.64)	44-0088-79
$C_{15}H_{18}Cl_3NO_5$			
Propanedioic acid, [3-[1-methyl-5-(trichloroacetyl)-1H-pyrrol-2-yl]propyl]-, dimethyl ester	MeOH	322(4.18)	35-1259-79
$C_{15}H_{18}F_6N_2O_6$			
Pyridinium, 1-(5-amino-5-carboxypentyl)-, trifluoroacetate	H_2O	254s(--),257(3.72), 265s(--)	39-2282-79C
$C_{15}H_{18}FeO$			
[4]Ferrocenophan-6-ol, 9-methyl-	H_2O	338(2.55),440(2.23)	44-2920-79
	70% H_2SO_4	260(3.8),342(2.73), 444(2.39)	44-2920-79
$C_{15}H_{18}IN_5O_5$			
Guanosine, N-acetyl-5'-deoxy-5'-iodo-2',3'-O-(1-methylethylidene)-	MeOH-HCl	266(4.28)	44-0400-79
	MeOH-NaOH	267(4.16)	44-0400-79
$C_{15}H_{18}N_2$			
9-Acridinamine, 1,2,3,4-tetrahydro-N,N-dimethyl-	EtOH	205(4.52),229(4.56), 250(3.44),295(3.44), 308(3.60),321(3.76), 340(3.66)	1-0313-79
1H-Indole-2-acetonitrile, α-(2,2-dimethylpropyl)-	EtOH	267(3.95),278(3.91), 288(3.75)	107-0505-79
Indolo[2,3-a]quinolizine, 1,2,3,4,6,7-12,12b-octahydro-	MeOH	278(3.94),290(3.83)	5-1643-79
$C_{15}H_{18}N_2O$			
Cycloocta[b][1,8]naphthyridin-5(1H)-one, 6,7,8,9,10,11-hexahydro-2-methyl-	EtOH	253(4.43),280(3.54), 291(3.52),336(3.94)	4-0137-79

Compound	Solvent	$\lambda_{max}(\log \epsilon)$	Ref.
12H-Cycloocta[d]pyrido[1,2-a]pyrimidin-12-one, 6,7,8,9,10,11-hexahydro-1-methyl-	EtOH	253(4.10),261(4.05), 360(3.98)	4-0137-79
4-Cycloocten-1-one, 8-(hydrazonophenyl-methyl)-	MeOH	224(3.88),280(4.10)	78-0277-79
6,10-Methano-5H-cyclohepta[b]quinoxa-lin-12-one, 5a,6,7,8,9,10,10a,11-octahydro-5-methyl-, (5aα,6β,10β,10aα)-	EtOH	220(4.64),250(3.94), 302(3.64)	30-0254-79
$C_{15}H_{18}N_2OS_2$			
[1]Benzothieno[2,3-d]pyrimidin-4(3H)-one, 2-(ethylthio)-5,6,7,8-tetra-hydro-3-(2-propenyl)-	n.s.g.	235(4.50),270(4.09), 325(4.26)	124-0871-79
$C_{15}H_{18}N_2O_2$			
8-Azabicyclo[3.2.1]oct-3-ene-6-carbo-nitrile, 8-(4,4-dimethyl-3-oxo-1-pentenyl)-2-oxo-, endo	EtOH	220(3.81),300(4.12)	56-0057-79
1-Piperidineacetic acid, 2-(1H-indol-2-yl)-	MeOH	267(3.99),280(3.90), 290(3.69)	5-1643-79
2-Piperidinone, 6-[3-(2-hydroxyethyl)-1H-indol-2-yl]-	MeOH	282(3.71),290(3.60)	5-1643-79
$C_{15}H_{18}N_2O_3$			
1H-Pyrazole-4-carboxylic acid, 3-(2-hy-droxyethyl)-5-methyl-1-phenyl-, ethyl ester	EtOH	218(4.01),245(4.09)	4-0657-79
1H-Pyrazole-4-carboxylic acid, 5-(2-hy-droxyethyl)-3-methyl-1-phenyl-, ethyl ester	EtOH	220s(4.00),241(4.10)	4-0657-79
4-Pyridazinecarboxylic acid, 1,6-di-hydro-5-hydroxy-1,6-dimethyl-3-phen-yl-, ethyl ester	EtOH	247(4.12),307(3.87)	44-3053-79
$C_{15}H_{18}N_2O_4$			
1H-Benzimidazole, 2-(tetrahydro-6-meth-oxy-2,2-dimethylfuro[2,3-d]-1,3-diox-ol-5-yl)-, [3aR-(3aα,5α,6α,6aα)]-	EtOH	212(3.70),244(3.74), 280(3.85),273(3.86)	33-1298-79
1H-Indazole-4,7-diol, 1-acetyl-6-(1,1-dimethylethyl)-, 4-acetate	n.s.g.	237(4.05)	70-1668-79
1H-Indole-1-acetic acid, 3-[2-(acetyl-amino)ethyl]-5-methoxy-	EtOH	228(4.36),282(3.77), 303(3.70)	12-0399-79
D-Ribitol, 1,4-anhydro-1-C-1H-indazol-3-yl-2,3-O-(1-methylethylidene)-	EtOH	213(4.16),254(3.48), 261(3.46),287(3.64), 292(3.63),300(3.57)	4-0081-79
$C_{15}H_{18}N_2O_4S_2$			
2H-1,4-Benzothiazin-3(4H)-one, 4-meth-yl-2-[(methylthio)-4-morpholinyl-methylene]-, 1,1-dioxide	dioxan	275(3.43),350(3.39)	83-0302-79
$C_{15}H_{18}N_2O_5S$			
5-Thia-1-azabicyclo[4.2.0]oct-2-ene-2-carboxylic acid, 3-(acetoxymethyl)-7-isocyano-8-oxo-, 1,1-dimethylethyl ester	EtOH	268(3.89)	39-2455-79C
$C_{15}H_{18}N_2O_6$			
2,4(1H,3H)-Pyrimidinedione, 1-[5,6,8-trideoxy-2,3-O-(1-methylethylidene)-β-D-ribo-oct-5-enofuranos-7-ulos-1-yl]-, (E)-	EtOH	216(4.05),255(3.92)	33-2788-79

Compound	Solvent	$\lambda_{max}(\log \epsilon)$	Ref.
$C_{15}H_{18}N_2O_6S$			
2,4(1H,3H)-Pyrimidinedione, 1-[2-hydroxy-3-[[(4-methylphenyl)sulfonyl]oxy]propyl]-5-methyl-	n.s.g.	220(4.20),268(4.00)	128-0281-79
$C_{15}H_{18}N_2O_7$			
β-D-ribo-Hept-5-enofuranuronic acid, 1,5,6-trideoxy-1-(3,4-dihydro-2,4-dioxo-1-(2H)-pyrimidinyl)-2,3-O-(1-methylethylidene)-, methyl ester, (E)-	EtOH	212(3.80),256(3.70)	33-2788-79
$C_{15}H_{18}N_3$			
Benzenaminium, N,N,N-trimethyl-4-(phenylazo)-, iodide, (Z)-	EtOH	210(4.09),232(4.17), 332(4.35),455(3.05)	7-0563-79
$C_{15}H_{18}N_4O$			
7-Azabicyclo[4.3.1]deca-3,8-dien-10-one, 7-(4,6-dimethyl-2-pyrimidinyl)-, oxime	$CHCl_3$	246(4.04)	39-1525-79C
$C_{15}H_{18}N_4O_3$			
1,2,4-Triazine-6-acetic acid, 3-amino-2,5-dihydro-α-methyl-5-oxo-2-(phenylmethyl)-, ethyl ester	EtOH	212(--),263(3.87)	39-1120-79C
$C_{15}H_{18}N_4O_4S$			
1H-1,2,4-Triazolium, 4-[bis(ethoxycarbonyl)amino]-2,3-dihydro-5-methyl-1-phenyl-3-thioxo-, hydroxide, inner salt	EtOH	250(4.31)	94-1683-79
$C_{15}H_{18}N_4O_5$			
Mitomycin C	MeOH	217(4.39),360(4.36), 555(2.32)	142-0411-79B
$C_{15}H_{18}N_4O_6$			
9H-Purine, 9-[2,3-O-(3-carboxy-1-methylpropylidene)-β-D-ribofuranosyl]-	MeOH	261(3.74)	136-0117-79G
$C_{15}H_{18}N_4O_6S$			
Inosine, 2',3'-O-(3-carboxy-1-methylpropylidene)-6-thio-	MeOH	325(4.35)	136-0117-79G
$C_{15}H_{18}N_6O$			
Acetamide, N-[8-(dimethylamino)-1,4-dimethyl-1H-cyclohepta[1,2-d:3,4-d']diimidazol-2-yl]-	MeOH	226(3.96),261(4.04), 306(4.56),414(4.14)	23-1707-79
	MeOH-acid	216(4.02),248(3.98), 298(4.53),415(4.26)	23-1707-79
$C_{15}H_{18}N_6O_5$			
1H-Purine-2,6-dione, 7-[3-(3,4-dihydro-5-methyl-2,4-dioxo-1(2H)-pyrimidinyl)-2-hydroxypropyl]-3,7-dihydro-1,3-dimethyl-	H_2O	274(4.19)	126-2303-79
$C_{15}H_{18}O$			
Cyclobuta[a]naphthalen-8b(1H)-ol, 2,2a-dihydro-2,2,3-trimethyl-	EtOH	258s(3.80),267(3.86), 276s(3.78),293s(3.27), 304s(3.06)	77-0276-79

Compound	Solvent	$\lambda_{max}(\log \epsilon)$	Ref.
$C_{15}H_{18}OS$			
1-Hepten-4-ol, 3-ethynyl-1-(phenylthio)-, cis	EtOH	266(4.00)	18-0135-79
6-Nonen-8-yn-4-ol, 5-(phenylthio)-, trans	EtOH	217(4.20)	18-0135-79
$C_{15}H_{18}O_2$			
2-Cyclohexene-1-acetic acid, phenylmethyl ester	n.s.g.	212(3.73)	12-2793-79
2,6-Naphthalenedione, 1,7,8,8a-tetrahydro-1,8a-dimethyl-7-(1-methylethylidene)-, cis-(±)- (warburgiadione)	EtOH	292(4.35)	94-0331-79
Naphtho[2,3-b]furan-2(4H)-one, 4a,5,6-7,8,8a-hexahydro-3,8a-dimethyl-5-methylene- (atractylenolide I)	hexane	274(4.16)	94-2954-79
1,2-Propanedione, 1-(5,6,7,8-tetrahydro-5,5-dimethyl-1-naphthalenyl)-	pentane	404(1.53)	39-0508-79C
$C_{15}H_{18}O_3$			
Anhydroperoxycostunolide	MeOH	233(3.60),300s(1.83)	44-3952-79
3-Acenaphthylenecarboxylic acid, 1,2,6,7,8,8a-hexahydro-5-hydroxy-1,6-dimethyl-, (1α,6α,8aα)-(-)-	MeOH	211(4.51),252(3.98), 310(3.58)	94-2874-79
Cyclodeca[b]furan-2,4-dione, 5,8,9,11a-tetrahydro-3,6,10-trimethyl-, [S-(E,E)]-	n.s.g.	218(4.14),314(2.87)	44-2575-79
Cyclohexanone, 3-[2-(4-methoxyphenyl)-2-oxoethyl]-	MeOH	273(4.27)	2-0152-79B
Furanoeremophilan-14β,6α-olide	MeOH	217(3.93)	18-1182-79
Istanbulin C	EtOH	220(4.15)	102-0338-79
2H-Naphtho[1,8-bc:3,2-b']difuran-2-one, 2a,3,4,5,5a,6,9b,9c-octahydro-9,9c-dimethyl-	MeOH	216(3.90)	18-1182-79
Naphtho[2,3-b]furan-4(4aH)-one, 5,6,7,8-tetrahydro-6-hydroxy-3,4a,5-trimethyl-	EtOH	240(3.88),247(3.88), 256s(--),265s(--), 333(3.79)	94-1747-79
$C_{15}H_{18}O_3S$			
2-Cyclohexen-1-one, 5,5-dimethyl-3-[(4-methylphenyl)sulfonyl]-	EtOH	220(4.08),291(4.21)	94-0676-79
$C_{15}H_{18}O_3S_2$			
3(2H)-Thiophenone, 2-[2-(6,7-dihydrobenzo[b]thien-4(5H)-ylidene)ethyl]-dihydro-2-methyl-, 1,1-dioxide, (±)-	MeOH	225(4.23),254(4.23)	13-0729-79B
$C_{15}H_{18}O_3Se$			
Cyclohexanecarboxylic acid, 2-oxo-1-(phenylseleno)-, ethyl ester	EtOH	226(4.07),272(2.85), 289(2.83)	33-2630-79
$C_{15}H_{18}O_4$			
Anhydroperoxyparthenolide	MeOH	228(3.60),310s(1.58)	44-3952-79
2H-1-Benzopyran-2-one, 8-(3-hydroxy-3-methylbutyl)-7-methoxy-	EtOH	250(3.72),258(3.74), 320(4.15)	2-0113-79A
5,9-Epoxy-5H-benzocycloheptene-5-acetic acid, 6,7,8,9-tetrahydro-9-hydroxy-, ethyl ester	isooctane	255(2.63),262(2.75), 268(2.72)	56-1751-79
	hexane	255(2.66),262(2.77), 269(2.76)	56-1751-79
	MeOH	250s(2.45),255(2.61), 262(2.77),268(2.74)	56-1751-79

Compound	Solvent	$\lambda_{max}(\log \epsilon)$	Ref.
(cont.)	25% MeOH	250s(2.53),255(2.64), 261(2.73),268(2.68)	56-1751-79
	25% MeOH-HCl	250s(2.52),255(2.63), 261(2.74),268(2.68)	56-1751-79
Ethanone, 1-(5,8-dimethoxy-2,2-dimethyl-2H-1-benzopyran-6-yl)-	MeOH	270(3.2),281(3.1), 310(3.9)	18-1203-79
Ethanone, 1-(7,8-dimethoxy-2,2-dimethyl-2H-1-benzopyran-6-yl)-	MeOH	255(3.6),286(3.2)	18-1203-79
Naphthalene, 1,2,3,6-tetramethoxy-8-methyl-	EtOH	240(4.85),276s(3.62), 283(3.66),315(3.09), 329(3.12)	150-0301-79
Parishin C	EtOH	247(4.16)	105-0577-79
$C_{15}H_{18}O_5$			
2H-1-Benzopyran-2-one, 8-(2,3-dihydroxy-3-methylbutyl)-7-methoxy-	EtOH	248(3.65),258(3.67), 324(4.17)	2-0113-79A
$C_{15}H_{18}O_6$			
Butanedioic acid, [(3,4-dimethoxyphenyl)methylene]-, dimethyl ester	EtOH	234(4.08),291(4.07), 310(4.09)	2-0202-79A
$C_{15}H_{18}S_3$			
2,4-Cyclohexadiene-1-thione, 6-(dihydrocyclooctadithiol-2-ylidene)-	CH_2Cl_2	269(4.00),350(3.57), 584(3.38)	18-0496-79
$C_{15}H_{18}Si$			
Silane, (1,2-dihydro-1-acenaphthylenyl)trimethyl-	C_6H_{12}	235(4.47),297(3.97)	44-4275-79
$C_{15}H_{19}BrN_4$			
1H-Imidazole, 2-[(4-bromophenyl)azo]-4,5-dipropyl-	MeOH	248(--),288(--), 408(4.48)	56-2340-79
$C_{15}H_{19}BrO_2$			
Phenol, 4-bromo-2-[3-(hydroxymethyl)-1,2-dimethyl-3-cyclopenten-1-yl]-5-methyl-, (1R-cis)-	EtOH	233(3.87),286(3.44), 293(3.42)	35-6136-79
$C_{15}H_{19}BrO_3$			
3aH,6H-Benz[3,4]oxeto[2,3-b]furan-5(4aH)-one, 7-bromo-1,2-dihydro-4a,8,8-trimethyl-2-(1-methylethenyl)-, [2R-(2α,3aα,4aβ,8aR*)]-	n.s.g.	250(4.04)	138-0301-79
$C_{15}H_{19}ClN$			
Cyclohepta[c]pyrrolium, 2-butyl-6-chloro-1,3-dimethyl-, perchlorate	CH_2Cl_2	242(4.11),267(4.04), 306(4.83),344(3.95), 668(3.14)	24-2087-79
$C_{15}H_{19}ClO$			
1-Butanone, 4-chloro-1-(6,7,8,9-tetrahydro-5H-benzocyclohepten-2-yl)-	MeOH	211(4.35),259(4.18)	73-3604-79
$C_{15}H_{19}N$			
2H-Pyrrole, 2,2-dimethyl-5-(1-methylethyl)-3-phenyl- (unstable)	EtOH	287.5(4.11)	78-2285-79
2H-Pyrrole, 5-ethyl-2,2,4-trimethyl-3-phenyl-	EtOH	252.5(3.78)	78-2285-79
$C_{15}H_{19}NO$			
2-Butanone, 1-(1,3-dihydro-1,3,3-tri-	pH 1	285(3.81)	88-4407-79

Compound	Solvent	λmax(log ε)	Ref.
methyl-2H-indol-2-ylidene)- (cont.)	H_2O	360(4.42)	88-4407-79
3-Buten-2-one, 1-(1-methyl-2-pyrrolidinyl)- (dehydrodarlinine)	EtOH	220(4.04),288(4.34)	12-2523-79
Ferrugine	EtOH	242(4.11)	12-2537-79
Ibalbidine, (±)-, hydrochloride?	EtOH	239(4.02),277(3.26)	150-0413-79
	EtOH-NaOH	261(4.07),295(3.55)	150-0413-79
2(1H)-Pyridinone, 5-ethyl-5,6-dihydro-4-methyl-1-(phenylmethyl)-	EtOH	253(3.58)	94-1847-79
$C_{15}H_{19}NO_2$			
8-Azabicyclo[3.2.1]octan-3-ol, 8-methyl-, benzoate	MeOH	273(2.85),280(2.72)	4-0625-79
epimer	MeOH	275(2.94),281(2.85)	4-0625-79
1(2H)-Phenanthridinone, 8-acetyl-3,4,5,6,6a,7,10,10a-octahydro-, cis	EtOH	231(4.12),298(4.40)	44-0124-79
$C_{15}H_{19}NO_3$			
Spiro[cyclohexane-1,3'(5'H)-quinoline]-2,5',6-trione, 1',2',4',6',7',8'-hexahydro-1'-methyl-	pH 1	296(4.29)	39-1593-79C
	H_2O	310(4.40)	39-1593-79C
	pH 13	314(4.48)	39-1593-79C
$C_{15}H_{19}NO_4$			
Benzene, 1-methoxy-3-[(3-methyl-2-butenyl)oxy]-5-(2-nitro-1-propenyl)-	EtOH	208(4.56),317(3.96)	150-0301-79
1H-Carbazole, 9-acetyl-2,3,4,4a,9,9a-hexahydro-4a-hydroperoxy-9a-methoxy-	EtOH	232(4.42),260(4.03), 325(3.50)	35-7332-79
$C_{15}H_{19}NO_4S$			
2,4-Hexadienoic acid, [[4-(dimethylamino)sulfonyl]phenyl]methyl ester	EtOH	231s(4.20),261(4.49)	118-0531-79
$C_{15}H_{19}NO_6$			
1,3-Benzenedicarboxylic acid, 4-ethyl-2-hydroxy-6-methyl-5-nitroso-, diethyl ester	DMF	690(1.81)	104-0311-79
$C_{15}H_{19}NS$			
Cyclohepta[c]pyrrole-6(2H)-thione, 2-butyl-1,3-dimethyl-	CH_2Cl_2	233(4.16),312(4.29), 423(4.39)	24-2087-79
$C_{15}H_{19}NS_2$			
2H-1,5,2-Dithiazepine, 3,4,6,7-tetramethyl-2-(4-methylphenyl)-	$CHCl_3$	226(4.35),263(3.96), 290s(3.75),320s(3.49)	5-1702-79
$C_{15}H_{19}N_2O_4$			
1H-Imidazol-1-yloxy, 4-[(benzoyloxy)-methyl]-2,5-dihydro-2,2,5,5-tetramethyl-, 3-oxide	EtOH	236(4.29)	70-0208-79
$C_{15}H_{19}N_2O_5PS$			
Phosphorothioic acid, O-[1,6-dihydro-5-methoxy-6-oxo-1-(phenylmethyl)-4-pyridazinyl] O-ethyl O-methyl ester	MeOH	213(4.38),288(3.80)	73-1761-79
$C_{15}H_{19}N_3$			
2,3,4-Triazatricyclo[5.4.1.0^{1,5}]dodec-2-ene, 4-phenyl-	pentane	216(4.17),283(3.99)	33-2025-79
2,3,4-Triazatricyclo[5.4.1.0^{1,5}]dodec-3-ene, 2-phenyl-	pentane	212(4.03),233(3.85), 283(4.05)	33-2025-79
2,3,4-Triazatricyclo[7.2.1.0^{1,5}]dodec-2-ene, 4-phenyl-	pentane	238(3.78),281(4.03)	33-2025-79

Compound	Solvent	λ_{max}(log ε)	Ref.
$C_{15}H_{19}N_3O$			
7-Azabicyclo[4.3.1]deca-3,8-dien-10-ol, 7-(4,6-dimethyl-2-pyrimidinyl)-	$CHCl_3$	279(4.32)	39-1525-79C
6,10-Methano-5H-cyclohepta[b]quinoxalin-12-one, 5a,6,7,8,9,10,10a,11-octahydro-5-methyl-, oxime, (5aα,6β,10β,10aα)-	EtOH	222(4.58),255(3.78), 302(3.57)	30-0254-79
Piperidine, 1-[2-(5-phenyl-1,2,4-oxadiazol-3-yl)ethyl]-	EtOH	236(4.06),275(4.08)	150-0801-79
$C_{15}H_{19}N_3OS$			
Cyclooctanone, 2-(1H-benzimidazol-2-ylthio)-, oxime	EtOH	251(3.825),289(4.126)	48-0249-79
$C_{15}H_{19}N_3O_2$			
N,N,N-Trimethyl-p-toluidinium 2,2-dicyano-1-methoxyethenolate	MeCN	231(3.88)	39-2219-79C
$C_{15}H_{19}N_3O_4$			
4-Imidazolidinepropanoic acid, 1-[4-(dimethylamino)phenyl]-2,5-dioxo-, methyl ester, (±)-	EtOH	264(4.27)	87-0869-79
$C_{15}H_{19}N_3O_9$			
1H-Imidazole, 2-methyl-4-nitro-1-(2,3,5-tri-O-acetyl-β-D-ribofuranosyl)-	n.s.g.	292(3.76)	111-0123-79
$C_{15}H_{19}N_3S$			
Isothiazolo[5,1-e][1,2,3]thiadiazole-7-S^{IV}, 5-(1,1-dimethylethyl)-1,6-dihydro-6-methyl-1-phenyl-	C_6H_{12}	242(4.15),248s(4.11), 278(3.78),428(4.39)	39-0926-79C
$C_{15}H_{19}N_5O_5$			
Guanine, 3,3'-anhydro-9-β-D-xylofuranosyl-2-N-pivaloyl-	pH 7	276(4.26)	24-0625-79
Guanosine, 2',3'-anhydro-N-(2,2-dimethyl-1-oxopropyl)-	MeOH	258(4.18),275(4.08)	24-0625-79
$C_{15}H_{19}N_5O_6$			
Adenosine, 3'-O-methyl-, 2',5'-diacetate	EtOH	260(4.16)	39-2088-79C
Guanosine, N-acetyl-2',3'-O-(1-methylethylidene)-	MeOH-HCl	264(4.22)	44-0400-79
	MeOH-NaOH	267(4.12)	44-0400-79
Guanosine, 2',3'-O-(1-methylethylidene)-, 5'-acetate	MeOH-HCl	260(4.13),278s(3.98)	44-0400-79
	MeOH-NaOH	212(4.37),259(4.08), 267(4.08)	44-0400-79
$C_{15}H_{19}N_5O_8$			
Pyrido[3,2-c]pyridazine-1,2-dicarboxylic acid, 4-[1,2-bis(methoxycarbonyl)hydrazino]-3,4-dihydro-, dimethyl ester	MeOH	229(3.95),276(3.55)	103-0518-79
$C_{15}H_{20}$			
Naphthalene, 1,2-dihydro-4,7-dimethyl-1-(1-methylethyl)-, (-)-cadalal,4,9-triene	EtOH	242(3.985)	102-0328-79
$C_{15}H_{20}BrClO$			
Oxonin, 3-bromo-8-chloro-2-ethyl-2,3,4-7,8,9-hexahydro-9-(2-penten-4-ynyl)-	MeOH	223(4.12)	88-1453-79
	$CHCl_3$	247(--)	88-1453-79

Compound	Solvent	$\lambda_{max}(\log \epsilon)$	Ref.
$C_{15}H_{20}F_2N_6O_5S$			
Adenosine, 5'-S-(3-amino-3-carboxy-4,4-difluorobutyl)-5'-thio-	H_2O	259(4.14)	44-2732-79
$C_{15}H_{20}INO_6$			
L-Serine, N-[(phenylmethoxy)carbonyl]-, 2-(2-iodoethoxy)ethyl ester	EtOH	253(2.76),258(2.79), 265(2.70),268(2.58)	118-0961-79
$C_{15}H_{20}N_2$			
1H-Pyrazole, 3,5-bis(1-methylethyl)-4-phenyl-	EtOH	230(3.84),240s(3.79)	103-0501-79
1H-Pyrazole, 4-phenyl-3,5-dipropyl-	EtOH	222s(3.86),270(4.04)	103-0501-79
$C_{15}H_{20}N_2O$			
1,4-Diazaspiro[4.4]non-1-ene, 3,3-dimethyl-2-phenyl-, 1-oxide	EtOH	224(3.89),290(3.99)	103-0092-79
1H-Indole-3-ethanol, 2-(2-piperidinyl)-	MeOH	282(3.92),290(3.85)	5-1643-79
4(1H)-Quinolinone, 3-[(diethylamino)-methylene]-2,3-dihydro-1-methyl-	EtOH	249(4.44),274s(3.86), 345(4.15),407(3.97)	4-0177-79
2-Quinoxaline-3-^{14}C-hexanol, 3-methyl-	EtOH	204(4.12),237(4.09), 315(3.99)	130-0311-79
$C_{15}H_{20}N_2O_2$			
Pyrrolo[2,3-b]indol-2(1H)-one, 5-ethoxy-3,3a,8,8a-tetrahydro-1,3a,8-trimethyl-	aq MeOH	248(4.00),318(3.47)	5-0927-79
$C_{15}H_{20}N_2O_2S$			
3-Methylindanylideneethylisothiouronium acetate	MeOH	214(4.28),219(4.25), 227s(4.11),252s(4.20), 258(4.28),293(3.96), 304(3.88)	2-0324-79A
$C_{15}H_{20}N_2O_3$			
Pyrazinemethanol, 3,6-diethoxy-2,5-dihydro-α-phenyl-	EtOH	208(3.93)	39-1889-79C
Quinoline, 6-ethoxy-1,2-dihydro-1,2,2,4-tetramethyl-8-nitro-	MeOH	232(4.74),335s(3.32), 470(3.51)	39-0488-79C
$C_{15}H_{20}N_2O_4$			
4-Quinolinecarboxylic acid, 1-(dimethylamino)-1,2,5,6,7,8-hexahydro-7,7-dimethyl-2,5-dioxo-, methyl ester	MeOH	207(4.00),284(4.15)	64-0102-79B
$C_{15}H_{20}N_2O_5$			
Pyridinium, 4-(dimethylamino)-1-[3-ethoxy-2-(ethoxycarbonyl)-1,3-dioxopropyl]-, hydroxide, inner salt	$CHCl_3$	260(4.2)	5-1388-79
$C_{15}H_{20}N_2O_6S$			
5-Thia-1-azabicyclo[4.2.0]oct-2-ene-2-carboxylic acid, 3-(acetoxymethyl)-7-(formylamino)-8-oxo-, 1,1-dimethylethyl ester	EtOH	266(3.87)	39-2455-79C
$C_{15}H_{20}N_2S$			
Benzenamine, N-(4-ethyl-3,4-dimethyl-5-methylene-2-thiazolidinylidene)-4-methyl-	EtOH	202(3.54),236(3.36)	103-0611-79
Benzenemethanamine, N-(4-ethyl-3,4-dimethyl-5-methylene-2-thiazolidinylidene)-	EtOH	227(3.42)	103-0611-79

Compound	Solvent	λ_{max}(log ϵ)	Ref.
$C_{15}H_{20}N_3OS$			
Isoxazolium, 2-ethyl-5-(ethylthio)-3-methyl-4-[(4-methylphenyl)azo]-, tetrafluoroborate	HOAc	290(4.03),354(3.89), 371(3.96),417s(3.06)	97-0446-79
1,3,4-Thiadiazolo[2,3-b]benzimidazolium, 9-ethyl-6-hydroxy-2-pentyl-, bromide	EtOH	273(3.79),508(3.81)	18-2033-79
$C_{15}H_{20}N_4$			
1H-Imidazole, 2-(phenylazo)-4,5-dipropyl-	MeOH	236(--),280(--), 400(4.40)	56-2340-79
$C_{15}H_{20}N_4O_6$			
α-D-Xylofuranose, 5-deoxy-3-O-methyl-1,2-O-(1-methylethylidene)-5-[3-(4-nitrophenyl)-1-triazenyl]-	EtOH	208(3.93),235(3.91), 349(4.32)	33-0971-79
$C_{15}H_{20}N_5O_8P$			
1,2,4-Triazine-3,5(2H,4H)-dione, 2-[5-O-(3,4-dihydro-6-methyl-4-oxo-1,3,2-diazaphosphorin-2(1H)-yl)-2,3-O-(1-methylethylidene)-β-D-ribofuranosyl]-	EtOH	259(4.20)	103-1147-79
$C_{15}H_{20}N_6$			
3H-Cyclohepta[1,2-d:4,5-d']diimidazole-2,6-diamine, N,N,N',N',1,4-hexamethyl-	MeOH	218(3.82),262(3.48), 314(4.07),373(3.45), 420(3.75)	23-1707-79
$C_{15}H_{20}O$			
Benzo[3,4]cyclobuta[1,2]cycloocten-4b(5H)-ol, 6,7,8,9,10,10a-hexahydro-4-methyl-	MeOH	261(2.85),267(2.94), 274(2.96)	39-2542-79C
isomer	MeOH	262(2.81),267(2.95), 275(2.99)	39-2542-79C
2,6,10,14-Cyclopentadecatetraen-1-one, (all-E)-	EtOH	235(4.14)	33-2661-79
(E,E,E,Z)-	EtOH	237(4.12)	33-2661-79
1,12-Methanobenzocyclodecen-12(5H)-ol, 6,7,8,9,10,11-hexahydro-	MeOH	262(2.72),267(2.85), 275(2.88)	39-2542-79C
cis	MeOH	261(2.76),266(2.88), 273(2.87)	39-2542-79C
trans	MeOH	261(2.77),266(2.90), 273(2.90)	39-2542-79C
6,10-Methano-5H-benzocyclononen-12-ol, 6,7,8,9,10,11-hexahydro-12-methyl-	MeOH	212(3.89),258(2.40), 267(2.58),274(2.59)	56-1221-79
1,10-Methanobenzocycloocten-10(5H)-ol, 6,7,8,9-tetrahydro-11,11-dimethyl-, cis	MeOH	260(2.75),265(2.89), 273(2.89)	39-2542-79C
1-Naphthalenol, 1,2-dihydro-1,2,2,3,4-pentamethyl-	hexane	210(4.15),217(4.19), 222(4.26),228(4.20), 244(3.68),273(3.98)	104-0685-79
$C_{15}H_{20}O_2$			
Anthemidin	EtOH	263(3.83)	100-0279-79
5,8-Epoxy-4H-indeno[6,5-b]furan, 4a,5,6,7,7a,8-hexahydro-4,4a,7,7a-tetramethyl- (pinguisanin)	EtOH	224(3.71)	102-1349-79
Furanoeremophilane, 9-oxo-, trans	EtOH	278(4.0)	39-1542-79C
2-Heptenoic acid, 7-(2,4-cyclopentadien-1-ylidene)-5,5-dimethyl-, methyl ester, (E)-	EtOH	258(4.32)	35-7129-79

Compound	Solvent	λ_{max}(log ε)	Ref.
2H-Naphtho[1,8-bc:3,2-b']difuran, 2a,3,4,5,5a,6,9b,9c-octahydro-9,9c-dimethyl-	MeOH	218(3.85)	18-1182-79
7H-Naphtho[2,1-b]pyran-7-one, 1,2,3,5-6,6a,8,9-octahydro-3,6aα-dimethyl-	EtOH	254(4.43)	56-0107-79
2,5-Nonadien-4-one, 9-(3-furanyl)-2,6-dimethyl-, (E)-	n.s.g.	255(3.99)	12-2003-79
1,7(2H,4bH)-Phenanthrenedione, 3,4,4a-5,6,9,10,10a-octahydro-10aα-methyl-	EtOH	240(4.42)	56-0107-79
$C_{15}H_{20}O_2S$			
1,3-Benzoxathiol-2-one, 4,6-bis(1,1-dimethylethyl)-	EtOH	226(4.01),266s(--), 272(3.28),280(3.28)	44-1977-79
$C_{15}H_{20}O_2Si$			
Silane, (2-methoxyethoxy)dimethyl-(1-naphthalenyl)-	EtOH	282.5(3.87)	3-0007-79
$C_{15}H_{20}O_3$			
Benzoic acid, 2,3-dimethyl-6-(3-methyl-1-oxobutyl)-, methyl ester	EtOH	255(4.15)	33-1525-79
Benzoic acid, 3,4-dimethyl-2-(3-methyl-1-oxobutyl)-, methyl ester	EtOH	243(4.14)	33-1525-79
2H-1-Benzopyran-6-propanol, 5-methoxy-2,2-dimethyl-	EtOH	226(4.45),263s(3.76), 270(3.83),275s(3.76), 317(3.23)	102-0351-79
Butanedial, (8-hydroxy-4,8-dimethyl-2,4,6-nonatrienylidene)-, (Z,E,E,E)-	MeOH	350(4.65)	88-0685-79
Naphtho[2,3-b]furan-5-carboxylic acid, 4,4a,5,6,7,8,8a,9-octahydro-3,4a-dimethyl-, [4aS-(4aα,5α,8aα)]-	MeOH	221(3.83)	18-1182-79
6,8-Nonadien-1-one, 1-(3-furanyl)-4-hydroxy-4,8-dimethyl-, [R-(E)]-	EtOH	230(4.28),240s(4.08)	12-2003-79
2-Propanone, 1-[3-methoxy-5-[(3-methyl-2-butenyl)oxy]phenyl]-	EtOH	211(4.27),245(4.33), 279(3.49)	150-0301-79
Toxethol	EtOH	229(3.78),285(3.36), 291(3.31)	100-0203-79
$C_{15}H_{20}O_4$			
1,5-Methano-1H-2,3-benzodioxepin-10-ol, 4,5-dihydro-4-methoxy-1,4,5,10-tetramethyl-	MeOH	252(2.30),258(2.53) 265(2.62),272(2.60)	44-0368-79
Peroxycostunolide (verlotorin)	MeOH	210(3.95)(end abs.)	44-3952-79
Sachalin	MeOH	210(4.08)	138-1503-79
$C_{15}H_{20}O_5$			
Artemolin	EtOH	223(4.07)	105-0577-79
Lactarolide A	EtOH	214(3.87)	102-0293-79
	EtOH-KOH	254(3.75)	102-0293-79
Lactarolide B	EtOH	213(3.84)	102-0293-79
	EtOH-KOH	264(3.74)	102-0293-79
Parvulenone, O-ethyl-	MeOH	224(4.21),288(4.15), 330s(3.49)	150-2685-79
Peroxyparthenolide	MeOH	210(3.90)(end abs.)	44-3952-79
$C_{15}H_{20}O_6$			
1H-2-Benzopyran-1-one, 3,4-dihydro-7,8-dihydroxy-3-(2-hydroxypentyl)-6-methoxy-	MeOH	232(4.28),277(4.09), 320(3.44)	39-2048-79C

Compound	Solvent	$\lambda_{max}(\log \epsilon)$	Ref.
$C_{15}H_{21}BrO_4$			
4H-Pyran-4-one, 3-bromo-2-methoxy-6-(1-oxononyl)-	EtOH	226(4.21),338(3.99)	23-1451-79
$C_{15}H_{21}BrO_6$			
α-D-galacto-Non-6-enopyranos-8-ulose, 7-bromo-6,7,9-trideoxy-1,2:3,4-bis-O-(1-methylethylidene)-, (Z)-	EtOH	239(3.87)	33-1632-79
$C_{15}H_{21}BrO_7$			
α-D-galacto-Oct-6-enopyranuronic acid, 7-bromo-6,7-dideoxy-1,2:3,4-bis-O-(1-methylethylidene)-, methyl ester, (Z)-	EtOH	234(3.99)	33-1632-79
$C_{15}H_{21}IN_4O_7$			
Uridine, 2'-deoxy-5-[[4-(iodoacetyl)amino]-1-oxobutyl]amino]-	H_2O	278(3.92)	87-0621-79
$C_{15}H_{21}NO$			
4a(2H)-Biphenylenol, 1,3,4,8b-tetrahydro-4-[(1-methylethyl)amino]-, hydrochloride	MeOH	260(3.03),266(3.19), 272(3.16)	111-0543-79
2-Cyclohexen-1-one, 3-(2-azabicyclo-[2.2.2]oct-5-en-2-yl)-5,5-dimethyl-	EtOH	306(4.56)	44-0124-79
1(2H)-Phenanthridinone, 3,4,5,6,6a,7,8-10a-octahydro-3,3-dimethyl-, cis	EtOH	302(4.35)	44-0124-79
2-Propen-1-one, 3-[bis(1-methylethyl)-amino]-1-phenyl-, (E)-	EtOH	247(4.04),347(4.38)	4-0093-79
2H-Pyrrole-5-ethanol, 3,4-dihydro-α,3,3-trimethyl-α-phenyl-	MeOH	205(4.10),242(3.78)	83-0498-79
2-Pyrrolidineethanol, 1-methyl-α-(2-phenylethenyl)- (darlinine)	EtOH	211(4.27),251(4.22)	12-2523-79
epidarlinine	EtOH	211(4.27),251(4.22)	12-2523-79
Quinoline, 6-ethoxy-1,2-dihydro-1,2,2,4-tetramethyl-	NeOH	232(4.56),365(3.46)	39-0488-79C
$C_{15}H_{21}NO_2$			
2-Octen-1-one, 3-hydroxy-8-(methylamino)-1-phenyl-, hydrochloride	pH 13	238(3.90),325(4.20)	103-0997-79
4-Octen-3-one, 8-hydroxy-5-[(phenylmethyl)amino]-	MeOH	242(4.15),315(4.31)	44-2073-79
$C_{15}H_{21}NO_4$			
2-Pyridinepropanoic acid, 3-(ethoxycarbonyl)-α,β-dimethyl-, ethyl ester, [S-(R*,R*)]-	EtOH	218(4.20),242s(3.82), 272(3.75),290(3.73)	39-2982-79C
$C_{15}H_{21}NO_5$			
1-Isoquinolinemethanol, 1,2,3,4-tetrahydro-5-hydroxy-6,7-dimethoxy-2-methyl-, α-acetate, hydrochloride	n.s.g.	258(2.70)	100-0197-79
$C_{15}H_{21}NO_6$			
D-Arabinitol, 1-deoxy-1-(2,5-dioxo-3-pyrrolidinylidene)-2,3:4,5-bis-O-(1-methylethylidene)-, (E)-	EtOH	224(4.20)	33-0977-79
$C_{15}H_{21}NS$			
2,1-Benzisothiazole, 5,7-bis(1,1-dimethylethyl)-	hexane	232(4.43),290(3.92), 301(4.00),324(2.72)	18-2002-79

Compound	Solvent	$\lambda_{max}(\log \epsilon)$	Ref.
$C_{15}H_{21}N_3$			
1H-Cyclooctatriazole, 3a,4,5,6,7,8,9,9a-octahydro-9a-methyl-1-phenyl-, trans	pentane	215(3.93),242(4.08), 275(3.89)	33-2025-79
$C_{15}H_{21}N_3O$			
7-Azabicyclo[4.3.1]decan-10-one, 7-(4,6-dimethyl-2-pyrimidinyl)-	$CHCl_3$	275(3.63)	39-1525-79C
$C_{15}H_{21}N_3O_3$			
4H-Pyrido[1,2-a]pyrimidine-3-carboxylic acid, 9-[(dimethylamino)methylene]-6,7,8,9-tetrahydro-6-methyl-4-oxo-, ethyl ester	EtOH	230(4.23),275(3.49), 299s(3.43),397(4.68)	88-2537-79
$C_{15}H_{21}N_3O_8$			
1,2,4-Triazine-3,5(2H,4H)-dione, 2-[2,3-O-(4-ethoxy-1-methyl-4-oxobutylidene)-β-D-ribofuranosyl]-, (R)-	MeOH	263(3.68)	87-1545-79
$C_{15}H_{21}N_5O_3$			
D-erythro-Pentitol, 1,4-anhydro-2-deoxy-1-C-[8-[(3-methyl-2-butenyl)amino]-1,2,4-triazolo[4,3-a]pyrazin-3-yl]-, (R)-	EtOH	235(4.32),244(4.24), 280(4.15)	44-1028-79
$C_{15}H_{21}N_5O_4$			
1H-Azepino[1,2-a]purin-11-imine, 3,5,6-7,8,9-hexahydro-3-β-D-ribofuranosyl-	pH 6.0	259(4.12)	5-1872-79
	pH 11.0	262(4.15),267s(4.13), 292s(3.85)	5-1872-79
D-Ribitol, 1,4-anhydro-1-C-[8-[(3-methyl-2-butenyl)amino]-1,2,4-triazolo-[4,3-a]pyrazin-3-yl]-, (S)-	EtOH	235(4.29),244(4.21), 280(4.11)	44-1028-79
$C_{15}H_{21}N_5O_5$			
Hexanoic acid, 6-[[6-(1,2-dihydroxypropyl)-1,4-dihydro-4-oxo-2-pteridinyl]amino]-	pH 0.25	212(4.03),242(4.23), 325(3.90)	18-2933-79
	pH 5.0	221(4.12),241s(4.06), 281(4.29),353(3.80)	18-2933-79
	pH 10.5	218(4.05),265(4.41), 372(3.89)	18-2933-79
$C_{15}H_{21}N_5O_6$			
Hexanoic acid, 6-[[1,4-dihydro-4-oxo-6-(1,2,3-trihydroxypropyl)-2-pteridinyl]amino]-	pH 0.25	213(4.22),242(4.26), 324(3.94)	18-2933-79
	pH 5.0	221(4.15),241s(4.08), 281(4.31),353(3.81)	18-2933-79
	pH 10.0	216(4.07),265(4.41), 372(3.90)	18-2933-79
$C_{15}H_{22}N_2O$			
4H-Cyclopenta[d]inden-4-one, 5-diazodecahydro-1,3a,6a-trimethyl-	EtOH	288(3.79)	33-1493-79
Pyrrolo[2,3-b]indole, 1,2,3,3a,8,8a-hexahydro-5-ethoxy-1,3a,8-trimethyl-	12M HCl	252(3.75),333(3.79)	5-0927-79
	MeOH	248(4.02),320(3.47)	5-0927-79
$C_{15}H_{22}N_2O_2$			
Butanoic acid, 3,3-dimethyl-2-[[1-(4-pyridinyl)ethyl]imino]-, ethyl ester, (S)-	C_6H_{12}	256(3.32),325(2.23)	35-0717-79
3H-Indazole-4,7-dione, 6,7a-bis(1,1-dimethylethyl)-3a,7a-dihydro-	n.s.g.	240(4.01)	70-1668-79

Compound	Solvent	λ_{max}(log ε)	Ref.
L-Valine, 3-methyl-N-[1-(4-pyridinyl)-ethylidene]-, ethyl ester	C_6H_{12}	235(2.90),270(2.78), 330(2.18)	35-0717-79
$C_{15}H_{22}N_2O_3$			
2-Butanone, 3,3-dimethyl-, O-[1-methyl-1-(4-nitrophenyl)ethyl]oxime, (E)-	MeOH	275(3.97)	12-2413-79
2,4(3H,5H)-Furandione, 3-[1-(cyclohexylamino)ethylidene]-5-[(dimethylamino)methylene]-	EtOH	248(4.14),297(4.22), 361(4.39)	4-1335-79
Spiro[cyclohexane-1,7'-[7H]pyrazolo-[1,5-c][1,3]oxazine]-3'-carboxylic acid, 4',5'-dihydro-2'-methyl-, ethyl ester	EtOH	233(4.03)	118-0440-79
$C_{15}H_{22}N_2O_4$			
1H-Benzimidazole, 4,5,6,7-tetrahydro-1-[2,3-O-(1-methylethylidene)-α-D-ribofuranosyl]-	MeOH	225(3.33)	44-4378-79
1-Cyclohexene-1-carbonitrile, 2-[[2,3-O-(1-methylethylidene)-D-ribofuranosyl]amino]-	MeOH	265(4.14)	44-4378-79
$C_{15}H_{22}N_2O_8$			
1(2H)-Pyrimidinebutanoic acid, 3,6-dihydro-2,6-dioxo-3-β-D-ribofuranosyl-, ethyl ester	MeOH	262(4.03)	24-3743-79
$C_{15}H_{22}N_2S_2$			
Spiro[cyclohexane-1,8'-[2H,8H]isothiazolo[4,3,2-ij]quinazoline]-2'-thione, 3',4',5',5'a,6',7'-hexahydro-6'-methyl-	EtOH	264(3.77),367(4.26)	150-0410-79S
$C_{15}H_{22}N_4O$			
7-Azabicyclo[4.3.1]decan-10-one, 7-(4,6-dimethyl-2-pyrimidinyl)-, oxime	$CHCl_3$	246(4.15)	39-1525-79C
$C_{15}H_{22}N_6O_4$			
9H-Purine-9-propanoic acid, 6-amino-α-[[(1,1-dimethylethoxy)carbonyl]-amino]-, ethyl ester	n.s.g.	260(4.15)	65-0989-79
$C_{15}H_{22}O$			
2(1H)-Azulenone, 6,7,8,8a-tetrahydro-3,8-dimethyl-5-(1-methylethyl)-	EtOH	293(4.22)	18-3755-79
epimer	EtOH	293(4.32)	18-3755-79
2-Butanone, 4-[2,2-dimethyl-3-(5-methylene-1-cyclopenten-1-yl)cyclopropyl]-, (1S-cis)- (taylorione)	EtOH	243(4.17)	39-2652-79C
Calamusenone, (+)-	EtOH	211(3.79),251(3.84)	102-0279-79
isomer	EtOH	210(3.74),249(3.69)	102-0279-79
Furanoeremophilane	MeOH	221(3.85)	18-1182-79
Marsupellone, (-)-	EtOH	241(3.65)	138-0073-79
Sclerosporal	hexane	228(3.99)	88-1773-79
Tetracyclo[6.3.1.0^{2,6}.0^{5,10}]dodecan-11-one, 2,5,9-trimethyl-	EtOH	294(1.35)	88-1125-79
$C_{15}H_{22}O_2$			
Cyclopenta[b]pyran-2(3H)-one, hexahydro-7a-methyl-3,5-bis(1-methylethylidene)-, cis	MeOH	234(3.20)	94-0275-79

Compound	Solvent	λ_{max}(log ε)	Ref.
Cyclopenta[b]pyran-2(3H)-one, hexahydro-7a-methyl-5-(1-methylethenyl)-3-(1-methylethylidene)-, (4aα,5α,7aα)-(+)-	MeOH	234(4.20)	94-0275-79
(4aα,5β,7aα)-(+)-	MeOH	232(4.26)	94-0275-79
4a,7-Methano-4aH-benzocycloheptene-5-carboxylic acid, 1,2,3,4,7,8,9,9a-octahydro-6,7-dimethyl-, (4aα,7α,9aα)-	EtOH	236(3.67)	12-0817-79
(4aα,7α,9aβ)-(±)-	EtOH	231(3.63)	12-0817-79
2(3H)-Naphthalenone, 4,4a,5,6,7,8-hexahydro-6-hydroxy-4a,5-dimethyl-3-(1-methylethylidene)- (isopetasol)	EtOH	247(4.08),279(3.86)	94-0331-79
3-epiisopetasol	EtOH	248(4.03),279(3.85)	94-0331-79
Naphtho[2,3-b]furan-5-methanol, 4,4a,5,6,7,8,8a,9-octahydro-3,4a-dimethyl-	MeOH	221(3.88)	18-1182-79
$C_{15}H_{22}O_3$			
Azuleno[5,6-c]furan-3(1H)-one, 4,4a,5-6,7,7a,8,9-octahydro-8-hydroxy-6,6,8-trimethyl-	EtOH	219(3.84)	102-0293-79
Germacrone, 4,5-diepoxy-	MeOH	249(3.68)	94-0275-79
isomer	MeOH	250(3.72)	94-0275-79
4,8-Methanoazulen-5(1H)-one, 2,3,3a,4-8,8a-hexahydro-9-hydroxy-6-methoxy-3a,8,8a-trimethyl-	EtOH	267(3.83)	35-6767-79
2(3H)-Naphthalenone, 4,4a,5,6,7,8-hexahydro-4-hydroxy-7-[1-(hydroxymethyl)-ethenyl]-1,4a-dimethyl- (heterophyllol)	MeOH	249(4.18)	88-3053-79
2(4aH)-Naphthalenone, 5,6,7,8-tetrahydro-6-hydroxy-3-(1-hydroxy-1-methylethyl)-4a,5-dimethyl- (3-epipetasitol)	EtOH	248(4.07)	94-0331-79
Naphtho[2,3-b]furan-5-methanol, 4,4a,5,6,7,8,8a,9-octahydro-4-hydroxy-3,4a-dimethyl-	MeOH	219(3.95)	18-1182-79
isomer	MeOH	224(3.88)	18-1182-79
Naphtho[2,3-b]furan-2(4H)-one, 4a,5,6,7,8,8a,9,9a-octahydro-9a-hydroxy-3,4a,5-trimethyl-	MeOH	223(4.40)	18-1964-79
$C_{15}H_{22}O_4$			
Azuleno[5,6-c]furan-3(1H)-one, 4,4a,5,6,7,7a,8,9-octahydro-4,8-dihydroxy-6,6,8-trimethyl-	EtOH	277(3.92)	102-0293-79
Benzene, 1,2,3-trimethoxy-5-(2-methoxy-4-pentenyl)-	EtOH	211(4.43),225s(3.92)	150-0301-79
Naphthalene, 1,2,3,4-tetrahydro-3,6,7,8-tetramethoxy-1-methyl-	EtOH	210(4.45),225s(4.04), 280(3.09)	150-0301-79
6-Nonen-1-one, 1-(3-furanyl)-4,8-dihydroxy-4,8-dimethyl-, [R-(E)]-	EtOH	216(3.59),248(3.36)	12-2003-79
4H-Pyran-4-one, 2-methoxy-6-(1-oxononyl)-	EtOH	220(4.07),255(3.12), 307(3.50)	23-1451-79
Spiro[1,3-dioxolane-2,1'(2'H)-naphthalen]-6'(5'H)-one, 3',4',4-a,8'a-tetrahydro-7'-hydroxy-5',5',8'a-trimethyl-, trans	MeOH	267(3.95)	44-2838-79
$C_{15}H_{22}O_6$			
α-D-galacto-Nonopyranose, 8,8,9,9-tetradehydro-7,8,9-trideoxy-1,2:3,4-bis-O-(1-methylethylidene)-	EtOH	222(3.79)	33-1632-79

Compound	Solvent	λ_{max}(log ε)	Ref.
$C_{15}H_{22}O_7$			
α-D-galacto-Oct-6-enopyranuronic acid, 6,7-dideoxy-1,2:3,4-bis-O-(1-methylethylidene)-, methyl ester	EtOH	215(3.90)	33-1632-79
$C_{15}H_{22}O_9$			
1-Propene-1,1,3,3-tetracarboxylic acid, 2-hydroxy-, tetraethyl ester	$CHCl_3$	256(3.9),303(2.7)	5-1388-79
$C_{15}H_{22}Si$			
Cyclohexene, 1-phenyl-3-(trimethylsilyl)-	isooctane	251(4.14)	101-0027-79K
$C_{15}H_{23}BrNO_2$			
Benzenebutanaminium, 4-bromo-N-(3-hydroxypropyl)-N,N-dimethyl-δ-oxo-, iodide	EtOH	255(4.23)	145-0983-79
$C_{15}H_{23}BrO$			
α-Chamigren-4-one, 10-bromo-	EtOH	284(1.48)	78-0823-79
$C_{15}H_{23}NO$			
1(2H)-Naphthalenone, 3,4,7,8-tetrahydro-3,3-dimethyl-6-[(1-methylethyl)amino]-	pH 1	252(3.91),380(4.33)	39-1411-79C
	H_2O	239(3.83),259(3.72), 415(4.51)	39-1411-79C
	EtOH	405(4.46)	39-1411-79C
Phenol, 2-[(octylimino)methyl]-	MeOH	216(4.31),253(3.98), 280(3.18),314(3.52)	150-3801-79
$C_{15}H_{23}NOS$			
Benzenamine, 2,4-bis(1,1-dimethylethyl)-6-methyl-N-sulfinyl-	hexane	226(4.00),255(3.73), 282s(3.43),392(3.41)	18-1998-79
2-Octanesulfenamide, 2-methyl-N-(4-oxo-2,5-cyclohexadien-1-ylidene)-	hexane	405(4.43)	138-1077-79
$C_{15}H_{23}NO_2$			
Pyridinium, 1-(1-carboxy-3-methylbutyl)-4-ethyl-3,5-dimethyl-, hydroxide, inner salt	MeOH	242(3.90),270(3.76)	44-1417-79
$C_{15}H_{23}NO_4$			
2-Butenoic acid, 2-methyl-, 6-acetoxy-8-methyl-8-azabicyclo[3.2.1]oct-3-yl ester, [1R-[1α,3β(E),5α,6α]]-	EtOH	217(4.15)	12-2071-79
1H-Pyrrole-3-propanoic acid, 2-[(1,1-dimethylethoxy)carbonyl]-4,5-dimethyl-, methyl ester	n.s.g.	249(3.71),285(4.19)	39-1927-79C
$C_{15}H_{23}NO_6$			
1,4,7,10,13,16-Hexaoxacyclooctadecino-[2,3-b]pyridine, 2,3,5,6,8,9,11,12-14,15-decahydro-	EtOH	220(3.9),275(3.9)	77-0285-79
$C_{15}H_{23}NS_2$			
Benzenamine, 2,4-bis(1,1-dimethylethyl)-6-methyl-N-sulfinothioyl-	hexane	270s(3.17),310s(3.29), 343(3.75),476(3.34), 536s(3.08)	18-1998-79
	hexane	476(3.34),536(3.08)	88-0745-79
	EtOH	343(3.78),478(3.34), 544s(3.10)	18-1998-79

Compound	Solvent	$\lambda_{max}(\log \epsilon)$	Ref.
(cont.)	CCl_4	345(3.77),480(3.35), 548s(3.11)	18-1998-79
2(3H)-Cyclooctathiazolethione, 3-cyclohexyl-4,5,6,7,8,9-hexahydro-	EtOH	329(3.861)	48-0249-79
$C_{15}H_{23}N_3O$			
7-Azabicyclo[4.3.1]decan-10-ol, 7-(4,6-dimethyl-2-pyrimidinyl)-	$CHCl_3$	255(3.95)	39-1525-79C
$C_{15}H_{23}N_3O_3$			
Benzenepropanamide, 4-(aminoiminomethyl)-α,α-dimethoxy-N-(1-methylethyl)-, monohydrochloride	n.s.g.	243(4.072)	106-0008-79
$C_{15}H_{23}N_4O_2$			
Pyridinium, 2-[(di-4-morpholinylmethylene)amino]-1-methyl-, iodide	EtOH	278(4.08),327(4.23)	94-2879-79
$C_{15}H_{23}N_5O_4$			
Uridine, 2',3'-didehydro-2',3',5'-trideoxy-5'-[(2,6-diamino-1-oxohexyl)-amino]-, (S)-	H_2O	261.5(3.95)	136-0113-79F
$C_{15}H_{23}N_5O_5$			
1H-Purine-2,6-dione, 3,7-dihydro-8-(hydroxymethyl)-7-[2-hydroxy-3-(4-morpholinyl)propyl]-1,3-dimethyl-, monohydrochloride	n.s.g.	210(4.66),275(4.25)	73-0424-79
$C_{15}H_{23}O_4PS_2$			
Benzeneethane(dithioic) acid, α-(diethoxyphosphinyl)-α-ethoxy-, methyl ester	isooctane	216s(--),245s(--), 319(3.91),477(1.41)	5-1715-79
Benzeneethane(dithioic) acid, α-(diethoxyphosphinyl)-α-methoxy-, ethyl ester	isooctane	246(3.48),322(3.90), 481(1.47)	5-1715-79
$C_{15}H_{24}$			
1,3,5,10-Dodecatetraene, 2,6,10-trimethyl-, (E,E,E)-	EtOH	281(3.46)	70-0509-79
1,6,11-Dodecatriene, 7,11-dimethyl-3-methylene-, (E)-	EtOH	225(4.20)	70-0509-79
$C_{15}H_{24}N_2O$			
Phenol, 2,6-bis(1,1-dimethylethyl)-4-(methylazo)-	C_6H_{12}	394(2.40)	24-2913-79
	acetone	395(3.18)	24-2913-79
$C_{15}H_{24}N_2O_4$			
Butanedioic acid, (methylhydrazono)-, dicyclopentyl ester, (E)-	MeOH	280(4.12)	5-1696-79
2-Butenedioic acid, 2-(1-methylhydrazino)-, dicyclopentyl ester, (E)-	MeOH	280(4.30)	5-1696-79
$C_{15}H_{24}N_2S$			
Thiourea, N,N'-diethyl-N'-tricyclo-[3.3.1.1^{3,7}]dec-2-ylidene-	C_6H_{12}	245s(4.00),258(4.06), 295s(3.80)	24-1102-79
$C_{15}H_{24}N_3$			
Cyclopropenylium, tripyrrolidino-, perchlorate	CH_2Cl_2	238(4.40)	24-1514-79

Compound	Solvent	λ_{max}(log ε)	Ref.
$C_{15}H_{24}N_3O_6$			
1H-Imidazolium, 5-amino-4-(ethoxycarbonyl)-3-methyl-1-[2,3-O-(1-methylethylidene)-α-D-ribofuranosyl]-, iodide	MeOH	271(4.02)	39-3107-79C
β-	MeOH	270(4.03)	39-3107-79C
$C_{15}H_{24}N_4$			
1H-Pyrrolo[2,3-d]pyrimidin-4-amine, N-(2-ethylhexyl)-2-methyl-	pH 1	280(4.14)	102-0217-79
	H_2O	279(4.14)	102-0217-79
	pH 13	278(4.12)	102-0217-79
1H-Pyrrolo[2,3-d]pyrimidin-4-amine, 2-methyl-N-octyl-	pH 1	276(4.20)	102-0217-79
	H_2O	276(4.19)	102-0217-79
	pH 13	275(4.12)	102-0217-79
$C_{15}H_{24}N_6$			
1,2,3-Triazine, 4,5,6-tripyrrolidino-	CH_2Cl_2	257(4.42),352(3.23)	24-1514-79
$C_{15}H_{24}N_6O_2$			
1,3,5-Triazin-2-amine, 4,6-bis(1-aziridinyl)-N-(5-ethyl-2,2-dimethyl-1,3-dioxan-5-yl)-	EtOH	222(4.82)	104-1144-79
$C_{15}H_{24}O$			
Bicyclohumulenone, (+)-	EtOH	205(4.02)	77-0174-79
2-Butanone, 4-[2,2-dimethyl-3-(2-methyl-1-cyclopenten-1-yl)cyclopropyl]-	EtOH	212(3.77)	39-2652-79C
2-Cyclohexen-1-one, 6-(1,5-dimethyl-4-hexenyl)-3-methyl-	EtOH	236(4.00)	12-1627-79
2,13-Cyclopentadecadien-1-one, (E,E)-	EtOH	229(4.07)	33-2661-79
2,14-Cyclopentadecadien-1-one, (E,E)-	EtOH	236(4.19)	33-2661-79
2,14-Cyclopentadecadien-1-one, (E,Z)-	EtOH	239(4.09)	33-2661-79
Cyclopropanepropanol, α,2,2-trimethyl-3-(5-methylene-1-cyclopenten-1-yl)-	EtOH	243(3.83)	39-2652-79C
2,4,8-Decatrien-1-ol, 3,9-dimethyl-6-(1-methylethenyl)-, (S)-	MeOH	240(4.22),282(3.25)	1-0551-79
Ionol	pH 12	215(3.20),225(2.62), 244(2.10)	135-1004-79B
	EtOH	212(3.90),230(3.95), 262(3.60),280(3.92)	135-1004-79B
$C_{15}H_{24}O_2$			
Caprylic acid, 2'-hydroxymethyl-2-cyclohexylidene-, lactone	MeOH	236(3.85)	146-0031-79
Cyclopenta[b]pyran-2(3H)-one, hexahydro-7a-methyl-5-(1-methylethyl)-3-(1-methylethylidene)-	MeOH	234(4.20)	94-0275-79
1H-Indene-2,4-diol, 6-ethenyl-2,3,3a,4-5,7a-hexahydro-3,3a,7,7a-tetramethyl-	EtOH	241(3.21)	102-1349-79
2(1H)-Naphthalenone, 3,4,4a,5,6,7,8,8a-octahydro-1-hydroxy-4a,5-dimethyl-3-(1-methylethylene)-	MeOH	252(3.65)	18-2372-79
$C_{15}H_{24}O_3$			
Cycloheptanone, 5-(1-methoxyethylidene)-2,2-dimethyl-7-(2-oxopropyl)-	n.s.g.	284(1.74)	33-1645-79
Cyclopenta[b]pyran-2(3H)-one, hexahydro-5-(1-hydroxy-1-methylethyl)-7a-methyl-3-(1-methylethylidene)-, (4aα,5α-7aα)-	MeOH	234(4.20)	94-0275-79
1,5-Hexanedione, 1-[2,2-dimethyl-3-(3-oxobutyl)cyclopropyl]-, (1R-cis)-	isooctane	203(3.48)	39-2652-79C

Compound	Solvent	$\lambda_{max}(\log \epsilon)$	Ref.
2(1H)-Naphthalenone, octahydro-5,6-dihydroxy-5,8a-dimethyl-3-(1-methylethylidene)- (cuauhtemone)	MeOH	254(3.89)	102-2033-79
$C_{15}H_{24}O_4$			
2-Furanacetic acid, 2,4-bis(1,1-dimethylethyl)-2,5-dihydro-5-oxo-, methyl ester	n.s.g.	214(4.04)	24-0389-79
2(1H)-Naphthalenone, 4a,5,6,7,8,8a-hexahydro-5,6-dihydroxy-3-(1-hydroxy-1-methylethyl)-5,8a-dimethyl-, [4aR-(4aα,5α,6α,8aβ)]- (plucheinol)	MeOH	243(3.79)	102-2033-79
$C_{15}H_{24}O_{10}$			
β-D-Glucopyranoside, 1,4a,5,6,7,7a-hexahydro-4a,5,7-trihydroxy-7-methylcyclopenta[c]pyran-1-yl (harpagide)	H_2O	206(4.01)	39-2473-79C
$C_{15}H_{25}N$			
3-Azabicyclo[3.2.0]hepta-1,4-diene, 6,7-bis(1,1-dimethylethyl)-3-methyl-, trans	EtOH	233(3.86)	44-2667-79
Piperidine, 1-(1,7,7-trimethylbicyclo[2.2.1]hept-2-en-2-yl)-	EtOH	214(3.45)	118-0830-79
$C_{15}H_{25}NO$			
15-Azabicyclo[12.1.0]pentadec-14-en-2-one, 1-methyl-	EtOH	238(3.18),293(1.86)	88-1875-79
14-Oxa-15-azabicyclo[11.2.1]hexadeca-13(16),15-diene, 16-methyl-	EtOH	225(3.76)	88-1875-79
Phenol, 2-[(octylamino)methyl]-, hydrochloride	EtOH	216(3.88),277(3.60)	150-3801-79
Piperidine, 1-(1,3,3-trimethyl-2-oxabicyclo[2.2.2]oct-5-en-6-yl)-	EtOH	232(3.68)	118-0830-79
$C_{15}H_{25}NO_2$			
2-Cyclohexen-1-one, 3,5,5-trimethyl-2-[2-(4-morpholinyl)ethyl]-	EtOH	245.5(3.97)	77-1084-79
$C_{15}H_{25}N_2O_4PS$			
Phosphonothioic acid, ethyl-, O-(1-cyclohexyl-1,6-dihydro-5-methoxy-6-oxo-4-pyridazinyl) O-ethyl ester	MeOH	215(4.38),289(3.77)	73-1761-79
$C_{15}H_{25}N_2O_5PS$			
Phosphorothioic acid, O-(1-cyclohexyl-1,6-dihydro-5-methoxy-6-oxo-4-pyridazinyl) O,O-diethyl ester	MeOH	214(4.27),289(3.68)	73-1761-79
$C_{15}H_{25}N_2O_6P$			
Phosphoric acid, 1-cyclohexyl-1,6-dihydro-5-methoxy-6-oxo-4-pyridazinyl diethyl ester	MeOH	213(4.32),289(3.74)	73-1761-79
$C_{15}H_{25}N_4O_8P$			
Uridine, 5-[(N-methylpiperazinyl)methyl]-2'-deoxy-, 5'-phosphate triethylamine salt	pH 1	266(3.95)	87-1134-79
	H_2O	264(3.97)	87-1134-79
	pH 13	264(3.81)	87-1134-79
$C_{15}H_{25}N_5O_4$			
1H-Purine-2,6-dione, 7-[3-(diethylami-	n.s.g.	211(4.57),277(4.11)	73-0424-79

Compound	Solvent	λ_{max}(log ε)	Ref.
no)-2-hydroxypropyl)-3,7-dihydro-8-(hydroxymethyl)-1,3-dimethyl-, mono-3-pyridinecarboxylate (cont.)			73-0424-79
1H-Purine-2,6-dione, 7-[[3-(1,1-dimethylethyl)amino]-2-hydroxypropyl]-3,7-dihydro-8-(hydroxymethyl)-1,3-dimethyl-, monohydrochloride	n.s.g.	211(4.44),234(3.73), 279(4.05)	73-0424-79
$C_{15}H_{26}N_3O_4PS$			
Phosphoramidothioic acid, (1-methylethyl)-, O-(1-cyclohexyl-1,6-dihydro-5-methoxy-6-oxo-4-pyridazinyl) O-methyl ester	MeOH	214(4.30),288(3.72)	73-1761-79
$C_{15}H_{26}N_5O_{13}P_3S$			
Adenosine, 5'-(tetrahydrogen triphosphate), 8-(pentylthio)-, tetrasodium salt	pH 7	281(4.27)	87-1529-79
$C_{15}H_{26}O_3$			
3(2H)-Furanone, 2,4-bis(1,1-dimethylethyl)-2-(2-hydroxypropyl)-	EtOH	268(3.81)	78-2493-79
$C_{15}H_{26}O_6$			
2H-3,9a-Methano-1-benzoxepin-4,5,6,7-tetrol, octahydro-5a-(hydroxymethyl)-2,2,9-trimethyl-	MeOH	210(3.55)(end abs.)	39-2972-79C
$C_{15}H_{28}O$			
2,4-Decadien-1-ol, 3,9-dimethyl-6-(1-methylethyl)-, (R)-	MeOH	238(4.39)	1-0551-79
$C_{15}H_{29}NO_2Si_2$			
1H-Azepine-1-carboxylic acid, 4,5-dihydro-4,5-bis(trimethylsilyl)-, ethyl ester, trans	EtOH	240(4.2)	142-0263-79
$C_{15}H_{29}N_5$			
1,2,3-Triazine-4,5-diamine, 6-(1,1-dimethylethyl)-N,N,N',N'-tetraethyl-	CH_2Cl_2	270(3.87),367s(--)	24-1514-79
1,2,3-Triazine-4,5-diamine, N,N,N',N'-tetrakis(1-methylethyl)-	CH_2Cl_2	269(4.09),350s(--)	24-1514-79
$C_{15}H_{30}N_5$			
Ethanaminium, N-[2,5-bis(diethylamino)-4H-imidazol-4-ylidene]-N-ethyl-, perchlorate	$CHCl_3$	330(4.30)	89-0156-79
$C_{15}H_{30}N_6$			
1,2,3-Triazine-4,5,6-triamine, N,N,N',N',N",N"-hexamethyl-	CH_2Cl_2	258(4.13),350(3.69)	24-1514-79
$C_{15}H_{35}N_2OP$			
Phosphorodiamidous acid, tetrapropyl-, propyl ester	hexane	215s(3.42),230(--)	22-0241-79I

Compound	Solvent	λ_{max}(log ε)	Ref.
$C_{16}Cl_{12}S_2$			
Benzene, 1,1'-[[3-(dichloromethylene)-1-propyne-1,3-diyl]bis(thio)]bis-[2,3,4,5,6-pentachloro-	heptane	203(4.89),280(4.10)	5-1626-79
$C_{16}F_{12}O_2$			
1(4H)-Naphthalenone, 2,3,4,4,6,7,8-heptafluoro-5-(pentafluorophenoxy)-	heptane or C_6H_{12}	220(4.09),237(3.98), 290(3.90)	104-1934-79
$C_{16}H_5F_9N_2O_3$			
Isoxazole, 4,5-dihydro-4-nitro-5-(pentafluorophenyl)-3-(2,3,5,6-tetrafluoro-4-methoxyphenyl)-	EtOH	213(4.36),232(4.32), 290(3.96)	104-2179-79
$C_{16}H_6ClF_6NO$			
2(1H)-Naphthalenone, 1-chloro-1,3,5,6-7,8-hexafluoro-4-(phenylamino)-	heptane	232s(4.15),246(4.18), 260s(4.10),315s(3.66), 393(3.91)	104-1934-79
$C_{16}H_6Cl_2O_3$			
Anthra[1,9-bc]pyran-2,7-dione, 4,6-dichloro-	benzene	353(3.98),390s(3.70)	104-0923-79
$C_{16}H_7BrClNO_3$			
2H-1-Benzopyran-2-one, 6-bromo-3-(5-chloro-2-benzoxazolyl)-	dioxan	358(4.53)	42-0505-79
$C_{16}H_7Br_2NO_3$			
2H-1-Benzopyran-2-one, 3-(5,7-dibromo-2-benzoxazolyl)-	dioxan	350(4.26)	42-0505-79
$C_{16}H_7Cl_2NO_3$			
Anthra[1,9-bc]pyran-2,7-dione, 1-amino-4,6-dichloro-	benzene	442(4.19)	104-0923-79
2H-1-Benzopyran-2-one, 3-(5,7-dichloro-2-benzoxazolyl)-	dioxan	349(4.28)	42-0505-79
$C_{16}H_7F_5N_4O_4$			
1H-Pyrazole, 1-(2,4-dinitrophenyl)-5-methyl-3-(pentafluorophenyl)-	EtOH	217s(4.31),294(3.94)	104-1964-79
$C_{16}H_8BrNO_3$			
2H-1-Benzopyran-2-one, 3-(2-benzoxazolyl)-6-bromo-	dioxan	360(4.24)	42-0505-79
2H-1-Benzopyran-2-one, 3-(5-bromo-2-benzoxazolyl)-	dioxan	350(4.56)	42-0505-79
$C_{16}H_8ClNO_3$			
2H-1-Benzopyran-2-one, 3-(7-chloro-2-benzoxazolyl)-	dioxan	340(4.20)	42-0505-79
$C_{16}H_8Cl_2$			
Benzo[a]biphenylene, 5,6-dichloro-	EtOH	229(4.37),266(4.66), 291(4.40),303(4.43), 386(3.55),404(3.65)	78-1177-79
$C_{16}H_8F_3N_5$			
5H-Indolo[2',3':5,6][1,2,4]triazino-[2,3-a]benzimidazole, 8-(trifluoromethyl)-	EtOH	234(4.11),278(4.38), 292(4.37),302(4.37), 368(3.96)	142-1001-79

Compound	Solvent	λ_{max}(log ε)	Ref.
$C_{16}H_8N_2O_2$			
Naphtho[2,3-f]quinoxaline-7,12-dione	EtOH	245(4.59),255(4.55), 260s(4.55),280s(4.22), 290s(4.14),342(3.95)	94-2596-79
$C_{16}H_8N_4O_2$			
Dipyrido[1,2-a:1',2'-a']benzo[1,2-d:4,5-d']diimidazole-6,13-dione, (E)-	EtOH	275(3.51),315(3.71), 453(3.94)	2-0525-79A
(Z)-	EtOH	281(3.75),327(3.98), 465(4.21)	2-0523-79A
$C_{16}H_8N_6$			
4,4'-Bipyridinium bis(dicyanomethylide)	MeCN	520(3.37)	5-0727-79
$C_{16}H_8O_3$			
7H,11H-Naphtho[1',8':4,5,6]cyclohepta-[1,2-c]furan-7,11-dione	CH_2Cl_2	239(4.25),295s(3.29), 347(3.87)	150-3518-79
$C_{16}H_8O_4$			
9,10-Anthracenedione, 6-ethynyl-1,4-dihydroxy-	MeOH	221(4.42),265(4.49), 280s(--),328(3.41), 484(3.91),515(3.69)	24-3453-79
[1]Benzopyrano[4,3-c][1]benzopyran-5,11-dione	EtOH	253(3.95),268(3.92), 380(4.10)	138-0511-79
$C_{16}H_8S_2$			
Anthra[1,9-bc:5,10-b'c']dithiophene	EtOH	252(4.59)	44-2491-79
$C_{16}H_9Br_2NO_3$			
Acetamide, N-(2,4-dibromo-9,10-dihydro-9,10-dioxo-1-anthracenyl)-	EtOH	212(4.43),265(4.57), 345(3.59)	40-1728-79
$C_{16}H_9Cl$			
Pyrene, 4-chloro-	heptane	233(4.57),242(4.86), 264(4.34),275(4.59), 297(3.67),309(4.07), 323(4.45),339(4.66), 354(3.02),365(2.62), 374(2.20)	49-1233-79
$C_{16}H_9Cl_2N_5O$			
5H-Indolo[2',3':5,6][1,2,4]triazino-[2,3-a]benzimidazole, 3,11-dichloro-8-methoxy-	EtOH	272(3.80),287(3.81), 297(3.88),365(3.29)	142-1001-79
$C_{16}H_9F_5N_2$			
1H-Pyrazole, 5-methyl-3-(pentafluorophenyl)-1-phenyl-	EtOH	209s(4.17),233(4.10)	104-1964-79
$C_{16}H_9F_5N_2OS$			
3H-Pyrazol-3-one, 2,4-dihydro-5-methyl-4-[(pentafluorophenyl)thio]-2-phenyl-	EtOH	207(4.28),248(4.14)	48-0495-79
$C_{16}H_9NO_2$			
5H-Benzo[b]carbazole-6,11-dione	EtOH	272(4.56),281s(4.55), 348s(3.64),380(3.8)	150-4801-79
	EtOH-NaOH	275s(--),295(--), 428(--),490s(--)	150-4801-79
Fluoranthene, 3-nitro-	CH_2Cl_2	255(4.18),301(3.79), 347(3.86),382(3.99)	124-1214-79

Compound	Solvent	$\lambda_{max}(\log \epsilon)$	Ref.
$C_{16}H_9NO_2S_3$			
5(4H)-Oxazolone, 4-[(2,2'-bithiophene)-5-ylmethylene]-2-(2-thienyl)-	toluene	315(4.32),465(4.81)	103-1303-79
$C_{16}H_9NO_3$			
Benzofuro[2,3-b]quinoline-11-carboxylic acid	EtOH	221(4.60),250s(4.60), 258(4.76),322(4.31), 334s(4.26)	4-0487-79
Benzofuro[3,2-c]quinoline-6-carboxylic acid	EtOH	212(4.26),228(4.23), 250s(4.54),259(4.68), 282(4.16),292(4.12)	4-0487-79
2H-1-Benzopyran-2-one, 3-(2-benzoxazolyl)-	dioxan	349(4.25)	42-0505-79
Liriodendronine	MeOH	260(4.08),297(3.84), 543(3.75),569s(3.73)	100-0325-79
	HCl	253(4.12),261s(4.08), 278s(3.88),477(3.56), 602s(3.06)	100-0325-79
$C_{16}H_9NO_4$			
Benzofuro[2,3-b]quinoline-11-carboxylic acid, 6-oxide	EtOH	223(4.34),254s(4.47), 264(4.73),281s(4.32), 323s(3.93)	4-0487-79
$C_{16}H_9N_3O_2$			
5H-Cyclopentapyrazine-5,7(6H)-dione, 6-(2-quinolinyl)-	DMF	425(4.52),451(4.56)	153-0173-79
$C_{16}H_{10}$			
Anthracene, 9-ethynyl-	$CHCl_3$	255(5.22),265(5.38), 313(3.35),348(3.65), 364(3.94),382(4.08), 403(4.04)	121-0203-79
polymer	$CHCl_3$	255(4.51),360(3.77), 375(3.87),394(3.85)	121-0203-79
Benzene, 1,1'-(1,3-butadiyne-1,4-diyl)-bis-	EtOH	204(4.63),218(4.51), 228(4.46),248(4.44), 260(4.43),288(4.32), 297(4.24),306(4.50), 317(4.12),327(4.47)	39-2289-79C
$C_{16}H_{10}BrN$			
3-Fluoranthenamine, 9-bromo-	CH_2Cl_2	261(4.57),310(4.49), 333(3.99),375(3.93), 409(3.91)	124-1214-79
$C_{16}H_{10}BrNO_3$			
Acetamide, N-(4-bromo-9,10-dihydro-9,10-dioxo-1-anthracenyl)-	EtOH	232(4.40),268(4.47), 300s(3.90),413(3.76)	40-1728-79
$C_{16}H_{10}ClN_3O_2$			
1H-Pyrimido[4,5-b]indole-2,4(3H,9H)-dione, 3-(4-chlorophenyl)-	$CHCl_3$	285(4.24),307(4.27), 313s(4.25)	103-0179-79
$C_{16}H_{10}Cl_2N_2$			
Pyrazine, 2,5-dichloro-3,6-diphenyl-	EtOH	270(4.08),327(4.14)	94-2980-79
$C_{16}H_{10}Cl_2N_4O_2$			
2,5-Cyclohexadiene-1,4-dione, 2,5-dichloro-3,6-bis(2-pyridinylamino)-	EtOH	245(3.75),351(3.98), 542(4.21)	2-0523-79A

Compound	Solvent	$\lambda_{max}(\log \epsilon)$	Ref.
$C_{16}H_{10}Cl_2OS$			
2H-Naphtho[1,8-bc]thiophen-3-ol, 6,8-dichloro-2-(2,4-cyclopentadien-1-yl)-	MeOH	230(4.4),253(4.3), 323(3.8),338(3.8), 354(3.8)	24-0349-79
$C_{16}H_{10}Cl_2O_2S$			
4-Cyclopentene-1,3-dione, 4,5-dichloro-2-(1,3-dimethyl-6H-cyclohepta[c]thien-6-ylidene)-	CH_2Cl_2	250(4.38),306(4.28), 314s(4.26),420s(4.42), 446(4.59),476(4.56)	83-0120-79
$C_{16}H_{10}Cl_4O_3$			
4a,8c-(Methanoxymethano)benzo[3',4']cyclobuta[1,2]benzene-9,11-dione, 5,6,7,8-tetrachloro-1,4,4b,4c,8a,8b-hexahydro-	CH_2Cl_2	290s(3.57),301(3.66), 313(3.62),327(3.32)	88-4545-79
$C_{16}H_{10}Cl_5N_3O_2$			
3-Butenimidamide, 3,4,4-trichloro-N,N'-bis(2-chlorophenyl)-2-aci-nitro-	EtOH	206(4.44),352(4.03)	104-0039-79
$C_{16}H_{10}CrMoO_6$			
Molybdenum, tricarbonyl(η^5-2,4-cyclopentadien-1-yl)[tricarbonyl(η^5-2,4-cyclopentadien-1-yl)chromium]-, (Cr-Mo)	PhCN	415(4.06),548(2.99)	64-0573-79B
$C_{16}H_{10}CrO_6W$			
Tungsten, tricarbonyl(η^5-2,4-cyclopentadien-1-yl)[tricarbonyl(η^5-2,4-cyclopentadien-1-yl)chromium]-, (Cr-W)	PhCN	402(4.05),520(3.06)	64-0573-79B
$C_{16}H_{10}Cr_2O_6$			
Chromium, hexacarbonylbis(η^5-2,4-cyclopentadien-1-yl)di-, (Cr-Cr)	PhCN	450(3.68),598(2.72)	64-0573-79B
$C_{16}H_{10}HgO_3$			
Mercury, (2,3-dihydro-1,3-dioxo-1H-indene-2-carboxaldehydato-O^1,O^2)-phenyl-	benzene	294(4.10),308(3.89), 320(3.96)	103-0056-79
	DMSO	275(4.05),287(4.28), 317(4.03),330(4.00)	103-0056-79
$C_{16}H_{10}Mo_2O_6$			
Molybdenum, hexacarbonylbis(η^5-2,4-cyclopentadien-1-yl)di-, (Mo-Mo)	PhCN	387(4.25),512(3.24)	64-0573-79B
$C_{16}H_{10}N_2$			
Dibenzo[f,h]quinoxaline	EtOH	256(5.0),330f(4.0)	152-0287-79
Naphtho[1,2-f]quinoxaline	EtOH	232(4.60),237s(4.56), 247(4.52),284(4.36), 299(4.37),345(3.63), 360(3.74),380(3.78)	94-2596-79
Naphtho[2,1-f]quinoxaline	EtOH	215(4.43),255(4.60), 273(4.42),281s(4.33), 301(4.35),357s(3.68), 353(3.67)	94-2596-79
Naphtho[2,3-f]quinoxaline	EtOH	222(4.38),247s(4.70), 254(4.72),276s(4.13), 308s(4.33),318(4.36), 339(3.94),358(3.86)	94-2596-79

Compound	Solvent	$\lambda_{max}(\log \epsilon)$	Ref.
$C_{16}H_{10}N_2O$			
Dibenzo[f,h]cinnolin-3(2H)-one	EtOH	236(4.51),255s(4.59), 267(4.67),279(4.54), 328(3.40),377(3.40)	39-2034-79C
3H-Pyrrolo[2,3-c]acridine-1-carboxalde- hyde	EtOH	215(4.36),234(4.49), 269(4.44),372(3.77)	103-0894-79
$C_{16}H_{10}N_2OS$			
Propanedinitrile, (3-ethoxy-2H-naphtho- [1,8-bc]thien-2-ylidene)-	MeOH	213(4.6),251(4.4), 268(4.5),276(4.6), 287(4.5),320(4.3), 356(4.3),373(4.5), 434(4.5),459(4.6), 485(4.4)	5-0965-79
$C_{16}H_{10}N_2O_2$			
3-Fluoranthenamine, 2-nitro-	DMSO	335(3.87),405(4.11), 445(4.19)	124-1214-79
3-Fluoranthenamine, 4-nitro-	CH_2Cl_2	304(4.33),345(4.14), 394(3.90),420(3.80)	124-1214-79
	DMSO	305(4.58),347(4.41), 405(3.95),430(3.84)	124-1214-79
protonated	isoPrOH	277(4.40),342(4.11), 382(4.13)	124-1214-79
	DMSO	280(4.40),346(4.14), 392(4.07)	124-1214-79
3-Fluoranthenamine, 8-nitro-	CH_2Cl_2	242(4.51),314(4.11), 340(4.19),444(3.98)	124-1214-79
	DMSO	346(4.18),484(4.11)	124-1214-79
protonated	isoPrOH	234(4.66),303(4.29), 346(4.08),379(4.07)	124-1214-79
	DMSO	333(4.18),361(4.21), 480(4.00)	124-1214-79
3-Fluoranthenamine, 9-nitro-	CH_2Cl_2	245(4.71),305(4.54), 340(4.20),401(4.12), 414(4.06)	124-1214-79
	DMSO	310(4.56),344(4.20), 420(4.01),431(4.02)	124-1214-79
protonated	isoPrOH	234(4.18),288(4.28), 326(3.78),361(3.91)	124-1214-79
	DMSO	288(4.12),328(3.89), 358(3.67)	124-1214-79
Indolo[7,6-g]indole-1,6-dicarboxalde- hyde, 3,8-dihydro-	EtOH	208(4.14),252(4.58), 260(4.61),276(4.71), 287(4.66),320(4.19), 335(4.04),350(3.82)	103-0989-79
$C_{16}H_{10}N_2O_3S$			
9H-Naphtho[1',2':4,5]thiazolo[3,2-a]- pyrimidine-11-carboxylic acid, 9- oxo-, methyl ester	MeOH	241(4.71),293(4.06), 346(3.97)	83-0619-79
$C_{16}H_{10}N_2O_6S$			
5-Thia-1-azabicyclo[4.2.0]oct-2-ene-2- carboxylic acid, 7-(1,3-dihydro-1,3- dioxo-2H-isoindol-2-yl)-3-methyl- 4,8-dioxo-, (6R-trans)-	EtOH	295(3.89),300s(3.88), 320s(3.78)	33-2681-79
$C_{16}H_{10}N_4$			
[Terpyridine]-x-carbonitrile	EtOH	225(4.39),245s(4.33), 276(4.27)	44-0041-79

Compound	Solvent	λ_{max}(log ε)	Ref.
$C_{16}H_{10}N_4O_2$			
1H-Imidazole-2-carbonitrile, 1-(4-nitrophenyl)-4-phenyl-	EtOH	270(4.15)	78-1331-79
$C_{16}H_{10}N_4S_3$			
[1,2,5]Thiadiazolo[2',3':2,3][1,2,4]-thiadiazolo[1,5-c][1,3,2]dithiazole-8-S^{IV}, 3,5-diphenyl- (or isomer)	EtOH	237(4.21),255(4.12), 322(3.98),364(4.04), 520(3.49)	4-1009-79
$C_{16}H_{10}N_6$			
1H-Tetrazolium, 5-(dicyanomethyl)-1,3-diphenyl-, hydroxide, inner salt	n.s.g.	223s(3.95),273(4.43), 394(3.13)	39-0744-79C
$C_{16}H_{10}O_2$			
Cyclohepta[de]naphthalene-8,9-dicarboxaldehyde	$CHCl_3$	258(4.68),310(3.77), 346s(3.91),372(4.10), 386s(4.03),460(2.89), 488(2.83),524(2.62), 564(2.17),620(0.92)	150-3518-79
$C_{16}H_{10}O_3S_8$			
1,3-Dithiole-4-carboxylic acid, 2-(1,3-dithiol-2-ylidene)-5-[[2-(1,3-dithiol-2-ylidene)-1,3-dithiol-4-yl]carbonyl]-, ethyl ester	MeCN	214s(4.27),253s(4.18), 290s(4.45),304(4.49), 314(4.50),475(3.43), 528(3.56)	44-1476-79
$C_{16}H_{10}O_4$			
4H-Difuro[3,2-c:2',3'-h]benzopyran-4-one, 2,7-dimethyl-	$CHCl_3$	255(4.50),268(4.41), 305(4.19),320(4.12), 330(4.05),336(4.01)	42-0056-79
$C_{16}H_{10}O_5$			
9,10-Anthracenedione, 6-acetyl-1,4-dihydroxy-	MeOH	214(4.07),255(4.20), 269s(--),320s(--), 488(3.53),570(2.94)	24-3453-79
$C_{16}H_{10}O_6W_2$			
Tungsten, hexacarbonylbis(η^5-2,4-cyclopentadien-1-yl)di-, (W-W)	PhCN	360(4.00),489(3.26)	64-0573-79B
$C_{16}H_{10}O_7$			
2-Anthraceneacetic acid, 9,10-dihydro-α,1,4-trihydroxy-9,10-dioxo-	EtOH	205(4.40),225(4.39), 249(4.52),280(4.03), 330s(--),486(3.90)	5-0019-79
$C_{16}H_{11}BrClN_3$			
Indolo[1,2-c]quinazolin-12-amine, 10-bromo-2-chloro-6-methyl-	dioxan	225(4.46),260(4.35), 290(4.79),386(4.11)	103-0681-79
$C_{16}H_{11}BrN_4O_2$			
1H-Pyrazole-3-carboxaldehyde, 1-(4-bromophenyl)-4,5-dihydro-5-oxo-4-(phenylhydrazono)-	n.s.g.	210(3.91),252(3.86), 406(4.11)	106-0531-79
$C_{16}H_{11}ClN_2$			
Pyrazine, 3-chloro-2,5-diphenyl-	EtOH	268(4.24),328(4.32)	94-2980-79
$C_{16}H_{11}ClN_2O$			
Pyrazine, 3-chloro-2,5-diphenyl-, 1-oxide	EtOH	272(4.46),335(3.89)	94-2980-79

Compound	Solvent	$\lambda_{max}(\log \epsilon)$	Ref.
2(1H)-Pyrazinone, 5-chloro-3,6-diphenyl-	EtOH	265(4.04),360(4.11)	94-2980-79
$C_{16}H_{11}ClN_2O_2$			
Phenol, 4,4'-(6-chloro-3,4-pyridazinediyl)bis-	EtOH	284(4.17)	111-0053-79
$C_{16}H_{11}ClN_4O_2$			
1H-Pyrazole-3-carboxaldehyde, 1-(4-chlorophenyl)-4,5-dihydro-5-oxo-4-(phenylhydrazono)-	n.s.g.	211(3.94),254(4.00), 409(4.21)	106-0531-79
$C_{16}H_{11}ClO_2$			
Cyclobut[a]acenaphthylen-7(6bH)-one, 8-acetyl-8-chloro-8,8a-dihydro-	EtOH	226(4.78),279(3.80), 290(3.89),300(3.73), 315(2.94),319(2.54)	39-2995-79C
$C_{16}H_{11}ClO_4$			
9,10-Anthracenedione, 2-(1-chloroethyl)-1,4-dihydroxy-	MeOH	206(4.37),231(4.38), 249(4.58),284(4.04), 484(4.00)	5-0019-79
$C_{16}H_{11}Cl_2NO_2$			
9(10H)-Anthracenone, 1,3-dichloro-10-(ethylimino)-4-hydroxy-	benzene	414(3.56),532(3.45)	104-0147-79
	EtOH	415s(3.40),512(3.72)	104-0147-79
	dioxan	411(3.50),523(3.49)	104-0147-79
$C_{16}H_{11}N$			
3-Fluoranthenamine	CH_2Cl_2	247(4.87),305(4.73), 326(4.08),367(4.16), 413(4.16)	124-1214-79
$C_{16}H_{11}NO$			
Benzofuro[2,3-b]quinoline, 11-methyl-	EtOH	222(4.56),250s(4.61), 257(4.74),279(3.70), 292s(3.76),310s(4.13), 324(4.42),337(4.20)	4-0487-79
Benzofuro[3,2-c]quinoline, 6-methyl-	EtOH	213(4.36),229(4.44), 247(4.75),256(4.87), 281(4.24),290(4.26), 315(3.35),329(3.06)	4-0487-79
$C_{16}H_{11}NOS$			
Benzofuro[3,2-b]quinoline-11(5H)-thione, 5-methyl-	dioxan	249(4.55),308(4.29), 336(4.16),439(4.32), 467(4.37)	83-0254-79
$C_{16}H_{11}NO_2$			
Benzamide, N-1H-2-benzopyran-1-ylidene-	EtOH	244(4.53),251(4.58), 327s(3.85)	39-0266-79C
Benzofuro[2,3-b]quinoline, 11-methyl-, 6-oxide	EtOH	224(4.34),251s(4.36), 263(4.75),281s(4.32), 323s(3.93),338(4.11), 350s(3.92),367(3.90)	4-0487-79
Benzofuro[3,2-c]quinoline, 6-methyl-, 7-oxide	EtOH	215(4.36),237s(4.44), 248(4.39),256s(4.43), 271(4.62),285s(4.33), 294(4.36),328(3.79), 339(3.78),355s(3.65)	4-0487-79
Benzofuro[3,2-b]quinolin-11(5H)-one, 5-methyl-	dioxan	235(4.21),261(4.56), 270(4.55),294(4.04),	83-0254-79

Compound	Solvent	λ_{max}(log ε)	Ref.
Benzofuro[3,2-b]quinolin-11(5H)-one, 5-methyl- (cont.)		307(4.19),354(4.06), 372(4.18)	83-0254-79
1H-Indene-1,3(2H)-dione, 2-[(phenyl-amino)methylene]-	hexane	234(4.38),291(3.67), 303(3.81),366(4.53)	131-0077-79D
	EtOH	367(4.54)	131-0077-79D
5(4H)-Oxazolone, 2-phenyl-4-(phenyl-methylene)-	toluene	360(4.59)	103-1303-79
3-Quinolinecarboxaldehyde, 1,4-dihydro-4-oxo-	EtOH	216(4.41),233(4.44), 264s(3.89),318s(4.23), 328(4.25)	4-0177-79
$C_{16}H_{11}NO_2S$			
5(4H)-Oxazolone, 2-phenyl-4-[3-(2-thi-enyl)-2-propenylidene]-	toluene	290(4.12),420(4.67)	103-1303-79
5(4H)-Oxazolone, 4-(3-phenyl-2-propen-ylidene)-2-(2-thienyl)-	toluene	295(4.13),405(4.71)	103-1303-79
$C_{16}H_{11}NO_3$			
2H-1-Benzopyran-2,4(3H)-dione, 3-[(phenylamino)methylene]-	hexane	240(4.24),366(4.38)	131-0077-79D
	EtOH	364(4.42)	131-0077-79D
Furan, 2-[2-(2-naphthalenyl)ethenyl]-5-nitro-, (E)-	MeOH	227(4.52),258(4.14), 318(4.03),411(4.34)	73-2096-79
5(4H)-Oxazolone, 4-[3-(2-furanyl)-2-propenylidene]-2-phenyl-	toluene	410(4.69),440(4.62)	103-1303-79
4(1H)-Quinolinone, 2-(1,3-benzodioxol-5-yl)- (norgraveoline)	EtOH	214(4.46),244(4.46), 276(4.13),324(4.30)	105-0716-79
	EtOH-acid	245(4.46),350(4.21)	105-0716-79
	EtOH-base	274(4.38),301(4.21)	105-0716-79
$C_{16}H_{11}NO_6$			
[1,3]Benzodioxolo[5,6-a]quinolizinium, 2,3-dicarboxy-6,7-dihydro-, hydroxide, inner salt (berberidic acid)	EtOH	230s(3.64),295(3.61), 385(3.56)	23-1647-79
$C_{16}H_{11}NO_8$			
2,5-Cyclohexadiene-1,4-dione, 3-hydr-oxy-2-[3-(4-hydroxy-3-nitrophenyl)-1-oxo-2-propenyl]-5-methoxy-	$CHCl_3$	277(4.32),382(4.54)	18-2596-79
$C_{16}H_{11}N_3OS$			
2H-Pyrimido[4,5-b]indol-2-one, 1,3,4,9-tetrahydro-3-phenyl-4-thioxo-	$CHCl_3$	262(4.31),352(4.32)	103-0179-79
$C_{16}H_{11}N_3O_2$			
1H-Pyrimido[4,5-b]indole-2,4(3H,9H)-di-one, 3-phenyl-	$CHCl_3$	285(4.20),305(4.24)	103-0179-79
$C_{16}H_{11}N_3O_2S$			
1-Indolizinecarbonitrile, 2-(methyl-thio)-3-(4-nitrophenyl)-	EtOH	243(4.47),305(4.03), 355(4.01)	95-0540-79
$C_{16}H_{11}N_3O_3S$			
Methanone, [4-amino-5-(4-nitrophenyl)-3-isothiazolyl]phenyl-	MeCN	267(4.31),405(4.04)	5-1534-79
$C_{16}H_{11}N_3O_4$			
1-Naphthalenamine, N-(2,4-dinitrophen-yl)-	EtOH	351(4.22)	73-1613-79
$C_{16}H_{11}N_3O_6S$			
Benzoic acid, 2-[(8-hydroxy-5-sulfo-	neutral	502(4.26),534(4.25)	73-2815-79

Compound	Solvent	λmax(log ε)	Ref.
7-quinolinyl)azo]- (cont.)	anion	510(4.24)	73-2815-79
	dianion	490(4.27)	73-2815-79
	trianion	470(4.05)	73-2815-79
Benzoic acid, 3-[(8-hydroxy-5-sulfo-7-quinolinyl)azo]-	neutral	500(4.28),530(4.31)	73-2815-79
	anion	500(4.17)	73-2815-79
	dianion	490(4.29)	73-2815-79
	trianion	480(4.29)	73-2815-79
Benzoic acid, 4-[(8-hydroxy-5-sulfo-7-quinolinyl)azo]-	neutral	505(4.38),535(4.40)	73-2815-79
	anion	500(4.37)	73-2815-79
	dianion	495(4.33)	73-2815-79
	trianion	485(4.25)	73-2815-79
$C_{16}H_{11}N_5O_4$			
1H-Pyrazole-3-carboxaldehyde, 4,5-dihydro-1-(4-nitrophenyl)-5-oxo-4-(phenylhydrazono)-	n.s.g.	230(3.97),410(4.36)	106-0531-79
$C_{16}H_{12}$			
Anthracene, 9-ethenyl-	$CHCl_3$	260(5.20),355(3.91), 372(3.93),390(3.87)	121-0203-79
Naphthalene, 1-phenyl-	MeCN	225(4.75),288(3.99)	44-2712-79
$C_{16}H_{12}BrN_3$			
Indolo[1,2-c]quinazolin-12-amine, 10-bromo-6-methyl-	dioxan	220(4.22),255(4.24), 287(4.44),380(4.58)	103-0681-79
$C_{16}H_{12}BrS_3$			
1,2-Dithiol-1-ium, 3-[(2-bromophenyl)-thio]-4-methyl-5-phenyl-, bromide	MeCN	218(4.50),270(3.91), 336s(3.99),372(4.35)	104-0955-79
triiodide	MeCN	220(4.36),290(4.54), 370(4.54)	104-0955-79
$C_{16}H_{12}ClN_3O_3$			
4(1H)-Quinazolinone, 6-chloro-1-methyl-8-nitro-2-(phenylmethyl)-	80% EtOH	239(4.30),265-336(3.7-3.22)	42-0708-79
4(1H)-Quinazolinone, 8-chloro-1-methyl-6-nitro-2-(phenylmethyl)-	80% EtOH	228(4.60),289-308(3.9-4.0)	42-0708-79
$C_{16}H_{12}Cl_2N_2S$			
2(1H)-Pyrimidinethione, 4,6-bis(4-chlorophenyl)-3,4-dihydro-	EtOH	238(4.35),265s(4.17)	23-2734-79
	$CHCl_3$	274(4.23)	23-2734-79
	CCl_4	278s(4.16),285(4.17), 300s(4.13)	23-2734-79
$C_{16}H_{12}Cl_2N_4$			
2-Propenimidamide, N-(2-chlorophenyl)-3-[(2-chlorophenyl)amino]-2-cyano-	EtOH	336(4.34)	24-0484-79
	MeCN	336(4.37)	24-0484-79
$C_{16}H_{12}Cl_3N_4S$			
1,3,4-Thiadiazolium, 5-[[chloro(4-chlorophenyl)methylene]hydrazino-3-methyl-2-phenyl-, hydroxide, inner salt	CH_2Cl_2	345(4.20),445(4.18)	39-0724-79C
$C_{16}H_{12}Cl_3N_3O_2$			
3-Butenimidamide, 3,4,4-trichloro-2-aci-nitro-N,N'-diphenyl-	EtOH	205(4.45),372(4.06)	104-0039-79
$C_{16}H_{12}FNO_4S$			
Ethanesulfonyl fluoride, 2-[(9,10-dihydro-9,10-dioxo-1-anthracenyl)amino]-	acetone	478(3.85)	44-3847-79

Compound	Solvent	λ_{max}(log ε)	Ref.
$C_{16}H_{12}NO_4$			
1,3-Benzodioxolo[5,6-a]furo[3,4-g]quin-olizinium, 5,6,9,11-tetrahydro-9-oxo-, iodide	EtOH	280(3.97),375(3.91)	23-1647-79
1,3-Benzodioxolo[5,6-a]furo[3,4-g]quin-olizinium, 5,6,9,11-tetrahydro-11-oxo-, iodide	EtOH	235(3.95),283(4.00), 375(3.79)	23-1647-79
$C_{16}H_{12}NP$			
9H-Pyrrolo[1,2-a]benzazaphosphole, 9-phenyl-	EtOH	212s(4.39),230(4.47), 265s(4.04),283(4.11)	101-0139-79C
$C_{16}H_{12}N_2$			
3,6'-Bi-1H-indole	EtOH	233(4.27),255s(3.95), 289(3.88),302(3.88)	94-0346-79
1,4-Ethenonaphthalene-2,3-dicarboni-trile, 1,4-dihydro-1,4-dimethyl-	EtOH	210(4.35),236(3.82), 245s(3.76),282(3.00), 312(2.95)	35-6660-79
1H-Phenanthro[9,10-d]imidazole, 1-meth-yl-	EtOH	225(4.15),245s(4.61), 252(4.77),278(3.92), 286s(3.83),298(3.67), 331(3.00),347(3.08)	44-0041-79
Pyrazine, [2-(1-naphthalenyl)ethenyl]-	EtOH	222(4.68),286(4.01)	94-2596-79
Pyrazine, [2-(2-naphthalenyl)ethenyl]-	EtOH	220(4.53),252s(4.26), 265s(4.30),272(4.31), 305s(4.20),332(4.27)	94-2596-79
$C_{16}H_{12}N_2O$			
Ethanone, 1-(3,8-dihydroindolo[7,6-g]-indol-2-yl)-	EtOH	204(4.10),249(4.51), 255(4.59),276(4.24), 287(4.40),360(4.26)	103-0989-79
1-Naphthalenol, 2-(phenylazo)-	EtOH	295(4.30),355(4.05), 493(4.26)	32-0351-79
	ether	300s(--),350(4.30), 490(4.45)	32-0351-79
	dioxan	295(4.35),360s(4.16), 494(4.34)	32-0351-79
	$CHCl_3$	360(4.08),496(4.32)	32-0351-79
	CCl_4	355(3.83),493(4.04)	32-0351-79
2-Naphthalenol, 1-(phenylazo)-	EtOH	228(4.56),258s(4.01), 312(3.81),420(3.96), 484(4.12)	4-1001-79
	EtOH	310(3.90),405(4.13), 470(4.28)	32-0351-79
	ether	320s(--),410(3.93), 465(3.97)	32-0351-79
	dioxan	230(4.33),256(--), 312(3.93),410(4.10), 480(4.24)	32-0351-79
	$CHCl_3$	315(3.63),410(3.85), 480(3.99)	32-0351-79
	CCl_4	315(4.00),410(4.20), 470(4.33)	32-0351-79
Pyrazine, 2,5-diphenyl-, 1-oxide	EtOH	273(4.34),329s(3.76)	94-2980-79
2(1H)-Pyrazinone, 3,6-diphenyl-	EtOH	263(4.08),362(4.28)	94-2980-79
Pyrrolo[2,3-c]carbazole, 6-acetyl-3,6-dihydro-	EtOH	223(4.55),250(4.37), 320(4.29),332(4.26)	103-0890-79
$C_{16}H_{12}N_2OS$			
Methanone, (4-amino-3-phenyl-5-isothia-zolyl)phenyl-	MeCN	237(4.26),386(4.08)	5-1534-79

Compound	Solvent	λ_{max}(log ε)	Ref.
Thiazolo[3,2-a]benzimidazol-6-ol, 3-methyl-2-phenyl-	pH 1	329(3.8),385(3.3)	18-3096-79
	pH 13	324(3.2),450(3.7)	18-3096-79
	EtOH	245(3.60),278(3.57), 364(3.60)	18-3096-79
Thiazolo[3,2-a]benzimidazol-6-ol, 3-(4-methylphenyl)-	pH 1	325(3.6),380(3.5)	18-3096-79
	pH 13	318(3.3),445(3.46)	18-3096-79
	EtOH	238(3.76),275(3.54), 362(3.65)	18-3096-79
$C_{16}H_{12}N_2OS_2$			
Benzamide, N-(4-phenyl-2-thioxo-3(2H)-thiazolyl)-	MeOH	226(4.35),321(4.18)	5-0656-79
	MeOH-NaOMe	227(4.30),316(4.08)	5-0656-79
Pyridinium, 1-(4-amino-5-benzoyl-2-mercapto-3-thienyl)-, hydroxide, inner salt	EtOH	247(4.21),324(4.03), 390(4.46)	95-1081-79
$C_{16}H_{12}N_2O_2$			
Acetic acid, (10-oxo-9(10H)-phenanthrenylidene)hydrazide	EtOH	242(4.44),249(4.44), 270(4.51),293(3.99), 303(4.07),372(4.08)	39-2034-79C
	EtOH-base	247(--),253(--), 262s(--),276s(--), 370(--),390(--)	39-2034-79C
Ethanone, 1,1'-(2,7-phenazinediyl)bis-	EtOH	273(5.08),366(4.16)	94-2316-79
Pyrazine, 2,5-diphenyl-, 1,4-dioxide	EtOH	283(4.26),327(3.92)	94-2980-79
Pyrazine, [2-(1-naphthalenyl)ethenyl]-, 1,4-dioxide	EtOH	222(4.77),253(4.22), 279(4.13),322(4.44)	94-2596-79
Pyrazine, [2-(2-naphthalenyl)ethenyl]-, 1,4-dioxide	EtOH	219(4.59),269(4.33), 280s(4.35),291(4.39), 321(4.64),350s(4.42)	94-2596-79
2(1H)-Pyrazinone, 3,6-diphenyl-, 4-oxide	EtOH	277(4.18),326(3.77)	94-2980-79
$C_{16}H_{12}N_2O_2S$			
Benzamide, N-(2-oxo-4-phenyl-3(2H)-thiazolyl)-	MeOH	226(4.28),265(3.92)	5-0656-79
	MeOH-NaOMe	230(4.28),275(3.83)	5-0656-79
1,3-Dioxolo[4,5-g]quinazoline, 8-[(phenylmethyl)thio]-	EtOH	205s(4.32),214(4.33), 234(4.32),263s(4.20), 270s(3.75),318s(3.90), 327(4.05),340(4.14)	1-0079-79
$C_{16}H_{12}N_2O_3$			
Benzamide, N-(2,3-dihydro-1,3-dioxo-1H-isoindol-4-yl)-2-methyl-	dioxan	229(4.56),264(4.31), 342(3.75)	4-0225-79
Benzamide, N-(2,3-dihydro-1,3-dioxo-1H-isoindol-4-yl)-3-methyl-	dioxan	221(4.53),270(4.31), 344(3.74)	4-0225-79
Benzamide, N-(2,3-dihydro-1,3-dioxo-1H-isoindol-4-yl)-4-methyl-	dioxan	229(4.56),272(4.41), 344(3.77)	4-0225-79
1,3-Dioxolo[4,5-g]quinazolin-8(5H)-one, 5-methyl-6-phenyl-	80% EtOH	248(4.44),324(4.03), 333(4.06)	42-0708-79
$C_{16}H_{12}N_2O_3S$			
Thiazolo[3,2-a]perimidine-9-acetic acid, 9,10-dihydro-10-oxo-, methyl ester	MeOH	212(4.32),233(4.52), 328(4.04)	83-0776-79
$C_{16}H_{12}N_2O_3S_2$			
2H-1,4-Benzothiazin-3(4H)-one, 2-(2(3H)-benzothiazolylidene)-4-methyl-, 1,1-dioxide, (E)-	dioxan	260(3.3),350(3.7)	83-0302-79
(Z)-	dioxan	260(3.2),350(3.3)	83-0302-79

Compound	Solvent	λ_{max}(log ε)	Ref.
$C_{16}H_{12}N_2O_4$			
Benzamide, N-(2,3-dihydro-1,3-dioxo-1H-isoindol-4-yl)-2-methoxy-	dioxan	224(4.56),272(4.29), 281(4.25),344(3.80)	4-0225-79
Benzamide, N-(2,3-dihydro-1,3-dioxo-1H-isoindol-4-yl)-4-methoxy-	dioxan	225(4.55),282(4.50), 346(3.77)	4-0225-79
$C_{16}H_{12}N_2O_5$			
4,5-Isoxazoledicarboxylic acid, 3-(2-quinolinyl)-, dimethyl ester	MeOH	210(4.35),246s(4.29), 263(4.35),304(4.07)	39-2171-79C
	MeOH-HClO₄	270(4.43),348(4.27)	39-2171-79C
$C_{16}H_{12}N_2O_6S$			
Benzoic acid, 2-nitro-5-[[2-(4-nitrophenyl)-2-propenyl]thio]-	n.s.g.	320(4.20)	35-3097-79
$C_{16}H_{12}N_2S$			
Quinazoline, 4-(benzo[b]thien-3(or 2)-yl)-1,4-dihydro-, hydrochloride	EtOH	225(4.62),261(4.04), 267(4.04),291(4.02), 301(3.99)	24-1348-79
$C_{16}H_{12}N_4$			
Tricyclo[3.2.1.0^{2,4}]octane, 6,7-bis-(methylene)-, tetracyanoethene adduct	EtOH	212.5(3.99)	33-2341-79
$C_{16}H_{12}N_4OS$			
8-Azabicyclo[3.2.1]oct-3-ene-6-carbonitrile, 2-oxo-8-(3-phenyl-1,2,4-thiadiazol-5-yl)-, endo	EtOH	246(4.45)	39-0399-79C
$C_{16}H_{12}N_4O_4$			
1H-Pyrazolo[4,3-e]pyrrolo[1,2-a]pyrimidine-4,8-dione, 6-acetyl-5,5a-dihydro-7-hydroxy-1-phenyl-	EtOH	229(4.34),261s(4.23), 334(3.96)	142-0397-79
$C_{16}H_{12}N_4O_4S$			
Isothiazolo[3,4-d]pyrimidine-3-acetic acid, α-cyano-4,5,6,7-tetrahydro-5-methyl-4,6-dioxo-7-phenyl-, methyl ester	EtOH	213(4.52),235(4.44), 294(3.87)	95-0989-79
	EtOH	217(4.41),258(3.92), 297(3.72)	142-0485-79
$C_{16}H_{12}N_4O_5S$			
3H-Pyrazol-3-one, 4-[(2,4-dinitrophenyl)thio]-2,4-dihydro-5-methyl-2-phenyl-	EtOH	247(4.30)	48-0495-79
$C_{16}H_{12}N_6O_4$			
9H-Purine-9-propanoic acid, 6-amino-α-(1,3-dihydro-1,3-dioxo-2H-isoindol-2-yl)-	n.s.g.	261(4.07)	65-0989-79
2-Pyridineacetonitrile, α-(1,3-dihydro-1,3-dimethyl-2H-benzimidazol-2-ylidene)-3,5-dinitro-	0.01N H_2SO_4	300(3.86),400(4.41)	104-0178-79
	pH 12	300(3.86),440(4.41)	104-0178-79
	EtOH	300(3.86),440(4.41)	104-0178-79
$C_{16}H_{12}O$			
Cyclopenta[a]fluoren-3(2H)-one, 1,10-dihydro-	EtOH	310(3.88)	25-0347-79
1-Naphthalenol, 3-phenyl-	EtOH	206(4.60),256(4.71), 300(3.85),340s(3.58)	104-1973-79
$C_{16}H_{12}O_2$			
9,10-Anthracenedione, 1,4-dimethyl-	C_6H_{12}	332s(--),346(3.69)	18-0329-79

Compound	Solvent	λ_{max}(log ϵ)	Ref.
4H-1-Benzopyran-4-one, 2-methyl-3-phenyl-	EtOH	224(4.31),285(3.91), 316(4.01)	150-1713-79
$C_{16}H_{12}O_3$			
2(3H)-Benzofuranone, 6-methoxy-3-(phenylmethylene)-	EtOH	216(3.81),239(3.79), 260(3.82),370(3.85)	78-2539-79
2H-1-Benzopyran-2-one, 4-(phenylmethoxy)-	MeOH	260s(3.55),267(4.06), 278(4.02),306(3.83), 315s(3.55)	150-0110-79S
4H-1-Benzopyran-4-one, 2,3-dihydro-3-[(3-hydroxyphenyl)methylene]-	EtOH	263(5.11),298(5.18), 345(5.01)	150-1713-79
4H-1-Benzopyran-4-one, 2,3-dihydro-3-[(4-hydroxyphenyl)methylene]-	EtOH	238(5.24),329(5.32), 357(5.32)	150-1713-79
4H-1-Benzopyran-4-one, 3-[(3-hydroxyphenyl)methyl]-	EtOH	229(4.16),328(2.51), 354(3.10)	150-1713-79
4H-1-Benzopyran-4-one, 3-[(4-hydroxyphenyl)methyl]-	EtOH	227(4.56),347(2.95), 354(2.95)	150-1713-79
Cyclohepta[de]naphthalene-8-carboxylic acid, 7,8-dihydro-7-oxo-, methyl ester	EtOH	220(4.6),317(3.8), 340(3.8),355(3.8)	18-0641-79
Cyclohepta[de]naphthalene-8-carboxylic acid, 7-hydroxy-, methyl ester	EtOH	217(4.5),250(4.2), 370(3.7),450(3.3)	18-0641-79
$C_{16}H_{12}O_4$			
1,2-Acenaphthylenedicarboxylic acid, dimethyl ester	CH_2Cl_2	336(4.10)	44-1359-79
Acetic acid, [(1-methyl-3-oxo-3H-benz[e]inden-2-yl)oxy]-	n.s.g.	252(4.26),290(4.20)	12-1159-79
Acetic acid, [(3-methyl-1-oxo-1H-benz[e]inden-2-yl)oxy]-	n.s.g.	252(4.30),290(4.21)	12-1159-79
9,10-Anthracenedione, 1,4-dihydroxy-2,3-dimethyl-	MeOH	228s(--),251(5.59), 255(4.59),290(3.93), 458s(--),485(3.99), 518s(--)	5-0019-79
9,10-Anthracenedione, 2-ethyl-1,4-dihydroxy-	MeOH	205(4.36),249(4.60), 284(4.01),330s(--), 484(4.00)	5-0019-79
9,10-Anthracenedione, 1-hydroxy-6-methoxy-3-methyl-	EtOH	241(4.33),267(4.26), 299(4.15),434(3.88), 450s(--)	32-0301-79
9,10-Anthracenedione, 1-hydroxy-6-methoxy-8-methyl-	dioxan	267(4.41),290s(3.94), 410(3.78)	118-0148-79
9(10H)-Anthracenone, 1-acetoxy-8-hydroxy-	MeOH	257(4.13),283(4.05), 359(3.56)	145-1083-79
4H-Difuro[3,2-c:3',2'-g][1]benzopyran-4-one, 2,6,8-trimethyl-	MeOH	304(4.09),332(4.19)	42-0056-79
[2.2]Metacyclophanequinone, anti	MeCN	258(4.57)	138-0595-79
$C_{16}H_{12}O_4S$			
Benzoic acid, 2-[[(1,3-dihydro-3-oxo-1-isobenzofuranyl)thio]methyl]-	dioxan	226s(4.29),277(3.47), 283(3.48)	78-1875-79
$C_{16}H_{12}O_5$			
9,10-Anthracenedione, 1,4-dihydroxy-2-(hydroxymethyl)-3-methyl-	MeOH	227(4.12),250(4.59), 255s(--),287(3.91), 459s(--),485(4.01), 519s(--)	5-0019-79
9,10-Anthracenedione, 1,8-dihydroxy-3-methoxy-6-methyl-	MeOH	224(4.28),255(3.94), 265(3.95),287(3.92), 435(2.70)	98-1342-79
4H-1-Benzopyran-4-one, 5-hydroxy-2-(4-hydroxyphenyl)-7-methoxy-	EtOH	265(4.17),368(4.27)	94-0984-79

Compound	Solvent	λ_{max}(log ε)	Ref.
$C_{16}H_{12}O_5S$			
2-Anthracenemethanesulfonic acid, 9,10-dihydro-3-methyl-9,10-dioxo-, sodium salt	H_2O	265(4.66),282(4.11), 338(3.72)	78-2255-79
$C_{16}H_{12}O_6$			
9,10-Anthracenedione, 1,4,5-trihydroxy-7-methoxy-2-methyl-	MeOH-10% dioxan	231(4.38),256(3.83), 278(3.96),302(3.83), 468(3.83),480(3.88), 491(3.92),510(3.80), 524(3.74)	98-1342-79
4H-1-Benzopyran-4-one, 5,6-dihydroxy-2-(2-hydroxyphenyl)-7-methoxy-	MeOH	273(4.8),337(4.7)	95-0657-79
4H-1-Benzopyran-4-one, 5,7-dihydroxy-2-(4-hydroxyphenyl)-6-methoxy-	MeOH	220(4.14),274(4.09), 333s(4.18),337s(4.18)	100-0450-79
(hispidulin)	MeOH-KOH	228(4.17),274(4.08), 325(3.97),385s(4.24), 390s(4.25)	100-0450-79
4H-1-Benzopyran-4-one, 3-(3,5-dihydroxy-4-methoxyphenyl)-7-hydroxy-	EtOH	222(4.49),248(4.91), 259s(4.86),312(4.54)	102-1037-79
1,4-Ethanoanthracene-2,9,10(1H)-trione, 3,4-dihydro-4,5,8-trihydroxy-	MeOH	215(4.36),246(4.16), 513(3.91)	24-2640-79
1,4-Naphthalenedione, 2-(2,4-dioxocyclohexyl)-	MeOH	212(4.60),284(4.38), 510(3.73),560(3.43)	24-2640-79
9H-Xanthene-1-carboxylic acid, 2-hydroxy-8-methoxy-6-methyl-9-oxo-	$CHCl_3$	246(4.27),261(4.29), 279(4.18),308(3.87)	44-4452-79
9H-Xanthene-1-carboxylic acid, 8-hydroxy-2-methoxy-9-oxo-, methyl ester	EtOH	237(4.29),262(4.34), 290(4.27),315s(4.21), 324s(4.20),386(--)	102-0311-79
$C_{16}H_{12}O_6S$			
1,1'-Spirobi[3H-2,1-benzoxathiole]-3,3'-dione, 5,5'-dimethoxy-	dioxan	255(4.24),295(3.76)	78-1869-79
$C_{16}H_{12}O_7$			
4H-1-Benzopyran-4-one, 2-(3,4-dihydroxyphenyl)-3,5-dihydroxy-7-methoxy-	EtOH	257(4.38),374(4.39)	94-0984-79
$C_{16}H_{12}O_8$			
Benzoic acid, 2-hydroxy-5-[[2-(methoxycarbonyl)-3,6-dioxo-1,4-cyclohexadien-1-yl]oxy]-	$CHCl_3$	245(4.28),319(3.76), 384(3.14)	33-2350-79
4H-1-Benzopyran-4-one, 2-(3,5-dihydroxy-4-methoxyphenyl)-3,5,7-trihydroxy- (mearnsetin)	MeOH	258(3.90),366(3.60)	2-0037-79A
$C_{16}H_{12}O_8S_2$			
2,3-Anthracenedimethanesulfonic acid, 9,10-dihydro-9,10-dioxo-, disodium salt	H_2O	265(4.69),281(4.12), 336(3.76)	78-2255-79
$C_{16}H_{12}S_3$			
Thiophene, 2,5-bis[2-(2-thienyl)ethenyl]-, (E,E)-	toluene	435(4.57)	103-0729-79
	DMF	412(4.73)	61-0417-79
	KBr	402(--)	61-0417-79
$C_{16}H_{12}Te_2$			
1,3-Ditellurole, 4-phenyl-2-(phenylmethylene)-	EtOH	260(5.09),357(5.05)	104-2346-79

Compound	Solvent	λ max (log ε)	Ref.
$C_{16}H_{13}AsO$			
4-Arsenincarboxaldehyde, 1,2-dihydro-1-(1-naphthalenyl)-	EtOH	220(4.42),825(3.70)	88-3141-79
$C_{16}H_{13}BrN_2O_3$			
4,8-Iminocyclohepta[c]pyrrole-1,3,5(2H)-trione, 4-bromo-3a,4,8,8a-tetrahydro-9-methyl-2-phenyl-, (3aα,4α,8β,8aα)-	EtOH	224(4.24)	39-2528-79C
$C_{16}H_{13}BrN_4O_2$			
1H-Pyrazole-4,5-dione, 1-(4-bromophenyl)-3-(hydroxymethyl)-, 4-(phenylhydrazone)	n.s.g.	212(3.60),257(4.02), 416(4.07)	106-0531-79
$C_{16}H_{13}BrO_2$			
Benzenemethanol, 4-bromo-α-(phenylmethylene)-, acetate	hexane	223(4.08),292(4.44)	23-1186-79
	EtOH	225(4.00),294(4.40)	23-1186-79
1,3-Butanedione, 1-(4-bromophenyl)-2-phenyl- (enol)	hexane	242(3.94),316(4.10)	23-1186-79
	EtOH	258(4.08),316(4.06)	23-1186-79
$C_{16}H_{13}ClN_2O$			
8-Azabicyclo[3.2.1]oct-3-ene-6-carbonitrile, 6-chloro-2-oxo-8-(2-phenylethenyl)-	EtOH	221(4.17),281(4.27)	39-2535-79C
4(1H)-Quinazolinone, 6-chloro-1-methyl-2-(phenylmethyl)- (in 80% EtOH)	neutral	231(4.48),279(3.9), 316(3.91)	42-0708-79
	acid	231(4.39),277(4.0), 304(3.79)	42-0708-79
	base	225(4.94),277(4.03), 315(3.97)	42-0708-79
4(1H)-Quinazolinone, 7-chloro-1-methyl-2-(phenylmethyl)- (in 80% EtOH)	neutral	237(4.49),280-308(3.6-4.0)	42-0708-79
	acid	242(4.55),280-309(3.6-3.8)	42-0708-79
	base	240(4.50),280-310(3.6-3.9)	42-0708-79
$C_{16}H_{13}ClN_2O_2S$			
Benzenepropanamide, α-[[(4-chlorophenyl)amino]thioxomethyl]-β-oxo-	EtOH	295(3.92),345(4.00)	104-1324-79
$C_{16}H_{13}ClN_2S$			
2(1H)-Pyrimidinethione, 4-(3-chlorophenyl)-3,4-dihydro-6-phenyl-	EtOH	267(4.09)	23-2734-79
	$CHCl_3$	274(4.09)	23-2734-79
	CCl_4	300(4.07)	23-2734-79
2(1H)-Pyrimidinethione, 4-(4-chlorophenyl)-3,4-dihydro-6-phenyl-	EtOH	230(4.36),267(4.12)	23-2734-79
	$CHCl_3$	274(4.08)	23-2734-79
	CCl_4	300(4.05)	23-2734-79
2(1H)-Pyrimidinethione, 6-(4-chlorophenyl)-3,4-dihydro-4-phenyl-	EtOH	232(4.32),253(4.28)	23-2734-79
	$CHCl_3$	272(4.20)	23-2734-79
	CCl_4	279(4.05)	23-2734-79
$C_{16}H_{13}ClN_4$			
2-Propenimidamide, N-(2-chlorophenyl)-2-cyano-3-(phenylamino)-	EtOH	336(4.30)	24-0484-79
5H-[1,2,4]Triazolo[5,1-a]isoindol-5-amine, 7-chloro-2-methyl-5-phenyl-	MeOH	244(4.31)	44-0084-79
$C_{16}H_{13}ClN_4O_2$			
1H-Pyrazole-4,5-dione, 1-(4-chlorophenyl)-3-(hydroxymethyl)-, 4-(phenylhydrazone)	n.s.g.	210(3.91),256(3.96), 406(4.01)	106-0531-79

Compound	Solvent	$\lambda_{max}(\log \epsilon)$	Ref.
$C_{16}H_{13}ClN_4S$			
Ethanethioamide, 2-[(4-chlorophenyl)-hydrazono]-2-cyano-N-(phenylmethyl)-	EtOH	385(4.37)	104-1082-79
1,3,4-Thiadiazolium, 5-[[(4-chlorophenyl)methylene]hydrazino]-3-methyl-2-phenyl-, hydroxide, inner salt	n.s.g.	253(4.38),342(4.19), 438(4.17)	39-0724-79C
1H-1,2,4-Triazolium, 4-[[(4-chlorophenyl)methylene]amino]-2,3-dihydro-1-methyl-5-phenyl-3-thioxo-, hydroxide, inner salt	n.s.g.	248(3.80),277s(3.71), 283(3.72),300s(3.55)	39-0724-79C
$C_{16}H_{13}ClO$			
Dibenzo[a,d]cycloocten-5-ol, 6-chloro-5,12-dihydro-	EtOH	240(4.60),270s(4.00)	44-4440-79
2-Propen-1-one, 2-chloro-3-(4-methylphenyl)-1-phenyl-	hexane	253(4.03),306(4.31)	97-0096-79
2-Propen-1-one, 2-chloro-1-(4-methylphenyl)-3-phenyl-, (Z)-	hexane	295(4.29)	97-0096-79
$C_{16}H_{13}ClO_2$			
2-Propen-1-one, 2-chloro-1-(4-methoxyphenyl)-3-phenyl-, (Z)-	hexane	297(4.39)	97-0096-79
2-Propen-1-one, 2-chloro-3-(4-methoxyphenyl)-1-phenyl-	hexane	245(3.94),323(4.23)	97-0096-79
$C_{16}H_{13}ClO_5$			
[1,1'-Biphenyl]-2,3-dicarboxylic acid, 4'-chloro-4-hydroxy-, dimethyl ester	EtOH	232(4.35),316(3.59)	103-0013-79
$C_{16}H_{13}Cl_3N_2O_2$			
15,16-Diazatricyclo[9.3.1.1^{4,8}]hexadeca-1(15),2,4,6,8(16),11,13-heptaene, 2,3,10-trichloro-9,9-dimethoxy-	90% EtOH	285(4.41),321(3.93)	12-1241-79
$C_{16}H_{13}HgNO_2$			
Mercury, (2,3-dihydro-1-methyl-3-oxo-1H-indole-2-carboxaldehydato-O,O')-phenyl-	benzene	315(4.07),340(3.89)	103-0056-79
	DMSO	270(4.18),325(4.12)	103-0056-79
$C_{16}H_{13}IN_2O$			
1H-Benzimidazole, 1-(2-iodobenzoyl)-5,6-dimethyl-	MeOH	214(4.24),235s(3.87), 274s(3.50),278(3.67), 282(3.69),288(3.74)	4-1235-79
$C_{16}H_{13}N$			
Benzeneacetonitrile, α-[(4-methylphenyl)methylene]-, cis	EtOH	229(4.24),299(4.22)	44-2896-79
Benzeneacetonitrile, 4-methyl-α-(phenylmethylene)-, cis	EtOH	225(4.22),299(4.04)	44-2896-79
Benzenepropanenitrile, α-(phenylmethylene)-, (E)-	$CHCl_3$	267(4.30)	24-2961-79
(Z)-	$CHCl_3$	280(4.22)	24-2961-79
Isoquinoline, 1-(phenylmethyl)-	EtOH	262(3.58),317(3.57)	44-3244-79
Quinoline, 2-(phenylmethyl)-	neutral	315(3.72)	39-0792-79B
	cation	319(4.00)	39-0792-79B
$C_{16}H_{13}NO$			
Benzeneacetonitrile, α-[(4-methoxyphenyl)methylene]-, cis	EtOH	235(4.20),318(4.27)	44-2896-79
Benzeneacetonitrile, 4-methoxy-α-(phenylmethylene)-, cis	EtOH	233(4.15),326(4.09)	44-2896-79

Compound	Solvent	$\lambda_{max}(\log \epsilon)$	Ref.
Benzoxazole, 2-[2-(4-methylphenyl)ethenyl]-	EtOH	230(3.97),328(4.66)	56-1033-79
2(1H)-Quinolinone, 1-methyl-3-phenyl-	EtOH	340(4.05)	4-0065-79
$C_{16}H_{13}NO_2$			
Benz[g]isoquinoline-5,10-dione, 3,5,7-trimethyl-	EtOH	206(4.44),266(4.42), 296s(4.14),340s(4.00), 390s(3.36)	103-0421-79
4H-1-Benzopyran-4-one, 2-[2-(methylamino)phenyl]-	MeOH	204(4.46),241(4.45), 298(4.05),381(3.78)	83-0248-79
Benzoxazole, 2-[2-(4-methoxyphenyl)ethenyl]-	EtOH	230(4.21),339(4.66)	56-1033-79
3,5-Pyridinedicarboxaldehyde, 4-ethynyl-1,4-dihydro-1-(2-methylphenyl)-	EtOH	207(4.30),229(4.37), 260(4.16),366(4.02)	49-0613-79
3,5-Pyridinedicarboxaldehyde, 4-ethynyl-1,4-dihydro-1-(3-methylphenyl)-	EtOH	207(4.29),226s(4.19), 238(4.13),277(4.31), 379(4.25)	49-0613-79
3,5-Pyridinedicarboxaldehyde, 4-ethynyl-1,4-dihydro-1-(4-methylphenyl)-	EtOH	208(4.25),228(4.27), 238(4.30),276(4.35), 375(3.99)	49-0613-79
2(1H)-Quinolinone, 3-(2-hydroxyphenyl)-4-methyl-	EtOH	207s(4.15),223(4.27), 248s(4.06),277(3.93), 317s(3.91),329(4.00), 341s(3.86)	4-0487-79
2(1H)-Quinolinone, 3-(2-methoxyphenyl)-	EtOH	222(4.61),267s(3.94), 280(3.98),332(4.04), 345s(3.96)	4-0487-79
4(1H)-Quinolinone, 2-(2-hydroxyphenyl)-1-methyl-	dioxan	214(4.51),246(4.19), 254(4.17),281(3.76), 330s(--),339(4.01)	83-0248-79
4(1H)-Quinolinone, 3-(2-methoxyphenyl)-	EtOH	212(4.57),249(4.24), 266s(4.05),283(3.89), 310s(3.86),323(3.94), 335(3.94)	4-0487-79
$C_{16}H_{13}NO_2S$			
Acetamide, N-(6,11-dihydro-11-oxodibenzo[b,e]thiepin-2-yl)-	MeOH	262(4.48),362(3.48)	73-2689-79
$C_{16}H_{13}NO_3$			
9,10-Anthracenedione, 1-methoxy-4-(methylamino)-	C_6H_{12}	514(3.88)	39-0702-79C
1H-Benzo[c]furo[3,4-f]quinolizine-1,12(3H)-dione, 5,6-dihydro-3-methyl-	MeOH	211(4.32),253(4.49), 295(3.93)	104-1247-79
4H-1-Benzopyran-4-one, 3-amino-2-(4-methoxyphenyl)-	EtOH	257(4.37),313(4.04), 386(4.23)	5-0162-79
4H-Pyrano[3,2-c]pyridine-4,5(6H)-dione, 6,7-dimethyl-2-phenyl-	n.s.g.	278(4.23),327(4.24)	94-0242-79
3,5-Pyridinedicarboxaldehyde, 4-ethynyl-1,4-dihydro-1-(2-methoxyphenyl)-	EtOH	224(4.36),240s(4.17), 267(4.16),283s(4.08), 369(3.96)	49-0613-79
3,5-Pyridinedicarboxaldehyde, 4-ethynyl-1,4-dihydro-1-(3-methoxyphenyl)-	EtOH	227(4.43),242s(4.19), 275(4.29),375(3.97)	49-0613-79
3,5-Pyridinedicarboxaldehyde, 4-ethynyl-1,4-dihydro-1-(4-methoxyphenyl)-	EtOH	213(4.26),239(4.40), 275(4.39),379(4.05)	49-0613-79
$C_{16}H_{13}NO_5$			
Bostrycoidin, 8-methoxy-	MeOH	248(4.50),318(3.92), 480(3.83)	78-1551-79
	MeOH-acid	227(4.32),262(4.20), 313(3.88),510(3.73)	78-1551-79

Compound	Solvent	λ_{max}(log ϵ)	Ref.
Bostrycoidin, 8-methoxy- (cont.)	MeOH-base	259(4.44),306(3.82), 546(4.00)	78-1551-79
$C_{16}H_{13}NO_5S$			
Thiazolo[3,2-a]indole-9-acetic acid, 2,3-dihydro-2-(2-methoxy-2-oxoethylidene)-3-oxo-, methyl ester, (Z)-	$CHCl_3$	284(4.35),433(3.72)	44-3994-79
$C_{16}H_{13}NS$			
1H-Indene-1-thione, 3-(methylamino)-2-phenyl-	$C_2H_4Cl_2$	303(4.28),322(4.18), 353(3.95),538(3.75)	99-0043-79
$C_{16}H_{13}NSSe$			
Benzenamine, N-[[3-(methylselenyl)benzo[b]thien-2-yl]methylene]-	$CHCl_3$	345(4.23)	103-0731-79
$C_{16}H_{13}N_2OS_2$			
Thiazolo[3,2-a]pyridinium, 2,3-dihydro-5-methyl-2-(3-methyl-2(3H)-benzothiazolylidene)-3-oxo-, methyl sulfate	MeCN	460(4.50),477(4.45)	103-1081-79
$C_{16}H_{13}N_2S_3$			
Benzo[1,2-d:5,4-d']bisthiazolium, 3,6-dimethyl-2-[2-(2-thienyl)ethenyl]-, iodide	DMF	267(4.35),420(4.36), 583(3.14)	126-1441-79
	KBr	422(--)	126-1441-79
$C_{16}H_{13}N_3$			
1H-Benzimidazole, 2-(1H-indol-3-ylmethyl)-	MeOH	224(4.84),275(4.57), 281(4.61),290(4.22)	120-0011-79
Indolo[1,2-c]quinazolin-12-amine, 6-methyl-	EtOH	245s(4.22),282(4.71), 370(4.11)	103-0681-79
Quinazoline, 1,4-dihydro-4-(1H-indol-3-yl)-, hydrochloride	EtOH	279(4.10),287s(4.06), 368(2.66)	24-1348-79
$C_{16}H_{13}N_3O_2$			
4(3H)-Quinazolinone, 3-[(hydroxyimino)-phenylmethyl]-2-methyl-	EtOH	286(3.47),295(3.50), 307(3.60),318(3.50)	142-0239-79A
$C_{16}H_{13}N_3O_2S$			
Acetonitrile, (1,3-dihydro-2H-benzimidazol-2-ylidene)[(4-methylphenyl)sulfonyl]-	EtOH	223(4.34),315(4.09)	95-0038-79
Benzenecarbothioic acid, 4-methoxy-, 2-(3-oxo-3H-indol-2-yl)hydrazide	$CHCl_3$	247(4.21),274(4.10), 349(4.02),417(3.60), 526(3.64)	104-0765-79
$C_{16}H_{13}N_3O_3$			
4(1H)-Quinazolinone, 1-methyl-6-nitro-2-(phenylmethyl)-	80% EtOH	217(4.28),310-320(4.1-4.2)	42-0708-79
4(1H)-Quinazolinone, 1-methyl-7-nitro-2-(phenylmethyl)-	80% EtOH	235(4.19),260(3.96), 280(3.75)	42-0708-79
$C_{16}H_{13}N_3O_4$			
1,3-Butanedione, 2-[(2-nitrophenyl)-azo]-	EtOH	395(3.255)	2-0502-79A'
	acetone	397(3.225)	2-0502-79A'
	dioxan	400(3.17)	2-0502-79A'
	$CHCl_3$	397(3.215)	2-0502-79A'
	CCl_4	395(3.123)	2-0502-79A'
1,3-Butanedione, 2-[(3-nitrophenyl)-azo]-	EtOH	355(4.225)	2-0502-79A'
	acetone	355(4.176)	2-0502-79A'

Compound	Solvent	λmax(log ε)	Ref.
1,3-Butanedione, 2-[(3-nitrophenyl)-azo]- (cont.)	dioxan	355(4.231)	2-0502-79A'
	$CHCl_3$	360(4.199)	2-0502-79A'
	CCl_4	363(4.267)	2-0502-79A'
1,3-Butanedione, 2-[(4-nitrophenyl)-azo]-	EtOH	395(3.519)	2-0502-79A'
	acetone	395(3.471)	2-0502-79A'
	dioxan	395(3.584)	2-0502-79A'
	$CHCl_3$	430(3.387)	2-0502-79A'
	CCl_4	395(3.552)	2-0502-79A'
$C_{16}H_{13}N_3O_4S$			
Benzenepropanamide, α-[[(4-nitrophenyl)amino]thioxomethyl]-β-oxo-	EtOH	312(4.17),350(4.29)	104-1324-79
$C_{16}H_{13}N_3O_5$			
Isoxazole, 4,5-dihydro-5-methyl-3,5-bis(4-nitrophenyl)-	MeOH	302(4.26)	12-1487-79
$C_{16}H_{13}N_3O_6$			
Isoxazole, 4,5-dihydro-5-methyl-3,5-bis(4-nitrophenyl)-, 2-oxide	MeOH	256(4.22),341(4.21)	12-1487-79
$C_{16}H_{13}N_3O_8S_2$			
2,7-Naphthalenedisulfonic acid, 3-hydroxy-4-[(6-methyl-2-pyridinyl)azo]-, disodium salt, N-oxide	pH 4	487(4.30)	74-0403-79B
copper chelate	pH 3.5	536(4.26)	74-0403-79B
$C_{16}H_{13}N_3S$			
Thiourea, N-phenyl-N'-4-quinolinyl-	EtOH	205s(4.03),220s(4.05), 226(4.09),323(3.63)	56-1895-79
Thiourea, N-phenyl-N'-5-quinolinyl-	EtOH	204.1(4.67),235.8(4.46)	56-1895-79
Thiourea, N-phenyl-N'-6-quinolinyl-	EtOH	206.2(4.55),275.5(4.47)	56-1895-79
Thiourea, N-phenyl-N'-7-quinolinyl-	EtOH	208(4.51),264(4.43), 339s(3.81)	56-1895-79
Thiourea, N-phenyl-N'-8-quinolinyl-	EtOH	201(4.61),247(4.47), 278(4.25),333s(3.96)	56-1895-79
$C_{16}H_{13}N_5O$			
3H-Pyrazol-3-one, 4-(2H-benzotriazol-2-yl)-2,4-dihydro-5-methyl-2-phenyl-	MeOH	210(4.34),245(4.26), 315(4.22)	48-0495-79
$C_{16}H_{13}N_5O_2S$			
Ethanethioamide, 2-cyano-2-[(4-nitrophenyl)hydrazono]-N-(phenylmethyl)-	EtOH	265(5.24),390(4.23), 405(4.16)	104-1082-79
$C_{16}H_{13}N_5O_3$			
3H-Pyrazol-3-one, 2,4-dihydro-5-methyl-4-[(2-nitrophenyl)azo]-2-phenyl-	EtOH	205(3.92),248(4.01), 410(3.91)	48-0495-79
$C_{16}H_{13}N_5O_4$			
1H-Pyrazole-4,5-dione, 3-(hydroxymethyl)-1-(4-nitrophenyl)-, 4-(phenylhydrazone)	n.s.g.	232(3.84),420(4.20)	106-0531-79
$C_{16}H_{13}N_7$			
1H-Tetrazole, 1-(1-azido-3-phenyl-2-propenyl)-5-phenyl-	MeOH	237(4.33)	44-3281-79
$C_{16}H_{13}N_9O$			
2H-Tetrazolium, 2-[3-(acetylamino)phenyl]-5-phenyl-3-(1H-tetrazol-5-yl)-	EtOH	250s(4.56),320s(--)	104-1793-79

Compound	Solvent	$\lambda_{max}(\log \epsilon)$	Ref.
$C_{16}H_{13}S_3$			
1,2-Dithiol-1-ium, 4-methyl-3-phenyl-5-(phenylthio)-, bromide	MeCN	218(4.57),265s(4.51), 340s(4.05),372(4.34)	104-0955-79
triiodide	MeCN	215(4.15),294(4.38), 370(4.39)	104-0955-79
$C_{16}H_{14}$			
Anthracene, 2-ethyl-	EtOH	254(4.91),334(4.05), 375(3.68)	2-0226-79A
Anthracene, 9-ethyl-	CCl_4	333(3.47),349(3.78), 368(3.98),388(3.97)	78-2131-79
Benzene, (cyclopropylidenephenylmethyl)-	EtOH	232(4.74),256s(--), 277(4.89)	44-0989-79
Benzo[1,2:3,4]dicycloheptene, 12a,12b-dihydro-, trans	isooctane	366(3.80)	88-4053-79
Cyclopenta[a]fluorene, 1,2,3,10-tetrahydro-	EtOH	270(4.46),282(4.22), 293(4.01),302(3.99)	25-0347-79
Phenanthrene, 3-ethyl-	EtOH	228(4.15),253(4.41), 319(2.73),335(2.72), 350(2.38),378(1.54)	2-0226-79A
$C_{16}H_{14}BrS$			
1H-Benzo[c]thiolium, 3-(3-bromophenyl)-1,1-dimethyl-	acid	357(4.23)	104-0937-79
1H-Benzo[c]thiolium, 3-(4-bromophenyl)-1,1-dimethyl-	acid	382(4.37)	104-0937-79
$C_{16}H_{14}Br_4$			
1,1'-Biphenyl, 2,2',6,6'-tetrakis(bromomethyl)-	EtOH	235(4.20)	44-1936-79
$C_{16}H_{14}ClNO_2$			
2-Propenamide, 3-(4-chlorophenyl)-N-hydroxy-N-(3-methylphenyl)-	EtOH	221(4.40),288(4.62)	34-0072-79
2-Propenamide, 3-(4-chlorophenyl)-N-hydroxy-N-(4-methylphenyl)-	EtOH	239(4.40),278(4.70)	34-0072-79
$C_{16}H_{14}ClN_3$			
1,5-Benzodiazocin-2-amine, 8-chloro-3,4-dihydro-6-phenyl-	EtOH	248(4.21)	94-2589-79
2-Quinazolineethanamine, 6-chloro-4-phenyl-	EtOH	231(4.67),263(3.91), 328(3.77)	94-2589-79
$C_{16}H_{14}ClN_3O$			
Benzamide, 4-chloro-N-(4,5-dihydro-1-phenyl-1H-pyrazol-3-yl)-	EtOH	243(4.28),272s(4.03), 345(4.06)	150-0801-79
Benzamide, N-[1-(4-chlorophenyl)-4,5-dihydro-1H-pyrazol-3-yl)-	EtOH	229(4.12),273(4.06), 333(4.08)	150-0801-79
1,2,4-Oxadiazole-3-ethanamine, N-(4-chlorophenyl)-5-phenyl-	EtOH	254(4.52),304(3.29)	150-0801-79
1,2,4-Oxadiazole-3-ethanamine, 5-(4-chlorophenyl)-N-phenyl-	EtOH	253(4.43)	150-0801-79
$C_{16}H_{14}ClN_5$			
1H-Pyrazol-3-amine, N-(2-chlorophenyl)-5-methyl-4-(phenylazo)-	EtOH	253(3.69)	48-0127-79
$C_{16}H_{14}ClS$			
1H-Benzo[c]thiolium, 3-(3-chlorophenyl)-1,1-dimethyl-	acid	358(4.30)	104-0937-79

Compound	Solvent	λ_{max}(log ε)	Ref.
1H-Benzo[c]thiolium, 3-(4-chlorophenyl)-1,1-dimethyl-	acid	380(4.35)	104-0937-79
$C_{16}H_{14}FS$			
1H-Benzo[c]thiolium, 3-(3-fluorophenyl)-1,1-dimethyl-	acid	358(4.38)	104-0937-79
1H-Benzo[c]thiolium, 3-(4-fluorophenyl)-1,1-dimethyl-	acid	369(4.36)	104-0937-79
$C_{16}H_{14}IN_3O_2$			
Butanamide, N-(4-iodophenyl)-3-oxo-2-(phenylhydrazono)-	EtOH	240(4.22),270(4.20), 380(4.60)	2-0585-79A
$C_{16}H_{14}NS$			
Benzothiazolium, 3-methyl-2-(2-phenylethenyl)-, iodide	DMF	374(4.38)	126-1441-79
perchlorate	DMF	373(4.40)	126-1441-79
	KBr	379(--)	126-1441-79
$C_{16}H_{14}N_2$			
1H-Imidazole, 1-(4-methylphenyl)-4-phenyl-	MeOH	263(4.44)	56-1147-79
1H-Pyrazole, 4-phenyl-3-(phenylmethyl)-	EtOH	243(4.13)	103-0501-79
Pyrimidine, dihydro-4,5-diphenyl-	EtOH	223(4.11),320(3.26)	39-1228-79C
$C_{16}H_{14}N_2O$			
Benzenamine, N-(1H-indol-3-ylmethylene)-4-methoxy-	EtOH	224(4.36),270(4.03), 335(4.25)	103-0741-79
5H-Dibenz[b,f]azepine-5-carboxamide, 2-methyl-	EtOH	215(4.46),239s(4.15), 286(4.04)	4-0257-79
1H-Pyrazole, 4-methoxy-3,5-diphenyl-	EtOH	255(4.45),291s(3.78)	23-0904-79
1H-Pyrazol-4-ol, 1-methyl-3,5-diphenyl-	EtOH	245(4.33),276s(4.03)	23-0904-79
Quinazoline, 4-methoxy-2-(phenylmethyl)- (glycophyrroline)	EtOH	230(4.35),268(3.85), 276(3.78),302(3.50), 312(3.45)	102-0694-79
4(1H)-Quinazolinone, 1-methyl-2-(phenylmethyl)-	neutral	231(4.19),266-306(3.5-3.8)	42-0708-79
	acid	235(4.33),270-305(3.6-3.7)	42-0708-79
	base	233(4.23),268-305(3.6-3.9)	42-0708-79
4(3H)-Quinazolinone, 3-methyl-2-(phenylmethyl)-	EtOH	227(4.25),268(3.68), 277(3.72),306(3.94), 315(3.87)	142-0929-79
$C_{16}H_{14}N_2OS_2$			
Acetamide, N-[2-(2-methyl-7-benzothiazolyl)thio]phenyl]-	MeOH	246(4.23),278(3.70)	39-1478-79C
$C_{16}H_{14}N_2O_2$			
9,10-Anthracenedione, 1,2(or 3)-bis-(methylamino)-	benzene	497(3.88),526s(3.78)	153-0033-79
9,10-Anthracenedione, 1,4-bis(methylamino)-	benzene	602(4.13),650(4.19)	153-0033-79
6,12-Epoxy-7,11-methano-6H-cyclonona-[b]quinoxalin-15-one, 7,8,9,10,11,12-hexahydro-, (6α,7β,11β,12α)-	EtOH	241(4.50),309(3.90), 319(4.00)	33-2325-79
1H-Isoindole-1,3(2H)-dione, 2-[(methylphenylamino)methyl]-	C_6H_{12}	361(1.83)	39-1103-79B
	benzene	364(1.79)	39-1103-79B
	EtOH	350(1.81)	39-1103-79B

Compound	Solvent	λ_{max}(log ε)	Ref.
2,6-Methano-2H-1,3,5-benzoxadiazocin-9-ol, 3,6-dihydro-2-phenyl-	EtOH	279(3.44),285(3.39)	24-0001-79
monohydrochloride	EtOH	276(3.38),281s(3.26)	24-0001-79
$C_{16}H_{14}N_2O_2S$			
Benzenepropanamide, β-oxo-α-[(phenylamino)thioxomethyl]-	EtOH	275(4.18),340(4.82)	104-1324-79
2-Propenoic acid, 2-cyano-3-[(5-phenyl-2-thienyl)amino]-, ethyl ester	DMF	296s(3.81),368(4.39)	49-1189-79
1,2,4-Thiadiazole, 3,5-bis(4-methoxyphenyl)-	EtOH	295(4.59)	40-0389-79
$C_{16}H_{14}N_2O_2S_2$			
1H-Pyrazole, 3-(methylthio)-5-phenyl-4-(phenylsulfonyl)-	EtOH	223(3.75)	95-0038-79
Thiazolo[3,2-a]pyridinium, 3-hydroxy-5-methyl-2-[[(6-methyl-2-pyridinyl)thio]acetyl]-, hydroxide, inner salt	MeOH	248(3.40),290(3.49), 429(3.50)	103-0872-79
Thiazolo[3,2-a]pyridinium, 3-hydroxy-7-methyl-2-[[(4-methyl-2-pyridinyl)thio]acetyl]-, hydroxide, inner salt	MeOH	250(3.33),280(3.29), 406(3.44)	103-0872-79
$C_{16}H_{14}N_2O_3$			
2H-Benz[f]indazole-4,9-dione, 2-(tetrahydro-2H-pyran-2-yl)-	EtOH	245(4.59)	111-0151-79
1,2,4-Oxadiazole, 3,5-bis(4-methoxyphenyl)-	EtOH	273(4.58)	40-0389-79
Phenol, 2-[3-[(4-methylphenyl)imino]-1-propenyl]-4-nitro-	MeOH	294(4.14),370(4.18), 420(3.99)	104-1715-79
	dioxan	280(4.45),345(4.37)	104-1715-79
	DMSO	291(4.25),410(4.34), 480(4.53)	104-1715-79
Phenol, 4-nitro-2-[3-[(phenylmethyl)-imino)-1-propenyl]-	MeOH	285(4.10),320(4.02), 370(3.93),428(3.82)	104-1715-79
	dioxan	300(4.10),345(3.68)	104-1715-79
	DMSO	330(3.95),384(4.07), 458(4.27)	104-1715-79
$C_{16}H_{14}N_2O_4$			
2-Propenamide, N-hydroxy-N-(3-methylphenyl)-3-(4-nitrophenyl)-	EtOH	312(4.04)	34-0072-79
2-Propenamide, N-hydroxy-N-(4-methylphenyl)-3-(4-nitrophenyl)-	EtOH	315(4.61)	34-0072-79
$C_{16}H_{14}N_2O_6$			
2-Butenedioic acid, 2-(nitro-2(1H)-quinolinylidenemethyl)-, dimethyl ester	MeOH	225(4.45),295s(3.75), 306(3.26),368(3.88), 370(3.86),421(3.86), 440(3.78)	39-2171-79C
	MeOH-$HClO_4$	227(4.46),248s(3.87), 306(3.85)	39-2171-79C
$C_{16}H_{14}N_2O_6S$			
5-Thia-1-azabicyclo[4.2.0]oct-2-ene-2-carboxylic acid, 3-methyl-4,8-dioxo-7-[(phenoxyacetyl)amino]-, (6R-trans)-	EtOH	268(3.69),274(3.73), 315(3.80)	33-2681-79
	EtOH	318(3.84)	87-0743-79

Compound	Solvent	$\lambda_{max}(\log \epsilon)$	Ref.
$C_{16}H_{14}N_2O_7S$			
4-Thia-1-azabicyclo[3.2.0]hept-2-ene-2-carboxylic acid, 3-(acetoxymethyl)-7-oxo-, (4-nitrophenyl)methyl ester	EtOH	262(4.08),319(3.96)	35-6296-79
$C_{16}H_{14}N_2O_7S_2$			
5-Thia-1-azabicyclo[4.2.0]oct-2-ene-2-carboxylic acid, 3-(acetoxymethyl)-8-oxo-7-(oxo-2-thienylacetyl)amino]-, (6R-trans)-	EtOH	316(3.77)	87-0743-79
$C_{16}H_{14}N_2S$			
2(1H)-Pyrimidinethione, 3,4-dihydro-4,6-diphenyl-	EtOH	226(4.36),267(4.18)	23-2734-79
	$CHCl_3$	275(4.16)	23-2734-79
	CCl_4	282(4.15),286-313s(4.1)	23-2734-79
2(1H)-Quinazolinethione, 1-ethyl-4-phenyl-	EtOH	293(4.45),408(3.70)	118-0120-79
$C_{16}H_{14}N_4$			
3,4-Diazabicyclo[4.1.0]hepta-2,4-diene, 1-methyl-2,5-di-2-pyridinyl-	hexane	320(3.98)	20-0905-79
	$CHCl_3$	318(4.07)	20-0905-79
2-Propenimidamide, 2-cyano-N-phenyl-3-(phenylamino)-	$C_6H_{11}Me$	333(4.35)	24-0484-79
	EtOH	337(4.36)	24-0484-79
	2-MeTHF	337(4.36)	24-0484-79
	$CHCl_3$	337(4.34)	24-0484-79
$C_{16}H_{14}N_4OS$			
Hydrazinecarbothioamide, 2-(1,3-dihydro-1-methyl-3-oxo-2H-indol-2-ylidene)-N-phenyl-	EtOH	282(4.34),373(4.18), 536(3.82)	104-0765-79
[1,3,4]Thiadiazino[5,6-b]indol-4a(9H)-ol, 9-methyl-3-(phenylamino)-	EtOH	274(4.08),383(3.72), 472(3.81)	104-0765-79
1H-1,2,4-Triazolium, 4-(acetylamino)-2,3-dihydro-1,5-diphenyl-3-thioxo-, hydroxide, inner salt	EtOH	250(4.42)	94-1683-79
$C_{16}H_{14}N_4O_3$			
1,2,4-Oxadiazole-3-ethanamine, N-(4-nitrophenyl)-5-phenyl-	EtOH	248(4.24),380(4.16)	150-0801-79
$C_{16}H_{14}N_4O_4S_4$			
5-Thia-1-azabicyclo[4.2.0]oct-2-ene-2-carboxylic acid, 8-oxo-3-[(1,2,3-thiadiazol-5-ylthio)methyl]-7-[(2-thienylacetyl)amino]-, monosodium salt, (6R-trans)-	H_2O	232(4.15),260(3.99)	87-1214-79
$C_{16}H_{14}N_4S$			
Ethanethioamide, 2-cyano-2-(phenylhydrazono)-N-(phenylmethyl)-	EtOH	380(4.34)	104-1082-79
1,3,4-Thiadiazolium, 3-methyl-2-phenyl-5-[(phenylmethylene)hydrazino]-, hydroxide, inner salt	n.s.g.	248(4.24),333(4.07), 434(3.98)	39-0724-79C
$C_{16}H_{14}N_6$			
1H-Indazole-5-carbonitrile, 3-[[4-(dimethylamino)phenyl]azo]-	EtOH	461(4.52)	103-1231-79
$C_{16}H_{14}N_6O_7$			
Benzamide, 4-azido-N-[2-hydroxy-1-(hydroxymethyl)-2-(4-nitrophenyl)ethyl]-	n.s.g.	252(4.30),265(4.27), 330s(3.32)	63-0721-79

Compound	Solvent	λ_{max}(log ε)	Ref.
2-nitro-, [R-(R*,R*)]- (cont.)			63-0721-79
$C_{16}H_{14}N_{10}O_2$			
2H-Tetrazolium, 2-[4-(dimethylamino)-phenyl]-5-(3-nitrophenyl)-3-(1H-tetrazol-5-yl)-, hydroxide, inner salt	EtOH	230(4.45),257(4.39), 475(4.10)	104-1793-79
2H-Tetrazolium, 2-[4-(dimethylamino)-phenyl]-5-(4-nitrophenyl)-3(1H-tetrazol-5-yl)-, hydroxide, inner salt	EtOH	275(4.43),470(4.06)	104-1793-79
$C_{16}H_{14}O$			
Anthracene, 1-(methoxymethyl)-	$C_6H_{11}Me$	254(5.19),328(3.46), 342(3.77),360(3.95), 379(3.94)	152-0231-79
$C_{16}H_{14}OS$			
Dibenzo[b,e]thiepin, 6,11-dihydro-11-(methoxymethylene)-	MeOH	231(4.24),265s(3.94), 306(3.53)	73-2536-79
$C_{16}H_{14}O_2$			
Cyclohepta[de]naphthalene-8,9-dimethanol	$CHCl_3$	246(4.41),280(3.84), 294s(3.80),333(3.74), 343(3.82),357(3.78), 369s(3.68),385(3.36), 412s(2.82),438(2.68), 470(2.50),506(2.25), 537(1.82),570(1.36)	150-3518-79
2-Propen-1-one, 1-(2-hydroxy-3-methyl-phenyl)-3-phenyl-	EtOH	225(4.10),319(4.37), 350(4.03)	78-2061-79
2-Propen-1-one, 2-methoxy-1,3-diphenyl-, (E)-	ether	250(4.31),311(3.43)	78-2501-79
(Z)-	ether	209(--),230(4.04), 250(4.14),310(4.21)	78-2501-79
9H-Xanthen-9-one, 2-(1-methylethyl)-	EtOH	242(4.62),262(4.10), 288(3.62),292(3.62), 342(3.81)	35-0665-79
$C_{16}H_{14}O_2S$			
Dibenzo[b,f]thiepin, 2,7-dimethoxy-	MeOH	227(4.50),269(4.12), 303(3.90),340s(3.34)	73-2987-79
Dibenzo[b,f]thiepin, 2,8-dimethoxy-	MeOH	228(4.45),262(4.47), 305(3.83),359(2.76)	73-2987-79
$C_{16}H_{14}O_3$			
Bicyclo[3.2.2]nona-3,6-dien-2-one, 1-(benzoyloxy)-	MeOH	231(4.33),333(1.83)	18-3355-79
Bicyclo[3.2.2]nona-3,6-dien-2-one, 3-(benzoyloxy)-	MeOH	232(4.37),330(2.04)	18-3355-79
1H-Phenalen-1-one, 3-(dimethoxymethyl)-	MeOH	225s(4.02),248(4.26), 255(4.22),306s(3.53), 319(3.60),364(3.94), 382s(3.91)	39-2995-79C
2-Propen-1-one, 1-(2-hydroxy-4-methoxy-phenyl)-3-phenyl-	EtOH	223(4.02),323(4.30), 349(4.28)	78-2061-79
2-Propen-1-one, 1-(2-hydroxyphenyl)-3-(4-methoxyphenyl)-	EtOH	225(4.09),320(4.28), 366(4.35)	78-2061-79
Spiro[cyclohepta[de]naphthalene-7(10H)-2'-[1,3]dioxolan]-10-one, 8,9-dihydro-	EtOH	306(3.88)	39-2995-79C

Compound	Solvent	$\lambda_{max}(\log \epsilon)$	Ref.
$C_{16}H_{14}O_3S$			
Dibenzo[b,f]thiepin-10(11H)-one, 2,8-dimethoxy-	MeOH	235(4.43),260s(4.15), 352(3.64)	73-2987-79
Dibenzo[b,f]thiepin-10(11H)-one, 3,8-dimethoxy-	MeOH	236(4.45),259s(4.11), 293(3.59),347(3.64)	73-2987-79
9H-Thioxanthen-9-one, 1,4-dimethoxy-7-methyl-	EtOH	205(4.34),257(4.56), 322(4.00),400(3.78)	33-2350-79
$C_{16}H_{14}O_4$			
9(10H)-Anthracenone, 1,8-dihydroxy-3-methoxy-6-methyl-	MeOH	231(4.47),256(4.08), 273(4.12),304(4.07), 355(4.36)	98-1342-79
7H-Furo[3,2-g][1]benzopyran-7-one, 9-(1,1-dimethyl-2-propenyl)-4-hydroxy-	MeOH	253(4.01),267s(4.22), 274(4.26),292(4.02), 315(3.95)	78-0697-79
	MeOH-base	237(4.05),262s(3.91), 291(4.31),332(3.85), 402(3.53)	78-0697-79
1,6-Heptalenedicarboxylic acid, dimethyl ester	EtOH	271(3.23),334(3.63), 420s(2.90)	89-0545-79
Methanone, (4-acetoxyphenyl)(4-methoxyphenyl)-	EtOH	291(4.23)	49-1057-79
Phenanthrene, 2,6-dihydroxy-5,7-dimethoxy-	$CHCl_3$	260(4.83),280(4.22), 298(4.10),301(3.91)	39-2449-79C
	$CHCl_3$	259(4.93),280s(4.23), 288s(4.12),300(3.94)	39-2449-79C
2-Propen-1-one, 1-(2,4-dihydroxy-5-methoxyphenyl)-3-phenyl-	EtOH	225(4.07),313(4.32)	78-2061-79
2-Propen-1-one, 1-(2,4-dihydroxy-6-methoxyphenyl)-3-phenyl-, (E)-	EtOH	223(4.23),322(4.30)	78-2061-79
9H-Xanthen-9-one, 1,4-dimethoxy-7-methyl-	EtOH	206(4.25),232(4.48), 258(4.45),367(3.75)	33-2350-79
$C_{16}H_{14}O_4S_2$			
1,3-Dithiole-4,5-dicarboxylic acid, 2-(3-phenyl-2-propenylidene)-, dimethyl ester	CH_2Cl_2	251(3.92),362(4.22), 376(4.21),680(2.53)	44-0930-79
$C_{16}H_{14}O_5$			
1,3-Benzenediol, 5-(5,6-dimethoxy-2-benzofuranyl)- (moracin F)	EtOH	217(4.51),282(4.08), 291(4.14),321(4.49), 334(4.42)	88-4675-79
4H-Naphtho[1,2-b]pyran-4-one, 5-hydroxy-8,10-dimethoxy-2-methyl-	EtOH	241(4.54),282(4.32), 371(3.69)	98-1347-79
$C_{16}H_{14}O_5S$			
Benzoic acid, 2,2'-[sulfinylbis(methylene)]bis-	dioxan	231s(4.21),285(3.54)	78-1875-79
$C_{16}H_{14}O_6$			
1,2-Benzenedicarboxylic acid, 3-hydroxy-6-phenoxy-, dimethyl ester	EtOH	222(4.39),326(3.63)	103-0013-79
4H-1-Benzopyran-4-one, 2,3-dihydro-6,7-dihydroxy-2-(4-hydroxyphenyl)-5-methoxy-	EtOH	287(4.16),350(3.67)	18-2596-79
4H-1-Benzopyran-4-one, 2,3-dihydro-2,5,7-trihydroxy-2-(4-methoxyphenyl)-	EtOH	289(4.36),375(3.66)	22-0119-79
	$EtOH-AlCl_3$	307(--),375(--)	22-0119-79
[1,1'-Biphenyl]-2,3-dicarboxylic acid, 4,4-dihydroxy-, dimethyl ester	EtOH	235(4.33),322(3.58)	103-0013-79
1,4-Ethanoanthracene-2,9,10(11H)-trione, 3,4,4a,9a-tetrahydro-4,5,8-trihydroxy-	MeOH	216(4.50),275s(3.92), 389(3.67)	24-2640-79

Compound	Solvent	λmax(log ε)	Ref.
Javanicin, 8-methoxy-	n.s.g.	226(4.56),283(4.04), 482(3.80),510(3.75), 550s(3.80)	78-1551-79
Propanedioic acid, (1,3-dihydro-1,3-dioxo-2H-inden-2-ylidene)-, diethyl ester	dioxan	233s(4.27),259(4.42), 306(3.60),318(3.58)	32-0329-79
1,3-Propanedione, 1-(2,6-dihydroxy-4-methoxyphenyl)-3-(2-hydroxyphenyl)-	EtOH	255(4.04),288(4.18), 330(3.88)	22-0119-79
2-Propen-1-one, 3-(4-hydroxyphenyl)-1-(2,4,6-trihydroxy-3-methoxyphenyl)-	EtOH	377(4.47)	18-2596-79
2-Propen-1-one, 3-(4-hydroxyphenyl)-1-(3,4,6-trihydroxy-2-methoxyphenyl)-	EtOH	368(4.36)	18-2596-79
$C_{16}H_{14}O_7$			
9,10-Anthracenedione, 3-acetyl-1,2,3,4-tetrahydro-1,3,5,8-tetrahydroxy-, cis-(±)-	MeOH	215(4.63),282(3.95), 474(3.84),509(3.92), 545(3.71)	24-3453-79
trans-(±)-	MeOH	213(4.53),281(3.91), 474(3.73),510(3.80), 540(3.24)	24-3453-79
2H-1-Benzopyran-6,8-dicarboxylic acid, 3-acetyl-5-methyl-2-oxo-, dimethyl ester	EtOH-H_2SO_4	225(4.64),250(4.69), 303(4.41),335s(4.27)	39-0472-79C
	EtOH-KOH	238(4.64),286(4.67), 440(4.08)	39-0472-79C
Propanedioic acid, 2-(2-ethenyl-5-hydroxy-4-oxo-4H-1-benzopyran-3-yl)-, dimethyl ester	EtOH	267(4.53),290s(3.98), 342(3.74)	102-0311-79
Spiro[anthracene-2(1H),2'-[1,3]dioxolane]-9,10-dione, 3,4-dihydro-4,5,8-trihydroxy-, (±)-	MeOH	219(4.55),281(3.88), 470(3.68),510(3.78), 547(3.55)	24-3453-79
9H-Xanthen-9-one, 3,6-dihydroxy-1,5,7-trimethoxy-	MeOH	233s(4.50),250(4.55), 315(4.20),353(3.91)	102-1029-79
	MeOH-NaOAc	312s(--),378(--)	102-1029-79
$C_{16}H_{14}O_7S$			
Benzoic acid, 2,2'-sulfinylbis[5-methoxy-	dioxan	237s(4.16),253s(4.10), 297(3.64)	78-1875-79
$C_{16}H_{15}$			
Cycloheptatrienylium, (4-cyclopropylphenyl)-	10% HCl	233(4.47),277(3.95), 415(4.28)	39-0262-79B
$C_{16}H_{15}Br$			
1,3,5-Cycloheptatriene, 1-bromo-7-(3a,7a-dihydro-1H-inden-1-yl)-	hexane	257s(3.82),264(3.86), 272s(3.81),283(3.62)	33-0718-79
$C_{16}H_{15}BrN_4O_3$			
1-Azabicyclo[4.2.0]oct-2-ene-2-carboxylic acid, 7-azido-4-bromo-3-methyl-8-oxo-, phenylmethyl ester	EtOH	284(3.82)	23-0227-79
$C_{16}H_{15}ClN_4$			
3H-1,4-Benzodiazepine, 7-chloro-2-(1-methylhydrazino)-5-phenyl-	EtOH	232(4.33),269(4.26), 352(3.47)	44-2688-79
$C_{16}H_{15}ClO_4$			
2H-1-Benzopyran-2-one, 7-acetoxy-6-(2-chloro-2-propenyl)-4,8-dimethyl-	EtOH	244(3.85),278(4.07), 315(3.84)	44-2176-79

Compound	Solvent	λmax(log ε)	Ref.
$C_{16}H_{15}N$			
Benzenamine, N-(3,4-dihydro-1(2H)-naphthalenylidene)-	CCl_4 or dioxan	255(4.30),329(3.32)	24-3490-79
Benzenemethanamine, 4-ethenyl-N-(phenylmethylene)-	$CHCl_3$	257(3.8)	24-2854-79
$C_{16}H_{15}NO$			
1H-Indole, 3-(4-methoxyphenyl)-5-methyl-	n.s.g.	212(4.31),230(4.33), 271(4.13)	2-0067-79A
6H-Pyrrolo[3,2,1-de]acridin-6-ol, 1,2-dihydro-1-methyl-	EtOH	215(4.2),262(3.6), 290(4.0)	103-1223-79
2H-Quinolizin-2-one, 1,9a-dihydro-9-methyl-4-phenyl-	MeOH	213(4.09),269(4.44), 401(4.10)	39-0584-79C
	MeOH-$HClO_4$	215(4.38),267(4.44), 285s(4.32),427(3.76)	39-0584-79C
$C_{16}H_{15}NO_2$			
Benzoic acid, 2-(2,3-dihydro-2-methyl-1H-indol-1-yl)-	EtOH	208(4.19),227(4.00), 285(3.65)	103-1223-79
2H-Indol-2-one, 1,3-dihydro-1-hydroxy-3,3-dimethyl-6-phenyl-	C_6H_{12}	246(4.5),300s(--)	5-0554-79
	pH 13	251(4.2),292(3.7)	5-0554-79
2H-Indol-2-one, 1,3-dihydro-1-hydroxy-3,3-dimethyl-5-phenyl-	pH 13	226(4.2),307(4.3)	5-0554-79
4H-Indol-4-one, 1,5,6,7-tetrahydro-5-(hydroxymethylene)-2-methyl-1-phenyl-	EtOH	222s(4.72),258(4.68), 326(4.59)	4-0913-79
$C_{16}H_{15}NO_2S$			
Benzeneacetic acid, α-[[(4-methylphenyl)thio]-, methyl ester	hexane	243(4.09),362(3.93)	44-1218-79
$C_{16}H_{15}NO_3$			
9(10H)-Acridinone, 1,4-dimethoxy-10-methyl-	EtOH	206(4.24),263(4.58), 316(3.92),407(3.87)	33-2350-79
1H-Benzo[a]furo[3,4-f]quinolizine-1,12(3H)-dione, 5,6,10b,11-tetrahydro-3-methyl-	MeOH	239(4.17),295(4.15)	104-1247-79
$C_{16}H_{15}NO_4$			
8H-1,3-Benzodioxolo[5,6-a]furo[3,4-g]-quinolizin-11(9H)-one, 5,6,12,12a-tetrahydro-	EtOH	290(3.53)	23-1647-79
9H-1,3-Benzodioxolo[5,6-a]furo[3,4-g]-quinolizin-9-one, 5,6,8,11,12,12a-hexahydro-	EtOH	292(3.70)	23-1647-79
6(5H)-Phenanthridinone, 8,9,10-trimethoxy-	EtOH	237(4.05),275(3.90), 283(3.89),295s(3.75), 325(3.30)	2-0503-79A
$C_{16}H_{15}NO_5$			
1,4-Cyclohexadiene-1-carboxylic acid, 2-[(4-methoxyphenyl)methylamino]-3,6-dioxo-, methyl ester	EtOH	207(4.21),241(4.22), 530(3.54)	33-2350-79
$C_{16}H_{15}NO_7S$			
Morpholine, 4-[(9-methoxy-7-oxo-7H-furo[3,2-g][1]benzopyran-4-yl)-sulfonyl]-	MeOH	225(4.27),255(4.20), 305(4.96)	48-1039-79
$C_{16}H_{15}N_2$			
Benzo[gh]perimidinium, 2,3-dihydro-1,3-	MeCN	259(4.48),387(4.47),	44-1704-79

Compound	Solvent	$\lambda_{max}(\log \epsilon)$	Ref.
dimethyl-, tetrafluoroborate (cont.)		535(3.75)	+138-0221-79
$C_{16}H_{15}N_2OS$			
Thiazolo[3,2-a]pyridinium, 2-[[4-(dimethylamino)phenyl]methylene]-2,3-dihydro-3-oxo-, perchlorate	MeCN	585(4.73)	103-1081-79
$C_{16}H_{15}N_2O_2S_2$			
Thiazolo[3,2-a]pyridinium, 2-[[(1-ethylpyridinium-2-yl)thio]acetyl]-3-hydroxy-, hydroxide, inner salt tetrafluoroborate	MeOH	251(3.9),284(3.9), 316(4.0),416(4.2)	103-0872-79
$C_{16}H_{15}N_3O$			
Benzamide, N-(4,5-dihydro-1-phenyl-1H-pyrazol-3-yl)-	EtOH	228(4.15),270(3.96), 338(4.00)	150-0801-79
1,2,4-Oxadiazole-3-ethanamine, N,5-diphenyl-	EtOH	249(4.44)	150-0801-79
$C_{16}H_{15}N_3OS$			
Benzothiazole, 2-[[4-(1-methylethoxy)-phenyl]azo]-	EtOH	418(3.13)	103-1185-79
2,5-Cyclohexadiene-1,4-dione, mono[[3-(1-methylethyl)-2(3H)-benzothiazolylidene]hydrazone]	EtOH	517(3.26)	103-1185-79
$C_{16}H_{15}N_3O_2$			
9,10-Anthracenedione, 1-amino-2,4-bis(methylamino)-	benzene	546(4.06),579(4.06)	153-0033-79
Benzenepropanamide, α-[(4-methylphenyl)hydrazono]-β-oxo-	EtOH	250(4.58),378(5.05)	104-1324-79
Butanamide, 3-oxo-N-phenyl-2-(phenylhydrazono)-	EtOH	245(4.3),385(4.5)	104-1416-79
1H-1,2,4-Triazole, 3,5-bis(4-methoxyphenyl)-	EtOH	264(4.43)	40-0389-79
$C_{16}H_{15}N_3O_3$			
Benzenepropanamide, α-[(4-methoxyphenyl)hydrazono]-β-oxo-	EtOH	257(4.41),387(4.75)	104-1324-79
$C_{16}H_{15}N_3O_3S$			
Furo[3',4':5,6]thiopyrano[2,3-c]pyrazole-5,7-dione, 1,4,4a,7a-tetrahydro-3-methyl-4-(methylamino)-1-phenyl-	EtOH	255(4.16)	103-0429-79
$C_{16}H_{15}N_3O_3Se$			
Furo[3',4':5,6]selenino[2,3-c]pyrazole-5,7-dione, 1,4,4a,7a-tetrahydro-3-methyl-4-(methylamino)-1-phenyl-	EtOH	255(4.08)	103-0429-79
$C_{16}H_{15}N_3O_4$			
Imidazo[1,5-b]pyridazine-4-carboxylic acid, 3,5,6,7-tetrahydro-6-methyl-5,7-dioxo-2-phenyl-, ethyl ester	50% EtOH	262(3.97),318s(3.27)	4-1105-79
1H-Pyrrolo[3,2-d]pyrimidine-7-carboxylic acid, 2,3,4,5-tetrahydro-1,3-dimethyl-2,4-dioxo-6-phenyl-, methyl ester	EtOH	238(4.80),290(4.64)	44-3830-79

Compound	Solvent	λmax(log ε)	Ref.
$C_{16}H_{15}N_3O_6$			
Benzene, 1,1'-(1,2-dimethyl-1-nitro-1,2-ethanediyl)bis[4-nitro-, (R*,R*)	MeOH	270(4.37)	12-1487-79
(R*,S*)-	MeOH	264(4.33)	12-1487-79
4H-Furo[3,4-d]-1,2,3-triazol-4-one, 6-(1,2-diacetoxyethyl)-2,6-dihydro-2-phenyl-	EtOH	217(3.64),282(4.11)	136-0087-79A
$C_{16}H_{15}N_5$			
1H-Pyrazol-5-amine, 3-methyl-1-phenyl-4-(phenylazo)-	EtOH	255(3.82)	48-0127-79
$C_{16}H_{15}N_5O_2$			
Benzoic acid, 4-[5-[4-(dimethylamino)-phenyl]-2H-tetrazol-2-yl]-	EtOH	260(4.27),288(4.36), 302(4.34),334(4.15)	4-0123-79
$C_{16}H_{15}N_5O_2S$			
Pyrido[3,2-d]pyrimidine-6-carboxamide, 4-amino-8-(methylthio)-2-(phenylmethoxy)-	pH 1	243(3.91),274(3.67), 335(3.56)	44-0435-79
	pH 7	247(3.92),287(3.49), 340(3.49),352s(3.45)	
	pH 11	248(3.59),340(3.52), 352(3.47)	
$C_{16}H_{15}N_5O_2S_2$			
Ethanethioamide, 2-[[4-(aminosulfonyl)-phenyl]hydrazono]-2-cyano-N-(phenylmethyl)-	EtOH	240(4.22),380(4.50)	104-1082-79
$C_{16}H_{15}N_5O_3S$			
3-Thiophenecarboxylic acid, 2-[(3-amino-1,5-dihydro-5-oxo-4H-pyrazol-4-ylidene)hydrazino]-5-phenyl-, ethyl ester	MeOH	230(4.07),294s(4.04), 472(4.33)	83-0726-79
$C_{16}H_{15}N_5O_5$			
Benzamide, 4-azido-N-[2-hydroxy-1-(hydroxymethyl)-2-(4-nitrophenyl)ethyl]-, [R-(R*,R*)]-	n.s.g.	271(4.37)	63-0721-79
$C_{16}H_{15}N_5O_6$			
Benzo[g]pteridine-3(2H)-acetic acid, 4,10-dihydro-7,10-dimethyl-6-nitro-2,4-dioxo-, ethyl ester	MeCN	327(3.83),428s(--), 446(4.02),470s(--)	5-1067-79
$C_{16}H_{15}N_9$			
2H-Tetrazolium, 2-[4-(dimethylamino)-phenyl]-5-phenyl-3-(1H-tetrazol-5-yl)-, hydroxide, inner salt	EtOH	245(4.37),460(4.10)	104-1793-79
$C_{16}H_{15}N_9O$			
Acetamide, N-[3-[3-phenyl-5-(1H-tetrazol-5-yl)-1-formazano]phenyl]-	EtOH	287(4.28),475(3.89)	104-1793-79
2H-Tetrazolium, 2-[4-(dimethylamino)-phenyl]-5-(2-hydroxyphenyl)-3(1H-tetrazol-5-yl)-, hydroxide, inner salt	EtOH	255(3.92),300(3.66), 452(3.65)	104-1793-79
	EtOH-NaOH	260(4.12),349(3.77), 435(3.86)	104-1793-79
$C_{16}H_{16}$			
1-Butene, 1,3-diphenyl-	EtOH	253(3.83),286(2.85), 293(2.43)	126-2979-79

Compound	Solvent	λ max (log ε)	Ref.
Cyclopropane, 1-methyl-1,2-diphenyl-, cis	EtOH or CCl_4	256(3.70),270(3.13), 277(2.92)	104-0080-79
trans	EtOH or CCl_4	258(3.40),270(3.16), 277(2.95)	104-0080-79
Propene, 2-[2-(phenylmethyl)phenyl]-	C_6H_{12}	254(2.96),261(2.80), 268(2.70)	44-3698-79
3,4,5-[1]Propen[1]yl[3]ylidene-3H-dicyclopenta[a,cd]pentalene, 2a,4,4a-4b,5,7a,7b,7c-octahydro-	C_6H_{12}	192(4.30)	35-6991-79
$C_{16}H_{16}BrNO_3$			
Furo[3,4-c]pyridine, 4-bromo-1,3-dihydro-1-methoxy-6-methyl-7-(phenylmethoxy)-	MeOH	225s(--),285(3.83)	88-2603-79
$C_{16}H_{16}ClNO_2$			
2H-Pyran-2-one, 3-chloro-6-phenyl-4-(1-piperidinyl)-	EtOH	235(4.00),264(4.51), 305(4.25),350s(4.02)	4-0093-79
$C_{16}H_{16}ClN_5O_3$			
Morpholine, 4-[(10-chloro-6,7-dihydro-7-methyl-6-oxo-5H-1,2,4-triazolo-[4,3-d][1,4]benzodiazepin-3yl)carbonyl]-	MeOH	235(4.56),298(3.44)	44-0088-79
$C_{16}H_{16}FN_3O_5$			
1(2H)-Pyrimidineacetic acid, α-(acetylamino)-5-fluoro-3,4-dihydro-α-methyl-2,4-dioxo-, phenylmethyl ester	MeOH	265(3.90)	44-2019-79
$C_{16}H_{16}FN_3O_6$			
1(2H)-Pyrimidineacetic acid, 5-fluoro-3,4-dihydro-2,4-dioxo-α-[[(phenylmethoxy)carbonyl]amino]-, ethyl ester	MeOH	265(3.86)	44-2019-79
$C_{16}H_{16}F_2O_3$			
Spiro[azuleno[4,5-b]furan-3(2H),1'-cyclopropane]-2,9(3aH)-dione, 2',2'-difluoro-4,5,9a,9b-tetrahydro-6,9a-dimethyl-, [3S-(3α,3aα,9aβ,9bα)]-	EtOH	297(3.92)	78-0815-79
$C_{16}H_{16}MoN_2O_6$			
Molybdenum, bis(N-hydroxy-N-phenylacetamidato-O,O')dioxo-	EtOH	251(4.26)	39-2481-79C
$C_{16}H_{16}NO$			
Phenalenylium, 1-ethoxy-9-(methylamino)-, tetrafluoroborate	n.s.g.	248(4.34),378(4.38), 447(4.18),472(4.20)	44-1704-79
$C_{16}H_{16}NO_2$			
[1,3]Benzodioxolo[5,6-a]quinolizinium, 6,7-dihydro-2,3-dimethyl-, iodide	EtOH	267(3.54),355(3.42)	23-1647-79
$C_{16}H_{16}N_2$			
Benzeneacetaldehyde, (2-phenylethylidene)hydrazone	EtOH	248(3.77),285(3.58), 296(3.57),310(3.51)	103-0501-79
$C_{16}H_{16}N_2O$			
1H-Imidazole, 2,5-dihydro-1-(4-methylphenyl)-4-phenyl-, 3-oxide	MeOH	245(4.37),291(4.23)	56-1147-79

Compound	Solvent	λmax(log ε)	Ref.
7,11-Methano-6H-cyclonona[b]quinoxalin-14-one, 7,8,9,10,11,12-hexahydro-	EtOH	206(4.36),238(4.40), 318(3.82)	56-1221-79
Quinazoline, 1,4-dihydro-4-(4-methoxy-phenyl)-2-methyl-, monohydrochloride	EtOH	241(3.86),274(3.85)	24-1348-79
$C_{16}H_{16}N_2OS_2$			
4-Thiazolidinone, 3-ethyl-5-(1-ethyl-2(1H)-quinolinylidene)-2-thioxo-	EtOH	452s(4.30),480(4.49), 498s(4.48)	73-1413-79
4-Thiazolidinone, 3-ethyl-5-(1-ethyl-4(1H)-quinolinylidene)-2-thioxo-	EtOH	460s(4.15),492s(4.65), 518(4.85)	73-1413-79
$C_{16}H_{16}N_2OS_3$			
Dianilinium 1,2,3-trithioquadratate	DMSO	300(3.87),340(3.89), 398(4.60)	24-0990-79
$C_{16}H_{16}N_2O_2$			
Benzamide, 2-[4-(dimethylamino)benzoyl]-	dioxan	342(4.39)	103-0634-79
Phenazine, 2,7-diethoxy-	EtOH	264(4.97),346(3.87), 408(4.00),427(4.03)	94-2316-79
$C_{16}H_{16}N_2O_2S$			
4-Oxazolidinone, 3-ethyl-5-(1-ethyl-2(1H)-quinolinylidene)-2-thioxo-	EtOH	402s(4.00),426(4.40), 448(4.53),454(4.38)	73-1413-79
$C_{16}H_{16}N_2O_2S_2$			
Dianilinium 1,3-dithioquadratate	DMSO	298(4.00),396(4.77)	24-0990-79
$C_{16}H_{16}N_2O_3$			
1H-Benzo[a]furo[3,4-f]quinolizine-1,12(3H)-dione, 5,6,10b,11-tetra-hydro-3-methyl-, 12-oxime	MeOH	213(4.00),298(4.25)	104-1247-79
1H-Pyrrolo[2,3-f]quinoline-8-carboxylic acid, 9-hydroxy-2,3-dimethyl-, ethyl ester	EtOH	213(4.48),240s(4.01), 296(4.44),339(3.99)	103-0888-79
3H-Pyrrolo[3,2-f]quinoline-8-carboxylic acid, 9-hydroxy-1,2-dimethyl-, ethyl ester	EtOH	224(4.60),260(4.16), 303(4.41),352(4.17)	103-0888-79
$C_{16}H_{16}N_2O_3S$			
Benzenesulfonic acid, 4-(4,5-dihydro-3-methyl-5-phenyl-1H-pyrazol-1-yl)-, sodium salt, (±)-	MeOH	294(4.31)	23-0360-79
Benzenesulfonic acid, 4-(4,5-dihydro-5-methyl-3-phenyl-1H-pyrazol-1-yl)-, sodium salt, (±)-	MeOH	234(4.11),267(4.11), 358(4.46)	23-0360-79
$C_{16}H_{16}N_2O_4S_2$			
2-Butenoic acid, 4,4-dicyano-2-[(4-methylphenyl)sulfonyl]-3-(methyl-thio)-, ethyl ester	EtOH	216s(4.28),324(4.01), 394(4.14)	95-1234-79
Spiro[benzothiazole-2(3H),2'-[2H]pyr-role]-3',4'-dicarboxylic acid, 3-methyl-5'-(methylthio)-, dimethyl ester	EtOH	220(4.23),254(4.33), 286(4.42),300(4.27), 405(3.78)	94-2879-79
$C_{16}H_{16}N_2O_5$			
Benzenepropanol, γ-hydroxy-β-[[(2-hy-droxyphenyl)methylene]amino]-4-ni-tro-, [R-(R*,R*)]-	MeOH	272(4.21),463(2.53)	94-1245-79

Compound	Solvent	$\lambda_{max}(\log \epsilon)$	Ref.
$C_{16}H_{16}N_2O_5S$			
Benzenepropanamide, N-[2-(aminosulfonyl)-5-methoxyphenyl]-β-oxo-	EtOH	205(4.41),230(4.44), 247(4.39),315(3.92)	104-1495-79
Benzenepropanamide, N-[2-(aminosulfonyl)phenyl]-4-methoxy-β-oxo-	EtOH	211(4.48),284(4.33), 322(3.67)	104-1495-79
Benzo[b][1,6]naphthyridine-2(1H)-propanesulfonic acid, 3,5-dihydro-5-methyl-1,3-dioxo-	pH 7	252(4.15),262(4.23), 283(4.54),303(4.38), 474(3.96)	149-0233-79A
$C_{16}H_{16}N_2O_5S_2$			
Benzenesulfonamide, 4-[(1,2-benzisothiazol-3-yloxy)methyl]-N,N-dimethyl-, S,S-dioxide	MeCN	229(4.29),274(3.45)	118-0531-79
$C_{16}H_{16}N_2O_6$			
5-Oxa-1-azabicyclo[4.2.0]oct-2-ene-2-carboxylic acid, 7-[(hydroxyphenylacetyl)amino]-3-methyl-8-oxo-, [6R-[(6α,7β(R*)]]-	EtOH	260(3.62)	39-2268-79C
5-Oxa-1-azabicyclo[4.2.0]oct-2-ene-2-carboxylic acid, 3-methyl-8-oxo-7-[(phenoxyacetyl)amino]-	EtOH	263(3.82)	39-2268-79C
5-Oxa-1-azabicyclo[4.2.0]oct-3-ene-2-carboxylic acid, 3-methyl-8-oxo-7-[(phenoxyacetyl)amino]-	EtOH	270(3.19),276(3.11)	39-2268-79C
1H-Pyrazole-3,4-dicarboxylic acid, 5-acetyl-1-(4-methoxyphenyl)-, dimethyl ester	CH_2Cl_2	end absorption	24-1193-79
$C_{16}H_{16}N_2O_6S$			
Uridine, 2',3'-didehydro-2',3'-dideoxy-, 5'-(4-methylbenzenesulfonate)	EtOH	224(4.17),262(3.99)	136-0113-79F
$C_{16}H_{16}N_2O_6S_3$			
Thiazolo[3,2-a]pyridinium, 2-[(1-methylpyridinium-2-ylthio)acetyl]-, 3-oxide, methyl sulfate	MeOH	251(3.9),284(3.9), 316(4.0),416(4.2)	103-0872-79
$C_{16}H_{16}N_2O_7$			
3,5-Pyridinedicarboxylic acid, 6-(3-cyano-4-methoxy-4-oxo-2-butenyl)-1,2-dihydro-1-methyl-2-oxo-, dimethyl ester	EtOH	213(4.34),262(4.04), 336(3.85),491(3.55)	39-0686-79C
	EtOH-HCl	213(4.34),264(4.04), 336(3.91)	39-0686-79C
	EtOH-NaOH	255(4.25),322(3.64), 488(4.82)	39-0686-79C
Uridine, 5'-benzoate	EtOH	230(4.16),261(4.01)	39-2088-79C
$C_{16}H_{16}N_3O_2$			
1H-1,2,3-Triazolium, 1,3-bis(4-methoxyphenyl)-, perchlorate	MeOH	317(4.24)	24-0445-79
$C_{16}H_{16}N_4$			
2,2'-Bi-1H-benzimidazole, 2,3-dihydro-1,1'-dimethyl-	MeOH	250(4.2),277(3.97)	103-0166-79
monohydrate	MeOH	250(4.45),277(4.35), 287(4.38),303(3.85), 353(3.27),385(3.22), 397(3.08)	103-0166-79
Propanedinitrile, [[4-(2-cyanoethyl)-ethylamino]-2-methylphenyl]methylene]-	EtOH	437(4.78)	110-1769-79
	EtOH-KOH	336(--)	110-1769-79
	CCl_4	421(--)	110-1769-79

Compound	Solvent	$\lambda_{max}(\log \epsilon)$	Ref.
1H-Tetrazole, 5-phenyl-1-(2,4,6-trimethylphenyl)-	EtOH	242(4.06)	39-1871-79C
$C_{16}H_{16}N_4O_2S$			
Isothiazolo[3,4-d]pyrimidine-4,6(5H,7H)-dione, 5-methyl-7-phenyl-3-pyrrolidino-	EtOH	234(4.35),276(4.00), 310(4.06)	95-0989-79
$C_{16}H_{16}N_4O_3$			
1-Azabicyclo[4.2.0]oct-2-ene-2-carboxylic acid, 7-azido-3-methyl-8-oxo-, phenylmethyl ester, trans	EtOH	268(3.97)	23-0227-79
Pyrimido[4,5-d]pyrimidine-2,4,5(1H,3H-6H)-trione, 1,3,7-trimethyl-6-(phenylmethyl)-	EtOH	236(4.59),270(3.89), 300(3.58)	95-0515-79
$C_{16}H_{16}N_4O_4$			
Benzo[g]pteridine-2,4(3H,10H)-dione, 10-(3-acetoxypropyl)-3-methyl-	EtOH	263(4.50),333(4.01), 419s(4.05),436(4.19), 455s(4.00)	4-1365-79
$C_{16}H_{16}N_4O_6$			
Bicyclo[2.2.1]hept-5-ene-2-carboxylic acid, 3-acetyl-, 2,4-dinitrophenylhydrazone	EtOH	384(4.31)	104-0043-79
$C_{16}H_{16}N_6O_2$			
Benzenamine, N,N-dimethyl-4-[(1-methyl-5-nitro-1H-indazol-3-yl)azo]-	EtOH	285(4.3),315(3.9), 475(4.30)	103-1231-79
Benzenamine, N,N-dimethyl-4-[(2-methyl-5-nitro-2H-indazol-3-yl)azo]-	EtOH	300(4.3),395(3.9), 530(4.52)	103-1231-79
$C_{16}H_{16}N_8$			
5H-Tetrazol-5-one, 1,2-dihydro-1-methyl-, [[(2-methylphenyl)azo]phenylmethylene]hydrazone	pH 13	285(3.86),445(4.45)	104-2000-79
	EtOH	271(4.15),322(4.02), 410(3.97)	104-2000-79
	dioxan	280(4.19),430(3.99)	104-2000-79
5H-Tetrazol-5-one, 1,2-dihydro-1-methyl-, [[(4-methylphenyl)azo]phenylmethylene]hydrazone	pH 13	257(3.99),455(4.52)	104-2000-79
	EtOH	245(4.40),275(4.37), 410(4.16)	104-2000-79
	dioxan	282(4.18),312(4.10), 420(4.04)	104-2000-79
5H-Tetrazol-5-one, 1,2-dihydro-2-methyl-, [[(2-methylphenyl)azo]phenylmethylene]hydrazone	pH 13	247(3.84),450(4.45)	104-2000-79
	EtOH	275(4.22),430(4.95)	104-2000-79
	dioxan	285(4.29),440(4.00)	104-2000-79
5H-Tetrazol-5-one, 1,2-dihydro-2-methyl-, [[(4-methylphenyl)azo]phenylmethylene]hydrazone	pH 13	255(3.98),470(4.54)	104-2000-79
	EtOH	250(4.25),280(4.28), 427(4.11)	104-2000-79
	dioxan	255(4.19),285(4.25), 435(4.10)	104-2000-79
$C_{16}H_{16}N_8O$			
5H-Tetrazol-5-one, 1,2-dihydro-1-methyl-, [[(4-methoxyphenyl)azo]phenylmethylene]hydrazone	pH 13	245(4.23),302(4.10), 466(4.49)	104-2000-79
	EtOH	365(4.15),415(4.16)	104-2000-79
	dioxan	282(4.11),355(4.19), 415(4.20)	104-2000-79
5H-Tetrazol-5-one, 1,2-dihydro-2-methyl-, [[(4-methoxyphenyl)azo]phenylmethylene]hydrazone	pH 13	259(4.05),455(4.59)	104-2000-79
	EtOH	254(4.14),365(4.07), 410(4.08)	104-2000-79

Compound	Solvent	λmax(log ε)	Ref.
(cont.)	dioxan	258(4.03),355(3.94), 420(3.95)	104-2000-79
$C_{16}H_{16}N_{10}O_2$			
Benzenamine, N,N-dimethyl-4-[3-(3-nitrophenyl)-5-(1H-tetrazol-5-yl)-1-formazano]-	EtOH	255(4.37),520(4.45)	104-1793-79
Benzenamine, N,N-dimethyl-4-[3-(4-nitrophenyl)-5-(1H-tetrazol-5-yl)-1-formazano]-	EtOH	265(4.24),392(4.10), 490(4.32)	104-1793-79
$C_{16}H_{16}O$			
Bicyclo[4.3.1]deca-2,4,8-trien-7-ol, 7-phenyl-, endo	C_6H_{12}	256(3.76)	5-0533-79
Gibba-1,3,4a(10a),4b-tetraen-8-one, 1-methyl-, (±)-	EtOH	258(4.22),266(4.16), 287(3.73)	44-4562-79
5H-3,4b-Methano-1H-benzo[1,3]cycloprop-[1,2-a]inden-4(4aH)-one, 2,3-dihydro-6-methyl-, (±)-	EtOH	234(4.07)	44-4562-79
$C_{16}H_{16}OS$			
6H-Cyclopenta[5,6]naphtho[2,1-b]thiophen-6-one, 4,5,5a,7,9,10-hexahydro-5a-methyl-	MeOH	312(4.13)	13-0601-79A
$C_{16}H_{16}O_2$			
5-Acenaphthylenemethanol, 1,2-dihydro-α-methyl-, acetate	hexane	225(4.81),231(5.01), 254(3.02),260(3.24), 284(4.89),296(4.97), 305(4.79),309(4.75), 323(3.20)	104-0340-79
Benzene, 4-ethenyl-1-methoxy-2-(phenylmethoxy)-	C_6H_{12}	218(4.24),259(4.02), 266s(4.00),285s(3.52)	39-0662-79C
Benzo[b]naphtho[2,1-d]furan-5(1H)-one, 2,3,4,4a,6,11b-hexahydro-, cis	EtOH	208(4.31),249(4.05), 276(3.61),283(3.58)	118-0122-79
1-Isobenzofuranol, 1,3-dihydro-3,3-dimethyl-1-phenyl-, cation	50% H_2SO_4	344(4.45)	104-1126-79
2,4,6,8-Nonatetraenal, 9-(4-methoxyphenyl)-	EtOH	406(4.70)	104-1669-79
$C_{16}H_{16}O_3$			
Benzoic acid, 2-[4-(1-methylethyl)phenoxy]-	EtOH	227(4.04),288(3.48)	35-0665-79
7,10-Epoxycyclohepta[de]naphthalene, 7.8.9.10-tetrahydro-7,10-dimethoxy-	MeOH	263s(3.58),274(3.79), 284(3.88),290s(3.75), 295(3.72)	39-2995-79C
6H-Furo[2,3-c]xanthen-6-one, 1,2,7,8-9,10-hexahydro-2-methyl-	MeOH	248(4.32),255(4.35), 302(4.12)	42-0052-79
Methanone, (2-hydroxy-3,5-dimethylphenyl)(2-methoxyphenyl)-	EtOH	223(4.16),269(3.98), 357(3.60)	49-1057-79
Methanone, (2-hydroxy-3,5-dimethylphenyl)(4-methoxyphenyl)-	EtOH	275(4.06),295(4.13), 351(3.76)	49-1057-79
Methanone, (4-hydroxy-3,5-dimethylphenyl)(2-methoxyphenyl)-	EtOH	229(4.16),300(4.18)	49-1057-79
Methanone, (4-hydroxy-3,5-dimethylphenyl)(4-methoxyphenyl)-	EtOH	302(4.30)	49-1057-79
$C_{16}H_{16}O_3S$			
3-Penten-2-one, 3-methyl-5-(2-naphthalenylsulfonyl)-	H_2O	226(4.410)	104-0578-79

Compound	Solvent	$\lambda_{max}(\log \epsilon)$	Ref.
$C_{16}H_{16}O_4$			
2H-1-Benzopyran-7-ol, 3,4-dihydro-3-(2-hydroxy-4-methoxyphenyl)- (vestitol)	MeOH	206(4.66),228(4.05), 285(3.75)	105-0644-79
4H-Difuro[3,2-c:3',2'-g]benzopyran-4-one, 2,3,8,9-tetrahydro-2,6,8-trimethyl-	MeOH	246(4.07),294(3.93), 324(4.33),338(4.29)	42-0056-79
1,3-Dioxane-4,6-dione, 2,2-dimethyl-5-(octahydro-1,2,4-metheno-3H-cyclobuta[cd]pentalen-3-ylidene)-	EtOH	245(4.04)	12-1767-79
2H-2,4a-Methanonaphthalene-3,4-dicarboxylic acid, 1-methyl-, dimethyl ester	EtOH	327(3.53+)	39-0673-79C
2H-2,4a-Methanonaphthalene-3,4-dicarboxylic acid, 9-methyl-, dimethyl ester	EtOH	320(3.49+)	39-0673-79C
2H-Naphtho[2,3-b]pyran-5,10-dione, 3,4-dihydro-4-methoxy-2,2-dimethyl-	EtOH	246(4.31),251(4.37), 284(4.03),335(3.39)	2-0016-79B
$C_{16}H_{16}O_4S$			
Benzoic acid, 3,6-dimethoxy-2-[(4-methylphenyl)thio]-	EtOH	209(4.47),305(3.79)	33-2350-79
Benzoic acid, 3,6-dimethoxy-2-(phenylthio)-, methyl ester	EtOH	213(4.34),239(4.13), 310(3.50)	33-2350-79
$C_{16}H_{16}O_5$			
Benzoic acid, 3,6-dimethoxy-2-(4-methylphenoxy)-	EtOH	209(4.31),221(4.28), 283(3.63)	33-2350-79
3,4-Furandicarboxylic acid, 2-phenyl-, diethyl ester	$CHCl_3$	250(4.763),275(4.555), 355(4.272)	104-0541-79
1H-Naphtho[2,3-c]pyran-1-one, 3,4-dihydro-9-hydroxy-7,10-dimethoxy-3-methyl-	MeOH	242(4.64),298s(--), 347(3.78)	24-0957-79
1-Propanone, 1-(2,4-dihydroxyphenyl)-3-(4-hydroxy-3-methoxyphenyl)-	EtOH	218(4.27),232s(4.11), 280(4.18),318(3.86)	102-1015-79
	EtOH-NaOH	227(3.86),249(4.11), 342(4.46)	102-1015-79
$C_{16}H_{16}O_7$			
9,10-Anthracenedione, 1,2,3,4-tetrahydro-1,2,3,5-tetrahydroxy-7-methoxy-2-methyl-	n.s.g.	220(4.61),238(3.97), 269(4.19),284s(3.99), 420(3.74)	88-2481-79
2H-1-Benzopyran-3,5,7-triol, 2-(3,5-dihydroxy-4-methoxyphenyl)-3,4-dihydro-, (2R-cis)-	n.s.g.	278(3.18)	2-0292-79B
Fusarubin, 8-methoxy-	n.s.g.	226(4.48),283(4.05), 484(3.83),510(3.80), 550s(3.49)	78-1551-79
Propanedioic acid, (2-ethyl-5-hydroxy-4-oxo-4H-1-benzopyran-3-yl)-, dimethyl ester	EtOH	328(3.69)	102-0311-79
1-Propanone, 3-(3,5-dihydroxy-4-methoxyphenyl)-1-(2,4-dihydroxyphenyl)-3-hydroxy- (gliricidol)	EtOH	281(4.05),320(3.86)	102-1037-79
	EtOH-NaOH	249(--),339(--)	102-1037-79
	EtOH-NaOAc	255(--),280(--), 338(--)	102-1037-79
Spiro[anthracene-2(1H),2'-[1,3]dioxolane]-9,10-dione, 3,4,4a,9a-tetrahydro-4,5,8-trihydroxy-	MeOH	215(4.36),259(3.94), 394(3.68)	24-3453-79
$C_{16}H_{16}O_8$			
9,10-Anthracenedione, 1,2,3,4-tetrahydro-1,2,3,5,8-pentahydroxy-6-methoxy-	EtOH	226(4.40),300(3.80), 470(3.68),501(3.74),	102-1579-79

Compound	Solvent	λ_{max}(log ϵ)	Ref.
3-methyl- (bostrycin) (cont.)		540(3.57)	102-1579-79
2H-Pyran-5-carboxylic acid, 3-acetyl-6-[4-hydroxy-3-(methoxycarbonyl)-1,3-pentadienyl]-2-oxo-, methyl ester	EtOH-H_2SO_4	301(4.12),437(4.30), 530s(3.58)	39-0472-79C
	EtOH-KOH	253(4.09),297(4.08), 320s(4.02),366(4.08), 498s(4.60),525(4.69)	39-0472-79C
2H-Pyran-5-carboxylic acid, 3-[5-hydroxy-4-(methoxycarbonyl)-1-oxo-2,4-hexadienyl]-6-methyl-2-oxo-, methyl ester	EtOH and EtOH-H_2SO_4	258(3.83),372(4.15)	39-0472-79C
	EtOH-KOH	283(4.45),320s(4.34), 427(4.57),542(3.98)	39-0472-79C
$C_{16}H_{17}$			
Propylium, 2-methyl-1,1-diphenyl-	H_2SO_4	432(4.22)	39-1395-79B
$C_{16}H_{17}BrN_2$			
Pyridine, 3-bromo-5-[1-(phenylmethyl)-2-pyrrolidinyl]-	EtOH	229(3.39),270s(3.53), 275(3.56),280s(3.48)	44-4332-79
$C_{16}H_{17}BrN_4O_2$			
Benzenamine, 3-bromo-N,N-diethyl-4-[(4-nitrophenyl)azo]-	EtOH	472(4.53)	39-1990-79C
	HOAc	474(4.52)	39-1990-79C
$C_{16}H_{17}ClF_3N_5O$			
Pyrrolidine, 1-[[3-[5-chloro-2-(methylamino)phenyl]-5-(trifluoromethyl)-4H-1,2,4-triazol-4-yl]acetyl]-, monohydrochloride	MeOH	257(4.08),333(3.54)	44-0088-79
$C_{16}H_{17}ClN_2O_2$			
8-Azabicyclo[3.2.1]oct-3-ene-6-carbonitrile, 6-chloro-8-(5,5-dimethyl-3-oxo-1-cyclohexen-1-yl)-2-oxo-	EtOH	218(3.83),294(4.25)	56-0057-79
$C_{16}H_{17}ClN_2O_2S$			
4-Imidazolidinone, 3-[3-[(2-chlorophenyl)hydroxymethyl]-5-ethyl-2-thienyl]-	MeOH	282(4.07)	73-3604-79
$C_{16}H_{17}ClN_4O_2$			
Benzenamine, 3-chloro-N,N-diethyl-4-[(4-nitrophenyl)azo]-	EtOH	472(4.53)	39-1990-79C
	HOAc	472(4.52)	39-1990-79C
$C_{16}H_{17}ClO_5$			
1H,7H-Cyclopropa[c]benzofuran-4,7(3aH)-dione, 3a-acetoxy-5-(1-chloro-1-propenyl)-1a,2-dihydro-2,2-dimethyl- (O-acetylmycorrhizin A)	EtOH	290(3.8)	33-1129-79
$C_{16}H_{17}F$			
1,1'-Biphenyl , 4'-fluoro-2,3,5,6-tetramethyl-	C_6H_{12}	261(3.06),266(3.17), 272(3.12)	12-1531-79
$C_{16}H_{17}FN_4O_2$			
Benzenamine, N,N-diethyl-3-fluoro-4-[(4-nitrophenyl)azo]-	EtOH	469(4.46)	39-1990-79C
	HOAc	472(4.39)	39-1990-79C
$C_{16}H_{17}IN_4O_2$			
Benzenamine, N,N-diethyl-3-iodo-4-[(4-nitrophenyl)azo]-	EtOH	476(4.52)	39-1990-79C
	HOAc	477(4.50)	39-1990-79C

Compound	Solvent	λ_{max}(log ε)	Ref.
$C_{16}H_{17}N$			
Benzeneethanamine, α-methyl-N-(phenyl- methylene)-	hexane	210s(4.38),241s(4.26), 248(4.28),255s(4.11), 277(3.11),287(2.98)	44-1690-79
	MeOH	247(4.26),277s(3.28), 287s(3.04)	44-1690-79
$C_{16}H_{17}NO$			
Benzenemethanamine, N-[(4-methoxyphen- yl)methylene]-α-methyl-, (S)-	EtOH	209(4.49),251(4.20), 304(3.80)	44-1690-79
Benzo[d]carbazol-6(7H)-one, 1,2,3,4,7a- 8-hexahydro-	MeOH	234(4.39),300(3.28)	5-1048-79
	dioxan	234(4.39),303(3.38)	5-1048-79
4a,9a-Butano-9H-carbazol-2(1H)-one	MeOH	228(4.33),302(3.14), 355s(3.04)	5-1048-79
	dioxan	230(4.21),315(3.26)	5-1048-79
A-Nor-3-aza-14α-estra-1,5(10),6,8- tetraen-17-one	EtOH	225(4.444),276(3.857), 285(3.806),292(3.682), 296(3.556)	104-1983-79
1H-Pyrrolizine-5-carboxaldehyde, 2,3- dihydro-2,2-dimethyl-6-phenyl-	MeOH	206(4.08),233(4.12), 306(4.25)	83-0896-79
$C_{16}H_{17}NO_2$			
Benzene, 2-butyl-1-nitroso-4-phenoxy-	$CHCl_3$	750(1.65)	44-2087-79
1,1'-Biphenyl, 3-(1,1-dimethylethyl)- 4-nitro-	C_6H_{12}	246(4.1),266s(4.0), 330s(3.0)	5-0554-79
	MeOH	248(4.1),274s(3.9), 334(3.1)	5-0554-79
1,1'-Biphenyl, 4-(1,1-dimethylethyl)- 3-nitro-	C_6H_{12}	239(4.3),290s(3.1), 340s(2.4)	5-0554-79
	MeOH	250(4.3),340s(2.5)	5-0554-79
Cyclopenta[c]carbazole-4-carboxylic acid, 1,2,3,3a,4,5,6,10c-octahydro-	EtOH	219(4.57),275s(3.84), 282(3.87),290(3.81)	44-4402-79
1H-Cyclopenta[f]pyrrolo[3,2,1-ij]quino- line-1,8-dione, 2,3,5,6,9,10-hexahy- dro-3,10-dimethyl-	MeOH	240(4.15),265(4.12), 320(4.32),380(3.80)	4-0949-79
$C_{16}H_{17}NO_2S$			
Benzene, 1-[2-methyl-1-(phenylthio)prop- yl]-4-nitro-	hexane	259(4.12)	12-1487-79
$C_{16}H_{17}NO_3$			
2H-1-Benzopyran-2,4(3H)-dione, 3-[(cy- clohexylamino)methylene]-	hexane	209(4.20),232(4.24), 243s(--),250s(--), 321s(--),331(4.34)	131-0077-79D
	EtOH	324(4.33)	131-0077-79D
C-Norerythrina-1(6),3-diene-2,10-dione, 14,15,16,17-tetrahydro-3-methoxy-	MeOH	232(4.34)	24-3795-79
$C_{16}H_{17}NO_4$			
1H-Azepine-4-carboxylic acid, 2,5-di- hydro-3-methoxy-2-oxo-7-phenyl-, ethyl ester	dioxan	222(4.17),249(4.11)	142-1427-79
Benzoic acid, 3,6-dimethoxy-2-(methyl- phenylamino)-	EtOH	208(4.35),243(4.19), 295(3.86)	33-2350-79
8H-1,3-Benzodioxolo[5,6-a]furo[3,4-g]- quinolizin-11(9H)-one, 5,6,8a,11a- 12,12a-hexahydro-, (8aα,11aβ,12aβ)-	EtOH	292(3.53)	23-1647-79
9H-1,3-Benzodioxolo[5,6-a]furo[3,4-g]- quinolizin-9-one, 5,6,8,8a,11,11a,12- 12a-octahydro-, (8aα,11aα,12aα)-	EtOH	290(3.61)	23-1647-79

Compound	Solvent	λ_{max}(log ε)	Ref.
2-Propenoic acid, 3-(2,4-dimethoxy-3-quinolinyl)-, ethyl ester	MeOH	307.5(4.52)	118-0903-79
2H-Pyrrole-4,5-dicarboxylic acid, 2,2-dimethyl-3-phenyl-, dimethyl ester	MeOH	293(3.57)	88-2983-79
$C_{16}H_{17}NO_4S$			
Benzenesulfonamide, 4-[(benzoyloxy)-methyl]-N,N-dimethyl-	EtOH	232(4.40),267(3.23), 274(3.20)	118-0531-79
$C_{16}H_{17}NO_5$			
Benzenepropanoic acid, α-(3-methyl-2-butenylidene)-4-nitro-β-oxo-, ethyl ester, (E)-	EtOH	274(4.39)	70-0758-79
$C_{16}H_{17}NO_5S_2$			
2,4-Pentanedione, 3-[(3,4-dihydro-4-methyl-3-oxo-2H-1,4-benzothiazin-2-ylidene)(methylthio)methyl]-, S,S-dioxide	dioxan	330(3.6)	83-0302-79
$C_{16}H_{17}NO_7S_2$			
Propanedioic acid, [(3,4-dihydro-4-methyl-3-oxo-2H-1,4-benzothiazin-2-ylidene)(methylthio)methyl]-, dimethyl ester, S,S-dioxide	dioxan	240(3.4),310(3.2)	83-0302-79
$C_{16}H_{17}N_2$			
Phenalenylium, 1-(dimethylamino)-9-(methylamino)-, tetrafluoroborate	n.s.g.	261(4.28),382(3.97), 467(3.63),491(3.67)	44-1704-79
$C_{16}H_{17}N_2S$			
1,2-Benzisothiazolium, 2-ethyl-3-[4-(methylamino)phenyl]-, chloride, hydrochloride	5M HCl	272(4.09),337(3.89)	24-3286-79
	MeOH	266(4.28),410(4.12)	24-3286-79
$C_{16}H_{17}N_3O$			
Ethanone, 1-[3-[[4-(dimethylamino)phenyl]azo]phenyl]-	MeOH	445(4.52)	65-2189-79
Piperidine, 1-[[(2-cyano-3-oxo-3-phenyl-1-propenyl)imino]methyl]-	MeOH	273(4.31),394(4.23)	83-0039-79
$C_{16}H_{17}N_3OS$			
Hydrazinecarboxamide, 2-[1-[5-methyl-2-(phenylthio)phenyl]ethylidene]-	MeOH	248(4.33),285s(3.94), 325(3.28)	73-2677-79
4-Imidazolidinone, 5-(1-ethyl-2(1H)-quinolinylidene)-1,3-dimethyl-2-thioxo-	EtOH	509(4.31)	73-1413-79
3H-Pyrazol-3-one, 4-(3-ethyl-4-methyl-2(3H)-thiazolylidene)-2,4-dihydro-5-methyl-2-phenyl-	EtOH	377(3.95)	73-1413-79
7H-Pyrrolo[2,3-d]pyrimidine, 4-methoxy-5-methyl-2-(methylthio)-7-(phenylmethyl)-	MeOH	247(4.29),288(4.00)	138-1283-79
$C_{16}H_{17}N_3O_2$			
β-Alanine, N-[4-(2,2-dicyanoethenyl)-phenyl]-N-ethyl-, methyl ester	EtOH	430(4.77)	110-1769-79
	EtOH-KOH	342(--)	110-1769-79
	CCl_4	421(--)	110-1769-79
	KBr	438(--)	110-1769-79
Carbamic acid, 1H-perimidin-2-yl-, butyl ester	n.s.g.	231(4.81),256(4.32), 318(3.93)	135-1183-79

Compound	Solvent	$\lambda_{max}(\log \epsilon)$	Ref.
Ergoline-8-methanol, 8,9-didehydro-6-methyl-1-nitroso-	MeOH	262(4.24),330(3.82)	87-0032-79
Pyrrolo[1,2-a]pyrazine-1,4-dione, hexahydro-3-(1H-indol-3-ylmethyl)-	EtOH	220(4.37),273(3.66), 279(3.66),279(3.69), 289(3.63)[sic]	39-3048-79C
1H-Pyrrolo[1",2":4',5']pyrazino[1',2'-1,5]pyrrolo[2,3-b]indole-5,13(5aH-13aH)-dione, 2,3,6,6a,11,11a-hexahydro-	EtOH	207(4.15),242(3.78), 297(3.31)	39-3048-79C
$C_{16}H_{17}N_3O_2S_2$			
Acetamide, N-[4-amino-5-cyano-2-(methylthio)-3-thienyl]-N-[(4-methoxyphenyl)methyl]-	EtOH	228(4.36),294(4.10), 320(3.98)	95-1081-79
$C_{16}H_{17}N_3O_3$			
Benzamide, 4-methoxy-N-[[nitroso(phenylmethyl)amino]methyl]-	EtOH	255(4.31),366(1.78)	94-0682-79
$C_{16}H_{17}N_3O_6$			
Cytidine, N-benzoyl-	MeOH-HOAc	259(4.40),303(4.06)	5-1855-79
5-Deazariboflavin, 7,8-didemethyl-8-hydroxy-	n.s.g.	420(4.6)	35-4419-79
$C_{16}H_{17}N_3O_7$			
Uridine, 5'-deoxy-5'-(2,5-dioxo-3-pyrrolidinylidene)-2',3'-O-(1-methylethylidene)-, (E)-	EtOH	220(4.06),253(3.85)	33-2788-79
$C_{16}H_{17}N_3S_2$			
5,11-Imino-5H,11H-[1,5]dithiocino[2,3-b:6,7-b']dipyridine, 13-(2-methylpropyl)-	EtOH	206(4.39),244(4.32), 302(3.93)	78-0869-79
$C_{16}H_{17}N_4O_2$			
1,2,3-Triazinium, 3,4,5,6-tetrahydro-1-(4-methylphenyl)-3-(4-nitrophenyl)-, perchlorate	MeOH	355(4.29)	24-0445-79
$C_{16}H_{17}N_4O_3$			
Phenol, 5-(diethylamino)-2-[(4-nitrophenyl)azo]-, ion(1-)	EtOH	567(4.63)	39-1990-79C
$C_{16}H_{17}N_4S$			
1H-1,2,4-Triazolium, 4-amino-3-(ethylthio)-1,5-diphenyl-, tetrafluoroborate	n.s.g.	229(4.25),270(3.84)	39-0724-79C
$C_{16}H_{17}N_5O_4$			
Benzenamine, N,N-diethyl-3-nitro-4-[(4-nitrophenyl)azo]-	EtOH	470(4.50)	39-1990-79C
	dioxan	459(4.47)	39-1990-79C
	HOAc	467(4.48)	39-1990-79C
	$HCONH_2$	498(4.47)	39-1990-79C
$C_{16}H_{17}N_9O$			
Phenol, 2-[1-[4-(dimethylamino)phenyl]-5-(1H-tetrazol-5-yl)formazanyl]-	EtOH	275(4.11),475(4.25)	104-1793-79
$C_{16}H_{17}O$			
Butylium, 4-hydroxy-1,1-diphenyl-	H_2SO_4	437(4.53)	39-1395-79B

Compound	Solvent	λmax(log ε)	Ref.
$C_{16}H_{17}OS$			
Thiophenium, tetrahydro-1-[2-(2-naphthalenyl)-2-oxoethyl]-, tetrafluoroborate	MeOH	300(4.34),360(3.00)	47-2877-79
$C_{16}H_{18}$			
1,1'-Biphenyl, 2,4,4',6-tetramethyl-	C_6H_{12}	273(2.80)	12-1531-79
Pentacyclo[8.4.1.1^{8,13}.0^{2,7}.0^{10,13}]-hexadeca-2,4,6-triene	C_6H_{12}	210(3.96),219s(3.81), 225(3.48),255(2.27), 259(2.36),262(2.35), 266(2.26),269(2.22)	12-2675-79
5,9-Propano-5H-benzocycloheptene, 6,7,8,9-tetrahydro-7,11-bis(methylene)-	C_6H_{12}	262(2.56),269(2.56)	12-2675-79
$C_{16}H_{18}ClN_2$			
Benzenaminium, 4-[[(4-chlorophenyl)-methylene]amino]-N,N,N-trimethyl-, iodide	EtOH	220(3.50),273(3.33), 315s(3.08)	2-0338-79B
$C_{16}H_{18}ClN_5O$			
5H-1,2,4-Triazolo[4,3-d][1,4]benzodiazepin-6(7H)-one, 10-chloro-7-methyl-3-(1-pyrrolidinylmethyl)-, monohydrochloride	MeOH	233(4.56),253s(4.11), 299(3.31)	44-0088-79
$C_{16}H_{18}ClN_5O_3$			
[1,2,4]Triazino[4,3-d][1,4]benzodiazepine-3,4,7(6H)-trione, 11-chloro-2-[2-(dimethylamino)ethyl]-2,8-dihydro-8-methyl-	MeOH	256(4.20),277(4.13), 307(4.01)	44-0088-79
$C_{16}H_{18}IN_5O_7$			
Guanosine, N-acetyl-5'-deoxy-5'-iodo-, 2',3'-diacetate	MeOH-HCl	261(4.27),275s(4.23)	44-0400-79
	MeOH-NaOH	265(4.14)	44-0400-79
$C_{16}H_{18}NO$			
Pyridinium, 1-ethyl-2-[2-(4-methoxyphenyl)ethenyl]-, iodide	EtOH	376(4.35)	80-1491-79
	$CHCl_3$	386(4.24)	80-1491-79
	CCl_4	380(4.33)	80-1491-79
$C_{16}H_{18}N_2O$			
Benzenamine, 4-[[(4-methoxyphenyl)imino]methyl]-N,N-dimethyl-	EtOH	376(3.25)	2-0338-79B
7,11-Methano-6H-cyclonona[b]quinoxalin-14-ol, 7,8,9,10,11,12-hexahydro-	EtOH	207(4.38),238(4.30), 319(3.83)	56-1221-79
7,10-Methanocycloocta[b]quinoxalin-13-ol, 6,7,8,9,10,11-hexahydro-13-methyl-	EtOH	207(4.50),238(4.48), 319(3.95)	56-1221-79
Pyridine, 2-(2-phenyl-1-piperidinyl)-, 1-oxide, (S)-(-)-	MeOH	315(3.36)	4-0591-79
Pyridine, 2-(3-phenyl-1-piperidinyl)-, 1-oxide, (S)-(+)-	MeOH	325(3.53)	4-0591-79
6H-Quino[2,1-f][1,6]naphthyridin-6-one, 4b,5,7,8,9,10,12,13-octahydro-	EtOH	330(4.08)	4-0527-79
$C_{16}H_{18}N_2O_2$			
1H-Indazole-5-carboxylic acid, 4,5,6,7-tetrahydro-1-phenyl-, ethyl ester	MeOH	250(4.12)	87-0048-79
2H-Indazole-5-carboxylic acid, 4,5,6,7-tetrahydro-2-phenyl-, ethyl ester	MeOH	268(4.28)	87-0048-79

Compound	Solvent	λ_{max}(log ε)	Ref.
$C_{16}H_{18}N_2O_3$			
Diazene, bis(4-ethoxyphenyl)-, 1-oxide	heptane	349.5(4.43)	18-1588-79
2H-Indazole-6-carboxylic acid, 3,3a,4,5,6,7-hexahydro-3-oxo-2-phenyl-, ethyl ester	EtOH	249(4.17),269s(4.02)	39-2099-79C
1H-Indole-3-acetic acid, 2-(6-oxo-2-piperidinyl)-, methyl ester	MeOH	272(3.89),282(3.87), 290(3.77)	5-1643-79
2-Propenoic acid, 2-(acetylamino)-3-(6-methyl-1H-indol-3-yl)-, ethyl ester, (Z)-	isoPrOH	342(4.32)	44-3741-79
7H-Pyrazolo[1,5-c][1,3]oxazine-3-carboxylic acid, 4,5-dihydro-2-methyl-7-phenyl-, ethyl ester	EtOH	231(4.10)	118-0440-79
$C_{16}H_{18}N_2O_4$			
1(4H)-Pyridinecarboxylic acid, 4-[1-(ethoxycarbonyl)-4(1H)-pyridinylidene]-, ethyl ester	MeCN	358s(4.49),377(4.82), 398(4.97)	5-0727-79
5-Pyrimidinecarboxylic acid, 2-(2-ethoxyphenyl)-1,4-dihydro-1-methyl-4-oxo-, ethyl ester	EtOH	204(4.30),241(4.24), 286(3.96)	87-0263-79
5-Pyrimidinecarboxylic acid, 2-(2-ethoxyphenyl)-1,6-dihydro-1-methyl-6-oxo-, ethyl ester	EtOH	205(4.21),217(4.12), 312(4.03)	87-0263-79
7,10,13,16-Tetraoxa-21,22-diazatricyclo-[15.3.1.1^{2,6}]docosa-1(21),2,4,6(22)-17,19-hexaene	EtOH	236(4.11),305(3.81), 310(3.90)	35-4472-79
L-Tryptophan, N,1-diacetyl-, methyl ester	EtOH	239(4.26),262(3.90), 270s(3.90),291(3.83), 299(3.86)	39-3048-79C
L-Tryptophan, N,2-diacetyl-, methyl ester	EtOH	236(4.20),312(4.27)	39-3048-79C
$C_{16}H_{18}N_2O_4Sn$			
Tin, diethylbis(2-pyridinecarboxylato-N^1,O^2)-	$CHCl_3$	238s(3.60),264(4.01)	131-0165-79D
	MeCN	221(3.85),263(3.81)	131-0165-79D
$C_{16}H_{18}N_3$			
1,2,3-Triazinium, 3,4,5,6-tetrahydro-1-(4-methylphenyl)-2-phenyl-, perchlorate	MeOH	240(3.86),342(4.17)	24-0445-79
1H-1,2,3-Triazolium, 4,5-dihydro-1,3-bis(4-methylphenyl)-, perchlorate	MeOH	246(4.09),254(4.08), 397(4.34)	24-0445-79
$C_{16}H_{18}N_3O$			
1H-1,2,3-Triazolium, 4,5-dihydro-1-(4-methoxyphenyl)-3-(4-methylphenyl)-, perchlorate	MeOH	250(3.97),255(3.94), 411(4.30)	24-0445-79
$C_{16}H_{18}N_3O_2$			
Benzenamine, N,N,N-trimethyl-4-[[(4-nitrophenyl)methylene]amino]-, iodide	EtOH	210(--),222(3.38), 290(3.26),336s(2.99)	2-0338-79B
1H-1,2,3-Triazolium, 4,5-dihydro-1,3-bis(4-methoxyphenyl)-, perchlorate	MeOH	233(3.99),252(3.99), 422(4.39)	24-0445-79
$C_{16}H_{18}N_3O_4$			
1H-Imidazol-1-yloxy, 4-[(1,3-dihydro-1,3-dioxo-2H-isoindol-2-yl)methyl]-2,5-dihydro-2,2,5,5-tetramethyl-, 3-oxide	EtOH	220(4.63),236(4.33), 292(3.33)	70-2521-79

Compound	Solvent	λ max (log ε)	Ref.
$C_{16}H_{18}N_3S_{12}$			
Methylium, tris[[4,5-bis(methylthio)-1,3-dithiol-2-ylidene]amino]-, tetrafluoroborate	MeCN	252(4.53),295(4.45), 520(4.74)	48-0827-79
$C_{16}H_{18}N_4O_2$			
Benzenamine, N,N-diethyl-4-[(4-nitrophenyl)azo]-	EtOH	486(4.53)	39-1990-79C
	dioxan	476(4.54)	39-1990-79C
	HOAc	489(4.52)	39-1990-79C
	$HCONH_2$	512(4.51)	39-1990-79C
4H-Pyrimido[4,5-b][1,4]oxazin-4-one, 2-amino-6-(4-phenylbutyl)-	2M HCl	262(3.85),347(3.89)	87-0797-79
	2M NaOH	276(3.89),323(3.89)	87-0797-79
$C_{16}H_{18}N_4O_3$			
Phenol, 5-(diethylamino)-2-[(4-nitrophenyl)azo]-	C_6H_{12}	478(--),499(4.71)	39-1990-79C
	+ base	548(4.54)	39-1990-79C
	EtOH	473(4.69)	39-1990-79C
	+ base	567(4.63)	39-1990-79C
	HOAc	471(4.74)	39-1990-79C
	$HCONH_2$	480(4.70)	39-1990-79C
	+ base	589(4.61)	39-1990-79C
$C_{16}H_{18}N_4O_7$			
Riboflavin, 8-demethyl-8-hydroxy-	pH -1.0	235(4.42),260(4.35), 427(4.48)	65-1658-79
	pH 3.0	235(4.42),263(4.47), 441(4.41)	65-1658-79
	pH 5.7	252(4.70),268s(4.41), 302(3.95),472(4.55)	65-1658-79
	pH 7.0	253(4.70),268s(4.42), 302(3.97),472(4.60)	65-1658-79
	pH 12.6	249(4.74),285(4.08), 476(4.70)	65-1658-79
	MeOH	253(4.62),305(4.01), 478(4.51)	65-1658-79
$C_{16}H_{18}N_4S$			
1,3,4-Thiadiazol-2-amine, N-butyl-5-(2-methyl-4-quinolinyl)-	EtOH	238(4.37),330s(--), 346(4.12)	106-0537-79
$C_{16}H_{18}N_6O_5$			
Adenosine, 8-cyano-2',3'-O-(1-methylethylidene)-, 5'-acetate	M HCl	276s(4.20),285(--), 294s(4.08)	94-0183-79
	H_2O	230(4.28),269s(3.82), 276s(3.93),299(4.11)	94-0183-79
$C_{16}H_{18}O$			
2,4-Cyclohexadien-1-one, 2,4,6-trimethyl-6-(4-methylphenyl)-	MeOH	227(4.28),280(3.58), 284(3.57)	12-1551-79
Gibba-1,3,4a(10a)-trien-8-one, 1-methyl-, (4bα)-(±)-	EtOH	263(2.59)	44-4562-79
(4bβ)-(±)-	EtOH	264(2.90)	44-4562-79
$C_{16}H_{18}OS$			
A-Nor-3-thiaestra-1,5(10),8-trien-17-one, cis	MeOH	226(4.35),277(3.63)	13-0601-79A
trans	MeOH	227(4.27),277(3.63)	13-0601-79A
A-Nor-3-thiaestra-1,5(10),9(11)-trien-17-one, (±)-	MeOH	227(4.27),250(4.16)	13-0601-79A

Compound	Solvent	λ max (log ε)	Ref.
$C_{16}H_{18}O_2$			
[1,1'-Biphenyl]-3-ol, 4'-methoxy-2,4,6-trimethyl-	n.s.g.	226(4.32),280(3.60), 286(3.58)	12-1551-79
2,4-Cyclohexadien-1-one, 6-(4-methoxyphenyl)-2,3,6-trimethyl-	MeOH	227(4.18)	12-1551-79
2,4-Cyclohexadien-1-one, 6-(4-methoxyphenyl)-2,4,6-trimethyl-	MeOH	227(4.26)	12-1551-79
2,4-Cyclohexadien-1-one, 6-(4-methoxyphenyl)-2,5,6-trimethyl-	MeOH	227(4.15)	12-1551-79
2,5-Cyclohexadien-1-one, 4-(4-methoxyphenyl)-2,4,6-trimethyl-	MeOH	235(3.99)	12-1551-79
2,5-Cyclohexadien-1-one, 4-(4-methoxyphenyl)-3,4,5-trimethyl-	MeOH	229(4.04)	12-1551-79
1H-Fluorene-1-carboxylic acid, 2,3,4,9-tetrahydro-1,8-dimethyl-, (±)-	EtOH	260(4.2)	44-4562-79
1H-Fluorene-2-carboxylic acid, 2,3,4,9-tetrahydro-2,8-dimethyl-, (±)-	EtOH	260(4.19)	44-4562-79
1H-Fluorene-2-carboxylic acid, 2,3,4,9-tetrahydro-8-methyl-, methyl ester, (±)-	EtOH	259(4.12)	44-4562-79
$C_{16}H_{18}O_3$			
4aH-Benzocycloheptene-5-carboxylic acid, 4-methoxy-4a-methyl-, ethyl ester	n.s.g.	282(4.60),425(3.95)	77-0528-79
2,5-Cyclohexadien-1-one, 4-methoxy-4-(4-methoxyphenyl)-2,6-dimethyl-	MeOH	236(4.00)	12-1551-79
2H-Pyran-5-carboxylic acid, 2,2-dimethyl-6-phenyl-, ethyl ester	EtOH	256(4.20),290(4.23)	70-0758-79
$C_{16}H_{18}O_4$			
[1,1'-Biphenyl]-2,2',6,6'-tetramethanol	EtOH	231(4.21),265(3.77)	44-1936-79
1,3-Dioxane-4,6-dione, 5-(2,3,3a,4,7,7a-hexahydro-4,7-methano-1H-inden-1-ylidene)-2,2-dimethyl-, (3aα,4α,7α,7aα)-	EtOH	242(3.89),268s(3.72)	12-1767-79
Ethanone, 1-(2,2-dimethyl-7-phenyl-1,3,6-trioxaspiro[4.4]non-7-en-8-yl)-, (±)-	$CHCl_3$	316(4.28)	136-0055-79B
2,5-Heptadienoic acid, 6-acetoxy-5-phenyl-, methyl ester, (?,E)-	EtOH	243(4.18)	1-0057-79
Methanone, phenyl(2,2,7-trimethyl-1,3,6-trioxaspiro[4.4]non-7-en-8-yl)-, (±)-	$CHCl_3$	316(4.45)	136-0055-79B
$C_{16}H_{18}O_5$			
Azuleno[4,5-b]furan-2,4,8(3H)-trione, octahydro-3-(methoxymethyl)-6,9-bis(methylene)-	EtOH	210(4.45)	102-0285-79
4H-Naphtho[1,2-d]-1,3-dioxin-4-carboxaldehyde, 4a,5,6,10b-tetrahydro-7-hydroxy-2,2,10b-trimethyl-6-oxo-	MeOH	259(3.92),335(3.59)	35-0689-79
$C_{16}H_{18}O_6$			
Solaniol, 8-methoxy-	n.s.g.	226(4.49),285(4.03), 476(3.82),510s(3.69)	78-1551-79
$C_{16}H_{18}O_9$			
4H-1-Benzopyran-4-one, 7-(β-D-glucopyranosyloxy)-5-hydroxy-2-methyl-	MeOH	255(4.15),285(3.85), 315(3.6)	102-0181-79

Compound	Solvent	$\lambda_{max}(\log \epsilon)$	Ref.
$C_{16}H_{18}S$			
Benzene, [(2-methyl-1-phenylpropyl)-thio]-	hexane	255(3.68)	12-1487-79
$C_{16}H_{19}N$			
3-Aza-A-norestra-1,5,7,9-tetraene, (14α)-	EtOH	224(4.471),274(3.941), 286(3.819),292(3.663), 298(3.580)	104-1983-79
(14β)-	EtOH	220(4.572),270(3.926), 284(3.763),290(3.580), 297(3.505)	104-1983-79
4-Azatricyclo[4.3.1.1^{3,8}]undec-4-ene, 5-phenyl-	MeOH	239(4.10),280(3.21)	44-3711-79
[1,1'-Biphenyl]-2-amine, N-ethyl-2',5'-dimethyl-	EtOH	305(3.47)	33-2129-79
[1,1'-Biphenyl]-2-amine, N,2',4',6'-tetramethyl-	EtOH	244(4.09),295(3.69)	33-2129-79
1H-Pyrrolizine, 2,3-dihydro-2,2,5-trimethyl-6-phenyl-	MeOH	209(4.25),279(4.00)	83-0896-79
$C_{16}H_{19}NO$			
3-Aza-A-norestra-1,5,7,9-tetraen-17-ol, (14β,17β)-	EtOH	220(4.486),270(3.898), 284(3.724),290(3.544), 296(3.462)	104-1983-79
(17β)-	EtOH	224(4.441),274(3.867), 287(3.771),292(3.634), 298(3.532)	104-1983-79
Benzo[d]carbazol-6(7H)-one, 1,2,3,4,4a-5,7a,8-octahydro-, cis	MeOH	246(3.76),298(3.40)	5-1048-79
	dioxan	247(3.98),300(3.44)	5-1048-79
trans	MeOH	248(3.76),305(3.36)	5-1048-79
	dioxan	248(4.02),305(3.50)	5-1048-79
isomer mixture	MeOH	244(3.93),295(3.45)	5-1048-79
4a,9a-Butano-9H-carbazol-2(1H)-one, 3,4-dihydro-	MeOH	243(3.86),294(3.47)	5-1048-79
	dioxan	248(3.98),397(3.49)	5-1048-79
$C_{16}H_{19}NO_2$			
4H-[1,3]Benzodioxolo[5,6-a]quinolizine, 1,6,7,12b-tetrahydro-2,3-dimethyl-	EtOH	292(3.51)	23-1647-79
1H-Carbazole-2-carboxylic acid, 4-ethyl-2,3,4,9-tetrahydro-3-methyl-	EtOH	228(4.49),276s(3.77), 283(3.81),290(3.85)	44-4402-79
1,3-Cyclohexanedione, 5,5-dimethyl-2-[[(4-methylphenyl)amino]methylene]-	hexane	232(4.18),251(4.01), 354(4.42)	131-0077-79D
	EtOH	351(4.44)	131-0077-79D
1,3-Cyclohexanedione, 5,5-dimethyl-2-[1-(phenylamino)ethylidene]-	hexane	235s(--),249(4.15), 317(4.30)	131-0077-79D
	EtOH	312(4.34)	131-0077-79D
2H-Indol-2-one, 1,3-dihydro-1,3-dimethyl-3-(2-oxocyclohexyl)-	EtOH	252(3.96),280s(3.24)	23-1694-79
6-Oxa-7-azabicyclo[3.2.2]non-8-en-4-one, 2,2,5-trimethyl-N-phenyl-	MeOH	208(4.02),244(3.88), 285s(2.21)	44-0001-79
$C_{16}H_{19}NO_3$			
1,3-Cyclohexanedione, 2-[[(4-methoxyphenyl)amino]methylene]-5,5-dimethyl-	hexane	232(3.97),252(4.03), 356(4.41)	131-0077-79D
	EtOH	359(4.41)	131-0077-79D
4-Pyridineacetic acid, 5-ethyl-1,2,5,6-tetrahydro-2-oxo-1-(phenylmethyl)-	EtOH	253(3.60)	94-1847-79
$C_{16}H_{19}NO_4$			
8H-1,3-Benzodioxolo[5,6-a]furo[3,4-g]-quinolizin-9-ol, 5,6,8a,9,11,11a,12,12a-octahydro-	EtOH	290(3.72)	23-1647-79

Compound	Solvent	λ_{max}(log ε)	Ref.
$C_{16}H_{19}NO_5$			
Pentanoic acid, 3-[ethoxy(phenylamino)-methylene]-2,4-dioxo-, ethyl ester	EtOH	287(4.38)	94-1792-79
$C_{16}H_{19}NO_7S$			
β-D-Ribofuranoside, 2-pyridinyl 1-thio-, 2,3,5-triacetate	EtOH	245(3.78),285(3.64)	44-1892-79
β-D-Ribofuranoside, 4-pyridinyl 1-thio-, 2,3,5-triacetate	EtOH	257(3.96)	44-1892-79
$C_{16}H_{19}N_2$			
Benzenaminium, N,N,N-trimethyl-4-[(phenylmethylene)amino]-, iodide	EtOH	220(3.38),263(3.26), 314s(2.95)	2-0338-79B
Pyridinium, 2-[2-[4-(dimethylamino)-phenyl]ethenyl]-1-methyl-, iodide	EtOH	460(4.57)	4-1579-79
Pyridinium, 4-[2-[4-(dimethylamino)-phenyl]ethenyl]-1-methyl-, iodide	EtOH	480(4.62)	4-1579-79
$C_{16}H_{19}N_3$			
Benzenamine, N,N-diethyl-4-(phenylazo)-	MeOH	415(4.51)	56-0989-79
$C_{16}H_{19}N_3O$			
[1,1'(4H,4'H)-Bipyridine]-4-carbonitrile, 5-ethyl-2,2',6'-trimethyl-4'-oxo-	EtOH	262.5(4.34)	39-1698-79C
Propanedinitrile, [[4-(diethylamino)-2-ethoxyphenyl]methylene]-	EtOH	444(4.77)	110-1769-79
	EtOH-KOH	345(--),355(--)	110-1769-79
	CCl_4	431(--)	110-1769-79
	KBr	443(--)	110-1769-79
$C_{16}H_{19}N_3OS$			
1H-Thieno[3,4-d]imidazol-2(3H)-one, tetrahydro-4-[3-(1H-indol-3-yl)-propyl]-, [3aS-(3aα,4β,6aα)]-	C_6H_{12} -1% EtOH	221(4.50),274s(3.74), 281(3.77),290(3.70)	35-0996-79
$C_{16}H_{19}N_3O_2$			
[1,1'-Biphenyl]-2,4'-diamine, N,N,N',N'-tetramethyl-5-nitro-	50% tert-BuOH	296(4.16),322(4.20), 405(4.04)	104-1915-79
$C_{16}H_{19}N_3O_2S$			
1H-Thieno[3,4-d]imidazol-2(3H)-one, tetrahydro-4-[3-(1H-indol-3-yl)-propyl]-, 5-oxide, [3aS-(3aα,4β,5α-6aα)]-	EtOH	275s(--),282(3.74), 291(3.67)	35-0996-79
$C_{16}H_{19}N_3O_3$			
5,8-Methanopyridazino[1,6-b]indazole-2-carboxylic acid, 1,4,5,6,7,8-hexahydro-8,11,11-trimethyl-4-oxo-, methyl ester, (5S)-	EtOH	245(4.30),315(3.91), 366(3.74)	95-0699-79
$C_{16}H_{19}N_3O_4S$			
1H-Pyrazole-3,4-dicarboxylic acid, 1-[4-(dimethylamino)phenyl]-5-(methylthio)-, dimethyl ester	CH_2Cl_2	265(4.20),300(4.11)	24-1193-79
$C_{16}H_{19}N_3O_6$			
Mitomycin A	MeOH	218(4.24),320(4.02), 520(3.15)	142-0411-79B

Compound	Solvent	$\lambda_{max}(\log \epsilon)$	Ref.
$C_{16}H_{19}N_3O_7$			
Imidazo[4,5-d][1,3]oxazin-7(3H)-one, 3-[5-O-acetyl-2,3-O-(1-methylethylidene)-β-D-ribofuranosyl]-5-methyl-	MeOH	208(4.07),237(3.97), 268(3.75)	39-1415-79C
$C_{16}H_{19}N_5O_2$			
1,3-Benzenediamine, N',N'-diethyl-4-[(4-nitrophenyl)azo]-	EtOH	514(4.65)	39-1990-79C
	HOAc	476(4.75)	39-1990-79C
$C_{16}H_{19}N_5O_3$			
1,3-Butanediol, 4-(6-amino-9H-purin-9-yl)-2-(phenylmethoxy)-, [R-(R*,R*)]-	pH 2,7,12	262(4.06)	73-0593-79
$C_{16}H_{19}N_5O_4S$			
Benzenesulfonamide, 5-(diethylamino)-2-[(4-nitrophenyl)azo]-	EtOH	484(4.50)	39-1990-79C
	HOAc	484(4.52)	39-1990-79C
$C_{16}H_{19}N_5O_4S_2$			
1H-Pyrazolo[3,4-d]pyrimidine-3-carbonitrile, 1-[2,3-O-(1-methylethylidene)-β-D-ribofuranosyl]-4,6-bis-(methylthio)-	EtOH	203(4.14),252(4.32), 293(4.08),315(3.92)	103-1361-79
$C_{16}H_{19}N_5O_7$			
Guanosine, N-acetyl-2',3'-O-(1-methylethylidene)-, 5'-formate	MeOH-HCl	264(4.24)	44-0400-79
$C_{16}H_{19}N_5O_7S$			
7H-Imidazo[4,5-d]-1,2,3-triazine, 4-(methylthio)-7-(2,3,5-tri-O-acetyl-β-D-ribofuranosyl)-	MeOH	208(4.21),233(4.04), 279(3.97),297(3.94)	103-0685-79
$C_{16}H_{19}N_5O_8$			
Guanosine, N-acetyl-, 3',5'-diacetate	EtOH	254(4.20),259(4.20), 280(4.06)	39-2088-79C
$C_{16}H_{20}$			
Bicyclo[2.2.1]hept-2-ene, 7-(2,4,6-trimethylphenyl)-, syn	hexane	267(--),269(2.26)	44-4899-79
2-Cyclopentene, 3-cyclopropyl-1,1-dimethyl-2-phenyl-	hexane	244(3.53)	35-5725-79
$C_{16}H_{20}BrN_3O_8$			
1H-Pyrazole-3-carboxamide, 1-(2,3,5-tri-O-acetyl-β-D-ribofuranosyl)-5-(bromomethyl)-	EtOH	223(3.92)	87-0807-79
1H-Pyrazole-5-carboxamide, 1-(2,3,5-tri-O-acetyl-β-D-ribofuranosyl)-3-(bromomethyl)-	EtOH	230(3.96)	87-0807-79
1H-Pyrazole-5-carboxamide, 1-(2,3,4-tri-O-acetyl-β-D-ribopyranosyl)-3-(bromomethyl)-	EtOH	226(3.85)	87-0807-79
$C_{16}H_{20}ClN_5O_2$			
3H-1,2,4-Triazolo[4,3-d][1,4]benzodiazepine-3,6(5H)-dione, 10-chloro-2-[3-(dimethylamino)propyl]-2,7-dihydro-7-methyl-	MeOH	253(4.26),274s(3.94), 305s(3.68)	44-0088-79

Compound	Solvent	λ max (log ε)	Ref.
$C_{16}H_{20}Cl_2N_2O_2$			
4-Cyclopentene-1,3-dione, 4,5-dichloro-2-(di-1-piperidinylmethylene)-	isoPrOH	252(4.46),299(4.45)	104-0454-79
$C_{16}H_{20}N_2O$			
Azoxybenzene, 4,4'-bis(dimethylamino)-	MeCN	400.3(4.61)	18-1588-79
2,2'-Dipyrromethene, 5'-oxo-4'-ethenyl-4-ethyl-1',5'-dihydro-3,3',5-trimethyl-	MeOH	438(4.60)	78-0463-79
	$CHCl_3$	433(4.56)	78-0463-79
6,10-Methano-5H-cyclohepta[b]quinoxalin-12-one, 5-ethyl-5a,6,7,8,9,10,10a,11-octahydro-	EtOH	221(4.53),250(3.91), 307(4.56)	30-0254-79
6,11-Methanocycloocta[b]quinoxalin-13-one, 5,5a,6,7,8,9,10,11,11a,12-decahydro-5-methyl-	EtOH	221(4.55),250(3.98), 309(3.68)	30-0254-79
4(1H)-Quinolinone, 2,3-dihydro-1-methyl-3-(1-piperidinylmethylene)-	EtOH	250(4.41),274s(3.92), 347(4.16)	4-0177-79
$C_{16}H_{20}N_2O_2$			
Benzeneacetonitrile, α-[3-(dimethylamino)-4,4-dimethoxy-2-butenylidene]-	EtOH	390(4.6)	88-0921-79
2-Pentanone, 4,4'-(1,3-phenylenedinitrilo)bis-	heptane	330(4.45)	40-1437-79
	EtOH	334(4.53)	40-1437-79
	dioxan	332(4.41)	40-1437-79
	$CHCl_3$	334(4.53)	40-1437-79
2-Pentanone, 4,4'-(1,4-phenylenedinitrilo)bis-	heptane	343(4.30)	40-1437-79
	EtOH	347(4.42)	40-1437-79
	dioxan	344(4.49)	40-1437-79
	$CHCl_3$	347(4.48)	40-1437-79
4-Pyridineacetamide, 5-ethyl-1,2,5,6-tetrahydro-2-oxo-1-(phenylmethyl)-	EtOH	252.5(3.54)	94-1847-79
$C_{16}H_{20}N_2O_2S_2$			
2-Propenenitrile, 3-(methylthio)-3-piperidino-2-[(4-methylphenyl)sulfonyl]-	EtOH	276(4.00),323(4.30)	95-0038-79
$C_{16}H_{20}N_2O_3$			
2-Pentanone, 4,4'-[(4-hydroxy-1,3-phenylene)dinitrilo]bis-	heptane	325(4.42)	40-1437-79
	EtOH	335(4.48)	40-1437-79
	dioxan	328(4.44)	40-1437-79
	$CHCl_3$	330(4.46)	40-1437-79
4-Pyridazinecarboxylic acid, 1,6-dihydro-5-methoxy-1,6-dimethyl-3-phenyl-, ethyl ester	EtOH	246(4.13),336(3.43)	44-3053-79
4-Pyridazinecarboxylic acid, 1,2,5,6-tetrahydro-1,2,6-trimethyl-5-oxo-3-phenyl-, ethyl ester	EtOH	247(4.15),315(3.93)	44-3053-79
$C_{16}H_{20}N_2O_4$			
1H-Indole-1-propanoic acid, 3-[2-(acetylamino)ethyl]-5-methoxy-	EtOH	228(4.36),282(3.66), 303(3.68)	12-0399-79
$C_{16}H_{20}N_2O_6$			
Pyrrolo[2,3-b]azepine-3,5-dicarboxylic acid, 1,4,5,6,7,8-hexahydro-1,8-dimethyl-4,7-dioxo-, diethyl ester	n.s.g.	235(4.07),330(4.14)	23-0044-79
$C_{16}H_{20}N_2O_7$			
β-D-ribo-Hept-5-enofuranuronic acid, 1,5,6-trideoxy-1-(3,4-dihydro-2,4-	EtOH	211(3.79),256(3.67)	33-2788-79

Compound	Solvent	λ max(log ε)	Ref.
dioxo-1(2H)-pyrimidinyl)-2,3-O-(1-methylethylidene)-, ethyl ester, (E)-(cont.)			33-2788-79
DL-threo-Hex-2-enopyranuronic acid, 1,2,3-trideoxy-1-(3,4-dihydro-2,4-dioxo-1(2H)-pyrimidinyl)-, butyl ester, 4-acetate, α-	MeOH	259(4.20)	136-0272-79E
β-	MeOH	259(4.00)	136-0272-79E
$C_{16}H_{20}N_4$			
Benzenamine, 2,2'-azobis[N,N-dimethyl-	EtOH	237(4.16),330(4.33), 465(2.96)	7-0563-79
2-Tetrazene, 1,4-dimethyl-1,4-bis(2-methylphenyl)-	MeCN	303(4.30)	40-0915-79
2-Tetrazene, 1,4-dimethyl-1,4-bis(3-methylphenyl)-	MeCN	345(4.42)	40-0915-79
2-Tetrazene, 1,4-dimethyl-1,4-bis(4-methylphenyl)-	MeCN	347(4.44)	40-0915-79
$C_{16}H_{20}N_4O_2$			
1(4H)-Pyridinecarboxamide, 4-[1-[(dimethylamino)carbonyl]-4(1H)-pyridinylidene]-N,N-dimethyl-	MeCN	384(4.73),402(4.82)	5-0727-79
$C_{16}H_{20}N_4O_3$			
Benzo[g]pteridine-2,4(3H,4aH)-dione, 5-ethyl-5,10-dihydro-4a-hydroxy-3,7,8,10-tetramethyl-	EtOH	222(4.56),286(3.84), 308(3.86),355(3.94)	88-3549-79
Spiro[imidazolidine-4,2'(3'H)-quinoxaline]-2,3',5-trione, 1'-ethyl-1',4'-dihydro-1,4',6',7'-tetramethyl-	EtOH	228(4.53),308(3.79)	88-3549-79
Spiro[imidazolidine-4,2'(3'H)-quinoxaline]-2,3',5-trione, 4'-ethyl-1',4'-dihydro-1,1',6',7'-tetramethyl-	EtOH	226(4.54),305(3.78)	88-3549-79
$C_{16}H_{20}N_4O_5$			
α-D-ribo-Hexopyranoside, methyl 3-(acetylamino)-6-azido-2,3,6-trideoxy-, 4-benzoate	MeOH	230(4.11),250(3.54), 272(3.23),280(3.18)	136-0059-79C
$C_{16}H_{20}N_4O_6$			
7H-Pyrrolo[2,3-d]pyrimidin-4-amine, 7-[2,3-O-(3-carboxy-1-methylpropylidene)-β-D-ribofuranosyl]-, (R)-	MeOH	272(4.07)	136-0117-79G
$C_{16}H_{20}N_6O_5S$			
Adenosine, 8-(aminothioxomethyl)-2',3'-O-(1-methylethylidene)-, 5'-acetate	M HCl	268(4.21),285s(4.07)	94-0183-79
	H_2O	218(4.23),263(4.04), 276(4.06),300s(4.03)	94-0183-79
	M NaOH	260(4.26)	94-0183-79
$C_{16}H_{20}OS$			
A-Thiophenoestrone	MeOH	230(4.05),247(3.88)	13-0601-79A
$C_{16}H_{20}O_2S$			
1,9-Dibenzothiophenedione, 2,3,4,6,7,8-hexahydro-3,3,7,7-tetramethyl-	EtOH	233(4.27),280(3.37)	94-0676-79
$C_{16}H_{20}O_4$			
2-Cyclohexen-1-one, 5-(2,3-dimethoxyphenyl)-3-ethoxy-	EtOH	251(4.23)	33-1549-79

Compound	Solvent	λ_{max}(log ε)	Ref.
1,3-Dioxane-4,6-dione, 2,2-dimethyl-5-(endo-tricyclo[5.2.1.0^{2,6}]decan-3-ylidene)-	EtOH	253(3.98)	12-1767-79
Naphthalene, 6-ethoxy-1,2,3-trimethoxy-8-methyl-	EtOH	240(4.76),275s(4.54), 283(3.57),315(2.99), 330(2.99)	150-0301-79
$C_{16}H_{20}O_6$			
O-Methylparvulenone acetate	MeOH	225(4.01),285(3.89), 330s(3.39)	150-2685-79
1,6,9,13-Tetraoxadispiro[4.2.4.2]tetradeca-2,10-diene, 3,11-diacetyl-2,10-dimethyl-, trans	$CHCl_3$	268(4.30)	136-0055-79B
$C_{16}H_{20}O_7$			
Butanedioic acid, [(3,4,5-trimethoxyphenyl)methylene]-, dimethyl ester	EtOH	283(4.01)	2-0202-79
$C_{16}H_{20}O_8$			
1,6,9,13-Tetraoxadispiro[4.2.4.2]tetradeca-2,10-diene-3,11-dicarboxylic acid, 2,10-dimethyl-, dimethyl ester, trans	EtOH	248(4.23)	136-0055-79B
$C_{16}H_{20}O_9$			
1,4-Epoxynaphthalene-5,8-dione, 1,2,3,4-tetrahydro-2,2,3,3,6,7-hexamethoxy-	ether	250s(3.61),284(3.88), 339(3.04),434(2.69)	33-2211-79
Pyrano[3,2-c][2]benzopyran-6(2H)-one, 3,4,4a,10b-tetrahydro-3,4-dihydroxy-2-(hydroxymethyl)-8,9,10-trimethoxy-(bergenin di-O-methyl ether)	EtOH	220(4.40),270(3.80)	39-2289-79C
$C_{16}H_{20}S$			
Azulene, 1,4-dimethyl-7-(1-methylethyl)-2-(methylthio)-	hexane	254(4.28),307(4.70), 316(4.74),348(3.45), 365(3.66),383(3.89), 403(4.03),570(2.60), 605(2.58),670s(2.18)	18-1549-79
$C_{16}H_{20}S_2Si$			
Silane, bis(ethylthio)diphenyl-	hexane	195(4.85),222s(4.28), 245s(3.50),261(3.01), 266(2.99),273(2.85)	114-0195-79D
$C_{16}H_{21}NO$			
2-Butanone, 1-(1,3-dihydro-1,3,3-trimethyl-2H-indol-2-ylidene)-3-methyl-	pH 1	286(3.83)	88-4407-79
	H_2O	361(4.45)	88-4407-79
6-Oxa-1-azabicyclo[3.1.0]hex-3-ene, 5-(1,1-dimethylethyl)-2,2-dimethyl-3-phenyl-	EtOH	217(3.85),261(3.89)	12-2041-79
2H-Pyrrole, 5-(1,1-dimethylethyl)-2,2-dimethyl-3-phenyl-, 1-oxide	EtOH	237(4.03),348(4.04)	12-1795-79
4(1H)-Quinolinone, 2-heptyl-	MeOH	213(4.41),236(4.46), 316(4.05),327(4.04)	49-0947-79
$C_{16}H_{21}NOS_3$			
4H-Dithieno[2,3-b:3',2'-e]thiopyran-4-ol, 4-[3-(dimethylamino)propyl]-2-ethyl-	MeOH	280s(3.96),300(4.05)	73-2997-79

Compound	Solvent	λ_{max}(log ϵ)	Ref.
$C_{16}H_{21}NO_2$			
14-Azabicyclo[11.2.2]heptadeca-13,15,16-triene-2,12-dione	MeOH	237(3.99),270(3.73)	49-0577-79
2H-Indol-2-one, 1,3-dihydro-3-(2-hydroxycyclohexyl)-1,3-dimethyl-	EtOH	253(3.93),281s(3.22)	23-1694-79
2(1H)-Pyridinone, 5-ethyl-5,6-dihydro-4-(2-hydroxyethyl)-1-(phenylmethyl)-	EtOH	252(3.52)	94-1847-79
$C_{16}H_{21}NO_4$			
8-Azabicyclo[3.2.1]oct-3-ene-6-carboxylic acid, 8-(4,4-dimethyl-3-oxo-1-pentenyl)-2-oxo-, methyl ester, endo	EtOH	223(3.36),302(3.92)	56-0057-79
2H-[1,3]Benzodioxolo[5,6-a]quinolizine-2,3-dimethanol, 1,3,4,6,7,12b-hexahydro-	EtOH	290(3.85)	23-1647-79
Butanoic acid, 2-(N-methylbenzamido)-3-oxo-, 1,1-dimethylethyl ester	EtOH	245(3.91),263s(3.85)	33-1236-79
$C_{16}H_{21}N_2O_2$			
1,4-Diazaspiro[4.5]dec-3-en-1-yloxy, 2,2-dimethyl-3-phenyl-, 4-oxide	EtOH	222(3.95),288(4.04)	103-0092-79
$C_{16}H_{21}N_2O_4PS$			
Phosphonothioic acid, ethyl-, O-[1,6-dihydro-5-methoxy-6-oxo-1-(phenylmethyl)-4-pyridazinyl] O-ethyl ester	MeOH	214(4.43),289(3.74)	73-1761-79
$C_{16}H_{21}N_2O_5PS$			
Phosphorothioic acid, O-[1,6-dihydro-5-methoxy-6-oxo-1-(phenylmethyl)-4-pyridazinyl] O,O-diethyl ester	MeOH	213(4.39),288(3.72)	73-1761-79
$C_{16}H_{21}N_2O_6P$			
Phosphoric acid, 1,6-dihydro-5-methoxy-6-oxo-1-(phenylmethyl)-4-pyridazinyl diethyl ester	MeOH	213(4.40),287(3.74)	73-1761-79
$C_{16}H_{21}N_3$			
Benzenamine, N-[2-methyl-2-(6,6-dimethyl-2,3-diazabicyclo[3.1.0]hex-2-en-4-yl)propylidene]-	MeOH	241(3.95),278(3.36)	44-1202-79
$C_{16}H_{21}N_3O$			
1,2,4-Oxadiazole-3-ethanamine, N-cyclohexyl-5-phenyl-, monohydrochloride	EtOH	252(4.24)	150-0801-79
$C_{16}H_{21}N_3OS$			
2-Butanone, 1-[(3-amino-6,7-dimethyl-2-quinoxalinyl)thio]-3,3-dimethyl-	EtOH	360(4.1),372(4.1)	103-0102-79
$C_{16}H_{21}N_3O_6$			
α-D-xylo-Hexofuranos-5-ulose, 6-deoxy-3-O-methyl-1,2-O-(1-methylethylidene)-, (4-nitrophenyl)hydrazone	EtOH	207(3.42),248(3.78), 384(4.29)	136-0287-79B
$C_{16}H_{21}N_3O_7$			
α-D-Glucofuranose, 6-deoxy-3-O-methyl-1,2-O-(1-methylethylidene)-5-C-[(4-nitrophenyl)azo]-	EtOH	207(4.02),278(4.20)	136-0287-79B

Compound	Solvent	λ max (log ε)	Ref.
α-L-Mannopyranoside, methyl 6-deoxy-2,3-O-(1-methylethylidene)-4-C-[(4-nitrophenyl)azo]-	EtOH	208(4.23),280(4.10)	136-0287-79B
$C_{16}H_{21}N_4O_8P$			
Uridine, 5'-O-(3,4-dihydro-6-methyl-4-oxo-1,3,2-diazaphosphorin-2(1H)-yl)-2',3'-O-(1-methylethylidene)-, P-oxide	EtOH	259(4.23)	103-1147-79
$C_{16}H_{21}N_5O_2$			
Butanamide, N-[1-[3-amino-2,5-dihydro-5-oxo-2-(phenylmethyl)-1,2,4-triazin-6-yl]ethyl]-	EtOH	259(3.86)	39-1120-79C
$C_{16}H_{21}N_5O_6$			
9H-Purin-6-amine, 9-[2,3-bis-O-(1-oxopropyl)-β-D-arabinofuranosyl]-	MeOH	259(4.19)	87-0273-79
9H-Purin-6-amine, 9-[3,5-bis-O-(1-oxopropyl)-β-D-arabinofuranosyl]-	MeOH	259(4.18)	87-0273-79
$C_{16}H_{21}N_5O_7S$			
Adenosine, 2',3'-O-(1-methylethylidene)-8-(methylsulfonyl)-, 5'-acetate	M HCl	270(4.20)	94-0183-79
	H_2O	221(4.28),284(4.09)	94-0183-79
$C_{16}H_{21}N_5O_8$			
Pyrido[3,2-c]pyridazine-1,2-dicarboxylic acid, 4-[1,2-bis(methoxycarbonyl)hydrazino]-3,4-dihydro-3-methyl-, dimethyl ester	MeOH	231(3.91),260s(3.62), 273(3.78)	103-0518-79
Pyrido[3,2-c]pyridazine-1,2-dicarboxylic acid, 4-[1,2-bis(methoxycarbonyl)hydrazino]-3,4-dihydro-6-methyl-, dimethyl ester	MeOH	233(4.00),283(3.60)	103-0518-79
Pyrido[3,2-c]pyridazine-1,2-dicarboxylic acid, 4-[1,2-bis(methoxycarbonyl)hydrazino]-3,4-dihydro-7-methyl-, dimethyl ester	MeOH	227(3.95),280(3.64)	103-0518-79
Pyrido[3,2-c]pyridazine-1,2-dicarboxylic acid, 4-[1,2-bis(methoxycarbonyl)hydrazino]-3,4-dihydro-8-methyl-, dimethyl ester	MeOH	220s(3.83),265(3.43)	103-0518-79
$C_{16}H_{22}ClN_5O_4$			
9H-Purin-6-amine, 9-[2-chloro-2-deoxy-5-O-(2,2-dimethyl-1-oxopropyl)-3-O-methyl-β-D-arabinofuranosyl]-	MeOH	258(4.16)	23-0274-79
$C_{16}H_{22}Cl_3NO_4$			
2H-Pyrrol-2-one, 1,5-dihydro-4-methoxy-5-(1-methylethyl)-1-(6,6,6-trichloro-3-methoxy-5-methyl-1-oxo-2-hexenyl)-, [S-[R*,R*(E)]]- (dysidin)	EtOH	225(4.20),264(4.43)	35-0240-79
$C_{16}H_{22}INO_5$			
L-Serine, N-[(phenylmethoxy)carbonyl]-, 5-iodopentyl ester	EtOH	253(2.82),257(2.85), 264(2.78),267(2.65)	118-0961-79
$C_{16}H_{22}NS$			
Cyclohepta[c]pyrrolium, 2-butyl-1,3-dimethyl-6-(methylthio)-, iodide	CH_2Cl_2	246(4.28),334(4.52), 412(4.65),594(3.29)	24-2087-79

Compound	Solvent	$\lambda_{max}(\log \epsilon)$	Ref.
$C_{16}H_{22}N_2$			
4,4'-Bipyridinium, 1,1'-bis(1-methylethyl)-, diperchlorate	MeCN	260(4.37)	5-0727-79
Cycloocta[1,2-c:5,6-c']dipyrrole, 2,7-diethyl-4,5,9,10-tetrahydro-	EtOH	227(4.04)	44-2667-79
$C_{16}H_{22}N_2O$			
1,4-Diazaspiro[4.5]dec-1-ene, 3,3-dimethyl-2-phenyl-, 1-oxide	EtOH	222(3.94)	103-0092-79
2-Propenenitrile, 2-ethoxy-3-[4-(diethylamino)-2-methylphenyl]-	EtOH	441(4.69)	110-1769-79
	CCl_4	424(--)	110-1769-79
	KBr	440(--)	110-1769-79
$C_{16}H_{22}N_2O_3S$			
5-Methoxy-3-methylindanylideneethylisothiouronium acetate	MeOH	218(4.03),235(4.14), 264(3.77),271(3.75), 304(3.21)	2-0324-79A
$C_{16}H_{22}N_2O_4$			
3,5-Cyclohexadiene-1,2-dione, 3,6-dimethyl-4,5-dimorpholino-	dioxan	430(3.71)	118-0695-79
$C_{16}H_{22}N_2O_7$			
Uridine, 2',3'-O-cyclohexylidene-4'-C-(hydroxymethyl)-	MeOH	260(4.03)	44-1309-79
$C_{16}H_{22}N_3O_4PS$			
Phosphoramidothioic acid, (1-methylethyl)-, O-[1,6-dihydro-5-methoxy-6-oxo-1-(phenylmethyl)-4-pyridazinyl] O-methyl ester	n.s.g.	213(4.48),287(3.62)	73-1761-79
$C_{16}H_{22}N_3S_2$			
2-Propanaminium, N-(1-methylethyl)-N-[6-(methylthio)-4-phenyl-2H-1,3,5-thiadiazin-2-ylidene]-, iodide	$CHCl_3$	247(4.26),339(4.34), 387(3.84),510(2.95)	78-0059-79
$C_{16}H_{22}N_4O_5$			
Azocino[1,2-a]purin-12(3H)-one, 5,6,7,8,9,10-hexahydro-3-β-D-ribofuranosyl-	pH -1.0	258(4.33)	5-1872-79
	pH 5.0	253(4.35),270s(4.11)	5-1872-79
$C_{16}H_{22}N_4O_6$			
α-D-Xylofuranose, 5-deoxy-3-O-methyl-1,2-O-(1-methylethylidene)-5-[1-methyl-3-(4-nitrophenyl)-2-triazenyl]-	EtOH	205(3.99),237(3.94), 270(3.56),360(4.38)	33-0971-79
$C_{16}H_{22}O$			
4bH-Benzo[3,4]cyclobuta[1,2]cyclononen-4b-ol, 5,6,7,8,9,10,11,11a-octahydro-4-methyl-	MeOH	261(2.79),266(2.92), 274(2.94)	39-2542-79C
Benzo[3,4]cyclobuta[1,2]cycloocten-4b(5H)-ol, 4-ethyl-6,7,8,9,10,10a-hexahydro-	MeOH	262(2.80),266(2.93), 273(2.93)	39-2542-79C
isomer	MeOH	260(2.82),267(2.84), 274(2.96)	39-2542-79C
1,11-Methano-5H-benzocyclononen-11(6H)-ol, 7,8,9,10-tetrahydro-12,12-dimethyl-	MeOH	260(2.75),265(2.89), 273(2.89)	39-1395-79C
1,11-Methano-5H-benzocyclononen-11(6H)-ol, 12-ethyl-7,8,9,10-tetrahydro-, cis	MeOH	262(2.77),267(2.92), 275(2.94)	39-2542-79C

Compound	Solvent	λ_{max}(log ε)	Ref.
1,11-Methano-5H-benzocyclononen-11(6H)-ol, 12-ethyl-7,8,9,10-tetrahydro-, trans	MeOH	261(2.96),267(2.99), 276(2.97)	39-2542-79C
1,13-Methano-5H-benzocycloundecen-13(6H)-ol, 7,8,9,10,11,12-hexahydro-	MeOH	262(2.76),267(2.88), 275(2.86)	39-2542-79C
$C_{16}H_{22}O_2$			
2,4-Pentadienoic acid, 3-methyl-5-(2,6,6-trimethyl-1,3-cyclohexadien-1-yl)-, methyl ester, (Z,E)-	MeOH	356(4.09)	39-1597-79C
$C_{16}H_{22}O_2S$			
2-Cyclohexen-1-one, 3,3'-thiobis[5,5-dimethyl-	EtOH	228(3.99),276(4.00), 311(3.97)	94-0676-79
$C_{16}H_{22}O_3$			
1H-Fluorene-1-carboxylic acid, 2,3,4-4a,4b,5,6,7,9,9a-decahydro-1,4a-dimethyl-7-oxo-	EtOH	242(4.38)	2-0183-79B
$C_{16}H_{22}O_3Si_2$			
Disiloxane, 1,3-dimethoxy-1,1-dimethyl-3,3-diphenyl-	C_6H_{12}	256(2.62),262(2.79), 267(2.86),274(2.74)	35-5703-79
$C_{16}H_{22}O_4$			
2H-1-Benzopyran-6-propanol, 5,7-dimethoxy-2,2-dimethyl-	EtOH	230(4.67),278(4.09), 285s(4.07),312(3.95)	102-0351-79
2-Cyclopenten-1-one, 4-acetyl-3,4-dihydroxy-2-(3-methyl-2-butenyl)-5-(2-methylpropylidene)-	MeOH-HCl	232(3.93)	20-0087-79
	MeOH-NaOH	232(3.89),262(4.12)	20-0087-79
$C_{16}H_{22}O_4S$			
2-Cyclohexen-1-one, 3,3'-sulfonylbis-[5,5-dimethyl-	EtOH	238(4.24),285(3.08)	94-0676-79
$C_{16}H_{22}O_5$			
Azuleno[4,5-b]furan-2(3H)-one, decahydro-4,8-dihydroxy-3-(methoxymethyl)-6,9-bis(methylene)-	EtOH	203(3.37)	102-0285-79
Benzeneethanol, 3,4,5-trimethoxy-α-2-propenyl-, acetate	EtOH	207(4.86),225s(3.99), 270(3.09)	150-0301-79
2-Naphthalenol, 1,2,3,4-tetrahydro-5,6,7-trimethoxy-4-methyl-	EtOH	212(4.42),226s(4.05), 279(3.08),281(3.12)	150-0301-79
4H-Pyran-3-carboxaldehyde, 2-methoxy-4-oxo-6-(1-oxononyl)- (phacidin)	EtOH	224(4.20),274(3.43), 342(3.90)	23-1451-79
$C_{16}H_{22}O_6$			
4,7-Benzofurandiol, 3-(acetoxymethyl)-2,3-dihydro-6-(2-hydroxypropyl)-2,2-dimethyl-	EtOH	256(4.2),302(3.9)	33-1129-79
1H-2-Benzopyran-1-one, 3,4-dihydro-8-hydroxy-3-(2-hydroxypentyl)-6,7-dimethoxy-	MeOH	274(4.13),308(3.51)	39-2048-79C
$C_{16}H_{22}O_7$			
1,4-Epoxynaphthalene, 1,2,3,4-tetrahydro-2,2,3,3,5,8-hexamethoxy-	ether	290(3.54)	33-2211-79
$C_{16}H_{22}O_{11}$			
1H,3H-Pyrano[3,4-c]pyran-1-one, 6-(β-D-glucopyranosyloxy)-4,4a,5,6-tetra-	MeOH	235.5(3.94)	102-1981-79

Compound	Solvent	λ_{max}(log ε)	Ref.
hydro-4a-hydroxy-5-oxiranyl- (eustomoside) (cont.)			102-1981-79
$C_{16}H_{22}S$			
1-Pentanethione, 5-cyclopropyl-2,2-dimethyl-1-phenyl-	C_6H_{12}	225(4.02),292(3.61), 561(2.02)	35-5725-79
$C_{16}H_{23}BrO_7$			
α-D-galacto-Oct-6-enopyranuronic acid, 7-bromo-6,7-dideoxy-1,2:3,4-bis-O-(1-methylethylidene)-, ethyl ester, (Z)-	EtOH	234(4.00)	33-1632-79
$C_{16}H_{23}ClO_{11}$			
1H,3H-Pyrano[3,4-c]pyran-1-one, 5-(2-chloro-1-hydroxyethyl)-6-(β-D-glucopyranosyloxy)-4,4a,5,6-tetrahydro-4a-hydroxy- (eustoside)	MeOH	237.0(3.86)	102-1981-79
$C_{16}H_{23}Cl_3O_2$			
Benzenemethanol, 2-hydroxy-5-(1,1,3,3-tetramethylbutyl)-α-(trichloromethyl)-	EtOH	221(3.92),288(3.45)	118-0824-79
$C_{16}H_{23}IN_4O_7$			
Uridine, 2'-deoxy-5-[[5-(iodoacetyl)amino]-1-oxopentyl]amino]-	H_2O	278(3.91)	87-0621-79
$C_{16}H_{23}NO$			
14-Azabicyclo[11.2.2]heptadeca-1(14),12,15-trien-2-one	MeOH	244(2.87),271(3.73)	49-0577-79
4bH-Benzo[3,4]cyclobuta[1,2]cyclohepten-4b-ol, 5,6,7,8,9,9a-hexahydro-5-[(1-methylethyl)amino]-, hydrochloride	MeOH	261(3.04),267(3.20), 273(3.19)	111-0543-79
4a(2H)-Biphenylenol, 4-[(1,1-dimethylethyl)amino]-1,3,4,8b-tetrahydro-, hydrochloride, (4α,4aβ,8bβ)-	MeOH	260(3.03),267(3.19), 273(3.17)	111-0543-79
$C_{16}H_{23}NO_2$			
14-Azabicyclo[11.2.2]heptadeca-13,15,16-trien-2-one, 14-oxide	MeOH	223(4.24),239(4.00), 267(3.91)	49-0577-79
3-Oxa-15-azabicyclo[12.2.2]octadeca-14,16,17-trien-2-one	MeOH	231(3.91),269(3.65)	49-0567-79
3-Oxa-16-azabicyclo[12.2.2]octadeca-14,16,17-trien-2-one	MeOH	234(3.94),271(3.69)	49-0577-79
6H-Pyrano[2,3-b]quinolin-6-one, 4,4a,5,7,8,9,10,10a-octahydro-2,8,8,10a-tetramethyl-	pH 1	296(4.20)	39-1411-79C
	H_2O	302(4.37)	39-1411-79C
$C_{16}H_{23}NO_3$			
Ethanone, 1-[1,2,4a,7,8,8a-hexahydro-2-methyl-7-(1-methyl-1,3-dioxolan-2-yl)-4-isoquinolinyl]-, (7α)-	EtOH	307(4.47)	44-0124-79
(7β)-	EtOH	307(4.20)	44-0124-79
3-Oxa-15-azabicyclo[12.2.2]octadeca-14,16,17-trien-2-one, 15-oxide	MeOH	232(4.41),273(3.91)	49-0567-79
3-Oxa-16-azabicyclo[12.2.2]octadeca-14,16,17-trien-2-one, 16-oxide	MeOH	226(4.22),272(4.05)	49-0577-79
Rudrakine	MeOH	272(3.86)	102-0700-79
$C_{16}H_{23}N_3$			
Bicyclo[2.2.1]heptan-2-one, 1,7,7-tri-	n.s.g.	216(4.36),264(4.06),	4-1001-79

Compound	Solvent	λ max(log ε)	Ref.
methyl-, (2-aminophenyl)hydrazone		300(3.86)	4-1001-79
Pyridine, 2-(2-piperidino-1-pyrrolidino-ethenyl)-	MeOH	230(3.89),264(3.92), 294(3.94)	22-0559-79
$C_{16}H_{23}N_3O_6S$			
2-Thiazolebutanoic acid, α-(acetylamino)-4-[[(2-ethoxy-2-oxoethyl)amino]-carbonyl]-, ethyl ester	EtOH	232(3.91)	44-0497-79
$C_{16}H_{23}N_4O_2$			
1-Imidazolidinyloxy, 2,2,3,5,5-pentamethyl-4-[[(4-methoxyphenyl)azo]-methylene]-	EtOH	400(4.37)	104-0364-79
$C_{16}H_{23}N_5$			
5,8-Ethenotetrazolo[1,5-d][1,4]diazacyclohexadecine, 9,10,11,12,13,14-15,16,17,18-decahydro-	MeOH	215(3.90),265(3.56)	49-0567-79
$C_{16}H_{23}N_5O_2$			
3H-Purine-3-butanoic acid, 6-[(3-methyl-2-butenyl)amino]-, ethyl ester, monohydrobromide, (S)-	MeOH	219(4.18),290(4.24)	24-3072-79
$C_{16}H_{23}N_5O_4$			
Adenosine, N,N,8-trimethyl-2',3'-O-(1-methylethylidene)-	EtOH	276(4.22)	88-0279-79
Azocino[1,2-a]purin-12(3H)-imine, 5,6,7,8,9,10-hexahydro-3-β-D-ribofuranosyl-	pH 6.0	261(4.13)	5-1872-79
	pH 11.0	262(4.12),268s(4.09), 293s(3.69)	5-1872-79
$C_{16}H_{23}N_5O_5$			
Adenosine, 5'-(2,2-dimethylpropanoate)	MeOH	259(4.13)	23-0274-79
$C_{16}H_{23}N_5O_6S$			
9H-Purin-6-amine, 9-[3,5-O-(2,2-dimethylpropylidene)-2-O-(methylsulfonyl)-β-D-xylofuranosyl]-	MeOH	258(4.18)	136-0314-79H
$C_{16}H_{23}N_5O_{11}$			
Polyoxin M	0.05M HCl	259(3.94)	142-0333-79B
	0.05M NaOH	261(3.81)	142-0333-79B
$C_{16}H_{23}N_5O_{12}$			
Polyoxin L	0.05M HCl	259(3.96)	142-0333-79B
	0.05M NaOH	262(3.85)	142-0333-79B
$C_{16}H_{24}$			
1,6,8,10,15-Hexadecapentaene, trans	EtOH	268(4.65)	104-1037-79
2,6,8,10,14-Hexadecapentaene, trans	EtOH	268(4.69)	104-1037-79
1,5,7,9,13-Tetradecapentaene, 3,12-dimethyl-	EtOH	269(4.62)	104-1037-79
$C_{16}H_{24}Cl_3N_3O_2$			
1,3-Butadiene-1,1-diamine, 3,4,4-trichloro-N,N'-dicyclohexyl-2-nitro-	EtOH	220(4.09),343(3.99)	104-0039-79
$C_{16}H_{24}N_2$			
Diazene, (1-butylcyclohexyl)phenyl-	C_6H_{12}	268(4.01)	39-2030-79C

Compound	Solvent	$\lambda_{max}(\log \epsilon)$	Ref.
$C_{16}H_{24}N_2O$			
14-Azabicyclo[11.2.2]heptadeca-13,15,16-trien-2-one, oxime	MeOH	234(3.96),276(3.53)	49-0577-79
12-Aza[12](2,5)-pyridinophan-11-one	MeOH	234(3.75),270(3.46)	49-0567-79
$C_{16}H_{24}N_2O_2$			
2,15-Diazabicyclo[12.2.2]octadeca-14,16,17-trien-3-one, 13-hydroxy-	MeOH	262(3.85)	49-0577-79
3H-Indazole-4,7-dione, 6,7a-bis(1,1-dimethylethyl)-3a,7a-dihydro-3-methyl-	n.s.g.	241(4.28)	70-1668-79
3-Pyrrolidinemethanol, 1-(1-oxohexyl)-2-(3-pyridinyl)-, trans	EtOH	259(3.20),264(3.25), 271(3.11)	44-4332-79
$C_{16}H_{24}N_2O_3$			
Spiro[cyclohexane-1,7'-[7H]pyrazolo-[1,5-c][1,3]oxazine-3'-carboxylic acid, 4',5'-dihydro-2',5'-dimethyl-, ethyl ester	EtOH	233(4.05)	118-0440-79
$C_{16}H_{24}N_2O_4$			
1,4-Benzenedicarboxylic acid, 2,5-bis-(ethylamino)-, diethyl ester	EtOH	483(3.74)	48-0905-79
$C_{16}H_{24}N_2O_5$			
2-Butenedioic acid, 2-[2-(2,2-dimethylhydrazino)-4,4-dimethyl-6-oxo-1-cyclohexen-1-yl]-, dimethyl ester, (Z)-	MeOH	224(3.95),296(4.11), 368(3.85)	64-0102-79B
2-Butenedioic acid, 2-[1-(5,5-dimethyl-3-oxo-1-cyclohexen-1-yl)-2,2-dimethylhydrazino)-, dimethyl ester, (E)-	MeOH	205(3.81),283(4.07), 343(4.10)	64-0102-79B
(Z)-	MeOH	290(4.44),326(3.38)	64-0102-79B
$C_{16}H_{24}N_2S$			
2,15-Diazabicyclo[12.2.2]octadeca-14,16,17-triene-3-thione	MeOH	289(4.16)	49-0567-79
$C_{16}H_{24}N_3$			
Isoindolium, 1,3-bis(diethylamino)-, perchlorate	$CHCl_3$	295(4.20),375(3.84)	89-0156-79
$C_{16}H_{24}N_4O_7$			
L-Alanine, N-[3-(3,4-dihydro-2,4-dioxo-1(2H)-pyrimidinyl)-N-[(1,1-dimethylethoxy)carbonyl]alanyl]-, methyl ester	EtOH	264(4.01)	65-0994-79
$C_{16}H_{24}N_4O_8$			
L-Serine, N-[3-(3,4-dihydro-2,4-dioxo-1(2H)-pyrimidinyl)-N-[(1,1-dimethylethoxy)carbonyl]alanyl]-, methyl ester	EtOH	264(3.96)	65-0994-79
$C_{16}H_{24}N_4S$			
Pyrido[2,3-d]pyrimidin-4-amine, N-(2-ethylhexyl)-2-(methylthio)-, picrate	0.2M HCl	223(4.36),294(4.03), 329(4.25),340(4.26)	102-1265-79
	0.2M NaOH	347(4.25)	102-1265-79
$C_{16}H_{24}N_6$			
5,8-Etheno-1H-tetrazolo[5,1-b][1,3,6]-triazacycloheptadecine, 9,10,11,12-13,14,15,16,17,18-decahydro-	MeOH	215(3.87),252(3.60)	49-0567-79

Compound	Solvent	λ max (log ε)	Ref.
$C_{16}H_{24}O$			
Calamenene, 8-methoxy-	MeOH	207(4.43),222s(4.04), 273(3.14),280(3.18)	78-0263-79
2,6,10-Cyclopentadecatrien-1-one, 14-methyl-, (E,E,E)-	EtOH	226(3.97)	33-2661-79
$C_{16}H_{24}O_2$			
Calamenene, 5-hydroxy-8-methoxy-	MeOH	290(3.38)	78-0263-79
2,4-Pentadienoic acid, 3-methyl-5-(2,6,6-trimethyl-1-cyclohexen-1-yl)-, methyl ester, (Z,E)-	MeOH	312(4.19)	39-1597-79C
2,4,6,8,10-Tetradecapentaene-1,13-diol, 12-ethyl-	MeOH	301(4.44),314(4.78), 329(4.99),347(5.00)	78-1851-79
Tricyclo[4.4.0.0^{3,10}]decane-2,5-dione, 1,3,4,6,8,9-hexamethyl-	MeOH	300(1.82)	23-2669-79
$C_{16}H_{24}O_3$			
1,5-Cyclotridecadiene-1-carboxylic acid, 13-oxo-, ethyl ester	EtOH	231(3.94)	33-2630-79
2(3H)-Naphthalenone, 7-(1-acetoxy-1-methylethyl)-4,4a,5,6,7,8-hexahydro-4a-methyl-	EtOH	236(4.16)	44-4981-79
Naphtho[2,3-b]furan-2(4H)-one, 4a,5,6-7,8,8a,9,9a-octahydro-9a-methoxy-3,4a,5-trimethyl-	MeOH	223(4.18)	18-1964-79
$C_{16}H_{24}O_4$			
3,5-Cyclohexadiene-1,2-dione, 4,5-bis(3-methylbutoxy)-	EtOH	290(4.14),414(2.71)	18-2169-79
3,5-Cyclohexadiene-1,2-dione, 4,5-bis(pentyloxy)-	EtOH	291(4.13),413(2.70)	18-2169-79
Naphthalene, 3-ethoxy-1,2,3,4-tetrahydro-6,7,8-trimethoxy-1-methyl-	EtOH	210(4.56),225s(4.14), 277(3.29)	150-0301-79
$C_{16}H_{24}O_5Si$			
Bicyclo[4.1.0]hept-2-ene-7-carboxylic acid, 7-[[[(1,1-dimethylethyl)dimethylsilyl]oxy]methyl]-4,5-dioxo-, methyl ester, (1α,6α,7β)-	MeCN	271(3.61),424(1.20)	88-2741-79
$C_{16}H_{24}O_7$			
α-D-galacto-Oct-6-enopyranuronic acid, 6,7-dideoxy-1,2:3,4-bis-O-(1-methylethylidene)-, ethyl ester	EtOH	217(3.81)	33-1632-79
α-D-galacto-Oct-6-enopyranuronic acid, 6,7-dideoxy-7-methyl-1,2:3,4-bis-O-(1-methylethylidene)-, methyl ester	EtOH	217(3.83)	33-1632-79
$C_{16}H_{24}O_8$			
Cyclopenta[c]pyran-4-carboxaldehyde, 1-(β-D-glucopyranosyloxy)-1,4a,5,6-7,7a-hexahydro-7-methyl-, [1S-(1α,4aα,7β,7aα)]- (boschnalosid)	MeOH	249(4.08)	33-2708-79
$C_{16}H_{24}O_9$			
Yuheinoside	MeOH	243(4.09)	33-2708-79
$C_{16}H_{24}O_{12}$			
Eustomorusside	MeOH	236.5(3.76)	102-1981-79

Compound	Solvent	λ_{max}(log ε)	Ref.
$C_{16}H_{24}S_{10}$			
5,10-Dithiadispiro[3.1.3.1]deca-1,7-diene, 1,2,3,3,7,8,9,9-octakis(methylthio)- (plus isomer)	CH_2Cl_2	272(4.31),322(4.35), 396s(3.57)	5-0595-79
$C_{16}H_{25}NO$			
14-Azabicyclo[11.2.2]heptadeca-13,15,16-triene, 14-oxide	MeOH	223(4.37),263(3.99)	49-0577-79
Cyclohexanamine, N-(3-methylene-1-oxaspiro[4.5]dec-2-ylidene)-, (Z)-(±)-	EtOH	214(3.86),233(3.74)	33-0205-79
1(2H)-Naphthalenone, 6-[(1,1-dimethylethyl)amino]-3,4,7,8-tetrahydro-3,3-dimethyl-	pH 1	256(3.88),390(4.41)	39-1411-79C
	H_2O	238(3.70),261(3.56), 417(4.54)	39-1411-79C
	EtOH	405(4.47)	39-1411-79C
$C_{16}H_{25}NO_3$			
Spiro[1,3-dioxolane-2,1'(2'H)-naphthalen]-6'(5'H)-one, 3',4',4'a,8'a-tetrahydro-5',5',8'a-trimethyl-7'-(methylamino)-, trans	MeOH	309(3.59)	44-2838-79
$C_{16}H_{25}NO_3S$			
2-Propenoic acid, 3-[(4-oxo-2-azetidinyl)thio]-, 5-methyl-2-(1-methylethyl)-cyclohexyl ester, (R)-	EtOH	278(4.17)	35-6306-79
(S)-	EtOH	277(4.18)	35-6306-79
$C_{16}H_{25}N_3$			
1H-Benzotriazole, 1-decyl-	EtOH	257(3.82),262(3.82), 280(3.65)	33-2129-79
$C_{16}H_{25}N_3O$			
2,15-Diazabicyclo[12.2.2]octadeca-14,16,17-triene, 2-nitroso-	MeOH	276(3.97)	49-0567-79
$C_{16}H_{25}N_3O_2$			
3H-Indazole-4,7-dione, 6,7a-bis(1,1-dimethylethyl)-3a,7a-dihydro-, 4-(O-methyloxime)	n.s.g.	287(4.14)	70-1668-79
$C_{16}H_{25}N_3O_5$			
Thymidine, 5'-deoxy-5'-[(1-oxohexyl)-amino]-	EtOH	267(3.97)	87-0621-79
$C_{16}H_{25}N_3O_6S$			
2-Thiazolebutanoic acid, α-(acetylamino)-4-[[(2-ethoxy-2-oxoethyl)amino]-carbonyl]-4,5-dihydro-, ethyl ester	EtOH	229(3.52),244s(3.45)	44-0497-79
	50% EtOH-HCl	267(3.73)	44-0497-79
$C_{16}H_{25}N_5O_4$			
1H-Purine-2,6-dione, 3,7-dihydro-8-(hydroxymethyl)-7-[2-hydroxy-3-(1-piperidinyl)propyl]-1,3-dimethyl-, mono-3-pyridinecarboxylate	n.s.g.	211(4.59),275(4.10)	73-0424-79
Thymidine, 2',3'-didehydro-3',5'-dideoxy-5'-[(2,6-diamino-1-oxohexyl)amino]-	H_2O	266(3.95)	136-0113-79F
$C_{16}H_{25}N_5O_6$			
Zeatin, O-β-D-glucopyranosyldihydro-	pH 1	272.7(4.16)	102-0819-79

Compound	Solvent	λ max (log ε)	Ref.
Zeatin, O-β-D-glucopyranosyldihydro- (cont.)	pH 13	275(4.18),282s(4.06)	102-0819-79
	EtOH	269.5(4.18)	102-0819-79
$C_{16}H_{26}N_2$			
2,15-Diazabicyclo[12.2.2]octadeca-14,16,17-triene	MeOH	208(3.90),256(4.03), 318(3.34)	49-0567-79
$C_{16}H_{26}N_2O_4$			
Pyrazine, 2,5-diethoxy-3-[3-[(tetrahydro-2H-pyran-2-yl)oxy]propyl]-	EtOH	245(3.94),345(3.50)	39-1889-79C
$C_{16}H_{26}N_2O_7$			
2,5,8,11,14,17,20-Heptaoxa-22,24-diazabicyclo[19.3.1]pentacosa-1(25),21,23-triene	EtOH	240(3.52),251(3.28)	44-3812-79
$C_{16}H_{26}N_4O_4$			
1H-Imidazol-1-yloxy, 4,4'-(1,2-ethenediyl)bis[2,5-dihydro-2,2,5,5-tetramethyl-, 3,3'-dioxide, (E)-	EtOH	244(3.79),360(4.11), 378(4.19)	70-2521-79
$C_{16}H_{26}N_4O_5$			
Thymidine, 5'-[[2-(acetylmethylamino)-ethyl]methylamino]-5'-deoxy-, monohydrochloride	H_2O	267(3.98)	87-0621-79
$C_{16}H_{26}O_2$			
3H-Cyclododecapyran-3-one, 1,5,6,7,8,9-10,11,12,13,14,14a-dodecahydro-4-methyl-	MeOH	231(3.85)	146-0031-79
$C_{16}H_{26}O_3$			
Cyclopenta[b]pyran-2(3H)-one, hexahydro-5-(1-methoxy-1-methylethyl)-7a-methyl-3-(1-methylethylidene)-, (4aα,5α,7aα)-	MeOH	234(4.20)	94-0275-79
1H-Indene-4-propanoic acid, octahydro-4,5,7a-trimethyl-1-oxo-, methyl ester	n.s.g.	286(2.02)	78-2301-79
1H-Inden-1-one, 2-(1-ethoxyethylidene)-octahydro-4-methoxy-3a,7a-dimethyl-, (2E,3aα,4β,7aβ)-	EtOH	272(4.00)	44-3666-79
$C_{16}H_{26}O_6S_4$			
D-Mannitol, 1,2:5,6-bis-O-(1-methylethylidene)-, bis(S-methyl carbonodithioate)	n.s.g.	280(4.37)	39-2378-79C
$C_{16}H_{27}NO_4$			
Propanedioic acid, [(dimethylamino)-methyl](3,7-dimethyl-2,6-octadien-yl)-, (E)-	EtOH	200(4.31)	70-1973-79
$C_{16}H_{27}NO_9S$			
α-D-Glucopyranoside, methyl 4,6-O-cyclohexylidene-2-deoxy-2-[(methoxycarbonyl)amino]-, 3-methanesulfonate	EtOH	200(2.30),223(2.20)	18-3015-79
$C_{16}H_{27}N_2O_5PS$			
Phosphorothioic acid, O-(1-cyclohexyl-1,6-dihydro-5-methoxy-6-oxo-4-pyridazinyl) O-ethyl O-(1-methylethyl) ester	MeOH	215(4.24),283(3.72)	73-1761-79

Compound	Solvent	λ_{max}(log ε)	Ref.
$C_{16}H_{27}N_3O_4$			
Thymidine, 5'-deoxy-5'-(hexylamino)-	pH 1	267(3.98)	87-0621-79
$C_{16}H_{27}N_4O_2P$			
Phosphinic acid, bis(4-methyl-1-piperazinyl)-, phenyl ester	EtOH	216(3.34),262(2.68), 268(2.57)	1-0319-79
$C_{16}H_{27}N_5O_4Si$			
9H-Purin-6-amine, 9-[5-O-[(1,1-dimethylethyl)dimethylsilyl]-β-D-arabinofuranosyl]-	MeOH	259(4.18)	87-0273-79
$C_{16}H_{27}N_6$			
1,2,3-Triazinium, 2-methyl-4,5,6-tripyrrolidino-, iodide	CH_2Cl_2	456(3.77)	24-1535-79
$C_{16}H_{28}N_2$			
Pyrazine, tetrakis(1-methylethyl)-	EtOH	282(3.965),277s(3.949)	12-1281-79
$C_{16}H_{28}N_2O_4$			
3-Hepten-2-one, 4,4'-(1,2-ethanediyldiimino)bis[7-hydroxy-	MeOH	321(4.53)	44-2073-79
$C_{16}H_{28}N_4$			
Cyanamide, [2,3-bis[bis(1-methylethyl)-amino]-2-cyclopropen-1-ylidene]-	CH_2Cl_2	246(4.27)	24-1514-79
$C_{16}H_{28}N_6$			
1-Triazene-1-carbonitrile, 3-[2,3-bis-[bis(1-methylethyl)amino]-2-cyclopropen-1-ylidene]-	CH_2Cl_2	365(4.28)	24-1514-79
$C_{16}H_{28}O_2Si$			
Phenol, 2-(1,1-dimethylethyl)-4-[[(1,1-dimethylethyl)dimethylsilyl]oxy]-	EtOH	204(4.23),227(3.76), 284(3.43)	87-0569-79
$C_{16}H_{30}N_4O_4P$			
1-Piperidinyloxy, 4-[2-[[[[bis(1-aziridinyl)phosphinyl]amino]carbonyl]oxy]-ethyl]-2,2,6,6-tetramethyl-	EtOH	244(3.33)	118-0269-79
$C_{16}H_{30}N_6O_2$			
1H-Imidazole, 1,1'-azobis[2,5-dihydro-2,2,4,5,5-pentamethyl-, 3,3'-dioxide	EtOH	230(4.32),288(4.05)	103-0092-79
$C_{16}H_{30}O_3$			
Malyngolide	EtOH	end absorption	44-4039-79
$C_{16}H_{32}N_2O_3$			
Acetamide, 2,2'-oxybis[N,N-dipropyl-	H_2O	203(4.20)	33-0754-79
$C_{16}H_{32}N_5$			
1,2,3-Triazinium, 4,5-bis[bis(1-methylethyl)amino]-2-methyl-, iodide	CH_2Cl_2	395(3.85)	24-1535-79
$C_{16}H_{32}OSi_4$			
Trisilane, 2-benzoyl-1,1,1,3,3,3-hexamethyl-2-(trimethylsilyl)-	C_6H_{12}	386(1.88),404(2.12), 424(2.19),446(1.96)	35-0083-79

Compound	Solvent	$\lambda_{max}(\log \epsilon)$	Ref.
$C_{16}H_{33}NO_2$			
Decanamide, 2,2,5-triethyl-N-hydroxy-	EtOH	209(3.57)	32-0357-79
$C_{16}H_{34}Cl_2N_4O_2Pt$			
Platinum, bis(3-amino-2,2,5,5-tetra-methyl-1-pyrrolidinyloxy-N)di-chloro-, (SP-4-2)-	EtOH	225(3.68)	77-0222-79
$C_{16}H_{37}N_2P$			
Phosphonous diamide, P-butyl-N,N,N',N'-tetrapropyl-	hexane	225(3.56)	22-0241-79I
$C_{16}H_{40}O_4Si_4$			
Cyclotetrasiloxane, octaethyl-	heptane	193(2.51),200s(--)	65-1333-79

Compound	Solvent	λ_{max}(log ε)	Ref.
$C_{17}H_3Cl_{11}S_2$			
Benzene, 1,1'-[[3-(1-chloroethylidene)-1-propyne-1,3-diyl]bis(thio)]bis-[2,3,4,5,6-pentachloro-	heptane	223(c.5.2),286(4.4)	5-1626-79
$C_{17}H_3F_5O_5$			
4,5,9,10-Pyrenetetrone, 1,2,3,6,7-pentafluoro-8-methoxy-	n.s.g.	227(4.41),255(4.20), 295(3.97)	39-1351-79C
$C_{17}H_5Cl_2NO_3$			
Anthra[1,9-bc]pyran-1-carbonitrile, 4,6-dichloro-2,7-dihydro-2,7-dioxo-	benzene	400s(3.85)	104-0923-79
$C_{17}H_6Cl_2N_2O_2$			
Propanedinitrile, (2,4-dichloro-1-hydroxy-10-oxo-9(10H)-anthracenylidene)-	benzene	345(3.91),429(3.68)	104-0923-79
$C_{17}H_7ClO_4$			
6H-Benzo[b]naphtho[2,3-d]pyran-6,7,12-trione, 2-chloro-	EtOH	214(4.52),311(3.74), 410(3.32)	33-2833-79
6H-Benzo[b]naphtho[2,3-d]pyran-6,7,12-trione, 3-chloro-	EtOH	213(4.51),245(4.26), 317(3.84),402(3.61)	33-2833-79
6H-Benzo[b]naphtho[2,3-d]pyran-6,7,12-trione, 4-chloro-	EtOH	213(4.48),227(4.28), 322(3.70)	33-2833-79
$C_{17}H_8ClNO_4$			
1,3-Isobenzofurandione, 5-[5-(4-chlorophenyl)-2-oxazolyl]-	toluene	365(4.29)	103-0028-79
$C_{17}H_8F_8N_2O_5$			
Isoxazole, 4,5-dihydro-4-nitro-3,5-bis-(2,3,5,6-tetrafluoro-4-methoxyphenyl)-	EtOH	235(4.34),298(3.90)	104-2179-79
$C_{17}H_8N_2O_4$			
Naphtho[2',3':4,5]furo[2,3-b]pyridine-3-carbonitrile, 1,2,5,10-tetrahydro-4-methyl-2,5,10-trioxo-	EtOH	294(4.34),340(4.06), 416(3.47),515(3.34)	2-0100-79A
$C_{17}H_9ClN_4$			
Pyrrolo[1,2-a:4,5-b']diquinoxaline, 6-chloro-	EtOH	274(4.93),304s(3.98), 358s(3.85),370(4.03), 387(4.06),447s(3.51), 467(3.61),493s(3.48)	78-2463-79
$C_{17}H_9NO_4$			
1,3-Isobenzofurandione, 5-(5-phenyl-2-oxazolyl)-	toluene	364(4.20)	103-0028-79
Oxopukateine	EtOH	248(4.14),260s(3.92), 274(4.04),311(3.39)	100-0325-79
$C_{17}H_{10}BrNO_3$			
2H-1-Benzopyran-2-one, 3-(5-bromo-7-methyl-2-benzoxazolyl)-	dioxan	353(4.11)	42-0505-79
2H-1-Benzopyran-2-one, 3-(7-bromo-5-methyl-2-benzoxazolyl)-	dioxan	348(4.25)	42-0505-79
2H-1-Benzopyran-2-one, 6-bromo-3-(5-methyl-2-benzoxazolyl)-	dioxan	362(4.41)	42-0505-79
$C_{17}H_{10}Cl_2N_2O_2$			
Propanenitrile, 3-[(2,4-dichloro-1-hy-	benzene	405(3.67),530s(2.61)	104-0147-79

Compound	Solvent	λ_{max}(log ε)	Ref.
droxy-10-oxo-9(10H)-anthracenylidene)amino]- (cont.)	EtOH	408(3.68),540s(2.81)	104-0147-79
	dioxan	405(3.66),525s(2.74)	104-0147-79
$C_{17}H_{10}Cl_2N_4O_2$			
Benzo[g]pteridine-2,4(3H,10H)-dione, 10-(3,4-dichlorophenyl)-3-methyl-	EtOH	265(4.34),332(3.80), 424s(3.80),437(3.84), 461s(3.71)	4-1365-79
$C_{17}H_{10}N_4$			
Quinoxalino[2',3':2,3]pyrrolo[1,2-c]-quinazoline	EtOH	255(4.45),290(4.56), 323(4.47),360(4.08), 372(4.03),420s(3.92), 438(3.99),460(3.87)	78-2463-79
$C_{17}H_{10}N_4O$			
1H-Benzo[3,4]cyclobut[1,2-b]imidazo-[4,5-g]quinoxaline, 1-acetyl-	EtOH	265(4.49),284(4.62), 306(4.36),371(4.10), 389(4.28),409(4.26)	78-0241-79
$C_{17}H_{10}O_4$			
4H-Furo[2,3-h]-1-benzopyran-4-one, 2-(2-hydroxyphenyl)-	n.s.g.	240(1.15),260(1.18), 300(1.10)	2-0525-79B
4H-Furo[2,3-h]-1-benzopyran-4-one, 2-(3-hydroxyphenyl)- (pongol)	MeOH	245(1.194),265(1.294), 300(1.032)	2-0525-79B
	MeOH-$AlCl_3$	245(1.70),265(1.618), 300(1.38)	2-0525-79B
4H-Furo[2,3-h]-1-benzopyran-4-one, 2-(4-hydroxyphenyl)-	n.s.g.	240(1.09),260(1.17), 305(0.985)	2-0525-79B
$C_{17}H_{10}O_6$			
1H-Anthra[2,3-c]pyran-3,6,11(4H)-trione, 5,12-dihydroxy-	MeOH	229(4.13),250(4.37), 255s(--),289(3.78), 479(3.75),509s(--)	5-0035-79
$C_{17}H_{11}BrN_4O$			
Imidazo[1,2-b][1,2,4]triazin-3(4H)-one, 6-(4-bromophenyl)-2-phenyl-	dioxan	285(4.35),376(4.07)	104-1798-79
$C_{17}H_{11}ClN_4O$			
Imidazo[1,2-b][1,2,4]triazin-3(4H)-one, 6-(4-chlorophenyl)-2-phenyl-	dioxan	285(4.33),377(4.04)	104-1798-79
$C_{17}H_{11}ClN_4O_2$			
Benzo[g]pteridine-2,4(3H,10H)-dione, 10-(4-chlorophenyl)-3-methyl-	EtOH	263(4.39),337(3.91), 422s(3.95),437(4.00), 461s(3.89)	4-1365-79
$C_{17}H_{11}ClO_4$			
6H-Benzo[b]naphtho[2,3-d]pyran-6,7,12-trione, 2-chloro-7a,8,11,11a-tetrahydro-	EtOH	213(4.51),307(3.94), 369(3.83)	33-2833-79
6H-Benzo[b]naphtho[2,3-d]pyran-6,7,12-trione, 3-chloro-7a,8,11,11a-tetrahydro-	EtOH	208(4.28),245(4.35), 272(3.91),288(3.89), 362(4.01)	33-2833-79
6H-Benzo[b]naphtho[2,3-d]pyran-6,7,12-trione, 4-chloro-7a,8,11,11a-tetrahydro-	EtOH	212(4.43),326(3.94)	33-2833-79
$C_{17}H_{11}N$			
Benzonitrile, 2-(2-naphthalenyl)-	C_6H_{12}	221(4.79),225(4.79),	39-1070-79C

Compound	Solvent	λ_{max}(log ε)	Ref.
Benzonitrile, 2-(2-naphthalenyl)- (cont.)		247(4.53),254s(4.48), 273(4.04),286(4.00)	39-1070-79C
	EtOH	220(4.70),222(4.69), 248(4.45),257s(4.40), 275(3.97),286(3.96)	39-1070-79C
Benzo[c]phenanthridine	EtOH	253(4.90),262(5.04), 310s(4.09),343(3.86), 360(3.90)	39-1070-79C
Benzo[i]phenanthridine	EtOH	218(4.34),233(4.36), 236(4.08),256s(4.62), 266(4.81),298(3.80), 313(3.87),326(3.88), 343(3.41),352(2.84), 359(3.30)	39-1070-79C
Naphthalene, 1-isocyano-2-phenyl-	EtOH	210(4.483),228(4.74), 252(4.70),297(4.13)	39-1070-79C
Naphthalene, 1-(2-isocyanophenyl)-	C_6H_{12}	222(4.83),282(3.82), 287(3.80),291(3.90)	39-1070-79C
	EtOH	221(4.85),280(3.80), 286(3.54),291(3.54)	39-1070-79C
Naphthalene, 2-(2-isocyanophenyl)-	C_6H_{12}	218(4.25),224(4.30), 246(3.95),255(3.95), 282(3.85)	39-1070-79C
	EtOH	219(4.32),226(4.37), 247(4.00),255(3.95), 282(3.85)	39-1070-79C
$C_{17}H_{11}NO$			
Benzo[b]naphth[1,8-de]azepin-7(8H)-one	EtOH	217(4.22),221(4.21), 240(4.11),282(4.29), 295(4.27),321(3.86), 333(3.89),400(3.46)	39-1070-79C
1H-Dibenz[e,g]indole-3-carboxaldehyde	EtOH	205(4.39),247(4.53), 255(4.58),262(4.62), 272(4.48),320(3.71), 336(3.47),352(3.26)	103-0302-79
$C_{17}H_{11}NO_2$			
5H-Benzo[b]carbazole-6,11-dione, 5-methyl-	EtOH	257s(4.27),274(4.37), 283s(4.36),350s(3.50), 366(3.67)	150-4801-79
$C_{17}H_{11}NO_3$			
2H-1-Benzopyran-2-one, 3-(4-methyl-2-benzoxazolyl)-	dioxan	350(4.13)	42-0505-79
2H-1-Benzopyran-2-one, 3-(7-methyl-2-benzoxazolyl)-	dioxan	350(4.31)	42-0505-79
$C_{17}H_{11}NO_6$			
1,3-Benzenedicarboxylic acid, 5-(4-ethynyl-3,5-diformyl-1(4H)-pyridinyl)-	EtOH	232(4.43),285(4.27), 363(3.89)	49-0613-79
$C_{17}H_{11}N_2O_2S_2$			
Thiazolo[3,2-a]pyridinium, 2,3-dihydro-2-[3-(3-hydroxythiazolo[3,2-a]pyridinium-2-yl)-2-propenylidene]-3-oxo-, hydroxide, inner salt, perchlorate	MeCN	640(4.75),685(4.98)	103-1081-79
$C_{17}H_{11}N_3$			
1H-Phenanthro[9,10-d]imidazole-2-carbonitrile, 1-methyl-	EtOH	223s(4.29),230(4.34), 246s(4.75),253(4.96),	44-0041-79

Compound	Solvent	λmax(log ε)	Ref.
1H-Phenanthro[9,10-d]imidazole-2-carbonitrile, 1-methyl- (cont.)		258s(4.77),277s(4.22), 296(4.18),309(4.22), 317s(4.00),330(4.03), 346(4.14)	44-0041-79
$C_{17}H_{11}N_5O$			
3H-Pyrazol-3-one, 2-acenaphtho[1,2-e]-[1,2,4]triazin-9-yl-2,4-dihydro-5-methyl-	MeOH	228(4.52),275(4.18), 332(4.42)	83-0147-79
$C_{17}H_{12}$			
8,16-Methano[2.2]metacyclophane-1,9-diene	C_6H_{12}	223(4.46),236(4.44), 246(4.45),305(4.17)	89-0946-79
$C_{17}H_{12}BrClN_2O_2$			
8-Azabicyclo[3.2.1]oct-3-ene-6-carbonitrile, 8-[3-(4-bromophenyl)-3-oxo-1-propenyl]-6-chloro-2-oxo-, trans	EtOH	217(4.09),267(4.18), 332(4.19)	56-0057-79
$C_{17}H_{12}BrNO_4S$			
2-Naphthalenesulfonic acid, 6-[[(4-bromophenyl)methylene]amino]-4-hydroxy-	MeOH	255(5.75),307(5.14)	104-2284-79
	MeOH-KOH	265(5.65),330(5.08)	104-2284-79
$C_{17}H_{12}ClFN_2O_3$			
1H-1,4-Benzodiazepine-1-acetic acid, 7-chloro-5-(2-fluorophenyl)-2,3-dihydro-2-oxo-	pH 0	240(4.41),285(4.12), 365(3.51)	59-0603-79
	pH 7	232(4.52),249s(4.21), 318(3.15)	59-0603-79
$C_{17}H_{12}ClNO_2$			
1-Naphthalenecarboxamide, N-(4-chlorophenyl)-N-hydroxy-	EtOH	222(4.63),282(4.10)	34-0072-79
$C_{17}H_{12}ClN_5S$			
1,3,4-Thiadiazolium, 5-[[(4-chlorophenyl)cyanomethylene]hydrazino]-3-methyl-2-phenyl-, hydroxide, inner salt	n.s.g.	259(4.25),351(3.89), 457(4.25)	39-0724-79C
$C_{17}H_{12}Cl_2$			
Dibenzo[a,e]cyclopropa[c]cycloheptene, 1,1-dichloro-1,1a,6,10b-tetrahydro-6-methylene-	$CHCl_3$	245(4.04),270(2.85), 272(2.93)	44-4440-79
$C_{17}H_{12}Cl_2OS$			
2H-Naphtho[1,8-bc]thiophene, 6,8-dichloro-2-(1,3(or 4)-cyclopentadien-1-yl)-3-methoxy-	MeOH	208(4.3),276(4.0), 407(4.0)	24-0349-79
$C_{17}H_{12}Cl_2O_6$			
Aflatoxin B_1, 8,9-dichloro-8,9-dihydro-	CH_2Cl_2	233(4.22),263(4.11), 353(4.23)	39-2664-79C
$C_{17}H_{12}Cl_4N_2O_2$			
1H-Isoindole-1,3(2H)-dione, 4,5,6,7-tetrachloro-2-[2-(methylphenylamino)ethyl]-	C_6H_{12}	402(1.95)	39-1103-79B
	benzene	400(1.88)	39-1103-79B
$C_{17}H_{12}FNO_4S$			
2-Naphthalenesulfonic acid, 6-[[(3-fluorophenyl)methylene]amino]-4-hydroxy-	MeOH	255(5.62),305(5.00)	104-2284-79
	MeOH-KOH	265(5.54),330(4.96)	104-2284-79

Compound	Solvent	$\lambda_{max}(\log \epsilon)$	Ref.
2-Naphthalenesulfonic acid, 6-[[(4-fluorophenyl)methylene]amino]-4-hydroxy-	MeOH	255(5.65),308(5.02)	104-2284-79
	MeOH-KOH	267(5.50),330(4.91)	104-2284-79
$C_{17}H_{12}F_3S_3$			
1,2-Dithiol-1-ium, 4-methyl-3-phenyl-5-[[4-(trifluoromethyl)phenyl]thio]-, bromide	MeCN	218(4.66),260s(3.89), 338s(4.05),372(4.37)	104-0955-79
$C_{17}H_{12}N_2$			
Isoquinoline, 1-(1H-indol-3-yl)-, monoperchlorate	MeCN	216(4.72),244s(4.68), 240s(4.32),270(4.05), 282s(3.92),333(3.61), 398(4.12)	103-0773-79
Quinoline, 2-(1H-indol-3-yl)-, monoperchlorate	MeCN	216(4.69),254(4.25), 269(4.27),300(3.95), 410(4.34)	103-0773-79
$C_{17}H_{12}N_2O$			
Pyrido[1,2-a]benzimidazol-9(5H)-one, 7-phenyl-	MeOH	265(4.6)	95-0880-79
3H-Pyrrolo[2,3-c]acridine, N-acetyl-	EtOH	215(4.23),244(4.41), 270(4.93),350(3.89), 368(4.14)	103-0894-79
Quinoline, 8-(2-benzoxazolyl)-2-methyl-	EtOH	306(4.16)	4-1579-79
monohydriodide	EtOH	308(4.18)	4-1579-79
Quinoline, 8-(2-benzoxazolyl)-4-methyl-	EtOH	310(4.19)	4-1579-79
monohydriodide	EtOH	312(4.21)	4-1579-79
$C_{17}H_{12}N_2O_2$			
Benzamide, N-(1-cyano-1H-2-benzopyran-1-yl)-	EtOH	228(4.37),265(4.46)	39-0266-79C
$C_{17}H_{12}N_2O_3S$			
9H-Naphtho[1',2':4,5]thiazolo[3,2-a]pyrimidine-11-carboxylic acid, 9-oxo-, ethyl ester	MeOH	242(4.72),292(4.08), 347(4.00)	83-0619-79
$C_{17}H_{12}N_2O_6S$			
1-Aza-4-thiabicyclo[3.2.0]hept-2-ene-2-carboxylic acid, 3-(2-furanyl)-7-oxo-, (4-nitrophenyl)methyl ester	EtOH	260(4.09),294(4.02), 307(3.98),358(4.08)	35-6296-79
2-Naphthalenesulfonic acid, 4-hydroxy-6-[[(3-nitrophenyl)methylene]amino]-	MeOH	255(5.67),305(5.03)	104-2284-79
	MeOH-KOH	267(5.52),330(4.90)	104-2284-79
2-Naphthalenesulfonic acid, 4-hydroxy-6-[[(4-nitrophenyl)methylene]amino]-	MeOH	255(5.49),293(5.22)	104-2284-79
	MeOH-KOH	267(5.46),325(4.95)	104-2284-79
$C_{17}H_{12}N_2S$			
Quinoline, 8-(2-benzothiazolyl)-2-methyl-	EtOH	330(4.26),345(4.24)	4-1579-79
Quinoline, 8-(2-benzothiazolyl)-4-methyl-	EtOH	330(4.29),338(4.30)	4-1579-79
$C_{17}H_{12}N_4$			
2-Butenedinitrile, 2-amino-3-[(diphenylmethylene)amino]-, (Z)-	EtOH	259(4.04),376(3.99)	44-0827-79
4-Pyridazinecarbonitrile, 3-amino-5,6-diphenyl-	DMF	369(3.93)	48-0071-79
$C_{17}H_{12}N_4O_2$			
1H-Pyrazole-4-carbonitrile, 3-methyl-1-(4-nitrophenyl)-5-phenyl-	EtOH	297(4.36)	78-1331-79

Compound	Solvent	λ_{max}(log ε)	Ref.
$C_{17}H_{12}N_4O_6$			
1H-Pyrazole-3-carboxylic acid, 1-(2,4-dinitrophenyl)-5-phenyl-, methyl ester	CH_2Cl_2	282s(4.11)	24-1193-79
1H-Pyrazole-4-carboxylic acid, 1-(2,4-dinitrophenyl)-5-phenyl-, methyl ester	CH_2Cl_2	285(4.03)	24-1193-79
$C_{17}H_{12}N_4S$			
Isothiazolo[3,4-c]pyridazin-3-amine, 4,5-diphenyl-	DMF	464(3.68)	48-0071-79
1,3,4-Thiadiazol-2-amine, N-phenyl-5-(4-quinolinyl)-	EtOH	236(4.64),270(4.13), 332s(--),356(4.20)	106-0537-79
$C_{17}H_{12}O$			
Methanone, 1-naphthalenylphenyl-	EtOH	220(4.79),250(4.20), 280s(3.75),290s(3.69), 306(3.67),320s(3.60)	18-3314-79
$C_{17}H_{12}O_2$			
1(4H)-Naphthalenone, 2-hydroxy-4-(phenylmethylene)-	$CHCl_3$	311(4.10),395(4.48)	138-1097-79
1-Pentyne-3,5-dione, 1,5-diphenyl-	MeOH	225s(4.05),255(3.97), 296(4.03),350(4.41)	4-0737-79
	MeOH-NaOMe	255(4.19),364(4.27)	4-0737-79
$C_{17}H_{12}O_3$			
5H-Furo[3,2-b]xanthen-5-one, 2,11-dimethyl-	MeOH	25?(3.90),290(3.10), 300(3.12),360(2.84)	42-0052-79
Spiro[1H-cyclopenta[b]naphtho[2,3-d]-furan-1,1'-cyclopropane]-5,10-dione, 3a,10b-dihydro-	n.s.g.	252(4.39),282(4.20), 327(3.45),393(3.07)	39-0719-79C
Spiro[cyclopropane-1,12'-[4a,9a]epoxy-[1,4]methanoanthracene]-9',10'-dione, 1',4'-dihydro-	n.s.g.	228(4.56),258(3.60), 298(3.33)	39-0719-79C
$C_{17}H_{12}O_4$			
1H-2-Benzopyran-4-carboxylic acid, 1-oxo-3-phenyl-, methyl ester	EtOH	233(4.32),292(4.22), 325(3.94)	117-0077-79
$C_{17}H_{12}O_5$			
9,10-Anthracenedione, 1,4-dihydroxy-2-(1-oxopropyl)-	MeOH	208(4.33),226(4.31), 250(4.46),283(3.92), 330s(--),484(3.90), 580s(--)	5-0019-79
11H-Benzofuro[2,3-b][1]benzopyran-11-one, 3,8-dimethoxy-	MeOH	261(4.48),287(4.22), 311s(4.00)	18-0529-79
2,5-Cyclohexadiene-1,4-dione, 2-(7-methoxy-2-methyl-4-oxo-4H-1-benzopyran-3-yl)-	MeOH	226(4.49),246(4.48), 252(4.48),297(4.17)	18-0529-79
$C_{17}H_{12}O_6$			
2-Anthracenecarboxylic acid, 9,10-dihydro-3,8-dihydroxy-1-methyl-9,10-dioxo-, methyl ester	MeOH	218(4.26),275(4.20), 308(3.27),410(3.51), 425(3.44)	118-0148-79
2-Anthracenecarboxylic acid, 9,10-dihydro-8-hydroxy-3-methoxy-6-methyl-9,10-dioxo-	EtOH	241(4.33),267(4.26), 299(4.15),434(3.88), 450s(--)	32-0301-79
$C_{17}H_{12}O_7$			
2-Anthraceneacetic acid, 9,10-dihydro-	EtOH	205(4.37),225(4.35)	5-0019-79

Compound	Solvent	λmax(log ε)	Ref.
α,1,4-trihydroxy-9,10-dioxo-, methyl ester (cont.)		249(4.54),281(4.01), 329s(--),480(4.00), 571(3.23)	5-0019-79
$C_{17}H_{12}O_8$			
[2]Benzopyrano[4,3-b][1]benzopyran-7(5H)-one, 3,4,8,10-tetrahydroxy-9-methoxy- (benthamianin)	MeOH	231(4.77),262(4.77), 280(4.87),381(4.77)	39-2696-79C
$C_{17}H_{13}$			
Cycloheptatrienylium, (1-naphthalenyl)-, tetrafluoroborate	MeCN	220(5.00),258(4.06), 279(4.06),290s(3.93), 446(3.78)	44-2712-79
$C_{17}H_{13}ClN_2O$			
4(1H)-Quinazolinone, 6-chloro-1-methyl-2-(2-phenylethenyl)-	80% EtOH	222(4.45),295(4.03)	42-0708-79
4(1H)-Quinazolinone, 7-chloro-1-methyl-2-(2-phenylethenyl)-	80% EtOH	225(4.48),310(4.16)	42-0708-79
$C_{17}H_{13}ClN_2O_2S$			
2(1H)-Pyrimidinethione, 4-(1,3-benzo-dioxol-5-yl)-6-(4-chlorophenyl)-3,4-dihydro-	EtOH	234(4.39),260(4.33)	23-2734-79
	$CHCl_3$	277s(4.14),292(4.20)	23-2734-79
	CCl_4	261(4.18),297(4.20)	23-2734-79
$C_{17}H_{13}ClN_4$			
1H-1,4-Benzodiazepine-1-carbonitrile, 7-chloro-2,3-dihydro-2-(methylimino)-5-phenyl-	EtOH	228(4.49),255s(4.14), 277s(3.75),305s(3.38)	44-2688-79
5H-[1,2,4]Triazolo[5,1-a][2,4]benzodiaz-epine, 9-chloro-2-methyl-7-phenyl-	MeOH	227(4.53),259(4.24)	44-0084-79
$C_{17}H_{13}ClN_4O$			
1H-1,2,4-Triazolo[4,3-a][1,4]benzodiaz-epinium, 8-chloro-2,4-dihydro-3-meth-yl-1-oxo-6-phenyl-, hydroxide, inner salt	EtOH	221(4.53),266(4.18)	44-2688-79
5H-1,2,4-Triazolo[4,3-d][1,4]benzodiaz-epin-6(7H)-one, 10-chloro-7-methyl-3-phenyl-	MeOH	244(4.60),298(3.59)	44-0088-79
$C_{17}H_{13}ClN_4S$			
1H-1,2,4-Triazolo[4,3-a][1,4]benzodiaz-epinium, 8-chloro-2,4-dihydro-3-meth-yl-6-phenyl-1-thioxo-, hydroxide, inner salt	EtOH	220(4.66),245s(4.28), 260s(4.05),278(3.92), 310s(3.62)	44-2688-79
$C_{17}H_{13}ClO_5$			
Furo[2,3-b]benzofuran-2,3-diol, 2,3,3a-8a-tetrahydro-, 2-(3-chlorobenzoate)	CH_2Cl_2	238(3.91),278(3.50), 284(3.49)	39-2664-79C
isomer 4m	CH_2Cl_2	238(3.90),278(3.52), 283(3.51)	39-2664-79C
Furo[2,3-b]benzofuran-2,3-diol, 2,3,3a-8a-tetrahydro-, 3-(3-chlorobenzoate)	CH_2Cl_2	239(3.90),278(2.54), 284(3.47)	39-2664-79C
$C_{17}H_{13}NO$			
Ethanone, 2-(1-isoquinolinyl)-1-phenyl-	MeCN	222(4.41),245(4.05), 294(3.90)	103-1337-79
Ethanone, 1-phenyl-2-(2-quinolinyl)-	neutral	423(4.35),444(4.33)	39-0792-79B
	cation	317(4.11)	39-0792-79B
	anion	398(4.36)	39-0792-79C

Compound	Solvent	$\lambda_{max}(\log \epsilon)$	Ref.
Ethanone, 1-phenyl-2-(4-quinolinyl)-	neutral	341(3.65),456(2.26)	39-0792-79B
	cation	313(3.95)	39-0792-79B
	anion	406(4.28)	39-0792-79B
10H-Indeno[1,2-b]quinolin-10-one, 5,11-dihydro-5-methyl-	MeOH	261s(--),269(4.57), 315(4.22),332(3.98), 347(4.13),364(4.12)	83-0254-79
Oxazole, 5-phenyl-2-(2-phenylethenyl)-	EtOH	261(3.75),338(4.22)	18-3597-79
$C_{17}H_{13}NOS$			
[1]Benzothieno[3,2-b]quinoline, 11-ethoxy-	MeOH	204(4.48),228(4.46), 247(4.60),274(4.79), 320(3.92),333(4.00), 355(3.71),372(3.73)	83-0254-79
$C_{17}H_{13}NO_2$			
[1]Benzofuro[3,2-b]quinoline, 11-ethoxy-	MeOH	202(4.38),220(4.56), 254(4.65),263(4.82), 287(3.74),323(4.29), 333s(4.17),350(3.94)	83-0254-79
Benzofuro[3,2-b][1]quinolin-11(5H)-one, 5-ethyl-5,11-dihydro-	MeOH	220(4.38),260(4.66), 310(4.29),337(3.98), 353(4.24),370(4.35)	83-0254-79
Benzonitrile, 4-(1-acetoxy-2-phenyleth-enyl)-	hexane	227(4.05),302(4.40)	23-1186-79
	EtOH	230(4.07),308(4.44)	23-1186-79
4H-Pyran-4-one, 2,6-diphenyl-, oxime	MeOH	270(4.31),308(4.16)	4-0737-79
	$MeOH-H_2SO_4$	257(4.24),310(4.50)	4-0737-79
$C_{17}H_{13}NO_3$			
2H-1-Benzopyran-2,4(3H)-dione, 3-[1-(phenylamino)ethylidene]-	hexane	212s(--),238(4.20), 337(4.29)	131-0077-79D
	EtOH	326(4.26)	131-0077-79D
Fuseine	EtOH	235(4.48),273(4.55), 317(3.91)	100-0325-79
$C_{17}H_{13}NO_4$			
Benzoic acid, 2-(4-ethynyl-3,5-diform-yl-1(4H)-pyridinyl)-, methyl ester	EtOH	227(4.37),271(4.10), 311(3.81),368(3.86)	49-0613-79
4-Quinolinecarboxylic acid, 1,2-dihydro-3-(2-methoxyphenyl)-2-oxo-	EtOH	222(4.54),278(3.90), 316(3.82),326(3.89), 338s(3.77)	4-0487-79
$C_{17}H_{13}NO_4S$			
2-Naphthalenesulfonic acid, 4-hydroxy-6-[(phenylmethylene)amino]-	MeOH	254(5.65),308(5.07)	104-2284-79
	MeOH-KOH	266(5.57),335(5.03)	104-2284-79
$C_{17}H_{13}NO_6$			
[1,3]Benzodioxolo[5,6-a]quinolizinium, 2-carboxy-6,7-dihydro-3-(methoxycar-bonyl)-, hydroxide, inner salt	EtOH	232(4.03),252(3.99), 271(4.02),292(4.05), 380(4.12)	23-1647-79
[1,3]Benzodioxolo[5,6-a]quinolizinium, 3-carboxy-6,7-dihydro-2-(methoxycar-bonyl)-, hydroxide, inner salt	EtOH	290(3.49),373(3.38)	23-1647-79
$C_{17}H_{13}NS$			
10H-Indeno[1,2-b]quinoline-10-thione, 5,11-dihydro-5-methyl-	dioxan	256(4.40),272(4.05), 317(4.30),370(3.48), 445(4.21),472(4.12)	83-0254-79
$C_{17}H_{13}N_3$			
1H-Imidazole-2-carbonitrile, 1-methyl-4,5-diphenyl-	EtOH	271(4.33)	44-0041-79

Compound	Solvent	λ_{max}(log ε)	Ref.
Pyrido[1,2-a]benzimidazol-9(5H)-imine, 7-phenyl-	MeOH	259(4.7)	95-0880-79
Quinoline, 8-(1H-benzimidazol-2-yl)-2-methyl-	EtOH	329(4.24),342(4.25)	4-1579-79
monohydriodide	EtOH	325(4.18),345(4.24)	4-1583-79
Quinoline, 8-(1H-benzimidazol-2-yl)-4-methyl-	EtOH	335(4.23),343(4.25)	4-1579-79
monohydriodide	EtOH	320(4.06),345(4.00)	4-1583-79
$C_{17}H_{13}N_3OS$			
2H-Pyrimido[4,5-b]indol-2-one, 1,3,4,9-tetrahydro-3-(4-methylphenyl)-4-thioxo-	$CHCl_3$	263(4.30),300s(3.65), 354(4.30)	103-0179-79
$C_{17}H_{13}N_3OS_2$			
3H-Pyrazol-3-one, 4-(2-benzothiazolylthio)-5-methyl-1-phenyl-	EtOH	222(4.50),244(4.32), 271(4.26),298(3.96)	48-0495-79
$C_{17}H_{13}N_3O_2$			
Imidazo[4,5-g][3,1]benzoxazin-8(3H)-one, 2,3-dimethyl-6-phenyl-	$CHCl_3$	273(4.71),317(4.38), 325(4.36)	39-1056-79C
1H-Pyrimido[4,5-b]indole-2,4(3H,9H)-dione, 3-(4-methylphenyl)-	$CHCl_3$	285(4.26),305(4.29), 312s(4.25)	103-0179-79
$C_{17}H_{13}N_3O_2S$			
1-Indolizinecarbonitrile, 8-methyl-2-(methylthio)-3-(4-nitrophenyl)-	EtOH	242(4.45),306(4.07), 340(3.99)	95-0540-79
3H-Pyrazol-3-one, 4-(2-benzoxazolylthio)-2,4-dihydro-5-methyl-2-phenyl-	EtOH	248(4.40),277(4.41), 285(4.28)	48-0495-79
2H-Pyrimido[4,5-b]indol-2-one, 1,3,4,9-tetrahydro-3-(4-methoxyphenyl)-4-thioxo-	$CHCl_3$	265(4.17),287(4.19), 327(4.03),345s(4.01)	103-0179-79
$C_{17}H_{13}N_3O_3S$			
Benzamide, N-(6-methyl-8-thioxo-1,3-dioxolo[4,5-g]quinazolin-7(8H)-yl)-	EtOH	226s(4.47),230(4.51), 255s(4.12),271(4.21), 322s(3.53),348s(3.87), 362(4.11),378(4.02), 387(4.06)	1-0079-79
Benzamide, N-[2-[(1,2,3,4-tetrahydro-2,4-dioxo-5-pyrimidinyl)thio]phenyl]-	MeOH	237(4.21)	4-0567-79
$C_{17}H_{13}N_3O_4$			
1H-Pyrazole-3-carboxylic acid, 1-(4-nitrophenyl)-5-phenyl-, methyl ester	CH_2Cl_2	298(4.17)	24-1193-79
1H-Pyrazole-4-carboxylic acid, 1-(4-nitrophenyl)-5-phenyl-, methyl ester	CH_2Cl_2	300(4.19)	24-1193-79
$C_{17}H_{13}N_5$			
5H-Indolo[2',3':5,6][1,2,4]triazino-[2,3-a]benzimidazole, 8,9-dimethyl-	EtOH	235(4.04),274(4.27), 282(4.44),292(4.50), 370(3.94)	142-1001-79
$C_{17}H_{13}N_5OS$			
1,2,4-Triazolo[3,4-b][1,3,4]thiadiazolium, 6-(benzoylamino)-3-methyl-2-phenyl-, hydroxide, inner salt	EtOH	313(4.49)	94-1688-79
$C_{17}H_{13}N_5S_2Se$			
Selenium, [4-phenyl-1-(phenylmethyl)-1H-1,2,4-triazolium-3-yl]bis(thiocyanato-S)-	MeCN	232(4.26),310(3.82)	70-2526-79

Compound	Solvent	λ_{max}(log ε)	Ref.
$C_{17}H_{13}N_5S_3$			
Sulfur, [4-phenyl-1-(phenylmethyl)-1H-1,2,4-triazolium-3-yl]bis(thiocyanato-S)-	MeCN	238(3.96),308(3.12)	70-2526-79
$C_{17}H_{14}$			
7H-Dibenzo[a,e]cyclobuta[c]cycloheptene, 2a,11b-dihydro-	C_6H_{12}	255(4.24),295s(3.38)	78-2359-79
5H-Dibenzo[a,c]cyclononene	EtOH	216(4.29),250s(3.60), 265s(3.34),273s(3.19), 293s(2.64),328s(2.00)	78-0667-79
7H-Dibenzo[a,c]cyclononene	EtOH	217(4.30),243s(3.85), 272s(3.18),280s(2.85), 293s(2.45)	78-0667-79
11H-Dibenzo[a,e]cyclononene	EtOH	250s(3.98),320s(3.07), 343(2.92)	78-0667-79
13H-Dibenzo[a,d]cyclononene, (E,Z)-	C_6H_{12}	258(4.04),280s(3.81), 335(3.26)	78-2359-79
(Z,Z)-	C_6H_{12}	255(4.08),290s(3.93)	78-2359-79
$C_{17}H_{14}BrN_2OS$			
Thiazolo[3,2-a]benzimidazolium, 3-(4-bromophenyl)-9-ethyl-6-hydroxy-, bromide	EtOH	260(3.40),512(3.81)	18-3096-79
$C_{17}H_{14}ClFN_2O_2$			
2H-1,4-Benzodiazepin-2-one, 7-chloro-5-(2-fluorophenyl)-1,3-dihydro-1-(2-hydroxyethyl)-	pH 0	243(4.33),288(4.03), 380(3.42)	59-0603-79
	pH 7	233(4.44),250s(4.15), 320(4.01)	59-0603-79
$C_{17}H_{14}ClN_3$			
Pyrazinamine, 5-(4-chlorophenyl)-3-(phenylmethyl)-	MeOH	285(4.31),342(4.07)	69-2204-79
$C_{17}H_{14}ClN_4$			
4H-[1,2,4]Triazolo[4,3-a][1,4]benzodiazepinium, 8-chloro-3-methyl-6-phenyl-, chloride	EtOH	224(4.55),250s(4.09), 265s(3.84),285(3.61)	44-2688-79
$C_{17}H_{14}Cl_2N_2O$			
4-Isoquinolinecarboxamide, 2-[(2,6-dichlorophenyl)methyl]-1,2-dihydro-	MeOH	272(4.0),339(4.0)	64-1593-79B
$C_{17}H_{14}IN_3O_4$			
Benzoic acid, 4-[[1-[[(4-iodophenyl)-amino]carbonyl]-2-oxopropylidene]-hydrazino]-	EtOH	248?(4.22),275(4.16), 385(4.55)	2-0585-79A
$C_{17}H_{14}N_2$			
4-Isoquinolinecarbonitrile, 1,2-dihydro-2-(phenylmethyl)-	CH_2Cl_2	242(4.1),343(3.9)	64-1593-79B
1H-Phenanthro[9,10-d]imidazole, 1,2-dimethyl-	EtOH	257(4.79),282(4.04), 306(3.93),340(3.11), 356(3.20)	44-0041-79
3-Quinolinecarbonitrile, 1,4-dihydro-1-(phenylmethyl)-	CH_2Cl_2	235(4.1),323s(4.1), 332(4.1)	64-1587-79B
$C_{17}H_{14}N_2O$			
3-Buten-2-one, 4-(1H-benzimidazol-1-yl)-4-phenyl-, (E)-	MeOH	211(4.43),228s(3.95), 254(4.05),274(4.23),	39-0584-79C

Compound	Solvent	$\lambda_{max}(\log \epsilon)$	Ref.
(cont.)		290s(4.15)	39-0584-79C
	MeOH-HClO₄	209(4.08),224(3.99), 270(4.20),277(4.20), 287s(4.15)	39-0584-79C
3-Buten-2-one, 4-(1H-benzimidazol-1-yl)-4-phenyl-, (Z)-	MeOH	215(4.28),255s(4.17), 267(4.18),303(4.05)	39-0584-79C
	MeOH-HClO₄	214(4.26),263(4.19), 268(4.18),274s(4.16)	39-0584-79C
Ellipticine, 9-hydroxy-	MeOH	245(4.41),276(4.60), 292(4.64),336(3.84), 353(3.45),405(3.44)	100-0643-79
	MeOH-KOH	249(4.41),277(4.55), 292(4.59),353(3.52), 368(3.40),415(3.36)	100-0643-79
Ethanone, 2-phenyl-1-(5-phenyl-1H-pyrazol-3-yl)-	MeOH	245(4.82)	4-0737-79
	MeOH-NaOMe	260(4.82),305s(4.35)	4-0737-79
4(1H)-Quinoxalinone, 1-methyl-2-(2-phenylethenyl)-	80% EtOH	220(4.42),305(4.13)	42-0708-79
$C_{17}H_{14}N_2OS$			
Acetamide, N-(3,4-diphenyl-2(3H)-thiazolylidene)-	EtOH	226(4.08),265(3.71), 310(4.08)	78-1199-79
Benzamide, N-(3-methyl-4-phenyl-2(3H)-thiazolylidene)-	EtOH	235(4.18),276(3.79), 286(3.77),331(4.35)	78-1199-79
$C_{17}H_{14}N_2O_2$			
1H-Pyrazole-3-carboxylic acid, 1,5-diphenyl-, methyl ester	CH_2Cl_2	235(4.34),255s(4.20)	24-1193-79
1H-Pyrazole-4-carboxylic acid, 1,5-diphenyl-, methyl ester	CH_2Cl_2	252(4.23)	24-1193-79
1H-Pyrazol-4-ol, 3,5-diphenyl-, acetate	EtOH	251(4.48)	23-0904-79
Pyrrolo[2,3-a]carbazole-2-carboxylic acid, 1,10-dihydro-, ethyl ester	EtOH	219(4.38),241(4.48), 256(4.59),284(4.67), 327(4.44)	103-1097-79
Pyrrolo[2,3-c]carbazole-2-carboxylic acid, 3,6-dihydro-, ethyl ester	EtOH	205(4.09),208(4.12), 225(4.19),250(3.00), 294(3.88),235[sic](3.94), 350(3.92)	103-0642-79
$C_{17}H_{14}N_2O_2S$			
1,3-Dioxolo[4,5-g]quinazoline, 6-methyl-8-[(phenylmethyl)thio]-	EtOH	203(4.26),214s(4.30), 234(4.26),242s(4.24), 281s(3.74),315s(3.74), 329(3.99),342(4.05)	1-0079-79
1,3-Dioxolo[4,5-g]quinazoline-8(7H)-thione, 6-methyl-7-(phenylmethyl)-	EtOH	228s(4.60),233(4.62), 256s(4.37),273(4.29), 325s(3.75),350s(4.05), 365(4.26),387(4.20)	1-0079-79
1H-Pyrazole-4-carboxylic acid, 1-phenyl-5-(phenylthio)-, methyl ester	CH_2Cl_2	247(4.33)	24-1193-79
1H-Pyrazole-5-carboxylic acid, 1-phenyl-3-(phenylthio)-, methyl ester	CH_2Cl_2	236(4.29)	24-1206-79
2(1H)-Pyrimidinethione, 4-(1,3-benzodioxol-5-yl)-3,4-dihydro-6-phenyl-	EtOH	257(4.16),279-96s(4.09)	23-2734-79
	$CHCl_3$	276(4.20),291s(4.19)	23-2734-79
	CCl_4	260(4.17),293(4.20)	23-2734-79
$C_{17}H_{14}N_2O_3$			
1,3-Dioxolo[4,5-g]quinazolin-8(5H)-one, 5-methyl-6-(phenylmethyl)-	80% EtOH	244(4.44),320(4.0), 333(4.01)	42-0708-79
Methanone, [3-(1,3-dioxolan-2-yl)-4-pyridinyl]-1H-indol-2-yl-	EtOH	228(4.27),324(4.39)	150-4801-79

Compound	Solvent	$\lambda_{max}(\log \epsilon)$	Ref.
$C_{17}H_{14}N_2O_3S$			
Propanoic acid, 2-[(3,4-dihydro-4-oxo-3-phenyl-2-quinoxalinyl)thio]-	MeOH	228(4.45),279(4.15), 317(3.61)	2-0039-79B
$C_{17}H_{14}N_2O_6$			
Pyrrolo[2,1-a]phthalazine-1,2,3-tricarboxylic acid, trimethyl ester	MeOH	225(4.08),247s(4.25), 254(4.27),264s(4.07), 302s(3.72),314(3.75)	150-4772-79
$C_{17}H_{14}N_2S$			
Quinazoline, 4-benzo[b]thien-2(or 3)-yl-1,4-dihydro-2-methyl-, hydrochloride	EtOH	268(3.63),285(3.47), 297(3.36)	24-1348-79
$C_{17}H_{14}N_4O$			
Acenaphtho[1,2-e][1,2,4]triazine, 9-morpholino-	MeOH	226(4.69),273(4.15), 333(4.47)	83-0147-79
2-Propenamide, 2-amino-3-cyano-3-[(diphenylmethylene)amino]-, (Z)-	EtOH	248(4.09),367(3.98)	44-0827-79
$C_{17}H_{14}N_4OS$			
3H-Pyrazol-3-one, 4-(1H-benzimidazol-2-ylthio)-2,4-dihydro-5-methyl-2-phenyl-	EtOH	282(4.29),290(4.31)	48-0495-79
$C_{17}H_{14}N_4OS_2$			
Urea, bis(3-methyl-2(3H)-benzothiazolylidene)-	MeCN	235(4.61),339(4.90), 352(5.02)	48-0827-79
$C_{17}H_{14}N_4O_2$			
1H-Pyrazole-3-carboxaldehyde, 4,5-dihydro-1-(4-methylphenyl)-5-oxo-4-(phenylhydrazono)-	n.s.g.	212(3.97),253(4.18), 410(4.18)	106-0531-79
$C_{17}H_{14}N_4O_5$			
2-Cyclopenten-1-one, 4,5-bis[(2-nitrophenyl)amino]-	n.s.g.	230(4.56),278(4.02), 414(3.95)	12-1079-79
2-Cyclopenten-1-one, 4,5-bis[(3-nitrophenyl)amino]-	n.s.g.	240(4.50),370(3.40)	12-1079-79
2-Cyclopenten-1-one, 4,5-bis[(4-nitrophenyl)amino]-	n.s.g.	224(4.15),375(4.48)	12-1079-79
$C_{17}H_{14}N_4S_3$			
Benzenamine, N,N'-(3,4-dihydro-2H,5H-1,6,6a-trithia(6a-S^{IV})-2a,4a-diazacyclopenta[cd]pentalene-2,5-diylidene)bis-	CH_2Cl_2	259(4.65),309(4.21)	39-2909-79C
Thiourea, N,N'-bis(3-methyl-2(3H)-benzothiazolylidene)-	MeOH	234(4.76),275(4.08), 400(4.85)	48-0827-79
$C_{17}H_{14}N_6OS$			
3H-Pyrazol-3-one, 2,4-dihydro-5-methyl-2-phenyl-4-[(1-phenyl-1H-tetrazol-5-yl)thio]-	EtOH	208(4.31),228(4.24), 245(4.21)	48-0495-79
$C_{17}H_{14}O$			
Naphthalene, 1-methoxy-3-phenyl-	EtOH	212(4.56),254(4.71), 300(3.97)	104-1973-79

Compound	Solvent	λ_{max}(log ε)	Ref.
$C_{17}H_{14}OS$			
Dibenzo[b,e]thiepin, 6,11-dihydro-11-(2-propenylidene)-, 5-oxide	MeOH	265(4.21),280s(4.18)	73-2536-79
$C_{17}H_{14}O_2$			
2-Cyclopenten-1-one, 5-hydroxy-3,4-diphenyl-, trans	n.s.g.	278(4.3)	39-0274-79C
5H-Dibenzo[a,c]cyclononene-5,9(6H)-dione, 7,8-dihydro-	EtOH	230(4.21),285s(3.34)	78-0667-79
$C_{17}H_{14}O_2S$			
Dibenzo[b,e]thiepin, 6,11-dihydro-11-(2-propenylidene)-, 5,5-dioxide	MeOH	265(4.34),282s(4.21)	73-2536-79
2-Propenoic acid, 3-(6,11-dibenzo[b,e]-thiepin-11-yl)-, (E)-	MeOH	254(3.96)	73-2536-79
$C_{17}H_{14}O_3$			
4H-1-Benzopyran-4-one, 2,3-dihydro-3-[(2-methoxyphenyl)methylene]-	EtOH	256(4.06),286(4.15), 344(4.12)	150-1713-79
4H-1-Benzopyran-4-one, 2,3-dihydro-3-[(3-methoxyphenyl)methylene]-	EtOH	259(4.09),295(4.29), 352(4.04)	150-1713-79
4H-1-Benzopyran-4-one, 2,3-dihydro-3-[(4-methoxyphenyl)methylene]-	EtOH	223(4.31),238(4.28), 328(4.36),356(4.35)	150-1713-79
4H-1-Benzopyran-4-one, 2-(2-methoxyphenyl)-3-methyl-	EtOH	227(4.41),282(3.95), 316(4.01)	150-1713-79
4H-1-Benzopyran-4-one, 2-(3-methoxyphenyl)-3-methyl-	EtOH	230(4.22),261(4.01), 316(4.27)	150-1713-79
4H-1-Benzopyran-4-one, 2-(4-methoxyphenyl)-3-methyl-	EtOH	241(4.31),364(4.02), 316(4.31)	150-1713-79
4H-1-Benzopyran-4-one, 3-[(2-methoxyphenyl)methyl]-	EtOH	225(4.65),298(4.03), 305(4.01)	150-1713-79
4H-1-Benzopyran-4-one, 3-[(3-methoxyphenyl)methyl]-	EtOH	226(4.23),282(3.47), 289(3.60),306(3.60)	150-1713-79
4H-1-Benzopyran-4-one, 3-[(4-methoxyphenyl)methyl]-	EtOH	227(4.56),298(3.74), 305(3.74)	150-1713-79
$C_{17}H_{14}O_4$			
9,10-Anthracenedione, 1,4-dihydroxy-2-propyl-	MeOH	205(4.41),250(4.62), 287(4.04),330s(--), 483(3.91)	5-0019-79
1H-2-Benzopyran-4-carboxylic acid, 3,4-dihydro-1-oxo-3-phenyl-, methyl ester, trans	EtOH	237(3.87),282(3.06), 293(3.00)	117-0077-79
1(3H)-Isobenzofuranone, 6-methoxy-2-[1-(4-hydroxyphenyl)ethylidene]-	EtOH	259(4.14),290(4.03), 368(4.26)	78-0531-79
$C_{17}H_{14}O_5$			
9,10-Anthracenedione, 1,4-dihydroxy-2-(2-hydroxyethyl)-3-methyl-	MeOH	229s(--),252(4.60), 255(4.61),292(3.77), 457s(--),486(3.99), 520s(--)	5-0019-79
9,10-Anthracenedione, 1,4-dihydroxy-2-(1-hydroxypropyl)-	MeOH	205(4.35),250(4.57), 285(4.01),330s(--), 484(3.97),580s(--)	5-0019-79
4H-1-Benzopyran-4-one, 5-hydroxy-7,8-dimethoxy-2-phenyl-	MeOH	276(4.50),340(3.83)	102-0149-79
1,4-Ethanoanthracene-9,10-dione, 1,4-dihydro-5,8-dihydroxy-1-methoxy-	MeOH	217(4.48),284(3.85), 492s(--),520(3.87), 560(3.66)	24-3453-79
Phenanthro[1,2-d]-1,3-dioxol-8-ol, 7,9-dimethoxy-	$CHCl_3$	308(3.98),339(3.86), 355(3.66),373(3.75)	39-2449-79C

Compound	Solvent	$\lambda_{max}(\log \epsilon)$	Ref.
(cont.)	$CHCl_3$	267(4.71),308s(4.01), 356(3.59),373(3.62)	39-2449-79C
$C_{17}H_{14}O_6$			
4H-1-Benzopyran-4-one, 5,7-dihydroxy-3,8-dimethoxy-2-phenyl-	MeOH	275(4.5),352(3.9)	2-0037-79A
4H-1-Benzopyran-4-one, 5-hydroxy-2-(2-hydroxyphenyl)-6,7-dimethoxy-	MeOH	272(4.2),338(4.1)	95-0657-79
	$MeOH-AlCl_3$	280s(--),287(--), 366(--)	95-0657-79
	EtOH	248(4.12),271(4.36), 339(4.26)	18-2950-79
	$EtOH-AlCl_3$	254(4.09),278s(4.35), 286(4.44),354(4.28)	18-2950-79
	EtOH-NaOAc	271(4.34),337(4.15), 415(3.73)	18-2950-79
4H-1-Benzopyran-4-one, 5-hydroxy-2-(2-hydroxyphenyl)-6,8-dimethoxy-	MeOH	287(3.7),330(3.4)	95-0657-79
	$MeOH-AlCl_3$	292s(--),307(--), 364(--)	95-0657-79
	EtOH	284(4.41),321(4.10), 339(4.11)	18-2950-79
	$EtOH-AlCl_3$	253(4.03),287s(4.29), 301(4.35),339(4.21), 355s(4.19)	18-2950-79
	EtOH-NaOAc	285(4.37),319s(4.02), 340(4.00),411(3.77)	18-2950-79
4H-1-Benzopyran-4-one, 5-hydroxy-2-(2-hydroxyphenyl)-7,8-dimethoxy-	MeOH	275(5.10),340(3.70)	95-0657-79
	$MeOH-AlCl_3$	283(--),292s(--), 353(--),410(--)	95-0657-79
	EtOH	271(4.40),340(4.05)	18-2950-79
	$EtOH-AlCl_3$	280(4.34),342(4.05), 400(3.84)	18-2950-79
syn	EtOH	273(4.44),343(4.11)	18-2950-79
	$EtOH-AlCl_3$	282(4.39),294s(4.34), 345(4.11),404(3.91)	18-2950-79
	EtOH-NaOAc	271(4.41),343(4.01), 416(3.81)	18-2950-79
4H-1-Benzopyran-4-one, 5-hydroxy-2-(3-hydroxyphenyl)-7,8-dimethoxy-	MeOH	273(4.43),340(4.07)	102-0149-79
Isoflavone, 3',7-dihydroxy-2',4'-dimethoxy- (3λ,2ε)	EtOH	240s(3.88),249s(3.58), 309s(?)	102-0815-79
	EtOH-NaOH	228(4.15),256s(4.09), 346(3.84)	102-0815-79
	EtOH-NaOAc	260s(3.89),355s(3.59)	102-0815-79
1,4-Naphthalenedione, 5,8-dihydroxy-2-(2-methoxy-4-oxo-2-cyclohexen-1-yl)- (and isomer)	MeOH	214(4.63),250(4.36), 283s(3.91),483(3.81), 509(3.84),554(3.60)	24-2640-79
$C_{17}H_{15}BF_2O_3$			
Boron, difluoro[1-(4-methoxyphenyl)-2-phenyl-1,3-butanedionato)-, (T-4)-	hexane	240(3.88),358(4.42)	23-1186-79
	EtOH	240(3.75),364(4.20)	23-1186-79
$C_{17}H_{15}BrN_2$			
1H-Pyrazole, 3-(4-bromophenyl)-1,5-dimethyl-4-phenyl-	hexane	243(4.28),263s(4.24)	23-1186-79
	EtOH	240(4.23),261s(4.15)	23-1186-79
1H-Pyrazole, 5-(4-bromophenyl)-1,3-dimethyl-4-phenyl-	hexane	228(4.21),244(4.21)	23-1186-79
	EtOH	230s(4.26),237(4.25)	23-1186-79
3H-Pyrazole, 5-(4-bromophenyl)-3,3-dimethyl-4-phenyl-	MeOH	245(4.25),305(3.76)	23-1403-79
$C_{17}H_{15}BrS$			
Dibenzo[b,e]thiepin, 11-(3-bromoprop-	heptane	233(4.31),262s(3.91),	73-2536-79

Compound	Solvent	λmax(log ε)	Ref.
ylidene)-6,11-dihydro-, (E)- (cont.)		308(3.43)	73-2536-79
$C_{17}H_{15}ClN_2OS$			
2(1H)-Pyrimidinethione, 6-(4-chloro-phenyl)-3,4-dihydro-4-(4-methoxy-phenyl)-	EtOH	232(4.35),253(4.31)	23-2734-79
	$CHCl_3$	271(4.22)	23-2734-79
	CCl_4	260(4.24),279(4.20), 288-309s(4.12)	23-2734-79
$C_{17}H_{15}ClN_2O_2S$			
Benzenesulfonamide, 4-chloro-N-[(1,3-dimethyl-1H-indol-2-yl)methylene]-	EtOH	225(4.61),255s(4.41), 350(4.34)	39-2154-79C
$C_{17}H_{15}ClN_2O_3$			
4(3H)-Quinazolinone, 6-chloro-3-[2-(3,4-dihydroxyphenyl)ethyl]-2-methyl-, hydrochloride	MeOH	276(4.19),316(3.58), 328(3.45)	4-0449-79
4(3H)-Quinazolinone, 7-chloro-3-[2-(3,4-dihydroxyphenyl)ethyl]-2-methyl-, hydrochloride	MeOH	282(4.06),308(3.58), 320(3.51)	4-0449-79
$C_{17}H_{15}ClN_2S$			
2(1H)-Quinazolinethione, 6-chloro-1-(1-methylethyl)-4-phenyl-	EtOH	302(4.45),417(3.72)	118-0120-79
$C_{17}H_{15}ClN_4$			
Acetaldehyde, (7-chloro-5-phenyl-3H-1,4-benzodiazepin-2-yl)hydrazone	EtOH	214s(4.47),230s(4.37), 260(4.42),335(3.40)	44-2688-79
$C_{17}H_{15}ClN_4S$			
Ethanethioamide, 2-[(3-chloro-2-methyl-phenyl)hydrazono]-2-cyano-N-(phenyl-methyl)-	EtOH	380(4.42)	104-1082-79
$C_{17}H_{15}ClN_5$			
4H-[1,2,4]Triazolo[4,3-a][1,4]benzodi-azepinium, 1-amino-8-chloro-3-methyl-6-phenyl-, chloride	EtOH	217(4.52),257(4.15)	44-2688-79
$C_{17}H_{15}ClO$			
2-Propen-1-one, 2-chloro-1-(4-ethyl-phenyl)-3-phenyl-, (Z)-	hexane	296(4.28)	97-0096-79
$C_{17}H_{15}ClO_2$			
Tricyclo[8.3.2.2^{4,7}]heptadeca-4,6,11,13-16-pentaene-14,15-dione, 12-chloro-	MeOH	228(4.18),248(4.07), 261(4.07),370(3.84), 414s(3.22)	88-1113-79
$C_{17}H_{15}ClO_3$			
Anthra[1,2-d]-1,3-dioxol-5(4H)-one, 4-chloro-3a,11b-dihydro-2,2-dimethyl-, (3aα,4α,11bα)-	ether	216(4.50),244s(4.50), 253(4.63),283s(3.70), 294(3.85),304(3.76), 338s(3.22),346(3.25)	22-0110-79
2-Propen-1-one, 2-chloro-1,3-bis(4-methoxyphenyl)-, (Z)-	hexane	319(4.41)	97-0096-79
$C_{17}H_{15}Fe$			
Methylium, ferrocenylphenyl-	$C_2H_4Cl_2$	260(4.01),337(4.05), 406(3.46)	32-0013-79
$C_{17}H_{15}IN_2O_3$			
4(3H)-Quinazolinone, 3-[2-(3,4-dihy-	MeOH	282(4.20),318(3.45),	4-0449-79

Compound	Solvent	$\lambda_{max}(\log \epsilon)$	Ref.
droxyphenyl)ethyl]-6-iodo-2-methyl-, hydrochloride (cont.)		330(3.30)	4-0449-79
$C_{17}H_{15}IN_4O_4$			
Butanamide, N-(5-iodo-2-methylphenyl)-2-[(4-nitrophenyl)hydrazono]-3-oxo-	EtOH	245(4.22),285(4.24), 395(4.71)	2-0585-79A
$C_{17}H_{15}N$			
16-Azabicyclo[9.2.2.1^{4,8}]hexadeca-2,4,6,8(16),9,11,13,14-octaene, 12,14-dimethyl-	MeCN	228(4.39),242(4.36), 294(3.55)	35-2121-79
Isoquinoline, 1-(1-phenylethyl)-	EtOH	262(3.61),317(3.59)	44-3244-79
1-Naphthalenamine, N-methyl-2-phenyl-	MeOH	213(4.79),245s(4.65), 310(3.75)	103-1117-79
$C_{17}H_{15}NO$			
Benzamide, N-1,3-butadienyl-N-phenyl-	MeOH	278(4.35)	88-0981-79
1H-Phenalen-1-one, 9-pyrrolidino-	n.s.g.	239(4.17),371(4.16), 432(3.84),546(3.80)	44-1704-79
Pyridine, 1,4-dihydro-1-hydroxy-2,6-diphenyl-	MeOH	254(4.25),305s(3.96)	4-0737-79
	$MeOH-H_2SO_4$	260(4.26),343(3.78)	4-0737-79
$C_{17}H_{15}NO_2$			
4H-1-Benzopyran-4-one, 2-[2-(ethylamino)phenyl]-	MeOH	205(4.53),242(4.48), 299(4.09),386(3.85)	83-0248-79
Benzoxazole, 2-[2-(4-ethoxyphenyl)ethenyl]-	EtOH	232(4.20),340(4.23)	56-1033-79
Cyclopenta[c]carbazole-4-carboxylic acid, 1,2,3,6-tetrahydro-, methyl ester	EtOH	227s(4.18),250(4.60), 308(4.34),361(3.56), 368(3.59)	44-4402-79
3,5-Pyridinedicarboxaldehyde, 1-(2,6-dimethylphenyl)-4-ethynyl-1,4-dihydro-	EtOH	209(4.32),229(4.42), 253(4.15),365(4.03)	49-0613-79
3,5-Pyridinedicarboxaldehyde, 1-(3,5-dimethylphenyl)-4-ethynyl-1,4-dihydro-	EtOH	215(4.37),224(4.39), 241(4.27),276(4.34), 375(3.99)	49-0613-79
2(1H)-Quinolinone, 3-(2-methoxyphenyl)-4-methyl-	EtOH	223(4.60),275(3.95), 317s(3.89),328(3.98), 342s(3.83)	4-0487-79
4(1H)-Quinolinone, 1-ethyl-2-(2-hydroxyphenyl)-	dioxan	218(4.44),244(4.31), 254(4.28),280(3.87), 326(4.08),339(4.15)	83-0248-79
4(1H)-Quinolinone, 3-(2-methoxyphenyl)-2-methyl-	EtOH	213(4.58),240(4.37), 247(4.38),281(3.84), 320(4.04),332(4.04)	4-0487-79
$C_{17}H_{15}NO_3$			
Benzoic acid, 2-(5-acetyl-2,3-dihydro-1H-indol-1-yl)-	EtOH	205(4.30),227(4.42), 298(3.40)	103-1223-79
Benzoxazole, 2-[2-(3,4-dimethoxyphenyl)-ethenyl]-, (E)-	EtOH	243(3.96),347(4.69)	56-1033-79
$C_{17}H_{15}NO_4$			
1H-Benzo[a]furo[3,4-f]quinolizine-1,12(3H)-dione, 5,6-dihydro-8-methoxy-3-methyl-	MeOH	219(4.20),231(4.13), 237(4.08),256(4.17), 275(4.22),285(4.25), 304(4.22),318(4.15)	104-1247-79
4H-Pyrano[3,2-c]pyridine-4,5(6H)-dione, 2-(4-methoxyphenyl)-6,7-dimethyl-	EtOH	302(4.20),325(4.32)	94-0242-79
3,5-Pyridinedicarboxaldehyde, 1-(3,5-dimethoxyphenyl)-4-ethynyl-1,4-dihydro-	EtOH	227(4.44),242s(4.17), 277(4.34),373(3.92)	49-0613-79

Compound	Solvent	$\lambda_{max}(\log \epsilon)$	Ref.
$C_{17}H_{15}NO_4S$			
Ethanone, 2-(2-oxazolidinylidene)-1-phenyl-2-(phenylsulfonyl)-	EtOH	275(4.28)	95-0038-79
$C_{17}H_{15}N_2OS$			
Thiazolo[3,2-a]benzimidazolium, 9-ethyl-6-hydroxy-3-phenyl-, bromide	EtOH	260(3.84),510(4.00)	18-3096-79
$C_{17}H_{15}N_2OS_2$			
Pyridinium, 1-[4-amino-5-benzoyl-2-(methylthio)-3-thienyl]-, iodide	EtOH	246(3.90),306(3.86), 364(4.01)	95-1081-79
$C_{17}H_{15}N_2O_2S$			
Thiazolo[3,2-a]benzimidazolium, 9-ethyl-6-hydroxy-3-(4-hydroxyphenyl)-, bromide	EtOH	255(3.38),508(3.63)	18-3096-79
$C_{17}H_{15}N_2PS_3$			
Phosphoramidotrithioic acid, 2-pyridinyl-, diphenyl ester	EtOH	211(4.49),230(4.43)	64-0297-79B
$C_{17}H_{15}N_3$			
Pyrazinamine, 5-phenyl-3-(phenylmethyl)-	MeOH	276(4.23),341(4.01)	69-2204-79
$C_{17}H_{15}N_3O_2$			
Propanoic acid, 2-oxo-, ethyl ester, 2-(1-carbazolylhydrazone)	EtOH	205(4.40),223(4.61), 250(4.61),292(4.22), 379(4.35)	103-1097-79
isomer	EtOH	211(4.85),222(4.90), 233(4.99),245(4.87), 292(4.63)	103-1097-79
$C_{17}H_{15}N_3O_3$			
2,4-Cyclohexadien-1-one, 6-[(1,3-dihydro-1,3-dimethyl-5-nitro-2H-benzimidazol-2-ylidene)ethylidene]-	EtOH	350(4.29)	42-0871-79
$C_{17}H_{15}N_3O_3S$			
8-Azabicyclo[3.2.1]oct-3-ene-6-carboxylic acid, 2-oxo-8-(3-phenyl-1,2,4-thiadiazol-5-yl)-, methyl ester, endo	MeCN	257(4.69)	39-0399-79C
exo	MeCN	235(4.45)	39-0399-79C
Benzoic acid, 4-[[(2-benzothiazolylamino)carbonyl]amino]-, ethyl ester	n.s.g.	240(4.09),290(4.66), 298(4.95),320(3.86)	87-0028-79
2H-1,4-Benzothiazine-2-acetamide, N-(2-aminophenyl)-3,4-dihydro-4-methyl-α,3-dioxo-	dioxan	350(3.9)	83-0302-79
$C_{17}H_{15}N_3O_4$			
Acetic acid, (5-acetoxy-6-phenyl-4(1H)-pyrimidinylidene)cyano-, ethyl ester	EtOH	208(4.17),298(4.23), 372(4.15)	103-0677-79
1H-Benz[f]indazole-3-carboxamide, 4,9-dihydro-4,9-dioxo-1-(tetrahydro-2H-pyran-2-yl)-, (±)-	EtOH	249(4.37),270(3.93)	111-0151-79
$C_{17}H_{15}N_3O_4S$			
Benzaldehyde, 4-methoxy-, [(3,4-dihydro-3-oxo-2H-1,4-benzothiazin-2-ylidene)methyl]hydrazone, S,S-dioxide	dioxan	270(3.46),350(3.82)	83-0302-79

Compound	Solvent	$\lambda_{max}(\log \epsilon)$	Ref.
$C_{17}H_{15}N_3O_6$			
1-Propanone, 2-methyl-1-(4-nitrophenyl)-, O-(4-nitrobenzoyl)oxime	MeOH	261(4.35)	12-1487-79
$C_{17}H_{15}N_3S$			
Thiourea, N-(6-methyl-5-quinolinyl)-N'-phenyl-	EtOH	213(4.54),238(4.61), 303s(3.87),323s(3.84)	56-1895-79
Thiourea, N-(8-methyl-5-quinolinyl)-N'-phenyl-	EtOH	203(4.67),239(4.51), 286s(4.12)	56-1895-79
Thiourea, N-(7-methyl-8-quinolinyl)-N'-phenyl-	EtOH	211(4.57),238(4.41)	56-1895-79
$C_{17}H_{15}N_5O_2$			
2,5-Piperazinedione, 3-(1H-imidazol-4-ylmethylene)-6-(1H-indol-3-ylmethyl)-, (E)-(+)-	EtOH	221(4.532),286s(4.027), 291(4.073),326(4.275)	98-0201-79
$C_{17}H_{15}N_5O_2S$			
Ethanethioamide, 2-cyano-2-[(2-methyl-5-nitrophenyl)hydrazono]-N-(phenylmethyl)-	EtOH	385(4.47)	104-1082-79
1,2,4-Triazolo[3,4-b]-1,3,4-thiadiazolium, 5-methyl-6-phenyl-, 2-p-tolylsulfonylaminide	EtOH	282(4.40)	94-1688-79
$C_{17}H_{15}N_5O_3S$			
Ethanethioamide, 2-cyano-2-[(2-methoxy-5-nitrophenyl)hydrazono]-N-(phenylmethyl)-	EtOH	245(4.34),290(4.01), 385(4.26),410(4.37)	104-1082-79
$C_{17}H_{15}N_5O_4$			
Adenosine, N-benzoyl-4',5'-didehydro-5'-deoxy-	MeOH	229(4.15),279(4.33)	44-0400-79
$C_{17}H_{15}N_5O_6$			
2-Pyridineacetic acid, α-(1,3-dihydro-1,3-dimethyl-2H-benzimidazol-2-ylidene)-3,5-dinitro-, methyl ester	0.01N H_2SO_4	358(4.05),395(4.34)	104-0178-79
	pH 12	335(4.2),465(4.31)	104-0178-79
	EtOH	335(4.2),465(4.31)	104-0178-79
$C_{17}H_{15}N_5O_6S_3$			
5-Thia-1-azabicyclo[4.2.0]oct-2-ene-2-carboxylic acid, 7-[[2-furanyl(methoxyimino)acetyl]amino]-8-oxo-3-[(1,2,3-thiadiazol-5-ylthio)methyl]-, sodium salt, anti	H_2O	269(4.21)	87-1214-79
syn	H_2O	219(4.37),278(4.32)	87-1214-79
$C_{17}H_{15}N_9$			
6H-Pyrazolo[5',3':3,4][1,2,4]triazino-[6,5-b]indole, 2,6-dimethyl-3-[(5-methyl-1H-pyrazol-3-yl)azo]-	DMF	375(4.00),390s(3.98), 480(3.86)	103-0657-79
$C_{17}H_{15}OS_3$			
1,2-Dithiol-1-ium, 3-[(2-methoxyphenyl)-thio]-4-methyl-5-phenyl-, bromide	MeCN	220(4.48),293(3.81), 340s(4.03),374(4.29)	104-0955-79
1,2-Dithiol-1-ium, 3-[(3-methoxyphenyl)-thio]-4-methyl-5-phenyl-, bromide	MeCN	219(4.42),340s(3.97), 372(4.15)	104-0955-79
1,2-Dithiol-1-ium, 3-[(4-methoxyphenyl)-thio]-4-methyl-5-phenyl-, bromide	MeCN	220(4.67),265s(4.09), 340s(4.26),372(4.41)	104-0955-79

Compound	Solvent	$\lambda_{max}(\log \epsilon)$	Ref.
$C_{17}H_{15}S_3$			
1,2-Dithiol-1-ium, 4-methyl-3-[(2-methylphenyl)thio]-5-phenyl-, bromide	MeCN	219(4.58),265s(3.72), 336s(4.03),372(4.39)	104-0955-79
1,2-Dithiol-1-ium, 4-methyl-3-[(3-methylphenyl)thio]-5-phenyl-, bromide	MeCN	218(4.62),265s(3.75), 339s(4.11),372(4.39)	104-0955-79
1,2-Dithiol-1-ium, 4-methyl-3-[(4-methylphenyl)thio]-5-phenyl-, bromide	MeCN	220(4.55),265s(3.67), 340s(3.98),372(4.29)	104-0955-79
1,2-Dithiol-1-ium, 4-methyl-3-[(4-methylphenyl)thio]-5-phenyl-, triiodide	MeCN	222(4.24),293(4.44), 370(4.40)	104-0955-79
$C_{17}H_{16}$			
Anthracene, 9-(1-methylethyl)-	CCl_4	335(3.48),350(3.77), 369(3.95),387(3.91)	78-2131-79
Anthracene, 9-propyl-	CCl_4	334(3.47),349(3.76), 368(3.96),388(3.94)	78-2131-79
1,4-Methanobenzo[b]biphenylene, 1,2,3,4,4a,10b-hexahydro-, (1α,4α,4aβ,10bβ)-	C_6H_{12}	260(3.68),268(3.85), 278(3.92),290(3.77), 308(3.26),312(3.08), 320(3.47)	35-1820-79
Phenanthrene, 3-(1-methylethyl)-	EtOH	224(4.12),252(4.56), 293(3.75),335(2.57), 349(2.39)	2-0226-79A
$C_{17}H_{16}ClN_3O$			
Benzamide, 2-chloro-N-[4,5-dihydro-1-(phenylmethyl)-1H-pyrazol-3-yl]-	EtOH	228s(3.99),290(3.88)	150-0801-79
1,2,4-Oxadiazole-3-ethanamine, 5-(3-chlorophenyl)-N-(phenylmethyl)-	EtOH	252(4.17),285(3.18), 295(3.05)	150-0801-79
$C_{17}H_{16}Cl_2N_2O_6$			
4-Oxa-1-azabicyclo[3.2.0]heptane-2-carboxylic acid, 3-[2-(dichloroacetyl)amino]ethylidene]-7-oxo-, phenylmethyl ester, [2R-(2α,3Z,5α)]-	EtOH	270(3.15),276(3.05)	39-2268-79C
$C_{17}H_{16}F_3NO$			
Acetamide, 2,2,2-trifluoro-N-(2',4',6'-trimethyl[1,1'-biphenyl]-4-yl)-	C_6H_{12}	256(4.21)	12-1531-79
$C_{17}H_{16}F_4O_3$			
5H-Cycloprop[7,8]azuleno[4,5-b]furan-5-one, 3-(difluoromethoxy)-8,8-difluoro-3a,3b,6,6a,7,7a,8,8a-octahydro-3a,8a-dimethyl-6-methylene-, [3aR-(3aα,3bβ,6aβ,7aα,8aα)]-	EtOH	270(3.65)	78-0815-79
1H-Dicycloprop[1,2:8,8a]azuleno[4,5-b]-furan-6,8-dione, 1,1,2,2-tetrafluorodecahydro-2a,7b-dimethyl-5-methylene-, [1aS-(1aα,1bS*,2aα,4aβ,7aβ,7bα,8aα)]-	EtOH	219(3.39)	78-0815-79
Spiro[cyclopropane-1,7'(8'H)-cycloprop-[8,8a]azuleno[4,5-b]furan]-1',8'(4'H)-dione, 2,2,4',4'-tetrafluoro-4'a,5'-6',6'a,9'a,9'b-hexahydro-4'a,9'b-dimethyl-, [4'aR-(3'aR*,4'aα,6'aβ,7'β-9'aβ,9'α)]-	EtOH	246(3.53)	78-0815-79
$C_{17}H_{16}IN_3O_2$			
Butanamide, N-(4-iodophenyl)-2-[(4-methylphenyl)hydrazono]-3-oxo-	EtOH	248(4.27),275(4.13), 385(4.53)	2-0585-79A

Compound	Solvent	λ_{max}(log ϵ)	Ref.
$C_{17}H_{16}IN_3O_3$			
Butanamide, N-(4-iodophenyl)-2-[(4-methoxyphenyl)hydrazono]-3-oxo-	EtOH	248(4.26),280(4.31), 395(4.51)	2-0585-79A
$C_{17}H_{16}IN_5O_4$			
Adenosine, N-benzoyl-5'-deoxy-5'-iodo-	MeOH	231(4.14),260s(4.11), 280(4.32)	44-0400-79
$C_{17}H_{16}N$			
Quinolinium, 1-methyl-2-(phenylmethyl)-,	neutral	415(4.48)(estd.)	39-0792-79B
iodide	cation	317(4.00)	39-0792-79B
Quinolinium, 4-methyl-1-(phenylmethyl)-,	EtOH	236(4.69),316(4.01)	103-1208-79
bromide			103-1208-79
chloride	EtOH	236(4.75),314(4.02)	103-1208-79
iodide	EtOH	234(4.79),315(4.15)	103-1208-79
perchlorate	EtOH	238(4.68),318(4.02)	103-1208-79
$C_{17}H_{16}N_2$			
1H-Pyrazole, 1,4-bis(4-methylphenyl)-	EtOH	276(4.34)	22-0017-79
1H-Pyrazole, 1,3-dimethyl-4,5-diphenyl-	hexane	239(4.20)	23-1186-79
	EtOH	233(4.16)	23-1186-79
1H-Pyrazole, 1,5-dimethyl-3,4-diphenyl-	hexane	237(4.23)	23-1186-79
	EtOH	231(4.21)	23-1186-79
4H-Pyrazole, 3,4-dimethyl-4,5-diphenyl-	hexane	274(4.08)	23-1186-79
	EtOH	277(4.15)	23-1186-79
$C_{17}H_{16}N_2O$			
2,4-Cyclohexadien-1-one, 6-[(1,3-di-	benzene	347(3.75)	42-0871-79
hydro-1,3-dimethyl-2H-benzimidazol-	EtOH	265(3.92),350(4.36)	42-0871-79
2-ylidene)ethylidene]-	$CHCl_3$	260(4.93),344(4.34), 520(2.44)	42-0871-79
2-Naphthaleneacetonitrile, α-(4-morpholinylmethylene)-	MeOH	213(4.57),260(4.22), 320(4.38)	83-0039-79
1H-Pyrazole, 4-methoxy-1-methyl-3,5-diphenyl-	EtOH	251(4.38)	23-0904-79
1H-Pyrazolium, 4-hydroxy-1,2-dimethyl-3,5-diphenyl-, hydroxide, inner salt	EtOH	226(4.15),248s(3.83), 325(3.99)	23-0904-79
1H-Pyrazolium, 4-hydroxy-1,3-dimethyl-2,5-diphenyl-, hydroxide, inner salt	H_2O	322(4.01)	23-0904-79
3-Quinolinecarboxamide, 1,4-dihydro-1-(phenylmethyl)-	CH_2Cl_2	238(4.0),331s(4.0), 342(4.0)	64-1587-79B
$C_{17}H_{16}N_2OS$			
2(1H)-Pyrimidinethione, 3,4-dihydro-6-(4-methoxyphenyl)-4-phenyl-	EtOH	225(4.31),247(4.22), 258-272s(4.14)	23-2734-79
	$CHCl_3$	272(4.16)	23-2734-79
	CCl_4	278(4.14),287-307s(4.11)	23-2734-79
$C_{17}H_{16}N_2O_2$			
Benz[f]imidazo[1,2-a]quinolin-11(1H)-one, 1-acetyl-2,3,5,6-tetrahydro-	MeOH	229(4.27),262(4.58), 300(4.19)	4-0517-79
1H-Isoindole-1,3(2H)-dione, 2-[2-(meth-	C_6H_{12}	357(1.99)	39-1103-79B
ylphenylamino)ethyl]-	benzene	363(1.96)	39-1103-79B
	EtOH	359(1.95)	39-1103-79B
3,5-Pyridinedicarboxaldehyde, 1-[4-(dimethylamino)phenyl]-4-ethynyl-1,4-dihydro-	EtOH	231(4.30),257(4.09), 289(4.35),390(3.82)	49-0613-79
$C_{17}H_{16}N_2O_2S$			
Benzenepropanamide, α-[[(4-methylphenyl)amino]thioxomethyl]-β-oxo-	EtOH	275(3.91),305(3.76), 345(3.89)	104-1324-79

Compound	Solvent	λ_{max}(log ε)	Ref.
$C_{17}H_{16}N_2O_2S_2$			
Acetamide, N-[2-[(6-methoxy-2-methyl-7-benzothiazolyl)thio]phenyl]-	MeOH	242(4.30),297(3.78), 308(3.70)	39-1478-79C
$C_{17}H_{16}N_2O_3$			
1,3-Butanedione, 2-[(4-methoxyphenyl)-azo]-1-phenyl-	acetone	403(4.279)	2-0502-79A'
	dioxan	402(4.246)	2-0502-79A'
	$CHCl_3$	405(4.322)	2-0502-79A'
	CCl_4	405(4.297)	2-0502-79A'
1H-Isoindole-1,3(2H)-dione, 5-(dimethylamino)-4-methoxy-2-phenyl-	EtOH	391(3.7)	88-0921-79
3-Pyrrolidinecarboxylic acid, 5-oxo-1-(phenylmethyl)-2-(3-pyridinyl)-, trans	EtOH	259s(3.20),264(3.25), 271s(3.11)	44-4332-79
Pyrrolo[2',3':4,5]furo[3,2-b]indole-2-carboxylic acid, 1-ethyl-1,9-dihydro-, ethyl ester	MeOH	360(4.47)	73-1805-79
4(3H)-Quinazolinone, 3-[2-(3,4-dihydroxyphenyl)ethyl]-2-methyl-, hydrochloride	MeOH	278(4.02),305(3.56), 320(3.38)	4-0449-79
$C_{17}H_{16}N_2O_3S$			
Ethanone, 2-(2-imidazolidinylidene)-1-phenyl-2-(phenylsulfonyl)-	EtOH	273(3.82)	95-0038-79
3-Quinolinesulfonamide, 1,2-dihydro-N,1-dimethyl-2-oxo-N-phenyl-	EtOH	252(3.80)	4-0065-79
$C_{17}H_{16}N_2O_4$			
1H-Benz[f]indazole-4,9-dione, 1-(tetrahydro-6-methoxy-2H-pyran-2-yl)-, trans-(±)-	EtOH	243(4.53),264(4.16)	111-0151-79
2H-Benz[f]indazole-4,9-dione, 2-(tetrahydro-6-(hydroxymethyl)-2H-pyran-2-yl]-, cis-(±)-	EtOH	246(4.86)	111-0151-79
$C_{17}H_{16}N_2O_5$			
4H-Furo[3,2-b]pyrrole-5-carboxylic acid, 4-ethyl-2-(2-nitrophenyl)-, ethyl ester	MeOH	322(4.64)	73-1805-79
$C_{17}H_{16}N_2S$			
2(1H)-Pyrimidinethione, 3,4-dihydro-4-(4-methylphenyl)-6-phenyl-	EtOH	224(4.36),265(4.18)	23-2734-79
	$CHCl_3$	272(4.16),277s(4.16)	23-2734-79
	CCl_4	258(4.13),291(4.14)	23-2734-79
2(1H)-Quinazolinethione, 1-(1-methylethyl)-4-phenyl-	EtOH	294(4.45),410(3.11)	118-0120-79
$C_{17}H_{16}N_3O_3$			
1H-Benzimidazolium, 2-[2-(2-hydroxyphenyl)ethenyl]-1,3-dimethyl-5-nitro-, iodide	EtOH-acid	269(3.92),371(4.56)	42-0871-79
	EtOH-base	318(4.36),398(4.35)	42-0871-79
1H-Benzimidazolium, 2-[2-(3-hydroxyphenyl)ethenyl]-1,3-dimethyl-5-nitro-, iodide	EtOH-acid	300(4.29),355(4.49)	42-0871-79
	EtOH-base	317(4.40),373(4.38)	42-0871-79
$C_{17}H_{16}N_4$			
3,4-Diazabicyclo[4.1.0]hepta-2,4-diene, 7,7-dimethyl-2,5-di-2-pyridinyl-	hexane	330(4.04)	20-0905-79
	$CHCl_3$	332(3.97)	20-0905-79
Ethanone, 1-phenyl-2-(5-phenyl-1H-pyrazol-3-yl)-, hydrazone	MeOH	248(4.29)	4-0737-79
	MeOH-NaOMe	250(4.31),337(4.02)	4-0737-79

Compound	Solvent	λ_{max}(log ε)	Ref.
Ethanone, 2-phenyl-1-(5-phenyl-1H-pyrazol-3-yl)hydrazone	MeOH	257(4.38)	4-0737-79
2-Propenimidamide, 2-cyano-3-[(2-methylphenyl)amino]-N-phenyl-	MeCN	338(4.37)	24-0484-79
$C_{17}H_{16}N_4O$			
1H-Indole-1,2,2(3H)-tripropanenitrile, 3-oxo-	EtOH	238(4.42),263(3.76), 404(3.64)	103-0884-79
$C_{17}H_{16}N_4OS$			
Ethanethioamide, 2-cyano-2-[(4-methoxyphenyl)hydrazono]-N-(phenylmethyl)-	EtOH	310(3.67),410(4.36)	104-1082-79
1,3,4-Thiadiazolium, 5-[[(4-methoxyphenyl)methylene]hydrazino]-3-methyl-2-phenyl-, hydroxide, inner salt	n.s.g.	253s(4.22),260(4.23), 335(4.22),440(4.14)	39-0724-79C
$C_{17}H_{16}N_4O_2$			
1,2,4-Oxadiazole-3-carboxamide, N-[4-(dimethylamino)phenyl]-5-phenyl-	EtOH	267(4.24),307(4.25), 442(4.11)	4-1477-79
1H-Pyrazole-5-carboxylic acid, 3-benzoyl-4,5-dihydro-4-phenyl-, hydrazide	EtOH	265s(3.27),295(3.42)	4-0849-79
1H-Pyrazole-4,5-dione, 3-(hydroxymethyl)-1-(4-methylphenyl)-, 4-(phenylhydrazone)	n.s.g.	212(3.66),253(4.00), 401(4.06)	106-0531-79
$C_{17}H_{16}N_4O_2S$			
1H-1,2,4-Triazolium, 4-[(ethoxycarbonyl)amino]-2,3-dihydro-1,5-diphenyl-3-thioxo-, hydroxide, inner salt	EtOH	251(4.41)	94-1683-79
$C_{17}H_{16}N_4O_3$			
2-Propenoic acid, 2-azido-3-(4-ethyl-4H-furo[3,2-b]indol-2-yl)-, ethyl ester	MeOH	420(4.39)	73-1805-79
$C_{17}H_{16}N_4O_3S$			
3-Thiophenecarboxylic acid, 2-[(1,5-dihydro-3-methyl-5-oxo-4H-pyrazol-4-ylidene)hydrazino]-5-phenyl-, ethyl ester	MeOH	240s(4.17),290(4.19), 490(4.31)	83-0726-79
$C_{17}H_{16}N_4O_6$			
Ethanone, 1-(3-nitrophenyl)-, O,O'-methylenedioxime	$CHCl_3$	235(4.41),253(4.53)	44-3970-79
Inosine, 5'-benzoate	EtOH	232(4.20),259s(4.02), 273s(3.66)	39-2088-79C
Inosine, 8-benzoyl-	H_2O	306(4.03)	88-2385-79
$C_{17}H_{16}N_4S$			
Ethanethioamide, 2-cyano-2-[(4-methylphenyl)hydrazono]-N-(phenylmethyl)-	EtOH	290(3.56),385(4.38)	104-1082-79
1,3,4-Thiadiazolium, 3-methyl-5-[[(4-methylphenyl)methylene]hydrazino]-2-phenyl-, hydroxide, inner salt	n.s.g.	255(4.46),335(4.30), 438(4.13)	39-0724-79C
$C_{17}H_{16}N_6$			
1H-Indazole-5-carbonitrile, 3-[[4-(dimethylamino)phenyl]azo]-1-methyl-	EtOH	470(<u>4.5</u>)	103-1231-79
2H-Indazole-5-carbonitrile, 3-[[4-(dimethylamino)phenyl]azo]-2-methyl-	EtOH	512(4.33)	103-1231-79

Compound	Solvent	λ_{max}(log ε)	Ref.
$C_{17}H_{16}N_6O_4$			
1,2-Cyclopentanedione, bis[(4-nitro-phenyl)hydrazone]	MeOH	446(4.31)	39-0603-79C
$C_{17}H_{16}O$			
2-Propenal, 3,3-bis(4-methylphenyl)-	EtOH	228(4.20),312(4.30)	35-6367-79
$C_{17}H_{16}OS$			
1H-Phenalen-1-one, 9-(butylthio)-	n.s.g.	366(4.29),431(3.85), 440(3.79)	44-1704-79
$C_{17}H_{16}O_2$			
Benzeneacetic acid, α-(1-hydroxy-5-methylbicyclo[2.2.2]oct-5-en-2-ylidene)-, lactone	MeOH	262(4.04)	44-1170-79
Benzeneacetic acid, α-(1-hydroxy-4-methylbicyclo[3.2.1]oct-3-en-2-ylidene)-, lactone	MeOH	308(4.26)	44-1170-79
[1,1'-Biphenyl]-4-propanal, α,α-dimethyl-β-oxo-	MeOH	211(4.27),265s(4.26), 274(4.29)	5-0617-79
5,9-Epoxy-5H-benzocyclohepten-5-ol, 6,7,8,9-tetrahydro-9-phenyl-	hexane	252s(2.65),257(2.80), 263(2.88),269(2.79)	56-1751-79
1(2H)-Naphthalenone, 3,4-dihydro-3-(4-methoxyphenyl)-	EtOH	248(4.13),279(3.51), 285(3.52),293s(3.39)	78-1167-79
[2]Paracyclo[2](3,7)tropolonophane	MeOH	228(4.14),248(4.05), 265s(4.03),364(3.74), 400s(3.14)	88-1113-79
1H-Phenalen-1-one, 9-butoxy-	n.s.g.	259(4.11),343(4.04), 395(3.71)	44-1704-79
9H-Xanthen-9-one, 2-(1,1-dimethylethyl)-	EtOH	242(4.60),262(4.02), 282(3.54),292(3.54), 341(3.73)	35-0665-79
$C_{17}H_{16}O_3$			
Anthracene, 1,8,9-trimethoxy-	MeOH	220(4.14),257(5.03), 369(4.04),384(3.92), 404(3.74)	145-1083-79
4H-1-Benzopyran-4-one, 2-(4-ethoxy-phenyl)-2,3-dihydro-	EtOH	223(4.35),253(4.01), 326(3.56)	56-1033-79
Bicyclo[2.2.2]oct-7-ene-2-carboxylic acid, 6-hydroxy-4,6-dimethyl-5-oxo-3-phenyl-, lactone	MeOH	252(2.46),259(2.50), 263(2.45),265(2.43), 270(2.30),310(2.00)	23-2853-79
1,3-Butanedione, 1-(4-methoxyphenyl)-2-phenyl- (contains enol)	hexane	220s(4.08),277(4.07), 330s(3.26)	23-1186-79
	EtOH	235s(4.02),286(4.04), 335s(3.23)	23-1186-79
2-Naphthalenecarboxylic acid, 3-cyclo-hexylidene-3,4-dihydro-4-oxo-	EtOH	245(4.62),295(3.80), 343s(--),350(3.71)	42-0068-79
$C_{17}H_{16}O_3S_3$			
2-Propen-1-one, 3,3-bis(methylthio)-1-phenyl-2-(phenylsulfonyl)-	EtOH	263(4.06)	95-0038-79
$C_{17}H_{16}O_4$			
4H-1-Benzopyran-4-one, 2,3-dihydro-7,8-dimethoxy-2-phenyl-	EtOH	284(4.21)	102-1765-79
7H-Furo[3,2-g][1]benzopyran-7-one, 9-(1,1-dimethyl-2-propenyl)-4-methoxy- (furopinnarin)	MeOH	227(4.11),254(3.94), 270(3.96),315(3.79)	78-0697-79
3-Phenanthrenol, 2,5,7-trimethoxy-	EtOH	254s(4.75),261(4.96),	64-0288-79C

Compound	Solvent	$\lambda_{max}(\log \epsilon)$	Ref.
3-Phenanthrenol, 2,5,7-trimethoxy- (batatasin) (cont.)		283(4.23),294(4.0), 305(3.97),328(3.65), 344(3.82),355(4.0)	64-0288-79C
2-Propen-1-one, 1-(2-hydroxy-4,5-dimethoxyphenyl)-3-phenyl-	EtOH	225(4.08),320(4.27), 373(4.38)	78-2061-79
2-Propen-1-one, 1-(2-hydroxy-4-methoxyphenyl)-3-(4-methoxyphenyl)-	EtOH	225(4.08),320(4.25), 365(4.39)	78-2061-79
$C_{17}H_{16}O_5$			
1,2-Benzenedicarboxylic acid, 3-hydroxy-6-(4-methylphenyl)-, dimethyl ester	EtOH	230(4.41),318(3.63)	103-0013-79
1,4-Ethanoanthracene-9,10-dione, 1,4,4a,9a-tetrahydro-5,8-dihydroxy-1-methoxy-	MeOH	211(4.12),235(4.21), 253(3.94),397(3.89), 417s(--)	24-2640-79
$C_{17}H_{16}O_6$			
1,2-Benzenedicarboxylic acid, 3-hydroxy-6-(4-methylphenoxy)-, dimethyl ester	EtOH	280(3.34)	103-0013-79
4H-1-Benzopyran-4-one, 2,3-dihydro-7-hydroxy-3-(3-hydroxy-2,4-dimethoxyphenyl)-	EtOH	279(4.02),318s(3.90)	102-0815-79
	EtOH-NaOH	250(4.18),294s(4.02), 339(4.24)	102-0815-79
	EtOH-NaOAc	281s(3.87),340(4.18)	102-0815-79
1H-Naphtho[2,3-c]pyran-1-one, 9-acetoxy-3,4-dihydro-10-hydroxy-7-methoxy-3-methyl-, (R)-	MeOH	261(5.69),305(3.74), 319s(--),352(3.80)	24-0957-79
1H-Phenalen-1-one, 3,9-dihydroxy-4,5,6-(or 4,7,8)-trimethoxy-7(or 6)-methyl-	EtOH	215(4.43),231s(4.25), 238s(4.17),256s(4.07), 273s(3.80),280s(3.70), 365(4.04),405(4.07)	150-0301-79
$C_{17}H_{16}O_7$			
Ethanone, 2-(1,3-benzodioxol-5-yl)-1-(4,6-dihydroxy-2,3-dimethoxyphenyl)-	EtOH	205(4.47),220s(4.26), 240s(4.11),286(4.18), 340(3.74)	39-2107-79C
Spiro[anthracene-2(1H),2'-dioxolane]-9,10-dione, 3,4-dihydro-5,8-dihydroxy-4-methoxy-	MeOH	216(4.59),277(3.95), 483(3.84),510(3.86), 545(3.61)	24-3453-79
$C_{17}H_{16}S$			
1H-Indene, 2-(ethylthio)-3-phenyl-	EtOH	233(4.28),301(4.09)	24-1495-79
$C_{17}H_{17}$			
Cycloheptatrienylium, (4-cyclopropyl-3-methylphenyl)-, perchlorate	10% HCl	232(4.44),276(3.92), 414(4.21)	39-0262-79B
$C_{17}H_{17}BrN_2O_6S_2$			
Acetic acid, [(4-bromophenyl)azo]-(methylsulfonyl)(phenylsulfonyl)-, ethyl ester	EtOH	320(3.90)	104-0919-79
$C_{17}H_{16}ClN_2O_6S_2$			
Acetic acid, [(2-chlorophenyl)azo]-(methylsulfonyl)(phenylsulfonyl)-, ethyl ester	EtOH	295(3.89)	104-0919-79
Acetic acid, [(4-chlorophenyl)azo]-(methylsulfonyl)(phenylsulfonyl)-, ethyl ester	EtOH	312(3.97)	104-0919-79

Compound	Solvent	$\lambda_{max}(\log \epsilon)$	Ref.
$C_{17}H_{17}ClN_5O_7P$			
Guanosine, cyclic 3',5'-[(4-chlorophenyl)methyl phosphate]	MeOH	256(4.20)	130-0009-79
$C_{17}H_{17}ClO_5$			
[1,1'-Biphenyl]-2-carboxylic acid, 4'-chloro-2',3,6-trimethoxy-, methyl ester	EtOH	214(4.44),285(3.75), 302(3.76)	33-2833-79
$C_{17}H_{17}ClO_5S$			
Spiro[benzofuran-2(3H),1'-[2]cyclohexen]-3-one, 7-chloro-2',4,6-trimethoxy-6'-methyl-4'-thioxo-, (1'S-trans)-	MeOH	295(4.30),323(3.78), 376(4.29)	39-1166-79C
$C_{17}H_{17}Cl_2N_3O$			
3-Pyridinecarbonitrile, 1-[(2,6-dichlorophenyl)methyl]-1,6-dihydro-6-morpholino-	CH_2Cl_2	258(3.5),316(3.6), 370s(3.1)	64-1019-79B
$C_{17}H_{17}F_3N_4O_2$			
Benzenamine, N,N-diethyl-4-[(4-nitrophenyl)azo]-3-(trifluoromethyl)-	EtOH	467(4.51)	39-1990-79C
	HOAc	466(4.52)	39-1990-79C
$C_{17}H_{17}F_3N_4O_9S_2$			
1-Azetidineacetic acid, 3-azido-2-[[(methylsulfonyl)oxy]methyl]-4-oxo-α-[1-[[(trifluoromethyl)sulfonyl]oxy]ethylidene]-, phenylmethyl ester	EtOH	242(3.80)	23-0222-79
$C_{17}H_{17}N$			
Azacyclooctadeca-1,3,5,7,9,11,13,15,17-nonaene	dioxan	276(3.87),329s(4.31), 349s(4.63),374(5.15), 410s(4.06),467(4.06), 611(2.86),682(2.76)	89-0312-79
$C_{17}H_{17}NO_2$			
Benzenamine, 2-[bis(5-methyl-2-furanyl)methyl]-	EtOH	225(4.57),287(3.28)	39-0599-79C
9H-Carbazole-2-carboxylic acid, 3,4-dimethyl-, ethyl ester	EtOH	227s(4.16),251(4.60), 302(4.19),351(3.48)	44-4402-79
9H-Carbazole-2-carboxylic acid, 4-ethyl-3-methyl-, methyl ester	EtOH	229s(4.33),252(4.73), 304(4.35),354(3.65)	44-4402-79
6-Isoquinolinol, 3,4-dihydro-7-methoxy-1-(phenylmethyl)-	pH 6.0	389(4.04)	39-2744-79C
7-Isoquinolinol, 3,4-dihydro-6-methoxy-1-(phenylmethyl)-	pH 6.0	355(3.82)	39-2744-79C
2-Propen-1-one, 1-[4-(dimethylamino)-2-hydroxyphenyl]-3-phenyl-	EtOH	220(4.30),286(4.20), 394(4.38)	78-2061-79
$C_{17}H_{17}NO_3$			
Acetamide, N-[2-[(2-acetoxyphenyl)methyl]phenyl]-	EtOH	235s(3.83)	78-1273-79
4H-1-Benzopyran-4-one, 2-(4-ethoxyphenyl)-2,3-dihydro-, oxime, (E)-	EtOH	228(4.44),255(4.10), 305(3.75),315(3.70)	56-1033-79
1,6(2H,5H)-Phenanthridinedione, 8-acetyl-3,4-dihydro-3,3-dimethyl-	EtOH	258(4.69)	44-0124-79
Phenol, 2-[4,5-dihydro-5-(4-methoxyphenyl)-3-isoxazolyl]-4-methyl-	isoBuOH	230(4.46),258(3.98), 312(3.70)	18-0584-79
2-Propen-1-one, 3-(4-ethoxyphenyl)-1-(2-hydroxyphenyl)-, oxime, (E,E)-	EtOH	222(4.18),311(4.33)	56-1033-79

Compound	Solvent	λ_{max}(log ϵ)	Ref.
$C_{17}H_{17}NO_4$			
9(10H)-Acridinone, 1,4,7-trimethoxy-10-methyl-	EtOH	208(4.35),269(4.35),227(3.69),425(3.90)	33-2350-79
1H-Benzo[a]furo[3,4-f]quinolizine-1,12(3H)-dione, 5,6,10b,11-tetrahydro-8-methoxy-3-methyl-	MeOH	235(4.35),292(4.18)	104-1247-79
Furo[3,4-c]pyridine-4-carboxaldehyde, 1,3-dihydro-1-methoxy-6-methyl-7-(phenylmethoxy)-	MeOH	275s(--),293(3.98)	88-2603-79
2-Propen-1-one, 3-(3,4-dimethoxyphenyl)-1-(2-hydroxyphenyl)-, oxime	EtOH	239(3.92),320(4.18)	56-1033-79
2(1H)-Pyridinone, 4-hydroxy-3-[3-(4-methoxyphenyl)-1-oxo-2-propenyl]-1,6-dimethyl-	EtOH	206(4.49),383(4.37)	94-0242-79
$C_{17}H_{17}NO_5$			
2H-Azepine-4-carboxylic acid, 6-ethoxy-3-hydroxy-2-oxo-7-phenyl-, ethyl ester	dioxan	251s(3.90),320(3.82),385(3.90)	142-1427-79
2H-Azepine-6-carboxylic acid, 4-ethoxy-3-hydroxy-2-oxo-7-phenyl-, ethyl ester	dioxan	265s(4.07),312(3.93),380(3.79)	142-1427-79
B-Norerythrinan-6-carboxylic acid, 13,16-dihydro-13-hydroxy-15-methoxy-7,16-dioxo-, γ-lactone, (13α)-	EtOH	269(3.91)	24-3795-79
$C_{17}H_{17}NO_6$			
1H-Azepine-4-carboxylic acid, 6-acetoxy-2,5-dihydro-3-hydroxy-2-oxo-7-phenyl-, ethyl ester	dioxan	220(4.15),258(4.19)	142-1427-79
$C_{17}H_{17}NO_6S$			
1H-Pyrrole-3-carboxylic acid, 1-(3-methoxy-3-oxo-1-propenyl)-5-[(4-methylphenyl)sulfonyl]-, methyl ester	EtOH	245(4.52),285(4.39)	94-2857-79
$C_{17}H_{17}N_2$			
Benzo[gh]perimidinium, 2,3-dihydro-1,2,3-trimethyl-, tetrafluoroborate	MeCN	260(4.58),390(4.54),534(3.89)	138-0221-79
$C_{17}H_{17}N_2O$			
1H-Benzimidazolium, 2-[2-(2-hydroxyphenyl)ethenyl]-1,3-dimethyl-, iodide	EtOH-acid	270(4.01),325(4.31)	42-0871-79
	EtOH-base	320(4.33),335(3.66)	42-0871-79
1H-Benzimidazolium, 2-[2-(3-hydroxyphenyl)ethenyl]-1,3-dimethyl-, iodide	EtOH-acid	248(3.99),337(4.45)	42-0871-79
	EtOH-base	365(4.85)	42-0871-79
Pyrrolizinium, 2-benzoyl-5-[(dimethylamino)methylene]-3,5-dihydro-, perchlorate	MeOH	206(3.96),241(4.06),377(5.27)	24-2465-79
$C_{17}H_{17}N_2S$			
Benzothiazolium, 3-methyl-2-[3-(1-methyl-2(1H)-pyridinylidene)-1-propenyl]-, iodide	EtOH	536(4.93)	4-1579-79
Benzothiazolium, 3-methyl-2-[3-(1-methyl-4(1H)-pyridinylidene)-1-propenyl]-, iodide	EtOH	557(4.98)	4-1579-79
$C_{17}H_{17}N_3$			
1H-Cyclopropa[c]cyclobuta[1,2-a:3,4-a']-dicyclooctene, 1-azido-1a,5a,5b,11a-11b,11c-hexahydro-	MeOH	251s(3.60)	89-0312-79

Compound	Solvent	λ_{max}(log ϵ)	Ref.
Pyrrolo[2,3-c]carbazole-1-methanamine, 3,6-dihydro-N,N-dimethyl-	EtOH	210(4.47),223(4.64), 244(4.56),317(4.37), 333(4.25)	103-0890-79
$C_{17}H_{17}N_3O$			
Benzamide, N-[4,5-dihydro-1-(4-methyl-phenyl)-1H-pyrazol-3-yl]-	EtOH	230(4.18),338(4.03)	150-0801-79
Benzamide, N-[4,5-dihydro-1-(phenyl-methyl)-7H-pyrazol-3-yl]-	EtOH	228(4.03),284(3.93)	150-0801-79
Benzamide, N-(4,5-dihydro-1-phenyl-1H-pyrazol-3-yl)-4-methyl-	EtOH	242(4.23),338(4.06)	150-0801-79
Methanone, [2-[(dimethylamino)methyl]-1H-indol-3-yl]-4-pyridinyl-	EtOH	269(3.92),325(3.75)	39-3155-79C
1,2,4-Oxadiazole-3-ethanamine, 5-(4-methylphenyl)-N-phenyl-	EtOH	252(4.43)	150-0801-79
1,2,4-Oxadiazole-3-ethanamine, 5-phen-yl-N-(phenylmethyl)-, monohydro-chloride	EtOH	254(4.27)	150-0801-79
3H-Pyrazol-3-one, 4-(1-ethyl-4(1H)-pyridinylidene)-2,4-dihydro-5-methyl-2-phenyl-	EtOH	320(4.08),394(4.36)	73-1413-79
$C_{17}H_{17}N_3OS$			
Benzothiazole, 2-[(4-butoxyphenyl)azo]-	EtOH	417(3.42)	103-1185-79
2,5-Cyclohexadiene-1,4-dione, mono[(3-butyl-2(3H)-benzothiazolylidene)hy-drazone]	EtOH	510(3.51)	103-1185-79
$C_{17}H_{17}N_3O_2$			
Benzamide, N-(4,5-dihydro-1-phenyl-1H-pyrazol-3-yl)-4-methoxy-	EtOH	229(4.10),338(4.05)	150-0801-79
1,2,4-Oxadiazole-3-ethanamine, N-(4-methoxyphenyl)-5-phenyl-	EtOH	248(4.40),287s(3.67)	150-0801-79
1,2,4-Oxadiazole-3-ethanamine, 5-(4-methoxyphenyl)-N-phenyl-	EtOH	249(4.40)	150-0801-79
Propanoic acid, 2-(9H-carbazol-3-yl-hydrazono)-, ethyl ester, anti	EtOH	205(3.36),225(3.52), 249(3.37),284(3.25), 335(3.33),349(3.3)	103-0642-79
syn	EtOH	205(3.31),231(3.45), 247(3.32),258(3.19), 306(3.18),357(3.19), 391(3.19)	103-0642-79
$C_{17}H_{17}N_3O_8S_2$			
Acetic acid, (methylsulfonyl)[(3-nitro-phenyl)azo](phenylsulfonyl)-, ethyl ester	EtOH	320(3.82)	104-0919-79
Acetic acid, (methylsulfonyl)[(4-nitro-phenyl)azo](phenylsulfonyl)-, ethyl ester	EtOH	295(4.08),360(3.95)	104-0919-79
$C_{17}H_{17}N_5$			
Benzenamine, N,N-dimethyl-4-[(1-phenyl-1H-pyrazol-3-yl)azo]-	EtOH	434(4.48)	104-1396-79
1H-Pyrazol-3-amine, 5-methyl-4-(phen-ylazo)-N-(phenylmethyl)-	EtOH	240(3.49)	48-0127-79
$C_{17}H_{17}N_5O_2$			
Benzonitrile, 5-(diethylamino)-2-[(4-nitrophenyl)azo]-	EtOH	472(4.51)	39-1990-79C
	HOAc	471(4.36)(changing)	39-1990-79C

Compound	Solvent	λ_{max}(log ε)	Ref.
$C_{17}H_{17}N_5O_3S$			
3-Thiophenecarboxylic acid, 2-[(3-amino-1,5-dihydro-1-methyl-5-oxo-4H-pyrazol-4-ylidene)hydrazino]-5-phenyl-, ethyl ester	MeOH	235s(4.00),285(3.94), 472(4.32)	83-0726-79
$C_{17}H_{17}N_5O_5$			
Adenosine, 5'-benzoate	EtOH	231(4.17),259(4.20)	39-2088-79C
$C_{17}H_{17}N_6O_9P$			
Guanosine, cyclic 3',5'-[(2-nitrophenyl)methyl phosphate]	MeOH	256(4.26)	130-0009-79
$C_{17}H_{17}OS$			
1H-Benzo[c]thiolium, 3-(2-methoxyphenyl)-1,1-dimethyl-	H_2SO_4	357(4.25)	104-0937-79
1H-Benzo[c]thiolium, 3-(3-methoxyphenyl)-1,1-dimethyl-	H_2SO_4	360(4.36)	104-0937-79
1H-Benzo[c]thiolium, 3-(4-methoxyphenyl)-1,1-dimethyl-	H_2SO_4	439(4.44)	104-0937-79
$C_{17}H_{17}S$			
1H-Benzo[c]thiolium, 1,1-dimethyl-3-(2-methylphenyl)-	H_2SO_4	359(4.19)	104-0937-79
1H-Benzo[c]thiolium, 1,1-dimethyl-3-(3-methylphenyl)-	H_2SO_4	364(4.27)	104-0937-79
1H-Benzo[c]thiolium, 1,1-dimethyl-3-(4-methylphenyl)-	H_2SO_4	396(4.28)	104-0937-79
$C_{17}H_{18}$			
4-Pentene, 1,4-diphenyl-	EtOH	238(3.88)	35-7367-79
$C_{17}H_{18}NO$			
Phenalenylium, 1-(dimethylamino)-9-ethoxy-, tetrafluoroborate	n.s.g.	251(4.32),393(4.17), 450(4.01)	44-1704-79
$C_{17}H_{18}N_2$			
Benzenamine, 4-methyl-N-[3-[(4-methylphenyl)amino]-2-propenylidene]-	benzene	381(4.4)	94-0403-79
	EtOH	245(4.0),307s(4.0), 365(4.6)	94-0403-79
1,4-Benzenediamine, N,N-dimethyl-N'-(3-phenyl-2-propenylidene)-	EtOH	222s(3.06),245s(--), 294(3.30),402(3.30)	2-0338-79B
Carbodiimide, N,N'-di-α-methylbenzyl-, (S)-(-)-	C_6H_{12}	210(4.42),238s(3.26), 246s(3.20),252s(3.15), 258(3.11),263(3.04), 267(2.99)	56-0631-79
Cinnoline, 1-ethyl-1,4-dihydro-3-methyl-4-phenyl-	MeCN	230(3.52),309(3.01)	104-2145-79
Pyrrolidine, 1-[phenyl(phenylimino)-methyl]-	EtOH	205(4.38),230s(--)	1-0319-79
Quinazoline, 1,4-dihydro-4-(2,4,6-trimethylphenyl)-, hydrochloride	EtOH	280(3.78)	24-1348-79
$C_{17}H_{18}N_2O$			
Benz[f]imidazo[1,2-a]quinoline, 11-ethoxy-2,3,5,6-tetrahydro-, hydriodide	EtOH	218(4.60),285(4.42)	4-0517-79
Ethanone, 1-[4-[[[4-(dimethylamino)-phenyl]methylene]amino]phenyl]-	toluene	373(4.60)	135-1491-79B
$C_{17}H_{18}N_2O_2$			
7,10-Methanocycloocta[b]quinoxalin-13-	EtOH	205(4.51),238(4.52),	56-1221-79

Compound	Solvent	λ_{max}(log ε)	Ref.
ol, 6,7,8,9,10,11-hexahydro-, acetate (cont.)		318(3.96)	56-1221-79
2-Propenoic acid, 3-[(phenylmethyl)amino]-3-(2-pyridinyl)-, ethyl ester, (E)-	ether	250(4.01),308(4.02)	22-0559-79
3-Pyridinecarboxylic acid, 5-[1-(phenylmethyl)-2-pyrrolidinyl]-	EtOH	230(3.52),268(3.50)	44-4332-79
3-Pyrrolidinecarboxylic acid, 1-(phenylmethyl)-2-(3-pyridinyl)-, trans	EtOH	237(3.52),262(3.49), 270s(3.47)	44-4332-79
$C_{17}H_{18}N_2O_3$			
Quinazoline, 1,4-dihydro-4-(2,4,5-trimethoxyphenyl)-, hydrochloride	EtOH	288(4.14)	24-1348-79
$C_{17}H_{18}N_2O_3S_3$			
Benzenesulfonic acid, 4-methyl-, [(methylthio)[(2-oxo-2-phenylethyl)thio]methylene]hydrazide, (E)-	EtOH	228(4.34),244(4.36)	5-0656-79
(Z)-	EtOH	229(4.30),248(4.36)	5-0656-79
$C_{17}H_{18}N_2O_5$			
1-Azabicyclo[4.2.0]oct-3-ene-2-carboxylic acid, 3-methyl-8-oxo-7-[(phenoxyacetyl)amino]-, (2α,6α,7β)-	EtOH	264(3.96)	23-0227-79
	EtOH-TEA	259(--)	23-0227-79
β-D-erythro-Pentodialdo-1,4-furanose, 1-deoxy-1-(3,4-dihydro-5-methyl-2,4-dioxo-1(2H)-pyrimidinyl)-3-O-(phenylmethyl)-	MeOH	265(3.98)	44-1309-79
$C_{17}H_{18}N_2O_6$			
Thymidine, 3'-benzoate	EtOH	264(4.03)	54-0537-79
$C_{17}H_{18}N_2O_6S$			
Benzenepropanamide, N-[2-(aminosulfonyl)-5-methoxyphenyl]-4-methoxy-β-oxo-	EtOH	206(4.30),227(4.58), 282(4.34),328(3.74)	104-1495-79
$C_{17}H_{18}N_2O_8$			
1H-Indole, 1-(2,4-di-O-acetyl-α-L-arabinopyranosyl)-6-nitro-	EtOH	248(3.92),318(3.87), 360(3.72)	103-0188-79
1H-Indole, 1-(3,4-di-O-acetyl-α-L-arabinopyranosyl)-6-nitro-	EtOH	250(3.94),318(3.81), 360(3.73)	103-0188-79
$C_{17}H_{18}N_2S$			
Benzenamine, 4-(1,2-benzisothiazol-3-yl)-N,N-diethyl-	5M HCl	263(4.13),338(3.94)	24-3286-79
	MeOH	270(4.16),345(4.22)	24-3286-79
$C_{17}H_{18}N_4$			
1,2-Cyclopentanedione, bis(phenylhydrazone)	MeOH	388(4.25)	39-0603-79C
$C_{17}H_{18}N_4O$			
Pyrazolo[3,4-d]pyrimidin-4-one, 1-cyclopentyl-1,5-dihydro-5-(phenylmethyl)-	MeOH	213(4.54),260(3.79)	83-0586-79
$C_{17}H_{18}N_4O_3S$			
D-erythro-Pentitol, 1,4-anhydro-2-deoxy-1-C-[8-[(phenylmethyl)thio]-1,2,4-triazolo[4,3-a]pyrazin-3-yl]-	EtOH	256(4.18),312(4.14)	44-1028-79
β-	EtOH	257(4.17),312(4.15)	44-1028-79

Compound	Solvent	λ max (log ε)	Ref.
$C_{17}H_{18}N_4O_4$			
Benzoic acid, 5-(diethylamino)-2-[(4-nitrophenyl)azo]-	C_6H_{12}	497(--),525(4.49)	39-1990-79C
	+ base	460(4.34)	39-1990-79C
	EtOH	493(4.48)	39-1990-79C
	+ base	492(4.48)	39-1990-79C
	dioxan	500(4.47)	39-1990-79C
	+ base	482(4.52)	39-1990-79C
	HOAc	523(4.52)	39-1990-79C
$C_{17}H_{18}N_4O_4S$			
D-Ribitol, 1,4-anhydro-1-C-[8-(phenylmethyl)thio]-1,2,4-triazolo[4,3-a]-pyrazin-3-yl]-, (S)-	EtOH	260(4.10),313(4.05)	111-0375-79
$C_{17}H_{18}N_4O_5$			
1-Propanone, 1-(3-methoxyphenyl)-2-methyl-, 2,4-dinitrophenylhydrazone	MeOH	224(4.46),254(4.18), 363(4.47)	5-0617-79
$C_{17}H_{18}N_4O_6$			
Inosine, 8-(hydroxyphenylmethyl)-	H_2O	251.5(4.17)	88-2385-79
$C_{17}H_{18}N_4O_8$			
D-Ribitol, 1,4-anhydro-1-C-[1-(2,4-dinitrophenyl)-1H-pyrazol-3-yl]-2,3-O-(1-methylethylidene)-, (R)-	CCl_4	280(3.95)	136-0061-79A
$C_{17}H_{18}N_5O_7P$			
Guanosine, cyclic 3',5'-(phenylmethyl phosphate)	MeOH	256(4.16)	130-0009-79
$C_{17}H_{18}N_6O_7$			
Adenosine, 8-cyano-, 2',3',5'-triacetate	0.5M HCl	264s(4.00),267(4.02), 296(3.82)	94-0183-79
	H_2O	264s(4.00),267(4.02), 298(3.81)	94-0183-79
$C_{17}H_{18}N_8O_5S$			
9H-Purin-6-amine, 9-[3-azido-3-deoxy-2-O-[(4-methylphenyl)sulfonyl]-β-D-arabinofuranosyl]-	MeOH	227(4.17),258(4.16)	44-1317-79
9H-Purin-6-amine, 9-[3-azido-3-deoxy-2-O-[(4-methylphenyl)sulfonyl]-β-D-xylofuranosyl]-	MeOH	228(4.14),260(4.16)	44-1317-79
$C_{17}H_{18}O$			
2H-Benz[e]inden-2-one, 1,3-dihydro-1,1,3,3-tetramethyl-	hexane	272(3.7),279(3.8), 291(3.6),308(3.0), 314(2.9),322(3.2)	35-3277-79
2H-Benz[f]inden-2-one, 1,3-dihydro-1,1,3,3-tetramethyl-	hexane	262(3.53),272(3.66), 283(3.70),294(3.53), 304(3.15),319(3.19)	35-3277-79
Bicyclo[4.3.1]deca-2,4,7-triene, 9-exo-methyl-7-phenyl-	C_6H_{12}	237(4.27)	5-0533-79
Cycloocta[a]naphthalen-12(7H)-one, 8,9,10,11-tetrahydro-7-methyl-	MeOH	225(4.90),271(3.74), 278(3.75),319(2.60)	39-1395-79C
Gibberone, (±)-	EtOH	260(4.43)	44-4562-79
5H-3,4b-Methano-1H-benzo[1,3]cycloprop-[1,2-a]inden-4(4aH)-one, 2,3-dihydro-3,6-dimethyl-	EtOH	238(3.92)	44-4562-79
1-Pentanone, 1,4-diphenyl-	EtOH	241(4.08),278(2.91)	35-7367-79
4-Penten-1-ol, 1,4-diphenyl-	EtOH	239(4.00)	35-7367-79

Compound	Solvent	$\lambda_{max}(\log \epsilon)$	Ref.
$C_{17}H_{18}O_2$			
Bicyclo[4.3.1]deca-2,4,8-trien-7-ol, 7-(2-methoxyphenyl)-	C_6H_{12}	256(3.81),267s(3.70), 277(3.47)	5-0533-79
2,4,6-Cycloheptatrien-1-one, 3-(2,4,6-cycloheptatrien-1-yl)-2-hydroxy-7-(1-methylethyl)-	MeOH	255(4.18),321(3.70), 363(3.68),374(3.72), 396(3.58)	18-1867-79
Dibenzo[a,c]cyclononene-5,9-diol, 6,7,8,9-tetrahydro-	EtOH	218(4.28),257(2.70), 263(2.72),272(2.57)	78-0667-79
1-Isobenzofuranol, 1,3-dihydro-3,3-dimethyl-1-(2-methylphenyl)-, cation	50% H_2SO_4	341(4.38)	104-1126-79
1-Isobenzofuranol, 1,3-dihydro-3,3-dimethyl-1-(3-methylphenyl)-, cation	50% H_2SO_4	342(4.43)	104-1126-79
1-Isobenzofuranol, 1,3-dihydro-3,3-dimethyl-1-(4-methylphenyl)-, cation	50% H_2SO_4	363(4.53)	104-1126-79
$C_{17}H_{18}O_3$			
Benzoic acid, 2-[4-(1,1-dimethylethyl)-phenoxy]-	EtOH	226(3.96),285(3.34)	35-0665-79
$C_{17}H_{18}O_4$			
Butanedioic acid, cyclohexylidene(phenylmethylene)-, (E)-	EtOH	258(4.10)	42-0068-79
5H-3,5a-Methanonaphth[2,1-c]oxepin-5-one, 2,3,6,7-tetrahydro-3,9-dimethoxy-	EtOH	268(4.28)	118-0374-79
2H-Naphtho[2,3-b]pyran-5,10-dione, 4-ethoxy-3,4-dihydro-2,2-dimethyl-	EtOH	248(4.45),250(4.44), 282(4.18),333(3.49)	2-0016-79B
1-Phenanthrenecarboxylic acid, 4b,5,6-7.9.10-hexahydro-2-methoxy-7-oxo-,	EtOH	233(4.34)	118-0374-79
1-Phenanthrenecarboxylic acid, 5,6,7-8,9,10-hexahydro-2-methoxy-7-oxo-, methyl ester	EtOH	272(4.21)	118-0374-79
1(2H)-Phenanthrenone, 10-acetoxy-3,4,9,10-tetrahydro-9-hydroxy-9-methyl-, cis	MeOH	228(4.11),233(4.09), 300(4.25)	24-0532-79
trans	MeOH	227(4.14),233(4.12), 301(4.25)	24-0532-79
$C_{17}H_{19}ClN_4O_5$			
DL-threo-Hex-2-enopyranuronic acid, 1-(6-chloro-9H-purin-9-yl)-1,2,3-trideoxy-, butyl ester 4-acetate	EtOH	265(3.95)	136-0272-79E
$C_{17}H_{19}IO_2$			
Benzene, 4-(3-iodopropyl)-1-methoxy-2-(phenylmethoxy)-	EtOH	209(4.30),226s(3.93), 278(3.48)	39-0662-79C
$C_{17}H_{19}N$			
16-Azatricyclo[9.2.2.1^{4,8}]hexadeca-4,6,8(16),11,13,14-hexaene, 12,14-dimethyl-	MeCN	265(3.43),300(2.72)	35-2121-79
$C_{17}H_{19}NO$			
Benzeneethanamine, N-[(2-methoxyphenyl)methylene]-α-methyl-, (S)-	hexane	208(4.49),246(4.20), 251(4.23),258s(4.04), 293s(3.67),302(3.81), 313(3.70)	44-1690-79
	EtOH	210(4.45),252(4.20), 305(3.75)	44-1690-79
Methanone, 4-azatricyclo[4.3.1.1^{3,8}]undec-4-en-5-ylphenyl-	MeOH	252(4.31),350(2.63)	44-3711-79

Compound	Solvent	$\lambda_{max}(\log \epsilon)$	Ref.
2-Propanamine, N-[3-(2-hydroxy-1-naphthalenyl)-2-propen-1-ylidene]-2-meth-	MeOH	280(4.04),310(3.95), 350(3.15),420(3.53), 500(4.09)	104-1715-79
	dioxan	300(3.90),310(3.90), 340(3.68),350(3.70)	104-1715-79
	DMSO	290(3.88),313(3.90), 344(3.96),520(4.11)	104-1715-79
	DMSO-NaOMe	312(4.04),370(3.88), 450(4.14)	104-1715-79
1H-Pyrrolizine-7-carboxaldehyde, 2,3-dihydro-2,2,5-trimethyl-6-phenyl-	MeOH	209(4.21),252(4.07), 270(4.05),304(3.73)	83-0896-79
$C_{17}H_{19}NO_2$			
Cyclopenta[c]carbazole-4-carboxylic acid, 1,2,3,3a,4,5,6,10c-octahydro-, methyl ester	EtOH	228(4.58),276s(3.87), 283(3.90),290(3.83)	44-4402-79
$C_{17}H_{19}NO_3$			
Benzamide, 3-acetyl-N-(5,5-dimethyl-3-oxocyclohexen-1-yl)-	EtOH	222(4.30),291(4.27)	44-0124-79
Cyclohexanecarboxaldehyde, 3-(2,3-dihydro-1,3-dimethyl-2-oxo-1H-indol-3-yl)-2-oxo-	EtOH	254(4.05),282(3.92)	23-1694-79
8-Isoquinolinol, 1,2,3,4-tetrahydro-1-[(4-hydroxyphenyl)methyl]-7-methoxy-, (R)-	n.s.g.	228(4.20),285(3.56)	105-0783-79
1-Oxaspiro[5.5]undecane-2,4-dione, 3-[(phenylamino)methylene]-	hexane	231(4.10),340(4.44)	131-0077-79D
	EtOH	338(4.42)	131-0077-79D
$C_{17}H_{19}NO_4$			
1H-Azepine-4-carboxylic acid, 6-ethyl-2,5-dihydro-3-hydroxy-2-oxo-7-phenyl-, ethyl ester	dioxan	227(4.11),263(4.13)	142-1427-79
Benzoic acid, 3,6-dimethoxy-2-(methylphenylamino)-, methyl ester	EtOH	207(4.30),241(4.16), 295(3.88)	33-2350-79
$C_{17}H_{19}NO_5$			
1H-Azepine-4-carboxylic acid, 6-ethoxy-2,5-dihydro-3-hydroxy-2-oxo-7-phenyl-, ethyl ester	dioxan	220(4.13),262(4.24)	142-1427-79
Benzoic acid, 3,6-dimethoxy-2-[(4-methoxyphenyl)methylamino]-	EtOH	207(4.44),243(4.19), 306(3.84)	33-2350-79
Ungminorine, (±)-	EtOH	290(3.40)	105-0370-79
$C_{17}H_{19}NS_2$			
3,11-Dithia-18-azatricyclo[11.2.2.1^{5,9}]octadeca-5,7,9(18),13,15,16-hexaene, 14,16-dimethyl-	MeCN	235(4.09),270(3.66)	35-2121-79
$C_{17}H_{19}N_2$			
1H-Imidazolium, 4,5-dihydro-1,3-bis(4-methylphenyl)-, chloride	MeOH	318(4.19)	24-0445-79
$C_{17}H_{19}N_2S$			
1,2-Benzisothiazolium, 3-[4-(dimethylamino)phenyl]-2-ethyl-, chloride hydrochloride	5M HCl	270(4.09),337(3.92)	24-3286-79
	MeOH	270(4.34),415(4.17)	24-3286-79
$C_{17}H_{19}N_3O$			
1H-Indole-3-methanol, 2-[(dimethylamino)methyl]-α-4-pyridinyl-	EtOH	224(4.3),267s(3.74), 275s(3.77),282(3.78),	39-3155-79C

Compound	Solvent	λ max (log ε)	Ref.
(cont.)		291(3.70)	39-3155-79C
$C_{17}H_{19}N_3O_2$			
1H-Naphth[2,3-d]imidazole-4,9-dione, 1,2-dimethyl-5-[(2-methylpropyl)-amino]-	C_6H_{12}	525(3.65)	39-0702-79C
	EtOH	532(--)	39-0702-79C
	EtOH-HCl	556(--)	39-0702-79C
1H-Naphth[2,3-d]imidazole-4,9-dione, 1,2-dimethyl-8-[(2-methylpropyl)-amino]-	C_6H_{12}	521(3.79)	39-0702-79C
	EtOH	530(--)	39-0702-79C
	EtOH-HCl	556(--)	39-0702-79C
Pyrrolo[1,2-a]pyrazin-4(3H)-one, 6,7,8,8a-tetrahydro-3-(1H-indol-3-ylmethyl)-1-methoxy-, (3S,8aS)-	EtOH	222(4.56),274(3.73), 282(3.77),290(3.70)	39-3048-79C
$C_{17}H_{19}N_3O_5$			
Glycine, N-(N-acetyl-1-formyl-L-trypto-phyl)-, methyl ester	MeOH-HCl	300(3.70)	63-0013-79
$C_{17}H_{19}N_3O_7$			
D-Ribitol, 1-deoxy-1-(3,4-dihydro-8-hy-droxy-7-methyl-2,4-dioxopyrimido[4,5-b]quinolin-10(2H)-yl)-	n.s.g.	426(4.65)	35-4419-79
$C_{17}H_{19}N_4O$			
1H-Tetrazolium, 5-ethoxy-1,3-bis(4-methylphenyl)-, tetrafluoroborate	n.s.g.	218(4.00),233s(3.80), 313(4.22)	39-0736-79C
$C_{17}H_{19}N_5O_2S$			
1H-Pyrazole, 3-[[4-(dimethylamino)phen-yl]azo]-1-(phenylsulfonyl)-	EtOH	482(4.63)	104-1396-79
$C_{17}H_{19}N_5O_5$			
Adenosine, 8-(hydroxyphenylmethyl)-	H_2O	263.5(4.07)	88-2385-79
Guanosine, N-(phenylmethyl)-	pH 1	259(4.15),282s(3.91)	44-3324-79
	pH 6.9	253(4.15),274s(3.97)	44-3324-79
	pH 13	257(4.10),270s(4.05)	44-3324-79
$C_{17}H_{19}N_5O_6S_2$			
1H-Pyrazolo[3,4-d]pyrimidine-3-carbo-nitrile, 1-(2,3-di-O-acetyl-α-D-ribofuranosyl)-4,6-bis(methylthio)-	EtOH	204(4.27),253(4.40), 293(4.15),316(3.98)	103-1361-79
$C_{17}H_{19}N_6O_2$			
1H-Indazolium, 3-[[4-(dimethylamino)-phenyl]azo]-5-nitro-, iodide	EtOH	581(4.68)	103-1231-79
$C_{17}H_{19}N_9$			
5H-Tetrazol-5-one, 1,2-dihydro-1-meth-yl-, [[[4-(dimethylamino)phenyl]azo]-phenylmethylene]hydrazone	pH 13	320(3.84),490(4.50)	104-2000-79
	EtOH	247(4.22),282(4.18), 490(4.49)	104-2000-79
	dioxan	280(4.24),480(4.54)	104-2000-79
5H-Tetrazol-5-one, 1,2-dihydro-2-meth-yl-, [[[4-(dimethylamino)phenyl]azo]-phenylmethylene]hydrazone	pH 13	240(3.84),452(4.29)	104-2000-79
	EtOH	250(4.26),480(4.51)	104-2000-79
	dioxan	255(4.22),475(4.50)	104-2000-79
$C_{17}H_{19}OSSe$			
Sulfonium, dimethyl-, 1-(methylphenyl-selenonio)-2-oxo-2-phenylethylide, tetrafluoroborate	n.s.g.	218s(4.352),257(4.102)	104-0332-79

Compound	Solvent	λ_{max}(log ε)	Ref.
$C_{17}H_{20}BrN_3O_{13}P_2$			
Uridine, 5'-(trihydrogen diphosphate), mono[4-[(bromoacetyl)amino]phenyl] ester	pH 7.0	258(4.20)	69-5332-79
$C_{17}H_{20}ClN_5O_3$			
[1,2,4]Triazino[4,3-d][1,4]benzodiazepine-3,4,7(6H)-trione, 11-chloro-2-[3-(dimethylamino)propyl]-2,8-dihydro-8-methyl-, hydrochloride	MeOH	257(4.16),278(4.09), 310s(3.97)	44-0084-79
$C_{17}H_{20}NO$			
Phenanthridinium, 5-ethyl-7,8,9,10-tetrahydro-9,9-dimethyl-7-oxo-, perchlorate	n.s.g.	255(4.31),330(4.08)	104-0495-79
$C_{17}H_{20}N_2$			
Cinnoline, 1,2,3,4-tetrahydro-3-methyl-4-phenyl-	MeCN	253(3.83),300(3.46)	104-2145-79
$C_{17}H_{20}N_2O$			
7,11-Methano-6H-cyclonona[b]quinoxalin-14-ol, 7,8,9,10,11,12-hexahydro-14-methyl-	EtOH	207(4.58),238(4.42), 319(3.69)	56-1221-79
Methanone, bis[4-(dimethylamino)phenyl]-	hexane	330(4.60)	60-0058-79
	EtOH	365(4.46)	60-0058-79
3-Pyrrolidinemethanol, 1-(phenylmethyl)-2-(3-pyridinyl)-, trans	EtOH	217(3.50),260s(3.59), 264(3.61),270s(3.50)	44-4332-79
$C_{17}H_{20}N_2OS$			
10H-Phenothiazine-10-propanamine, N,N-dimethyl-, S-oxide	MeOH	232(4.47),274(4.12), 300(3.97),343(3.8)	133-0197-79
$C_{17}H_{20}N_2O_2$			
Benzenemethanamine, α-(1,1-dimethylethyl)-N-(4-nitrophenyl)-, (R)-	MeOH	229(3.95),260s(3.48), 298s(3.00),386(4.32)	35-5186-79
1H-Indole, 2-[2-(1,2,3,6-tetrahydro-1-methyl-4-pyridinyl)-1,3-dioxolan-2-yl]-	EtOH	222(4.06),281(3.93), 290(3.81)	39-3155-79C
$C_{17}H_{20}N_2O_3$			
7H-Pyrazolo[1,5-c][1,3]oxazine-3-carboxylic acid, 4,5-dihydro-2,5-dimethyl-7-phenyl-, ethyl ester, cis	EtOH	231(4.09)	118-0440-79
trans	EtOH	231(4.10)	118-0440-79
$C_{17}H_{20}N_2O_4$			
Propanedioic acid, [[(2-methyl-1H-indol-5-yl)amino]methylene]-, diethyl ester	EtOH	255(4.29),285(4.31), 334(4.42)	103-0888-79
$C_{17}H_{20}N_2O_5$			
1H-Indazole-4,7-diol, 1-acetyl-6-(1,1-dimethylethyl)-, diacetate	n.s.g.	232(4.21)	70-1668-79
Propanedioic acid, (formylamino)(1H-indol-3-ylmethyl)-, diethyl ester	isoPrOH	221(4.57),273(3.76), 281(3.80),289(3.75)	44-3748-79
$C_{17}H_{20}N_2O_5S$			
Benzo[b]thiophen-3(2H)-one, 2-(di-4-morpholinylmethylene)-, 1,1-dioxide	EtOH	241(3.94),276(4.02)	95-0038-79

Compound	Solvent	λ_{max}(log ε)	Ref.
$C_{17}H_{20}N_2O_6$			
Neosidomycin	MeOH	270(3.91),279(3.89), 283s(3.87),298(3.76)	88-1701-79
Pyrrolo[2,3-b]indole-1,2(2H)-dicarboxylic acid, 8-acetyl-3,3a,8,8a-tetrahydro-5-methoxy-, dimethyl ester	MeOH	253(4.15),295(3.46)	142-1027-79
Pyrrolo[2,3-b]indole-1,2(2H)-dicarboxylic acid, 8-acetyl-3,3a,8,8a-tetrahydro-6-methoxy-, dimethyl ester	MeOH	218(4.39),248(4.01), 289(3.66),295(3.65)	142-1027-79
$C_{17}H_{20}N_2O_7S$			
2,4(1H,3H)-Pyrimidinedione, 1-[2-acetoxy-3-[[(4-methylphenyl)sulfonyl]-oxy]propyl]-5-methyl-	n.s.g.	223(4.28),267(4.07), 273s(4.04)	128-0281-79
$C_{17}H_{20}N_2S$			
Isopromethazine, hydrochloride	MeOH	206(4.39),253(4.51), 305(3.61)	133-0197-79
Methanethione, bis[4-(dimethylamino)-phenyl]-	EtOH	209(4.40),220(4.33), 247(4.15)	56-0631-79
10H-Phenothiazine-10-propanamine, N,N-dimethyl-, hydrochloride (promazine)	MeOH	205(4.43),254(4.51), 306(3.64)	133-0197-79
Promethazine, hydrochloride	MeOH	205(4.42),253(4.49), 304(3.61)	133-0197-79
	EtOH	205(4.55),255(4.58), 305(3.71)	56-0415-79
lead picrate complex	EtOH	208(4.89),255(4.85), 360(4.56)	56-0415-79
$C_{17}H_{20}N_3$			
1,2,3-Triazinium, 3,4,5,6-tetrahydro-1,3-bis(4-methylphenyl)-, perchlorate	MeOH	248(3.79),348(4.20)	24-0445-79
$C_{17}H_{20}N_3O$			
1,2,3-Triazinium, 3,4,5,6-tetrahydro-1-(4-methoxyphenyl)-3-(4-methyl-phenyl)-, perchlorate	MeOH	225(3.05),360(4.17)	24-0445-79
$C_{17}H_{20}N_3O_4$			
1H-Imidazol-1-yloxy, 4-[1-(1,3-dihydro-1,3-dioxo-2H-isoindol-2-yl)ethyl]-2,5-dihydro-2,2,5,5-tetramethyl-, 3-oxide	EtOH	220(4.65),238(4.25), 290(3.39)	70-2521-79
$C_{17}H_{20}N_4O$			
Hydrazinecarboxamide, 2-(1,2,3,4,7,8-hexahydrobenzo[d]carbazol-6(7H)-yl-idene)-	MeOH	270(4.32)	5-1048-79
$C_{17}H_{20}N_4O_2$			
Benzenamine, N,N-diethyl-3-methyl-4-[(4-nitrophenyl)azo]-	EtOH	497(4.52)	39-1990-79C
	dioxan	486(4.53)	39-1990-79C
	HOAc	507(4.52)	39-1990-79C
	$HCONH_2$	526(4.51)	39-1990-79C
$C_{17}H_{20}N_4O_2S$			
Benzenamine, N,N-diethyl-3-(methylthio)-4-[(4-nitrophenyl)azo]-	EtOH	513(4.55)	39-1990-79C
	HOAc	512(4.65)	39-1990-79C
$C_{17}H_{20}N_4O_3$			
Benzenamine, N,N-diethyl-3-methoxy-4-	EtOH	501(4.52)	39-1990-79C

Compound	Solvent	λ_{max}(log ϵ)	Ref.
[(4-nitrophenyl)azo]- (cont.)	HOAc	480(4.80)	39-1990-79C
$C_{17}H_{20}N_4O_4S$			
Benzamide, N-[[[[4-[(dimethylamino)sulfonyl]phenyl]methyl]nitrosoamino]-methyl]-	EtOH	233(4.47),367(1.81)	118-0531-79
$C_{17}H_{20}N_4O_4S$			
Benzenamine, N,N-diethyl-3-(methylsulfonyl)-4-[(4-nitrophenyl)azo]-	EtOH	477(4.51)	39-1990-79C
	HOAc	478(4.53)	39-1990-79C
$C_{17}H_{20}N_4O_4S_2$			
Formazan, 1,5-bis(4-methylphenyl)-3-[[(methylsulfonyl)methyl]sulfonyl]-	EtOH	454(4.39)	104-0370-79
	HOAc-H_2SO_4	612(4.53)	104-0370-79
$C_{17}H_{20}N_4O_7$			
Riboflavin, 8-demethyl-8-methoxy-	pH -1.0	234(4.46),261(4.41), 428(4.55)	65-1658-79
	pH 3.0	235(4.54),263(4.47), 441(4.39)	65-1658-79
	pH 7.0	235(4.54),263(4.47), 380s(3.92),441(4.40)	65-1658-79
	pH 12.6	230(4.54),265(4.51), 389s(4.04),443(4.33)	65-1658-79
	MeOH	233(4.56),267(4.44), 385s(3.91),439(4.32), 450s(4.31)	65-1658-79
$C_{17}H_{20}N_6O_3$			
Urea, [5-(diethylamino)-2-[(4-nitrophenyl)azo]phenyl]-	EtOH	518(4.61)	39-1990-79C
	HOAc	502(4.68)	39-1990-79C
$C_{17}H_{20}N_8O_5$			
1H-Purine-2,6-dione, 7,7'-(2-hydroxy-1,3-propanediyl)bis[3,7-dihydro-1,3-dimethyl-	H_2O	274(4.23)	126-2303-79
$C_{17}H_{20}N_8O_{12}$			
Cytidine, 5'-deoxy-5'-(methylureido)-, picrate (spectra of free compound)	pH 1	279(4.30)	87-1109-79
	pH 7 and 13	234s(3.82),272(3.87)	87-1109-79
$C_{17}H_{20}O$			
Gibba-1,3,4a(10a)-trien-8-one, 1,7-dimethyl-, (4bα)-(±)-	EtOH	260(2.92),265(2.94), 274(2.83)	44-4562-79
2(1H)-Naphthalenone, 3,4,5,6,7,8-hexahydro-1-(phenylmethyl)-	MeOH	213(3.66),248(3.10), 280(1.63)	33-0119-79
2(3H)-Naphthalenone, 4,4a,5,6,7,8-hexahydro-1-(phenylmethyl)-	MeOH	250(4.01)	33-0119-79
2(3H)-Naphthalenone, 4,4a,5,6,7,8-hexahydro-4a-(phenylmethyl)-, (±)-	isooctane	235(4.05),335(1.53)	33-0119-79
$C_{17}H_{20}O_2$			
1,1'-Biphenyl, 2',4'-dimethoxy-2,4,6-trimethyl-	C_6H_{12}	280(3.29),286(3.25)	12-1531-79
1H-Fluorene-1-carboxylic acid, 2,3,4,9-tetrahydro-1,8-dimethyl-, methyl ester, (±)-	EtOH	259(4.20)	44-4562-79
1H-Fluorene-2-carboxylic acid, 2,3,4,9-tetrahydro-2,8-dimethyl-, methyl ester, (±)-	EtOH	259(4.19)	44-4562-79

Compound	Solvent	$\lambda_{max}(\log \epsilon)$	Ref.
$C_{17}H_{20}O_3$			
Benzenepropanol, 4-methoxy-3-(phenylmethoxy)-	EtOH	208(4.12),225s(3.73), 278(3.26)	39-0662-79C
2H-Benz[e]inden-3-ol, 3,3a,4,5-tetrahydro-7-methoxy-3a-methyl-, acetate, (3S-cis)-	EtOH	266(4.27),297(3.51), 308(3.36)	39-1322-79C
2,4-Cyclohexadien-1-one, 6-(2,4-dimethoxyphenyl)-2,4,6-trimethyl-	MeOH	227(4.17),280(3.67), 285(3.65)	12-1551-79
2,4-Hexadienoic acid, 2-benzoyl-4,5-dimethyl-, ethyl ester	EtOH	207(4.24),245(3.96), 285(3.67)	70-0758-79
$C_{17}H_{20}O_4$			
Naphtho[2,3-b]furan-2(3H)-one, 6-acetoxy-3a,4,4a,5,6,8a,9,9a-octahydro-8a-methyl-3,5-bis(methylene)-	MeOH	211(4.11)	102-1743-79
$C_{17}H_{20}O_5$			
α-D-ribo-Hept-5-enodialdo-1,4-furanose, 5,6-dideoxy-1,2-O-(1-methylethylidene)-3-O-(phenylmethyl)-, (E)-	MeOH	205(4.53),225(4.22)	136-0151-79H
α-D-xylo-Hept-5-enodialdo-1,4-furanose, 5,6-dideoxy-1,2-O-(1-methylethylidene)-3-O-(phenylmethyl)-, (E)-	MeOH	210(4.48),222(4.33)	136-0151-79H
1H-Indene-2-acetic acid, 5,6-dimethoxy-α-methyl-3-(1-methylethyl)-1-oxo-	EtOH	261(4.61),430(2.67)	2-0122-79B
1-Naphthalenecarboxaldehyde, 2-ethoxy-5,6,7-trimethoxy-4-methyl-	EtOH	237(4.80),257(4.44), 356(4.15)	150-0301-79
1-Naphthalenecarboxaldehyde, 7-ethoxy-2,3,4-trimethoxy-5-methyl-	EtOH	221(4.57),226(4.26), 337(3.82),366(3.89)	150-0301-79
1-Naphthalenepropanoic acid, β-hydroxy-2,7-dimethoxy-, ethyl ester	EtOH	238(4.64),280s(4.54), 288(3.57),297s(3.56), 315(3.47),329(3.51), 349s(3.11)	150-0301-79
1,3,6-Trioxaspiro[4.4]non-7-ene-8-carboxylic acid, 2,2-dimethyl-7-phenyl-, ethyl ester, (±)-	EtOH	208(4.14),246(4.08)	136-0055-79B
$C_{17}H_{20}O_6$			
Bicyclo[3.2.2]nona-3,6,8-triene-6,7-dicarboxylic acid, 3-(1-methylethyl)-1-methoxy-2-oxo-, dimethyl ester	MeOH	222(4.43),292s(2.82), 362(2.27)	18-2023-79
Bicyclo[3.2.2]nona-3,6,8-triene-6,7-dicarboxylic acid, 4-(1-methylethyl)-1-methoxy-2-oxo-, dimethyl ester	MeOH	224(4.25),287s(3.22), 335s(2.55)	18-2023-79
Bicyclo[3.2.2]nona-3,6,8-triene-6,7-dicarboxylic acid, 9-(1-methylethyl)-1-methoxy-2-oxo-, dimethyl ester	MeOH	215(4.13),285s(3.15), 345(2.60)	18-2023-79
Bicyclo[3.2.2]nona-3,6,8-triene-6,7-dicarboxylic acid, 9-(1-methylethyl)-3-methoxy-2-oxo-, dimethyl ester	MeOH	227(3.96),289(3.41), 364s(2.58)	18-2023-79
1H-Indene-1,7-dicarboxylic acid, 2,3-dihydro-6-methoxy-1-(1-methylethyl)-3-oxo-, dimethyl ester	MeOH	228(4.31),271(4.20), 285s(4.10),294s(3.95)	18-2962-79
1H-Indene-1,7-dicarboxylic acid, 2,3-dihydro-6-methoxy-2-(1-methylethyl)-3-oxo-, dimethyl ester, trans	MeOH	233(4.28),270(4.16), 296(3.88)	18-2962-79
1H-Indene-1,7-dicarboxylic acid, 2,3-dihydro-6-methoxy-4-(1-methylethyl)-3-oxo-, dimethyl ester	MeOH	236(4.41),275(4.17), 300s(3.69)	18-2962-79
1H-Indene-3a,7a-dicarboxylic acid,	MeOH	220(4.16),283(3.68),	18-2023-79

Compound	Solvent	λ max (log ε)	Ref.
7-methoxy-2-(1-methylethyl)-1-oxo-, dimethyl ester, cis (cont.)		340(2.86)	18-2023-79
1H-Indene-3a,7a-dicarboxylic acid, 7-methoxy-3-(1-methylethyl)-1-oxo-, dimethyl ester, cis	MeOH	221(4.16),284(3.57), 338(2.75)	18-2023-79
1H-Indene-3a,7a-dicarboxylic acid, 7-methoxy-5-(1-methylethyl)-1-oxo-, dimethyl ester, cis	MeOH	215(4.13),282(3.61), 347(2.92)	18-2023-79
$C_{17}H_{20}O_6Si$			
2,9,10(1H)-Anthracenetrione, 3,4,4a,9a-tetrahydro-5,8-dihydroxy-4-[(trimethylsilyl)oxy]-	MeOH	224(4.30),259(4.06), 394(3.89)	24-3453-79
$C_{17}H_{20}O_7$			
4H-Bisoxireno[1,8a:2,3]azuleno[4,5-b]-furan-2(3H)-one, 4-acetoxyoctahydro-6-hydroxy-6,8a-dimethyl-3-methylene-(yomogiartemin)	MeOH	214(4.04)	138-0081-79
Parvulenone diacetate	MeOH	255(3.98),286(3.85), 330s(3.39)	150-2685-79
$C_{17}H_{21}ClN_2O_2$			
2-Propenoic acid, 3-[4-(2-chloroethyl)-ethylamino]-2-methylphenyl]-2-cyano-, ethyl ester	EtOH	242(4.58)	110-1769-79
	EtOH-KOH	341(--)	110-1769-79
	CCl_4	417(--)	110-1769-79
	KBr	437(--)	110-1769-79
$C_{17}H_{21}N$			
Benz[g]isoquinoline, 1,2,3,4-tetrahydro-2,3,7,8-tetramethyl-	EtOH	205(4.14),234(4.82), 260(3.31),266(3.36), 278(3.44),278(3.40), 298(3.18),313(2.68), 320(2.35),328(2.78)	103-0421-79
Cyclohepta[b]pyrrole, 2,4,5,6,7,8-hexahydro-2,2-dimethyl-3-phenyl-	EtOH	255(3.82)	78-2285-79
Cyclopent[cd]azulen-2-amine, N,N-diethyl-1,8a-dihydro-1-methyl-	hexane	213(4.16),252s(3.89), 267s(4.04),273(4.08), 319s(4.13),336(4.25), 400(3.62)	89-0161-79
Cyclopent[cd]azulen-2-amine, N,N-diethyl-3,4-dihydro-1-methyl-	hexane	224s(4.10),256(4.17), 295s(4.26),306s(4.58), 316(4.75),337s(3.83), 363s(3.61),392s(3.59), 403s(3.75),410(3.88), 429s(3.89),436(4.06), 530(2.51)	89-0161-79
5aH-Cyclopent[c]inden-4-amine, N,N-diethyl-5-methyl-	hexane	259(3.89),328s(3.09)	89-0161-79
$C_{17}H_{21}NO$			
Benzamide, N-1,3-butadienyl-N-cyclohexyl-	MeOH	250(4.17)	88-0981-79
3,5-Hexadien-2-one, 1-(1-methyl-2-pyrrolidinyl)-6-phenyl-, (E,E)-(+)-	EtOH	233(3.78),322(4.51)	12-2523-79
4,7-Methano-1,2-benzisoxazole, 3a,4,5,6,7,7a-hexahydro-3-(2,4,6-trimethylphenyl)-	EtOH	230(3.8)	33-2025-79
4(1H)-Quinolinone, 2,3,5,6,7,8-hexahydro-3-methyl-1-(phenylmethyl)-	EtOH	340(4.26)	103-1261-79

Compound	Solvent	λ_{max}(log ε)	Ref.
$C_{17}H_{21}NO_2$			
1H-Carbazole-2-carboxylic acid, 4-ethyl-2,3,4,9-tetrahydro-3-methyl-, methyl ester	EtOH	227(4.48),274s(3.80), 282(3.84),290(3.78)	44-4402-79
1H-Carbazole-2-carboxylic acid, 2,3,4,9-tetrahydro-3,4-dimethyl-, ethyl ester	EtOH	226(4.43),276s(3.71), 283(3.75),291(3.68)	44-4402-79
1H-Carbazole-2-carboxylic acid, 2,3,4,9-tetrahydro-4-(2-methylpropyl)-	EtOH	228(4.56),275s(3.82), 282(3.86),290(3.81)	44-4402-79
$C_{17}H_{21}NO_3$			
Dibenz[c,e]azocin-5(1H)-one, 2,3,4,6,7-8-hexahydro-10,11-dimethoxy-	MeOH	211(4.45),284(3.57)	24-3795-79
B-Norerythrinan-8-one, 15,16-dimethoxy-, cis	MeOH	208(4.46),278(3.62)	24-3795-79
4-Pyridineacetic acid, 5-ethyl-1,2,5,6-tetrahydro-2-oxo-1-(phenylmethyl)-, methyl ester	EtOH	253(3.54)	94-1847-79
$C_{17}H_{21}NO_5$			
Pentanoic acid, 2,4-dioxo-3-[(phenylamino)propoxymethylene]-, ethyl ester	EtOH	287(4.36)	94-1792-79
Pentanoic acid, 3-[(1-methylethoxy)-(phenylamino)methylene]-2,4-dioxo-, ethyl ester	EtOH	288(4.36)	94-1792-79
$C_{17}H_{21}NSi$			
5-Acenaphthylenamine, N,N-dimethyl-2-(trimethylsilyl)-	C_6H_{12}	242(4.39),328(3.97), 364(3.90)	44-4275-79
$C_{17}H_{21}N_2$			
Pyridinium, 2-[2-[4-(dimethylamino)-phenyl]ethenyl]-1-ethyl-, iodide	EtOH	464(4.65)	80-1491-79
	$CHCl_3$	478(4.22)	80-1491-79
	CCl_4	468(4.22)	80-1491-79
$C_{17}H_{21}N_2O$			
Benzenaminium, 4-[[(4-methoxyphenyl)imino]methyl]-N,N,N-trimethyl-, iodide	EtOH	222(3.41),310(3.38)	2-0338-79B
$C_{17}H_{21}N_3$			
1,4-Benzenediamine, N-[[4-(dimethylamino)phenyl]methylene]-N,N-dimethyl-	toluene	383(4.50)	135-1491-79B
$C_{17}H_{21}N_3OS$			
1H-Thieno[3,4-d]imidazol-2(3H)-one, tetrahydro-4-[4-(1H-indol-3-yl)-butyl]-2-oxo-, [3aS-(3aα,4β,6aα)]-	C_6H_{12} -1% EtOH	221(4.50),273s(3.74), 281(3.77),290(3.68)	35-0996-79
$C_{17}H_{21}N_3O_2$			
Debenzoevodiaminic acid, ethyl ester, hydrochloride	EtOH	242(4.12),324(4.30)	114-0127-79D
$C_{17}H_{21}N_3O_5$			
Glycine, N-[N-acetyl-3-(1-formyl-2,3-dihydro-1H-indol-3-yl)-L-alanyl]-, methyl ester	MeOH-HCl	251(3.67),289(3.23)	63-0013-79
$C_{17}H_{21}N_3O_{10}$			
Cytosine, 1-(5-O-carboxymethyl-2,3-di-O-acetyl-β-D-arabinofuranosyl)-N^4-acetyl-	pH 1	245(4.00),305(3.99)	73-3023-79
	pH 7-10.5	248(4.16),298(3.88)	73-3023-79

Compound	Solvent	λ_{max}(log ε)	Ref.
$C_{17}H_{21}N_3O_{10}S$			
1,2,4-Triazin-5(2H)-one, 3,4-dihydro-3-thioxo-2-[2,3,5-tri-O-acetyl-4-C-(acetoxymethyl)-β-D-erythro-pento-furanosyl]-	MeOH	217(4.11),272(4.22)	44-1301-79
$C_{17}H_{21}N_3O_{11}$			
1H-Imidazole, 4-nitro-1-(2,3,4,6-tetra-O-acetyl-β-D-glucopyranosyl)-	n.s.g.	280(4.01)	111-0123-79
1H-Imidazole, 5-nitro-1-(2,3,4,6-tetra-O-acetyl-β-D-glucopyranosyl)-	n.s.g.	288(3.89)	111-0123-79
1H-Pyrazole, 3-nitro-1-(2,3,4,6-tetra-O-acetyl-β-D-glucopyranosyl)-	n.s.g.	258(4.03)	111-0123-79
1H-Pyrazole, 5-nitro-1-(2,3,4,6-tetra-O-acetyl-β-D-glucopyranosyl)-	n.s.g.	272(3.88)	111-0123-79
$C_{17}H_{21}N_5O_4S$			
Methanesulfonamide, N-[5-(diethylamino)-2-[(4-nitrophenyl)azo]phenyl]-	EtOH	498(4.64)	39-1990-79C
	HOAc	495(4.63)	39-1990-79C
$C_{17}H_{21}N_5O_7S$			
Adenosine, 2-(methylthio)-, 2',3',5'-triacetate	M HCl	220(4.21),271(4.21), 282s(4.11)	94-0183-79
	H_2O	236(4.33),274(4.16)	94-0183-79
Adenosine, 8-(methylthio)-, 2',3',5'-triacetate	M HCl	281(4.27)	94-0183-79
	H_2O	280(4.25)	94-0183-79
$C_{17}H_{21}N_5O_9S$			
Adenosine, 2-(methylsulfonyl)-, 2',3',5'-triacetate	0.5M HCl	263(4.08),278s(3.88)	94-0183-79
	H_2O	263(4.09),280s(3.83)	94-0183-79
Adenosine, 8-(methylsulfonyl)-, 2',3',5'-triacetate	M HCl	269(4.23)	94-0183-79
	H_2O	221(4.31),284(4.09)	94-0183-79
$C_{17}H_{22}BrN_3O_9$			
1H-1,2,3-Triazole, 4-(bromomethyl)-1-(2,3,4,6-tetra-O-acetyl-β-D-glucopyranosyl)-	EtOH	235(3.39)	87-0496-79
$C_{17}H_{22}ClN_3O_9$			
1H-1,2,3-Triazole, 4-(chloromethyl)-1-(2,3,4,6-tetra-O-acetyl-β-D-glucopyranosyl)-	EtOH	226(3.37)	87-0496-79
1H-1,2,3-Triazole, 5-(chloromethyl)-1-(2,3,4,6-tetra-O-acetyl-β-D-glucopyranosyl)-	EtOH	232(3.37)	87-0496-79
$C_{17}H_{22}IN_3O_9$			
1H-1,2,3-Triazole, 4-(iodomethyl)-1-(2,3,4,6-tetra-O-acetyl-β-D-glucopyranosyl)-	EtOH	239(3.62)	87-0496-79
$C_{17}H_{22}N_2O$			
4-Piperidinone, 1-phenyl-3-(1-piperidinylmethylene)-	EtOH	252(4.06),330(4.24)	4-0177-79
$C_{17}H_{22}N_2O_2$			
1,3-Cyclohexanedione, 2-[[[4-(dimethylamino)phenyl]amino]methylene]-5,5-dimethyl-	hexane	248(4.12),344s(4.06), 377(4.42)	131-0077-79D
	EtOH	392(4.36)	131-0077-79D

Compound	Solvent	λ_{max}(log ε)	Ref.
1H-Indole-3-methanol, 2-(methoxymethyl)- -(1,2,3,6-tetrahydro-1-methyl-4-pyridinyl)-	EtOH	276s(3.84),283(3.85), 290s(3.79)	39-3155-79C
2-Pentanone, 4,4'-[(2-methyl-1,4-phenylene)dinitrilo]bis-	heptane	332(4.38)	40-1437-79
	EtOH	339(4.48)	40-1437-79
	dioxan	334(4.46)	40-1437-79
	$CHCl_3$	336(4.47)	40-1437-79
2-Pentanone, 4,4'-[(4-methyl-1,3-phenylene)dinitrilo]bis-	heptane	332(4.38)	40-1437-79
	EtOH	338(4.38)	40-1437-79
	dioxan	334(4.39)	40-1437-79
	$CHCl_3$	336(4.41)	40-1437-79
$C_{17}H_{22}N_2O_3$			
2-Pentanone, 4,4'-(2-methoxy-1,4-phenylene)dinitrilo]bis-	heptane	318(4.31)	40-1437-79
	EtOH	326(4.38)	40-1437-79
	dioxan	320(4.33)	40-1437-79
	$CHCl_3$	322(4.38)	40-1437-79
$C_{17}H_{22}N_2O_6$			
1H-Azepine-3,6-dicarboxylic acid, 4,5-dihydro-4-(2,5-dioxo-1-pyrrolidinyl)-2,5,7-trimethyl-, dimethyl ester	n.s.g.	235(4.02),328(4.17)	23-0044-79
$C_{17}H_{22}N_2O_7$			
DL-threo-Hex-2-enopyranuronic acid, 1,2,3-trideoxy-1-(3,4-dihydro-5-methyl-2,4-dioxo-1(2H)-pyrimidinyl)-, butyl ester, 4-acetate (both α and β)	MeOH	263(3.95)	136-0272-79E
$C_{17}H_{22}N_4O_3$			
1,2,3-Triazine-2(5H)-carboxylic acid, 4-[bis(1-methylethyl)amino]-5-oxo-6-phenyl-, methyl ester	CH_2Cl_2	402(3.86)	24-1535-79
$C_{17}H_{22}N_4O_5$			
8-Azabicyclo[3.2.1]oct-3-ene-6-carboxylic acid, 8-(4,6-dimethoxy-1,3,5-triazin-2-yl)-2-oxo-, 1,1-dimethylethyl ester, endo	$CHCl_3$	247(3.63)	39-2528-79C
exo	$CHCl_3$	247(3.50)	39-2528-79C
$C_{17}H_{22}N_4O_6S$			
Inosine, 2',3'-O-(4-ethoxy-1-methyl-4-oxobutylidene)-6-thio-	MeOH	325(4.37)	136-0117-79G
$C_{17}H_{22}N_4O_7$			
α-D-Xylofuranose, 5-[1-acetyl-3-(4-nitrophenyl)-2-triazenyl)-5-deoxy-3-O-methyl-1,2-O-(1-methylethylidene)-	EtOH	218(3.97),311(4.22)	33-0971-79
$C_{17}H_{22}N_4O_8$			
1H-Purine-2,6-dione, 9-(4,6-di-O-acetyl-2-deoxy-β-D-arabino-hexopyranosyl)-3,9-dihydro-1,3-dimethyl-	MeOH	274(3.91)	136-0061-79A
$C_{17}H_{22}N_4O_9$			
Polyoxin I	0.05M HCl	262.5(3.94)	142-0333-79B
	0.05M NaOH	264(3.78)	142-0333-79B
$C_{17}H_{22}O_2$			
6-Oxabicyclo[3.2.1]octan-7-one, 1,5-di-	EtOH	253(2.93),259(2.44)	44-1992-79

Compound	Solvent	λ max(log ε)	Ref.
methyl-8-(2-phenylethyl)-, anti-(±)-			44-1992-79
$C_{17}H_{22}O_3$			
1H-Fluorene-1-carboxylic acid, 2,3,4-4a,9,9a-hexahydro-7-methoxy-1,4a-dimethyl-	EtOH	278(3.46)	2-0183-79B
$C_{17}H_{22}O_4$			
Furanoeremophilan-6-one, 3 -acetoxy-	EtOH	270(3.52)	94-1747-79
2H-Oxocin-3(4H)-one, 8-(1-acetoxy-3-hexen-5-ynyl)-2-ethyl-7,8-dihydro-	EtOH	224(4.15),230s(4.06), 293(2.51),300(2.48), 310(2.45),322(2.29)	18-0135-79
$C_{17}H_{22}O_5$			
Cedr-8-ene-12,15-dioic acid, 10-oxo-, dimethyl ester	MeOH	247(3.96)	2-0320-79B
Helenimarin	MeOH	226(2.53),278(1.82)	100-0450-79
Tenulin	EtOH	225(3.91)	36-0715-79
$C_{17}H_{22}O_5S_3$			
α-D-Allopyranoside, methyl 2-O,3-S-[bis(methylthio)methylene]-4,6-O-(phenylmethylene)-3-thio-	MeOH	205(3.90)	136-0127-79G
α-D-Mannopyranoside, methyl 3-O,2-S-[bis(methylthio)methylene]-4,6-O-(phenylmethylene)-2-thio-	MeOH	205(3.78)	136-0127-79G
$C_{17}H_{22}O_6$			
Lactarolide A, 8-acetyl-	EtOH	210(3.90)	102-0293-79
	EtOH-KOH	254(3.78)	102-0293-79
$C_{17}H_{22}O_7$			
Butanoic acid, 3-methyl-, 4-(acetoxymethyl)-7-formyl-1,3,4a,7a-tetrahydro-1-hydroxycyclopenta[c]pyran-4-yl ester	MeOH	276(4.36)	83-0555-79
$C_{17}H_{23}BrN_4O_8$			
1H-1,2,3-Triazole, 4-(bromomethyl)-1-[3,4,6-tri-O-acetyl-2-(acetylamino)-2-deoxy-β-D-glucopyranosyl]-	EtOH	230(3.41)	87-0496-79
$C_{17}H_{23}ClN_4O_8$			
1H-1,2,3-Triazole, 4-(chloromethyl)-1-[3,4,6-tri-O-acetyl-2-(acetylamino)-2-deoxy-β-D-glucopyranosyl]-	EtOH	225(3.23)	87-0496-79
1H-1,2,3-Triazole, 5-(chloromethyl)-1-[3,4,6-tri-O-acetyl-2-(acetylamino)-2-deoxy-β-D-glucopyranosyl]-	EtOH	224(3.66)	87-0496-79
$C_{17}H_{23}NO$			
6-Oxa-1-azabicyclo[3.1.0]hexane, 5-(1,1-dimethylethyl)-2,2-dimethyl-4-(phenylmethylene)-	EtOH	212(3.94),252(4.14)	12-2041-79
2H-Pyrrole, 5-(1,1-dimethylethyl)-3,4-dihydro-2,2-dimethyl-4-(phenylmethylene)-, 1-oxide	EtOH	236(3.88),318(4.45)	12-2025-79
2H-Pyrrole, 5-(1,1-dimethylethyl)-2,2-dimethyl-4-(phenylmethyl)-, 1-oxide	EtOH	300(3.72)	12-2025-79
2-Pyrrolidineethanol, 1-methyl-α-(4-phenyl-1,3-butadienyl)- (darlingianine)	EtOH	207(4.20),285(4.36)	12-2523-79

Compound	Solvent	λ_{max}(log ϵ)	Ref.
2-Pyrrolidineethanol, 1-methyl-α-(4-phenyl-1,3-butadienyl)- (isodarlingianine)	EtOH	214(4.16),274(4.24)	12-2523-79
$C_{17}H_{23}NO_3$			
2-Cyclohexen-1-one, 3-[7-(2-methyl-1,3-dioxolan-2-yl)-2-azabicyclo[2.2.2]-oct-5-en-2-yl]-	EtOH	304(4.15)	44-0124-79
1(2H)-Phenanthridinone, 3,4,5,6,6a,7-10,10a-octahydro-8-(2-methyl-1,3-dioxolan-2-yl)-, cis	EtOH	301(4.42)	44-0124-79
$C_{17}H_{23}N_2O_5PS$			
Phosphorothioic acid, O-[1,6-dihydro-5-methoxy-6-oxo-1-(phenylmethyl)-4-pyridazinyl] O-ethyl O-(1-methylethyl) ester	MeOH	212(4.34),289(3.67)	73-1761-79
$C_{17}H_{23}N_3O_{10}$			
1H-1,2,3-Triazole-4-methanol, 1-(2,3,4-6-tetra-O-acetyl-β-D-glucopyranosyl)-	EtOH	228(3.33)	87-0496-79
$C_{17}H_{23}N_5O_8$			
Pyrido[3,2-c]pyridazine-1,2-dicarboxylic acid, 4-[1,2-bis(methoxycarbonyl)hydrazino]-7-ethyl-3,4-dihydro-, dimethyl ester	MeOH	227(3.94),281(3.63)	103-0518-79
$C_{17}H_{23}N_5O_{13}$			
5-Pyrimidinecarboxylic acid, 1-[5-[[2-amino-5-O-(aminocarbonyl)-2,3-dideoxy-L-erythro-pentonoyl]amino]-5-deoxy-β-D-allofuranuronosyl]-1,2,3,4-tetrahydro-2,4-dioxo- (Polyoxin E)	0.05M HCl	276(4.00)	142-0333-79B
	0.05M NaOH	271(3.81)	142-0333-79B
$C_{17}H_{23}N_5O_{14}$			
Polyoxin D	0.05M HCl	276(4.05)	142-0333-79B
	0.05M NaOH	271(3.85)	142-0333-79B
$C_{17}H_{24}N_2$			
Benzenamine, N-[[5-methyl-2-(1-methylethyl)cyclohexyl]carbonimidoyl]-, [1R-(1α,2β,3α)]-	C_6H_{12}	209(4.26),252(4.13), 280s(3.60),287s(3.43)	56-0631-79
$C_{17}H_{24}N_2O_4S$			
Thieno[3,2-c]pyridazine-1,2-dicarboxylic acid, 1,2-dihydro-4-methyl-, bis(1,1-dimethylethyl) ester	EtOH	229(3.98),269(3.80), 307(3.73)	78-2027-79
$C_{17}H_{24}N_2S$			
1-Piperidinecarbothioamide, N-(2,2-dimethyl-1-phenylpropylidene)-	C_6H_{12}	264(4.00)	24-1956-79
$C_{17}H_{24}N_4O_4S$			
1H-1,2,4-Triazole, 3-nitro-1-[[2,4,6-tris(1-methylethyl)phenyl]sulfonyl]-	EtOH	242(4.18),285(3.63)	54-0537-79
$C_{17}H_{24}N_4O_8$			
1,3(2H,4H)-Pyrimidinediacetic acid, α,α'-bis(acetylamino)-5-methyl-2,4-dioxo-, diethyl ester	pH 1	268(3.96)	44-2019-79
	pH 12	273(3.95)	44-2019-79
	MeOH	267(3.97)	44-2019-79

Compound	Solvent	λ_{max}(log ε)	Ref.
$C_{17}H_{24}N_4O_9$			
1H-1,2,3-Triazole-4-methanol, 1-[3,4,6-tri-O-acetyl-2-(acetylamino)-2-deoxy-β-D-glucopyranosyl]-	EtOH	228(3.41)	87-0496-79
1H-1,2,3-Triazole-5-methanol, 1-[3,4,6-tri-O-acetyl-2-(acetylamino)-2-deoxy-β-D-glucopyranosyl]-	EtOH	229(3.36)	87-0496-79
$C_{17}H_{24}N_6O_8$			
1,2-Hydrazinedicarboxylic acid, 1,1'-[(dimethylamino)-4-pyridinylethenylidene]bis-, tetramethyl ester	n.s.g.	230(4.15),320(3.63)	104-2203-79
$C_{17}H_{24}O$			
Benzo[3,4]cyclobuta[1,2]cyclodecen-4b(5H)-ol, 6,7,8,9,10,11,12,12a-octahydro-4-methyl-, (4bR*,12aS*)-	MeOH	261(2.76),267(2.85), 274(2.86)	39-2542-79C
4bH-Benzo[3,4]cyclobuta[1,2]cyclononen-4b-ol, 4-ethyl-5,6,7,8,9,10,11,11a-octahydro-, (4bR*,11aS*)-	MeOH	261(2.82),266(2.96), 273(2.96)	39-2542-79C
Benzo[3,4]cyclobuta[1,2]cycloocta-4b(5H)-ol, 6,7,8,9,10,10a-hexahydro-4-(1-methylethyl)-, cis	MeOH	261(2.91),266(3.06), 273(3.06)	39-2542-79C
trans	MeOH	261(2.83),266(2.97), 274(2.95)	39-2542-79C
2,16-Cycloheptadecadien-9-yn-1-one, (E,E)-	EtOH	240(4.18)	33-2661-79
1,12-Methanobenzocyclododecen-12(5H)-ol, 6,7,8,9,10,11-hexahydro-13,13-dimethyl-	MeOH	261(2.79),266(2.93), 273(2.94)	39-2542-79C
1,13-Methano-5H-benzocycloundecen-13(6H)-ol, 7,8,9,10,11,12-hexahydro-14-methyl-	MeOH	261(2.74),267(2.86), 274(2.82)	39-2542-79C
$C_{17}H_{24}OSi$			
Ethanone, 1-[2-phenyl-6-(trimethylsilyl)-2-cyclohexen-1-yl]-	isooctane	244(3.29)	101-0027-79K
$C_{17}H_{24}O_2$			
1,9-Heptadecadiene-4,6-diyne-3,8-diol, (Z)-(+)-	ether	233(3.0),245(3.0), 259(2.8)	102-1195-79
A-Norestr-1(10)-en-2-one, 17-hydroxy-, (5α,17β)-	n.s.g.	232(4.26)	22-0157-79
$C_{17}H_{24}O_3$			
6H-Cycloprop[e]azulen-6-one, 2-acetoxy-1,1a,2,3,4,7,7a,7b-octahydro-3,3,5,7b-tetramethyl-, (1aα,2α,7aβ,7bα)-(±)-	EtOH	240(4.01)	88-3891-79
Marsupellone, acetoxy-, (+)-	EtOH	239(3.61)	138-0073-79
2(3H)-Naphthalenone, 1-acetoxy-4,4a,5,6-7,8-hexahydro-4a,5-dimethyl-3-(1-methylethylidene)-, (4aR-cis)-	MeOH	255(3.97),285(3.85)	18-2372-79
$C_{17}H_{24}O_4$			
2,5-Cyclohexadiene-1,4-dione, 2,3,5-trimethyl-6-[2-(2,2,4-trimethyl-1,3-dioxolan-4-yl)ethyl]-, (S)-	EtOH	262(4.26),269(4.26), 344(2.43)	35-6710-79
1β-Phenanthrenecarboxylic acid, 1,2,3-4,4a,4b,5,6,7,9,10,10a-dodecahydro-10β-hydroxy-1,4a-dimethyl-7-oxo-	EtOH	248(4.19)	18-0608-79

Compound	Solvent	λmax(log ε)	Ref.
Spiro[1,3-dioxolane-2,2'(6'H)-naphthalen]-6'-one, 1',3',4',8'a-tetrahydro-7'-(1-hydroxy-1-methylethyl)-1',8'a-dimethyl-, cis-(±)-	EtOH	244(4.15)	94-0331-79
$C_{17}H_{24}O_4S_2$			
2-Propanone, 1-[2-[(3,4,5-trimethoxyphenyl)methyl]-1,3-dithian-2-yl]-	EtOH	211(4.52),234s(3.95), 270(3.54)	150-0301-79
$C_{17}H_{24}O_5$			
Acetylhumulinic acid, anti-cis-	MeOH-HCl	225(4.06),265s(3.96)	78-0989-79
	MeOH-NaOH	255(4.17)	78-0989-79
trans	MeOH-HCl	227(4.09),256s(4.11)	78-0989-79
	MeOH-NaOH	260(4.16)	78-0989-79
$C_{17}H_{24}O_{11}$			
Hastatoside	H_2O	234(3.98)	64-0311-79C
$C_{17}H_{25}IN_4O_7$			
Uridine, 2'-deoxy-5-[[6-[(iodoacetyl)-amino]-1-oxohexyl]amino]-	H_2O	278(3.90)	87-0621-79
$C_{17}H_{25}N$			
Dicycloocta[b,e]pyridine, 1,2,3,4,5,6-8,9,10,11,12,13-dodecahydro-	EtOH	218(3.96),235(3.45), 272(3.80),275(3.87), 279(3.86),284(3.84)	1-0313-79
$C_{17}H_{25}NO$			
4bH-Benzo[3,4]cyclobuta[1,2]cyclohepten-4b-ol, 5-[(1,1-dimethylethyl)amino]-5,6,7,8,9,9a-hexahydro-, monohydrochloride, (4bα,5β,9aα)-	MeOH	260(3.04),266(3.21), 273(3.20)	111-0543-79
Benzo[3,4]cyclobuta[1,2]cycloocten-4b(5H)-ol, 6,7,8,9,10,10a-hexahydro-5-[(1-methylethyl)amino]-, monohydrochloride, (4bα,5β,10aα)-	MeOH	260(3.23),266(3.33), 273(3.30)	111-0543-79
4(1H)-Pyridinone, 1,3-dicyclohexyl-	EtOH	272(5.0414)	104-0396-79
2-Pyrrolidineethanol, 1-methyl-α-(4-phenyl-3-butenyl)-, [R*,S*-(E)]-(+)-(dihydrodarlingianine)	EtOH	211(4.25),251(4.21)	12-2523-79
$C_{17}H_{25}NO_2$			
2H-Pyrrol-4-ol, 5-(1,1-dimethylethyl)-3,4-dihydro-2,2-dimethyl-4-(phenylmethyl)-, 1-oxide	EtOH	211(3.89),239(4.05)	12-2025-79
$C_{17}H_{25}NO_3$			
2-Cyclohexen-1-ol, 4-(3,4-dimethoxyphenyl)-4-[2-(methylamino)ethyl]-(joubertinamine)	EtOH	231(3.9),280(3.5), 284s(3.45)	39-1063-79C
$C_{17}H_{25}NO_4$			
3,5-Cyclohexadiene-1,3-dicarboxylic acid, 4-methyl-6-pyrrolidino-, diethyl ester	EtOH	383(4.48)	39-1837-79C
$C_{17}H_{25}NO_6$			
1H-Pyrrole-3-propanoic acid, 5-(acetoxymethyl)-2-[(1,1-dimethylethoxy)-carbonyl]-4-methyl-, methyl ester	n.s.g.	275(4.17)	39-1927-79C

Compound	Solvent	λ_{max}(log ε)	Ref.
1H-Pyrrole-3-propanoic acid, 2-[(1,1-dimethylethoxy)carbonyl]-4-(2-methoxy-2-oxoethyl)-5-methyl-, methyl ester	n.s.g.	282(3.73)	39-1927-79C
$C_{17}H_{25}N_3O_4$			
Pyrido[3,2-c]pyridazine-1,2-dicarboxylic acid, 3,4-dihydro-, bis(1,1-dimethylethyl) ester	EtOH	234(3.89),281(3.60)	78-2027-79
Pyrido[3,4-c]pyridazine-1,2-dicarboxylic acid, 3,4-dihydro-, bis(1,1-dimethylethyl) ester	EtOH	235(3.90),277(3.52)	78-2027-79
1H-Pyrido[1,2-c]triazine-1,2(3H)-dicarboxylic acid, bis(1,1-dimethylethyl) ester	EtOH	253(3.27),261(3.28), 262(3.17)	78-2027-79
$C_{17}H_{25}N_3O_8$			
Thymidine, 3'-O-(carboxymethyl)-5'-deoxy-, 5'-[[(1,1-dimethylethoxy)carbonyl]amino]-	EtOH	268(3.95)	39-1389-79C
$C_{17}H_{25}N_3O_{10}S$			
D-Galactose, (aminothioxomethyl)hydrazone, 2,3,4,5,6-pentaacetate	EtOH	235(3.87),277(4.34)	136-0325-79H
$C_{17}H_{25}N_3O_{11}$			
D-Galactose, (aminocarbonyl)hydrazone, 2,3,4,5,6-pentaacetate	EtOH	235(4.15)	136-0325-79H
$C_{17}H_{25}N_5O_4$			
Adenosine, N,N,8-trimethyl-5'-O-methyl-2',3'-O-(1-methylethylidene)-	EtOH	273(4.30)	88-0279-79
5,14-Iminoimidazo[4,5-b][1,5]diazacyclotridecine, 3,6,7,8,9,10,11,12-octahydro-3-β-D-ribofuranosyl-	pH 1.0	277(4.24)	5-1872-79
	pH 7.0	272(4.26)	5-1872-79
$C_{17}H_{25}N_5O_{12}$			
Polyoxin G	0.05M HCl	262(3.92)	142-0333-79B
	0.05M NaOH	264(3.82)	142-0333-79B
Polyoxin J	0.05M HCl	264(3.91)	142-0333-79B
	0.05M NaOH	267(3.81)	142-0333-79B
$C_{17}H_{25}N_5O_{13}$			
Polyoxin B	0.05M HCl	262(3.94)	142-0333-79B
	0.05M NaOH	264(3.82)	142-0333-79B
$C_{17}H_{26}N_2S_2$			
Spiro[cyclohexane-1,8'-[2H,8H]isothiazolo[4,3,2-ij]quinazoline]-2'-thione, 3',4',5',5'a,6',7'-hexahydro-6'-(1-methylethyl)-	EtOH	264(3.50),369(4.31)	150-0410-79S
$C_{17}H_{26}N_3OP$			
Phosphorodiamidous acid, tetraethyl-, 8-quinolinyl ester	n.s.g.	233(4.58),293(3.66)	93-1271-79
$C_{17}H_{26}N_3O_8P$			
Octanoic acid, 2,3,3a,9a-tetrahydro-6-imino-2-[(phosphonooxy)methyl]-6H-furo[2',3':4,5]oxazolo[3,2-a]pyrimidin-3-yl ester, [2R-(2α,3β,3aβ,9aβ)]-	MeOH	235(3.90),265(3.95)	87-0639-79

Compound	Solvent	λ_{max}(log ε)	Ref.
$C_{17}H_{26}N_4O$			
7H-Indazol-7-one, 4-(1-aziridinylimino)-6,7a-bis(1,1-dimethylethyl)-3,3a,4,7a-tetrahydro-	n.s.g.	255(4.40)	70-1668-79
$C_{17}H_{26}O_3$			
Cyclopropa[d]naphthalen-2(3H)-one, 7-(1-acetoxy-1-methylethyl)-octahydro-4a-methyl-	EtOH	207(3.75)	44-4981-79
2(1H)-Naphthalenone, 1-acetoxyoctahydro-4a,5-dimethyl-3-(1-methylethylidene)-, [1R-(1α,4aα,5α,8aα)]-	MeOH	253(3.76)	18-2372-79
Naphtho[1,2-b]furan-2(4H)-one, 9a-ethoxy-4a,5,6,7,8,8a,9,9a-octahydro-3,4a,5-trimethyl-, [4aR-(4aα,5α,8aβ-9aβ)]-	EtOH	222(4.14)	39-1542-79C
Phenol, 2,3,6-trimethyl-5-[2-(2,2,4-trimethyl-1,3-dioxolan-4-yl)ethyl]-, (S)-	EtOH	223s(3.98),274(2.98), 281(2.99)	35-6710-79
$C_{17}H_{26}O_4$			
Azuleno[5,6-c]furan-3(1H)-one, 8-ethoxy-4,4a,5,6,7,7a,8,9-octahydro-4-hydroxy-6,6,8-trimethyl-	EtOH	216(3.89)	102-0293-79
2,6,10-Dodecatrienedioic acid, 3,6,10-trimethyl-, dimethyl ester, (E,E,E)-	EtOH	219(4.42)	40-0255-79
2(3H)-Naphthalenone, 1-acetoxy-4,4a,5-6,7,8-hexahydro-3-hydroxy-4a,5-dimethyl-3-(1-methylethyl)-	MeOH	249(3.91)	18-2372-79
Spiro[1,3-dioxolane-2,2'(6'H)-naphthalen]-6'-one, 1',3',4',7',8',8'a-hexahydro-7'-(1-hydroxy-1-methylethyl)-1',8'-dimethyl-	EtOH	239(4.20)	94-0331-79
$C_{17}H_{26}O_4S_2$			
1,3-Dithiane-2-ethanol, α-methyl-2-[(3,4,5-trimethoxyphenyl)methyl]-	EtOH	211(4.50),288s(4.01), 272(3.54)	150-0301-79
$C_{17}H_{27}NO$			
2-Pyrrolidineethanol, 1-methyl-α-(4-phenylbutyl)- (tetrahydrodarlingianine)	EtOH	212(3.78)	12-2523-79
$C_{17}H_{27}NO_7S_2$			
α-D-Glucopyranoside, methyl 4,6-O-cyclohexylidene-2-deoxy-2-[(methoxycarbonyl)amino]-, 3-(S-methyl carbonodithioate)	EtOH	203(3.85),227(3.78), 281(4.00)	18-3015-79
$C_{17}H_{27}NO_8$			
α-D-Glucopyranoside, methyl 4,6-O-cyclohexylidene-2-deoxy-2-[(methoxycarbonyl)amino]-, 3-acetate	EtOH	203(2.43)	18-3015-79
$C_{17}H_{27}NO_8S$			
α-D-Glucofuranose, 1,2:5,6-bis-O-(1-methylethylidene)-, 3-(2-ethoxy-2-oxoethyl)carbonothioate)	EtOH	241(4.10)	136-0141-79A

Compound	Solvent	λ_{max}(log ϵ)	Ref.
$C_{17}H_{27}NS_2$			
Benzenamine, 2,4-bis(1,1-dimethyleth-yl)-6-(1-methylethyl)-N-sulfinothi-oyl-	pentane	272s(3.31),305s(3.37), 343(3.84),483(3.26), 542s(3.05)	18-1998-79
$C_{17}H_{27}N_2O_8P$			
L-Ascorbic acid, 3-deoxy-3-(di-4-mor-pholinylphosphinyl)-5,6-O-(1-meth-ylethylidene)-	EtOH	236(3.98)	78-1483-79
$C_{17}H_{27}N_5O_4$			
1H-Purine-2,6-dione, 7-[3-(cyclohexyl-amino)-2-hydroxypropyl]-3,7-dihydro-8-(hydroxymethyl)-1,3-dimethyl-, hydrochloride	n.s.g.	211(4.44),235(3.89), 279(4.05)	73-0424-79
$C_{17}H_{28}N$			
13-Azoniabicyclo[9.3.1]pentadeca-1(15),11,13-triene, 12,13,14-trimethyl-, iodide	C_6H_{12}	197(4.3),217(3.9), 273(3.5),280s(3.5)	18-0257-79
$C_{17}H_{28}N_4$			
1H-Pyrrolo[2,3-d]pyrimidin-4-amine, N-decyl-2-methyl-	pH 1	268(4.26),357(3.95)	102-0217-79
	H_2O	268(4.23),358(4.00)	102-0217-79
	pH 13	264(4.22),356(4.03)	102-0217-79
$C_{17}H_{28}O$			
2,4-Cyclopentadien-1-one, 2,3,5-tris-(1,1-dimethylethyl)-	C_6H_{12}	220(3.68),417(2.67)	44-2983-79
$C_{17}H_{28}O_2$			
3H-Cyclododeca[c]pyran-3-one, 4-ethyl-1,5,6,7,8,9,10,11,12,13,14,14a-do-decahydro-	MeOH	231(3.81)	146-0031-79
$C_{17}H_{28}O_3$			
1-Cyclopentadecene-1-carboxylic acid, 15-oxo-, methyl ester	EtOH	225.5(3.88)	33-2630-79
geometric isomer	EtOH	222(3.61)	33-2630-79
$C_{17}H_{28}O_5$			
Methynolide, (+)-	EtOH	225(4.03)	138-1021-79
$C_{17}H_{28}O_7$			
2-Butenoic acid, 3-methyl-4-[tetrahy-dro-3,4-dihydroxy-5-[[3-(2-hydroxy-1-methylpropyl)oxiranyl]methyl]-2H-pyran-2-yl]-, [2S-(2α(E),3β,4β,5α-[2R*.3R*(1R*,2R*)]]]-	EtOH	221(4.05)	39-0308-79C
sodium salt	EtOH	214(4.16)	39-0308-79C
$C_{17}H_{29}N$			
Benzenamine, 2,4-bis(1,1-dimethyleth-yl)-N,N,6-trimethyl-	50% EtOH	260s(2.82)	54-0071-79
	+ H_2SO_4	265(2.64),274(2.55)	54-0071-79
$C_{17}H_{29}NO$			
Propanamide, N-1,3-butadienyl-2-methyl-N-(1-propyl-4-hexenyl)-	MeOH	274(3.92)	88-0981-79

Compound	Solvent	$\lambda_{max}(\log \epsilon)$	Ref.
$C_{17}H_{30}O_2Si$			
Silane, (1,1-dimethylethyl)[3-(1,1-dimethylethyl)-4-methoxyphenoxy]dimethyl-	EtOH	204(4.23),227(3.88), 284(3.45)	87-0569-79
$C_{17}H_{30}O_4Si$			
3(2H)-Furanone, 5-(1,1-dimethylethyl)-2-(3,3-dimethyl-2-oxobutyl)-2-[(trimethylsilyl)oxy]-	MeOH	266(3.65)	4-0417-79
$C_{17}H_{30}O_5$			
2-Cyclobuten-1-one, 3,4,4-tributoxy-2-methoxy-	BuOH	250(4.0)	44-1208-79
$C_{17}H_{32}N_4$			
1,2,3-Triazin-5-amine, 4,6-bis(1,1-dimethylethyl)-N,N-bis(1-methylethyl)-	CH_2Cl_2	305(3.02),343(3.09)	24-1514-79
$C_{17}H_{33}N_3O$			
Acetamide, N-(1-dodecyl-4,5-dihydro-1H-pyrazol-3-yl)-	EtOH	263(3.83)	150-0801-79
$C_{17}H_{34}N_6$			
1,2,3-Triazine-4,5,6-triamine, N^4,N^4-dimethyl-N^5,N^5,N^6,N^6-tetrakis(1-methylethyl)-	CH_2Cl_2	260(4.12),360s(--)	24-1514-79

Compound	Solvent	λ_{max}(log ε)	Ref.
$C_{18}F_{14}O_3$			
2,4-Cyclohexadien-1-one, 2,3,4,6-tetra-fluoro-5,6-bis(pentafluorophenoxy)-	EtOH	266s(3.59),344(3.37)	104-1290-79
2,5-Cyclohexadien-1-one, 2,3,4,4,5-pentafluoro-6-[2,3,4,6-tetrafluoro-5-(pentafluorophenoxy)phenoxy]-	EtOH	209(4.45)	104-1290-79
2,5-Cyclohexadien-1-one, 2,3,4,4-tetra-fluoro-5,6-bis(pentafluorophenoxy)-	EtOH	213(4.20),225(4.15), 303(3.36)	104-1290-79
2,5-Cyclohexadien-1-one, 2,4,4,5-tetra-fluoro-3,6-bis(pentafluorophenoxy)-	heptane	228(4.14),303s(3.28)	104-1290-79
$C_{18}H_6Br_2Cl_2N_2S_2$			
Triphenodithiazine, 3,10-dibromo-6,13-dichloro-	H_2SO_4	335(4.85)	40-0432-79
	o-$C_6H_4Cl_2$	572(4.64)	40-0432-79
$C_{18}H_6Cl_4N_2O$			
12H-Phthaloperin-12-one, 8,9,10,11-tetrachloro-	xylene	477(3.90),504(3.91)	153-0173-79
$C_{18}H_6Cl_4N_2S_2$			
Triphenodithiazine, 3,6,10,13-tetra-chloro-	H_2SO_4	334(4.89)	40-0432-79
	o-$C_6H_4Cl_2$	571(4.67)	40-0432-79
$C_{18}H_8Cl_2N_2O_2$			
Triphenodioxazine, 6,13-dichloro-	H_2SO_4	293(4.67)	40-0432-79
	o-$C_6H_4Cl_2$	517(4.75)	40-0432-79
$C_{18}H_8Cl_2N_2S_2$			
Triphenodithiazine, 6,13-dichloro-	H_2SO_4	332(4.94)	40-0432-79
	o-$C_6H_4Cl_2$	556(4.72)	40-0432-79
$C_{18}H_8Cl_4$			
Naphthacene, 5,6,11,12-tetrachloro-	benzene	453(3.18),482(3.59), 513(3.89),551(3.92)	104-0343-79
$C_{18}H_8Se_4$			
Naphthaceno[5,6-cd:11,12-c'd']bis[1,2]-diselenole	benzene	470(3.84),650(3.90), 720(4.18)	104-0343-79
$C_{18}H_9FO_2$			
Benz[a]anthracene-7,12-dione, 2-fluoro-	MeOH	234(4.16),246(4.16), 252(4.15),278(4.42), 336(3.42),395(3.42)	44-3715-79
Benz[a]anthracene-7,12-dione, 3-fluoro-	MeOH	232(4.30),246(4.30), 252(4.30),281(4.51), 330(3.57),362(3.57)	44-3715-79
$C_{18}H_9N_7O_{12}$			
Benzenamine, N,N-bis(2,4-dinitrophen-yl)-2,4-dinitro-	EtOH	368(3.72)	73-1613-79
$C_{18}H_{10}Br_2O_3$			
3(2H)-Furanone, 5-(4-bromophenyl)-2-[2-(4-bromophenyl)-2-oxoethylidene]-	hexane	243(4.43),318(4.65), 366(4.15)	4-0417-79
$C_{18}H_{10}ClN_3O$			
12H-Phthaloperin-12-one, 3-amino-4-chloro-	xylene	440(4.01),460(4.07)	153-0043-79
12H-Phthaloperin-12-one, 4-amino-3-chloro-	xylene	434(4.19),458(4.16)	153-0043-79

Compound	Solvent	λ_{max}(log ε)	Ref.
$C_{18}H_{10}Cl_2O_3$			
3(2H)-Furanone, 5-(4-chlorophenyl)-2-[2-(4-chlorophenyl)-2-oxoethylidene]-	hexane	240(4.33),316(4.55), 364(4.05)	4-0417-79
$C_{18}H_{10}Cl_4OS$			
2H-Naphtho[1,8-bc]thiophene, 3-ethoxy-2-(2,3,4,5-tetrachloro-2,4-cyclopentadien-1-ylidene)-	MeOH	208(4.7),304(4.3), 348(4.1),378(3.9), 398(4.1),542(4.4), 570(4.4)	5-1789-79
$C_{18}H_{10}Cl_4O_5$			
1,4-Ethano-4c,8a-(methanoxymethano)-benzo[3',4']cyclobuta[1',2':3,4]-cyclobuta[1,2]benzene-9,11,12,13-tetrone, 1,2,3,4-tetrachloro-1,4,4a,4b,5,8,8b,8c-octahydro-	CH_2Cl_2	238(3.40),280(3.11), 442(2.42)	88-4545-79
$C_{18}H_{10}IN_3O_3$			
12H-Phthaloperin-12-one, 3-iodo-4-nitro-	xylene	420(4.15)	153-0043-79
$C_{18}H_{10}N_2O$			
12H-Phthaloperin-12-one	xylene	450(3.88),475(3.86)	153-0173-79
$C_{18}H_{10}N_2O_2$			
Triphenodioxazine	H_2SO_4	256(4.81)	40-0432-79
	o-$C_6H_4Cl_2$	508(4.68)	40-0432-79
$C_{18}H_{10}N_2O_4$			
Naphtho[2',3':4,5]furo[2,3-b]pyridine-3-carbonitrile, 1,2,5,10-tetrahydro-1,4-dimethyl-2,5,10-trioxo-	$CHCl_3$	276(4.48),342(4.01), 440(3.96)	2-0100-79A
$C_{18}H_{10}N_2S_2$			
Triphenodithiazine	H_2SO_4	321(4.72)	40-0432-79
	o-$C_6H_4Cl_2$	560(4.28)	40-0432-79
$C_{18}H_{10}O$			
Benz[1,10]acephenanthryleno[4,5-b]oxirene, 6b,7a-dihydro-	CH_2Cl_2	232(4.64),246(4.68), 264(4.34),275(4.54), 315(4.01),330(4.36), 347(4.49),353(4.12), 366(3.39),374(3.63)	77-0903-79
Cyclopenta[cd]pyrenone	EtOH	250(4.68),256(4.68), 350(4.58)	77-0302-79
$C_{18}H_{10}O_2$			
Benzo[1,2-b:4,5-b']bisbenzofuran	dioxan	217(4.61),261(4.28), 311(4.65),327(4.77), 338(4.49)	1-0405-79
7,12-Pleiadenedione	EtOH	206(4.66),240(4.47), 280s(3.62),335(3.39)	18-3314-79
$C_{18}H_{10}O_2S$			
Triphenyleno[1,12-bcd]thiophene, 4,4-dioxide	ether	252s(4.84),257(4.94), 284(4.31)	4-0599-79
$C_{18}H_{10}O_2S_3$			
2H-1-Benzopyran-2-thione, 4,4'-thiobis-	MeCN	273(4.09),316(3.85), 385(4.08),400s(4.00)	39-1166-79C

Compound	Solvent	λ_{max}(log ε)	Ref.
$C_{18}H_{10}O_3$			
Benz[a]anthracene-7,12-dione, 1-hydroxy-	EtOH	222(4.61),250(4.35), 311(4.36)	44-2150-79
Benz[a]anthracene-7,12-dione, 2-hydroxy-	EtOH	211(4.52),224(4.61), 254(4.63),290(4.33)	44-2150-79
Benz[a]anthracene-7,12-dione, 3-hydroxy-	EtOH	222(4.47),304(4.43)	44-2150-79
Benz[a]anthracene-7,12-dione, 4-hydroxy-	EtOH	218(4.61),244(4.36), 306(4.38)	44-2150-79
Benz[a]anthracene-7,12-dione, 8-hydroxy-	EtOH	210(4.65),231(4.51), 283(4.57),308(3.77), 360(3.67),405(3.92)	44-0699-79
Benz[a]anthracene-7,12-dione, 11-hydroxy-	EtOH	213(4.80),233(4.66), 287(4.67),310(3.82), 367(3.80),409(3.94), 425(3.99),450(3.93)	44-0699-79
1H-Indene-1,3(2H)-dione, 2-(6H-cyclohepta[c]furan-6-ylidene)-	$CHCl_3$	244(4.33),274(4.37), 296(4.08),327s(3.50), 414s(4.43),432(4.49), 458s(4.38)	83-0120-79
$C_{18}H_{10}O_4$			
6H-Benzo[b]naphtho[2,3-d]pyran-6,7,12-trione, 2-methyl-	EtOH	214(4.59),314(3.91), 414(3.61)	33-2833-79
6H-Benzo[b]naphtho[2,3-d]pyran-6,7,12-trione, 3-methyl-	EtOH	213(4.60),240(4.23), 319(3.89),416(3.80)	33-2833-79
Naphtho[1,2-b]furan-2,3-dione, 5-hydroxy-4-phenyl-	EtOH	229(4.44),275(4.26), 421(3.70)	103-0597-79
$C_{18}H_{10}O_4S$			
2H-1-Benzopyran-2-one, 4,4'-thiobis-	MeOH	275(4.26),315(4.08)	39-1166-79C
$C_{18}H_{10}O_5$			
5,12-Naphthacenedione, 6,8,11-trihydroxy-	MeOH	224(4.16),249(4.51), 272(4.59),301s(--), 435s(--),455(4.09), 480(4.26),512(4.18)	24-3453-79
$C_{18}H_{10}S$			
Triphenyleno[1,12-bcd]thiophene	EtOH	233s(4.53),243(4.58), 254(4.49),264(4.41), 280(4.40),304(4.02), 317(4.01),341(3.15), 348(2.82),357(2.85)	4-0599-79
$C_{18}H_{11}BrO$			
Cyclopenta[cd]pyren-3-ol, 4-bromo-3,4-dihydro-, trans	CH_2Cl_2	233(4.01),246(4.26), 255(3.52),267(3.81), 277(4.08),296(3.11), 314(3.46),328(3.79), 345(3.92)	77-0903-79
$C_{18}H_{11}BrO_6S_2$			
7H-Furo[3,2-g][1]benzopyran-4-sulfonic acid, 9-methoxy-7-thioxo-, 4-bromophenyl ester	MeOH	225(4.58),255(4.46), 305(4.20),350(3.90)	48-1039-79
$C_{18}H_{11}BrO_7S$			
7H-Furo[3,2-g][1]benzopyran-4-sulfonic acid, 9-methoxy-7-oxo-, 4-bromophenyl ester	MeOH	225(4.54),255(4.43), 305(4.17),350(3.86)	48-1039-79

Compound	Solvent	λ_{max}(log ε)	Ref.
$C_{18}H_{11}ClO_6S_2$			
7H-Furo[3,2-g][1]benzopyran-4-sulfonic acid, 9-methoxy-7-thioxo-, 2-chlorophenyl ester	MeOH	230(4.24),255(4.34), 305(4.02),355(3.68)	48-1039-79
7H-Furo[3,2-g][1]benzopyran-4-sulfonic acid, 9-methoxy-7-thioxo-, 4-chlorophenyl ester	MeOH	225(4.45),255(4.42), 305(4.15),350(3.83)	48-1039-79
$C_{18}H_{11}ClO_7S$			
7H-Furo[3,2-g][1]benzopyran-4-sulfonic acid, 9-methoxy-7-oxo-, 2-chlorophenyl ester	MeOH	230(4.21),255(4.31), 305(3.99),355(3.72)	48-1039-79
7H-Furo[3,2-g][1]benzopyran-4-sulfonic acid, 9-methoxy-7-oxo-, 4-chlorophenyl ester	MeOH	225(4.49),255(4.41), 305(4.15),350(3.85)	48-1039-79
$C_{18}H_{11}NO_2$			
1H-Indene-1,3(2H)-dione, 2-(2-quinolinyl)-	DMF	418(4.52),442(4.49)	153-0173-79
5,11-Naphthacenedione, 12-amino-	benzene	452(3.93),476s(3.83)	153-0033-79
5,12-Naphthacenedione, 6-amino-	benzene	473(3.98),496s(3.87)	153-0033-79
$C_{18}H_{11}NO_2S_2$			
5(4H)-Oxazolone, 4-([2,2'-bithiophen]-5-ylmethylene)-2-phenyl-	toluene	300(4.19),455(4.69)	103-1303-79
$C_{18}H_{11}NO_4$			
1,3-Isobenzofurandione, 5-[5-(4-methylphenyl)-2-oxazolyl]-	toluene	370(4.34)	103-0028-79
Lanuginosine	EtOH	246(4.52),273(4.42), 315(3.88)	102-1584-79
Oxolaureline	MeOH	247(4.26),267(4.19), 309(3.78),349(3.81), 400(3.81)	100-0325-79
Oxoputerine	MeOH	250(4.52),278(4.46), 320(3.78),432(4.06)	100-0325-79
Oxostephanine	MeOH	248(4.23),270(4.15), 308(2.90),356(3.41)	100-0325-79
	HCl	258(4.30),287(4.14), 324(3.11)	100-0325-79
$C_{18}H_{11}NO_5$			
1H-Indene-1,3(2H)-dione, 5-nitro-2-(1-oxo-3-phenyl-2-propenyl)-	pH 1	246(4.41),318(4.09), 398(4.62)	65-1600-79
	pH 13	232(4.50),269(4.24), 313(4.38),365(4.43)	65-1600-79
1,3-Isobenzofurandione, 5-[5-(4-methoxyphenyl)-2-oxazolyl]-	toluene	380(4.20)	103-0028-79
$C_{18}H_{11}NO_6$			
1H-Indene-1,3(2H)-dione, 2-[3-(4-hydroxyphenyl)-1-oxo-2-propenyl]-5-nitro-	pH 1	252(4.38),310(3.98), 443(4.67)	65-1600-79
	pH 6.65	232(4.47),320(4.34), 374(4.54)	65-1600-79
	pH 13	230(4.43),263(4.26), 308(4.20),417(4.53)	65-1600-79
$C_{18}H_{11}NO_8S_2$			
7H-Furo[3,2-g][1]benzopyran-4-sulfonic acid, 9-methoxy-7-thioxo-, 4-nitrophenyl ester	MeOH	230(4.46),255(4.54), 300(4.21),355(3.94)	48-1039-79

Compound	Solvent	$\lambda_{max}(\log \epsilon)$	Ref.
$C_{18}H_{11}NO_9S$			
7H-Furo[3,2-g][1]benzopyran-4-sulfonic acid, 9-methoxy-7-oxo-, 4-nitrophenyl ester	MeOH	230(4.41),255(4.51), 305(4.18),350(3.84)	48-1039-79
$C_{18}H_{11}N_3O_4S$			
10H-Phenothiazine, 1,3-dinitro-10-phenyl-	dioxan	238(4.49),273s(4.19), 294s(4.08),431(3.54)	104-2316-79
$C_{18}H_{11}N_5O_2$			
Benzonitrile, 4-(3,4-dihydro-3-methyl-2,4-dioxobenzo[g]pteridin-10(2H)-yl)-	EtOH	266(4.46),323(3.96), 421s(3.91),437(3.95), 465s(3.78)	4-1365-79
$C_{18}H_{11}N_5O_8$			
Benzenamine, N-(2,4-dinitrophenyl)-2,4-dinitro-N-phenyl-	EtOH	240(4.28),356(3.68), 413(3.61)	73-1613-79
$C_{18}H_{12}$			
Chrysene	EtOH	245(4.31),257(4.89), 266(5.12),294(4.16), 304(4.25),319(4.23), 341(4.15),358(2.68)	2-0233-79B
$C_{18}H_{12}BrNO_3$			
1,4-Naphthalenedione, 2-acetyl-3-[(4-bromophenyl)amino]-	dioxan	232(4.26),273(4.40), 444(3.68)	5-0503-79
$C_{18}H_{12}BrNO_5S_2$			
7H-Furo[3,2-g][1]benzopyran-4-sulfonamide, N-(4-bromophenyl)-9-methoxy-7-thioxo-	MeOH	230(4.48),260(4.37), 310(4.12),360(3.70)	48-1039-79
$C_{18}H_{12}BrNO_6S$			
7H-Furo[3,2-g][1]benzopyran-4-sulfonamide, N-(4-bromophenyl)-9-methoxy-7-oxo-	MeOH	230(4.53),250(4.41), 310(4.14)	48-1039-79
$C_{18}H_{12}BrN_3S_2$			
5,11-Imino-5H,11H-[1,5]dithiocino[2,3-b:6,7-b']dipyridine, 13-(4-bromophenyl)-	EtOH	212(4.42),247(4.45), 296(3.96)	78-0869-79
$C_{18}H_{12}Br_2$			
1,1':4',1"-Terphenyl, 4,4"-dibromo-	hexane	288(5.18)	65-0146-79
$C_{18}H_{12}ClNO_2$			
Pyrano[2,3-e]indol-2(7H)-one, 3-chloro-8-methyl-7-phenyl-	EtOH	273(5.36),340(4.78)	4-0913-79
$C_{18}H_{12}ClNO_3$			
1,4-Naphthalenedione, 2-acetyl-3-[(3-chlorophenyl)amino]-	dioxan	237s(4.1),272(4.35), 435(3.56)	5-0503-79
1,4-Naphthalenedione, 2-acetyl-3-[(4-chlorophenyl)amino]-	dioxan	234(4.25),273(4.41), 450(3.67)	5-0503-79
$C_{18}H_{12}ClNO_5S_2$			
7H-Furo[3,2-g][1]benzopyran-4-sulfonamide, N-(3-chlorophenyl)-9-methoxy-7-thioxo-	MeOH	230(4.50),260(4.33), 310(4.08),365(3.67)	48-1039-79

Compound	Solvent	$\lambda_{max}(\log \epsilon)$	Ref.
$C_{18}H_{12}ClNO_6S$			
7H-Furo[3,2-g][1]benzopyran-4-sulfonamide, N-(3-chlorophenyl)-9-methoxy-7-oxo-	MeOH	230(4.46),250(4.35), 310(4.08)	48-1039-79
$C_{18}H_{12}ClN_3$			
1H-Benz[g]indole, 3-[(4-chlorophenyl)-azo]-	n.s.g.	380(4.30)	104-2288-79
$C_{18}H_{12}Cl_2N_2O_2$			
4-Cyclopentene-1,3-dione, 2-[bis(phenylamino)methylene]-4,5-dichloro-	n.s.g.	252(4.46),306(4.60)	104-0454-79
$C_{18}H_{12}Cl_4$			
Benzene, 1,1'-(1,3,5-hexatriene-1,6-diyl)bis[2,4-dichloro-, (E,E,E)-	hexane	350(5.02),368(5.05), 382(4.87)	65-0146-79
$C_{18}H_{12}FNO_3$			
1,4-Naphthalenedione, 2-acetyl-3-[(4-fluorophenyl)amino]-	dioxan	234(4.25),270(4.37), 436(3.66)	5-0503-79
$C_{18}H_{12}F_6N_4$			
2-Propenimidamide, 2-cyano-N-[3-(trifluoromethyl)phenyl]-3-[[3-(trifluoromethyl)phenyl]amino]-	MeCN	333(4.38)	24-0484-79
$C_{18}H_{12}N_2O$			
5H-Indeno[1,2-d]pyrimidin-5-one, 4-methyl-2-phenyl-	EtOH	246(4.46),290(4.55)	39-1871-79C
Propanedinitrile, (9-ethoxy-1H-phenalen-1-ylidene)-	MeCN	270(3.6),388(4.0), 497(3.8)	83-0288-79
$C_{18}H_{12}N_2O_2$			
5,5'-Bioxazole, 4,4'-diphenyl-	MeOH	239(4.26),264s(--), 285s(--)	5-1370-79
5,12-Naphthacenedione, 6,11-diamino-	benzene	528(4.14),567(4.15)	153-0033-79
$C_{18}H_{12}N_2O_2S$			
10H-Phenothiazine, 3-nitro-10-phenyl-	dioxan	260(4.43),286s(4.03), 321(4.15),448(3.83)	104-2316-79
$C_{18}H_{12}N_2O_3$			
10H-Phenoxazine, 3-nitro-10-phenyl-	MeCN	446(4.14)	44-3310-79
$C_{18}H_{12}N_2O_5$			
Ethanone, 1-[2-(2-furanyl)-1-(5-nitro-2-furanyl)-3-indolizinyl]-	EtOH	380(4.25),429(4.32)	94-3078-79
1,4-Naphthalenedione, 2-acetyl-3-[(4-nitrophenyl)amino]-	dioxan	232s(4.3),289(4.30), 319s(4.2),433(3.80)	5-0503-79
$C_{18}H_{12}N_4$			
Quinoxalino[2',3':2,3]pyrrolo[1,5-c]-phthalazine, 5-methyl-	EtOH	253(4.53),275(4.42), 288(4.51),341(4.41), 374(4.11),438s(3.67), 456(3.78),480(3.63)	78-2463-79
Quinoxalino[2',3':2,3]pyrrolo[1,5-c]-quinazoline, 6-methyl-	EtOH	256(4.49),289(4.56), 318(4.49),356(4.05), 368(4.03),434(4.00)	78-2463-79
$C_{18}H_{12}N_4O$			
Pyrrolo[1,2-a:4,5-b']diquinoxaline,	EtOH	268s(4.54),274(4.60),	78-2463-79

Compound	Solvent	λ max (log ε)	Ref.
6-methoxy- (cont.)		295(4.24),304s(4.14), 342s(3.76),360(4.04), 376(4.09),437s(3.62), 452(3.67),490(3.46)	78-2463-79
$C_{18}H_{12}N_4O_6S$			
Benzenamine, N-phenyl-2-[(2,4,6-tri- nitrophenyl)thio]-	dioxan	230s(4.35),286(4.24), 354(3.87)	104-2316-79
$C_{18}H_{12}O$			
Benz[a]anthracen-1-ol	EtOH	227(4.65),255(4.70), 273(4.81),282(4.84), 309(4.54)	44-2150-79
Benz[a]anthracen-2-ol	EtOH	227(4.71),263(4.64), 270(4.68),278(4.67), 287(4.68),298(4.64)	44-2150-79
Benz[a]anthracen-3-ol	EtOH	244(4.54),288(4.81)	44-2150-79
Benz[a]anthracen-4-ol	EtOH	204(4.42),230(4.64), 245(4.71),257(4.69), 277(4.71),287(4.79), 313(4.39)	44-2150-79
7(12H)-Pleiadenone	EtOH	210(4.63),245(4.26), 336(3.92)	18-3314-79
$C_{18}H_{12}O_2$			
Cyclobuta[1,2-a:4,3-a']diindene-9,10- dione, 4b,4c,9a,9b-tetrahydro-	EtOH	245(4.16),288(3.34), 333(<2),346(<2)	44-1388-79
$C_{18}H_{12}O_3$			
1H-Indene-1,3(2H)-dione, 2-(1-oxo- 3-phenyl-1-propenyl)-	pH 1	246(4.38),314(3.93), 390(4.63)	65-1600-79
	pH 13	237(4.48),302(4.32), 361(4.41)	65-1600-79
$C_{18}H_{12}O_6S_2$			
7H-Furo[3,2-g][1]benzopyran-4-sulfonic acid, 9-methoxy-7-thioxo-, phenyl ester	MeOH	230(4.42),255(4.41), 305(4.14),355(3.83)	48-1039-79
$C_{18}H_{12}O_7S$			
7H-Furo[3,2-g][1]benzopyran-4-sulfonic acid, 9-methoxy-7-oxo-, phenyl ester	MeOH	230(4.38),255(4.37), 305(4.11),355(3.80)	48-1039-79
$C_{18}H_{12}S_2Se_2$			
1,3-Thiaselenole, 5-phenyl-2-(5-phenyl- 1,3-thiaselenol-2-ylidene)-	THF	241(4.30),269(4.39), 294(4.35),323s(4.14), 400(3.54),505s(2.54)	97-0192-79
$C_{18}H_{12}Se_4$			
1,3-Diselenole, 4-phenyl-2-(4-phenyl- 1,3-diselenol-2-ylidene)-	THF	247s(4.36),266(4.38), 295(4.36),350s(3.38), 388(3.70),483(2.55)	97-0192-79
$C_{18}H_{13}ClN_4$			
Pyridazine, 6-(4-chlorophenyl)-3,4-di- 1H-pyrrol-1-yl-	EtOH	262(4.66)	80-0453-79
$C_{18}H_{13}ClO_2$			
5-Oxaspiro[2.4]hept-6-en-4-one, 1-(4- chlorophenyl)-6-phenyl-	EtOH	224s(--),281(218?)	28-0133-79A

Compound	Solvent	λ_{max}(log ε)	Ref.
$C_{18}H_{13}FO_2$			
Benzoic acid, 2-[(6-fluoro-2-naphthalenyl)methyl]-	MeOH	263(3.77),271(3.82), 280(3.75),294(3.00), 302(2.90),308(3.10), 315(3.00),323(3.24)	44-3715-79
Benzoic acid, 2-[(7-fluoro-1-naphthalenyl)methyl]-	MeOH	263(3.65),268(3.58), 273(3.66),278(3.87), 283(3.82),288(3.77), 306(2.88),313(2.86), 320(3.17)	44-3715-79
5-Oxaspiro[2.4]hept-6-en-4-one, 6-(4-fluorophenyl)-1-phenyl-	EtOH	222s(--),279(218?)	28-0133-79A
$C_{18}H_{13}NO$			
Ethanone, 1-(1H-dibenz[e,g]indol-2-yl)-	EtOH	201(4.34),247(4.54), 259(4.66),266(4.71), 275(4.39),334(4.22), 347(4.13)	103-0302-79
Ethanone, 1-(1H-dibenz[e,g]indol-3-yl)-	EtOH	204(4.41),262(4.70), 289(3.99),311(3.49)	103-0302-79
$C_{18}H_{13}NO_3$			
2H-Cyclopenta[l]phenanthrene-1-carboxamide, 3,3a-dihydro-3a-hydroxy-2-oxo-	EtOH	220s(4.11),260(4.50), 300(4.0),353(3.50)	39-2034-79C
Liriodendronine, N,O-dimethyl-	MeOH	247s(4.03),311(4.29), 420(3.46),585(3.44), 602(3.44)	100-0325-79
	HCl	251(4.16),286(4.16), 387(3.56),473(3.37)	100-0325-79
1,4-Naphthalenedione, 2-acetyl-3-(phenylamino)-	dioxan	232(4.21),271(4.36), 445(3.60)	5-0503-79
$C_{18}H_{13}NO_4$			
5,12-Naphthacenedione, 7,8,9,10-tetrahydro-1-nitro-	EtOH	213(4.58),236(4.48), 269(4.79),336(3.91)	94-2229-79
Norcepharadione B	EtOH	213(4.55),241(4.60), 303(4.24),315(4.27), 440(4.22)	100-0325-79
$C_{18}H_{13}NO_5S_2$			
7H-Furo[3,2-g][1]benzopyran-4-sulfonamide, 9-methoxy-N-phenyl-7-thioxo-	MeOH	230(4.46),260(4.36), 315(4.46),360(3.95)	48-1039-79
$C_{18}H_{13}NO_5S_3$			
[1]Benzothieno[3,2-b]pyridin-2(1H)-one, 4-(methylthio)-3-(phenylsulfonyl)-, 5,5-dioxide	EtOH	220s(4.52),262(4.34), 384(4.06)	95-1234-79
$C_{18}H_{13}NO_6S$			
7H-Furo[3,2-g][1]benzopyran-4-sulfonamide, 9-methoxy-7-oxo-N-phenyl-	MeOH	215(4.40),250(4.34), 305(4.08)	48-1039-79
$C_{18}H_{13}N_3$			
1H-Benzimidazole, 5-phenyl-2-(2-pyridinyl)-	anion	325(3.97)	94-1235-79
3-Pyridinecarbonitrile, 2-amino-4,5-diphenyl-	CH_2Cl_2	260(4.35),342(3.84)	118-0376-79
$C_{18}H_{13}N_3O_2$			
4H,7H-Pyrrolo[1',2':1,2]imidazo[4,5-g]-3,1-benzoxazin-4-one, 8,9-dihydro-2-phenyl-	$CHCl_3$	274(4.71),318(4.33), 325(4.30)	39-1056-79C

Compound	Solvent	λ_{max}(log ε)	Ref.
$C_{18}H_{13}N_3O_3$			
4H,7H-[1,4]Oxazino[4',3':1,2]imidazo-[4,5-g]-3,1-benzoxazin-4-one, 9,10-dihydro-2-phenyl-	$CHCl_3$	272(4.83),317(4.09), 322(4.08)	39-1056-79C
$C_{18}H_{13}N_3O_4$			
Benzenamine, 2,4-dinitro-N,N-diphenyl-	EtOH	247(4.25),405(4.08)	73-1613-79
Spiro[5H-indeno[1,2-b]pyridine-5,3'-[3H]pyrazole]-4',5'-dicarboxylic acid, dimethyl ester	EtOH	208(4.78),285(4.35), 295(4.33),308(4.32), 445(3.17),606(2.62)	103-0777-79
$C_{18}H_{13}N_3O_4S$			
Benzenamine, 2-[(2,4-dinitrophenyl)-thio]-N-phenyl-	dioxan	296(4.33),324s(4.22)	104-2316-79
$C_{18}H_{13}N_3O_5S$			
4-Thia-1-azabicyclo[3.2.0]hept-2-ene-2-carboxylic acid, 7-oxo-3-(3-pyridin-yl)-, (4-nitrophenyl)methyl ester	EtOH	259(4.19),333(3.82)	35-6296-79
$C_{18}H_{13}N_3S_2$			
5H-Imino-5H,11H-[1,5]dithiocino[2,3-b:6m7-b']dipyridine, 13-phenyl-	EtOH	210(4.46),244(4.46), 299(3.89)	78-0869-79
$C_{18}H_{13}N_5$			
Acenaphtho[1,2-e][1,2,4]triazine, 9-(3,5-dimethyl-1H-pyrazol-1-yl)-	MeOH	233(4.63),260(4.23), 316(4.60)	83-0147-79
$C_{18}H_{13}N_5O_3$			
Pyrazinecarboxamide, 3-cyano-4,5-di-hydro-6-(4-nitrophenyl)-5-phenyl-	MeOH	260(4.35),430(4.16)	44-4871-79
$C_{18}H_{13}N_5O_5$			
Isoxazole, 3-methyl-4-[(4-nitrophenyl)-azo]-5-[2-(4-nitrophenyl)ethenyl]-	$CHCl_3$	310(4.37),389(4.44)	103-0968-79
$C_{18}H_{14}$			
1,1':4',1"-Terphenyl	hexane	276(4.70)	65-0146-79
$C_{18}H_{14}BrN_3O$			
Isoxazole, 4-[(4-bromophenyl)azo]-3-methyl-5-(2-phenylethenyl)-	$CHCl_3$	297(4.42),377(4.43)	103-0968-79
$C_{18}H_{14}Br_2$			
1,3,5-Hexatriene, 1,6-bis(4-bromophen-yl)-	hexane	343(5.07),360(5.18), 380(5.02)	65-0146-79
$C_{18}H_{14}ClNO_2$			
2H-Pyran-2-one, 3-chloro-4-(methylphen-ylamino)-6-phenyl-	EtOH	229(4.12),272(4.26), 319(4.22)	4-0093-79
$C_{18}H_{14}Cl_2N_2$			
Pyrazine, 2-chloro-3-(chlorophenylmeth-yl)-6-(phenylmethyl)-	EtOH	223s(4.16),286(4.01), 310s(3.71)	94-2980-79
Pyrazine, 2,5-dichloro-3,6-bis(phenyl-methyl)-	EtOH	223(4.13),287s(3.88), 301(4.00)	94-2980-79
$C_{18}H_{14}Cl_4O_4$			
1,4-Ethenobiphenylene-2,3-dicarboxylic acid, 5,6,7,8-tetrachloro-1,4,4a,4b-8a,8b-hexahydro-, dimethyl ester	EtOH	295(3.64)	78-1177-79

Compound	Solvent	λ_{max}(log ε)	Ref.
$C_{18}H_{14}N_2$			
5H-Indeno[1,2-d]pyrimidine, 4-methyl-2-phenyl-	EtOH	226(4.35),255(4.64), 287(4.26),301(4.29)	39-1871-79C
1H-Indole, 2-(3H-indol-3-ylidenemethyl)-3-methyl-, perchlorate	CH_2Cl_2	220(4.43),544(4.73)	56-0073-79
Quinazoline, 1,4-dihydro-4-(1-naphthalenyl)-, hydrochloride	EtOH	282(4.13)	24-1348-79
$C_{18}H_{14}N_2O$			
Acetamide, 2-cyano-2-(2,3-dihydro-1H-inden-1-ylidene)-N-phenyl-	$CHCl_3$	240(4.20),335(4.43)	80-1485-79
$C_{18}H_{14}N_2O_2$			
2-Propen-1-one, 3-(2-furanyl)-1-(4-methyl-2-phenyl-5-pyrimidinyl)-	EtOH	205(4.22),248s(4.06), 294(4.23),342(4.49)	103-0551-79
Pyrazinol, 3,6-diphenyl-, acetate	EtOH	266(4.24),326(4.36)	94-2980-79
$C_{18}H_{14}N_2O_3$			
1H-Pyrrole-2,5-dione, 3-acetyl-1-phenyl-4-(phenylamino)-	EtOH	289(4.36),342(3.98)	94-1792-79
	EtOH	288(4.30),343(3.93)	95-0818-79
$C_{18}H_{14}N_2S$			
Diazene, (3-ethenylphenyl)(2-naphthalenylthio)-	toluene	332(4.0)	126-1651-79
$C_{18}H_{14}N_4$			
Diazene, 1,1'-(1,2-phenylene)bis[2-phenyl-	EtOH	210(4.32),305(4.90), 445(3.08)	7-0563-79
Pyrazine, 2,5-bis[2-(2-pyridinyl)ethenyl]-	EtOH	223s(3.88),280s(3.89), 299(3.99),310(3.99)	94-2596-79
Pyridazine, 3,4-di-1H-pyrrol-1-yl-6-phenyl-	EtOH	266(4.63)	80-0453-79
1H-Tetrazole, 1-(2-methyl-1-naphthalenyl)-5-phenyl-	EtOH	276(3.89),285(3.87)	39-1871-79C
$C_{18}H_{14}N_4O$			
Pyrazinecarboxamide, 3-cyano-1,6-dihydro-5,6-diphenyl-	MeOH	254(4.24),383(3.97)	44-4871-79
Pyrazinecarboxamide, 3-cyano-4,5-dihydro-5,6-diphenyl-	MeOH	262(4.34),383(4.04)	44-4871-79
	MeOH	265(4.34),409(4.04)	44-4871-79
$C_{18}H_{14}N_4OS$			
4H-Pyrimido[4,5-b][1,4]thiazin-4-one, 2-amino-1,7-dihydro-6,7-diphenyl-	MeOH	230(4.270),271(4.306), 381(4.152)	83-0076-79
$C_{18}H_{14}N_4O_2$			
Benzo[g]pteridine-2,4(3H,10H)-dione, 3,6-dimethyl-10-phenyl-	EtOH	270(4.35),304s(3.72), 356(3.77),423s(3.72), 443(3.78),471s(3.64)	4-1365-79
Benzo[g]pteridine-2,4(3H,10H)-dione, 3-methyl-10-(3-methylphenyl)-	EtOH	264(4.44),332(3.86), 428s(3.89),440(3.92), 463s(3.89)	4-1365-79
Benzo[g]pteridine-2,4(3H,10H)-dione, 3-methyl-10-(phenylmethyl)-	EtOH	236s(4.31),264(4.24), 305(4.08),436(3.91)	4-1365-79
Methanone, phenyl-2-pyridinyl-, (4-nitrophenyl)hydrazone, anti	benzene	415(4.66)	151-0039-79B
syn	benzene	390(4.61)	151-0039-79B
Methanone, phenyl-3-pyridinyl-, (4-nitrophenyl)hydrazone, anti	benzene	387.5(4.61)	151-0039-79B
syn	benzene	387.5(4.57)	151-0039-79B

Compound	Solvent	λ max (log ε)	Ref.
Pyrazine, 2,5-bis[2-(2-pyridinyl)ethen-yl]-, 1,4-dioxide	EtOH	315 s(4.41),329(4.58)	94-2596-79
$C_{18}H_{14}N_4O_3$			
Isoxazole, 3-methyl-4-[(4-nitrophenyl)-azo]-5-(2-phenylethenyl)-	$CHCl_3$	302(4.42),400(4.32)	103-0968-79
Isoxazole, 3-methyl-5-[2-(4-nitrophen-yl)ethenyl]-4-(phenylazo)-	$CHCl_3$	310(4.32),380(4.49)	103-0968-79
$C_{18}H_{14}N_4O_8$			
[5,4':5',5":4",5"'-Quateroxazole]-4,4"'-dicarboxylic acid, diethyl ester	MeOH	224(4.31),312(4.00)	5-1370-79
$C_{18}H_{14}N_4S$			
1,3,4-Thiadiazol-2-amine, 5-(2-methyl-4-quinolinyl)-N-phenyl-	EtOH	240(4.34),270(4.01), 335s(--),355(4.09)	106-0537-79
$C_{18}H_{14}N_6$			
1H-Tetrazolium, 5-(dicyanomethyl)-1,3-bis(4-methylphenyl)-, hydroxide, inner salt	n.s.g.	222s(4.46),279(4.55), 349s(3.32),394s(3.16)	39-0744-79C
$C_{18}H_{14}N_8O$			
Naphtho[2,1-e]pyrazolo[5,1-c][1,2,4]-triazin-5-ol, 2-methyl-1-[(5-methyl-1H-pyrazol-3-yl)azo]-	DMF	330(4.00),345(4.02), 450(3.86)	103-0657-79
$C_{18}H_{14}O_2$			
Benzo[c]phenanthrene-1,2-diol, 1,2-di-hydro-	MeOH	220(4.5),253(4.44), 305(3.9),330(3.9)	88-2849-79
Benzo[c]phenanthrene-3,4-diol, 3,4-di-hydro-	MeOH	228(4.7),273(4.64), 310(3.8),335(3.7)	88-2849-79
Benzo[c]phenanthrene-5,6-diol, 5,6-di-hydro-	MeOH	220(4.6),230(4.5), 310f(4.12)	88-2849-79
5-Oxaspiro[2.4]hept-6-en-4-one, 1,6-di-phenyl-	EtOH	281(221?)	28-0133-79A
1-Pentyne-3,5-dione, 5-(4-methylphenyl)-1-phenyl-	MeOH	227(4.03),260s(3.96), 295(4.02),351(4.31)	4-0737-79
	MeOH-NaOMe	263(4.20),360(4.31)	4-0737-79
5,12-Tetracenedione, 7,8,9,10-tetra-hydro-	EtOH	211(4.33),263(4.65), 330(3.68)	94-2229-79
$C_{18}H_{14}O_2S$			
Naphtho[2,3-c]thiophene, 4,9-dihydro-4-phenyl-, 2,2-dioxide	EtOH	230s(4.04),275s(3.36)	44-2667-79
$C_{18}H_{14}O_3$			
Ethanone, 1-(3,4-dihydroxy-2-naphtha-lenyl)-2-phenyl-	$CHCl_3$	271(3.52),340(3.36), 404(3.38)	138-1097-79
Methanone, (8-hydroxy-4-methoxy-1-naph-thalenyl)phenyl-	MeOH	300(3.9),315(3.8), 329(3.7)	5-0959-79
5,12-Naphthacenedione, 7,8,9,10-tetra-hydro-1-hydroxy-	EtOH	217(4.58),268(4.61), 400(3.83)	94-2229-79
1-Pentyne-3,5-dione, 1-(4-methoxyphen-yl)-5-phenyl-	MeOH	233(4.03),252(4.03), 297(3.93),366(4.45)	4-0737-79
	MeOH-NaOMe	279(4.10),366(4.36)	4-0737-79
1-Pentyne-3,5-dione, 5-(4-methoxyphen-yl)-1-phenyl-	MeOH	226(4.06),262s(3.93), 296(4.03),354(4.38)	4-0737-79
	MeOH-NaOMe	267(4.19),360(4.34)	4-0737-79

Compound	Solvent	λ_{max}(log ε)	Ref.
$C_{18}H_{14}O_4$			
6H-Benzo[b]naphtho[2,3-d]pyran-6-one, 8,11-dihydro-7,12-dihydroxy-2-methyl-	EtOH	210(4.41),241(4.56), 271(4.09),367(4.00)	33-2833-79
6H-Benzo[b]naphtho[2,3-d]pyran-6,7,12-trione, 7a,8,11,11a-tetrahydro-2-methyl-	EtOH	210(4.40),242(4.46), 273(3.97),368(3.95)	33-2833-79
6H-Benzo[b]naphtho[2,3-d]pyran-6,7,12-trione, 7a,8,11,11a-tetrahydro-3-methyl-	EtOH	210(4.36),237(4.17), 364(3.87)	33-2833-79
1,3,4,6-Hexanetetrone, 1,6-diphenyl-	MeOH	248(4.00),320(4.00), 364(4.17)	4-0417-79
	CH_2Cl_2	370(4.44)	4-0417-79
1,3-Propanedione, 1-(4-methoxy-5-benzofuranyl)-3-phenyl- (pongamol)	MeOH	245(4.37),345(4.33)	88-4879-79
$C_{18}H_{14}O_5$			
9,10-Anthracenedione, 1,4-dihydroxy-2-(3-oxobutyl)-	MeOH	205(4.35),249(4.58), 284(4.00),330s(--), 486(3.98)	5-0019-79
9(10H)-Anthracenone, 1,8-diacetoxy-	MeOH	241(4.14),259(4.49), 353s(3.09),370(3.29), 386(3.20),405s(3.04)	145-1083-79
Cyclohepta[de]naphthalene-8,9-dicarboxylic acid, 7,8-dihydro-7-oxo-, dimethyl ester	EtOH	208(4.5),237(4.5), 325(4.0)	18-0641-79
3H,7H-Pyrano[2,3-c]xanthen-7-one, 6,11-dihydroxy-3,3-dimethyl-	EtOH	232(4.26),250(4.54), 268(4.51),308(3.92), 329(4.02)	142-0269-79
$C_{18}H_{14}O_6$			
2-Anthraceneacetic acid, 9,10-dihydro-1,4-dihydroxy-3-methyl-9,10-dioxo-, methyl ester	MeOH	229s(--),250(4.54), 256(4.54),286(3.89), 460(3.91),510s(--)	5-0035-79
2-Anthracenebutanoic acid, 9,10-dihydro-1,4-dihydroxy-9,10-dioxo-	MeOH	205(4.42),250(4.66), 286(3.80),486(3.78), 520s(--)	5-0019-79
2-Anthracenecarboxylic acid, 9,10-dihydro-8-hydroxy-3-methoxy-1-methyl-9,10-dioxo-, methyl ester	dioxan	268(4.37),291s(3.88), 410(3.69)	118-0148-79
4H-1-Benzopyran-4-one, 2-(1,3-benzodioxol-5-yl)-6,7-dimethoxy-	EtOH	235(5.28),265(5.02), 335(5.32)	2-0552B-79B
2,5-Cyclohexadiene-1,4-dione, 2-(6,7-dimethoxy-2-methyl-4-oxo-4H-1-benzopyran-3-yl)-	MeOH	289(4.08),323(4.13)	18-0529-79
2,5-Cyclohexadiene-1,4-dione, 2-methoxy-5-(7-methoxy-2-methyl-4-oxo-4H-1-benzopyran-3-yl)-	MeOH	223(4.37),247(4.41), 252(4.43),298(4.20)	18-0529-79
Ellagic acid, tetramethyl-	EtOH	242(3.41),354(3.12)	102-1017-79
1,4-Ethanoanthracene-9,10-dione, 3-c-ethynyl-1,2,3,4-tetrahydro-1,3,5,8-tetrahydroxy-	MeOH	215(4.45),288(3.74), 513(3.84),554(3.65)	24-2640-79
3-t-	MeOH	215(4.53),288(3.89), 518(3.91),560(3.79)	24-2640-79
$C_{18}H_{14}O_7$			
4H-1-Benzopyran-4-one, 3-(1,3-benzodioxol-5-yl)-7-hydroxy-5,6-dimethoxy- (dipteryxine)	EtOH	208(4.59),220s(4.50), 262(4.30),292s(4.28)	39-2107-79
9H-Xanthene-1-carboxylic acid, 8-acetoxy-2-methoxy-9-oxo-, methyl ester	EtOH	240(4.34),250s(4.27), 270s(3.72),302s(2.90), 360(3.58),373(3.53)	102-0311-79

Compound	Solvent	$\lambda_{max}(\log \epsilon)$	Ref.
$C_{18}H_{14}O_9$			
Flavellagic acid, tetramethyl-	EtOH	244(3.80),306(3.11), 357(3.16),371(3.14)	102-1017-79
$C_{18}H_{14}S$			
Naphtho[2,3-c]thiophene, 4,9-dihydro-4-phenyl-	EtOH	247(3.92),272(2.97), 337(2.78)	44-2667-79
$C_{18}H_{14}S_2$			
Benzene, 1,4-bis(2-thienylethenyl)-	DMF	377(4.73)	61-0417-79
$C_{18}H_{15}BrN_4O_3$			
1H-Pyrazole-4,5-dione, 3-(acetoxymethyl)-1-(4-bromophenyl)-, 4-(phenylhydrazone)	n.s.g.	210(3.79),257(4.16), 400(4.22)	106-0531-79
$C_{18}H_{15}BrN_{10}$			
Pyrazolo[2,3-c:3,4-e][1,2,4]triazine, 6-(4-bromo-3-methyl-5-pyrazolylazo)-3,7-dimethyl-1-phenyl-	MeOH	420(3.78)	103-0657-79
$C_{18}H_{15}BrO$			
2-Cyclohexen-1-one, 3-(4-bromophenyl)-5-phenyl-	H_2SO_4	380(4.48)	124-1093-79
$C_{18}H_{15}ClN_2$			
Pyrazine, 3-chloro-2,5-bis(phenylmethyl)-	EtOH	283(4.11)	94-2980-79
$C_{18}H_{15}ClN_2O$			
Pyrazine, 3-chloro-2,5-bis(phenylmethyl)-, 1-oxide	EtOH	235(4.28),275(3.95), 304(3.55),315s(3.84)	94-2980-79
$C_{18}H_{15}ClN_2OS$			
2(1H)-Pyrimidinethione, 1-acetyl-4-(3-chlorophenyl)-3,4-dihydro-6-phenyl-	EtOH	242(4.37),327(4.01)	23-2734-79
2(1H)-Pyrimidinethione, 1-acetyl-4-(4-chlorophenyl)-3,4-dihydro-6-phenyl-	EtOH	242(4.44),326(4.08)	23-2734-79
2(1H)-Pyrimidinethione, 1-acetyl-6-(4-chlorophenyl)-3,4-dihydro-4-phenyl-	EtOH	244(4.41),325(4.11)	23-2734-79
$C_{18}H_{15}ClN_2O_2$			
Pyridazine, 6-chloro-3,4-bis(4-methoxyphenyl)-	hexane	273(4.26)	111-0053-79
$C_{18}H_{15}ClN_4$			
Pyridazine, 6-(4-chlorophenyl)-4,5-dihydro-3,4-di-1H-pyrrol-1-yl-	EtOH	234(4.57)	80-0453-79
$C_{18}H_{15}ClN_4O_3$			
1H-Pyrazole-4,5-dione, 3-(acetoxymethyl)-1-(4-chlorophenyl)-, 4-(phenylhydrazone)	n.s.g.	212(3.74),252(4.04), 398(4.24)	106-0531-79
$C_{18}H_{15}ClN_4O_4$			
L-xylo-2-Hexulosonic acid, γ-lactone, 2-(phenylhydrazone)	n.s.g.	230(3.83),288(3.89), 364(3.98)	106-0531-79
$C_{18}H_{15}ClO$			
5H-Benzocyclohepten-5-one, 6,7,8,9-	isooctane	232(4.11),263(4.08),	65-1407-79

Compound	Solvent	λmax(log ε)	Ref.
tetrahydro-6-[(4-chlorophenyl)methylene]- (cont.)		296(4.23)	65-1407-79
	MeOH	230(4.06),272(4.05),306(3.99)	65-1407-79
2-Cyclohexen-1-one, 3-(4-chlorophenyl)-5-phenyl-	H_2SO_4	383(4.49)	124-1093-79
$C_{18}H_{15}ClP$			
Phosphorus(1+), chlorotriphenyl-	$C_2H_4Cl_2$	229(4.46),270(4.05),345(2.04)	65-0275-79
	MeCN	229(4.42),269(3.98),345(2.00)	65-0275-79
	$MeNO_2$	270(4.00),345(1.95)	65-0275-79
tetrachloroaluminate	MeCN	207(4.53),229(4.45),270(3.69)	65-0275-79
	CH_2Cl_2-MeCN	229(4.45),269(3.71)	65-0275-79
$C_{18}H_{15}Cl_2NO_2$			
9(10H)-Anthracenone, 10-(butylimino)-1,3-dichloro-4-hydroxy-	benzene	415(3.57),531(3.40)	104-0147-79
	EtOH	415s(3.45),512(3.66)	104-0147-79
	dioxan	411(3.54),520(3.45)	104-0147-79
$C_{18}H_{15}Cl_2P$			
Phosphorus, dichlorotriphenyl-	$C_2H_4Cl_2$	227(4.47),272(3.65)	65-0275-79
	MeCN	207(4.54),226(4.47),271(3.63)	65-0275-79
$C_{18}H_{15}F$			
Naphthalene, 1-(4-fluorophenyl)-2,3-dimethyl-	$CHCl_3$	267s(3.73),277(3.82),286(3.85),295s(3.78)	12-1531-79
$C_{18}H_{15}F_3N_2O_5S$			
8H-3,8a-(Iminomethano)-4H,6H-oxazolo-[4,3-b][1,3]thiazine-4,8-dione, dihydro-9-hydroxy-2,2-dimethyl-6-(phenylmethylene)-10-(trifluoroacetyl)-	THF	284(4.42)	39-0170-79C
$C_{18}H_{15}F_3N_4O$			
2-Propenimidamide, 2-cyano-3-[(2-methoxyphenyl)amino]-N-[3-(trifluoromethyl)phenyl]-	EtOH	348(4.36)	24-0484-79
	$CHCl_3$	351(4.34)	24-0484-79
	MeCN	348(4.38)	24-0484-79
$C_{18}H_{15}F_6IO_2$			
1,2-Benziodoxole, 1,3-dihydro-3,3-dimethyl-1-[2,2,2-trifluoro-1-phenyl-1-(trifluoromethyl)ethoxy]-	pentane	195(4.54),225(4.27),295(2.90)	44-1779-79
$C_{18}H_{15}N$			
5H-Benzo[b]carbazole, 6,11-dimethyl-	EtOH	235(4.42),277(4.73),283s(4.72),298(4.52),344(3.86),374(3.68),370s(3.60),386(3.65),405(3.71)	150-4801-79
11H-Benzo[a]carbazole, 7,10-dimethyl-	EtOH	255(4.37),283(4.41),303(4.11)	39-2506-79C
Pyrrolo[2,1-a]isoquinoline, 5,6-dihydro-2-phenyl-	MeOH	213(4.15),254(4.22),284(4.18),312(4.21)	83-0896-79
$C_{18}H_{15}NO$			
Ethanone, 2-(1-methyl-2(1H)-quinolinylidene)-1-phenyl-	neutral	429(4.51),445s(4.47)	39-0792-79B
	cation	323(4.15)	39-0792-79B

Compound	Solvent	$\lambda_{max}(\log \epsilon)$	Ref.
Ethanone, 2-(1-methyl-4(1H)-quinolin-ylidene)-1-phenyl-	neutral	465(4.57)	39-0792-79B
	cation	317(4.05)	39-0792-79B
11H-Indeno[1,2-b]quinoline, 11-ethoxy-	MeOH	206(4.59),265(4.76), 311(4.19),320(4.26), 334(4.24)	83-0254-79
Indeno[1,2-b]quinolin-11-one, 5-ethyl-5,11-dihydro-	MeOH	262(4.54),271(4.59), 316(4.24),333(4.02), 348(4.20),365(4.22)	83-0254-79
$C_{18}H_{15}NO_2$			
Dehydroroemerine	EtOH	254(4.61),262(4.76), 332(4.12)	100-0325-79
4-Isoquinolinecarboxaldehyde, 1-ethoxy-3-phenyl-	EtOH	247(4.54),329(4.01)	39-0266-79C
1-Naphthalenecarboxamide, N-hydroxy-N-(3-methylphenyl)-	EtOH	225(4.70),284(3.98)	34-0072-79
Pyrano[3,4-b]indol-1(3H)-one, 4,9-di-hydro-9-(phenylmethyl)-	EtOH	232(4.64),297(4.55)	23-0289-79
4H-Pyran-4-one, 2-(4-methylphenyl)-6-phenyl-, oxime	MeOH	276(4.37),310s(4.19)	4-0737-79
	MeOH-H_2SO_4	263(4.24),317(4.52)	4-0737-79
$C_{18}H_{15}NO_3$			
5H-Benzocyclohepten-5-one, 6,7,8,9-tetrahydro-6-[(4-nitrophenyl)meth-ylene]-	isooctane	230(3.94),306(4.18)	65-1407-79
	MeOH	230(3.76),308(4.17)	65-1407-79
2-Cyclohexen-1-one, 3-(4-nitrophenyl)-5-phenyl-	H_2SO_4	347(4.41)	124-1093-79
4H-Pyran-4-one, 2-(4-methoxyphenyl)-6-phenyl-, oxime	MeOH	287(4.43),320s(4.22)	4-0737-79
	MeOH-H_2SO_4	274s(4.29),330(4.47)	4-0737-79
$C_{18}H_{15}NO_4$			
Benzoic acid, 4-(4-ethynyl-3,5-diform-yl-1(4H)-pyridinyl)-, ethyl ester	EtOH	228(4.23),293(4.33), 360(3.89)	49-0613-79
Spiro[cyclopropane-1,5'-[5H]indeno-[1,2-b]pyridine]-2,3-dicarboxylic acid, dimethyl ester	EtOH	208(4.90),245(4.24), 297(4.44),310(4.39)	103-0777-79
$C_{18}H_{15}NO_6$			
Bostrycoidin, 5-acetoxy-8-methoxy-	MeOH	237(4.49),263(4.08), 287(4.09),406(3.75)	78-1551-79
$C_{18}H_{15}N_2OS_2$			
Thiazolo[3,2-a]pyridinium, 2-[(3-ethyl-2(3H)-benzothiazolylidene)ethylid-ene]-2,3-dihydro-3-oxo-, iodide	MeCN	553(4.73),574(4.72)	103-1081-79
$C_{18}H_{15}N_2O_2$			
Quinolinium, 1-methyl-4-[2-(4-nitro-phenyl)ethenyl]-, methyl sulfate	MeOH	375(4.53)	64-1556-79B
$C_{18}H_{15}N_2O_2S$			
Thiazolo[3,2-a]pyridinium, 2-[(3-ethyl-2(3H)-benzoxazolylidene)ethylidene]-2,3-dihydro-3-oxo-, iodide	MeCN	525(4.75),545(4.71)	103-1081-79
$C_{18}H_{15}N_2S$			
Benzothiazolium, 3-methyl-2-(2-methyl-8-quinolinyl)-, iodide	EtOH	307(4.09),318(4.10)	4-1579-79
Benzothiazolium, 3-methyl-2-(4-methyl-8-quinolinyl)-, iodide	EtOH	306(4.08),316(4.09)	4-1579-79

Compound	Solvent	λ_{max}(log ϵ)	Ref.
$C_{18}H_{15}N_2S_2$			
Benzo[1,2-d:5,4-d']bisthiazolium, 3,6-dimethyl-2-(2-phenylethenyl)-, iodide	DMF	265(4.40),379(4.26)	126-1441-79
	KBr	275(--),398(--)	126-1441-79
$C_{18}H_{15}N_3$			
Benzenamine, N-phenyl-4-(phenylazo)-	MeOH	415(4.51)	56-0989-79
Benzonitrile, 4-(1,3-dimethyl-4-phenyl-1H-pyrazol-5-yl)-	hexane	229(4.24),280(3.91)	23-1186-79
	EtOH	231(4.19),285s(3.83)	23-1186-79
Benzonitrile, 4-(1,5-dimethyl-4-phenyl-1H-pyrazol-3-yl)-	hexane	227s(4.09),244s(4.06), 282(4.18)	23-1186-79
	EtOH	232s(4.23),285(4.20)	23-1186-79
Benzonitrile, 4-(4,5-dimethyl-4-phenyl-4H-pyrazol-3-yl)-	hexane	285(4.22)	23-1186-79
	EtOH	284(4.18)	23-1186-79
$C_{18}H_{15}N_3O$			
Acetamide, N-(6-methylindolo[1,2-c]-quinazolin-12-yl)-	dioxan	247(4.51),273(4.74), 283(4.98),292s(4.17), 346(4.20),360s(4.16)	103-0681-79
Aziridine, 2-(phenylmethyl)-1-(2-quinoxalinylcarbonyl)-, (S)-	isooctane	204(4.53),242(4.56), 245(4.55),318(3.75), 328(3.68)	39-2881-79C
	EtOH	203(4.53),245(4.52), 319(3.83)	39-2881-79C
	MeCN	204(4.47),244(4.51), 318(3.76)	39-2881-79C
5H-1-Benzazepino[5,4,3-de]quinolin-7-one, 2-(dimethylamino)-7,8-dihydro-	dioxan	260(4.5),330(3.9), 392(3.9)	83-0708-79
5H-1-Benzazepino[5,4,3-de]quinolin-8-one, 2-(dimethylamino)-7,8-dihydro-	dioxan	260(4.5),330(3.9), 392(3.7)	83-0708-79
Isoxazole, 3-methyl-4-(phenylazo)-5-(2-phenylethenyl)-	$CHCl_3$	291(4.40),368(4.41)	103-0968-79
$C_{18}H_{15}N_3OS$			
Pyrido[3',2':4,5]thieno[3,2-d]pyrimidin-4(3H)-one, 7,9-dimethyl-3-(phenylmethyl)-	EtOH	248(4.90),286(3.96), 297(4.12),324(3.83), 336(3.64)	103-1078-79
$C_{18}H_{15}N_3O_2$			
Acetic acid, cyano-, (9-ethoxy-1H-phenalen-1-ylidene)hydrazide	CH_2Cl_2	256(4.3),281(3.5), 388(4.3),484(3.7), 513(3.4),542(4.0)	83-0288-79
$C_{18}H_{15}N_3O_2S$			
Propanedinitrile, [1-[(phenylmethyl)-amino]-2-(phenylsulfonyl)ethylidene]-	EtOH	297(4.19)	95-1234-79
$C_{18}H_{15}N_3O_3$			
2H-Cyclopenta[l]phenanthrene-1-carboxamide, 3,3a-dihydro-3a-hydroxy-2-oxo-, hydrazone	EtOH	254(4.40),277s(4.22), 322(4.14),402(3.27)	39-2034-79C
Phenol, 4,4'-[(2-amino-5-hydroxy-2,5-cyclohexadiene-1,4-diylidene)dinitrilo]bis-	pH 2	438(4.12)	39-0308-79B
	pH 7	395(--)	39-0308-79B
	pH 9	470(--)	39-0308-79B
	pH 11.9	530(4.07)	39-0308-79B
	pH 14	485(4.08)	39-0308-79B
$C_{18}H_{15}N_3O_4$			
Carbamic acid, [2-(1,2,3,4-tetrahydro-2,4-dioxo-5-pyrimidinyl)phenyl]-, phenylmethyl ester	EtOH	238(4.18),277(3.95)	39-2902-79C

Compound	Solvent	λ max (log ε)	Ref.
$C_{18}H_{15}N_3S_2$			
Pyrido[3',2':4,5]thieno[3,2-d]pyrimidine, 7,9-dimethyl-4-[(phenylmethyl)thio]-	EtOH	228(4.39),245(4.38), 299(4.34),328(3.92), 339(3.93)	103-1078-79
$C_{18}H_{15}N_4$			
Phenazinium, 3,7-diamino-5-phenyl-	cation	523(4.59)	59-0421-79
$C_{18}H_{15}N_5$			
5H-Indolo[2',3':5,6][1,2,4]triazino-[2,3-a]benzimidazole, 5,8,9-trimethyl-	EtOH	234(3.65),270(4.09), 280(4.12),288(4.19), 376(3.67)	142-1001-79
6H-Indolo[2',3':5,6]triazino[2,3-a]-benzimidazole, 6,8,9-trimethyl-	EtOH	234(4.07),272(4.17), 282(4.41),292(4.46), 367(3.88)	142-1001-79
7H-Indolo[2',3':5,6][1,2,4]triazino-[2,3-a]benzimidazole, 7,8,9-trimethyl-	EtOH	234(3.93),275(4.19), 284(4.38),294(4.46), 372(3.82)	142-1001-79
$C_{18}H_{15}N_5O_5$			
1H-Pyrazole-4,5-dione, 3-(acetoxymethyl)-1-(4-nitrophenyl)-, 4-(phenylhydrazone)	n.s.g.	230(4.00),400(4.24)	106-0531-79
$C_{18}H_{15}N_5O_6$			
L-xylo-2-Hexulosonic acid, 3,6-anhydro-3-C-[(4-nitrophenyl)azo]-, γ-lactone, 2-(phenylhydrazone)	n.s.g.	235(3.91),288(4.10), 350(4.11)	106-0531-79
$C_{18}H_{15}OP$			
Phosphine oxide, triphenyl-	dioxan	223(4.40),260(3.15), 266(3.26),272(3.18)	65-0479-79
	MeCN	224(4.38),259(3.15), 266(3.26),272(3.20)	65-0275-79
	$C_2H_4Cl_2$	224(4.39),260(3.18), 266(3.26),272(3.20)	65-0275-79
$C_{18}H_{15}O_3P$			
4(1H)-Phosphorinone, 1-methoxy-2,6-diphenyl-, 1-oxide	MeOH	315(4.03),337(4.02)	24-1272-79
$C_{18}H_{15}P$			
Phosphine, triphenyl-	C_6H_{12}	262(4.01)	65-0479-79
	hexane	262.3(4.15)	22-0241-79I
	12M HCl	228(4.45),269(3.56), 276(3.48)	65-0479-79
	MeCN	208(4.81),268(3.69), 274(3.68)	65-0275-79
	$C_2H_4Cl_2$	273(3.76)	65-0275-79
	n.s.g.	264(4.03)	65-1036-79
hydrochloride	12M HCl	228(4.42),269(3.56), 276(3.48)	65-0275-75
$C_{18}H_{15}S$			
Sulfonium, triphenyl-, hexafluoroarsenate	MeOH	227(4.32),298(4.00)	47-0977-79
tetrafluoroborate	MeOH	227(4.32)	47-0977-79
$C_{18}H_{15}Se$			
Selenonium, triphenyl-, hexafluoroarsenate	MeOH	275(3.32)	47-1047-79

Compound	Solvent	$\lambda_{max}(\log \epsilon)$	Ref.
Selenonium, triphenyl-, hexafluorostibnate	MeOH	275(3.32)	47-1047-79
tetrafluoroborate	MeOH	258(4.04),266(3.45), 275(3.32)	47-1047-79
$C_{18}H_{16}$			
Benzocyclotetradecene	C_6H_{12}	231(3.95),305(4.70), 360s(3.67)	24-3895-79
Benzocyclotetradecene, 9,10,11,12-tetradehydro-7,8,13,14-tetrahydro-	EtOH	232(4.36),256s(4.23)	24-3895-79
1,2'-Bi-1H-indene, 2,3-dihydro-	EtOH	224s(4.17),259(4.21), 263s(4.18),269s(4.11), 272s(3.99),282s(3.32), 288s(2.84)	44-1358-79
[1,2:9,10]Bismethano[2.2]paracyclophane, anti	EtOH	230(4.18),260s(3.70), 304(2.95)	35-6475-79
Chrysene, 5,6,11,12-tetrahydro-	C_6H_{12}	207(4.48),231(4.29), 237(4.37),244(4.16), 311(4.42),324(4.54), 340(4.38)	44-4933-79
1,3,5-Hexatriene, 1,6-diphenyl-	hexane	335(4.99),351(5.08), 370(4.60)	65-0146-79
Pentacyclo[10.2.2.2^{5,8}.0^{2,4}.0^{9,11}]octadeca-5,7,12,14,15,17-hexaene	EtOH	240s(3.16)	88-1939-79
$C_{18}H_{16}Br_2N_2O_3$			
1-Propanone, 1,1'-[azoxybis(4-bromo-2,1-phenylene)]bis-	EtOH	255(4.22),315(3.83)	104-0847-79
$C_{18}H_{16}ClNO$			
2,1-Benzisoxazole, 5-chloro-3-(6,7,8,9-tetrahydro-5H-benzocyclohepten-2-yl)-	MeOH	254(4.16),263(4.22), 360(4.25)	73-3604-79
$C_{18}H_{16}ClNO_2$			
9,10-Anthracenedione, 1-(butylamino)-x-chloro-	benzene	500(3.68)	153-0033-79
$C_{18}H_{16}ClN_4$			
4H-[1,2,4]Triazolo[4,3-a][1,4]benzodiazepinium, 8-chloro-1,2-dimethyl-6-phenyl-, bromide	EtOH	222(4.58),245s(4.21), 280s(3.68)	44-2688-79
4H-[1,2,4]Triazolo[4,3-a][1,4]benzodiazepinium, 8-chloro-1,3-dimethyl-6-phenyl-, chloride	EtOH	223(4.58),247s(4.14), 265s(3.88),285s(3.69)	44-2688-79
$C_{18}H_{16}CrO_7$			
Chromate(1-), bis[α-hydroxy-α-methylbenzeneacetato(2-)]oxo-, sodium	H_2O	520s(2.11)	35-3206-79
$C_{18}H_{16}F_6O_3$			
Spiro[cyclopropane-1,6'(3'aH)-[5H]cycloprop[7,8]azuleno[4,5-b]furan-5'-one, 3'-(difluoromethoxy)-2,2,8',8'-tetrafluoro-3'b,6'a,7',7'a,8',8'a-hexahydro-3'a,8'a-dimethyl-, [3'aR-(3'aα,3'bβ,6'β,6'aβ,7'aα,8'aα)]-	EtOH	270(3.65)	78-0815-79
$C_{18}H_{16}NO_6$			
[1,3]Benzodioxolo[5,6-a]quinolizinium, 6,7-dihydro-2,3-bis(methoxycarbonyl)-, chloride	EtOH	277(4.28),303(4.43), 405(4.47)	23-1647-79

Compound	Solvent	$\lambda_{max}(\log \epsilon)$	Ref.
$C_{18}H_{16}N_2$			
3,4-Diazabicyclo[4.1.0]hepta-2,4-diene, 1-methyl-2,5-diphenyl-	hexane	310(4.16)	20-0905-79
	$CHCl_3$	311(4.17)	20-0905-79
Hydrazine, triphenyl-	MeCN	248(4.52),288(4.38)	103-1243-79
1H-Indole, 2-(1H-indol-3-ylmethyl)-3-methyl-	EtOH	276(4.11),283(4.16), 291(4.11)	56-0073-79
1H-Pyrazole, 1,5-diphenyl-3-(1-propenyl)-	EtOH	212(4.22),245(4.44)	4-0657-79
$C_{18}H_{16}N_2O$			
1,6-Benzodiazocin-2(1H)-one, 1,3-dimethyl-5-phenyl-	MeOH	258(4.24),323(3.36)	39-0584-79C
	MeOH-$HClO_4$	246(3.64),305(3.92)	39-0584-79C
Ethanone, 1-[5-(4-methylphenyl)-1H-pyrazol-3-yl]-2-phenyl-	MeOH	250(4.27)	4-0737-79
Pyrazine, 2,5-bis(phenylmethyl)-, 1-oxide	EtOH	227(4.38),269(4.05)	94-2980-79
Pyrazine, 3-ethoxy-2,5-diphenyl-	EtOH	265(4.13),340(4.42)	94-2980-79
6H-Pyrido[4,3-b]carbazole, 9-methoxy-5,11-dimethyl-	MeOH	211(4.23),245(4.31), 276(4.55),291(4.62), 337(3.71),354(3.45), 403(3.44)	100-0643-79
$C_{18}H_{16}N_2OS$			
2(1H)-Pyrimidinethione, 1-acetyl-3,4-dihydro-4,6-diphenyl-	EtOH	243(4.00),327(4.35)	23-2734-79
$C_{18}H_{16}N_2O_2$			
Ethanone, 1-[5-(4-methoxyphenyl)-1H-pyrazol-3-yl]-2-phenyl-	MeOH	258(4.39)	4-0737-79
1-Naphthalenemethanamine, α-methyl-N-(4-nitrophenyl)-, (S)-	MeOH	223(4.92),263s(3.77), 272(3.85),282(3.89), 290s(3.79),308s(3.40), 384(4.30)	35-5186-79
Pyrazine, 2,5-bis(phenylmethyl)-, 1,4-dioxide	EtOH	234(4.36),311(4.27)	94-2980-79
2(1H)-Pyrazinone, 3,6-bis(phenylmethyl)-, 4-oxide	EtOH	233(4.22),280(3.82), 332(3.91)	94-2980-79
1H-Pyrazole, 1-acetyl-4-methoxy-3,5-diphenyl-	EtOH	233(4.29),287(4.30)	23-0904-79
1H-Pyrazol-4-ol, 1-methyl-3,5-diphenyl-, acetate	EtOH	247(4.44)	23-0904-79
$C_{18}H_{16}N_2O_2S$			
4(3H)-Quinazolinone, 2-[(1-methyl-2-oxo-1-propyl)thio]-3-phenyl-	MeOH	230(4.51),275(4.14), 314(3.66)	2-0039-79B
$C_{18}H_{16}N_2O_3$			
8H-Isoquino[2,1-b][2,7]naphthyridin-8-one, 5,6-dihydro-2,3-dimethoxy-	MeOH	240(4.20),257s(4.06), 257s(4.06),280s(3.72), 365(4.39),366(4.33), 415(3.35)	4-0433-79
Methanone, 1H-indol-2-yl[3-(2-phenyl-1,3-dioxolan-2-yl)-4-pyridinyl]-	EtOH	230(4.27),322(4.40)	77-0642-79
$C_{18}H_{16}N_2O_3S$			
5H-Thiazolo[3,2-a]quinazoline-1,5(2H)-dione, dihydro-3a-methoxy-2-methyl-4-phenyl-	MeOH	230(4.50),276(4.13), 315(3.65)	2-0039-79B
$C_{18}H_{16}N_2O_3S_2$			
Acetic acid, [(3,4,5,6,7,8-hexahydro-	n.s.g.	235(4.17),280(3.79),	124-0871-79

Compound	Solvent	λ_{max}(log ε)	Ref.
4-oxo-3-phenyl-[1]benzothieno[2,3-d]-pyrimidin-2-yl)thio]- (cont.)		322(4.16),335(4.09)	124-0871-79
$C_{18}H_{16}N_2O_4$			
2,3-Dioxa-5,7-diazabicyclo[2.2.2]octane-6,8-dione, 1,4-bis(phenylmethyl)-	EtOH	220(3.89),313(3.49)	39-1885-79C
2,7-Phenazinedicarboxylic acid, diethyl ester	EtOH	266(5.10),366(4.17)	94-2316-79
$C_{18}H_{16}N_2O_5$			
1H-Indole-3-carboxylic acid, 6-hydroxy-2-methyl-1-(4-nitrophenyl)-, ethyl ester	MeOH	245(4.43),285s(4.18), 345s(3.63)	83-0515-79
$C_{18}H_{16}N_2O_6$			
3-Benzofurancarboxylic acid, 5-hydroxy-2-methyl-6-[(4-nitrophenyl)amino]-, ethyl ester	MeOH	248s(4.27),270s(4.10), 395(4.30)	83-0515-79
$C_{18}H_{16}N_2O_7S$			
Benzoic acid, 2,2'-sulfinylbis[5-(acetylamino)-	dioxan	228(4.47),272(4.25)	78-1875-79
$C_{18}H_{16}N_3$			
1H-Benzimidazolium, 1-methyl-2-[2-(4-methylquinolinyl)]-, iodide	EtOH	284(4.36),332(4.37), 347(4.31)	4-1583-79
Quinolinium, 4(1H)-benzimidazol-2-yl-1,2-dimethyl-, iodide	EtOH	332(4.12),392(4.25)	4-1583-79
Quinolinium, 6(1H)-benzimidazol-2-yl-1,2-dimethyl-, iodide	EtOH	303(4.42),370(3.91)	4-1583-79
Quinolinium, 6(1H)-benzimidazol-2-yl-1,4-dimethyl-, iodide	EtOH	303(4.44),371(3.89)	4-1583-79
$C_{18}H_{16}N_4$			
Pyridazine, 4,5-dihydro-6-phenyl-3,4-di-1H-pyrrol-1-yl-	EtOH	244(4.51)	80-0453-79
$C_{18}H_{16}N_4O$			
Azepino[4,5-b]indole-4,5-dione, 1,2,3,6-tetrahydro-, 5-(phenylhydrazone)	EtOH	236(4.38),295(3.94), 384(4.28)	103-0780-79
$C_{18}H_{16}N_4O_2S$			
5H-2a-Thia(2a-S^{IV})-2,3,4a,7a-tetraazacyclopent[cd]indene-1,4(2H,3H)-dione, 6,7-dihydro-2,3-diphenyl-	EtOH	235(4.31),263(4.08)	39-2909-79C
1H-1,2,4-Triazolium, 4-(diacetylamino)-2,3-dihydro-1,5-diphenyl-3-thioxo-, hydroxide, inner salt	EtOH	249(4.38),330(3.61)	94-1683-79
$C_{18}H_{16}N_4O_5S_3$			
5-Thia-1-azabicyclo[4.2.0]oct-2-ene-2-carboxylic acid, 7-[(hydroxyphenylacetyl)amino]-8-oxo-3-[(1,2,3-thiadiazol-5-ylthio)methyl]-	MeOH	267(4.03)	87-1214-79
5-Thia-1-azabicyclo[4.2.0]oct-2-ene-2-carboxylic acid, 8-oxo-7-[(phenoxyacetyl)amino]-3-[(1,2,3-thiadiazol-5-ylthio)methyl-, sodium salt, (6R-trans)-	H_2O	268(4.06)	87-1214-79

Compound	Solvent	λ_{max}(log ϵ)	Ref.
$C_{18}H_{16}N_4O_7$			
D-Arabinitol, 1,4-anhydro-1-C-(6-nitro-[1,2,4]triazolo[1,5-a]pyridin-2-yl)-, 5-benzoate, (R)-	EtOH	235(4.39),320(3.56)	111-0375-79
D-Arabinitol, 1,4-anhydro-1-C-(8-nitro-[1,2,4]triazolo[1,5-a]pyridin-2-yl)-, 5-benzoate, (R)-	EtOH	230(4.46),330(3.66)	111-0375-79
1-Propanone, 1,1'-[azoxybis(4-nitro-2,1-phenylene)]bis-	EtOH	258(4.47),318(3.97)	104-0847-79
Sydnone, 4-[[4,5-bis(ethoxycarbonyl)-3H-pyrazol-3-yl]carbonyl]-3-phenyl-	n.s.g.	255(3.56),337(4.18)	103-1153-79
$C_{18}H_{16}N_4S_3$			
5H-2a-Thia(2a-S^{IV})-2,3,4a,7a-tetraaza-cyclopent[cd]indene-1,4(2H,3H)-dithione, 6,7-dihydro-2,3-diphenyl-	EtOH	219(4.53),267(4.39)	39-2909-79C
$C_{18}H_{16}N_6$			
Benzenamine, 2,2'-[1,2-phenylenebis-(azo)]bis-	benzene	313(4.34),350s(4.11), 422(4.08),475s(3.92)	118-0545-79
8(1H)-Cycloheptapyrazolone, (3-methyl-8(1H)-cycloheptapyrazolylidene)hydrazone	MeOH	224(4.32),283s(3.69), 450(4.13)	18-1972-79
$C_{18}H_{16}N_6O_8$			
L-threo-2,3-Hexodiulosonic acid, γ-lactone, 3-[(2,4-dinitrophenyl)hydrazone] 2-(phenylhydrazone)	n.s.g.	228(4.28),268(4.28), 42?(4.48),410s(4.22), 500s(3.52)	106-0531-79
$C_{18}H_{16}N_6S_2$			
1H-1,2,4-Triazole, 3,3'-dithiobis[1-methyl-5-phenyl-	n.s.g.	223(4.40)	39-0724-79C
1H-1,2,4-Triazole, 3,3'-dithiobis[5-methyl-1-phenyl-	n.s.g.	240(4.30)	39-0724-79C
$C_{18}H_{16}N_8O_2$			
2,3-Naphthalenediol, 1-[[5-methyl-4-[(5-methyl-1H-pyrazol-3-yl)azo]-1H-pyrazol-3-yl]azo]-	DMF	294(3.84),355(3.85), 495(3.85)	103-0657-79
$C_{18}H_{16}O$			
5H-Benzocyclohepten-5-one, 6,7,8,9-tetrahydro-6-(phenylmethylene)-	isooctane	233(4.08),262(4.03), 297(4.16)	65-1407-79
	MeOH	233(4.28),270(4.23), 300(4.41)	65-1407-79
Bicyclo[3.1.0]hexen-2-one, 6,6-diphenyl-	EtOH	230(4.24),250(3.67), 305(1.70)	35-1841-79
2-Cyclohexen-1-one, 3,5-diphenyl-	H_2SO_4	368(4.50)	124-1093-79
2,4,6,12,14-Cyclopentadecapentaene-8,10-diyn-1-one, 2,7,12-trimethyl-	ether	250s(4.5),295(4.7), 370(3.9)	138-1035-79
$C_{18}H_{16}O_2$			
1H-Indene-1-methanol, α-phenyl-, acetate	hexane	224s(4.36),254(4.01), 268s(3.77),282s(2.93), 288s(2.75)	33-0718-79
1(2H)-Naphthalenone, 2-(4-methoxyphenyl)-2-methyl-	MeOH	238(4.65)	12-1551-79
$C_{18}H_{16}O_2S$			
1-Benzothiepin, 3,5-dimethoxy-4-phenyl-	MeOH	266(4.11)	24-0781-79

Compound	Solvent	$\lambda_{max}(\log \epsilon)$	Ref.
$C_{18}H_{16}O_3$			
2-Benzoxepin-1-carboxylic acid, 1,3-dihydro-5-phenyl-, methyl ester	EtOH	236(4.29),259(4.04)	88-4049-79
1,4-Epoxyanthracene, 1,2,3,4-tetrahydro-5,8-dimethoxy-2,3-bis(methylene)-	EtOH	208(5.26),226(4.73), 322(3.67),336(3.70)	88-4533-79
Ethanone, 1-(1,4,4a,5,8,8a-hexahydro-3-phenyl-1,4:5,8-diepoxynaphthalen-2-yl)-, trans	MeOH and MeOH-$HClO_4$	215(4.03),284(3.89)	39-0584-79C
1H,3H-Furo[3,4-c]furan-1-one, tetrahydro-4,6-diphenyl-	MeOH	258(2.78)	78-0861-79
2(1H)-Naphthalenone, 3,4-dihydro-1-(4-methoxybenzoyl)-	EtOH	210s(4.42),263(4.16), 365(3.95)	87-0962-79
Oxiranecarboxylic acid, 3-(2,2-diphenylethenyl)-, methyl ester, trans	EtOH	233s(4.20),263(4.24)	88-4049-79
$C_{18}H_{16}O_3S$			
1-Benzothiepin, 3,5-dimethoxy-4-phenyl-, 1-oxide	C_6H_{12}	280s(3.90),330(3.08)	24-0781-79
	MeOH at -10°	270s(4.01)	24-0781-79
$C_{18}H_{16}O_4$			
9,10-Anthracenedione, 2-butyl-1,4-dihydroxy-	MeOH	205(4.36),250(4.59), 286(3.99),325s(--), 487(4.00)	5-0019-79
4H-1-Benzopyran-4-one, 2,3-dihydro-5,7-dimethoxy-3-(phenylmethylene)-	EtOH	233(5.24),340(5.11), 358(5.12)	150-1713-79
4H-1-Benzopyran-4-one, 3-[(2,4-dimethoxyphenyl)methyl]-	EtOH	226(4.54),267(3.78), 285(3.84),298(3.93), 306(3.93)	150-1713-79
4H-1-Benzopyran-4-one, 3-[(2,4-dimethoxyphenyl)methylene]-2,3-dihydro-	EtOH	263(4.42),365(4.23)	150-1713-79
4H-1-Benzopyran-4-one, 5,7-dimethoxy-3-(phenylmethyl)-	EtOH	220(4.01),256(3.71), 287(4.02)	150-1713-79
4H-1-Benzopyran-4-one, 7-methoxy-3-[(4-methoxyphenyl)methyl]-	EtOH	219(4.57),240(4.37), 280(4.13),295(4.15), 305(4.10)	150-1713-79
4H-1-Benzopyran-4-one, 7-methoxy-3-[(4-methoxyphenyl)methylene]-2,3-dihydro-	EtOH	235(4.16),310(4.23), 355(4.39)	150-1713-79
1,5-Biphenylenedicarboxylic acid, 3,7-dimethyl-, dimethyl ester	n.s.g.	204(4.65),254(4.45), 262(4.46),383(4.01), 410(4.12)	70-1916-79
9H-Xanthen-9-one, 1,5-dihydroxy-6-(3-methyl-2-butenyl)-	EtOH	252(4.62),318(4.04), 368(3.57)	142-0269-79
$C_{18}H_{16}O_4S$			
1-Benzothiepin, 3,5-dimethoxy-4-phenyl-, 1,1-dioxide	MeOH	286(3.95)	24-0781-79
$C_{18}H_{16}O_5$			
9,10-Anthracenedione, 1,4-dihydroxy-2-(1-hydroxybutyl)-	MeOH	206(4.33),250(4.56), 285(4.00),330s(--), 483(3.96),580s(--)	5-0019-79
4H-1-Benzopyran-4-one, 3-(2-hydroxy-4-methoxyphenyl)-7-methoxy-2-methyl-	MeOH	247(4.40),251(4.40), 290(4.20)	18-0529-79
4H-1-Benzopyran-4-one, 3-(2-hydroxyphenyl)-6,7-dimethoxy-2-methyl-	MeOH	298(4.13),324(4.07)	18-0529-79
4H-1-Benzopyran-4-one, 5,7,8-trimethoxy-2-phenyl-	n.s.g.	270(4.46),330(3.95)	2-0552-79
2,7-Dibenzofurandiol, 1,3-dimethyl-, diacetate	EtOH	223(4.60),247(4.12), 254(4.26),287(4.34), 298s(4.16)	1-0271-79

Compound	Solvent	λmax(log ε)	Ref.
2,7-Dibenzofurandiol, 1,4-dimethyl-, diacetate	EtOH	225(4.57),247(4.09), 256(4.19),284(4.27), 296s(3.93),306s(3.64)	1-0271-79
2,7-Dibenzofurandiol, 3,4-dimethyl-, diacetate	EtOH	220(4.50),244(4.15), 253(4.22),291(4.28), 300(4.21),330(2.86)	1-0271-79
9H-Xanthen-9-one, 1,3,5-trihydroxy-2-(3-methyl-2-butenyl)-	EtOH	235s(4.42),248(4.40), 301(4.26),358(3.50)	142-0269-79
9H-Xanthen-9-one, 1,3,5-trihydroxy-4-(3-methyl-2-butenyl)-	EtOH	239(4.48),244(4.48), 256(4.45),310(4.11), 318(4.15),368(3.62)	142-0269-79
$C_{18}H_{16}O_6$			
4H-1-Benzopyran-4-one, 5-hydroxy-7,8-dimethoxy-2-(3-methoxyphenyl)-	MeOH	273(4.43),330(4.05)	102-0149-79
4H-1-Benzopyran-4-one, 3-(2-hydroxy-3,4-dimethoxyphenyl)-7-methoxy-	EtOH	248(4.52),262s(4.42), 305(4.21)	102-0815-79
	EtOH-NaOH	236(4.65),273(4.34), 297(4.34)	102-0815-79
4H-1-Benzopyran-4-one, 3-(3-hydroxy-2,4-dimethoxyphenyl)-7-methoxy-	EtOH	240s(4.51),248(4.48), 269s(4.28),308s(4.17)	102-0815-79
	EtOH-NaOH	247(4.58),305(4.29)	102-0815-79
1,3-Propanedione, 1-(1,3-benzodioxol-5-yl)-3-(2,4-dimethoxyphenyl)-	MeOH	225(5.15),255(4.97), 275(4.83),305(4.97), 315(4.99),375(5.40)	2-0552B-79B
9H-Xanthen-9-one, 2,3,6,8-tetrahydroxy-1-(3-methyl-2-butenyl)-	MeOH	241(4.29),256(4.36), 313(4.11),364(3.77)	100-0301-79
	MeOH-NaOMe	267(--),378(--)	100-0301-79
	MeOH-NaOAc	241(--),259(--), 374(--)	100-0301-79
$C_{18}H_{16}O_7$			
4H-1-Benzopyran-4-one, 5-hydroxy-2-(4-hydroxy-3-methoxyphenyl)-3,7-dimethoxy-	MeOH	254(4.01),268(4.00), 302s(3.79),355(4.27)	100-0320-79
	MeOH-NaOMe	230s(4.16),263(4.21), 293s(3.88),412(4.50)	100-0320-79
	MeOH-NaOAc	254(4.11),268(4.00), 300s(3.74),355(4.23)	100-0320-79
	MeOH-$AlCl_3$	272(4.15),300(3.68), 370(4.14),405(4.27)	100-0320-79
	MeOH-$AlCl_3$-HCl	273(4.14),300(3.77), 365(4.14),404(4.24)	100-0320-79
	MeOH-NaOMe-H_3BO_3	253(4.14),268(4.03), 300s(3.82),355(4.27)	100-0320-79
1,4-Ethanoanthracene-9,10-dione, 3-acetyl-1,2,3,4-tetrahydro-1,3,5,8-tetrahydroxy-, (1α,3α,4β)-	MeOH	217(4.43),280(3.70), 483s(3.73),518(3.80), 557(3.62)	24-2640-79
(1α,3β,4β)-	MeOH	216(4.43),290(3.76), 480(3.86),510(3.91), 567(3.73)	24-2640-79
$C_{18}H_{16}O_8$			
9,10-Anthracenedione, 1,3,6,8-tetrahydroxy-2-[3-hydroxy-1-(hydroxymethyl)propyl]- (versiconol)	MeOH	224(4.48),266(4.15), 294(4.38),315(4.09), 455(3.87)	39-0451-79C
4H-1-Benzopyran-4-one, 5,6-dihydroxy-2-(2-hydroxy-6-methoxyphenyl)-7,8-dimethoxy-	MeOH	276(4.5),311s(4.1), 364(3.7)	95-0657-79
4H-1-Benzopyran-4-one, 2-(3,5-dihydroxy-4-methoxyphenyl)-5-hydroxy-3,7-dimethoxy-	EtOH	265(4.30),347(4.26)	2-0037-79A

Compound	Solvent	$\lambda_{max}(\log \epsilon)$	Ref.
Propanedioic acid, (5-acetoxy-2-ethenyl-4-oxo-4H-1-benzopyran-3-yl)-, dimethyl ester	EtOH	251(4.48),258(4.48), 286(4.04),313(4.00)	102-0311-79
$C_{18}H_{16}S_3$			
1,2,5-Trithiepin, dimethyldiphenyl-	$CHCl_3$	216(4.33),238s(4.24), 279(4.21),300s(4.17)	5-1702-79
$C_{18}H_{16}Te_2$			
1,3-Ditellurole, 4-(4-methylphenyl)-2-[(4-methylphenyl)methylene]-	dioxan	345(5.37)	104-2346-79
$C_{18}H_{17}BrN_2$			
13,14-Diazatetracyclo[8.2.1.1^{4,7}0^{1,14}]-tetradeca-2,4,6-triene, 13-(4-bromophenyl)-	isooctane	253(3.86),292(3.85), 301s(3.78)	44-2499-79
$C_{18}H_{17}BrN_2O_2$			
1-Propanone, 1-[4-bromo-2-[(2-cyclopropylphenyl)-NNO-azoxy]phenyl]-	EtOH	255(3.92),316(3.37)	104-0847-79
$C_{18}H_{17}BrN_4O_4$			
L-threo-2,3-Hexodiulosonic acid, γ-lactone, 3-[(4-bromophenyl)hydrazone] 2-(phenylhydrazone)	n.s.g.	205(4.03),263s(4.19), 280(4.27),350(3.90), 445(4.22)	106-0531-79
1H-Pyrazole-4,5-dione, 1-(4-bromophenyl)-3-(1,2,3-trihydroxypropyl)-, 4-(phenylhydrazone), [S-(R*,R*)]-	n.s.g.	216(4.12),255(4.23), 403(4.56)	106-0531-79
$C_{18}H_{17}Br_2NO_4$			
Erythrinan-2,8-dione, 1,3-dibromo-3,4-didehydro-15,16-dimethoxy-, (1β)-(±)-	MeOH	232(4.06),262(3.93), 342s(3.08)	24-1126-79
$C_{18}H_{17}ClN_4$			
Acetaldehyde, (7-chloro-5-phenyl-3H-1,4-benzodiazepin-2-yl)methylhydrazone	EtOH	233(4.42),248s(4.36), 279(4.36),293(4.43), 347(3.64)	44-2688-79
1H-1,2,4-Triazolo[4,3-a][1,4]benzodiazepine, 8-chloro-2,6-dihydro-1,2-dimethyl-6-phenyl-	EtOH	214(4.53),267(4.27), 350s(3.06)	44-2688-79
$C_{18}H_{17}ClN_4O$			
Acetic acid, 2-(7-chloro-5-phenyl-3H-1,4-benzodiazepin-2-yl)-1-methylhydrazide	EtOH	227(4.50),330(3.40)	44-2688-79
Acetic acid, 2-(7-chloro-5-phenyl-3H-1,4-benzodiazepin-2-yl)-2-methylhydrazide	EtOH	231(4.47),262(4.28), 340(3.47),241s(4.03)	44-2688-79
$C_{18}H_{17}ClN_4O_4$			
L-threo-2,3-Hexodiulosonic acid, γ-lactone, 3-[(4-chlorophenyl)hydrazone] 2-(phenylhydrazone)	n.s.g.	208(4.28),260s(4.28), 280(4.48),350(4.22), 438(4.21)	106-0531-79
1H-Pyrazole-4,5-dione, 1-(4-chlorophenyl)-3-(1,2,3-trihydroxypropyl)-, 4-(phenylhydrazone), [S-(R*,R*)]-	n.s.g.	210(3.94),256(4.00), 402(4.36)	106-0531-79
$C_{18}H_{17}Fe$			
Ethylium, 1-ferrocenyl-1-phenyl-	$C_2H_4Cl_2$	253(3.82),341(3.60), 465s(2.97)	32-0013-79

Compound	Solvent	$\lambda_{max}(\log \epsilon)$	Ref.
$C_{18}H_{17}N$			
5H-Benzo[a]carbazole, 6,11-dihydro-7,10-dimethyl-	EtOH	255(4.39),347(3.79)	39-2506-79C
1-Naphthalenamine, N-ethyl-2-phenyl-	n.s.g.	213(4.86),245s(4.71), 310(3.88)	103-1117-79
1H-Pyrrole, 2,3-dimethyl-4,5-diphenyl-	EtOH	258(4.03),313(4.06)	88-1587-79
1H-Pyrrole, 2,4-dimethyl-3,5-diphenyl-	EtOH	238(4.13),303(4.32)	78-2285-79
1H-Pyrrole, 2,5-dimethyl-3,4-diphenyl-	EtOH	222s(4.21),240(4.23), 276(3.99)	103-0501-79
1H-Pyrrole, 3,4-dimethyl-2,5-diphenyl-	EtOH	203(4.39),321(4.41)	44-3281-79
2H-Pyrrole, 2,2-dimethyl-3,5-diphenyl-	EtOH	273(4.47),357(3.95)	12-1795-79
	EtOH	248(4.25)	78-2285-79
2H-Pyrrole, 2,3-dimethyl-2,5-diphenyl-	EtOH	247(4.49)	78-2285-79 +88-1587-79
$C_{18}H_{17}NO$			
2-Butanone, 4-(1a,9b-dihydro-1H-phenanthro[9,10-b]azirin-1-yl)-	$CHCl_3$	240(3.89),272s(4.28), 278(4.31),293s(4.08), 305(3.70)	78-2901-79
2-Cyclohexen-1-one, 3-(4-aminophenyl)-5-phenyl-	H_2SO_4	346(4.18)	124-1093-79
1H-Cyclopropa[c]cyclobuta[1,2-a:3,4-a']dicyclooctene, 1a,5a,5b,11a,11b-11c-hexahydro-1-isocyanato-	dioxan	260s(3.51)	89-0312-79
1-Pyridinol, 1,4-dihydro-2-(4-methylphenyl)-6-phenyl-	MeOH	258(4.27),306s(3.99)	4-0737-79
	MeOH-H_2SO_4	262(4.25),350(3.92)	4-0737-79
$C_{18}H_{17}NO_2$			
11H-Benzo[f]pyrrolo[1,2-b]isoquinoline, 9,10-dihydro-2,3-dimethoxy-, perchlorate	MeOH	222(4.37),237(4.39), 256(4.16),295(4.66), 333(3.97)	5-1212-79
4-Isoquinolinemethanol, 1-ethoxy-3-phenyl-	EtOH	244(4.45),294(4.06)	39-0266-79C
1-Pyridinol, 1,4-dihydro-2-(4-methoxyphenyl)-6-phenyl-	MeOH	266(4.37),314s(4.00)	4-0737-79
	MeOH-H_2SO_4	266(4.30),366(3.93)	4-0737-79
$C_{18}H_{17}NO_3$			
9,10-Anthracenedione, 1-[2-(dimethylamino)ethoxy]-, hydrochloride	EtOH	252(4.52),270(4.15), 370(3.63)	87-0501-79
1(2H)-Isoquinolinone, 3-(3,4-dimethoxyphenyl)-2-methyl-	EtOH	207(4.71),295(4.22)	78-1861-79
Oliveroline	EtOH	235(4.03),275(4.08), 315(3.56)	100-0325-79
Pachypodanthine	EtOH	232(4.20),274(4.25), 318(3.58)	100-0325-79
Puterine	EtOH	265s(4.11),274(4.17), 295(3.91)	100-0325-79
Xylopine, (-)-	EtOH	280(4.32)	102-1584-79
$C_{18}H_{17}NO_4$			
Benzoxazole, 2-[2-(3,4,5-trimethoxyphenyl)ethenyl]-	EtOH	241(3.92),346(4.51)	56-1033-79
Elmerrilicine	MeOH	221(4.60),241s(4.27), 271s(4.14),277(4.17), 298(4.01)	100-0325-79
Launobine	EtOH	218(3.98),263(3.67), 303(3.28)	100-0325-79
Litseferine	EtOH	282(4.10),310(4.12)	100-0325-79
Michelanugine	HCl	217(4.49),237s(4.16), 279(4.29),322s(3.62)	100-0325-79

Compound	Solvent	λ_{max}(log ε)	Ref.
5,12-Naphthacenedione, 5a,6,7,8,9,10-11,11a-octahydro-1-nitro-	EtOH	220(4.33),267(4.05), 330(3.06)	94-2229-79
Norpachystaudine	EtOH	237(4.16),274(4.18), 315(3.50)	100-0325-79
Oliveroline, N-oxide	EtOH	237(4.14),274(4.05), 314(3.53)	100-0325-79
$C_{18}H_{17}NO_4S$			
Benzene, 4-[2-isocyano-2-[(4-methylphenyl)sulfonyl]ethenyl]-1,2-dimethoxy-	EtOH	239(4.08),324(4.08), 338(4.18)	39-0652-79C
$C_{18}H_{17}NO_5$			
1H-Benzo[a]furo[3,4-f]quinolizine-1,12(3H)-dione, 5,6-dihydro-8,9-dimethoxy-3-methyl-	MeOH	227(4.24),243(4.30), 250(4.34),260(4.25), 278(4.12),287(4.17), 329(4.15)	104-1247-79
2-Butenedioic acid, 2-[2-oxo-1-(2(1H)-quinolinylidene)propyl]-, dimethyl ester	MeOH	217(4.46),294(4.05), 299s(4.05),312s(4.00), 420(4.04)	39-2171-79C
	MeOH-$HClO_4$	220(4.43),241(4.12), 284(3.99),321(3.76), 384(4.02)	39-2171-79C
$C_{18}H_{17}NO_6$			
2H-Azepine-4-carboxylic acid, 6-acetoxy-3-methoxy-2-oxo-7-phenyl-, ethyl ester	dioxan	263(4.00),287(3.95), 355s(3.60)	142-1427-79
Benzo[g]quinoline-5,10-dione, 7-butyl-3,4,9-trihydroxy-8-methoxy-	MeOH	229(4.34),270(4.47), 435(3.96)	39-0807-79C
[1,1'-Biphenyl]-2,3-dicarboxylic acid, 4'-(acetylamino)-4-hydroxy-, dimethyl ester	EtOH	265(4.42),320(3.63)	103-0013-79
Decarboxyphomazarin, di-O-methyl-	MeOH	225(4.39),268(4.55), 350(3.86)	39-0807-79C
$C_{18}H_{17}NO_6S_4$			
1,3-Dithiole-4,5-dicarboxylic acid, 2-(3,4-dihydro-2H-1,4-benzothiazin-2-ylidene)-, diethyl ester, S,S-dioxide	dioxan	250(3.5),300(3.1), 410(3.6)	83-0302-79
$C_{18}H_{17}N_2OS$			
Thiazolo[3,2-a]benzimidazolium, 9-ethyl-6-hydroxy-3-methyl-2-phenyl-, bromide	EtOH	250(3.50),512(3.81)	18-3096-79
Thiazolo[3,2-a]benzimidazolium, 9-ethyl-6-hydroxy-3-(4-methylphenyl)-, bromide	EtOH	264(3.72),526(3.94)	18-3096-79
$C_{18}H_{17}N_3$			
3,4-Diazabicyclo[4.1.0]hepta-2,4-diene, 7,7-dimethyl-2-phenyl-5-(2-pyridinyl)-	hexane	326(4.07)	20-0905-79
	$CHCl_3$	329(3.98)	20-0905-79
Pyrazinamine, 5-(4-methylphenyl)-3-(phenylmethyl)-	MeOH	277(4.18),345(3.91)	69-2204-79
Pyridazine, 3-(1H-pyrrol-1-yl)-6-(1,2,3,4-tetrahydro-2-naphthalenyl)-	EtOH	294(4.34)	80-0453-79
3H-Pyrrolo[2,3-c]acridine-1-methanamine, N,N-dimethyl-	EtOH	222(4.38),236(4.41), 279(4.75),372(3.86)	103-0894-79

Compound	Solvent	λ_{max}(log ε)	Ref.
$C_{18}H_{17}N_3O$			
1H-Cyclopropa[c]cyclobuta[1,2-a:3,4-a']dicyclooctene-1-carbonyl azide, 1a,5a,5b,11a,11b,11c-hexahydro-	dioxan	227s(3.20)	89-0312-79
Morpholine, 4-[[[2-cyano-2-(2-naphthalenyl)ethenyl]imino]methyl]-	MeOH	211(4.60),233(4.57), 281(4.16),293(4.24), 342(4.58)	83-0039-79
$C_{18}H_{17}N_3O_2$			
8-Azabicyclo[3.2.1]octane-8-propanenitrile, 4-benzoyl-6-cyano-2-oxo-	EtOH	210(4.24),245(4.18)	56-0057-79
isomer	EtOH	210(4.24),245(4.18)	56-0057-79
Propanoic acid, 2-(3-acridinylhydrazono)-, ethyl ester, anti	EtOH	223(4.32),241(4.54), 322(4.54),383(3.69)	103-0894-79
syn	EtOH	222(4.22),243(4.56), 350(4.54)	103-0894-79
$C_{18}H_{17}N_3O_2S$			
Carbamic acid, [3-[(phenylamino)thioxomethyl]-1H-indol-2-yl]-, ethyl ester	$CHCl_3$	267(4.28),287(4.29), 355(4.21)	103-0179-79
Carbamic acid, [3-[(methylamino)thioxomethyl]-1H-indol-2-yl]-, phenylmethyl ester	$CHCl_3$	260(4.32),285(4.28), 343(4.09)	103-0179-79
$C_{18}H_{17}N_3O_3$			
Carbamic acid, [3-[(phenylamino)carbonyl]-1H-indol-2-yl]-, ethyl ester	$CHCl_3$	283(4.34),304(4.36), 312s(4.34),352s(2.08)	103-0179-79
1-Imidazolidinecarboxamide, 5,5-dimethyl-2,4-dioxo-N,3-diphenyl-	MeCN	244.5(4.28)	33-1429-79
$C_{18}H_{17}N_3O_4$			
2,5-Cyclohexadien-1-one, 4-[(1,3-dihydro-1,3-dimethyl-5-nitro-2H-benzimidazolylidene)ethylidene]-2-methoxy-	EtOH	285(4.05),345(4.05)	42-0871-79
	benzene-10% EtOH	254(4.75),522(3.47)	42-0871-79
	$CHCl_3$-10% EtOH	285(4.24),350(4.27), 522(3.47)	42-0871-79
$C_{18}H_{17}N_3O_4S$			
Benzoic acid, 4-[[[(6-methoxy-2-benzothiazolyl)amino]carbonyl]amino]-, ethyl ester	n.s.g.	243(4.13),298(4.60)	87-0028-79
$C_{18}H_{17}N_3O_5$			
D-Arabinitol, 1,4-anhydro-1-C-1,2,4-triazolo[4,3-a]pyridin-3-yl-, 5-benzoate, (R)-	EtOH	263(4.05),266(4.08), 280(4.01)	111-0375-79
Phenol, 2,2'-[(hydroxyimino)bis[4,5-dihydro-5,3-isoxazolediyl]]bis-	EtOH	214(4.58),261(4.44), 270(4.30),305(4.08)	56-0229-79
$C_{18}H_{17}N_5O_2$			
Benzoic acid, 2-[[5-methyl-4-(phenylazo)-1H-pyrazol-3-yl]amino]-, methyl ester	EtOH	232(4.41),333(4.05)	48-0127-79
$C_{18}H_{17}N_5O_6$			
L-threo-2,3-Hexodiulosonic acid, γ-lactone, 3-[(4-nitrophenyl)hydrazone] 2-(phenylhydrazone)	n.s.g.	247(4.09),352(4.34), 460(4.36)	106-0531-79
1H-Pyrazole-4,5-dione, 1-(4-nitrophenyl)-3-(1,2,3-trihydroxypropyl)-, 4-(phenylhydrazone)	n.s.g.	227(4.04),400(4.32)	106-0531-79

Compound	Solvent	λ_{max}(log ε)	Ref.
$C_{18}H_{18}$			
Anthracene, 9-(1,1-dimethylethyl)-	CCl_4	340(3.38),358(3.68), 376(3.83),395(3.76)	78-2131-79
Anthracene, 9-(2-methylpropyl)-	CCl_4	336(3.45),352(3.78), 370(3.98),385(3.95)	78-2131-79
Benzene, 1,2-di-1-hexen-5-ynyl-	EtOH	234(4.39),260(4.26)	24-3895-79
$C_{18}H_{18}ClNO$			
Methanone, (2-amino-5-chlorophenyl)-(6,7,8,9-tetrahydro-5H-benzocyclohepten-2-yl)-	MeOH	233(4.41),263(3.89), 388(3.83)	73-3604-79
$C_{18}H_{18}ClNO_4$			
Butanoic acid, 4-[4-chloro-N-(4-methoxyphenyl)benzamido]-	n.s.g.	230(4.25)	145-0001-79
$C_{18}H_{18}F_3N_3O_7$			
1-Oxa-1-dethiaceph-3-em-4-carboxylic acid, 7-(D-α-phenylglycylamino)-3-methyl-, trifluoroacetate, (6R,7S)-	EtOH	260(3.85)	39-2268-79C
$C_{18}H_{18}N$			
Quinolinium, 4,6-dimethyl-1-(phenylmethyl)-, bromide	EtOH	241(4.60),317(3.85)	103-1208-79
chloride	EtOH	242(4.80),320(4.16)	103-1208-79
iodide	EtOH	240(4.85),318(4.05)	103-1208-79
perchlorate	EtOH	241(4.72),318(4.02)	103-1208-79
$C_{18}H_{18}NO$			
Quinolinium, 1-(4-ethoxyphenyl)-2-methyl-, perchlorate	EtOH	238(4.65),318(4.27)	104-1160-79
Quinolinium, 6-methoxy-4-methyl-1-(phenylmethyl)-, bromide	EtOH	251(4.70),318(4.90)	103-1208-79
iodide	EtOH	251(4.70),312(4.02)	103-1208-79
perchlorate	EtOH	252(4.68),315(4.02)	103-1208-79
$C_{18}H_{18}NO_2S$			
Benzothiazolium, 2-[2-(2,5-dimethoxyphenyl)ethenyl]-3-methyl-, iodide	DMF	358(4.25),438(4.23)	126-1441-79
perchlorate	DMF	354(4.19),437(4.18)	126-1441-79
$C_{18}H_{18}N_2$			
2-Naphthaleneacetonitrile, α-(1-piperidinylmethylene)-	MeOH	214(4.56),263(4.18), 324(4.36)	83-0039-79
3H-Pyrazole, 3,3-dimethyl-5-(4-methylphenyl)-4-phenyl-	MeOH	240(4.23),305(3.69)	23-1403-79
2H-Pyrrol-5-amine, 2,2-dimethyl-3,4-diphenyl-	EtOH	252(4.28)	78-2285-79
$C_{18}H_{18}N_2O$			
Diazene, bis(2-cyclopropylphenyl)-, 1-oxide	EtOH	239(3.53),310(3.34)	104-0847-79
1H-Pyrazole, 3-(4-methoxyphenyl)-1,5-dimethyl-4-phenyl-	hexane	245(4.29),257s(4.25)	23-1186-79
	EtOH	242(4.16),255s(4.12)	23-1186-79
1H-Pyrazole, 5-(4-methoxyphenyl)-1,3-dimethyl-4-phenyl-	hexane	243(4.29),260s(4.12)	23-1186-79
	EtOH	239(4.33),255s(4.06)	23-1186-79
4H-Pyrazole, 3-(4-methoxyphenyl)-4,5-dimethyl-4-phenyl-	hexane	296(4.28)	23-1186-79
	EtOH	307(4.31)	23-1186-79
Pyrrolo[2,3-b]indol-2(1H)-one, 3,3a,8-8a-tetrahydro-3a-methyl-8-(phenylmethyl)-	MeOH	251(4.04),302(3.45)	5-0927-79

Compound	Solvent	$\lambda_{max}(\log \epsilon)$	Ref.
4(1H)-Quinolinone, 2,3-dihydro-1-methyl-3-[(methylphenylamino)methylene]-	EtOH	251(4.60),293(3.78), 330(4.07),342(4.05)	4-0177-79
$C_{18}H_{18}N_2OS$			
2(1H)-Pyrimidinethione, 3,4-dihydro-6-(4-methoxyphenyl)-4-(4-methylphenyl)-	EtOH	250(4.40),264s(4.32)	23-2734-79
	$CHCl_3$	251(4.37),273(4.31)	23-2734-79
	CCl_4	285(4.24)	23-2734-79
$C_{18}H_{18}N_2O_2$			
9,10-Anthracenedione, 1-amino-4-(butylamino)-	benzene	582(3.86),625(3.85)	153-0033-79
$C_{18}H_{18}N_2O_2S$			
2(1H)-Pyrimidinethione, 3,4-dihydro-4,6-bis(4-methoxyphenyl)-	EtOH	253(4.40),266s(4.31)	23-2734-79
	$CHCl_3$	253(4.30),274(4.25)	23-2734-79
	CCl_4	282(4.21)	23-2734-79
$C_{18}H_{18}N_2O_3$			
9,10-Anthracenedione, 1-[[2-(dimethylamino)ethyl]amino]-4-hydroxy-	EtOH	248(4.37),548(3.89), 591(3.85)	87-0501-79
Isoquinoline, 1,2,3,4-tetrahydro-6,7-dimethoxy-1-methylene-2-(3-pyridinylcarbonyl)-	MeOH	231s(4.27),265(4.23), 303(3.90),315s(3.78)	4-0433-79
1-Propanone, 1,1'-(azoxydi-2,1-phenylene)bis-	EtOH	323(3.81)	104-0847-79
4(3H)-Quinazolinone, 3-[2-(3,4-dihydroxyphenyl)ethyl]-2,6-dimethyl-, hydrochloride	MeOH	280(4.10),313(3.53), 324(3.30)	4-0449-79
4(3H)-Quinazolinone, 3-[2-(3,4-dihydroxyphenyl)ethyl]-2,8-dimethyl-, hydrochloride	MeOH	282(4.02),310(3.58), 324(3.45)	4-0449-79
$C_{18}H_{18}N_2O_3S_2$			
Acetamide, N-[4-methoxy-2-[(6-methoxy-2-methyl-7-benzothiazolyl)thio]phenyl]-	MeOH	246(4.30),297(3.78), 308(3.70)	39-1478-79C
$C_{18}H_{18}N_2O_4$			
9,10-Anthracenedione, 1-hydroxy-4-[[2-(2-hydroxyethyl)amino]ethyl]amino]-	EtOH	252(4.42),276(4.19), 545(3.95),578(4.12), 635(4.08)	87-0501-79
2,5-Pyrazinedione, 3,6-dihydroxy-3,6-bis(phenylmethyl)-	EtOH	287(3.40)	39-1885-79C
$C_{18}H_{18}N_2O_4S$			
2-Thiazolin-5-one, 4-[N-acetyl-N-(1-benzyloxycarbonyl-2-methyl-1-propenyl)aminomethylene]-	EtOH	225s(--),272(3.92), 340(4.17)	39-2455-79C
3-Thiophenecarboxylic acid, 2-[(1-acetyl-2-oxopropylidene)hydrazino]-5-phenyl-	MeOH	268(4.22),300s(3.94), 435(4.26)	83-0726-79
$C_{18}H_{18}N_2O_5$			
Benzoic acid, 3,3'-azoxybis-, diethyl ester	heptane	321.7(4.20)	18-1588-79
Benzoic acid, 4,4'-azoxybis-, diethyl ester	heptane	335.5(4.35)	18-1588-79
$C_{18}H_{18}N_2O_7$			
1-Azabicyclo[4.2.0]oct-2-ene-2,4-dicarboxylic acid, 3-methyl-8-oxo-7-[(phen-	EtOH	268(3.71)	23-0222-79

Compound	Solvent	λmax(log ε)	Ref.
oxyacetyl)amino]-, [4R-(4α,6β,7α)]-			23-0222-79
$C_{18}H_{18}N_2O_8$			
2,6-Pyridinedicarboxylic acid, 4-[[[1-carboxy-2-(3,4-dihydroxypehnyl)ethyl)imino]ethylidene]-1,2,3,4-tetrahydro-, (E,E)- (dopaxanthin)	n.s.g.	478(4.62)	33-1330-79
$C_{18}H_{18}N_3OS$			
Isoxazolium, 2-ethyl-5-(methylthio)-3-phenyl-4-(phenylazo)-, tetrafluoroborate	HOAc	263(4.12),289(4.13), 297(4.13),339(4.15), 349s(4.14),370s(4.03), 483s(3.10)	97-0446-79
$C_{18}H_{18}N_3O_4$			
1H-Benzimidazolium, 2-[2-(4-hydroxy-3-methoxyphenyl)ethenyl]-1,3-dimethyl-5-nitro-, (±)-	EtOH-acid	251(4.15),382(4.59)	42-0871-79
	EtOH-base	400(4.40)	42-0871-79
$C_{18}H_{18}N_4$			
Ethanone, 1-[5-(4-methylphenyl)-1H-pyrazol-3-yl]-2-phenyl-	MeOH	257(4.43)	4-0737-79
2-Propenimidamide, 2-cyano-N-(2-methylphenyl)-3-[(2-methylphenyl)amino]-	EtOH	333(4.35)	24-0484-79
	MeCN	335(4.36)	24-0484-79
$C_{18}H_{18}N_4O$			
8-Azabicyclo[3.2.1]oct-3-en-2-one, 8-(4,6-dimethyl-2-pyrimidinyl)-6-(2-pyridinyl)-, endo	$CHCl_3$	256(4.20),293(3.56)	39-1525-79C
exo	$CHCl_3$	250(4.28),293(3.63)	39-1525-79C
8-Azabicyclo[3.2.1]oct-3-en-2-one, 8-(4,6-dimethyl-2-pyrimidinyl)-6-(4-pyridinyl)-, endo	$CHCl_3$	254(4.20),290(3.59)	39-1525-79C
Ethanone, 1-[5-(4-methoxyphenyl)-1H-pyrazol-3-yl]-2-phenyl-	MeOH	265(4.44)	4-0737-79
$C_{18}H_{18}N_4O_2$			
2-Propenimidamide, 2-cyano-N-(2-methoxyphenyl)-3-(2-methoxyphenyl)amino]-	EtOH	348(4.34)	24-0484-79
	$CHCl_3$	352(4.34)	24-0484-79
	MeCN	348(4.36)	24-0484-79
$C_{18}H_{18}N_4O_3S$			
3-Thiophenecarboxylic acid, 2-[(1,5-dihydro-1,3-dimethyl-5-oxo-4H-pyrazol-4-ylidene)hydrazino]-5-phenyl-, ethyl ester	MeOH	278(4.21),310s(4.01), 475(4.34)	83-0726-79
$C_{18}H_{18}N_4O_4$			
1H-Benz[f]indazole-3-carboxamide, 4,9-dihydro-4-imino-9-oxo-1-[tetrahydro-6-(hydroxymethyl)-2H-pyran-2-yl]-, cis-(±)- (or isomer)	EtOH	247(4.34),273(4.07)	111-0151-79
trans	EtOH	249(4.58),267(4.19)	111-0151-79
D-erythro-2,3-Hexodiulosonic acid, γ-lactone, 2,3-bis(phenylhydrazone)	EtOH	208(4.00),261(4.11), 352(4.25),442(4.20)	136-0087-79A
L-threo-2,3-Hexodiulosonic acid, γ-lactone, 2,3-bis(phenylhydrazone)	MeOH	462(4.27)	39-0603-79C
after mutarotation	MeOH	444(4.31)	39-0603-79C
1H-Pyrazole-4,5-dione, 1-phenyl-3-(1,2,3-trihydroxypropyl)-, 4-(phenylhydrazone), [S-(R*,R*)]-	EtOH	208(4.21),252(4.41), 402(4.31)	136-0087-79A

Compound	Solvent	λ_{max}(log ε)	Ref.
$C_{18}H_{18}N_4O_5$			
D-Arabinitol, 1-C-(6-amino-[1,2,4]triazolo[1,5-a]pyridin-2-yl)-1,4-anhydro-, 5-benzoate, (R)-	EtOH	233(4.51),305(3.49)	111-0375-79
D-Arabinitol, 1-C-(8-amino-[1,2,4]triazolo[1,5-a]pyridin-2-yl)-1,4-anhydro-, 5-benzoate, (R)-	EtOH	278(4.11),295(3.99)	111-0375-79
$C_{18}H_{18}N_8O_6$			
DL-Aspartic acid, N-[4-[[(2-amino-3,4-dihydro-4-oxo-6-pteridinyl)methyl]-amino]phenylcarbamoyl]-	pH 1	243(4.38),280s(3.62), 319(3.83),360s(2.77)	87-0874-79
	pH 13	255(4.51),366(3.96)	87-0874-79
$C_{18}H_{18}O$			
B-Norestra-1,3,5(10),8,14-pentaen-17-one, 6-methyl-	MeOH	212(4.03),227(4.02), 234(4.08),242(3.97), 299(4.39),302(4.39)	2-0324-79A
$C_{18}H_{18}O_2$			
Bicyclo[6.1.0]nona-2,4,6-triene-9-methanol, α-phenyl-, acetate	MeCN	210(4.12),246(3.66)	33-0718-79
1,3,5-Cycloheptatrien-1-ol, 7-(3a,7a-dihydro-1H-inden-1-yl)-, acetate	hexane	258s(3.80),264(3.85), 272s(3.83),283s(3.69)	33-0718-79
5,9-Epoxy-5H-benzocyclohepten-5-ol, 6,7,8,9-tetrahydro-9-(phenylmethyl)-	hexane	257(2.81),262(2.91), 269(2.87)	56-1751-79
3(2H)-Furanone, dihydro-2,2-dimethyl-5,5-diphenyl-	C_6H_{12}	249s(2.47),253(2.46), 259(2.65),264(2.65), 268s(2.40),289(1.59), 298(1.65),309(1.61), 320(1.32)	19-0665-79
	EtOH	248(2.51),253(2.59), 258(2.65),348(2.54), 262(4.20),288s(1.65), 296(1.71),306(1.66), 318s(1.36)	19-0665-79
	50% EtOH	253(2.65),258(2.70), 264(2.62),267s(2.51), 290(2.11)	19-0665-79
	40% EtOH	252(3.08),258(3.06), 263s(2.95),267s(2.87), 290(2.62)	19-0665-79
1H-Indene-1-methanol, 3a,7a-dihydro-α-phenyl-, acetate	MeCN	254s(3.58),263(3.62), 273s(3.51),284s(3.20)	33-0718-79
1H-Inden-1-one, 2,3-dihydro-2-[(4-methoxyphenyl)methyl]-3-methyl-	EtOH	225(4.16),246(4.13), 279s(3.62),286(3.63), 292s(3.50)	78-1167-79
5,12-Naphthacenedione, 5a,6,7,8,9,10-11,11a-octahydro-	EtOH	223(4.52),250(4.06), 305(3.30)	94-2229-79
1(2H)-Naphthalenone, 3,4-dihydro-3-(4-methoxyphenyl)-	EtOH	248(4.12),278(3.56), 285(3.58),295s(3.48)	78-1167-79
$C_{18}H_{18}O_2S_4$			
Carbonodithioic acid, O,O'-(1,2-diphenyl-1,2-ethanediyl) S,S'-dimethyl ester, (±)-	n.s.g.	280(4.29)	39-2378-79C
meso-	n.s.g.	280(4.34)	39-2378-79C
$C_{18}H_{18}O_3$			
1,4-Epoxyanthracene, 1,2,3,4,9,10-hexahydro-5,8-dimethoxy-2,3-bis(methylene)-	dioxan	228(4.34),255s(3.88), 285(3.75),291s(3.72)	88-4533-79

Compound	Solvent	λ_{max}(log ε)	Ref.
5,12-Naphthacenedione, 5a,6,7,8,9,10-11,11a-octahydro-1-hydroxy-	EtOH	210(4.15),228(4.25), 264(3.83),347(3.64)	94-2229-79
1(2H)-Naphthalenone, 3-(3,4-dimethoxyphenyl)-3,4-dihydro-	EtOH	245(4.11),283(3.71), 294s(3.51)	78-1167-79
$C_{18}H_{18}O_4$			
2-Buten-1-one, 1-(2-hydroxy-4-methoxyphenyl)-3-(4-methoxyphenyl)-	EtOH	354(4.78)	78-0531-79
[2.2]Metaparacyclophanequinhydrone, di-O-methyl-	$CHCl_3$	490(2.77)	88-2513-79
isomer 2	$CHCl_3$	420(2.90)	88-2513-79
Perbenzoic acid, 4-benzoyl-, 1,1-dimethylethyl ester	CCl_4	347(2.4)	44-4123-79
Tricyclo[11.3.1.1^{5,9}]octadeca-1(17),5-8,13,15-pentaene-7,18-dione, 15,17-dihydroxy-	dioxan	275(4.0),446(3.40)	138-0541-79
$C_{18}H_{18}O_5$			
4H-1-Benzopyran-4-one, 2,3-dihydro-2-(3,4,5-trimethoxyphenyl)-	EtOH	223(4.35),250(4.05), 320(3.52)	56-1033-79
1,6-Naphthalenedicarboxylic acid, 3-acetyl-4,7-dimethyl-, dimethyl ester	EtOH	240(4.47),260(4.69), 310(3.75)	39-0464-79C
2-Propen-1-one, 3-(3,4-dimethoxyphenyl)-1-(2-hydroxy-4-methoxyphenyl)-	EtOH	221(4.36),269(4.03), 360(4.39)	78-2061-79
$C_{18}H_{18}O_5S$			
Secrolin	EtOH	217s(4.22),263s(4.15), 278(4.27),328(4.07)	105-0635-79
$C_{18}H_{18}O_6$			
4H-1-Benzopyran-4-one, 2,3-dihydro-3-(2-hydroxy-3,4-dimethoxyphenyl)-	EtOH	235s(4.23),309(4.11), 370(3.93)	102-0815-79
7-methoxy-, (±)-	EtOH-NaOH	231(4.38),305(4.07), 365s(3.93)	102-0815-79
4H-1-Benzopyran-4-one, 2,3-dihydro-	EtOH	275(4.05),317s(3.83)	102-0815-79
3-(3-hydroxy-2,4-dimethoxyphenyl)-7-methoxy-, (±)-	EtOH-NaOH	235(4.00),275(3.95), 319s(3.67)	102-0815-79
2-Naphthalenecarboxylic acid, 3,4-diacetoxy-5,8-dimethyl-, methyl ester	EtOH	220(4.83),250(5.08), 285(4.10),295(4.16), 305(4.07)	39-0237-79C
1H-Naphtho[2,3-c]pyran-1-one, 9-acetoxy-3,4-dihydro-7,10-dimethoxy-3-methyl-	MeOH	235(4.73),294(3.88)	24-0957-79
1H-Phenalen-1-one, 4-ethoxy-3,9-dihydroxy-7,8-dimethoxy-6-methyl-	EtOH	214(4.67),227s(4.43), 240s(4.34),253s(4.26), 271s(4.00),279s(3.90), 365(4.23),404(4.14)	150-0301-79
$C_{18}H_{18}O_8$			
Fusarubin, 5-acetoxy-8-methoxy-	n.s.g.	218(4.38),269(4.10), 285s(3.86),415(3.52)	78-1551-79
Spiro[anthracene-2(1H),2'-[1,3]dioxolane]-9,10-dione, 8-acetoxy-3,4,4a,9a-tetrahydro-4,5-dihydroxy-	MeOH	227(4.35),244s(--), 360(3.79)	24-3453-79
$C_{18}H_{18}S_3$			
4-Thiahepta-1,6-diyne trimer	EtOH	243.5(4.09)	44-2667-79

Compound	Solvent	λ_{max}(log ε)	Ref.
$C_{18}H_{19}$			
Cycloheptatrienylium, (4-cyclopropyl-3,5-dimethylphenyl)-, perchlorate	10% HCl	230(4.48),277(3.91), 408(4.21)	39-0262-79B
$C_{18}H_{19}BrN_2O_2S$			
Benzenesulfonamide, N-(5-bromo-1,3-dihydro-1,3,3-trimethyl-2H-indol-2-ylidene)-4-methyl-	EtOH	222(4.60),290(4.57), 300s(4.42)	39-2154-79C
$C_{18}H_{19}BrN_2O_3$			
Hydrazinecarboxylic acid, 2-[3-(4-bromophenyl)-3-oxo-1-phenylpropyl]-, ethyl ester	EtOH	230(4.30),253(4.40)	94-0257-79
$C_{18}H_{19}BrN_2O_6S_2$			
Acetic acid, [(4-bromophenyl)azo]-[[(4-methylphenyl)sulfonyl](methylsulfonyl)-, ethyl ester	EtOH	315(4.11)	104-0919-79
$C_{18}H_{19}ClN_2O$			
Methanone, (2-amino-5-chlorophenyl)-(6,7,8,9-tetrahydro-5H-benzocyclohepten-2-yl)-, oxime	MeOH	245(4.33),265s(4.16), 313s(3.77)	73-3604-79
$C_{18}H_{19}ClN_2OS$			
Dibenzo[b,f]thiepin, 2-chloro-10,11-dihydro-10-piperazino-, S-oxide, dimethanesulfonate	MeOH	250s(3.87)	73-3008-79
$C_{18}H_{19}ClN_2O_6S_2$			
Acetic acid, [(2-chlorophenyl)azo]-[(4-methylphenyl)sulfonyl](methylsulfonyl)-, ethyl ester	EtOH	295(4.06)	104-0919-79
$C_{18}H_{19}ClN_2O_7$			
2H-Pyrrole-2,2-dicarboxylic acid, 1-acetyl-4-(4-chloro-2-nitrophenyl)-1,3-dihydro-, diethyl ester	isoPrOH	215(4.25),268(4.12), 285s(4.09),349(3.46)	44-3748-79
$C_{18}H_{19}Cl_4N_2O_8P$			
3'-Thymidylic acid, 2-chlorophenyl 2,2,2-trichloroethyl ester	MeOH	264(4.01)	54-0537-79
$C_{18}H_{19}F_3N_2O_4$			
2-Cyclohexen-1-one, 2-(3,4-dihydro-4-quinazolinyl)-3-hydroxy-5,5-dimethyl-, hydrotrifluoroacetate	EtOH	260(4.25)	24-1348-79
$C_{18}H_{19}NO$			
9-Acridineacetaldehyde, 9,10-dihydro-α,α,10-trimethyl-	EtOH	282(4.15)	103-0541-79
1H-Phenanthro[9,10-b]azirine-1-propanol, 1a,9b-dihydro-α-methyl-	$CHCl_3$	242(3.90),272s(4.16), 278(4.18),293s(3.91), 305(3.55)	78-2901-79
2H-Pyrrole-5-ethanol, 3,4-dihydro-α,α-diphenyl-	MeOH	205(4.31),253(3.54)	83-0498-79
$C_{18}H_{19}NO_2$			
Benzo[d]carbazol-6(7H)-one, 8-acetyl-1,2,3,4,7a,8-hexahydro-	MeOH	238(4.21)	5-1048-79

Compound	Solvent	λ_{max}(log ε)	Ref.
9H-Carbazole-2-carboxylic acid, 4-(2-methylpropyl)-, methyl ester	EtOH	225(4.31),253(4.81), 307(4.48),352(3.73), 361(3.73)	44-4402-79
1H-Indole-3-acetic acid, 2,3-dihydro-3-methyl-1-(phenylmethyl)-	MeOH	254(4.42),301(3.80)	5-0927-79
Isoquinoline, 3,4-dihydro-6,7-dimethoxy-3-(phenylmethyl)-	MeOH	238(4.23),311(4.07), 367(3.89)	83-0273-79
Isoquinoline, 3-(3,4-dimethoxyphenyl)-1,2-dihydro-2-methyl-	EtOH	205(4.49),280(3.98), 349(4.18)	78-1861-79
2H-Pyrrol-4-ol, 3,4-dihydro-2,2-dimethyl-4,5-diphenyl-, 1-oxide	EtOH	212(4.08),290(4.08)	12-2025-79
$C_{18}H_{19}NO_2S$			
Benzenepropanoic acid, α-[[(4-methylphenyl)thio]imino]-, ethyl ester	hexane	230(4.08),337(3.94)	44-1218-79
$C_{18}H_{19}NO_3$			
Aegeline	EtOH	224(4.36),277(4.72)	2-0385B-79A
Benzo[f]pyrrolo[1,2-b]isoquinolin-12(7H)-one, 9,10,11,11a-tetrahydro-2,3-dimethoxy-, (S)-	MeOH	222(4.68),350(3.97)	5-1212-79
Crotsparine, N-methyl-	MeOH	205(4.54),232(4.43), 288(3.55)	100-0399-79
	MeOH-base	240(--),310(--)	100-0399-79
1,7-Cycloerythrinan-8-one, 2,3-didehydro-15,16-dimethoxy-, (±)-	MeOH	204(4.79),233s(4.00), 284(3.66)	24-1110-79
Isopiline	EtOH	220(4.39),275(4.15), 292s(3.91),310(3.78)	100-0325-79
5a,9-Methano-5aH-cyclooct[b]indol-10(5H)-one, 5-acetyl-6,7,8,9-tetrahydro-8-hydroxy-8-methyl-	EtOH	206(4.17),250(4.28), 298(4.06),435(3.88)	103-0696-79
Pachyconfine	EtOH	227(4.29),274(4.18), 307(3.65)	100-0325-79
$C_{18}H_{19}NO_3S$			
Acetic acid, (9-methyl-3-oxothiazolo-[3,2-a]indol-2(3H)-ylidene)-, 2,2-dimethylpropyl ester, (Z)-	$CHCl_3$	287(4.42),435(3.84)	44-3994-79
2-Propenoic acid, 2-[(4-methylphenyl)-sulfinyl]amino]-3-phenyl-, ethyl ester	CH_2Cl_2	305(4.19)	44-1218-79
$C_{18}H_{19}NO_4$			
2H-Azepine-4-carboxylic acid, 6-ethyl-3-methoxy-2-oxo-7-phenyl-, ethyl ester	dioxan	220(4.09),262(4.11), 345s(3.52)	142-1427-79
Ethanone, 1-[1,3-dihydro-1-methoxy-6-methyl-7-(phenylmethoxy)furo[3,4-c]-pyridin-4-yl]-	MeOH	260(3.92),294(4.05)	88-2603-79
$C_{18}H_{19}NO_5$			
2H-Azepine-4-carboxylic acid, 6-ethoxy-3-methoxy-2-oxo-7-phenyl-, ethyl ester	dioxan	260(4.13),360(3.53)	142-1427-79
2H-Azepine-6-carboxylic acid, 4-ethoxy-3-methoxy-2-oxo-7-phenyl-, ethyl ester	dioxan	254(4.15),290s(3.95), 357(3.81)	142-1427-79
1H-Benzo[a]furo[3,4-f]quinolizine-1,12(3H)-dione, 5,6,10b,11-tetrahydro-8,9-dimethoxy-3-methyl-	MeOH	237(4.36),292(4.27)	104-1247-79

Compound	Solvent	$\lambda_{max}(\log \epsilon)$	Ref.
4H-1-Benzopyran-4-one, 2,3-dihydro-2-(3,4,5-trimethoxyphenyl)-, oxime	EtOH	225(4.40),250(4.09), 304(3.71),315(3.61)	56-1033-79
Erythrinan-1,8-dione, 2,3-didehydro-2,3-didehydro-7β-hydroxy-15,16-dimethoxy-, (±)-	MeOH	211(4.31),211s(4.25), 273s(3.79),285s(3.69)	24-1329-79
Erythrinan-3,8-dione, 1,2-didehydro-7β-hydroxy-15,16-dimethoxy-, (±)-	MeOH	211(4.32),230s(4.12), 288(3.42)	24-1329-79
β-L-threo-Pentofuranose, 3,5-dideoxy-5-(2,5-dioxo-1-phenyl-3-pyrrolidinylidene)-1,2-O-(1-methylethylidene)-, (E)-	EtOH	227(4.16)	33-0977-79
2-Propen-1-one, 1-(2-hydroxyphenyl)-3-(3,4,5-trimethoxyphenyl)-, oxime, (E,E)-	EtOH	238(4.24),311(4.33)	56-1033-79
L-Serine, N-[(phenylmethoxy)carbonyl]-O-(phenylmethyl)-	EtOH	248(2.37),253(2.51), 258(2.63),263(2.51), 264(2.55),268(2.35)	118-0957-79
$C_{18}H_{19}NO_5S$			
Formamide, N-[2-(3,4-dimethoxyphenyl)-1-[(4-methylphenyl)sulfonyl]ethenyl]-, (E)-	EtOH	235(4.34),295(4.26), 324(4.40)	39-0652-79C
4-Thia-1-azabicyclo[3.2.0]heptane-2-carboxylic acid, 6-(2-methoxy-2-oxoethylidene)-3,3-dimethyl-7-oxo-, phenylmethyl ester, (2S-cis)-	isooctane	218.5(4.15)	39-2455-79C
$C_{18}H_{19}NO_6$			
1H-Azepine-4-carboxylic acid, 6-acetoxy-2,5-dihydro-3-methoxy-2-oxo-7-phenyl-, ethyl ester	dioxan	222(4.15),253(4.13)	142-1427-79
$C_{18}H_{19}NO_7$			
3-Pyridinecarboxylic acid, 4-[[2,6-dimethoxy-4-(methoxycarbonyl)phenoxy]-methyl]-, methyl ester	EtOH	215(4.63),267(4.19), 292(3.64)	39-2982-79C
$C_{18}H_{19}NS$			
Benzothiazole, 2-ethyl-6-(2,4,6-trimethylphenyl)-	EtOH	215s(3.87),258(4.21), 294s(3.35)	33-0021-79
	$CHCl_3$	260(4.15),296s(3.33)	33-0021-79
$C_{18}H_{19}N_2$			
1H-Pyrazolium, 1,2,3-trimethyl-4,5-diphenyl-, iodide	EtOH	215(4.18),255s(3.60)	23-1186-79
4H-Pyrazolium, 1,4,5-trimethyl-3,4-diphenyl-, iodide	EtOH	219(4.36),299(3.99)	23-1186-79
$C_{18}H_{19}N_3O$			
Benzeneacetamide, N-(4,5-dihydro-1-methyl-1H-pyrazol-3-yl)-α-phenyl-	EtOH	266(3.99)	150-0801-79
3(2H)-Pyridazinone, 4,5-dihydro-4-(1H-pyrrol-1-yl)-6-(1,2,3,4-tetrahydro-2-naphthalenyl)-	EtOH	276(4.24)	80-0453-79
Pyrrolo[2,3-b]indol-2(1H)-one, 3,3a,8-8a-tetrahydro-3a,8-dimethyl-1-(phenylamino)-	MeOH	238(4.13),250s(4.11)	5-0927-79
$C_{18}H_{19}N_3O_7$			
Cytidine, N-benzoyl-4'-C-(hydroxymethyl)-2',3'-O-methylene-	MeOH	258(4.39),303(4.03)	44-1309-79

Compound	Solvent	λ_{max}(log ε)	Ref.
$C_{18}H_{19}N_3O_8S_2$			
Acetic acid, [(4-methylphenyl)sulfonyl](methylsulfonyl)[(3-nitrophenyl)azo]-, ethyl ester	EtOH	310(3.89)	104-0919-79
Acetic acid, [(4-methylphenyl)sulfonyl](methylsulfonyl)[(4-nitrophenyl)azo]-, ethyl ester	EtOH	290(4.16),360(4.05)	104-0919-79
$C_{18}H_{19}N_4O$			
2,10-Methano-1H-pyrido[2,3-b]indolizin-5-ium, 1-(4,6-dimethyl-2-pyrimidinyl)-2,3,4,4a,10,10a-hexahydro-3-oxo-, chloride	$CHCl_3$	246(4.27),270(4.11)	39-1525-79C
$C_{18}H_{19}N_5O$			
1H-Azepine-2,3,4(5H)-trione, dihydro-, 3,4-bis(phenylhydrazone)	EtOH	277(4.30),400(4.20)	103-0780-79
$C_{18}H_{19}N_5O_9$			
3-Pyrrolidinemethanol, 1-acetyl-2-(3-pyridinyl)-, picrate	EtOH	260s(3.33),265(3.38), 271s(3.25)	44-4332-79
hemisuccinate	EtOH	259s(3.38),265(3.42), 270s(3.30)	44-4332-79
$C_{18}H_{19}N_6$			
1H-Indazolium, 5-cyano-3-[[(4-dimethylamino)phenyl]azo]-1,2-dimethyl-, iodide	EtOH	579(4.76)	103-1231-79
$C_{18}H_{19}OS$			
Thiophenium, 1-(2-[1,1'-biphenyl]-4-yl-2-oxoethyl)tetrahydro-, tetrafluoroborate	MeOH	259(4.06),288(4.06), 296(3.63),360(3.28)	47-2877-79
$C_{18}H_{20}$			
Cyclopropane, 1-ethyl-3-methyl-1,2-diphenyl-, cis	EtOH or CCl_4	225(4.13),260(2.88), 266(2.85),276(2.59)	104-0080-79
trans	EtOH or CCl_4	223(4.34),254(2.86), 260(2.90),266(2.86), 275(2.51)	104-0080-79
Cyclopropane, 1-methyl-1,2-bis(4-methylphenyl)- (isomeric mixture)	EtOH or CCl_4	226(4.03),265(3.21), 274(3.14),281(2.90)	104-0080-79
$C_{18}H_{20}ClN_5O_3$			
[1,2,4]Triazino[4,3-d][1,4]benzodiazepine-3,4,7(6H)-trione, 11-chloro-2,8-dihydro-8-methyl-2-[2-(1-pyrrolidinyl)ethyl]-, hydrochloride	H_2O	253(4.18),273(4.09), 305(3.96)	44-0084-79
$C_{18}H_{20}Cl_2N_2O_4$			
[2.2](2,6)Pyridinophane, 2,9-dichloro-1,1,10,10-tetramethoxy-	90% EtOH	246(3.48),273(3.51)	12-1241-79
$C_{18}H_{20}F_2O_5$			
Spiro[azuleno[6,5-b]furan-3(2H),1'-cyclopropane]-2,5(3aH)-dione, 4-acetoxy-2',2'-difluoro-4,4a,6,8,9,9a-hexahydro-4a,8-dimethyl-, [3R-(3α,3aα,4α-4aβ,8α,9aα)]-	EtOH	211(3.07)	78-0815-79
Spiro[azuleno[6,5-b]furan-3(2H),1'-cyclopropane]-2,5(3aH)-dione, 4-acet-	EtOH	238(3.53)	78-0815-79

Compound	Solvent	λ max(log ε)	Ref.
oxy-2',2'-difluoro-4,4a,7a,8,9,9a-hexahydro-4a,8-dimethyl-, [3R-(3α,3aα,4α,4aβ,7aα,8α,9aα)]-			78-0815-79
$C_{18}H_{20}NO_2$			
9H-Benzo[f]pyrrolo[1,2-b]isoquinolinium, 10,11,11a,12-tetrahydro-2,3-dimethoxy-, chloride	MeOH	226(4.50),260(4.36), 269(4.40),279(4.45), 365(4.33)	5-1212-79
Isoquinolinium, 3,4-dihydro-6,7-dimethoxy-2-(phenylmethyl)-, iodide	EtOH	250(4.30),312(4.08), 365(4.08)	39-0283-79C
	EtOH-NaOH	282(3.62)	39-0283-79C
$C_{18}H_{20}N_2$			
2-Propanone, 1-phenyl-, (1-methyl-2-phenylethylidenehydrazone)	EtOH	216(4.07),237(3.93), 269(3.12)	103-0501-79
$C_{18}H_{20}N_2O$			
2H-Benz[d]azepin-2-one, 7-amino-4,4-dimethyl-5-phenyl-1,3,4,5-tetrahydro-	EtOH	241(4.05),288(3.20)	4-1525-79
[3,7'-Bi-1H-indol]-2(3H)-one, 4',5',6'-7'-tetrahydro-1,3-dimethyl-, form A	EtOH	253(3.85),279s(3.20)	23-1694-79
form B	EtOH	254(--),280s(--)	23-1694-79
4H-Indol-4-one, 5-[(dimethylamino)methylene]-1,5,6,7-tetrahydro-2-methyl-1-phenyl-	EtOH	256(4.10),353(4.04)	4-0913-79
Pyrano[3,2-c]carbazole-6-carbonitrile, 4a-ethyl-2,3,4,4a,5,6,7,11c-octahydro-	EtOH	272(3.88),280(3.86), 289(3.72)	107-0505-79
Urea, (1a,5a,5b,11a,11b,11c-hexahydro-1H-cyclopropa[c]cyclobuta[1,2-a:3,4-a']dicycloocten-1-yl)-	dioxan	249s(3.32)	89-0312-79
$C_{18}H_{20}N_2O_2$			
3-Pyrrolidinecarboxylic acid, 1-(phenylmethyl)-2-(3-pyridinyl)-, methyl ester, trans	EtOH	242(3.49),263(3.48)	44-4332-79
$C_{18}H_{20}N_2O_4$			
Benzeneacetamide, N-(2-hydroxy-1,1-dimethyl-2-phenylethyl)-4-nitro-	EtOH	272(3.98)	4-1525-79
$C_{18}H_{20}N_2O_5$			
8-Aza-16-oxagona-1,3,5(10),13-tetraen-17-one, 12-(hydroxyimino)-2,3-dimethoxy-15-methyl-	MeOH	235(4.04),294(4.30)	104-1247-79
$C_{18}H_{20}N_2O_5S$			
4-Thia-1-azabicyclo[3.2.0]hept-2-ene-2-carboxylic acid, 7-oxo-3-pentyl-, (4-nitrophenyl)methyl ester	EtOH	270(4.13),310(3.99)	35-6296-79
$C_{18}H_{20}N_2O_7$			
Benzonitrile, 2-[(2,3,5-tri-O-acetyl-β-D-ribofuranosyl)amino]-	MeOH	217(4.50),247(3.97), 318(3.66)	44-0173-79
Benzonitrile, 2-[(2,3,4-tri-O-acetyl-β-D-ribopyranosyl)amino]-	MeOH	218(4.42),247(4.03), 316(3.67)	44-0173-79
$C_{18}H_{20}N_4O$			
Benzenamine, 4,4'-(1,2,4-oxadiazole-3,5-diyl)bis[N,N-dimethyl-	EtOH	333(4.72)	40-0389-79

Compound	Solvent	$\lambda_{max}(\log \epsilon)$	Ref.
$C_{18}H_{20}N_4O_3$			
Ethanone, 1-[5-(diethylamino)-2-[(4-nitrophenyl)azo]phenyl]-	EtOH	488(4.56)	39-1990-79C
	HOAc	546(4.66)	39-1990-79C
$C_{18}H_{20}N_4O_4$			
1,2-Cyclohexanediamine, N,N'-bis(4-nitrophenyl)-, (1R-trans)-	MeOH	231(4.28),303s(3.49), 314s(3.63),392(4.68)	35-5186-79
Uridine, 5'-[(2-amino-1-oxo-3-phenylpropylamino]-2',3'-didehydro-2',3',5'-trideoxy-, (S)-	H_2O	261.5(3.93)	136-0113-79F
$C_{18}H_{20}N_4O_8$			
1(2H)-Pyrimidinepropanoic acid, α-[[(1,1-dimethylethoxy)carbonyl]amino]-3,4-dihydro-2,4-dioxo-, 4-nitrophenyl ester	n.s.g.	266(4.22)	65-0989-79
$C_{18}H_{20}N_4S$			
Benzenamine, 4,4'-(1,2,4-thiadiazole-3,5-diyl)bis[N,N-dimethyl-	EtOH	348(4.63)	40-0389-79
$C_{18}H_{20}N_5O_7P$			
Guanosine, cyclic 3',5'-[(4-methylphenyl)methyl phosphate]	MeOH	256(4.15)	130-0009-79
$C_{18}H_{20}N_6O_3$			
9H-Purine-9-acetic acid, α-(acetylamino)-6-amino-α-(phenylmethyl)-, ethyl ester	MeOH	257(4.18)	44-2019-79
$C_{18}H_{20}N_6O_6$			
2-Propenoic acid, 2-methyl-, 1-[(3,4-dihydro-2,4-dioxo-1(2H)-pyrimidinyl)methyl]-2-(1,2,3,6-tetrahydro-1,3-dimethyl-2,6-dioxo-7H-purin-7-yl)ethyl ester	H_2O	270(4.13)	126-2303-79
$C_{18}H_{20}N_{10}$			
2H-Tetrazolium, 2,5-bis[4-(dimethylamino)phenyl]-3-(1H-tetrazol-5-yl)-, hydroxide, inner salt	M HCl	242(4.38),320s(--), 490(3.34)	104-1793-79
	6M HCl	245(4.36),320s(--)	104-1793-79
	EtOH	265(3.91),327(4.28), 450(3.84)	104-1793-79
$C_{18}H_{20}O$			
B-Norestra-1,3,5(10),8,14-pentaen-17β-ol, 6-methyl-	MeOH	213(4.11),228(4.05), 236(4.03),244(3.95), 302(4.21)	2-0324-79A
$C_{18}H_{20}O_2$			
9H-Benzo[a]fluoren-9-one, 5,6,6a,6b-7,8,11,11a-octahydro-3-methoxy-, (6aα,6bβ,11aβ)-(±)-	MeOH	234(4.36)	44-0958-79
Bicyclo[4.3.1]deca-2,4,7-triene, 9-methoxy-7-(2-methoxyphenyl)-, endo	C_6H_{12}	234(4.15),252s(3.85), 263(3.70),280(3.48)	5-0533-79
1H-Indene-1,4(2H)-dione, hexahydro-3a,7a-dimethyl-2-(phenylmethylene)-, trans	EtOH	294(4.40)	44-3666-79
1-Isobenzofuranol, 3,3-diethyl-1,3-dihydro-1-phenyl-	50% H_2SO_4	344(4.40)	104-1126-79

Compound	Solvent	λmax(log ε)	Ref.
8,14-Seco-B-norestra-1,3,5(10),9(11)-tetraene-14,17-dione, 6-methyl-	MeOH	209(4.38),257(4.31), 294(3.91)	2-0324-79A
$C_{18}H_{20}O_3S$			
Phenanthro[2,1-b]thiophene, 2,4,5,10,11-11a-hexahydro-7-methoxy-, 1,1-dioxide	MeOH	230(4.04),311(4.16)	13-0619-79B
$C_{18}H_{20}O_4$			
Anthra[1,9-de]-1,3-dioxin-7(3aH)-one, 6,6a,11b,11c-tetrahydro-8-hydroxy-2,2,11b-trimethyl-	MeOH	217(4.26),256(3.91), 333(3.64)	35-0689-79
1,2-Azulenedicarboxylic acid, 4-methyl-7-(1-methylethyl)-, dimethyl ester	hexane	205(4.22),218s(4.19), 244(4.40),297(4.62), 308s(4.51),345(3.79), 367(3.74)	27-0324-79
2H-2,4a-Methanonaphthalene-3,4-dicarboxylic acid, 1,5,8-trimethyl-, dimethyl ester	EtOH	325(3.82)	39-0673-79C
$C_{18}H_{21}BrO_5$			
α-D-xylo-Oct-5-enofuranos-7-ulose, 6-bromo-5,6,8-trideoxy-1,2-O-(1-methylethylidene)-3-O-(phenylmethyl)-, (Z)-	EtOH	212(3.74),246(3.80)	33-1303-79
$C_{18}H_{21}ClN_2O_5$			
2H-Pyrrole-2,2-dicarboxylic acid, 1-acetyl-4-(2-amino-4-chlorophenyl)-1,3-dihydro-, diethyl ester	isoPrOH	211(4.28),244(4.36), 282(4.16),293(4.12), 325(4.05)	44-3748-79
$C_{18}H_{21}ClN_6O_3$			
Urea, N-(2-chloroethyl)-N'-[(8)-6-methyl-1-nitrosoergolin-8-yl]-N-nitroso-	MeOH	262(4.28),330(3.67)	87-0032-79
$C_{18}H_{21}FN_2O_{11}$			
Uridine, 4'-C-(acetoxymethyl)-5-fluoro-, 2',3',5'-triacetate	MeOH	263(3.92)	44-1301-79
$C_{18}H_{21}N$			
1H-3-Benzazepine, 2,3,4,5-tetrahydro-2,2-dimethyl-1-phenyl-	EtOH	259(2.61)	4-1525-79
1H-Pyrrolizine, 2,3-dihydro-3,3-dimethyl-1-(1-methylethylidene)-6-phenyl-	MeOH	210(4.12),252(4.22), 275(4.18),290(4.09)	83-0896-79
$C_{18}H_{21}NO$			
1H-3-Benzazepin-7-ol, 2,3,4,5-tetrahydro-4,4-dimethyl-5-phenyl-	EtOH	205(4.52),280(3.34), 288s(3.30)	4-1525-79
$C_{18}H_{21}NO_2$			
Benzo[f]pyrrolo[1,2-b]isoquinoline, 7,9,10,11,11a,12-hexahydro-2,3-dimethoxy-, (S)-	MeOH	238(4.78),263(3.65), 271(3.68),281(3.66), 291(3.49),304(3.07), 313(3.36),320(3.22), 327(3.54)	5-1212-79
A-Nor-3-aza-14α-estra-1,5,7,9-tetraen-17β-ol, acetate	EtOH	223(4.498),274(3.919), 286(3.826),292(3.699), 298(3.58)	104-1983-79
14β-	EtOH	220(4.508),270(3.919), 283(3.771),288(3.633), 296(3.505)	104-1983-79

Compound	Solvent	λ_{max}(log ε)	Ref.
$C_{18}H_{21}NO_2S_2$			
2-Azetidinone, 4-[[1-(cyclohexylthio)-3-oxo-3-phenyl-1-propenyl]thio]-, (E)-	dioxan	261(3.92),277(3.91), 338(4.24)	142-1315-79
(Z)-	dioxan	262(3.89),279(3.88), 337(4.25)	142-1315-79
$C_{18}H_{21}NO_3$			
Benzo[f]pyrrolo[1,2-b]isoquinolin-12-ol, 7,9,10,11,11a,12-hexahydro-2,3-dimethoxy-	n.s.g.	236(4.89),262(3.72), 270(3.75),280(3.73), 313(3.50),328(3.69)	5-1212-79
diastereomer 14b	n.s.g.	237(4.83),262(3.62), 271(3.66),281(3.66), 313(3.40),328(3.58)	5-1212-79
Coclaurine, N-methyl-, (R)-(-)-	EtOH	227(4.21),284(3.80)	100-0430-79
1,7-Cycloerythrinan-8-one, 15,16-dimethoxy-, (±)-	MeOH	204(4.73),232s(3.92), 284(3.68)	24-1110-79
Cyclohexaneacetaldehyde, 3-(2,3-dihydro-1,3-dimethyl-2-oxo-1H-indol-3-yl)-2-oxo-	EtOH	253(3.97)	23-1694-79
form A	EtOH	254(--),279s(--)	23-1694-79
$C_{18}H_{21}NO_4$			
1H-Azepine-4-carboxylic acid, 6-ethyl-2,5-dihydro-3-methoxy-2-oxo-7-phenyl-, ethyl ester	dioxan	222(4.12),252(4.09)	142-1427-79
Benzoic acid, 4-[[(4,4-dimethyl-2,6-dioxocyclohexylidene)methyl]amino]-, ethyl ester	hexane	233(4.19),247s(4.12), 360(4.56)	131-0077-79D
	EtOH	360(4.53)	131-0077-79D
Estra-1,3,5(10)-trien-17-one, 3-hydroxy-2-nitro-	MeOH	217(4.19),293(3.89), 361(3.55)	145-0463-79
Estra-1,3,5(10)-trien-17-one, 3-hydroxy-4-nitro-	MeOH	207(4.06),215(4.04), 277(3.35)	145-0463-79
L-Proline, 1-[(6,7-dimethoxy-2-naphthalenyl)methyl]-	MeOH	237(4.90),269(3.81), 312(3.49),326(3.62)	5-1212-79
hydrochloride	MeOH	237(4.26),240(4.23), 268(3.11),312(2.65), 326(2.83)	5-1212-79
2H-Pyrrole-4,5-dicarboxylic acid, 2,2-dimethyl-3-phenyl-, diethyl ester	MeOH	292(3.67)	88-2983-79
Wisanin, all-cis	MeOH	220(4.21),244(4.06), 295(4.06),350(4.09)	78-0385-79
cis-trans	MeOH	217(4.23),245(4.10), 295(4.12),353(4.17)	78-0385-79
$C_{18}H_{21}NO_4S$			
Benzene, 1-[2,2-dimethyl-1-[(4-nitrophenyl)sulfonyl]propyl]-4-nitro-	MeOH	224(4.20)	12-1487-79
$C_{18}H_{21}NO_5$			
1H-Azepine-4-carboxylic acid, 6-ethoxy-2,5-dihydro-3-methoxy-2-oxo-7-phenyl-, ethyl ester	dioxan	225(3.96),252(4.04)	142-1427-79
Benzoic acid, 3,6-dimethoxy-2-[(4-methoxyphenyl)methylamino]-, methyl ester	EtOH	210(4.30),230(4.15), 305(3.86)	33-2350-79
Benzo[g]quinoline-5,10-dione, 7-bromo-1,2,3,4-tetrahydro-8,9-dihydroxy-3-methoxy-	MeOH	277(4.32),338(3.74), 432(3.50)	39-0807-79C
B-Norerythrinan-6α-carboxylic acid, 15,16-dimethoxy-7-oxo-, (±)-	MeOH	209(4.48),283(3.57)	24-3795-79

Compound	Solvent	λmax(log ε)	Ref.
$C_{18}H_{21}NO_6$			
2H-[1,3]Benzodioxolo[5,6-a]quinolizine-2,3-dicarboxylic acid, 1,3,4,6,7,12b-hexahydro-, dimethyl ester	EtOH	292(3.62)	23-1647-79
$C_{18}H_{21}NO_8$			
Pyridinium, 1-[3-ethoxy-2-(ethoxycarbonyl)-1-[2-methoxy-1-(methoxycarbonyl)-2-oxoethyl]-3-oxo-1-propenyl]-, hydroxide, inner salt	$CHCl_3$	363(3.1),470(2.3)	5-1406-79
$C_{18}H_{21}N_3$			
Piperazine, 1-methyl-4-[phenyl(phenylimino)methyl]-	EtOH	203(4.44),230s(--)	1-0319-79
$C_{18}H_{21}N_3O_2$			
2-Propenoic acid, 2-cyano-3-[4-[(2-cyanoethyl)ethylamino]-2-methylphenyl]-, ethyl ester	EtOH	426(4.61)	110-1769-79
	EtOH-KOH	338(--)	110-1769-79
	CCl_4	410(--)	110-1769-79
	KBr	429(--)	110-1769-79
Pyrrolo[1,2-a]pyrazin-4(3H)-one, 6,7,8,8a-tetrahydro-1-ethoxy-3-[(1H-indol-3-yl)methyl]-, (3S-trans)-	EtOH	221(4.87),275(3.65), 282(3.69),290(3.62)	39-3048-79C
$C_{18}H_{21}N_3O_5$			
1(2H)-Pyrimidineacetic acid, α-(acetylamino)-3,4-dihydro-5-methyl-2,4-dioxo-α-(phenylmethyl)-, ethyl ester	MeOH	264(4.06)	44-2019-79
$C_{18}H_{21}N_3O_7$			
α-D-Arabinopyranosylamine, N-1H-benzimidazol-2-yl-, 2,3,4-triacetate	MeOH	242(4.0),248(4.8), 282(4.1),287(4.1)	94-1153-79
$C_{18}H_{21}N_5$			
Benzenamine, 4,4'-(1H-1,2,4-triazole-3,5-diylbis[N,N-dimethyl-	EtOH	309(4.69)	40-0389-79
$C_{18}H_{21}N_5O_3$			
Acetamide, N-[5-(diethylamino)-2-[(4-nitrophenyl)azo]phenyl]-	EtOH	511(4.67)	39-1990-79C
	HOAc	511(4.68)	39-1990-79C
$C_{18}H_{21}P$			
Phosphine, cyclohexyldiphenyl-	hexane	255(3.39)	22-0241-79I
$C_{18}H_{22}$			
5,14-Ethenobenzocyclododecene, 6,7,8,9,10,11,12,13-octahydro-	EtOH	234(4.59),292(3.71)	35-6660-79
$C_{18}H_{22}ClN_5O_2$			
Urea, N-(2-chloroethyl)-N'-[(8β)-6-methylergolin-8-yl]-N-nitroso-	MeOH	222(4.50),272(3.85), 280(3.81),292(3.67)	87-0032-79
$C_{18}H_{22}ClN_5O_3$			
[1,2,4]Triazino[4,3-d][1,4]benzodiazepine-3,4,7(6H)-trione, 11-chloro-2-[2-(diethylamino)ethyl]-2,8-dihydro-8-methyl-, monohydrochloride	H_2O	252(4.18),270(4.10), 303s(3.95)	44-0084-79
$C_{18}H_{22}FN_3O_6S_3$			
Ethanesulfonyl fluoride, 2-[[4-[[2,4-bis(methylsulfonyl)phenyl]azo]phen-	acetone	451(4.48)	44-3847-79

Compound	Solvent	λ_{max}(log ε)	Ref.
yl]ethylamino]- (cont.)			44-3847-79
$C_{18}H_{22}F_2O_5$			
Spiro[azuleno[6,5-b]furan-3(2H),1'-cyclopropane]-2,6(4H)-dione, 5-acetoxy-2',2'-difluorooctahydro-4a,8-dimethyl-, [3R-(3α,3aα,4aβ,5β,7aα,8β,9aα)]-	EtOH	225(3.39)	78-0815-79
$C_{18}H_{22}N_2$			
1H-3-Benzazepin-7-amine, 2,3,4,5-tetrahydro-4,4-dimethyl-5-phenyl-	EtOH	271(3.98)	4-1525-79
2,2'-Biquinolizinium, 6,6',7,7',8,8'-9,9'-octahydro-, dichloride	n.s.g.	600(4.21)	39-2704-79C
$C_{18}H_{22}N_2OS$			
10H-Phenothiazine-10-propanamine, N,N,2-trimethyl-, 5-oxide	MeOH	237(4.51),275(4.10), 299(3.95),342(3.80)	133-0197-79
Promazine, 2-methoxy- (maleate)	MeOH	210(4.62),253(4.43), 307(3.69)	133-0197-79
$C_{18}H_{22}N_2OS_2$			
Spiro[cyclohexane-1,8'[2H,8H]isothiazolo[4,3,2-ij]quinazoline]-2'-thione, 6'-(2-furanyl)-3',4',5',5'a,6',7'-hexahydro-	EtOH	267(3.56),369(4.13)	150-0410-79S
$C_{18}H_{22}N_2O_2$			
Benzeneacetamide, 4-amino-N-(2-hydroxy-1,1-dimethyl-2-phenylethyl)-	EtOH	242(4.03),289(3.15)	4-1525-79
$C_{18}H_{22}N_2O_2S$			
10H-Phenothiazine-10-propanamine, 2-methoxy-N,N-dimethyl-	MeOH	244(4.54),276(4.11), 296(3.84),335(3.76)	133-0197-79
10H-Phenothiazine-10-propanamine, N,N,β-trimethyl-, S,S-dioxide	EtOH-HCl	226(4.64),270(4.27), 296(4.04),33(3.87)	56-0415-79
lead picrate complex	EtOH	223(4.86),270(4.38), 298(4.20),340(4.55), 360(4.56)	56-0415-79
$C_{18}H_{22}N_2O_4$			
Propanedioic acid, [[(2,3-dimethyl-1H-indol-5-yl)amino]methylene]-, diethyl ester	EtOH	230(4.33),297(4.37), 336(4.40)	103-0888-79
Propanedioic acid, [[(2,3-dimethyl-1H-indol-6-yl)amino]methylene]-, diethyl ester	EtOH	225(4.20),286(3.97), 350(4.22)	103-0888-79
2-Propenoic acid, 2-cyano-3-[4-[ethyl-(3-methoxy-3-oxopropyl)amino]phenyl]-, ethyl ester	EtOH	424(4.67)	110-1769-79
	EtOH-KOH	347(--)	110-1769-79
	CCl_4	413(--)	110-1769-79
	KBr	429(--)	110-1769-79
$C_{18}H_{22}N_2O_5$			
7,10,13,16,19-Pentaoxa-24,25-diazatricyclo[18.3.1.1^{2,6}]pentacosa-1(24),2,4,6(25),20,22-hexaene	EtOH	230(4.42),310(4.49), 317(4.26)	35-4472-79
Propanedioic acid, (formylamino)[(6-methyl-1H-indol-3-yl)methyl]-, diethyl ester	isoPrOH	223(4.60),276(3.76), 282(3.78),293(3.72)	44-3748-79
$C_{18}H_{22}N_2O_6$			
Thymidine, 4'-C-(hydroxymethyl)-3'-O-	MeOH	266(4.00)	44-1309-79

Compound	Solvent	λ_{max}(log ε)	Ref.
(phenylmethyl)- (cont.)			44-1309-79
$C_{18}H_{22}N_2O_7$			
L-Tryptophan, N^{in}-formyl-, tert-butyl ester, oxalate	MeOH-HCl	299(3.65)	63-0013-79
$C_{18}H_{22}N_2O_{11}$			
2,4(1H,3H)-Pyrimidinedione, 1-[2,3,5-tri-O-acetyl-4-C-(acetoxymethyl)-α-L-threo-pentofuranosyl]-	MeOH	257(3.98)	44-1309-79
Uridine, 4'-C-(acetoxymethyl)-, 2',3',5'-triacetate	MeOH	257(3.98)	44-1309-79
$C_{18}H_{22}N_2S$			
10H-Phenothiazine-10-propanamine, N,N,β-trimethyl-	pH 7.4	300(3.76)	149-0531-79A
10H-Phenothiazine-10-propanamine, N,N,2-trimethyl-, hydrochloride	MeOH	207(4.45),255(4.49), 306(3.65)	133-0197-79
$C_{18}H_{22}N_4O_2$			
1H-Pyrazole-4-carbonitrile, 3,5-bis-(1,1-dimethylethyl)-1-(4-nitrophenyl)-	EtOH	274(3.90)	78-1331-79
$C_{18}H_{22}N_4O_2S$			
5-Pyrimidinecarbothioamide, 6-amino-N-cyclohexyl-1,2,3,4-tetrahydro-3-methyl-2,4-dioxo-1-phenyl-	EtOH	262(4.42)	95-0515-79
$C_{18}H_{22}N_4O_9$			
2,5-Pyrrolidinedione, 1-[[[1-[5-O-acetyl-2,3-O-(1-methylethylidene)-β-D-ribofuranosyl]-5-amino-1H-imidazol-4-yl]carbonyl]oxy]-	MeOH	235(3.64),277(4.18)	39-1415-79C
$C_{18}H_{22}N_4O_9S$			
Isothiazolo[3,4-d]pyrimidine-4,6(5H,7H)-dione, 5,7-dimethyl-3-[(2,3,4-tri-O-acetyl-α-D-arabinopyranosyl)amino]-	dioxan	224(4.0),259(4.2), 271(4.1),314(4.2)	94-1147-79
$C_{18}H_{22}N_4O_{10}Se_2$			
Uridine, 5,5''-diselenobis[2'-deoxy-	pH 7.2	270(4.08)	87-0618-79
	+ DTT	330(3.32)	87-0618-79
$C_{18}H_{22}N_{12}O_3$			
Alanine, 3-(6-amino-9H-purin-9-yl)-N-[3-(6-amino-9H-purin-9-yl)alanyl]-, ethyl ester, trihydrochloride	EtOH	260(4.39)	65-0994-79
$C_{18}H_{22}O$			
1H-Inden-1-one, octahydro-3a-(1-methyl-2-phenylethenyl)-, (E)-	MeOH	241(3.79)	33-0119-79
3a,7a-Methano-1H-inden-1-one, hexahydro-8-methyl-8-(phenylmethyl)-	MeOH	244(3.03),258(2.79), 264(2.67),290(2.43)	33-0119-79
2(1H)-Naphthalenone, 3,4,5,6,7,8-hexahydro-1-methyl-1-(phenylmethyl)-, (±)-	MeOH	225(3.40),247(3.01), 252(2.97),256(2.90), 265(2.76),285(2.21)	33-0119-79
2(3H)-Naphthalenone, 4,4a,5,6,7,8-hexahydro-1-methyl-4a-(phenylmethyl)-, (±)-	isooctane	245(4.27),324(1.60)	33-0119-79

Compound	Solvent	λ_{max}(log ε)	Ref.
$C_{18}H_{22}O_2$			
1,1'-Biphenyl, 2',4'-dimethoxy-2,3,5,6-tetramethyl-	C_6H_{12}	280(3.62),286(3.52)	12-1531-79
Estra-4,9-diene-3,17-dione	MeOH	233(4.23)	24-3748-79
Estra-1,3,5(10)-trien-17-one, 3-hydroxy- (estrone)	dioxan	220s(--),230s(--), 282(3.37),290(3.33)	13-0485-79B
	dioxan-base	240(3.97),297(3.45)	13-0485-79B
Estra-5,7,9-trien-3-one, 17β-hydroxy-	MeOH	221s(3.99),262s(2.72), 265s(2.76),269(2.79), 273s(2.76),278(2.72)	24-2631-79
Estra-5,7,9-trien-17-one, 3α-hydroxy-	MeOH	218s(4.02),223s(3.96), 262s(2.41),265s(2.46), 269(2.54),273s(2.45), 279(2.41),293s(1.57)	24-2631-79
$C_{18}H_{22}O_3$			
Benzaldehyde, 3,6-dihydroxy-2-(1,3,5-undecatrienyl)-, (E,E,E)-	n.s.g.	266(4.55),314(4.42), 413(4.10)	88-3233-79
$C_{18}H_{22}O_3S$			
17-Thiaestra-1,3,5(10),8-tetraene, 3-methoxy-, S,S-dioxide, (14β)-	MeOH	213(4.32),272(4.21)	13-0619-79B
$C_{18}H_{22}O_4S$			
3(2H)-Thiophenone, 2-[2-(3,4-dihydro-6-methoxy-1(2H)-naphthalenylidene)-ethyl]dihydro-2-methyl-, 1,1-dioxide, (±)-	MeOH	210(4.23),265(4.20)	13-0619-79B
$C_{18}H_{22}O_5$			
2-Naphthaleneacetic acid, 3-acetoxy-1,2,3,4,4a,6,7,8,8a-octahydro-4a-methyl- ,8-bis(methylene)-7-oxo-, methyl ester (gerin)	EtOH	202(4.06),239(4.04)	102-1741-79
$C_{18}H_{22}O_6$			
Spiro[bicyclo[2.2.2]octa-5,7-diene-2,2'-oxirane]-4,5-dicarboxylic acid, 7-(1,1-dimethylethyl)-6-methyl-3-oxo-, dimethyl ester	EtOH	225(3.69),243s(3.48), 298s(2.49),306(2.51), 320s(2.30)	12-1231-79
Spiro[bicyclo[2.2.2]octa-5,7-diene-2,2'-oxirane]-5,6-dicarboxylic acid, 7-(1,1-dimethylethyl)-4-methyl-3-oxo-, dimethyl ester	EtOH	227s(3.71),245s(3.63), 304s(2.63),314(2.67), 327s(2.51)	12-1231-79
Spiro[cyclopropa[cd]pentalene-1(2H),2'-oxirane]-2b,4b(2aH,4aH)-dicarboxylic acid, 4-(1,1-dimethylethyl)-2a-methyl-2-oxo-, dimethyl ester	EtOH	256s(2.72),312s(1.93), 323s(1.81),337s(1.48)	12-1231-79
$C_{18}H_{22}O_6S_4$			
α-D-Glucopyranoside, methyl 4,6-O-(phenylmethylene)-, bis(S-methyl carbonodithioate)	MeOH	220(3.59),278(3.98)	136-0127-79G
α-D-Idopyranoside, methyl 4,6-O-(phenylmethylene)-, bis(S-methyl carbonodithioate)	n.s.g.	283(4.35)	39-2378-79C
α-D-Mannopyranoside, methyl 4,6-O-(phenylmethylene)-, bis(S-methyl carbonodithioate), (R)-	n.s.g.	280(4.17)	39-2378-79C

Compound	Solvent	$\lambda_{max}(\log \epsilon)$	Ref.
$C_{18}H_{23}BrN_2O_9$			
1H-Pyrazole-5-carboxylic acid, 3-(bromomethyl)-1-(2,3,5-tri-O-acetyl-β-D-ribofuranosyl)-, ethyl ester	EtOH	235(4.01),245s(3.96)	87-0807-79
1H-Pyrazole-5-carboxylic acid, 3-(bromomethyl)-1-(2,3,4-tri-O-acetyl-β-D-ribopyranosyl)-, ethyl ester	EtOH	230(4.00),245s(3.88)	87-0807-79
$C_{18}H_{23}Br_2N_3O_9$			
1H-1,2,3-Triazole, 4,5-bis(bromomethyl)-1-(2,3,4,6-tetra-O-acetyl-β-D-glucopyranosyl)-	EtOH	254(3.63)	87-0496-79
$C_{18}H_{23}ClN_4O$			
Urea, N-(2-chloroethyl)-N'-[(8β)-6-methylergolin-8-yl]-	MeOH	222(4.67),274(4.07), 281(4.07),293(3.97)	87-0032-79
$C_{18}H_{23}Cl_2N_3O_9$			
1H-1,2,3-Triazole, 4,5-bis(chloromethyl)-1-(2,3,4,6-tetra-O-acetyl-β-D-glucopyranosyl)-	EtOH	236(3.49)	87-0496-79
$C_{18}H_{23}NO$			
1-Propanol, 3-[bis(phenylmethyl)amino]-2-methyl-	EtOH	207(3.95),252(2.46), 256(2.54),264s(2.42)	4-1525-79
4(1H)-Quinolinone, 2-(1-nonenyl)-	MeOH	258(4.59),267(4.58), 308(3.94),330(4.05)	49-0947-79
$C_{18}H_{23}NO_2$			
1H-Carbazole-2-carboxylic acid, 2,3,4,9-tetrahydro-4-(2-methylpropyl)-, methyl ester	EtOH	227(4.60),276s(3.83), 282(3.87),290(3.78)	44-4402-79
Estra-1,3,5(10)-trien-17-one, 2-amino-3-hydroxy-	MeOH	210(4.41),297(3.62)	145-0463-79
Estra-1,3,5(10)-trien-17-one, 4-amino-3-hydroxy-	MeOH	210(4.44),287(3.50)	145-0463-79
Spiro[benzo[d]carbazole-6(7H),2'-[1,3]-dioxolane], 1,2,3,4,7a,8-hexahydro-	MeOH	240(3.77),290(3.42)	5-1048-79
$C_{18}H_{23}NO_3$			
4-Pyridineacetic acid, 5-ethyl-1,2,5,6-tetrahydro-2-oxo-1-(phenylmethyl)-, ethyl ester	EtOH	253(3.52)	94-1847-79
$C_{18}H_{23}NO_4$			
8-Azabicyclo[3.2.1]octane-2-carboxylic acid, 8-methyl-3-[(4-methylbenzoyl)-oxy]-, methyl ester, hydrochloride, [1R-(exo,exo)]-	MeOH	270(3.01),282(2.73)	4-0625-79
$C_{18}H_{23}NO_5$			
8-Azabicyclo[3.2.1]octane-2-carboxylic acid, 3-[(4-methoxybenzoyl)oxy]-8-methyl-, methyl ester, hydrochloride, [1R-(exo,exo)]-	MeOH	272(3.86),282(3.38)	4-0625-79
$C_{18}H_{23}N_3O$			
1,5-Methano-[1,3]diazocino[1,8-a]indol-6(1H)-one, 7-[(dimethylamino)methyl]-2,3,4,5-tetrahydro-2-methyl-	EtOH	212(4.45),241(4.35), 320(4.40)	39-3155-79C

Compound	Solvent	λ_{max}(log ε)	Ref.
Methanone, [2-[(dimethylamino)methyl]-1H-indol-3-yl](1,2,3,6-tetrahydro-1-methyl-4-pyridinyl)-	EtOH	250(3.88),278s(3.80), 314(3.65)	39-3155-79C
Methanone, [3-[(dimethylamino)methyl]-1H-indol-2-yl](1,2,3,6-tetrahydro-1-methyl-4-pyridinyl)-	EtOH	217(4.44),243(4.19), 321(4.15)	39-3155-79C
$C_{18}H_{23}N_3O_7S$			
Thiourea, N-(2-aminophenyl)-N'-(2,3,4-tri-O-acetyl-α-D-arabinopyranosyl)-	MeOH	242(4.6),299(4.0)	94-1153-79
$C_{18}H_{23}N_3O_8$			
α-L-Mannopyranoside, methyl 6-deoxy-2,3-O-(1-methylethylidene)-4-C-[(4-nitrophenyl)azo]-, 4-acetate	EtOH	210(4.30),281(4.23)	136-0287-79B
$C_{18}H_{23}N_3O_{11}$			
1H-Imidazole, 2-methyl-4-nitro-1-(2,3,4,6-tetra-O-acetyl-β-D-glucopyranosyl)-	n.s.g.	288(3.91)	111-0123-79
$C_{18}H_{23}N_5O_4S$			
Benzenesulfonamide, 5-(diethylamino)-N,N-dimethyl-2-[(4-nitrophenyl)azo]-	EtOH	471(4.50)	39-1990-79C
	HOAc	470(4.48)	39-1990-79C
$C_{18}H_{23}N_5O_9$			
1H-Purine-2,6-dione, 3,7-dihydro-1,3-dimethyl-8-[(2,3,4-tri-O-acetyl-α-D-arabinopyranosyl)amino]-	MeOH	212(4.5),289(4.3)	94-1153-79
$C_{18}H_{23}N_9$			
Imidazo[5,1-f][1,2,4]triazin-2-amine, 5-methyl-N-(5-methyl-7-propylimidazo[5,1-f][1,2,4]triazin-2-yl)-7-propyl-	EtOH	243(4.38),261(4.39)	39-1120-79C
$C_{18}H_{24}N_2$			
[1,1'-Biphenyl]-4,4'-diamine, N,N,N',N',2,2'-hexamethyl-	MeCN	265(4.36),300s(3.9)	18-1573-79
6H-Cyclohepta[b]quinolin-11-amine, N-butyl-7,8,9,10-tetrahydro-	EtOH	226(4.18),235(4.12), 308(3.49),320(3.52)	1-0313-79
$C_{18}H_{24}N_2O$			
Cyclohexanol, 1-[2-(phenylazo)-1-cyclohexen-1-yl]-	hexane	231(4.13),237(4.13), 242(3.96),333(4.55), 417(2.78)	104-0676-79
2-Cyclohexen-1-one, 2-(1-hydroxycyclohexyl)-, phenylhydrazone	hexane	248(3.98),298(4.47), 319(4.54)	104-0676-79
1H-Indole-2-methanol, 3-[2-(3-ethyl-5,6-dihydro-1(2H)-pyridinyl)ethyl]-	EtOH	223(4.45),274(3.76), 284(3.81),292(3.73)	23-0289-79
Spiro[cyclohexane-1,3'-[3H]indazol]-2-ol, 2',3'a,4',5',6',7'-hexahydro-2'-phenyl-	hexane	279(3.86)	104-0457-79
$C_{18}H_{24}N_2O_2$			
Butanamide, 2-methyl-N-[1-(1-oxo-3-phenyl-2-propenyl)-2-pyrrolidinyl]-	EtOH	283(4.20)	88-2247-79
$C_{18}H_{24}N_2O_3$			
Cyclohexanol, 1-[6-hydroperoxy-6-(phenylazo)-1-cyclohexen-1-yl]-	hexane	323(4.62),337(4.62), 431(2.54)	104-0676-79

Compound	Solvent	λ max (log ε)	Ref.
1,4-Naphthalenedione, 2(or 3),5-bis(butylamino)-8-hydroxy-	benzene	555(4.10),599(4.06)	138-0627-79
Odorinol	EtOH	283(4.25)	88-2247-79
Propanoic acid, 2-methyl-2-[[[5-[(phenylmethyl)amino]-2,4-pentadienylidene]amino]oxy]-, ethyl ester	MeOH	340(4.66)	78-0341-79
	ether	329(4.80)	78-0341-79
$C_{18}H_{24}N_2O_4$			
1,4-Benzenedicarboxylic acid, 2,5-bis-(2-propenylamino)-, diethyl ester	EtOH	476(3.72)	48-0905-79
1H-Indole-1-pentanoic acid, 3-[2-(acetylamino)ethyl]-5-methoxy-	EtOH	228(4.36),282(3.76), 303(3.68)	12-0399-79
1,4-Naphthalenedione, 6,7-bis(butylamino)-5,8-dihydroxy-	benzene	463(4.04),501(4.07), 541(4.11)	138-0627-79
$C_{18}H_{24}N_2O_9S$			
4-Isothiazolecarboxylic acid, 3-methyl-5-[(2,3,4-tri-O-acetyl-α-D-arabinopyranosyl)amino]-, ethyl ester	dioxan	225(3.4),273(4.1), 382(2.7)	94-1147-79
$C_{18}H_{24}N_2O_{15}$			
β-D-Glucopyranoside, 3,4-dinitrophenyl 4-O-β-D-glucopyranosyl-	pH 5	284(3.8)	130-0147-79
$C_{18}H_{24}N_3$			
Benzenaminium, 4-[[[4-(dimethylamino)-phenyl]methylene]amino]-N,N,N-trimethyl-, iodide	EtOH	220(2.97),251(2.92), 313s(2.46),357(2.87)	2-0338-79B
$C_{18}H_{24}N_4$			
2-Tetrazene, 1,4-bis(2,6-dimethylphenyl)-1,4-dimethyl-, (E)-	MeCN	302(4.20)	40-0915-79
2-Tetrazene, 1,4-bis(3,4-dimethylphenyl)-1,4-dimethyl-, (E)-	MeCN	346(4.38)	40-0915-79
$C_{18}H_{24}N_4O_2$			
3,5-Methanofuro[3,2-b]pyridine, 4-(4,6-dimethyl-2-pyrimidinyl)-2,3,3a,4,5,7a-hexahydro-6-morpholino-	$CHCl_3$	250(4.02)	39-1525-79C
$C_{18}H_{24}N_4O_4$			
2,6(1H,3H)-Pyridinedione, 1-ethyl-5-(ethylamino)-3-[1-ethyl-5-(ethylamino)-1,6-dihydro-2,6-dioxo-3(2H)-pyridinylidene]-	$CHCl_3$	284(4.22),628(4.51)	118-0948-79
$C_{18}H_{24}N_4O_6$			
7H-Pyrrolo[2,3-a]pyrimidin-4-amine, 7-[2,3-O-(4-ethoxy-1-methyl-4-oxobutylidene)-β-D-ribofuranosyl]-	MeOH	271(4.06)	136-0117-79G
$C_{18}H_{24}N_4O_7$			
α-D-Allofuranose, 3-deoxy-1,2:5,6-bis-O-(1-methylethylidene)-3-[3-(4-nitrophenyl)-1-triazenyl]-	EtOH	208(3.84),236(3.75), 351(4.24)	33-0971-79
α-D-Galactofuranose, 3-deoxy-1,2:5,6-bis-O-(1-methylethylidene)-3-[3-(4-nitrophenyl)-1-triazenyl]-	EtOH	208(3.95),231(3.86), 272(3.66),349(4.33)	33-0971-79
α-D-Glucofuranose, 3-deoxy-1,2:5,6-bis-O-(1-methylethylidene)-3-[3-(4-nitrophenyl)-1-triazenyl]-	EtOH	208(3.94),236(3.85), 276(3.68),350(4.29)	33-0971-79

Compound	Solvent	λ_{max}(log ε)	Ref.
α-D-Galactopyranose, 6-deoxy-1,2:3,4-bis-O-(1-methylethylidene)-6-[3-(4-nitrophenyl)-1-triazenyl]-	EtOH	207(3.95),236(3.86), 268(3.51),353(4.28)	33-0971-79
$C_{18}H_{24}N_4O_8$			
2,5-Cyclohexadiene-1,4-dione, 2,5-bis-[2-[(aminocarbonyl)oxy]-1-methoxyethyl]-3,6-bis(1-aziridinyl)-	50% EtOH	317(4.25),336(4.15)	87-0491-79
$C_{18}H_{24}N_4O_8S$			
Glycine, N-[S-[5-(acetylamino)-2-hydroxyphenyl]-N-L-γ-glutamyl-L-cysteinyl]-	H_2O	202(3.96),245(3.65), 298(3.08)	12-1307-79
$C_{18}H_{24}N_4O_{16}P_2Se_2$			
5'-Uridylic acid, 5,5"-diselenobis[2'-deoxy-, tetrasodium salt	pH 2	270(4.02)	87-0618-79
	pH 8	272(4.30)	87-0618-79
$C_{18}H_{24}N_6S$			
4H-Imidazole-2,5-diamine, 4-(2-benzothiazolylimino)-N,N,N',N'-tetraethyl-	$CHCl_3$	260(3.88),425(4.27), 445(4.30),480(4.01)	89-0156-79
$C_{18}H_{24}O$			
Phenanthrene, 1,2,3,4,4a,10a-hexahydro-7-methoxy-1,1,4a-trimethyl-	EtOH	266(3.96)	18-0608-79
$C_{18}H_{24}O_2$			
Bicyclo[3.2.1]oct-2-en-1-ol, 4-ethyl-3-(4-methoxyphenyl)-2-methyl-	MeOH	240(4.02)	2-0152-79B
2H,8H-3,6a:9,12a-Dimethanocyclobuta-[1,2:3,4]dicyclooctene-1,7(6bH,12bH)-dione, octahydro-	EtOH	298(1.79)	44-3793-79
3,6a:6b,10-Dimethanocyclobuta[1,2:3,4]-dicyclooctene-1,12(2H,7H)-dione, decahydro-, (6bα,10α,1aβ)-	EtOH	295(1.82)	44-3793-79
(6bβ,10β,12aα)-	EtOH	283.5(1.83)	44-3793-79
Estra-5,7,9-triene-3α,17β-diol	MeOH	218s(3.90),223s(3.85), 262s(2.34),265s(2.40), 269(2.49),273s(2.38), 279(2.36)	24-2631-79
$C_{18}H_{24}O_3$			
2,7-Epidioxynaphth[2,3-b]oxirene, 1a,2,7,7a-tetrahydro-1a,2,3,4,5,6,7-7a-octamethyl-, (1aα,2α,7α,7aα)-	C_6H_{12}	225(3.83),275(2.62)	44-0368-79
Ethanone, 1-[2-hydroxy-5-(3-methyl-2-butenyl)-4-[(3-methyl-2-butenyl)oxy]phenyl]-	MeOH	278(4.16),318(3.78)	78-0413-79
1H-Fluorene-1-carboxylic acid, 2,3,4-4a,9,9a-hexahydro-7-methoxy-1,4a-dimethyl-, methyl ester, (1α,4aα,9aα)-(±)-	EtOH	278(3.58)	2-0183-79B
2-Phenanthrenecarboxaldehyde, 4b,5,6-7,8,8a,9,10-octahydro-1,4-dihydroxy-4b,8,8-trimethyl-, (4bS-trans)-(premnolal)	EtOH or C_6H_{12}	208(3.69),236(4.14), 288(4.16)	2-0513-79B
	EtOH-NaOH	220(4.74),252(4.30), 305(3.99)	2-0513-79B
$C_{18}H_{24}O_3S$			
17-Thiaestra-1,3,5(10)-triene, 3-methoxy-, 17,17-dioxide, (8α,14β)-(±)-	MeOH	278(3.31),286(3.29)	13-0619-79B

Compound	Solvent	$\lambda_{max}(\log \epsilon)$	Ref.
$C_{18}H_{24}O_3Se$			
Cyclononanecarboxylic acid, 2-oxo-1-(phenylseleno)-, ethyl ester	EtOH	227(4.00),290(2.68)	33-2630-79
$C_{18}H_{24}O_4S$			
Hexanoic acid, 2-(1-methyl-2-propenyl)-3-oxo-6-(phenylsulfinyl)-, ethyl ester	EtOH	252(3.26),267s(3.10)	33-2630-79
4-Pentenoic acid, 2-acetyl-3-methyl-2-[2-(phenylsulfinyl)ethyl]-, ethyl ester	EtOH	243(3.60),266s(3.19), 273s(2.97)	33-2630-79
$C_{18}H_{24}O_8$			
1,6,9,13-Tetraoxadispiro[4.2.4.2]tetradeca-2,10-diene-3,11-dicarboxylic acid, diethyl ester, trans	$CHCl_3$	248(4.24)	136-0055-79B
$C_{18}H_{25}NO$			
4(1H)-Quinolinone, 2-nonyl-	MeOH	213(4.37),236(4.43), 316(4.02),327(4.00)	49-0947-79
$C_{18}H_{25}NO_5$			
1,3-Benzenedicarboxylic acid, 2-hydroxy-4-methyl-6-piperidino-, diethyl ester	MeOH	255(3.92),322(4.18)	83-0591-79
$C_{18}H_{25}N_3$			
5,6,7-Triazatricyclo[9.4.0.0^{4,8}]pentadec-5-ene, 7-phenyl-	C_6H_{12}	280(3.96)	39-3077-79C
$C_{18}H_{25}N_3O$			
1H-Indole-2-methanol, 3-[(dimethylamino)methyl]- -(1,2,3,6-tetrahydro-1-methyl-4-pyridinyl)-	EtOH	224(4.26),276(3.75), 283(3.78),290(3.72)	39-3155-79C
Methanone, [3-[(dimethylamino)methyl]-1H-indol-2-yl](1-methyl-4-piperidinyl)-	EtOH	237(4.15),315(4.3)	39-3155-79C
$C_{18}H_{25}N_3O_{11}$			
1H-1,2,3-Triazole-4,5-dimethanol, 1-(2,3,4,6-tetra-O-acetyl-β-D-glucopyranosyl)-	EtOH	233(3.23)	87-0496-79
$C_{18}H_{25}N_4O_7$			
1H-Pyrrol-1-yloxy, 3-[[(1,2-dihydro-2-oxo-1-β-D-ribofuranosyl-4-pyrimidinyl)amino]carbonyl]-2,5-dihydro-2,2,5,5-tetramethyl-	n.s.g.	260(4.23)	118-0267-79
$C_{18}H_{25}N_5O_6$			
9H-Purin-6-amine, 9-[2,3-bis-O-(2-methyl-1-oxopropyl)-β-D-arabinofuranosyl]-	MeOH	259(4.18)	87-0273-79
9H-Purin-6-amine, 9-[3,5-bis-O-(2-methyl-1-oxopropyl)-β-D-arabinofuranosyl]-	MeOH	259(4.19)	87-0273-79
$C_{18}H_{25}N_5O_8$			
1,2-Hydrazinedicarboxylic acid, 1,1'-[(dimethylamino)phenylethenylidene]-bis-, tetramethyl ester	n.s.g.	223(4.32),292(3.75)	104-2203-79

Compound	Solvent	λ_{max}(log ε)	Ref.
$C_{18}H_{26}BrN_2O_2$			
2H-Isoindol-2-yloxy, 5-[(bromoacetyl)-amino]-1,1,3,3-tetraethyl-1,3-dihydro-	C_6H_{12}	254(4.20)	22-0048-79
$C_{18}H_{26}N_2O_2$			
3,5-Cyclohexadiene-1,2-dione, 3,6-di-methyl-4,5-di-1-piperidinyl-	dioxan	440(3.83)	118-0695-79
$C_{18}H_{26}N_2O_3$			
14-Azabicyclo[11.2.2]heptadeca-13,15,16-trien-2-one, 12-acetoxy-, oxime	MeOH	240(3.88),270s(3.56)	49-0577-79
$C_{18}H_{26}N_2O_8$			
1(2H)-Pyrimidinebutanoic acid, 3,6-di-hydro-3-[2,3-O-(1-methylethylidene)-β-D-ribofuranosyl]-2,6-dioxo-, ethyl ester	MeOH	261(3.88)	24-0700-79
$C_{18}H_{26}N_2O_9S$			
2-Butenoic acid, 3-amino-2-[thioxo-[(2,3,4-tri-O-acetyl-α-D-arabino-pyranosyl)amino]methyl]-, ethyl ester	dioxan	224(4.3),269(4.0), 388(2.6)	94-1147-79
$C_{18}H_{26}N_2S_2$			
Dispiro[cyclohexane-1,8'-[2H,8H]isothi-azolo[4,3,2-ij]quinazoline-6'(7'H),1"-cyclopentane]-2'-thione, 3',4',5',5'a-tetrahydro-	EtOH	263(3.55),367(4.16)	150-0410-79S
$C_{18}H_{26}N_4O_9$			
L-Aspartic acid, N-[[5-amino-1-[2,3-O-(1-methylethylidene)-β-D-ribofurano-syl]-1H-imidazol-4-yl]carbonyl]-, dimethyl ester	MeOH	232(3.77),268(3.85)	39-1415-79C
$C_{18}H_{26}O$			
4bH-Benzo[3,4]cyclobuta[1,2]cyclononen-4b-ol, 5,6,7,8,9,10,11,11a-octahydro-4-(1-methylethyl)-	MeOH	260(2.87),266(2.98), 274(2.96)	39-2542-79C
1,14-Methanobenzocyclododecen-14(5H)-ol, 6,7,8,9,10,11,12,13-octahydro-15-methyl-	MeOH	260(2.73),266(2.85), 274(2.84)	39-2542-79C
1,13-Methano-5H-benzocycloundecen-13(6H)-ol, 7,8,9,10,11,12-hexahydro-14,14-dimethyl-	MeOH	260(2.73),266(2.86), 273(2.82)	39-2542-79C
$C_{18}H_{26}O_5$			
Spiro[1,3-dioxolane-2,1'-[1H]inden]-5'(6'H)-one, 2',3',7',7'a-tetrahydro-4'-[2-(2-methyl-1,3-dioxolan-2-yl)-ethyl]-, (R)-	EtOH	253(4.11)	28-0053-79A
$C_{18}H_{27}NO$			
Benzo[3.4]cyclobuta[1,2]cycloocten-4b(5H)-ol, 5-(1,1-dimethylethyl)-amino]-6,7,8,9,10,10a-hexahydro-, hydrochloride	MeOH	260(3.09),267(3.23), 273(3.19)	111-0543-79
$C_{18}H_{27}N_3O_4$			
Pyrido[2,3-c]pyridazine-1,2-dicarbox-ylic acid, 3,4-dihydro-7-methyl-,	EtOH	229(3.93),282(3.73)	78-2027-79

Compound	Solvent	λ_{max}(log ε)	Ref.
bis(1,1-dimethylethyl) ester (cont.)			78-2027-79
Pyrido[3,2-c]pyridazine-1,2-dicarboxylic acid, 3,4-dihydro-3-methyl-, bis(1,1-dimethylethyl) ester	EtOH	235(3.99),283(3.66)	78-2027-79
Pyrido[4,3-c]pyridazine-1,2-dicarboxylic acid, 3,4-dihydro-7-methyl-, bis(1,1-dimethylethyl) ester	EtOH	243(4.00),268(3.53), 277(3.40)	78-2027-79
$C_{18}H_{27}N_5O_4$			
Adenosine, 8-ethyl-N,N-dimethyl-5'-O-methyl-2',3'-O-(1-methylethylidene)-	EtOH	275(4.28)	88-0279-79
$C_{18}H_{27}N_7O_5$			
Alanine, 3-(6-amino-9H-purin-9-yl)-N-[N-[(1,1-dimethylethoxy)carbonyl]-L-alanyl]-, ethyl ester	EtOH	261(4.12)	65-0994-79
$C_{18}H_{27}P$			
Phosphine, dicyclohexylphenyl-	hexane	262.5(3.36)	22-0241-79I
$C_{18}H_{28}Cr_2O_2$			
Chromium, bis(η^5-2,4-cyclopentadien-1-yl)bis[μ-(2-methyl-2-propanolato)]-di-, (Cr-Cr)-	hexane	520(2.78),668(2.00)	125-0120-79
$C_{18}H_{28}N_2O_4$			
1,4-Benzenedicarboxylic acid, 2,5-bis-[(1-methylethyl)amino]-, diethyl ester	EtOH	482(3.77)	48-0905-79
	dioxan	488(3.72)	48-0905-79
	butanone	495(3.81)	48-0905-79
	o-$C_6H_4Cl_2$	500(3.78)	48-0905-79
	DMF	490(3.85)	48-0905-79
	DMSO	493(3.74+)	48-0905-79
1,4-Benzenedicarboxylic acid, 2,5-bis-(propylamino)-, diethyl ester	EtOH	486(3.73)	48-0905-79
$C_{18}H_{28}O_2S$			
4-Thiepincarboxylic acid, 2,7-bis(1,1-dimethylethyl)-5-methyl-, ethyl ester	C_6H_{12}	234(4.11),356(2.95)	35-5059-79
$C_{18}H_{28}O_3$			
1,5-Cyclohexadecadienecarboxylic acid, 16-oxo-, methyl ester	EtOH	222.5(3.76)	33-2630-79
$C_{18}H_{29}NOS$			
Benzenamine, 2,4,6-tris(1,1-dimethylethyl)-N-sulfinyl-	hexane	231(4.09),410(2.54)	18-1998-79
$C_{18}H_{29}NOS_2$			
7aH-1,2,3-Benzodithiazole, 4,6,7a-tris-(1,1-dimethylethyl)-, 1-oxide, trans	hexane	233(3.98),345(3.31)	18-3615-79
$C_{18}H_{29}NS_2$			
Benzenamine, 2,4,6-tris(1,1-dimethylethyl)-N-sulfinothioyl-	hexane	268(3.42),292(3.41), 340(3.31),410(3.54), 535(weak)	18-1998-79
$C_{18}H_{29}N_3O_5$			
Thymidine, 5'-(acetylhexylamino)-5'-deoxy-	pH 1	267(3.98)	87-0621-79

Compound	Solvent	λ_{max}(log ε)	Ref.
$C_{18}H_{30}N_2O_7S$			
α-D-Glucopyranoside, methyl 4,6-O-cyclohexylidene-2-deoxy-2-[(methoxycarbonyl)amino]-, 3-(dimethylcarbamothioate)	EtOH	203(3.95),248(4.18), 285(3.00)	18-3015-79
$C_{18}H_{30}N_4O_5$			
Thymidine, 5'-[[4-(methylacetylamino)-butyl]methylamino]-5'-deoxy-	n.s.g.	267(3.98)	87-1524-79
$C_{18}H_{30}O_3$			
1,4-Benzenediol, 2-(hydroxymethyl)-3-undecyl- (octahydroaurocitrin)	n.s.g.	295(3.58)	88-3233-79
	+ NaOH	280(--)	88-3233-79
$C_{18}H_{30}O_7$			
2-Butenoic acid, 4-[5S-(2S,3S-epoxy-5S-hydroxy-4S-methylhexyl)-3R,4R-dihydroxytetrahydropyran-2S-yl]-3-methyl-, methyl ester (methyl monate A)	EtOH	221(4.17)	39-0308-79C
methyl isomonate A	EtOH	222(3.98)	39-0308-79C
$C_{18}H_{32}$			
Cyclopentane, 1,1,3,3-tetramethyl-2-(2,2,5,5-tetramethylcyclopentylidene)-	C_6H_{12}	203.0(4.18)	88-1305-79
Decalene, 1,2,3,4,5,6,7,8,9,10,11,12-13,14,15,16-hexadecahydro-, (E)-(±)-	hexane	201s(3.52),223(3.73)	35-0147-79
(Z)-	hexane	202(4.02),206s(4.00), 213s(3.75)	35-0147-79
$C_{18}H_{32}N_2O_4$			
4-Octen-3-one, 5,5'-(1,2-ethanediyldiimino)bis[8-hydroxy-	MeOH	323(4.41)	44-2073-79
$C_{18}H_{32}N_4$			
Methanaminium, N,N'-[4,5-bis[(dimethylamino)methylene]-2,6-octadiene-1,8-diylidene]bis[N-methyl-, diperchlorate	EtOH	413(5.00)	89-0214-79
$C_{18}H_{32}O_2$			
2-Cyclopenten-1-one, 5-dodecyl-4-hydroxy-4-methoxy-	EtOH	222(4.04)	102-0488-79
$C_{18}H_{34}N_4O_4P$			
1-Piperidinyloxy, 4-[[[[bis(2,2-dimethyl-1-aziridinyl)phosphinyl]amino]-carbonyl]oxy]-2,2,6,6-tetramethyl-	EtOH	243(3.33)	118-0269-79
$C_{18}H_{36}N_2O_4$			
Acetamide, 2,2'-[1,2-ethanediylbis-(oxy)]bis[N,N-bis(1-methylethyl)-	H_2O	203(4.18)	33-0754-79
Acetamide, 2,2'-[1,2-ethanediylbis-(oxy)]bis[N,N-dipropyl-	H_2O	203(4.21)	33-0754-79
$C_{18}H_{37}N_6$			
1,2,3-Triazinium, 5-[bis(1-methylethyl)-amino]-4,6-bis(diethylamino)-2-methyl-, iodide	CH_2Cl_2	458(3.80)	24-1535-79

Compound	Solvent	$\lambda_{max}(\log \epsilon)$	Ref.
$C_{19}H_9Br_3FN$			
Benzenamine, 2,4,6-tribromo-N-(2-fluoro-9H-fluoren-9-ylidene)-	dioxan	251(4.69),259(4.82), 269(4.47),288(4.01), 300(4.06),321s(3.23), 390(3.04)	24-3490-79
$C_{19}H_9Br_3FNO$			
Benzenamine, 2,4,6-tribromo-N-(2-fluoro-9H-fluoren-9-ylidene)-, N-oxide, (Z)-	dioxan	242(4.71),266(4.28), 275s(4.21),296(3.77), 345(4.26),360(4.30), 428s(2.39)	24-3490-79
$C_{19}H_9F_5N_2O_3$			
Isoxazole, 4,5-dihydro-5-(1-naphthalenyl)-4-nitro-3-(pentafluorophenyl)-	EtOH	223(4.80),270(4.08), 345(3.45)	104-2179-79
$C_{19}H_9N_9O_8$			
2-Pyridineacetonitrile, α-[1-(3,5-dinitro-2-pyridinyl)-1,3-dihydro-2H-benzimidazol-2-ylidene)-3,5-dinitro-	0.01N H_2SO_4	295(4.32),460(4.6)	104-0178-79
	pH 12	300(4.33),500(4.6)	104-0178-79
	EtOH	295(4.32),460(4.59)	104-0178-79
$C_{19}H_{10}O_5$			
1H-Naphtho[2,1,8-mna]xanthen-1-one, 5,8,9-trihydroxy-	MeOH	242(4.50),259s(4.43), 284(4.24),331(3.78), 362(3.75),395(3.76), 545(4.30),578(4.39)	12-1841-79
1H-Naphtho[2,1,8-mna]xanthen-1-one, 8,9,11-trihydroxy-	MeOH	232(4.40),257(4.36), 273(4.36),299s(4.04), 311s(4.00),396(4.04), 528(3.89),558(3.97)	12-1841-79
$C_{19}H_{11}F_2N$			
Benzenamine, N-(2,7-difluoro-9H-fluoren-9-ylidene)-	dioxan	249s(4.61),257(4.68), 268s(4.34),287s(3.86), 297s(3.79),398(3.19)	24-3490-79
$C_{19}H_{11}N_3O_2$			
5H-Pyrido[1',2':1,2]pyrimido[4,5-b]-acridine-7,15-dione	n.s.g.	283(4.72),311(4.59)	40-0398-79
$C_{19}H_{11}N_5O_2S$			
Isothiazolo[4,3-b]pyridine-6-carbonitrile, 5-amino-3-(4-nitrophenyl)-7-phenyl-	DMF	332(4.12),452(4.11)	5-1534-79
$C_{19}H_{12}BrNO_2$			
Furo[2,3-c]pyridin-2(6H)-one, 3-(4-bromophenyl)-6-phenyl-	EtOH	395(4.42)	97-0020-79
Furo[3,2-b]pyridin-2(4H)-one, 3-(4-bromophenyl)-4-phenyl-	EtOH	384(4.12)	97-0020-79
$C_{19}H_{12}Br_2O$			
2,5-Cyclohexadien-1-one, 2,6-dibromo-4-(diphenylmethylene)-	n.s.g.	276(4.18),396(4.45)	35-5717-79
$C_{19}H_{12}FN$			
Benzenamine, N-(2-fluoro-9H-fluoren-9-ylidene)-	dioxan	249s(4.65),257(4.73), 285(3.89),296(3.88), 318s(3.11),396(3.21)	24-3490-79

Compound	Solvent	$\lambda_{max}(\log \epsilon)$	Ref.
$C_{19}H_{12}N_2$			
6H-Benzo[b]phenaleno[1,9-ef][1,4]diazepine, tetrafluoroborate	n.s.g.	285(4.50),370(3.93), 510(3.16)	44-1704-79
$C_{19}H_{12}N_2OS$			
Thiazolo[3,2-a]benzimidazol-6-ol, 3-(2-naphthalenyl)-	pH 1	339(3.51),383(3.47)	18-3096-79
	pH 13	322(3.31),451(3.57)	18-3096-79
	EtOH	254(3.84),279(4.12), 372(3.71)	18-3096-79
$C_{19}H_{12}N_2O_2$			
15H-Cyclohepta[1,2-b:3,4-b']bis[1,4]-benzoxazine	MeOH	207(4.10),254(3.99), 355(3.43),500(3.68)	18-1156-79
	MeOH-HCl	207(4.08),223(4.02), 275(4.00),325s(3.57), 410(3.68),535(3.54)	18-1156-79
$C_{19}H_{12}N_2O_2S_2$			
Quinoline, 2-[2-(3'-nitro[2,2'-bithiophene]-5-yl)ethenyl]-, (E)-	EtOH	242(5.00),291(5.09), 312(5.06),391(5.02)	103-0970-79
Quinoline, 2-[2-(5'-nitro[2,2'-bithiophene]-5-yl)ethenyl]-, (E)-	EtOH	236(5.04),274(5.12), 315(5.10),442(4.94)	103-0970-79
$C_{19}H_{12}N_2O_3$			
Benzonitrile, 4-[(3-acetyl-1,4-dihydro-1,4-dioxo-2-naphthalenyl)amino]-	dioxan	229s(4.3),279(4.46), 445(3.74)	5-0503-79
1H-Pyrrolo[3,4-c]pyridine-1,3,6(2H,5H)-trione, 2,4-diphenyl-	MeOH	245(4.15),298(4.15)	44-0626-79
$C_{19}H_{12}N_2O_4$			
Furo[2,3-c]pyridin-2(6H)-one, 3-(4-nitrophenyl)-6-phenyl-	EtOH	432(4.36)	97-0020-79
Naphtho[2',3':4,5]furo[2,3-b]pyridine-3-carbonitrile, 1-ethyl-1,2,5,10-tetrahydro-4-methyl-2,5,10-trioxo-	$CHCl_3$	277(4.40),345(4.09), 442(3.94)	2-0100-79A
$C_{19}H_{12}N_2S_5$			
Thiourea, bis(4-phenyl-1,3-dithiol-2-ylidene)-	MeCN	230(4.71),254(4.71), 456(4.86)	48-0827-79
$C_{19}H_{12}N_4$			
2-Butenedinitrile, 2-amino-3-[(9-anthracenylmethylene)amino]-	EtOH	252(4.98),426(4.42)	44-0827-79
Pyrazino[2',3':4,5]pyrrolo[1,2-a]quinoxaline, 6-phenyl-	EtOH	257s(4.02),272s(4.11), 282(4.16),296s(3.99), 330(3.60),345(3.71), 355(3.73),408s(3.52), 421(3.56),441(3.42)	78-2463-79
$C_{19}H_{12}N_4O$			
Ethanone, 1-pyrrolo[1,2-a:4,5-b']diquinoxalin-6-yl-	EtOH	274s(4.55),284(4.68), 294(4.62),321(3.91), 360s(3.90),378(4.08), 397(4.12),498s(3.59), 516(3.60),548s(3.42)	78-2463-79
$C_{19}H_{12}N_4O_7$			
Methanone, (2,4-dinitrophenyl)[4-nitro-2-(phenylamino)phenyl]-	EtOH	225(4.42),260(4.41), 278(4.33),444(3.76)	39-1364-79C

Compound	Solvent	$\lambda_{max}(\log \epsilon)$	Ref.
$C_{19}H_{12}N_4S_2$			
Benzonitrile, 4-(5,11-imino-5H,11H-[1,5]dithiocino[2,3-b:6,7-b']di-pyridin-13-yl)-	EtOH	206(4.58),242(4.31), 281(4.49)	78-0869-79
$C_{19}H_{12}OS$			
4H-Cyclopenta[b]thiophen-4-one, 5,6-di-phenyl-	CH_2Cl_2	267(4.67),448(3.44)	103-1173-79
6H-Cyclopenta[b]thiophen-6-one, 4,5-di-phenyl-	CH_2Cl_2	267(4.40),510(3.16)	103-1173-79
$C_{19}H_{12}O_2$			
Benzo[a]anthracene-7,12-dione, 9-meth-yl-	CH_2Cl_2	255(4.22),286(4.58), 344(3.59),394s(3.34)	44-1941-79
$C_{19}H_{12}O_3$			
Benzo[a]anthracene-7,12-dione, 9-meth-oxy-	EtOH	217(4.47),256s(4.14), 278(4.43),288(4.63), 399(3.81)	44-0699-79
$C_{19}H_{12}O_5$			
5,12-Naphthacenedione, 6,11-dihydroxy-8-methoxy-	MeOH	216(4.14),250(4.41), 271(4.61),300s(--), 425s(--),455(4.06), 480(4.23),514(4.15)	24-3453-79
$C_{19}H_{12}O_7$			
Daphnoretin	MeOH	228(1.18),265(0.86), 325(1.28),343(1.31)	100-0159-79
$C_{19}H_{13}ClN_2$			
Benzenamine, N-(1H-benz[g]indol-3-yl-methylene)-4-chloro-	EtOH	208(4.46),218s(4.36), 253(4.39),280s(4.25), 319s(4.27),328(4.27), 343s(4.24)	103-0741-79
$C_{19}H_{13}ClO_2$			
9H-Xanthen-9-ol, 1-chloro-9-phenyl-	EtOH	236(4.12),281(3.48), 290(3.64)	36-1453-79
$C_{19}H_{13}NO_2$			
Benzo[j]phenanthridine-7,12-dione, 3,6-dimethyl-	dioxan	217(4.62),235(4.44), 248s(4.4),284(4.42), 379(3.81)	5-0503-79
Furo[2,3-c]pyridin-2(6H)-one, 3,6-di-phenyl-	EtOH	392(4.50)	97-0020-79
Furo[3,2-b]pyridin-2(4H)-one, 3,4-di-phenyl-	EtOH	384(3.96)	97-0020-79
5,12-Naphthacenedione, 6-(methylamino)-	benzene	510(4.05),538s(3.89)	153-0033-79
$C_{19}H_{13}NO_3$			
1H-Benz[f]isoindole-1,3(2H)-dione, 4-(2-hydroxyphenyl)-2-methyl-	ether	257(4.77),292(3.93), 340(3.51),357(3.61)	89-0413-79
Benzo[j]phenanthridine-7,12-dione, 3-methoxy-6-methyl-	dioxan	217(4.57),241(4.49), 257s(4.4),293(4.39), 393(3.88)	5-0503-79
$C_{19}H_{13}NO_7$			
1H-Indene-1,3(2H)-dione, 2-[3-(2-hy-droxy-3-methoxyphenyl)-1-oxo-2-prop-enyl]-5-nitro-	pH 1	245(4.37),424(4.45)	65-1600-79
	pH 6.20	230(4.51),264(4.21), 314(4.32),376(4.46)	65-1600-79

Compound	Solvent	λ_{max}(log ε)	Ref.
(cont.)	pH 13	230(4.52),314(4.18), 368(4.24),436(4.23)	65-1600-79
$C_{19}H_{13}NS_2$			
Quinoline, 2-(2-[2,2'-bithiophen]-5-yl-ethenyl)-, (E)-	EtOH	220(4.00),260(4.17), 314(3.93),390(3.65)	103-0970-79
$C_{19}H_{13}N_3O$			
Benzo[b]cyclohept[e][1,4]oxazine, 8-(phenylazo)-	MeOH	205(4.45),231(4.32), 263(4.44),322(4.30), 450s(4.43),471(4.48), 500s(4.40),570s(3.76)	18-3123-79
	MeOH-HCl	205(4.38),235(4.37), 265(4.38),274(4.41), 333(4.26),535(4.39)	18-3123-79
	MeOH-NaOH	258(4.32),321(4.14), 448(4.52),505s(4.28), 570s(4.16)	18-3123-79
$C_{19}H_{13}N_3O_2$			
3-Pyridinecarbonitrile, 5-benz[cd]ind-ol-2-yl-1,2-dihydro-6-hydroxy-1,4-dimethyl-2-oxo-	DMF	510(3.93)	2-0140-79A
5H-Pyrido[1',2':1,2]pyrimido[4,5-b]-acridine-7,15-dione	n.s.g.	210(4.45),234(4.71), 317(4.31)	40-0398-79
$C_{19}H_{13}N_3O_2S_2$			
14,17-Dithia-22,23,24-triazatetracyclo-[16.3.1.1^{3,7}.1^{9,13}]tetracosa-1(24)-3,5,7(24),9,11,13(23),18,20-nonaene-2,8-dione	EtOH	235(5.01),277(4.72), 360(3.64)	44-3816-79
$C_{19}H_{13}N_3O_3$			
Imidazo[1,5-b]pyridazine-5,7(3H,6H)-di-one, 4-benzoyl-2-phenyl-	pH 13	255(3.74)	4-1105-79
	50% EtOH	264(4.44),290s(4.29)	4-1105-79
$C_{19}H_{13}N_3O_8S$			
7H-Furo[3,2-g][1]benzopyran-4-sulfonic acid, 9-methoxy-7-oxo-, [(2-nitro-phenyl)methylene]hydrazide	MeOH	230(4.49),265(4.42), 300(4.13)	48-1039-79
$C_{19}H_{14}$			
Chrysene, 3-methyl-	EtOH	268(5.11),294(4.13), 306(4.16),321(4.11), 363(2.73)	2-0233-79B
1H-Indene, 1-(1H-inden-3-ylmethylene)-	C_6H_{12}	206(4.50),263(4.59), 346(4.18),360s(4.14), 382s(3.75)	33-0718-79
$C_{19}H_{14}BrNO$			
3H-Naphtho[2,1-b]pyran-3-amine, N-(4-bromophenyl)-	MeOH	285(3.91),297(3.97), 310(3.95),339(3.60), 346(3.64),385(2.60)	104-1715-79
	CCl_4	316(4.01),341(3.69), 355(3.71)	104-1715-79
	DMSO	290(3.61),302(3.64), 314(3.54),342(3.28), 355(3.32),510(3.11)	104-1715-79
	DMSO-NaOMe	292(3.92),338(3.51), 500(3.68)	104-1715-79

Compound	Solvent	$\lambda_{max}(\log \epsilon)$	Ref.
$C_{19}H_{14}Br_2O_2$			
Benzenemethanol, 3,5-dibromo-4-hydroxy-α,α-diphenyl-	n.s.g.	285(3.34),293(3.43)	35-5717-79
$C_{19}H_{14}ClNOS$			
Benzenamine, 4-chloro-N-(3-ethoxy-2H-naphtho[1,8-bc]thien-2-ylidene)-	MeOH	204(4.9),220(4.8), 268(4.8),342(4.4), 389(4.6)	5-1789-79
$C_{19}H_{14}ClN_3O$			
Pyrimido[1,2-a][1,4]benzodiazepin-1(5H)-one, 9-chloro-3-methyl-7-phenyl-	EtOH	216(4.65)	94-2927-79
Pyrimido[1,2-a][1,4]benzodiazepin-3(5H)-one, 9-chloro-1-methyl-7-phenyl-	EtOH	221(4.49),264(4.47)	94-2927-79
$C_{19}H_{14}ClN_3O_2$			
Pyrimido[4,5-b]quinoline-2,4(3H,10H)-dione, 5-(4-chlorophenyl)-3,10-dimethyl-	EtOH	223(4.50),266(4.44), 322(3.85),408(3.73)	142-0691-79
$C_{19}H_{14}ClN_3O_7$			
Butanedioic acid, [5-(2-chlorophenyl)-2,3-dihydro-7-nitro-2-oxo-1H-1,4-benzodiazepin-3-yl] ester	isoPrOH	215(4.52),248(4.22), 308(4.08)	36-0845-79
$C_{19}H_{14}NP$			
Benzonitrile, 3-(diphenylphosphinyl)-	C_6H_{12}	230(4.40),264(4.00), 269(3.51)	65-0479-79
	12M HCl	230(4.40),276(3.48), 285(3.08)	65-0479-79
Benzonitrile, 4-(diphenylphosphinyl)-	C_6H_{12}	230(4.37),269(3.67), 285(3.96)	65-0479-79
	12M HCl	231(4.53),276(3.57), 291(3.20)	65-0479-79
$C_{19}H_{14}N_2$			
Benzenamine, N-(1H-benz[g]indol-3-ylmethylene)-	EtOH	216(4.45),263(4.51), 285s(4.31),319(4.30), 328(4.30),343(4.21)	103-0741-79
Benzenamine, N-(3H-benz[e]indol-1-ylmethylene)-	EtOH	222(4.55),249s(4.22), 279(4.24),315(4.03), 347(3.80)	103-0741-79
$C_{19}H_{14}N_2O_2$			
5,12-Naphthacenedione, 6-amino-11-(methylamino)-	benzene	550(4.09),590(4.08)	153-0033-79
$C_{19}H_{14}N_2O_3$			
3H-Naphtho[2,1-b]pyran-3-amine, N-(4-nitrophenyl)-	MeOH	300(3.88),312(3.98), 353(3.32)	104-1715-79
	CCl_4	317(4.23),336(4.33)	104-1715-79
	DMSO	302(3.93),317(4.00), 360(4.34),373(4.36)	104-1715-79
	DMSO-NaOMe	367(4.19),600(4.48)	104-1715-79
$C_{19}H_{14}N_2O_4$			
1,3-Isobenzofurandione, 5-[5-[4-(dimethylamino)phenyl]-2-oxazolyl]-	toluene	330(4.30),425(3.91)	103-0028-79
$C_{19}H_{14}N_2O_4S_2$			
Pyrrolo[1,2-b]isoquinoline-5,10-dione,	EtOH	238(4.48),266(4.17),	95-1234-79

Compound	Solvent	λ max (log ε)	Ref.
3-amino-1-(methylthio)-2-(phenylsulfonyl)- (cont.)		317(3.89),450(4.04)	95-1234-79
$C_{19}H_{14}N_2O_5$			
Ethanone, 1-[2-(2-furanyl)-5-methyl-1-(5-nitro-2-furanyl)-3-indolizinyl]-	EtOH	380(4.14),443(4.32)	94-3078-79
Ethanone, 1-[2-(2-furanyl)-7-methyl-1-(5-nitro-2-furanyl)-3-indolizinyl]-	EtOH	385(4.25),441(4.33)	94-3078-79
$C_{19}H_{14}N_2O_5S$			
4-Thia-1-azabicyclo[3.2.0]hept-2-ene-2-carboxylic acid, 7-oxo-3-phenyl-, (4-nitrophenyl)methyl ester	EtOH	258(4.24),327(3.91)	35-6296-79
$C_{19}H_{14}N_2O_6S$			
7H-Furo[3,2-g][1]benzopyran-4-sulfonic acid, 9-methoxy-7-oxo-, (phenylmethylene)hydrazide	MeOH	230(4.52),255(4.40), 305(4.12)	48-1039-79
$C_{19}H_{14}N_2O_8S$			
7H-Furo[3,2-g][1]benzopyran-4-sulfonamide, 9-methoxy-N-methyl-N-(4-nitrophenyl)-7-oxo-	MeOH	230(4.55),260(4.39), 310(4.13)	48-1039-79
$C_{19}H_{14}N_4O$			
2-Propenamide, 2-amino-3-[(9-anthracenylmethylene)amino]-3-cyano-	EtOH	254(4.57),424(3.98)	44-0827-79
Pyrrolo[1,2-a:4,5-b']diquinoxaline, 6-ethoxy-	EtOH	268s(4.53),275(4.60), 296(4.22),305s(4.12), 345s(3.76),362(4.01), 378(4.06),433s(3.53), 455(3.64),490s(3.48)	78-2463-79
$C_{19}H_{14}N_4O_8$			
1H-Pyrazole-3,4-dicarboxylic acid, 1-(2,4-dinitrophenyl)-5-phenyl-, dimethyl ester	CH_2Cl_2	278s(4.02)	24-1193-79
$C_{19}H_{14}N_6O_2$			
1H-Pyrazole-4-carboxylic acid, 1-(acenaphtho[1,2-e][1,2,4]triazin-9-yl)-5-amino-, ethyl ester	MeOH	234(4.81),250s(4.53), 311(3.67)	83-0147-79
$C_{19}H_{14}O$			
Benz[a]anthracene, 8-methoxy-	EtOH	231(4.25),269(4.29), 28C(4.40),291(4.34), 319(3.29),335(3.42), 350(3.48),370(3.33), 384(3.05)	44-0699-79
Benz[a]anthracene, 9-methoxy-	EtOH	224(4.59),245(4.57), 252(4.64),276(4.80), 287(4.95),301(4.52)	44-0699-79
Benz[a]anthracene, 10-methoxy-	EtOH	222(4.58),258(4.61), 264(4.70),278(4.81), 287(4.82),302(4.27), 317(3.94),332(3.93), 348(3.79),370(3.55), 391(3.55)	44-0699-79
Benz[a]anthracene, 11-methoxy-	EtOH	231(4.24),261(4.27), 271(4.25),282(4.37), 294(4.37),319(3.33),	44-0699-79

Compound	Solvent	$\lambda_{max}(\log \epsilon)$	Ref.
Benz[a]anthracene, 11-methoxy- (cont.)		335(3.44),352(3.46), 370(3.25),382(3.00)	44-0699-79
Benz[a]anthracen-12(7H)-one, 9-methyl-	CH_2Cl_2	257(4.24),274s(4.18), 284(4.26),292(4.25), 325(3.89),392s(3.05)	44-1941-79
5(12H)-Naphthacenone, 2-methyl-	EtOH	223(4.68),261(4.40), 304s(4.11),315(4.19), 360(3.34)	44-1941-79
$C_{19}H_{14}OS_2$			
4H,5H-Thiopyrano[2,3-b][1]benzopyran-5-thione, 2-methyl-4-phenyl-	MeOH	210(4.57),228s(4.35), 305s(3.60),353(4.14), 389(4.20)	39-1166-79C
4H,5H-Thiopyrano[3,2-c][1]benzopyran-5-thione, 2-methyl-4-phenyl-	MeOH	215(4.22),246(4.23), 270s(3.95),281(3.98), 310(3.71),355s(3.96), 368(4.04),390(4.11), 410(4.08)	39-1166-79C
$C_{19}H_{14}O_2S$			
4H,5H-Pyrano[3,2-c][1]benzopyran-5-thione, 2-methyl-4-phenyl-	hexane	278(4.15),310s(3.66), 371(4.11),387(4.06)	39-1166-79C
4H,5H-Thiopyrano[2,3-b][1]benzopyran-5-one, 2-methyl-4-phenyl-	MeOH	217(4.37),294(3.86), 302(3.96),314s(3.84)	39-1166-79C
4H,5H-Thiopyrano[3,2-c][1]benzopyran-5-one, 2-methyl-4-phenyl-	MeOH	213(4.52),240(4.18), 248(4.16),286(4.05), 310(4.00),320s(3.97)	39-1166-79C
$C_{19}H_{14}O_3$			
1H-Cyclopenta[1]phenanthrene-1-carboxylic acid, 2,3-dihydro-2-oxo-, methyl ester	EtOH	249(4.70),257(4.94), 278(4.18),288(4.07), 300(4.12),335(3.97), 350(3.97)	39-2034-79C
1-Naphthalenecarboxylic acid, 2-(3-methylbenzoyl)-	EtOH	240(4.30),285s(3.73), 301(3.80),325s(3.49)	44-1941-79
2-Naphthalenecarboxylic acid, 1-(3-methylbenzoyl)-	EtOH	233(4.71),283(3.88), 294(3.79),322(3.20), 335(3.24)	44-1941-79
2-Naphthalenecarboxylic acid, 3-(3-methylbenzoyl)-	EtOH	231(4.75),327s(3.20), 337(3.28)	44-1941-79
4H,5H-Pyrano[3,2-c][1]benzopyran-5-one, 2-methyl-4-phenyl-	MeOH	260(4.06),267(4.03), 273(4.02),302s(3.90), 312(3.90),328s(3.68)	39-1166-79C
$C_{19}H_{14}O_4$			
1H-Cyclopenta[1]phenanthrene-1-carboxylic acid, 2,3-dihydro-1-hydroxy-2-oxo-, methyl ester	EtOH	257(4.76),279(4.08), 290(4.00),301(4.00), 334(3.84),350(3.84)	39-2034-79C
1H-Cyclopenta[1]phenanthrene-3-carboxylic acid, 2,11b-dihydro-11b-hydroxy-2-oxo-, methyl ester	EtOH	257(4.56),264(4.65), 300(4.02),352(3.90)	39-2034-79C
$C_{19}H_{14}O_5$			
5,12-Naphthacenedione, 9,10-dihydro-1,6,11-trihydroxy-8-methyl-	MeOH	223(4.36),272(4.39), 511(4.18),546(4.02)	5-2018-79
$C_{19}H_{14}O_6$			
Methanone, [3-(1,3-benzodioxol-5-yl)-oxiranyl](4-methoxy-5-benzofuranyl)-	MeOH	240(4.5),290s(--)	88-4879-79
Naphthaceno[1,2-b]oxirene-5,10-dione,	MeOH	235(4.54),251(4.47),	5-2018-79

Compound	Solvent	λmax(log ε)	Ref.
1a,2,3,11b-tetrahydro-4,6,11-trihydroxy-1a-methyl- (cont.)		293(3.89),491(4.14), 525s(--)	5-2018-79
$C_{19}H_{14}O_6S_2$			
7H-Furo[3,2-g][1]benzopyran-4-sulfonic acid, 9-methoxy-7-thioxo-, 4-methylphenyl ester	MeOH	225(4.44),255(4.43), 305(4.18),350(3.91)	48-1039-79
$C_{19}H_{14}O_7S$			
7H-Furo[3,2-g][1]benzopyran-4-sulfonic acid, 9-methoxy-7-oxo-, 4-methylphenyl ester	MeOH	225(4.41),255(4.39), 305(4.13),350(3.80)	48-1039-79
$C_{19}H_{15}$			
Cycloheptatrienylium, [1,1'-biphenyl]-2-yl-	CH_2Cl_2	236(--),270(--), 365(3.90),420s(3.64)	88-4999-79
	MeCN	355(3.8),400s(3.7)	88-4999-79
$C_{19}H_{15}ClN_2O_3S$			
2(1H)-Pyrimidinethione, 1-acetyl-4-(1,3-benzodioxol-5-yl)-6-(4-chlorophenyl)-3,4-dihydro-	EtOH	244(4.32),255-294s(4.12), 326(3.85)	23-2734-79
$C_{19}H_{15}ClN_4O_3$			
4H-[1,2,4]Triazino[4,3-d][1,4]benzodiazepine-3,4,7(6H)-trione, 11-chloro-2,8-dihydro-8-methyl-2-(phenylmethyl)-	MeOH	257(4.19),279(4.12), 300s(4.00)	44-0088-79
$C_{19}H_{15}ClO_6$			
Furo[2,3-b]benzopyran-2,3-diol, 3-acetate 2-(3-chlorobenzoate), 2α,3β,3aβ-8a β-tetrahydro-	CH_2Cl_2	235(3.82),279(3.48), 285(3.47)	39-2664-79C
5,12-Naphthacenedione, 7-chloro-7,8,9,10-tetrahydro-1,6,8,11-tetrahydroxy-8-methyl-, trans	MeOH	232(4.51),249(4.41), 288(3.87),489(4.15), 522(3.99)	5-2018-79
$C_{19}H_{15}K$			
Potassium, (triphenylmethyl)-	ether	414s(--),476(4.40)	44-0317-79
$C_{19}H_{15}Li$			
Lithium, (triphenylmethyl)-	ether	390s(--),446(4.34)	44-0317-79
$C_{19}H_{15}NO$			
11H-Benzo[a]carbazole-5-carboxaldehyde, 7,10-dimethyl-	EtOH	250(4.34),290(4.49), 360?(3.80)	39-2506-79C
3H-Benzo[c]quinolizin-3-one, 4,4a-dihydro-1-phenyl-	MeOH	210(4.40),229(4.51), 287(4.31),343(3.61), 394(3.65)	39-0584-79C
3H-Naphtho[2,1-b]pyran-3-amine, N-phenyl-	MeOH	284(3.95),297(4.00), 310(4.00),333(3.79), 346(3.80),370(3.28)	104-1715-79
	MeCN	302(3.93),315(3.90), 340(3.65),352(3.66)	104-1715-79
	CCl_4	287(3.98),300(3.96), 316(3.90),341(3.64), 357(3.66)	104-1715-79
	DMSO	289(4.00),301(4.02), 315(3.95),340(3.76), 354(3.76),384(3.08), 504(2.60)	104-1715-79

Compound	Solvent	$\lambda_{max}(\log \epsilon)$	Ref.
$C_{19}H_{15}NOS$			
Benzenamine, N-(3-ethoxy-2H-naphtho-[1,8-bc]thien-2-ylidene)-	MeOH	203(4.8),223(4.8), 268(4.7),340(4.4), 387(4.6)	5-1789-79
$C_{19}H_{15}NO_2$			
Ethanone, 2-(5-methyl-2-furanyl)-1-phenyl-2-(phenylimino)-	MeOH	293(4.27)	142-1005-79
$C_{19}H_{15}NO_3$			
Benzoic acid, 2-[[1-(phenylmethyl)-1H-pyrrol-2-yl]carbonyl]-	EtOH	205(4.57),296(4.19)	103-0747-79
1,4-Naphthalenedione, 2-acetyl-3-(4-amino-2-methylphenyl)-	dioxan	254(4.29),263(4.30), 333s(3.6),490(3.71)	5-0503-79
1,4-Naphthalenedione, 2-acetyl-3-[4-(methylamino)phenyl]-	dioxan	247s(4.2),253(4.21), 269(4.26),295s(4.2), 510(3.75)	5-0503-79
1,4-Naphthalenedione, 2-acetyl-3-[(2-methylphenyl)amino]-	dioxan	230(4.24),270(4.31), 435(3.62)	5-0503-79
1,4-Naphthalenedione, 2-acetyl-3-[(3-methylphenyl)amino]-	dioxan	230s(4.2),274(4.36), 445(3.63)	5-0503-79
1,4-Naphthalenedione, 2-acetyl-3-[(4-methylphenyl)amino]-	dioxan	232(4.26),273(4.37), 450(3.63)	5-0503-79
$C_{19}H_{15}NO_4$			
7H-Dibenzo[de,g]quinolin-7-one, 1,2,9-trimethoxy-	EtOH	244(4.46),271(4.44), 292s(4.16),377(3.68), 444(3.62)	95-0102-79
7H-Dibenzo[de,g]quinolin-7-one, 1,2,10-trimethoxy-	EtOH	240(4.49),268(4.47), 282s(4.20),302s(3.86), 309(3.87),348(4.09), 385(4.02)	33-1549-79
	EtOH	242(4.45),272(4.44), 284s(4.19),312(3.84), 351(4.07),387(4.00)	95-0102-79
7H-Dibenzo[de,g]quinolin-7-one, 2,3,9-trimethoxy-	EtOH	238s(4.18),275(4.23), 304s(4.14),355s(3.28), 375(3.21),482(3.35)	95-0102-79
4,9-Epoxy-1H-benz[f]isoindole-1,3(2H)-dione, 3a,4,9,9a-tetrahydro-4-(2-hydroxyphenyl)-2-methyl-, endo	ether	276(3.50),283(3.47)	89-0413-79
exo	ether	271(3.39),273(3.40), 281(3.35)	89-0413-79
1,4-Naphthalenedione, 2-acetyl-3-(4-amino-3-methoxyphenyl)-	dioxan	248(4.37),290s(4.0), 336s(3.5),500(3.47)	5-0503-79
1,4-Naphthalenedione, 2-acetyl-3-[(2-methoxyphenyl)amino]-	dioxan	228s(4.3),279(4.10), 440(3.64)	5-0503-79
1,4-Naphthalenedione, 2-acetyl-3-[(3-methoxyphenyl)amino]-	dioxan	224(4.36),279(4.35), 445(3.62)	5-0503-79
1,4-Naphthalenedione, 2-acetyl-3-[(4-methoxyphenyl)amino]-	dioxan	232(4.27),274(4.37), 438(3.58),480(3.59)	5-0503-79
Oxoaporphine, trimethoxy- (m. 256-8°)	EtOH	234(4.52),247(4.61), 322(3.87),470(3.77)	95-0102-79
Splendidine	EtOH	237(4.36),270(4.34), 290s(4.15),415(4.05)	23-1642-79
$C_{19}H_{15}NO_5$			
7H-Dibenzo[de,g]quinolin-7-one, 11-hydroxy-1,2,10-trimethoxy- (glaunine)	EtOH	250(4.40),272(4.22), 310s(3.97),348(3.87), 406(2.75),600(2.68)	105-0367-79

Compound	Solvent	λ max (log ε)	Ref.
Glaunine (cont.)	EtOH-acid	248(4.46),263s(4.41), 285(4.30),320s(3.88), 375(2.94),470s(2.60)	105-0367-79
$C_{19}H_{15}NO_6$			
1,3-Benzenedicarboxylic acid, 5-(4-ethynyl-3,5-diformyl-1(4H)-pyridinyl)-, dimethyl ester	EtOH	207(4.62),232(4.50), 285(4.33),362(3.94)	49-0613-79
Spiro[1,3-dioxolo[4,5-g]isoquinoline-5(6H),7'-[7H]indeno[4,5-d][1,3]dioxol]-6'(8'H)-one, 7,8-dihydro-8'-hydroxy-, cis-(±)-	MeOH	212(4.27),237(4.38), 294(4.03),308s(3.92)	23-1569-79
$C_{19}H_{15}NO_6S$			
7H-Furo[3,2-g][1]benzopyran-4-sulfonamide, 9-methoxy-N-(2-methylphenyl)-7-oxo-	MeOH	225(4.45),260(4.40), 310(4.14)	48-1039-79
7H-Furo[3,2-g][1]benzopyran-4-sulfonamide, 9-methoxy-N-(3-methylphenyl)-7-oxo-	MeOH	225(4.53),255(4.42), 300(4.15)	48-1039-79
7H-Furo[3,2-g][1]benzopyran-4-sulfonamide, 9-methoxy-N-(4-methylphenyl)-7-oxo-	MeOH	215(4.38),255(4.27), 305(4.05)	48-1039-79
7H-Furo[3,2-g][1]benzopyran-4-sulfonamide, 9-methoxy-7-oxo-N-(phenylmethyl)-	MeOH	225(4.49),265(4.13), 300(4.10)	48-1039-79
$C_{19}H_{15}N_2PS$			
Phosphine sulfide, (diazophenylmethyl)-diphenyl-	EtOH	267(4.24),465(1.99)	88-2415-79
$C_{19}H_{15}N_3$			
Benzo[c]cinnolinium 5-[(2-methylphenyl)amino]-, hydroxide, inner salt	CH_2Cl_2	253(4.57),305(4.01), 319(3.93),420(4.15)	39-0185-79C
1H-Benzotriazole, 1-(diphenylmethyl)-	EtOH	258(3.91),280(3.65)	33-2129-79
$C_{19}H_{15}N_3O$			
Benzamide, N-[2-(phenylazo)phenyl]-	EtOH	232(4.24),272(4.21), 327(4.06)	7-0563-79
2(10H)-Phenazinone, 8-amino-7-methyl-10-phenyl-	neutral	513(4.48)	59-0421-79
	cation	436(4.16),498(4.25)	59-0421-79
$C_{19}H_{15}N_3O_2$			
Benzo[b]cyclohept[e][1,4]oxazin-8(5aH)-one, 5a-hydroxy-, phenylhydrazone	MeOH	205(4.73),234(4.36), 278(4.06),440(4.32)	18-3123-79
	MeOH-NaOH	277(4.05),410s(4.00), 472(4.20)	18-3123-79
Naphth[2,3-d]imidazole-4,9-dione, 1,2-dimethyl-5-(phenylamino)-	C_6H_{12}	519(3.70)	39-0702-79C
	EtOH	524(--)	39-0702-79C
	EtOH-HCl	548(--)	39-0902-79C
Naphth[2,3-d]imidazole-4,9-dione, 1,2-dimethyl-8-(phenylamino)-	C_6H_{12}	515(3.70)	39-0702-79C
	EtOH	523(--)	39-0702-79C
	EtOH-HCl	548(--)	39-0702-79C
4H-Pyrido[1',2':1,2]imidazo[4,5-g]-3,1-benzoxazin-4-one, 7,8,9,10-tetrahydro-2-phenyl-	$CHCl_3$	274(4.70),318(4.32), 326(4.30)	39-1056-79C
Pyrimido[4,5-b]quinoline-2,4(3H,10H)-dione, 3,10-dimethyl-5-phenyl-	EtOH	222(4.59),264(4.61), 323(3.98),403(3.94)	142-0691-79
8-Quinolinol, 2,2'-(methylimino)bis-	acid	246(4.50),288(4.47), 333(4.13)	123-0070-79

Compound	Solvent	λ max (log ε)	Ref.
8-Quinolinol, 2,2'-(methylimino)bis- (cont.)	neutral	238(4.40),293(4.52), 361(4.18)	123-0070-79
	dianion	310(4.55)	123-0070-79
$C_{19}H_{15}N_3O_2S$			
Benzenesulfonic acid, 4-methyl-, 5H-indeno[1,2-b]pyridin-5-ylidenehydrazide	EtOH	228(4.88),314(4.48), 386(4.34)	103-0777-79
$C_{19}H_{15}N_3O_3S$			
2H-Naphtho[1,8-bc]thiophen-2-one, 3-ethoxy-, (4-nitrophenyl)hydrazone	MeOH	213(4.7),276(4.6), 355(4.3),450(4.7)	5-1789-79
$C_{19}H_{15}N_3O_5$			
Carbamic acid, [2-(1,2-dihydro-5-nitro-2-oxo-3-pyridinyl)phenyl]-, phenylmethyl ester	EtOH	230(4.17),315(4.09)	39-2902-79C
Carbamic acid, [2-(1,4-dihydro-5-nitro-4-oxo-3-pyridinyl)phenyl]-, phenylmethyl ester	EtOH	233(4.13),337(3.59)	39-2902-79C
$C_{19}H_{15}N_3O_6$			
1H-Pyrazole-3,4-dicarboxylic acid, 1-(4-nitrophenyl)-5-phenyl-, dimethyl ester	CH_2Cl_2	291(4.15)	24-1193-79
$C_{19}H_{15}N_3O_7$			
Butanedioic acid, mono(2,3-dihydro-7-nitro-2-oxo-5-phenyl-1H-1,4-benzodiazepin-3-yl) ester	isoPrOH	219(4.39),264(4.23), 305(4.04)	36-0845-79
$C_{19}H_{15}N_3S_2$			
5,11-Imino-5H,11H-[1,5]dithiocino[2,3-b:6,7-b']dipyridine, 13-(phenylmethyl)-	EtOH	207(4.51),244(4.28), 302(3.88)	78-0869-79
$C_{19}H_{15}O_2$			
[1,1':3',1"-Terphenyl]-2'-yloxy, 5'-methoxy-	PrOH	405(4.70),650(3.60) (anom.)	39-1540-79B
$C_{19}H_{15}S$			
9H-Thioxanthenium, 10-phenyl-, hexafluoroarsenate	MeOH	280(4.35),316(3.89)	47-0977-79
$C_{19}H_{16}BrNO_4$			
1,3-Dioxolo[4,5-g]isoquinoline, 5-[1-(6-bromo-1,3-benzodioxol-5-yl)ethyl]-7,8-dihydro-	EtOH	229(4.39),290(3.88), 310(3.86)	39-0283-79C
$C_{19}H_{16}ClN_5O$			
4H-[1,2,4]triazolo[4,3-a][1,4]benzodiazepinium, 1-(acetylamino)-8-chloro-3-methyl-6-phenyl-, hydroxide, inner salt (hydrate)	EtOH	221(4.58),272s(4.06)	44-2688-79
$C_{19}H_{16}N$			
5H-Indeno[1,2-b]pyridinium, 1-(phenylmethyl)-, bromide	EtOH	208(4.59),294(4.38)	103-1214-79
9H-Indeno[2,1-c]pyridinium, 2-(phenylmethyl)-, bromide	EtOH	205(4.28),300(3.59)	103-1214-79

Compound	Solvent	λ_{max}(log ε)	Ref.
$C_{19}H_{16}NO_5$			
7H-Dibenzo[de,g]quinolinium, 1,11-dihydroxy-2,10-dimethoxy-6-methyl-7-oxo- (arosinine)	EtOH	244(4.58),317(4.53), 413(4.01),590(3.76)	88-4589-79
	EtOH-HCl	246(4.65),292s(4.42), 316s(4.35),391(3.99), 480(3.62)	88-4589-79
$C_{19}H_{16}N_2O$			
Acetamide, 2-cyano-2-(2,3-dihydro-1H-inden-1-ylidene)-N-(2-methylphenyl)-	$CHCl_3$	245(4.19),335(4.47)	80-1485-79
Acetamide, 2-cyano-2-(2,3-dihydro-1H-inden-1-ylidene)-N-(3-methylphenyl)-	$CHCl_3$	240(4.19),335(4.45)	80-1485-79
Acetamide, 2-cyano-2-(2,3-dihydro-1H-inden-1-ylidene)-N-(4-methylphenyl)-	$CHCl_3$	240(4.25),338(4.46)	80-1485-79
Acetamide, 2-cyano-2-(2,3-dihydro-1H-inden-1-ylidene)-N-(phenylmethyl)-	$CHCl_3$	295s(4.31),326(4.32)	80-1485-79
$C_{19}H_{16}N_2OS_2$			
Methanone, [3-amino-5-(methylthio)-4-[(phenylmethylene)amino]-2-thienyl]phenyl-	EtOH	260(4.27),340(4.39)	95-1081-79
$C_{19}H_{16}N_2O_3$			
4-Isoquinolinecarbonitrile, 1,2-dihydro-6,7-dimethoxy-1-oxo-2-(phenylmethyl)-	CH_2Cl_2	230(3.9),254(4.2), 308(3.5),318(3.5)	64-1593-79B
1H-Pyrazole-3-carboxylic acid, 5-benzoyl-4-phenyl-, ethyl ester	EtOH	254(3.21)	4-0849-79
1H-Pyrazol-4-ol, 1-acetyl-3,5-diphenyl-, acetate	EtOH	232(4.31),273(4.31)	23-0904-79
1H-Pyrrole-2,5-dione, 3-acetyl-2,5-dihydro-4-[(4-methylphenyl)amino]-	EtOH	288(4.39),344(4.03)	95-0818-79
$C_{19}H_{16}N_2O_3S$			
2(1H)-Pyrimidinethione, 1-acetyl-4-(1,3-benzodioxol-5-yl)-3,4-dihydro-6-phenyl-	EtOH	239(4.42),253-291s(4.17), 328(3.99)	23-2734-79
$C_{19}H_{16}N_2O_3S_2$			
Propanenitrile, 3-(1,2-dihydro-1-methyl-2-oxo-3H-indol-3-ylidene)-3-(methylthio)-2-(phenylsulfonyl)-	EtOH	262(4.35),297(3.79), 345(3.97),357(3.97)	95-1234-79
$C_{19}H_{16}N_2O_4$			
1,3-Dioxolo[4,5-g]quinoline-7-carboxylic acid, 5-ethyl-5,8-dihydro-8-(phenylimino)-	MeOH	230(4.5),265(4.5), 285(4.5),328(4.1)	4-1353-79
$C_{19}H_{16}N_2O_4S$			
1H-Pyrazole-3,4-dicarboxylic acid, 1-phenyl-5-(phenylthio)-, dimethyl ester	CH_2Cl_2	241(4.27)	24-1193-79
$C_{19}H_{16}N_2O_5$			
Benzoic acid, 2,2'-[(5-oxo-3-cyclopentene-1,2-diyl)diimino]bis-	n.s.g.	252(4.23),342(4.0)	12-1079-79
$C_{19}H_{16}N_2O_6$			
Methanone, (5,6-dimethyl-1-isoquinolinyl)(5-methoxy-2-nitrophenyl)-	EtOH	264(4.32),322(3.91)	95-0102-79

Compound	Solvent	$\lambda_{max}(\log \epsilon)$	Ref.
$C_{19}H_{16}N_3O$			
Phenazinium, 3-amino-7-hydroxy-2-methyl-5-phenyl-	neutral	513(4.48)	39-0304-79B
	cation	436(4.16),498(4.25)	39-0304-79B
	cation	436(4.14),498(4.28)	44-0025-79
$C_{19}H_{16}N_4$			
Pyridazine, 6-(4-methylphenyl)-3,4-di-1H-pyrrol-1-yl-	EtOH	269(4.65)	80-0453-79
$C_{19}H_{16}N_4O$			
Pyrazinecarboxamide, 3-cyano-1,6-dihydro-5-(4-methylphenyl)-6-phenyl-	MeOH	265(4.26),386(4.02)	44-4871-79
Pyrazinecarboxamide, 3-cyano-1,6-dihydro-6-(4-methylphenyl)-5-phenyl-	MeOH	254(4.25),383(3.97)	44-4871-79
Pyrazinecarboxamide, 3-cyano-4,5-dihydro-5-(4-methylphenyl)-6-phenyl-	MeOH	263(4.26),385(3.93)	44-4871-79
$C_{19}H_{16}N_4O_2$			
Benzo[g]pteridine-2,4(3H,10H)-dione, 10-(3,4-dimethylphenyl)-3-methyl-	EtOH	264(4.52),336(3.97), 429s(4.03),440(4.06), 461s(3.95)	4-1365-79
Benzo[g]pteridine-2,4(3H,10H)-dione, 3-methyl-10-(2-phenylethyl)-	EtOH	263(4.43),336(3.91), 422s(4.10),440(3.93), 461s(3.95)	4-1365-79
3,3'(4H,4'H)-Spirobi[2H-[1,3]oxazino-[3,2-a]benzimidazole]	CH_2Cl_2	250(4.45),282(4.22), 288(4.21)	18-0930-79
$C_{19}H_{16}N_4O_2S$			
Isothiazolo[3,4-d]pyrimidine-4,6(5H,7H)-dione, 5-methyl-7-phenyl-3-[(phenylmethyl)amino]-	EtOH	230(4.41),270(4.14), 294(3.98)	95-0989-79
$C_{19}H_{16}N_4O_3S$			
1H-Pyrazole-4,5-dione, 3-[(2-hydroxy-1-naphthalenyl)azo]-1-(phenylsulfonyl)-	$CHCl_3$	480(4.18)	104-1396-79
$C_{19}H_{16}N_4O_7S_3$			
5-Thia-1-azabicyclo[4.2.0]oct-2-ene-2-carboxylic acid, 3-[[(4-carboxy-1,2,3-thiadiazol-5-yl)thio]methyl]-7-[(hydroxyphenylacetyl)amino]-8-oxo-, disodium salt	MeOH	265(3.85),302(3.81)	87-1214-79
$C_{19}H_{16}N_4S_2$			
3,3'(4H,4'H)-Spirobi[2H-[1,3]thiazino-[3,2-a]benzimidazole]	CH_2Cl_2	235(4.41),264(4.37), 271(4.38),291(4.48), 299(4.50)	18-0930-79
$C_{19}H_{16}O_2$			
Benzenemethanol, 4-hydroxy-α,α-diphenyl-	n.s.g.	280(3.24),286(3.14)	35-5717-79
1-Naphthalenecarboxylic acid, 2-[(3-methylphenyl)methyl]-	EtOH	235(4.23),275(3.65), 321(2.50)	44-1941-79
2-Naphthalenecarboxylic acid, 3-[(3-methylphenyl)methyl]-	EtOH	232(4.82),267(3.78), 280(3.78),330s(3.04), 338(3.05)	44-1941-79
5-Oxaspiro[2.4]hept-6-en-4-one, 6-(4-methylphenyl)-1-phenyl-	EtOH	223s(--),282(217)[sic]	28-0133-79A
[1,1':3',1"-Terphenyl]-2'-ol, 5'-methoxy-	PrOH	315(3.95)	39-1540-79B

Compound	Solvent	λ_{max}(log ε)	Ref.
$C_{19}H_{16}O_3$			
2-Cyclopenten-1-one, 5-acetoxy-3,4-diphenyl-, trans	n.s.g.	290(4.8)	39-0274-79C
Methanone, (4-ethoxy-8-hydroxy-1-naphthalenyl)phenyl-	MeOH	300(3.7),318(3.7), 328(3.6)	5-0959-79
5,12-Naphthacenecione, 7,8,9,10-tetrahydro-1-methoxy-	EtOH	215(4.51),265(4.63), 376(3.78)	94-2229-79
5-Oxaspiro[2.4]hept-6-en-4-one, 1-(4-methoxyphenyl)-6-phenyl-	EtOH	222s(--),280(217)[sic]	28-0133-79A
$C_{19}H_{16}O_3S$			
1-Benzothiepin-3-ol, 5-methoxy-4-phenyl-, acetate	MeOH	265(4.17)	24-0781-79
1-Benzothiepin-5-ol, 3-methoxy-4-phenyl-, acetate	MeOH	259(4.15)	24-0781-79
$C_{19}H_{16}O_4S$			
1-Benzothiepin-3-ol, 5-methoxy-4-phenyl-, acetate, 1-oxide	MeOH at -10°	288(3.84)	24-0781-79
1-Benzothiepin-5-ol, 3-methoxy-4-phenyl-, acetate, 1-oxide	MeOH at -10°	265(4.06)	24-0781-79
$C_{19}H_{16}O_5$			
1,4-Naphthalenedione, 8-(3,4-dimethoxyphenyl)-2-methoxy-	MeOH	240(4.32),275(4.27), 350s(4.40)	12-0071-79
$C_{19}H_{16}O_5S$			
1-Benzothiepin-3-ol, 5-methoxy-4-phenyl-, acetate, 1,1-dioxide	MeOH	295(4.06)	24-0781-79
1-Benzothiepin-5-ol, 3-methoxy-4-phenyl-, acetate, 1,1-dioxide	MeOH	283s(3.92)	24-0781-79
$C_{19}H_{16}O_6$			
2-Anthracenebutanoic acid, 9,10-dihydro-1,4-dihydroxy-9,10-dioxo-, methyl ester	MeOH	205(4.34),226(4.32), 250(4.56),283(3.99), 489(3.98),518s(--)	5-0019-79
2-Anthracenebutanoic acid, 9,10-dihydro-1,8-dihydroxy-9,10-dioxo-, methyl ester	MeOH	204(4.21),229(4.57), 260(4.40),291(3.93), 438(4.03)	5-0019-79
Anthra[2,3-e][1,3]dioxepin-7,12-dione, 1,5-dihydro-6,13-dihydroxy-3,3-dimethyl-	MeOH	236s(--),251(4.63), 255s(--),291(3.95), 479(4.02),514(3.79)	5-0019-79
11bH-Benzofuro[2,3-b][1]benzopyran-11-one, 10b-acetoxy-5a,10b-dihydro-3-methoxy-5a-methyl-, cis	MeOH	287(4.23)	18-0529-79
4H-1-Benzopyran-4-one, 3-(1,3-benzodioxol-5-ylmethyl)-5,7-dimethoxy-	EtOH	226(4.40),254(4.01), 287(4.41)	150-1713-79
4H-1-Benzopyran-4-one, 3-(1,3-benzodioxol-5-ylmethylene)-2,3-dihydro-5,7-dimethoxy-	EtOH	238(5.21),346(5.10), 352(5.10)	150-1713-79
Phenanthro[1,2-d]-1,3-dioxol-8-ol, 7,9-dimethoxy-, acetate	$CHCl_3$	268(4.69)	39-2449-79C
$C_{19}H_{16}O_7$			
11H-Benzofuro[2,3-b][1]benzopyran-11-one, 10b-acetoxy-5a,10b-dihydro-3,8-dimethoxy-	MeOH	233(4.14),283(4.19), 311s(3.94)	18-0529-79
4H-1-Benzopyran-4-one, 3-(1,3-benzodioxol-5-yl)-5,6,7-trimethoxy- (odoratine)	EtOH	207(4.73),264(4.65), 292s(4.44)	39-2107-79C

Compound	Solvent	$\lambda_{max}(\log \epsilon)$	Ref.
4H-1-Benzopyran-4-one, 3-(1,3-benzodioxol-5-yl)-5,7,8-trimethoxy-	EtOH	207(4.52),226s(4.37), 262(4.53),294s(4.10)	39-2107-79C
4H-1-Benzopyran-4-one, 3-(1,3-benzodioxol-5-yl)-6,7,8-trimethoxy-	$CHCl_3$	264(4.38),292s(4.15), 320(3.86)	102-0366-79
2,5-Cyclohexadiene-1,4-dione, 2-(6,7-dimethoxy-2-methyl-4-oxo-4H-1-benzopyran-3-yl)-5-methoxy-	MeOH	322(4.17)	18-0529-79
β_1-Rhodomycinone, (±)-	MeOH	234(4.32),253(4.23), 294(3.65),492(3.98), 513(3.83),526(3.83)	5-2018-79
10-epi-	MeOH	234(4.42),253(4.29), 289(3.76),492(4.02), 524(3.87)	5-2018-79
$C_{19}H_{16}O_9$			
Pentamethylflavellagic acid	EtOH	248(3.76),350(3.24), 359(3.26)	102-1017-79
$C_{19}H_{17}BrN_8O$			
2-Naphthalenol, 1-[[4-[(4-bromo-5-methyl-1H-pyrazol-3-yl)azo]-1,3-dimethyl-1H-pyrazol-5-yl]azo]-	MeOH	345s(4.05),380(4.20), 405(4.14)	103-0657-79
$C_{19}H_{17}BrO_7$			
Cyclopenta[c]furo[3',2':4,5]furo[2,3-h][1]benzopyran-1,11-dione, 9-bromo-8-ethoxy-2,3,6a,8,9,9a-hexahydro-4-methoxy-, (6aα,8β,9α,9aα)-	CH_2Cl_2	230(4.29),260(4.10), 346(4.21)	39-2664-79C
$C_{19}H_{17}ClN$			
Quinolinium, 4-[2-(4-chlorophenyl)ethenyl]-1-ethyl-, iodide, (E)-	MeOH	391(4.48)	64-1556-79B
$C_{19}H_{17}ClN_2O_2$			
6H-Anthra[1,9-cd]isoxazol-6-one, 3-chloro-5-(pentylamino)-	dioxan	500(4.20),538(4.24)	104-0510-79
$C_{19}H_{17}ClN_2O_2S$			
2(1H)-Pyrimidinethione, 1-acetyl-6-(4-chlorophenyl)-3,4-dihydro-4-(4-methoxyphenyl)-	EtOH	245(4.34),255-281s(4.18), 328(3.97)	23-2734-79
$C_{19}H_{17}Cl_2N_5$			
4',5-Bipyrimidine, 2,2'-dichloro-6-phenyl-4'-(1-piperidinyl)-	EtOH	245(4.53),286(4.57), 346(3.92)	103-0671-79
$C_{19}H_{17}F_3N_2O_5S$			
8H-3,8a-(Iminomethano)-4H,6H-oxazolo-[4,3-b][1,3]thiazine-4,8-dione, dihydro-9-methoxy-2,2-dimethyl-6-(phenylmethylene)-10-(trifluoroacetyl)-	THF	284(4.38)	39-0170-79C
$C_{19}H_{17}HgNO_2$			
1H-Inden-1-one, 2-[(1-methylethyl)iminomethyl]-3-(phenylmercurioxy)-	benzene	287(4.07),300(4.21), 340(4.25)	103-0056-79
	DMSO	286(3.91),297(4.18), 338(4.38)	103-0056-79
$C_{19}H_{17}N$			
2H-Benz[f]isoindole, 4,9-dihydro-2-methyl-4-phenyl-	EtOH	263(3.46),272(3.29), 348(3.05)	44-2667-79

Compound	Solvent	λ_{max}(log ε)	Ref.
5H-Benzo[b]carbazole, 5,6,11-trimethyl-	EtOH	237(4.05),270s(4.31), 278(4.36),287(4.35), 300(4.21),323(3.77), 337s(3.47),370s(3.28), 388(3.55),406(3.59)	150-4801-79
[1,1'-Biphenyl]-2-amine, N-(phenylmethyl)-	EtOH	310(3.58)	33-2129-79
$C_{19}H_{17}NO$			
2-Propen-1-one, 1-(1,3-dimethyl-1H-indol-2-yl)-3-phenyl-	EtOH	225(4.47),285s(4.18), 315s(4.29),340(4.30)	39-2154-79C
$C_{19}H_{17}NO_2$			
Benzoic acid, 2-[[1-(phenylmethyl)-1H-pyrrol-2-yl]methyl]-	EtOH	206(4.57)	103-0747-79
$C_{19}H_{17}NO_2S$			
7H-Pyrano[2,3-c]acridine-7-thione, 3,12-dihydro-6-hydroxy-3,3,12-trimethyl-	CH_2Cl_2-DMF	410(4.26),490(3.75)	36-0036-79
$C_{19}H_{17}NO_3$			
Anonaine, N-acetyl-	MeOH	217(4.24),269(4.12), 312(3.49)	100-0325-79
Dehydroisolaureline	EtOH	264(4.75),334(4.08)	100-0325-79
Methanone, phenyl(2,3,3a,6a-tetrahydro-5-methyl-2-phenylfuro[2,3-d]isoxazol-3-yl)-	MeOH	246(4.43)	142-1005-79
9-Phenanthreneacetic acid, 10-(2-amino-2-oxoethyl)-, methyl ester	EtOH	225(4.36),249(4.69), 256(4.80),279(4.09), 288(3.98),300(4.02)	39-2034-79C
7H-Pyrano[2,3-c]acridin-7-one, 3,12-dihydro-6-hydroxy-3,3,12-trimethyl- (noracronine)	CH_2Cl_2-DMF	410(3.70)	36-0036-79
1H-Pyrrole-2-carboxylic acid, 3-hydroxy-1-(phenylmethyl)-, phenylmethyl ester	EtOH	266(4.27)	94-1448-79
$C_{19}H_{17}NO_4$			
11H-Indeno[1,2-c]isoquinolin-2-ol, 3,8,9-trimethoxy-, hydrochloride	EtOH	243(4.37),277(4.50), 308(4.25),330(4.19)	78-2555-79
4-Isoquinolinecarboxaldehyde, 3-(3,4-dimethoxyphenyl)-1,2-dihydro-2-methyl-1-oxo-	EtOH	237(4.24)	78-1861-79
$C_{19}H_{17}NO_5$			
2-Anthracenecarboperoxoic acid, 1-amino-9,10-dihydro-9,10-dioxo-, 1,1-dimethylethyl ester	toluene	490(3.94)	93-0903-79
1,3-Dioxolo[4,5-g]isoindolo[1,2-a]isoquinolin-8(6H)-one, 5,12b-dihydro-9,10-dimethoxy-, (±)-	EtOH	260(3.92),280s(3.22)	44-4347-79
$C_{19}H_{17}NO_8$			
Benzo[g]quinoline-2-carboxylic acid, 7-butyl-5,10-dihydro-3,4,9-trihydroxy-8-methoxy-5,10-dioxo- (phomazarin)	MeOH	231(4.54),277(4.77), 430(3.92)	39-0807-79C
$C_{19}H_{17}N_2O_2$			
Quinolinium, 1-ethyl-4-[2-(4-nitrophen-	MeOH	375(4.49)	64-1556-79B

Compound	Solvent	$\lambda_{max}(\log \epsilon)$	Ref.
yl)ethenyl]-, iodide (cont.)			64-1556-79B
$C_{19}H_{17}N_3$			
Propanedinitrile, [[4-[ethyl(phenylmethyl)amino]phenyl]methylene]-	EtOH	433(4.67)	110-1769-79
	EtOH-KOH	341(--)	110-1769-79
	CCl_4	423(--)	110-1769-79
	KBr	443(--)	110-1769-79
$C_{19}H_{17}N_3O$			
Isoxazole, 3-methyl-4-[[(4-methylphenyl)azo]-5-(2-phenylethenyl)-	$CHCl_3$	296(4.44),372(4.45)	103-0968-79
$C_{19}H_{17}N_3OS$			
3H-Pyrazol-3-one, 4-(3-ethyl-2(3H)-benzothiazolylidene)-2,4-dihydro-5-methyl-2-phenyl-	EtOH	378(4.25)	73-1413-79
$C_{19}H_{17}N_3O_2$			
Isoxazole, 4-[(4-methoxyphenyl)azo]-3-methyl-5-(2-phenylethenyl)-	$CHCl_3$	309(4.41),382(4.45)	103-0968-79
3H-Pyrazol-3-one, 4-(3-ethyl-2(3H)-benzoxazolylidene)-2,4-dihydro-5-methyl-2-phenyl-	EtOH	342(4.40)	73-1413-79
$C_{19}H_{17}N_3O_3$			
1H-Pyrazole-3-carboxylic acid, 5-[(hydroxyimino)phenylmethyl]-4-phenyl-, ethyl ester	EtOH	252(3.17)	4-0849-79
$C_{19}H_{17}N_3O_3S$			
3-Indolethiocarboxamide, N-acetyl-2-[(phenylmethoxycarbonyl)amino]-	$CHCl_3$	268(4.20),287(4.30), 393(4.16)	103-0179-79
$C_{19}H_{17}N_3O_4$			
1H-Pyrazole-5-carboxylic acid, 3-benzoyl-4,5-dihydro-1-nitroso-4-phenyl-, ethyl ester	EtOH	249(3.33),286(3.14)	4-0849-79
$C_{19}H_{17}N_3O_5$			
Butanedioic acid, mono(7-amino-2,3-dihydro-2-oxo-5-phenyl-1H-1,4-benzodiazepin-3-yl) ester	isoPrOH	243(4.49),354(3.43)	36-0845-79
$C_{19}H_{17}N_4$			
Phenazinium, 3,7-diamino-2-methyl-5-phenyl-	cation	520(4.58)	59-0421-79
$C_{19}H_{17}O_3P$			
Phosphorin, dihydro-4-(hydroxymethylene)-2,6-diphenyl-1-methoxy-, P-oxide, lithium salt	MeOH	343(4.54)	24-1272-79
$C_{19}H_{17}Se$			
Selenonium, (4-methylphenyl)diphenyl-, hexafluoroarsenate	MeOH	225(4.34),265(3.57), 272(3.40)	47-1047-79
$C_{19}H_{18}$			
Bicyclo[3.1.0]hex-2-ene, 3-methyl-2,6-diphenyl-, (4-endo,6-exo)	n.s.g.	271(4.02)	54-0192-79
(4-exo,6-exo)	n.s.g.	270(3.79)	54-0192-79

Compound	Solvent	λmax(log ε)	Ref.
Bicyclo[6.1.0]nona-2,4,6-triene, 9-(4-phenyl-1,3-butadienyl)-, [1α,8α,9α(1E,3Z)]-	MeCN	226(4.28),233s(4.26), 240s(4.14),295s(4.64), 303(4.65),322s(4.46)	33-0718-79
1,3-Cyclohexadiene, 6-methyl-1,5-diphenyl-, cis	pentane	305(4.32)	54-0192-79
trans	pentane	305(4.11)	54-0192-79
1,3,5-Heptatriene, 1,5-diphenyl-, (E,E,E)-	pentane	309(4.48),320(4.60), 334(4.44)	54-0192-79
(E,E,Z)-	pentane	309(--),320(--), 335(--)	54-0192-79
(E,Z,E)-	pentane	265(4.18),303(4.34)	54-0192-79
(E,Z,Z)-	pentane	309(4.45),320(4.49), 337(4.32)	54-0192-79
(Z,E,E)-	pentane	250(4.13),308(4.44)	54-0192-79
(Z,E,Z)-	pentane	306(4.35)	54-0192-79
(Z,Z,E)-	pentane	257(4.30),290(4.26)	54-0192-79
(Z,Z,Z)-	pentane	301(4.37)	54-0192-79
Pyrene, 9,10-dihydro-1-(1-methylethyl)-	EtOH	217(4.47),259(4.67), 280(4.06),292(4.00), 304(4.01)	42-0907-79
$C_{19}H_{18}BrNO_4$			
1,3-Dioxolo[4,5-g]isoquinoline, 5-[1-(6-bromo-1,3-benzodioxol-5-yl)ethyl]-5,6,7,8-tetrahydro-	EtOH	229s(3.98),287(3.92)	39-0283-79C
$C_{19}H_{18}BrN_3O_4$			
1H-Indole-3-propanamide, α-amino-6-bromo-N-[2-(3,4,5-trihydroxyphenyl)ethenyl]-, [S-(E)]-	MeOH	227(4.49),291(4.04), 296(4.08),311s(3.97)	23-2325-79
$C_{19}H_{18}BrN_5O_4$			
1H-Purine-2,6-dione, 8-bromo-7-[4-(1,3-dihydro-1,3-dioxo-2H-isoindol-2-yl)-butyl]-3,7-dihydro-1,3-dimethyl-	EtOH	279(4.06)	118-0581-79
$C_{19}H_{18}ClNO_5$			
Benzo[g]quinoline-5,10-dione, 7-butyl-4-chloro-9-hydroxy-3,8-dimethoxy-	MeOH	245(4.17),270(4.31), 297(4.16),402(3.68)	39-0807-79C
$C_{19}H_{18}ClNO_6$			
[1,1'-Biphenyl]-2,4-dicarboxylic acid, 4'-chloro-3-hydroxy-5-methyl-6-nitroso-, diethyl ester	DMF	690(1.99)	104-0311-79
$C_{19}H_{18}FN_5O_4S_2$			
4H-1,4-Benzoxazine-4-ethanesulfonyl fluoride, 6-(acetylamino)-7-(2,1-benzisothiazol-3-ylazo)-2,3-dihydro-	acetone	568(4.42)	44-3847-79
$C_{19}H_{18}N$			
Quinolinium, 1-ethyl-4-(2-phenylethenyl)-, iodide, (E)-	MeOH	388(4.46)	64-1556-79B
$C_{19}H_{18}NO$			
Quinolinium, 1-ethyl-2-[2-(2-hydroxyphenyl)ethenyl]-, iodide	EtOH	393(4.40),563(4.44)	80-1491-79
	$CHCl_3$	413(4.41),620(4.36)	80-1491-79
	CCl_4	413(4.29),615(4.02)	80-1491-79
Quinolinium, 1-ethyl-2-[2-(4-hydroxyphenyl)ethenyl]-, iodide	EtOH	433(4.52),560(4.02)	80-1491-79
	$CHCl_3$	425(4.49),590(3.88)	80-1491-79

Compound	Solvent	$\lambda_{max}(\log \epsilon)$	Ref.
$C_{19}H_{18}NOPS_3$			
Phosphoramidotrithioic acid, (4-methoxyphenyl)-, diphenyl ester	EtOH	212(4.52),233(4.50)	64-0297-79B
$C_{19}H_{18}NO_4P$			
Phosphorin, 1,1-dihydro-1,1-dimethoxy-2,6-diphenyl-	MeOH	248(3.86),396(4.33)	24-1272-79
$C_{19}H_{18}N_2$			
3,4-Diazabicyclo[4.1.0]hepta-2,4-diene, 7,7-dimethyl-2,5-diphenyl-	hexane	321(4.10)	20-0905-79
	$CHCl_3$	324(4.08)	20-0905-79
1H-Dibenz[e,g]indole-3-methanamine, N,N-dimethyl-	EtOH	207(4.40),253(4.67), 261(4.84),292(4.27), 313(3.88)	103-0302-79
1H-Pyrazole, 4-methyl-5-(1-methylethenyl)-1,3-diphenyl-	CH_2Cl_2	240(4.18),272(4.27)	24-1206-79
1H-Pyrazole, 3-(2-methyl-1-propenyl)-1,5-diphenyl-	EtOH	212(4.24),245(4.44)	4-0657-79
Pyrazolo[1,5-a]quinoline, 4,5-dihydro-3,4-dimethyl-2-phenyl-	CH_2Cl_2	280(4.30),298(4.28)	24-1206-79
Pyridazine, 4-(1-methylethyl)-3,6-diphenyl-	hexane	260(4.37)	20-0905-79
$C_{19}H_{18}N_2O$			
1,6-Benzodiazocin-2(1H)-one, 1-ethyl-3-methyl-5-phenyl-	MeOH	258(4.26),327(3.40)	39-0584-79C
	MeOH-$HClO_4$	244(3.72),307(3.95)	39-0584-79C
[1,1'-Biphenyl]-4-acetonitrile, α-(4-morpholinylmethylene)-	MeOH	267(4.03),328(4.42)	83-0039-79
4H-Pyrazol-4-one, 1,5-dihydro-5-methyl-5-(1-methylethenyl)-1,3-diphenyl-	CH_2Cl_2	252(4.12),260(4.11), 281(4.24),427(4.20)	24-1206-79
$C_{19}H_{18}N_2OS$			
2(1H)-Pyrimidinethione, 1-acetyl-3,4-dihydro-4-(4-methylphenyl)-6-phenyl-	EtOH	238(4.32),325(3.9)	23-2734-79
$C_{19}H_{18}N_2O_2$			
Anthra[1,9-cd]isoxazol-6-one, 3-(pentylamino)-	dioxan	503(5.69)	104-0510-79
Anthra[1,9-cd]isoxazol-6-one, 5-(pentylamino)-	dioxan	495(4.17),533(4.22)	104-0510-79
$C_{19}H_{18}N_2O_2S$			
2(1H)-Pyrimidinethione, 1-acetyl-3,4-dihydro-4-(4-methoxyphenyl)-6-phenyl-	EtOH	239(4.39),253-281s(4.15), 330(4.06)	23-2734-79
$C_{19}H_{18}N_2O_3$			
Acetic acid, (10-carbazoylmethyl-9-phenanthrenyl)-, methyl ester	EtOH	225(4.41),249(4.67), 257(4.76),278(4.03), 289(3.95),301(4.00)	39-2034-79C
Indolo[2,3-a]quinolizine-3-carboxylic acid, 1-ethyl-4,6,7,12-tetrahydro-4-oxo-, methyl ester	MeOH	215(4.31),266(3.75), 280(3.56),320(3.46), 420(4.17)	24-1889-79
2-Propenenitrile, 3-[1,3-dihydro-1-methoxy-6-methyl-7-(phenylmethoxy)-furo[3,4-c]pyridin-4-yl]-	EtOH	223s(--),272(4.11), 320(4.32)	88-2603-79
Spiro[2H-1-benzopyran-2,2'-[2H]indole], 1',3'-dihydro-1',3',3'-trimethyl-6-nitro-	n.s.g.	254(4.03),270(4.12), 301(3.81),341(3.95)	103-1329-79
$C_{19}H_{18}N_2O_3S$			
5H-Thiazolo[3,2-a]quinazoline-1,5(2H)-	MeOH	230(4.51),276(4.24),	2-0039-79B

Compound	Solvent	λ_{max}(log ε)	Ref.
dione, 3a-ethoxy-3a,4-dihydro-2-methyl-4-phenyl- (cont.)		315(3.65)	2-0039-79B
$C_{19}H_{18}N_2O_4$			
10bH-Oxazolo[2,3-a]isoquinoline, 2,3-dihydro-10b-[(3-methoxy-2-nitrophenyl)methyl]-	EtOH	219(4.38),236(4.45), 331(3.54)	44-0285-79
3-Quinolinecarboxylic acid, 1-ethyl-1,4-dihydro-6-hydroxy-7-methoxy-4-(phenylimino)-	MeOH	248(4.5),260(4.4), 282(4.4)	4-1353-79
$C_{19}H_{18}N_2O_5$			
4H-Benzofuro[3,2-f]indazol-4-one, 8-acetyl-1,4a-dihydro-5,7-dihydroxy-1,3,4a,6-tetramethyl-, (-)-	MeOH	227(4.62),246(4.44), 285(4.31)	87-1380-79
1H-Benz[f]indazole-3-carboxylic acid, 4,9-dihydro-4,9-dioxo-1-(tetrahydro-2H-pyran-2-yl)-, ethyl ester, (±)-	EtOH	246(4.49),265(4.11)	111-0151-79
1H-Benz[f]indazole-4,9-dione, 1-[6-(acetoxymethyl)tetrahydro-2H-pyran-2-yl]-, trans	EtOH	246(4.47),270(3.98)	111-0151-79
2H-Benz[f]indazole-4,9-dione, 2-[6-(acetoxymethyl)tetrahydro-2H-pyran-2-yl]-, cis	EtOH	246(4.68)	111-0151-79
$C_{19}H_{18}N_2O_6$			
Methanone, (3,4-dihydro-5,6-dimethoxy-1-isoquinolinyl)(5-methoxy-2-nitrophenyl)-	EtOH	317(4.23)	95-0102-79
Methanone, (3,4-dihydro-6,7-dimethoxy-1-isoquinolinyl)(5-methoxy-2-nitrophenyl)-	EtOH	234(4.16),265s(4.02), 325(3.92)	95-0102-79
$C_{19}H_{18}N_2S$			
Benzenamine, N-(4,5,6,7-tetrahydro-3-phenyl-2(3H)-benzothiazolylidene)-	EtOH	284(3.835),311(3.884)	48-0249-79
$C_{19}H_{18}N_3$			
4H-Pyrazolium, 3-(4-cyanophenyl)-1,4,5-trimethyl-4-phenyl-	EtOH	217s(4.45),250s(4.05), 355s(4.04),390(4.10)	23-1186-79
$C_{19}H_{18}N_4$			
Pyridazine, 4,5-dihydro-6-(4-methylphenyl)-3,4-di-1H-pyrrol-1-yl-	EtOH	248(4.54)	80-0453-79
$C_{19}H_{18}N_4O_3$			
1H-Pyrazole-4,5-dione, 3-(acetoxymethyl)-1-(4-methylphenyl)-, 4-(phenylhydrazone)	n.s.g.	212(3.86),254(3.95), 398(4.21)	106-0531-79
$C_{19}H_{18}N_4O_3S$			
Benzoic acid, 4-[(4a,9a-dihydro-4a-hydroxy-9-methyl-[1,3,4]thiadiazino-[5,6-b]indol-3-yl)amino]-, methyl ester	EtOH	288(4.01),366(3.98), 452(3.70)	104-0765-79
Benzoic acid, 4-[[[1,3-dihydro-1-methyl-3-oxo-2H-indol-2-ylidene)hydrazino]thioxomethyl]amino]-, ethyl ester	EtOH	283(3.97),372(3.81), 538(3.67)	104-0765-79

Compound	Solvent	$\lambda_{max}(\log \epsilon)$	Ref.
$C_{19}H_{18}N_4O_4$			
L-xylo-2-Hexulosonic acid, 3,6-anhydro-3-C-[(4-methylphenyl)azo]-, γ-lactone, 2-(phenylhydrazone)	n.s.g.	237(3.85),284(3.92), 344(4.00)	106-0531-79
$C_{19}H_{18}N_4O_5S$			
Benzenesulfonamide, N-[[8-(5-nitro-2-pyridinyl)-2-oxo-8-azabicyclo[3.2.1]-oct-3-en-6-yl]methyl]-, endo	$CHCl_3$	245(3.65),348(4.04)	39-1525-79C
3,5-Methano-6H-pyrrolo[3,2-b]pyridin-6-one, octahydro-4-(5-nitro-2-pyridinyl)-1-(phenylsulfonyl)-	$CHCl_3$	245(3.74),352(4.20)	39-1525-79C
$C_{19}H_{18}N_4O_6$			
2H-Pyrrole-5-carboxaldehyde, 3,4-dihydro-2,2-dimethyl-3-phenyl-, O-(2,4-dinitrophenyl)oxime, 1-oxide	EtOH	212(4.31),327(4.43)	12-1775-79
$C_{19}H_{18}N_4O_7$			
2-Cyclopenten-1-one, 4,5-bis[(2-methoxy-4-nitrophenyl)amino]-	n.s.g.	231(4.22),258(4.11), 385(4.45)	12-1079-79
$C_{19}H_{18}O$			
5H-Benzocyclohepten-5-one, 6,7,8,9-tetrahydro-6-[(4-methylphenyl)methylene]-	isooctane	235(4.00),250(3.86), 302(4.17)	65-1407-79
	MeOH	238(4.15),268(4.00), 314(4.34)	65-1407-79
2-Cyclohexen-1-one, 3-(4-methylphenyl)-5-phenyl-	H_2SO_4	394(4.51)	124-1093-79
$C_{19}H_{18}O_2$			
5H-Benzocyclohepten-5-one, 6,7,8,9-tetrahydro-6-[(4-methoxyphenyl)-methylene]-	isooctane	249(4.18),321(4.20)	65-1407-79
	MeOH	260(3.96),332(4.33)	65-1407-79
2,8-Chrysenediol, 4b,5,6,12-tetrahydro-4b-methyl-	EtOH	217(4.33),270(4.10), 304(3.49),320(3.36)	12-1107-79
2-Cyclohexen-1-one, 3-(4-methoxyphenyl)-5-phenyl-	H_2SO_4	415(4.53)	124-1093-79
Phenanthro[10,1-bc]pyran-9(8H)-one, 4,5-dihydro-3,8,8-trimethyl-	EtOH	215(4.850),250(4.676), 272(4.456),397(4.155)	88-0405-79
$C_{19}H_{18}O_2S$			
1-Benzothiepin, 3,5-dimethoxy-2-methyl-4-phenyl-	heptane	244(4.25),270s(4.11), 305s(3.74)	64-1145-79B
$C_{19}H_{18}O_3$			
1(2H)-Naphthalenone, 2-acetyl-3,4-dihydro-2-(4-methoxyphenyl)-	MeOH	234(4.15),250(4.15)	12-1561-79
Phenol, 4-[7-methoxy-3-methyl-5-(1-propenyl)-2-benzofuranyl]-, (E)-	EtOH	226s(4.25),267(4.55), 292(4.46),302s(4.43), 320s(4.17)	12-2317-79
$C_{19}H_{18}O_3S_2$			
3-Cyclohexene-1-carboxylic acid, 2-oxo-6-(2-thienyl)-4-[2-(2-thienyl)ethenyl]-, ethyl ester	EtOH	236(4.29),275s(--), 358(4.22)	104-1059-79
$C_{19}H_{18}O_4$			
2H-1-Benzopyran-7-ol, 3,4-dihydro-5-(6-hydroxy-2-benzofuranyl)-2,2-dimethyl-	EtOH	217(4.55),314(4.56), 326s(4.45)	88-4675-79

Compound	Solvent	λ_{max}(log ε)	Ref.
$C_{19}H_{18}O_4S$			
3-Cyclohexene-1-carboxylic acid, 4-[2-(2-furanyl)ethenyl]-2-oxo-6-(2-thienyl)-, ethyl ester	EtOH	240(4.20),270s(--), 358(4.29)	104-1059-79
$C_{19}H_{18}O_5$			
4H-1-Benzopyran-4-one, 3-[(2,4-dimethoxyphenyl)methylene]-2,3-dihydro-7-methoxy-	EtOH	246(4.10),300(4.04), 367(4.30)	150-1713-79
4H-1-Benzopyran-4-one, 3-[(2,4-dimethoxyphenyl)methyl]-7-methoxy-	EtOH	218(4.34),241(4.20), 284(4.39),296(3.90), 305(3.90)	150-1713-79
4H-1-Benzopyran-4-one, 6,7-dimethoxy-3-(2-methoxyphenyl)-2-methyl-	MeOH	288(4.08),324(4.01)	18-0529-79
3-Cyclohexene-1-carboxylic acid, 6-(2-furanyl)-4-[2-(2-furanyl)ethenyl]-2-oxo-, ethyl ester	EtOH	350(3.72)	104-1059-79
	isooctane	340(--)	104-1059-79
2,7-Dibenzofurandiol, 1,3,4-trimethyl-, diacetate	EtOH	224(4.61),247(4.15), 256(4.26),286(4.35), 297s(4.12)	1-0271-79
$C_{19}H_{18}O_6$			
4H-1-Benzopyran-4-one, 2,3-dihydro-3-[(3-hydroxy-4-methoxyphenyl)methylene]-5,7-dimethoxy-	EtOH	235(5.10),348(5.05), 360(5.15)	150-1713-79
4H-1-Benzopyran-4-one, 2-(2,4-dimethoxyphenyl)-5,7-dimethoxy-	MeOH	245(4.34),340(4.51)	102-1245-79
4H-1-Benzopyran-4-one, 3-(2-hydroxy-4-methoxyphenyl)-6,7-dimethoxy-2-methyl-	MeOH	291(4.21),324(4.11)	18-0529-79
4H-1-Benzopyran-4-one, 3-[(3-hydroxy-4-methoxyphenyl)methyl]-5,7-dimethoxy-	EtOH	220(4.26),225(3.91), 296(4.35)	150-1713-79
7H-Phenaleno[1,2-b]furan-7-one, 8,9-dihydro-1,2,3,6-tetrahydroxy-4,8,8,9-tetramethyl-	EtOH	228s(4.37),262(4.31), 273(4.31),282s(4.28), 342(3.76),382(4.18), 420(4.17)	150-0301-79
7H-Phenaleno[1,2-b]furan-7-one, 8,9-dihydro-1,4,5,6-tetrahydroxy-3,8,8,9-tetramethyl-	EtOH	220(4.49),264(4.38), 384(4.10)	150-0301-79
Phenol, 4-[2-(1,3-benzodioxol-4-yl)-ethenyl]-2,6-dimethoxy-, acetate	$CHCl_3$	302(4.16)	39-2449-79C
$C_{19}H_{18}O_7$			
4H-1-Benzopyran-4-one, 2-(3,4-dimethoxyphenyl)-5-hydroxy-3,7-dimethoxy-	MeOH	232(4.21),254(3.82), 272(3.82),288(3.59), 352(3.88)	39-2696-79C
	MeOH	253(4.28),269(4.20), 303s(4.05),352(4.35)	100-0320-79
	MeOH-NaOMe	253(4.32),270(4.27), 303s(4.18),352(4.40)	100-0320-79
	MeOH-NaOAc	253(4.30),269(4.21), 302s(4.06),352(4.39)	100-0320-79
	MeOH-$AlCl_3$	275(4.31),298(3.94), 365(4.28?)	100-0320-79
	MeOH-NaOAc-H_3BO_3	252(4.32),268(4.24), 305s(4.07),352(4.40)	100-0320-79
4H-1-Benzopyran-4-one, 2-(3,4-dimethoxyphenyl)-5-hydroxy-6,7-dimethoxy-	EtOH	242(4.27),275(4.28), 338(4.44)	100-0496-79
4H-1-Benzopyran-4-one, 5-hydroxy-2-(4-methoxyphenyl)-6,7,8-trimethoxy-	EtOH	217s(4.43),289(4.33), 328(4.39)	100-0496-79

Compound	Solvent	$\lambda_{max}(\log \epsilon)$	Ref.
1H-Naphtho[2,3-c]pyran-1-one, 9,10-di-acetoxy-3,4-dihydro-7-methoxy-3-methyl-, (R)-	MeOH	254(4.62),316(3.89)	24-0957-79
Petalostetin, dihydro-	$CHCl_3$	238(4.19),280(4.09), 337(3.60)	102-0366-79
$C_{19}H_{18}O_8$			
4H-1-Benzopyran-4-one, 5,7-dihydroxy-6-methoxy-3-(2,4,5-trimethoxyphenyl)-	MeOH	263(4.47),297(4.26), 360s(3.53)	42-0081-79
(caviunin)	MeOH-$AlCl_3$	224(--),275(--), 298(--),380s(--), 400s(--)	42-0081-79
4H-1-Benzopyran-4-one, 2-(3,4-dimethoxyphenyl)-5,6-dihydroxy-3,7-dimethoxy-	MeOH	259(3.98),282(3.88), 343(3.93)	39-2696-79C
4H-1-Benzopyran-4-one, 5-hydroxy-2-(2-hydroxy-4,5-dimethoxyphenyl)-3,7-dimethoxy-	MeOH	259(4.53),320(4.09), 364(4.20)	39-2696-79C
4H-1-Benzopyran-4-one, 5-hydroxy-2-(3-hydroxy-4,5-dimethoxyphenyl)-3,7-dimethoxy-	MeOH	263(3.95),306s(3.69), 343(3.79)	100-0320-79
	MeOH-NaOMe	263(4.02),350(3.77)	100-0320-79
	MeOH-NaOAc	263(4.02),340(3.79)	100-0320-79
	MeOH-$AlCl_3$	276(3.85),300s(3.52), 398(3.66)	100-0320-79
	MeOH-$AlCl_3$-HCl	276(3.84),300s(3.54), 348(3.69),398(3.61)	100-0320-79
	MeOH-NaOAc-H_3BO_3	263(4.02),340(3.80)	100-0320-79
4H-1-Benzopyran-4-one, 5-hydroxy-2-(2-hydroxy-6-methoxyphenyl)-6,7,8-trimethoxy-	MeOH	271(4.3),310(3.9), 345(3.7)	95-0657-79
$C_{19}H_{18}Si$			
Silane, methyltriphenyl-	C_6H_{12}	247(2.67),253(2.84), 259(2.98),263(2.96), 266(2.93),270(2.81)	35-5703-79
$C_{19}H_{19}BrN_2O_9$			
1H-Indole, 3-bromo-6-nitro-1-(2,3,4-tri-O-acetyl-α-L-arabinopyranosyl)-	EtOH	262(3.89),310(3.75), 362(3.60)	103-0188-79
$C_{19}H_{19}ClN_2O_2S$			
1H-Pyrido[1,2-a]indolium, 4a-[[(4-chlorophenyl)sulfonyl]amino]-2,3,4,4a-tetrahydro-10-methyl-, hydroxide, inner salt	EtOH	213(4.29),248(4.24), 325(3.69)	23-0558-79
$C_{19}H_{19}ClN_2O_3$			
4(3H)-Quinazolinone, 6-chloro-3-[2-(3,4-dimethoxyphenyl)ethyl]-2-methyl-	MeOH	274(3.78),316(3.15), 328(3.04)	4-0449-79
4(3H)-Quinazolinone, 7-chloro-3-[2-(3,4-dimethoxyphenyl)ethyl]-2-methyl-	MeOH	280(3.63),305(3.15), 320(3.08)	4-0449-79
$C_{19}H_{19}HgNO$			
Mercury, [2,3-dihydro-2-[[(1-methylethyl)imino]methyl]-1-oxo-1H-inden-2-yl]phenyl-	benzene	300(3.55),380(4.31)	103-0056-79
	DMSO	285(3.43),297(3.47), 360(4.28)	103-0056-79
$C_{19}H_{19}IN_2O_3$			
4(3H)-Quinazolinone, 3-[2-(3,4-dimethoxyphenyl)-6-iodo-2-methyl-	MeOH	280(3.88),320(3.08), 330(2.95)	4-0449-79

Compound	Solvent	$\lambda_{max}(\log \epsilon)$	Ref.
$C_{19}H_{19}IN_2O_9$			
1H-Indole, 3-iodo-6-nitro-1-(2,3,4-tri-O-acetyl-α-L-arabinopyranosyl)-	EtOH	264(4.41),311(3.88), 361(3.71)	103-0188-79
$C_{19}H_{19}N$			
16-Azatricyclo[0.2.2.1^{4,8}]hexadeca-2,4,6,8(16),9,11,13,14-octaene, 12,13,14,15-tetramethyl-	MeCN	228(4.47),243(4.39), 252(4.36),260(4.22), 285(3.65)	35-2121-79
$C_{19}H_{19}NO$			
Cyclopentanone, 2-(9,10-dihydro-10-methyl-9-acridinyl)-	EtOH	287(4.32)	103-0541-79
Ethanone, 2-(1,3-dihydro-1,3,3-trimethyl-2H-indol-2-ylidene)-1-phenyl-	pH 1	285(3.99)	88-4407-79
	H_2O	391(4.48)	88-4407-79
Methanone, (2-ethyl-1,2-dihydro-1-methylisoquinolin-3-yl)phenyl-	ether	305s(3.72),410(3.68)	78-2501-79
2H-Pyrrole, 3,4-dihydro-2,2-dimethyl-5-phenyl-4-(phenylmethylene)-	EtOH	245(3.95),271(4.03), 323(4.39),334s(--)	12-2025-79
$C_{19}H_{19}NO_2$			
1,8(2H,5H)-Acridinedione, 3,4,6,7,9,10-hexahydro-9-phenyl-	H_2O	251(4.25),380(3.95)	39-1593-79C
Carbamic acid, 1,3-butadienyl(phenylmethyl)-, phenylmethyl ester	MeOH	254(4.44)	88-0981-79
2-Propen-1-one, 2-(4-morpholinyl)-1,3-diphenyl-, (E)-	ether	205(--),252(4.25), 276(4.22),365(3.19)	78-2501-79
(Z)-	ether	205(--),250(4.22), 300(3.94),391(3.54)	78-2501-79
$C_{19}H_{19}NO_3$			
4-Isoquinolinecarboxaldehyde, 3-(3,4-dimethoxyphenyl)-1,2-dihydro-2-methyl-	EtOH	228(4.24),290(4.14), 354(4.03)	78-1861-79
Pachypodanthine, N-methyl-	EtOH	235(4.02),273(4.03), 317(3.45)	100-0325-79
$C_{19}H_{19}NO_4$			
Bulbocapnine	MeOH	269(4.15),282s(4.12), 305(3.75)	100-0174-79
5,13-(Iminomethano)benzo[4,5]cycloocta-[1,2-f][1,3]benzodioxol-2-ol, 5,6,7,13-tetrahydro-3-methoxy-, (±)-	EtOH	224(3.88),291(3.72)	78-1857-79
	EtOH-NaOH	224(3.99),245(3.88), 297(3.76)	
Isodomesticine	EtOH	282(3.95)	2-0525-79A
	EtOH-NaOH	294(3.97)	2-0525-79A
6-Isoquinolinol, 4-[(3,4-dimethoxyphenyl)methylene]-1,4-dihydro-7-methoxy-, hydrochloride	EtOH	236(4.20),275(4.05), 366(4.05)	78-2555-79
Litsedine	EtOH	285(3.93),308(4.11)	100-0325-79
Nordicentrine	EtOH	216(4.32),277(3.99), 302(4.04),309s(4.03)	100-0325-79
Noroliverine	EtOH	217(4.38),235(4.06), 282(4.21),320(3.64)	100-0325-79
Pachystaudine	EtOH	237(4.24),274(4.20), 314(3.58)	100-0325-79
Palaudine	pH 2	252(4.76),286(3.74), 313(3.82),333(3.76)	106-0194-79
Spiro[2H-indene-2,1'(2'H)-isoquinolin]-1(3H)-one, 3',4'-dihydro-3-hydroxy-6',7'-dimethoxy-	MeOH	214(4.18),239(4.23), 285(3.75),343(2.65)	23-1569-79
$C_{19}H_{19}NO_5$			
Bulbocapnine, 4-hydroxy-	MeOH	270(4.10),280s(4.05),	100-0174-79

Compound	Solvent	$\lambda_{max}(\log \epsilon)$	Ref.
Bulbocapnine, 4-hydroxy- (cont.)		303(3.71)	100-0174-79
Guatterine N-oxide	EtOH	244(4.29),281(4.24)	100-0325-79
Oliveridine N-oxide	EtOH	222(4.42),240s(4.15), 287(4.28),320s(3.88)	100-0325-79
2-Propenoic acid, 3-[1,3-dihydro-1-methoxy-6-methyl-7-(phenylmethoxy)-furo[3,4-c]pyridin-4-yl]-	MeOH	285(3.84)	88-2603-79
$C_{19}H_{19}NO_5S_2$			
2-Naphthalenesulfonic acid, [4-[(dimethylamino)sulfonyl]phenyl]methyl ester	EtOH	230(4.88),269(3.61), 276(3.74)	118-0531-79
$C_{19}H_{19}NO_6$			
Benzo[g]quinoline-5,10-dione, 7-butyl-4,9-dihydroxy-3,8-dimethoxy-	MeOH	260(4.42),272s(4.37), 290s(4.07),432(3.86)	39-0807-79C
[1,1'-Biphenyl]-2,4-dicarboxylic acid, 3-hydroxy-5-methyl-6-nitroso-, diethyl ester	DMF	690(1.83)	104-0311-79
$C_{19}H_{19}N_2O_2$			
Pyridinium, 1-[2-(1H-indol-3-yl)ethyl]-3-(3-methoxy-3-oxo-1-propenyl)-, bromide	MeOH	218(4.62),256(4.21), 288(3.93)	35-5370-79
$C_{19}H_{19}N_3$			
Piperidine, 1-[[[2-cyano-2-(2-naphthalenyl)ethenyl]imino]methyl]-	MeOH	213(4.60),233(4.37), 282(4.12),294(4.21)	83-0039-79
Propanedinitrile, [3,4-dihydro-4a,9a-butano-9H-carbazol-2(1H)-ylidene]-	MeOH	242(4.35),295(3.58), 339(3.37)	5-1048-79
Propanedinitrile, (1,2,3,4,4a,5,7a,8-octahydrobenzo[d]carbazol-6(7H)-ylidene)-	MeOH	241(4.15),295(3.44), 361(3.21)	5-1048-79
$C_{19}H_{19}N_3O$			
2H-1,5-Benzodiazepin-2-one, 4-[2-[4-(dimethylamino)phenyl]ethenyl]-1,3-dihydro-, boron trifluoride adduct	$CHCl_3$	544(4.95)	124-0231-79
$C_{19}H_{19}N_3OS$			
7-Azabicyclo[4.3.1]deca-3,8-dien-10-one, 3,4-dimethyl-7-(3-phenyl-1,2,4-thiadiazol-5-yl)-	MeCN	257(4.53)	39-0399-79C
$C_{19}H_{19}N_3O_3$			
Carbamic acid, [3-[(ethylamino)carbonyl]-1H-indol-2-yl]-, phenylmethyl ester	$CHCl_3$	237(4.30),284(4.29)	103-0179-79
1H-Pyrazole-5-carboxylic acid, 4,5-dihydro-3-[(hydroxyimino)phenylmethyl]-4-phenyl-, ethyl ester	EtOH	233(3.08),295(3.39), 383(3.43)	4-0849-79
$C_{19}H_{19}N_3O_6$			
Cytosine, N^4-benzoyl-1-(2,3-O-isopropylidene-β-D-ribopentodialdo-1,4-furanosyl)-, hydrate	MeOH	259(4.37),304(4.00)	44-1309-79
$C_{19}H_{19}N_5$			
4,5'-Bipyrimidine, 6-phenyl-4'-(1-piperidinyl)-	EtOH	207(4.41),233(4.31), 277(4.39),385(3.82)	103-0671-79

Compound	Solvent	$\lambda_{max}(\log \epsilon)$	Ref.
$C_{19}H_{19}N_5O$			
Benzaldehyde, [hexahydro-2-oxo-4-(phenylhydrazono)-3H-azepin-3-ylidene]hydrazone	EtOH	244(4.19),292(4.24), 435(4.21)	103-0780-79
$C_{19}H_{19}N_5O_6$			
Adenosine, N-benzoyl-4'-C-(hydroxymethyl)-2',3'-O-methylene-	MeOH	233(4.05),280(4.25)	44-1309-79
$C_{19}H_{20}$			
Cyclopropene, 2-methyl-1,3-diphenyl-3-propyl-	EtOH	264(4.21)	35-5743-79
Cyclopropene, 3-methyl-1,2-diphenyl-3-propyl-	EtOH	229(4.21),321(4.46), 338(4.34)	35-5743-79
Phenanthrene, 6,9-dimethyl-1-(1-methylethyl)-	n.s.g.	259(4.76),280(4.13), 291(4.09),303(4.16)	88-0963-79
$C_{19}H_{20}BrNO_4$			
Isoquinoline, 5-bromo-1-(3,4-dimethoxyphenyl)-3,4-dihydro-7,8-dimethoxy-	MeOH	312(3.77)	2-0198-79A
6-Isoquinolinol, 1-[(6-bromo-1,3-benzodioxol-5-yl)methyl]-1,2,3,4-tetrahydro-7-methoxy-2-methyl-	EtOH	290(3.93)	2-0525-79A
	EtOH-NaOH	295(3.97)	2-0525-79A
$C_{19}H_{20}FN_5O_6$			
Glycine, N-[N-[4-[(5-fluoro-1,2-dihydro-2-oxo-4-pyrimidinyl)amino]-1,4-dioxobutyl]glycyl]-, phenylmethyl ester	H_2O-DMSO	241(4.04),305(3.76)	87-1104-79
$C_{19}H_{20}F_4O_5$			
Spiro[azuleno[6,5-b]furan-3(2H),1'-cyclopropan]-2-one, 4-acetoxy-5-(difluoromethoxy)-2,2'-difluoro-3a,4,4a-8,9,9a-hexahydro-4a,8-dimethyl-, [3R-(3α,3aα,4α,4aβ,8α,9aα)]-	EtOH	265(3.55)	78-0815-79
$C_{19}H_{20}HgN_2O$			
Mercury, [1,2-dihydro-1-methyl-2-[[(1-methylethyl)imino]methyl]-3H-indol-3-onato-N^2,O^3]phenyl-	benzene	285(4.23),320(3.80), 365(4.18)	103-0056-79
$C_{19}H_{20}INO_6$			
1H-Pyrrole-3-propanoic acid, 2-iodo-4-(2-methoxy-2-oxoethyl)-5-[(phenylmethoxy)carbonyl]-, methyl ester	n.s.g.	253(3.82),282(4.25)	39-1927-79C
$C_{19}H_{20}NO$			
Phenalenylium, 1-ethoxy-9-pyrrolidino-, tetrafluoroborate	n.s.g.	256(4.65),352(4.37), 464(4.27)	44-1704-79
Quinolinium, 6-ethoxy-4-methyl-1-(phenylmethyl)-, bromide	EtOH	252(4.64),313(4.06)	103-1208-79
chloride	EtOH	254(4.71),315(4.08)	103-1208-79
iodide	EtOH	252(4.76),314(4.06)	103-1208-79
perchlorate	EtOH	254(4.82),317(4.27)	103-1208-79
Quinolinium, 2-methyl-1-[4-(1-methylethoxy)phenyl]-, perchlorate	EtOH	239(4.71),318(4.23)	104-1160-79
Quinolinium, 2-methyl-1-(4-propoxyphenyl)-, perchlorate	EtOH	238(4.75),318(4.30)	104-1160-79

Compound	Solvent	λmax(log ε)	Ref.
$C_{19}H_{20}NO_4$			
Isoquinolinium, 2-(1,3-benzodioxol-4-ylmethyl)-3,4-dihydro-6,7-dimethoxy-, iodide	EtOH	248(4.34),312(4.08), 367(4.08)	39-0283-79C
	EtOH-NaOH	284(3.93)	39-0283-79C
$C_{19}H_{20}NO_5$			
Pyridinium, 4-[2-[4-(2-methoxy-2-oxoethoxy)phenyl]ethenyl]-1-(2-methoxy-2-oxoethyl)-, chloride, (E)-	MeOH	394(4.26)	56-1649-79
$C_{19}H_{20}N_2$			
1H-Pyrazole, 4,5-dihydro-5-methyl-5-(1-methylethenyl)-1,3-diphenyl-	CH_2Cl_2	238(4.14),310s(3.85), 358(4.31)	24-1206-79
1H-Pyrazole, 4-methyl-5-(1-methylethyl)-1,3-diphenyl-	CH_2Cl_2	264(4.23)	24-1206-79
$C_{19}H_{20}N_2O$			
2-Cyclopenten-1-one, 4,5-bis(methylphenylamino)-	n.s.g.	250(4.21),293(3.53)	12-1079-79
1H-Pyrazol-4-ol, 4,5-dihydro-5-methyl-5-(1-methylethenyl)-1,3-diphenyl-	CH_2Cl_2	241(--),357(4+)	24-1206-79
Pyrrolo[2,3-b]indol-2(1H)-one, 3,3a,8-8a-tetrahydro-1,3a-dimethyl-8-(phenylmethyl)-	MeOH	251(4.02),301(3.50)	5-0927-79
Pyrrolo[2,3-b]indol-2(1H)-one, 3,3a,8-8a-tetrahydro-3a,8-dimethyl-1-(phenylmethyl)-	MeOH	248(4.1),298(2.97)	5-0927-79
Vellosimine	EtOH	226(4.52),283(3.82), 300(3.14)	2-0087-79B
$C_{19}H_{20}N_2O_2$			
9,10-Anthracenedione, 1-amino-2-(pentylamino)-	dioxan	508(4.02)	104-0510-79
9,10-Anthracenedione, 1-amino-4-(pentylamino)-	dioxan	578(4.11),620(4.13)	104-0510-79
Eburnamonin-19-one	MeOH	245(4.34),267(4.08), 295(3.76),305(3.76)	24-1902-79
Epiisoeburnamonin-19-one	MeOH	245(4.20),265(4.00), 295(3.64),304(3.64)	24-1902-79
1H-Pyrido[4,3-b]carbazol-5-ol, 2,3,4,6-tetrahydro-2,6-dimethyl-, acetate	EtOH	240(4.52),250s(4.36), 263(4.25),286s(3.86), 296(4.16),317(3.56), 330(3.60),345(3.56)	39-3155-79C
$C_{19}H_{20}N_2O_3$			
Indolo[2,3-a]quinolizine-3-carboxylic acid, 1-ethyl-2,3,4,6,7,12-hexahydro-4-oxo-, methyl ester, (±)-	MeOH	230(4.21),309(4.03), 320(4.04)	24-1889-79
2-Propenamide, 2-(acetylamino)-3-(4-hydroxyphenyl)-N-(1-phenylethyl)-, (S)-	$CHCl_3$	293(4.18)	70-0129-79
Pyrrolo[2',3':4,5]furo[3,2-b]indole-2-carboxylic acid, 1,9-diethyl-1,9-dihydro-, ethyl ester	MeOH	361(4.59)	73-1805-79
$C_{19}H_{20}N_2O_5$			
Isoquinoline, 3,4-dihydro-5,6-dimethoxy-1-[(5-methoxy-2-nitrophenyl)-methyl]-	EtOH	277(4.33)	95-0102-79
$C_{19}H_{20}N_2O_6S$			
5-Thia-1-azabicyclo[4.2.0]oct-2-ene-2-	hexane	266(3.53),273(3.58),	33-2681-79

Compound	Solvent	λmax(log ε)	Ref.
carboxylic acid, 4,8-dioxo-7-[(phenoxyacetyl)amino]-, 1,1-dimethylethyl ester, (6R-trans)-		306(3.76)	33-2681-79
$C_{19}H_{20}N_2O_7$			
1-Azabicyclo[4.2.0]oct-2-ene-2,4-dicarboxylic acid, 3-methyl-8-oxo-7-[(phenoxyacetyl)amino]-, 4-methyl ester	EtOH	265(3.91)	23-0222-79
$C_{19}H_{20}N_2O_9$			
1H-Indole, 5-nitro-1-(2,3,4-tri-O-acetyl-α-L-arabinopyranosyl)-	EtOH	264(4.35),313(3.76)	103-0188-79
1H-Indole, 6-nitro-1-(2,3,4-tri-O-acetyl-α-L-arabinopyranosyl)-	EtOH	246(4.03),317(3.95), 350(3.84)	103-0188-79
$C_{19}H_{20}N_4O_4$			
L-threo-2,3-Hexodiulosonic acid, γ-lactone, 3-[(4-methylphenyl)hydrazone] 2-(phenylhydrazone)	n.s.g.	212(4.00),252(4.11), 350(4.21),442(4.36)	106-0531-79
1H-Pyrazole-4,5-dione, 1-(4-methylphenyl)-3-(1,2,3-trihydroxypropyl)-, 4-(phenylhydrazone)-, [S-(R*,R*)]-	n.s.g.	210(3.93),250(3.99), 410(4.14)	106-0531-79
2-Quinazolinamine, 1,4-dihydro-4-imino-N-phenyl-1-β-D-ribopyranosyl-	MeOH	215s(4.20),229(4.30), 249(4.33),277s(4.20), 327(4.77)	44-0173-79
$C_{19}H_{20}N_6O_4$			
L-Tyrosine, N-acetyl-3-[(4-azidophenyl)azo]-, ethyl ester	n.s.g.	246(3.44),344(3.53), 394s(3.37)	33-1217-79
$C_{19}H_{20}N_8O_6$			
DL-Glutamic acid, N-[[[4-[[(2-amino-1,4-dihydro-4-oxo-6-pteridinyl)methyl]amino]phenyl]amino]carbonyl]-	pH 1	243(4.38),280s(3.61), 319(3.83),360s(--)	87-0874-79
	pH 13	255(4.51),366(3.96)	87-0874-79
$C_{19}H_{20}O$			
Furan, 2,5-dihydro-2,2,5-trimethyl-3,5-diphenyl-	MeOH	252(3.99)	44-4021-79
4-Hexen-2-one, 5-methyl-3,4-diphenyl-	MeOH	294(4.31)	44-4021-79
6,9-Methanobenzocycloocten-11-ol, 5,6,7,8,9,10-hexahydro-11-phenyl-	MeOH	212(4.20),252(2.51), 258(2.63),263(2.64), 266(2.46),271(2.45)	56-1221-79
2-Oxabicyclo[2.1.0]pentane, 1,3,3-trimethyl-4,5-diphenyl-, exo	MeOH	218(4.06)	44-4021-79
$C_{19}H_{20}O_2$			
2,8-Chrysenediol, 4b,5,6,10b,11,12-hexahydro-4b-methyl-, cis	EtOH	223(4.19),281(3.68), 288(3.62)	12-1107-79
trans	EtOH	223(4.20),281(3.60), 287(3.54)	12-1093-79
B-Norestra-1,3,5(10),8,14-pentaen-17-one, 3-methoxy-6-methyl-	MeOH	213(4.20),227(4.10), 234(4.07),240(3.92), 309(4.51)	2-0324-79A
2,4-Pentanedione, 3,3-bis(4-methylphenyl)-	EtOH	227s(4.29),266(3.08), 274(3.04),295(3.08)	12-1561-79
Phenanthro[10,1-bc]pyran-9(8H)-one, 4,5,10,11-tetrahydro-3,8,8-trimethyl-	EtOH	224(4.703),242(4.697), 307(3.907),322(3.782), 338(3.715)	88-0405-79
Spiro[2,5-cyclohexadiene-1,7'(6'H)-[5,9]methanobenzocycloocten]-4-one,	EtOH	230(4.15),278(3.32)	39-3017-79C

Compound	Solvent	$\lambda_{max}(\log \epsilon)$	Ref.
5',8',9',10'-tetrahydro-3'-hydroxy-5'-methyl- (cont.)			39-3017-79C
$C_{19}H_{20}O_2S_2$			
5H-1,4-Dithiepin, 6,7-dihydro-2-[3-methoxy-4-(phenylmethoxy)phenyl]-	EtOH	250s(4.02),390(4.1)	4-1081-79
$C_{19}H_{20}O_3$			
1H-Inden-1-one, 2-[(3,4-dimethoxyphenyl)methyl]-2,3-dihydro-3-methyl-	n.s.g.	237(4.16),244s(4.13), 284(3.72)	78-1167-79
5,12-Naphthacenedione, 5a,6,7,8,9,10-11,11a-octahydro-1-methoxy-	EtOH	207(4.16),227(4.44), 260s(--),336(3.79)	94-2229-79
Phenol, 4-(5,6,7,8-tetrahydro-6,7-dimethylnaphtho[2,3-d]-1,3-dioxol-5-yl)- (±-attenuol)	EtOH	223s(4.16),287(3.69), 294s(3.63)	78-1665-79
	CH_2Cl_2	227(4.05),285(3.80), 294(3.73)	88-1389-79
$C_{19}H_{20}O_3S_2$			
1,3-Dithiane-2-carboxaldehyde, 2-[3-methoxy-4-(phenylmethoxy)phenyl]-	EtOH	238(4.08),283(3.67)	4-1081-79
$C_{19}H_{20}O_4$			
1(2H)-Naphthalenone, 3,4-dihydro-3-(2,4,6-trimethoxyphenyl)-	EtOH	241(4.23),250(4.15), 293(3.48)	78-1167-79
2,4-Pentanedione, 3,3-bis(4-methoxyphenyl)-	MeOH	237(4.26),276(3.59), 283(3.57)	12-1561-79
2-Propenoic acid, 3-[4-methoxy-3-(phenylmethoxy)phenyl]-, ethyl ester	EtOH	237(4.06),295(4.10), 322(4.18)	39-0662-79C
$C_{19}H_{20}O_5$			
6H-Dibenzo[a,c]cyclononen-6-one, 5,7,8,9-tetrahydro-3,11-dihydroxy-2,12-dimethoxy-	EtOH	210(4.54),289(3.90)	39-0662-79C
	EtOH-KOH	213(4.63+),248(4.20), 308(3.86)	39-0662-79C
Perbenzoic acid, 4-(4-methoxybenzoyl)-, 1,1-dimethylethyl ester	CCl_4	325(2.6)	44-4123-79
Phenanthrene, 2,3,4,7,8-pentamethoxy-	$CHCl_3$	264(5.04)	39-2449-79C
$C_{19}H_{20}O_6$			
1H-Phenalen-1-one, 4-ethoxy-3-hydroxy-7,8,9-trimethoxy-6-methyl-	EtOH	212(4.46),265(4.33), 360(4.00),391(3.98), 409(3.99)	150-0301-79
$C_{19}H_{20}O_7$			
Benzoic acid, 2-(2,6-dimethoxy-4-methylbenzoyl)-3,6-dimethoxy-	$CHCl_3$	240(4.21),285(3.62), 324(3.93)	44-4452-79
2,5-Cyclohexadiene-1,4-dione, 5-(3,4-dihydro-6,7-dimethoxy-2H-1-benzopyran-3-yl)-2,3-dimethoxy-, (S)-	EtOH	269(4.16),397(3.11)	32-0009-79
$C_{19}H_{20}O_8$			
2,5-Cyclohexadiene-1,4-dione, 5-(3,4-dihydro-6-hydroxy-7,8-dimethoxy-2H-1-benzopyran-3-yl)-2,3-dimethoxy-, (S)-	EtOH	268(3.97),388(2.95)	32-0009-79
$C_{19}H_{21}BrN_2O_3S$			
Benzenesulfonic acid, 4-bromo-, (1,6,7-8,9,10a-hexahydro-4H-1,4-epoxy-4a,8-methanobenzocycloocten-10(5H)-ylidene)hydrazide, (1α,4α,4aα,8α,10aβ)-	EtOH	234(4.09),278s(3.18)	44-3793-79
(1α,4α,4aβ,8β,10aα)-	EtOH	234(4.15),278s(3.20)	44-3793-79

Compound	Solvent	λ_{max}(log ε)	Ref.
$C_{19}H_{21}ClN_4O_9$			
9H-Purine, 6-chloro-9-[2,3,5-tri-O-acetyl-4-C-(acetoxymethyl)-β-D-erythro-pentofuranosyl]-	EtOH	250s(3.81),264(3.92)	44-1301-79
$C_{19}H_{21}NO$			
1-Propanone, 2-(3,3-dimethyl-2-phenyl-2-aziridinyl)-1-phenyl-	EtOH	240(4.17)	78-2285-79
2-Propen-1-one, 2-(diethylamino)-1,3-diphenyl-, (E)-	ether	292(4.12),420(3.12)	78-2501-79
$C_{19}H_{21}NOS$			
Dibenzo[b,e]thiepin, 6,11-dihydro-11-[3-(dimethylamino)propylidene]-, 5-oxide	EtOH	247s(4.07),275s(3.76)	73-2536-79
Dibenzo[b,e]thiepin-2-ol, 6,11-dihydro-11-[3-(dimethylamino)propylidene]-, cis	MeOH	240(4.14),284(3.76), 316(3.87)	73-2536-79
trans	MeOH	228(4.36),263(3.95), 323(3.52)	73-2536-79
$C_{19}H_{21}NO_2$			
2-Hexen-1-one, 6-hydroxy-1-phenyl-3-[(phenylmethyl)amino]-	MeOH	241(4.41),338(4.48)	44-2073-79
Noratherosperminine	EtOH	235(4.27),251(4.58), 279(3.97),306(3.99), 314(3.97)	100-0325-79
2H-Pyrrol-4-ol, 3,4-dihydro-2,2-dimethyl-5-phenyl-4-(phenylmethyl)-, 1-oxide	EtOH	211(4.12),285(4.08)	12-2025-79
$C_{19}H_{21}NO_2S$			
Dibenzo[b,e]thiepin, 6,11-dihydro-11-[3-(dimethylamino)propylidene]-, 5,5-dioxide	MeOH	240(4.06),276(3.41)	73-2536-79
$C_{19}H_{21}NO_2S_2$			
2-Propenoic acid, 2-[(4-methylphenyl)-thio]-3-[[(4-methylphenyl)thio]-amino]-, ethyl ester	hexane	252(4.37)	44-1218-79
$C_{19}H_{21}NO_2S_3$			
Propanoic acid, 3-[(4-methylphenyl)dithio]-2-[[(4-methylphenyl)thio]imino]-, ethyl ester	hexane	238(4.26),355(3.93)	44-1218-79
$C_{19}H_{21}NO_3$			
Dibenzo[de,g]quinoline, 5,6,6a,7-tetrahydro-1,2,10-trimethoxy-, hydrochloride, (±)-	EtOH	22?(4.55),266(4.12), 274(4.13),301(3.83)	33-1549-79
Liridinine	EtOH	221(4.41),281(4.16)	100-0325-79
Nuciferine, 3-hydroxy-	EtOH	215(4.69),240s(4.28), 283(4.49),292s(4.46)	100-0325-79
$C_{19}H_{21}NO_4$			
2,4,6-Heptatrienamide, 7-cyclohexyl-N-(2,5-dioxo-7-oxabicyclo[4.1.0]-hept-3-en-3-yl)-, (E,E,E)-	MeOH	300(4.10),347(4.16)	35-3402-79
Isoboldine, hydrobromide	H_2O	220(4.53),279(4.03), 305(4.08)	106-0435-79
Isoquinoline, 2-(1,3-benzodioxol-5-ylmethyl)-1,2,3,4-tetrahydro-6,7-dimethoxy-	EtOH	233(3.99),285(3.85)	39-0283-79C

Compound	Solvent	λ_{max}(log ε)	Ref.
6-Isoquinolinol, 4-(1,3-benzodioxol-5-ylmethyl)-1,2,3,4-tetrahydro-7-methoxy-2-methyl-	EtOH	235(4.08),289(4.00)	78-2555-79
	EtOH-NaOH	235(4.13),298(4.03)	78-2555-79
Liriotulipiferine	MeOH	218(4.54),274s(4.06), 281(4.12),303(4.10), 313s(4.03)	100-0325-79
Phenylalanine, N-[(phenylmethoxy)carbonyl]-, ethyl ester	EtOH	243(2.30),248(2.41), 253(2.54),258(2.64), 265(2.56),268(2.40)	118-0961-79
Salutaridine	pH 2	238(4.12),280(3.72)	106-0194-79
$C_{19}H_{21}NO_6$			
α-D-Xylofuranose, 5-deoxy-5-(2,5-dioxo-1-phenyl-3-pyrrolidinylidene)-3-O-methyl-1,2-O-(1-methylethylidene)-, (E)-	EtOH	225(4.22)	33-0977-79
$C_{19}H_{21}NO_9$			
Pyrido[1,2-a]azepine-6,7,8,9-tetracarboxylic acid, 6,7-dihydro-10-methoxy-, tetramethyl ester	MeOH	208(3.98),236(3.86), 252(3.90),405(4.07), 505(4.16)	39-0584-79C
	MeOH-$HClO_4$	207(4.05),255(3.76), 321(3.77)	39-0584-79C
$C_{19}H_{21}N_2O$			
4H-Pyrazolium, 3-(4-methoxyphenyl)-1,4,5-trimethyl-4-phenyl-, iodide	EtOH	215s(4.39),245s(3.81), 340(4.09)	23-1186-79
$C_{19}H_{21}N_3O$			
Benzenepropanamide, N-(4,5-dihydro-1-methyl-1H-pyrazol-3-yl)-β-phenyl-	EtOH	263.5(3.98)	150-0801-79
Lysergic acid amide, N-2-propenyl-	MeOH	241(4.32),316(4.05)	94-3029-79
$C_{19}H_{21}N_3O_2$			
1H-Naphth[2,3-d]imidazole-4,9-dione, 5-(cyclohexylamino)-1,2-dimethyl-	C_6H_{12}	520(3.75)	39-0702-79C
	EtOH	535(--)	39-0702-79C
	EtOH-HCl	560(--)	39-0702-79C
1H-Naphth[2,3-d]imidazole-4,9-dione, 8-(cyclohexylamino)-1,2-dimethyl-	C_6H_{12}	519(3.77)	39-0702-79C
	EtOH	535(--)	39-0702-79C
	EtOH-HCl	560(--)	39-0702-79C
$C_{19}H_{21}N_3O_3$			
Benzamide, N-[4,5-dihydro-1-(phenylmethyl)-1H-pyrazol-3-yl]-3,4-dimethoxy-	EtOH	274s(4.14),301(4.28)	150-0801-79
Eburnamenin-14(15H)-one, 9-nitro-, (3α,16α)- (9-nitrovincamone)	MeOH	269(3.92),306(3.72), 360(3.64)	20-0093-79
Eburnamenin-14(15H)-one, 11-nitro-(11-nitrovincamone)	MeOH	226(4.34),315(3.97), 354(4.06)	20-0093-79
1,2,4-Oxadiazole-3-ethanamine, 5-(3,4-dimethoxyphenyl)-N-(phenylmethyl)-	EtOH	228(4.38),279(4.32), 302(4.23)	150-0801-79
$C_{19}H_{21}N_3O_5$			
Ethenetricarbonitrile, (2,3,5,6-tetraethoxy-4-hydroxyphenyl)-	MeOH	416(4.22)	49-0737-79
	MeOH-NH_3	270(4.25),544(4.68)	49-0737-79
$C_{19}H_{21}N_4O$			
Pyridinium, 2-[8-(4,6-dimethyl-2-pyrimidinyl)-2-oxo-8-azabicyclo[3.2.1]oct-3-en-6-yl]-1-methyl-, iodide, endo	$CHCl_3$	248(4.31)	39-1525-79C

Compound	Solvent	λ_{max}(log ε)	Ref.
$C_{19}H_{21}N_5O_7S_2$			
1H-Pyrazolo[3,4-d]pyrimidine-3-carbonitrile, 4,6-bis(methylthio)-1-(2,3,5-tri-O-acetyl-α-D-ribofuranosyl)-	EtOH	206(4.11),253(4.32), 293(4.08),316(3.92)	103-1361-79
β-	EtOH	205(4.27),254(4.42), 296(4.19),322(4.04)	103-1361-79
$C_{19}H_{21}N_9O_5$			
DL-Aspartic acid, N-[[[4-[[(2,4-diamino-6-pteridinyl)methyl]methylamino]-phenyl]amino]carbonyl]-	pH 1	244(4.51),337(4.00), 287s(3.82),350s(3.94)	87-0869-79
	pH 13	258(4.48),390(3.76)	87-0869-79
$C_{19}H_{21}OS$			
Phenalenylium, 1-(butylthio)-9-ethoxy-, tetrafluoroborate	n.s.g.	283(4.26),350(3.91), 406(4.13),505(3.56)	44-1704-79
$C_{19}H_{21}O_2$			
Phenalenylium, 1-butoxy-9-ethoxy-, tetrafluoroborate	n.s.g.	261(4.03),371(4.44), 431(4.06),457(4.05)	44-1704-79
$C_{19}H_{21}S$			
1H-Benzo[c]thiolium, 1,1-dimethyl-3-(2,4,6-trimethylphenyl)-	dil H_2SO_4	359(4.17)	104-0937-79
$C_{19}H_{22}$			
5,8-Etheno-9H-benzocyclotridecene, 10,11,12,13,14,15-hexahydro-	EtOH	233s(3.97)	44-2160-79
$C_{19}H_{22}BrNO_5$			
Benzamide, N-[2-(2-bromo-4,5-dimethoxyphenyl)ethyl]-3,4-dimethoxy-	MeOH	255(4.16),287(4.01)	2-0198-79
$C_{19}H_{22}ClN_3O_2$			
Carbamic acid, (2-chloroethyl)-, (8,9-didehydro-6-methylergolin-8-yl)methyl ester	MeOH	222(4.42),274(3.76), 283(3.79),294(3.71)	87-0032-79
$C_{19}H_{22}NO_2$			
Isoquinolinium, 3,4-dihydro-6,7-dimethoxy-2-methyl-3-(phenylmethyl)-, perchlorate	MeOH	250(4.34),313(4.03), 370(4.00)	83-0273-79
$C_{19}H_{22}NS$			
Benzothiazolium, 2-ethyl-3-methyl-6-(2,4,6-trimethylphenyl)-, iodide	EtOH	215(4.75),241(4.23), 293(4.00)	33-0021-79
$C_{19}H_{22}N_2$			
Pyrrolo[2,3-b]indole, 1,2,3,3a,8,8a-hexahydro-1,3a-dimethyl-8-(phenylmethyl)-	MeOH	248(4.19),299(3.64)	5-0927-79
$C_{19}H_{22}N_2O$			
[1,1'-Biphenyl]-3-amine, N-cyclohexyl-5-methyl-6-nitroso-	EtOH	411(4.57),701(2.00)	104-1437-79
Yohimban-6-one (mixture with epialloyohimban-6-one)	MeOH	241(3.94),262(3.81), 296(3.80)	5-1643-79
$C_{19}H_{22}N_2O_2$			
1H-Indole-2-acetonitrile, α-[(3-ethyltetrahydro-2-methoxy-2H-pyran-3-yl)-	EtOH	249(3.95),273(3.57), 321(4.30)	107-0505-79

Compound	Solvent	λ max(log ε)	Ref.
methylene]- (cont.)			107-0505-79
6H-Pyrrolo[3,2-f]indolizine-2-carboxylic acid, 4-ethyl-3,7,8-trimethyl-6-methylene-, ethyl ester, monohydrochloride	KBr	277(4.79),285(4.80), 338(3.85),353(3.88)	104-0967-79
$C_{19}H_{22}N_2O_2S$			
Dibenzo[b,f]thiepin-2,8-diol, 10,11-dihydro-10-(4-methylpiperazino)-	MeOH	260s(4.01),295s(3.52)	73-2987-79
$C_{19}H_{22}N_2O_3$			
2,4(3H,5H)-Furandione, 3-[1-(cyclohexylamino)ethylidene]-5-[(phenylamino)-methylene]-	EtOH	254(4.20),297(4.23), 378(4.59)	4-1335-79
$C_{19}H_{22}N_2O_3S$			
Benzenesulfonic acid, 4-[3-(1,1-dimethylethyl)-4,5-dihydro-5-phenyl-1H-pyrazol-1-yl]-, sodium salt, (±)-	MeOH	295(4.10)	23-0360-79
$C_{19}H_{22}N_2O_9$			
1H-Indole, 2,3-dihydro-5-nitro-1-(2,3,4-tri-O-acetyl-α-L-arabino-pyranosyl)-	EtOH	227(3.75)	103-0188-79
1H-Indole, 2,3-dihydro-6-nitro-1-(2,3,4-tri-O-acetyl-α-L-arabino-pyranosyl)-	EtOH	252(4.18),360(3.22)	103-0188-79
$C_{19}H_{22}N_4O_4$			
Benzoic acid, 5-(diethylamino)-2-[(4-nitrophenyl)azo]-, ethyl ester	EtOH	479(4.51)	39-1990-79C
	HOAc	479(4.49)	39-1990-79C
Thymidine, 5'-[(2-amino-1-oxo-3-phenyl-propyl)amino]-2',3'-didehydro-3',5'-dideoxy-, monohydrochloride, (S)-	H_2O	267(4.04)	136-0113-79F
$C_{19}H_{22}N_4O_4S$			
Benzamide, N-[[nitroso[[4-(1-pyrrolidinylsulfonyl)phenyl]methyl]amino]-methyl]-	EtOH	234(4.40),367(1.79)	118-0531-79
$C_{19}H_{22}N_4O_9S$			
Inosine, 4'-C-(acetoxymethyl)-6-thio-, 2',3',5'-triacetate	pH 13	232(4.16),311(4.34)	44-1301-79
$C_{19}H_{22}N_6O_6$			
2-Propenoic acid, 2-methyl-, 1-[(3,4-dihydro-5-methyl-2,4-dioxo-1(2H)-pyrimidinyl)methyl]-2-(1,2,3,6-tetrahydro-1,3-dimethyl-2,6-dioxo-7H-purin-7-yl)ethyl ester	H_2O	274(4.19)	126-2303-79
$C_{19}H_{22}O_2$			
14β-Estra-1,3,5(10),15-tetraen-17-one, 3-methoxy-	MeOH	228(4.05),279(3.34), 288(3.28)	150-2525-79
1-Isobenzofuranol, 3,3-diethyl-1,3-dihydro-1-(2-methylphenyl)-, cation	50% H_2SO_4	343(4.35)	104-1126-79
1-Isobenzofuranol, 3,3-diethyl-1,3-dihydro-1-(3-methylphenyl)-, cation	50% H_2SO_4	345(4.39)	104-1126-79
1-Isobenzofuranol, 3,3-diethyl-1,3-dihydro-1-(4-methylphenyl)-, cation	50% H_2SO_4	368(4.50)	104-1126-79

Compound	Solvent	λ_{max}(log ε)	Ref.
B-Norestra-1,3,5(10),8,14-pentaen-17β-ol, 3-methoxy-6-methyl-	MeOH	215(4.08),227(3.99), 233(3.97),240(3.83), 309(4.36)	2-0324-79A
$C_{19}H_{22}O_2S$			
15-Thiaestra-1,3,5(10),8-tetraen-17-one, 3-methoxy-14β-methyl-	EtOH	280.5(4.27)	39-0990-79C
$C_{19}H_{22}O_3$			
2H,6H-Benzo[1,2-b:5,4-b']dipyran-2-one, 7,8-dihydro-8,8-dimethyl-3-(3-methyl-2-butenyl)- (same spectrum in acid or base)	EtOH	221(4.12),250s(3.72), 262s(3.76),332(4.24)	102-1073-79
2H-1-Benzopyran-2-one, 7-[(3,7-dimethyl-2,6-octadienyl)oxy]- (aurapten)	EtOH	210(4.30),326(4.09)	2-0385B-79A
2H-1-Benzopyran-2-one, 7-hydroxy-3,6-bis(3-methyl-2-butenyl)- (balsamiferone)	EtOH	219(4.16),250s(3.64), 258s(3.56),334(4.23)	102-1073-79
	EtOH-base	237(4.00),273s(3.52), 305s(3.42),368(4.35)	102-1073-79
D-Homo-16-oxaestra-1,3,5(10),8-tetraen-17a-one, 3-methoxy-	EtOH	277(4.21)	4-0637-79
18-Norandrosta-4,8,11,13-tetraen-3-one, 17α-hydroxy-11-methoxy-	EtOH	245(3.92),285(3.57)	44-2457-79
17β-	EtOH	245(3.85),283(3.58)	44-2457-79
18-Norandrosta-4,8,11,13-tetraen-17-one, 3-hydroxy-11-methoxy-	EtOH	219(4.68),262(4.54), 320(4.18)	44-2457-79
8,14-Seco-B-norestra-1,3,5(10),9(11)-tetraene-14,17-dione, 3-methoxy-6-methyl-	MeOH	214(4.18),263(4.24), 304(3.84)	2-0324-79A
$C_{19}H_{22}O_3S_2$			
Carbonodithioic acid, O-[3-[4-methoxy-3-(phenylmethoxy)phenyl]propyl] S-methyl ester	EtOH	211(4.14),225s(4.11), 277(4.07)	39-0662-79C
1,3-Dithiane-2-methanol, 2-[3-methoxy-4-(phenylmethoxy)phenyl]-	EtOH	237(3.80),281(3.31)	4-1081-79
$C_{19}H_{22}O_4$			
Spiro[bicyclo[4.2.0]octane-7,5'[1,3]-dioxane]-4',6'-dione, 2,2'-dimethyl-8-phenyl-, cis	hexane	243(3.04)	24-3293-79
$C_{19}H_{22}O_4S$			
D-Homo-16-thiaestra-1,3,5(10),8(14)-tetraen-17a-one, 3-methoxy-, 16,16-dioxide	EtOH	278(3.40),282(3.36)	39-0990-79C
(9β)-	EtOH	278(3.34),282(3.32)	39-0990-79C
D-Homo-16-thiaestra-1,3,5(10),8-tetraen-17a-one, 3-methoxy-, 16,16-dioxide	EtOH	276(4.19)	39-0990-79C
$C_{19}H_{22}O_5$			
Benzene, 5-[2-(2,3-dimethoxyphenyl)ethenyl]-1,2,3-trimethoxy-	$CHCl_3$	319(4.09)	39-2449-79C
2-Oxaspiro[4.5]dec-3-ene-3-carboxylic acid, 1-oxo-8-(phenylmethoxy)-, ethyl ester, cis	MeOH	238(4.1)	24-1550-79
trans	MeOH	239(4.0)	24-1550-79
2-Pentanone, 1,5-bis(3-hydroxy-4-methoxyphenyl)-	EtOH	210(4.30),225s(4.15), 281(3.85)	39-0662-79C
	EtOH-KOH	216(4.40),239s(4.15), 296(3.90)	39-0662-79C

Compound	Solvent	λmax(log ε)	Ref.
$C_{19}H_{22}O_6Si$			
1,4-Ethanoanthracene-2,9,10(1H)-trione, 3,4,4a,9a-tetrahydro-5,8-dihydroxy-4-[(trimethylsilyl)oxy]-	MeOH	215(4.44),223s(4.34), 252(4.23),392(4.06), 414s(4.03),428s(3.96)	24-2640-79
$C_{19}H_{22}O_7$			
Ethanone, 1-(2-hydroxy-4,6-dimethoxyphenyl)-2-(2,4,5-trimethoxyphenyl)-	MeOH	232(4.1),276(3.82), 346(3.69)	2-0076-79B
$C_{19}H_{22}O_{10}$			
Butanedioic acid, 2-acetoxy-2-[(3,4-diacetoxyphenyl)methyl]-, dimethyl ester, (R)-	MeOH	207(4.46),266s(3.31), 272(3.42),281s(3.24)	102-1211-79
$C_{19}H_{23}BrO_4$			
Phenol, 2-[3-(acetoxymethyl)-1,2-dimethyl-3-cyclopenten-1-yl]-4-bromo-5-methyl-	EtOH	231s(4.16),274(3.20), 283(3.16),290(2.95)	35-6136-79
$C_{19}H_{23}BrO_6$			
α-D-xylo-Hept-5-enofuranuronic acid, 6-bromo-5,6-dideoxy-1,2-O-(1-methylethylidene)-3-O-(phenylmethyl)-, ethyl ester, (Z)-	EtOH	211(3.81),235(3.74)	33-1303-79
$C_{19}H_{23}ClN_2O_2S$			
Ethanol, 2,2'-[[3-(2-chloro-10H-phenothiazin-10-yl)propyl]imino]bis-	MeOH	272(4.04),305s(3.91)	73-3617-79
$C_{19}H_{23}N$			
16-Azatricyclo[9.2.2.$1^{4,8}$]hexadeca-4,6,8(16),11,13,14-hexaene, 12,13,14,15-tetramethyl-	MeCN	235(3.75),270(3.19), 305(2.51)	35-2121-79
1H-3-Benzazepine, 2,3,4,5-tetrahydro-2,2,3-trimethyl-1-phenyl-	EtOH	257(2.79)	4-1525-79
Cyclonona[cd]pentalen-5-amine, N,N-diethyl-1,2-dihydro-6-methyl-	hexane	293s(3.96),320(4.06), 378(4.09)	89-0162-79
$C_{19}H_{23}NO$			
1(2H)-Naphthalenone, 3,4,7,8-tetrahydro-3,3-dimethyl-6-[(phenylmethyl)amino]-	pH 1	255(3.94),394(4.41)	39-1411-79C
	H_2O	412(4.42)	39-1411-79C
	EtOH	403(4.43)	39-1411-79C
$C_{19}H_{23}NO_2$			
2H-Indol-2-one, 1,3-dihydro-1,3-dimethyl-3-[2-oxo-3-(2-propenyl)cyclohexyl]-, A	EtOH	253(3.92),279s(3.28)	23-1694-79
B	EtOH	253(--),280s(--)	23-1694-79
$C_{19}H_{23}NO_3$			
Armepavine, (R)-(-)-	EtOH	229(4.18),284(3.74)	100-0430-79
	EtOH-base	290(--)	100-0430-79
Demethylcolletine, (R)-(-)-	EtOH	226(4.03),283(3.74)	100-0430-79
$C_{19}H_{23}NO_4$			
2-Azaspiro[4.5]dec-3-ene-3-carboxylic acid, 1-oxo-8-(phenylmethoxy)-, ethyl ester, cis	MeOH	282(3.8),308(2.4)	24-1550-79
Reticuline, (+)-	pH 2	226(4.23),282(3.80)	106-0194-79

Compound	Solvent	$\lambda_{max}(\log \epsilon)$	Ref.
$C_{19}H_{23}NO_6S$			
Erythrinan-6-en-8-one, 7-hydroxy-15,16-dimethoxy-, 7-methylsulfonate	MeOH	212(4.3),280(3.56)	24-2472-79
$C_{19}H_{23}NS_2$			
3,11-Dithia-18-azatricyclo[11,2,2,1^{5,9}]-octadeca05,7,9(18),13,15,16-hexaene, 14,15,16,17-tetramethyl-	MeCN	243(3.89),270(3.33)	35-2121-79
$C_{19}H_{23}N_2S$			
1,2-Benzisothiazolium, 3-[4-(diethyl-amino)phenyl]-2-ethyl-, chloride, hydrochloride	5M HCl	270(4.09),337(3.90)	24-3286-79
	MeOH	273(4.27),424(4.21)	24-3286-79
$C_{19}H_{23}N_3$			
1H-Indole-2-acetonitrile, 3-[2-(3-ethyl-5,6-dihydro-1(2H)-pyridinyl)ethyl]-	EtOH	221(4.69),274(3.84), 281(3.85),291(3.77)	23-0289-79
$C_{19}H_{23}N_3O$			
Eburnamenin-14(15H)-one, 9-amino-, (3α,16α)-, (9-aminovincamone)	MeOH	237(3.97),261s(3.66), 330(3.55)	20-0093-79
Eburnamenin-14(15H)-one, 11-amino-(11-aminovincamone)	MeOH	212(4.30),251(4.29), 294(4.09)	20-0093-79
$C_{19}H_{23}N_3O_2S$			
4H-Pyrrolo[2,3-d]pyrimidin-4-one, 3,7-dihydro-5-methyl-3-[(1-methylethoxy)-methyl]-2-(methylthio)-7-(phenylmethyl)-	MeOH	227(4.35),280s(3.94), 303(4.04)	138-1283-79
$C_{19}H_{23}N_3O_6$			
α-D-Galactopyranose, 6-deoxy-1,2:3,4-bis-O-(1-methylethylidene)-6-(4-oxo-1,2,3-benzotriazin-3(4H)-yl)-	EtOH	222(4.27),281(3.90)	33-0971-79
1H-Imidazole-4-carboxylic acid, 5-amino-1-[2,3-O-(1-methylethylidene)-α-D-ribofuranosyl]-, phenylmethyl ester	pH 3	235(3.94),272(4.17)	39-1415-79C
	pH 10	235(3.77),272(4.18)	39-1415-79C
Bratton-Marshall product	n.s.g.	529(4.35)	39-1415-79C
β-form	pH 3	248(3.92),271(4.05)	39-1415-79C
	pH 10	240(3.81),271(4.16)	39-1415-79C
Bratton-Marshall product	n.s.g.	524(4.27)	39-1415-79C
$C_{19}H_{23}N_3O_8S$			
β-D-Ribofuranoside, 5-methyl-2-(methylthio)-1H-pyrrolo[2,3-d]pyrimidin-4-yl, 2,3,5-triacetate	MeOH	244(4.37),284(4.02)	24-0799-79
$C_{19}H_{23}N_7O_3$			
Alanine, 3-(6-amino-9H-purin-9-yl)-N-L-phenylalanyl-, ethyl ester, dihydrochloride	EtOH	260(4.09)	65-0994-79
$C_{19}H_{24}$			
5,15-Etheno-6H-benzocyclotridecene, 7,8,9,10,11,12,13,14-octahydro-	EtOH	234(4.67),296(3.79)	35-6660-79
$C_{19}H_{24}BrN_3O_{10}$			
1H-Pyrazole-5-carboxamide, 3-(bromomethyl)-1-(2,3,4,6-tetra-O-acetyl-β-D-glucopyranosyl)-	EtOH	218(4.09)	87-0807-79

Compound	Solvent	λ_{max}(log ε)	Ref.
$C_{19}H_{24}N_2O_2$			
1H-Indole-2-acetonitrile, α-[(3-ethyltetrahydro-2-methoxy-2H-pyran-3-yl)-methyl]-	EtOH	266(3.98),278(3.94), 287(3.77)	107-0505-79
$C_{19}H_{24}N_4O_2$			
Benzo[d]cyclopenta[i]tetrazolo[1,5-a]-[1]benzazepine-1,10(3bH,8H)-dione, 2,3,3a,11,12,12a,12b,13,14,14a-decahydro-12a,14a-dimethyl-, [3aR-(3aα,3bβ,12bα,14bβ)]-	EtOH	240(4.18)	39-3166-79C
$C_{19}H_{24}N_4O_7S$			
Benzenesulfonic acid, 4-methyl-, [[5-[(3,4-dihydro-2,4-dioxo-1(2H)-pyrimidinyl)methoxymethyl]-2,2-dimethyl-1,3-dioxolan-4-yl]methylene]hydrazide	MeOH	235(4.11),260s(3.95)	44-4713-79
$C_{19}H_{24}N_4O_9$			
1H-Purine-2,6-dione, 9-(2,3-di-O-acetyl-4,6-O-ethylidene-β-D-glucopyranosyl)-3,9-dihydro-1,3-dimethyl-	MeOH	274.5(3.92)	136-0061-79A
1H-Purine-2,6-dione, 3,9-dihydro-1,3-dimethyl-9-(3,4,6-tri-O-acetyl-2-deoxy-β-D-arabino-hexopyranosyl)-	MeOH	274(3.96)	136-0061-79A
$C_{19}H_{24}N_4O_{10}$			
1H-Purine-2,6-dione, 3,9-dihydro-1,3-dimethyl-9-(2,3,6-tri-O-acetyl-β-D-glucopyranosyl)-	MeOH	274(3.91)	136-0061-79A
$C_{19}H_{24}O$			
Androsta-2,4,6-trien-17-one	n.s.g.	297(4.16),308(4.23), 322(4.08)	39-3042-79C
2(3H)-Naphthalenone, 4,4a,5,6,7,8-hexahydro-3,4a-dimethyl-3-(phenylmethyl)-, trans-(±)-	EtOH	239(4.16)	78-0961-79
$C_{19}H_{24}OS$			
Androsta-1,4-dien-17-one, 3-thioxo-	MeOH	330(4.28)	39-1166-79C
$C_{19}H_{24}O_2$			
5α-Androsta-2,7-diene-6,17-dione	n.s.g.	241(4.01)	32-0651-79
2,4-Cyclohexadien-1-one, 2-(1,1-dimethylethyl)-6-(4-methoxyphenyl)-4,6-dimethyl-	MeOH	229(4.28)	12-1551-79
Estra-2,5,7,9-tetraen-17α-ol, 3-methoxy-	MeOH	221s(3.97),262s(2.55), 269(2.71),273s(2.68), 279(2.71)	24-2631-79
Estra-2,5,7,9-tetraen-17β-ol, 3-methoxy-	MeOH	221s(3.97),262s(2.55), 269(2.68),273s(2.62), 279(2.61)	24-2631-79
Ethanone, 1-(1,2,3,4,9,10-hexahydro-7-methoxy-1,2-dimethyl-2-phenanthrenyl)-	EtOH	272.5(4.20)	39-0990-79C
Gona-4,8(14)-diene-3,17-dione, 13-ethyl-	MeOH	234(4.21),255s(3.94)	24-3748-79
	MeCN	230(4.23),250s(3.99)	24-3748-79
4H-Inden-4-one, 1,2,3,5,6,7-hexahydro-1-[3-(3-methoxyphenyl)propyl]-	MeOH	252(4.13),279(3.46)	13-0361-79A
B-Norestra-1,3,5(10),8-tetraen-17β-ol, 3-methoxy-6-methyl-	MeOH	212(3.43),271(4.26), 303(3.77)	2-0324-79A

Compound	Solvent	λ_{max}(log ϵ)	Ref.
$C_{19}H_{24}O_2S$			
D-Homo-16-thiaestra-1,3,5(10),8(14)-tetraen-17a-ol, 3-methoxy-, (17aα)-	EtOH	278(3.36),283(3.34)	39-0990-79C
(14β,17aα)-	EtOH	277(4.29)	39-0990-79C
15-Thia-14β-estra-1,3,5(10),8-tetraen-17α-ol, 3-methoxy-14β-methyl-	EtOH	282(4.23)	39-0990-79C
$C_{19}H_{24}O_3$			
Estra-1,3,5(10)-trien-17-one, 3-hydroxy-2-methoxy-	EtOH	286(3.60)	13-0485-79B
anion	EtOH	244(3.91),300(3.70)	13-0485-79B
D-Homo-16-oxaestra-1,3,5(10),8-tetraen-17a-ol, 3-methoxy-, (8α)-	EtOH	273.5(4.21)	4-0637-79
(9β)-	EtOH	276(4.21)	4-0637-79
$C_{19}H_{24}O_4$			
Nagilactone F	EtOH	260(4.19)	102-1691-79
Phenol, 3,3'-(1,5-pentanediyl)bis[6-methoxy-	EtOH	207(4.06),220(3.89), 281(3.56)	39-0662-79C
	EtOH-KOH	211(4.52),243(3.97), 294(3.69)	39-0662-79C
$C_{19}H_{24}O_4S$			
D-Homo-16-thiaestra-1,3,5(10),8(14)-tetraen-17a-ol, 3-methoxy-, 16,16-dioxide, (17aα)-	EtOH	278(3.30),283(3.28)	39-0990-79C
(17aβ)-	EtOH	278(3.34),283(3.32)	39-0990-79C
D-Homo-16-thia-14β-estra-1,3,5(10),8-tetraen-17aα-ol, 3-methoxy-, 16,16-dioxide	EtOH	275(4.18)	39-0990-79C
$C_{19}H_{24}O_5$			
Nagilactone G	EtOH	218(4.00)	102-1691-79
$C_{19}H_{24}O_7$			
Cedr-8-ene-12,14-dioic acid, 13-acetoxy-10-oxo-, dimethyl ester	MeOH	252(4.08)	2-0320-79B
Lactarolide A acetate	EtOH	220(3.84)	102-0293-79
	EtOH-KOH	231(changing)	102-0293-79
$C_{19}H_{25}BrO_3$			
Androst-4-ene-3,17-dione, 6-bromo-16-hydroxy-, (6β,16α)-	EtOH	246(4.02)	13-0347-79B
$C_{19}H_{25}NO$			
2-Oxa-3-azatricyclo[5.4.1.0^{1,5}]dodec-3-ene, 4-(2,4,6-trimethylphenyl)-	EtOH	233(3.85)	33-2025-79
$C_{19}H_{25}NO_2$			
Darlingianine, O-acetyl-	EtOH	285(4.36)	12-2523-79
$C_{19}H_{25}NO_3$			
Epilupinyl cis-p-coumarate	MeOH	207(4.18),308(4.18)	100-0385-79
	MeOH-KOH	204(4.10),225s(--), 359(4.33)	100-0385-79
Epilupinyl trans-p-coumarate	MeOH	208(4.15),225s(--), 313(4.42)	100-0385-79
	MeOH-KOH	205(4.33),239s(--), 360(4.52)	100-0385-79

Compound	Solvent	λ_{max}(log ε)	Ref.
$C_{19}H_{25}NO_5$			
Ungvedine	n.s.g.	206(4.50),235s(3.66), 295(3.62)	105-0513-79
$C_{19}H_{25}N_3O_2$			
Acetic acid, cyano(phenylhydrazono)-, 2-(1-methylethyl)cyclohexyl ester, (E)-	MeOH	240(3.91),360(4.37)	80-1061-79
(Z)-	MeOH	240(3.91),360(4.39)	80-1061-79
$C_{19}H_{25}N_4O_8P$			
5'-Thymidylic acid, α-(3,4-dihydro-4-methyl-1(2H)-quinoxalinyl)-, bis-(triethylamine) salt	pH 1	220s(4.23),270(3.96)	87-1134-79
	H_2O	250(4.28),262(3.96)	87-1134-79
	pH 13	220(4.28),262(3.98)	87-1134-79
$C_{19}H_{26}N_2O$			
3-Pyridinecarboxamide, 1,4-dihydro-2,4-dimethyl-N-(1-phenylethyl)-1-propyl-, (R,R)-	EtOH	322(3.50)	35-7036-79
(R,S)-	EtOH	322(3.57)	35-7036-79
(S,R)-	EtOH	322(3.52)	35-7036-79
(S,S)-	EtOH	322(3.53)	35-7036-79
$C_{19}H_{26}N_4O_2$			
Benzo[d]cyclopenta[i]tetrazolo[1,5-a]-[1]benzazepin-10(8H)-one, 1,2,3,3a-3b,11,12,12a,12b,13,14,14a-dodecahydro-1-hydroxy-12a,14a-dimethyl-, [1S-(1α,3aα,3bα,12aα,12bβ,14aα)]-	MeOH	235(4.07)	39-3166-79C
$C_{19}H_{26}N_4O_7$			
Acetamide, N-[4,7-dihydro-3-(methoxymethyl)-5-methyl-7-[2,3-O-(1-methylethylidene)-β-D-ribofuranosyl]-4-oxo-3H-pyrrolo[2,3-d]pyrimidin-2-yl]-	MeOH	275s(3.81),302(3.94)	35-3629-79
α-D-Galactopyranose, 6-deoxy-1,2:3,4-bis-O-(1-methylethylidene)-6-[1-methyl-3-(4-nitrophenyl)-2-triazenyl]-	EtOH	205(4.00),238(3.93), 273(3.56),363(4.38)	33-0971-79
$C_{19}H_{26}N_6O_9P$			
1H-Pyrrol-1-yloxy, 2,5-dihydro-2,2,5,5-tetramethyl-3-[[[9-(3-O-phosphono-β-D-ribofuranosyl)-9H-purin-6-yl]amino]-carbonyl]-	H_2O	282(4.29)	118-0267-79
1H-Pyrrol-1-yloxy, 2,5-dihydro-2,2,5,5-tetramethyl-3-[[[9-(5-O-phosphono-β-D-ribofuranosyl)-9H-purin-6-yl]amino]-carbonyl]-	H_2O	282(4.29)	118-0267-79
$C_{19}H_{26}O$			
Androsta-2,4-dien-1-one, (10α)-	hexane	312(3.77),322s(3.69), 343s(3.14),371(2.27), 395s(2.10),410s(1.74)	24-0310-79
	MeOH	322(3.75)	24-0310-79
	ether	315(3.76)(plus shoulders)	24-0310-79
	CF_3CH_2OH	331(3.76)	24-0310-79
diastereomer	hexane	317(3.72),380(2.15), 402(1.93),412s(1.56)	24-0310-79
	MeOH	328(3.71)	24-0310-79
	CF_3CH_2OH	336(3.72)	24-0310-79

Compound	Solvent	λ_{max}(log ε)	Ref.
Furan, 3-[2-(1,2,3,4,4a,8a-hexahydro-1,2,4a-trimethyl-1-naphthalenyl)-ethyl]-	EtOH	262(3.47)	2-0529-79B
	EtOH	225(3.866),265(3.927)	102-0494-79
$C_{19}H_{26}O_2$			
Bicyclo[3.3.1]non-3-en-1-ol, 4-ethyl-3-(4-methoxyphenyl)-2-methyl-	EtOH	236(3.98)	2-0152-79B
Estra-4,8(14)-dien-3-one, 17β-hydroxy-17-methyl-	MeOH	233(4.20)	24-3748-79
Gon-4-ene-3,17-dione, 13-ethyl-	MeOH	239(4.24)	24-3748-79
	MeCN	237(4.24)	24-3748-79
2-Phenanthrenemethanol, 1,2,3,4,9,10-hexahydro-7-methoxy-α,1,2-trimethyl-	EtOH	273(4.18)	39-0990-79C
$C_{19}H_{26}O_2S$			
D-Homo-16-thiaestra-1,3,5(10)-trien-17a-ol, 3-methoxy-	EtOH	279(3.30),288(3.26)	39-0990-79C
$C_{19}H_{26}O_3$			
Androst-4-ene-3,17-dione, 6β-hydroxy-, retro-	EtOH	241(4.23)	22-0056-79
A-Norestr-3(5)-en-2-one, 17β-acetoxy-	n.s.g.	233(4.22)	22-0157-79
16-Oxa-15,16-seco-D-homoestra-1,3,5(10)-8-tetraen-17aβ-ol, 3-methoxy-, (14ξ)-	EtOH	273(4.15)	4-0637-79
Premnolal monomethyl ether	EtOH	220s(4.29),232(4.36), 282(4.23)	2-0513-79B
	EtOH-base	219(4.82),265(4.52), 310(4.16)	2-0513-79B
$C_{19}H_{26}O_5$			
1,4,7-Trioxaspiro[4.7]dodec-10-ene-8-methanol, 6-ethyl-α-2-penten-4-ynyl-, acetate, [6α,8α(R*)]-	EtOH	223(4.11),230(4.02)	18-0135-79
$C_{19}H_{26}O_7$			
1,3-Benzenedicarboxylic acid, 2-hydroxy-4-methyl-6-[2-(2,2,4-trimethyl-1,3-dioxolan-4-yl)ethyl]-, dimethyl ester, (S)-	EtOH	214(4.43),251(4.01), 314(3.76)	35-6710-79
$C_{19}H_{27}BrO$			
5α-Androst-2-en-1-one, 4α-bromo-	MeOH	221(3.86)	24-0310-79
5α-Androst-2-en-1-one, 4β-bromo-	MeOH	221(3.97)	24-0310-79
$C_{19}H_{27}BrO_2$			
Androst-4-en-3-one, 6α-bromo-7β-hydroxy-	EtOH	237.5(4.01)	13-0347-79B
6β-	EtOH	247.5(3.96)	13-0347-79B
$C_{19}H_{27}NO$			
4(1H)-Quinolinone, 1-methyl-2-nonyl-	MeOH	236(--),323(4.19), 335(4.19)	102-1768-79
	MeOH-HCl	233(--),301(--)	102-1768-79
$C_{19}H_{27}NO_6$			
Propanedioic acid, [2,2-dimethyl-1-(4-nitrophenyl)propyl]methyl-, diethyl ester	hexane	266(4.08)	12-1487-79
$C_{19}H_{27}NO_8$			
1H-Pyrrole-3-propanoic acid, 5-(acet-	n.s.g.	272(4.23)	39-1927-79C

Compound	Solvent	λ_{max}(log ε)	Ref.
oxymethyl)-2-[(1,1-dimethylethoxy)-carbonyl]-4-(2-methoxy-2-oxoethyl)-, methyl ester (cont.)			39-1927-79C
$C_{19}H_{27}N_3OS$			
Cyclododecanone, 2-(1H-benzimidazol-2-ylthio)-, oxime	EtOH	250(3.818),287(4.098), 292(4.098)	48-0249-79
$C_{19}H_{27}N_3O_7S$			
α-D-Glucopyranoside, methyl 4,6-O-cyclo-hexylidene-2-deoxy-2-[(methoxycarbo-nyl)amino]-, 3-(1H-imidazole-1-carbo-thioate)	EtOH	201(3.70),219(3.70), 276(4.08)	18-3015-79
$C_{19}H_{27}N_3O_8$			
Propanoic acid, 3-ethoxy-, 2-[(3-eth-oxy-1-oxopropoxy)methyl]-2,3,3a,9a-tetrahydro-6-imino-6H-furo[2',3'-4,5]oxazolo[3,2-a]pyrimidin-3-yl ester, monohydrochloride	MeOH	235(4.02),264(4.08)	87-0639-79
$C_{19}H_{27}N_4S$			
Pyrrolidinium, 1-[6-[bis(1-methyleth-yl)amino]-4-phenyl-2H-1,3,5-thiadi-azin-2-ylidene]-, iodide	$CHCl_3$	307(4.33),360(4.01), 374s(3.93)	78-0059-79
$C_{19}H_{27}N_5O_4$			
1H-Purine-2,6-dione, 7-[3,4-(cyclohex-ylimino)-3,4,6-trideoxy-α-L-galacto-pyranosyl]-3,7-dihydro-1,3-dimethyl-	MeOH	274(3.92)	39-2682-79C
$C_{19}H_{27}N_5O_8$			
Pyrido[3,2-c]pyridazine-1,2-dicarbox-ylic acid, 4-[1,2-bis(ethoxycarbo-nyl)hydrazino]-3,4-dihydro-, diethyl ester	MeOH	230(3.91),277(3.51)	103-0518-79
Pyrido[3,4-c]pyridazine-1,2-dicarbox-ylic acid, 4-[1,2-bis(ethoxycarbo-nyl)hydrazino]-3,4-dihydro-, diethyl ester	MeOH	230(3.68),275(3.35)	103-0518-79
$C_{19}H_{27}N_6S$			
Benzothiazolium, 2-[[2,5-bis(diethyl-amino)-4H-imidazol-4-ylidene]amino]-3-methyl-, perchlorate	$CHCl_3$	370(4.19),385(4.26), 405(4.24),450(4.40), 480(4.18)	89-0156-79
$C_{19}H_{28}$			
5,8-Etheno-1H-benzocyclotridecene, 2,3,4,4a,9,10,11,12,13,14,15,15a-dodecahydro-, (4aR*,15aS*)-	EtOH	266(3.91),273(2.45), 279(2.51)	44-2160-79
$C_{19}H_{28}N_2O_3$			
2,4(3H,5H)-Furandione, 3-[1-(cyclohex-ylamino)ethylidene]-5-[(cyclohexyl-amino)methylene]-	EtOH	250(4.19),296(4.22), 358(4.44)	4-1335-79
$C_{19}H_{28}N_4O_2$			
7a-Aza-B-homoandrost-5-eno[7a,7-d]-tetrazole-3β,17β-diol	EtOH	244(4.30)	39-3166-79C

Compound	Solvent	λ_{max}(log ϵ)	Ref.
$C_{19}H_{28}O$			
5α-Androst-1-en-3-one	MeOH	229(4.01)	24-0310-79
5α-Androst-2-en-1-one	MeOH	225(3.88)	24-0310-79
Benzo[3,4]cyclobuta[1,2]cyclododecen-4b(5H)-ol, 6,7,8,9,10,11,12,13,14,14a-4-methyl-	MeOH	260(2.78),266(2.86), 273(2.85)	39-2542-79C
$C_{19}H_{28}O_4$			
1H-Indene-2,4-diol, 6-ethenyl-2,3,3a,4-5,7a-hexahydro-3,4a,7,7a-tetramethyl-, diacetate	EtOH	237.5(3.00)	102-1349-79
$C_{19}H_{28}O_5$			
2H-Pyran, tetrahydro-2-[(1,2,3,4-tetrahydro-5,6,7-trimethoxy-4-methyl-2-naphthalenyl)oxy]-	EtOH	213(4.40),224(3.90), 273(3.23)	150-0301-79
$C_{19}H_{29}NO_8$			
1-Propene-1,1,3,3-tetracarboxylic acid, 2-(1-pyrrolidinyl)-, tetraethyl ester	$CHCl_3$	306(4.2)	5-1388-79
$C_{19}H_{29}NO_9$			
β-D-Glucopyranoside, 1,2,3,4-tetrahydro-1-(hydroxymethyl)-6,7-dimethoxy-2-methyl-5-isoquinolinyl (pterocereine)	H_2O	214s(3.29),268(2.60)	100-0197-79
$C_{19}H_{29}N_5O_4$			
5,16-Iminoimidazo[4,5-b][1,5]diazacyclopentadecine, 3,6,7,8,9,10,11,12,13,14-decahydro-3-β-D-ribofuranosyl-	pH 1.0	273(4.23)	5-1872-79
	pH 7.0	272(4.25)	5-1872-79
$C_{19}H_{30}ClN_3O_2$			
4-Cyclopentene-1,3-dione, 2-[bis(diethylamino)methylene]-4-chloro-5-piperidino-	isoPrOH	263(4.24),326(4.50)	104-0454-79
$C_{19}H_{30}O_3$			
Kolavonic acid, methyl ester	n.s.g.	217(3.91)	78-0979-79
$C_{19}H_{30}O_4$			
1-Naphthalenepropanoic acid, 1,2,3,4-4a,7,8,8a-octahydro-5-(methoxycarbonyl)-1,2,4a-trimethyl-, methyl ester, [1S-(1α,2β,4aβ,8aα)]-	EtOH	220(3.61)	78-2301-79
$C_{19}H_{30}O_5$			
Cyclohexanepropanoic acid, 6-(methoxycarbonyl)-2,3,6-trimethyl-2-(3-oxo-1-butenyl)-, methyl ester, (1α,2β,3α-6β)-	EtOH	227(4.11)	78-2301-79
$C_{19}H_{30}S_4$			
7H,15H-6a,14a-Methano-6H,14H-[1,6]benzodithiocino[3,4-c][1,6]benzodithiocin, dodecahydro-, (4aα,6aα,8aβ,12aα-14aα,16aβ)]-	dioxan	230(2.89)	48-0437-79
$C_{19}H_{31}N$			
Benzenamine, 2,4,6-tris(1,1-dimethylethyl)-N-methylene-	isooctane	213(4.18),220(3.98), 225s(3.97),275(3.00)	54-0071-79

Compound	Solvent	$\lambda_{max}(\log \epsilon)$	Ref.
1-Butanamine, N-[3-methyl-5-(2,6,6-trimethyl-1-cyclohexen-1-yl)-2,4-pentadienylidene)-, all trans	3-Mepentane	260s(4.23),287(4.40)	149-0689-79B
protonated	3-Mepentane	300(4.05),389(4.32)	149-0689-79B
9-cis	3-Mepentane	249(4.26),250s(4.09)	149-0689-79B
9-cis, protonated	3-Mepentane	296(4.05),382(4.19)	149-0689-79B
2,4-Cyclohexadiene-1-carbonitrile, 1,3,5-tris(1,1-dimethylethyl)-	hexane	261(3.77)	18-0175-79
2,4-Octadienenitrile, 2,4-bis(1,1-dimethylethyl)-7,7-dimethyl-6-methylene-, (Z,E)-	hexane	262(3.83)	18-0175-79
2,3,5-Octatrienenitrile, 2,4-bis(1,1-dimethylethyl)-6,7,7-trimethyl-, (E)-	hexane	258(4.17)	18-0175-79
2,4,5-Octatrienenitrile, 2,4-bis(1,1-dimethylethyl)-6,7,7-trimethyl-, (Z)-	hexane	270.5(3.96)	18-0175-79
2,4,7-Octatrienenitrile, 2,4-bis(1,1-dimethylethyl)-6,6,7-trimethyl-, (Z,E)-	hexane	257(3.18)	18-0175-79
$C_{19}H_{31}NO$			
Phenol, 2-[(dodecylimino)methyl]-	MeOH	216(3.66),253(4.30), 280(3.58),315(3.85)	150-3801-79
$C_{19}H_{32}N_6O_4$			
1,3,5-Triazin-2-amine, N-(5-ethyl-2,2-dimethyl-1,3-dioxan-5-yl)-4,6-dimorpholino-	EtOH	228(4.63)	104-1144-79
$C_{19}H_{32}O_7$			
2-Butenoic acid, 3-methyl-4-[tetrahydro-3,4-dihydroxy-5-[[3-(2-hydroxy-1-methylpropyl)oxiranyl]methyl]-2H-pyran-2-yl]-, ethyl ester, (E)-	EtOH	220(4.05)	39-0308-79C
(Z)-	EtOH	221(3.99)	39-0308-79C
$C_{19}H_{32}O_8$			
3-Buten-2-one, 4-[2-(β-D-glucopyranosyloxy)-1-hydroxy-2,6,6-trimethylcyclohexyl]-	EtOH	232(4.04)	94-2807-79
$C_{19}H_{33}N$			
2,5-Octadienenitrile, 2,4-bis(1,1-dimethylethyl)-6,7,7-trimethyl-	hexane	240s(3.91)	18-0175-79
$C_{19}H_{33}NO$			
3,5-Octadienenitrile, 2,4-bis(1,1-dimethylethyl)-7-methoxy-6,7-dimethyl-	hexane	293s(2.99)	18-0175-79
Phenol, 2-[(dodecylamino)methyl]-, hydrochloride	EtOH	216(3.81),277(3.45)	150-3801-79
$C_{19}H_{33}NO_3$			
2-Pyridineundecanol, 4-hydroxy-5-methoxy-α,6-dimethyl- (melochinine)	MeOH	263(4.13)	24-0376-79
	MeOH-HCl	240(3.75),261(3.7)	24-0376-79
	MeOH-NaOH	245(3.99)	24-0376-79
$C_{19}H_{36}N_3$			
Cyclopropenylium, bis[bis(1-methylethyl)amino]-1-pyrrolidinyl]-, perchlorate	CH_2Cl_2	235(4.27)	24-1514-79

Compound	Solvent	λ_{max}(log ε)	Ref.
$C_{19}H_{38}N_2O_4$			
Acetamide, 2,2'-[(1-methyl-1,2-ethanediyl)bis(oxy)]bis[N,N-dipropyl-	H_2O	204(4.18)	33-0754-79
$C_{19}H_{39}Cl_2N_2PPd$			
Palladium, [2,3-bis(dimethylamino)-2-cyclopropen-1-ylidene]dichloro(tributylphosphine)-, (SP-4-3)-	CH_2Cl_2	309(3.41)	101-0199-79J

Compound	Solvent	λ_{max}(log ε)	Ref.
$C_{20}H_8Br_4O_5$			
Eosin	10M H_2SO_4	453(4.7)	22-0375-79I
	H_2SO_4	455(4.64)	140-0807-79
	pH 1	480(3.85)	140-0807-79
	pH 1.89	490(2.7)	22-0375-79I
	pH 3.6	518(4.9)	22-0375-79I
	pH 8	515(5.0)	22-0375-79I
	pH 8	520(4.94)	140-0807-79
$C_{20}H_8N_2O_7$			
1,8-Naphthalenedicarboxylic acid anhydride, 4-nitro-5-phthalimido-	xylene	343(3.99)	153-0043-79
$C_{20}H_8O_7$			
[2]Benzopyrano[6,5,4-def][2]benzopyran-1,3,6,8-tetrone, 4-phenoxy-	$CHCl_3$	417(4.00)	104-2279-79
$C_{20}H_9Cl_3N_2O_4$			
9(10H)-Anthracenone, 1,3-dichloro-10-[(2-chloro-4-nitrophenyl)imino]-4-hydroxy-	benzene	419(3.94)	104-0147-79
	dioxan	414(3.96)	104-0147-79
$C_{20}H_{10}BrNO_2S$			
6H-Anthra[1,9-cd]isoxazol-6-one, 3-[(4-bromophenyl)thio]-	EtOH	235(4.52),255(4.52), 449(4.22),477(4.37)	104-1514-79
8H-Naphtho[2,3-a]phenothiazin-8,13(14H)-dione, 2-bromo-	EtOH	245(4.39),275(4.70), 585(3.84)	104-1514-79
$C_{20}H_{10}BrNO_3S$			
6H-Anthra[1,9-cd]isoxazol-6-one, 3-[(4-bromophenyl)thio]-5-hydroxy-	EtOH	245(4.62),443(3.98), 455(3.98),490(3.54)	104-1514-79
8H-Naphtho[2,3-a]phenothiazine-8,13-(14H)-dione, 2-bromo-7-hydroxy-	EtOH	250(4.50),280(4.68), 633(4.17),684(4.11)	104-1514-79
$C_{20}H_{10}BrN_3O_2S$			
9,10-Anthracenedione, 1-azido-2-[(4-bromophenyl)thio]-	EtOH	235(4.54),252(4.55), 275(4.33),305(4.26), 422(3.69),444(3.67), 475(3.44)	104-1514-79
$C_{20}H_{10}BrN_3O_3S$			
9,10-Anthracenedione, 1-azido-2-[(4-bromophenyl)thio]-4-hydroxy-	EtOH	235(4.51),256(4.57), 458(3.93)	104-1514-79
$C_{20}H_{10}Br_2O_5$			
Fluorescein, 4,5-dibromo-	H_2SO_4	450(4.62)	140-0807-79
	pH 1.5	490(3.70)	140-0807-79
	pH 8	510(4.86)	140-0807-79
$C_{20}H_{10}ClNO_2S$			
6H-Anthra[1,9-cd]isoxazol-6-one, 3-[(4-chlorophenyl)thio]-	EtOH	230(4.46),255(4.51), 448(4.22),477(4.37)	104-1514-79
8H-Naphtho[2,3-a]phenothiazine-8,13-(14H)-dione, 2-chloro-	EtOH	242(4.41),275(4.74), 586(3.87)	104-1514-79
$C_{20}H_{10}ClNO_3S$			
6H-Anthra[1,9-cd]isoxazol-6-one, 3-[(4-chlorophenyl)thio]-5-hydroxy-	EtOH	245(4.62),443(3.96), 457(3.96),490(3.53)	104-1514-79
8H-Naphtho[2,3-a]phenothiazine-8,13-(14H)-dione, 2-chloro-7-hydroxy-	EtOH	250(4.45),280(4.64), 633(4.15),685(4.03)	104-1514-79

Compound	Solvent	$\lambda_{max}(\log \epsilon)$	Ref.
$C_{20}H_{10}ClN_3O_2S$			
9,10-Anthracenedione, 1-azido-2-[(4-chlorophenyl)thio]-	EtOH	232(4.46),252(4.50), 280(4.27),421(3.72), 443(3.72),475(3.53)	104-1514-79
$C_{20}H_{10}ClN_3O_3S$			
9,10-Anthracenedione, 1-azido-2-[(4-chlorophenyl)thio]-4-hydroxy-	EtOH	230(4.49),256(4.57), 458(3.95)	104-1514-79
$C_{20}H_{10}Cl_2N_2O_4$			
9(10H)-Anthracenone, 1,3-dichloro-4-hydroxy-10-[(4-nitrophenyl)imino]-	benzene	417(3.98)	104-0147-79
	EtOH	408(3.98)	104-0147-79
	dioxan	412(3.98)	104-0147-79
$C_{20}H_{10}F_4O$			
Benzofuran, 4,5,6,7-tetrafluoro-2,3-diphenyl-	C_6H_{12}	232(4.34),297(4.40)	18-2657-79
$C_{20}H_{10}F_4O_3$			
1-Pyrenebutanoic acid, α,α,β,β-tetrafluoro-γ-oxo-	$CHCl_3$	240(4.5),295(4.2), 430(3.7)	24-2907-79
$C_{20}H_{10}N_2O$			
Propanedinitrile, (2-phenyl-5H-naphtho-[1,8-bc]furan-5-ylidene)-	MeOH	229(3.8),280(3.7), 304(3.8),471(4.6)	5-0959-79
$C_{20}H_{10}O_2S_2$			
Naphtho[1,8-bc]thiopyran-3(2H)-one, 2-(3-oxobenzo[b]thien-2(3H)-ylidene)-, cis	n.s.g.	482(4.19)	124-0768-79
trans	n.s.g.	592(4.49)	124-0768-79
$C_{20}H_{10}O_3$			
Indeno[1,2-a]phenalene-7,8-dione, 3-hydroxy-	MeOH	350(4.17),390(4.01), 420(3.84),535(4.26)	135-0220-79A
	C_6H_5Cl	345(4.49),420(4.10)	135-0220-79A
	DMSO	340(4.21),420(3.91), 535(4.02)	135-0220-79A
$C_{20}H_{10}O_4$			
[2,2'-Binaphthalene]-1,1',4,4'-tetrone	MeOH	246(4.4),333(3.96)	2-0079-79A
tetraleucoacetate	MeOH	247(4.79),285(4.34)	2-0079-79A
$C_{20}H_{11}BrN_2O_2$			
6H-Anthra[1,9-cd]isoxazol-6-one, 3-bromo-5-(phenylamino)-	dioxan	502(4.16),532(4.23)	104-0510-79
$C_{20}H_{11}Cl_2NO_2$			
9(10H)-Anthracenone, 1,3-dichloro-4-hydroxy-10-(phenylimino)-	benzene	417(3.86)	104-0147-79
	EtOH	417(3.85),540s(2.78)	104-0147-79
	dioxan	417(3.87)	104-0147-79
$C_{20}H_{11}F$			
Benzo[a]pyrene, 7-fluoro-	hexane	297(4.8),386(4.5), 404(2.9)	24-2907-79
Benzo[a]pyrene, 9-fluoro-	hexane	296(4.6),385(4.2), 408(3.9)	24-2907-79
$C_{20}H_{11}NO_2S$			
6H-Anthra[1,9-cd]isoxazol-6-one, 3-(phenylthio)-	EtOH	255(4.44),449(4.31), 477(4.41)	104-1514-79

Compound	Solvent	$\lambda_{max}(\log \epsilon)$	Ref.
8H-Naphtho[2,3-a]phenothiazine-8,13-(14H)-dione	EtOH	240(4.43),275(4.62), 590(3.79)	104-1514-79
$C_{20}H_{11}NO_3$			
3H-Naphtho[2,1-b]pyran-3-one, 2-(2-benzoxazolyl)-	dioxan	391(4.40)	42-0505-79
$C_{20}H_{11}NO_3S$			
6H-Anthra[1,9-cd]isoxazol-6-one, 5-hydroxy-3-(phenylthio)-	EtOH	245(4.60),440(4.00), 454(4.00),490(3.54)	104-1514-79
8H-Naphtho[2,3-a]phenothiazine-8,13-(14H)-dione, 7-hydroxy-	EtOH	240(4.42),280(4.55), 636(4.18),689(4.06)	104-1514-79
$C_{20}H_{11}N_3O_2S$			
9,10-Anthracenedione, 1-azido-2-(phenylthio)-	EtOH	252(4.48),280(4.25), 305(4.24),422(3.72), 442(3.68),474(3.33)	104-1514-79
$C_{20}H_{11}N_3O_3S$			
9,10-Anthracenedione, 1-azido-4-hydroxy-2-(phenylthio)-	EtOH	256(4.57),460(3.96)	104-1514-79
$C_{20}H_{12}$			
Benzo[4,5]cyclohept[1,2,3-bc]acenaphthylene	C_6H_{12}	223(4.39),258(4.55), 277(4.77),287(4.87), 329(4.08),344(4.10), 361(4.10),395(3.74), 416(3.78),453(3.26), 478(3.25),542(2.68)	138-0537-79
Benzo[a]fluoranthene	hexane	194(4.79),214(4.56), 257(4.82),302(3.83), 363(3.66),422(3.86)	5-1443-79
Benzo[a]naphth[3,4,4a,5-cde]azulene	C_6H_{12}	256(4.70),286(4.54), 298(4.39),318(3.83), 357(3.96),365(3.96), 372(3.97),403(3.39), 419(3.12),429(3.38), 509(3.03),546(3.11), 581(2.97),595(3.01), 636(2.60),654(2.60)	138-0537-79
$C_{20}H_{12}BrN_3$			
Benzimidazo[1,2-c]quinazoline, 6-(2-bromophenyl)-	n.s.g.	268(4.65),278(4.75)	124-0225-79
$C_{20}H_{12}ClN_3$			
Benzimidazo[1,2-c]quinazoline, 6-(2-chlorophenyl)-	n.s.g.	268(4.62),278(4.72)	124-0225-79
$C_{20}H_{12}Cl_2$			
Benzo[a]pyrene, 7,8-dichloro-9,10-dihydro-	$CHCl_3$	302(4.6),347(4.4), 410(3.3)	24-2907-79
$C_{20}H_{12}Cl_2N_2O_2S_2$			
Triphenodithiazine, 6,13-dichloro-3,10-dimethoxy-	H_2SO_4	331(4.79)	40-0432-79
	o-$C_6H_4Cl_2$	584(4.04)	40-0432-79
$C_{20}H_{12}Cl_2N_2S_2$			
Triphenodithiazine, 6,13-dichloro-3,10-dimethyl-	H_2SO_4	333(4.90)	40-0432-79
	o-$C_6H_4Cl_2$	571(4.72)	40-0432-79

Compound	Solvent	$\lambda_{max}(\log \epsilon)$	Ref.
$C_{20}H_{12}FN_3$			
Benzimidazo[1,2-c]quinazoline, 6-(4-fluorophenyl)-	n.s.g.	267(4.60),277(4.70)	124-0225-79
$C_{20}H_{12}IN_2O_4$			
Iodonium, bis[4-(2,5-dihydro-2,5-dioxo-1H-pyrrol-1-yl)phenyl]-, chloride	MeOH	288(abs=0.7)	47-3845-79
$C_{20}H_{12}N_2OS$			
9H-Naphtho[1',2':4,5]thiazolo[3,2-a]-pyrimidin-9-one, 11-phenyl-	MeOH	248(4.63),321(4.05), 348(4.05)	83-0619-79
$C_{20}H_{12}N_2O_2$			
6H-Anthra[1,9-cd]isoxazol-6-one, 5-(phenylamino)-	dioxan	493(4.16),522(4.19)	104-0510-79
Benzoxazole, 2,2'-(1,3-phenylene)bis-	H_2SO_4	205(4.70),388(3.80)	103-1299-79
Benzoxazole, 2,2'-(1,4-phenylene)bis-	H_2SO_4	205(4.70),400(3.90)	103-1299-79
$C_{20}H_{12}N_2O_4$			
2-Hexenedinitrile, 2,5-dibenzoyl-3-hydroxy-4-oxo-, sodium salt	H_2O	377(4.57)	48-0443-79
$C_{20}H_{12}N_4O$			
[1,2,5]Oxadiazolo[3,4-f]quinoxaline, 7,8-diphenyl-	EtOH	230(4.38),289(4.33), 348(4.14)	78-0241-79
$C_{20}H_{12}N_4O_2$			
Benzimidazo[1,2-c]quinazoline, 6-(4-nitrophenyl)-	n.s.g.	267(4.60),279(4.72)	124-0225-79
$C_{20}H_{12}O_2$			
Benzo[a]pyrene-7,10-dione, 8,9-dihydro-	$CHCl_3$	290(4.4),368(4.3), 410(2.5)	24-2907-79
[2,2'-Binaphthalene]-1,4-dione	MeOH	222(4.45),252(4.24), 320(3.5)	2-0079-79A
$C_{20}H_{12}O_5$			
Fluorescein	pH 1	440(4.42)	140-0807-79
	pH 3	445(3.90)	140-0807-79
	pH 5	455-475(4.28)	140-0807-79
	pH 8	495(4.68)	140-0807-79
dianion	MeOH-NaOH	497(4.92)	151-0467-79A
$C_{20}H_{12}O_6$			
Helioxanthin	$CHCl_3$	268(4.65),290(3.70), 355(3.90)	2-0415-79A
Justicidin E	$CHCl_3$	250(4.60),258(4.63), 313(4.10),345?(3.65)	2-0415-79A
$C_{20}H_{12}O_7$			
Prostalidin C	MeOH	235(4.64),258(4.59), 293s(3.84),310(3.82), 317(3.84),350s(2.98)	25-0854-79
$C_{20}H_{13}BrNO_2$			
Pyridinium, 1-[(1-bromo-9,10-dihydro-9,10-dioxo-2-anthracenyl)methyl]-, bromide	H_2O	261(4.68),272(4.19), 342(3.75)	78-2255-79
$C_{20}H_{13}BrN_2O_2$			
9,10-Anthracenedione, 1-amino-2-bromo-4-anilino-	dioxan	570(0.01),614(4.03)	104-0510-79

Compound	Solvent	λ_{max}(log ε)	Ref.
$C_{20}H_{13}ClNO_2$			
Pyridinium, 1-[(1-chloro-9,10-dihydro-9,10-dioxo-2-anthracenyl)methyl]-, bromide	H_2O	253(4.69),272(4.18), 339(3.77)	78-2255-79
$C_{20}H_{13}ClN_4$			
Indolo[7,6-g]indole, 1-[(4-chlorophenyl)azo]-3,8-dihydro-	EtOH	203(4.24),262(4.60), 335(4.01),341(3.89), 476(4.54)	103-0989-79
Pyrrolo[2,3-c]carbazole, 1-[(4-chlorophenyl)azo]-3,6-dihydro-	EtOH	204(4.51),227(4.73), 326(4.40),422(4.24)	103-0890-79
$C_{20}H_{13}INO_2$			
Pyridinium, 1-[(9,10-dihydro-1-iodo-9,10-dioxo-2-anthracenyl)methyl]-, bromide	H_2O	260(4.60),348(3.65)	78-2255-79
$C_{20}H_{13}NO$			
Propanenitrile, 2-(2-phenyl-5H-naphtho-[1,8-bc]furan-5-ylidene)-	MeOH	241(3.7),251(3.7), 281(4.0),395s(--), 407(4.6)	5-0959-79
$C_{20}H_{13}NOS_2$			
[2,2'-Bithiophene]-5-carboxaldehyde, 5'-[2-(2-quinolinyl)ethenyl]-, (E)-	EtOH	240(4.38),330(3.68), 380(4.04),420(3.96)	103-0970-79
$C_{20}H_{13}NO_2$			
1H-Phenalene-1,3(2H)-dione, 2-[(phenylamino)methylene]-	hexane	234(4.73),349s(4.40), 373(4.46),395s(4.39)	131-0077-79D
	EtOH	340s(--),361(4.47), 372s(--),395s(--)	131-0077-79D
$C_{20}H_{13}N_2O_4$			
Pyridinium, 1-[(9,10-dihydro-1-nitro-9,10-dioxo-2-anthracenyl)methyl]-, bromide	H_2O	260(4.63),331(3.63)	78-2255-79
$C_{20}H_{13}N_3$			
Benzimidazo[1,2-c]quinazoline, 6-phenyl-	n.s.g.	268(4.62),278(4.70)	124-0225-79
$C_{20}H_{13}N_5O_2$			
Indolo[7,6-g]indole, 3,8-dihydro-1-[(4-nitrophenyl)azo]-	EtOH	204(3.87),261(4.11), 291(3.63),526(4.22)	103-0989-79
Pyrrolo[2,3-c]carbazole, 3,6-dihydro-1-[(4-nitrophenyl)azo]-	EtOH	205(4.31),223(4.58), 322(4.38),522(4.12)	103-0890-79
$C_{20}H_{14}$			
5,5'-Biazulene	EtOH	274(4.49),304(4.78), 382(4.20),594(3.04), 615(3.03),645(3.04), 716(2.74)	89-0214-79
2,7-(Etheno[1,4]benzenoetheno)naphthalene	hexane	240(5.76)	12-1067-79
$C_{20}H_{14}BrNO_2$			
Furo[2,3-c]pyridin-2(6H)-one, 3-(4-bromophenyl)-6-(phenylmethyl)-	EtOH	382(4.34)	97-0020-79
Furo[3,2-b]pyridin-2(4H)-one, 3-(4-bromophenyl)-4-(phenylmethyl)-	EtOH	370(3.64)	97-0020-79

Compound	Solvent	λ_{max}(log ε)	Ref.
$C_{20}H_{14}Cl_2N_6O$			
Cyclohexanone, 2,6-bis[(4-azido-2-chlorophenyl)methylene]-	MeOH	340(4.58)	93-0333-79
$C_{20}H_{14}Cl_2S$			
Thiophene, 2,5-bis[2-(4-chlorophenyl)-ethenyl]-	toluene	397(4.86)	103-0729-79
$C_{20}H_{14}NO_2$			
Pyridinium, 1-[(9,10-dihydro-9,10-di-oxo-2-anthracenyl)methyl]-, bromide	H_2O	257(4.72),276(4.17), 332(3.72)	78-2255-79
$C_{20}H_{14}N_2$			
Diazene, di-2-naphthalenyl-	hexane	335(4.3),480s(3.0)	19-0793-79
	$H_2NCH_2CH_2NH_2$	325(4.1),502(3.7)	19-0793-79
$C_{20}H_{14}N_2O$			
2H-Cyclopenta[d]pyridazine-5-carbox-aldehyde, 1,4-diphenyl-	EtOH	245(4.5),265s(4.4), 300(4.3),340(4.0), 405(3.8)	5-0675-79
9-Phenanthrenol, 10-(phenylazo)-	EtOH	265(4.54),290(4.19), 396(3.90),480(4.38)	32-0351-79
	ether	290(3.93),390(3.86), 470(4.36)	32-0351-79
	dioxan	210(4.58),255(4.58), 290(4.29),405(3.98), 480(4.49)	32-0351-79
	CCl_4	290(4.36),395(4.02), 475(4.39)	32-0351-79
$C_{20}H_{14}N_2OS$			
Benzenepropanenitrile, β-oxo-α-[[(5-phenyl-2-thienyl)amino]methylene]-	DMF	261(4.00),295(4.06), 395(4.30)	49-1189-79
$C_{20}H_{14}N_2OS_2$			
1,3,2-Benzodithiazole, 2-[4-(2-benz-oxazolyl)phenyl]-5-methyl-	CH_2Cl_2	315(4.55)	4-0183-79
$C_{20}H_{14}N_2O_2$			
9,10-Anthracenedione, 1-amino-2-(phen-ylamino)-	dioxan	506(4.76)	104-0510-79
$C_{20}H_{14}N_2O_2S_2$			
Triphenodithiazine, 3,10-dimethoxy-	H_2SO_4	299(4.70)	40-0432-79
	o-$C_6H_4Cl_2$	583(4.28)	40-0432-79
$C_{20}H_{14}N_2O_4$			
3H-Indol-3-one, 1-acetyl-2-(1-acetyl-1,3-dihydro-3-oxo-2H-indol-2-yli-dene)-1,2-dihydro-, cis	benzene	438(3.65)	18-3397-79 +25-0415-79
trans	benzene	562(3.85)	18-3397-79
Naphtho[2',3':4,5]furo[2,3-b]pyridine-3-carbonitrile, 1,2,5,10-tetrahydro-4-methyl-1-(1-methylethyl)-2,5,10-trioxo-	$CHCl_3$	278(4.40),345(4.07), 445(3.91)	2-0100-79A
$C_{20}H_{14}N_2O_4S$			
Thiophene, 2,5-bis[2-(4-nitrophenyl)-ethenyl]-, (E,E)-	toluene	415(4.69),435(4.66)	103-0729-79

Compound	Solvent	$\lambda_{max}(\log \epsilon)$	Ref.
$C_{20}H_{14}N_2O_5S$			
2-Anthracenesulfonic acid, 1-amino-9,10-dihydro-9,10-dioxo-4-(phenylamino)-, monosodium salt	glycerol	637(4.22)	112-0139-79
$C_{20}H_{14}N_2S_2$			
Triphenodithiazine, 3,10-dimethyl-	H_2SO_4	322(4.69)	40-0432-79
	$o-C_6H_4Cl_2$	570(4.42)	40-0432-79
$C_{20}H_{14}N_3O$			
9H-Fluorene-2-diazonium, 7-(benzoylamino)-, tetrafluoroborate	EtOH-HBF_4	414(4.49)	104-0733-79
$C_{20}H_{14}N_4$			
Indolo[7,6-g]indole, 3,8-dihydro-1-(phenylazo)-	EtOH	204(4.25),261(4.49), 300(4.01),322(3.91), 337(3.79)	103-0989-79
Pyrrolo[2,3-c]carbazole, 3,6-dihydro-1-(phenylazo)-	EtOH	206(4.65),317(4.24), 412(4.06)	103-0890-79
$C_{20}H_{14}N_4O_2$			
Pyrrolo[1,2-a:4,5-b']diquinoxaline-6-carboxylic acid, ethyl ester	EtOH	279s(4.46),284(4.51), 290s(4.44),317s(3.78), 364s(3.73),378(3.93), 397(4.02),491s(3.48), 507(3.51),555(3.18)	78-2463-79
$C_{20}H_{14}N_6$			
Pyrimidine, 5,5'-azobis[4-phenyl-	EtOH	268(4.35),341(4.01)	103-0808-79
$C_{20}H_{14}N_6O_2$			
Tribenzo[c,g,m][1,2,5,6,9,12]hexaazacyclotetradecine-12,13-dione, 11,14-dihydro-	benzene	339(4.66),420s(4.05)	118-0545-79
$C_{20}H_{14}N_8O_5$			
Cyclohexanone, 2,6-bis[(4-azido-3-nitrophenyl)methylene]-	MeOH	328(4.51)	93-0333-79
$C_{20}H_{14}O$			
2-Styrylbiphenylene oxide	dioxan	298(4.55)	104-1944-79
$C_{20}H_{14}O_2$			
6H-Cyclopenta[b]furan-6-one, 2-methyl-4,5-diphenyl-	CH_2Cl_2	267(4.47),470(3.66)	103-1173-79
$C_{20}H_{14}O_2S$			
1H-Indene-1,3(2H)-dione, 2-(1,3-dimethyl-6H-cyclohepta[c]thien-6-ylidene)-	$CHCl_3$	248(4.39),276(4.34), 308(4.19),321(4.18), 436s(4.39),466(4.55), 496(4.55)	83-0120-79
$C_{20}H_{14}O_3$			
4H-Naphtho[1,2-b]pyran-4-one, 2-(3-methoxyphenyl)-	MeCN	277(4.51)	87-1244-79
$C_{20}H_{14}O_4S_2$			
1,3-Dithiole-4,5-dicarboxylic acid, 2-(9H-fluoren-9-ylidene)-, dimethyl ester	CH_2Cl_2	245(4.83),377(4.51), 396s(4.49)	44-0930-79

Compound	Solvent	λ_{max}(log ε)	Ref.
$C_{20}H_{14}O_5$			
Benzenepropanoic acid, α-(1,3-dihydro-1,3-dioxo-2H-inden-2-ylidene)-β-oxo-, ethyl ester	dioxan	256(4.59),305(3.83), 317(3.72)	32-0329-79
$C_{20}H_{14}O_6$			
1,4-Ethanonaphthacene-2,6,11(1H)-trione, 3,4-dihydro-4,5,12-trihydroxy-	MeOH	204(4.46),251(4.61), 256(4.60),283(4.08), 325s(3.91),464(4.11), 486(4.15),518(4.02)	24-2640-79
5,12-Naphthacenedione, 9-ethynyl-7,8,9,10-tetrahydro-6,7,9,11-tetrahydroxy-, cis	MeOH	215(4.13),249(4.46), 286(3.84),481(3.85), 514(3.65)	24-3453-79
$C_{20}H_{15}BrNP$			
Acetonitrile, bromo(triphenylphosphoranylidene)-	MeCN	199(4.72),220s(4.43)	33-1401-79
$C_{20}H_{15}BrN_2O$			
2-Propen-1-one, 3-(4-bromophenyl)-1-(4-methyl-2-phenyl-5-pyrimidinyl)-	EtOH	206(4.45),228s(4.25), 317(4.50)	103-0551-79
$C_{20}H_{15}ClNP$			
Acetonitrile, chloro(triphenylphosphoranylidene)-	MeCN	199(4.60),220s(4.35)	33-1401-79
$C_{20}H_{15}ClN_2$			
Benzenamine, 4-chloro-N-(10-methyl-9(10H)-acridinylidene)-, monohydriodide	EtOH	244(4.57),271(4.67), 337(3.75),449(4.13)	104-0183-79
$C_{20}H_{15}ClO_3$			
1H-Cyclopenta[l]phenanthrene-1-carboxylic acid, 1-chloro-2,3-dihydro-2-oxo-, ethyl ester	EtOH	219s(4.27),257(4.65), 281s(4.16),295s(4.13), 307(4.07),336(3.19), 352(3.16)	39-2034-79C
$C_{20}H_{15}Cl_2N_3S$			
Sulfur, dichloro(1,4,5-triphenyl-1H-1,2,4-triazolium-3-yl)-	MeOH	238(4.24)	70-2526-79
$C_{20}H_{15}F$			
Benzo[a]anthracene, 2-fluoro-7,12-dimethyl-	MeOH	227(3.28),262(4.67), 274(4.67),284(4.84), 294(4.84),305(3.18), 345(2.88),363(2.88)	44-3715-79
$C_{20}H_{15}INP$			
Acetonitrile, iodo(triphenylphosphoranylidene)-	MeCN	198(4.67),220s(4.34)	33-1401-79
$C_{20}H_{15}NO_2$			
Benzo[j]phenanthridine-7,12-dione, 2,3,6-trimethyl-	dioxan	220s(4.6),240(4.45), 250(4.44),287(4.40), 385(3.82)	5-0503-79
Furo[2,3-c]pyridin-2(6H)-one, 3-phenyl-6-(phenylmethyl)-	EtOH	380(4.39)	97-0020-79
Furo[3,2-b]pyridin-2(4H)-one, 3-phenyl-4-(phenylmethyl)-	EtOH	374(4.10)	97-0020-79

Compound	Solvent	$\lambda_{max}(\log \epsilon)$	Ref.
$C_{20}H_{15}NO_3$			
Furo[2,3-c]pyridin-2(6H)-one, 3-(4-methoxyphenyl)-6-phenyl-	EtOH	398(4.40)	97-0020-79
Furo[3,2-b]pyridin-2(4H)-one, 3-(4-methoxyphenyl)-4-phenyl-	EtOH	388(3.94)	97-0020-79
$C_{20}H_{15}NO_4$			
1,3-Isobenzofurandione, 5-[5-(2,4,5-trimethylphenyl)-2-oxazolyl]-	toluene	372(4.16)	103-0028-79
$C_{20}H_{15}NO_6$			
5H-[1,3]Dioxolo[4,5-g]-1,3-dioxolo-[6',7']indeno[2',1':4,5]oxazolo-[4,3-a]isoquinolin-14(3cH)-one, 7,8-dihydro-, (3cR*,14aR*)-(±)-	MeOH	212(4.37),237(4.50), 295(4.16),314(4.07)	23-1569-79
$C_{20}H_{15}NO_7$			
Spiro[1,3-dioxolo[4,5-g]isoquinolin-5(6H),7'-[7H]indeno[4,5-d][1,3]dioxole]-6-carboxaldehyde, 6',7,8,8'-tetrahydro-8'-hydroxy-6'-oxo-, cis-(±)-	MeOH	212(4.11),236(4.17), 293(3.88),308s(3.73)	23-1569-79
$C_{20}H_{15}N_3O$			
Benzamide, N-(2-phenyl-1H-benzimidazol-1-yl)-	EtOH	230s(4.40),279(4.18), 291(4.23)	4-1005-79
Benzo[b]cyclohept[e][1,4]oxazine, 8-[(4-methylphenyl)azo]-	MeOH	206(4.39),230(4.25), 264(4.41),328(4.28), 455s(4.45),474(4.49), 500s(4.41),560s(4.37)	18-3123-79
	MeOH-HCl	206(4.31),233(4.28), 265(4.36),275(4.39), 341(4.17),540(4.37)	18-3123-79
	MeOH-NaOH	268(4.35),333(4.21), 475(4.50),510s(4.37), 570s(4.02)	18-3123-79
3(2H)-Isoquinolinone, 1,4-dihydro-1-(3-pyridinyl)-4-(3-pyridinylmethylene)-	n.s.g.	308(4.19)	114-0305-79D
3(2H)-Isoquinolinone, 1-(3-pyridinyl)-4-(3-pyridinylmethyl)-	n.s.g.	286(3.73),296(3.69), 350(3.86),430(2.95)	114-0305-79D
3(2H)-Isoquinolinone, 1-(4-pyridinyl)-4-(4-pyridinylmethyl)-	n.s.g.	281(--),293(--), 359(3.92),434(3.07)	114-0305-79D
$C_{20}H_{15}N_3OS$			
Benzothiazole, 2-[[4-(phenylmethoxy)-phenyl]azo]-	EtOH	410(3.45)	103-1185-79
$C_{20}H_{15}N_3O_2$			
3-Pyridinecarbonitrile, 5-benz[cd]indol-2-yl-1-ethyl-1,2-dihydro-6-hydroxy-4-methyl-2-oxo-	DMF	510(3.90)	2-0140-79A
$C_{20}H_{15}N_3O_2S_2$			
Benzamide, N,N'-[2-cyano-5-(methylthio)-3,4-thiophenediyl]bis-	EtOH	235(4.45),310(4.04)	95-1081-79
$C_{20}H_{15}N_3O_3$			
Imidazo[1,5-b]pyridazine-5,7(3H,6H)-dione, 4-benzoyl-6-methyl-2-phenyl-	50% EtOH	255(4.10),317s(3.50)	4-1105-79
2-Propen-1-one, 1-(4-methyl-2-phenyl-5-pyrimidinyl)-3-(4-nitrophenyl)-	EtOH	204(4.35),219s(4.16), 302(4.37)	103-0551-79

Compound	Solvent	λmax(log ε)	Ref.
$C_{20}H_{15}N_3S$			
3H-1,2,4-Triazole-3-thione, 2,4-dihydro-2,4,5-triphenyl-	MeOH	245(4.44),325(3.88)	24-0517-79
	dioxan	233(4.08),275s(--), 340s(--)	24-0517-79
1H-1,2,4-Triazolium, 3-mercapto-1,4,5-triphenyl-, hydroxide, inner salt	MeOH	241(4.39),390(3.50)	70-2526-79
$C_{20}H_{15}N_3S_2$			
2-Thiophenecarbonitrile, 5-(methylthio)-3,4-bis[(phenylmethylene)amino]-	EtOH	250(4.43),290(4.20), 330(3.99)	95-1081-79
$C_{20}H_{15}S_2$			
1-Benzothiopyrylium, 4-(2H-1-benzothiopyran-2-ylidenemethyl)-2-methyl-, perchlorate	acetone	616(4.79)	18-0160-79
$C_{20}H_{15}S_3$			
1,3-Dithiol-1-ium, 4-methyl-3-(1-naphthalenylthio)-5-phenyl-, bromide	MeCN	220(4.88),300(3.98), 324s(4.03),370(4.33)	104-0955-79
$C_{20}H_{16}$			
Azuleno[1,2,3-cd]phenalene, 4,5,11,12-tetrahydro-	C_6H_{12}	249(4.12),262s(4.02), 294s(4.49),310(4.80), 323(4.94),479(2.13), 576s(2.45),610(2.56), 666(2.45),725(2.05), 739(2.09),809s(0.75)	138-0771-79
Bicyclo[4.2.0]octa-1,3,5-triene, 2,5-diphenyl-	C_6H_{12}	289.5(4.47)	18-3765-79
1,1'-Biphenyl, 4-(2-phenylethenyl)-	C_6H_{12}	325(4.51)	104-1944-79
$C_{20}H_{16}ClNO$			
9H-Carbazole, 6-chloro-3-methoxy-2-methyl-1-phenyl-	EtOH	220(4.51),235(4.51), 242(4.52),255s(4.30), 272s(4.16),300s(4.12), 310(4.26),348(3.64), 360(3.62)	88-4915-79
$C_{20}H_{16}ClN_3O$			
1H-Pyrimido[1,2-a][1,5]benzodiazocin-1-one, 10-chloro-5,6-dihydro-3-methyl-8-phenyl-	EtOH	252(4.13)	94-2927-79
3H-Pyrimido[1,2-a][1,5]benzodiazocin-3-one, 10-chloro-5,6-dihydro-1-methyl-8-phenyl-	EtOH	252.5(4.48)	94-2927-79
$C_{20}H_{16}ClN_3O_2$			
Pyrimido[4,5-b]quinoline-2,4(3H,10H)-dione, 5-(4-chlorophenyl)-10-ethyl-3-methyl-	EtOH	244(4.54),265(4.50), 324(3.83),406(3.82)	142-0691-79
$C_{20}H_{16}Cl_2N_2O$			
Benzenecarboximidamide, N'-(4-chloro-2-methylphenyl)-N-(4-chlorophenyl)-N-hydroxy-, hydrochloride	EtOH	208(4.62),258(4.11), 318(4.13)	56-2597-79
$C_{20}H_{16}NO$			
5H-Indeno[1,2-b]pyridinium, 1-(2-oxo-2-phenylethyl)-, bromide	EtOH	210(4.66),290(4.00), 330(4.14)	103-1214-79

Compound	Solvent	$\lambda_{max}(\log \epsilon)$	Ref.
9H-Indeno[2,1-c]pyridinium, 2-(2-oxo-2-phenylethyl)-, bromide	EtOH	210(4.65),328(4.20)	103-1214-79
$C_{20}H_{16}N_2$			
Benzenamine, N-(10-methyl-9(10H)-acridinylidene)-	EtOH	225(4.52),246(4.49), 406(4.05)	104-0183-79
Propanedinitrile, [3,3-bis(4-methylphenyl)-2-propenylidene]-	EtOH	245(4.08),382(4.51)	35-6367-79
$C_{20}H_{16}N_2O$			
Benzenamine, N-(1H-benz[g]indol-3-ylmethylene)-4-methoxy-	EtOH	206(4.44),217s(4.40), 265(4.46),332(4.34), 343s(4.32)	103-0741-79
Benzenamine, N-(3H-benz[e]indol-1-ylmethylene)-4-methoxy-	EtOH	222(4.62),286(4.29), 323(4.27),345(4.19)	103-0741-79
Benzo[g]quinazolin-4(1H)-one, 1-methyl-2-(phenylmethyl)- (spectra in 80% EtOH)	neutral	243(4.59),282(4.30), 310(4.47)	42-0708-79
	acid	244(4.42),283(4.43), 315(3.52)	42-0708-79
	base	244(4.72),283(4.49), 315(4.4)	42-0708-79
2-Propen-1-one, 1-(4-methyl-2-phenyl-5-pyrimidinyl)-3-phenyl-	EtOH	206(4.48),228(4.23), 310(4.51)	103-0551-79
$C_{20}H_{16}N_2O_3$			
3aH-Cyclopenta[l]phenanthrene-1-carboxamide, 2-(acetylamino)-3a-hydroxy-	EtOH	248(4.64),291(4.02), 353(3.50)	39-2034-79C
$C_{20}H_{16}N_2O_4$			
Camptothecin	MeOH	218(4.63),253(4.51), 289(3.81),358(4.34), 368(4.34)	100-0475-79
5,12-Naphthacenedione, 1,4-bis(methylamino)-6,11-dihydroxy-	benzene	526(4.23),562(4.32)	153-0033-79
$C_{20}H_{16}N_2O_6$			
3-Indolizinecarboxylic acid, 2-(2-furanyl)-5-methyl-1-(5-nitro-2-furanyl)-, ethyl ester	EtOH	449(4.20)	94-3078-79
3-Indolizinecarboxylic acid, 2-(2-furanyl)-7-methyl-1-(5-nitro-2-furanyl)-, ethyl ester	EtOH	447(4.31)	94-3078-79
$C_{20}H_{16}N_4$			
[1,1'-Biphenyl]-2-amine, 2'-(3-phenyl-1H-1,2,4-triazol-1-yl)-	n.s.g.	233(4.38),255(4.38)	39-0185-79C
$C_{20}H_{16}N_4O_4$			
Pyrimido[4,5-b]quinoline-2,4(3H,10H)-dione, 10-ethyl-3-methyl-5-(2-nitrophenyl)-	EtOH	224(4.48),265(4.49), 327(3.88),405(3.85)	142-0691-79
$C_{20}H_{16}N_4O_6$			
Methanone, (4-hydroxyphenyl)(4-methoxyphenyl)-, 2,4-dinitrophenylhydrazone	EtOH	395(4.29)	49-1057-79
$C_{20}H_{16}N_4O_6S_2$			
Bisthiazolo[3,2-a:3',2'-a']benzo[1,2-d:4,5-d']diimidazole-2,8-dicarboxylic acid, 5,11-dihydro-3,9-dimethyl-5,11-dioxo-, diethyl ester	EtOH	277(4.42),327(4.36), 471(4.27)	2-0525-79A

Compound	Solvent	$\lambda_{max}(\log \epsilon)$	Ref.
Bisthiazolo[3,2-a:3',2'-a']benzo[1,2-d:5,4-d']diimidazole-2,8-dicarboxylic acid, 5,11-dihydro-3,7-dimethyl-5,11-dioxo-, diethyl ester	EtOH	255(4.28),312(4.10), 455(3.90)	2-0525-79A
$C_{20}H_{16}N_6O$			
Cyclohexanone, 2,6-bis[(4-azidophenyl)-methylene]-	MeOH	356(4.32)	93-0333-79
$C_{20}H_{16}N_8O$			
7H-Benzo[e]perimidin-7-one, 6-[[4,6-bis(methylamino)-1,3,5-triazin-2-yl]amino]-	DMF	466(4.28)	2-0195-79B
$C_{20}H_{16}O$			
Benz[a]anthracen-2-ol, 7,12-dimethyl-	EtOH	226(4.44),267(4.51), 277(4.52),291(4.59), 302(4.55)	44-2150-79
Benz[a]anthracen-3-ol, 7,12-dimethyl-	EtOH	244(4.15),298(4.82)	44-2150-79
Benz[a]anthracen-4-ol, 7,12-dimethyl-	EtOH	228(4.62),265(4.68), 281(4.78),292(4.74), 322(4.61)	44-2150-79
$C_{20}H_{16}O_2$			
2,4,6-Cycloheptatrien-1-one, 3-(2,4,6-cycloheptatrien-1-yl)-2-hydroxy-7-phenyl-	MeOH	242(4.36),268(4.33), 348(3.84),385(3.86), 410(3.70)	18-1867-79
Ethanone, 1,1'-(1-phenyl-2,3-naphthalenediyl)bis-	MeOH	215s(4.42),230(4.58), 250(4.55),279s(3.84), 288(3.91),295s(3.84), 305(3.15),347(3.15)	39-0584-79C
	MeOH-$HClO_4$	215(3.42),220(3.79), 277(3.81),286(3.88), 293(3.81)	39-0584-79C
$C_{20}H_{16}O_3$			
4H,8H-Benzo[1,2-b:3,4-b']dipyran-4-one, 8,8-dimethyl-2-phenyl-	MeOH	224(4.27),253(4.32), 306(4.38)	78-0413-79
4H-1-Benzopyran-4-one, 7-[(1,1-dimethyl-2-propynyl)oxy]-2-phenyl-	MeOH	253(4.41),300(4.21)	78-0413-79
1H-Cyclopenta[l]phenanthrene-1-carboxylic acid, 2,3-dihydro-2-oxo-, ethyl ester	EtOH	249(4.67),257(4.83), 278(4.19),289(4.08), 300(4.13),335(3.86), 350(3.86)	39-2034-79C
$C_{20}H_{16}O_4$			
2H,8H-Benzo[1,2-b:3,4-b']dipyran-2-one, 5-hydroxy-8,8-dimethyl-4-phenyl-	EtOH	283(4.33)	2-0111-79A
4H,8H-Benzo[1,2-b:3,4-b']dipyran-4-one, 5-hydroxy-8,8-dimethyl-3-phenyl-	MeOH	265(4.62)	2-0123-79A
4H-1-Benzopyran-4-one, 7-[(1,1-dimethyl-2-propynyl)oxy]-5-hydroxy-3-phenyl-	MeOH	263(4.38)	2-0123-79A
1H-Cyclopenta[l]phenanthrene-1-carboxylic acid, 2,3-dihydro-1-hydroxy-2-oxo-, ethyl ester	EtOH	249s(4.60),257(4.74), 279(4.07),290(4.04), 301(4.03),334(3.84), 349(3.84)	39-2034-79C
1H-Cyclopenta[l]phenanthrene-1-carboxylic acid, 2,11b-dihydro-11b-hydroxy-2-oxo-, ethyl ester	EtOH	257(4.46),264(4.56), 300(4.03),352(3.68)	39-2034-79C

Compound	Solvent	$\lambda_{max}(\log \epsilon)$	Ref.
2,9:3,8-Diethanodibenzo[a,e]cyclooctene-1,4,7,10-tetrone, 5,6,11,12-tetrahydro-	MeOH	256(4.26),273(4.02)	5-1258-79
	dioxan	257(4.24),277(3.97)	5-1258-79
Pyrano[2",3":7,6]isoflavone, 5-hydroxy-6",6"-dimethyl-	MeOH	271(4.68)	2-0123-79A
$C_{20}H_{16}O_4S$			
1-Benzothiepin-3,5-diol, 4-phenyl-, diacetate	MeOH	260(4.09)	24-0781-79
$C_{20}H_{16}O_5$			
2H,6H-Benzo[1,2-b:5,4-b']dipyran-2,6-dione, 7,8-dihydro-4-hydroxy-8,8-dimethyl-3-phenyl-	dioxan	300(4.18),340(4.15)	2-0456-79B
$C_{20}H_{16}O_5S$			
1-Benzothiepin-3,5-diol, 4-phenyl-, diacetate, 1-oxide	MeOH at -10°	282s(3.82)	24-0781-79
$C_{20}H_{16}O_6$			
Polygamain	EtOH	288(3.49)	100-0378-79
$C_{20}H_{16}O_6S$			
1-Benzothiepin-3,5-diol, 4-phenyl-, diacetate, dioxide	MeOH	287(3.98)	24-0781-79
$C_{20}H_{16}O_7$			
Isoversicolorin C, 3,6-O,O-dimethyl-	MeOH	217(4.87),265(4.30), 274(4.45),315(3.96), 430(3.92)	39-0451-79C
5,12-Naphthacenedione, 9-acetyl-7,8,9,10-tetrahydro-6,7,9,11-tetrahydroxy- (±-4-demethoxydaunomycinone)	MeOH	203(4.42),219s(--), 249(4.59),286(3.96), 328s(--),481(4.01), 514(3.83),567s(--)	24-3453-79
7-epi-	MeOH	205(4.41),255(4.61), 288(3.89),328(3.36), 480(4.00),512(3.85), 560s(--)	24-3453-79
Spiro[1,3-dioxolane-2,2'(1'H)-naphthacene]-6',11'-dione, 3',4'-dihydro-4',5',12'-trihydroxy-	MeOH	225(4.12),240(4.41), 288(3.81),482(3.85), 512(3.67)	24-3453-79
$C_{20}H_{16}O_9$			
Versiconal acetate	MeOH	223(4.41),265(4.16), 291(3.39),315(4.01), 452(3.85)	39-0451-79C
$C_{20}H_{16}S$			
Thiophene, 2,5-bis(2-phenylethenyl)-, (E,E)-	toluene	395(4.66)	103-0729-79
	DMF	391(4.72)	61-0417-79
$C_{20}H_{17}$			
Cycloheptatrienylium, (4'-methyl-[1,1'-biphenyl]-2-yl)-	CH_2Cl_2	370(3.89),442(3.60)	88-4999-79
Ethylium, 1,1,2-triphenyl-	H_2SO_4	430(4.32)	39-1395-79B
$C_{20}H_{17}BrO_2$			
Chrysene, 1-bromo-5,6-dihydro-2,8-dimethoxy-	EtOH	270(4.72),280(4.86), 301(4.16),312(4.21), 325(4.19)	12-1107-79

Compound	Solvent	λ_{max}(log ε)	Ref.
$C_{20}H_{17}ClN_2O$			
Benzenecarboximidamide, N'-(4-chloro-2-methylphenyl)-N-hydroxy-N-phenyl-, hydrochloride	EtOH	208(4.54),258(4.06), 317(4.09)	56-2597-79
$C_{20}H_{17}ClN_2O_2S$			
Benzenesulfonamide, 4-chloro-N-(4,5,9-10-tetrahydropyrrolo[3,2,1-jk]carbazol-7(8H)-ylidene)-	EtOH	255s(4.49),352(4.75)	39-2387-79C
$C_{20}H_{17}ClN_4O_5$			
L-xylo-2-Hexulosonic acid, 3,6-anhydro-3-C-[(4-chlorophenyl)azo]-, γ-lactone, 2-(phenylhydrazone), 5-acetate	n.s.g.	232(4.00),291(3.89), 367(3.91)	106-0531-79
$C_{20}H_{17}ClO_9$			
7-Oxabicyclo[2.2.1]hepta-2,5-diene-2,3,5,6-tetracarboxylic acid, 1-(4-chlorophenyl)-, tetramethyl ester	MeOH	224(4.15),332(3.69)	44-0626-79
$C_{20}H_{17}NO$			
9H-Carbazole, 3-methoxy-2-methyl-1-phenyl- (same spectrum in acid or base)	EtOH	226s(4.53),232(4.56), 238s(4.54),250s(4.30), 260s(4.13),292s(4.10), 304(4.27),338(3.65), 352(3.70)	88-4915-79
3H-Naphtho[2,1-b]pyran-3-amine, N-(4-methylphenyl)-	hexane	287(4.02),299(4.06), 311(4.00),337(3.68), 352(3.67)	104-1715-79
	MeOH	284(4.24),298(3.97), 313(3.94),338(3.80), 348(3.79),380(3.58), 547(?)	104-1715-79
	MeCN	302(3.97),313(3.93), 340(3.69),352(3.69)	104-1715-79
	DMSO	277(4.24),340(3.76), 355(3.76),380(3.38), 506(2.30)	104-1715-79
	DMSO-NaOMe	357(3.81),480(4.09)	104-1715-79
3H-Naphtho[2,1-b]pyran-3-amine, N-(phenylmethyl)-	MeOH	280(3.53),300(3.56), 313(3.69),327(3.62), 355(3.64),510(3.58)	104-1715-79
	CCl_4	300(3.82),314(3.83), 343(3.62),355(3.67), 355(3.67),405(3.56), 520(3.53)	104-1715-79
	DMSO	293(3.72),304(3.85), 315(3.36),320(3.92), 357(3.94),520(3.60)	104-1715-79
	DMSO-NaOMe	290(3.96),315(3.94), 360(3.83),472(3.81)	104-1715-79
1H-Pyrrolizine-5-carboxaldehyde, 2,3-dihydro-6,7-diphenyl-	MeOH	208(4.29),235(4.26), 317(4.21)	83-0896-79
$C_{20}H_{17}NO_2$			
Benzene, 1,1',1"-(nitroethylidyne)tris-	MeCN	238(3.38)	78-0177-79
Ethanone, 2-(5-ethyl-2-furanyl)-1-phenyl-2-(phenylimino)-	MeOH	298(4.14)	142-1005-79
3H-Naphtho[2,1-b]pyran-3-amine, N-(4-methoxyphenyl)-	MeOH	297(3.93),310(3.97), 332(3.68),346(3.74), 386(3.23)	104-1715-79

Compound	Solvent	λmax(log ε)	Ref.
3H-Naphtho[2,1-b]pyran-3-amine, N-(4-methoxyphenyl)- (cont.)	CCl_4	292(3.83),302(3.90), 315(3.91),340(3.64), 353(3.64)	104-1715-79
	DMSO	300(4.09),310(4.05), 337(3.95),357(3.95), 384(3.91),498(3.89)	104-1715-79
	DMSO-NaOMe	351(3.95),484(4.17)	104-1715-79
$C_{20}H_{17}NO_3$			
1,4-Naphthalenedione, 2-acetyl-3-(4-amino-2,6-dimethylphenyl)-	dioxan	253(4.29),265(4.30), 290s(4.1),340s(3.5), 496(3.72)	5-0503-79
1,4-Naphthalenedione, 2-acetyl-3-[4-(dimethylamino)phenyl]-	dioxan	248(4.23),278(4.26), 295s(4.2),346s(3.4), 520(3.78)	5-0503-79
1,4-Naphthalenedione, 2-acetyl-3-[(2,6-dimethylphenyl)amino]-	dioxan	232(4.28),262(4.28), 272(4.27),430(3.61)	5-0503-79
1,4-Naphthalenedione, 2-acetyl-3-[(3,4-dimethylphenyl)amino]-	dioxan	231s(4.2),275(4.37), 466(3.63)	5-0503-79
$C_{20}H_{17}NO_4$			
7H-Dibenzo[de,g]quinolin-7-one, 2-ethoxy-10,11-dimethoxy-	EtOH	269(4.50),284s(4.28), 317(3.80),334s(3.90), 347(4.03),396(3.97)	33-1549-79
$C_{20}H_{17}NO_5$			
1,4-Naphthalenedione, 2-acetyl-3-(4-amino-2,6-dimethoxyphenyl)-	dioxan	246(4.42),309(4.19), 541(3.46)	5-0503-79
1,4-Naphthalenedione, 2-acetyl-3-[(2,6-dimethoxyphenyl)amino]-	dioxan	227(4.32),265(4.17), 291(4.28),425(3.53)	5-0503-79
$C_{20}H_{17}NO_7$			
Benzofuro[3,2-f]-1,2-benzisoxazol-4(4aH)-one, 5-acetoxy-8-acetyl-7-hydroxy-3,4a,6-trimethyl-	MeOH	250(4.13),265(4.08), 357(3.76)	87-1380-79
Norhydrastine, 1,2-dehydro-9-hydroxy-	EtOH	238(3.95),290(3.75), 300s(3.74)	44-4343-79
$C_{20}H_{17}N_2O$			
Acridinium, 9-[(4-hydroxyphenyl)amino]-10-methyl-, iodide	EtOH	249(4.68),271(4.63), 333(3.50),450(4.16)	104-0183-79
$C_{20}H_{17}N_2OS$			
Thiazolo[3,2-a]pyridinium, 2-[(1-ethyl-2(1H)-quinolinylidene)ethylidene]-2,3-dihydro-3-oxo-, perchlorate	MeCN	562(4.78),580(4.81)	103-1081-79
$C_{20}H_{17}N_3$			
Benzaldehyde, [2-[(phenylmethylene)-amino]phenylhydrazone	EtOH	265s(4.01),298(3.99), 364(4.25)	4-1005-79
2-Phenazinamine, x-(4-methylbenzyl)-	MeOH	280(4.74),361(3.84), 465(3.80)	32-0175-79
Propanedinitrile, [3-(dimethylamino)-1,2-diphenyl-2-propenylidene]-	CH_2Cl_2	394(4.37)	118-0376-79
$C_{20}H_{17}N_3O$			
Benzamide, N-methyl-N-[2-(phenylazo)-phenyl]-	EtOH	207(4.32),227(4.24), 260(4.17),455(2.62)	7-0563-79
Benzoic acid, 2-[2-[(phenylmethylene)-amino]phenyl]hydrazide	EtOH	254s(3.94),302(3.80)	4-1005-79

Compound	Solvent	λ_{max}(log ε)	Ref.
Imidazo[1,2-a]pyrazin-3(7H)-one, 2-methyl-6-phenyl-8-(phenylmethyl)-	MeOH	247(4.21),351(3.75), 425(3.88)	69-2204-79
1,2,4-Oxadiazole-3-ethanamine, N-(2-naphthalenyl)-5-phenyl-	EtOH	246(4.79),280s(4.03), 290s(3.89),343(3.39)	150-0801-79
$C_{20}H_{17}N_3O_2$			
4H,7H-Azepino[1',2':1,2]imidazo[4,5-g]-3,1-benzoxazin-4-one, 8,9,10,11-tetrahydro-2-phenyl-	$CHCl_3$	275(4.70),318(4.35), 326(4.34)	39-1056-79C
Benzo[b]cyclohept[e][1,4]oxazin-8(5aH)-one, 5a-hydroxy-, (4-methylphenyl)hydrazone	MeOH	205(4.72),250(4.35), 300(4.04),442(4.33)	18-3123-79
	MeOH-NaOH	293(4.05),405(4.09), 480(4.26)	18-3123-79
Pyrimido[4,5-b]quinoline-2,4(3H,10H)-dione, 10-ethyl-3-methyl-5-phenyl-	EtOH	222(4.50),265(4.49), 324(3.81),402(3.82)	142-0691-79
$C_{20}H_{17}N_3O_3S_2$			
Propanenitrile, 3-(1,5-dihydro-3-methyl-5-oxo-1-phenyl-4H-pyrazol-4-ylidene)-3-(methylthio)-2-(phenylsulfonyl)-	EtOH	244(4.23),270s(4.03), 326(4.11),414(3.87)	95-1234-79
$C_{20}H_{17}N_5O_7$			
L-xylo-2-Hexulosonic acid, 3,6-anhydro-3-C-[(4-nitrophenyl)azo]-, γ-lactone, 2-(phenylhydrazone), 5-acetate	n.s.g.	235(3.91),285(3.97), 354(3.91)	106-0531-79
$C_{20}H_{17}N_5O_{10}$			
α-D-Arabinofuranoside, methyl 3-azido-3-deoxy-, 2,5-bis(4-nitrobenzoate)	EtOH	257(4.50)	136-0071-79B
$C_{20}H_{17}O$			
Cycloheptatrienylium, (4'-methoxy[1,1'-biphenyl]-2-yl)-	CH_2Cl_2	373(3.93),476(3.50)	88-4999-79
Ethylium, 2-phenoxy-1,1-diphenyl-	H_2SO_4	447(3.23)	39-1395-79B
$C_{20}H_{17}O_2$			
[1,1':3',1"-Terphenyl]-2'-yloxy, 5'-ethoxy-	PrOH	405(4.48),650(3.42) (anom.)	39-1540-79B
$C_{20}H_{17}O_2P$			
Benzoic acid, 3-(diphenylphosphino)-, methyl ester	C_6H_{12}	230(4.48),258(4.06)	65-0479-79
	12M HCl	230(4.34),269(3.52), 276(3.49)	65-0479-79
Benzoic acid, 4-(diphenylphosphino)-, methyl ester	heptane	228(4.33),272(3.97), 280(3.98),287(3.98)	65-0479-79
	12M HCl	231(4.48),268(3.64), 276(3.58),293(3.20)	65-0479-79
$C_{20}H_{17}O_3P$			
Benzoic acid, 4-(diphenylphosphinyl)-, methyl ester	EtOH	225(4.43),240(4.32), 265(3.46),273(3.38), 287(3.11)	65-0479-79
	dioxan	236(4.59),289(4.30)	65-0479-79
$C_{20}H_{18}$			
Bicyclo[4.2.0]octa-2,4-diene, 2,5-diphenyl-	C_6H_{12}	233(4.06),358(4.36), 366s(4.34)	18-3765-79
$C_{20}H_{18}Br_3ClN_2O_2S$			
Benzenesulfonamide, 4-chloro-N-(2,3,5'-	EtOH	225(4.42),287(4.29),	39-2154-79C

Compound	Solvent	λ_{max}(log ε)	Ref.
tribromo-1'-methylspiro[cyclohexane-1,3'-[3H]indol]-2'(1'H)-ylidene)- (cont.)		312s(4.00)	39-2154-79C
$C_{20}H_{18}ClN_3O_2$			
Butanamide, N-[7-chloro-5-(4-methoxyphenyl)-3H-1,4-benzodiazepin-2-yl]-3-oxo-	EtOH	235(4.45)	94-2927-79
1H-Pyrimido[1,2-a][1,5]benzodiazocin-1-one, 10-chloro-2,3,5,6-tetrahydro-3-hydroxy-3-methyl-8-phenyl-	EtOH	247(4.39)	94-2927-79
$C_{20}H_{18}ClN_5O_2$			
2-Propenamide, N-[4-[4-[(3-chlorophenyl)azo]-4,5-dihydro-3-methyl-5-oxo-1H-pyrazol-1-yl]phenyl]-2-methyl-	benzene	393(4.40)	40-1774-79
2-Propenamide, N-[4-[4-[(4-chlorophenyl)azo]-4,5-dihydro-3-methyl-5-oxo-1H-pyrazol-1-yl]phenyl]-2-methyl-	benzene	400(4.45)	40-1774-79
$C_{20}H_{18}Cl_2N_2O$			
Quinazoline, 6-chloro-2-(chloromethyl)-4-(6,7,8,9-tetrahydro-5H-benzocyclohepten-2-yl)-, 3-oxide	MeOH	270(4.50),340s(3.78)	73-3604-79
$C_{20}H_{18}Cl_2N_4O_6S_2$			
5-Thiazolecarboxylic acid, 2,2'-[(2,5-dichloro-3,6-dioxo-1,4-cyclohexadiene-1,4-diyl)diimino]bis[4-methyl-, diethyl ester	EtOH	254(3.61),352(4.10), 495(4.22)	2-0523-79A
$C_{20}H_{18}N$			
9H-Indeno[2,1-c]pyridinium, 3-methyl-2-(phenylmethyl)-, bromide	EtOH	207(4.49),310(4.25), 460(3.12)	103-1214-79
$C_{20}H_{18}NO_2P$			
Phosphorin, 4-cyano-1,1-dihydro-1,1-dimethoxy-2,6-diphenyl-	MeOH	231(4.24),254(4.23), 372(4.24)	24-1272-79
$C_{20}H_{18}NO_5$			
7H-Dibenzo[de,g]quinolinium, 1-hydroxy-2,10,11-trimethoxy-6-methyl-7-oxo-(arosine or glaunidine) (same spectrum in base)	EtOH	238(4.47),314(4.40), 410(3.78),610(3.60)	88-4589-79
	EtOH	235(4.53),315(4.46), 410(3.72),620(3.59)	105-0367-79
	EtOH-HCl	221(4.50),253(4.57), 282s(4.41),383(3.95), 430s(3.60)	88-4589-79
	EtOH-HCl	250(4.54),290s(4.36), 380(3.87),450(3.55)	105-0367-79
$C_{20}H_{18}N_2O$			
Benzenecarboximidamide, N-hydroxy-N-(2-methylphenyl)-N'-phenyl-	EtOH	208(4.60),258(4.20), 312(4.20)	56-2597-79
$C_{20}H_{18}N_2O_2$			
Pyrazinemethanol, α-phenyl-5-(phenylmethyl)-, acetate	EtOH	279(3.99),308s(3.23)	94-2980-79
$C_{20}H_{18}N_2O_2S$			
1,1-Ethenediamine, N,N'-diphenyl-2-(phenylsulfonyl)-	EtOH	278(4.20)	95-0038-79

Compound	Solvent	λ_{max}(log ε)	Ref.
$C_{20}H_{18}N_2O_3$			
1H-Cyclopenta[l]phenanthrene-1-carboxylic acid, 2-hydrazono-2,3-dihydro-1-hydroxy-, ethyl ester	EtOH	249(4.76),256(4.84), 278(4.14),388(4.04), 300(4.08),333(3.68), 349(3.71)	39-2034-79C
2,4(3H,5H)-Furandione, 5-[(phenylamino)methylene]-3-[1-[(phenylmethyl)amino]ethylidene]-	EtOH	254(4.20),298(4.23), 381(4.57)	4-1335-79
1H-Pyrazole-4-carboxylic acid, 5-acetyl-1,3-diphenyl-, ethyl ester	EtOH	239(4.30)	44-3053-79
$C_{20}H_{18}N_2O_4$			
8H-Benzo[g]-1,3-benzodioxolo[5,6-a]quinolizin-8-imine, 5,6-dihydro-9,10-dimethoxy-	EtOH	282(3.48),358(3.76), 377s(3.61),400(3.41)	36-0705-79
	EtOH-acid	253s(3.77),343(3.83), 386(3.48),403s(3.40)	36-0705-79
$C_{20}H_{18}N_2O_6S$			
5-Thia-1-azabicyclo[4.2.0]oct-2-ene-2-carboxylic acid, 7-(1,3-dihydro-1,3-dioxo-2H-isoindol-2-yl)-3-methyl-4,8-dioxo-, 1,1-dimethylethyl ester, (6R-trans)-	EtOH	294(3.84),300(3.83), 318(3.71)	33-2681-79
$C_{20}H_{18}N_2O_6S_3$			
2H-1,4-Benzothiazin-3(4H)-one, 2-[(3,4-dihydro-4-methyl-3-oxo-2H-1,4-benzothiazin-2-ylidene)(methylthio)methyl]-4-methyl-, tetraoxide	dioxan	330(4.1)	83-0302-79
$C_{20}H_{18}N_2O_8$			
4H-Pyrido[2,1-a]phthalazine-1,2,3,4-tetracarboxylic acid, tetramethyl ester	MeOH	225(4.76),260(4.20), 309(4.24),326s(4.11), 449(4.26)	150-4772-79
11bH-Pyrido[2,1-a]phthalazine-1,2,3,4-tetracarboxylic acid, tetramethyl ester	MeOH	224s(4.37),268(4.21), 302s(3.83),334(3.72), 454(4.02)	150-4772-79
$C_{20}H_{18}N_3$			
Acridinium, 9-(3,4-diaminophenyl)-10-methyl-, iodide	EtOH	257(4.45),453(4.11)	104-0183-79
$C_{20}H_{18}N_4O_2$			
Benzo[g]pteridine-2,4(3H,10H)-dione, 10-(3,4-dimethylphenyl)-3,6-dimethyl-	EtOH	271(4.34),358(3.78), 430s(3.70),444(3.75), 468s(3.63)	4-1365-79
$C_{20}H_{18}N_4O_4$			
1-Propanone, 2-methyl-1-(1-naphthalenyl)-, 2,4-dinitrophenylhydrazone	MeOH	221(5.02),268(4.19), 360(4.40)	5-0617-79
orange-red isomer	MeOH	221(4.98),363(4.40)	5-0617-70
Pyridinium, 4,4'-(1,2-ethenediyl)bis-[1-[2-(cyanomethoxy)-2-oxoethyl]-, diperchlorate	MeCN	231(4.51),253s(--), 524(4.74)	5-0727-79
$C_{20}H_{18}N_4O_8$			
α-D-Arabinofuranoside, methyl 2-azido-2-deoxy-, 5-benzoate 3-(4-nitrobenzoate)	MeOH	230(4.30),257(4.22)	136-0071-79B

Compound	Solvent	λ_{max}(log ϵ)	Ref.
$C_{20}H_{18}N_6$			
Tribenzo[c,g,m][1,2,5,6,9,12]hexaaza-cyclotetradecine, 11,12,13,14-tetra-hydro-	benzene	315(4.28),336(4.28), 405s(4.00),425s(4.00), 466(4.03)	118-0545-79
$C_{20}H_{18}N_6O_4$			
2-Propenamide, N-[4-[4,5-dihydro-3-methyl-4-[(3-nitrophenyl)azo]-5-oxo-1H-pyrazol-1-yl]phenyl]-2-methyl-	benzene	390(4.37)	40-1774-79
2-Propenamide, N-[4-[4,5-dihydro-3-methyl-4-[(4-nitrophenyl)azo]-5-oxo-1H-pyrazol-1-yl]phenyl]-2-methyl-	benzene	405(4.54)	40-1774-79
$C_{20}H_{18}N_7$			
1H-Tetrazolium, 5-[imino(phenylhydra-zino)methyl]-1,3-diphenyl-, chloride	EtOH	245(4.11),282(4.14), 376(4.32)	24-2369-79
$C_{20}H_{18}O$			
Benzo[3,4]cyclobuta[1,2-l]phenanthren-8c(9H)-ol, 10,11,12,12a-tetrahydro-, cis	C_6H_{12}	251s(4.94),258(5.03), 280(4.32),292(4.27), 305(4.37),340(3.18), 357(3.37)	150-3686-79
$C_{20}H_{18}O_2$			
Benz[a]anthracene-3,4-diol, 3,4-dihy-dro-7,12-dimethyl-, trans	MeOH	271(5.16),386(3.77), 407(4.03),432(4.01)	35-0237-79
Chrysene, 5,6-dihydro-2,8-dimethoxy-	EtOH	224(4.50),253s(4.39), 262(4.61),271(4.71), 306(4.35),319(4.35)	12-1093-79
2,9:3,8-Diethanodibenzo[a.e]cyclooct-ene-1,4-dione, 5,6,11,12-tetrahydro-	CH_2Cl_2	271(3.94),277(3.94), 300(3.29),330(3.24)	35-2128-79
1-Isobenzofuranol, 3,3-dimethyl-1-(1-naphthalenyl)-, cation	50% H_2SO_4	440(4.20)	104-1126-79
1-Isobenzofuranol, 3,3-dimethyl-1-(2-naphthalenyl)-, cation	50% H_2SO_4	371(4.51)	104-1126-79
1,1':4',1"-Terphenyl, 2,2"-dimethoxy-	hexane	264(4.39)	65-0146-79
1,1':4',1"-Terphenyl, 4,4"-dimethoxy-	hexane	294(4.79)	65-0146-79
[1,1':3',1"-Terphenyl]-2'-ol, 5'-eth-oxy-	PrOH	315(3.85)	39-1540-79B
$C_{20}H_{18}O_3$			
9(10H)-Anthracenone, 1,8-dihydroxy-10,10-di-2-propenyl-	MeOH	258(3.95),273(3.89), 299(4.03),373(4.01)	145-1083-79
Benz[a]anthracene-3,4-diol, 3,4-dihy-dro-7-(hydroxymethyl)-12-methyl-, trans	MeOH	270(5.20),383(3.79), 404(4.05),428(4.03)	35-0237-79
Methanone, (8-hydroxy-4-propoxy-1-naph-thalenyl)phenyl-	MeOH	304(3.8),314(3.8), 325(3.7)	5-0959-79
$C_{20}H_{18}O_4$			
Dibenzo[a,e]cyclooctene-5,6-dicarbox-ylic acid, 5,6-dihydro-, dimethyl ester, trans	n.s.g.	250(3.78)	44-4477-79
2,9:3,8-Diethanodibenzo[a,e]cyclooct-ene-1,4-dione, 5,6,11,12-tetrahydro-7,10-dihydroxy-	MeOH	258(4.01),278s(3.77)	5-1258-79
	dioxan	258(4.01),277s(3.78)	5-1258-79
Licoflavone A	MeOH	330(4.54)	78-0413-79
$C_{20}H_{18}O_5$			
1,3-Benzenediol, 5-(7,10-dihydro-4-methoxy-8-methylfuro[2,3-g][1]benz-	EtOH	217(4.52),306(4.49), 315(4.52),329(4.34)	88-4675-79

Compound	Solvent	λ_{max}(log ε)	Ref.
oxepin-2-yl)- (moracin H) (cont.)			88-4675-79
$C_{20}H_{18}O_7$			
11H-Benzofuro[2,3-b][1]benzopyran-11-one, 10b-acetoxy-5a,10b-dihydro-2,3-dimethoxy-5a-methyl-, cis	MeOH	286(4.15),347(3.94)	18-0529-79
11H-Benzofuro[2,3-b][1]benzopyran-11-one, 10b-acetoxy-5a,10b-dihydro-3,8-dimethoxy-5a-methyl-, cis	MeOH	233(4.14),284(4.20)	18-0529-79
4H-1-Benzopyran-4-one, 3-(1,3-benzodioxol-5-yl)-6-ethoxy-5,7-dimethoxy-	EtOH	207(4.32),264(4.22), 292s(4.00)	39-2107-79C
$C_{20}H_{18}O_8$			
1,3-Benzodioxole, 5,5'-[(tetrahydro-1H,3H-furo[3,4-c]furan-1,4-diyl)-bis(oxy)]bis- (simplexolin)	MeOH	235(4.12),292(4.04)	102-0503-79
$C_{20}H_{18}O_8S_4$			
1,3-Dithiole-4,5-dicarboxylic acid, 2,2'-(2-cyclohexene-1,4-diylidene)-bis-, tetramethyl ester	CH_2Cl_2	391(4.59),410(4.61)	44-0930-79
$C_{20}H_{18}O_9$			
9,10-Anthracenedione, 2-[3-acetoxy-1-(hydroxymethyl)propyl]-1,3,6,8-tetrahydroxy- (versiconol acetate)	MeOH	225(4.49),265s(4.20), 294(4.41),315(4.11), 453(3.93)	39-0451-79C
7-Oxabicyclo[2.2.1]hepta-2,5-diene-2,3,5,6-tetracarboxylic acid, 1-phenyl-, tetramethyl ester	MeOH	207s(3.29),216s(3.27), 275s(3.00)	44-0626-79
$C_{20}H_{18}O_9S_4$			
1,3-Dithiole-4,5-dicarboxylic acid, 2-[4-[4,5-bis(methoxycarbonyl)-1,3-dithiol-2-ylidene]-2-cyclohexen-1-ylidene]-, dimethyl ester, 1-oxide, (Z)-	CH_2Cl_2	257s(4.08),343(4.05), 457(4.47)	44-0930-79
$C_{20}H_{18}O_{10}$			
[1]Benzopyrano[5,4,3-cde][1]benzopyran-5,10-dione, 1,2,3,6,7,8-hexamethoxy- (hexamethyl coruleoellagic acid)	EtOH	245?(4.01),284(3.22), 356(3.39),360(3.46)	102-1017-79
$C_{20}H_{18}S_2$			
10H,12H-1,13:5,9-Dimethano-2H,4H-cyclohepta[d][1,8]dithiacyclopentadecin	C_6H_{12}	243(4.27),307(4.34), 366(3.60),384(3.55), 624(2.38),750s(1.77)	138-0771-79
$C_{20}H_{19}ClN_2O_2$			
Pyridazine, 6-chloro-3,4-bis(4-ethoxyphenyl)-	hexane	274(4.28)	111-0053-79
$C_{20}H_{19}ClN_2O_2S$			
Benzenesulfonamide, 4-chloro-N-(4,5,7-8,9,10-hexahydropyrrolo[3,2,1-jk]-carbazol-7-yl)-	EtOH	233(4.61),282(3.93), 308s(3.70)	39-2387-79C
Benzenesulfonamide, 4-chloro-N-(1'-methylspiro[2-cyclohexen-1,3'-[3H]indol]-2'(1'H)-ylidene)-	EtOH	226(4.48),284s(4.24), 288(4.26),297s(4.18)	39-2154-79C
Benzenesulfonamide, 4-chloro-N-(7,8,9-10-tetrahydrocyclohept[b]indol-6(5H)-ylidene)-	EtOH	201(4.59),251(4.14), 349(4.43)	39-2154-79C

Compound	Solvent	λ_{max}(log ϵ)	Ref.
$C_{20}H_{19}ClN_2O_3S$			
Benzenesulfonamide, 4-chloro-N-(1'-methyl-2-oxospiro[cyclohexan-1,3'-[3'H]indol]-2'(1'H)-ylidene)-	EtOH	225(4.33),287(4.26), 300s(4.10)	39-2154-79C
Benzenesulfonamide, 4-chloro-N-(1-methylspiro[3H-indole-3,2'-[7]oxabicyclo-[4.1.0]heptan]-2(1H)-ylidene)-	EtOH	205(4.40),225(4.41), 280s(4.16),286(4.21), 300s(4.14)	39-2154-79C
$C_{20}H_{19}ClO_4$			
Tricyclo[9.2.2.1^{4,8}]hexadeca-4,6,8(16)-11,13,14-hexaene-12,14-dicarboxylic acid, 16-chloro-, dimethyl ester	MeCN	263(3.94),332(3.17)	35-2121-79
$C_{20}H_{19}ClO_4S_2$			
3,11-Dithiatricyclo[11.2.2.1^{5,9}]octadeca-5,7,9(18),13,15,16-hexaene-14,16-dicarboxylic acid, 18-chloro-, dimethyl ester	MeCN	260(3.77),313(3.28)	35-2121-79
$C_{20}H_{19}Cl_2NO_2$			
Acetamide, 2-chloro-N-[4-chloro-2-benzocyclohepten-2-yl)carbonyl]phenyl]-	MeOH	236(4.36),273(4.19), 327s(3.61)	73-3604-79
4-Cyclopentene-1,3-dione, 2-(2-butyl-1,3-dimethylcyclohepta[c]pyrrol-6(2H)-ylidene)-4,5-dichloro-	CH_2Cl_2	248(4.33),314(4.39), 459(4.65)	83-0120-79
$C_{20}H_{19}N$			
2H-Benz[g]indole, 4,5-dihydro-2,2-dimethyl-3-phenyl-	EtOH	255(4.37)	78-2285-79
1H-Pyrrolizine, 2,3-dihydro-5-methyl-6,7-diphenyl-	MeOH	209(4.43),244(4.27), 277(4.12)	83-0896-79
$C_{20}H_{19}NO$			
Methanone, phenyl(1,3,4,11b-tetrahydro-2H-benzo[a]quinolizin-6-yl)-	ether	315(3.71),414(3.64)	78-2501-79
$C_{20}H_{19}NO_2$			
Benzoic acid, 2-[[1-(phenylmethyl)-1H-pyrrol-2-yl]methyl]-, methyl ester	EtOH	212(4.51),228s(4.10)	103-0747-79
1H-Carbazole-2-carboxylic acid, 2,3,4,9-tetrahydro-4-methyl-3-phenyl-	EtOH	232(4.85),278s(3.93), 284(3.98),291(3.93)	44-4402-79
2-Propenoic acid, 3-[2-(1-pyrrolidinyl)-1-acenaphthylenyl]-, methyl ester	EtOH	227(4.7),254(4.4), 320(4.3),357(4.5), 390(4.2),520(3.8)	18-0641-79
$C_{20}H_{19}NO_3$			
Ethanone, 1-[3-(4-amino-3,5-dimethylphenyl)-1,4-dihydroxy-2-naphthalenyl]-	dioxan	224(4.64),253(4.38), 282(4.39),315s(3.8), 405(3.86)	5-0503-79
Ethanone, 1-[3-[4-(dimethylamino)phenyl]-1,4-dihydroxy-2-naphthalenyl]-	dioxan	223(4.57),263(4.45), 281(4.43),322(3.93), 406(3.89)	5-0503-79
Methanone, (5-ethyl-2,3,3a,6a-tetrahydro-2-phenylfuro[2,3-d]isoxazol-3-yl)phenyl-, (3α,3aα,6aα)-	MeOH	248(4.37)	142-1005-79
1(2H)-Naphthalenone, 3-acetyl-2-(4-amino-3,5-dimethylphenyl)-4-hydroxy-	dioxan	220(4.45),244(4.35), 274(4.06),323(3.89), 360s(3.7)	5-0503-79
7H-Pyrano[2,3-c]acridin-7-one, 3,12-dihydro-6-methoxy-3,3,12-trimethyl-(acronine)	CH_2Cl_2-$MeCONMe_2$	390(3.83)	36-0036-79

Compound	Solvent	λmax(log ε)	Ref.
$C_{20}H_{19}NO_4$			
4H-Indeno[2',1':4,5]oxazolo[4,3-a]isoquinolin-10(5aH)-one, 1,2-dihydro-12,13-dimethoxy-, (5aR*,10aR*)-(±)-	MeOH	214(4.26),242(4.26), 286(3.74)	23-1569-79
1(3H)-Isobenzofuranone, 3-(3,4-dihydro-6,7-dimethoxy-2-methyl-1(2H)-isoquinolinylidene)-	MeOH	219(4.37),307(3.98), 342(4.07),400(4.20)	23-1598-79
Nantenine, dehydro-	EtOH	217(4.22),244s(4.45), 262(4.66),299s(4.02), 337(3.93)	100-0325-79
Thalphenine, N-demethyl-	MeOH	233s(4.13),277s(3.61), 288(3.76),314(3.87), 325s(3.85)	100-0325-79
$C_{20}H_{19}NO_5$			
8H-Benzo[a][1,3]benzodioxolo[5,6-g]quinolizin-8-one, 5,6,14,14a-tetrahydro-2,3-dimethoxy-	n.s.g.	225(4.61),265(3.86), 273(3.90),291(3.90), 305(3.88)	107-0895-79
Isoquino[1,2-c][2,4]benzoxazepine, 5,6,7,8,13,14a-hexahydro-13-methyl-2,3:10,11-bis(methylenedioxy)-	EtOH	245(4.05),292(3.92), 307(3.38),366(3.33)	39-0283-79C
	EtOH-HCl	250(4.41),295(3.95), 309(3.96),365(4.08)	39-0283-79C
	EtOH-NaOH	290(3.92)	39-0283-79C
Spiro[2H-indene-2,1'(2'H)-isoquinoline]-2'-carboxaldehyde, 1,3,3',4'-tetrahydro-1-hydroxy-6',7'-dimethoxy-3-oxo-	MeOH	212(4.24),238(4.13), 288(3.52)	23-1569-79
$C_{20}H_{19}NO_6$			
2-Anthracenecarboxylic acid, 1-amino-9,10-dihydro-9,10-dioxo-, [(1,1-dimethylethyl)dioxy]methyl ester	toluene	489(3.97)	93-0903-79
1,3-Dioxolo[4,5-g]isoquinoline-6(5H)-carboxaldehyde, 7,8-dihydro-5-[(2-hydroxy-3,4-dimethoxyphenyl)methylene]-, (Z)-	EtOH	220(4.59),292(4.21), 332(4.19)	88-4521-79
Spiro[7H-indeno[4,5-d]-1,3-dioxole-7,1'(2'H)-isoquinolin]-6(8H)-one, 3',4'-dihydro-8-hydroxy-6',7'-dimethoxy-	MeOH	212(4.31),236(4.46), 289(4.03),310(3.93)	23-1569-79
$C_{20}H_{19}NO_8$			
Benzo[g]quinoline-2-carboxylic acid, 7-butyl-5,10-dihydro-4,6,9-trihydroxy-8-methoxy-5,10-dioxo-, methyl ester (isophomazarin methyl ester)	MeOH	248(4.53),263(4.60)	39-0823-79C
Phomazarin methyl ester	MeOH	229(4.34),278(4.60), 427(3.92)	39-0807-79C
$C_{20}H_{19}NS_4$			
Benzenamine, N-(3'a,4',5',6',7',7'a-hexahydrospiro[4H-1,3-benzodithiin-4,2'-[1,3]benzodithiol]-2-ylidene)-	C_6H_{12}	244s(4.24),275(4.06), 318(3.87)	18-0496-79
$C_{20}H_{19}N_2OS$			
Thiazolo[3,2-a]pyridinium, 2-[(1,3-dihydro-1,3,3-trimethyl-2H-indol-2-ylidene)ethylidene]-2,3-dihydro-3-oxo-, perchlorate	MeCN	550(4.76),576(4.76)	103-1081-79

Compound	Solvent	λ_{max}(log ε)	Ref.
$C_{20}H_{19}N_2O_2S_2$			
Benzo[1,2-d:5,4-d']bisthiazolium, 2-[2-(2,5-dimethoxyphenyl)ethenyl]-3,6-dimethyl-, iodide	DMF	269(4.31),370(4.20), 447(4.13)	126-1441-79
$C_{20}H_{19}N_3$			
2,4-Diazabicyclo[3.2.0]hept-2-ene-6-carbonitrile, 3,4-dimethyl-1,5-diphenyl-	EtOH	222s(4.31),255s(3.60)	44-0041-79
isomer 4c'	EtOH	220s(4.20),257(3.59)	44-0041-79
Ethenamine, 2-(3,6-diphenyl-4-pyridazinyl)-N,N-dimethyl-	MeOH	254(4.33),278(4.11), 381(4.31)	5-0675-79
$C_{20}H_{19}N_3O$			
Morpholine, 4-[[(2-[1,1'-biphenyl]-4-yl-2-cyanoethenyl)imino]methyl]-	MeOH	262(4.20),352(4.64)	83-0039-79
$C_{20}H_{19}N_3O_3$			
Butanoic acid, 2-(3-acridinylazo)-2-methyl-3-oxo-, ethyl ester	EtOH	223(4.38),239(4.68), 283(4.68),378(4.3)	103-0894-79
$C_{20}H_{19}N_3O_4S$			
Benzenesulfonamide, N-(1'-methylspiro-[2-cyclohexene-1,3'-[3H]indol]-2'(1'H)-ylidene)-4-nitro-	EtOH	216(4.34),270s(4.21), 280(4.25),287s(4.13)	39-2154-79C
$C_{20}H_{19}N_5O_2$			
7-Azabicyclo[4.3.1]deca-3,8-dien-10-one, 7-(5-nitro-2-pyridinyl)-, phenylhydrazone	$CHCl_3$	345(3.70)	39-1525-79C
3,5-Methanofuro[2',3':5,6]pyrido[3,4-b]quinoxaline, 4-(4,6-dimethyl-2-pyrimidinyl)-2,3,3a,4,5,11b-hexahydro-, 11-oxide	$CHCl_3$	253(4.39)	39-1525-79C
2-Propenamide, N-[4-[4,5-dihydro-3-3-methyl-5-oxo-4-(phenylazo)-1H-pyrazol-1-yl]phenyl]-2-methyl-	benzene	395(4.43)	40-1774-79
$C_{20}H_{19}N_5O_3$			
Benzenamine, N,N-dimethyl-4-[2-(3-methyl-4-[(4-nitrophenyl)azo]-5-isoxazolyl]ethenyl]-	$CHCl_3$	290s(--),360(4.48), 518(4.34)	103-0968-79
3,5-Methanofuro[2',3':5,6]pyrido[3,4-b]quinoxaline, 4-(4,6-dimethyl-2-pyrimidinyl)-2,3,3a,4,5,11b-hexahydro-, 6,11-dioxide	$CHCl_3$	248(3.82),270(3.87)	39-1525-79C
$C_{20}H_{19}N_7$			
1H-Pyrazol-5-amine, 3-methyl-4-[(3-methyl-1-phenyl-1H-pyrazol-5-yl)-azo]-1-phenyl-	MeOH	420(4.49)	103-0657-79
$C_{20}H_{19}O_3P$			
Phosphorin, 4-formyl-1,1-dihydro-1,1-dimethoxy-2,6-diphenyl-	MeOH	325(4.43),367(4.28)	24-1272-79
$C_{20}H_{19}O_4P$			
Phosphorin, 4-carboxy-1,1-dihydro-1,1-dimethoxy-2,6-diphenyl-	MeOH	297(4.13),375(4.22)	24-1272-79

Compound	Solvent	λ_{max}(log ε)	Ref.
$C_{20}H_{19}S$			
Sulfonium, (2,5-dimethylphenyl)diphenyl-, hexafluoroarsenate	MeOH	263(4.40),275(4.63), 287(4.57),307(4.38)	47-0977-79
$C_{20}H_{19}Se$			
Selenonium, (3,4-dimethylphenyl)diphenyl-, hexafluoroarsenate	MeOH	265(3.60),272(3.51)	47-1047-79
$C_{20}H_{20}$			
Bicyclo[3.1.0]hexane, 5-methyl-3-methylene-1,6-diphenyl-, exo	EtOH	225(4.17)	35-5743-79
1,2'-Bi-1H-indene, 2,3-dihydro-1,3'-dimethyl-	EtOH	227s(3.84),261(4.04), 272s(3.90)	44-1358-79
1,3-Cyclopentadiene, 1,5,5-trimethyl-2,3-diphenyl-	EtOH	227s(4.35),237(4.39), 280(3.60)	44-2331-79
1,3-Cyclopentadiene, 2,5,5-trimethyl-1,3-diphenyl-	EtOH	230(4.11)	44-2331-79
1,3-Cyclopentadiene, 3,5,5-trimethyl-1,2-diphenyl-	EtOH	230(4.23),287(3.70)	44-2331-79
[2.2.2.2](1,2,3,4)-Cyclophane	EtOH	200(4.96),225s(4.15), 240s(3.60),283(2.57), 297s(2.45)	89-0329-79
[2.2.2.2](1,2,4,5)-Cyclophane	EtOH	248s(3.56),294s(2.82), 303(3.02)	35-2128-79
Cyclopropene, 3-isobutenyl-1-methyl-2,3-diphenyl-	EtOH	266(4.23)	44-2331-79
Cyclopropene, 3-isobutenyl-3-methyl-1,2-diphenyl-	EtOH	228(4.44),237s(4.29), 307s(4.43),317(4.50), 334(4.39)	44-2331-79
Cyclopropene, 2-methyl-3-(2-methylallyl)-1,3-diphenyl-	EtOH	263(4.25)	35-5743-79
Cyclopropene, 3-methyl-3-(2-methylallyl)-1,2-diphenyl-	EtOH	229(4.28),321(4.43), 337(4.28)	35-5743-79
1H-Indene, 1-methyl-3-(2-methyl-1-propenyl)-2-phenyl-	EtOH	238(4.30),299(4.18)	44-2331-79
1H-Indene, 2-methyl-3-(2-methyl-1-propenyl)-1-phenyl-	EtOH	226(3.94)	44-2331-79
Tricyclo[2.2.0.0^{2,6}]hexane, 4,6-dimethyl-1,2-diphenyl-	EtOH	263(4.12)	35-5743-79
$C_{20}H_{20}BrNO_2$			
7-Azabicyclo[4.3.1]deca-3,8-dien-10-one, 7-[3-(4-bromophenyl)-3-oxo-1-propenyl]-3,4-dimethyl-, (E)-	EtOH	207(4.24),265(4.47), 375(4.50)	56-0057-79
$C_{20}H_{20}BrNO_2S_2$			
4-Bromophenacylpyridinium 2-oxocyclohexanedithiocarboxylate	EtOH	262(4.34),345(4.15), 425(3.70)	150-1732-79
$C_{20}H_{20}BrNO_4$			
1,3-Dioxolo[4,5-g]isoquinoline, 5-[1-[(2-bromo-4,5-dimethoxyphenyl)ethyl]-7,8-dihydro-	EtOH	281(4.06),313(4.04)	39-0283-79C
Isoquinoline, 1-[1-[6-bromo-1,2-benzodioxol-5-yl)ethyl]-3,4-dihydro-6,7-dimethoxy-	EtOH	230(4.37),282(3.94), 305(3.95)	39-0283-79C
$C_{20}H_{20}ClNO_2S$			
4-Cyclopentene-1,3-dione, 4-(butylamino)-5-chloro-2-(1,3-dimethyl-6H-cyclohepta[c]thien-6-ylidene)-	CH_2Cl_2	256(4.23),265s(4.22), 290s(4.37),304(4.27), 317(4.31),380(4.13),	83-0120-79

Compound	Solvent	$\lambda_{max}(\log \epsilon)$	Ref.
(cont.)		442s(4.45),470(4.56), 497(4.44)	83-0120-79
$C_{20}H_{20}ClNO_5$			
Benzo[g]quinoline-5,10-dione, 7-butyl-4-chloro-3,8,9-trimethoxy-	MeOH	262(4.46),292(4.38), 350(3.82)	39-0807-79C
$C_{20}H_{20}ClN_3O_2$			
8-Quinazolineacetic acid, 2-(2-aminoethyl)-6-chloro-4-phenyl-, ethyl ester	EtOH	234(4.65),272s(--), 330(3.79)	94-2618-79
$C_{20}H_{20}IN_5O_4$			
Adenosine, N-benzoyl-5'-deoxy-5'-iodo-2',3'-O-(1-methylethylidene)-	MeOH	230(4.12),266s(4.09), 280(4.16)	44-0400-79
$C_{20}H_{20}NO$			
Quinolinium, 1-ethyl-2-[2-(4-methoxyphenyl)ethenyl]-	EtOH	418(4.45)	80-1491-79
	$CHCl_3$	434(4.41)	80-1491-79
	CCl_4	418(4.38)	80-1491-79
Quinolinium, 1-ethyl-4-[2-(4-methoxyphenyl)ethenyl]-, bromide	MeOH	432(4.50)	64-1556-79B
p-toluenesulfonate	MeOH	432(4.53)	64-1556-79B
Quinolinium, 1-ethyl-4-[2-(4-methoxyphenyl)ethenyl]-, iodide	H_2O	412(4.46)	64-1556-79B
	MeOH	429(4.54)	64-1556-79B
	acetone	428(4.53)	64-1556-79B
	$CHCl_3$	439(4.53)	64-1556-79B
perchlorate	H_2O	412(4.37)	64-1556-79B
	MeOH	431(4.42)	64-1556-79B
	$CHCl_3$	439(4.41)	64-1556-79B
$C_{20}H_{20}NO_3P$			
Phosphorin, 1,1-dihydro-4-[(hydroxyimino)methyl]-1,1-dimethoxy-2,6-diphenyl-	MeOH	255(4.18),309(4.27), 403(4.19)	24-1272-79
$C_{20}H_{20}NO_4$			
Stylopine methohydroxide	n.s.g.	244(3.90),294(3.88)	105-0783-79
$C_{20}H_{20}N_2$			
Benz[c]acridin-7-amine, 5,6-dihydro-N,N,5-trimethyl-	EtOH	213(4.56),223(4.44), 250(4.49),264(4.52), 276(4.30),289(4.25), 315(3.95),330(4.06), 343(4.06)	1-0313-79
[1,1'-Biphenyl]-4-acetonitrile, α-(1-piperidinylmethylene)-	MeOH	264(3.99),339(4.42)	83-0039-79
3H-Pyrazole, 5-methyl-3-(2-methyl-1-propenyl)-3,4-diphenyl-	EtOH	271(3.76),307(3.77)	44-2331-79
$C_{20}H_{20}N_2O$			
Pyrazine, 3-ethoxy-2,5-bis(phenylmethyl)-	EtOH	284s(3.87),301(3.99)	94-2980-79
$C_{20}H_{20}N_2O_2$			
5,22-Dioxokopsane	EtOH	207(3.38),243(2.89), 296(2.54)	2-0651-79A
Pyrazine, 2,5-dimethyl-3,6-bis(phenylmethoxy)-	EtOH	275(3.24),317(3.99)	94-2027-79

Compound	Solvent	λ_{max}(log ε)	Ref.
$C_{20}H_{20}N_2O_2S$			
2(1H)-Pyrimidinethione, 1-acetyl-3,4-dihydro-6-(4-methoxyphenyl)-4-(4-methylphenyl)-	EtOH	259(4.42),329(3.92)	23-2734-79
$C_{20}H_{20}N_2O_3$			
9,10-Phenanthrenediacetic acid, mono-ethyl ester, hydrazide	EtOH	225(4.45),250(4.69), 257(4.79),279(4.08), 289(3.98),301(3.99)	39-2034-79C
4-Pyridazinecarboxylic acid, 1,6-di-hydro-5-hydroxy-6-methyl-1,3-diphen-yl-, ethyl ester	EtOH	246(4.29),304(3.95), 369(3.72)	44-3053-79
Spiro[2H-1-benzopyran-2,2'-[2H]indole], 1',3'-dihydro-1',3',3',8-tetramethyl-6-nitro-	EtOH	550(4.49)	103-1101-79
$C_{20}H_{20}N_2O_3S$			
2(1H)-Pyrimidinethione, 1-acetyl-3,4-dihydro-4,6-bis(4-methoxyphenyl)-	EtOH	259(4.45),329(3.95)	23-2734-79
$C_{20}H_{20}N_2O_4$			
Dibenzo[f,h]cinnoline-12b(1H)-acetic acid, 2,3,4,4a-tetrahydro-4a-hydroxy-3-oxo-, ethyl ester	EtOH	274(4.14),293s(3.90)	39-2034-79C
Spiro[2H-1-benzopyran-2,2'-[2H]indole], 1',3'-dihydro-8-methoxy-1',3',3'-tri-methyl-6-nitro-	EtOH	560(4.43)	103-1101-79
	toluene	601(--)	103-1101-79
$C_{20}H_{20}N_2O_6$			
1H-Benz[f]indazole-3-carboxylic acid, 4,9-dihydro-4,9-dioxo-1-(tetrahydro-6-methoxy-2H-pyran-2-yl)-, ethyl ester, cis	EtOH	246(4.51),265(4.13)	111-0151-79
trans	EtOH	246(4.53),265(4.20)	111-0151-79
2,4(1H,3H)-Pyrimidinedione, 1-[5,6-di-deoxy-2,3-O-(1-methylethylidene)-7-C-phenyl-β-D-ribo-hept-5-enodialdo-1,4-furanosyl]-, (E)-	EtOH	206(3.65),255(4.06)	33-2788-79
$C_{20}H_{20}N_2O_8$			
1,5-Hexanediol, bis(4-nitrobenzoate)-, (+)-	$CHCl_3$	260.5(4.42)	39-1154-79C
(-)-	$CHCl_3$	260(4.48)	39-1154-79C
$C_{20}H_{20}N_2S_2$			
1H-Indole, 2,2'-dithiobis[1,3-dimethyl-	MeOH	228(3.29),320(2.93)	103-0282-79
$C_{20}H_{20}N_4$			
Benzimidazo[1,2-c]quinazoline, 6-(pip-eridinylmethyl)-	n.s.g.	266(4.57),275(4.64)	124-0225-79
$C_{20}H_{20}N_4O$			
Benzenamine, N,N-dimethyl-4-[2-[3-meth-yl-4-(phenylazo)-5-isoxazolyl]ethen-yl]-	$CHCl_3$	321(4.42),448(4.92)	103-0968-79
Urea, N'-[4-cyano-1,2-dihydro-2-(phen-ylmethyl)-1-isoquinolinyl]-N,N-di-methyl-	CH_2Cl_2	240(4.3),321(4.3)	64-1593-79B
Urea, N'-[3-cyano-1,4-dihydro-1-(phen-ylmethyl)-4-quinolinyl]-N,N-dimethyl-	CH_2Cl_2	230(4.0),312(4.1)	64-0064-79B

Compound	Solvent	λ_{max}(log ε)	Ref.
$C_{20}H_{20}N_4O_7$			
1-Azabicyclo[4.2.0]oct-2-ene-2,4,4-tricarboxylic acid, 7-azido-3-methyl-8-oxo-, 4,4-dimethyl 2-(phenylmethyl) ester, trans	EtOH	270(4.05)	23-0222-79
$C_{20}H_{20}N_5O_4$			
8,12-Epoxy-7H-[1,3]dioxolo[5,6][1,3]diazocino[1,2,3-cd]purin-6-ium, 3-(benzoylamino)-8,8a,11a,12-tetrahydro-10,10-dimethyl-, iodide	MeOH	220(4.43),306(4.21), 333s(4.02)	44-0400-79
$C_{20}H_{20}N_6O_6S$			
11-Thiohomofolic acid	pH 1	255(4.18),290(4.17)	87-0850-79
	pH 13	256(4.47),275s(4.29), 366(3.90)	
$C_{20}H_{20}N_8O_5$			
1H-Pyrrole-2-carboxamide, N-[5-[[(cyanomethyl)amino]carbonyl]-1-methyl-1H-pyrrol-3-yl]-1-methyl-4-[[(1-methyl-4-nitro-1H-pyrrol-2-yl)carbonyl]amino]-	DMF	297(4.57)	87-1296-79
$C_{20}H_{20}O$			
Dibenz[b,e]oxepin, 1,2,3,4,4a,6-hexahydro-6-phenyl-	EtOH	225s(4.31),263(4.22)	88-4049-79
9H-Fluoren-9-one, 1,2,3,4,4a,9a-hexahydro-9a-(phenylmethyl)-	EtOH	246(4.13),290(3.56), 297(3.57)	78-1167-79
3,5-Heptadien-2-one, 6-methyl-3,4-diphenyl-, trans	EtOH	230(4.16),298(3.98)	44-2331-79
1-Oxaspiro[2.5]octane, 2-phenyl-4-(phenylmethylene)-	EtOH	245(4.11)	88-4049-79
$C_{20}H_{20}O_2$			
Benzene, 1,1'-(1,3,5-hexatriene-1,6-diyl)bis[4-methoxy-, (E,E,E)-	hexane	345(4.71)	65-0146-79
Chrysene, 5,6,11,12-tetrahydro-2,8-dimethoxy-	EtOH	238(4.15),307s(4.28), 319(4.46),333(4.54), 349(4.39)	12-1093-79
1,3,5-trinitrobenzene adduct (2:3)	EtOH	219(4.80),230s(4.78), 306(4.34),319(4.51), 333(4.58),349(4.42)	12-1093-79
2,9:3,8-Diethanodibenzo[a,e]cycloocten-1(4H)-one, 5,6,11,12-tetrahydro-4-hydroxy-	EtOH	252(3.72),292(3.32)	35-2128-79
7,14-Epidioxy-3,11:4,10-dimethenobenzo-[1,2:4,5]dicyclooctene, 1,2,5,6,7,8-9,12,13,14-decahydro-	CH_2Cl_2	298(3.15)	35-2128-79
6,9-Methanobenzocycloocten-11-ol, 5,6,7,8,9,10-hexahydro-, benzoate	MeOH	212(4.15),230(4.17), 264(3.0),267(3.02), 272(3.03),282(2.93)	56-1221-79
Tricyclo[8.2.2.2^{4,7}]hexadeca-4,6,10,12-13,15-hexaene-5,15-dicarboxaldehyde, 11,13-dimethyl-	EtOH	313(3.58),321(3.59), 363(3.21)	35-2128-79
$C_{20}H_{20}O_3$			
2-Cyclohexen-1-one, 3,5-bis(4-methoxyphenyl)-	H_2SO_4	417(4.54)	124-1093-79
4b,10b-Epoxychrysene, 5,6,11,12-tetrahydro-2,8-dimethoxy-	EtOH	242(4.40),275(4.40), 285(3.43)	12-1093-79

Compound	Solvent	λ_{max}(log ε)	Ref.
3(2H)-Phenanthrenone, 2-(2-furanylmethylene)-1,4,4a,9,10,10a-hexahydro-7-methoxy-, trans-(±)-	MeOH	328(4.41)	44-0958-79
$C_{20}H_{20}O_6$			
6H-Benz[5,6]indeno[1,7-de]-1,3-dioxin-5-carboxaldehyde, 7-acetoxy-3a,5a-10b,10c-tetrahydro-2,2,10b-trimethyl-6-oxo-	MeOH	248(3.88),290(3.26)	35-0689-79
4H-1-Benzopyran-4-one, 3-(2,4-dimethoxyphenyl)-6,7-dimethoxy-2-methyl-	MeOH	291(4.09),325(3.99)	18-0529-79
1,4,9(4aH)-Phenanthrenetrione, 10-ethyl-10,10a-dihydro-5,8-dihydroxy-4a-(1-oxobutyl)-	EtOH	222(4.49),275(3.59), 300(3.56),388(3.77)	18-3019-79
Stilbene, 3',4-diacetoxy-3,5-dimethoxy-	$CHCl_3$	301(4.04)	39-2449-79C
$C_{20}H_{20}O_7$			
1H,3H-Furo[3,4-c]furan-1-one, tetrahydro-3,6-bis(4-hydroxy-3-methoxyphenyl)-	MeOH	236(2.99),287(2.72)	78-0861-79
1H-Phenalen-1-one, 3-acetoxy-4-ethoxy-9-hydroxy-7,8-dimethoxy-6-methyl-	EtOH	213(4.50),230(4.29), 263s(3.94),286s(3.62), 374(4.06),419(4.10)	150-0301-79
$C_{20}H_{20}O_8$			
4H-1-Benzopyran-4-one, 2-(2-hydroxy-4,5-dimethoxyphenyl)-3,5,7-trimethoxy-	MeOH	232(4.08),254(3.94), 288(3.74),329(3.68)	39-2696-79C
4H-1-Benzopyran-4-one, 5-hydroxy-3,7-dimethoxy-2-(2,4,5-trimethoxyphenyl)-	MeOH	234(4.54),267(4.54), 286(4.04),303(4.04), 342(4.23)	39-2696-79C
4H-1-Benzopyran-4-one, 5-hydroxy-3,6,7,8-tetramethoxy-2-(4-methoxyphenyl)-	EtOH	225s(4.21),282(4.23), 336(4.24)	100-0496-79
4H-Naphtho[1,2-d]-1,3-dioxin-5-acetaldehyde, 7-acetoxy-4-formyl-4a,5-6,10b-tetrahydro-2,2,10b-trimethyl-α,6-dioxo-	MeOH-NaOH	220(4.38),250(4.07), 350(4.06)	35-0689-79
$C_{20}H_{20}O_8S_4$			
1,3-Dithiole-4,5-dicarboxylic acid, 2,2'-(1,4-cyclohexanediylidene)-bis-, tetramethyl ester	CH_2Cl_2	267(4.58),324(3.62), 403(3.67)	44-0930-79
$C_{20}H_{20}O_9$			
4H-1-Benzopyran-4-one, 6-hydroxy-2-(2-hydroxy-4,5-dimethoxyphenyl)-3,5,7-trimethoxy-	MeOH	238(4.43),254(4.38), 314(4.35)	39-2696-79C
4,7-Epoxy-7H-benzo[h]-1,3-dioxino-[4,5,6-ef][2,3]benzodioxepin-7-carboxaldehyde, 9-acetoxy-3a,4,7a,8,12b-12c-hexahydro-2,2,12b-trimethyl-8-oxo-	ether	245(3.84),290(3.23)	35-0689-79
$C_{20}H_{20}O_9S_4$			
1,3-Dithiole-4,5-dicarboxylic acid, 2-[4-[4,5-bis(methoxycarbonyl)-1,3-dithiol-2-ylidene]cyclohexylidene]-, dimethyl ester, 1-oxide	CH_2Cl_2	260(4.59),337(4.04)	44-0930-79
$C_{20}H_{21}BrN_2OS_2$			
4-Bromophenacylpyridinium 2-iminocyclohexanedithiocarboxylate	EtOH	248s(4.13),262(4.23), 305(3.97),392(4.39),	150-1732-79

Compound	Solvent	λmax(log ε)	Ref.
(cont.)		424s(4.10)	150-1732-79
$C_{20}H_{21}BrN_4O_{11}$			
1,4,7,10,13-Benzopentaoxacyclopentadec-in-15-amine, 16-bromo-2,3,5,6,8,9,11-12-octahydro-N-(2,4,6-trinitrophenyl)-	$CHCl_3$	402(4.01)	86-0921-79
$C_{20}H_{21}ClN_2O_3S$			
Benzenesulfonamide, 4-chloro-N-(2-hydroxy-1'-methylspiro[cyclohexane-1,3'-[3H]indol]-2'(1'H)-ylidene)-	EtOH	224(4.42),279s(4.20), 284(4.21),297s(4.11)	39-2154-79C
$C_{20}H_{21}ClN_4$			
Benzenamine, 4,4'-(6-chloro-3,4-pyridazinediyl)bis[N,N-dimethyl-	hexane	313(4.44)	111-0053-79
$C_{20}H_{21}N$			
1H-Pyrrole, 2,5-diethyl-3,4-diphenyl-	EtOH	239(4.18),274(3.91)	103-0501-79
$C_{20}H_{21}NO$			
5H-Benzocyclohepten-5-one, 6-[[4-(dimethylamino)phenyl]methylene]-6,7,8,9-tetrahydro-	isooctane	256(4.24),323(3.85), 372(4.25)	65-1407-79
	MeOH	265(4.28),402(4.41)	65-1407-79
1-Butanone, 4-(3,4-dihydro-2H-pyrrol-5-yl)-1,3-diphenyl-	MeOH	207(4.30),258(2.91)	83-0498-79
Cyclohexanone, 2-(9,10-dihydro-10-methyl-9-acridinyl)-	EtOH	284(4.17)	103-0541-79
2-Cyclohexen-1-one, 3-[4-(dimethylamino)phenyl]-5-phenyl-	H_2SO_4	342(4.42)	124-1093-79
$C_{20}H_{21}NO_2$			
Benzo[d]carbazol-6(7H)-one, 1,2,3,4,7a-8-hexahydro-8-(3-oxo-1-butenyl)-	MeOH	228(4.33),293(3.95), 340(4.43)	5-1048-79
$C_{20}H_{21}NO_3$			
4H-Dibenzo[de,g]quinoline, 5,6-dihydro-1,2,10-trimethoxy-6-methyl-	EtOH	252(4.66),264s(4.57), 297(3.95),322(4.03), 396(3.40)	95-0102-79
1H-Indole-2-acetic acid, 3-(2-hydroxyethyl)-1-(phenylmethyl)-, methyl ester	EtOH	274(3.40)	23-0289-79
Nornuciferine, N-acetyl-	MeOH	211(4.09),268(3.78), 300s(3.10)	100-0325-79
2-Propen-1-one, 1-(4-methoxyphenyl)-3-(4-morpholinyl)-3-phenyl-	EtOH	246(3.83),340(4.18)	39-2606-79C
$C_{20}H_{21}NO_4$			
Aegeline acetate	EtOH	225(4.45),277(4.70)	2-0385B-79A
6H-Benzo[g]1,3-benzodioxolo[5,6-a]quinolizine, 5,8,13,13a-tetrahydro-9,10-dimethoxy-	n.s.g.	232s(4.04),289(3.95)	107-0895-79
Corydine, hydrochloride	H_2O	222(4.51),263(4.08), 304(3.74)	106-0435-79
1,3-Dioxolo[4,5-g]isoquinoline, 6-[(6-ethyl-1,3-benzodioxol-5-yl)methyl]-5,6,7,8-tetrahydro-	EtOH	205(4.38),229s(4.14), 290(4.14)	39-0283-79C
Isocorydine	H_2O	221(4.49),268(4.09), 303(3.69)	106-0435-79
Spiro[2H-indene-2,1'(2'H)-isoquinolin]-1(3H)-one, 3',4'-dihydro-3-hydroxy-6',7'-dimethoxy-2'-methyl-, cis-(±)-	MeOH	213(4.12),243(4.11), 286(3.68)	23-1569-79

Compound	Solvent	$\lambda_{max}(\log \epsilon)$	Ref.
$C_{20}H_{21}NO_5$			
Benzo[g]quinoline-5,10-dione, 7-butyl-3,8,9-trimethoxy-	MeOH	256(4.31),295(4.30), 355(3.65)	39-0807-79C
Erythrinan-8-one, 7β-acetoxy-1,2,3,4-tetradehydro-15,16-dimethoxy-, (±)-	MeOH	212(4.30),276(3.83)	24-1329-79
Leucoxine	MeOH	220(4.59),284(4.29)	100-0325-79
Oliverine N-oxide	EtOH	223(4.38),238s(4.03), 283(4.18),317s(3.70)	100-0325-79
Polyalthine	EtOH	246(4.18),287(4.25)	100-0325-79
$C_{20}H_{21}NO_6$			
1,1'-Biphenyl-2,4-dicarboxylic acid, 3-hydroxy-4',5-dimethyl-6-nitroso-, diethyl ester	DMF	695(1.83)	104-0311-79
3,4-Isoquinolinediol, 1-[(3,4-dimethoxyphenyl)methyl]-6,7-dimethoxy-	MeOH	268(3.9),278(3.9), 306(4.0)	63-0721-79
$C_{20}H_{21}NO_{10}$			
Pyrido[1,2-a]azepine-6,7,8,9-tetracarboxylic acid, 10-acetoxy-6,7-dihydro-, tetramethyl ester	MeOH	254(3.94),384s(4.05), 394(4.10),489(4.20)	39-0584-79C
	$MeOH-HClO_4$	213(4.09),301(3.95)	39-0584-79C
$C_{20}H_{21}N_3O_3$			
Carbamic acid, [[2,5-dihydro-2-methyl-5-oxo-1-(phenylmethyl)-1H-pyrazol-3-yl]methyl]-, phenylmethyl ester	MeOH	248(3.95)	1-0294-79
$C_{20}H_{21}N_5O_5$			
Benzamide, N-[(6-formyl-3a,4,5,6,11,11a-hexahydro-2,2-dimethyl-4,11-epoxy-1,3-dioxolo[4,5-f]imidazo[1,5-a][1,3]diazocin-7-yl)iminomethyl]-, [3aR-(3aα,4α,11α,11aα)]-	MeOH	266(4.10),308(4.10)	44-0400-79
$C_{20}H_{21}N_5O_{13}$			
1,4,7,10,13-Benzopentaoxacyclopentadecin-15-amine, 2,3,5,6,8,9,11,12-octahydro-16-nitro-N-(2,4,6-trinitrophenyl)-	$CHCl_3$	424(4.16)	86-0921-79
$C_{20}H_{22}$			
Benzene, 1,1'-[3-(2-butenyl)-3-methyl-1,2-cyclopropanediyl]bis-, [1α,2α-3β(E)]-	EtOH	225s(4.14)	35-5743-79
[1α,2α,3β(Z)]-	EtOH	225s(4.14)	35-5743-79
Benzene, 1,1'-(3-butyl-2-methyl-1-cyclopropene-1,3-diyl)bis-	EtOH	263(4.24)	35-5743-79
Benzene, 1,1'-(3-butyl-3-methyl-1-cyclopropene-1,2-diyl)bis-	EtOH	229(4.24),321(4.46), 338(4.34)	35-5743-79
Bicyclo[3.1.0]hexane, 2,5-dimethyl-1,6-diphenyl-	EtOH	225s(4.13)	35-5743-79
$C_{20}H_{22}BrNO_4$			
1,3-Dioxolo[4,5-g]isoquinoline, 5-[1-(2-bromo-4,5-dimethoxyphenyl)ethyl]-5,6,7,8-tetrahydro-	EtOH	225s(4.14)	39-0283-79C
Isoquinoline, 1-[1-(6-bromo-1,3-benzodioxol-5-yl)ethyl]-1,2,3,4-tetrahydro-6,7-dimethoxy-, (R*,R*)-(±)-	EtOH	231s(4.16),291(3.90)	39-0283-79C

Compound	Solvent	$\lambda_{max}(\log \epsilon)$	Ref.
$C_{20}H_{22}Cl_2N_{10}O_5S$			
Adenosine, 5'-chloro-2',5'-dideoxy-, 3',3"'-sulfite	pH 1	257(4.43)	44-3100-79
	pH 13	260(4.42)	44-3100-79
$C_{20}H_{22}NO$			
Quinolinium, 1-(4-butoxyphenyl)-2-methyl-, perchlorate	EtOH	239(4.63),318(4.14)	104-1160-79
$C_{20}H_{22}NO_3$			
Isoquinolinium, 3-(3,4-dimethoxyphenyl)-1,4-dihydro-4-(methoxymethylene)-2-methyl-, tetrafluoroborate	EtOH	228(4.38),290(4.20), 354(4.10)	78-1861-79
$C_{20}H_{22}NO_4$			
Caryachine methiodide, (±)-	MeOH	290(4.00)	100-0163-79
	MeOH-NaOH	297.5(--)	100-0163-79
Caryachine methoperchlorate, (-)-	MeOH	225s(4.07),292(3.95)	100-0163-79
	MeOH-NaOH	296(--)	100-0163-79
Isocaryachine methiodide, (±)-	MeOH	290(3.76)	100-0163-79
	MeOH-NaOH	296(--)	100-0163-79
Isoquinolinium, 4-[(3,4-dimethoxyphenyl)methyl]-6-hydroxy-7-methoxy-2-methyl-, iodide	EtOH	242(4.84),283(4.18), 313(3.92),327(3.81)	78-2555-79
	EtOH-NaOH	222(4.74),253(4.79), 340(4.18)	78-2555-79
$C_{20}H_{22}N_2$			
Benzenamine, 4-[2-(3,3-dimethyl-3H-indol-2-yl)ethenyl]-N,N-dimethyl-, BF_3 adduct	$CHCl_3$	534(4.99)	124-0231-79
$C_{20}H_{22}N_2O$			
Acetamide, N-methyl-N-[2-[1-(phenylmethyl)-1H-indol-3-yl]ethyl]-	EtOH	281s(3.70),289(3.74), 299s(3.69)	23-1694-79
4-Oxazolamine, 2-(diphenylmethylene)-2,5-dihydro-N,N,%,%-tetramethyl-	MeCN	230(4.17),332(4.39)	33-1429-79
4-Piperidinone, 3-[(methylphenylamino)-methylene]-1-(phenylmethyl)-	EtOH	250(4.13),308(3.69)	4-0177-79
$C_{20}H_{22}N_2O_2$			
Acetamide, N-[2-[2,3-dihydro-2-oxo-1-(phenylmethyl)-1H-indol-3-yl]ethyl]-N-methyl-	EtOH	256(3.85),280s(3.14)	23-1694-79
2H-Benz[d]azepin-2-one, 7-(acetylamino)-4,4-dimethyl-5-phenyl-1,3,4,5-tetrahydro-	EtOH	205(4.53),247(4.26)	4-1525-79
5-Norcatharanthine	MeOH	228(4.53),276s(4.03), 284(4.04),291(3.99)	23-2572-79
	MeOH-HCl	224(4.50),260(4.08), 272s(4.07),288(3.98)	23-2572-79
Pyrrolo[2,3-b]indol-2(1H)-one, 1-(2-hydroxyethyl)-3,3a,8,8a-tetrahydro-3a-methyl-8-(phenylmethyl)-	MeOH	249(3.92),298(3.38)	5-0927-79
$C_{20}H_{22}N_2O_3$			
2-Propenamide, 2-(acetylamino)-3-(4-methoxyphenyl)-N-(1-phenylethyl)-, (S)-	$CHCl_3$-20% MeOH	302(4.28)	70-0129-79
4(3H)-Quinazolinone, 3-[2-(3,4-dimethoxyphenyl)ethyl]-2,6-dimethyl-	MeOH	278(3.68),312(3.18), 325(3.08)	4-0449-79
4(3H)-Quinazolinone, 3-[2-(3,4-dimethoxyphenyl)ethyl]-2,8-dimethyl-	MeOH	282(3.65),312(3.22), 324(3.11)	4-0449-79

Compound	Solvent	λ_{max}(log ε)	Ref.
Tabersonine, 19-oxo-	EtOH	225(4.15),300(4.13), 330(4.30)	44-2468-79
$C_{20}H_{22}N_2O_4$			
Benzenemethanol, α,α'-azobis[α-methyl-, diacetate	hexane	358(1.61)	49-0699-79
Tricyclo[4.2.2.0^{2,5}]deca-3,7-diene-3,4-dicarboxylic acid, 7,8-dicyano-1,5,10-10-tetramethyl-, dimethyl ester	MeOH	222(4.20),247s(3.90)	39-0042-79C
$C_{20}H_{22}N_2O_6S$			
5-Thia-1-azabicyclo[4.2.0]oct-2-ene-2-carboxylic acid, 3-methyl-4,8-dioxo-7-[(phenoxyacetyl)amino]-, 1,1-dimethylethyl ester, (6R-trans)-	EtOH	267(3.68),274(3.72), 312(3.80)	33-2681-79
$C_{20}H_{22}N_4$			
2-Propenimidamide, 2-cyano-N-(2,3-dimethylphenyl)-3-[(2,3-dimethylphenyl)amino]-	$CHCl_3$	333(4.34)	24-0484-79
	MeCN	333(4.35)	24-0484-79
$C_{20}H_{22}N_4O_2$			
1,4-Benzenediacetonitrile, α,α'-bis(4-morpholinylmethylene)-	MeOH	233(4.09),341(4.42)	83-0535-79
$C_{20}H_{22}N_4O_3S$			
3,5-Methano-6H-pyrrolo[3,2-b]pyridin-6-one, 4-(4,6-dimethyl-2-pyrimidinyl)octahydro-1-(phenylsulfonyl)-	$CHCl_3$	248(4.21),290(3.66)	39-1525-79C
$C_{20}H_{22}N_4O_6$			
3H-Phenoxazine-1,9-dicarboxamide, 2-amino-N,N'-bis(2-hydroxyethyl)-4,6-dimethyl-3-oxo-	n.s.g.	445(4.34)	104-0951-79
$C_{20}H_{22}N_4O_9$			
α-D-galacto-Octopyranos-6-ulose, 7,7,8,8-tetradehydro-7,8-dideoxy-1,2:3,4-bis-O-(1-methylethylidene)-, 2,4-dinitrophenylhydrazone	MeOH	206(4.31),254(4.23), 356(4.58)	136-0151-79H
$C_{20}H_{22}N_4O_{11}$			
1,4,7,10,13-Benzopentaoxacyclopentadecin-15-amine, 2,3,5,6,8,9,11,12-octahydro-N-(2,4,6-trinitrophenyl)-	$CHCl_3$	395(4.03)	86-0921-79
$C_{20}H_{22}O$			
Bicyclo[6.1.0]nona-2,4,6-triene, 9,9'-(methoxymethylene)bis-	MeCN	205(4.52),245(4.08)	33-0718-79
2-Chrysenol, 4b,5,6,10b,11,12-hexahydro-7,8-dimethyl-	EtOH	281(3.52)	39-1333-79C
6,10-Methano-5H-benzocyclononen-12-ol, 6,7,8,9,10,11-hexahydro-12-phenyl-	MeOH	212(4.23),252(2.62), 258(2.75),265(2.79), 273(2.70)	56-1221-79
18-Norandrosta-4,6,8,11,13-pentaen-3-one, 17,17-dimethyl-	MeOH	245(4.17),360(4.16)	39-1333-79C
$C_{20}H_{22}O_2$			
D-Homoestra-1,3,5(10),6,8-pentaen-17a-one, 3-methoxy-	MeOH	267(3.86),277(3.73), 321(3.58),324(3.69)	13-0361-79A

Compound	Solvent	λ_{max}(log ε)	Ref.
D-Homoestra-1,3,5(10),8,14-pentaen-17a-one, 3-methoxy-	MeOH	230(4.14),294(4.29), 307(4.38),320(4.27)	13-0361-79
1,5-Pentanedione, 2,3,3-trimethyl-1,5-diphenyl-	EtOH	245(4.31),322(2.07)	44-2331-79
$C_{20}H_{22}O_3$			
9(10H)-Anthracenone, 1,8-dihydroxy-10,10-dipropyl-	MeOH	258(3.95),273(3.89), 299(4.03),373(4.01)	145-1083-79
$C_{20}H_{22}O_5$			
Anthra[1,9-de]-1,3-dioxin-7(3aH)-one, 8-acetoxy-6,6a,11b,11c-tetrahydro-2,2,11b-trimethyl-	MeOH	242(3.91),290(3.23)	35-0689-79
Crotofolin E	EtOH	215(4.20)	88-3345-79
$C_{20}H_{22}O_6$			
1,2-Benzenedicarboxylic acid, 3-(4-butoxyphenyl)-6-hydroxy-, dimethyl ester	EtOH	236(4.33),320(3.56)	103-0013-79
$C_{20}H_{22}O_6Se$			
2-Oxaspiro[4.5]dec-6-ene-3-carboxylic acid, 3-ethoxy-1,8-dioxo-9-(phenylseleno)-, ethyl ester, (3SR,5RS)-	MeOH	218(4.09),236(3.90), 266(3.39)	24-1571-79
(3SR,5SR)-	MeOH	220(4.05),276s(3.35)	24-1571-79
$C_{20}H_{22}O_7$			
2-Butenoic acid, 2-methyl-, 2,3,3a,4,9-10,11,11a-octahydro-6-(hydroxymethyl)-10-methyl-3-methylene-2,9-dioxo-7,10-epoxycyclodeca[b]furan-4-yl ester (centratherin)	MeOH	217(4.02),267(3.87)	102-0681-79
Nortrachelogenin, (+)-	MeOH	230(2.05),282(1.35)	100-0159-79
	MeOH-base	249(2.65),298(1.75)	100-0159-79
$C_{20}H_{22}O_8$			
Abruquinone B, (3S)-	EtOH	268(4.03),395(3.01)	32-0009-79
$C_{20}H_{23}BrO_6$			
α-D-galacto-Oct-6-enodialdo-1,5-pyranose, 7-bromo-6,7-dideoxy-1,2:3,4-bis-O-(1-methylethylidene)-8-C-phenyl-, (E)-	EtOH	208(3.74),254(4.00)	33-1632-79
(Z)-	EtOH	209(3.84),255(3.97)	33-1632-79
$C_{20}H_{23}NO$			
2H-Pyrrole-5-ethanol, 3,4-dihydro-3,3-dimethyl-α,α-diphenyl-	MeOH	206(4.32),252(3.59)	83-0498-79
$C_{20}H_{23}NOS$			
1-Propanamine, 3-(2-methoxydibenzo-[b,e]thiepin-11(6H)-ylidene)-N,N-dimethyl-	MeOH	229(4.40),261(3.99), 321(3.53)	73-2536-79
$C_{20}H_{23}NO_2$			
2-Hexen-1-one, 6-hydroxy-1-(4-methylphenyl)-3-[(phenylmethyl)amino]-	MeOH	249(4.23),344(4.64)	44-2073-79
$C_{20}H_{23}NO_3$			
Cyclohexanecarboxaldehyde, 3-(2,3-dihydro-1,3-dimethyl-2-oxo-1H-indol-3-yl)-2-oxo-1-(2-propenyl)-	EtOH	253(3.95),280s(3.30)	23-1694-79

Compound	Solvent	$\lambda_{max}(\log \epsilon)$	Ref.
4H-Dibenzo[de,g]quinoline, 2-ethoxy-5,6,6a,7-tetrahydro-10,11-dimethoxy-, hydrochloride, (±)-	EtOH	219(4.60),230s(4.50), 268(4.20),275(4.19), 299(3.80)	33-1549-79
4H-Dibenzo[de,g]quinoline, 5,6,6a,7-tetrahydro-1,2,10-trimethoxy-6-methyl-, hydrochloride, (±)-	EtOH	221(4.58),266(4.15), 274(4.16),301(3.87)	33-1549-79
2H-Indol-2-one, 1,3-dihydro-1,3-dimethyl-3-[2-oxo-3-[(2-propenyloxy)methylene]cyclohexyl]-	EtOH	254(4.10),280(3.69)	23-1694-79
Nuciferine, 3-methoxy-	EtOH	212(4.63),228s(4.39), 275(4.33)	100-0325-79
Thebaine (as methochloride)	EtOH	214(4.41),226(4.42), 285(4.22)	102-1089-79
$C_{20}H_{23}NO_4$			
4H-Dibenzo[de,g]quinolin-9-ol, 5,6,6a-7-tetrahydro-2,9,10-trimethoxy-N-methyl-	EtOH	233(4.32),281(4.11), 305(4.12)	78-2555-79
	EtOH-NaOH	233(4.32),270(4.04), 311(3.78),344(3.91)	78-2555-79
Isocorypalmine	MeOH	206(4.78),283(3.76)	106-0194-79
Lirioferine	MeOH	220(4.50),273s(4.02), 280(4.09),303(4.07), 312s(4.02)	100-0325-79
Unknown compound, m. 108°	EtOH	232(4.03),287(3.79)	78-1857-79
L-Valine, N-[(phenylmethoxy)carbonyl]-, phenylmethyl ester	EtOH	248(2.39),252(2.52), 258(2.63),262(2.52), 264(2.55),268(2.36)	118-0957-79
$C_{20}H_{23}NO_5$			
Colchicine, N-deacetyl-	EtOH	245(4.47),353(4.24)	33-0965-79
Demecolceine	EtOH	244(4.44),350(4.23)	33-0965-79
Erythrinan-8-one, 7-acetoxy-6,7-didehydro-15,16-dimethoxy-, (±)-	MeOH	220(4.36),280(3.63)	24-2472-79
Glaufidine	n.s.g.	223(4.51),269(4.03), 305(3.69)	105-0091-79
6-Isoquinolinol, 3,4-dihydro-7-methoxy-1-((3,4,5-trimethoxyphenyl)methyl]-	pH 6.0	392(4.24)	39-2744-79C
Srilankine	EtOH	210(4.68),277(4.35), 301(4.22)	100-0325-79
$C_{20}H_{23}NO_6$			
3,4-Isoquinolinediol, 1-[(3,4-dimethoxyphenyl)methyl]-3,4-dihydro-6,7-dimethoxy-	MeOH	281(4.2),329(4.1)	63-0721-79
$C_{20}H_{23}NO_7$			
3-Pyridinecarboxylic acid, 4-[[4-(ethoxycarbonyl)-2,6-dimethoxyphenoxy]-methyl]-, ethyl ester	EtOH	215(4.55),265(4.06), 291s(3.58)	39-2982-79C
$C_{20}H_{23}N_2O_2$			
Pyridinium, 1-[2-[2-(ethoxycarbonyl)-1H-indol-3-yl]ethyl]-3-ethyl-, chloride	EtOH	220(4.30),226(4.35), 276(3.90),296(4.20)	23-0289-79
Pyridinium, 3-ethyl-1-[2-[2-(2-methoxy-2-oxoethyl)-1H-indol-3-yl]ethyl]-, perchlorate	EtOH	219(4.56),265(4.01), 271(3.98),280(3.91), 289(3.83)	23-0289-79
$C_{20}H_{23}N_3O_3$			
1H-Naphth[2,3-d]imidazole-4,9-dione,	C_6H_{12}	541(3.83)	39-0702-79C

Compound	Solvent	λmax(log ε)	Ref.
5-(cyclohexylamino)-8-methoxy-2,3-dimethyl- (cont.)	EtOH	566(--)	39-0702-79C
	EtOH-HCl	586(--)	39-0702-79C
1H-Naphth[2,3-d]imidazole-4,9-dione, 8-(cyclohexylamino)-5-methoxy-2,3-dimethyl-	C_6H_{12}	539(3.87)	39-0702-79C
	EtOH	563(--)	39-0702-79C
	EtOH-HCl	586(--)	39-0702-79C
$C_{20}H_{23}N_3O_7$			
Carbamic acid, [1,2-dihydro-1-[2,3-O-(1-methylethylidene)-β-D-ribofuranosyl]-2-oxo-4-pyrimidinyl]-, phenylmethyl ester	MeOH	242(4.13),293(3.76)	87-0639-79
Cytidine, N-benzoyl-4'-C-(hydroxymethyl)-2',3'-O-(1-methylethylidene)-	MeOH	259(4.38),303(4.02)	44-1309-79
$C_{20}H_{23}N_3O_7S$			
2(1H)-Quinazolinethione, 3,4-dihydro-4-imino-3-methyl-1-(2,3,4-tri-O-acetyl-β-D-ribopyranosyl)-	MeOH	208(4.07),220(4.07), 240(4.11),281(4.28)	44-0173-79
$C_{20}H_{23}N_5O$			
3,5-Methanofuro[3,2-b]pyridin-6(2H)-one, 4-(4,6-dimethyl-2-pyrimidinyl)hexahydro-, phenylhydrazone	$CHCl_3$	348(4.02)	39-1525-79C
$C_{20}H_{23}N_7O_7$			
Folic acid, 5-formyl-5,6,7,8-tetrahydro-, L-(±)-, calcium salt	pH 13	282(4.46)	87-0731-79
$C_{20}H_{23}N_9O_5$			
DL-Glutamic acid, N-[[[4-[[(2,4-diamino-6-pteridinyl)methyl]methylamino]-phenyl]amino]carbonyl]-	pH 1	245(4.54),337(4.00), 285(3.80),350s(3.85)	87-0869-79
	pH 13	258(4.48),390(3.76)	87-0869-79
$C_{20}H_{24}$			
Benzene, 1,1'-(3-ethyl-1-propyl-1,2-cyclopropanediyl)bis- (isomer mixture)	EtOH or CCl_4	257(3.21),278(2.64)	104-0080-79
Bicyclo[4.1.0]heptane, 7,7'-[2,4-bis-(methylene)-1,3-cyclobutanediylidene]-bis-	heptane	202(4.06),256(3.24)	35-4772-79
2,9:3,8-Diethanodibenzo[a,e]cyclooctene, 1,4,5,6,7,10,11,12-octahydro-	EtOH	235(4.04)	44-2160-79
$C_{20}H_{24}ClN_3S$			
10H-Phenothiazine, 2-chloro-10-[3-(4-methyl-1-piperazinyl)propyl]-	MeOH	206(4.45),258(4.54), 310(3.65)	133-0197-79
$C_{20}H_{24}N_2$			
7-Azabicyclo[3.2.1]oct-2-ene, 6-(1H-indol-3-ylmethyl)-8-methylene-7-(1-methylethyl)-, exo- (peduncularine)	EtOH	223(4.51),274s(3.73), 281(3.77),290(3.71)	33-0481-79
2-Butanone, 1-phenyl-, [1-(phenylmethyl)propylidene]hydrazone	EtOH	218(4.36),241(4.04), 269(3.21)	103-0501-79
2-Butanone, 3-phenyl-, (1-methyl-2-phenylpropylidene)hydrazone	EtOH	216(4.58),238(4.11), 258(3.84),265(3.04), 269(2.95)	103-0501-79
Sorelline	EtOH	224(4.72),241s(4.24), 276s(3.81),282(3.85), 291(3.80)	33-2539-79

Compound	Solvent	λ_{max}(log ϵ)	Ref.
$C_{20}H_{24}N_2O_3$			
Tabersonine, 19R-hydroxy-	EtOH	220(4.02),300(4.02), 330(4.13)	44-2468-79
Tabersonine, 19S-hydroxy-	EtOH	220(4.11),300(4.00), 330(4.15)	44-2468-79
$C_{20}H_{24}N_2O_3S$			
Benzenesulfonamide, 4-methyl-N-(1,2,3,4-tetrahydro-1,3,3,4-tetramethyl-2-oxo-4-quinolinyl)-	EtOH	233(4.32),256(4.21)	23-0558-79
$C_{20}H_{24}N_2O_6$			
Butanoic acid, [(4,4'-diamino[1,1'-biphenyl]-3,3'-diyl)bis(oxy)]bis-	pH 1	250(4.13),287(3.92)	145-0187-79
	pH 10	283(4.27),300(4.30)	145-0187-79
oxidized form	pH 7	450(4.1)	145-0187-79
5-Oxa-1-azabicyclo[4.2.0]oct-2-ene-2-carboxylic acid, 3-methyl-8-oxo-7-[(phenoxyacetyl)amino]-, 1,1-dimethylethyl ester, (6R-trans)-	EtOH	264(3.96)	39-2268-79C
5-Oxa-1-azabicyclo[4.2.0]oct-3-ene-2-carboxylic acid, 3-methyl-8-oxo-7-[(phenoxyacetyl)amino]-, 1,1-dimethylethyl ester, (6R-trans)-	EtOH	270(3.18),276(3.11)	39-2268-79C
$C_{20}H_{24}N_2O_8$			
Phenol, 4,4'-(2,3-dimethyl-1,4-butanediyl)bis[2-methoxy-6-nitro-, (R*,S*)-	EtOH	225(4.32),254s(3.87), 296(3.90)	94-1583-79
$C_{20}H_{24}N_2S$			
Piperazine, 1-(10,11-dihydro-2-methyldibenzo[b,f]thiepin-10-yl)-4-methyl-	MeOH	261(4.41),297s(3.95), 340s(2.87)	73-2677-79
$C_{20}H_{24}N_2S_2$			
Spiro[cyclohexane-1,8'-[2H,8H]isothiazolo[4,3,2-ij]quinazoline]-2'-thione, 3',4',5',5'a,6',7'-hexahydro-6'-phenyl-	EtOH	266(3.65),370(4.25)	150-0410-79S
$C_{20}H_{24}N_3$			
1H-Indolo[2,3-a]quinolizin-5-ium, 1-(2-cyanoethyl)-1-ethyl-2,3,4,6,7,12-hexahydro-, perchlorate	MeOH	248(3.86),253(3.80), 366(4.26)	114-0387-79C
$C_{20}H_{24}N_4O_3$			
Acetamide, N-[4,7-dihydro-5-methyl-3-[(1-methylethoxy)methyl]-4-oxo-7-(phenylmethyl)-3H-pyrrolo[2,3-d]-pyrimidin-2-yl]-	MeOH	225(4.29),270s(3.79), 302(3.95)	138-1283-79
$C_{20}H_{24}N_4O_{10}$			
α-D-galacto-Octodialdo-1,5-pyranos-6-ulose, 7-deoxy-1,2:3,4-bis-O-(1-methylethylidene)-, 8-(2,4-dinitrophenylhydrazone)	MeOH	222(4.15),252(4.05), 355(4.26)	136-0151-79H
$C_{20}H_{24}O$			
18-Norandrosta-4,8,11,13-tetraen-3-one, 17,17-dimethyl-	EtOH	238(4.29),278(3.13)	39-1333-79C
$C_{20}H_{24}O_2$			
14β-Estra-1,3,5(10),16-tetraen-15-one, 3-methoxy-14-methyl-	MeOH	227(4.07),279(3.32), 288(3.27)	150-2525-79

Compound	Solvent	λmax(log ε)	Ref.
D-Homoestra-1,3,5(10),9(11)-tetraen-17a-one, 3-methoxy-	MeOH	262(4.25),292(3.48)	13-0361-79A
1-Isobenzofuranol, 1,3-dihydro-3,3-bis(1-methylethyl)-1-phenyl-, cation	50% H_2SO_4	343(4.41)	104-1126-79
19-Norpregna-4,9-dien-20-yn-3-one, 17-hydroxy-	MeOH	231(4.24)	24-3748-79
$C_{20}H_{24}O_3$			
Furan, tetrahydro-2,4-bis(4-methoxyphenyl)-3,5-dimethyl-	MeOH	205(3.25),230(3.42), 278(2.60)	106-0022-79
5H-Inden-5-one, 1,2,3,6,7,7a-hexahydro-1-hydroxy-4-[2-(3-methoxyphenyl)-2-propenyl]-7a-methyl-, (1S-cis)-	EtOH	211(4.37),244(4.18)	54-0496-79
1,6(2H,7H)-Naphthalenedione, 3,4,8,8a-tetrahydro-5-[2-(3-methoxyphenyl)-ethyl]-8a-methyl-, (S)-	MeOH	252(4.01),280(3.57)	13-0361-79A
2(3H)-Naphthalenone, 4a-(acetoxyphenylmethyl)-4,4a,5,6,7,8-hexahydro-1-methyl-, (R*)-	MeOH	259(4.14),290(1.48)	33-0119-79
(S*)-	MeOH	259(4.14),290(1.48)	33-0119-79
$C_{20}H_{24}O_4$			
2-Naphthalenecarboxylic acid, 4-acetoxy-3,6,7-trimethyl-1-(1-methylethyl)-, methyl ester	EtOH	235(4.92),288(4.11)	2-0122-79B
1H-Naphtho[1',2':5,6]cyclohepta[1,2-b]-furan-4-carboxylic acid, 2,3,4,4a,5-6,7,11,12,12b-decahydro-4,12b-dimethyl-7-oxo- (hispanonic acid)	EtOH	254s(3.77),273(3.95), 281s(3.93),311(4.03)	44-2219-79
[2.2]Paracyclophane-4,7,12,15-tetramethanol	EtOH	230(4.26),290(2.52)	35-2128-79
2,4,12-Tridecatrienoic acid, 13-(1,3-benzodioxol-5-yl)-, (E,E,E)-	n.s.g.	260(4.36),305(3.98)	2-0538B-79A
$C_{20}H_{24}O_5$			
2H-10,4a-(Epoxymethano)phenanthrene-5,6,9(1H)-trione, 3,4,10,10a-tetrahydro-10-hydroxy-1,1-dimethyl-7-(1-methylethyl)-, [4aR-(4aα,10α,10aβ)]-	ether	221(4.13),408(3.41)	33-2754-79
$C_{20}H_{24}O_5S$			
2-Cyclohexen-1-one, 2,4,4-trimethyl-6-[[(4-methylphenyl)sulfonyl]oxy]-3-(3-oxo-1-butenyl)-, (E)-	MeCN	228(4.30),270(4.08), 349s(2.35)	33-0553-79
$C_{20}H_{24}O_6$			
3-Dehydroleptocarpin	n.s.g.	227(3.98),243(3.94)	102-1527-79
Ethanone, 2-(3,4-dimethoxyphenyl)-1-[2-(2-hydroxyethyl)-4,5-dimethoxyphenyl]-	MeOH	233(4.3),275(4.2), 358(3.9)	63-0721-79
2-Naphthalenecarboxylic acid, 4-acetoxy-6,7-dimethoxy-3-methyl-1-(1-methylethyl)-, methyl ester	EtOH	246(4.81),286(3.80)	2-0122-79B
α-D-galacto-Oct-6-enodialdo-1,5-pyranose, 6,7-dideoxy-1,2:3,4-bis-O-(1-methylethylidene)-8-C-phenyl-	EtOH	206(3.67),256(4.12)	33-1632-79
$C_{20}H_{24}O_6S$			
2-Propenoic acid, 3-[2,6,6-trimethyl-4-[[(4-methylphenyl)sulfonyl]oxy]-3-oxo-1-cyclohexen-1-yl]-, methyl ester, (E)-	MeCN	225(4.25),265(4.14), 340s(1.95)	33-0553-79

Compound	Solvent	$\lambda_{max}(\log \epsilon)$	Ref.
$C_{20}H_{24}O_6Se$			
2-Oxaspiro[4.5]decane-3-carboxylic acid, 3-ethoxy-1,8-dioxo-7-(phenylseleno)-, (3RS,5SR)-	MeOH	218(4.15),268(3.5)	24-1550-79
(3SR,5SR)-	MeOH	215(4.1),237(3.9), 273(3.6)	24-1550-79
$C_{20}H_{24}O_7$			
Anthra[1,9-de]-1,3-dioxin-7(3aH)-one, 8-acetoxy-4,5,6,6a,11b,11c-hexahydro-4,5-dihydroxy-2,2,11b-trimethyl-	MeOH	241(3.96),289(3.27)	35-0689-79
Eupachifolin E	MeOH	213(4.26)	138-1473-79
$C_{20}H_{25}NO_2$			
1H-3-Benzazepine, 2,3,4,5-tetrahydro-7,8-dimethoxy-2,2-dimethyl-1-phenyl-, hydrochloride	EtOH	235(3.89),270s(3.20), 284(3.28)	4-1525-79
$C_{20}H_{25}NO_3$			
Isoquinoline, 1,2,3,4-tetrahydro-6,7-dimethoxy-1-[(4-methoxyphenyl)methyl]-2-methyl-, (+-O-methylarmepavine)	EtOH	280(3.78)	102-1584-79
(R)-(-)-	EtOH	227(4.14),282(3.76)	100-0430-79
$C_{20}H_{25}NO_4$			
6-Isoquinolinol, 4-[(3,4-dimethoxyphenyl)methyl]-1,2,3,4-tetrahydro-7-methoxy-2-methyl-	EtOH	230(4.15),286(3.81)	78-2555-79
	EtOH-NaOH	226(4.26),288(3.70), 304(3.74)	78-2555-79
7-Isoquinolinol, 4-[(3,4-dimethoxyphenyl)methyl]-1,2,3,4-tetrahydro-6-methoxy-2-methyl-	EtOH	239(4.21),285(3.85)	78-2555-79
	EtOH-NaOH	233(4.20),254(4.16), 288(3.86),300s(3.75)	78-2555-79
Laudanine	pH 2	226(4.20),282(3.71)	106-0194-79
Phenol, 2-methoxy-4-[(1,2,3,4-tetrahydro-6,7-dimethoxy-2-methyl-4-isoquinolinyl)methyl]-	EtOH	237(4.22),284(4.00)	78-2555-79
	EtOH-NaOH	241(4.22),292(4.03)	78-2555-79
Phenol, 2-methoxy-5-[(1,2,3,4-tetrahydro-6,7-dimethoxy-2-methyl-4-isoquinolinyl)methyl]-	EtOH	234(4.05),285(3.82)	78-2555-79
	EtOH-NaOH	233(4.10),293(3.89)	78-2555-79
$C_{20}H_{25}NO_5$			
Benzo[g]quinoline-5,10-dione, 7-butyl-1,2,3,4-tetrahydro-3,8,9-trimethoxy-	MeOH	236(4.23),281(4.47), 361(3.65),480(3.45)	39-0807-79C
$C_{20}H_{25}NO_8$			
Pyridinium, 1-[3-ethoxy-2-(ethoxycarbonyl)-1-[2-ethoxy-1-(ethoxycarbonyl)-2-oxoethyl]-3-oxo-1-propenyl]-, hydroxide, inner salt	$CHCl_3$	365(2.7),475(1.9)	5-1388-79 +5-1406-79
$C_{20}H_{25}N_2O_3$			
2H-Isoindol-2-yloxy, 5-(2,5-dihydro-2,5-dioxo-1H-pyrrol-1-yl)-1,1,3,3-tetraethyl-1,3-dihydro-	C_6H_{12}	275(3.94)	22-0048-79
$C_{20}H_{25}N_3O$			
Ethanamine, N,N-diethyl-2-[(4-methyl-1-phenyl-1H-pyrrolo[2,3-b]pyridin-6-yl)oxy]-	n.s.g.	258(4.19),330(3.85)	103-0310-79
$C_{20}H_{25}N_3O_2S$			
2-Cyclododecathiazolamine, 4,5,6,7,8,9-	EtOH	275(4.174),389(3.926)	48-0249-79

Compound	Solvent	λmax(log ε)	Ref.
10,11,12,13-decahydro-N-[(4-nitrophenyl)methylene]- (cont.)			48-0249-79
$C_{20}H_{25}N_3O_5$			
α-D-Galactopyranose, 6-deoxy-6-(4-methylene-1,2,3-benzotriazin-3(4H)-yl)-1,2:3,4-bis-O-(1-methylethylidene)-	EtOH	212(4.34),270(4.15), 327(3.48)	33-0971-79
$C_{20}H_{25}N_3O_5S$			
Carbamic acid, [3-methyl-8-oxo-7-[(phenoxyacetyl)amino]-5-thia-1-azabicyclo[4.2.0]oct-2-en-2-yl]-, 1,1-dimethylethyl ester, (6R-trans)-	EtOH	273(3.61)	39-1659-79C
Carbamic acid, [3-methyl-8-oxo-7-[(phenoxyacetyl)amino]-5-thia-1-azabicyclo[4.2.0]oct-3-en-2-yl]-, 1,1-dimethylethyl ester, (6R-trans)-	EtOH	266(3.60)	39-1659-79C
$C_{20}H_{25}N_3O_6$			
Glycine, N-[N-[(1,1-dimethylethoxy)-1-formyl-L-tryptophyl]-, methyl ester	MeOH-HCl	299(3.63)	63-0013-79
$C_{20}H_{25}N_3O_9$			
α-D-Galactofuranose, 1,2:5,6-bis-O-(1-methylethylidene)-3-C-[(4-nitrophenyl)azo]-, 3-acetate	EtOH	213(4.33),284(4.31), 406(2.52)	136-0287-79B
α-D-Glucofuranose, 1,2:5,6-bis-O-(1-methylethylidene)-3-C-[(4-nitrophenyl)azo]-, 3-acetate	EtOH	283(4.23),407(2.53)	136-0287-79B
$C_{20}H_{25}N_5O_3$			
Acetamide, N-[5-(diethylamino)-2-[(4-nitrophenyl)azo]phenyl]-N-ethyl-	EtOH	482(4.56)	39-1990-79C
	HOAc	475(4.53)	39-1990-79C
$C_{20}H_{25}N_7$			
[4,5'-Bipyrimidine]-2,2',4'-triamine, N,N,N',N',N",N"-hexamethyl-6-phenyl-	EtOH	259(4.62),323(4.04), 360(4.12)	103-0671-79
$C_{20}H_{26}$			
Benzene, (5-ethyl-3,7-dimethyl-1,3,5,8-decatetraenyl)-, (all-E)-	hexane	302(4.51)	44-3109-79
(E,E,E,Z)-	hexane	295(4.51),311(4.54)	44-3109-79
Benzene, 1-ethyl-4-[2-(2,3-dimethylphenyl)ethyl]-2,3-dimethyl-, tetracyanoethylene complex	MeCN	227(4.24),255(4.18), 261(4.18),270(4.12), 460(3.18)	88-1209-79
5,16-Ethenobenzocyclotetradecene, 6,7,8,9,10,11,12,13,14,15-decahydro-	EtOH	230(4.64),282(3.67), 291(3.68),300(3.51)	35-6660-79
$C_{20}H_{26}N_2$			
Hobartine	EtOH	223(4.60),275s(3.80), 283(3.84),291(3.78)	33-2539-79
$C_{20}H_{26}N_2O_2$			
1H-Indole-2-acetic acid, 3-[2-(3-ethyl-5,6-dihydro-1(2H)-pyridinyl)ethyl]-, methyl ester	EtOH	223(4.43),274(3.87), 283(3.92),292(3.83)	23-0289-79
Pyridine, 1-(2,2-dimethyl-1-oxopropyl)-4-[1-(2,2-dimethyl-1-oxopropyl)-4(1H)-pyridinylidene]-1,4-dihydro-	MeCN	412(4.64),432(4.69)	5-0727-79

Compound	Solvent	$\lambda_{max}(\log \epsilon)$	Ref.
$C_{20}H_{26}N_2O_4Sn$			
Tin, dibutylbis(2-pyridinecarboxylato-N[1],O[2])-	$CHCl_3$	238s(3.58),264(4.00)	131-0165-79D
	MeCN	221(4.08),263(3.95)	131-0165-79D
$C_{20}H_{26}N_2O_5$			
1H-Pyrrole-3-propanoic acid, 5-[(1,5-dihydro-3-methyl-5-oxo-2H-pyrrol-2-ylidene)methyl]-2-[(1,1-dimethylethoxy)carbonyl]-4-methyl-, methyl ester	MeOH	228s(--),230(4.26), 390(4.43),406s(--)	24-2243-79
$C_{20}H_{26}N_2O_6$			
7,10,13,16,19,22-Hexaoxa-27,28-diazatricyclo[21.3.1.1^{2,6}]octacosa-1(27),2,4,6(28),23,25-hexaene	EtOH	220(4.57),307(3.90), 315(4.30)	35-4472-79
$C_{20}H_{26}N_2O_8$			
Pyridinium, 4-(dimethylamino)-1-[3-ethoxy-2-(ethoxycarbonyl)-1-[2-methoxy-1-(methoxycarbonyl)-2-oxoethyl]-3-oxo-1-propenyl]-, hydroxide, inner salt	$CHCl_3$	253(4.1),307(4.5), 412(4.1)	5-1406-79
$C_{20}H_{26}N_4$			
1,4-Butanedione, 1,4-diphenyl-, bis(dimethylhydrazone)	MeOH	233(4.35),306(3.46)	44-3281-79
$C_{20}H_{26}N_4O_8$			
α-D-Allofuranose, 3-[1-acetyl-3-(4-nitrophenyl)-2-triazenyl]-3-deoxy-1,2:5,6-bis-O-(1-methylethylidene)-	EtOH	218(4.03),313(4.30)	33-0971-79
α-D-Galactofuranose, 3-[1-acetyl-3-(4-nitrophenyl)-2-triazenyl]-3-deoxy-1,2:5,6-bis-O-(1-methylethylidene)-	EtOH	210(3.96),306(4.13)	33-0971-79
α-D-Galactopyranose, 6-[1-acetyl-3-(4-nitrophenyl)-2-triazenyl]-6-deoxy-1,2:3,4-bis-O-(1-methylethylidene)-	EtOH	215(4.00),311(4.23)	33-0971-79
α-D-Glucofuranose, 3-[1-acetyl-3-(4-nitrophenyl)-2-triazenyl]-3-deoxy-1,2:5,6-bis-O-(1-methylethylidene)-	EtOH	218(3.91),310(4.14)	33-0971-79
$C_{20}H_{26}N_4O_8S_2$			
D-Arabinitol, 1-C-(1,6-dihydro-6-thioxo-9H-purin-9-yl)-1-S-ethyl-1-thio-, 2,3,4,5-tetraacetate, (R)-	EtOH	227(4.0),325(4.4)	136-0117-79B
D-Ribitol, 1-C-(1,6-dihydro-6-thioxo-9H-purin-9-yl)-1-S-ethyl-1-thio-, 2,3,4,5-tetraacetate, (R)-	EtOH	227(4.0),325(4.4)	136-0117-79B
D-Xylitol, 1-C-(1,6-dihydro-6-thioxo-9H-purin-9-yl)-1-S-ethyl-1-thio-, 2,3,4,5-tetraacetate, (S)-	EtOH	227(4.0),325(4.4)	136-0117-79B
$C_{20}H_{26}O$			
18-Norandrosta-4,6,8(14)-trien-3-one, 17,17-dimethyl-	EtOH	286(3.89),353(4.38)	94-0783-79
Retinal, 3,4-didehydro-, all-trans	hexane	384(4.65)	149-0695-79A
	EtOH	399(4.62)	149-0695-79A
7-cis	hexane	364(4.59)	149-0695-79A
	EtOH	376(4.56)	149-0695-79A
9-cis	hexane	373(4.55)	149-0695-79A
	EtOH	388(4.53)	149-0695-79A

Compound	Solvent	λ max(log ε)	Ref.
$C_{20}H_{26}O_2$			
Benzene, 2,4-dimethoxy-1-(2,3,3,4,5-pentamethyl-6-methylene-1,4-cyclohexadien-1-yl)-	C_6H_{12}	231(4.20),258(4.31)	12-1531-79
D-Homoestra-1,3,5(10)-trien-17-one, 3-methoxy-	MeOH	278(3.23),285(3.18)	13-0361-79A
D-Homoestra-1,3,5(10)-trien-17a-one, 3-methoxy-	MeOH	279(3.32),284(3.27)	13-0361-79A
4H-Inden-4-one, 2,3,3a,5,6,7-hexahydro-1-[3-(3-methoxyphenyl)propyl]-3a-methyl-	MeOH	273(3.30),279(3.27), 294(2.48)	13-0361-79A
$C_{20}H_{26}O_3$			
1,3-Cyclodecadiene-1-carboxylic acid, 6-[2-(3-furanyl)ethyl]-6,7-dimethyl-10-methylene-, [6S-(1E,3Z.6R*,7S*)]-(strictic acid)	hexane	227(4.413),240(3.434)	102-0494-79
	EtOH	212(4.28),254(3.72)	2-0529-79B
	EtOH	215s(--),225(4.719)	102-0494-79
Estra-5,7,9-trien-17-one, 3-hydroxy-, cyclic 1,2-ethanediyl acetal, (3α)-	MeOH	218s(4.03),223s(3.96), 262s(2.53),265s(2.59), 269(2.64),273s(2.55), 279(2.54)	24-2631-79
(3β)-	MeOH	218s(4.01),223s(3.95), 262s(2.48),265s(2.53), 269(2.61),273s(2.52), 279(2.51)	24-2631-79
1,6(2H,5H)-Naphthalenedione, hexahydro-5-[2-(3-methoxyphenyl)ethyl]-8a-methyl-	MeOH	272(3.26),278(3.20)	13-0361-79A
2(3H)-Naphthalenone, 4,4a,5,6,7,8-hexahydro-5-hydroxy-1-[2-(3-methoxyphenyl)ethyl]-4a-methyl-	MeOH	249.5(4.02)	13-0361-79A
17-Norkaura-1,15-diene-3,12-dione, 2-hydroxy-13-methyl-	EtOH	210(3.56),270(3.97)	39-1004-79C
	NaOH	215(3.56),314(3.69)	39-1004-79C
$C_{20}H_{26}O_4$			
10αH-Furanoeremophilane, 3α-angeloyloxy-9-oxo-	EtOH	217(3.98),280(4.05)	39-1542-79C
2H-Naphtho[1,8-bc]furan-2-one, 6-[2-(2,5-dihydro-5-oxo-3-furanyl)ethyl]-4,5,5a,6,7,8,8a,8b-octahydro-6,7,8b-trimethyl-	MeOH	216(4.01)	102-0129-79
Phenol, 4,4'-(2,3-dimethyl-1,4-butanediyl)bis[2-methoxy-	EtOH	205(4.60),229(4.09), 282(3.74)	94-1583-79
Premnolal monoacetate	EtOH	215s(4.19),226(4.33), 273(4.22)	2-0513-79B
	EtOH-base	221(4.82),250(4.61), 294(4.26)	2-0513-79B
$C_{20}H_{26}O_5$			
Carnosolone	ether	234(4.19),285(4.06)	33-2754-79
$C_{20}H_{26}O_6$			
Eupachifolin A	MeOH	212(4.01),312(1.53)	138-1473-79
Leptocarpin	n.s.g.	209(4.22)	102-1527-79
Montafrusin	EtOH	213(4.37)	102-0843-79
$C_{20}H_{26}O_7$			
α-D-ribo-Hexofuranose, 3-deoxy-4-C-hyhydroxy-1,2:5,6-bis-O-(1-methylethylidene)-3-(2-oxo-2-phenylethyl)-, (4ξ)-	EtOH	242(4.01)	33-1298-79
Sachalinin	MeOH	211(4.23)	138-1503-79

Compound	Solvent	λmax(log ε)	Ref.
$C_{20}H_{26}O_8$			
Glaucarubolone	n.s.g.	239(4.01)	28-0269-79A
Peroxysachalinin	MeOH	211(4.22)	138-1503-79
$C_{20}H_{26}O_{10}$			
2H-Pyran-2-one, 5,6-dihydro-6-(3,4,5,6-tetraacetoxy-1-heptenyl)- (anamarine)	EtOH	220(3.40)	88-3579-79
$C_{20}H_{26}Si_2$			
Silane, 9,10-anthracenediylbis[trimethyl-	CCl_4	350(3.56),365(3.86), 384(4.07),405(4.07)	78-2131-79
$C_{20}H_{27}Br$			
Cyclohexene, 2-(9-bromo-3,7-dimethyl-3,5,7-nonatrien-1-ynyl)-1,3,3-trimethyl-, (E,E,E)-	C_6H_{12}	338.2(4.58)	5-1945-79
$C_{20}H_{27}Cl$			
Cyclohexene, 2-(9-chloro-3,7-dimethyl-3,5,7-nonatrien-1-ynyl)-1,3,3-trimethyl-, (E,E,E)-	C_6H_{12}	328(4.11)	5-1945-79
$C_{20}H_{27}ClN_6O$			
Pyrrolidine, 1-[[3-[5-chloro-2-(methylamino)phenyl]-5-(1-pyrrolidinylmethyl)-4H-1,2,4-triazol-4-yl]acetyl]-, monohydrochloride	MeOH	259(4.10),330(3.58)	44-0088-79
$C_{20}H_{27}N$			
Cyclopent[a]inden-8-amine, N,N-diethyl-3b,7a-dihydro-3b,5,7,7a-tetramethyl-, cis	hexane	217s(3.98),266(3.84), 333(4.24)	89-0161-79
$C_{20}H_{27}NO$			
4(1H)-Quinolinone, 2-(3-undecenyl)-	MeOH	213(4.58),236(4.58), 316(4.09),327(4.11)	49-0947-79
$C_{20}H_{27}NO_3$			
Benzenemethanol, α-[1-[[2-(3,4-dimethoxyphenyl)ethyl]amino]-1-methylethyl-	EtOH	215s(4.08),226s(3.98), 279(3.45),286s(3.36)	4-1525-79
$C_{20}H_{27}NO_4$			
Epilupinyl trans-ferulate	MeOH	235(4.07),295s(--), 327(4.31)	100-0385-79
	MeOH-KOH	250(3.92),308s(--), 378(4.47)	100-0385-79
$C_{20}H_{27}NO_5$			
17-Norkaur-15-ene-2,12-dione, 13-methyl-3-(nitrooxy)-, (3α,8β,13β)-	EtOH	210(3.73),295(2.33)	39-1004-79C
$C_{20}H_{27}N_3O$			
Ethanamine, 2-[(2,3-dihydro-4-methyl-1-phenyl-1H-pyrrolo[2,3-b]pyridin-6-yl)oxy]-N,N-diethyl-	n.s.g.	278(4.20),331(4.32)	103-0310-79
$C_{20}H_{27}N_3O_2$			
Hydrazinecarboxamide, 2-[1,2,3,5,6,7-hexahydro-1-[3-(3-methoxyphenyl)propyl]-4H-inden-4-ylidene]-	MeOH	262(4.40),270(4.48), 279s(4.40),319(2.81)	13-0361-79A

Compound	Solvent	$\lambda_{max}(\log \epsilon)$	Ref.
1H-Indole-3-methanamine, N,N-dimethyl-2-[2-(1,2,3,6-tetrahydro-1-methyl-4-pyridinyl)-1,3-dioxolan-2-yl]-	EtOH	221(4.45),274(3.92), 282(3.94),290(3.86)	39-3155-79C
$C_{20}H_{27}N_3O_7$			
α-D-Galactopyranose, 6-deoxy-6-[3-[2-(methoxycarbonyl)phenyl]-1-triazen-yl]-1,2:3,4-bis-O-(1-methylethylidene)-	EtOH	215(4.20),236(3.99), 285(4.07),320(4.01)	33-0971-79
$C_{20}H_{27}N_4O_5P$			
Phosphonic acid, [5-(diethylamino)-2-[(4-nitrophenyl)azo]phenyl]-, diethyl ester	EtOH	476(4.49)	39-1990-79C
	HOAc	475(4.50)	39-1990-79C
$C_{20}H_{27}N_5O_2$			
1,3-Benzenediamine, N,N,N',N'-tetraethyl-4-[(4-nitrophenyl)azo]-	EtOH	542(4.49)	39-1990-79C
	HOAc	480(4.63)	39-1990-79C
$C_{20}H_{27}N_5O_6$			
Guanosine, 2',3'-anhydro-N-(2,2-dimethyl-1-oxopropyl)-, 5'-(2,2-dimethylpropanoate)	MeOH	257(4.15),280s(4.02)	24-0625-79
$C_{20}H_{28}$			
Naphthalene, 4-(1,5-dimethylhexyl)-1,6-dimethyl-, (S)-	EtOH	234(4.30),290(3.74)	12-2079-79
$C_{20}H_{28}ClN_5O_6$			
Propanoic acid, 2,2-dimethyl-, 5'-ester with N-[9-(3-chloro-3-deoxy-β-D-xylofuranosyl)-6,9-dihydro-6-oxo-1H-purin-2-yl]-2,2-dimethylpropanamide	MeOH	256(4.18),278s(4.05)	24-0625-79
$C_{20}H_{28}IN_5O_6$			
Propanoic acid, 2,2-dimethyl-, 5'-ester with N-[9-(2-deoxy-2-iodo-β-D-arabinofuranosyl)-6,9-dihydro-6-oxo-1H-purin-2-yl]-2,2-dimethylpropanamide	MeOH	257(4.33),278s(4.19)	24-0625-79
Propanoic acid, 2,2-dimethyl-, 5'-ester with N-[9-(3-deoxy-3-iodo-β-D-xylofuranosyl)-6,9-dihydro-6-oxo-1H-purin-2-yl]-2,2-dimethylpropanamide	MeOH	258(4.20),280s(4.08)	24-0625-79
$C_{20}H_{28}N_2O_2$			
Aspidospermidine-3-methanol, 20-hydroxy-, (2β,3α,5α,12β,19α,20R)-	EtOH	248(3.85),302(3.47)	78-1151-79
8bH-Pyrrolo[3',2':2,3]pentaleno[1,2-b]-indole-8b-methanol, 11a-ethyl-1,2,3-8,8a,9,10,11,11a,11b-decahydro-10-hydroxy-1-methyl-	EtOH	210(--),249(3.86), 307(3.53)	78-0641-79
$C_{20}H_{28}N_2O_6$			
Pyridinium, 4-(dimethylamino)-1-[3-ethoxy-1-[2-ethoxy-1-(ethoxycarbonyl)-2-oxoethyl]-2-methyl-3-oxo-1-propenyl]-, hydroxide, inner salt	$CHCl_3$	255(4.3),297(4.4), 379(3.7)	5-1406-79
$C_{20}H_{28}N_2O_{12}$			
D-Arabinitol, 5-C-(3-acetyl-2,3-dihydro-	EtOH	236(4.03)	136-0325-79H

Compound	Solvent	λ_{max}(log ε)	Ref.
5-methyl-1,3,4-oxadiazol-2-yl)-, 1,2,3,4,5-pentaacetate (cont.)			136-0325-79H
D-Galactose, diacetylhydrazone, 2,3,4,5,6-pentaacetate	EtOH	224(3.95)	136-0325-79H
$C_{20}H_{28}N_4$			
2-Tetrazene, 1,4-dimethyl-1,4-bis(2,4,6-trimethylphenyl)-, (E)-	MeCN	300(4.21)	40-0915-79
$C_{20}H_{28}N_4O_{10}$			
L-Aspartic acid, N-[[1-[5-O-acetyl-2,3-O-(1-methylethylidene)-β-D-ribofuranosyl]-5-amino-1H-imidazol-4-yl]carbonyl]-, dimethyl ester	MeOH	206(3.88),268(3.93)	39-1415-79C
$C_{20}H_{28}N_5S$			
Benzothiazolium, 2-[[2,5-bis(diethylamino)-4H-imidazol-4-ylidene]methyl]-3-methyl-, perchlorate	$CHCl_3$	375(4.02),390(4.03), 410(3.87),500(4.51), 575(4.55)	89-0156-79
$C_{20}H_{28}N_6O_6$			
1H-Purine-2,6-dione, 7-[3,4-(cyclohexylimino)-3,4,6-trideoxy-2-C-(nitromethyl)-α-L-allopyranosyl]-3,7-dihydro-1,3-dimethyl-	MeOH	276(3.88)	39-2682-79C
$C_{20}H_{28}O$			
Retinal, 11-cis	hexane	363(4.42)	35-5078-79
Retinal, 7,11-di-cis	hexane	355(4.27)	35-5078-79
Spiro[cyclohexane-1,2'(1'H)-naphthalen]-1'-one, 7'-ethyl-3',4'-dihydro-2-propyl-	EtOH	254(4.05),299(4.21)	2-0226-79A
$C_{20}H_{28}O_2$			
1,3-Cyclodecadiene-1-methanol, 6-[2-(3-furanyl)ethyl]-6,7-dimethyl-10-methylene-, (1E,3Z,6R*,7S*)-	EtOH	212(4.15)	2-0529-79B
Cyclohept[e]indene-8-carboxaldehyde, 2,3,3a,4,5,5a,6,7,10,10a-decahydro-3a,5a-dimethyl-1-(1-methylethyl)-6-oxo-, [3aR-(3aα,5aβ,10aα)]-	MeOH	228(3.79)	23-3332-79
Cyclohept[e]indene-8-carboxaldehyde, 2,3,3a,4,5,5a,6,7-octahydro-6-hydroxy-3a,5a-dimethyl-1-(1-methylethyl)- (allocyathin B_2)	hexane	266(3.71),325(4.08)	23-3332-79
Cyclotetradeca[b]furan-2(3H)-one, 3a,4,7,8,11,12,15,15a-octahydro-6,10,14-trimethyl-3-methylene-, [3aR-(3aR*,5E,9E,13E,15aS*)]-	EtOH	210(4.00)	12-1273-79
3(2H)-Furanone, 2,2-dimethyl-5-(2-methyl-4-(2,6,6-trimethyl-1-cyclohexen-1-yl)-1,3-butadienyl]-, (E,E)-	EtOH	350(4.40)	142-0505-79
(Z,E)-	EtOH	350(4.37)	142-0505-79
Retinal, 7,8-epoxy-7,8-dihydro-	EtOH	337(4.43)	44-4458-79
Retinoic acid	pH 7.4	370(4.30)	149-0531-79A
Spruceanol	MeOH	218(4.48),278(3.58)	100-0658-79
	MeOH-KOH	221(4.81),289(3.49)	100-0658-79
$C_{20}H_{28}O_3$			
Gon-4-ene-3,17-dione, 13β-(3-hydroxypropyl)-	MeOH	237(4.23)	87-0966-79

Compound	Solvent	λ_{max}(log ϵ)	Ref.
Ketone from cleomeolide	EtOH	224.5(3.53)	35-4720-79
17-Norkaur-15-ene-2,12-dione, 3β-hydroxy-13-methyl-	EtOH	215(3.61),296(2.38)	39-1004-79C
Premnolal dimethyl ether	C_6H_{12}	216(4.59),225s(4.53), 268(4.14)	2-0513-79B
Retinoic acid, 7,8-epoxy-7,8-dihydro-	EtOH	302(4.70)	44-4458-79
$C_{20}H_{28}O_3Se$			
Cyclododecanecarboxylic acid, 2-oxo-1-(phenylseleno)-, methyl ester	EtOH	225(4.05),289(2.93)	33-2630-79
$C_{20}H_{28}O_4$			
Isoxeniolide A	MeOH	263(4.12)	20-0071-79
1(3aH)-Pentalenone, 4,5,6,6a-tetrahydro-2-hydroxy-6a-(3-hydroxy-5-methyl-1-oxo-2-hexenyl)-4,4-dimethyl-5-(1-methylethenyl)-, [3aR-(3aα-5α,6aα)]-	MeOH	277(4.16)	39-1250-79C
	MeOH-base	297(4.26)	39-1250-79C
Prosta-8(12),13-dien-1-oic acid, 4-hydroxy-11,15-dioxo-, γ-lactone, (13E)-	MeOH	275(4.35)	44-0168-79
$C_{20}H_{28}O_5$			
Nellionol	EtOH	220(4.34),240(4.21), 295(4.01)	2-0513-79B
Oxireno[5,6]cyclonona[1,2-c]pyran-5(laH)-one, decahydro-10-hydroxy-4-(4-hydroxy-4-methyl-2-pentenylidene)-la-methyl-8-methylene-	MeOH	263.5(4.30)	20-0071-79
4a,7-Methano-4aH-benzocycloheptene-1,2-diacetic acid, 1,2,3,4,7,8,9,9a-octahydro-α^2,α^2,1,7-tetramethyl-8-oxo-, [1S-(1α,2β,4aα,7α,9aα)]-	EtOH	210(3.55),297(2.33)	39-1004-79C
2H-Naphtho[1,8-bc]furan-2-one, 4,5,5a-6,7,8,8a,8b-octahydro-4-hydroxy-6,7-8b-trimethyl-6-[2-(tetrahydro-5-oxo-3-furanyl)ethyl]-	MeOH	213(3.89)	102-0129-79
$C_{20}H_{28}O_6$			
Butanoic acid, 2-methyl-, la,2,3,5a,7-8,8a,9,10,10a-decahydro-3-hydroxy-4,10a-dimethyl-8-methylene-7-oxo-oxireno[5,6]cyclodeca[1,2-b]furan-9-yl ester (dihydroleptocarpin)	n.s.g.	213(3.95)	102-1527-79
Butanoic acid, 2-methyl-, 2,3,3a,4,5-8,9,11a-octahydro-5,9-dihydroxy-6,10-dimethyl-3-methylene-2-oxocyclodeca[b]-furan-4-yl ester	MeOH	212(4.00)	102-1337-79
Spiro[4.5]deca-1,3-diene-6,7,8-triacetic acid, α^8,α^8,2,7-tetramethyl-, [5S-(5α,6β,7α,8β)]-	EtOH	210(3.14),254(3.14)	39-1004-79C
$C_{20}H_{28}O_7$			
1H-Inden-1-one, 6-[2-(β-D-glucopyranosyloxy)ethyl]-2,3-dihydro-2,5,7-trimethyl-, (R)- (pteroside B)	EtOH	218(4.40),260(4.04), 305(3.18)	94-0592-79
$C_{20}H_{28}O_8$			
1H-Inden-1-one, 6-[2-(β-D-glucopyranosyloxy)ethyl]-2,3-dihydro-5-(hydroxymethyl)-2,7-dimethyl-, (S)- (pteroside P)	EtOH	217(4.61),258(4.19), 305(3.48)	94-0592-79

Compound	Solvent	λ max(log ε)	Ref.
1H-Inden-1-one, 6-[2-(β-D-glucopyranosyloxy)ethyl]-2,3-dihydro-3-hydroxy-2,5,7-trimethyl- (pteroside C)	EtOH	220(4.53),261(4.16), 302(3.30)	94-0592-79
$C_{20}H_{29}BrN_2O_2S$			
Benzenesulfonic acid, 4-bromo-, [2-(1,1-dimethylethyl)octahydro-4-(2H)-azulenylidene]hydrazide, cis	EtOH	232(4.11)	44-3031-79
trans	EtOH	233(4.10)	44-3031-79
$C_{20}H_{29}ClN_6O_6S_3$			
Benzenesulfonamide, 4-[[4-[[2-(aminosulfonyl)ethyl][2-[[(1,1-dimethylethyl)amino]sulfonyl]ethyl]amino]-phenyl]azo]-3-chloro-	acetone	438(4.44)	44-3847-79
$C_{20}H_{29}NO_6$			
Schizanthin A	EtOH	221.5(4.43)	102-0171-79
$C_{20}H_{29}N_5O_6$			
9H-Purin-6-amine, 9-[3,5-bis-O-(2,2-dimethyl-1-oxopropyl)-β-D-arabino-furanosyl]-	MeOH	259(4.18)	87-0273-79
$C_{20}H_{30}$			
5,8-Ethenobenzocyclotetradecene, 1,2,3-4,4a,9,10,11,12,13,14,15,16,16a-tetradecahydro-, (4aR*,16aS*)-	EtOH	223(3.92),262(2.45), 269(2.57),277(2.51)	44-2160-79
2,6,10,14-Hexadecatetraen-8-yne, 2,6,11-15-tetramethyl-, (E,E)-	hexane	268(4.28),276(4.38), 292(4.31)	39-2429-79C
Phenanthrene, 1,2,3,4,4a,9,10,10a-octahydro-6,9,10a-trimethyl-1-(1-methylethyl)-	n.s.g.	271(2.8),278(2.9)	88-0963-79
$C_{20}H_{30}N_2$			
4,4'-Bipyridinium, N,N'-dibutyl-2,2'-dimethyl-, dibromide	n.s.g.	600(4.14)	39-2704-79C
1H-Indole-3-ethanamine, α-(2-methylcyclohexyl)-N-(1-methylethyl)-	EtOH	224(4.35),282(3.67), 290(3.61)	33-0481-79
$C_{20}H_{30}N_2OS$			
Androst-16-eno[17,16-d]thiazol-3-ol, 2'-amino-, (3β,5α)-	$CHCl_3$	271(3.77)	4-0763-79
$C_{20}H_{30}N_2P_2$			
Hypophosphonous diamide, N,N,N',N'-tetraethyl-P,P'-diphenyl-	hexane	258(3.16),265(3.12), 272(3.01)	22-0241-79I
$C_{20}H_{30}N_2S$			
Androst-16-eno[17,16-d]thiazol-2'-amine, (5α)-	$CHCl_3$	269(3.92)	4-0763-79
$C_{20}H_{30}O$			
Cyclotetradeca[b]furan, 2,4,5,8,9,12-13,15a-octahydro-3,6,10,14-tetramethyl-, (3Z,6E,10E,14E)-	EtOH	213(3.29)	12-0653-79
Vitamin A, all-trans	EtOH	325(4.65)	39-1729-79C
$C_{20}H_{30}O_2$			
2-Cyclohexen-1-one, 2,2'-(1,2-ethanediyl)bis[3,5,5-trimethyl-	EtOH	244.5(4.22)	77-1084-79

Compound	Solvent	λ max (log ε)	Ref.
Cyclotetradeca[b]furan, 6,7-epoxy-2,4,5,6,7,8,9,12,13,15a-decahydro-3,6,10,14-tetramethyl-, (3Z,10E,14E)-	EtOH	215(3.62)	12-0653-79
Dibenz[b,d]oxepin-6(1H)-one, 3-ethenyl-2,4a,7,7a,8,9,10,11,11a,11b-decahydro-4,8,8,11a-tetramethyl-	EtOH	238(4.23)	78-1449-79
Dictyodial	EtOH	232(3.86)	44-2044-79
Dictyolactone	MeOH	226(3.67)	44-2044-79
2,6,11,13,15-Hexadecapentaen-4-one, 10-hydroxy-2,6,10,14-tetramethyl-, (E,E,E)-	hexane	253(4.48),261(4.62), 272(4.72),282(4.62)	44-0968-79
(E,Z,E)-	hexane	248(4.42),254(4.53), 264(4.58),274(4.46)	44-0968-79
Perrottetianal A	EtOH	204(3.80),245(3.81)	102-1681-79
Retinol, 7,8-epoxy-7,8-dihydro-, all-trans	EtOH	284(4.54)	44-4458-79
$C_{20}H_{30}O_3$			
Cleomeolide	EtOH	225(3.54)	35-4720-79
Cyclotetradeca[b]furan, 6,7:14,15-di-epoxy-2,4,5,6,7,8,9,12,13,14,15,15a-dodecahydro-3,6,10,14-tetramethyl-, (3Z,10E)-	EtOH	216(3.26)	12-0653-79
Dibenz[b,d]oxepin-4-carboxaldehyde, 3-ethenyl-1,2,4a,6,7,7a,8,9,10,11-11a,11b-dodecahydro-6-hydroxy-8,8,11a-trimethyl-	EtOH	218(4.23),273(4.08)	78-1449-79
4,6,8-Nonatrien-3-one, 2,5-dihydroxy-2,7-dimethyl-9-(2,6,6-trimethyl-1-cyclohexen-1-yl)-, (E)-	EtOH	358(4.41)	142-0505-79
	EtOH-NaOH	340(--)	142-0505-79
(Z)-	EtOH	361(4.41)	142-0505-79
	EtOH-NaOH	340(--)	142-0505-79
17-Norkaurane-2,12-dione, 3-hydroxy-13-methyl-, (3α,8β,13β)-	EtOH	210(3.33),285(1.85)	39-1004-79C
Perrottetianal B	EtOH	207(3.23),246(3.15)	102-1681-79
$C_{20}H_{30}O_4$			
Kolavic acid	EtOH	216(4.32)	78-0979-79
Pachyclavulariadiol	EtOH	221(3.98)	12-2265-79
Prosta-8(12),13-dien-1-oic acid, 4,15-dihydroxy-11-oxo-, γ-lactone	MeOH	228(4.12),236s(4.00), 263(4.01)	44-0168-79
$C_{20}H_{30}O_5$			
4a,7-Methano-4aH-benzocycloheptene-1,2-diacetic acid, decahydro-α^2,α^2,1,7-tetramethyl-8-oxo-, [1S-(1α,2β,4aα-7α,9aα)]-	EtOH	210(2.42),283(1.67)	39-1004-79C
$C_{20}H_{31}N_4O_8$			
1-Piperidinyloxy, 4-[[[[1-(2-deoxy-β-D-erythro-pentofuranosyl)-1,2,3,4-tet-rahydro-2,4-dioxo-5-pyrimidinyl]oxy]-acetyl]amino]-2,2,6,6-tetramethyl-	pH 7	275(3.88)	33-1677-79
	pH 12	273(3.82)	33-1677-79
$C_{20}H_{31}N_4O_9$			
1-Piperidinyloxy, 2,2,6,6-tetramethyl-4-[[[(1,2,3,4-tetrahydro-2,4-dioxo-1-β-D-ribofuranosyl-5-pyrimidinyl)-oxy]acetyl]amino]-	pH 7	275(3.88)	33-1677-79
	pH 12	273(3.80)	33-1677-79

Compound	Solvent	λmax(log ε)	Ref.
$C_{20}H_{32}$			
1,3,6,10,14-Hexadecapentaene, 2,6,10-14-tetramethyl-, (all-E)-	EtOH	232(5.29)	70-0509-79
2,6,8,10,14-Hexadecapentaene, 2,6,11-15-tetramethyl-, (6E,8Z,10E)-	hexane	263s(--),276(4.48), 286(4.56),297(4.42)	39-2429-79C
$C_{20}H_{32}N_2O_2$			
Dispiro[2-oxabicyclo[2.2.2]octane-6,3'(4'H)-[1,2]diazete-4',6"-[2]-oxabicyclo[2.2.2]octane], 1,1",3,3-3',3"-hexamethyl-	EtOH	340(2.08)	39-0885-79C
2-Oxabicyclo[2.2.2]octan-6-one, 1,3,3-trimethyl-, (1,3,3-trimethyl-2-oxa-bicyclo[2.2.2]oct-6-ylidene)hydra-zone, [1S-[1α,4α,6(1R*,4S*)]]-	hexane	223(3.79),234(3.76), 240(3.72)	39-0885-79C
$C_{20}H_{32}N_2O_4$			
1,4-Benzenedicarboxylic acid, 2,5-bis-(butylamino)-, diethyl ester	EtOH	484(3.76)	48-0905-79
1,4-Benzenedicarboxylic acid, 2,5-bis-[(1-methylpropyl)amino]-, diethyl ester	EtOH	483(3.72)	48-0905-79
$C_{20}H_{32}O$			
1H-Inden-1-ol, 5,7-bis(1,1-dimethyleth-yl)-2,3-dihydro-1,3,3-trimethyl-	EtOH	239(3.23),266(2.54), 307(1.89)	44-0894-79
Pentaleno[1,6-cd]azulen-1(2H)-one, dodecahydro-2a,4,4,6a,10-pentamethyl-	$CHCl_3$	290(1.53)	39-1774-79C
2-Pentenal, 3-methyl-5-(1,2,3,4,4a,7-8,8a-octahydro-1,2,4a,5-tetramethyl-1-naphthalenyl)- (kolavenal)	EtOH	238(4.12)	78-0985-79
Sarcophytol A	EtOH	252(4.30)	94-2382-79
$C_{20}H_{32}O_2$			
3,5,9,13-Cyclotetradecatetraene-1,2-di-ol, 6,10,14-trimethyl-3-(1-methyl-ethyl)- (sarcophytol B)	EtOH	253(4.24)	94-2382-79
Dibenz[b,d]oxepin-6-ol, 3-ethenyl-1,2,4a,6,7,7a,8,9,10,11,11a,11b-dodecahydro-4,8,8,11a-tetramethyl-	EtOH	239(4.28)	78-1449-79
2-Oxabicyclo[2.2.2]octane, 1,3,3-tri-methyl-6-(1,3,3-trimethyl-2-oxabi-cyclo[2.2.2]oct-6-ylidene)-	hexane	213(2.74),218s(2.45)	39-0885-79C
2-Propanone, 1-(3a-acetyldecahydro-3,5a,9-trimethyl-1H-cyclopent[c]-inden-3-yl)-	EtOH	223(2.54),225(2.54), 251(2.15),276(2.11), 283(2.11)	39-1774-79C
$C_{20}H_{32}O_3$			
Cyclopent[c]azulene-1-acetic acid, dodecahydro-1,3,3,5a,9-pentamethyl-10-oxo-	EtOH	220(2.49),281(1.89)	39-1774-79C
$C_{20}H_{34}N_4O_5$			
Thymidine, 5'-[[6-(acetylmethylamino)-hexyl]methylamino]-5'-deoxy-, mono-hydrochloride	n.s.g.	267(3.99)	87-1524-79
$C_{20}H_{34}O$			
2(1H)-Naphthalenone, 4a,5,6,7,8,8a-hexahydro-3,4a,8,8-tetramethyl-4-(3-methylpentyl)-	EtOH	247(3.91)	102-1681-79

Compound	Solvent	$\lambda_{max}(\log \epsilon)$	Ref.
$C_{20}H_{34}O_2$			
3,7-Cyclodecadiene-1-methanol, 2-hydroxy-α,4,8-trimethyl-α-(4-methyl-3-pentenyl)- (hydroxydilophol)	MeOH	208(3.85)	44-1354-79
2,3-Naphthalenediol, decahydro-2,5,5,8a-tetramethyl-1-(3-methyl-2,4-pentadienyl)-	EtOH	239(3.95)	102-1681-79
$C_{20}H_{35}NO$			
3,5-Octadienenitrile, 2,4-bis(1,1-dimethylethyl)-2-methoxy-6,7,7-trimethyl-, (E,E)-	hexane	234s(3.61),262s(3.18)	18-0175-79
$C_{20}H_{36}$			
Cyclodecacyclododecene, 1,2,3,4,5,6,7-8,9,10,11,12,13,14,15,16,17,18-octadecahydro-, cis	hexane	202(3.95),206s(3.94), 213s(3.70)	35-0147-79
trans	hexane	200s(3.59),218(3.82)	35-0147-79
$C_{20}H_{36}Cl_3N_3O_2$			
1,3-Butadiene-1,1-diamine, N,N,N',N'-tetrabutyl-3,4,4-trichloro-2-nitro-	MeOH	364(4.04)	104-0981-79
$C_{20}H_{36}CrO_7$			
Chromate(1-), bis[2-butyl-2-hydroxyhexanoato(2-)-O^1,O^2]oxo-, sodium	H_2O	250(3.84),350(3.13), 506(2.30),739(1.60), 750(1.60),800(1.53)	35-3206-79
$C_{20}H_{36}S_4$			
1-Buten-3-yne, 1,1,2,4-tetrakis[(1,1-dimethylethyl)thio]-	heptane	196(4.39),339(3.94)	5-1606-79
$C_{20}H_{38}N_2O_4$			
1,4-Dioxa-7,10-diazacyclododecane-6,11-dione, 7,10-dihexyl-	H_2O	203(4.30)	33-0754-79
$C_{20}H_{38}N_4O_4P$			
1-Piperidinyloxy, 4-[2-[[[[bis(2,2-dimethyl-1-aziridinyl)phosphinyl]amino]carbonyl]oxy]ethyl]-2,2,6,6-tetramethyl-	EtOH	245(3.32)	118-0269-79
$C_{20}H_{40}N_2O_2$			
Octanediamide, N,N,N',N'-tetrapropyl-	H_2O	202(4.20)	33-0754-79
$C_{20}H_{40}N_2O_4$			
Acetamide, 2,2'-[(1,2-dimethyl-1,2-ethanediyl)bis(oxy)]bis[N,N-dipropyl-	H_2O	204(4.18)	33-0754-79
$C_{20}H_{40}N_2O_5$			
3,6,9-Trioxa-12-azapentadecanamide, 11-oxo-N,N,12-tripropyl-	H_2O	203(4.20)	33-0754-79
$C_{20}H_{42}N_2P_2$			
Hypophosphonous diamide, P,P'-dicyclohexyl-N,N,N',N'-tetraethyl-	hexane	240(2.75)	22-0421-79I
	EtOH	240(3.09)	22-0421-79I

Compound	Solvent	λ max(log ε)	Ref.
$C_{21}H_{10}Cl_6$			
9,12-Methanobenzo[e]pyrene, 9,10,11,12-13,13-hexachloro-8b,9,12,12a-tetrahydro-	dioxan	259(4.45),268(4.45), 284s(--),289(4.04), 302(4.03),327(2.87), 337(2.55),345(2.37), 353(2.44)	49-1233-79
$C_{21}H_{11}NO_4$			
1,3-Isobenzofurandione, 5-[5-(1-naphthalenyl)-2-oxazolyl]-	toluene	365(4.19)	103-0028-79
1,3-Isobenzofurandione, 5-[5-(2-naphthalenyl)-2-oxazolyl]-	toluene	380(4.41)	103-0028-79
1H,3H-Naphtho[1,8-cd]pyran-1,3-dione, 6-(5-phenyl-2-oxazolyl)-	toluene	295(4.03),398(4.34)	103-0028-79
$C_{21}H_{12}ClN_3O$			
8H-Quinazolino[4,3-b]quinazolin-8-one, 6-(4-chlorophenyl)-	EtOH	232(4.46),248(4.49), 287(4.37),350(4.17)	2-0349-79A
$C_{21}H_{12}N_3P$			
Benzonitrile, 4,4',4"-phosphinidyne-tris-	dioxan	231(4.59),288(4.25)	65-0479-79
	$C_2H_4Cl_2$	232(4.59),242(4.75), 282(3.81),287(4.25)	65-0479-79
	70% H_2SO_4	248(4.77),290(3.77)	65-0479-79
$C_{21}H_{12}OS$			
14H-Dinaphtho[1,8-bc:1',8'-fg]thiocin-14-one	EtOH	214(4.89),253s(4.28), 258s(4.27),270s(4.09), 293(4.01),308(3.98), 333(3.84)	18-3314-79
$C_{21}H_{12}O_2$			
14H-Dinaphth[1,8-bc:1',8'-fg]oxocin-14-one	EtOH	215(4.89),257(4.42), 293(3.87),303s(3.82), 333(3.81),356s(3.76)	18-3314-79
$C_{21}H_{12}O_2S$			
Anthra[1,2-b]benzo[d]thiophene-5,13-dione, 6-methyl-	$CHCl_3$	270(4.56),301s(4.45), 313(4.45),395(3.80)	12-0145-79
Anthra[1,2-b]benzo[d]thiophene-5,13-dione, 7-methyl-	$CHCl_3$	270(4.55),302s(4.45), 313(4.42),395(3.79)	12-0145-79
Anthra[2,3-b]benzo[d]thiophene-7,12-dione, 6-methyl-	$CHCl_3$	255(4.8),273(4.78), 300(4.76),403(3.92)	12-0145-79
Anthra[2,3-b]benzo[d]thiophene-7,12-dione, 13-methyl-	$CHCl_3$	254(4.81),272(4.78), 300(4.76),402(3.93)	12-0145-79
$C_{21}H_{12}O_3$			
Indeno[1,2-a]phenalene-3,8-dione, 7-methoxy-	C_6H_5Cl	340(3.90),410(3.60)	135-0220-79A
Indeno[1,2-a]phenalene-7,8-dione, 3-methoxy-	C_6H_5Cl	340(3.49),410(3.67), 480(3.51)	135-0220-79A
$C_{21}H_{12}O_4$			
Dinaphtho[1,2-b:2',1'-d]furan-5,6-dione, 8-methoxy-	n.s.g.	259s(4.41),273s(4.54), 279(4.55),299s(4.00), 307s(3.95),311s(3.93), 327(3.82),345(3.74), 530(3.34),580s(3.27)	39-2679-79C
Dinaphtho[1,2-b:2',3'-d]furan-7,12-dione, 5-methoxy-	$CHCl_3$	267(4.85),291s(4.10), 313s(3.91),325(3.72), 342s(3.42),475(3.86)	39-2679-79C

Compound	Solvent	$\lambda_{max}(\log \epsilon)$	Ref.
$C_{21}H_{13}BrClN$			
Quinoline, 2-(4-bromophenyl)-6-chloro-4-phenyl-	n.s.g.	273(4.47)	124-0447-79
$C_{21}H_{13}BrO$			
2,5-Cyclohexadien-1-one, 4-(9-anthracenylbromomethylene)-	HOAc	253(4.79),327(4.36), 354s(4.16),374(4.12), 393(4.00),450(3.15)	44-3687-79
$C_{21}H_{13}ClN_2O_2$			
Quinoline, 6-chloro-2-(3-nitrophenyl)-4-phenyl-	n.s.g.	292(4.40)	124-0447-79
$C_{21}H_{13}ClN_4$			
3H-Pyrrolo[2,3-c]acridine, 1-[(4-chlorophenyl)azo]-	EtOH	215(4.59),246(4.64), 282(4.92),360(4.41), 386(4.45)	103-0894-79
$C_{21}H_{13}NO_2S$			
6H-Anthra[1,9-cd]isoxazol-6-one, 3-[(4-methylphenyl)thio]-	EtOH	255(4.53),450(4.27), 478(4.42)	104-1514-79
8H-Naphtho[2,3-a]phenothiazine-8,13-(14H)-dione, 2-methyl-	EtOH	240(4.43),280(4.68), 610(3.85)	104-1514-79
$C_{21}H_{13}NO_3S$			
6H-Anthra[1,9-cd]isoxazol-6-one, 5-hydroxy-3-[(4-methylphenyl)thio]-	EtOH	245(4.64),440(4.00), 454(3.98),492(3.53)	104-1514-79
6H-Anthra[1,9-cd]isoxazol-6-one, 3-[(4-methoxyphenyl)thio]-	EtOH	235(4.52),255(4.51), 451(4.28),479(4.43)	104-1514-79
8H-Naphtho[2,3-a]phenothiazine-8,13-(14H)-dione, 7-hydroxy-2-methyl-	EtOH	240(4.42),285(4.55), 647(4.20),704(4.13)	104-1514-79
8H-Naphtho[2,3-a]phenothiazine-8,13-(14H)-dione, 2-methoxy-	EtOH	240(4.45),282(4.70), 626(3.87)	104-1514-79
$C_{21}H_{13}NO_4S$			
6H-Anthra[1,9-cd]isoxazol-6-one, 5-hydroxy-3-[(4-methoxyphenyl)thio]-	EtOH	245(4.61),436(3.99), 454(3.97),492(3.51)	104-1514-79
8H-Naphtho[2,3-a]phenothiazine-8,13-(14H)-dione, 7-hydroxy-2-methoxy-	EtOH	245(4.35),285(4.54), 661(4.20),721(4.15)	104-1514-79
$C_{21}H_{13}NO_5$			
Aminofluorescein	pH 1	445(4.74)	140-0807-79
	pH 3.5	440(4.54)	140-0807-79
	pH 5	455-475(4.68)	140-0807-79
	pH 8	495(4.04)	140-0807-79
$C_{21}H_{13}N_3O$			
8H-Quinazolino[4,3-b]quinazolin-8-one, 6-phenyl-	EtOH	229(4.42),247(4.46), 287(4.36),350(4.15)	2-0349-79A
$C_{21}H_{13}N_3O_2S$			
9,10-Anthracenedione, 1-azido-2-[(4-methylphenyl)thio]-	EtOH	252(4.52),280(4.28), 305(4.28),424(3.76), 444(3.74),475(3.46)	104-1514-79
$C_{21}H_{13}N_3O_3$			
5,4':5',5"-Teroxazole, 4,4"-diphenyl-	MeOH	225(4.40),308(4.03)	5-1370-79
$C_{21}H_{13}N_3O_3S$			
9,10-Anthracenedione, 1-azido-4-hydroxy-2-[(4-methylphenyl)thio]-	EtOH	256(4.56),460(3.94)	104-1514-79

Compound	Solvent	λ_{max}(log ε)	Ref.
9,10-Anthracenedione, 1-azido-2-[(4-methoxyphenyl)thio]-	EtOH	241(4.56),252(4.57), 280(4.32),305(4.28), 426(3.72),448(3.78), 477(3.65)	104-1514-79
$C_{21}H_{13}N_3O_4S$			
9,10-Anthracenedione, 1-azido-4-hydroxy-2-[(4-methoxyphenyl)thio]-	EtOH	235(4.51),256(4.62), 463(3.94)	104-1514-79
$C_{21}H_{13}N_5O_2$			
3H-Pyrrolo[2,3-c]acridine, 1-[(4-nitrophenyl)azo]-	EtOH	215(4.36),236(4.69), 286(4.94),385(4.5), 410(4.55)	103-0894-79
$C_{21}H_{14}$			
Benzo[a]pyrene, 9-methyl-	EtOH	222(4.36),228(4.39), 256(4.58),267(4.69), 273(4.48),286(4.65), 298(4.76),335s(3.72), 350s(4.05),367(4.31), 379(4.42),384(4.31), 386(4.32),407(3.81)	44-2941-79
$C_{21}H_{14}BrN_5O_5S$			
Benzenepropanethioamide, N-(2-bromo-5-nitrophenyl)-α-[(4-nitrophenyl)-hydrazono]-β-oxo-	EtOH	247(4.36),275(4.38), 355(3.90),405(4.00)	104-1324-79
$C_{21}H_{14}Br_3N$			
Benzenamine, 2,4,6-tribromo-N-(2,7-dimethyl-9H-fluoren-9-ylidene)-	dioxan	258(4.76),266(4.91), 276s(4.51),292(4.05), 305(4.11),325s(3.11), 391(3.05)	24-3490-79
$C_{21}H_{14}Br_3NO$			
Benzenamine, 2,4,6-tribromo-N-(2,7-dimethyl-9H-fluoren-9-ylidene)-, N-oxide	dioxan	245(4.70),270(4.41), 279(4.42),300(3.83), 344(4.25),360(4.32), 428s(2.60)	24-3490-79
$C_{21}H_{14}ClN$			
Quinoline, 6-chloro-2,4-diphenyl-	n.s.g.	263(4.51)	124-0447-79
$C_{21}H_{14}N_2$			
Propanedinitrile, (5,6-diphenylbicyclo-[3.1.0]hex-3-en-2-ylidene)-, cis	EtOH	225s(4.15),348(4.07)	35-1841-79
trans	EtOH	220s(4.22),312(4.07)	35-1841-79
Propanedinitrile, (6,6-diphenylbicyclo-[3.1.0]hex-3-en-2-ylidene)-	EtOH	225s(4.19),342(3.98)	35-1841-79
Propanedinitrile, (4,4-diphenyl-2,5-cyclohexadien-1-ylidene)-	EtOH	220(4.30),252(3.45), 326(4.50)	35-1841-79
Propanedinitrile, [1,1':2',1"-terphenyl]-3'-yl-	EtOH	236(4.18)	35-1841-79
Propanedinitrile, [1,1':2',1"-terphenyl]-4'-yl-	EtOH	237(4.48),257s(4.21)	35-1841-79
$C_{21}H_{14}N_2O_2$			
6H-Anthra[1,9-cd]isoxazol-6-one, 5-[(phenylmethyl)amino]-	dioxan	488(4.18),523(4.22)	104-0510-79

Compound	Solvent	λ max(log ε)	Ref.
$C_{21}H_{14}N_2O_4S$			
1H-Indole, 2-[(3-formyl-4-pyridinyl)-carbonyl]-1-(phenylsulfonyl)-	EtOH	227(4.20),305(3.98)	150-4801-79
$C_{21}H_{14}O$			
1H-Inden-1-one, 2,3-diphenyl-	CH_2Cl_2	263(4.56),436(3.22)	103-1173-79
$C_{21}H_{14}O_3$			
[1,1'-Binaphthalene]-3,4-dione, 4'-methoxy-	n.s.g.	213(4.72),237(4.58), 254(4.42),297(4.06), 408(3.51),480s(--), 550(2.78)	12-1749-79
$C_{21}H_{14}O_4$			
[2,2'-Binaphthalene]-1,4-dione, 1'-hydroxy-4'-methoxy-	n.s.g.	247(4.48),316(4.11), 348s(3.64),510(3.07)	39-2679-79C
1H-Naphtho[2,1,8-mna]xanthen-1-one, 2,5-dimethoxy-	MeOH	238(4.55),253s(4.45), 277s(4.16),288s(4.08), 322(4.02),334s(3.99), 364(3.85),385(3.90), 544(4.12)	12-1841-79
$C_{21}H_{14}O_5S_2$			
Benzo[b]thiophen-3(2H)-one, 2-[5-(3-hydroxybenzo[b]thien-2-yl)-2,4-pentadienylidene]-, S,S,1,1-tetraoxide	CH_2Cl_2	264(4.35),290(4.07), 365(3.73),451(4.17)	44-0930-79
$C_{21}H_{14}O_8$			
Furo[3',4':6,7]naphtho[2,3-d]-1,3-dioxol-6(8H)-one, 9-(6-hydroxy-1,3-benzodioxol-5-yl)-4-methoxy-	MeOH	230(4.93),255(4.86), 303s(3.33),310(3.28), 315(3.25),345s(2.98)	25-0854-79
$C_{21}H_{15}BrN_4$			
1H-Imidazole, 2-[(4-bromophenyl)azo]-4,5-diphenyl-	MeOH	223(--),293(--), 425(4.44)	56-2340-79
$C_{21}H_{15}Cl$			
Anthracene, 9-(chlorophenylmethyl)-	n.s.g.	338(3.39),354(3.68), 373(3.83),393(3.78)	39-2948-79C
$C_{21}H_{15}ClN_4O_3S$			
Benzenepropanethioamide, N-(4-chlorophenyl)-α-[(4-nitrophenyl)hydrazono]-β-oxo-	EtOH	255(4.29),380(4.22)	104-1324-79
$C_{21}H_{15}ClN_4S$			
1,3,4-Thiadiazolium, 5-[[(4-chlorophenyl)methylene]hydrazino]-2,3-diphenyl-, hydroxide, inner salt	n.s.g.	253(4.41),346(4.32), 454(4.04)	39-0724-79C
$C_{21}H_{15}Cl_2OS_2$			
1-Benzothiopyrylium, 7-chloro-4-[(7-chloro-4-methoxy-2H-1-benzothiopyran-2-ylidene)methyl]-2-methyl-, perchlorate	acetone	590(4.72)	18-0160-79
$C_{21}H_{15}NO_4S$			
2-Propen-1-one, 1-(2-hydroxyphenyl)-3-[(4-nitrophenyl)thio]-3-phenyl-	EtOH	268(4.02),342(4.34), 365s(4.17)	104-1805-79

Compound	Solvent	λ_{max}(log ε)	Ref.
$C_{21}H_{15}NO_5$			
Pyrrolo[2,1,5-cd]indolizine-5,6-dicarboxylic acid, 4-benzoyl-, dimethyl ester	EtOH	204(4.38),253(4.48), 338(3.94),424(3.94)	24-2465-79
$C_{21}H_{15}NS$			
1H-Indene-1-thione, 2-phenyl-3-(phenylamino)-	$C_2H_4Cl_2$	314(4.16),544(3.79)	99-0043-79
$C_{21}H_{15}N_2S_4$			
Benzo[1,2-d:5,4-d']isothiazolium, 3-methyl-2,6-bis[2-(2-thienyl)ethenyl]-, perchlorate	DMF	357(4.43),458(4.38)	126-1441-79
	KBr	455(--)	126-1441-79
$C_{21}H_{15}N_3$			
Anthracene, 9-azido-9,10-dihydro-10-(phenylmethylene)-	n.s.g.	308(3.81)	39-2948-79C
Anthracene, 9-(azidophenylmethyl)-	n.s.g.	263(4.17),335(3.23), 351(3.60),369(3.78), 389(3.76)	39-2948-79C
$C_{21}H_{15}N_3O$			
4(1H)-Pyrimidinone, 5,6-diphenyl-2-(2-pyridinyl)-	MeOH	246(4.27),270s(4.25), 335(4.10)	138-1213-79
$C_{21}H_{15}N_3O_2S$			
1H-Pyrrolo[3',4':5,6]thiopyrano[2,3-c]-pyrazole-5,7(6H,7aH)-dione, 3-methyl-1,6-diphenyl-	EtOH	257(4.40)	103-0429-79
$C_{21}H_{15}N_3O_4$			
1,3-Propanedione, 2-[(2-nitrophenyl)-azo]-1,3-diphenyl-	EtOH	405(4.114)	2-0502-79A'
	acetone	410(4.19)	2-0502-79A'
	dioxan	395(4.255)	2-0502-79A'
	$CHCl_3$	410(4.243)	2-0502-79A'
	CCl_4	405(4.29)	2-0502-79A'
1,3-Propanedione, 2-[(4-nitrophenyl)-azo]-1,3-diphenyl-	EtOH	390(4.362)	2-0502-79A'
	acetone	390(4.579)	2-0502-79A'
	dioxan	390(4.532)	2-0502-79A'
	$CHCl_3$	396(4.568)	2-0502-79A'
	CCl_4	390(4.47)	2-0502-79A'
$C_{21}H_{16}$			
Anthracene, 9,10-dihydro-9-(phenylmethylene)-	n.s.g.	243(4.11),304(3.98)	39-2948-79C
Anthracene, 9-(phenylmethyl)-	n.s.g.	249(5.15),332(3.52), 348(3.83),367(4.00), 386(4.00)	39-2948-79C
9H-Fluorene, 2-(2-phenylethenyl)-	dioxan	339(4.76)	104-1944-79
$C_{21}H_{16}BrNO_4$			
2-Azabicyclo[3.2.0]hept-6-ene-5-carboxylic acid, 1-(4-bromophenyl)-3,4-dioxo-7-phenyl-, ethyl ester	dioxan	258(4.26),382(2.85), 402(2.78)	142-1423-79
2H-Azepine-4-carboxylic acid, 7-(4-bromophenyl)-3-hydroxy-2-oxo-6-phenyl-, ethyl ester	dioxan	235(4.31),282(4.00), 375(3.97)	142-1423-79
$C_{21}H_{16}ClNO_2$			
1H-Pyrrolizine-5-acetyl chloride, 2,3-dihydro-α-oxo-6,7-diphenyl-	ether	208(4.42),234(4.25), 333(4.16)	83-0896-79

Compound	Solvent	λ_{max}(log ε)	Ref.
$C_{21}H_{16}ClN_5$			
1H-Pyrazol-3-amine, N-(2-chlorophenyl)-5-phenyl-4-(phenylazo)-	EtOH	265(4.45),323(4.12)	48-0127-79
$C_{21}H_{16}NO_2$			
Pyridinium, 1-[(9,10-dihydro-3-methyl-9,10-dioxo-2-anthracenyl)methyl]-, bromide	H_2O	262(4.71),278(4.13), 334(3.72)	78-2255-79
$C_{21}H_{16}N_2$			
6H-Benzo[b]pyrido[3,4-h]carbazole, 5,13-dimethyl-	EtOH	273(4.58),309(4.48), 320(4.53),340(4.23)	39-2504-79C
Propanedinitrile, (5,6-diphenylbicyclo-[3.1.0]hex-2-ylidene)-, cis	EtOH	220s(4.10),279(4.10)	35-1841-79
trans	EtOH	219s(4.26),289(4.11)	35-1841-79
Propanedinitrile, (6,6-diphenylbicyclo-[3.1.0]hex-2-ylidene)-	EtOH	230s(4.03)	35-1841-79
Propanedinitrile, (4,5-diphenyl-2-cyclo-hexen-1-ylidene)-	EtOH	350(4.44)	35-1841-79
1H-Pyrazole, 3,4,5-triphenyl-	EtOH	238s(4.52),247(4.54)	103-0501-79
$C_{21}H_{16}N_2O$			
Ethanone, 1-(1,4-diphenyl-2H-cyclo-penta[d]pyridazin-5-yl)-	MeOH	234(4.57),261(4.52), 289s(--),336(3.94), 395(3.70)	5-0675-79
$C_{21}H_{16}N_2O_2$			
9,10-Anthracenedione, 1-amino-4-[(phen-ylmethyl)amino]-	dioxan	472(4.06),617(4.07)	104-0510-79
$C_{21}H_{16}N_2O_2S_5$			
Thiourea, bis[4-(4-methoxyphenyl)-1,3-dithiol-2-ylidene]-	MeCN	268(4.76),296(4.63), 470(4.82)	48-0827-79
$C_{21}H_{16}N_2O_4$			
Naphtho[2',3':4,5]furo[2,3-b]pyridine, 1-butyl-1,2,5,10-tetrahydro-4-methyl-2,5,10-trioxo-3-cyano-	EtOH	278(4.37),345(4.07), 445(3.91)	2-0100-79A
$C_{21}H_{16}N_2S_5$			
Thiourea, bis[4-(4-methylphenyl)-1,3-dithiol-2-ylidene]-	MeCN	262(4.88),294(4.69), 468(4.84)	48-0827-79
$C_{21}H_{16}N_3OPS_5$			
Phosphoramidotrithioic acid, (4-meth-oxyphenyl)-, bis(2-benzothiazolyl) ester	EtOH	224(4.65),236(4.48), 275(4.37),316(4.24)	64-0297-79B
$C_{21}H_{16}N_4$			
1H-Imidazole, 4,5-diphenyl-2-(phenyl-azo)-	MeOH	222(--),290(--), 419(4.38)	56-2340-79
$C_{21}H_{16}N_4O_5$			
1H-Phenalen-1-one, 9-ethoxy-, 2,4-di-nitrophenylhydrazone	MeCN	250(4.7),364(4.8), 377(4.8),494(4.5)	83-0288-79
$C_{21}H_{16}N_4O_{10}$			
Butanedioic acid, [(3,4-dihydro-2,4-di-oxo-1(2H)-pyrimidinyl)methyl]-, bis(4-nitrophenyl) ester	MeOH	266(4.40)	126-2323-79

Compound	Solvent	λ_{max}(log ε)	Ref.
$C_{21}H_{16}N_4S$			
1H-1,2,4-Triazolium, 2,3-dihydro-1,5-diphenyl-4-[(phenylmethylene)amino]-3-thioxo-, hydroxide, inner salt	n.s.g.	250(4.03),352(3.98)	39-0724-79C
$C_{21}H_{16}O$			
9-Anthracenemethanol, α-phenyl-	n.s.g.	260(3.97),318(3.06), 331(3.42),350(3.73), 367(3.91),388(3.87)	39-2948-79C
$C_{21}H_{16}O_4$			
3H-2-Benzopyran-3-one, 1,4-dihydro-1,1-bis(4-hydroxyphenyl)-	pH 9.8	553(4.45+)	24-1226-79
1H-Phenalen-1-one, 6-hydroxy-2,5-dimethoxy-7(or 9)-phenyl-	MeOH	218(4.63),282(4.42), 305s(4.20),356(3.80), 373(3.86),514(3.90)	12-1841-79
$C_{21}H_{16}O_6$			
Furo[3',4':6,7]naphtho[2,3-d]-1,3-dioxol-6(8H)-one, 9-(3,4-dimethoxyphenyl)-	EtOH	260(4.58),295(4.15), 312(4.15),350(3.45)	25-0667-79
	n.s.g.	250(4.61),315(3.95), 350s(3.57)	77-0165-79
$C_{21}H_{16}O_7$			
1H-Anthra[2,3-c]pyran-3,6,11(4H)-trione, 5,12-dihydroxy-1-(3-oxobutyl)-	MeOH	232(4.41),249(4.60), 255(4.57),286(4.02), 463(3.99),513s(--)	5-0035-79
1H-Cyclopenta[b]anthracene-1-carboxylic acid, 3-acetyl-2,3,5,10-tetrahydro-4,11-dihydroxy-5,10-dioxo-, methyl ester	MeOH	226s(--),251(4.59), 256(4.59),288(3.91), 463(3.97),510s(--)	5-0035-79
1H-Cyclopenta[b]anthracene-1-carboxylic acid, 3-formyl-2,3,5,10-tetrahydro-4,11-dihydroxy-3-methyl-5,10-dioxo-, methyl ester	MeOH	251(4.60),255(4.60), 289(3.93),479(3.97), 510(3.74)	150-3643-79
isomer m. 208°	MeOH	251(4.63),255(4.62), 289(3.94),477(3.99), 510(3.76)	150-3643-79
$C_{21}H_{16}O_8$			
9,10-Anthracenedione, 1,4-diacetoxy-2-(acetoxymethyl)-	MeOH	232s(--),253(4.43), 272s(--),340(3.74)	5-0019-79
$C_{21}H_{16}O_9$			
1H-Cyclopenta[b]anthracene-1-carboxylic acid, 3-formyl-2,3,5,10-tetrahydro-3,4,6,11-tetrahydroxy-2-methyl-5,10-dioxo-, methyl ester	MeOH	234(4.46),253(4.29), 492(3.99)	150-3643-79
$C_{21}H_{17}BrN_2$			
1H-Pyrazole, 1-(4-bromophenyl)-4,5-dihydro-3,5-diphenyl-	C_6H_{12}	360(4.39)	12-1601-79
	MeOH	356(4.35)	12-1601-79
1H-Pyrazole, 3-(4-bromophenyl)-4,5-dihydro-1,5-diphenyl-	C_6H_{12}	368(4.35)	12-1601-79
	MeOH	364(4.38)	12-1601-79
1H-Pyrazole, 5-(2-bromophenyl)-4,5-dihydro-1,3-diphenyl-	C_6H_{12}	357(4.31)	12-1601-79
	MeOH	355(4.25)	12-1601-79
1H-Pyrazole, 5-(3-bromophenyl)-4,5-dihydro-1,3-diphenyl-	C_6H_{12}	356(4.30)	12-1601-79
	MeOH	355(4.27)	12-1601-79
1H-Pyrazole, 5-(4-bromophenyl)-4,5-dihydro-1,3-diphenyl-	C_6H_{12}	354(4.28)	12-1601-79
	MeOH	352(4.29)	12-1601-79

Compound	Solvent	$\lambda_{max}(\log \epsilon)$	Ref.
$C_{21}H_{17}BrN_2O_3S$			
Benzenesulfonic acid, 4-bromo-, (9-ethoxy-1H-phenalen-1-ylidene)hydrazide	MeCN	278(4.3),352(4.9), 369(5.2),388(4.8), 502(4.4)	83-0288-79
$C_{21}H_{17}ClN_2$			
1H-Pyrazole, 1-(4-chlorophenyl)-4,5-dihydro-3,5-diphenyl-	C_6H_{12}	361(4.31)	12-1601-79
	MeOH	357(4.32)	12-1601-79
1H-Pyrazole, 3-(4-chlorophenyl)-4,5-dihydro-1,5-diphenyl-	C_6H_{12}	366(4.37)	12-1601-79
	MeOH	363(4.39)	12-1601-79
1H-Pyrazole, 5-(4-chlorophenyl)-4,5-dihydro-1,3-diphenyl-	C_6H_{12}	355(4.30)	12-1601-79
	MeOH	353(4.27)	12-1601-79
$C_{21}H_{17}ClN_4O_7S$			
3-Butenoic acid, 2-acetyl-4-[(4-chlorophenyl)sulfonyl]-4-cyano-2-[(3-nitrophenyl)azo]-, ethyl ester	EtOH	260(4.25),395(3.47)	104-0500-79
$C_{21}H_{17}Cl_2N_3O_5S$			
3-Butenoic acid, 2-acetyl-2-[(4-chlorophenyl)azo]-4-[(4-chlorophenyl)sulfonyl]-4-cyano-, ethyl ester	EtOH	257(4.22),380(3.48)	104-0500-79
$C_{21}H_{17}FN_2$			
1H-Pyrazole, 1-(4-fluorophenyl)-4,5-dihydro-3,5-diphenyl-	C_6H_{12}	360(4.30)	12-1601-79
	MeOH	355(4.23)	12-1601-79
1H-Pyrazole, 3-(4-fluorophenyl)-4,5-dihydro-1,5-diphenyl-	C_6H_{12}	358(4.25)	12-1601-79
	MeOH	352(4.26)	12-1601-79
1H-Pyrazole, 5-(4-fluorophenyl)-4,5-dihydro-1,3-diphenyl-	C_6H_{12}	356(4.3)	12-1601-79
	MeOH	353(4.28)	12-1601-79
$C_{21}H_{17}IN_2$			
1H-Pyrazole, 4,5-dihydro-1-(4-iodophenyl)-3,5-diphenyl-	C_6H_{12}	360(4.45)	12-1601-79
	MeOH	357(4.42)	12-1601-79
1H-Pyrazole, 4,5-dihydro-3-(4-iodophenyl)-1,5-diphenyl-	C_6H_{12}	373(4.42)	12-1601-79
	MeOH	368(4.36)	12-1601-79
1H-Pyrazole, 4,5-dihydro-5-(4-iodophenyl)-1,3-diphenyl-	C_6H_{12}	357(4.28)	12-1601-79
	MeOH	355(4.27)	12-1601-79
$C_{21}H_{17}N$			
Benzenamine, N-(p-biphenylylmethylene)-4-ethenyl-	$CHCl_3$	302(4.0),343(4.0)	24-2854-79
Benzenamine, N-(2,7-dimethyl-9H-fluoren-9-ylidene)-	dioxan	256(4.70),264(4.79), 300(3.90),306s(3.83), 390(3.24)	24-3490-79
Benzenepropanenitrile, β,β-diphenyl-	MeCN	235(2.9),261(2.85)	78-0177-79
$C_{21}H_{17}NO$			
Benzenamine, N-(2,7-dimethyl-9H-fluoren-9-ylidene)-, N-oxide	dioxan	246(4.65),269(4.41), 279(4.43),304(3.85), 342(4.24),356(4.37), 430s(2.65)	24-3490-79
2-Propen-1-one, 3-(diphenylamino)-1-phenyl-, (E)-	EtOH	256(4.24),362(4.46)	4-0093-79
$C_{21}H_{17}NO_3S$			
8H-Benzo[a][1]benzothieno[2,3-g]quinolizin-8-one, 5,6-dihydro-2,3-dimethoxy-	MeOH	236(4.33),246(4.35), 259(4.45),268s(4.40), 275(4.38),313(4.02), 325(4.10),352s(4.11), 367(4.29),384(5.24)	4-0433-79

Compound	Solvent	$\lambda_{max}(\log \epsilon)$	Ref.
$C_{21}H_{17}NO_4$			
8H-Benzo[a]benzofuro[2,3-g]quinolizin-8-one, 5,6-dihydro-2,3-dimethoxy-	MeOH	225(4.46),238(4.42), 254s(4.35),262(4.44), 271(4.41),290s(4.11), 304s(4.00),316(4.10), 334s(4.13),347(4.22), 361(4.13)	4-0433-79
$C_{21}H_{17}NO_5$			
Acetamide, N-[4-(3-acetyl-1,4-dihydro-1,4-dioxo-2-naphthalenyl)-2-methoxyphenyl]-	dioxan	254(4.49),288(4.10), 332(3.57),434(3.31)	5-0503-79
[1,3]Benzodioxolo[5,6-c]-1,3-dioxolo-[4,5-i]phenanthridine, 13,14-dihydro-14-methoxy-13-methyl-, (-)-	n.s.g.	210(4.16),235(4.23), 280(4.28),327(4.12)	102-0695-79
$C_{21}H_{17}NS$			
2-Azetidinethione, 1,3,3-triphenyl-	EtOH	312(4.32)	97-0109-79
2-Azetidinethione, 1,3,4-triphenyl-	EtOH	309(4.32)	97-0109-79
$C_{21}H_{17}N_2OS$			
Thiazolo[3,2-a]benzimidazolium, 9-ethyl-6-hydroxy-3-(2-naphthalenyl)-, bromide	EtOH	276(3.51),519(3.87)	18-3096-79
$C_{21}H_{17}N_2PS_3$			
Phosphoramidotrithioic acid, 5-quinolinyl-, diphenyl ester	EtOH	222(4.47),278(4.61)	64-0297-79B
$C_{21}H_{17}N_3$			
Pyridine, 2-(1-methyl-4,5-diphenyl-1H-imidazol-2-yl)-	EtOH	235s(4.12),305(4.31)	44-0041-79
$C_{21}H_{17}N_3OS$			
8-Azabicyclo[3.2.1]oct-3-en-2-one, 6-endo-phenyl-8-(3-phenyl-1,2,4-thiadiazol-5-yl)-	EtOH	247(4.49)	39-0399-79C
$C_{21}H_{17}N_3O_2$			
1H-Pyrazole, 4,5-dihydro-3-(4-nitrophenyl)-1,5-diphenyl-	toluene	445(4.33)	135-1491-79B
$C_{21}H_{17}N_3O_2S_3$			
14,17,20-Trithia-25,26,27-triazatetracyclo[19.3.1.1^{3,7}.1^{9,13}]heptacosa-1(25),3,5,7(27),9,11,13(26),21,23-nonaene-2,8-dione	EtOH	237(4.46),275(4.18), 362(3.66)	44-3816-79
$C_{21}H_{17}N_3O_3$			
Indolo[2',3':3,4]pyrido[2,1-b]quinazolin-5(14H)-one, 2,3-dimethoxy-14-methyl-	MeOH	249(4.63),347(3.82)	142-0353-79
1H-Phenalen-1-one, 9-ethoxy-, (4-nitrophenyl)hydrazone	MeCN	246(5.1),357(5.0), 461(4.9),560(5.0)	83-0288-79
$C_{21}H_{17}N_3O_3S$			
Thiopyrano[2,3-c]pyrazole-5-carboxylic acid, 1,6-dihydro-3-methyl-1-phenyl-6-[(phenylamino)carbonyl]-	EtOH	257(4.48)	103-0429-79

Compound	Solvent	λ_{max}(log ε)	Ref.
$C_{21}H_{17}N_3O_3S_2$			
17-Oxa-14,20-dithia-25,26,27-triaza-tetracyclo[19.3.1.1^{3,7}.1^{9,13}]hepta-cosa-1(25),3,5,7(27),9,11,13(26),21-23-nonaene-2,8-dione	EtOH	235(4.47),275(4.17), 362(3.70)	44-3816-79
$C_{21}H_{17}N_3O_5$			
14,17,20-Trioxa-25,26,27-triazatetracy-clo[9.3.1.1^{3,7}.1^{9,13}]heptacosa-1(25)-3,5,7(27),9,11,13(26),21,23-nonaene-2,8-dione	EtOH	218(4.40),251(3.97), 300(3.98)	44-3816-79
$C_{21}H_{17}N_3O_6S_3$			
1-Azetidineacetic acid, 2-(2-benzothia-zolyldithio)-α-(1-hydroxyethylidene)-4-oxo-, (4-nitrophenyl)hydrazone	EtOH	274(4.53)	77-0665-79
$C_{21}H_{17}OS_2$			
1-Benzothiopyrylium, 4-[(4-methoxy-2H-1-benzothiopyran-2-ylidene)methyl]-2-methyl-, perchlorate	acetone	590(4.80)	18-0160-79
$C_{21}H_{18}$			
Anthracene, 9,10-dihydro-9-methyl-9-phenyl-	C_6H_{12}	263(3.23),271(3.19)	44-3698-79
Benzene, 1-(2,2-diphenylethenyl)-2-methyl-	MeOH	230(4.30),293(4.12)	54-0452-79
$C_{21}H_{18}Cl_2N_2O$			
Benzenecarboximidamide, N'-(3-chloro-4-methylphenyl)-N-(4-chlorophenyl)-N-hydroxy-4-methyl-	EtOH	209(4.61),259(4.23), 320(4.21)	56-2597-79
$C_{21}H_{18}F_2$			
1,1':3',1"-Terphenyl, 4,4"-difluoro-2',4',6'-trimethyl-	C_6H_{12}	266(3.39),272(3.30)	12-1531-79
$C_{21}H_{18}N$			
Benzo[f]quinolinium, 1-methyl-4-(phen-ylmethyl)-, perchlorate	EtOH	229(4.76),282(4.74), 365(3.85)	103-1208-79
Benzo[h]quinolinium, 4-methyl-1-(phen-ylmethyl)-, perchlorate	EtOH	370(3.12)	103-1208-79
$C_{21}H_{18}NO$			
9H-Indeno[2,1-c]pyridinium, 3-methyl-2-(2-oxo-2-phenylethyl)-, bromide	EtOH	246(4.18),310(4.40), 450(3.22)	103-1214-79
$C_{21}H_{18}N_2$			
Benzenamine, 4-methyl-N-(10-methyl-9(10H)-acridinylidene)-	EtOH	225(4.54),247(4.55), 406(4.09)	104-0183-79
1H-1,5-Benzodiazepine, 2,3-dihydro-2,4-diphenyl-	octane	370(3.73)	103-0697-79
Cinnoline, 1,4-dihydro-3-methyl-1,4-di-phenyl-	MeCN	288(3.84)	104-2145-79
1H-Pyrazole, 4,5-dihydro-1,3,5-triphen-yl-	C_6H_{12}	356(4.30)	12-1601-79
	MeOH	355(4.29)	12-1601-79
$C_{21}H_{18}N_2O$			
Benzenamine, 4-methoxy-N-(10-methyl-9(10H)-acridinylidene)-	EtOH	225(4.53),247(4.60), 406(4.08)	104-0183-79

Compound	Solvent	$\lambda_{max}(\log \epsilon)$	Ref.
$C_{21}H_{18}N_2O_2$			
2-Propen-1-one, 3-(4-methoxyphenyl)-1-(4-methyl-2-phenyl-5-pyrimidinyl)-	EtOH	205(4.34),243(4.15), 291(4.25),345(4.43)	103-0551-79
Spiro[1H-indene-1,1'-[1H]indeno[2,1-c]-pyridine]-4'-carboxamide, 2,2',3,3'-4',9'-hexahydro-3'-oxo-	$CHCl_3$	256(4.35),283(2.99), 293(2.64)	80-1485-79
$C_{21}H_{18}N_2O_3$			
Pyridinium, 2,5-dimethyl-4-(4-nitro-phenyl)-, 2-oxo-2-phenylethylide	EtOH	210(4.52),265(4.78), 320(3.67),390(3.69), 440s(2.20)	103-0316-79
$C_{21}H_{18}N_2O_3S$			
Benzamide, N-[[[(4-methylphenyl)sulfon-yl]imino]phenylmethyl]-	CH_2Cl_2	259(4.46)	44-4435-79
Benzenesulfonic acid, (9-ethoxy-1H-phenalen-1-ylidene)hydrazide	EtOH	265(4.6),280(4.7), 338(4.7),460(4.6)	83-0288-79
Benzenesulfonic acid, 4-(4,5-dihydro-3,5-diphenyl-1H-pyrazol-1-yl)-, sodium salt, (±)-	MeOH	234(4.16),276(4.15), 357(4.49)	23-0360-79
$C_{21}H_{18}N_2O_4$			
2-Butenedioic acid, (3,5-diphenyl-1H-pyrazol-1-yl)-, dimethyl ester	EtOH	239(4.36),275s(4.13), 335(3.62)	23-0904-79
4,8-Iminocyclohepta[c]pyrrole-1,3,5(2H)-trione, 3a,4,8,8a-tetrahydro-9-(3-oxo-1-cyclohexen-1-yl)-2-phenyl-, (3aα,4α,8α,8aα)-	EtOH	217(4.21),290(4.52)	56-0057-79
$C_{21}H_{18}N_2O_5$			
1H-Pyrano[3',4':6,7]indolizino[1,2-b]-quinoline-3,14(4H,12H)-dione, 4-ethyl-4-hydroxy-9-methoxy-	MeOH	218(4.52),262(4.38), 305(3.85),320(4.05), 356(4.30),371s(4.28)	100-0475-79
2,4,6(1H,3H,5H)-Pyrimidinetrione, 5-(3,4-diethoxy-1H-phenalen-1-ylidene)-	MeOH	234(4.5),255(4.6), 290(4.8),373(4.6), 448(4.6),606(4.5)	83-0288-79
$C_{21}H_{18}N_2O_7$			
1H-Benz[f]indazole-4,9-dione, 1-(4,6-di-O-acetyl-2,3-dideoxy-α-D-erythro-hex-2-enopyranosyl)-	EtOH	243(4.61),263(4.21)	111-0151-79
2H-Benz[f]indazole-4,9-dione, 2-(4,6-di-O-acetyl-2,3-dideoxy-D-erythro-hex-2-enopyranosyl)-	EtOH	246(4.62)	111-0151-79
$C_{21}H_{18}N_3O_2S$			
9H-Fluorene-2-diazonium, 7-[methyl[(4-methylphenyl)sulfonyl]amino]-, tetra-fluoroborate	$EtOH-HBF_4$	388(4.12)	104-0733-79
$C_{21}H_{18}N_4$			
[1,1'-Biphenyl]-2-amine, 2'-(5-methyl-3-phenyl-1H-1,2,4-triazol-1-yl)-	CH_2Cl_2	233(4.37),242(4.33), 303(3.48)	39-0185-79C
$C_{21}H_{18}N_4O_6$			
Methanone, (4-methoxyphenyl)(4-methyl-phenyl)-, 2,4-dinitrophenylhydrazone	EtOH	397(4.50)	49-1057-79
$C_{21}H_{18}N_6O$			
Cyclohexanone, 2,6-bis[(4-azidophenyl)-methylene]-4-methyl-	MeOH	360(4.64)	93-0333-79

Compound	Solvent	$\lambda_{max}(\log \epsilon)$	Ref.
$C_{21}H_{18}N_6O_2$			
Propanoic acid, (phenylazo)bis(phenylhydrazono)-	dioxan	250(4.34),287s(4.11), 296(4.12),367(4.44), 400s(4.43)	24-2369-79
methanol adduct	dioxan	250(4.31),287s(4.10), 296(4.11),367(4.44), 400s(4.40)	24-2369-79
$C_{21}H_{18}O$			
Benzenemethanol, α-phenyl-α-(2-phenylethenyl)-	96% H_2SO_4	308(3.74),418(4.14)	39-1395-79B
2,5-Cyclohexadien-1-one, 4-(diphenylmethylene)-2,6-diphenyl-	n.s.g.	262(4.19),365(4.49)	35-5717-79
2-Cyclopropen-1-one, 2,3-bis(2-cyclopropylphenyl)-	EtOH	289(4.23),312(4.17), 324(4.15),341s(4.08)	18-0856-79
2-Cyclopropen-1-one, 2,3-bis(4-cyclopropylphenyl)-	EtOH	277s(4.45),295(4.59), 301s(4.50),313(4.52)	18-0856-79
2-Cyclopropen-1-one, 2-(2-cyclopropylphenyl)-3-(4-cyclopropylphenyl)-	EtOH	294s(4.30),307(4.40), 325(4.38),337s(4.32)	18-0856-79
$C_{21}H_{18}OP$			
4H-1,4-Benzoxaphosphoninium, 2-methyl-4,4-diphenyl-, perchlorate	MeCN	255(3.97)	78-0775-79
$C_{21}H_{18}O_2$			
1H,3H-Naphtho[1,8-cd]pyran-1-one, 3-(2,4,6-trimethylphenyl)-	hexane	214(4.67),245(4.39), 312(3.89),329(3.76)	44-1931-79
$C_{21}H_{18}O_4$			
4H-1-Benzopyran-4-one, 7-[(1,1-dimethyl-2-propynyl)oxy]-5-hydroxy-2-methyl-3-phenyl-	MeOH	253(4.30),278(4.52)	2-0123-79A
Pyrano[2",3":7,6]isoflavone, 5-hydroxy-2-methyl-6",6"-dimethyl-	MeOH	230(4.50),261(4.67)	2-0123-79A
Pyrano[2",3":7,8]isoflavone, 5-hydroxy-2-methyl-6",6"-dimethyl- (3λ,2ε)-	MeOH	222(4.47),241(--), 278(4.70)	2-0123-79A
$C_{21}H_{18}O_5$			
2H-Anthra[1,2-b]pyran-7,12-dione, 11-hydroxy-5-methoxy-2,2,9-trimethyl-	$CHCl_3$	256(4.13),292(4.24), 427(3.96),445s(3.94)	32-0301-79
$C_{21}H_{18}O_6$			
β-Apopolygamatin	EtOH	293(3.98)	100-0378-79
Benzeneacetic acid, 4-methoxy-α-(3-methoxy-5-oxo-4-phenyl-2(5H)-furanylidene)-, methyl ester, (E)-	EtOH	353(4.32)	39-0084-79C
Benzeneacetic acid, α-[3-methoxy-4-(4-methoxyphenyl)-5-oxo-2(5H)-furanylidene]-, methyl ester, (E)-	EtOH	340(4.12)	39-0084-79C
Furo[3',4':6,7]naphtho[2,3-d]-1,3-dioxol-6(5aH)-one, 9-(3,4-dimethoxyphenyl)-5,8-dihydro-3,4-dimethoxy-	EtOH	247(4.1),294(3.64)	25-0667-79
7-Oxabicyclo[4.1.0]hept-4-ene-2,3-diol, 1-[(benzoyloxy)methyl]-, 3-benzoate (pipoxide)	EtOH	228(4.46),274(3.29), 280(3.19)	88-2427-79
$C_{21}H_{18}O_7$			
2-Anthraceneacetic acid, 9,10-dihydro-1,4-dihydroxy-α-(3-oxobutyl)-, methyl ester	MeOH	233(4.32),249(4.49), 255s(--),285(4.02), 468(3.85),515s(--)	5-0035-79

Compound	Solvent	λ max(log ε)	Ref.
Averufin, 6-O-methyl-	MeOH	223(4.52),265(4.19), 291(4.44),320(3.82), 448(3.98)	39-0451-79C
11H-Benzofuro[2,3-b][1]benzopyran-11-one, 1,3,8-trihydroxy-9-methoxy-7-(3-methyl-2-butenyl)- (lisetin)	EtOH	259(4.48),285(4.28), 344(4.13)	142-1539-79
Spiro[1,3-dioxolane-2,2'(1'H)-naphthacene]-6',11'-dione, 3',4'-dihydro-5',12'-dihydroxy-4'-methoxy-	MeOH	229s(--),251(4.58), 255s(--),285(3.92), 337(3.33),458s(--), 483(4.01),513(3.83)	24-3453-79
$C_{21}H_{18}O_8$			
4H-1-Benzopyran-4-one, 5-acetoxy-2-(2-acetoxyphenyl)-6,7-dimethoxy-	EtOH	254(4.31),301(4.28)	18-2950-79
4H-1-Benzopyran-4-one, 5-acetoxy-2-(2-acetoxyphenyl)-7,8-dimethoxy-	EtOH	257(4.45),303(4.13)	18-2950-79
Daunomycinone, (±)-	MeOH	215(4.47),231(4.54), 249(4.39),285(3.93), 470(4.04),490(4.05), 529(3.80)	24-3453-79
7-Epidaunomycinone, (±)-	MeOH	217(4.43),232(4.53), 250(4.43),290(3.92), 466(4.06),496(4.06), 530(3.79)	24-3453-79
5,12-Naphthacenedione, 8-acetyl-7,8,9-10-tetrahydro-6,8,10,11-tetrahydroxy-2-methoxy-, (±)-	MeOH	224(4.53),269(4.50), 470(3.99),513(3.79)	24-3453-79
5,12-Naphthacenedione, 8-acetyl-7,8,9-10-tetrahydro-6,8,10,11-tetrahydroxy-3-methoxy-, (±)-	MeOH	229(4.45),269(4.52), 470(4.01),513(3.79)	24-3453-79
β_1-Rhodomycinone, 10-acetate, (±)-	MeOH	234(4.57),253(4.45), 291(3.94),490(4.22), 524(4.07)	5-2018-79
ε_1-Rhodomycinone, 9-deoxy-7-epi-	MeOH	234(4.53),252(4.31), 289(3.87),491(4.09), 523(3.90)	150-3643-79
ε_1-Rhodomycinone, 9-deoxy-10-epi-	MeOH	233(4.47),251(4.29), 294(3.81),490(4.03), 526(3.85)	150-3643-79
Trioxadicyclopent[a,hi]indene-7-carboxylic acid, 3,3a,7a,9b-tetrahydro-3-[(4-hydroxy-3-methoxyphenyl)methylene]-2-oxo-, methyl ester (oruwacin)	EtOH	205(4.05),241(4.08), 317s(3.84),348(4.13)	102-0175-79
$C_{21}H_{18}O_9$			
5,12-Naphthacenedione, 8-acetyl-7,8,9-10-tetrahydro-6,7,8,10,11-pentahydroxy-1(or 4)-methoxy-, (7α,8β,10β)-(±)-	MeOH	229(4.52),246(4.24), 283(3.99),487(3.92), 524(3.67)	24-3453-79
$C_{21}H_{19}$			
Cyclopropenylium, bis(4-cyclopropylphenyl)-, tetrafluoroborate	EtOH	220(4.17),279(4.10), 343(4.63)	18-0856-79
$C_{21}H_{19}ClN_2O$			
Benzenecarboximidamide, N'-(3-chloro-2-methylphenyl)-N-hydroxy-4-methyl-N-phenyl-	EtOH	209(4.61),257(4.03), 317(4.07)	56-2597-79
Benzenecarboximidamide, N'-(4-chloro-2-methylphenyl)-N-hydroxy-N-(2-methylphenyl)-, hydrochloride	EtOH	209(4.69),258(4.29), 310(4.32)	56-2597-79

Compound	Solvent	λmax(log ε)	Ref.
Benzenecarboximidamide, N'-(4-chloro-2-methylphenyl)-N-hydroxy-N-(4-methylphenyl)-, hydrochloride	EtOH	208(4.53),258(4.00), 315(4.05)	56-2597-79
Benzenecarboximidamide, N-(4-chloro-phenyl)-N'-(3,4-dimethylphenyl)-N-hydroxy-	EtOH	208(4.43),258(4.04), 323(4.01)	56-2597-79
$C_{21}H_{19}ClN_4O_7$			
D-Ribitol, 1,4-anhydro-1-C-(8-chloro-1,2,4-triazolo[4,3-a]pyrazin-3-yl)-, 2,3-diacetate 5-benzoate, (S)-	EtOH	280(3.95),305(3.80)	44-1028-79
$C_{21}H_{19}ClO_6$			
4-Cyclohexene-1,2,3-triol, 1-[(benz-oyloxy)methyl]-6-chloro-, 3-benzoate, [1S-(1α,2α,3β,6β)]-	EtOH	230(4.44),274(3.28), 281(3.19)	88-2427-79
$C_{21}H_{19}Fe_2$			
Methylium, diferrocenyl-	$C_2H_4Cl_2$	255(4.22),352(4.13), 605(3.89)	32-0013-79
$C_{21}H_{19}NO$			
Ethanone, 1-(2,3-dihydro-6,7-diphenyl-1H-pyrrolizin-5-yl)-	MeOH	206(4.35),248(4.20), 314(4.19)	83-0896-79
$C_{21}H_{19}NOS$			
Benzenamine, N-(3-ethoxy-2H-naphtho-[1,8-bc]thien-2-ylidene)-2,6-dimeth-yl-	MeOH	267(4.7),325(4.2), 339(4.4),375(4.5), 389(4.5)	5-1789-79
$C_{21}H_{19}NO_3$			
1(3H)-Isobenzofuranone, 3-ethoxy-3-[1-(phenylmethyl)-1H-pyrrol-2-yl]-	EtOH	207(4.29),230(4.26)	103-0747-79
$C_{21}H_{19}NO_3S$			
8H-Benzo[a][1]benzothieno[2,3-g]quino-lizin-8-one, 5,6,14,14a-tetrahydro-2,3-dimethoxy-	MeOH	254(4.28),310(3.95)	4-0433-79
Isoquinoline, 2-(benzo[b]thien-2-yl-carbonyl)-1,2,3,4-tetrahydro-6,7-dimethoxy-1-methylene-	MeOH	223(4.58),270(4.33), 300(4.22)	4-0433-79
$C_{21}H_{19}NO_4$			
1H-Azepine-4-carboxylic acid, 2,5-di-hydro-3-hydroxy-2-oxo-6,7-diphenyl-, ethyl ester	dioxan	226(4.28),269(4.25)	142-1427-79
8H-Benzo[a]benzofuro[2,3-g]quinolizin-8-one, 5,6,14,14a-tetrahydro-2,3-di-methoxy-	MeOH	253(4.30),284(3.95), 310(3.99)	4-0433-79
Isoquinoline, 2-(2-benzofuranylcarbo-nyl)-1,2,3,4-tetrahydro-6,7-dimeth-oxy-1-methylene-	MeOH	232s(4.34),268(4.44), 296(4.28)	4-0433-79
$C_{21}H_{19}NO_4S$			
1H-Azepine-4-carboxylic acid, 2,5-di-hydro-3-hydroxy-2-oxo-7-phenyl-6-(phenylthio)-, ethyl ester	dioxan	220(4.31),263(4.26)	142-1427-79
$C_{21}H_{19}NO_6$			
Δ^1-Aporhoeadene, 1,12,13-trimethoxy-7,8-(methylenedioxy)-14-oxo-	EtOH	275(3.91),308(4.00), 328s(3.90),380(4.44),	44-4347-79

Compound	Solvent	λ_{max}(log ε)	Ref.
(cont.)		393s(4.37)	44-4347-79
Benzo[g]-1,3-benzodioxolo[5,6-a]quinolizinium, 5,6-dihydro-13-hydroxy-8,9,10-trimethoxy-, hydroxide, inner salt	EtOH	230(4.50),262s(4.11), 313(4.09),359(3.81), 374(3.80),455(3.83)	44-4337-79
12H-[1,3]Dioxolo[6',7']indeno[2',1'-4,5]oxazolo[4,3-a]isoquinolin-5(10aH)-one, 14,15-dihydro-2,3-dimethoxy-, (4bR*,10cR*)-(±)-	MeOH	211(4.20),236(4.35), 290(3.91),314(3.87)	23-1569-79
$C_{21}H_{19}NO_6S_2$			
Furo[2,3-d]-1,3-dioxol-6-ol, 5-(2-benzothiazolyl)-3a,6a-dihydro-2,2-dimethyl-, 4-methylbenzenesulfonate	EtOH	225(4.23),305s(4.16), 316(4.19),333s(3.96)	33-1298-79
$C_{21}H_{19}NO_7$			
Aporhoeadane, 1,14-dioxo-2,12,13-trimethoxy-7,8-(methylenedioxy)-	MeOH	278s(3.88),316(4.01)	44-4343-79
Norlumidine	n.s.g.	220(4.43),235s(3.57), 285(3.36),317(3.18)	25-0744-79
Spiro[7H-indeno[4,5-d]-1,3-dioxole-7,1'(2'H)-isoquinoline]-2'-carboxaldehyde, 3',4',6,8-tetrahydro-8-hydroxy-6',7'-dimethoxy-6-oxo-, cis-(±)-	MeOH	212(4.37),235(4.37), 290(3.99),310(3.87)	23-1569-79
$C_{21}H_{19}NO_8$			
Narceimine	n.s.g.	237(4.39),292(4.05), 335(4.15)	25-0744-79
$C_{21}H_{19}N_2$			
Acridinium, 10-methyl-9-[(4-methylphenyl)amino]-, iodide	EtOH	244(4.49),270(4.60), 334(3.66),450(4.15)	104-0183-79
$C_{21}H_{19}N_2O$			
Acridinium, 9-[(4-methoxyphenyl)amino]-10-methyl-, iodide	EtOH	248(4.61),272(4.61), 333(3.60),450(4.16)	104-0183-79
perchlorate	EtOH	249(4.57),271(4.53), 379(3.73),449(4.15)	104-0183-79
$C_{21}H_{19}N_3$			
Benzenamine, 4-(4,5-dihydro-1,3-diphenyl-1H-pyrazol-5-yl)-	C_6H_{12}	361(4.32)	12-1601-79
	MeOH	356(4.31)	12-1601-79
Benzenamine, 4-(4,5-dihydro-1,5-diphenyl-1H-pyrazol-3-yl)-	C_6H_{12}	353(4.33)	12-1601-79
	MeOH	354(4.44)	12-1601-79
Benzenamine, 4-(4,5-dihydro-3,5-diphenyl-1H-pyrazol-1-yl)-	C_6H_{12}	375(4.13)	12-1601-79
	MeOH	377(4.17)	12-1601-79
$C_{21}H_{19}N_3O$			
3H-Pyrazol-3-one, 2,4-dihydro-4-(1-ethyl-2(1H)-quinolinylidene)-2,4-dihydro-5-methyl-2-phenyl-	EtOH	462(4.04)	73-1413-79
$C_{21}H_{19}N_3O_3$			
5,9-Methano-1H-[1,2,4]triazolo[1,2-a]pyridazine-1,3(2H)-dione, 5,8-dihydro-2-phenyl-10-[(phenylmethoxy)methyl]-, anti	MeCN	230(3.85),248(3.58)	35-3315-79
syn	MeCN	230(3.84),252(3.65)	35-3315-79
Pyrimido[4,5-b]quinoline-2,4(3H,10H)-dione, 10-ethyl-5-(4-methoxyphenyl)-3-methyl-	EtOH	224(4.61),264(4.63), 324(3.97),400(4.05)	142-0691-79

Compound	Solvent	λmax(log ε)	Ref.
$C_{21}H_{19}N_3O_3S_2$			
5,11-Imino-5H,11H-[1,5]dithiocino[2,3-b:6,7-b']dipyridine, 13-(3,4,5-trimethoxyphenyl)-	EtOH	212(4.66),246(4.43), 298(3.90)	78-0869-79
$C_{21}H_{19}O_4P$			
Methanol, (1-methoxy-2,6-diphenyl-4(1H)-phosphorinylidene)-, acetate, P-oxide	MeOH	341(4.23)	24-1272-79
$C_{21}H_{20}$			
1,1':4',1"-Terphenyl, 2,4,6-trimethyl-	C_6H_{12}	248(4.39)	12-1531-79
$C_{21}H_{20}BrN$			
Benzenamine, 4-[4-(4-bromophenyl)-1,3,5-cycloheptatrien-1-yl]-N,N-dimethyl-	EtOH	368(4.430)	78-2269-79
$C_{21}H_{20}Br_2O_2$			
Chrysene, 1,11-dibromo-4b,5,6,12-tetrahydro-2,8-dimethoxy-4b-methyl-	EtOH	265(4.18)	12-1107-79
$C_{21}H_{20}ClN$			
Benzenamine, 4-[4-(4-chlorophenyl)-1,3,5-cycloheptatrien-1-yl]-N,N-dimethyl-	EtOH	368(4.436)	78-2269-79
$C_{21}H_{20}Cl_2O_2$			
4b,10b-Methanochrysene, 13,13-dichloro-5,6,11,12-tetrahydro-2,8-dimethoxy-	EtOH	241(4.32),281(3.64), 287(3.64)	12-1107-79
$C_{21}H_{20}F_3NO_6$			
Acetamide, 2,2,2-trifluoro-N-(5,6,7,9-tetrahydro-10-hydroxy-1,2,3-trimethoxy-9-oxobenzo[a]heptalen-7-yl)-, (S)-	EtOH	243(4.57),352(4.37)	33-0965-79
$C_{21}H_{20}NO$			
Phenanthridinium, 7,8,9,10-tetrahydro-9,9-dimethyl-7-oxo-5-phenyl-, perchlorate	n.s.g.	254(4.12),325(4.18)	104-0495-79
$C_{21}H_{20}NO_2PS_3$			
Benzoic acid, 4-[[bis(phenylthio)phosphinothioyl]amino]-, ethyl ester	EtOH	210(4.86),231(4.86)	64-0297-79B
$C_{21}H_{20}N_2$			
Cinnoline, 1,2,3,4-tetrahydro-3-methyl-1,4-diphenyl-	MeCN	299(4.11)	104-2145-79
5H-Cyclohepta[d]pyridazine, 6,7,8,9-tetrahydro-1,4-diphenyl-	EtOH	265(4.35)	23-0904-79
$C_{21}H_{20}N_2O$			
Benzenecarboximidamide, N'-(3,4-dimethylphenyl)-N-hydroxy-N-phenyl-	EtOH	209(4.64),257(4.23), 320(4.21)	56-2597-79
Cinnoline, 1,2,3,4-tetrahydro-4-methoxy-1,2-diphenyl-	MeCN	248(4.45),282(4.38)	103-1243-79
7,10-Methanocycloocta[b]quinoxalin-13-ol, 6,7,8,9,10,11-hexahydro-13-phenyl-	EtOH	205(4.67),238(4.56), 319(4.02)	56-1221-79
Pyrazolo[1,5-a]pyridin-3(3aH)-one, 4,7-dihydro-5,6-dimethyl-2,3a-diphenyl-	EtOH	270(4.24),392(3.91)	23-0904-79

Compound	Solvent	λ_{max}(log ε)	Ref.
$C_{21}H_{20}N_2O_2$			
1H-Indole-3-acetic acid, α-1H-indol-3-yl-α-methyl-, ethyl ester	EtOH	276s(4.08),283(4.11), 291(4.02)	94-0346-79
1H-Pyrazole-4-carboxylic acid, 1,5-diphenyl-3-(1-propenyl)-, ethyl ester	EtOH	217s(4.33),236(4.46)	4-0657-79
3,5-Pyrazolidinedione, 4-(1-cyclopenten-1-yl)-4-methyl-1,2-diphenyl-	EtOH	238(4.3)	103-0215-79
Pyridine, 1,4-dihydro-2,5-dimethyl-4-[(4-nitrophenyl)methylene]-1-(phenylmethyl)-	$CHCl_3$	260(3.98),332(3.90), 560(4.50)	103-0316-79
$C_{21}H_{20}N_2O_2S$			
1,1-Ethenediamine, 2-[(4-methylphenyl)-sulfonyl]-N,N'-diphenyl-	EtOH	275(4.22)	95-0038-79
$C_{21}H_{20}N_2O_3$			
2,4(3H,5H)-Furandione, 3-[[1-(phenylmethyl)amino)ethylidene]-5-[[(phenylmethyl)amino]methylene]-	EtOH	250(4.17),298(4.24), 358(4.43)	4-1335-79
Pyridazinium, 4-(ethoxycarbonyl)-5-hydroxy-6-methyl-3-phenyl-1-(phenylmethyl)-	EtOH	216(4.12),248(4.23), 328(3.84)	44-3053-79
$C_{21}H_{20}N_2O_4$			
Benzamide, N-[3-acetoxy-4-(formylamino)-2-methyl-1-phenyl-1,3-butadienyl]-	MeOH	234(4.49),280s(4.15)	44-2683-79
1,3-Dioxolo[4,5-g]quinoline-7-carboxylic acid, 5-ethyl-5,8-dihydro-8-(phenylimino)-, ethyl ester	MeOH	245(4.5),290s(4.5)	4-1353-79
Ethanone, 1-(1',3'-dihydro-1',3',3'-trimethyl-6-nitrospiro[2H-1-benzopyran-2,2'-[2H]indol]-5'-yl)-	n.s.g.	255(4.32),270(4.06), 301(4.10),340(3.98)	103-1329-79
photochromic form	EtOH	535(--)	103-1329-79
Methanamine, N-(5,6-dihydro-9,10-dimethoxy-8H-benzo[g]-1,3-benzodioxolo[5,6-a]quinolizin-8-ylidene)-	EtOH	283(3.83),360(4.16)	36-0705-79
	EtOH-acid	253(4.18),340(4.25), 395(3.78)	36-0705-79
$C_{21}H_{20}N_2O_5$			
Phenanthrene, 1,2,3,9,10,10a-hexahydro-7-methoxy-1-nitro-2-(4-nitrophenyl)-	MeOH	216(4.41),268(4.52)	2-0071-79B
Phenanthrene, 1,2,3,9,10,10a-hexahydro-7-methoxy-2-nitro-1-(4-nitrophenyl)-	MeOH	214(4.32),263(4.37)	2-0071-79B
$C_{21}H_{20}N_2O_6S$			
Furo[2,3-d]-1,3-dioxol-6-ol, 5-(1H-benzimidazol-2-yl)-3a,6a-dihydro-2,2-dimethyl-, 4-methylbenzenesulfonate	EtOH	205(4.08),225(4.10), 295s(4.02),307(4.11), 322s(3.90)	33-1298-79
$C_{21}H_{20}N_4O_8$			
1,2,4-Triazolo[4,3-a]pyrazin-8(7H)-one, 3-(2,3-di-O-acetyl-5-O-benzoyl-α-D-arabinofuranosyl)-8-oxo-	EtOH	265(3.86)	111-0375-79
$C_{21}H_{20}N_4S$			
1,3,4-Thiadiazol-2-amine, N-butyl-5-(2-phenyl-4-quinolinyl)-	EtOH	244s(--),265(4.94), 345(4.23)	106-0537-79
$C_{21}H_{20}O$			
Benzo[3,4]cyclobuta[1,2-1]phenanthren-8c(9H)-ol, 10,11,12,12a-tetrahydro-12a-methyl-	C_6H_{12}	257(4.78),282(4.05), 293(4.00),305(4.09), 340(2.90),358(3.09)	150-3686-79

Compound	Solvent	λmax(log ε)	Ref.
8cH-Cyclohepta[3,4]cyclobuta[1,2-l]-phenanthren-8c-ol, 9,10,11,12,13,13a-hexahydro-, cis	tert-BuOH	213(4.41),256(4.68), 291(3.88),304(4.00), 338(2.98),356(3.00)	150-3686-79
$C_{21}H_{20}O_2$			
Benzenemethanol, 4-hydroxy-3,5-dimethyl-α,α-diphenyl-	n.s.g.	277(3.20),284(3.20)	35-5717-79
1H,3H-Naphtho[1,8-cd]pyran-1-ol, 3-(2,4,6-trimethylphenyl)-, trans	hexane	206(4.58),229(4.85), 288(3.90)	44-1934-79
$C_{21}H_{20}O_3$			
11H-Benzo[a]fluoren-11-one, 6a,11a-dihydro-2,9-dimethoxy-6,11a-dimethyl-, cis	EtOH	252(4.28),277(3.20)	44-1388-79
$C_{21}H_{20}O_3S$			
3-Cyclohexene-1-carboxylic acid, 2-oxo-6-phenyl-4-[2-(2-thienyl)ethenyl]-, ethyl ester	EtOH	240(4.01),274(3.59), 358(4.38)	104-1059-79
$C_{21}H_{20}O_4$			
3-Cyclohexene-1-carboxylic acid, 4-[2-(2-furanyl)ethenyl]-2-oxo-6-phenyl-, ethyl ester	EtOH	242(4.09),265s(--), 358(4.42)	104-1059-79
$C_{21}H_{20}O_5$			
9,10-Anthracenedione, 1,8-dihydroxy-3-methoxy-6-methyl-2-(3-methyl-1-butenyl)-, (E)-	$CHCl_3$	262(4.74),293(4.84), 445(4.54)	32-0301-79
2H-Anthra[1,2-b]pyran-7,12-dione, 3,4-dihydro-11-hydroxy-5-methoxy-2,2,9-trimethyl-	$CHCl_3$	270(4.43),305s(4.0), 430(4.0)	32-0301-79
$C_{21}H_{20}O_6$			
2-Anthracenebutanoic acid, 4-ethoxy-9,10-dihydro-1-hydroxy-9,10-dioxo-, methyl ester	MeOH	206(4.45),228(4.45), 251(4.54),282(4.07), 330s(--),471(3.88)	5-0035-79
2(3H)-Furanone, 3-(1,3-benzodioxol-5-ylmethyl)-4-[(3,4-dimethoxyphenyl)-methylene]dihydro-	EtOH	226(4.4),280(3.9)	25-0667-79
Polygamatin	EtOH	286(3.84)	100-0378-79
$C_{21}H_{20}O_8$			
11H-Benzofuro[2,3-b][1]benzopyran-11-one, 10b-acetoxy-5a,10b-dihydro-2,3,8-trimethoxy-5a-methyl-	MeOH	286(4.17),347(3.97)	18-0529-79
$C_{21}H_{20}O_{10}$			
Afzelin	MeOH	266(4.32),345(4.15)	95-0439-79
	MeOH-NaOMe	275(4.37),326(4.09), 391(4.32)	95-0439-79
$C_{21}H_{21}BrO_2$			
Chrysene, 11-bromo-4b,5,6,12-tetrahydro-2,8-dimethoxy-4b-methyl-	EtOH	262(4.27)	12-1107-79
$C_{21}H_{21}ClN_2O_3S$			
Benzenesulfonamide, 4-chloro-N-[(1',2'-dihydro-1'-methyl-2'-oxospiro[cyclopentane-1,3'-[3H]indol]-2-ylidene)-methyl]-N-methyl-, (E)-(±)-	EtOH	210(4.58),230s(4.30), 260s(4.05)	39-2154-79C

Compound	Solvent	λ_{max}(log ϵ)	Ref.
$C_{21}H_{21}ClN_2O_8$			
2-Naphthacenecarboxamide, 7-chloro-4-(dimethylamino)-1,4,4a,5,5a,6,11,12a-octahydro-3,6,10,12,12a-pentahydroxy-1,11-dioxo-	pH 7.4	280(4.15),380(4.19)	149-0531-79A
$C_{21}H_{21}N$			
1-Azaspiro[4.5]deca-1,3-diene, 2,4-diphenyl-	EtOH	248(4.29)	78-2285-79
Benzenamine, N,N-dimethyl-4-(4-phenyl-1,3,5-cycloheptatrien-1-yl)-	EtOH	363(4.412)	78-2269-79
Benzenamine, 4-methyl-N,N-bis(4-methylphenyl)-	$CHCl_3$	300(4.64)	88-1561-79
[1,1'-Biphenyl]-2-amine, 2',5'-dimethyl-N-(phenylmethyl)-	n.s.g.	220(4.20)(end abs.)	33-2129-79
Cyclohepta[b]pyrrole, 1,4,5,6,7,8-hexahydro-2,3-diphenyl-	EtOH	260(4.01),313(4.11)	88-1587-79
$C_{21}H_{21}NO_2$			
1H-Carbazole-2-carboxylic acid, 2,3,4,9-tetrahydro-4-methyl-3-phenyl-, methyl ester	EtOH	228(4.54),275s(3.84), 283(3.86),290(3.81)	44-4402-79
$C_{21}H_{21}NO_3$			
1H-Indole-2-acetic acid, 3-(2-hydroxyethyl)- -methylene-1-(phenylmethyl)-, methyl ester	EtOH	275(3.30)	23-0289-79
Phenanthrene, 1,2,3,9,10,10a-hexahydro-7-methoxy-1-nitro-2-phenyl-, (1α,2β-10aβ)-	MeOH	222(4.13),264(4.29)	2-0071-79B
1H-Pyrrole-2-carboxylic acid, 3-(phenylmethoxy)-1-(phenylmethyl)-, ethyl ester	EtOH	266(4.29)	94-1448-79
$C_{21}H_{21}NO_4$			
1-Naphthalenamine, N-[(3,4-dimethoxyphenyl)methylene]-6,7-dimethoxy-	EtOH	211(4.56),240(4.70), 276(4.20),318(4.16), 350(4.10)	44-0293-79
$C_{21}H_{21}NO_4S_2$			
Benzothiazolium, 2-ethyl-6-(2-furanyl)-3-methyl-, p-toluenesulfonate	EtOH	220(4.39),227s(--), 271(4.14),293s(--), 309s(--),335(3.88)	33-0021-79
$C_{21}H_{21}NO_6$			
β-Hydrastine, (±)-	EtOH	298(3.90)	44-4343-79
$C_{21}H_{21}NO_7$			
1(3H)-Isobenzofuranone, 6,7-dimethoxy-3-(5,6,7,8-tetrahydro-4-hydroxy-6-methyl-1,3-dioxolo[4,5-g]isoquinolin-5-yl)-	EtOH	210(4.50),228(4.37), 280(4.20),308(4.19)	44-4337-79
Narcotoline	pH 2	291(3.15),309(3.71)	106-0194-79
	M KOH	282(3.72),311(2.05)	106-0194-79
$C_{21}H_{21}NO_8$			
Benzo[g]quinoline-2-carboxylic acid, 7-butyl-5,10-dihydro-4,9-dihydroxy-3,8-dimethoxy-5,10-dioxo-, methyl ester	MeOH	236(4.23),265(4.28), 293s(3.98),446(3.61)	39-0807-79C

Compound	Solvent	$\lambda_{max}(\log \epsilon)$	Ref.
Benzo[g]quinoline-2-carboxylic acid, 7-butyl-5,10-dihydro-4-hydroxy-3,8,9-trimethoxy-5,10-dioxo-	MeOH	272(4.53),370(3.90)	39-0807-79C
Cyclopenta[a]quinolizine-6,7,9,10-tetracarboxylic acid, 6,7-dihydro-8-methyl-, tetramethyl ester	MeOH	228s(4.01),268(4.05), 347(3.90),449(4.24)	39-0584-79C
	MeOH-$HClO_4$	241(3.84),254s(3.70), 296(3.48),373(4.18), 449(3.00)	39-0584-79C
$C_{21}H_{21}NO_{10}S$			
1H-Pyrrole-3,4-dicarboxylic acid, 1-[3-methoxy-1-(methoxycarbonyl)-3-oxo-1-propenyl]-2-[(4-methylphenyl)sulfonyl]-, dimethyl ester	EtOH	225(4.58),260(4.55)	94-2857-79
$C_{21}H_{21}N_2O_4$			
1,3-Dioxolo[4,5-g]quinolinium, 7-(ethoxycarbonyl)-5-ethyl-8-(phenylamino)-, iodide	MeOH	265(4.7),288(4.7)	4-1353-79
$C_{21}H_{21}N_3$			
Piperidine, 1-[[(2-[1,1'-biphenyl]-4-yl-2-cyanoethenyl)imino]methyl]-	MeOH	262(4.21),354(4.64)	83-0039-79
$C_{21}H_{21}N_3O_2$			
3,5-Methanofuro[3,2-b]pyridin-6(2H)-one, 4-(4,6-dimethyl-2-pyrimidinyl)hexahydro-7-(phenylmethylene)-	$CHCl_3$	250(4.21),295(4.25)	39-1525-79C
$C_{21}H_{21}N_3O_3$			
Benzenemethanol, 4,5-dimethoxy-2-(methyl-9H-pyrido[3,4-b]indol-1-ylamino)-	MeOH	244(4.42),294(3.94), 345(3.77)	142-0353-79
Indolo[2',3':3,4]pyrido[2,1-b]quinazolin-5(7H)-one, 8,13,13b,14-tetrahydro-2,3-dimethoxy-14-methyl-	MeOH	268(4.11),290(3.90)	142-0353-79
5,8-Methano-1H-[1,2,4]triazolo[1,2-a]pyridazine-1,3(2H)-dione, tetrahydro-2-phenyl-10-[(phenylmethoxy)methyl]-, anti	MeCN	229(3.99)	35-3315-79
syn	MeCN	229(3.97)	35-3315-79
$C_{21}H_{21}N_3S_3$			
2,11,20-Trithia[3,3,5](2,6)pyridophane	90% EtOH	270(4.03)	12-1241-79
$C_{21}H_{21}N_5O_2$			
2-Propenamide, N-[4-(4,5-dihydro-3-methyl-4-[(3-methylphenyl)azo]-5-oxo-1H-pyrazol-1-yl]phenyl]-2-methyl-	benzene	398(4.43)	40-1774-79
2-Propenamide, N-[4-(4,5-dihydro-3-methyl-4-[(4-methylphenyl)azo]-5-oxo-1H-pyrazol-1-yl]phenyl]-2-methyl-	benzene	402(4.43)	40-1774-79
$C_{21}H_{21}N_5O_3$			
2-Propenamide, N-[4-[4,5-dihydro-4-[(3-methoxyphenyl)azo]-3-methyl-5-oxo-1H-pyrazol-1-yl]phenyl]-2-methyl-	benzene	401(4.43)	40-1774-79
2-Propenamide, N-[4-[4,5-dihydro-4-[(4-methoxyphenyl)azo]-3-methyl-5-oxo-1H-pyrazol-1-yl]phenyl]-2-methyl-	benzene	415(4.43)	40-1774-79

Compound	Solvent	λ max(log ε)	Ref.
$C_{21}H_{21}N_5O_8$			
Guanosine, N-benzoyl-, 3',5'-diacetate	EtOH	238(4.21),257(4.14), 264(4.14),269(4.16)	39-2088-79C
$C_{21}H_{21}O_3S$			
Sulfonium, tris(4-methoxyphenyl)-, hexafluoroarsenate	EtOH	225(4.34),280(4.00)	47-0977-79
$C_{21}H_{21}O_4P$			
Phosphorin, 1,1-dihydro-1,1-dimethoxy-4-(methoxycarbonyl)-2,6-diphenyl-	MeOH	300(4.26),372(4.30)	24-1272-79
$C_{21}H_{21}S$			
Sulfonium, tris(4-methylphenyl)-, tetrafluoroborate	EtOH	243(4.39),278(3.69)	47-0977-79
$C_{21}H_{22}$			
Cyclopropane, 3-methyl-3-(2,4-pentadienyl)-1,2-diphenyl-, cis-cis	EtOH	227(4.27)	35-5743-79
Cyclopropene, 1-methyl-3-(4-pentenyl)-2,3-diphenyl-	EtOH	263(4.19)	35-5743-79
Cyclopropene, 3-methyl-3-(4-pentenyl)-1,2-diphenyl-	EtOH	223(4.23),319(4.45), 337(4.32)	35-5743-79
$C_{21}H_{22}BrNO_4$			
8-Azabicyclo[3.2.1]oct-3-ene-6-carboxylic acid, 8-[3-(4-bromophenyl)-3-oxo-1-propenyl]-2-oxo-, 1,1-dimethylethyl ester, endo	$CHCl_3$	265(4.27),334(4.43)	39-1525-79C +39-2528-79C
exo	$CHCl_3$	265(4.23),334(4.41)	39-1525-79C
$C_{21}H_{22}BrN_5$			
Pyrazolo[4,3-c][1,2,5]benzotriazepine, 5-(2-bromo-4-methylphenyl)-1,5-dihydro-3,7-dimethyl-1-propyl-	MeOH	345(3.47),400(3.75)	103-0654-79
$C_{21}H_{22}ClN_3O$			
3H-1,4-Benzodiazepin-2-amine, 7-chloro-N-methyl-5-(6,7,8,9-tetrahydro-5H-benzocyclohepten-2-yl)-, 4-oxide	MeOH	260(4.54),315s(3.93)	73-3604-79
$C_{21}H_{22}N_2$			
1-Azaspiro[4.5]deca-1,3-dien-2-amine, 3,4-diphenyl-	EtOH	253(4.18)	78-2285-79
$C_{21}H_{22}N_2O$			
4(1H)-Quinolinone, 2,3-dihydro-1-phenyl-3-(1-piperidinylmethylene)-	EtOH	242(4.34),302(4.08), 339(4.12),415(3.84)	4-0177-79
$C_{21}H_{22}N_2OS_2$			
Benzenecarbodithioic acid, [4-(dimethylamino)-5,5-dimethyl-2(5H)-oxazolylidene]phenylmethyl ester	MeCN	231(4.33),317(4.47), 440(3.21)	33-1236-79
$C_{21}H_{22}N_2O_2$			
2-Propenoic acid, 2-cyano-3-[4-[ethyl-(phenylmethyl)amino]phenyl]-, ethyl ester	EtOH	424(4.67)	110-1769-79
	EtOH-KOH	350(--)	110-1769-79
	CCl_4	415(--)	110-1769-79
	KBr	429(--)	110-1769-79
Yohimban, 17,18-dimethoxy-15,16,17,18-19,20-hexadehydro-	n.s.g.	216(4.48),225(4.56), 284(3.99),291(3.94)	142-1483-79

Compound	Solvent	λ_{max}(log ε)	Ref.
$C_{21}H_{22}N_2O_3$			
1H-Cyclopenta[a]indolo[3,2-h]quinolizine-4-carboxylic acid, 2,3,3a,7,8,13-13b,13c-octahydro-1-methyl-3-oxo-, methyl ester, [1S-(1α,3aα,13bα,13cα)]-	EtOH	224(4.50),285(4.41), 292(4.40)	28-0057-79A
4-Isoquinolineacetonitrile, 3-(3,4-dimethoxyphenyl)-1,2-dihydro-α-methoxy-2-methyl-	EtOH	240(4.09),344(3.89)	78-1861-79
2-Propenoic acid, 2-cyano-3-[4-[(4-ethoxyphenyl)methylamino]phenyl]-, ethyl ester	EtOH	425(4.64)	110-1769-79
	EtOH-KOH	347(--)	110-1769-79
	CCl_4	415(--)	110-1769-79
	KBr	435(--)	110-1769-79
4-Pyridazinecarboxylic acid, 1,6-dihydro-5-hydroxy-6-methyl-3-phenyl-1-(phenylmethyl)-, ethyl ester	EtOH	244(4.14),310(3.93)	44-3053-79
4-Pyridazinecarboxylic acid, 1,6-dihydro-5-methoxy-6-methyl-1,3-diphenyl-, ethyl ester	EtOH	247(4.36),290(3.71), 373(4.03)	44-3053-79
4-Pyridazinecarboxylic acid, 1,2,5,6-tetrahydro-2,6-dimethyl-5-oxo-1,3-diphenyl-, ethyl ester	EtOH	243(4.24),314(4.04)	44-3053-79
Spiro[2H-1-benzopyran-2,2'-[2H]indole], 8-ethyl-1',3'-dihydro-1',3',3'-trimethyl-6-nitro-	EtOH	555(4.48)	103-1101-79
	toluene	597(--)	103-1101-79
Strychnine, 15-hydroxy-	EtOH	255(4.08),280(3.60), 291(3.49)	78-2545-79
$C_{21}H_{22}N_2O_4$			
Eburnamenine-14-carboxylic acid, 17,18-didehydro-14,15-dihydro-14-hydroxy-19-oxo-, methyl ester, (3α,14β,16α)-	MeOH	246(4.24),266(4.05), 295(3.72),305(3.72)	24-1902-79
L-Tryptophan, N-[(phenylmethoxy)carbonyl]-, ethyl ester	EtOH	274(3.77),281(3.80), 290(3.72)	118-0957-79
$C_{21}H_{22}N_2O_6S$			
Furo[2,3-d]-1,3-dioxol-6-ol, 5-(1H-benzimidazol-2-yl)tetrahydro-2,2-dimethyl-, 4-methylbenzenesulfonate	EtOH	209(4.21),227(3.91), 274(3.76),281(3.75)	33-1298-79
$C_{21}H_{22}N_2O_8$			
2-Naphthacenecarboxamide, 4-(dimethylamino)-1,4,4a,5,5a,6,11,12a-octahydro-3,8,10,12,12a-pentahydroxy-1,11-dioxo-, monohydriodide	MeOH-HCl	220(4.40),254(4.25), 269(4.24),289s(4.09), 355(4.42)	35-2171-79
	MeOH-NaOH	216(4.48),270(4.16), 290s(4.07),370(4.50)	35-2171-79
	MeOH-borax	218(4.47),253(4.19), 264(4.19),289s(4.09), 368s(4.26),398(4.37)	35-2171-79
$C_{21}H_{22}N_2O_8S_2$			
2,4(1H,3H)-Pyrimidinedione, 1-[2,3-bis-[[(4-methylphenyl)sulfonyl]oxy]propyl]-	n.s.g.	225(4.26),261(3.85), 272(3.71)	128-0281-79
$C_{21}H_{22}N_2O_9$			
4-Oxa-1-azabicyclo[3.2.0]heptane-2-carboxylic acid, 3-[3-(ethoxycarbonyl)-4-oxopentylidene]-7-oxo-, (4-nitrophenyl)methyl ester	EtOH	267(3.98)	23-0222-79

Compound	Solvent	$\lambda_{max}(\log \epsilon)$	Ref.
$C_{21}H_{22}N_2S$			
4(3H)-Pyridinethione, 2-(dimethylamino)-3,3-dimethyl-5,6-diphenyl-	EtOH	283(4.23),487(4.26), 620s(2.30)	33-0086-79
$C_{21}H_{22}N_4O_3S$			
Benzo[b]thiophene-3-carboxylic acid, 2-[(4,5-dihydro-3-methyl-5-oxo-1-phenyl-1H-pyrazol-4-yl)azo]-4,5,6,7-tetrahydro-, ethyl ester	MeOH	220(4.28),245(4.34), 300s(3.89),462(4.34)	83-0726-79
$C_{21}H_{22}N_4O_8$			
α-D-ribo-Pentodialdo-1,4-furanose, 1,2-O-(1-methylethylidene)-3-O-(phenylmethyl)-, 2,4-dinitrophenylhydrazone	MeOH	207(4.29),226(4.13), 252(4.05),354(4.33)	136-0151-79H
$C_{21}H_{22}N_6O_2$			
1H-Isoindole-1,3(2H)-dione, 2-[3-[6-[(3-methyl-2-butenyl)amino]-3H-purin-3-yl]propyl]-, monohydrobromide	MeOH	219(4.73),289(4.28)	24-3072-79
$C_{21}H_{22}O$			
Chrysene, 4b,5,6,12-tetrahydro-2,8-dimethoxy-4b-methyl-	EtOH	266(4.20),301(3.48)	12-1107-79
9H-Fluoren-9-one, 1,2,3,4,4a,9a-hexahydro-9a-[(4-methoxyphenyl)methyl]-	EtOH	225(4.14),286(3.63), 292(3.61)	78-1167-79
$C_{21}H_{22}O_2Si$			
Silane, (2-methoxyethoxy)triphenyl-	EtOH	264(3.03)	3-0007-79
$C_{21}H_{22}O_3$			
2H-1-Benzopyran-2-one, 7-hydroxy-8-(3-methylbutyl)-4-(methylphenyl)-	EtOH	275(3.56),280s(3.53)	2-0113-79A
$C_{21}H_{22}O_4$			
9(10H)-Anthracenone, 1,8-dihydroxy-3-methoxy-6-methyl-2-(3-methyl-1-butenyl)-, (E)-	$CHCl_3$	271(4.71),355(4.50)	32-0301-79
$C_{21}H_{22}O_4S_2$			
5H-1,4-Dithiepin-2-carboxylic acid, 6,7-dihydro-3-[3-methoxy-4-(phenylmethoxy)phenyl]-, methyl ester	EtOH	231(4.17),333(3.83)	4-1081-79
$C_{21}H_{22}O_4Si$			
3(2H)-Furanone, 2-(2-oxo-2-phenylethyl)-5-phenyl-2-[(trimethylsilyl)oxy]-	MeOH	247(4.04),312(4.00)	4-0417-79
$C_{21}H_{22}O_5$			
11H-Anthra[1,2-b]pyran-11-one, 2,8,9,10-tetrahydro-9,12-dihydroxy-5-methoxy-2,2,9-trimethyl- (vismione B)	$CHCl_3$	245(4.13),305(4.41), 410(3.84)	32-0301-79
$C_{21}H_{22}O_5S_2$			
1,3-Dithiane-2-acetic acid, 2-[3-methoxy-4-(phenylmethoxy)phenyl]-α-oxo-, methyl ester	EtOH	238(4.08),284(3.66)	4-1081-79
$C_{21}H_{22}O_6$			
2-Furanol, 3-(1,3-benzodioxol-5-ylmethyl)-4-[(3,4-dimethoxyphenyl)methylene]tetrahydro- (podotoxin)	EtOH	232(4.59),282(3.78)	25-0667-79

Compound	Solvent	$\lambda_{max}(\log \epsilon)$	Ref.
2(3H)-Furanone, 4-(1,3-benzodioxol-5-ylmethyl)-3-[(3,4-dimethoxyphenyl)-methyl]dihydro-, (3R-trans)-	EtOH	232(4.08),286(3.78)	95-0674-79
$C_{21}H_{22}O_8$			
4H-1-Benzopyran-4-one, 3,5,7-trimethoxy-2-(2,4,5-trimethoxyphenyl)-	MeOH	246(4.30),293(3.86), 325(3.98)	39-2696-79C
Butanedioic acid, [(2,3-dimethoxyphenyl)(3,4-dimethoxyphenyl)methylene]-	MeOH	277(4.04)	2-0198-79
geometric isomer	MeOH	280(4.06)	2-0198-79
4-Cyclohexene-1,3-dione, 4-acetyl-2-[(5-acetyl-2,4-dihydroxy-3,3-dimethyl-6-oxo-1,4-cyclohexadien-1-yl)methylene]-5-hydroxy-6,6-dimethyl-	EtOH	320(4.17),490(4.85)	138-0201-79
1H,3H-Furo[3,4-c]furan-1-one, tetrahydro-3-(4-hydroxy-3,5-dimethoxyphenyl)-6-(4-hydroxy-3-methoxyphenyl)-	MeOH	236(2.99),290(2.72)	78-0861-79
$C_{21}H_{22}O_9$			
2,5-Cyclohexadiene-1,4-dione, 5-(6-acetoxy-3,4-dihydro-7,8-dimethoxy-2H-1-benzopyran-3-yl)-2,3-dimethoxy-, (S)-	EtOH	284(4.27),350(2.96)	32-0009-79
$C_{21}H_{22}O_{10}$			
4H-1-Benzopyran-4-one, 3-[(6-deoxy-α-L-mannopyranosyl)oxy]-2,3-dihydro-5,7-dihydroxy-2-(4-hydroxyphenyl)- (astilbin)	MeOH	292(3.86),330s(--)	106-0841-79
$C_{21}H_{22}O_{12}$			
9H-Xanthen-9-one, 5-(β-D-glucopyranosyloxy)-1,6-dihydroxy-3,7-dimethoxy-	EtOH	242(4.35),260(4.39), 277s(4.0),317(3.98)	102-1029-79
	EtOH-NaOAc	245(--),258s(--), 273(--),338(--)	102-1029-79
$C_{21}H_{23}BrN_3OS$			
4H-Imidazolium, 2-[[2-(4-bromophenyl)-2-oxoethyl]thio]-5-(dimethylamino)-4,4-dimethyl-1-phenyl-, bromide	n.s.g.	254(4.37)	33-0160-79
$C_{21}H_{23}ClFN_3O$			
2H-1,4-Benzodiazepin-2-one, 7-chloro-1-[2-(diethylamino)ethyl]-5-(2-fluorophenyl)-1,3-dihydro- (flurazepam)	pH 0	241(4.36),287(4.08), 370(3.51)	59-0603-79
	pH 7	231(4.46),250s(4.16), 315(3.08)	59-0603-79
$C_{21}H_{23}NO_2$			
2-Aziridinecarboxylic acid, 3-[1,1'-biphenyl]-4-yl-1-(1-methylethyl)-, 2-propenyl ester, trans	MeOH	256(4.42)	44-0255-79
2H-Indol-2-one, 1,3-dihydro-3-(2-hydroxycyclohexyl)-1-(phenylmethyl)-	EtOH	253(3.91),280s(3.22)	23-1694-79
form B	EtOH	253(3.91),280s(3.01)	23-1694-79
$C_{21}H_{23}NO_3S_2$			
2-Propen-1-one, 3-(methylthio)-1-phenyl-2-(phenylsulfonyl)-3-(1-piperidinyl)-	EtOH	282(3.93),374(4.31)	95-0038-79

Compound	Solvent	λ_{max}(log ε)	Ref.
$C_{21}H_{23}NO_4$			
5H-Benzo[g]-1,3-benzodioxolo[6,5,4-de]-quinolin-12-ol, 6,7,7a,8-tetrahydro-11-methoxy-7-propyl-, hydrochloride, (±)-	EtOH	228(4.39),275(3.97), 306(3.72)	4-0087-79
1-Naphthalenamine, 2-(3,4-dimethoxy-phenyl)-6,7-dimethoxy-N-methyl-	MeOH	231(4.64),261(4.62)	103-1260-79
1-Naphthalenamine, N-[(3,4-dimethoxy-phenyl)methyl]-6,7-dimethoxy-	EtOH	206(4.58),221(4.69), 259(4.48),283s(3.78), 316(3.80)	44-0293-79
Tuliferoline	MeOH	224(4.06),273(4.10)	100-0325-79
$C_{21}H_{23}NO_5$			
Allocryptopine	MeOH	229(4.49),286(4.22)	56-0079-79
Benzaldehyde, 2,3-dimethoxy-6-[(5,6,7-8-tetrahydro-6-methyl-1,3-dioxolo-[4,5-g]isoquinolin-5-yl)methyl]-, (±)-canadaline)	MeOH	288(3.85)	142-0497-79A
6H-[1,3]Dioxoloisoquino[1,2-c][2,4]-benzoxazepine, 5,8,13,14a-tetrahydro-10,11-dimethoxy-13-methyl-	EtOH	243(4.18),288(3.81), 306s(3.50),366(3.59)	39-0283-79C
	EtOH-HCl	248(4.33),293(3.71), 308(3.87),367(4.01)	39-0283-79C
	EtOH-NaOH	224s(4.02),287(3.98)	39-0283-79C
10,5-(Iminomethano)-1H-dibenzo[a,d]cy-clohepten-12-one, 10,11-dihydro-2,3,7,8-tetramethoxy-11-methyl-, (±)-	EtOH	290(4.0)	44-1162-79
$C_{21}H_{23}NO_6$			
Ocoxylonine	MeOH	224(4.55),284(4.38), 305s(4.08)	100-0325-79
$C_{21}H_{23}NO_9$			
2H-Quinolizine-2,3,4-tricarboxylic acid, 2-(2-methoxy-2-oxoethyl)-1-(1-oxopro-pyl)-, trimethyl ester	MeOH	213(4.24),273(4.15), 323(3.78),470(3.68)	39-0584-79C
	MeOH-$HClO_4$	212(4.14),275(3.94)	39-0584-79C
$C_{21}H_{23}N_2$			
Quinolinium, 2-[2-[4-(dimethylamino)-phenyl]ethenyl]-1-ethyl-	EtOH	530(4.79)	80-1491-79
	$CHCl_3$	548(4.81)	80-1491-79
	CCl_4	548(4.54)	80-1491-79
Quinolinium, 4-[2-[4-(dimethylamino)-phenyl]ethenyl]-1-ethyl-, iodide, (E)-	MeOH	545(4.62)	64-1556-79B
$C_{21}H_{23}N_3O$			
7-Azabicyclo[4.3.1]deca-3,8-dien-10-ol, 7-(4,6-dimethyl-2-pyrimidinyl)-10-phenyl-	$CHCl_3$	279(4.49)	39-1525-79C
$C_{21}H_{23}N_3O_2$			
Indolo[2',3':3,4]pyrido[2,1-b]quinazo-line, 5,7,8,13,13b,14-hexahydro-2,3-dimethoxy-14-methyl-	MeOH	272s(--),282(3.94), 290(3.92)	142-0353-79
Pyrrolo[1,2-a]pyrazine-1,4-dione, 3-[(1,1-dimethyl-1H-pyrrolo[1,2-a]-indol-9-yl)methyl]hexahydro-, (3S-trans)-	EtOH	220(4.25),232s(4.16), 245s(3.90),313(3.86), 325s(3.74),341(3.34)	39-3053-79C
$C_{21}H_{23}N_3O_3$			
Indolo[2',3':3,4]pyrido[2,1-b]quinazo-lin-5(7H)-one, 8,9,10,11,12,14-hexa-hydro-2,3-dimethoxy-14-methyl-	MeCN	239(4.00),252(3.94), 376(4.44)	142-0353-79

Compound	Solvent	$\lambda_{max}(\log \epsilon)$	Ref.
$C_{21}H_{23}N_3O_6$			
2-Pentanone, 4-[[2-hydroxy-2-(4-nitro-phenyl)-1-[[[(phenylamino)carbonyl]-oxy]methyl]ethyl]imino]-, [R-(R*,R*)]-	MeOH	280(4.19),311(4.34)	94-1245-79
$C_{21}H_{23}N_3O_7$			
Carbamic acid, [2-[(2,5-dioxo-1-pyrrol-idinyl)oxy]-1-[(1-formyl-1H-indol-3-yl)methyl]-2-oxoethyl]-, 1,1-dimeth-ylethyl ester, (S)-	MeOH-HCl	300(3.72)	63-0013-79
$C_{21}H_{23}N_3O_8S$			
Acetamide, N-[1,2-dihydro-2-thioxo-1-(2,3,4-tri-O-acetyl-β-D-ribo-pyranosyl)-4-quinazolinyl]-	MeOH	212(4.17),234(3.97), 287(4.52),312s(4.06)	44-0173-79
$C_{21}H_{23}N_5O_2$			
4',5-Bipyrimidine, 2,2'-dimethoxy-6-phenyl-4'-piperidino-	EtOH	208(4.65),235(4.37), 260(4.19),288(4.28), 335(4.15)	103-0671-79
$C_{21}H_{23}N_5O_6$			
Adenosine, N-benzoyl-4'-C-(hydroxymeth-yl)-2',3'-O-(1-methylethylidene)-	MeOH	230(4.11),280(4.30)	44-1309-79
$C_{21}H_{24}$			
Anthracene, 1,2,3,4,4a,9,9a,10-octa-hydro-9-methyl-9-phenyl-	C_6H_{12}	256(2.80),262(2.84), 266(2.79),269(2.73), 273(2.63)	44-3698-79
Bicyclo[3.1.0]hexane, 2,2,5-trimethyl-1,6-diphenyl-	EtOH	225s(4.14)	35-5743-79
Bicyclo[3.1.0]hexane, 2,2,6-trimethyl-1,5-diphenyl-	EtOH	225(4.23)	35-5743-79
Cyclopropane, 3-methyl-2-(3-methyl-2-butenyl)diphenyl-, cis	EtOH	220(4.18)	35-5743-79
Cyclopropane, 3-methyl-3-(3-methyl-2-butenyl)-1,2-diphenyl-, cis	EtOH	223s(4.16)	35-5743-79
Cyclopropene, 2-methyl-3-(3-methyl-butyl)-1,3-diphenyl-	EtOH	264(4.22)	35-5743-79
Cyclopropene, 3-methyl-3-(3-methyl-butyl)-1,2-diphenyl-	EtOH	229(4.23),321(4.46), 338(4.33)	35-5743-79
$C_{21}H_{24}Cl_2O_7$			
Centaurepensin	MeOH	210(4.7)	100-0427-79
$C_{21}H_{24}NO_4$			
Nantenine, N-methyl- (cation)	EtOH	225(4.24),278s(3.65), 285(3.79),310(3.94), 320s(3.84)	100-0325-79
$C_{21}H_{24}NO_5$			
Pyridinium, 4-[2-[4-(2-ethoxy-2-oxoeth-yl)phenyl]ethenyl]-1-(2-ethoxy-2-oxo-ethyl)-, (E)-, bromide	MeOH	398(4.42)	56-1649-79
chloride	MeOH	385(4.26)	56-1649-79
$C_{21}H_{24}N_2O$			
Benzenamine, 4-[2-(2,3-dihydro-2,2-di-methyl-1,5-benzoxazepin-4-yl)ethen-yl]-N,N-dimethyl-, BF_3 adduct	$CHCl_3$	530(4.58)	124-0231-79

Compound	Solvent	λ_{max}(log ε)	Ref.
4H-Indol-4-one, 1,5,6,7-tetrahydro-2-methyl-1-phenyl-5-(1-piperidinylmethylene)-	EtOH	255(4.18),296(3.85), 360(4.43)	4-0913-79
$C_{21}H_{24}N_2O_2$			
Pyrrolo[2,3-b]indol-2(1H)-one, 3,3a,8-8a-tetrahydro-1-(3-hydroxypropyl)-3a-methyl-8-(phenylmethyl)-	MeOH	251(3.93),300(3.42)	5-0927-79
$C_{21}H_{24}N_2O_3$			
1H-Cyclopent[a]indolo[3,2-h]quinolizine-4-carboxylic acid, 2,3,3a,7,8-13,13b,13c-octahydro-3-hydroxy-1-methyl-, methyl ester, [1S-(1α,3α-3aα,13bα,13cα)]-	EtOH	222(4.46),285(4.41), 290(4.42)	28-0057-79A
3β-	EtOH	224(4.36),286(4.42), 292(4.45)	28-0057-79A
Lochnericine	EtOH	227(4.10),299(4.15), 328(4.32)	2-0175-79A
1,6-Naphthalenediamine, 2-(3,4-dimethoxyphenyl)-7-methoxy-N,N'-dimethyl-	MeOH	230(4.53),256(4.59), 344s(3.47)	103-1260-79
$C_{21}H_{24}N_2O_3S$			
Benzenesulfonamide, N-(2-hydroxy-1'-methylspiro[cyclohexane-1,3'-[3H]-indol]-2'(1'H)-ylidene)-4-methyl-	EtOH	221(4.37),278s(4.14), 283(4.16),300s(4.03)	39-2154-79C
$C_{21}H_{24}N_2O_4$			
Benzenepropanamide, α-(acetylamino)-4-(acetyloxy)-N-(1-phenylethyl)-, [S-(R*,S*)]-	$CHCl_3$	258(2.50),265(2.51), 273(2.40)	70-0129-79
Butanedioic acid, mono[[1-(phenylmethyl)-2-(3-pyridinyl)-3-pyrrolidinyl]-methyl] ester, trans	EtOH	257s(3.38),262(3.40), 267s(3.28)	44-4332-79
8bH-Pyrrolo[3',2':2,3]pentaleno[1,2-b]-indole-8b-carboxylic acid, 11a-ethyl-1-formyl-1,2,3,8,8a,9,10,11,11a,11b-decahydro-10-oxo-, methyl ester, (3aS*,8aα,8bβ,11aβ,11bβ)-(±)-	EtOH	211(--),248(4.11), 305(3.40)	78-0641-79
$C_{21}H_{24}N_2O_5$			
Rumberine	EtOH	227(4.10),255(4.26), 312(3.46)	88-3197-79
$C_{21}H_{24}N_2O_8$			
Acetamide, N-[1-(2,3,4-tri-O-acetyl-α-L-arabinopyranosyl)-1H-indol-5-yl]-	EtOH	263(4.17),313(3.76)	103-0188-79
Acetamide, N-[1-(2,3,4-tri-O-acetyl-α-L-arabinopyranosyl)-1H-indol-6-yl]-	EtOH	235(4.38),279(4.08), 300s(3.73)	103-0188-79
$C_{21}H_{24}N_2S$			
Benzenamine, 4-[2-(2,3-dihydro-2,2-dimethyl-1,5-benzothiazepin-4-yl)ethenyl]-N,N-dimethyl-, BF_3 adduct	$CHCl_3$	530(4.71)	124-0231-79
$C_{21}H_{24}N_4$			
1,2,3-Triazin-5-amine, N,N-bis(1-methylethyl)-4,6-diphenyl-	CH_2Cl_2	374(3.50)	24-1514-79
$C_{21}H_{24}N_4S$			
Hydrazinecarbothioamide, 2-[2-(9,10-di-	EtOH	275(4.64)	103-0541-79

Compound	Solvent	λ_{max}(log ε)	Ref.
hydro-10-methyl-9-acridinyl)cyclohexylidene]- (cont.)			103-0541-79
$C_{21}H_{24}N_8O_6$			
2-Propenoic acid, 2-methyl-, 1-[(1,2,3-6-tetrahydro-1,3-dimethyl-2,6-dioxo-7H-purin-7-yl)methyl]-2-(1,2,3,4-tetrahydro-1,3-dimethyl-2,6-dioxo-7H-purin-7-yl)ethyl ester	H_2O	273(4.23)	126-2303-79
$C_{21}H_{24}O_2$			
Chrysene, 4b,5,6,10b,11,12-hexahydro-2,8-dimethoxy-4b-methyl-, cis	EtOH	220(4.24),280(3.63), 287(3.59)	12-1107-79
trans	EtOH	220(4.28),262(3.43), 272(3.64),277(3.64), 286(3.60)	12-1093-79
$C_{21}H_{24}O_3$			
5-Chrysenol, 4b,5,6,10b,11,12-hexahydro-2,8-dimethoxy-10b-methyl-, (4bα,5α,10bα)-	EtOH	222(4.27),278(3.60), 286(3.60)	12-1107-79
(4bα,5α,10bβ)-	EtOH	222(4.25),278(3.54), 285(3.51)	12-1107-79
Estr-4-ene-3,17-dione, 10-(1-oxo-2-propynyl)-	n.s.g.	216s(4.01),225s(4.07), 243(4.12)	88-2105-79
Tricyclo[9.3.1.1^{4,8}]hexadeca-1(15),4,7-11,13-pentaene-6,16-dione, 13-(1,1-dimethylethyl)-15-methoxy-	MeCN	257(4.26)	138-0595-79
$C_{21}H_{24}O_4$			
Anthracene, 9-[2-[2-(2-methoxyethoxy)-ethoxy]ethoxy]-	C_6H_{12}	249(4.94),257(5.27), 320(3.09),335(3.45), 351(3.76),370(3.96), 390(3.91)	108-0220-79
	benzene	392(3.90)	108-0220-79
	MeOH	256(5.27),389(3.90)	108-0220-79
Benzenecarboperoxoic acid, 4-(2,4,6-trimethylbenzoyl)-, 1,1-dimethylethyl ester	CCl_4	349(2.2),360s(2.2)	44-4123-79
1,2-Heptalenedicarboxylic acid, 5,10-dimethyl-7-(1-methylethyl)-, dimethyl ester	hexane	209(4.38),253(4.17), 277(4.09),330s(3.13)	27-0324-79
1,3-Heptalenedicarboxylic acid, 5,10-dimethyl-7-(1-methylethyl)-, dimethyl ester	hexane	210(4.39),279(4.33), 334s(3.5),424(3.17)	27-0324-79
1H-Naphtho[1',2':5,6]cyclohepta[1,2-b]-furan-4-carboxylic acid, 2,3,4,4a,5-6,7,12b-octahydro-4,12b-dimethyl-7-oxo-, methyl ester, [4S-(4α,4aβ,12bα)]-	EtOH	233s(4.01),258(4.25), 308s(3.53),319(3.57), 331(3.56),346(3.40)	44-2219-79
$C_{21}H_{24}O_5$			
2(3H)-Benzofuranone, 7-(1,1-dimethylethyl)-3-[5-(1,1-dimethylethyl)-3-oxo-2(3H)-furanylidene]-5-methoxy-, (E)-	EtOH	271(4.01),365(4.09), 455(3.60)	39-0290-79C
(Z)-	EtOH	275(4.03),357(3.96), 290s(3.88),455(3.50)	39-0290-79C
$C_{21}H_{24}O_5S_2$			
1,3-Dithiane-2-acetic acid, α-hydroxy-2-[3-methoxy-4-(phenylmethoxy)phen-	EtOH	240(5.00),281(3.55)	4-1081-79

Compound	Solvent	λ_{max}(log ε)	Ref.
yl]-, methyl ester (cont.)			4-1081-79
$C_{21}H_{24}O_8$			
4H-1-Benzopyran-4-one, 2,3-dihydro-6,7-dimethoxy-3-(2,3,4,5-tetramethoxyphenyl)-, (S)-	EtOH	280(4.17),337(3.94)	32-0009-79
$C_{21}H_{24}O_{10}$			
Eranthin-β-D-glucoside	MeOH	227(4.26),238s(4.12),253(4.18),258(4.19),292s(3.59),325(3.62)	102-2053-79
$C_{21}H_{25}BrN_2O_2$			
Aspidospermidine-3-carboxylic acid, 15-bromo-2,3-didehydro-, methyl ester, (±)-	MeOH	225s(4.11),310(4.19),331(4.17)	44-1063-79
$C_{21}H_{25}ClN_2O_2$			
Aspidospermidine-3-carboxylic acid, 15-chloro-2,3-didehydro-, methyl ester, (±)- (15-chlorovincadifformine)	MeOH	225s(4.11),311(4.20),338(4.17)	44-1063-79
$C_{21}H_{25}FN_4O_6$			
L-Glutamine, N -[(1,1-dimethylethoxy)-carbonyl]-N-(5-fluoro-1,2-dihydro-2-oxo-4-pyrimidinyl)-, phenylmethyl ester	EtOH	209(4.24),244(4.02),313(3.73),347(3.79)	87-1104-79
$C_{21}H_{25}N$			
2H-Pyrrole, 3,4-dihydro-3,3-dimethyl-5-[2-phenyl-1-(phenylmethyl)ethyl]-	MeOH	210(4.17),214s(4.11),218s(4.06)	83-0498-79
$C_{21}H_{25}NO_2$			
Benzenemethanamine, N-2,4-hexadienyl-4-methoxy-2-(4-methoxyphenyl)-, (E,E)-	n.s.g.	231(4.62),274(3.53),284(3.43)	44-3451-79
19-Norpregna-1,3,5(10),17(20)-tetraene-21-nitrile, 14-hydroxy-3-methoxy-, (14β)-	MeOH	222(4.33)	97-0451-79
2H-Pyrrole-5-ethanol, 3,4-dihydro-α-(4-methoxyphenyl)-3,3-dimethyl-α-phenyl-	MeOH	205(4.37),230(3.85)	83-0498-79
$C_{21}H_{25}NO_3$			
4H-Dibenzo[de,g]quinoline, 2-ethoxy-5,6,6a,7-tetrahydro-10,11-dimethoxy-6-methyl-, hydrochloride, (±)-	EtOH	219(4.59),230s(4.50),268(4.19),275(4.18),298(3.80)	33-1549-79
$C_{21}H_{25}NO_4$			
Atherosperminine, methoxy-	EtOH	216(4.40),260(4.80),284s(4.16),296(4.05),308(4.16)	100-0325-79
5,12-(Iminomethano)dibenzo[a,d]cyclooctene, 5,6,7,12-tetrahydro-2,3,9,10-tetramethoxy-, (±)-	EtOH	233(4.13),287(3.82)	78-1857-79
Isoquinoline, 2-[(6-ethyl-1,3-benzodioxol-5-yl)methyl]-1,2,3,4-tetrahydro-6,7-dimethoxy-	EtOH	230s(4.11),286(3.90)	39-0283-79C
L-Phenylalanine, N-[(phenylmethoxy)-carbonyl]-, butyl ester	EtOH	248(2.48),253(2.57),259(2.64),265(2.55),268(2.39)	118-0961-79

Compound	Solvent	$\lambda_{max}(\log \epsilon)$	Ref.
$C_{21}H_{25}NO_5$			
Benzo[a]heptalen-9(5H)-one, 6,7-dihydro-1,2,3,10-tetramethoxy-7-(methylamino)-, (S)- (demecolcine)	EtOH	243(4.48),350(4.21)	33-0965-79
Isodemecolcine	EtOH	247(4.52),344(4.29)	33-0965-79
$C_{21}H_{25}NO_6$			
D-Arabinitol, 1-deoxy-1-(2,5-dioxo-1-phenyl-3-pyrrolidinylidene)-2,3:4,5-bis-O-(1-methylethylidene)-, (E)-	EtOH	226(4.15)	33-0977-79
Benzeneacetamide, N-[2-(3,4-dimethoxyphenyl)ethenyl]-α,3,4-trimethoxy-, cis	EtOH	227(4.25),280(4.29), 294s(4.12)	39-0652-79C
trans	EtOH	218(4.13),285(4.20), 292(4.21),308(4.13), 324s(3.94)	39-0652-79C
$C_{21}H_{25}N_3OS$			
Benzothiazole, 2-[[4-(octyloxy)phenyl]-azo]-	EtOH	417(3.27)	103-1185-79
2,5-Cyclohexadiene-1,4-dione, mono[(3-octyl-2(3H)-benzothiazolylidene)hydrazone]	EtOH	518(3.83)	103-1185-79
$C_{21}H_{25}N_3O_2$			
5H,11H-6a,11a-Propano-13H-pyrrolo[1",2"-1,5]pyrrolo[2,3-b]indole-5,13-dione, 1,2,3,5a,6,13a-hexahydro-14,14-dimethyl-, [5aS-(5aα,6aβ,11aβ,13aβ)]-	EtOH	229(3.91),244(3.80), 296(3.42)	39-3053-79C
Pyrrolo[1,2-a]pyrazine-1,4-dione, 3-[(2,3-dihydro-1,1-dimethyl-1H-pyrrolo[1,2-a]indol-9-yl)methyl]-hexahydro-, (3S-trans)-	EtOH	227(4.47),278s(3.76), 284(3.70),292(3.65)	39-3053-79C
Pyrrolo[1,2-a]pyrazine-1,4-dione, 3-[(5,6-dihydro-6,6-dimethyl-4H-pyrrolo[3,2,1-ij]quinolin-1-yl)methyl]hexahydro-, (3S-trans)-	EtOH	223(4.34),248s(3.53), 290(3.64),300(3.62)	39-3053-79C
Pyrrolo[1,2-a]pyrazine-1,4-dione, hexahydro-3-[[1-(3-methyl-2-butenyl)-1H-indol-3-yl]methyl]-, (3S-trans)-	EtOH	278s(3.60),288(3.63), 292s(3.56)	39-3048-79C
1H-Pyrrolo[1",2":4',5']pyrazino[1',2'-1,5]pyrrolo[2,3-b]indole-5,13(5aH-13aH)-dione, 2,3,6,6a,11,11a-hexahydro-11-(3-methyl-2-butenyl)-	EtOH	209(4.37),256(3.91), 306(3.28)	39-3048-79C
$C_{21}H_{25}N_3O_3$			
Indolo[2',3':3,4]pyrido[2,1-b]quinazolin-5(7H)-one, 8,13,13b,14-tetrahydro-2,3-dimethoxy-14-methyl-, tetrahydro deriv.	MeOH	233(4.37),315(3.57), 373(3.62)	142-0353-79
Pyrrolo[1,2-a]pyrazine-1,4-dione, 3-[(2,3-dihydro-3-hydroxy-1,1-dimethyl-1H-pyrrolo[1,2-a]indol-9-yl)-methyl]hexahydro-	EtOH	226(4.51),279(3.79), 285(3.78),291(3.73)	39-3053-79C
less polar isomer	EtOH	226(4.50),280(3.74), 296(3.79),293(3.75)	39-3053-79C
$C_{21}H_{25}N_3O_4$			
Pyrrolo[1,2-a]pyrazine-1,4-dione, 3-[2-[2-(3,3-dimethyl-2-oxo-1-pyrrolidinyl)phenyl]-2-oxoethyl]hexahydro-, (3S-trans)-	EtOH	211(4.13),225(4.11), 281(3.0)	39-3053-79C

Compound	Solvent	λ_{max}(log ε)	Ref.
$C_{21}H_{25}N_3O_5$			
Eburnamenine-14-carboxylic acid, 14,15-dihydro-14-hydroxy-9-nitro-, methyl ester, (3α,14β,16α)-	MeOH	213(4.48),243(4.04), 250(4.05),390(3.69)	20-0093-79
Eburnamenine-14-carboxylic acid, 14,15-dihydro-14-hydroxy-11-nitro-, methyl ester (11-nitrovincamine)	MeOH	220(4.43),269(3.95), 329(3.90),381(4.00)	20-0093-79
$C_{21}H_{25}N_3O_7$			
1H-Imidazole-4-carboxylic acid, 5-amino-1-[2,3-O-(1-methylethylidene)-5-acetoxy-β-D-ribofuranosyl]-, phenylmethyl ester	MeOH	206(4.10),268(4.18)	39-1415-79C
Bratton-Marshall product	n.s.g.	524(4.23)	39-1415-79C
$C_{21}H_{25}N_3O_9$			
β-D-Glucopyranosylamine, N-1H-benzimidazol-2-yl-, 2,3,4,6-tetraacetate	MeOH	246(4.8),280(4.0), 285(4.0)	94-1153-79
$C_{21}H_{25}N_5O_5S$			
Guanosine, 2',3'-O-(1-methylethylidene)-N-[(4-methylphenyl)thio]methyl-	EtOH	256(4.29),272s(4.18)	130-0339-79
$C_{21}H_{26}$			
5,8-Etheno-9H-benzocyclopentadecene, 10,11,12,13,14,15,16,17-octahydro-	EtOH	238(4.08)	44-2160-79
$C_{21}H_{26}ClN_3OS$			
10H-Phenothiazine, 2-chloro-7-methoxy-10-[3-(4-methyl-1-piperazinyl)propyl]- (perphenazine)	MeOH	207(4.46),257(4.56), 312(3.66)	133-0197-79
$C_{21}H_{26}N_2$			
2-Cyclohexen-1-amine, 5-[2-(1H-indol-3-yl)ethenyl]-N-methyl-6-methylene-N-(1-methylethyl)-, [1α,5α(E)]-	EtOH	224(4.42),252s(4.21), 258(4.29),280(3.98), 297s(3.80)	33-0481-79
$C_{21}H_{26}N_2O_2$			
6H-Pyrrolo[3,2-f]indolizine-2-carboxylic acid, 3,7,8-trimethyl-6-methylene-4-(2-methylphenyl)-, ethyl ester, hydrochloride	KBr	277(4.68),285(4.67), 330(3.95),353(3.89)	104-0967-79
$C_{21}H_{26}N_2O_3$			
1H-Cyclopent[a]indolo[3,2-h]quinolizine-4-carboxylic acid, 2,3,3a,4,5,7-8,13,13b,13c-decahydro-3-hydroxy-1-methyl-, methyl ester	EtOH	227(4.48),284(3.84), 292(3.82)	28-0057-79A
isomer	EtOH	227(4.39),284(3.84), 292(3.81)	28-0057-79A
$C_{21}H_{26}N_2O_4$			
8bH-Pyrrolo[3',2':2,3]pentaleno[1,2-b]-indole-8b-carboxylic acid, 11a-ethyl-1-formyl-1,2,3,8,8a,9,10,11,11a,11b-decahydro-10-hydroxy-, methyl ester	EtOH	248(3.86),305(3.40)	78-0641-79
Yohimban-16-carboxylic acid, 1,2-didehydro-2,7-dihydro-7,17-dihydroxy-, methyl ester, (16α,17α)-	EtOH	222(4.11),261(3.53)	78-0633-79

Compound	Solvent	λ_{max}(log ϵ)	Ref.
$C_{21}H_{26}N_2O_5$			
5H-Indazole-5,5-dicarboxylic acid, 3-ethoxy-2,4,6,7-tetrahydro-2-phenyl-, diethyl ester	EtOH	253(4.19)	39-2099-79C
$C_{21}H_{26}N_4O_{11}S$			
Isothiazolo[3,4-d]pyrimidine-4,6(5H,7H)-dione, 5,7-dimethyl-3-[(2,3,4,6-tetra-O-acetyl-β-D-glucopyranosyl)amino]-	dioxan	221(4.2),258(4.4), 276(4.3),314(4.4)	94-1147-79
Thiazolo[4,5-d]pyrimidine-5,7(4H,6H)-dione, 2,3-dihydro-4,6-dimethyl-2-[(2,3,4,6-tetra-O-acetyl-β-D-glucopyranosyl)imino]-	MeOH	223(4.5),272(4.5), 293(4.0)	94-1147-79
$C_{21}H_{26}O$			
Euserotin	n.s.g.	217(4.48),265(3.51)	44-2784-79
$C_{21}H_{26}O_2$			
D-Dihomoestra-1,3,5(10),16-tetraen-17a-one, 3-methoxy-, (±)-	n.s.g.	220(4.03)	23-3308-79
2(3H)-Furanone, 4-(2-ethyl-4-methyl-6-phenyl-1,3,5-hexatrienyl)dihydro-3,5-dimethyl-	hexane	227(4.12),301(4.58)	44-3109-79
1-Isobenzofuranol, 1,3-dihydro-3,3-bis(1-methylethyl)-1-(2-methylphenyl)-	50% H_2SO_4	344(4.33)	104-1126-79
1-Isobenzofuranol, 1,3-dihydro-3,3-bis(1-methylethyl)-1-(3-methylphenyl)-	50% H_2SO_4	346(4.39)	104-1126-79
1-Isobenzofuranol, 1,3-dihydro-3,3-bis(1-methylethyl)-1-(4-methylphenyl)-	50% H_2SO_4	370(4.48)	104-1126-79
19-Norpregna-1,3,5(10),16-tetraen-20-one, 3-methoxy-, (±)-	n.s.g.	229(4.15),277(3.43), 287(3.38)	23-3308-79
19-Norpregna-1,3,5(10)-trien-20-yn-16-ol, 3-methoxy-, (16α,17α)-	EtOH	278(3.31),287(3.29)	87-1538-79
3-Oxabicyclo[4.1.0]heptan-4-one, 2-ethyl-5,7-dimethyl-2-(2-methyl-4-phenyl-1,3-butadienyl)-	hexane	219(4.23),289(4.52), 306(4.29)	44-3109-79
$C_{21}H_{26}O_3$			
3,5-Cyclohexadiene-1,2-dione, 3,6-bis-(1,1-dimethylethyl)-4-(4-methoxyphenyl)-	C_6H_{12}	357(3.6)	44-2983-79
Estr-4-ene-3,17-dione, 10-(1-hydroxy-2-propynyl)-	n.s.g.	239(4.18)	88-2105-79
stereoisomer	n.s.g.	238(4.16)	88-2105-79
Pregna-4,16-diene-3,12,20-trione	MeOH	230(4.08),280(3.92)	102-1240-79
Pregna-4,6,16-triene-3,20-dione, 12-hydroxy-, (12β)- (neridienone A)	MeOH	245(4.08),284(4.36)	102-1240-79
$C_{21}H_{26}O_3S$			
D-Homo-16-thiaestra-1,3,5(10),8(14)-tetraen-17aα-ol, 3-methoxy-, acetate	EtOH	278(3.30),283(3.28)	39-0990-79C
D-Homo-16-thiaestra-1,3,5(10),8-tetraen-17aβ-ol, 3-methoxy-, acetate	EtOH	276(4.27)	39-0990-79C
D-Homo-16-thia-14 -estra-1,3,5(10),8-tetraen-17aβ-ol, 3-methoxy-, acetate	EtOH	277(4.29)	39-0990-79C
D-Homo-16-thiaestra-1,3,5(10),9(11)-tetraen-17aβ-ol, 3-methoxy-, acetate	EtOH	263(4.27)	39-0990-79C
15-Thiaestra-1,3,5(10),8-tetraen-17β-ol, 3-methoxy-14β-methyl-, acetate	EtOH	278(4.24)	39-0990-79C
15-Thia-14β-estra-1,3,5(10),8-tetraen-17α-ol, 3-methoxy-14β-methyl-, acetate	EtOH	282(4.27)	39-0990-79C

Compound	Solvent	λ_{max}(log ε)	Ref.
$C_{21}H_{26}O_4$			
1H-Naphtho[1',2':5,6]cyclohepta[1,2-b]-furan-4-carboxylic acid, 2,3,4,4a,5-6,7,11,12,12b-decahydro-4,12b-dimethyl-7-oxo-, methyl ester (methyl hispanonate)	EtOH	258s(3.85),273(3.97), 284s(3.94),313(4.06)	44-2219-79
1H-Naphtho[1',2':5,6]cyclohepta[1,2-b]-furan-4-carboxylic acid, 2,3,4,4a,5-6,9,11,12,12b-decahydro-4,12b-dimethyl-9-oxo-, methyl ester (methyl hispaninate)	EtOH	233(3.72),260(3.79), 357(4.02)	44-2219-79
Pregna-2,16-diene-1,20-dione, 5,6-epoxy-4-hydroxy-	EtOH	219(3.94),235(4.00)	150-1178-79
$C_{21}H_{26}O_5$			
2(3H)-Benzofuranone, 7-(1,1-dimethylethyl)-3-[5-(1,1-dimethylethyl)-2,3-dihydro-3-oxo-2-furanyl]-5-methoxy-	C_6H_{12}	260(4.06),296(3.43), 368(2.78)	39-0290-79C
2(3H)-Benzofuranone, 7-(1,1-dimethylethyl)-3-(4-hydroxy-5,5-dimethyl-2-oxo-3-hexenylidene)-5-methoxy-, (Z,E)-	EtOH	266(4.05),294(3.45), 372(3.43)	39-0290-79C
Cyclopentanepentanoic acid, 1-[3-(3-methoxyphenyl)-2-propenyl]- ,2-dioxo-, methyl ester	MeOH	254(3.98),291(3.46)	13-0361-79A
Lumiprednisone	EtOH	215(3.65),265(3.27)	35-5019-79
19-Norpregna-1,3,5(10)-triene-11,20-dione, 2,17α,21-trihydroxy-1-methyl-	EtOH	214(3.90),284(3.31)	35-5019-79
	EtOH-base	243(4.08),300(3.69)	35-5019-79
$C_{21}H_{26}O_5S$			
D-Homo-16-thiaestra-1,3,5(10),8(14)-tetraen-17a-ol, 3-methoxy-, acetate, 16,16-dioxide, (17aα)-	EtOH	278(3.30),283(3.28)	39-0990-79C
(17aβ)-	EtOH	278(3.32),283(3.28)	39-0990-79C
$C_{21}H_{26}O_6$			
7a,12a-Epidioxy-9H-naphtho[1',2':5,6]-cyclohepta[1,2-b]furan-4-carboxylic acid, 1,2,3,4,4a,5,6,11,12,12b-decahydro-4,12b-dimethyl-9-oxo-, methyl ester, [4S-(4α,4aβ,7aβ,12aβ,12bα)]-	EtOH	222(4.20)	44-2219-79
$C_{21}H_{26}O_7$			
2H-1-Benzopyran, 3,4-dihydro-6,7-dimethoxy-3-(2,3,4,5-tetramethoxyphenyl)-, (S)-	EtOH	289(3.90)	32-0009-79
1-Naphthalenepropanoic acid, 2-ethoxy-5,6,7-trimethoxy-4-methyl-β-oxo-, ethyl ester	EtOH	238(4.79),259s(4.34), 357(3.67)	150-0301-79
$C_{21}H_{27}BrN_2O_{11}$			
1H-Pyrazole-3-carboxylic acid, 5-(bromomethyl)-1-(2,3,4,6-tetra-O-acetyl-β-D-glucopyranosyl)-, ethyl ester	EtOH	214(4.18)	87-0807-79
1H-Pyrazole-5-carboxylic acid, 3-(bromomethyl)-1-(2,3,4,6-tetra-O-acetyl-α-D-glucopyranosyl)-, ethyl ester	EtOH	222(4.01),240s(3.83)	87-0807-79
β-	EtOH	222(4.02),240s(3.83)	87-0807-79
$C_{21}H_{27}BrO_4$			
Androst-4-ene-3,17-dione, 16α-acetoxy-6α-bromo-	EtOH	241(4.04)	13-0347-79B

Compound	Solvent	λ_{max}(log ε)	Ref.
Androst-4-ene-3,17-dione, 16α-acetoxy-6β-bromo-	EtOH	248(4.09)	13-0347-79B
$C_{21}H_{27}NO_3$			
1H-3-Benzazepine, 2,3,4,5-tetrahydro-7,8-dimethoxy-2,2-dimethyl-1-(3-methoxyphenyl)-, hydrochloride	EtOH	281(3.68)	4-1525-79
$C_{21}H_{27}NO_4$			
Isoquinoline, 4-[(3,4-dimethoxyphenyl)-methyl]-1,2,3,4-tetrahydro-6,7-di-methoxy-2-methyl-	EtOH	234(4.23),283(3.90)	78-2555-79
Naphtho[1,2-c][1,3]dioxin, 7-hydroxy-2,2,10b-trimethyl-6-oxo-4-(piperi-dinomethylene)-	MeOH	217(4.38),256(4.10), 338(3.62)	35-0689-79
$C_{21}H_{27}NO_6$			
Propanoic acid, 2-amino-2-[(3,4-dimeth-oxyphenyl)methyl]-3-(3,4-dimethoxy-phenyl)-, methyl ester	EtOH	280(3.78)	44-2732-79
$C_{21}H_{27}NO_8$			
Pyridinium, 1-[3-ethoxy-2-(ethoxycarbo-nyl)-1-[2-ethoxy-1-(ethoxycarbonyl)-2-oxoethyl]-3-oxo-1-propenyl]-2-methyl-	$CHCl_3$	367(3.1),440(2.3)	5-1406-79
Pyridinium, 1-[3-ethoxy-2-(ethoxycarbo-nyl)-1-[2-ethoxy-1-(ethoxycarbonyl)-2-oxoethyl]-3-oxo-1-propenyl]-3-methyl-	$CHCl_3$	363(3.3),465(2.5)	5-1406-79
Pyridinium, 1-[3-ethoxy-2-(ethoxycarbo-nyl)-1-[2-ethoxy-1-(ethoxycarbonyl)-2-oxoethyl]-3-oxo-1-propenyl]-4-methyl-	$CHCl_3$	362(3.6),450(2.9)	4-1406-79
$C_{21}H_{27}NSi_3$			
Silanamine, 1-methyl-N,N-bis(methyl-phenylsilyl)-1-phenyl-	heptane	188.8(5.15)	65-1333-79
$C_{21}H_{27}N_3$			
1H-Pyrrole, 2-[[5-[(3,4-dimethyl-1H-pyrrol-2-yl)methyl]-3,4-dimethyl-2H-pyrrol-2-ylidene]methyl]-3,4,5-tri-methyl-, monohydrobromide	$CHCl_3$-HBr	498(4.75)	104-0970-79
1H-Pyrrole, 2-[[2-[(3,4-dimethyl-1H-pyrrol-2-yl)methylene]-3,4-dimethyl-2H-pyrrol-5-yl]methyl]-3,4,5-tri-methyl-, monohydrobromide	$CHCl_3$-HBr	487(4.76)	104-0970-79
$C_{21}H_{27}N_3O$			
7H-Indazol-7-one, 6,7a-bis(1,1-dimeth-ylethyl)-3,3a,4,7a-tetrahydro-4-(phenylimino)-	n.s.g.	260(4.29)	70-1668-79
$C_{21}H_{27}N_3O_3$			
Eburnamenine-14-carboxylic acid, 9-ami-no-14,15-dihydro-14-hydroxy-, methyl ester, (3α,14β,16α)-	MeOH	231(4.49),276(3.88), 302(3.82)	20-0093-79
Eburnamenine-14-carboxylic acid, 11-ami-no-14,15-dihydro-14-hydroxy-, methyl ester (11-aminovincamine)	MeOH	236(4.43),278(3.88), 307(3.62)	20-0093-79

Compound	Solvent	λ_{max}(log ε)	Ref.
$C_{21}H_{27}N_3O_9S$			
Thiourea, N-(2-aminophenyl)-N'-(2,3,4,6-tetra-O-acetyl-β-D-glucopyranosyl)-	MeOH	240(4.5),295(4.4)	94-1153-79
$C_{21}H_{27}N_3O_{10}$			
Butanedioic acid, 2-[(4-ethoxy-1,4-dioxobutoxy)methyl]-2,3,3a,9a-tetrahydro-6-imino-6H-furo[2',3':4,5]oxazolo-[3,2-a]pyrimidin-3-yl ethyl ester, monohydrochloride, [2R-(2α,3β,3aβ,9aβ)]-	MeOH	235(3.90),263(3.98)	87-0639-79
$C_{21}H_{27}N_5O_{11}$			
1H-Purine-2,6-dione, 3,7-dihydro-1,3-dimethyl-8-[(2,3,4,6-tetra-O-acetyl-β-D-glucopyranosyl)amino]-	MeOH	216(4.5),290(4.3)	94-1153-79
$C_{21}H_{27}N_{13}O_4$			
Alanine, 3-(6-amino-9H-purin-9-yl)-N-[N-[3-(6-amino-9H-purin-9-yl)alanyl]-L-alanyl]-, ethyl ester, trihydrochloride	EtOH	206(4.38)	65-1000-79
$C_{21}H_{28}$			
6H-5,15-Methenocyclopentacyclopentadecene, 7,8,9,10,11,12,13,14-octahydro-4,16-dimethyl-	C_6H_{12}	253(4.71),292(4.87), 298(4.85),340(3.97), 350(4.06),365(3.87), 565s(2.92),581(2.94), 600(2.91),627s(2.82), 660s(2.56),690(2.29)	18-0257-79
$C_{21}H_{28}N_2O_3$			
Secodin-17-ol, 16,17-dihydro-	EtOH	222(4.49),274(3.87), 284(3.93),292(3.86)	23-0289-79
$C_{21}H_{28}N_2O_6$			
1,1,3-Cyclohexanetricarboxylic acid, 4-(phenylhydrazono)-, triethyl ester	EtOH	239(3.82),278(4.18), 291s(4.06)	39-2099-79C
$C_{21}H_{28}N_2O_8$			
Pyridinium, 4-(dimethylamino)-1-[3-ethoxy-2-(ethoxycarbonyl)-1-[1-(ethoxycarbonyl)-2-methoxy-2-oxoethyl]-3-oxo-1-propenyl]-, hydroxide, inner salt	$CHCl_3$	306(4.5),413(4.0)	5-1388-79 +5-1406-79
$C_{21}H_{28}N_2O_{11}S$			
4-Isothiazolecarboxylic acid, 3-methyl-5-[(2,3,4,6-tetra-O-acetyl-β-D-glucopyranosyl)amino]-, ethyl ester	dioxan	223(3.3),273(4.1), 380(2.6)	94-1147-79
$C_{21}H_{28}N_4O_2$			
Benzo[d]cyclopenta[i]tetrazolo[1,5-a]-[1]benzazepin-10(8H)-one, 1-acetyl-1,2,3,3a,3b,11,12,12a,12b,13,14,14a-dodecahydro-12a,14a-dimethyl-, [1S-(1α,3aα,3bβ,12aα,12bβ,14aα)]-	MeOH	235(4.77)	39-3166-79C
$C_{21}H_{28}N_4O_3$			
Benzo[d]cyclopenta[i]tetrazolo[1,5-a]-[1]benzazepin-10(8H)-one, 1-acetoxy-1,2,3,3a,3b,11,12,12a,12b,13,14,14a-	MeOH	234(4.10)	39-3166-79C

Compound	Solvent	λ_{max}(log ε)	Ref.
dodecahydro-12a,14a-dimethyl-, [1S-(1α,3aβ,3bα,12aα,12bβ,14aα)]- (cont.)			39-3166-79C
$C_{21}H_{28}N_6O_4$			
1H-Purine-2,6-dione, 3,7-dihydro-8-(hydroxymethyl)-7-[2-hydroxy-3-(4-methyl-1-piperazinyl)propyl]-1,3-dimethyl-, dinicotinate	n.s.g.	212(4.74),276(4.18)	73-0424-79
$C_{21}H_{28}O$			
Pregna-1,4,20-trien-3-one	MeOH	244(4.19)	39-2064-79C
$C_{21}H_{28}O_2S_2$			
Androsta-3,5-diene-11,17-dione, 3-(ethyldithio)-	MeOH	248(4.26)	39-1166-79C
$C_{21}H_{28}O_3$			
1,2-Benzenediol, 3,6-bis(1,1-dimethylethyl)-4-(4-methoxyphenyl)-	EtOH	279(3.5)	44-2983-79
Estra-1,3,5(10)-trien-17-one, 3-methoxy-, cyclic 1,2-ethanediyl acetal	n.s.g.	263(4.29),298(3.49)	88-0629-79
18-Norpregna-8,11,13-trien-3-one, 20,21-dihydroxy-17-methyl-, (5β,17α,20R)-	MeOH	269(2.65)	39-1048-79C
Pregna-4,16-diene-3,20-dione, 12-hydroxy-	MeOH	240(4.42)	102-1240-79
9β,10α-Pregna-4,6-diene-3,20-dione, 17α-hydroxy-	MeOH	284(4.43)	54-0078-79
Strictic acid, methyl ester	EtOH	212(4.16),255(3.34)	2-0529-79B
$C_{21}H_{28}O_4$			
Androst-5-ene-7,17-dione, 3β-acetoxy-	EtOH	235(4.11)	150-0501-79
8,15-Isopimaradien-18-oic acid, 7,11-dioxo-, methyl ester	EtOH	266(3.89)	102-1835-79
Pregna-4,8(14)-diene-3,20-dione, 16,17-dihydroxy-	MeOH	233(4.27),256s(3.99)	24-3748-79
	MeCN	228(4.21),250s(3.97)	24-3748-79
$C_{21}H_{28}O_5$			
2(3H)-Benzofuranone, 7-(1,1-dimethylethyl)-3-(4-hydroxy-5,5-dimethyl-2-oxo-3-hexenyl)-5-methoxy-, (Z)-	EtOH	243(3.74),281(3.92)	39-0290-79C
Carnosolone methyl ether	ether	228(4.24),273(4.02), 316(3.61)	33-2754-79
Cyclopentanepentanoic acid, 1-[3-(3-methoxyphenyl)propyl]-δ,2-dioxo-, methyl ester	MeOH	272(3.36),278(3.32), 300(2.59)	13-0361-79A
Tricyclo[6.3.0^{1,5}.0^{1,8}]undeca-2,4,6-trione, 5-hydroxy-9,9-dimethyl-3-(3-methylbutanoyl)-10-(1-methylethenyl)-	EtOH-acid	237(4.02),268(4.04)	39-1250-79C
	EtOH-base	257(4.26)	39-1250-79C
$C_{21}H_{28}O_6$			
B(9a)-Homo-A,19-dinorpregn-3(5)-ene-2,11,20-trione, 9a,17,21-trihydroxy-9a-methyl-, (9aα,10α)-	EtOH	233(4.49)	35-5019-79
Rhipocephalin or 1,6,8,10-Dodecatetraene-1,4-diol, 3-(acetoxymethylene)-7,11-dimethyl-, diacetate, (Z,E,E,E)-	MeOH	257(4.48),266(4.52), 277(4.54),287(4.43)	88-0685-79
$C_{21}H_{29}BrO_3$			
Androst-4-en-3-one, 6α-bromo-17β-acetoxy-	EtOH	240(4.05)	13-0347-79B

Compound	Solvent	λ max (log ε)	Ref.
Androst-4-en-3-one, 6β-bromo-17β-acetoxy- (cont.)	EtOH	245.5(4.11)	13-0347-79B
$C_{21}H_{29}ClO_7$			
1H-Inden-1-one, 6-(2-chloroethyl)-2-[(β-D-glucopyranosyloxy)methyl]-2,3-dihydro-2,5,7-trimethyl-, (S)-	EtOH	221(4.52),261(4.17), 306(3.35)	94-0592-79
$C_{21}H_{29}NO_3$			
1H-[1]Benzopyrano[2,3-b]quinoline-1,10(2H)-dione, 3,4,5a,6,7,8,9,11,11a-12-decahydro-3,3,5a,8,8-pentamethyl-	pH 1	265(4.28),301(4.37)	39-1411-79C
	H_2O	268(4.28),300(4.32)	39-1411-79C
	pH 13	295(4.46)	39-1411-79C
	EtOH	262(4.33),293(4.34)	39-1411-79C
$C_{21}H_{29}NO_4$			
Benzenemethanol, α-[1-[[2-(3,4-dimethoxyphenyl)ethyl]amino]-1-methylethyl]-3-methoxy-, hydrochloride	EtOH	220(4.06),278(3.58)	4-1525-79
$C_{21}H_{29}N_3O_{12}S$			
D-Arabinitol, 5-C-[3-acetyl-5-(acetylamino)-2,3-dihydro-1,3,4-thiadiazol-2-yl]-, 1,2,3,4,5-pentaacetate, (±)-	EtOH	214(3.92),254(3.78), 283(3.93)	136-0325-79H
(-)-	EtOH	215(4.02),286(4.34)	136-0325-79H
$C_{21}H_{29}N_5O_4S_2$			
Benzenesulfonamide, 4-[[4-[[2-[(cyclohexylamino)sulfonyl]ethyl]methylamino]phenyl]azo]-	acetone	424(4.46)	44-3847-79
$C_{21}H_{30}NO_4$			
Benzo[a]quinolizinium, 2-(2-ethoxy-2-oxoethyl)-3-ethyl-1,2,3,4,6,7-hexahydro-, cis, iodide	EtOH	246(4.21),305(3.95), 356(3.96)	94-2497-79
perchlorate	EtOH	246(4.23),304(3.97), 354(3.97)	94-2497-79
$C_{21}H_{30}N_2OS$			
Androsta-5,16-dieno[17,16-d]thiazol-3-ol, 2'-(methylamino)-, (3β)-	$CHCl_3$	273(3.82)	4-0763-79
Formamide, N-[(5α)-androst-16-eno-[17,16-d]thiazol-2'-yl]-	$CHCl_3$	291(3.95)	4-0763-79
$C_{21}H_{30}N_2O_3$			
Aspidospermidine-3-methanol, 20-hydroxy-16-methoxy-, (2β,3α,5α,12β-19α,20R)-	EtOH	247(3.76),304(3.69)	78-1151-79
$C_{21}H_{30}N_2O_{11}S$			
2-Butenoic acid, 3-amino-2-[[(2,3,4,6-tetra-O-acetyl-β-D-glucopyranosyl)-amino]thioxomethyl]-, ethyl ester	dioxan	224(4.3),271(4.0), 388(2.6)	94-1147-79
$C_{21}H_{30}N_4O_2$			
Benzo[d]cyclopenta[i]tetrazolo[1,5-a]-[1]benzazepin-10(8H)-one, 1-acetyl-1,2,3,3a,3b,8a,9,11,12,12a,12b,13-14,14a-tetradecahydro-12a,14a-dimethyl-, [1S-(1α,3aβ,3bα,8aβ,12aα-12bα,14aα)]-	MeOH	242(4.07)	39-3166-79C

Compound	Solvent	λ_{max}(log ε)	Ref.
$C_{21}H_{30}N_4O_3$			
Benzo[d]cyclopenta[i]tetrazolo[1,5-a]-[1]benzazepine-1,10-diol, 1,2,3,3a-3b,9,10,11,12,12a,12b,13,14,14a-tetradecahydro-12a,14a-dimethyl-, 1-acetate, [1S-(1α,3aβ,3bα,10α,12aα-12bβ,14aα)]-	MeOH	241(4.14)	39-3166-79C
$C_{21}H_{30}O$			
Spiro[cyclohexane-1,2'(1'H)-naphthalen]-1'-one, 3',4'-dihydro-7'-(1-methylethyl)-2-propyl-	EtOH	254(4.07),292(4.22)	2-0226-79A
$C_{21}H_{30}O_2$			
17,18-Cyclo-5β-pregnane-3,20-dione	EtOH	217(3.8)	12-2323-79
$C_{21}H_{30}O_3$			
Androst-4-en-3-one, 17β-acetoxy-	EtOH	241(4.13)	150-0501-79
Hardwickiic acid, methyl ester	EtOH	213(4.10)	78-2301-79
Retinoic acid, 7,8-epoxy-7,8-dihydro-, methyl ester, all-trans	EtOH	324(4.20)	44-4458-79
13-cis	EtOH	315(4.04)	44-4458-79
Retinoic acid, 13,14-epoxy-13,14-dihydro-, methyl ester, (13R*,14S*)-(±)-	hexane	293(4.3)	44-4988-79
$C_{21}H_{30}O_4$			
Androst-4-ene-1-acetic acid, 17-hydroxy-3-oxo-, (1α,17β)-	EtOH	243(4.18)	56-0149-79
Androst-4-en-3-one, 17β-acetoxy-15β-hydroxy-	EtOH	241(4.20)	150-0201-79
7a,10-Methano-7aH-cyclohepta[g]-3-benzoxepin-2,11(1H,10H)-dione, 4,5,5a,6-7,12,12a,12b-octahydro-4-methoxy-5,5,10,12b-tetramethyl-	EtOH	213(3.47),296(2.33)	39-1004-79C
1H-Naphtho[1',2':5,6]cyclohepta[1,2-b]-furan-4-carboxylic acid, 2,3,4,4a-5,6,7,7a,9,10,10a,11,12,12b-tetradecahydro-4,12b-dimethyl-7-oxo-, methyl ester	EtOH	252(3.86)	44-2219-79
Pregn-4-ene-3,20-dione, 16,17-dihydroxy-, (16α)-	MeOH	240(4.23)	24-3748-79
	MeCN	238(4.24)	24-3748-79
$C_{21}H_{30}O_5$			
Isohumulone, cis-anti	MeOH-HCl	224(4.05),270(3.99)	78-0989-79
	MeOH-NaOH	255(4.20)	78-0989-79
trans	MeOH-HCl	255(4.02),275s(3.74)	78-0989-79
	MeOH-NaOH	255(4.16)	78-0989-79
$C_{21}H_{30}O_8$			
Pteroside A, (2S)-	EtOH	216(4.37),260(4.25), 305(3.46)	94-0592-79
Pteroside D, (3S)-	EtOH	216(4.46),258(4.07), 300(3.27)	94-0592-79
$C_{21}H_{30}S$			
Methanethione, bis(tricyclo[3.3.1.1^{3,7}]-dec-1-yl)-	benzene	548(1.22)	88-3673-79
	hexane	548(1.14)	88-3673-79
$C_{21}H_{31}FO_2$			
A-Homoandrost-2-en-4-one, 3-fluoro-17-hydroxy-2-methyl-, (5α,17β)-	n.s.g.	248(4.00)	44-2929-79

Compound	Solvent	λ max (log ε)	Ref.
$C_{21}H_{31}NO_2$			
Pregn-17(20)-ene-21-nitrile, 3,14-dihydroxy-, (3β,5β,14β)-	MeOH	222(4.14)	97-0451-79
$C_{21}H_{31}N_2OP$			
Benzenamine, 4,4'-[(diethylphosphinyl)methylene]bis[N,N-dimethyl-	EtOH	268(4.61),300s(3.79)	65-1275-79
$C_{21}H_{31}N_2P$			
Benzenamine, 4,4'-[(diethylphosphino)methylene]bis[N,N-dimethyl-	EtOH	268(4.65),300s(3.80), 360(2.98)	65-1275-79
$C_{21}H_{31}N_5O_{10}$			
β-D-Glucopyranoside, 2-methyl-4-(9-β-D-ribofuranosyl-9H-purin-6-yl)amino]-2-butenyl, (E)-	pH 1	265.5(4.30)	102-0819-79
	pH 13	269(4.29)	102-0819-79
	EtOH	269(4.29)	102-0819-79
$C_{21}H_{32}$			
5,8-Etheno-1H-benzocyclopentadecene, 2,3,4,4a,9,10,11,12,13,14,15,16,17-17a-tetradecahydro-, (4aR*,17aS*)-	EtOH	222(3.92),262(2.46), 269(2.58),277(2.52)	44-2160-79
$C_{21}H_{32}F_2O_2$			
A-Homoandrostan-4-one, 3,3-difluoro-17-hydroxy-2-methyl-, (2α,5α,17β)-	n.s.g.	286(1.90)	44-2929-79
$C_{21}H_{32}N_2O_2S$			
Benzenesulfonic acid, 4-methyl-, [2-(1,1-dimethylethyl)octahydro-4(2H)-azulenylidene]hydrazide, cis	EtOH	226(4.01),274(2.93)	44-3031-79
trans	EtOH	230(4.01),274(2.98)	44-3031-79
$C_{21}H_{32}N_4O_9$			
DL-Aspartic acid, N-[[5-amino-1-[2,3-O-(1-methylethylidene)-β-D-ribofuranosyl]-1H-imidazol-4-ylcarbonyl]-3-methyl-, diethyl ester, threo-	MeOH	230(3.90),268(3.97)	39-1415-79C
$C_{21}H_{32}O$			
Pregna-3,5-dien-20α-ol	MeOH	228(4.23),235(4.26), 243(4.07)	13-0467-79A
$C_{21}H_{32}O_2$			
17,18-Cyclo-5β-pregnan-20-one, 3α-hydroxy-	EtOH	220(3.8)	12-2323-79
$C_{21}H_{32}O_3$			
Oxiranebutanoic acid, 3-(1,3,5,8-tetradecatetraenyl)-, methyl ester	MeOH	269(4.48),278(4.60), 287(4.54)	35-6748-79
Pregn-4-en-3-one, 17α,20α-dihydroxy-	EtOH	242(4.28)	150-0501-79
Pregn-4-en-3-one, 17α,20β-dihydroxy-	EtOH	241(4.18)	150-0501-79
$C_{21}H_{32}O_4$			
Cannabiripsol	MeOH	227(3.39),286(2.90)	31-1278-79
5α-Pregn-16-en-20-one, 2α,3β,6β-trihydroxy-	EtOH	239(3.97)	105-0446-79
Tricyclo[$6.3.0^{1,5}.0^{1,8}$]undeca-2,4,6-trione, 5-hydroxy-3-isopentyl-10-isopropyl-9,9-dimethyl-	EtOH-acid	259(3.93)	39-1250-79C
	EtOH-base	278(3.97)	39-1250-79C

Compound	Solvent	λ_{max}(log ε)	Ref.
$C_{21}H_{33}ClN_7$			
1,2,3-Triazinium, 2-[2-chloro-1-(diethylamino)-2-phenylethenyl]-4,5,6-tris-(dimethylamino)-, chloride	CH_2Cl_2	481(3.97)	24-1535-79
$C_{21}H_{33}NO$			
17a-Aza-D-homopregn-4-en-3-one	MeOH	240(4.29)	39-0305-79C
$C_{21}H_{33}NO_2$			
17a-Aza-D-homopregn-4-en-3-one, 21-hydroxy-	MeOH	241(4.19)	39-2451-79C
$C_{21}H_{33}NO_8$			
1-Propene-1,1,3,3-tetracarboxylic acid, 2-[2-(diethylamino)ethenyl]-, tetraethyl ester	$CHCl_3$	328(3.3)	5-1388-79
$C_{21}H_{33}N_2$			
Cyclopropenylium, bis[bis(1-methylethyl)amino]phenyl-, perchlorate	CH_2Cl_2	209(4.31),246(3.79)	24-1514-79
$C_{21}H_{33}N_5$			
1,2,3-Triazine-4,5-diamine, N,N,N',N'-tetrakis(1-methylethyl)-6-phenyl-	CH_2Cl_2	274(4.16),382s(--)	24-1514-79
$C_{21}H_{33}N_5O_4$			
5,18-Iminoimidazo[4,5-b][1,5]diazacycloheptadecine, 3,6,7,8,9,10,11,12-13,14,15,16-dodecahydro-3-β-D-ribofuranosyl-	pH 1.0	266(4.21)	5-1872-79
	pH 7.0	270(4.24)	5-1872-79
$C_{21}H_{34}N_2$			
Carbodiimide, N,N'-di-1-endo-fenchyl-	C_6H_{12}	200(end abs.)	56-0631-79
$C_{21}H_{34}N_2O_8$			
1-Propene-1,1,3,3-tetracarboxylic acid, 2-[2,2-bis(dimethylamino)ethenyl]-, tetraethyl ester	$CHCl_3$	428(4.1)	5-1388-79
$C_{21}H_{34}O_2$			
Methyl kolavenate	EtOH	219(4.19)	78-0979-79
$C_{21}H_{34}O_3$			
1,5-Cyclononadecadiene-1-carboxylic acid, 19-oxo-, methyl ester	EtOH	226(3.76)	33-2630-79
Methyl tetrahydrohardwickiate	EtOH	215(3.84)	78-2301-79
$C_{21}H_{34}O_4$			
2,5-Furandione, 3-methyl-4-(15-oxohexadecyl)-	EtOH	254(3.74)	32-0151-79
$C_{21}H_{35}NO_4S$			
Dodecanoic acid, [4-[(dimethylamino)-sulfonyl]phenyl]methyl ester	EtOH	230(4.09),274(2.79)	118-0531-79
$C_{21}H_{36}O$			
Methanone, (4-tert-butyl-2-cyclohexen-1-yl)(4-tert-butyl-1-cyclohexyl)-	hexane	209(3.43)	35-5660-79
$C_{21}H_{36}O_8$			
Aeginetoside	EtOH	237(4.15)	94-2807-79

Compound	Solvent	λ_{max}(log ε)	Ref.
$C_{21}H_{38}N_3O_8P$			
Phosphorus(1+), [3-ethoxy-2-(ethoxy-carbonyl)-1-[2-ethoxy-1-(ethoxycarb-onyl)-2-oxoethyl]-3-oxo-1-propenyl]-tris(N-methylmethanaminato)-, hydroxide, inner salt	$CHCl_3$	248(4.2),473(3.3)	5-1406-79
$C_{21}H_{38}OSi$			
Silane, (1,1-dimethylethyl)dimethyl-(2,4,6,9-pentadecatetraenyloxy)-, (E,E,Z,Z)-	EtOH	263(4.58),272(4.69), 283(4.56)	35-6748-79
$C_{21}H_{39}NO_5$			
Butanoic acid, 4-[(7-methoxy-1-oxo-tetradecyl)methylamino]-3-oxo-, methyl ester, (S)-	MeOH	213(3.73)	35-0240-79
	MeOH-NaOH	214(3.90)	35-0240-79
$C_{21}H_{42}N_4$			
1H-Imidazol-4-amine, 5-[[bis(1-methyl-ethyl)amino]methylene]-2,5-dihydro-2,2-dimethyl-N,N,1-tris(1-methyl-ethyl)-	CH_2Cl_2	297(4.08)	24-1535-79
tetrafluoroborate	CH_2Cl_2	321(4.25)	24-1535-79
$C_{21}H_{42}N_6$			
1,2,3-Triazine-4,5,6-triamine, N,N,N',N',N",N"-hexakis(1-methylethyl)-	CH_2Cl_2	358(3.76)	24-1514-79
$C_{21}H_{46}N_5P$			
Phosphorus(1+), [[bis(1-methylethyl)am-ino]cyclopropenyliumyl]tris(methyl-methanaminato)-, diperchlorate, (T-4)-	n.s.g.	210(4.33),266(4.30)	89-0472-79

Compound	Solvent	λ_{max}(log ε)	Ref.
$C_{22}H_{12}Cl_2O_3$			
Dinaphtho[1,2-b:2',3'd]furan-7(12H)-one, 12-(dichloromethylene)-5-methoxy-	n.s.g.	257(4.67),276s(4.42), 300s(4.22),332s(4.08), 433(3.64)	39-2679-79C
$C_{22}H_{12}N_4$			
5H-Cyclopenta[2,1-b:3,4-b']dipyridine, 5-(5H-cyclopenta[2,1-b:3,4-b']dipyridin-5-ylidene)-	EtOH	291(5.45)	44-0502-79
$C_{22}H_{12}O_2$			
7H,14H-Cycloocta[1,2,3-de:5,6,7-d'e']-dinaphthalene-7,14-dione	EtOH	212(4.95),226(4.73), 250s(3.49),259(3.56), 269(3.77),280(3.87), 316(4.03),326(4.05)	18-3314-79
Dibenz[a,h]anthracene-3,4-dione	dioxan	228(4.64),280(4.68), 290(4.74),332(4.45), 420(3.61),505(3.11)	44-3086-79
$C_{22}H_{12}O_3S$			
4H,8H-Thieno[3,4-f]isobenzofuran-4,8-dione, 5,7-diphenyl-	CH_2Cl_2	242(4.33),266(4.25), 340(4.03)	150-3518-79
$C_{22}H_{12}O_4$			
4H,8H-Benzo[1,2-c:4,5-c']difuran-4,8-dione, 1,3-diphenyl-	CH_2Cl_2	242(4.47),257(4.43), 362(4.20),378s(4.13), 396s(4.05)	150-3518-79
$C_{22}H_{12}O_5$			
2H-Naphtho[1,8-bc]furan-2,6(7H)-dione, 7-(4-methoxy-1-oxo-2(1H)-naphthalenylidene)-	$CHCl_3$	264s(4.45),268(4.47), 301(4.18),326s(4.03), 380s(3.65),560(3.76)	39-2679-79C
$C_{22}H_{13}NO_2$			
Dibenzo[a,j]phenanthridine-9,14-dione, 8-methyl-	dioxan	221(4.73),262(4.66), 310(4.23),324(4.18), 416(3.69)	5-0503-79
Dibenzo[c,j]phenanthridine-7,12-dione, 6-methyl-	dioxan	220(4.52),244(4.62), 261(4.78),301(4.33), 312(4.32),427(3.84)	5-0503-79
5,13-Pentacenedione, 6-amino-	toluene	505(4.32),541(4.24)	104-0344-79
6,13-Pentacenedione, 7-amino-	benzene	462(4.04),484s(3.99)	153-0033-79
$C_{22}H_{13}NO_3$			
2H-1-Benzopyran-2-one, 3-(5-phenyl-2-benzoxazolyl)-	dioxan	355(4.28)	42-0505-79
$C_{22}H_{13}NO_4S$			
5H-Benzo[b]carbazole-6,11-dione, 5-(phenylsulfonyl)-	EtOH	262(4.51),268s(4.50), 300(3.87),360(3.76)	150-4801-79
$C_{22}H_{13}N_3O_4$			
Pyridinium, 1-[3-(5-cyano-1,2-dihydro-6-hydroxy-4-methyl-2-oxo-3-pyridinyl)-1,4-dihydro-1,4-dioxo-2-naphthalenyl]-, hydroxide, inner salt	EtOH	253(4.21),337(4.27), 606(3.33)	2-0100-79A
$C_{22}H_{14}$			
Dibenzo[c,g]phenanthrene	$C_6H_{11}Me$	257(4.6),298(4.5), 300s(4.5),322(4.1)	151-0197-79B

Compound	Solvent	λ max (log ε)	Ref.
$C_{22}H_{14}ClHgNO_2$			
Mercury, [2-[[(4-chlorophenyl)imino]-methyl]-2,3-dihydro-1,3-dioxo-1H-inden-2-yl]phenyl-	benzene	293(3.70),305(3.89), 370(4.42)	103-0056-79
	DMSO	295(3.88),305(3.94), 370(4.50)	103-0056-79
$C_{22}H_{14}ClNO_3$			
Furo[3,2-b]pyridin-2(4H)-one, 4-[3-(4-chlorophenyl)-3-oxo-1-propenyl]-3-phenyl-, (E)-	$CHCl_3$	450(4.20)	97-0020-79
$C_{22}H_{14}ClN_3$			
1H-Dibenz[e,g]indole, 3-[(4-chlorophenyl)azo]-	EtOH	203(4.44),247(4.54), 257(4.51),268(4.37), 276(4.38),347(3.77), 415(4.47)	103-0302-79
$C_{22}H_{14}N_2$			
Quinazoline, 4-(9-anthracenyl)-	EtOH	252(5.26),314(3.67), 328(3.65),346(3.86), 364(4.00),383(3.95)	24-1348-79
$C_{22}H_{14}N_2O$			
Furo[3.4-g]phthalazine, 6,8-diphenyl-	CH_2Cl_2	288(4.70),350(4.23), 548(3.90)	150-3518-79
$C_{22}H_{14}N_2O_2$			
Benzo[a]naphthacene-7,14-dione, 8,13-diamino-	benzene	562(4.11),605(4.11)	153-0033-79
6,13-Pentacenedione, 5,14-diamino-	benzene	522(4.00),562(3.92)	153-0033-79
$C_{22}H_{14}N_2O_2S$			
5H-Thiazolo[3.2-a]quinazolinium, 1-hydroxy-5-oxo-2,4-diphenyl-, hydroxide, inner salt	MeOH	272(3.68),425(3.41)	2-0039-79B
	MeCN	444(--)	2-0039-79B
	$CHCl_3$	454(--)	2-0039-79B
	benzene	466(--)	2-0039-79B
$C_{22}H_{14}N_2O_2S_2$			
Thiazolo[3,2-a]quinolinium, 1-hydroxy-2-[(2-quinolinylthio)acetyl]-, hydroxide, inner salt	n.s.g.	297(3.96),328(3.87), 455(4.22)	103-0811-79
$C_{22}H_{14}N_2S$			
Thieno[3,4-g]phthalazine, 6,8-diphenyl-	CH_2Cl_2	290(4.64),510(3.83)	150-3518-79
$C_{22}H_{14}N_4$			
2,7-Pyrenediacetonitrile, α,α'-dicyano-4,5,9,10-tetrahydro-	THF	292(3.90)	152-0647-79
$C_{22}H_{14}N_4O_2$			
1H-Dibenz[e,g]indole, 3-[(4-nitrophenyl)azo]-	EtOH	203(4.44),246(4.52), 258(4.48),277(4.31), 482(4.49)	103-0302-79
$C_{22}H_{14}O$			
6H-6,10b[1',2']-Benzenoaceanthrylen-2(1H)-one	$CHCl_3$	277(3.5),310(3.58)	104-1341-79
$C_{22}H_{14}O_2$			
[1]Benzopyrano[3,4-b][1]benzopyran, 6-phenyl-	EtOH	242(4.50),261(4.41), 268(4.36),400(3.92),	138-0511-79

Compound	Solvent	λ_{max}(log ε)	Ref.
(cont.)		423(4.06),447(4.11), 473(3.89)	138-0511-79
[1,1'-Binaphthalene]-8,8'-dicarboxaldehyde	benzene	333(4.27)	104-1744-79
Dibenz[a,h]anthracene-3,4-diol	dioxan	293(4.47),302(4.69), 330(4.16),342(4.09), 354(3.89),383(3.31), 405(3.40)	44-3086-79
$C_{22}H_{14}O_2S$			
Benzo[c]thiophene-5,6-dicarboxaldehyde, 1,3-diphenyl-	CH_2Cl_2	297(4.80),416(3.98)	150-3518-79
$C_{22}H_{14}O_3$			
5,6-Isobenzofurandicarboxaldehyde, 1,3-diphenyl-	CH_2Cl_2	283(5.08),420(4.17), 440s(4.15)	150-3518-79
$C_{22}H_{14}O_3S$			
1H-Indene-1,3(2H)-dione, 2-(3-ethoxy-2H-naphtho[1,8-bc]thien-2-ylidene)-	MeOH	210(4.9),246(4.8), 228(4.7),342(4.4), 363(4.4),382(4.6), 524(4.8)	5-1789-79
$C_{22}H_{14}O_4$			
Dinaphtho[1,2-b:2',3'-d]furan-7,12-dione, 5-ethoxy-	n.s.g.	262s(4.69),268(4.71), 292s(4.11),326s(3.73), 342s(3.52),475(3.81)	39-2679-79C
$C_{22}H_{14}O_6$			
Zeylanone	dioxan	235(4.85),246(4.72), 350(4.00),430(3.83)	78-1777-79
$C_{22}H_{15}BrN_2O$			
4(1H)-Pyrimidinone, 2-(4-bromophenyl)-5,6-diphenyl-	MeOH	262(4.45),328(4.17)	138-1213-79
$C_{22}H_{15}BrO_2$			
9(10H)-Anthracenone, 10-[bromo(4-methoxyphenyl)methylene]-	EtOH	233(4.63),275s(4.22), 359(3.95)	44-3687-79
$C_{22}H_{15}ClCuN_6O_4$			
Copper, [2-chloro-11,12,13,14-tetrahydro-8,17-dinitrotribenzo[b,f,l]-[1,4,8,11]tetraazacyclotetradecinato(2-)-N^5,N^{11},N^{14},N^{20}]-	$CHCl_3$	388(4.15),434s(3.90), 465s(3.78)	12-2303-79
$C_{22}H_{15}ClN_2O$			
4(1H)-Pyrimidinone, 2-(4-chlorophenyl)-5,6-diphenyl-	MeOH	261(4.39),327(4.07)	138-1213-79
9H-Xanthene, 1-chloro-9-(1-imidazolyl)-9-phenyl-	EtOH	285(3.52)	36-1453-79
9H-Xanthene, 1-chloro-9-(2-imidazolyl)-9-phenyl-	EtOH	285(3.50)	36-1453-79
$C_{22}H_{15}ClN_2OS$			
Benzamide, N-[3-(4-chlorophenyl)-4-phenyl-2(3H)-thiazolylidene]-	EtOH	240s(4.35),337(4.33)	39-1762-79C
Methanone, [2-[(4-chlorophenyl)amino]-4-phenyl-5-thiazolyl]phenyl-	EtOH	253s(4.36),278(4.38), 380(4.27)	39-1762-79C

Compound	Solvent	λmax(log ε)	Ref.
$C_{22}H_{15}ClO_4$			
3-Phenanthrenecarboxylic acid, 4-(4-chlorophenyl)-1-hydroxy-9-methoxy-	n.s.g.	227(4.57),258(4.48), 306(4.03),347(3.48)	33-0090-79
$C_{22}H_{15}CuN_7O_6$			
Copper, [11,12,13,14-tetrahydro-2,8,17-trinitrotribenzo[b,f,l][1,4,8,11]-tetraazacyclotetradecinato(2-)-N^5-N^{11},N^{14},N^{20}]-, (SP-4-4)-	$CHCl_3$	345(4.46),418s(4.27), 510s(3.78)	12-2303-79
$C_{22}H_{15}HgNO_2$			
Mercury, phenyl[2-[(phenylimino)methyl]-1H-indene-1,3(2H)-dionato-N,O]-	benzene	305(3.80),370(4.39)	103-0056-79
	DMSO	307(3.83),375(4.43)	103-0056-79
$C_{22}H_{15}N$			
9-Anthraceneacetonitrile, α-phenyl-	n.s.g.	334(3.38),351(3.71), 369(3.87),388(3.83)	39-2948-79C
9-Anthracenecarbonitrile, 10-(phenylmethyl)-	n.s.g.	351(3.39),368(3.65), 388(3.77),410(3.72)	39-2948-79C
$C_{22}H_{15}NO_2$			
5(4H)-Oxazolone, 4-([1,1'-biphenyl]-4-ylmethylene)-2-phenyl-	toluene	390(4.65)	103-1303-79
$C_{22}H_{15}NO_2S$			
6H-Anthra[1,9-cd]isoxazol-6-one, 3-[(3,4-dimethylphenyl)thio]-	EtOH	230(4.51),255(4.58), 451(4.32),480(4.46)	104-1514-79
6H-Anthra[1,9-cd]isoxazol-6-one, 3-[(4-ethylphenyl)thio]-	EtOH	230(4.44),255(4.51), 451(4.27),479(4.37)	104-1514-79
8H-Naphtho[2,3-a]phenothiazine-8,13-(14H)-dione, 2,3-dimethyl-	EtOH	242(4.48),282(4.66), 620(3.90)	104-1514-79
8H-Naphtho[2,3-a]phenothiazine-8,13-(14H)-dione, 2-ethyl-	EtOH	240(4.48),280(4.67), 610(3.86)	104-1514-79
$C_{22}H_{15}NO_3$			
1,4-Naphthalenedione, 2-acetyl-3-(4-amino-1-naphthalenyl)-	dioxan	247(4.60),336(4.14), 540(3.29),638s(2.9)	5-0503-79
1,4-Naphthalenedione, 2-acetyl-3-(1-naphthalenylamino)-	dioxan	278(4.37),426(3.56)	5-0503-79
$C_{22}H_{15}NO_3S$			
6H-Anthra[1,9-cd]isoxazol-6-one, 3-[(2,4-dimethylphenyl)thio]-5-hydroxy-	EtOH	245(4.62),442(3.99), 454(3.98),492(3.54)	104-1514-79
6H-Anthra[1,9-cd]isoxazol-6-one, 3-[(3,4-dimethylphenyl)thio]-5-hydroxy-	EtOH	245(4.54),441(4.00), 453(3.99),492(3.54)	104-1514-79
6H-Anthra[1,9-cd]isoxazol-6-one, 3-[(4-ethylphenyl)thio]-5-hydroxy-	EtOH	245(4.57),442(3.97), 454(3.96),491(3.51)	104-1514-79
8H-Naphtho[2,3-a]phenothiazine-8,13-(14H)-dione, 2-ethyl-7-hydroxy-	EtOH	245(4.46),285(4.61), 647(4.19),704(4.08)	104-1514-79
8H-Naphtho[2,3-a]phenothiazine-8,13-(14H)-dione, 7-hydroxy-2,3-dimethyl-	EtOH	240(4.48),285(4.54), 652(4.15),710(4.17)	104-1514-79
8H-Naphtho[2,3-a]phenothiazine-8,13-(14H)-dione, 7-hydroxy-2,4-dimethyl-	EtOH	245(4.51),285(4.60), 653(4.20),712(4.15)	104-1514-79
$C_{22}H_{15}NO_4S$			
1H-Indole, 2-(2-formylbenzoyl)-1-(phenylsulfonyl)-	EtOH	304(4.1)	150-4801-79
$C_{22}H_{15}N_3$			
1H-Dibenz[e,g]indole, 3-(phenylazo)-	EtOH	203(4.50),247(4.59), 255(4.54),275(4.41),	103-0302-79

Compound	Solvent	λ_{max}(log ε)	Ref.
(cont.)		345(3.86),445(4.47)	103-0302-79
$C_{22}H_{15}N_3O$			
8H-Quinazolino[4,3-b]quinazolin-8-one, 6-(4-methylphenyl)-	EtOH	233(4.52),247(4.54), 288(4.44),354(4.24)	2-0349-79A
$C_{22}H_{15}N_3O_2$			
8H-Quinazolino[4,3-b]quinazolin-8-one, 6-(4-methoxyphenyl)-	EtOH	222(4.45),245(4.51), 285(4.34),359(4.23)	2-0349-79A
$C_{22}H_{15}N_3O_2S$			
9,10-Anthracenedione, 1-azido-2-[(2,4-dimethylphenyl)thio]-	EtOH	230(4.45),255(4.53), 280(4.26),305(4.26), 427(3.74),445(3.76), 477(3.48)	104-1514-79
9,10-Anthracenedione, 1-azido-2-[(3,4-dimethylphenyl)thio]-	EtOH	252(4.50),280(4.23), 305(4.23),428(3.76), 448(3.85),478(3.79)	104-1514-79
9,10-Anthracenedione, 1-azido-2-[(4-ethylphenyl)thio]-	EtOH	252(4.54),280(4.29), 305(4.28),425(3.72), 445(3.74),475(3.44)	104-1514-79
$C_{22}H_{15}N_3O_3$			
4(1H)-Pyrimidinone, 2-(3-nitrophenyl)-5,6-diphenyl-	MeOH	258(4.54),322(4.05)	138-1213-79
$C_{22}H_{15}N_3O_3S$			
9,10-Anthracenedione, 1-azido-2-[(2,4-dimethylphenyl)thio]-4-hydroxy-	EtOH	256(4.53),460(3.95)	104-1514-79
9,10-Anthracenedione, 1-azido-2-[(3,4-dimethylphenyl)thio]-4-hydroxy-	EtOH	256(4.55),460(3.94)	104-1514-79
9,10-Anthracenedione, 1-azido-2-[(4-ethylphenyl)thio]-4-hydroxy-	EtOH	256(4.53),460(3.92)	104-1514-79
$C_{22}H_{15}N_3O_4$			
Benzo[lmn][3,8]phenanthroline-1,3,6,8-(2H,7H)-tetrone, 2,7-dimethyl-4-(phenylamino)-	$CHCl_3$	514(4.09)	104-2279-79
$C_{22}H_{15}N_5OS$			
1,2,4-Triazolo[3,4-b][1,3,4]thiadiazol-ium, 6-(benzoylamino)-5,6-diphenyl-, hydroxide, inner salt	EtOH	285(4.13),329(4.45)	94-1688-79
$C_{22}H_{16}$			
Anthracene, 9-(4-ethenylphenyl)-	EtOH	256(5.09),331(3.44), 348(3.79),365(3.96), 384(3.98)	18-0253-79
	CH_2Cl_2	258(5.12),332(3.45), 349(3.81),367(4.01), 387(3.97)	18-0253-79
Benzo[g]chrysene, 9,10-dihydro-	MeOH	242(4.59),254(4.60), 262(4.65),268s(4.56), 278(4.39),305s(4.17), 318(4.34),331(4.29), 363(3.10)	54-0187-79
Phenanthrene, 1-ethenyl-9-phenyl-	MeOH	244s(4.45),262(4.61), 306(4.16)	54-0452-79
$C_{22}H_{16}ClNO$			
Quinoline, 6-chloro-2-(4-methoxyphenyl)-	n.s.g.	280(4.40)	124-0447-79

Compound	Solvent	λ_{max}(log ε)	Ref.
4-phenyl- (cont.)			124-0447-79
$C_{22}H_{16}CuN_6O_4$			
Copper, [11,12,13,14-tetrahydro-8,17-dinitrotribenzo[b,f,l][1,4,8,11]-tetraazacyclotetradecinato(2-)-N^5,N^{11},N^{14},N^{20}]-, (SP-4-2)-	$CHCl_3$	390(4.18),424s(4.06), 520s(3.65)	12-2303-79
$C_{22}H_{16}N_2$			
1H-Phenanthro[9,10-d]imidazole, 1-methyl-2-phenyl-	EtOH	258(4.81),285(4.26), 305s(4.22),340(3.71), 356(3.71)	44-0041-79
$C_{22}H_{16}N_2O$			
Acetamide, 2-cyano-2-(2,3-dihydro-1H-inden-1-ylidene)-N-1-naphthalenyl-	$CHCl_3$	240(4.25),345(4.39)	80-1485-79
4(1H)-Pyrimidinone, 2,5,6-triphenyl-	MeOH	256(4.35),325(4.07)	138-1213-79
$C_{22}H_{16}N_2OS$			
Benzamide, N-(3,4-diphenyl-2(3H)-thiazolylidene)-	EtOH	235s(4.38),337(4.37)	39-1762-79C
	EtOH	245(4.13),275(3.82), 336(4.12)	78-1199-79
Methanone, phenyl[4-phenyl-2-(phenylamino)-5-thiazolyl]-	EtOH	254(4.36),275s(4.33), 382(4.22)	39-1762-79C
$C_{22}H_{16}N_2O_2S_2$			
Thiazolo[3,2-a]quinolinium, 2-acetyl-1-hydroxy-5-[(3-methyl-2(3H)-benzothiazolylidene)methyl]-, hydroxide, inner salt	$MeNO_2$	566(4.63)	103-0811-79
$C_{22}H_{16}N_2O_3S$			
Benzeneacetic acid, α-[(3,4-dihydro-4-oxo-3-phenyl-2-quinazolinyl)thio]-	MeOH	224(4.54),280(4.18), 316(3.67)	2-0039-79B
$C_{22}H_{16}O_2$			
9(10H)-Anthracenone, 10-[(4-methoxyphenyl)methylene]-	EtOH	236(4.61),294s(4.17), 388(4.21)	44-3687-79
Methanone, 9-anthracenyl(4-methoxyphenyl)-	EtOH	253(5.08),290(4.22), 330(3.56),346(3.81), 364(3.96),385(3.93)	44-3687-79
$(C_{22}H_{16}O_2)_n$			
Poly[2-(vinylbenzyloxy)-9-fluorenone]	THF	261(4.69),268(4.69), 298s(3.69),312s(3.57), 423(2.78)	47-0777-79
$C_{22}H_{16}O_3$			
Benzo[b]phenanthro[9,10-d]furan, 11,12-dimethoxy-	EtOH	226(4.54),259(4.81), 285(4.28),301(4.22), 333(4.51),363(3.52)	19-0109-79
Spiro[isobenzofuran-1(3H),9'-[9H]xanthen]-3-one, 2'-ethyl-	EtOH	202(4.76),216(4.68), 267(3.72)	56-0403-79
	80% H_2SO_4	203(4.71),228(4.45), 265(4.72),285(3.83), 383(4.65),454(3.62)	56-0403-79
Spiro[isobenzofuran-1(3H),9'-[9H]xanthen]-3-one, 3'-ethyl-	EtOH	202(4.82),218(4.75), 284(3.79)	56-0403-79
	80% H_2SO_4	204(4.68),227s(--), 261(4.74),282(3.70), 388(4.61),440s(--)	56-0403-79

Compound	Solvent	λ_{max}(log ε)	Ref.
Spiro[isobenzofuran-1(3H),9'-[9H]xanthen]-3-one, 4'-ethyl-	EtOH	202(4.78),218(4.69), 285(3.79),294(3.77)	56-0403-79
	80% H_2SO_4	205(4.74),265(4.72), 282(3.74),382(4.60), 459(3.59)	56-0403-79
$C_{22}H_{16}O_4$			
9,10-Anthracenedione, 1,4-dihydroxy-2-(1-phenylethyl)-	MeOH	206(4.46),250(4.60), 384(3.94),484(4.01)	5-0019-79
[2,2'-Binaphthalene]-1,4-dione, 4'-ethoxy-1'-hydroxy-	n.s.g.	249(4.72),321(4.21), 536(3.19)	39-2679-79C
1(2H)-Naphthalenone, 4-methoxy-2-(4-methoxy-1-oxo-2(1H)-naphthalenylidene)-	$CHCl_3$	282(4.41),319(4.15), 608s(4.23),638(4.28)	39-2679-79C
3-Phenanthrenecarboxylic acid, 1-hydroxy-9-methoxy-4-phenyl-	n.s.g.	226(4.52),256(4.47), 307s(3.99),349(3.44)	33-0090-79
$C_{22}H_{16}O_5$			
1H-Naphtho[2,1,8-mna]xanthen-1-one, 5,8,9-trimethoxy-	MeOH	214s(4.51),222(4.54), 236(4.59),250(4.57), 283(4.34),362(3.81), 390(3.85),550(4.45), 566(4.46)	12-1841-79
1H-Naphtho[2,1,8-mna]xanthen-1-one, 8,9,11-trimethoxy-	MeOH	218s(4.59),232(4.72), 264(4.42),273(4.39), 296(3.91),330(3.68), 517(4.51),548(4.57)	12-1841-79
$C_{22}H_{16}O_6$			
2(6H)-Benzofuranone, 6,7-bis(benzoyloxy)-7,7a-dihydro- (griffonilide dibenzoate)	MeOH	234(4.14),252(4.04)	100-0500-79
Dasycarponilide dibenzoate	MeOH	228(4.29),256s(3.69)	100-0500-79
1,4-Ethanonaphthacene-6,11-dione, 3-ethynyl-1,2,3,4-tetrahydro-1,3,5,12-tetrahydroxy-, (1α,3α,4β)-	MeOH	203(4.37),252(4.60), 290(3.80),488(3.97), 520(3.73)	24-2640-79
(1α,3β,4β)-	MeOH	203(4.39),252(4.61), 292(3.84),486(3.99), 517(3.78)	24-2640-79
$C_{22}H_{16}O_8$			
Naphtho[2,3-d]-1,3-dioxole-6,7-dicarboxylic acid, 5-(1,3-benzodioxol-5-yl)-, dimethyl ester	EtOH	259(5.03),292(4.16)	2-0202-79
$C_{22}H_{16}O_{10}$			
9,10-Anthracenedione, 1,3,5,8-tetraacetoxy-	MeOH	211(4.45),254(4.46), 334(4.01)	24-2640-79
$C_{22}H_{16}S_4$			
Thiophene, 2-[2-(5-thienyl)ethenyl]-2-[2-(5-thienyl)ethenyl]-2-[2-(5-thienyl)ethenyl]-	DMF	460(4.81)	61-0417-79
	KBr	458(--)	61-0417-79
$C_{22}H_{17}Br$			
9H-Fluorene, 9-(bromophenylmethylene)-2,7-dimethyl-	$CHCl_3$	258(4.49),267(4.61), 286(4.20),305(4.19), 318(4.19)	24-3490-79
$C_{22}H_{17}BrO_2$			
9-Anthracenol, 10-[bromo(4-methoxyphen-	EtOH	230(4.22),301(3.96)	44-3687-79

Compound	Solvent	λ_{max}(log ε)	Ref.
yl)methylene]-9,10-dihydro- (cont.)			44-3687-79
$C_{22}H_{17}ClCuN_4$ Copper, [2-chloro-11,12,13,14-tetrahydrotribenzo[b,f,l][1,4,8,11]tetraazacyclotetradecinato(2-)-N^5,N^{11}-N^{14},N^{20}]-, (SP-4-4)-	$CHCl_3$	265(4.51),287(4.41), 336(4.11),355(4.08), 434(4.08),510(3.90)	12-2303-79
$C_{22}H_{17}ClN_2O_2$ Benzoic acid, 4-chloro-, (9-ethoxy-1H-phenalen-1-ylidene)hydrazide	MeOH	268(5.1),321(5.7), 389(5.6),413(5.6), 494(5.5),525(5.4), 564s(5.4)	83-0288-79
$C_{22}H_{17}ClN_4O_4S$ Benzenepropanethioamide, α-[(4-chlorophenyl)hydrazono]-N-(2-methoxy-5-nitrophenyl)-β-oxo-	EtOH	245(4.30),285(4.21), 355(4.12),400(4.08)	104-1324-79
$C_{22}H_{17}ClO_2$ Phenanthrene, 4-(4-chlorophenyl)-1,9-dimethoxy-	n.s.g.	225(4.72),258(4.52), 282s(4.36),311s(4.03), 345(3.50)	33-0090-79
$C_{22}H_{17}CuN_5O_2$ Copper, [11,12,13,14-tetrahydro-2-nitrotribenzo[b,f,l][1,4,8,11]tetraazacyclotetradecinato(2-)-N^5,N^{11}-N^{14},N^{20}]-, (SP-4-4)-	$CHCl_3$	253(4.42),328(4.15), 348(4.10),484(4.11)	12-2303-79
$C_{22}H_{17}HgNO$ Mercury, [2,3-dihydro-2-[(phenylimino)-methyl]-1H-inden-1-onato-N,O]phenyl-	benzene	295(3.77),395(4.39)	103-0056-79
	DMSO	390(4.47)	103-0056-79
$C_{22}H_{17}NO_2$ Spiro[9H-fluorene-9,1'(8'aH)-indolizine]-2'-carboxylic acid, methyl ester	n.s.g.	376(4.03)	89-0945-79
$C_{22}H_{17}NO_2S_2$ 4-Quinolinecarboxylic acid, 2-(2-[2,2'-bithiophen]-5-ylethenyl)-, ethyl ester, (E)-	EtOH	220(4.52),270(4.16), 336(4.20),414(4.09)	103-0970-79
$C_{22}H_{17}NO_5$ 6H,7H-Benzo[a][1]benzopyrano[3,4-g]-quinolizine-6,7-dione, 9,10-dihydro-12,13-dimethoxy-	MeOH	239s(4.00),253(3.96), 293(4.02),310(4.03), 388s(4.15),409(4.36), 430(4.34)	4-0433-79
$C_{22}H_{17}NO_5S$ Benzenesulfonamide, N-[2-[(3-hydroxy-2-benzofuranyl)carbonyl]phenyl]-4-methyl-	MeOH	202(4.55),356(4.16)	83-0254-79
$C_{22}H_{17}NSi$ 9H-Pyrrolo[1,2-a][1,3]benzazasilole, 9,9-diphenyl-	EtOH	210(4.52),226(4.60), 263(4.21),279s(3.94), 286s(3.89)	101-0139-79C
$C_{22}H_{17}N_2OS_2$ Thiazolo[3,2-a]quinolinium, 2-[2-(3-	n.s.g.	588(4.80)	103-0811-79

Compound	Solvent	λ_{max}(log ε)	Ref.
ethylbenzothiazolium-2-yl)ethenyl]- 1-hydroxy-, hydroxide, inner salt (cont.)			103-0811-79
$C_{22}H_{17}N_3$			
Benzonitrile, 2-(4,5-dihydro-1,3-di- phenyl-1H-pyrazol-5-yl)-	C_6H_{12} MeOH	350(4.27) 348(4.24)	12-1601-79 12-1601-79
Benzonitrile, 3-(4,5-dihydro-1,3-di- phenyl-1H-pyrazol-5-yl)-	C_6H_{12} MeOH	352(4.25) 353(4.24)	12-1601-79 12-1601-79
Benzonitrile, 4-(4,5-dihydro-1,3-di- phenyl-1H-pyrazol-5-yl)-	C_6H_{12} MeOH	343(4.24) 346(4.23)	12-1601-79 12-1601-79
Benzonitrile, 4-(4,5-dihydro-1,5-di- phenyl-1H-pyrazol-3-yl)-	C_6H_{12} MeOH	396(4.45) 397(4.45)	12-1601-79 12-1601-79
Benzonitrile, 4-(4,5-dihydro-3,5-di- phenyl-1H-pyrazol-1-yl)-	C_6H_{12} MeOH	360(4.51) 357(4.56)	12-1601-79 12-1601-79
$C_{22}H_{17}N_3OS$			
Ethanone, 2-[(3-amino-2-quinoxalinyl)- thio]-1,2-diphenyl-	EtOH	360(4.1),377(4.2)	103-0102-79
$C_{22}H_{17}N_3O_6S$			
2-Anthracenesulfonic acid, 4-[[2-(acet- ylamino)phenyl]amino]-1-amino-9,10- dihydro-9,10-dioxo-, sodium salt	glycerol	631(4.13)	112-0139-79
2-Anthracenesulfonic acid, 4-[[3-(acet- ylamino)phenyl]amino]-1-amino-9,10- dihydro-9,10-dioxo-, sodium salt	glycerol	637(4.23)	112-0139-79
2-Anthracenesulfonic acid, 4-[[4-(acet- ylamino)phenyl]amino]-1-amino-9,10- dihydro-9,10-dioxo-, sodium salt	glycerol	635(4.16)	112-0139-79
$C_{22}H_{17}N_5NiO_2$			
Nickel, [11,12,13,14-tetrahydro-2-ni- trotribenzo[b,f,l][1,4,8,11]tetra- azacyclotetradecinato(2-)-N^5,N^{11}- N^{14},N^{20}]-, (SP-4-4)-	$CHCl_3$	297(4.20),344(4.11), 398(4.04),498(3.48), 580(3.00)	12-2303-79
$C_{22}H_{17}N_5O_2S_2$			
1,2,4-Triazolo[3,4-b][1,3,4]thiadiazol- ium, 6-[[(4-methylphenyl)sulfonyl]- amino]-2,3-diphenyl-, hydroxide, inner salt	EtOH	291(4.31)	94-1688-79
$C_{22}H_{17}N_5O_6S$			
Benzenepropanethioamide, N-(2-methoxy- 5-nitrophenyl)-α-[(4-nitrophenyl)hy- drazono]-β-oxo-	EtOH	230(3.97),282(3.88), 302(3.89),400(3.98)	104-1324-79
$C_{22}H_{17}S_3$			
1,2-Dithiol-1-ium, 3-([1,1'-biphenyl]- 4-ylthio)-4-methyl-5-phenyl-, tri- iodide	MeCN	211(4.22),288(4.39), 370(4.24)	104-0955-79
$C_{22}H_{18}$			
Benzene, 1,4-bis(2-phenylethenyl)-	dioxan DMF	356(4.78) 355(4.75)	104-1944-79 61-0417-79
Benzene, 1-(1,2-diphenylethenyl)-2-eth- enyl-, (E)-	MeOH	229(4.39),225(4.22), 294(4.23)[sic]	54-0187-79
(Z)-	MeOH	227(4.29),295(4.35)	54-0187-79
Benzene, 1-(2,2-diphenylethenyl)-2-eth- enyl-	MeOH	239(4.39),298(4.12)	54-0452-79

Compound	Solvent	λ max(log ε)	Ref.
Benzo[c]chrysene, 5,6,13,14-tetrahydro-	C_6H_{12}	248(4.63),259(4.12), 268(3.95),279(4.15), 290(4.21),318(4.43), 332(4.58),349(4.44)	44-4933-79
Cycloprop[a]indene, 1,1a,6,6a-tetrahydro-1,1a-diphenyl-, endo	n.s.g.	253s(3.16),258(3.12), 265(3.12),271(3.09), 279(2.98)	54-0187-79
Cycloprop[a]indene, 1,1a,6,6a-tetrahydro-6,6a-diphenyl-	MeOH	259(3.22),261s(3.12), 265(3.20),269s(3.19), 272(3.20),280(3.17), 295s(2.50)	54-0452-79
9H-Fluorene, 1,8-dimethyl-9-(phenylmethylene)-	dioxan	268(4.51),288(4.03), 333(4.21)	24-3490-79
9H-Fluorene, 2,7-dimethyl-9-(phenylmethylene)-	$CHCl_3$	255(4.49),264(4.51), 301(4.21),311(4.21), 327(4.15)	24-3490-79
Picene, 7,8,13,14-tetrahydro-	C_6H_{12}	242(4.32),250(4.23), 270(4.20),281(4.53), 292(4.63),332(4.31), 347(4.46),365(4.35)	44-4933-79
$C_{22}H_{18}BrClN_2O_2$			
Benzoic acid, 2-[3-(4-bromophenyl)-1-(4-chlorophenyl)-3-oxopropyl]hydrazide	EtOH	225(4.53),253(4.46), 318(4.32)	94-0257-79
$C_{22}H_{18}BrNO_4$			
2H-Azepine-4-carboxylic acid, 7-(4-bromophenyl)-3-methoxy-2-oxo-6-phenyl-, ethyl ester	dioxan	263(4.27),280(4.27), 360s(--)	142-1423-79
2,3-Pyridinedicarboxylic acid, 6-(bromophenyl)-5-phenyl-, 3-ethyl 2-methyl ester	EtOH	235(4.27),305s(4.08)	142-1423-79
2,5-Pyridinedicarboxylic acid, 6-(4-bromophenyl)-3-phenyl-, 5-ethyl 2-methyl ester	EtOH	273(4.31)	142-1423-79
$C_{22}H_{18}ClNO_4$			
2-Naphthaleneacetic acid, 3-chloro-1,4-dihydro-1,4-dioxo-α-[1-(phenylamino)-ethylidene]-, ethyl ester	MeOH	245(4.24),251(4.24), 278(4.35),303(4.40), 490(3.29)	83-0431-79
$C_{22}H_{18}ClN_5$			
1H-1,2,4-Triazolium, 3-[[(4-chlorophenyl)methylene]hydrazino]-1-methyl-4,5-diphenyl-, hydroxide, inner salt	n.s.g.	310(4.35),367(4.52)	39-0724-79C
$C_{22}H_{18}CuN_4$			
Copper, [11,12,13,14-tetrahydrotribenzo[b,f,l][1,4,8,11]tetraazacyclotetradecinato(2-)-N^5,N^{11},N^{14},N^{20}]-, (SP-4-2)-	$CHCl_3$	267(4.56),334(3.30), 355(3.18),425(3.18), 506(3.00)	12-2303-79
$C_{22}H_{18}HgN_2O$			
Mercury, [1,2-dihydro-1-methyl-2-[(phenylimino)methyl]-3H-indol-3-onato-N^2,O^3]phenyl- (or isomer)	benzene	292(4.16),387(4.26)	103-0056-79
	DMSO	283(4.00),290(3.99), 380(4.28)	103-0056-79
$C_{22}H_{18}N_2$			
Pyrimidine, 1,4-dihydro-4,4,6-triphenyl-	EtOH	237(4.35),293(3.26)	39-1228-79C

Compound	Solvent	λ max (log ε)	Ref.
$C_{22}H_{18}N_2O$			
2H-Indol-2-one, 3-(9H-carbazol-1-yl)-1,3-dihydro-1,3-dimethyl-	EtOH	236(4.56),245(4.43), 259(4.18),283(4.01), 293(4.13),324(3.55), 337(3.49)	23-1694-79
1H-Pyrazole, 1-(4-formylphenyl)-4,5-dihydro-3,5-diphenyl-	C_6H_{12}	369(4.58)	12-1601-79
	MeOH	386(4.68)	12-1601-79
1H-Pyrazolium, 4-hydroxy-1-methyl-2,3,5-triphenyl-, hydroxide, inner salt	H_2O	341(4.06)	23-0904-79
$C_{22}H_{18}N_2O_4S$			
1H-Indole, 2-[[3-(1-hydroxyethyl)-4-pyridinyl]carbonyl]-1-(phenylsulfonyl)-	EtOH	230(4.20),307(3.93)	77-0642-79
$C_{22}H_{18}N_2O_5$			
1H-Pyrano[3',4':6,7]indolizino[1,2-b]quinoline-3,14(4H,12H)-dione, 4-acetoxy-4-ethyl-, (S)-	MeOH	218(4.42),252(4.26), 288(3.52),356(4.07), 368(4.07)	100-0475-79
$C_{22}H_{18}N_2S_4$			
Benzo[1,2-d:5,4-d']bisthiazolium, 3,5-dimethyl-2,6-bis[2-(2-thienyl)ethenyl]-, diperchlorate	DMF	309(4.16),385(4.45), 491(4.26),521s(4.21)	126-1465-79
$C_{22}H_{18}N_4O_2$			
Acetamide, N-acetyl-N-(6-methyl-12H-pyrimido[1,6-a:5,4-b']diindol-13-yl)-	n.s.g.	210(4.41),235(4.33), 247(4.45),258(4.38), 279(4.36),289(4.31), 302(4.21),313(4.30), 339(4.42),358(4.25), 379(4.15),389(3.97)	103-1193-79
$C_{22}H_{18}N_4O_{10}$			
Butanedioic acid, [(3,4-dihydro-5-methyl-2,4-dioxo-1(2H)-pyrimidinyl)methyl]-, bis(4-nitrophenyl) ester	MeOH	270(4.42)	126-0325-79
$C_{22}H_{18}O$			
Anthracene, 9-(methoxymethyl)-10-phenyl-	$C_6H_{11}Me$	258(5.19),338(3.52), 354(3.88),373(4.10), 393(4.08)	39-0411-79B
Anthracene, 9-(methoxyphenylmethyl)-	n.s.g.	333(3.41),350(3.68), 378(3.83),388(3.79)	39-2948-79C
Anthracene, 9-methoxy-10-(phenylmethyl)-	n.s.g.	343(3.40),361(3.65), 380(3.82),402(3.77)	39-2948-79C
1(2H)-Naphthalenone, 3,4-dihydro-4,4-diphenyl-	EtOH	212(4.58),252(4.19), 269(3.48)	104-1973-79
$C_{22}H_{18}O_2$			
9-Anthracenol, 9,10-dihydro-10-[(4-methoxyphenyl)methylene]-	EtOH	248(4.36),255s(4.30), 320(4.13)	44-3687-79
[1]Benzopyrano[3,4-b][1]benzopyran, 6,6a,12,12a-tetrahydro-6-phenyl-	EtOH	283(3.69),310(3.70)	138-0511-79
3-Buten-1-one, 1-(2-hydroxyphenyl)-4,4-diphenyl-	MeOH	205(4.0),252(4.3), 322(3.8)	24-1791-79
1,4-Naphthacenedione, 2,3,7,10-tetramethyl-	$CHCl_3$	268(4.97),317s(3.29), 329(4.24),345(4.38), 374(3.42),397(3.58), 421(3.70),479(3.92)	150-3518-79

Compound	Solvent	λ_{max}(log ε)	Ref.
Phenanthrene, 1,9-dimethoxy-4-phenyl-	n.s.g.	224(4.70),253(4.53), 304s(4.10),342s(3.45)	33-0090-79
1,3-Propanedione, 1-(4-methylphenyl)-2,3-diphenyl-	MeOH	252(4.43)	44-4021-79
Spiro[2H-1-benzopyran-2,9'-[9H]xanthene], 3,4-dihydro-4-methyl-	EtOAc	277(3.62)	104-0761-79
$(C_{22}H_{18}O_2)_n$			
Poly(p-benzoylphenoxymethylstyrene)	THF	225s(--),250(4.03), 277s(--),285(4.23)	47-0777-79
$C_{22}H_{18}O_2S$			
2-Propen-1-one, 1-(2-hydroxyphenyl)-3-[(4-methylphenyl)thio]-3-phenyl-	EtOH	260(4.19),352(4.34), 363s(4.32)	104-1805-79
$C_{22}H_{18}O_3$			
Benzoic acid, 2-(2-ethyl-9H-xanthen-9-yl)-	EtOH	202(4.74),287(3.60)	56-0403-79
Benzoic acid, 2-(3-ethyl-9H-xanthen-9-yl)-	EtOH	203(4.75),284(3.59)	56-0403-79
1,3-Propanedione, 1-(4-methoxyphenyl)-2,3-diphenyl-	MeOH	283(4.27)	44-4021-79
$C_{22}H_{18}O_4$			
4H-Furo[2,3-h]-1-benzopyran-4-one, 6-[(3-methyl-2-butenyl)oxy]-2-phenyl-(ovalifolin)	EtOH	268(6.27),300(6.07)[sic]	2-0552B-79B
$C_{22}H_{18}O_5$			
1,4-Ethanonaphthacene-6,11-dione, 1,4-dihydro-5,12-dihydroxy-1-methoxy-8-methyl- (plus isomer)	MeOH	221(4.36),257(4.64), 285(3.91),463s(--), 482(4.06)	5-2018-79
Pyrano[2",3":7,8]isoflavone, 5-acetoxy-6",6"-dimethyl-	MeOH	270(4.6)	2-0123-79A
$C_{22}H_{18}O_6$			
2(4H)-Benzofuranone, 6,7-bis(benzoyloxy)-5,6,7,7a-tetrahydro- (dihydrogriffonilide dibenzoate)	MeOH	228(4.96),266(4.63)	100-0500-79
Dasycarponilide, dihydro-, dibenzoate	MeOH	225(4.88),272(3.84)	100-0500-79
6H-Benzo[b]naphtho[2,3-d]pyran-6-one, 7,12-diacetoxy-8,11-dihydro-2-methyl-	EtOH	217(4.39),242(4.50), 293(3.66),305(3.71), 331(3.87)	33-2833-79
4H-1-Benzopyran-4-one, 2,3-dihydro-2,5,7-trihydroxy-2-phenyl-3-(phenylmethoxy)-	EtOH	293(4.20),330s(--)	22-0125-79
	EtOH-NaOH	328(--)	22-0125-79
	EtOH-$AlCl_3$	314(--),370(--)	22-0125-79
1,4-Cyclohexadiene-1-carboxylic acid, 2,5-bis(4-methylphenoxy)-3,6-dioxo-, methyl ester	$CHCl_3$	274(4.30),344(3.44)	33-2350-79
Diospyrin, tetrahydro-	EtOH	216(4.5),263(4.1), 330(3.5),430(3.7)	102-0684-79
$C_{22}H_{18}O_7$			
1,4-Ethanonaphthacene-6,11-dione, 3-acetyl-1,2,3,4-tetrahydro-1,3,5,12-tetrahydroxy-, (1α,3α,4β)-	MeOH	202(4.36),252(4.56), 288(3.80),487(3.92), 520(3.75)	24-2640-79
(1α,3β,4β)-	MeOH	205(4.39),252(4.61), 289(3.84),483(4.02), 510(3.80)	24-2640-79

Compound	Solvent	$\lambda_{max}(\log \epsilon)$	Ref.
$C_{22}H_{18}O_8$			
Butanedioic acid, bis(1,3-benzodioxol-5-ylmethylene)-, dimethyl ester, (E,E)-	EtOH	236(4.31),293(4.27), 329(4.42)	2-0202-79
Naphtho[2,3-d]-1,3-dioxole-6,7-dicarboxylic acid, 5-(1,3-benzodioxol-5-yl)-5,6-dihydro-, dimethyl ester, trans	EtOH	245(4.38),295(3.96), 340(4.14)	2-0202-79
$C_{22}H_{18}O_9$			
1H-Cyclopenta[b]anthracene-1-carboxylic acid, 2-ethyl-3-formyl-2,3,5,10-tetrahydro-3,4,6,11-tetrahydroxy-5,10-dioxo-, methyl ester	MeOH	234(4.50),254(4.35), 292(3.80),490(4.06), 523(3.85)	150-3643-79
$C_{22}H_{19}BrN_2O_2$			
Benzenepropanamide, α-(benzoylamino)-N-(4-bromophenyl)-, (±)-	EtOH	230(4.34),253(4.42)	94-0257-79
$C_{22}H_{19}N$			
Benzenemethanamine, 4-ethenyl-N-([1,1'-biphenyl]-4-ylmethylene)-	$CHCl_3$	284(4.5)	24-2854-79
$C_{22}H_{19}NOS$			
2-Azetidinethione, 1-(2-methoxyphenyl)-3,4-diphenyl-, trans	EtOH	314(4.05)	97-0109-79
$C_{22}H_{19}NO_4$			
2H-Azepine-4-carboxylic acid, 3-methoxy-2-oxo-6,7-diphenyl-, ethyl ester	dioxan	253(4.23),300(4.09)	142-1427-79
Bisacodyl	MeOH	220s(--),252s(--), 259s(--),263(3.9), 270s(--)	106-0027-79
$C_{22}H_{19}NO_4S$			
2H-Azepine-4-carboxylic acid, 3-methoxy-2-oxo-7-phenyl-6-(phenylthio)-, ethyl ester	dioxan	222(4.21),250(4.21), 345s(3.76)	142-1427-79
$C_{22}H_{19}NO_5$			
6H,7H-Benzo[a][1]benzopyrano[3,4-g]-quinolizine-6,7-dione, 9,10,14b,15-tetrahydro-12,13-dimethoxy-	MeOH	283(3.85),310(3.35)	4-0433-79
Isoquinoline, 1,2,3,4-tetrahydro-6,7-dimethoxy-1-methylene-2-[(2-oxo-2H-1-benzopyran-3-yl)carbonyl]-	MeOH	274(4.26),316(4.12), 386(3.74),405(3.81)	4-0433-79
$C_{22}H_{19}NO_5S$			
Benzenesulfonamide, N-[2-[3-(2-hydroxyphenyl)-1,3-dioxopropyl]phenyl]-4-methyl-	MeOH	203(4.53),213(4.53), 367(4.10)	83-0248-79
$C_{22}H_{19}NO_7$			
8H-1,3-Dioxolo[4,5-h]isoindolo[1,2-b]-[3]benzazepin-8-one, 13-acetoxy-5,6-dihydro-9,10-dimethoxy- (4λ,3ε)	MeOH	263s(3.84),274s(3.85), 303(4.31),377(?)	44-4347-79
$C_{22}H_{19}NO_8$			
Benzofuro[3,2-f]-1,2-benzisoxazol-4-(4aH)-one, 5,7-diacetoxy-8-acetyl-3,4a,6-trimethyl-	MeOH	247(4.16),305(3.74), 357(3.54)	87-1380-79

Compound	Solvent	λmax(log ε)	Ref.
1,3-Cyclopentadiene-1,2,3,4-tetracarboxylic acid, 5-(2(1H)-quinolinylidene)-	MeOH	221(4.24),231s(4.10), 264(4.26),293s(3.92), 340s(3.46)	39-2171-79C
	MeOH-$HClO_4$	227(4.08),261(4.16), 267s(4.13),285s(3.92), 428(3.83)	39-2171-79C
6H-1,3-Dioxolo[4,5-h]isoindolo[1,2-b]-[3]benzazepine-8,13(5H,12bH)-dione, 12b-acetoxy-9,10-dimethoxy-, (±)-	MeOH	263s(3.84),274s(3.84), 303(3.85),377(4.31)	44-4347-79
$C_{22}H_{19}NS$			
2-Azetidinethione, 1-(4-methylphenyl)-3,4-diphenyl-, trans	EtOH	312(4.25)	97-0109-79
$C_{22}H_{19}N_3$			
3H-Benzo[c][1,2,3]triazolo[1,2-a]cinnoline, 3,3-dimethyl-2-phenyl-	n.s.g.	254(4.51),260(4.49), 388(3.89)	39-0192-79C
Methanamine, 1-(1,4-diphenyl-5H-cyclopenta[d]pyridazin-5-ylidene)-N,N-dimethyl-	MeOH	239(4.43),273(4.22), 306(4.05),380(4.37), 407s(--)	5-0675-79
$C_{22}H_{19}N_3O_3S$			
1H-Indole-3-carboxamide, 2-[[(4-methylphenyl)sulfonyl]amino]-N-phenyl-	$CHCl_3$	240s(4.48),263s(4.14), 297(3.83)	103-0179-79
$C_{22}H_{19}N_3O_5S_3$			
1-Azetidineacetic acid, 2-(2-benzothiazolyldithio)-α-(1-methylethenyl)-4-oxo-, (4-nitrophenyl)methyl ester, [R-(R*,R*)]-	EtOH	266(4.33)	77-0665-79
$C_{22}H_{19}N_3O_7S$			
4-Thia-1-azabicyclo[3.2.0]hept-2-ene-2-carboxylic acid, 7-oxo-3-[[(phenoxyacetyl)amino]methyl]-, (4-nitrophenyl)methyl ester, (±)-	dioxan	261(4.17),266(4.17), 272s(4.10),318(4.00)	35-6296-79
$C_{22}H_{19}N_3O_8S_4$			
1-Azetidineacetic acid, 2-(2-benzothiazolyldithio)-α-[1-[(methylsulfonyl)oxy]ethylidene]-4-oxo-, (4-nitrophenyl)methyl ester, [R-(E)]-	EtOH	267(4.40)	77-0665-79
$C_{22}H_{19}N_5$			
1H-Pyrazol-3-amine, N-(4-methylphenyl)-5-phenyl-4-(phenylazo)-	EtOH	266(4.09),330(4.12)	48-0127-79
1H-1,2,4-Triazolium, 1-methyl-4,5-diphenyl-3-[(phenylmethylene)hydrazino]-, hydroxide, inner salt	n.s.g.	303(3.98),357(3.90)	39-0724-79C
$C_{22}H_{19}OS$			
Phenalenylium, 1-ethoxy-9-[(phenylmethyl)thio]-, tetrafluoroborate	n.s.g.	275(4.18),283(4.26), 368(3.99),406(3.88)	44-1704-79
$C_{22}H_{20}$			
Benzocyclooctadecene	C_6H_{12}	341(4.81),415(3.89)	24-3907-79
Benzocyclooctadecene, 11,12,13,14-tetradehydro-9,10,15,16-tetrahydro-	C_6H_{12}	263(4.68),298(4.16)	24-3907-79
$C_{22}H_{20}BrN_3O_5S$			
3-Butenoic acid, 2-acetyl-2-[(4-bromo-	EtOH	260(4.29),380(3.50)	104-0500-79

Compound	Solvent	$\lambda_{max}(\log \epsilon)$	Ref.
phenyl)azo]-4-cyano-4-[(4-methylphenyl)sulfonyl]-, ethyl ester (cont.)			104-0500-79
$C_{22}H_{20}Br_2N_2$			
Quinolinium, 1,1'-(1,2-ethanediyl)bis-[6-bromo-4-methyl-, salt with 4-methylbenzenesulfonic acid (1:2)	EtOH	243(4.62),322(3.93)	104-0566-79
$C_{22}H_{20}ClN_3O_5S$			
3-Butenoic acid, 2-acetyl-2-[(4-chlorophenyl)azo]-4-cyano-4-[(4-methylphenyl)sulfonyl]-, ethyl ester	EtOH	265(4.23),395(3.61)	104-0500-79
$C_{22}H_{20}F_2$			
1,1':4',1"-Terphenyl, 4,4"-difluoro-2',3',5',6'-tetramethyl-	$CHCl_3$	267(3.49),273(3.37)	12-1531-79
$C_{22}H_{20}NO_6$			
Benzo[g]-1,3-benzodioxolo[5,6-a]quinolizinium, 8-(carboxymethyl)-5,6-dihydro-9,10-dimethoxy-, chloride	EtOH	272(4.26),353(4.22), 411s(3.70),430s(3.68)	36-0705-79
$C_{22}H_{20}N_2O$			
1H-Imidazol-5-ol, 4,5-dihydro-1-methyl-2,4,4-triphenyl-	EtOH	222(3.85),260s(3.26)	44-0041-79
2-Propen-1-one, 1-(1,3-dimethyl-1H-indol-2-yl)-3-(3-methyl-1H-indol-2-yl)-	EtOH	268(4.09),435(4.49)	39-2154-79C
1H-Pyrazole, 4,5-dihydro-1-(4-methoxyphenyl)-3,5-diphenyl-	C_6H_{12}	366(4.22)	12-1601-79
	MeOH	363(4.20)	12-1601-79
1H-Pyrazole, 4,5-dihydro-3-(4-methoxyphenyl)-1,5-diphenyl-	C_6H_{12}	363(4.25)	12-1601-79
	MeOH	351(4.27)	12-1601-79
1H-Pyrazole, 4,5-dihydro-5-(4-methoxyphenyl)-1,3-diphenyl-	C_6H_{12}	360(4.27)	12-1601-79
	MeOH	354(4.30)	12-1601-79
$C_{22}H_{20}N_2O_2$			
3H-Benz[f]indol-3-one, 1,2-dihydro-2-[1-[3-(1-methoxyethyl)-4-pyridinyl]ethylidene]-, (E)-	EtOH	210(3.01),235(3.24), 277(4.24),304(4.29)	39-2504-79C
Benzoic acid, 2-(3-oxo-1,3-diphenylpropyl)hydrazide	EtOH	243(4.25)	94-0257-79
$C_{22}H_{20}N_2O_2S$			
1H-Pyrazole, 4,5-dihydro-1-[4-(methylsulfonyl)phenyl]-3,5-diphenyl-	C_6H_{12}	355(4.48)	12-1601-79
	MeOH	354(4.56)	12-1601-79
1H-Pyrazole, 4,5-dihydro-3-[4-(methylsulfonyl)phenyl]-1,5-diphenyl-	C_6H_{12}	393(4.36)	12-1601-79
	MeOH	389(4.42)	12-1601-79
1H-Pyrazole, 4,5-dihydro-5-[4-(methylsulfonyl)phenyl]-1,3-diphenyl-	C_6H_{12}	354(4.23)	12-1601-79
	MeOH	352(4.22)	12-1601-79
$C_{22}H_{20}N_2O_3$			
1H-Cyclopenta[l]phenanthrene-1-carboxylic acid, 2-(acetylhydrazono)-2,3-dihydro-, ethyl ester	EtOH	248(4.73),256(4.82), 278(4.06),288(4.00), 300(4.01),335(3.31), 350(3.31)	39-2034-79C
Ethanone, 2-[2,5-dimethyl-4-[(4-nitrophenyl)methylene]-1(4H)-pyridinyl]-1-phenyl-	$CHCl_3$	252(4.07),450(3.97), 560(2.80)	103-0316-79
$C_{22}H_{20}N_2O_3S$			
Benzenesulfonic acid, 4-methyl-, (9-ethoxy-1H-phenalen-1-ylidene)hydrazide	EtOH	282(4.4),369(4.6), 387(4.6),503(4.2)	83-0288-79

Compound	Solvent	λ_{max}(log ε)	Ref.
$C_{22}H_{20}N_2O_4$			
1H-Cyclopenta[l]phenanthrene-1-carboxylic acid, 2-(acetylhydrazono)-2,3-dihydro-1-hydroxy-, ethyl ester	EtOH	249(4.71),256(4.74), 265s(4.42),278(4.18), 288(4.06),301(4.07)	39-2034-79C
1H-Cyclopenta[l]phenanthrene-1-carboxylic acid, 2-(acetylhydrazono)-2,3-dihydro-1-methoxy-, methyl ester	EtOH	249(4.85),257(4.97), 278(4.20),289(4.07), 301(4.14),333(3.12), 348(3.13)	39-2034-79C
$C_{22}H_{20}N_2O_5$			
Acetamide, N-(5,6-dihydro-9,10-dimethoxy-8H-benzo[g]-1,3-benzodioxolo-[5,6-a]quinolizin-8-ylidene)-	EtOH	263(4.22),348(4.23), 408(3.68),420(3.69)	36-0705-79
$C_{22}H_{20}N_2O_8$			
3-Benzofurancarboxylic acid, 6-[acetyl-(4-nitrophenyl)amino]-5-acetoxy-2-methyl-, ethyl ester	MeOH	256(4.23),291(4.15), 313s(4.08)	83-0515-79
2H-Benzo[b]furo[4,3,2-kl]acridinium, 4-cyano-2a,3,4,5,5a,6,6a,7,12,12a-12b,12c-dodecahydro-2a,8,12-trihydroxy-6,6,12-trimethyl-2,3,5,7-tetraoxo-, hydroxide, inner salt	MeOH-HCl	233(4.02),280(4.32), 352(3.59)	44-0691-79
$C_{22}H_{20}N_2S$			
1H-Pyrazole, 4,5-dihydro-1-[4-(methylthio)phenyl]-3,5-diphenyl-	C_6H_{12}	367(4.37)	12-1601-79
	MeOH	364(4.34)	12-1601-79
1H-Pyrazole, 4,5-dihydro-3-[4-(methylthio)phenyl]-1,5-diphenyl-	C_6H_{12}	368(4.34)	12-1601-79
	MeOH	365(4.28)	12-1601-79
1H-Pyrazole, 4,5-dihydro-5-[4-(methylthio)phenyl]-1,3-diphenyl-	C_6H_{12}	357(4.31)	12-1601-79
	MeOH	355(4.28)	12-1601-79
Thiourea, bis(phenylmethyl)(phenylmethylene)-	C_6H_{12}	250(4.45),280(4.52)	24-1956-79
$C_{22}H_{20}N_4$			
Pyridazine, 3,4-di-1H-pyrrol-1-yl-6-(1,2,3,4-tetrahydro-2-naphthalenyl)-	EtOH	272(4.68)	80-0453-79
$C_{22}H_{20}N_4O_4$			
Quinolinium, 1,1'-(1,2-ethanediyl)bis-[4-methyl-6-nitro-, salt with 4-methylbenzenesulfonic acid (1:2)	EtOH	245(4.42),318(3.78)	104-0566-79
$C_{22}H_{20}N_4O_6$			
Methanone, (4-hydroxy-3,5-dimethylphenyl)(4-methoxyphenyl)-, 2,4-dinitrophenylhydrazone	EtOH	396.5(4.43)	49-1057-79
high melting isomer	EtOH	398(4.46)	49-1057-79
$C_{22}H_{20}N_4O_7S$			
3-Butenoic acid, 2-acetyl-4-cyano-4-[(4-methylphenyl)sulfonyl]-2-[(4-nitrophenyl)azo]-, ethyl ester	EtOH	250(4.22),340(3.94)	104-0500-79
$C_{22}H_{20}N_6$			
[1,1'-Biphenyl]-4,4'-diamine, N-[5-methyl-4-(phenylazo)-1H-pyrazol-3-yl]-	EtOH	345(3.43)	48-0127-79
$C_{22}H_{20}N_6O$			
Cyclohexanone, 2,6-bis[(4-azido-3-meth-	MeOH	362(4.68)	93-0333-79

Compound	Solvent	$\lambda_{max}(\log \epsilon)$	Ref.
ylphenyl)methylene]- (cont.)			93-0333-79
$C_{22}H_{20}N_6O_3$			
Cyclohexanone, 2,6-bis[(4-azido-3-methoxyphenyl)methylene]-	MeOH	368(5.02)	93-0333-79
$C_{22}H_{20}N_6O_{10}$			
L-threo-2,3-Hexodiulosonic acid, γ-lactone, 3-[(2,4-dinitrophenyl)hydrazone] 2-(phenylhydrazone), 5,6-diacetate (3λ,4ε)	n.s.g.	225(4.44),322(4.46), 475(4.55),?(3.78)	106-0531-79
$C_{22}H_{20}N_8O$			
7H-Benzo[e]perimidin-7-one, 6-[[4,6-bis(dimethylamino)-1,3,5-triazin-2-yl]amino]-	DMF	466(4.33)	2-0195-79B
7H-Benzo[e]perimidin-7-one, 6-[[4,6-bis(ethylamino)-1,3,5-triazin-2-yl]amino]-	DMF	468(4.29)	2-0195-79B
$C_{22}H_{20}N_8O_3$			
7H-Benzo[e]perimidin-7-one, 6-[[4,6-bis[(2-hydroxyethyl)amino]-1,3,5-triazin-2-yl]amino]-	DMF	467(4.27)	2-0195-79B
$C_{22}H_{20}O$			
2-Butanone, 4,4,4-triphenyl-	MeCN	236(3.28),261(2.91)	78-0177-79
9H-Fluoren-9-ol, 2,7-dimethyl-9-(phenylmethyl)-	$CHCl_3$	285(4.21),294s(4.14)	24-3490-79
$C_{22}H_{20}O_2$			
1-Isobenzofuranol, 1-p-biphenylyl-3,3-dimethyl-, cation	50% H_2SO_4	404(4.57)	104-1126-79
2-Naphthalenol, 5,6,7,8-tetrahydro-5-(4-hydroxyphenyl)-6-phenyl-	n.s.g.	281(3.57)	87-1509-79
$C_{22}H_{20}O_2S$			
Thiophene, 2,5-bis[2-(4-methoxyphenyl)-ethenyl]-	toluene	405(4.77)	103-0729-79
$C_{22}H_{20}O_4$			
Cyclobuta[1,2-a:3,4-a']diindene-5,10-dione, 5,5b,10a,10b-tetrahydro-3,8-dimethoxy-5a,10a-dimethyl-, endo	$C_2H_4Cl_2$	220(4.76),252(4.21), 314(3.86)	44-1388-79
exo	$C_2H_4Cl_2$	224(4.69),250(4.39), 318(3.87)	44-1388-79
$C_{22}H_{20}O_5$			
5,12-Naphthacenedione, 2-acetyl-1,2,3,4-tetrahydro-7,10-dimethoxy-	EtOH	255(4.78),476(3.72)	88-4533-79
$C_{22}H_{20}O_6$			
4H-1-Benzopyran-4-one, 3-(3,4-dimethoxyphenyl)-7-[(1,1-dimethyl-2-propynyl)oxy]-5-hydroxy-	MeOH	238(4.21),276(4.47)	2-0123-79A
9-Phenanthreneacetic acid, α-acetyl-α-acetoxy-9,10-dihydro-10-oxo-, ethyl ester	EtOH	237s(4.33),246(4.53), 254(4.52),279(3.89), 340(3.48)	39-2034-79C
Pyrano[2,3-h]isoflavone, 5-hydroxy-2',4'-dimethoxy-8,8-dimethyl-	MeOH	255(4.52),266(4.58), 305(3.91)	39-0279-79C

Compound	Solvent	λ_{max}(log ϵ)	Ref.
Pyrano[3,2-g]isoflavone, 5-hydroxy-2',4'-dimethoxy-8,8-dimethyl-	MeOH	265(4.64),308(3.80)	39-0279-79C
Pyrano[2",3":7,6]isoflavone, 5-hydroxy-3',4'-dimethoxy-6",6"-dimethyl-	MeOH	208(4.03),276(4.07)	2-0123-79A
Pyrano[2",3":7,8]isoflavone, 5-hydroxy-3',4'-dimethoxy-6",6"-dimethyl-	MeOH	224(4.05),260(4.61)	2-0123-79A
$C_{22}H_{20}O_7$			
2-Anthraceneacetic acid, 9,10-dihydro-1,4-dihydroxy-3-methyl-9,10-dioxo-α-(3-oxobutyl)-, methyl ester	MeOH	226s(--),251(4.56),255(4.55),289(3.97),484(3.98),517s(--)	5-0035-79
2,6-Epoxy-2H-anthra[2,3-b]oxocin-8,13-dione, 3,4,5,6-tetrahydro-7-hydroxy-9,11-dimethoxy-2-methyl-	MeOH	225(4.57),250(4.16),287(4.50),313(3.92),439(3.90)	39-0451-79C
2,6-Epoxy-2H-anthra[2,3-b]oxocin-8,13-dione, 3,4,5,6-tetrahydro-9-hydroxy-7,11-dimethoxy-2-methyl-	MeOH	223(4.48),252(4.08),272(4.38),288(4.56),313(3.96),428(3.83)	39-0451-79C
$C_{22}H_{20}O_8$			
ε-Rhodomycinone, 9-deoxy-10-epi-	MeOH	234(4.60),251(4.46),293(3.98),491(4.16),526(4.10),568(3.78)	150-3643-79
$C_{22}H_{20}O_9$			
Versiconal, 3,6-O,O-dimethyl-, acetate	MeOH	225(4.60),265(4.34),284(4.52),321(4.04),442(4.07)	39-0451-79C
$C_{22}H_{21}As$			
Arsine, (diphenylmethylene)(2,4,6-trimethylphenyl)-	THF	346(3.52)	89-0395-79
$C_{22}H_{21}BrN_4O_6$			
L-threo-2,3-Hexodiulosonic acid, γ-lactone, 3-[(4-bromophenyl)hydrazone] 2-(phenylhydrazone), 5,6-diacetate	n.s.g.	203(4.12),262(4.26),355(4.28),446(4.26)	106-0531-79
$C_{22}H_{21}BrO_2$			
4-Cyclopentene-1,3-dione, 4-(1-bromo-1-methylethyl)-2,2-bis(phenylmethyl)-	EtOH	397(1.70)	25-0057-79
$C_{22}H_{21}Br_4N_3O_8$			
Fistularin 1	n.s.g.	230(4.18),284(3.75)	88-3921-79
$C_{22}H_{21}ClN_2O$			
Benzenecarboximidamide, N'-(3-chloro-4-methylphenyl)-N-hydroxy-4-methyl-N-(4-methylphenyl)-	EtOH	210(4.73),260(4.19),319(4.22)	56-2597-79
Benzenecarboximidamide, N-(4-chlorophenyl)-N'-(2,3-dimethylphenyl)-N-hydroxy-4-methyl-, monohydrochloride	EtOH	209(4.60),253(4.13),320(4.17)	56-2597-79
$C_{22}H_{21}ClN_4O_6$			
L-threo-2,3-Hexodiulosonic acid, γ-lactone, 3-[(4-chlorophenyl)hydrazone] 2-(phenylhydrazone), 5,6-diacetate	n.s.g.	210(4.21),255(4.32),362(4.11),436(3.96)	106-0531-79
$C_{22}H_{21}NO_4$			
1H-Azepine-4-carboxylic acid, 2,5-dihydro-3-methoxy-2-oxo-6,7-diphenyl-, ethyl ester	dioxan	228(4.27),300s(4.00)	142-1427-79

Compound	Solvent	λ max (log ε)	Ref.
6-Oxa-1-azabicyclo[5.2.0]non-4-ene-3,9-dione, 2,2-dimethyl-4-phenyl-5-(phenylmethoxy)-	EtOH	279(4.05)	88-0391-79
$C_{22}H_{21}NO_4S$			
1H-Azepine-4-carboxylic acid, 2,5-dihydro-3-methoxy-2-oxo-7-phenyl-6-(phenylthio)-, ethyl ester	dioxan	220(4.33),260s(4.19), 315s(3.88)	142-1427-79
$C_{22}H_{21}NO_5$			
[1,3]Benzodioxolo[5,6-c]phenanthridine, 12,13-dihydro-1,2,13-trimethoxy-12-methyl-	EtOH	210(4.43),226(4.47), 282(4.55),320(4.10)	2-0299-79A
$C_{22}H_{21}NO_6$			
1,3-Dioxolo[4,5-h]indeno[2,1-a][3]benzazepin-12(5H)-one, 6,7-dihydro-10,11,13-trimethoxy-7-methyl-	EtOH	238(4.43),303s(--), 312(4.54),487(3.38)	24-3486-79
$C_{22}H_{21}N_2O$			
Acridinium, 9-[(4-ethoxyphenyl)amino]-10-methyl-, iodide	EtOH	249(4.63),271(4.59), 334(3.54),452(4.12)	104-0183-79
$C_{22}H_{21}N_2O_8$			
2H-Benzo[b]furo[4,3,2-kl]acridinium, 4-(aminocarbonyl)-2a,5,5a,6,12b,12c-hexahydro-2a,3,7,8-tetrahydroxy-6,6,12-trimethyl-2,5-dioxo-, chloride	MeOH-HCl	234(4.81),264(4.30), 316(3.90),330(4.01), 345(4.06)	44-0691-79
$C_{22}H_{21}N_3$			
Benzenamine, 4-(4,5-dihydro-1,3-diphenyl-1H-pyrazol-5-yl)-N-methyl-	C_6H_{12}	363(4.32)	12-1601-79
	MeOH	356(4.26)	12-1601-79
Benzenamine, 4-(4,5-dihydro-1,5-diphenyl-1H-pyrazol-3-yl)-N-methyl-	C_6H_{12}	360(4.38)	12-1601-79
	MeOH	361(4.37)	12-1601-79
$C_{22}H_{21}N_3O_4$			
Benzoic acid, 4,5-dimethoxy-2-(methyl-9H-pyrido[3,4-b]indol-1-ylamino)-	MeCN	228(4.51),246(4.58), 292(4.05),353(3.95)	142-0353-79
Epieburnamonin-18-carboxylic acid, 15-cyano-19-oxo-, methyl ester	MeOH	247(4.30),275(4.03), 304(3.73),300(3.69)	24-1902-79
$C_{22}H_{21}N_3O_7$			
Uridine, 5'-deoxy-5'-(2,5-dioxo-1-phenyl-3-pyrrolidinylidene)-2',3'-O-(1-methylethylidene)-, (E)-	EtOH	223(4.10)	33-2788-79
$C_{22}H_{21}N_3S$			
Imidazo[1,2-c]quinazoline-5(3H)-thione, 2,6,7,8,9,10-hexahydro-2,3-diphenyl-	EtOH	266(3.93),350(4.08)	106-0390-79
	EtOH-HCl	270(3.96),333(4.19)	106-0390-79
	EtOH-NaOH	266(4.09),350(4.12)	106-0390-79
$C_{22}H_{21}N_5O_8$			
L-threo-2,3-Hexodiulosonic acid, γ-lactone, 3-[(4-nitrophenyl)hydrazone] 2-(phenylhydrazone), 5,6-diacetate	n.s.g.	253(5.60),352(6.02), 440(5.05)	106-0531-79
$C_{22}H_{21}OSSe$			
Sulfonium, dimethyl-, 1-(diphenylselenonio)-2-oxo-2-phenylethylide, tetrafluoroborate	n.s.g.	220s(4.477),263(4.119)	104-0332-79

Compound	Solvent	λ_{max}(log ε)	Ref.
$C_{22}H_{21}P$			
Phosphine, (diphenylmethylene)(2,4,6-trimethylphenyl)-	THF	254(3.20)	89-0395-79
$C_{22}H_{22}$			
Benzene, 1,2-di-1,3-octadien-7-ynyl-, (all-E)-	C_6H_{12}	267(4.58),304(4.53)	24-3907-79
1,10:2,9:4,7-Triethanodibenzo[a,e]cyclooctene, 5,6,11,12-tetrahydro-	THF	294(2.55),313(2.30)	35-3125-79
$C_{22}H_{22}BrNO_6$			
8-Azabicyclo[3.2.1]oct-2-ene-6,7-dicarboxylic acid, 8-[3-(4-bromophenyl)-3-oxo-1-propenyl]-4-oxo-, diethyl ester, (6-endo,7-exo)-	EtOH	216(4.17),263(4.03), 337(4.28)	56-0057-79
(6-exo,7-endo)-	EtOH	218(4.18),264(4.05), 337(4.30)	56-0057-79
$C_{22}H_{22}ClN_3O_2$			
4-Cyclopentene-1,3-dione, 2-[bis(phenylamino)methylene]-4-chloro-5-(diethylamino)-	isoPrOH	263(4.28),339(4.61)	104-0454-79
$C_{22}H_{22}F_3NO_6$			
Colchicine, N-(trifluoroacetyl)deacetyl-	EtOH	227(4.43),236(4.44), 346(4.21)	33-0965-79
Isocolchicine, N-(trifluoroacetyl)-deacetyl-	EtOH	226(4.42),244(4.48), 340(4.27)	33-0965-79
$C_{22}H_{22}NO_7$			
Hydrastine, 9-oxo-1,2-dehydro-, methyl ester, iodide	EtOH	240s(4.31),257s(4.23), 310(4.19),388(3.87)	44-4343-79
$C_{22}H_{22}N_2$			
1,4:5,14-Diethenobenzocyclododecene-2,3-dicarbonitrile, 1,4,6,7,8,9,10-11,12,13-decahydro-	EtOH	213(4.28),241(3.79), 252s(3.76),285s(2.87), 331(2.60)	35-6660-79
5,8-Etheno-1,4-octanonaphthalene-6,7-dicarbonitrile, 5,8-dihydro-	EtOH	208s(4.47),222(4.39), 248s(3.06),270s(3.06), 323(2.49)	35-6660-79
$C_{22}H_{22}N_2O$			
Benzenecarboximidamide, N'-(2,3-dimethylphenyl)-N-hydroxy-4-methyl-N-phenyl-, hydrochloride	EtOH	209(4.56),250(4.13), 314(4.13)	56-2597-79
Benzenecarboximidamide, N'-(2,6-dimethylphenyl)-N-hydroxy-N-(2-methylphenyl)-, hydrochloride	EtOH	208(4.60),310(4.10)	56-2597-79
Benzenecarboximidamide, N'-(3,4-dimethylphenyl)-N-hydroxy-N-(2-methylphenyl)-	EtOH	209(4.62),259(4.16), 315(4.08)	56-2597-79
Benzenecarboximidamide, N'-(3,4-dimethylphenyl)-N-hydroxy-N-(4-methylphenyl)-	EtOH	208(4.45),259(4.06), 320(4.03)	56-2597-79
Cinnoline, 4-ethoxy-1,2,3,4-tetrahydro-1,2-diphenyl-	MeCN	245(4.23),280(4.11)	103-1243-79
Cinnoline, 1,2,3,4-tetrahydro-4-methoxy-3-methyl-1,2-diphenyl-	MeCN	246(4.21),289(4.23)	104-2145-79
6,10-Imino-11H-cyclooct[b]indol-11-one, 5,6,7,8,9,10-hexahydro-5-methyl-12-(phenylmethyl)-, cis	EtOH	248(4.30),267(4.25), 307(4.09)	88-1025-79

Compound	Solvent	$\lambda_{max}(\log \epsilon)$	Ref.
2H-Indol-2-one, 1,3-dihydro-1,3-dimethyl-3-(2,3,4,9-tetrahydro-1H-carbazol-1-yl)-	EtOH	228(4.54),256(4.02), 286(3.99),293(3.90)	23-1694-79
7,11-Methano-6H-cyclonona[b]quinoxalin-14-ol, 7,8,9,10,11,12-hexahydro-14-phenyl-	EtOH	208(4.58),241(4.40), 319(3.96)	56-1221-79
$C_{22}H_{22}N_2O_2$			
1H-Pyrazole-4-carboxylic acid, 3-(2-methyl-1-propenyl)-1,5-diphenyl-, ethyl ester	EtOH	219s(4.30),239(4.38)	4-0657-79
3,5-Pyrazolidinedione, 4-(1-cyclohexen-1-yl)-4-methyl-1,2-diphenyl-	EtOH	238(4.3)	103-0215-79
3,5-Pyrazolidinedione, 4-(1-cyclopenten-1-yl)-4-ethyl-1,2-diphenyl-	EtOH	239(4.3)	103-0215-79
$C_{22}H_{22}N_2O_3$			
Spiro[2H-1-benzopyran-2,2'-[2H]indole], 1',3'-dihydro-1',3',3'-trimethyl-6-nitro-8-(2-propenyl)-	EtOH	540(4.53)	103-1101-79
	toluene	600(--)	103-1101-79
$C_{22}H_{22}N_2O_4$			
4,8-Iminocyclohepta[c]pyrrole-1,3,5-(2H)-trione, 9-(4,4-dimethyl-3-oxo-1-pentenyl)-3a,4,8,8a-tetrahydro-2-phenyl-, (3aα,4α,8α,8aα)-	EtOH	217(4.19),295(4.35)	56-0057-79
$C_{22}H_{22}N_2O_5$			
Dibenzo[f,h]cinnoline-12b(1H)-acetic acid, 1-acetyl-2,3,4,4a-tetrahydro-4a-hydroxy-3-oxo-, ethyl ester	EtOH	274(4.12),293s(3.89)	39-2034-79C
Ethanone, 1-(1',3'-dihydro-8-methoxy-1',3',3'-trimethyl-6-nitrospiro[2H-1-benzopyran-2,2'-[2H]indol]-5'-yl)-	n.s.g.	255(4.13),281(3.68), 301(3.59),357(3.99)	103-1329-79
photochromic form	EtOH	565(--)	103-1329-79
$C_{22}H_{22}N_2O_7$			
1H-Benz[f]indazole-3-carboxylic acid, 1-[6-(acetoxymethyl)tetrahydro-2H-pyran-2-yl]-4,9-dihydro-4,9-dioxo-, ethyl ester, cis	EtOH	246(4.54),265(4.18)	111-0151-79
2-Naphthacenecarbonitrile, 4-(dimethylamino)-1,4,4a,5,5a,6,11,12a-octahydro-3,5,10,12,12a-pentahydroxy-6-methyl-1,11-dioxo-	MeOH	270(4.26),360(4.11)	88-2701-79
$C_{22}H_{22}N_4$			
Pyridazine, 4,5-dihydro-6-(1,2,3,4-tetrahydro-2-naphthalenyl)-3,4-di-1H-pyrrol-1-yl-	EtOH	252(4.57)	80-0453-79
$C_{22}H_{22}N_4O_4S$			
Benzamide, N-[[[[4-[(methylphenylamino)sulfonyl]phenyl]methyl]nitrosoamino]methyl]-	EtOH	225(4.44),366(1.81)	118-0531-79
$C_{22}H_{22}N_4O_6$			
L-threo-2,3-Hexodiulosonic acid, γ-lactone, 2,3-bis(phenylhydrazone), 5,6-diacetate	EtOH	207(4.02),256(4.11), 282(4.21),355(3.98), 445(4.21)	136-0087-79A

Compound	Solvent	λ_{max}(log ε)	Ref.
$C_{22}H_{22}N_{12}Ni$			
Nickel, (1,11-diethyl-1,10,11,20-tetrahydro-3,13-dimethyldipyrazolo[4,3-c-4',3'-j]dipyrido[2,3-f:2',3'-m]-[1,2,5,8,9,12]hexaazacyclotetradecinato(2-)-N^4,N^{10},N^{14},N^{20})-, (SP-4-1)-	n.s.g.	470(3.49)	103-0572-79
$C_{22}H_{22}O_2$			
1H,7H-1a,6a:7a,12a-Dimethanodicyclopropa[e,e']benzo[1,2-a:4,5-a']dicyclooctene-13,14-dione, 2,3,5,6,8,9-11,12-octahydro-	C_6H_{12}	262s(3.13),287(3.04), 297(3.02)	35-2128-79
1-Isobenzofuranol, 3,3-diethyl-1,3-dihydro-1-(1-naphthalenyl)-, cation	50% H_2SO_4	422(4.18)	104-1126-79
1-Isobenzofuranol, 3,3-diethyl-1,3-dihydro-1-(2-naphthalenyl)-, cation	50% H_2SO_4	373(4.47)	104-1126-79
1H,3H-Naphtho[1,8-cd]pyran-1-ol, 1-methyl-3-(2,4,6-trimethylphenyl)-	hexane	206(4.58),229(4.85), 288(3.88)	44-1934-79
$C_{22}H_{22}O_4$			
Ethanone, 1-(1,2,3,4,5,12-hexahydro-7,10-dimethoxy-5,12-epoxynaphthacen-2-yl)-	EtOH	220(4.58),260(4.57), 300(3.74),325(3.67), 340(3.63)	88-4533-79
1,1':4',1"-Terphenyl, 3,3",4,4"-tetramethoxy-	hexane	271(4.78),279(4.79)	65-0146-79
$C_{22}H_{22}O_6$			
4H,8H-Benzo[1,2-b:3,4-b']dipyran-4-one, 3-(2,4-dimethoxyphenyl)-9,10-dihydro-5-hydroxy-8,8-dimethyl-	MeOH	258(4.48),288(4.19)	39-0279-79C
4H-1-Benzopyran-4-one, 3-(2,4-dimethoxyphenyl)-5,7-dihydroxy-6-(3-methyl-2-butenyl)-	MeOH	259(4.45),288(4.69)	39-0279-79C
4H-1-Benzopyran-4-one, 3-(2,4-dimethoxyphenyl)-5,7-dimethoxy-8-(3-methyl-2-butenyl)-	MeOH	266(4.62),290(4.29)	39-0279-79C
4H-1-Benzopyran-4-one, 3-(2,4-dimethoxyphenyl)-5-hydroxy-7-[(3-methyl-2-butenyl)oxy]-	MeOH	256(4.45),302(3.98)	39-0279-79C
$C_{22}H_{22}O_7$			
Desoxypicropodophyllin	EtOH	246(4.19),294(3.84)	95-0674-79
Desoxypodophyllotoxin	EtOH	294(4.67)	95-0674-79
	EtOH	291(3.79)	100-0378-79
Herqueichrysin monoacetate	MeOH	235(3.56),282(3.56), 325(2.85),432(3.54)	39-1233-79C
1,4-Ethanonaphthacene-6,8,11(7H)-trione, 1,4,6a,9,10,10a-hexahydro-5,12-dihydroxy-1,10-dimethoxy- (or isomer)	MeOH	228s(--),243(4.32), 267(3.74),255s(--), 402(3.97),420s(--)	24-3453-79
$C_{22}H_{22}O_8$			
[1,1'-Biphenyl]-2,2',4,5'-tetrol, 3',4'-dimethyl-, tetraacetate	EtOH	220s(4.69),236s(4.51), 291(3.11),300(3.05)	1-0271-79
1H-Phenalen-1-one, 3,9-diacetoxy-4-ethoxy-7,8-dimethoxy-6-methyl-	EtOH	210(4.43),246(4.16), 273(4.16),280s(3.91), 340(3.74),424(3.91)	150-0301-79
$C_{22}H_{22}O_{13}$			
4H-1-Benzopyran-4-one, 2-(3,4-dihydroxyphenyl)-7-(β-D-glucopyranosyloxy)-	MeOH	259(4.36),373(4.27)	100-0126-79

Compound	Solvent	λ_{max}(log ε)	Ref.
3,5-dihydroxy-6-methoxy- (cont.)			100-0126-79
acetyl deriv.	MeOH	258(4.39),373(4.32)	100-0126-79
$C_{22}H_{23}ClN_2O_8$			
5-Isobenzofurancarboxamide, 1-(3-chloro-1,2,3,4-tetrahydro-5-hydroxy-1-methyl-4-oxo-2-naphthalenyl)-7-(dimethylamino)-1,3,3a,6,7,7a-hexahydro-3a,4-dihydroxy-3,6-dioxo-, monohydrochloride	MeOH-HCl	269(4.39),352(3.56)	44-0691-79
$C_{22}H_{23}ClN_6$			
4H-[1,2,4]Triazolo[4,3-a][1,4]benzodiazepine, 8-chloro-4-methyl-1-(4-methyl-1-piperazinyl)-6-phenyl-	EtOH	218(4.61),245s(4.23), 265s(3.97),300s(3.28)	87-1390-79
6H-[1,2,4]Triazolo[4,3-a][1,4]benzodiazepine, 8-chloro-4-methyl-1-(4-methyl-1-piperazinyl)-6-phenyl-	EtOH	204(4.72),285(3.77)	87-1390-79
$C_{22}H_{23}IN_2O_4$			
L-Tryptophan, N-[(phenylmethoxy)carbonyl]-, 3-iodopropyl ester	EtOH	274(3.79),282(3.81), 291(3.75)	118-0957-79
$C_{22}H_{23}N$			
Benzenamine, N,N-dimethyl-4-[4-(4-methylphenyl)-1,3,5-cycloheptatrien-1-yl]-	EtOH	362(4.445)	78-2269-79
$C_{22}H_{23}NO$			
Benzenamine, 4-[4-(4-methoxyphenyl)-1,3,5-cycloheptatrien-1-yl]-N,N-dimethyl-	EtOH	361(4.431)	78-2269-79
$C_{22}H_{23}NO_2$			
1-Naphthaleneacetamide, N-(2-hydroxy-1,1-dimethyl-2-phenylethyl)-	EtOH	224(4.86),281(3.85)	4-1525-79
$C_{22}H_{23}NO_3$			
2H-1-Benzopyran-2,4(3H)-dione, 3-[[[2,6-bis(1-methylethyl)phenyl]amino]methylene]-	hexane	210s(--),236(4.22), 337(4.31)	131-0077-79D
	EtOH	333(4.37)	131-0077-79D
1-Isoquinolinepropanoic acid, 3,4-dihydro-α-[2-(4-methylphenyl)-2-oxoethyl]-, methyl ester	EtOH	205(6.00),254(5.79), 320(5.10)	103-0770-79
1H-Pyrrole-3-carboxylic acid, 4,5-dihydro-2-methyl-5-oxo-1,4-bis(phenylmethyl)-	EtOH	212(4.02),291(3.93)	44-0808-79
$C_{22}H_{23}NO_4$			
1,3-Cyclohexadiene-1-carboxylic acid, 5-[[bis(4-methoxyphenyl)methyl]amino]-, (±)-	MeOH	236(4.25),275(3.94)	44-3451-79
1H-Indole-2-acetic acid, 3-(2-hydroxyethyl)- -(methoxymethylene)-1-(phenylmethyl)-, methyl ester, (E)-	EtOH	226(4.56),288(3.86)	23-0289-79
(Z)-	EtOH	226(4.56),289(3.89)	23-0289-79
Phenanthrene, 1,2,3,4,9,10-hexahydro-7-methoxy-1-(4-methoxyphenyl)-2-nitro-	MeOH	230(4.12),276(4.27)	2-0071-79B
Phenanthrene, 1,2,3,9,10,10a-hexahydro-7-methoxy-1-(4-methoxyphenyl)-2-nitro-	MeOH	219(4.29),264(4.16)	2-0071-79B
Phenanthrene, 1,2,3,9,10,10a-hexahydro-7-methoxy-2-(4-methoxyphenyl)-1-nitro-	MeOH	219(4.29),265(4.16)	2-0071-79B

Compound	Solvent	λ_{max}(log ε)	Ref.
$C_{22}H_{23}NO_6$			
8-Canadinylacetic acid, hydrochloride	EtOH-acid	267s(3.44),287(3.86)	36-0705-79
Corynolamine	MeOH	237(3.25),288(3.24)	94-2194-79
1(3H)-Isobenzofuranone, 3-(3,4-dihydro-6,7-dimethoxy-2-methyl-1(2H)-isoquinolinylidene)-6,7-dimethoxy-	MeOH	225(4.39),307(4.18), 330(4.16),404(4.28)	23-1598-79
$C_{22}H_{23}NO_7$			
Dehydrohydrastine methyl ester	EtOH	258(4.61),298(4.70), 302(4.68),387(3.92)	44-4337-79
Dehydronorhydrastine ethyl ester	EtOH	210(4.46),230(4.35), 282(4.21),309(4.20)	44-4337-79
8H-1,3-Dioxolo[4,5-h]isoindolo[1,2-b]-[3]benzazepin-8-one, 5,6,12b,13-tetrahydro-9,10,12b,13-tetramethoxy-, cis	EtOH	292(3.66),312s(3.19)	44-4347-79
trans	EtOH	293(3.72),314s(3.20)	44-4347-79
$C_{22}H_{23}NO_8$			
Benzo[g]quinoline-2-carboxylic acid, 7-butyl-5,10-dihydro-4-hydroxy-3,8,9-trimethoxy-5,10-dioxo-, methyl ester	MeOH	259(4.36),272(4.44), 404(3.73)	39-0807-79C
Benzo[g]quinoline-2-carboxylic acid, 7-butyl-5,10-dihydro-9-hydroxy-3,4,8-trimethoxy-5,10-dioxo-, methyl ester	MeOH	258(4.32),273(4.40), 414(3.94)	39-0807-79C
Isophomazarin, di-O-methyl-, methyl ester	MeOH	256(4.29),276s(4.10), 450(3.63)	39-0823-79C
$C_{22}H_{23}N_2O_8$			
2H-Benzo[b]furo[4,3,2-kl]acridinium, 4-(aminocarbonyl)-2a,5,5a,6,6a,7,12-12a,12b,12c-decahydro-2a,3,8-trihydroxy-6,6,12-trimethyl-2,5,7-trioxo-, chloride	MeOH-HCl	273(4.41),360(3.61)	44-0691-79
$C_{22}H_{23}N_2O_9$			
2H-Benzo[b]furo[4,3,2-kl]acridinium, 4-(aminocarbonyl)-2a,5,5a,6,6a,7,12-12a,12b,12c-decahydro-2a,3,8,12-tetrahydroxy-6,6,12-trimethyl-2,5,7-trioxo-, chloride	MeOH-HCl	271(4.40),352(3.65)	44-0691-79
	MeOH-NaOH	217(4.24),249(4.27), 282(4.21),389(3.41)	44-0691-79
$C_{22}H_{23}N_3O$			
Propanamide, N-[4-cyano-1,2-dihydro-2-(phenylmethyl)-1-isoquinolinyl]-2,2-dimethyl-	CH_2Cl_2	230(4.2),308(4.1), 321s(4.1)	64-1593-79B
Propanamide, N-[3-cyano-1,2-dihydro-1-(phenylmethyl)-2-quinolinyl]-2,2-dimethyl-	CH_2Cl_2	243(3.8),254s(3.8), 289(3.8),299(3.8), 393(3.5)	64-0064-79B
$C_{22}H_{23}N_3O_4S$			
1H-1,2,4-Triazolium, 3-[[2-ethoxy-1-(ethoxycarbonyl)-2-oxoethyl]-thio]-4-phenyl-1-(phenylmethyl)-, hydroxide, inner salt	MeOH	249(4.31)	70-2526-79
$C_{22}H_{23}N_5O_2$			
Roquefortine photoisomer (3Z)	EtOH	212(4.236),240(4.113), 311(4.434)	98-0201-79

Compound	Solvent	λ_{max}(log ε)	Ref.
$C_{22}H_{23}N_7O_2$			
1H-Pyrazole-3-acetonitrile, 4-cyano-α-(4-morpholinylmethylene)-5-[(4-morpholinylmethylene)amino]-1-phenyl-	MeOH	233(4.30),302(4.52)	83-0535-79
$C_{22}H_{23}N_7O_6$			
Benzoic acid, 4,4'-[1H-1,2,4-triazole-3,5-diylbis(iminocarbonylimino)]bis-, diethyl ester	n.s.g.	282(4.75)	87-0028-79
$C_{22}H_{23}S$			
Sulfonium, [4-(1,1-dimethylethyl)phenyl]diphenyl-, hexafluorophosphate	MeOH	237(4.31),249(4.29)	47-0977-79
$C_{22}H_{23}Se$			
Selenonium, [4-(1,1-dimethylethyl)phenyl]diphenyl-, hexafluoroarsenate	MeOH	226(4.34),264(3.57), 372(3.36)	47-1047-79
$C_{22}H_{24}$			
1,10:2,9-Diethanodibenzo[a,e]cyclooctene, 5,6,11,12-tetrahydro-3,8-dimethyl-	CH_2Cl_2	287(2.58),295s(2.55), 301s(2.50)	35-3126-79
3,11:4,10-Dimetheno-1H-cyclohepta[1,2-4,5]dicyclooctene, 2,5,6,7,8,9,12,13-octahydro-14-methyl-	EtOH	278(3.54)	35-2128-79
$C_{22}H_{24}NO_2P$			
2-Propanamine, N-[(1-methoxy-2,6-diphenyl-4(1H)-phosphorinylidene)methyl]-, P-oxide	MeOH	245(4.05),368(4.50)	24-1272-79
$C_{22}H_{24}NO_5$			
Isoquinolinium, 4-[(3,4-dimethoxyphenyl)acetyl]-7,8-dimethoxy-2-methyl-, tetrafluoroborate	EtOH	275(4.19),336(3.81)	78-1861-79
$C_{22}H_{24}N_2O_2$			
2-Propenoic acid, 2-cyano-3-[4-[ethyl(phenylmethyl)amino]-2-methylphenyl]-, ethyl ester	EtOH	437(4.62)	110-1769-79
	EtOH-KOH	344(--)	110-1769-79
	CCl_4	424(--)	110-1769-79
	KBr	440(--)	110-1769-79
Pyrazine, 2,5-diethyl-3,6-bis(phenylmethoxy)-	EtOH	273(3.14),317(3.99)	94-2027-79
$C_{22}H_{24}N_2O_3$			
Spiro[2H-1-benzopyran-2,2'-[2H]indole], 1',3'-dihydro-1',3',3'-trimethyl-8-(1-methylethyl)-6-nitro-	EtOH	555(4.56)	103-1101-79
$C_{22}H_{24}N_2O_3S$			
Formamide, N-(3-acetoxyestra-1,3,5(10)-16-tetraeno[17,16-d]thiazol-2'-yl)-	$CHCl_3$	285(3.63)	4-0763-79
$C_{22}H_{24}N_2O_4$			
Indolo[2,3-a]quinolizine-3-carboxylic acid, 1,2,6,7,12,12b-hexahydro-2-[1-(methoxycarbonyl)propylidene]-, methyl ester, (E)-(±)-	MeOH	222(4.58),282(3.97), 289(3.73),354(4.64)	35-5370-79
$C_{22}H_{24}N_2O_7S$			
2-Naphthacenecarbothioamide, 4-(dimeth-	MeOH	270(4.26),360(4.15)	88-2701-79

Compound	Solvent	$\lambda_{max}(\log \epsilon)$	Ref.
ylamino)-1,4,4a,5,5a,6,11,12a-octahydro-3,5,10,12,12a-pentahydroxy-6-methyl-1,11-dioxo- (cont.)			88-2701-79
$C_{22}H_{24}N_2O_8$			
Tetracycline	pH 7.4	270(4.20),360(4.19)	149-0531-79A
$C_{22}H_{24}N_2O_8S_2$			
Thymine, 1-(2,3-di-p-toluenesulfonyloxypropyl)-	n.s.g.	225(4.65),267(4.16), 272s(4.11)	128-0281-79
$C_{22}H_{24}N_2S$			
6H,8H-Pyrimido[2,1-a:4,3-a']diisoquinoline-6-thione, 4b,5,9,13b,15,16-hexahydro-5,5-dimethyl-	$CHCl_3$	288(4.15),360(1.76)	5-1702-79
$C_{22}H_{24}N_2S_2$			
1H-Indole, 2,2'-dithiobis[3-ethyl-1-methyl-	MeOH	236(3.21),310(1.32)	103-0282-79
$C_{22}H_{24}N_3S_6$			
Methylium, tris[(4,5,6,7-tetrahydro-1,3-benzodithiol-2-ylidene)amino]-, tetrafluoroborate	MeCN	246(4.51),302(4.06), 500(4.82)	48-0827-79
$C_{22}H_{24}N_6O_2$			
1,4-Benzenediacetonitrile, α,α'-bis-[[(4-morpholinylmethylene)amino]-methylene]-	MeOH	255(4.55),314(4.67), 382(4.94)	83-0535-79
2-Propenamide, N-[4-[4-[[4-(dimethylamino)phenyl]azo]-4,5-dihydro-3-methyl-5-oxo-1H-pyrazol-1-yl]-phenyl]-2-methyl-	benzene	478(4.40)	40-1774-79
$C_{22}H_{24}N_8O_4$			
1H-Pyrrole-2-carboxamide, N-[5-[[(2-cyanoethyl)amino]carbonyl]-1-methyl-1H-pyrrol-3-yl]-4-[[[4-(formylamino)-1-methyl-1H-pyrrol-2-yl]carbonyl]amino]-1-methyl-	EtOH	241(4.23),300(4.34)	87-1296-79
$C_{22}H_{24}N_8O_5$			
1H-Pyrrole-2-carboxamide, N-[5-[[(2-cyano-1-methylethyl)amino]carbonyl]-1-methyl-1H-pyrrol-3-yl]-1-methyl-4-[[(1-methyl-4-nitro-1H-pyrrol-2-yl)-carbonyl]amino]-	DMF	295(4.44)	87-1296-79
$C_{22}H_{24}O$			
3,11:4,10-Dimetheno-1H-cyclohepta[1,2-4,5]dicyclooctene-14-methanol, 2,5,6,7,8,9,12,13-octahydro-	EtOH	280(3.52)	35-2128-79
$C_{22}H_{24}OSi_2$			
Disilane, 1-acetyl-1,1-dimethyl-2,2,2-triphenyl-	C_6H_{12}	328(1.98),345(2.27), 360(2.54),374(2.66), 389(2.57)	35-0083-79
$C_{22}H_{24}O_2$			
1,3-Cyclohexanedione, 5,5-dimethyl-2,2-bis(4-methylphenyl)-	MeOH	266(3.00),274(2.95), 295(2.60)	12-1561-79

Compound	Solvent	λ_{max}(log ϵ)	Ref.
6H-Dibenzo[b,d]pyran-1-ol, 6a,7,10,10a-tetrahydro-6,6,9-trimethyl-3-phenyl-, trans-(-)-	EtOH	210(4.31),232(4.39), 266(4.17)	2-0250-79A
$C_{22}H_{24}O_3$			
Estra-1,3,5,7,9,14-hexaen-17β-ol, 3-methoxy-, acetate	EtOH	252(4.55),258(4.70), 268(4.72),288(4.08), 299(4.19),312(4.15), 336(3.26),353(3.08)	54-0496-79
19-Norpregna-1,3,5(10)-trien-20-yn-3-ol, 16α,17α-epoxy-, acetate	EtOH	275(2.87)	87-1538-79
$C_{22}H_{24}O_4$			
Benzene, 1,1'-(1,3,5-hexatriene-1,6-diyl)bis[3,4-dimethoxy-, (E,E,E)-	hexane	350(5.50),370(5.58), 389(5.48)	65-0146-79
1,3-Cyclohexanedione, 2,2-bis(4-methoxyphenyl)-5,5-dimethyl-	MeOH	227(--),276(--), 282(--)	12-1561-79
$C_{22}H_{24}O_7$			
2(3H)-Furanone, 4-(1,3-benzodioxol-5-ylmethyl)dihydro-3-[(3,4,5-trimethoxyphenyl)methyl]- (yatein)	EtOH	214(4.31),258(2.87), 288(3.56)	102-1495-79
2-Naphthalenecarboxylic acid, 1-(3,4-dimethoxyphenyl)-1,2,3,4-tetrahydro-7,8-dimethoxy-4-oxo-, methyl ester	MeOH	232(4.33),282(4.13), 312(3.60)	2-0198-79
$C_{22}H_{24}O_8$			
Cleroda-13(16),14-dieno-20,12-lactone, 18-acetoxy-4-epi,17:15,16-diepoxy-6,7-dioxo-	n.s.g.	280(3.81)	39-2526-79C
Podorhizol	EtOH	232(4.05),287(3.61)	95-0674-79
$C_{22}H_{24}O_8S_2$			
4H-Thiopyran-2,6-dicarboxylic acid, 4-[2,6-bis(ethoxycarbonyl)-4H-thiopyran-4-ylidene]-, diethyl ester	MeCN	217(4.46),445s(4.45), 475(4.70)	44-0880-79
$C_{22}H_{24}O_9$			
4H-1-Benzopyran-4-one, 3,5,6,7-tetramethoxy-2-(2,3,4-trimethoxyphenyl)-	MeOH	238(4.45),256(4.30), 305(4.22)	39-2696-79C
$C_{22}H_{24}O_9S$			
4H-Pyran-2,6-dicarboxylic acid, 4-[2,6-bis(ethoxycarbonyl)-4H-thiopyran-4-ylidene]-, diethyl ester	MeCN	270(4.52),415s(4.57), 443(4.66),545s(3.27)	44-0880-79
$C_{22}H_{24}O_{10}$			
4H-Pyran-2,6-dicarboxylic acid, 4-[2,6-bis(ethoxycarbonyl)-4H-pyran-4-ylidene]-, diethyl ester	MeCN	214(4.32),365s(4.24), 388(4.58),409(4.74), 470(3.73),500s(3.50), 535s(3.10)	44-0880-79
$C_{22}H_{25}N$			
1H-Pyrrole, 3,4-diphenyl-2,5-dipropyl-	EtOH	222s(4.26),240(4.27), 277(3.99)	103-0501-79
$C_{22}H_{25}NO$			
Benzenemethanol, α-[1-methyl-1-[[2-(1-naphthalenyl)ethyl]amino]ethyl]-, hydrochloride	EtOH	223(4.92),281(3.81)	4-1525-79

Compound	Solvent	$\lambda_{max}(\log \epsilon)$	Ref.
1-Butanone, 4-(3,4-dihydro-3,3-dimethyl-2H-pyrrol-5-yl)-1,3-diphenyl-	MeOH	206(4.33),243(3.05)	83-0498-79
Ipalbidine, O-(phenylmethyl)-	EtOH	238(4.06),276(3.34)	150-0413-79
$C_{22}H_{25}NO_2S_2$			
4-Cyclopentene-1,3-dione, 2-(2-butyl-1,3-dimethylcyclohepta[c]pyrrol-6(2H)-ylidene)-4,5-bis(methylthio)-	CH_2Cl_2	506(4.62)	83-0120-79
$C_{22}H_{25}NO_3$			
8-Azabicyclo[3.2.1]octane-2-methanol, 3-(benzoyloxy)-8-methyl-α-phenyl-	EtOH	210(4.02),232(4.01), 280(3.0)	12-2537-79
$C_{22}H_{25}NO_5$			
Ethanone, 1-(1,2-dihydro-7,8-dimethoxy-2-methyl-4-isoquinolinyl)-2-(3,4-dimethoxyphenyl)-	EtOH	220(4.12),289(3.99), 355(3.72)	78-1861-79
1-Isoquinolinecarboxylic acid, 8-(2,3-dimethoxyphenyl)-6-ethoxy-3,4-dihydro-	EtOH	254s(4.01),290(4.01)	33-1549-79
$C_{22}H_{25}NO_6$			
Leucoxylonine	EtOH	283(4.32)	100-0325-79
$C_{22}H_{25}N_3$			
Benzo[d]carbazol-6(7H)-one, 1,2,3,4,4a-5,7a,8-octahydro-, phenylhydrazone	MeOH	275(4.30)	5-1048-79
$C_{22}H_{25}N_3O$			
Ergoline-8-carboxamide, 9,10-didehydro-6-methyl-N,N-di-2-propenyl-, (8β)-	EtOH	241(4.31),314(3.97)	94-3029-79
$C_{22}H_{25}N_3O_2$			
Benzamide, N-[[4-(dimethylamino)-5,5-dimethyl-2(5H)-oxazolylidene]phenylmethyl]-N-methyl-, (E)-	MeCN	232(4.25),337(4.45), 347s(4.39)	33-1236-79
(Z)-	MeCN	232(4.33),334(4.38), 344s(4.33)	33-1236-79
$C_{22}H_{25}N_3O_3$			
Carbamic acid, [3-[(pentylamino)carbonyl]-1H-indol-2-yl]-, phenylmethyl ester	$CHCl_3$	283(4.28),326s(3.08)	103-0179-79
$C_{22}H_{26}$			
Anthracene, 2,6-bis(1,1-dimethylethyl)-	CCl_4	340(3.56),358(3.68), 377(3.58)	78-2131-79
$C_{22}H_{26}BF_2N_3O$			
2H-Pyrrol-2-one, 5-[[2-[[1-(difluoroboryl)-4-ethyl-3,5-dimethyl-1H-pyrrol-2-yl]methylene]-3,4-dimethyl-2H-pyrrol-5-yl)methylene]-1,5-dihydro-3,4-dimethyl-, (Z,E)-	EtOH	238(4.06),261(4.10), 337(4.04),385(3.85), 538(4.57)	49-1127-79
(Z,Z)-	EtOH	245(4.34),255(4.27), 340(4.36),385(4.22), 575(4.89)	49-1127-79
$C_{22}H_{26}F_3N_3OS$			
1-Piperazineethanol, 4-[3-[2-(trifluoromethyl)-10H-phenothiazin-10-yl]propyl]-	MeOH	206(4.37),260(4.52), 312(3.59)	133-0197-79

Compound	Solvent	$\lambda_{max}(\log \epsilon)$	Ref.
$C_{22}H_{26}N_2O_2$			
9,10-Anthracenedione, 1,2(or 3)-bis(butylamino)-	benzene	502(3.90),530s(3.81)	153-0033-79
9,10-Anthracenedione, 1,4-bis(butylamino)-	benzene	604(4.12),652(4.18)	153-0033-79
$C_{22}H_{26}N_2O_5$			
Palmirine	EtOH	220(4.49),255(4.40), 312(3.48)	88-3197-79
$C_{22}H_{26}N_2O_7$			
1,11(4H,5H)-Naphthacenedione, 2-(aminomethyl)-4-(dimethylamino)-4a,5a,6,12a-tetrahydro-3,5,10,12,12a-pentahydroxy-6-methyl-	MeOH	265(4.21),360(4.08)	88-2701-79
$C_{22}H_{26}O_2$			
1H,7H-1a,6a:7a,12a-Dimethanodicyclopropa[e,e']benzo[1,2-a:4,5-a']dicyclooctene-13,14-diol, 2,3,5,6-8,9,11,12-octahydro-	CH_2Cl_2	294(3.00)	35-2128-79
$C_{22}H_{26}O_5$			
Pregna-1,4,6-triene-3,11,20-trione, 17α,21-dihydroxy-16α-methyl-	MeOH	220(4.04),252(3.98), 296(4.04)	145-1662-79
$C_{22}H_{26}O_6$			
Coleon Z	EtOH	230(4.15)	33-2374-79
$C_{22}H_{26}O_7$			
Eupachifolin C	MeOH	217(4.06)	138-1473-79
$C_{22}H_{26}O_8$			
Eupachifolin B	MeOH	213(4.19)	138-1473-79
Gibb-2-ene-4,4a,10-tricarboxylic acid, 1-methyl-4,8-dioxo-, trimethyl ester, (1α,4aα,4bβ,10β)-	n.s.g.	222(3.80)	39-1918-79C
$C_{22}H_{26}O_9$			
4H-1-Benzopyran-4-one, 2,3-dihydro-6,7,8-trimethoxy-3-(2,3,4,5-tetramethoxyphenyl)-	EtOH	280(4.18),343(3.78)	32-0009-79
2H-Cyclohepta[b]furan-3,3(3aH)-dicarboxylic acid, 2-[2-ethoxy-1-(ethoxycarbonyl)-2-oxoethylidene]-, diethyl ester	$CHCl_3$	305(3.9)	5-1388-79
$C_{22}H_{26}O_{10}$			
[1,1'-Biphenyl]-2,2'-dicarboxylic acid, 4,4',5,5',6,6'-hexamethoxy-, dimethyl ester	EtOH	221(4.61),254(4.22), 301(3.71)	94-1383-79
$C_{22}H_{26}O_{11}$			
Veronicoside	MeOH	205(4.09),232(4.18), 275(3.02)	33-0530-79
$C_{22}H_{27}ClO_8$			
Eupachifolin D	MeOH	213.5(4.25)	138-1473-79
$C_{22}H_{27}NO_3$			
Vincetene	MeOH	247(4.58),331(3.43)	5-1212-79

Compound	Solvent	$\lambda_{max}(\log \epsilon)$	Ref.
$C_{22}H_{27}NO_4$			
5,12-(Iminomethano)dibenzo[a,d]cyclo-octene, 5,6,7,12-tetrahydro-2,3,9,10-tetramethoxy-14-methyl-, (±)-	EtOH	233(4.09),285(3.83)	78-1857-79
Morphinan-7-one, 5,6,8,14-tetradehydro-3,4,6-trimethoxy-17-propyl-, (±)-	EtOH	239(4.33),283(3.89)	4-0087-79
$C_{22}H_{27}NO_5$			
Demecolcine, N-methyl-	EtOH	245(4.52),353(4.23)	33-0965-79
$C_{22}H_{27}N_3$			
Benzonitrile, 4-[5-(4-pentylcyclohex-yl)-2-pyrimidinyl]-, trans	EtOH	268s(4.50),276(4.52), 288s(4.31)	64-1535-79B
$C_{22}H_{27}N_3O_2$			
9,10-Anthracenedione, 1-amino-2,4-bis(butylamino)-	benzene	557(4.07),598(4.07)	153-0033-79
$C_{22}H_{27}N_3O_3$			
1,2,4-Oxadiazole-3-ethanamine, 5-[(3,4-diethoxyphenyl)methyl]-N-(phenyl-methyl)-, monohydrochloride	EtOH	279(3.46)	150-0801-79
$C_{22}H_{27}N_3O_7$			
Uridine, [(3-benzoylamino)propyl]-2',3'-O-(1-methylethylidene)-	MeOH	218(4.19),256(4.00)	24-0700-79
$C_{22}H_{27}N_9O_4$			
1H-Pyrrole-2-carboxamide, N-[5-[[(3-am-ino-3-iminopropyl)amino]carbonyl]-1-methyl-1H-pyrrol-3-yl]-4-[[[4-(form-ylamino)-1-methyl-1H-pyrrol-2-yl]-carbonyl]amino]-1-methyl-	EtOH	243(4.44),303(4.52)	87-1296-79
hydrochloride	EtOH	238(4.48),300(4.55)	87-1296-79
$C_{22}H_{28}$			
5,8-Ethenobenzocyclohexadecene, 9,10-11,12,13,14,15,16,17,18-decahydro-	EtOH	238(4.10)	44-2160-79
$C_{22}H_{28}N_2$			
2-Butanone, 3-methyl-1-phenyl-, [2-methyl-1-(phenylmethyl)propylidene]-hydrazone	EtOH	278(4.23),305(4.27)	103-0501-79
2-Pentanone, 1-phenyl-, [1-(phenylmeth-yl)butylidene]hydrazone	EtOH	218(4.39),269(3.15)	103-0501-79
$C_{22}H_{28}N_2O_3$			
Vincadifformine, 15-methoxy-, (±)-	MeOH	228s(4.10),313(4.23), 331(4.14)	44-1063-79
Vincadifformine, 16-methoxy-, (±)-	EtOH	249(4.00),330(4.12)	44-1063-79
$C_{22}H_{28}N_2O_8$			
Benzene, 1,1'-(2,3-dimethyl-1,4-butane-diyl)bis[3,4-dimethoxy-5-nitro-	EtOH	222(4.43),265(3.66), 330(3.23)	94-1583-79
$C_{22}H_{28}N_4O$			
Androst-4-eno[3,2-f](s-triazolo[4,3-b]-pyridazine), 17β-hydroxy-	MeOH	243(4.40),250(4.42), 288(3.95)	39-1816-79C
Androst-5-eno[17,16-f](s-triazolo[4,3-b]pyridazine), 3β-hydroxy-	MeOH	215(4.28),291(3.50)	39-1816-79C

Compound	Solvent	$\lambda_{max}(\log \epsilon)$	Ref.
$C_{22}H_{28}N_4O_2$			
9,10-Anthracenedione, 1,4-bis[[2-(dimethylamino)ethyl]amino]-	EtOH	255(4.41),273(4.11), 310(3.65),594(4.07), 630(4.16)	87-0501-79
$C_{22}H_{28}N_4O_6$			
1H-Imidazole-4-carboxylic acid, 5-[[(dimethylamino)methylene]amino]-1-[2,3-O-(1-methylethylidene)-β-D-ribofuranosyl]-, phenylmethyl ester	MeOH	211(4.30),234(4.08), 300(3.98)	39-1415-79C
$C_{22}H_{28}O_2$			
Androst-4-en-3-one, 17β-(1-oxo-2-propynyl)-	MeCN	214s(4.04),222s(4.11), 237(4.24)	13-0199-79B
16,18-Cyclo-D-dihomoestr-4-en-3-one, 18-ethynyl-18-hydroxy-, (13α,16β,18R)-(±)-	MeOH	240(4.16)	87-0966-79
11,18-Cyclo-C-dihomo-19-norpregn-4-en-20-yn-3-one, 17-hydroxy-, (11β,13α-17α)-(±)-	MeOH	240(4.17)	87-0966-79
Cyclopenta[1,4]cyclobuta[1,2]benzen-5(6H)-one, octahydro-6-[(4-methoxyphenyl)methylene]-1,4,4-trimethyl-	EtOH	231(4.03),325(4.35)	39-1407-79C
2H-1,4a-Methanonaphthalen-8(5H)-one, hexahydro-7-[(4-methoxyphenyl)methylene]-4,9,9-trimethyl-	EtOH	325(4.27)	39-1407-79C
$C_{22}H_{28}O_3$			
9β,10α-Pregna-4,7-diene-3,20-dione, 16,17α-epoxy-16β-methyl-	MeOH	238(4.14)	54-0078-79
$C_{22}H_{28}O_4$			
14β-Estra-1,3,5(10),16-tetraen-15-one, 3-methoxy-17-(2-methoxyethoxy)-	MeOH	234(4.21),280(3.30), 288(3.27)	150-2525-79
19-Norpregna-1,3,5(10),17(20)-tetraen-21-oic acid, 14-hydroxy-3-methoxy-, methyl ester, (14β)-	MeOH	226(4.34)	97-0451-79
Spiro[androst-4-ene-17,2'(3'H)-furan]-3,3'-dione, 11-hydroxy-, (11β,17α)-	benzene	345(2.08)	44-1597-79
	MeOH	248(4.09)	44-1597-79
$C_{22}H_{28}O_5$			
3(2H)-Furanone, 5-(1,1-dimethylethyl)-2-[7-(1,1-dimethylethyl)-2-(2,5-dimethoxy-3-benzofuranyl)-	C_6H_{12}	253(4.33),289(3.71), 297(3.69)	39-0290-79C
$C_{22}H_{28}O_6$			
Coleon N, 7-deoxy-12-O-demethyl-3-acetoxy-	EtOH	225(3.89),260s(3.80)	33-2374-79
Dibenzo[a,c]cyclooctene-3,10-diol, 5,6,7,8-tetrahydro-1,2,11,12-tetramethoxy-6,7-dimethyl- (gomisin J)	EtOH	214(4.70),248(4.15), 276(3.53)	94-1583-79
Hiyodorilactone D	EtOH	210(4.41)(end abs.)	94-2539-79
$C_{22}H_{28}O_8$			
2H-1-Benzopyran, 3,4-dihydro-6,7,8-trimethoxy-3-(2,3,4,5-tetramethoxyphenyl)-	EtOH	286(3.72)	32-0009-79
Coleon X	ether	278(3.79),320(3.78), 400(3.64)	33-2374-79
Eupalinin A	MeOH	220(4.17)	138-1473-79
Eupalinin B	MeOH	220(4.10)	138-1473-79

Compound	Solvent	λ_{max}(log ϵ)	Ref.
Eupalinin C	MeOH	215(4.10)	138-1473-79
Eupalinin D	MeOH	217(4.17)	138-1473-79
Hiyodorilactone E	EtOH	210(4.28)(end abs.)	94-2539-79
$C_{22}H_{29}ClO_2$			
18,19-Dinorpregn-4-en-3-one, 13β-(3-chloropropyl)-17β-hydroxy-	MeOH	239(4.19)	87-0966-79
$C_{22}H_{29}Cl_2NO_2$			
Estra-1,3,5-trien-17-one, 2-[bis(2-chloroethyl)amino]-3-hydroxy-	MeOH	206(4.29),289(3.56)	145-0463-79
Estra-1,3,5-trien-17-one, 4-[bis(2-chloroethyl)amino]-3-hydroxy-	MeOH	206(4.29),216(4.08), 284(3.41)	145-0463-79
$C_{22}H_{29}NO_3$			
Vincetene, dihydro-	MeOH	240(4.3),263(3.9), 275(3.8),288(3.8), 315(3.4),330(3.5)	5-1212-79
$C_{22}H_{29}NO_7S$			
α-D-Glucopyranoside, methyl 4,6-O-cyclohexylidene-2-deoxy-2-[(methoxycarbonyl)amino]-, 3-benzenecarbothioate	EtOH	202(4.04),217(3.90), 253(3.90),292(4.00)	18-3015-79
$C_{22}H_{29}N_3O_2$			
Ergoline-8-carboxamide, 9,10-didehydro-N-(2-hydroxypropyl)-6-methyl-N-propyl-, monohydrochloride, (8β)-	MeOH	240s(4.28),314(3.95)	94-3029-79
$C_{22}H_{29}N_3O_4$			
Yohimbine oxindole, 5-(aminocarbonyl)-2-deoxo-, (5β)-	EtOH	247(3.84),298(3.45)	78-0633-79
$C_{22}H_{29}N_3O_{11}$			
Aconitan-3-one, 1,2-didehydro-8,13,14-15-tetrahydroxy-6,16-dimethoxy-4-(methoxymethyl)-2-nitro-20-nitroso-, (6α,14α,15α,16β)-	EtOH	230(4.1),343(3.1)	138-1163-79
$C_{22}H_{29}N_9O_7$			
Alanine, 3-(6-amino-9H-purin-9-yl)-N-[3-(3,4-dihydro-2,4-dioxo-1(2H)-pyrimidinyl)-N-[(1,1-dimethylethoxy)-carbonyl]alanyl]-, ethyl ester	EtOH	262(4.31)	65-0994-79
$C_{22}H_{30}I_2N_4O_9S$			
L-Methionine, N-[N-[N-(N-acetyl-L-seryl)-3,5-diiodo-L-tyrosyl]-L-seryl]-	pH 13	310(3.64)	33-2460-79
	50% HOAc	287(3.37),295(3.36)	33-2460-79
$C_{22}H_{30}N_2O_6$			
1H-Pyrrole-3-propanoic acid, 5-[[1,5-dihydro-4-(1-hydroxyethyl)-3-methyl-5-oxo-2H-pyrrol-2-ylidene]methyl]-2-[(1,1-dimethylethoxy)carbonyl]-4-methyl-, methyl ester	MeOH	254s(--),260(4.37), 388(4.56),406s(--)	24-2243-79
$C_{22}H_{30}N_2O_7$			
7,10,13,16,19,22,25-Heptaoxa-30,31-diazatricyclo[24.3.1.$1^{2,6}$]hentriaconta-	EtOH	236(4.42),301(4.20), 310(4.26)	35-4472-79

Compound	Solvent	λmax(log ε)	Ref.
1(30),2,4,6(31),26,28-hexaene (cont.)			35-4472-79
$C_{22}H_{30}N_2O_8$			
Pyridinium, 4-(dimethylamino)-1-[3-ethoxy-2-(ethoxycarbonyl)-1-[2-ethoxy-1-(ethoxycarbonyl)-2-oxoethyl]-3-oxo-1-propenyl]-, hydroxide, inner salt	$CHCl_3$	305(4.5),413(4.0)	5-1406-79
$C_{22}H_{30}N_4O$			
1H-Naphth[2',1':4,5]indeno[2,1-e]-[1,2,4]triazolo[4,3-b]pyridazin-2-ol, 2,3,4,4a,4b,5,6,6a,13,13a,13b,14,15-15a-tetradecahydro-4a,6a-dimethyl-, [2S-(2α,4aα,4bβ,6aα,13aβ,13bα,15aβ)]-	MeOH	215(4.27),291(3.56)	39-1816-79C
$C_{22}H_{30}N_5$			
Quinolinium, 2-[[2,5-bis(diethylamino)-4H-imidazol-4-ylidene)methyl]-1-methyl-, perchlorate	EtOH	230(4.26),260(4.21), 390(3.94),520(4.48), 550(4.55)	89-0156-79
$C_{22}H_{30}N_6O_{13}$			
Polyoxin K	0.05M HCl	259(3.95)	142-0333-79B
	0.05M NaOH	262(3.86)	142-0333-79B
$C_{22}H_{30}O_2$			
Androst-4-en-3-one, 17-(1-hydroxy-2-propynyl)-, [17β(R)]	MeCN	238(4.22)	13-0199-79B
[17β(S)]-	MeCN	236(4.22)	13-0199-79B
2,5-Cyclohexadien-1-one, 2,6-bis(1,1-dimethylethyl)-4-(4-methoxyphenyl)-4-methyl-	MeOH	235(4.00)	12-1551-79
Retinol, 7,8-didehydro-, acetate	C_6H_{12}	320.6(4.06)	5-1945-79
$C_{22}H_{30}O_3$			
Androsta-4,6-dien-3-one, 17-acetoxy-7-methyl-, (17β)-	n.s.g.	295(4.43)	13-0361-79B
Androst-4-ene-3,17-dione, 15β-(2-propenyloxy)-	EtOH	240(4.23)	150-0201-79
5,7,9-Decatrienoic acid, 6-ethyl-3-hydroxy-2,4,8-trimethyl-10-phenyl-, methyl ester	hexane	305(4.52)	44-3109-79
17-Norkaura-2,15-dien-12-one, 2,3-[1,2-ethanediylbis(oxy)]-13-methyl-, (8β,13β)-	EtOH	210(3.77),296(2.31)	39-1004-79C
$C_{22}H_{30}O_4$			
Benzene, 1,1'-(1,1,2,2-tetramethyl-1,2-ethanediyl)bis[3,4-dimethoxy-	EtOH	205(4.80),229(4.26), 280(3.80),285s(3.72)	94-1583-79
Ilimaquinone	MeOH	214(4.02),286(4.12), 435(2.73)	78-0609-79
	MeOH-acid	204(4.01),212s(3.92), 285(4.21),425(2.90)	78-0609-79
	MeOH-base	209(4.12),238s(3.97), 288(4.11),523(3.20)	78-0609-79
	$CHCl_3$	285(4.21),420(2.76)	78-0609-79
Juniferdin	EtOH	211(4.0),260(4.2)	105-0771-79
Labda-8,13(16),14-trien-7-one, 3-acetoxy-15,16-epoxy- (calyenone)	EtOH	217(4.07),251(4.10)	39-1305-79C
17-Norkaur-1-ene-3,12-dione, 2-acetoxy-13-methyl-, (8β,13β)-	EtOH	238(4.00),329(1.94)	39-1004-79C

Compound	Solvent	λmax(log ε)	Ref.
17-Norkaur-15-ene-2,12-dione, 3-acetoxy-13-methyl-, (3α,8β,13β)-	EtOH	212(3.92),298(2.41)	39-1004-79C
(3β,8β,13β)-	EtOH	210(3.60),296(2.37)	39-1004-79C
17-Norkaur-15-ene-3,12-dione, 2-acetoxy-13-methyl-, (2β,8β,13β)-	EtOH	210(3.54),296(2.35)	39-1004-79C
1,4-Phenanthrenediol, 4b,5,6,7,8,8a,9-10-octahydro-2,4b,8,8-tetramethyl-, diacetate, (4bS-trans)-	EtOH	218(4.20),272(2.99)	2-0513-79B
$C_{22}H_{30}O_4S$			
Cyclononanecarboxylic acid, 9-ethenyl-2-oxo-1-[2-(phenylsulfinyl)ethyl]-, ethyl ester	EtOH	242(3.44),265s(2.89), 273s(2.49)	33-2630-79
$C_{22}H_{30}O_5$			
Fertenin	EtOH	260(3.80)	105-0135-79
Oxireno[4,5]cyclotetradeca[1,2-b]furan-12(1aH)-one, 10-acetoxy-2,3,6,7,10-10a,13,13a,14,14a-decahydro-1a,5,9-trimethyl-13-methylene-	EtOH	210(3.94)	12-1273-79
more polar form	EtOH	211(3.87)	12-1273-79
$C_{22}H_{30}O_6$			
19H-1,20-Metheno-2H-3,6,9,12,15,18-benzohexaoxacyclotricosin, 4,5,7,8-10,11,13,14,16,17-decahydro-	MeOH	230(3.54)	89-0311-79
Phenol, 3,3'-(2,3-dimethyl-1,3-butanediyl)bis[5,6-dimethoxy-, (R*,S*)-	EtOH	208(4.81),225s(4.30), 270(3.15)	94-1583-79
$C_{22}H_{30}O_7$			
2H-3,9a-Methano-1-benzoxepin-4,5,6,7-tetrol, octahydro-5a-(hydroxymethyl)-2,2,9-trimethyl-, 5-benzoate	MeOH	230(4.05)	39-2972-79C
Royleanone, 7α-acetoxy-6β,20-dihydroxy-	ether	270(4.12),409(2.97)	33-2754-79
$C_{22}H_{30}O_8$			
2-Butenoic acid, 2-methyl-, 2-acetoxy-3-oxo-1-[tetrahydro-4-methyl-2-(2-methyl-5-oxo-3-pentenyl)-5-oxo-3-furanyl]butyl ester	MeOH	220(3.94)	102-1745-79
Clerodane	MeOH	290(1.54)	88-2511-79
$C_{22}H_{30}O_{12}$			
1-Propene-1,1,3,3-tetracarboxylic acid, 2-[2-ethoxy-1-(ethoxycarbonyl)-2-oxoethyl]-, tetraethyl ester, ion(2-)-disodium	H_2O	263(4.1),386(3.8)	5-1388-79
$C_{22}H_{31}BrO_4$			
17-Norkaurane-2,12-dione, 3-acetoxy-11-bromo-13-methyl-, (3α,8β,11β,13β)-	EtOH	210(3.30),238s(2.65), 294(1.93)	39-1004-79C
$C_{22}H_{31}FO_3$			
A-Homoandrost-2-en-4-one, 17-acetoxy-3-fluoro-, (5α,17β)-	n.s.g.	240(3.67)	44-2929-79
$C_{22}H_{31}IN_4O_9S$			
L-Methionine, N-[N-[N-(N-acetyl-L-seryl)-3-iodo-L-tyrosyl]-L-seryl]-	pH 13	305(3.52)	33-2460-79
	50% HOAc	283(3.29),289s(3.27)	33-2460-79

Compound	Solvent	λ max (log ε)	Ref.
$C_{22}H_{31}N$			
[1,1'-Biphenyl]-2-amine, N-decyl-	EtOH	227(4.25),310(3.45)	33-2129-79
$C_{22}H_{31}NO_2S$			
Spiro[androst-4-ene-17,5'-oxazolidin]-3-one, 3'-methyl-2'-thioxo-, (17β)-	EtOH	243(4.50)	114-0089-79B
$C_{22}H_{31}NO_4$			
Estra-1,3,5(10)-trien-17-one, 2-[bis(2-hydroxyethyl)amino]-3-hydroxy-	MeOH	208(4.61),282(3.74)	145-0463-79
Estra-1,3,5(10)-trien-17-one, 4-[bis(2-hydroxyethyl)amino]-3-hydroxy-	MeOH	206(4.28),218(4.00), 283(3.39)	145-0463-79
$C_{22}H_{31}NO_9S$			
α-D-Glucopyranoside, methyl 4,6-O-cyclohexylidene-2-deoxy-2-[(methoxycarbonyl)amino]-, 3-(4-methylbenzenesulfonate)	EtOH	199(3.88),223(4.00)	18-3015-79
$C_{22}H_{31}N_3O_6Si$			
Cytidine, N-benzoyl-2'-O-[(1,1-dimethylethyl)dimethylsilyl]-	MeOH-HOAc	259(4.42),304(4.06)	5-1855-79
Cytidine, N-benzoyl-3'-O-[(1,1-dimethylethyl)dimethylsilyl]-	MeOH-HOAc	259(4.40),304(4.04)	5-1855-79
Cytidine, N-benzoyl-5'-O-[(1,1-dimethylethyl)dimethylsilyl]-	MeOH-HOAc	258(4.35),303(4.02)	5-1855-79
$C_{22}H_{32}N_2O$			
1,7-Secopeduncularine, 7-acetyl-1,2,3,7,8,9-hexahydro-	EtOH	222(4.36),275s(3.56), 282(3.63),290(3.57)	33-0481-79
$C_{22}H_{32}N_2O_2$			
1,4-Naphthalenedione, 2-butyl-5,8-bis-(butylamino)-	benzene	630(4.10),681(4.10)	138-0627-79
$C_{22}H_{32}N_2O_3$			
3-Azetidinecarboxylic acid, 1,3-bis(1,1-dimethylethyl)-2-oxo-4-[(1-phenylethyl)imino]-, ethyl ester	C_6H_{12}	251s(2.90),257s(2.75), 267s(2.53)	56-0643-79
$C_{22}H_{32}N_4O_4$			
2,6(1H,3H)-Pyridinedione, 3-[1,6-dihydro-2,6-dioxo-1-propyl-5-(propylamino)-3(2H)-pyridinylidene]-1-propyl-5-(propylamino)-	$CHCl_3$	286(4.26),631(4.51)	118-0948-79
$C_{22}H_{32}N_4O_9S$			
L-Methionine, N-[N-[N-(N-acetyl-L-seryl)-L-tyrosyl]-L-seryl]-	pH 13	293(3.35)	33-2460-79
	M HOAc	275(3.11),281s(3.03)	33-2460-79
$C_{22}H_{32}OS$			
Retinthiol, acetate, cis	EtOH	327(4.48)	87-1532-79
Retinthiol, acetate, trans	EtOH	330(4.48)	87-1532-79
$C_{22}H_{32}O_3$			
5α-Androsta-8,14-dien-17β-ol, 3β,19-epoxy-3α-methoxy-4,4-dimethyl-	n.s.g.	246s(4.33),252(4.35), 260s(4.22)	33-2732-79
5α-Androstano[17,16-b]furan-5'-one, 4',5',16β,17β-tetrahydro-3β-hydroxy-4-methylene-	EtOH	215(3.99)	33-1586-79

Compound	Solvent	$\lambda_{max}(\log \epsilon)$	Ref.
Androst-4-en-3-one, 17-acetoxy-7α-methyl-	n.s.g.	242(4.18)	13-0361-79B
Androst-4-en-3-one, 17-acetoxy-7β-methyl-	n.s.g.	241(4.18)	13-0361-79B
$C_{22}H_{32}O_4$			
17-Norkaurane-2,12-dione, 3α-acetoxy-13-methyl-	EtOH	210(2.94),292(1.94)	39-1004-79C
17-Norkaurane-2,12-dione, 3β-acetoxy-13-methyl-	EtOH	210(2.75),288(1.77)	39-1004-79C
17-Norkaurane-3,12-dione, 2α-acetoxy-13-methyl-	EtOH	210(2.63),288(1.79)	39-1004-79C
17-Norkaurane-3,12-dione, 2β-acetoxy-13-methyl-	EtOH	210(2.48),286(1.94)	39-1004-79C
$C_{22}H_{32}O_5$			
Calyone	EtOH	213(3.67)	39-1305-79C
Cyclotetradeca[b]furan-5-ol, 4-acetoxy-6,9-epoxy-3,4,5,6,7,8,9,10,11,12-decahydro-3,6,10,14-tetramethyl-, (4R*,5S*,6R*,9S*,10R*,13E)-	EtOH	207(4.01),220(4.07)	12-2265-79
Epicalyone	EtOH	213(3.71)	39-1305-79C
Evillosin, 3-keto-	EtOH	209(4.17)	44-1322-79
Labd-14-en-7-one, 3-acetoxy-9,13:15,16-diepoxy- (precalyone)	EtOH	223(3.98)	39-1305-79C
$C_{22}H_{32}O_6$			
Cauferinin	n.s.g.	218(4.22),244(3.80), 255(3.85),328(4.08)	105-0127-79
$C_{22}H_{32}O_6P_2$			
Phosphonic acid, [[1,1'-biphenyl]-2,2'-diylbis(methylene)]bis-, tetraethyl ester	EtOH	238(4.27)	44-1936-79
$C_{22}H_{32}S_3$			
Benzene, [1,4,4-tris[(1,1-dimethylethyl)thio]-1,2,3-butatrienyl]-	heptane	200(4.57),410(4.49)	5-1626-79
$C_{22}H_{33}NO_8$			
2-Cyclobutene-1,1-dicarboxylic acid, 2-(diethylamino)-4-[2-ethoxy-1-(ethoxycarbonyl)-2-oxoethylidene]-3-methyl-, diethyl ester	$CHCl_3$	362(4.3),452(2.8)	5-1388-79
$C_{22}H_{33}N_3$			
Cyclohexanecarbonitrile, 4-[5-(4-pentylcyclohexyl)-2-pyrimidinyl]-, [trans(trans)]-	EtOH	249s(3.42),254(3.48), 261s(3.36),282(2.49)	64-1535-79B
$C_{22}H_{33}N_3O_2$			
1,4-Naphthalenedione, 2,5,8-tris(butylamino)-	benzene	598(4.20),649(4.46)	138-0627-79
1,4-Naphthalenedione, 5,6,8-tris(butylamino)-	benzene	614(4.05),662(4.09)	138-0627-79
$C_{22}H_{33}N_3O_3$			
1,4-Naphthalenedione, 5,6,7-tris(butylamino)-8-hydroxy-	benzene	523(4.20),562(4.39)	138-0627-79

Compound	Solvent	$\lambda_{max}(\log \epsilon)$	Ref.
$C_{22}H_{34}$			
5,8-Ethenobenzocyclohexadecene, 1,2,3-4,4a,9,10,11,12,13,14,15,16,17,18,18a-hexadecahydro-, (4aR*,18aS*)-	EtOH	221(3.92),260(2.48), 268(2.61),276(2.56)	44-2160-79
$C_{22}H_{34}N_2$			
4,4'-Bipyridinium, N,N'-dibutyl-2,2'-diethyl-, dibromide	n.s.g.	600(4.11)	39-2704-79C
$C_{22}H_{34}O_2$			
2,4,6,10,14-Hexadecapentaen-4-one, 10-ethoxy-2,6,10,14-tetramethyl-, (E,E,E)-(±)-	hexane	254(4.45),265(4.60), 275(4.71),282(4.61)	44-0968-79
Pentaleno[1,6-cd]azulen-1-ol, 2,2a,3,4-4a,5,6,6a,7,8,9,10-dodecahydro-2a,4-4,6a,10-pentamethyl-, acetate, [2aS-(2aα,4aβ,6aα,10α,10bS*)]-	$CHCl_3$	246(2.80)	39-1774-79C
Pregna-6,8(14)-diene-3β,21-diol, 20-methyl-, (3β)-	EtOH	247(4.34),250(4.36), 252(4.37)	44-0643-79
$C_{22}H_{34}O_3$			
1,6-Octadien-4-yn-3-ol, 7-(1-ethoxy-ethoxy)-3-methyl-1-(2,6,6-trimethyl-1-cyclohexen-1-yl)-	isoPrOH	238(4.29)	54-0316-79
$C_{22}H_{34}O_4$			
Kolavic acid, dimethyl ester	EtOH	217(4.33)	78-0979-79
$C_{22}H_{34}O_5$			
Evillosin	EtOH	209(4.18)	44-1322-79
Marrubenol, 19-acetyl-	EtOH	218(3.60)	102-0859-79
2,3-Secobeyerane-2,3-dioic acid, ent-12-oxo-, dimethyl ester	EtOH	210(2.47),216s(2.43), 276(1.83)	39-1004-79C
$C_{22}H_{35}NO_2$			
Androst-4-en-3-one, 17β-hydroxy-, O-(1-methylethyl)oxime, anti	EtOH	250(4.42)	78-0233-79
syn	EtOH	257(4.25)	78-0233-79
$C_{22}H_{36}N_2O$			
2,4-Cyclopentadiene-1-carboxamide, N-cyclohexyl-1-(cyclohexylamino)-2,3,4,5-tetramethyl-	hexane	273(4.58)	88-0271-79
$C_{22}H_{36}N_2O_4$			
Acetamide, 2,2'-[1,2-phenylenebis(oxy)]-bis[N,N-dipropyl-	H_2O	273(3.28)	33-0754-79
$C_{22}H_{36}O_3$			
2,3-Naphthalenediol, decahydro-2,5,5,8a-tetramethyl-1-(3-methyl-2,4-pentadienyl)-, 3-acetate	EtOH	240(3.96)	102-1681-79
$C_{22}H_{36}O_4$			
1,3,12,14-Cyclodocosanetetrone	$CHCl_3$	275(3.74)	121-0503-79
copper chelate	$CHCl_3$	250(3.98),295(3.90)	121-0503-79
$C_{22}H_{37}NO_{10}$			
Cathedulin E , 8-denicotinyl-	MeOH	227(4.15),256s(3.43), 264(3.48),270s(3.43), 283s(2.95)	39-2972-79C

Compound	Solvent	$\lambda_{max}(\log \epsilon)$	Ref.
$C_{22}H_{37}N_4O_4$			
Pyridinium, 1-(5-amino-5-carboxypentyl)-3-[1-(5-amino-5-carboxypentyl)-2-piperidinyl]-, chloride (anabilysine)	2M NH_3	263(3.60),268s(--)	39-2282-79C
$C_{22}H_{37}O_6P$			
Phosphonium, tributyl[3,6-dihydroxy-2-(methoxycarbonyl)phenyl]-, acetate	EtOH	211(4.23),252(3.57), 361(3.64)	33-2350-79
$C_{22}H_{38}ClNO_3$			
4-Tetradecenamide, N-[2-(chloromethylene)-4-oxopentyl]-7-methoxy-N-methyl-, [S-(E,E)]-	MeOH	212(3.59)	35-0240-79
$C_{22}H_{40}N_7O$			
Cyclopropenylium, [4,6-bis(dimethylamino)-5-oxo-1,2,3-triazin-2(5H)-yl]bis-[bis(1-methylethyl)amino]-, perchlorate	CH_2Cl_2	417(4.29)	24-1535-79
$C_{22}H_{44}N_2O_4$			
Propanamide, 3,3'-oxybis[N-heptyl-N-methyl-	H_2O	203(4.18)	33-0754-79
$C_{22}H_{45}N_4$			
1H-Imidazolium, 4-[bis(1-methylethyl)-amino]-5-[[bis(1-methylethyl)amino]-methylene]-2,5-dihydro-2,2,3-trimethyl-1-(1-methylethyl)-, perchlorate	CH_2Cl_2	351(4.34)	24-1535-79
$C_{22}H_{45}N_6$			
1,2,3-Triazinium, 4,5,6-tris[bis(1-methylethyl)amino]-2-methyl-, perchlorate	CH_2Cl_2	470(3.83)	24-1535-79

Compound	Solvent	$\lambda_{max}(\log \epsilon)$	Ref.
$C_{23}H_3Cl_{15}S_4$			
Benzene, 1,1',1"-[[1-(methylthio)-1-buten-3-yne-1,2,4-triyl]tris(thio)]-tris[2,3,4,5,6-pentachloro-	heptane	196(4.77),212(4.79), 349(4.28)	5-1606-79
$C_{23}H_{12}N_2O_4$			
Naphtho[2',3':4,5]furo[2,3-b]pyridine-3-carbonitrile, 1,2,5,10-tetrahydro-4-methyl-2,5,10-trioxo-1-phenyl-	$CHCl_3$	273(4.48),343(4.08), 440(3.90)	2-0100-79A
$C_{23}H_{13}NO_4$			
1,3-Isobenzofurandione, 5-(5-[1,1'-biphenyl]-4-yl-2-oxazolyl)-	toluene	375(4.47)	103-0028-79
$C_{23}H_{14}N_2O_5$			
Methanone, [2-(2-furanyl)-1-(5-nitro-2-furanyl)-3-indolizinyl]phenyl-	EtOH	431(4.39)	94-3078-79
$C_{23}H_{14}N_4$			
Phthalazino[2',1':1,5]pyrrolo[2,3-b]-quinoxaline, 5-phenyl-	EtOH	256(4.51),288(4.44), 346(4.51),375s(4.08), 433(3.66),458(3.76), 487(3.63)	78-2463-79
Pyrrolo[1,2-a:4,5-b']diquinoxaline, 6-phenyl-	EtOH	243s(4.36),277s(4.58), 284(4.63),290s(4.46), 318s(4.09),362s(3.97), 375(4.13),391(4.19), 470s(3.72),483(3.75), 506(3.68)	78-2463-79
Quinoxalino[2',3':4,5]pyrrolo[1,2-c]-quinazoline, 6-phenyl-	EtOH	256(4.46),293(4.49), 325(4.50),361(4.03), 440(3.91)	78-2463-79
$C_{23}H_{14}N_4O$			
Pyrrolo[1,2-a:4,5-b']diquinoxaline, 6-phenoxy-	EtOH	275(4.70),364(3.18), 380(4.20),466(3.73)	78-2463-79
$C_{23}H_{14}N_4O_2$			
1H-Isoindole-1,3(2H)-dione, 2-(benzimidazo[1,2-c]quinazolin-6-ylmethyl)-	n.s.g.	265(4.64),274(4.67)	124-0225-79
$C_{23}H_{14}O_2$			
3H-Cyclopenta[b]benzofuran-3-one, 1,2-diphenyl-	CH_2Cl_2	259(4.59),263(4.58), 464(3.88)	103-1173-79
$C_{23}H_{14}O_3$			
1H-Indene-1,3(2H)-dione, 2-(oxodiphenylethylidene)-	dioxan	250(4.56),331(4.22)	32-0329-79
$C_{23}H_{14}O_4$			
2H-Furo[2,3-c][1]benzopyran-2-one, 1-(2-hydroxyphenyl)-4-phenyl-	EtOH	312(4.03),391(4.30)	138-0511-79
$C_{23}H_{15}Br_4N_2P$			
4-Pyridinamine, 2,3,5,6-tetrabromo-N-(triphenylphosphoranylidene)-	EtOH	230(3.95),294(4.49)	103-1197-79
$C_{23}H_{15}Br_4N_4P$			
Pyridine, 2,3,5,6-tetrabromo-4-[3-(triphenylphosphoranylidene)-1-triazenyl]-	EtOH	258(4.24)	103-1197-79

Compound	Solvent	$\lambda_{max}(\log \epsilon)$	Ref.
$C_{23}H_{15}NO$			
Benzofuro[2,3-b]quinoline, 11-(2-phenylethenyl)-	EtOH	205(4.64),224(4.68), 261(4.69),340(4.35)	4-0487-79
Benzofuro[3,2-c]quinoline, 6-(2-phenylethenyl)-	EtOH	207(4.88),226(4.89), 260(4.98),289(4.92), 330s(4.29)	4-0487-79
$C_{23}H_{15}NO_2S$			
Methanone, (5-phenyl-3,4-isothiazolediyl)bis[phenyl-	CH_2Cl_2	258(4.57)	24-0260-79
$C_{23}H_{15}NS_2$			
Thieno[3,4-c]isothiazole-5-S^{IV}, 3,4,6-triphenyl-	CH_2Cl_2	243(4.31),280(4.41), 300(4.17),321(3.91), 530(4.12)	24-0260-79
$C_{23}H_{15}N_3O_4$			
Pyridinium, 1-[3-(5-cyano-1,6-dihydro-2-hydroxy-1,4-dimethyl-6-oxo-3-pyridinyl)-1,4-dihydro-1,4-dioxo-2-naphthalenyl]-, hydroxide, inner salt	EtOH	250(4.27),337(4.26), 625(3.38)	2-0100-79A
$C_{23}H_{16}BrN_3$			
Quinoline, 2-(4-bromophenyl)-4-(1-methyl-1H-benzimidazol-2-yl)-	n.s.g.	270(4.70)	124-0447-79
$C_{23}H_{16}ClNO_2$			
2H-Pyran-2-one, 3-chloro-4-(diphenylamino)-6-phenyl-	EtOH	236s(4.54),274(4.62), 298s(4.48),335(4.60)	4-0093-79
$C_{23}H_{16}N_2O_4$			
1H-Isoindole-1,3(2H)-dione, 2-[(1,3-dihydro-1-hydroxy-3-oxo-1-phenyl-2H-isoindol-2-yl)methyl]-	isoPrOH	218(4.75),277(3.35), 286(3.35),300(3.24)	4-0339-79
$C_{23}H_{16}N_4O_2$			
Quinoline, 4-(1-methyl-1H-benzimidazol-2-yl)-2-(nitrophenyl)-	n.s.g.	288(4.34)	124-0447-79
$C_{23}H_{16}N_4S$			
1,3,4-Thiadiazol-2-amine, N-phenyl-5-(2-phenyl-4-quinolinyl)-	EtOH	244s(--),265(4.60), 346(4.28)	106-0537-79
$C_{23}H_{16}O$			
7H-7,11b[1',2']-Benzeno-3H-benz[de]anthracen-3-one, 1,2-dihydro-	$CHCl_3$	280(3.55),310(4.7)	104-1341-79
$C_{23}H_{16}O_2$			
4H-1-Benzopyran-4-one, 3-(1,2-diphenylethenyl)-	MeOH	219(4.4),289(4.12)	24-1791-79
4H-1-Benzopyran-4-one, 3-(2,2-diphenylethenyl)-	MeOH	224(4.6),277(4.5), 304(4.4)	24-1791-79
1,2-Naphthalenedione, 4-(diphenylmethyl)-	$CHCl_3$	328(3.58),405(3.39)	138-1097-79
1(4H)-Naphthalenone, 4-(diphenylmethylene)-2-hydroxy-	$CHCl_3$	428(4.34)	138-1097-79
$C_{23}H_{16}O_4$			
[1]Benzopyrano[3,4-b][1]benzopyran-12-carboxylic acid, 6,12-dihydro-6-phenyl-	EtOH	282(3.79),293(3.84), 312(3.97)	138-0511-79

Compound	Solvent	λ_{max}(log ε)	Ref.
$C_{23}H_{16}O_5$			
[2,2'-Binaphthalene]-1,4-dione, 1'-acetoxy-4'-methoxy-	n.s.g.	243(4.46),299(4.08), 336s(3.63),436(2.99)	39-2679-79C
$C_{23}H_{17}$			
Cycloheptatrienylium, (8-phenyl-1-naphthalenyl)-, perchlorate	MeCN	225(4.86),271(4.05), 300s(3.91),373(3.76), 464(3.65)	44-2712-79
	CH_2Cl_2	273(4.04),310s(3.85), 392(3.75),500(3.62)	44-2712-79
$C_{23}H_{17}BrN_4O$			
Acetamide, N-(benzimidazo[1,2-c]quinazolin-6-ylmethyl)-N-(4-bromophenyl)-	n.s.g.	263(4.61),273(4.69)	124-0225-79
$C_{23}H_{17}ClCuN_6O_4$			
Copper, [2-chloro-12,13,14,15-tetrahydro-8,18-dinitro-11H-tribenzo[b,f,m]-[1,4,8,12]tetraazacyclopentadecinato-(2-)-N^5,N^{11},N^{15},N^{22}]-, (SP-4-4)-	$CHCl_3$	274(4.56),385(4.61), 510s(3.30)	12-2303-79
$C_{23}H_{17}ClN_2O$			
Benzenecarboximidamide, N-(4-chlorophenyl)-N-hydroxy-N'-1-naphthalenyl-, hydrochloride	EtOH	221(4.87),322(4.29)	56-2597-79
$C_{23}H_{17}ClN_4O$			
Acetamide, N-(benzimidazo[1,2-c]quinazolin-6-ylmethyl)-N-(4-chlorophenyl)-	n.s.g.	262(4.61),273(4.72)	124-0225-79
$C_{23}H_{17}ClO_2$			
4H-1-Benzopyran-4-one, 3-(1-chloro-2,2-diphenylethyl)-	MeOH	224(4.3),299(3.7)	24-1791-79
2H-Pyran-2-one, 4-(4-chlorophenyl)-3,4-dihydro-3,6-diphenyl-	EtOH	220(4.23),247(4.20)	4-0001-79
$C_{23}H_{17}ClO_4$			
3-Phenanthrenecarboxylic acid, 4-(4-chlorophenyl)-1,9-dimethoxy-	n.s.g.	226(4.66),260(4.56), 306s(4.17),317(4.13), 345(3.74)	33-0090-79
$C_{23}H_{17}Cl_2NO_2$			
9(10H)-Anthracenone, 1,3-dichloro-4-hydroxy-10-[(2,4,6-trimethylphenyl)imino]-	benzene	417(3.78)	104-0147-79
	EtOH	417(3.73)	104-0147-79
	dioxan	417(3.74)	104-0147-79
$C_{23}H_{17}Cl_2N_3O_6$			
Benzoic acid, 2-chloro-, 2-[[(2-chlorobenzoyl)oxy]methyl]-2,3,3a,9a-tetrahydro-6-imino-6H-furo[2',3':4,5]oxazolo[3,2-a]pyrimidin-3-yl ester, monohydrochloride	MeOH	234(4.32),265(4.06)	87-0639-79
Benzoic acid, 3-chloro-, 2-[[(3-chlorobenzoyl)oxy]methyl]-2,3,3a,9a-tetrahydro-6-imino-6H-furo[2',3':4,5]oxazolo[3,2-a]pyrimidin-3-yl ester, monohydrochloride	MeOH	234(4.44),265(4.05)	87-0639-79
Benzoic acid, 4-chloro-, 2-[[(4-chlorobenzoyl)oxy]methyl]-2,3,3a,9a-tetrahydro-6-imino-6H-furo[2',3':4,5]oxazolo[3,2-a]pyrimidin-3-yl ester, HCl salt	MeOH	243(4.63),270s(4.08)	87-0639-79

Compound	Solvent	λ_{max}(log ε)	Ref.
$C_{23}H_{17}CuN_7O_6$			
Copper, [12,13,14,15-tetrahydro-2,8,18-trinitro-11H-tribenzo[b,f,m][1,4,8,12]-tetraazacyclopentadecinato(2-)-N^5,N^{11},N^{15},N^{21}]-, (SP-4-4)-	$CHCl_3$	317(4.62),414(4.54), 466(4.30)	12-2303-79
$C_{23}H_{17}F_2N_3O_6$			
Benzoic acid, 4-fluoro-, 2-[[(4-fluorobenzoyl)oxy]methyl]-2,3,3a,9a-tetrahydro-6-imino-6H-furo[2',3':4,5]oxazolo[3,2-a]pyrimidin-3-yl ester, hydrochloride	MeOH	234(4.56),263(4.13)	87-0639-79
$C_{23}H_{17}HgNO_3$			
Mercury, [2-[[(4-methoxyphenyl)imino]-methyl]-1H-indene-1,3(2H)-dionato-N^2,O^1]phenyl-	benzene	293(3.79),306(3.91), 375(4.40)	103-0056-79
	DMSO	293(3.82),305(3.83), 380(4.48)	103-0056-79
$C_{23}H_{17}NO_2$			
Benzenepropanenitrile, α-(2,2-diphenyl-ethylidene)-2-hydroxy-β-oxo-	MeOH	320(4.4)	24-1791-79
$C_{23}H_{17}NO_3S_2$			
4-Quinolinecarboxylic acid, 2-[2-(5'-formyl[2,2'-bithiophen]-5-yl)ethenyl]-, ethyl ester	EtOH	230(4.11),250(4.08), 280(3.93),420(4.70)	103-0970-79
$C_{23}H_{17}N_3$			
Quinoline, 4-(1-methyl-1H-benzimidazol-2-yl)-2-phenyl-	n.s.g.	265(4.55)	124-0447-79
$C_{23}H_{17}N_3O$			
Isoxazole, 3-phenyl-4-(phenylazo)-5-(2-phenylethenyl)-	$CHCl_3$	299(4.45),386(4.28)	103-0968-79
$C_{23}H_{17}N_3O_4$			
Propanedinitrile, (5,6-dihydro-9,10-dimethoxy-8H-benzo[g]-1,3-benzodioxolo-[5,6-a]quinolizin-8-ylidene)-	EtOH	255s(3.97),278(3.85), 345(3.84),386s(3.73), 466(3.51)	36-0705-79
$C_{23}H_{17}N_5S$			
Benzenamine, N,N'-(3-phenyl-2H-thiazolo[3,2-a]-1,3,5-triazine-2,4(3H)-diylidene)bis-	dioxan	280(4.09),325(3.96)	97-0059-79
$C_{23}H_{18}$			
Naphthalene, 3-methyl-1,2-diphenyl-	MeOH	228(4.77),280(4.03)	54-0452-79
Phenanthrene, 9-phenyl-1-(1-propenyl)-, cis	MeOH	215s(4.5),260(4.59), 305(4.08)	54-0452-79
$C_{23}H_{18}BrN_3O_2S$			
Carbamic acid, [3-[[(4-bromophenyl)amino]thioxomethyl]-1H-indol-2-yl]-, phenylmethyl ester	$CHCl_3$	267(4.24),287(4.28), 360(4.25)	103-0179-79
$C_{23}H_{18}ClNO$			
2(1H)-Pyridinone, 4-(4-chlorophenyl)-3,4-dihydro-3,6-diphenyl-	EtOH	249(4.18)	4-0001-79

Compound	Solvent	$\lambda_{max}(\log \epsilon)$	Ref.
$C_{23}H_{18}ClN_3O_2S$			
Carbamic acid, [3-[[(4-chlorophenyl)amino]thioxomethyl]-1H-indol-2-yl]-, phenylmethyl ester	$CHCl_3$	267(4.34),287(4.36), 354(4.28)	103-0179-79
$C_{23}H_{18}ClN_3O_3$			
Carbamic acid, [3-[[(4-chlorophenyl)amino]carbonyl]-1H-indol-2-yl]-, phenylmethyl ester	$CHCl_3$	285(4.36),306(4.38), 313s(4.34),358(2.92), 376(2.76)	103-0179-79
$C_{23}H_{18}CuN_6O_4$			
Copper, [12,13,14,15-tetrahydro-8,18-dinitro-11H-tribenzo[b,f,m][1,4,8,12]-tetraazacyclopentadecinato(2-)-N^5,N^{11},N^{15},N^{21}]-, (SP-4-2)-	$CHCl_3$	286(4.34),424(4.46), 456s(4.32)	12-2303-79
$C_{23}H_{18}F_3NO_5$			
Ethanone, 2,2,2-trifluoro-1-(2,3,8,9-tetramethoxybenzo[c]phenanthridin-4-yl)-	EtOH	227(4.43),282(4.82), 313(4.29),328s(4.03), 352(3.54),370(3.40)	44-0293-79
$C_{23}H_{18}Fe_2O$			
Ferrocene, 1,1''-(3-oxo-1-cyclopropene-1,2-diyl)bis-	EtOH	243(4.15),275(4.08), 300(4.08),348(3.71), 477(3.33)	78-0733-79
$C_{23}H_{18}N_2O$			
Benzenecarboximidamide, N-hydroxy-N'-(1-naphthalenyl)-N-phenyl-, hydrochloride	EtOH	222(4.81),322(4.21)	56-2597-79
Phenol, 2-[4-(2,2-diphenylethenyl)-1H-pyrazol-3-yl]-	MeOH	198(4.6),300(4.2)	24-1791-79
4(1H)-Pyrimidinone, 2-(4-methylphenyl)-5,6-diphenyl-	MeOH	262(4.43),328(4.18)	138-1213-79
4(1H)-Quinazolinone, 2-(1,2-diphenylethenyl)-1-methyl-	80% EtOH	230(4.47),275-305(4.3-4.2)	42-0708-79
$C_{23}H_{18}N_2OS$			
2-Thiazolamine, 5-benzoyl-N-methyl-N,4-diphenyl-	EtOH	258(4.23),377(4.01)	39-1762-79C
$C_{23}H_{18}N_2O_2$			
1H-Pyrazol-4-ol, 1,3,5-triphenyl-, acetate	EtOH	248(4.44),271s(4.33), 283s(4.17)	23-0904-79
4(1H)-Pyrimidinone, 2-(4-methoxyphenyl)-5,6-diphenyl-	MeOH	226s(4.33),276(4.35), 332(4.27)	138-1213-79
$C_{23}H_{18}N_2O_2S$			
2H-1,3-Thiazine, 2-(nitromethyl)-2,4,6-triphenyl-	EtOH	244(4.44)	18-3767-79
$C_{23}H_{18}N_2O_4$			
Spiro[9H-fluorene-9,5'(4'aH)-pyrrolo-[1,2-b]pyridazine]-6',7'-dicarboxylic acid, dimethyl ester	n.s.g.	389(3.98)	89-0945-79
$C_{23}H_{18}N_2O_5S$			
1H-Indole, 2-[[3-(1,3-dioxolan-2-yl)-4-pyridinyl]carbonyl]-1-(phenylsulfonyl)-	EtOH	306(3.78)	150-4801-79

Compound	Solvent	$\lambda_{max}(\log \epsilon)$	Ref.
$C_{23}H_{18}N_4O$			
Acetamide, N-(benzimidazo[1,2-c]quinazolin-6-ylmethyl)-N-phenyl-	n.s.g.	263(4.68),270(4.73)	124-0225-79
$C_{23}H_{18}N_4O_5$			
Carbamic acid, [3-[[(4-nitrophenyl)amino]carbonyl]-1H-indol-2-yl]-, phenylmethyl ester	$CHCl_3$	244(4.46),280(4.32), 302(4.25),385(3.73)	103-0179-79
$C_{23}H_{18}N_6NiO_4$			
Nickel, [11,12,13,14-tetrahydro-2-methyl-8,17-dinitrotribenzo[b,f,l]-[1,4,8,11]tetraazacyclotetradecinato-(2-)-N^5,N^{11},N^{14},N^{20}]-, (SP-4-4)-	$CHCl_3$	436(3.98)	12-2303-79
$C_{23}H_{18}O$			
3H-Cyclohepta[2,1-a:3,4-a']dinaphthalen-4-ol, 4,5-dihydro-, (S)-	dioxan	220(4.90),232(4.79), 267s(4.67),306(3.99)	44-4588-79
Methanone, bis(2-methyl-1-naphthalenyl)-	CCl_4	314(3.99)	73-2946-79
isomer	CCl_4	290(3.79)	73-2946-79
2-Propanone, 1,3-di-1-naphthalenyl-	MeCN	273(4.11),283(4.20), 295(4.08)	39-1545-79B
$C_{23}H_{18}O_2$			
2H-Pyran-2-one, 3,4-dihydro-3,4,6-triphenyl-	EtOH	225(4.67),248(4.19), 284(3.84)	4-0001-79
$C_{23}H_{18}O_3$			
Spiro[isobenzofuran-1(3H),9'-[9H]xanthen]-3-one, 2'-ethyl-6'-methyl-	EtOH	202(4.77),220(4.72), 288(3.77),298(3.72)	56-0403-79
	80% H_2SO_4	204(4.65),230(4.42), 263(4.70),391(4.79), 450(3.72)	56-0403-79
Spiro[isobenzofuran-1(3H),9'-[9H]xanthen]-3-one, 2'-ethyl-7'-methyl-	EtOH	202(4.74),217(4.69), 292(3.72),302(3.76)	56-0403-79
	80% H_2SO_4	202(4.66),230(4.43), 268(4.76),391(4.85), 461(3.73)	56-0403-79
Spiro[isobenzofuran-1(3H),9'-[9H]xanthen]-3-one, 5'-ethyl-2'-methyl-	EtOH	202(4.79),215(4.70), 290(3.72),301(3.71)	56-0403-79
	80% H_2SO_4	202(4.68),238(4.46), 265(4.72),393(4.79), 455(3.70)	56-0403-79
Spiro[isobenzofuran-1(3H),9'-[9H]xanthen]-3-one, 5'-ethyl-3'-methyl-	EtOH	202(4.79),220(4.76), 285(3.79),294(3.79)	56-0403-79
	80% H_2SO_4	205(4.71),228(4.37), 265(4.65),286(3.79), 392(4.60),450s(--)	56-0403-79
Spiro[isobenzofuran-1(3H),9'-[9H]xanthen]-3-one, 6'-ethyl-2'-methyl-	EtOH	202(4.81),220(4.74), 288(3.73),299(3.73)	56-0403-79
	80% H_2SO_4	202(4.76),230(4.52), 265(4.79),286(3.67), 392(4.72),444(3.67)	56-0403-79
$C_{23}H_{18}O_4$			
2H-1-Benzopyran-2-acetic acid, 3,4-dihydro-4-oxo-α,α-diphenyl-	MeOH	218(4.3),247(4.0), 314(3.5)	24-1791-79
3-Phenanthrenecarboxylic acid, 1,9-dimethoxy-4-phenyl-	n.s.g.	225(4.66),257(4.57), 309(4.15),342(3.63)	33-0090-79

Compound	Solvent	λ_{max}(log ε)	Ref.
$C_{23}H_{18}O_5$			
[1,1'-Binaphthalene]-2-carboxylic acid, 4-hydroxy-4',6-dimethoxy-	n.s.g.	211(4.86),288(4.24), 298(4.25),318(4.15)	33-0090-79
3-Phenanthrenecarboxylic acid, 1-hydroxy-9-methoxy-4-(4-methoxyphenyl)-	n.s.g.	226(4.61),251(4.57), 282s(4.34),316s(4.04), 348(3.53)	33-0090-79
$C_{23}H_{19}BrO_3$			
Benzenepentanoic acid, 4-bromo-δ-oxo-α,β-diphenyl-	EtOH	255(4.33)	94-2767-79
$C_{23}H_{19}ClCuN_4$			
Copper, [2-chloro-12,13,14,15-tetrahydro-11H-tribenzo[b,f,m][1,4,8,12]-tetraazacyclopentadecinato(2-)-N^5,N^{11},N^{15},N^{21}]-, (SP-4-4)-	$CHCl_3$	250(4.40),269(4.45), 334(3.95),436(3.90), 470(3.88)	12-2303-79
$C_{23}H_{19}ClN_4Ni$			
Nickel, [2-chloro-12,13,14,15-tetrahydro-11H-tribenzo[b,f,m][1,4,8,12]-tetraazacyclopentadecinato(2-)-N^5,N^{11},N^{15},N^{21}]-, (SP-4-4)-	$CHCl_3$	260(4.49),280(4.51), 430(4.02),560(3.00)	12-2303-79
$C_{23}H_{19}ClO_3$			
Benzenepentanoic acid, β-(4-chlorophenyl)-δ-oxo-α-phenyl-	EtOH	241(4.08)	4-0001-79
$C_{23}H_{19}Cl_2N_3O_4S_2$			
Benzenesulfonamide, 4-chloro-N-[5-[[(4-chlorophenyl)sulfonyl]amino]-1,2-dihydro-5-methylpyrrolo[3,2,1-hi]indol-4(5H)-ylidene]-	EtOH	228(4.69),272(4.31), 280(4.26),314(4.08)	39-2387-79C
$C_{23}H_{19}CuN_5O_2$			
Copper, [12,13,14,15-tetrahydro-2-nitro-11H-tribenzo[b,f,m][1,4,8,12]tetraazacyclopentadecinato(2-)-N^5,N^{11},N^{15}-N^{21}]-, (SP-4-4)-	$CHCl_3$	253(4.57),325(4.19), 488(4.23)	12-2303-79
$C_{23}H_{19}Fe$			
Methylium, ferrocenyldiphenyl-	$C_2H_4Cl_2$	260(3.84),375(3.92), 615(3.19)	32-0013-79
$C_{23}H_{19}HgNO_2$			
Mercury, [2,3-dihydro-2-[[(4-methoxyphenyl)imino]methyl]-1H-inden-1-onato-N^2,O^1]phenyl-	benzene	303(3.75),405(4.33)	103-0056-79
	DMSO	295(3.85),395(4.44)	103-0056-79
$C_{23}H_{19}NO$			
Butanenitrile, 3,3-dimethyl-2-(2-phenyl-5H-naphtho[1,8-bc]furan-5-ylidene)-	MeOH	240(4.1),292(4.1), 406s(--),422(4.5)	5-0959-79
2(1H)-Pyridinone, 3,4-dihydro-3,4,6-triphenyl-	EtOH	248(4.15)	4-0001-79
$C_{23}H_{19}NO_4S$			
Benzenesulfonamide, N-[2-[(1,3-dihydro-1-oxo-2H-inden-2-ylidene)hydroxymethyl]phenyl]-4-methyl-	MeOH	202(4.56),353(4.14)	83-0254-79
$C_{23}H_{19}NO_5S$			
Benzenesulfonamide, N-[2-[(3-hydroxy-	MeOH	204(4.59),235(4.34),	83-0254-79

Compound	Solvent	λmax(log ε)	Ref.
2-benzofuranyl)carbonyl]phenyl]-N,4-dimethyl- (cont.)		325(4.19)	83-0254-79
$C_{23}H_{19}NO_{11}$			
Carbonic acid, 2'-formyl-3',4',6,8-tetrahydro-8-hydroxy-6-oxospiro-[7H-indeno[4,5-d]-1,3-dioxole-7,1'(2'H)-isoquinoline]-6',7'-diyl dimethyl ester, cis-(±)-	MeOH	214(4.33),238(4.35), 295(3.91),313(3.97)	23-1569-79
$C_{23}H_{19}N_3OS$			
Ethanone, 2-[[3-(methylamino)-2-quinoxalinyl]thio]-1,2-diphenyl-	n.s.g.	359(4.0),372(4.0)	103-0102-79
$C_{23}H_{19}N_3O_2S$			
Carbamic acid, [3-[(phenylamino)thioxomethyl]-1H-indol-2-yl]-, phenylmethyl ester	$CHCl_3$	268(4.42),288(4.43), 355(4.41)	103-0179-79
$C_{23}H_{19}N_3O_3$			
Carbamic acid, [3-[(phenylamino)carbonyl]-1H-indol-2-yl]-, phenylmethyl ester	$CHCl_3$	285(4.30),305(4.26)	103-0179-79
$C_{23}H_{19}N_3O_6S$			
2-Anthracenesulfonic acid, 4-[[5-(acetylamino)-2-methylphenyl]amino]-1-amino-9,10-dihydro-9,10-dioxo-	glycerol	633(4.16)	112-0139-79
$C_{23}H_{19}N_3O_8$			
2-Propenoic acid, 3-(2-furanyl)-2-[[[3-(2-furanyl)-1-oxo-2-propenyl]oxy]-methyl]-2,3,3a,9a-tetrahydro-6-imino-6H-furo[2',3':4,5]oxazolo[3,2-a]pyrimidin-3-yl ester, monohydrochloride, [2R-(2α,3β,3aβ,9aβ)]-	MeOH	235(3.82),312(4.36)	87-0639-79
$C_{23}H_{19}N_5O_2$			
Benzoic acid, 2-[[5-phenyl-4-(phenylazo)-1H-pyrazol-3-yl]amino]-, methyl ester	EtOH	245(4.51)	48-0127-79
$C_{23}H_{20}$			
Benzene, 1-(2,2-diphenylethenyl)-2-(2-propenyl)-, cis	MeOH	236(4.37),299(4.22)	54-0452-79
trans	MeOH	239(4.37),258s(4.28), 299(4.17)	54-0452-79
Benzobicyclo[3.1.0]hex-2-ene, 6-methyl-4,5-diphenyl-, (endo,exo)-	MeOH	263(3.07),267(3.07), 271(3.12),279(3.09)	54-0452-79
$C_{23}H_{20}CuN_4$			
Copper, [11,12,13,14-tetrahydro-2-methyltribenzo[b,f,l][1,4,8,11]tetraazacyclotetradecinato(2-)-N^5,N^{11},N^{14}-N^{20}]-, (SP-4-4)-	$CHCl_3$	266(4.61),336(4.18), 354(4.15),427(4.26), 510(4.13)	12-2303-79
Copper, [12,13,14,15-tetrahydro-11H-tribenzo[b,f,m][1,4,8,12]tetraazacyclopentadecinato(2-)-N^5,N^{11},N^{15}-N^{21}]-, (SP-4-2)-	$CHCl_3$	267(4.63),328(4.18), 436(4.04),470(4.08)	12-2303-79

Compound	Solvent	λ max(log ε)	Ref.
$C_{23}H_{20}N_2O$			
4(1H)-Quinolinone, 2,3-dihydro-3-[(methylphenylamino)methylene]-1-phenyl-	EtOH	240(4.31),295(4.13), 361(4.21),424(3.94)	4-0177-79
$C_{23}H_{20}N_2O_2$			
Benzoic acid, 4-(4,5-dihydro-1,3-diphenyl-1H-pyrazol-5-yl)-, methyl ester	C_6H_{12}	355(4.27)	12-1601-79
	MeOH	350(4.23)	12-1601-79
Benzoic acid, 4-(4,5-dihydro-1,5-diphenyl-1H-pyrazol-3-yl)-, methyl ester	C_6H_{12}	391(4.40)	12-1601-79
	MeOH	390(4.47)	12-1601-79
Benzoic acid, 4-(4,5-dihydro-3,5-diphenyl-1H-pyrazol-1-yl)-, methyl ester	C_6H_{12}	364(4.48)	12-1601-79
	MeOH	364(4.59)	12-1601-79
Phenol, 4-(4,5-dihydro-1,3-diphenyl-1H-pyrazol-5-yl)-, acetate	C_6H_{12}	357(4.26)	12-1601-79
	MeOH	355(4.27)	12-1601-79
Phenol, 4-(4,5-dihydro-1,5-diphenyl-1H-pyrazol-3-yl)-, acetate	C_6H_{12}	362(4.31)	12-1601-79
	MeOH	357(4.29)	12-1601-79
$C_{23}H_{20}N_2O_4$			
Benzoic acid, 2-[1-(1,3-benzodioxol-5-yl)-3-oxo-3-phenylpropyl)hydrazide	EtOH	227(4.41),240(4.45), 282(3.99)	94-0257-79
$C_{23}H_{20}N_2O_8$			
Uridine, 3',5'-dibenzoate	EtOH	230(4.39),258(4.04)	39-2088-79C
$C_{23}H_{20}N_4$			
1H-Imidazole-5-carbonitrile, 4,5-dihydro-1,2-dimethyl-4,5-diphenyl-4-(2-pyridinyl)-	EtOH	220s(4.21),254(3.72), 263s(3.67),270s(3.51)	44-0041-79
$C_{23}H_{20}N_4Ni$			
Nickel, [11,12,13,14-tetrahydro-2-methyltribenzo[b,f,l][1,4,8,11]tetraazacyclotetradecinato(2-)-N^5,N^{11},N^{14}-N^{20}]-, (SP-4-4)-	$CHCl_3$	289(4.56),388(4.33), 411(4.34),585(3.60), 646(3.65)	12-2303-79
Nickel, [12,13,14,15-tetrahydro-11H-tribenzo[b,f,m][1,4,8,12]tetraazacyclopentadecinato(2-)-N^5,N^{11},N^{15}-N^{21}]-, (SP-4-2)-	$CHCl_3$	280(4.50),425(4.02)	12-2303-79
$C_{23}H_{20}N_4O_3S_3$			
5-Thia-1-azabicyclo[4.2.0]oct-2-ene-2-carboxylic acid, 7-amino-8-oxo-3-[(1,2,3-thiadiazol-5-ylthio)methyl]-, diphenylmethyl ester, (6R-trans)-	MeOH	275(3.92)	87-1214-79
$C_{23}H_{20}N_4O_4S$			
Benzenepropanethioamide, N-(2-methoxy-5-nitrophenyl)-α-[(4-methylphenyl)-hydrazono]-β-oxo-	EtOH	247(4.30),352(4.15), 382(4.08)	104-1324-79
$C_{23}H_{20}N_4O_5$			
Tryptoquivaline L	MeOH	216s(4.53),226(4.52), 231s(4.49),252s(4.24), 264s(4.09),274s(3.92), 290s(3.57),302(3.48), 315(3.38)	94-1611-79

Compound	Solvent	$\lambda_{max}(\log \epsilon)$	Ref.
$C_{23}H_{20}N_4O_6$			
Acetic acid, 2,2'-[(3-phenyl-1,5-formazandiyl)bis(2,1-phenyleneoxy)]bis-	60% EtOH	505(3.50)	140-1195-79
$C_{23}H_{20}N_4O_9S_2$			
4-Thia-1-azabicyclo[3.2.0]hept-2-ene-2-carboxylic acid, 3-[2-[[[(4-nitrophenyl)methoxy]carbonyl]amino]ethyl]-7-oxo-, (4-nitrophenyl)methyl ester	dioxan	268(4.39),318(4.00)	35-2210-79
$C_{23}H_{20}O$			
Anthracene, 9-ethoxy-9,10-dihydro-10-(phenylmethylene)-	n.s.g.	242(4.04),308(4.01)	39-2948-79C
Anthracene, 9-ethoxy-10-(phenylmethyl)-	n.s.g.	345(3.30),361(3.56), 381(3.74),402(3.70)	39-2948-79C
Anthracene, 9-(ethoxyphenylmethyl)-	n.s.g.	257(4.00),318(3.05), 333(3.41),350(3.72), 367(3.90),387(3.86)	39-2948-79C
Pentaleno[2,1-a]naphthalen-10(6bH)-one, 7,8,9,9a-tetrahydro-9a-(phenylmethyl)-	EtOH	233(4.40),300s(3.85), 309(3.95),317s(3.86), 333s(3.69)	78-1167-79
$C_{23}H_{20}O_2$			
3(2H)-Furanone, dihydro-2-methyl-2,5,5-triphenyl-	C_6H_{12}	248s(2.70),253(2.79), 258(2.86),264(2.77), 268s(2.62),290s(2.41), 298(2.51),308(2.51), 320(2.30)	19-0665-79
	EtOH	248s(2.82),253(2.83), 258(2.87),264(2.78), 267s(2.66),288s(2.42), 298(2.52),307(2.51), 318s(2.28)	19-0665-79
	50% EtOH	252(2.96),258(2.95), 264(2.85),267s(2.76), 298(2.60)	19-0665-79
	40% EtOH	251s(3.09),258(3.06), 263(2.96),267s(2.86), 298(2.67)	19-0665-79
$C_{23}H_{20}O_3$			
Benzenepentanoic acid, δ-oxo-α,β-diphenyl-	EtOH	241(4.07)	4-0001-79
Benzoic acid, 2-(2-ethyl-6-methyl-9H-xanthen-9-yl)-	EtOH	202(4.76),253(3.92), 286(3.53)	56-0403-79
Benzoic acid, 2-(2-ethyl-7-methyl-9H-xanthen-9-yl)-	EtOH	202(4.78),253(4.03), 290(3.66)	56-0403-79
Benzoic acid, 2-(5-ethyl-3-methyl-9H-xanthen-9-yl)-	EtOH	202(3.76?),282(3.64)	56-0403-79
Benzoic acid, 2-(6-ethyl-2-methyl-9H-xanthen-9-yl)-	EtOH	202(4.75),290(3.58)	56-0403-79
Phenanthrene, 1,9-dimethoxy-4-(4-methoxyphenyl)-	n.s.g.	227(4.65),241(4.56), 275s(4.33),285s(4.31), 347s(3.74)	33-0090-79
$C_{23}H_{20}O_5$			
Chamanetin 5-methyl ether, (±)-	MeOH	223(4.22),255(3.63), 286(4.01),324(3.99)	100-0264-79
	MeOH-NaOAc	228(4.35),253(4.10), 284(3.91),324(4.35)	100-0264-79

Compound	Solvent	λ_{max}(log ϵ)	Ref.
Pyrano[2",3":7,8]isoflavone, 5-acetoxy-2-methyl-6",6"-dimethyl-	MeOH	246(4.50),297(4.32)	2-0123-79A
$C_{23}H_{20}O_8$			
9,10-Anthracenedione, 1,4-diacetoxy-2-(2-acetoxyethyl)-3-methyl-	MeOH	235s(--),257(4.59), 275s(--),343(3.76)	5-0019-79
$C_{23}H_{21}BrO_3$			
3-Cyclohexene-1-carboxylic acid, 6-(4-bromophenyl)-2-oxo-4-(2-phenylethenyl)-, ethyl ester	EtOH	228(4.24),244(4.13), 328(4.28)	104-1059-79
$C_{23}H_{21}ClN_2O_2$			
Benzeneacetic acid, 2-[1-(4-chlorophenyl)-3-oxo-3-phenylpropyl]hydrazide	EtOH	223(4.62),243(4.32)	94-0257-79
$C_{23}H_{21}ClO_3$			
3-Cyclohexene-1-carboxylic acid, 6-(4-chlorophenyl)-2-oxo-4-(2-phenylethenyl)-, ethyl ester	EtOH	225(4.30),231(4.20), 328(4.40)	104-1059-79
	isooctane	236(--),241(--), 321(--)	104-1059-79
$C_{23}H_{21}Cl_3N_2O_3S$			
Pyrrolo[2,1-b]thiazole-3-carboxylic acid, hexahydro-2,2-dimethyl-5-oxo-6-phenyl-7-(phenylimino)-, 2,2,2-trichloroethyl ester	n.s.g.	250(4.09),332(3.99)	142-0227-79B
1,4-Thiazepine-3-carboxylic acid, 2,3,6,7-tetrahydro-2,2-dimethyl-7-oxo-6-[phenyl(phenylamino)methylene]-, 2,2,2-trichloroethyl ester, (S)-	n.s.g.	243(4.16),320(4.07)	142-0227-79B
$C_{23}H_{21}NO$			
Benzo[d]carbazol-6(7H)-one, 1,2,3,4-7a,8-hexahydro-7-(phenylmethylene)-	MeOH	235(4.29),295(4.95)	5-1048-79
$C_{23}H_{21}NO_3$			
1H-Benz[f]indole-3-carboxylic acid, 4-hydroxy-2-methyl-1-(phenylmethyl)-, ethyl ester	dioxan	263(4.65),343(3.87), 367(4.00),381(3.96)	83-0431-79
$C_{23}H_{21}NO_3S$			
Benzeneacetic acid, α-[[(4-methylphenyl)thio]imino]-4-(phenylmethoxy)-, methyl ester	hexane	243(4.18),365(4.09)	44-1218-79
$C_{23}H_{21}NO_4S$			
Benzeneacetic acid, α-[[(4-methylphenyl)sulfinyl]imino]-4-(phenylmethoxy)-, methyl ester	CH_2Cl_2	313(4.37)	44-1218-79
5(4H)-Thiazolone, 2-phenyl-4-[2-(1,2,3-4-tetrahydro-5,7-dimethoxy-4-oxo-2-naphthalenyl)ethylidene]-, (±)-	MeCN	220s(4.42),226(4.44), 231s(4.43),272(4.57), 307(4.18),325s(4.13)	35-2171-79
$C_{23}H_{21}NO_5$			
3-Cyclohexene-1-carboxylic acid, 6-(3-nitrophenyl)-2-oxo-4-(2-phenylethenyl)-, ethyl ester	EtOH	247(4.14),267(4.14), 334(4.33)	104-1059-79
	isooctane	263(--),323(--), 373(--)	104-1059-79
3-Cyclohexene-1-carboxylic acid, 6-(4-nitrophenyl)-2-oxo-4-(2-phenylethen-	EtOH	245(4.24),273(4.35), 329(4.42)	104-1059-79

Compound	Solvent	λmax(log ε)	Ref.
yl)-, ethyl ester (cont.)	isooctane	268(--),323(--), 373(--)	104-1059-79
$C_{23}H_{21}NO_5S$			
Benzenesulfonamide, N-[2-[3-(2-hydroxy-phenyl)-1,3-dioxopropyl]phenyl]-N,4-dimethyl-	MeOH	202(4.58),358(4.19)	83-0248-79
$C_{23}H_{21}N_3$			
Ethanamine, 1-(1,4-diphenyl-5H-cyclo-penta[d]pyridazin-5-ylidene)-N,N-dimethyl-	n.s.g.	249(4.51),311(4.10), 400(4.06)	5-0675-79
$C_{23}H_{21}N_3O$			
Acetamide, N-[4-(4,5-dihydro-1,3-di-	C_6H_{12}	355(4.28)	12-1601-79
phenyl-1H-pyrazol-5-yl)phenyl]-	MeOH	356(4.27)	12-1601-79
Acetamide, N-[4-(4,5-dihydro-1,5-di-	C_6H_{12}	364(4.33)	12-1601-79
phenyl-1H-pyrazol-3-yl)phenyl]-	MeOH	363(4.40)	12-1601-79
Acetamide, N-[4-(4,5-dihydro-3,5-di-	C_6H_{12}	368(4.32)	12-1601-79
phenyl-1H-pyrazol-1-yl)phenyl]-	MeOH	365(4.30)	12-1601-79
$C_{23}H_{21}N_3O_2$			
1H-Imidazole-5-carboxylic acid, 4,5-di-hydro-1,2-dimethyl-4,5-diphenyl-4-(2-pyridinyl)-, hydrochloride	EtOH	239(4.01),258s(4.89), 264s(3.85),271s(3.69)	44-0041-79
$C_{23}H_{21}N_3O_4S_2$			
Dispiro[1,3-dioxolane-2,2'-[14,17]di-thia[22,23,24]triazatetracyclo[16.3-1.1^{3,7}.1^{9,13}]tetracosa-1(22),3,5,7-(24),9,11,13(23),18,20-nonaene-8',2"-[1,3]dioxolane]	EtOH	223(4.68),261(5.05), 305(5.12)	44-3816-79
$C_{23}H_{21}N_3O_6$			
Dispiro[1,3-dioxolane-2,2'-[14,17]di-oxa[22,23,24]triazatetracyclo[16.3-1.1^{3,7}.1^{9,13}]tetracosa-1(22),3,5,7-(24),9,11,13(23),18,20-nonaene-8',2"-[1,3]dioxolane]	EtOH	220(4.22),275(4.12)	44-3816-79
1,3-Propanediol, 2-[[(2-hydroxyphenyl)-methylene]amino]-1-(4-nitrophenyl)-, 3-(phenylcarbamate), [R-(R*,R*)]-	MeOH	258(4.30),318(3.74), 404(2.77)	94-1245-79
Spiro[1,3-dioxolane-2,2'-[14,17,20]tri-oxa[25,26,27]triazatetracyclo[19.3-1.1^{3,7}.1^{9,13}]heptacosa-1(25),3,5,7-(27),9,11,13(26),21,23-nonaen]-8'-one	EtOH	215(4.39),265(3.91), 300(3.92)	44-3816-79
14,17,20,23-Tetraoxa-28,29,30-triaza-tetracyclo[22.3.1.1^{3,7}.1^{9,13}]tria-conta-1(28),3,5,7(30),9,11,13(29)-24,26-nonaene-2,8-dione	EtOH	216(4.41),250(3.94), 312(3.97)	44-3816-79
$C_{23}H_{21}N_4S$			
1H-1,2,4-Triazolium, 3-(ethylthio)-1,5-diphenyl-4-[(phenylmethylene)amino]-, tetrafluoroborate	n.s.g.	273(3.68)	39-0724-79C
$C_{23}H_{21}N_5$			
1H-1,2,4-Triazolium, 1-methyl-3-[[(4-methylphenyl)methylene]hydrazino]-4,5-diphenyl-, hydroxide, inner salt	n.s.g.	308(4.16),357(4.32)	39-0724-79C

Compound	Solvent	$\lambda_{max}(\log \epsilon)$	Ref.
$C_{23}H_{21}N_5O$			
1H-1,2,4-Triazolium, 3-[[(4-methoxyphenyl)methylene]hydrazino]-1-methyl-4,5-diphenyl-, hydroxide, inner salt	n.s.g.	306s(4.39),330s(4.46), 353(4.51)	39-0724-79C
$C_{23}H_{21}O_3S_2$			
1-Benzothiopyrylium, 4-[(4,7-dimethoxy-2H-1-benzothiopyran-2-ylidene)methyl]-7-methoxy-2-methyl-, perchlorate	acetone	596(4.84)	18-0160-79
$C_{23}H_{21}O_4S$			
1-Benzopyrylium, 7-methoxy-4-[(7-methoxy-4-[(7-methoxy-4-methyl-2H-1-benzopyran-2-ylidene)methyl]-, perchlorate	acetone	556(4.78)	18-0160-79
$C_{23}H_{22}ClNO_8$			
4aH-Benzo[c]quinolizine-1,2,3,4-tetracarboxylic acid, 4a-(chloromethyl)-8-methyl-, tetramethyl ester	MeOH	218(4.31),257(4.29), 284s(3.81),304s(3.59), 408(3.73)	39-2171-79C
$C_{23}H_{22}FN_2S_2$			
Benzothiazolium, 3-ethyl-2-[5-(3-ethyl-2(3H)-benzothiazolylidene)-3-fluoro-1,3-pentadienyl]-, perchlorate	EtOH	666(4.38)	124-0872-79
$C_{23}H_{22}N_2O$			
4H-Indol-4-one, 1,5,6,7-tetrahydro-2-methyl-5-[(1-methylphenylamino)methylene]-1-phenyl-	EtOH	260(4.15),298(3.87), 370(4.36)	4-0913-79
$C_{23}H_{22}N_2O_2$			
Benzoic acid, 2-[1-(4-methylphenyl)-3-oxo-3-phenylpropyl]hydrazide	EtOH	223(4.15),240(4.22), 320(3.41)	94-0257-79
6H-Pyrrolo[3,2-f]indolizine-2-carboxylic acid, 3,7,8-trimethyl-6-methylene-, ethyl ester, hydrochloride	KBr	280(4.69),286(4.68), 340(3.86),356(3.79)	104-0967-79
$C_{23}H_{22}N_2O_3$			
Benzoic acid, 2-[1-(3-methoxyphenyl)-3-oxo-3-phenylpropyl]hydrazide	EtOH	243(4.38),279s(3.87)	94-0257-79
$C_{23}H_{22}N_2O_5$			
Hydrazinecarboxylic acid, [1,3-dihydro-1-methoxy-1-(methoxycarbonyl)-2H-cyclopenta[l]phenanthren-2-ylidene]-, ethyl ester	EtOH	249(5.07),257(5.13), 278(4.42),289(4.13), 301(4.34),333(3.28), 348(3.30)	39-2034-79C
Hydrazinecarboxylic acid, [1-(ethoxycarbonyl)-1,3-dihydro-1-hydroxy-2H-cyclopenta[l]phenanthren-2-ylidene]-, ethyl ester	EtOH	249(4.90),257(4.98), 278(4.06),288(4.03), 300(4.05),335(3.95), 350(3.96)	39-2034-79C
2,4,6(1H,3H,5H)-Pyrimidinetrione, 5-(3,4-diethoxy-1H-phenalen-1-ylidene)-1,3-dimethyl-	MeOH	258s(5.0),374(5.2), 452(5.0),618(5.0)	83-0288-79
$C_{23}H_{22}N_3O$			
Pyridinium, 3-(2-benzoxazolyl)-4-[2-[4-(dimethylamino)phenyl]ethenyl]-1-methyl-, iodide	EtOH	535(4.63)	4-1579-79
Pyridinium, 5-(2-benzoxazolyl)-2-[2-	EtOH	530(4.82)	4-1579-79

Compound	Solvent	λ_{max}(log ε)	Ref.
[4-(dimethylamino)phenyl]ethenyl]- 1-methyl- (cont.)			4-1579-79
$C_{23}H_{22}N_3S$			
Pyridinium, 3-(2-benzothiazolyl)-4-[2- [4-(dimethylamino)phenyl]ethenyl]- 1-methyl-, iodide	EtOH	524(4.60)	4-1579-79
Pyridinium, 5-(2-benzothiazolyl)-2-[2- [4-(dimethylamino)phenyl]ethenyl]- 1-methyl-, iodide	EtOH	525(4.78)	4-1579-79
$C_{23}H_{22}O_2$			
8cH-Cyclohepta[3,4]cyclobuta[1,2-1]- phenavthren-8c-ol, 9,10,11,12,13,13a- hexahydro-, acetate	C_6H_{12}	252(4.62),258(4.68), 280(3.92),291(3.86), 303(3.95),338(2.76), 355(2.98)	150-3686-79
A-Nor-3-oxaestra-1,5,7,9-tetraen-17-one, 7-methyl-2-phenyl-, (13α)-(±)-	hexane	213(4.38),236(4.16), 242(4.12),248(4.01), 260(3.95),278s(4.11), 288s(4.27),298(4.39), 311(4.50),328(4.41)	13-0153-79A
$C_{23}H_{22}O_3$			
3-Cyclohexene-1-carboxylic acid, 2-oxo- 6-phenyl-4-(2-phenylethenyl)-, ethyl ester	EtOH isooctane	238(3.94),327(4.40) 235(--),242(--), 319(--)	104-1059-79 104-1059-79
$C_{23}H_{22}O_7$			
Isolisetin dimethyl ether	EtOH	257(4.49),275s(4.26), 304(4.12),326(4.11)	142-1539-79
2-Naphthalenecarboxylic acid, 3,4-di- hydro-5,7-dimethoxy-4-oxo-3-[(3,5- dimethoxyphenyl)methylene]-, methyl ester	EtOH	224(4.55),256(4.67), 364(3.61)	2-0202-79
$C_{23}H_{22}O_8$			
1,3-Dioxolane-2-butanoic acid, α-(9,10- dihydro-1,4-dihydroxy-9,10-dioxo-2- anthracenyl)-2-methyl-, methyl ester	MeOH	232(4.37),250(4.58), 255s(--),285(4.01), 482(3.98),513s(--)	5-0035-79
Tephrosin, 11-hydroxy-	MeOH	228(4.43),234(4.43), 263(4.54),272(4.59), 294(4.24),311(4.16)	142-1033-79
$C_{23}H_{22}O_9$			
2-Anthraceneacetaldehyde, α-(2-acetoxy- ethyl)-9,10-dihydro-8-hydroxy-1,3,6- trimethoxy-9,10-dioxo-	MeOH	218(4.90),270(4.38), 285(4.50),315(3.96), 430(3.80)	39-0451-79C
$C_{23}H_{22}O_{10}$			
Granaticin, dihydro-3'-oxo-, methyl ester	$CHCl_3$	490(3.40),518(3.44), 554(3.24)	100-0627-79
$C_{23}H_{22}O_{12}$			
β-D-Glucopyranosiduronic acid, 5-hy- droxy-6-methoxy-2-(4-methoxyphenyl)- 4-oxo-4H-1-benzopyran-7-yl (camantho- side B)	MeOH	276(4.16),329(4.30)	94-1252-79
$C_{23}H_{23}$			
Cycloheptatrienylium, [4'-(1,1-dimethyl- ethyl)[1,1'-biphenyl]-2-yl]-	CH_2Cl_2	369(3.91),446(3.61)	88-4999-79

Compound	Solvent	λ_{max}(log ε)	Ref.
$C_{23}H_{23}BrO_5$			
α-D-xylo-Hept-5-enodialdo-1,4-furanose, 6-bromo-5,6-dideoxy-1,2-O-(1-methylethylidene)-7-C-phenyl-3-O-(phenylmethyl)-	EtOH	210(4.05),254(4.03)	33-1303-79
$C_{23}H_{23}NO_7S$			
5,12-Naphthacenedione, 8-acetyl-10-[(2-aminoethyl)thio]-7,8,9,10-tetrahydro-6,8,11-trihydroxy-1-methoxy-, hydrochloride, (8S-cis)-	MeOH	233(4.51),256(4.42), 286s(--),480(4.11), 498(4.10),532(3.82)	87-0922-79
$C_{23}H_{23}NO_8$			
5,12-Naphthacenedione, 8-acetyl-10-(2-aminoethoxy)-7,8,9,10-tetrahydro-6,8,11-trihydroxy-1-methoxy-, hydrochloride, (8S-cis)-	MeOH	233(4.60),252(4.40), 288(3.94),476(4.09), 494(4.08),528s(3.80)	87-0922-79
$C_{23}H_{23}NO_{11}S$			
4H-1-Benzothiopyran-2,3,5,7,8-pentacarboxylic acid, 4-oxo-6-pyrrolidino-, pentamethyl ester	EtOH	230(4.33),265(4.21), 361(3.89)	88-1529-79
$C_{23}H_{23}N_3$			
Benzenamine, 4-(4,5-dihydro-1,3-diphenyl-1H-pyrazol-5-yl)-N,N-dimethyl-	C_6H_{12}	361(4.34)	12-1601-79
	MeOH	356(4.30)	12-1601-79
Benzenamine, 4-(4,5-dihydro-1,5-diphenyl-1H-pyrazol-3-yl)-N,N-dimethyl-	C_6H_{12}	360(4.40)	12-1601-79
	MeOH	363(4.32)	12-1601-79
$C_{23}H_{23}N_3O_5$			
Benzamide, N-[3-(benzoyloxy)-4-(3,4-dihydro-5-methyl-2,4-dioxo-1(2H)-pyrimidinyl)butyl]-	EtOH	226(4.35),267(3.99)	128-0051-79
$C_{23}H_{23}N_3O_6$			
Glycine, N-[1-formyl-N-(phenylmethoxy)-carbonyl]-L-tryptophyl]-, methyl ester	MeOH-HCl	300(3.69)	63-0013-79
$C_{23}H_{23}N_4$			
Pyridinium, 3-(2-benzimidazolyl)-4-[2-[4-(dimethylamino)phenyl]ethenyl]-1-methyl-, iodide	EtOH	515(4.57)	4-1583-79
Pyridinium, 4-(2-benzimidazolyl)-2-[2-[4-(dimethylamino)phenyl]ethenyl]-1-methyl-, iodide	EtOH	507(4.56)	4-1583-79
Pyridinium, 5-(2-benzimidazolyl)-2-[2-[4-(dimethylamino)phenyl]ethenyl]-1-methyl-, iodide	EtOH	515(4.74)	4-1583-79
$C_{23}H_{23}N_8OPS$			
Thiourea, N-[[(4-methoxyphenyl)amino]-bis(2-pyridinylamino)phosphoranylidene]-N'-2-pyridinyl-	EtOH	214(4.60),235s(4.47), 274(4.53)	64-0297-79B
$C_{23}H_{24}$			
1,1':3',1"-Terphenyl, 2',4,4',4",6'-pentamethyl-	C_6H_{12}	223(4.60),273(3.15)	12-1531-79
$C_{23}H_{24}Cl_2N_2O_2$			
Pyrano[2,3-e]indol-2(3H)-one, 3,3-dichloro-4,5,6,7-tetrahydro-8-methyl-	EtOH	221(4.13),276(3.88), 324(3.76)	4-0913-79

Compound	Solvent	λ max (log ε)	Ref.
7-phenyl-4-piperidino- (cont.)			4-0913-79
$C_{23}H_{24}CrO_3$			
Chromium, tricarbonyl[(10,11,12,13,14-η)-5,6,11,12-tetramethyltricyclo-[8.2.2.2^{4,7}]hexadeca-4,6,10,12,13,15-hexaene]-	MeCN	334(3.74)	88-1209-79
$C_{23}H_{24}F_3NO_6$			
Acetamide, 2,2,2-trifluoro-N-methyl-N-(5,6,7,9-tetrahydro-1,2,3,10-tetramethoxy-9-oxobenzo[a]heptalen-7-yl)-, (S)-	EtOH	235(4.47),242(4.48), 350(4.24)	33-0965-79
Acetamide, 2,2,2-trifluoro-N-methyl-N-(5,6,7,10-tetrahydro-1,2,3,9-tetramethoxy-10-oxobenzo[a]heptalen-7-yl)-, (S)-	EtOH	245(4.47),343(4.26)	33-0965-79
$C_{23}H_{24}N_2O$			
Benzenecarboximidamide, N'-(2,3-dimethylphenyl)-N-hydroxy-4-methyl-N-(4-methylphenyl)-, hydrochloride	EtOH	209(4.60),257(4.21), 315(4.17)	56-2597-79
Cinnoline, 4-ethoxy-1,2,3,4-tetrahydro-3-methyl-1,2-diphenyl-	MeCN	246(3.92),289(4.02)	104-2145-79
Cinnoline, 3-ethyl-1,2,3,6-tetrahydro-4-methoxy-1,2-diphenyl-	MeCN	246(3.92),289(4.02)	104-2145-79
Cinnoline, 1,2,3,4-tetrahydro-4-methoxy-3,3-dimethyl-1,2-diphenyl-	MeCN	240(4.06),267(4.14), 299(4.13)	103-1243-79
$C_{23}H_{24}N_2O_2$			
Ethanamine, N-[(7,10-dimethyl-11H-benzo[a]carbazol-5-yl)methylene]-2,2-dimethoxy-	EtOH	280(4.49),295(4.43), 348(4.27)	39-2506-79C
3,5-Pyrazolidinedione, 4-(1-cyclohexen-1-yl)-4-ethyl-1,2-diphenyl-	EtOH	239(4.3)	103-0215-79
$C_{23}H_{24}N_2O_4$			
1-Propanamine, N-(5,6-dihydro-9,10-dimethoxy-8H-benzo[g]-1,3-benzodioxolo-[5,6-a]quinolizin-8-ylidene)-	EtOH	283(4.09),363(4.22)	36-0705-79
	EtOH-acid	254(4.36),340(4.42), 397(3.90)	36-0705-79
Propanedioic acid, [1'-(phenylmethyl)-spiro[3H-indole-3,3'-pyrrolidin]-2(1H)-ylidene]-, dimethyl ester	MeOH-HCl	206(4.25),237(4.24), 298(3.93),340(4.27)	44-1063-79
	MeOH-base	325(--)	44-1063-79
$C_{23}H_{24}N_2O_4S$			
Imidazo[5,1-b]thiazole-3,7-dicarboxylic acid, 2,3,7,7a-tetrahydro-2,2-dimethyl-7-(phenylmethyl)-, 3-(phenylmethyl) ester, monohydrochloride, [3S-(3α,7α,7aα)]-	EtOH	233(3.90)	39-2455-79C
$C_{23}H_{24}N_2O_6$			
Epieburnamonin-15,18-dicarboxylic acid, 19-oxo-, dimethyl ester	MeOH	250(4.33),266(4.08), 306(3.76)	24-1902-79
$C_{23}H_{24}N_4O_4S$			
Benzamide, N-[[[[4-[[methyl(phenylmethyl)amino]sulfonyl]phenyl]methyl]nitrosoamino]methyl]-	EtOH	234(4.49),367(1.80)	118-0531-79

Compound	Solvent	$\lambda_{max}(\log \epsilon)$	Ref.
$C_{23}H_{24}N_4O_5$			
2,4(1H,3H)-Pyrimidinedione, 1-[5-(1,3-diphenyl-2-imidazolidinyl)tetrahydro-3,4-dihydroxy-2-furanyl]-, [2R-(2α,3β,4β,5α)]-	MeOH	253(4.59)	44-1309-79
$C_{23}H_{24}N_4O_6$			
L-threo-2,3-Hexodiulosonic acid, γ-lactone 3-[(4-methylphenyl)hydrazone] 2-(phenylhydrazone, 5,6-diacetate	n.s.g.	210(3.96),252(4.00), 350(4.21),442(4.36)	106-0531-79
$C_{23}H_{24}N_4O_8$			
α-D-ribo-Hept-5-enodialdo-1,4-furanose, 5,6-dideoxy-1,2-O-(1-methylethylidene)-3-O-(phenylmethyl)-, 2,4-dinitrophenylhydrazone, (5E)-	MeOH	208(4.06),258(4.02), 372(4.13)	136-0151-79H
$C_{23}H_{24}N_4O_9$			
Nocardicin A, 4-hydroxyphenyl-, DL-	EtOH-H_2O	220(4.31),273(4.15)	23-1932-79
	EtOH-NaOH	245(4.36),286(4.06)	23-1932-79
$C_{23}H_{24}N_8O_2$			
1H-Pyrazole-3-acetonitrile, 4-cyano-5-[(4-morpholinylmethylene)amino]-α-[[(4-morpholinylmethylene)amino]-methylene]-1-phenyl-	MeOH	251(4.52),340(4.33), 384(4.13)	83-0535-79
$C_{23}H_{24}OS_2$			
Spiro[thietane-2,9'-[9H]thioxanthene], 4-(1,1-dimethylethoxy)-3-(2-methyl-1-propenylidene)-	hexane	266(3.12),297s(2.49)	88-4857-79
$C_{23}H_{24}O_2$			
A-Nor-3-oxa-14β-estra-1,5,7,9-tetraen-17α-ol, 7-methyl-2-phenyl-	MeOH	205(4.35),234(3.87), 244(3.70),265s(2.62), 284s(4.02),298(4.17), 310(4.27),325(4.15)	13-0153-79A
$C_{23}H_{24}O_5$			
11H-Benzo[a]fluoren-11-one, 6a,11a-dihydro-2,3,8,9-tetramethoxy-6,11a-dimethyl-, cis	$C_2H_4Cl_2$	235(4.59),268(4.26), 288(4.11)	44-1388-79
$C_{23}H_{24}O_6$			
4H-1-Benzopyran-4-one, 3-(2,4-dimethoxyphenyl)-5-hydroxy-7-methoxy-6-(3-methyl-2-butenyl)-	MeOH	263(4.42),287(4.20)	39-0279-79C
4H-1-Benzopyran-4-one, 3-(2,4-dimethoxyphenyl)-5-hydroxy-7-methoxy-8-(3-methyl-2-butenyl)-	MeOH	267(4.64),293(4.23)	39-0279-79C
Pyrano[2,3-f]isoflavone, 7,8-dihydro-2',4',9-trimethoxy-6,6-dimethyl-	MeOH	264(4.40),292(4.05)	39-0279-79C
$C_{23}H_{24}O_{10}$			
Granaticin, dihydro-, methyl ester	$CHCl_3$	490(3.37),518(3.40), 550(3.25),565s(--)	100-0627-79
$C_{23}H_{25}Cl_4N_2O_{10}P$			
3'-Thymidylic acid, 2-chlorophenyl 2,2,2-trichloroethyl ester, 5'-(4-oxopentanoate)	MeOH	264(3.99)	54-0537-79

Compound	Solvent	λ_{max}(log ε)	Ref.
$C_{23}H_{25}IN_2O_5$			
L-Tryptophan, N-[(phenylmethoxy)carbonyl]-, 2-(2-iodoethoxy)ethyl ester	EtOH	275(3.76),282(3.78), 291(3.72)	118-0957-79
$C_{23}H_{25}N$			
1H-Naphth[1,2-d]azepine, 2,3,4,5-tetrahydro-3,4,4-trimethyl-5-phenyl-	EtOH	232(4.93),286(4.02)	4-1525-79
$C_{23}H_{25}NO$			
Benzo[d]carbazole, 8-benzoyl-1,2,3,4-4a,5,6,7,7a,8-decahydro-	MeOH	215(4.17),260(4.11)	5-1048-79
$C_{23}H_{25}NO_3$			
2H-Indol-2-one, 3-(2-acetoxycyclohexyl)-1,3-dihydro-1-(phenylmethyl)-	EtOH	253(3.91),279s(3.14)	23-1694-79
$C_{23}H_{25}NO_4$			
2-Aziridinecarboxylic acid, 3-[1,1'-biphenyl]-4-yl-1-(1-methylethyl)-, 4-methoxy-4-oxo-2-butenyl ester, [2α(E),3α]-	MeOH	256(4.28)	44-0255-79
[2α(E),3β]-	MeOH	258(4.41)	44-0255-79
1H-Furo[3,4-b]pyrrole-3-carboxylic acid, 2-[1,1'-biphenyl]-4-ylhexahydro-1-(1-methylethyl)-6-oxo-, methyl ester, (2α,3α,3aα,6aα)-	MeOH	255(4.32)	44-0255-79
$C_{23}H_{25}NO_8$			
Benzo[g]quinoline-2-carboxylic acid, 7-butyl-5,10-dihydro-3,4,8,9-tetramethoxy-5,10-dioxo-, methyl ester	MeOH	270(4.69),355(3.80)	39-0807-79C
Isophomazarin, tri-O-methyl-, methyl ester	MeOH	260(4.31),452(3.54)	39-0823-79C
$C_{23}H_{25}NS$			
Thieno[2',3':3,4]cyclohept[1,2-b]indole, 2,4-bis(1,1-dimethylethyl)-	n.s.g.	610(4.0+)	88-1445-79
$C_{23}H_{25}N_2$			
Methylium, bis[4-(dimethylamino)phenyl]-phenyl-, perchlorate	EtOH	250(3.78),318(4.12), 428(4.15),622(4.86)	65-0860-79
	acetone	426(4.27),622(5.12)	65-0860-79
$C_{23}H_{25}N_3$			
5,9:7,11-Dimethano-1H-1,2,4-triazolo-[4,3-a]azonine, 5,6,7,8,9,10,11,11a-octahydro-1,3-diphenyl-	MeOH	220(4.08),258(3.91), 346(3.89)	44-3711-79
$C_{23}H_{25}N_3O_4$			
2-Propenoic acid, 2-cyano-3-[4-[ethyl-[2-[[(phenylamino)carbonyl]oxy]ethyl]-amino]phenyl]-, ethyl ester	EtOH	424(4.69)	110-1769-79
	EtOH-KOH	342(--)	110-1769-79
	CCl_4	411(--)	110-1769-79
	KBr	424(--)	110-1769-79
$C_{23}H_{25}N_3O_8$			
Uridine, 3-[3-(1,3-dihydro-1,3-dioxo-2H-isoindol-2-yl)propyl]-2',3'-O-(1-methylethylidene)-	MeOH	261(3.95)	24-0700-79
$C_{23}H_{25}N_5O_4$			
Meleagrin	EtOH	232(4.39),285s(3.92),	100-0374-79

Compound	Solvent	λ_{max}(log ϵ)	Ref.
Meleagrin (cont.)		349(4.44)	100-0374-79
	EtOH-HCl	232(4.44),285s(4.04), 330(4.44),344s(4.38)	100-0374-79
$C_{23}H_{26}F_3N_3O_4$			
Acetic acid, trifluoro-, 1,1-dimethyl-3-(2,3,5a,6,11,11a,13,13a-octahydro-5,13-dioxo-1H-pyrrolo[1",2":4',5']pyrazino[1',2':1,5]pyrrolo[2,3-b]indol-6a(5H)-yl)propyl ester	EtOH	241(3.70),295(3.29)	39-3053-79C
$C_{23}H_{26}N_2O$			
Acridine, 9,10-dihydro-10-methyl-9-[2-(4-morpholinyl)-2-cyclopenten-1-yl]-	EtOH	283(4.36),318(3.75)	103-0541-79
$C_{23}H_{26}N_2O_3$			
Spiro[2H-1-benzopyran-2,2'-[2H]indole], 1',3'-dihydro-1',3',3'-trimethyl-8-(1-methylpropyl)-6-nitro-	EtOH	560(4.52)	103-1101-79
	toluene	605(--)	103-1101-79
Spiro[2H-1-benzopyran-2,2'-[2H]indole], 1',3'-dihydro-1',3',3'-trimethyl-8-(1,1-dimethylethyl)-6-nitro-	EtOH	565(4.53)	103-1101-79
	toluene	600(--)	103-1101-79
$C_{23}H_{26}N_2O_4$			
L-Tryptophan, N-[(phenylmethoxy)carbonyl]-, 1-methylpropyl ester	EtOH	275(3.71),282(3.81), 292(3.76)	118-0961-79
$C_{23}H_{26}N_2O_6$			
Azacycloundecino[5,4-b]indole-9,10(1H)-dicarboxylic acid, 5-ethyl-3-formyl-2,3,6,7,8,9-hexahydro-7-oxo-, dimethyl ester, (S)-	EtOH	227(4.38),259(4.06), 265(4.05),281s(3.78), 293(3.67)	23-1682-79
$C_{23}H_{26}N_2S$			
6H,8H-Pyrimido[2,1-a:4,3-a']diisoquinoline-6-thione, 5-ethyl-4b,5,9,13b-15,16-hexahydro-5-methyl-	$CHCl_3$	289(4.19),359(1.75)	5-1702-79
$C_{23}H_{26}N_8O_4$			
1H-Pyrrole-2-carboxamide, N-[5-[[(2-cyano-1-methylethyl)amino]carbonyl]-1-methyl-1H-pyrrol-3-yl]-4-[[[4-(formylamino)-1-methyl-1H-pyrrol-2-yl]carbonyl]amino]-1-methyl-	EtOH	238(4.23),303(4.31)	87-1296-79
$C_{23}H_{26}N_8O_7$			
3,11-Diazatricyclo[5.3.1.1^{2,6}]dodec-4-ene-10,12-dione, 3,11-bis(4,6-dimethoxy-1,3,5-triazin-2-yl)-8-(2-propenyloxy)-	$CHCl_3$	270(4.2)	39-1525-79C
$C_{23}H_{26}O_3$			
6H-Dibenzo[b,d]pyran-1-ol, 6a,7,10,10a-tetrahydro-3-(4-methoxyphenyl)-6,6,9-trimethyl-	EtOH	211(4.46),233(3.29), 268(4.25)	2-0250-79A
$C_{23}H_{26}O_6$			
1(2H)-Anthracenone, 3-acetoxy-3,4-dihydro-8,9-dihydroxy-6-methoxy-3-methyl-7-(3-methyl-1-butenyl)- (vismione A)	$CHCl_3$	245(4.25),298(4.59), 335s(3.98),410(3.94)	32-0301-79

Compound	Solvent	λ_{max}(log ε)	Ref.
7H-Phenaleno[1,2-b]furan-7-one, 1-ethoxy-8,9-dihydro-6-hydroxy-4,5-dimethoxy-3,8,8,9-tetramethyl-	EtOH	219(4.66),258(4.28), 279(4.17),358(4.14), 410(4.23)	150-0301-79
7H-Phenaleno[1,2-b]furan-7-one, 6-ethoxy-8,9-dihydro-1-hydroxy-2,3-dimethoxy-4,8,8,9-tetramethyl-	EtOH	215(4.56),245(4.24), 256(4.20),277(4.28), 286(4.35),358(4.14), 409(4.13),424s(4.05)	150-0301-79
1H-Phenalen-1-one, 2-(1,1-dimethyl-2-propenyl)-4-ethoxy-3,9-dihydroxy-7,8-dimethoxy-6-methyl-	EtOH	219(4.62),256s(4.20), 273(4.04),278s(4.03), 370(4.20),402(4.20)	150-0301-79
1H-Phenalen-1-one, 4-ethoxy-9-hydroxy-7,8-dimethoxy-6-methyl-3-[(3-methylbutenyl)oxy]-	EtOH	216(4.61),241s(4.37), 255(4.33),273s(4.15), 373(4.22),404(4.34)	150-0301-79
1H-Phenalen-1-one, 4-ethoxy-3,9-dihydroxy-7,8-dimethoxy-6-methyl-2-(3-methyl-2-butenyl)-	EtOH	219(4.65),257(4.29), 275(4.22),368(4.19), 406(4.19)	150-0301-79
$C_{23}H_{26}O_7$			
Benzo[3,4]cycloocta[1,2-f][1,3]benzodioxol-5(6H)-one, 7,8-dihydro-1,2,3,13-tetramethoxy-4,7-dimethyl-	EtOH	209(4.52),229(4.51), 250s(4.20),272s(4.02), 319(3.62)	94-2695-79
$C_{23}H_{26}O_8$			
Benzaldehyde, 3,4,5-trimethoxy-2-[4-methoxy-6-(2-methyl-3-oxobutyl)-1,3-benzodioxol-5-yl]-	EtOH	218s(4.59),280(4.01), 320s(3.57)	94-1383-79
Benzo[3,4]cycloocta[1,2-f][1,3]benzodioxol-5(6H)-one, 7,8-dihydro-6-hydroxy-1,2,3,13-tetramethoxy-6,7-dimethyl-	EtOH	217(4.56),249s(4.18), 256s(4.11),293s(3.48)	94-1383-79
Benzo[3,4]cycloocta[1,2-f][1,3]benzodioxol-8(5H)-one, 6,7-dihydro-7-hydroxy-1,2,3,13-tetramethoxy-6,7-dimethyl-	EtOH	218(4.56),247s(4.23)	94-1383-79
$C_{23}H_{26}O_9$			
1,4-Benzenediol, 5-(3,4-dihydro-6,7-dimethoxy-2H-1-benzopyran-3-yl)-2,3-dimethoxy-, diacetate, (S)-	EtOH	293(3.78)	32-0009-79
$C_{23}H_{27}NO_8S$			
Benzothiazolium, 2-[3-ethoxy-2-(ethoxycarbonyl)-1-[2-ethoxy-1-(ethoxycarbonyl)-2-oxoethyl]-3-oxo-1-propenyl]-3-methyl-, hydroxide, inner salt	$CHCl_3$	359(4.3),477(3.6)	5-1406-79
$C_{23}H_{27}N_3O_4$			
1H,12H-Pyrrolo[1,2-a]pyrrolo[1",2":-4',5']pyrazino[1',2':1,5]pyrrolo-[2,3-b]indole-10,15(8bH,13H)-dione, 8b-acetoxy-2,3,9,9a,14,14a-hexahydro-1,1-dimethyl-, [8bS-(8bα,9aα,14aα-16aS*)]-	EtOH	256(3.88),299(3.25)	39-3053-79C
$C_{23}H_{27}N_3O_8$			
1H-Imidazole-4-carboxylic acid, 5-(acetylamino)-1-[5-O-acetyl-2,3-O-(1-methylethylidene)-β-D-ribofuranosyl]-, phenylmethyl ester	MeOH	218(4.22),240(3.97)	39-1415-79C

Compound	Solvent	λmax(log ε)	Ref.
$C_{23}H_{28}ClN_3O_2$			
Pentanamide, N-(4-chlorophenyl)-2-[[4-(diethylamino)phenyl]imino]-4,4-dimethyl-3-oxo-	heptane	417(3.79)	73-1460-79
	EtOH	436(3.81)	73-1460-79
$C_{23}H_{28}NO_5$			
Pyridinium, 4-[2-[4-(2-ethoxy-1-methyl-2-oxoethoxy)phenyl]ethenyl]-1-(2-ethoxy-1-methyl-2-oxoethyl)-, bromide	MeOH	390(4.32)	56-1649-79
Pyridinium, 4-[2-[4-(2-oxo-2-propoxyethoxy)phenyl]ethenyl]-1-(2-oxo-2-propoxyethyl)-, chloride, (E)-	MeOH	388(4.35)	56-1649-79
$C_{23}H_{28}N_2O_4$			
1H-2-Pyrindine-7-methanol, 5-acetoxy-2,3,4,4a,5,7a-hexahydro-2-[2-(1H-indol-3-yl)ethyl]-, acetate	EtOH	223(4.48),283(3.73), 292(3.74)	28-0057-79A
$C_{23}H_{28}N_2O_5$			
L-Glutamic acid, N-[4-[(phenylmethyl)-amino]benzoyl]-, diethyl ester	EtOH	299(4.38)	4-1645-79
free acid	EtOH	291(4.33)	4-1645-79
10H-3,13-Methanooxireno[9,10]azacycloundecino[5,4-b]indole-10,11-dicarboxylic acid, 1a-ethyl-1a,2,4,5,11-12,13,13a-octahydro-, dimethyl ester, [1aS-(1aR*,3S*,11R*,13R*,13aS*)]-	EtOH	227(4.32),262(4.09), 268(4.08),283s(3.76), 294(3.66)	23-1682-79
$C_{23}H_{28}N_2O_6$			
Azacycloundecino[5,4-b]indole-9,10(1H)-dicarboxylic acid, 5-ethyl-3-formyl-2,3,6,7,8,9-hexahydro-7-hydroxy-, dimethyl ester	EtOH	224(4.32),262(4.03), 281s(3.68),293(3.50)	23-1682-79
$C_{23}H_{28}O_3$			
3'H-Benz[4,5]androst-6-ene-3,3',17-trione, 4,6'-dihydro-, (4α,5S)-	MeOH	222(3.95)	44-4299-79
Tricyclo[11.3.1.1^{5,9}]octadeca-1(17),5-8,13,15-pentaene-7,18-dione, 17-(1,1-dimethylethyl)-15-methoxy-	dioxan	260f(4.0),360(3.3)	138-0541-79
$C_{23}H_{28}O_4$			
Gona-1,3,5(10),8-tetraen-17β-ol, 11β,13β-(1ξ-hydroxypropano)-3-methoxy-, acetate	MeOH	278(4.06)	87-0966-79
Pregna-1,4,6-triene-3,11,20-trione, 21-hydroxy-6,16α-dimethyl-	MeOH	226(4.01),258(3.93), 293(4.07)	24-0979-79
$C_{23}H_{28}O_5S$			
Pregna-1,4-dien-11-one, 17α,20:20,21-bis[methylenebis(oxy)]-3-thioxo-	MeCN	330(4.29),565(1.30)	39-1166-79C
$C_{23}H_{28}O_6$			
Benzo[3,4]cycloocta[1,2-f][1,3]benzodioxole, 5,6,7,8-tetrahydro-1,2,3,13-tetramethoxy-6,7-dimethyl- (gomisin N)	EtOH	218(4.73),251s(4.14), 278s(3.61)	94-2695-79
1,5-Cyclo-1,10-secopregna-3,9-diene-2,11,20-trione, 21-acetoxy-17-hydroxy-, (5S)-	EtOH	266(3.40)	35-5019-79
19-Norpregna-1,3,5(10)-triene-11,20-dione, 21-acetoxy-2,17 -dihydroxy-1-	EtOH	214(3.90),284(3.32)	35-5019-79
	EtOH-base	242(3.95),303(3.50)	35-5019-79

Compound	Solvent	λ max (log ε)	Ref.
1-methyl- (cont.)			35-5019-79
Vismione A, dihydro-	$CHCl_3$	242s(4.06),283(4.48), 318(3.85),332s(3.79), 405(3.92)	32-0301-79
$C_{23}H_{28}O_6S$			
Pregna-1,4-dien-11-one, 17α,20:20,21-bis[methylenebis(oxy)]-3-sulfinyl-	MeCN	358(4.20)	39-1166-79C
$C_{23}H_{28}O_7$			
Benzo[3,4]cycloocta[1,2-f][1,3]benzodioxol-5-ol, 5,6,7,8-tetrahydro-1,2,3-13-tetramethoxy-6,7-dimethyl- (gomisin O)	EtOH	214(4.60),253s(3.93), 282(3.54)	94-2695-79
Epigomisin O	EtOH	218(4.53),253s(3.95), 277s(3.39),289s(3.33)	94-2695-79
Gomisin A	EtOH	218(4.88),253(4.30), 281s(3.70),290s(3.57)	94-1383-79
$C_{23}H_{28}O_8$			
Benzo[3,4]cycloocta[1,2-f][1,3]benzodioxole-5,6-diol, 5,6,7,8-tetrahydro-1,2,3,13-tetramethoxy-6,7-dimethyl-, (5α,6β,7β)-(-)-	EtOH	217(4.85),257s(4.12), 284s(3.59)	94-1383-79
Benzo[3,4]cycloocta[1,2-f][1,3]benzodioxole-7,8-diol, 5,6,7,8-tetrahydro-1,2,3,13-tetramethoxy-6,7-dimethyl-	EtOH	220(4.76),253s(4.19), 284s(3.58)	94-1383-79
Dibenzo[a,c]cyclooctene-1,4-dione, 5,6,7,8-tetrahydro-7-hydroxy-2,3,10,11,12-pentamethoxy-6,7-dimethyl-	EtOH	216(4.59),241s(4.16), 274(4.01),365(3.44)	94-1576-79
$C_{23}H_{28}O_{10}$			
2-Propen-1-one, 1-[2-hydroxy-3,4,6-tris(methoxymethoxy)phenyl]-3-[4-(methoxymethoxy)phenyl]-	EtOH	367(4.42)	18-2596-79
$C_{23}H_{29}BrN_4O_9$			
Acetamide, N-acetyl-N-[7-[5-O-acetyl-2,3-O-(1-methylethylidene)-β-D-ribofuranosyl]-6-bromo-4,7-dihydro-3-(methoxymethyl)-5-methyl-4-oxo-3H-pyrrolo[2,3-d]pyrimidin-2-yl]-	MeOH	272(3.94),311(4.05)	35-3629-79
$C_{23}H_{29}NO_4$			
4H-Dibenzo[de,g]quinoline, 5,6,6a,7-tetrahydro-1,2,10,11-tetramethoxy-6-propyl-	EtOH	222(4.59),272(4.12), ?(3.76)	4-0087-79
$C_{23}H_{29}NO_8$			
Isophomazarin, tetrahydrotri-O-methyl-, methyl ester	MeOH	272(4.34),313(3.97), 374(3.66)	39-0823-79C
$C_{23}H_{29}N_3O_2$			
Pentanamide, 2-[[4-(diethylamino)phenyl]imino]-4,4-dimethyl-3-oxo-N-phenyl-	heptane	415(3.62)	73-1460-79
	EtOH	432(3.66)	73-1460-79
$C_{23}H_{29}N_3O_5$			
Yohimbine oxindole, 5-(aminocarbonyl)-1,2-didehydro-2-deoxo-2-methoxy-	EtOH	212(4.27),258(3.63)	78-0633-79

Compound	Solvent	λ_{max}(log ε)	Ref.
$C_{23}H_{29}N_3O_6$			
α-D-Galactopyranose, 6-deoxy-6-[(2,3-dihydro-1,5-dimethyl-3-oxo-2-phenyl-1H-pyrazol-4-yl)imino]-1,2:3,4-bis-O-(1-methylethylidene)-	EtOH	208(3.85),238(3.95), 288(3.96)	33-1632-79
$C_{23}H_{29}N_3O_{11}$			
D-Galactose, [(phenylamino)carbonyl]hydrazone, 2,3,4,5,6-pentaacetate	EtOH	230(4.15),252(4.28)	136-0325-79H
$C_{23}H_{30}N_2O_3S$			
Formamide, N-[(3β)-3-acetoxyandrosta-5,16-dieno[17,16-d]thiazol-2'-yl]-	$CHCl_3$	285(4.02)	4-0763-79
$C_{23}H_{30}N_4O_3$			
Ethanone, 1-(10-acetoxy-3,3a,3b,9,10-11,12,12a,12b,13,14,14a-dodecahydro-12a,14a-dimethylbenzo[d]cyclopenta-[i]tetrazolo[1,5-a][1]benzazepin-1-yl]-, [3aR-(3aα,3bβ,10β,12aβ,12bα-14aβ)]-	EtOH	241(3.94)	39-3166-79C
$C_{23}H_{30}N_4O_9$			
Acetamide, N-acetyl-N-[7-[5-O-acetyl-2,3-O-(1-methylethylidene)-β-D-ribofuranosyl]-4,7-dihydro-3-(methoxymethyl)-5-methyl-4-oxo-3H-pyrrolo-[2,3-d]pyrimidin-2-yl]-	MeOH	270s(3.74),305(3.92)	35-3629-79
$C_{23}H_{30}N_4O_{12}$			
1H-Purine-2,6-dione, 3,9-dihydro-1,3-dimethyl-9-[2,3,6-tri-O-acetyl-4-O-(1-acetoxyethyl)-β-D-glucopyranosyl]-	MeOH	273(4.03)	136-0061-79A
$C_{23}H_{30}N_6O_{15}$			
Polyoxin F	0.05M HCl	276(4.06)	142-0333-79B
	0.05M NaOH	271(3.87)	142-0333-79B
$C_{23}H_{30}N_{12}O_5$			
Alanine, 3-(6-amino-9H-purin-9-yl)-N-[3-(6-amino-9H-purin-9-yl)-N-[(1,1-dimethylethoxy)carbonyl]alanyl]-, ethyl ester	EtOH	262(4.39)	65-0994-79
$C_{23}H_{30}O_3$			
2,4,6,8-Nonatetraenoic acid, 3,7-dimethyl-3-(4-methoxy-2,3,6-trimethylphenyl)-, ethyl ester, (all-E)-	pH 7.4	380(4.35)	149-0531-79A
Pregna-1,4,20-trien-3-one, 18-acetoxy-	n.s.g.	242(4.09)	88-4701-79
$C_{23}H_{30}O_4$			
14β-Estra-1,3,5(10),16-tetraen-15-one, 3-methoxy-17-(2-methoxyethoxy)-14-methyl-	MeOH	211(3.90),234(4.17), 279(3.33),288(3.28)	150-2525-79
Gona-1,3,5(10),9(11)-tetraene-3-propanol, 17-acetoxy-3-methoxy-, (17β)-	MeOH	263(4.23)	87-0966-79
19-Norpregna-1,3,5(10),17(20)-tetraen-21-oic acid, 14-hydroxy-3-methoxy-, ethyl ester, (14β)-	MeOH	226(4.40)	97-0451-79

Compound	Solvent	λ_{max}(log ϵ)	Ref.
Pregna-4,6-diene-3,20-dione, 17α-acetoxy-	EtOH	283(4.39)	150-0501-79
Pregna-1,4,6-triene-3,20-dione, 11,21-dihydroxy-6,16-dimethyl-, (11α,16α)-	MeOH	225(4.07),261(4.06), 300(4.05)	24-0979-79
(11β,16α)-	MeOH	227(4.11),252(3.93), 303(4.02)	24-0979-79
$C_{23}H_{30}O_5$			
Pregna-4,8(14)-dien-3-one, 17,20:20,21-bis[methylenebis(oxy)]-	MeOH	236(4.16)	24-3748-79
	MeCN	233(4.16)	24-3748-79
$C_{23}H_{30}O_5S$			
Pregna-1,4-dien-20-one, 21-acetoxy-11,17-dihydroxy-3-thioxo-, (11β)-	MeOH	334(4.34)	39-1166-79C
$C_{23}H_{30}O_6$			
Dibenzo[a,c]cycloocten-6-ol, 5,6,7,8-tetrahydro-1,2,3,10,11-pentamethoxy-6,7-dimethyl-	EtOH	213(4.63),254(4.14), 282(3.76),293s(3.67)	94-1576-79
Pregna-4,8(14)-diene-3,20-dione, 21-acetoxy-11,17-dihydroxy-, (9β,11β)-	MeOH	240(4.22)	24-3748-79
	MeCN	237(4.23)	24-3748-79
$C_{23}H_{30}O_7$			
Asteltoxin	MeOH	267(4.47),237(4.47), 367(4.52)	77-0441-79
Gomisin H	EtOH	219(4.81),248s(4.32), 276(3.76),285s(3.65)	94-1576-79
B(9a)-Homo-A,19-dinorpregn-3(5)-ene-2,11,20-trione, 21-acetoxy-9a,17-dihydroxy-9a-methyl-, (9aα,10α)-	EtOH	231(4.26)	35-5019-79
10α-Pregn-4-ene-2,20-dione, 21-acetoxy-11α,17α-dihydroxy-1β,11β-epoxy-	MeOH	288(2.32)	35-5019-79
$C_{23}H_{31}BrN_2O_8$			
1H-Pyrrole-3-propanoic acid, 2-[bromo-[4-(3-methoxy-3-oxopropyl)-3,3-dimethyl-5-oxo-2-pyrrolidinylidene]-methyl]-4,5-dihydro-4-(2-methoxy-2-oxoethyl)-4-methyl-5-oxo-, methyl ester, [S-(R*,R*)]-	MeOH	236(4.80)	5-1440-79
$C_{23}H_{31}N_2S$			
1,2-Benzisothiazolium, 3-[4-(dibutylamino)phenyl]-2-ethyl-, chloride, hydrochloride	5M HCl	269(4.14),338(3.95)	24-3286-79
	MeOH	273(4.39),430(4.29)	24-3286-79
$C_{23}H_{31}NO_2$			
2,4,6,8-Nonatetraenamide, N-ethyl-9-(4-methoxy-2,3,6-trimethylphenyl)-3,7-dimethyl-, (all-E)-	pH 7.4	290(4.03)	149-0531-79A
$C_{23}H_{31}N_7O_{10}$			
L-Alanine, N-[3-(3,4-dihydro-2,4-dioxo-1(2H)-pyrimidinyl)-N-[3-(3,4-dihydro-2,4-dioxo-1(2H)-pyrimidinyl)-N-[(1,1-dimethylethoxy)carbonyl]alanyl]alanyl]-, methyl ester	EtOH	264(4.27)	65-1000-79
$C_{23}H_{32}N_2O_2S$			
Benzenecarbothioic acid, 4-(hexyloxy)-, S-(5-hexyl-2-pyrimidinyl) ester	EtOH	222(4.27),294(4.4)	48-0619-79

Compound	Solvent	$\lambda_{max}(\log \epsilon)$	Ref.
Formamide, N-[5-[(3β,17β)-3-hydroxy-androst-5-en-17-yl]-2-thiazolyl]-	$CHCl_3$	273(3.82)	4-0763-79
$C_{23}H_{32}N_2O_3S$			
Formamide, N-[(3α,5α)-3-acetoxyandrost-16-eno[17,16-d]thiazol-2'-yl]-	$CHCl_3$	287(4.13)	4-0763-79
(3β,5α)-	$CHCl_3$	287(4.01)	4-0763-79
(3β,5β)-	$CHCl_3$	288(3.63)	4-0763-79
$C_{23}H_{32}N_4O_3$			
Ethanone, 1-(3-acetoxy-1,2,3,4,4a,5,6-6a,6b,7,9a,14,14a,14b-tetradecahydro-9a,14b-dimethylcyclopenta[f]naphtho-[1,2-d]tetrazolo[1,5-a]azepin-9-yl)-, [3S-(3α,4aβ,6aα,6bβ,9aα,14aβ,14bα)]-	MeOH	241(4.03)	39-3166-79C
$C_{23}H_{32}N_4O_4$			
Benzo[d]cyclopenta[i]tetrazolo[1,5-a]-[1]benzazepine-1,10-diol, 1,2,3,3a-3b,9,10,11,12,12a,12b,13,14,14a-tetradecahydro-12a,14a-dimethyl-, diacetate	EtOH	242(4.21)	39-3166-79C
$C_{23}H_{32}N_6O_{13}$			
Polyoxin H	0.05M HCl	265(3.88)	142-0333-79B
	0.05M NaOH	266(3.79)	142-0333-79B
$C_{23}H_{32}N_6O_{14}$			
Polyoxin A	0.05M HCl	262(3.94)	142-0333-79B
	0.05M NaOH	264(3.80)	142-0333-79B
$C_{23}H_{32}OS_2$			
Pregna-1,4-diene-3,20-dione, cyclic 20-(1,2-ethanediyl mercaptole)	MeOH	245(4.13)	39-2064-79C
$C_{23}H_{32}O_3$			
Pregna-4,6-diene-3,20-dione, cyclic 20-(1,2-ethanediyl acetal)	EtOH	284(4.42)	150-0501-79
Pregna-4,6-diene-3,20-dione, 21-hydr-oxy-6,16α-dimethyl-	MeOH	289(4.37)	24-0979-79
Pregna-4,20-dien-3-one, 11α-acetoxy-	n.s.g.	243(4.10)	31-0298-79
$C_{23}H_{32}O_4$			
Androsta-5,7-dien-3-one, 17-acetoxy-19-hydroxy-4,4-dimethyl-, (13α,17β)-	n.s.g.	265s(3.81),277(3.94), 285(3.97),295s(3.83)	33-2732-79
(17β)-	n.s.g.	265s(3.83),274(3.96), 286(3.97),296(3.75)	33-2732-79
Oleagenin	MeOH	207(4.32)	94-1604-79
Pregna-4,6-diene-3,20-dione, 11,21-di-hydroxy-6,16-dimethyl-, (11α)-	MeOH	289(4.36)	24-0979-79
(11β)-	MeOH	289(4.37)	24-0979-79
Pregn-5-ene-3,7,20-trione, cyclic 3-(1,2-ethanediyl acetal)	EtOH	241(4.11)	150-0501-79
$C_{23}H_{32}O_5$			
Androst-5-ene-3,7-dione, 17β-acetoxy-, cyclic 3-(1,2-ethanediyl acetal)	EtOH	241(4.09)	150-0501-79
Androst-5-ene-7,17-dione, 3β-acetoxy-, cyclic 17-(1,2-ethanediyl acetal)	EtOH	234.5(4.10)	150-0501-79
Pregn-4-en-3-one, 17,20:20,21-bis-[methylenebis(oxy)]-	MeOH	240(4.21)	24-3748-79
	MeCN	238(4.23)	24-3748-79

Compound	Solvent	$\lambda_{max}(\log \epsilon)$	Ref.
$C_{23}H_{33}I_2N_3O_8S$			
L-Methionine, N-[N-[N-[(1,1-dimethylethoxy)carbonyl]-3,5-diiodo-L-tyrosyl]-L-seryl]-, methyl ester	EtOH	287(3.46),296s(3.42)	33-2460-79
$C_{23}H_{33}NO_3S$			
Pregn-4-ene-21-thioamide, 17α-hydroxy-N,N-dimethyl-3,20-dioxo-	EtOH	245(4.40)	94-1352-79
$C_{23}H_{33}NO_6$			
Benzenepropanamine, N-(2,2-dimethoxyethyl)-α-(3,4-dimethoxyphenyl)-3,4-dimethoxy-	EtOH	235(4.24),282(3.89)	78-1857-79
$C_{23}H_{34}N_4O_{10}$			
DL-Aspartic acid, N-[[1-[5-O-acetyl-2,3-O-(1-methylethylidene)-β-D-ribofuranosyl]-5-nitro-1H-imidazol-4-yl]carbonyl]-3-methyl-, diethyl ester, threo-	MeOH	207(3.84),268(3.85)	39-1415-79C
$C_{23}H_{34}O_2$			
8,15-Cyclo-C,18-dinor-14,15-secoandrost-15-ene-2,3-diol, 4,4-dimethyl-17-methylene-, cyclic 1-methylethylidene acetal, (2α,3α,5β,9β,10α)-	EtOH	210(3.73),239(4.25)	39-1004-79C
2,4-Norchola-5,7-dien-23-al, 3β-hydroxy-	EtOH	282(4.01)	65-0202-79
$C_{23}H_{34}O_2S_2$			
Estr-4-en-3-one, 17β-acetoxy-, cyclic 3-(1,3-propanediyl mercaptole)	MeOH	248(4.20)	39-1166-79C
$C_{23}H_{34}O_3$			
5α-Androstano[16,17-b]furan-5'-one, 4',5',16β,17β-tetrahydro-3β-methoxy-4'-methylene-	EtOH	214(3.95)	33-1586-79
5α-Androstano[17,16-b]furan-5'-one, 4',5',16β,17β-tetrahydro-3β-methoxy-4'-methylene-	EtOH	216(3.89)	33-1586-79
Card-20(22)-enolide, 3-hydroxy-	EtOH	213(3.97)	33-1586-79
17,18-Cyclo-5β-pregnan-20-one, 3α-acetoxy-	EtOH	219(3.9)	12-2323-79
Pregn-4-ene-3,20-dione, cyclic 20-(1,2-ethanediyl acetal)	EtOH	241(4.19)	150-0501-79
$C_{23}H_{34}O_3Se$			
Cyclopentadecanecarboxylic acid, 2-oxo-1-(phenylseleno)-, methyl ester	EtOH	227(3.86),294(2.62)	33-2630-79
$C_{23}H_{34}O_4$			
Pregna-5,17(20)-dien-21-oic acid, 3,14-dihydroxy-, ethyl ester, (3β,14β)-	MeOH	227(4.27)	97-0451-79
Pregn-4-ene-3,20-dione, 6α,21-dihydroxy-6β,16α-dimethyl-	MeOH	243(4.14)	24-0979-79
$C_{23}H_{34}O_5$			
Digitoxigenin, 18,20-epoxy-20,22-dihydro-	MeOH	220(2.50)	44-3511-79

Compound	Solvent	$\lambda_{max}(\log \epsilon)$	Ref.
$C_{23}H_{34}O_5S$			
Androstane-16-acetic acid, 17-hydroxy-α-methylene-3-[(methylsulfonyl)oxy]-, γ-lactone, (3β,5α,16α,17α)-	EtOH	214(3.94)	33-1586-79
$C_{23}H_{36}NO_3$			
Spiro[androstane-3,2'-oxazolidin]-3'-yloxy, 4',4'-dimethyl-17-oxo-	ether	437(0.93)	4-0807-79
photoisomer	ether	439(0.93)	4-0807-79
$C_{23}H_{36}O_4$			
Pregn-17(20)-ene-21-carboxylic acid, 3,14-dihydroxy-, ethyl ester, (3β,5β,14β)-	MeOH	227(4.20)	97-0451-79
$C_{23}H_{39}NO_2$			
Pyridinium, 1-(carboxymethyl)-2-hexyl-3,5-dipentyl-, hydroxide, inner salt	MeOH	241s(--),282(4.00)	44-1417-79
$C_{23}H_{40}O_2$			
4H-Pyran-4-one, 3,5-dibutyl-2,6-dipentyl-	EtOH	258(3.89)	35-4386-79
$C_{23}H_{42}NO$			
Pyridinium, 2-hexyl-1-(2-hydroxyethyl)-3,5-dipentyl-, chloride	MeOH	283(3.99)	44-1417-79
$C_{23}H_{46}N_2O_4$			
Acetamide, 2,2'-[1,3-propanediylbis(oxy)]bis[N-heptyl-N-methyl-	H_2O	203(4.22)	33-0754-79

Compound	Solvent	λmax(log ε)	Ref.
$C_{24}F_{16}S_8$			
2,3,8,9,14,15,20,21-Octathiapentacyclo-[20.2.2.2^{4,7}.2^{10,13}.2^{16,19}]dotriaconta-4,6,10,12,16,18,22,24,25,27,29,31-dodecaene, 5,6,11,12,17,18,23,24,25-26,27,28,29,30,31,32-hexadecafluoro-	n.s.g.	255(4.67),308(4.28)	44-2629-79
$C_{24}H_{12}Br_2$			
Naphtho[2',3':3,4]cyclobut[1,2-a]anthracene, 6,7-dibromo-	$CHCl_3$	315(5.26),330(4.91), 340(4.59),365(4.12), 362(4.13),384(4.15), 408(4.11),432(4.31)	44-3790-79
$C_{24}H_{12}ClNO_5$			
Naphtho[2,3-c]furan-1,3-dione, 4-(3-chlorophenyl)-9-(4-nitrophenyl)-	n.s.g.	222(4.70),263(4.39), 312(4.21)	80-1177-79
$C_{24}H_{12}Cl_2O_3$			
Naphtho[2,3-c]furan-1,3-dione, 4-(3-chlorophenyl)-9-(4-chlorophenyl)-	n.s.g.	222(4.59),310(4.02)	80-1177-79
$C_{24}H_{12}N_4O_2S_2$			
Bisthiazolo[3,2-a:3',2'-a]benzo[1,2-d:4,5-d']diimidazole-5,11-dione, 2,8-diphenyl-	EtOH	291(4.35),324(4.27), 468(4.20)	2-0523-79A
Bisthiazolo[3,2-a:3',2'-a]benzo[1,2-d:5,4-d']diimidazole-5,11-dione, 3,9-diphenyl-, (E)-	EtOH	290(4.43),311(4.31), 460(4.25)	2-0523-79A
(Z)-	EtOH	285(4.21),315(4.01), 452(3.97)	2-0523-79
Bisthiazolo[3,2-a:3',2'-a]benzo[1,2-d:5,4-d']diimidazole-5,11-dione, 2.8-diphenyl-	EtOH	275(4.17),317(4.04), 461(3.99)	2-0523-79A
$C_{24}H_{12}O_2S_2$			
Naphtho[1,8-bc]thiopyran-3(2H)-one, 2-(3-oxonaphtho[1,2-b]thien-2(3H)-ylidene)-, cis	n.s.g.	487(4.15)	124-0768-79
trans	n.s.g.	600(4.51)	124-0768-79
$C_{24}H_{13}ClO_3$			
Naphtho[2,3-c]furan-1,3-dione, 4-(3-chlorophenyl)-9-phenyl-	n.s.g.	222(4.68),509(4.14)	80-1177-79
$C_{24}H_{13}NO_5$			
5,11-Naphthacenedione, 6-(4-nitrophenoxy)-	toluene	480(4.20)	135-0691-79A
5,12-Naphthacenedione, 6-(4-nitrophenoxy)-	toluene	395(3.78)	135-0691-79A
$C_{24}H_{14}ClNO_5$			
2,5-Furandione, 3-[(3-chlorophenyl)-phenylmethylene]dihydro-4-[(4-nitrophenyl)methylene]-	n.s.g.	208(4.32),340(3.54)	80-1177-79
$C_{24}H_{14}Cl_2N_4O_2S_2$			
2,5-Cyclohexadiene-1,4-dione, 2,5-dichloro-3,6-bis[(4-phenyl-2-thiazolyl)amino]-	EtOH	248(3.72),345(3.95), 545(4.27)	2-0523-79A
2,5-Cyclohexadiene-1,4-dione, 2,5-dichloro-3,6-bis[(5-phenyl-2-thiazo-	EtOH	235(3.85),362(3.99), 537(4.25)	2-0523-79A

Compound	Solvent	λ$_{max}$(log ε)	Ref.
lyl)amino]- (cont.)			2-0523-79A
$C_{24}H_{14}Cl_2O_3$			
2,5-Furandione, 3-[(4-chlorophenyl)-methylene]-4-[(3-chlorophenyl)phenyl-methylene]dihydro-	n.s.g.	222(4.61),266(4.27), 308(4.09)	80-1177-79
$C_{24}H_{14}O_3$			
5,11-Naphthacenedione, 6-phenoxy-	toluene	480(4.23)	135-0691-79A
5,12-Naphthacenedione, 6-phenoxy-	toluene	400(3.78)	135-0691-79A
$C_{24}H_{14}O_4$			
1H-Indene-1,3(2H)-dione, 2-(1-benzoyl-2-oxo-2-phenylethylidene)-	dioxan	257(4.83),304(4.08), 318(3.96),398(2.22)	32-0329-79
5,11-Naphthacenedione, 6-(4-hydroxy-phenoxy)-	toluene	480(4.23)	135-0691-79A
5,12-Naphthacenedione, 6-(4-hydroxy-phenoxy)-	toluene	400(3.72)	135-0691-79A
Spiro[1H-indene-1,2'-[2H]indene]-1',3,3'(2H)-trione, 2-benzoyl-	dioxan	227(4.70),247s(4.36), 307(4.04),325(4.05)	32-0329-79
	Et_3N	360(4.07)	32-0329-79
$C_{24}H_{15}ClO_4$			
9H-Indeno[2,1-c]phenanthren-9-one, 7-acetoxy-11-chloro-5-methoxy-	n.s.g.	220(4.75),237(4.68), 263(4.34),280(4.29), 290s(4.26),330(4.38), 347(4.50),390(3.65), 460(3.39)	33-0090-79
$C_{24}H_{15}NO$			
5H-Indeno[1,2-c]pyridin-5-one, 1,3-di-phenyl-	EtOH	220(2.66),258(4.6), 360(4.28),453(3.25)	103-0899-79
$C_{24}H_{15}N_3$			
5H-Diindolo[2,3-a:2',3'-c]carbazole, 6,11-dihydro-	EtOH	216(4.92),254(4.91), 272s(4.23),298(4.74), 305(4.81),317s(4.39), 333(4.45),347(4.62), 373(4.24)	142-0471-79
5H-Indeno[1,2-b]pyridine, 5-diazo-2,4-diphenyl-	EtOH	212(4.08),248(4.20), 267(4.23),330(3.97)	103-0777-79
$C_{24}H_{16}As_4$			
5,12[1',2']:6,11[1",2"]-Dibenzenodiben-zo[c,g][1,2,5,6]tetrarsocin	THF	229(4.79),279(4.57), 328(4.02)	78-0155-79
$C_{24}H_{16}ClNO_6$			
Butanedioic acid, [(3-chlorophenyl)-phenylmethylene][(4-nitrophenyl)-methylene]-	n.s.g.	222(4.65),263(4.33)	80-1177-79
$C_{24}H_{16}Cl_2O_4$			
Butanedioic acid, [(4-chlorophenyl)-methylene][(3-chlorophenyl)phenyl-methylene]-	n.s.g.	217(4.57),272(4.37), 325(3.78)	80-1177-79
$C_{24}H_{16}F_3$			
Cycloheptatrienylium, [8-[4-(trifluoro-methyl)phenyl]-1-naphthalenyl]-, perchlorate	MeCN	223(4.88),265(4.12), 291(4.09),345(3.63), 453(3.72)	44-2712-79

Compound	Solvent	$\lambda_{max}(\log \epsilon)$	Ref.
$C_{24}H_{16}N_2$			
25,26-Diazapentacyclo[19.3.1.1^{9,13}-0^{4,16}.0^{6,18}]hexacosa-1(25),2,4,6(18)-7,9,11,13(26),14,15,19,21,23-tridecaene	EtOH	247(4.33),253(4.34), 260(4.27),294(3.87)	35-2121-79
$C_{24}H_{16}N_2O$			
5-Chrysenol, 6-(phenylazo)-	EtOH	255(4.52),334(4.03), 415(3.76),502(4.03)	32-0351-79
	ether	275(4.28),330(3.98), 410(3.70),495(3.95)	32-0351-79
	dioxan	255(4.36),270(4.53), 330(4.01),418(3.69), 505(4.00)	32-0351-79
	$CHCl_3$	335(4.19),415(3.90), 504(4.16)	32-0351-79
	CCl_4	335(4.13),410(3.83), 500(4.10)	32-0351-79
6-Chrysenol, 5-(phenylazo)-	EtOH	255(4.44),340(3.81), 400(4.12),512(4.40)	32-0351-79
	ether	340(3.76),405(4.26), 500(4.49)	32-0351-79
	dioxan	235(4.59),250(4.64), 335(3.76),400(4.20), 505(4.42)	32-0351-79
	$CHCl_3$	340(3.88),405(4.21), 510(4.48)	32-0351-79
	CCl_4	340(3.60),405(3.98), 510(4.19)	32-0351-79
$C_{24}H_{16}N_2O_2$			
Oxazole, 2,2'-(1,4-phenylene)bis[5-phenyl-	EtOH	346(4.68),360(4.74), 369(4.52)	18-3597-79
Oxazole, 5,5'-(1,4-phenylene)bis[2-phenyl-	EtOH	341(4.67),353(4.74)	18-3597-79
$C_{24}H_{16}N_2O_5$			
Methanone, [2-(2-furanyl)-5-methyl-1-(5-nitro-2-furanyl)-3-indolizinyl]phenyl-	EtOH	448(4.20)	94-3078-79
Methanone, [2-(2-furanyl)-7-methyl-1-(5-nitro-2-furanyl)-3-indolizinyl]phenyl-	EtOH	448(4.20)	94-3078-79
$C_{24}H_{16}O_2$			
Benzo[rst]pentaphene-3,4-diol, 3,4-dihydro-	EtOH-10% THF	307(4.8)	88-3819-79
Dibenzo[b,def]chrysene-1,2-diol, 1,2-dihydro-	EtOH-10% THF	240(4.57),398(4.44)	88-3819-79
Methanone, 1,8-naphthalenediylbis[phenyl-	EtOH	206(4.72),230s(4.40), 250(4.40),290(3.99), 310s(3.91)	18-3314-79
$C_{24}H_{16}O_4$			
[1]Benzopyrano[3,4-b][1]benzopyran-12-carboxylic acid, 6-phenyl-, methyl ester	EtOH	241(4.47),264(4.41), 445(4.05)	138-0511-79
Dibenz[a,h]anthracene-7,14-dione, 3,4-dimethoxy-	dioxan	312(4.52),385(3.74)	44-3086-79
2H-Furo[2,3-c][1]benzopyran-2-one, 1-(2-methoxyphenyl)-4-phenyl-	EtOH	237(4.50),243s(--), 312(4.29),389(4.45)	138-0511-79

Compound	Solvent	λ max(log ε)	Ref.
9H-Indeno[2,1-c]phenanthren-9-one, 7-acetoxy-5-methoxy-	n.s.g.	215(4.74),224(4.72), 260(4.32),281(4.29), 298(4.24),320s(4.28), 327(4.35),344(4.47), 388(3.60),466(--)	33-0090-79
3H,10H-Pyrano[4,3-b][1]benzopyran-3,10-dione, 4,4a-dihydro-4,4-diphenyl-	MeOH	285(4.0),345(3.1)	24-1791-79
$C_{24}H_{17}BrN_2O_4$			
4,8-Iminocyclohepta[c]pyrrole-1,3,5-(2H)-trione, 9-[3-(4-bromophenyl)-3-oxo-1-propenyl]-3a,4,8,8a-tetrahydro-2-phenyl-, [3aα,4β,8β,8aα,9(E)]-	EtOH	270(3.94),324(4.16)	56-0057-79
$C_{24}H_{17}ClO_4$			
Butanedioic acid, [(3-chlorophenyl)-phenylmethylene](phenylmethylene)-	n.s.g.	222(4.53),263(4.22), 309(4.01)	80-1177-79
$C_{24}H_{17}F_3N_2O_2$			
Quinazolinium, 4-(9-anthracenyl)-3,4-dihydro-, trifluoroacetate	EtOH	256(5.04),335(3.59), 351(3.82),368(4.00), 388(3.94)	24-1348-79
$C_{24}H_{17}N$			
5H-Indeno[1,2-c]pyridine, 1,3-diphenyl-	EtOH	224s(4.5),242s(4.3), 304(4.56)	103-0899-79
$C_{24}H_{17}NO_2$			
Isoquinoline, 2-benzoyl-1,2-dihydro-1-(2-oxo-2-phenylethylidene)-	MeCN	226(4.53),261(4.23)	103-1337-79
$C_{24}H_{17}NO_2S_2$			
Ethanone, 2,2'-(4-phenyl-1,2,4-dithiazolidine-3,5-diylidene)bis[1-phenyl-, cis	EtOH	267(3.53),286(4.04), 366(4.41),380(4.34)	103-1187-79
trans	EtOH	270(3.85),310(3.6), 395(3.75),445(4.02)	103-1187-79
$C_{24}H_{17}NO_4$			
4H-[1]Benzopyrano[3,4-d]isoxazole-4-acetic acid, α,α-diphenyl-	MeOH	229(4.3),269(3.9), 280(3.9),322(3.8)	24-1791-79
$C_{24}H_{17}N_2O$			
Isoquinolinium, 2-benzoyl-1-(1H-indol-3-yl)-, perchlorate	MeCN	211(4.72),225s(4.57), 241s(4.51),267s(4.25), 332(3.69),408(3.88)	103-0773-79
Quinolinium, 1-benzoyl-2-(1H-indol-3-yl)-, perchlorate	MeCN	225s(4.50),255(4.45), 299s(4.01),333s(3.75), 430(4.26)	103-0773-79
$C_{24}H_{17}N_3O_4$			
Pyridinium, 1-[3-(5-cyano-1-ethyl-1,6-dihydro-2-hydroxy-4-methyl-6-oxo-3-pyridinyl)-1,4-dihydro-1,4-dioxo-2-naphthalenyl]-, hydroxide, inner salt	EtOH	252(4.28),338(4.27), 630(3.49)	2-0100-79A
$C_{24}H_{17}O$			
[1,1':3',1"-Terphenyl]-2'-yloxy, 5'-phenyl-	PrOH	550(3.78),750(3.34) (anom.)	39-1540-79B

Compound	Solvent	$\lambda_{max}(\log \epsilon)$	Ref.
$C_{24}H_{18}ClN_7O_2S$			
Benzaldehyde, 4-chloro-, (dihydro-10-methyl-6,8-dioxo-4,7-diphenyl-2H-1,4-imino-4H,6H-[1,2,4]triazolo[1,2-c]-[1,3,4,5]thiatriazin-2-ylidene)hydrazone	DMF	279(4.16),349(4.17),451(4.29)	39-0724-79C
$C_{24}H_{18}GeO$			
10H-Phenoxagermanin, 10,10-diphenyl-	pentane	247(4.15),285(3.79),295(3.67)	65-0672-79
$C_{24}H_{18}GeS$			
10H-Phenothiagermanin, 10,10-diphenyl-	pentane	270(3.90),280(3.74),290(3.62)	65-0672-79
$C_{24}H_{18}N_2$			
9H-Carbazol-9-amine, N-[1,1'-biphenyl]-2-yl-	EtOH	231(4.85),290(4.45),320(3.85),332(3.92)	39-1536-79C
$C_{24}H_{18}N_2O_2S_2$			
Thiazolo[3,2-a]quinolinium, 1-hydroxy-5-methyl-2-[[(4-methyl-2-quinolinyl)-thio]acetyl]-, hydroxide, inner salt	n.s.g.	297(4.05),328(3.93),452(4.30)	103-0811-79
$C_{24}H_{18}N_4O_4$			
1,2-Benzenediol, 4,4'-[[1,1'-biphenyl]-4,4'-diylbis(azo)]bis-	cation	520(4.65)	140-1133-79
	neutral	380(4.28)	140-1133-79
	dianion	480(4.40)	140-1133-79
	tetraanion	500(4.48)	140-1133-79
$C_{24}H_{18}N_6$			
Benzenamine, N,N'-(3-phenyl-2H-pyrimido[1,2-a]-1,3,5-triazine-2,4(3H)-diylidene)bis-	dioxan	270s(4.23),300(4.13),395(3.48)	97-0059-79
Diazene, bis[2-(phenylazo)phenyl]-	EtOH	212(4.26),307(4.40),430(3.11)	7-0563-79
Diazene, bis[2-(phenylazo)phenyl]-	EtOH	202(4.60),223(4.38),300(4.57),350s(4.37)	12-0643-79
$C_{24}H_{18}O$			
8H-8,12b[1',2']-Benzenocyclohept[de]-anthracen-4(1H)-one, 2,3-dihydro-	$CHCl_3$	280(3.6),300(3.56)	104-1341-79
Ethanone, 1-(1-azulenyl)-2,2-diphenyl-	benzene	530(2.66)	70-0221-79
[1,1':3',1"-Terphenyl]-2'-ol, 5'-phenyl-	PrOH	310s(3.65)	39-1540-79B
$C_{24}H_{18}OSi$			
10H-Phenoxasilin, 10,10-diphenyl-	pentane	250(4.19),290(3.86),300(3.95)	65-0672-79
$C_{24}H_{18}OSn$			
10H-Phenoxastannin, 10,10-diphenyl-	pentane	250(4.06),285(3.78),295(3.67)	65-0672-79
$C_{24}H_{18}O_2$			
4H-1-Benzopyran-4-one, 3-(2,2-diphenylethenyl)-6-methyl-	MeOH	227(4.4),285(4.4),305(4.2)	24-1791-79
Dibenz[a,h]anthracene, 3,4-dimethoxy-	EtOH	225(4.46),278(4.32),291(4.64),302(4.87),324(4.26),338(4.07),351(3.76)	44-3086-79

Compound	Solvent	λ_{max}(log ϵ)	Ref.
$C_{24}H_{18}O_3$			
1-Naphthaleneacetic acid anhydride	MeCN	281.5(4.15)	39-1545-79B
2-Naphthaleneacetic acid anhydride	MeCN	277(4.17)	39-1545-79B
$C_{24}H_{18}O_4$			
9(10H)-Anthracenone, 10-[acetoxy(4-methoxyphenyl)methylene]-	EtOH	233(4.47),363(3.82)	44-3687-79
[1]Benzopyrano[3,4-b][1]benzopyran-12-carboxylic acid, 6,12-dihydro-6-phenyl-, methyl ester	EtOH	280(3.79),295(3.77), 312(3.93)	138-0511-79
Methanone, (10-acetoxy-9-anthracenyl)-(4-methoxyphenyl)-	EtOH	254(5.17),286(4.30), 332(3.64),350(3.91), 365(4.09),385(4.05)	44-3687-79
Pyrano[2,3-c][1]benzopyran-5(1H)-one, 2,3-dihydro-3-hydroxy-1,3-diphenyl-	MeOH	240(4.08)	142-1203-79
	MeOH-NaOH	240(4.08)	142-1203-79
	MeOH-$AlCl_3$	240(4.08)	142-1203-79
$C_{24}H_{18}O_4S$			
Benzene, 1,1'-sulfonylbis[4-phenoxy-	C_6H_{12}	260(4.55)	39-0007-79B
$C_{24}H_{18}O_5$			
[1]Benzopyrano[3,4-b][1]benzopyran-12-carboxylic acid, 6,6a-dihydro-6a-hydroxy-6-phenyl-, methyl ester	EtOH	240(4.16),296(4.03), 306(3.94),345(4.18), 370(4.14)	138-0511-79
$C_{24}H_{18}SSi$			
10H-Phenothiasilin, 10,10-diphenyl-	pentane	272(4.09),285(3.90), 290(3.90)	65-0672-79
$C_{24}H_{18}SSn$			
10H-Phenothiastannin, 10,10-diphenyl-	pentane	260(3.38),275(2.06), 290(1.88)	65-0672-79
$C_{24}H_{19}$			
Cycloheptatrienylium, [8-(4-methylphenyl)-1-naphthalenyl]-, perchlorate	MeCN	224(4.87),273(4.06), 302(4.03),389(3.89), 463(3.65)	44-2712-79
$C_{24}H_{19}ClN_2O_4$			
4-Imidazolidinecarboxylic acid, 1-(4-chlorophenyl)-2,5-dioxo-3,4-diphenyl-, ethyl ester	MeOH	233(4.60)	118-0794-79
$C_{24}H_{19}ClN_4O_3$			
Benzoic acid, 2-[(7-chloro-4-quinolinyl)amino]-, 2-[(3-pyridinylcarbonyl)-amino]ethyl ester (nicafenine)	MeOH	255(4.37),356(4.28)	146-1659-79
$C_{24}H_{19}ClO_4$			
3-Phenanthrenecarboxylic acid, 4-(4-chlorophenyl)-1,9-dimethoxy-, methyl ester	n.s.g.	225(4.66),260(4.58), 305(4.22),314(4.23), 336(3.95)	33-0090-79
$C_{24}H_{19}F_3N_2O_5S$			
8H-3,8a-(Iminomethano)-4H,6H-oxazolo-[4,3-b][1,3]thiazine-4,8-dione, 6-(diphenylmethylene)dihydro-9-hydroxy-2,2-dimethyl-10-(trifluoroacetyl)-	THF	230(4.24),292(4.24)	39-0170-79C
$C_{24}H_{19}N$			
Pyridine, 4-methyl-2,3,6-triphenyl-	EtOH	243(4.4),286(4.2)	103-0899-79

Compound	Solvent	$\lambda_{max}(\log \epsilon)$	Ref.
$C_{24}H_{19}NO_2PbS$			
Plumbane, [(4-nitrophenyl)thio]triphenyl-	benzene	343(4.1)	70-1585-79
$C_{24}H_{19}NO_2S$			
6H-Anthra[1,9-cd]isoxazol-6-one, 3-[[4-(1,1-dimethylethyl)phenyl]thio]-	EtOH	230(4.48),255(4.53), 451(4.32),479(4.46)	104-1514-79
$C_{24}H_{19}NO_2SSn$			
Stannane, [(4-nitrophenyl)thio]triphenyl-	benzene	322(4.06)	70-1585-79
$C_{24}H_{19}NO_3S$			
6H-Anthra[1,9-cd]isoxazol-6-one, 3-[[4-(1,1-dimethylethyl)phenyl]thio]-5-hydroxy-	EtOH	245(4.54),442(3.97), 455(3.96),490(3.53)	104-1514-79
6H-Anthra[1,9-cd]isoxazol-6-one, 5-hydroxy-3-[[4-(1-methylpropyl)phenyl]-thio]-	EtOH	245(4.60),442(3.98), 454(3.98),491(3.54)	104-1514-79
8H-Naphtho[2,3-a]phenothiazine-8,13-(14H)-dione, 7-hydroxy-2-(1-methyl-propyl)-	EtOH	240(4.45),285(4.61), 647(4.18),704(4.09)	104-1514-79
8H-Naphtho[2,3-a]phenothiazine-8,13-(14H)-dione, 2-(1,1-dimethylethyl)-7-hydroxy-	EtOH	245(4.51),285(4.57), 647(4.21),704(4.15)	104-1514-79
$C_{24}H_{19}NO_4$			
2H-1-Benzopyran-2-acetamide, 3,4-dihydro-3-(hydroxymethylene)-4-oxo-α,α-diphenyl-, monoammonium salt	MeOH	217(4.4),313(3.9), 357(3.9)	24-1791-79
Spiro[9H-fluorene-9,1'(8'aH)-indolizine]-2',3'-dicarboxylic acid, dimethyl ester	n.s.g.	384(4.02)	89-0945-79
$C_{24}H_{19}N_3$			
1H-Imidazole-1-propanenitrile, α,α,β-triphenyl-	EtOH	266(3.88)	44-0041-79
$C_{24}H_{19}N_3O$			
Benzamide, N-[4-cyano-1,2-dihydro-2-(phenylmethyl)-1-isoquinolinyl]-	CH_2Cl_2	239(4.2),325(4.0)	64-1593-79B
Benzamide, N-[3-cyano-1,2-dihydro-1-(phenylmethyl-2-quinolinyl]-	CH_2Cl_2	241(4.1),255s(4.0), 289(3.6),299(3.6), 390(3.4)	64-0064-79B
Benzamide, N-[3-cyano-1,4-dihydro-1-(phenylmethyl)-4-quinolinyl]-	CH_2Cl_2	233(4.0),317(3.8)	64-0064-79B
Phenol, 2-[2-amino-5-(2,2-diphenyl-ethenyl)-4-pyrimidinyl]-	MeOH	230(4.3),307(4.1)	24-1791-79
Quinoline, 2-(4-methoxyphenyl)-4-(1-methyl-1H-benzimidazol-2-yl)-	n.s.g.	280(4.46)	124-0447-79
$C_{24}H_{19}N_3O_2S$			
9,10-Anthracenedione, 1-azido-2-[[4-(1,1-dimethylethyl)phenyl]thio]-	EtOH	252(4.53),280(4.28), 305(4.27),427(3.74), 447(3.78),477(3.59)	104-1514-79
$C_{24}H_{19}N_3O_3S$			
9,10-Anthracenedione, 1-azido-2-[[4-(1,1-dimethylethyl)phenyl]thio]-4-hydroxy-	EtOH	256(4.53),460(3.94)	104-1514-79

Compound	Solvent	$\lambda_{max}(\log \epsilon)$	Ref.
9,10-Anthracenedione, 1-azido-4-hydroxy-2-[[4-(1-methylpropyl)phenyl]-thio]-	EtOH	256(4.56),460(3.95)	104-1514-79
Carbamic acid, [3-[(benzoylamino)thioxomethyl]-1H-indol-2-yl]-, phenylmethyl ester	$CHCl_3$	265s(4.29),285(4.34), 410(4.22)	103-0179-79
$C_{24}H_{19}N_3O_4$			
Carbamic acid, [3-[(benzoylamino)carbonyl]-1H-indol-2-yl]-, phenylmethyl ester	$CHCl_3$	242s(4.38),282(4.15), 322(4.21)	103-0179-79
$C_{24}H_{19}O$			
Cycloheptatrienylium, 8-(4-methoxyphenyl)-1-naphthalenyl]-, perchlorate	MeCN	222(4.76),290(4.06), 306s(4.01),411(3.84), 490(3.44)	44-2712-79
$C_{24}H_{19}OP$			
2,5-Cyclohexadien-1-one, 6-(triphenylphosphoranylidene)-	MeOH	337(3.70)	46-1213-79
	MeCN	359(3.70)	46-1213-79
	+2% H_2O	348(--)	46-1213-79
	+5% H_2O	344(--)	46-1213-79
$C_{24}H_{20}$			
Chrysene, 5,6,11,12-tetrahydro-2-phenyl-	C_6H_{12}	205(4.48),235s(4.13), 241(4.13),326s(4.39), 339(4.48),355s(4.34)	44-4933-79
6,18:9,15-Dimethenodicyclohepta[a,g]-cyclododecene, 7,8,16,17-tetrahydro-	CH_2Cl_2	289(4.75),315s(4.70), 366(4.07),380(3.85), 415(2.51),646(2.69)	88-1055-79
Naphthalene, 1,1'-(1-methyl-1,2-cyclopropanediyl)bis-	EtOH or CCl_4	247(4.60),278(4.30), 287(4.38),297(4.30)	104-0080-79
$C_{24}H_{20}CuN_6O_4$			
Copper, [11,12,13,14-tetrahydro-2,3-dimethyl-8,17-dinitrotribenzo[b,f,l]-[1,4,8,11]tetraazacyclotetradecinato(2-)-N^5,N^{11},N^{15},N^{20}]-, (SP-4-2)-	$CHCl_3$	297(4.28),347(4.15), 438(3.81)	12-2303-79
Copper, [12,13,14,15-tetrahydro-2-methyl-8,18-dinitro-11H-tribenzo[b,f,m]-[1,4,8,12]tetraazacyclopentadecinato(2-)-N^5,N^{11},N^{15},N^{21}]-, (SP-4-4)-	$CHCl_3$	295(4.38),420(4.57), 455(4.49)	12-2303-79
$C_{24}H_{20}N_2$			
Benzenamine, 4-ethenyl-N-[(4-styryliminomethyl)phenyl]methylene]-	$CHCl_3$	287(4.4),370(4.1)	24-2854-79
3,12:4,11-Dimethenocyclooct[c]octalene-7,16-dicarbonitrile, 1,2,5,6,9,10,13-14-octahydro-	CH_2Cl_2	260(3.62),318(3.02)	35-2128-79
7,14-Etheno-3,11:4,10-dimethenobenzo-[1,2:4,5]dicyclooctene-15,16-dicarbonitrile, 1,2,5,6,7,8,9,12,13,14-decahydro-	n.s.g.	253s(3.61),299(3.04), 370(2.38)	35-2128-79
$C_{24}H_{20}N_2O$			
Cyclopenta[3,4]pyrazolo[1,5-a]pyridin-5-ium, 1,3a,4,9b-tetrahydro-2,9b-dimethyl-1-oxo-3,3a-diphenyl-, hydroxide, inner salt	EtOH	206(4.41),278(4.12), 340(3.96),430s(3.45)	88-1765-79

Compound	Solvent	$\lambda_{max}(\log \epsilon)$	Ref.
$C_{24}H_{20}N_2OS$			
Benzamide, N-(5,6,7,8-tetrahydro-2-phenyl[1]benzothieno[2,3-b]pyridin-4-yl)-	DMF	274(4.47),317(4.25)	49-1189-79
Benzo[b]thiophene-3-carbonitrile, 4,5,6,7-tetrahydro-2-[(3-oxo-1,3-diphenyl-1-propenyl)amino]-	DMF	271(4.18),415(4.28)	49-1189-79
$C_{24}H_{20}N_2O_3S$			
5H-Thiazolo[3,2-a]quinazoline-1,5(2H)-dione, 3a-ethoxy-3a,4-dihydro-2,4-diphenyl-	MeOH	228(4.58),276(4.17), 315(3.69)	2-0039-79B
$C_{24}H_{20}N_2O_4$			
4-Imidazolidinecarboxylic acid, 2,5-dioxo-1,3,4-triphenyl-, ethyl ester	MeOH	230(4.45)	118-0794-79
$C_{24}H_{20}N_2O_5S$			
1H-Indole, 2-[[3-(2-methyl-1,3-dioxolan-2-yl)-4-pyridinyl]carbonyl]-1-(phenylsulfonyl)-	EtOH	232(4.17),310(4.19)	77-0642-79
$C_{24}H_{20}N_2S$			
4H-1,2-Diazepine, 4-(methylthio)-3,5,7-triphenyl-	EtOH	252(4.33),277(4.30)	118-0130-79
4H-1,2-Diazepine, 6-(methylthio)-3,5,7-triphenyl-	EtOH	263s(4.42),293(4.22)	118-0130-79
$C_{24}H_{20}N_2S_3$			
Benzothiazolium, 2,2'-(2,5-thiophenediyldi-2,1-ethenediyl)bis[3-methyl-,	DMF	263(4.49),305s(4.17), 367(4.00)	126-1441-79
diiodide	KBr	505(--)	126-1441-79
diperchlorate	DMF	263(4.16),294(4.20), 426(4.40),572s(--)	126-1441-79
	KBr	500(--)	126-1441-79
$C_{24}H_{20}N_3OS$			
Benzothiazolium, 2-[3-[3-(2-benzoxazolyl)-1-methyl-4(1H)-pyridinylidene]-1-propenyl]-3-methyl-, iodide	EtOH	596(4.95)	4-1579-79
Benzothiazolium, 2-[3-[5-(2-benzoxazolyl)-1-methyl-2(1H)-pyridinylidene]-1-propenyl]-3-methyl-, iodide	EtOH	587(5.21)	4-1579-79
$C_{24}H_{20}N_3S_2$			
Benzothiazolium, 2-[3-[3-(2-benzothiazolyl)-1-methyl-4(1H)-pyridinylidene]-1-propenyl]-3-methyl-, iodide	EtOH	590(4.89)	4-1579-79
Benzothiazolium, 2-[3-[5-(2-benzothiazolyl)-1-methyl-2(1H)-pyridinylidene]-1-propenyl]-3-methyl-, iodide	EtOH	588(5.17)	4-1579-79
$C_{24}H_{20}N_4$			
6,15:8,17-Dimethanocyclodeca[1,2-b:6,7-b']diquinoxaline, 6,7,8,15,16,17-hexahydro-	$CHCl_3$	240(4.87),317(4.31)	88-2347-79
4-Quinolinamine, 3-(4,5-dimethylbenzo[h]-1,6-naphthyridin-2-yl)-2-methyl-	DMF	274s(4.43),307s(4.20), 352(3.71)	48-0695-79
$C_{24}H_{20}N_4O_6$			
Isoxazole, 5,5'-(2,4-diphenyl-1,3-cyclo-	MeOH	260s(3.94)	4-0253-79

Compound	Solvent	$\lambda_{max}(\log \epsilon)$	Ref.
butanediyl)bis[3-methyl-4-nitro- (cont.)			4-0253-79
Isoxazole, 5,5'-(3,4-diphenyl-1,2-cyclo-butanediyl)bis[3-methyl-4-nitro-	MeOH	265(4.04)	4-0253-79
2-Oxa-3-azabicyclo[3.2.0]hept-3-ene, 4-methyl-7-(3-methyl-4-nitro-5-isox-azolyl)-5-nitro-6-phenyl-1-(2-phenyl-ethenyl)-, [1α(E),5α,6β,7α]-	MeOH	253(4.19)	4-0253-79
$C_{24}H_{20}N_4O_7$			
Inosine, 3',5'-dibenzoate	EtOH	231(4.41),251s(4.05), 273s(3.77),282s(3.60)	39-2088-79C
$C_{24}H_{20}N_6NiO_4$			
Nickel, [11,12,13,14-tetrahydro-2,3-di-methyl-8,17-dinitrotribenzo[b,f,l]-[1,4,8,11]tetraazacyclotetradecin-ato(2-)-N^5,N^{11},N^{14},N^{20}]-, (SP-4-2)-	$CHCl_3$	325s(4.00),375(3.95), 435(3.78),525s(3.48)	12-2303-79
$C_{24}H_{20}N_6O_{10}$			
Butanedioic acid, [(1,2,3,6-tetrahydro-1,3-dimethyl-2,6-dioxo-7H-purin-7-yl)methyl]-, bis(4-nitrophenyl) ester	MeOH	274(4.36)	126-0325-79
$C_{24}H_{20}O_2$			
2H-Pyran-2-one, 3,4-dihydro-4-(4-meth-ylphenyl)-3,6-diphenyl-	EtOH	248(4.16)	4-0001-79
$C_{24}H_{20}O_3$			
9-Anthracenemethanol, α-(4-methoxyphen-yl)-, acetate	EtOH	254(4.94),315s(3.30), 333(3.54),349(3.80), 366(3.95),386(3.93)	44-3687-79
3-Buten-1-one, 1-(2-acetoxyphenyl)-4,4-diphenyl-	MeOH	246(4.4),298-320(4.3)	24-1791-79
Methanone, [3,4-dihydro-2-(4-methoxy-phenyl)-1-naphthalenyl](4-hydroxy-phenyl)-	EtOH	221(4.38),293(4.52)	87-0962-79
2H-Pyran-2-one, 3,4-dihydro-4-(4-meth-oxyphenyl)-3,6-diphenyl-	EtOH	246(4.15)	4-0001-79
Spiro[isobenzofuran-1(3H),9'-[9H]xan-then]-3-one, 2',6'-diethyl-	EtOH	202(4.81),220(4.73), 287(3.72),308(3.73)	56-0403-79
	80% H_2SO_4	202(4.71),227(4.43), 265(4.69),286(3.70), 391(4.60),444s(--)	56-0403-79
Spiro[isobenzofuran-1(3H),9'-[9H]xan-then]-3-one, 2',7'-diethyl-	EtOH	202(4.76),218(4.67), 292(3.71),302(3.74)	56-0403-79
	80% H_2SO_4	202(5.03),230(4.79), 268(5.09),288(3.88), 391(4.66),462(3.71)	56-0403-79
Spiro[isobenzofuran-1(3H),9'-[9H]xan-then]-3-one, 3',5'-diethyl-	EtOH	202(4.81),221(4.77), 285(3.79),294(3.79)	56-0403-79
	80% H_2SO_4	206(4.64),233(4.32), 265(4.62),391(4.76), 434s(--)	56-0403-79
Spiro[isobenzofuran-1(3H),9'-[9H]xan-then]-3-one, 3',6'-diethyl-	EtOH	202(4.78),221(4.76), 284(3.72),294(3.72)	56-0403-79
	80% H_2SO_4	202(4.84),229(4.68), 267(5.07),286(3.88), 397(4.58),445s(--)	56-0403-79
$C_{24}H_{20}O_4$			
[1]Benzopyrano[3,4-b][1]benzopyran,	EtOH	239(4.39),294(4.20),	138-1301-79

Compound	Solvent	λmax(log ε)	Ref.
6,6a-dihydro-6,6a-dimethoxy-6-phenyl-		332(4.39),350(4.32)	138-1301-79
2H-1-Benzopyran-2-acetic acid, 3,4-dihydro-4-oxo-α,α-diphenyl-, methyl ester	MeOH	224(4.1),248(3.9), 279(3.4),318(3.6)	24-1791-79
4H-1-Benzopyran-4-one, 2,3-dihydro-3-[[4-methoxy-3-(phenylmethoxy)phenyl]-methylene]-	EtOH	265(4.00),360(4.04)	150-1713-79
4H-1-Benzopyran-4-one, 2-[4-methoxy-3-(phenylmethoxy)phenyl]-3-methyl-	EtOH	218(4.11),228(4.23), 240(4.30),313(4.28)	150-1713-79
4H-1-Benzopyran-4-one, 3-[[4-methoxy-3-(phenylmethoxy)phenyl]methyl]-	EtOH	226(4.29),298(3.59)	150-1713-79
3-Phenanthrenecarboxylic acid, 1,9-dimethoxy-4-phenyl-, methyl ester	n.s.g.	224(4.62),261(4.59), 315(4.19),339(3.77)	33-0090-79
1H,3H-Pyrano[4,3-b][1]benzopyran-3-one, 4,4a,10,10a-tetrahydro-10-hydroxy-4,4-diphenyl-	MeOH	220(3.8),268(3.0)	24-1791-79
$C_{24}H_{20}O_5$			
1,3-Benzodioxole-5-propanoic acid, β-(2-oxo-2-phenylethyl)-α-phenyl-	EtOH	240(4.24),285(3.80)	94-2767-79
2H-1-Benzopyran-2-one, 3,4-dihydro-5,7-dihydroxy-8(or 6)-(1-oxo-3-phenylpropyl)-4-phenyl-	MeOH	236(4.25),284(4.19), 325s(3.77)	88-4269-79
7H-Oxireno[b][1]benzopyran-7-one, 1a,7a-dihydro-7a-[[4-methoxy-3-(phenylmethoxy)phenyl]methyl]-	MeOH	216(4.08),252(3.78), 280(3.31),310(3.27)	150-1713-79
3-Phenanthrenecarboxylic acid, 1,9-dimethoxy-4-(4-methoxyphenyl)-	n.s.g.	226(4.60),250(4.56), 316s(4.05),345(3.49)	33-0090-79
$C_{24}H_{20}O_8$			
4H-1-Benzopyran-4-one, 3,5,7-trihydroxy-2-[4,5-dimethoxy-3-(phenylmethoxy)phenyl]-	MeOH	250(3.99),300s(3.89), 365(3.99)	2-0168-79A
	MeOH-$AlCl_3$	255(--),268(--), 355(--)	2-0168-79A
$C_{24}H_{20}P$			
Phosphonium, tetraphenyl-	MeCN	226(4.63),262(3.90), 267(3.99),275(3.92), 345(2.04)	65-0275-79
	$C_2H_4Cl_2$	226s(4.64),262(3.90), 268(4.00),274(3.96), 345(2.00)	65-0275-79
chloride	MeCN	226s(4.59),262(3.54), 267(3.66),274(3.59)	65-0275-79
	$C_2H_4Cl_2$	227s(4.60),262(3.58), 269(3.70),276(3.63)	65-0275-79
$C_{24}H_{20}P_2$			
Diphosphine, tetraphenyl-	EtOH	222(4.42),260s(3.72)	22-0241-79I
$C_{24}H_{20}S_2$			
2,13-Dithia[3.3]azulenophane	CH_2Cl_2	271(4.73),299s(4.49), 365(3.86),630(2.70)	88-1055-79
$C_{24}H_{21}Cl_2N_3O_4S_2$			
Benzenesulfonamide, 4-chloro-N-[4-[[(4-chlorophenyl)sulfonyl]imino]-1,2,4,5-tetrahydro-5-methylpyrrolo-[3,2,1-hi]indol-5-yl]-N-methyl-	EtOH	226(4.60),272(4.23), 282(4.20),312(4.05)	39-2387-79C

Compound	Solvent	$\lambda_{max}(\log \epsilon)$	Ref.
$C_{24}H_{21}Cl_2N_7O_7$			
9H-Purine, 2,6-dichloro-9-[2,3,5-tri-O-acetyl-5-C-(1-phenyl-1H-1,2,3-triazol-4-yl)-β-D-xylofuranosyl]-	MeOH	245(4.12),268(4.03)	136-0141-79H
$C_{24}H_{21}FeO$			
Methylium, [1'-(hydroxyphenylmethyl)-ferrocenyl]phenyl-	$C_2H_4Cl_2$	255(3.56),336(3.49), 397s(2.98)	32-0013-79
$C_{24}H_{21}NO$			
2(1H)-Pyridinone, 3,4-dihydro-4-(4-methylphenyl)-3,6-diphenyl-	EtOH	248(4.15)	4-0001-79
$C_{24}H_{21}NO_2$			
2(1H)-Pyridinone, 3,4-dihydro-4-(4-methoxyphenyl)-3,6-diphenyl-	EtOH	249(4.18)	4-0001-79
$C_{24}H_{21}NO_4$			
Benzoic acid, 2-[6-(diethylamino)-3-oxo-3H-xanthen-9-yl]- (chromogen red B)	MeOH-NaOH	517(4.59)	151-0467-79A
$C_{24}H_{21}NO_4S$			
Benzene, 4-[2-isocyano-2-[(4-methylphenyl)sulfonyl]ethenyl]-1-methoxy-2-(phenylmethoxy)-	EtOH	248(4.12),320(4.03), 345(4.26)	39-0662-79C
Benzenesulfonamide, N-[2-[(1,3-dihydro-1-oxo-2H-inden-2-ylidene)hydroxymethyl]phenyl]-N,4-dimethyl-	MeOH	203(4.58),230(4.21), 330(4.14)	83-0254-79
$C_{24}H_{21}NO_5S$			
Benzenesulfonamide, N-ethyl-N-[2-[(3-hydroxy-2-benzofuranyl)carbonyl]-phenyl]-4-methyl-	MeOH	203(4.64),233(4.35), 317(4.14)	83-0254-79
$C_{24}H_{21}NO_8$			
Indolo[2,1-a]isoquinoline-2,3,9,10-tetrol, 5,6-dihydro-, tetraacetate	EtOH	255(4.44),258(4.27), 331(4.45)	142-1413-79
$C_{24}H_{21}N_3OS$			
2H-1,4-Thiazino[2,3-b]quinoxalin-3-ol, 3,4-dihydro-7,8-dimethyl-2,3-diphenyl-	EtOH	377(4.2)	103-0102-79
	dioxan	370(4.3),385s(4.2)	103-0102-79
$C_{24}H_{21}N_3O_3$			
Carbamic acid, [3-[[(4-methylphenyl)amino]carbonyl]-1H-indol-2-yl]-, phenylmethyl ester	$CHCl_3$	282(4.36),300s(4.26), 357(2.65),375(2.59)	103-0179-79
4,8-Etheno-3H-pyrazolo[1,5-c][1,3]diazepine-7(8H)-carboxylic acid, 3a,4-dihydro-3-oxo-2,3a-diphenyl-, ethyl ester, (3aα,4β,8β)-	benzene	400(3.60)	142-0453-79
$C_{24}H_{21}N_3O_3S$			
Carbamic acid, [3-[[(4-methoxyphenyl)-amino]thioxomethyl]-1H-indol-2-yl]-, phenylmethyl ester	$CHCl_3$	265(4.34),287(4.36), 352(4.27)	103-0179-79
$C_{24}H_{21}N_3O_7$			
Carbamic acid, [2-[(2,5-dioxo-1-pyrrolidinyl)oxy]-1-[(1-formyl-1H-indol-3-	MeOH-HCl	299(3.65)	63-0013-79

Compound	Solvent	λ_{max}(log ε)	Ref.
yl)methyl]-2-oxoethyl]-, phenylmethyl ester, (S)- (cont.)			63-0013-79
$C_{24}H_{21}N_4S$			
Benzothiazolium, 2-[3-[3-(1H-benzimidazol-2-yl)-1-methyl-4(1H)-pyridinylidene]-1-propenyl]-3-methyl-, iodide	EtOH	564(4.84)	4-1583-79
Benzothiazolium, 2-[3-[4-(1H-benzimidazol-2-yl)-1-methyl-2(1H)-pyridinylidene]-1-propenyl]-3-methyl-, iodide	EtOH	558(4.85)	4-1583-79
Benzothiazolium, 2-[3-[5-(1H-benzimidazol-2-yl)-1-methyl-2(1H)-pyridinylidene]-1-propenyl]-3-methyl-, iodide	EtOH	559(5.03)	4-1583-79
$C_{24}H_{21}N_5O_5$			
Adenosine, N-benzoyl-2'-deoxy-, 3'-benzoate	EtOH	280(4.35)	54-0537-79
$C_{24}H_{21}N_5O_6$			
Adenosine, 3',5'-dibenzoate	EtOH	246(4.13)	39-2088-79C
9H-Purin-6-amine, 9-(2,3-di-O-benzoyl-β-D-arabinofuranosyl)-	MeOH	232(4.50),259(4.20)	87-0273-79
$C_{24}H_{21}O_6P$			
Benzoic acid, 4,4',4"-phosphinidynetris-, trimethyl ester	12M HCl	242(4.66),285(3.79)	65-0479-79
	MeCN	231(4.56),290(4.31)	65-0479-79
$C_{24}H_{22}$			
Cyclopropene, 3-methyl-1,2-diphenyl-2-(2-phenylethyl)-	EtOH	227(4.24),238(4.12), 312(4.32),321(4.40), 338(4.28)	35-5743-79
$C_{24}H_{22}CuN_4$			
Copper, [11,12,13,14-tetrahydro-2,3-dimethyltribenzo[b,f,l][1,4,8,11]tetraazacyclotetradecinato(2-)-N^5,N^{11},N^{14}-N^{20}]-, (SP-4-2)-	$CHCl_3$	267(4.57),288(4.54), 296(4.52),338(4.34), 356(4.33),426(4.18)	12-2303-79
$C_{24}H_{22}N_2O_4$			
2H-1-Benzopyran-2-acetamide, 3,4-dihydro-3-(hydroxymethylene)-4-oxo-α,α-diphenyl-, monoammonium salt	MeOH	217(4.4),313(3.9), 357(3.9)	24-1791-79
$C_{24}H_{22}N_2O_9$			
1H-Benz[f]indazole-3-carboxylic acid, 1-(4,6-di-O-acetyl-2,3-dideoxy-α-D-erythro-hex-2-enopyranosyl)-4,9-dihydro-4,9-dioxo-, ethyl ester	EtOH	245(4.53),263(4.25)	111-0151-79
D-ribo-Hex-1-enitol, 1,5-anhydro-2,3-dideoxy-3-[3-(ethoxycarbonyl)-4,9-dihydro-4,9-dioxo-1H-benz[f]indazol-1-yl]-, 4,6-diacetate	EtOH	248(4.50),266(4.24)	111-0151-79
$C_{24}H_{22}N_4Ni$			
Nickel, [11,12,13,14-tetrahydro-2,3-dimethyltribenzo[b,f,l][1,4,8,11]tetraazacyclotetradecinato(2-)-N^5,N^{11},N^{14}-N^{20}]-, (SP-4-2)-	$CHCl_3$	290(4.48),390(4.28), 412(4.30),645(3.40)	12-2303-79
Nickel, [12,13,14,15-tetrahydro-2-methyl-11H-tribenzo[b,f,m][1,4,8,12]tetra-	$CHCl_3$	263(4.42),295(4.35), 307(4.32),370(4.15)	12-2303-79

Compound	Solvent	λ_{max}(log ε)	Ref.
azacyclopentadecinato(2-)-N^5,N^{11},N^{15}-N^{21}]-, (SP-4-4)- (cont.)			12-2303-79
$C_{24}H_{22}N_4O_5S$			
D-Arabinitol, 1,4-anhydro-1-C-[8-[(phenylmethyl)thio]-1,2,4-triazolo[4,3-a]pyrazin-3-yl]-, 5-benzoate, (R)-	EtOH	260(4.08),313(4.00)	111-0375-79
D-Ribitol, 1,4-anhydro-1-C-[8-[(phenylmethyl)thio]-1,2,4-triazolo[4,3-a]-pyrazin-3-yl]-, 5-benzoate, (S)-	EtOH	258(4.01),312(4.00)	44-1028-79
$C_{24}H_{22}O$			
Anthracene, 9-[(1-methylethoxy)phenylmethyl]-	n.s.g.	332(3.51),351(3.80), 368(3.94),387(3.89)	39-2948-79C
Anthracene, 9-(1-methylethoxy)-10-(phenylmethyl)-	n.s.g.	351(3.58),365(3.82), 383(3.96),404(3.91)	39-2948-79C
11H-Benzo[a]fluoren-11-one, 6b,7,8,9-10,10a-hexahydro-10a-(phenylmethyl)-	EtOH	233(4.65),300s(3.87), 310(3.98),333s(3.73)	78-1167-79
Furan, 2,5-dihydro-2,2-dimethyl-3,5,5-triphenyl-	MeOH	253(4.27)	44-4021-79
Furan, 2,5-dihydro-5,5-dimethyl-2,2,3-triphenyl-	MeOH	250(3.99)	44-4021-79
Methanone, [9-(1,1-dimethylethyl)-9H-fluoren-9-yl]phenyl-	EtOH	258(4.27),289s(3.77), 302(3.60)	118-0616-79
Pentaleno[2,1-a]naphthalen-10(6bH)-one, 7,8,9,9a-tetrahydro-6b-methyl-9a-(phenylmethyl)-	EtOH	233(4.36),296s(3.83), 309(3.94),316s(3.85), 333s(3.69)	78-1167-79
$C_{24}H_{22}O_2$			
Anthracene, 9-[ethoxy(4-methoxyphenyl)-methyl]-	EtOH	256(5.03),315s(3.42), 333(3.68),348(3.81), 366(3.97),386(3.94)	44-3687-79
Furan, 2,5-dihydro-2-methoxy-2-methyl-3,5,5-triphenyl-	MeOH	252(4.33)	44-4021-79
$C_{24}H_{22}O_3$			
Benzoic acid, 2-(2,6-diethyl-9H-xanthen-9-yl)-	EtOH	204(4.76),288(3.56)	56-0403-79
Benzoic acid, 2-(2,7-diethyl-9H-xanthen-9-yl)-	EtOH	202(4.81),253(4.06), 290(3.64)	56-0403-79
Benzoic acid, 2-(3,5-diethyl-9H-xanthen-9-yl)-	EtOH	203(3.75),284(3.65)	56-0403-79
Benzoic acid, 2-(3,6-diethyl-9H-xanthen-9-yl)-	EtOH	210(4.76),284(3.54)	56-0403-79
Butanoic acid, 4-benzoyl-3-(4-methylphenyl)-2-phenyl-	EtOH	242(4.21),275s(3.60)	4-0001-79
2,3,5-Trioxabicyclo[2.2.1]heptane, 6,6-dimethyl-1,4,7-triphenyl-	MeOH	250(3.30)	44-4021-79
$C_{24}H_{22}O_4$			
Benzenepentanoic acid, β-(4-methoxyphenyl)-δ-oxo-α-phenyl-	EtOH	242(4.09)	4-0001-79
$C_{24}H_{23}BrN_4O_7$			
1H-Pyrazole-4,5-dione, 1-(4-bromophenyl)-3-(1,2,3-triacetoxypropyl)-, 4-(phenylhydrazone), [S-(R*,R*)]-	n.s.g.	209(3.96),255(4.00), 396(4.02)	106-0531-79
$C_{24}H_{23}ClN_4O_7$			
1H-Pyrazole-4,5-dione, 1-(4-chlorophen-	n.s.g.	208(3.90),252(4.11),	106-0531-79

Compound	Solvent	λ_{max}(log ε)	Ref.
yl)-3-(1,2,3-triacetoxypropyl)-, 4-(phenylhydrazone), [S-(R*,R*)]-		400(4.20)	106-0531-79
$C_{24}H_{23}F_3N_2O_4S_2$			
2H-1,3-Thiazine-2-carbothioic acid, tetrahydro-6,6-dimethyl-4-oxo-3-(phenylacetyl)-5-[(trifluoroacetyl)-amino]-, S-(phenylmethyl) ester, (2S-trans)-	EtOH-ether	218(4.17),237s(3.88)	39-0170-79C
$C_{24}H_{23}N$			
Benzenamine, N-(2,7-dimethyl-9H-fluoren-9-ylidene)-2,4,6-trimethyl-	dioxan	254(4.69),264(4.77), 296(4.05),306s(3.95), 409(3.01)	24-3490-79
$C_{24}H_{23}NO$			
4-Piperidinone, 1-methyl-2,3,6-triphenyl-	EtOH	248-266(2.8-29)	103-0899-79
$C_{24}H_{23}NO_2$			
9H-Cyclopenta[a]fluoranthen-9-one, 8-[(1,1-dimethylethyl)amino]-10,11-dihydro-11-hydroxy-11-methyl-	CH_2Cl_2	244(4.68),280(4.44), 298(4.29),321s(4.07), 360(4.11),377(4.12), 384(4.05),442(3.85), 470s(3.76)	24-3166-79
1H-Indene-1,3(2H)-dione, 2-(2-butyl-1,3-dimethyl-6H-cyclohepta[c]pyrrol-6-ylidene)-	$CHCl_3$	248(4.36),276(4.28), 308(4.29),474s(4.63), 506(4.73)	83-0120-79
$C_{24}H_{23}NO_4$			
Butanedioic acid, [(1,1-dimethylethyl)-carbonimidoyl]-9H-fluoren-9-ylidene-, dimethyl ester	CH_2Cl_2	244(4.45),255s(4.49), 264(4.57),303(3.88), 319(3.81),372(3.91)	89-0067-79
1,2-Fluoranthenedicarboxylic acid, 3-[(1,1-dimethylethyl)amino]-, dimethyl ester	CH_2Cl_2	240(4.58),276(4.47), 310(3.92),381(3.94)	24-3166-79
L-Phenylalanine, N-[(phenylmethoxy)-carbonyl]-, phenylmethyl ester	EtOH	243(2.34),248(2.48), 253(2.62),259(2.73), 262(2.61),265(2.65), 288(2.44)	118-0957-79
$C_{24}H_{23}NO_4S$			
Benzene, 4-[2-isocyano-2-[(4-methyl-phenyl)sulfonyl]ethyl]-1-methoxy-2-(phenylmethoxy)-	EtOH	227(4.21),274(3.38)	39-0662-79C
$C_{24}H_{23}NO_5S$			
Benzenesulfonamide, N-ethyl-N-[2-[3-(2-hydroxyphenyl)-1,3-dioxopropyl]phenyl]-4-methyl-	MeOH	203(4.69),359(4.27)	83-0248-79
Formamide, N-[2-[4-methoxy-3-(phenyl-methoxy)phenyl]-1-[(4-methylphenyl)-sulfonyl]ethenyl]-	EtOH	208(4.54),234(4.41), 294(4.27),321(4.38)	39-0662-79C
$C_{24}H_{23}NO_7S$			
Semiglycinecresol Red	neutral	442(4.43)	86-0479-79
	anion	442(4.43)	86-0479-79
	dianion	578(4.81)	86-0479-79
	trianion	582(4.83)	86-0479-79
	cation	518(4.62)	86-0479-79
	dication	518(4.83)	86-0479-79

Compound	Solvent	λ max(log ε)	Ref.
$C_{24}H_{23}NO_9$			
Cyclobuta[4,5]pyrrolo[1,2-a]quinoline-7a,8,9,9a-tetracarboxylic acid, 7-acetyl-8,9-dihydro-, tetramethyl ester, (7aα,8α,9β,9aα)-	MeOH	224(4.43),282(4.12), 300(4.16),314(4.28), 332s(4.24),412(3.91), 430(4.08),460(4.09), 492s(3.93)	39-2171-79C
	MeOH-HClO₄	227(4.53),293(4.50), 410(4.52)	39-2171-79C
$C_{24}H_{23}N_3O$			
Benzeneacetamide, N-[4,5-dihydro-1-(phenylmethyl)-1H-pyrazol-3-yl]-α-phenyl-	EtOH	270(4.05)	150-0801-79
$C_{24}H_{23}N_3O_8$			
Phenol, 2,2'-[(acetoxyimino)bis(4,5-dihydro-5,3-isoxazolediyl)]bis-, diacetate	EtOH	210(4.56),256(4.49)	56-0229-79
$C_{24}H_{23}N_5O_7$			
1,7-Cycloerythrinan-2,8-dione, 15,16-dimethoxy-, 2-(2,4-dinitrophenylhydrazone), (±)-	MeOH	361(4.20)	24-1110-79
$C_{24}H_{23}N_5O_9$			
1H-Pyrazole-4,5-dione, 1-(4-nitrophenyl)-3-(1,2,3-triacetoxypropyl)-, 4-(phenylhydrazone), [S-(R*,R*)]-	n.s.g.	230(3.89),390(4.23)	106-0531-79
$C_{24}H_{23}O_3P$			
6-Phosphanthridineacetic acid, 5,6-dihydro-5-methyl-6-phenyl-, ethyl ester, 5-oxide	EtOH	218(4.52),230s(4.23), 272(3.91),286s(3.73)	39-1499-79C
$C_{24}H_{24}$			
[2.2.2.2.2.2](1,2,3,4,5,6)Cyclophane	CH_2Cl_2	296(2.62),306s(2.60), 311s(2.51)	35-3126-79
1-Hexene, 1,3,5-triphenyl-	EtOH	255(3.56),285(2.65), 293(2.30)	126-2979-79
$C_{24}H_{24}Br_2O_4S_3$			
Benzene, 1,1'-[thiobis(3,4-dimethyl-1,3-butadiene-4,1-diyl)sulfonyl]]-bis[4-bromo-	n.s.g.	245(4.52),350(4.39)	104-2018-79
$C_{24}H_{24}Cl_2O_4S_3$			
Benzene, 1,1'-[thiobis[(3,4-dimethyl-1,3-butadiene-4,1-diyl)sulfonyl]]-bis[4-chloro-	n.s.g.	256(4.83),352(4.69)	104-2018-79
$C_{24}H_{24}N$			
9-Anthracenaminium, 9,10-dihydro-N,N,N-trimethyl-10-(phenylmethylene)-, chloride	n.s.g.	323(4.11)	39-2948-79C
$C_{24}H_{24}N_2O$			
2-Buten-1-one, 1,3-bis(1,3-dimethyl-1H-indol-2-yl)-, trans	EtOH	226(4.61),328(4.11)	39-2154-79C
$C_{24}H_{24}N_2O_5$			
1-Azabicyclo[4.2.0]oct-2-ene-2-carbox-	EtOH	269(4.11)	23-0227-79

Compound	Solvent	λ_{max}(log ε)	Ref.
ylic acid, 3-methyl-8-oxo-7-[(phenoxyacetyl)amino]-, phenylmethyl ester, trans (cont.)	EtOH	269(4.11)	23-0227-79
$C_{24}H_{24}N_2O_8S_3$			
Benzene, 1,1'-[thiobis[(3,4-dimethyl-1,3-butadiene-4,1-diyl)sulfonyl]]-bis[4-nitro-	n.s.g.	250(4.49),350(4.33)	104-2018-79
$C_{24}H_{24}N_2O_{13}$			
2,6-Pyridinedicarboxylic acid, 4-[2-[2-carboxy-5-(β-D-glucopyranosyloxy)-2,3-dihydro-6-hydroxy-1H-indol-1-yl]ethenyl]-, [S-(E)]-	H_2O	469(4.26)	33-1330-79
	MeOH	472(4.20)	33-1330-79
	MeOH-acid	500(4.27)	33-1330-79
$C_{24}H_{24}N_4$			
Pyrido[1,2-a]indole, 10,10'-azobis-[1,2,3,4-tetrahydro-	EtOH	260(4.22),468s(4.35), 504(4.35)	23-0558-79
$C_{24}H_{24}O_2$			
1-Isobenzofuranol, 1-[1,1'-biphenyl]-4-yl-3,3-diethyl-1,3-dihydro-, cation	50% H_2SO_4	407(4.56)	104-1126-79
$C_{24}H_{24}O_4$			
3-Cyclohexene-1-carboxylic acid, 4-[2-(4-methoxyphenyl)ethenyl]-2-oxo-6-phenyl-, ethyl ester	EtOH	251(4.20),351(4.23)	104-1059-79
	isooctane	244(--),343(--)	104-1059-79
$C_{24}H_{24}O_6$			
Cyclobuta[1,2-a:3,4-a']diindene-5,10-dione, 4b,4c,9b,9c-tetrahydro-2,3,7,8-tetramethoxy-4c,9c-dimethyl-, endo	$C_2H_4Cl_2$	231(4.52),270(4.30), 307(4.22)	44-1388-79
exo	$C_2H_4Cl_2$	236(4.60),270(4.33), 310(4.27)	44-1388-79
Cyclobuta[1,2-a:3,4-a']diindene-5,10-dione, 4b,4c,9b,9c-tetrahydro-2,4,7,9-tetramethoxy-4c,9c-dimethyl-, endo	$C_2H_4Cl_2$	266(3.93),330(3.60)	44-1388-79
exo	$C_2H_4Cl_2$	234(4.61),264(4.19), 327(3.83)	44-1388-79
$C_{24}H_{24}O_8$			
2,7-Anthracenedibutanoic acid, 9,10-dihydro-1,8-dihydroxy-9,10-dioxo-, dimethyl ester	MeOH	205(4.42),230(4.67), 260(4.48),292(4.02), 439(4.10)	5-0019-79
1,3-Dioxolane-2-butanoic acid, α-(9,10-dihydro-1,4-dihydroxy-3-methyl-9,10-dioxo-2-anthracenyl)-2-methyl-, methyl ester	MeOH	228s(--),251(4.68), 256(4.68),290(4.03), 457s(--),485(4.08), 518s(--)	5-0035-79
$C_{24}H_{24}O_{12}$			
β-D-Glucopyranosiduronic acid, 5-hydroxy-6-methoxy-2-(4-methoxyphenyl)-4-oxo-4H-1-benzopyran-7-yl, methyl ester	MeOH	276(4.15),328(4.27)	94-1252-79
	MeOH-NaOAc	276(4.15),328(4.28)	94-1252-79
	MeOH-$AlCl_3$	259s(3.87),286s(3.90), 298(4.19),344(4.24)	94-1252-79
$C_{24}H_{25}N$			
1H-3-Benzazepine, 2,3,4,5-tetrahydro-2,2-dimethyl-1,5-diphenyl-	EtOH	256(2.87),270(2.68)	4-1525-79

Compound	Solvent	$\lambda_{max}(\log \epsilon)$	Ref.
$C_{24}H_{25}NO$			
2-Azatetracyclo[6.3.1.1^{6,10}.0^{2,5}]tri-decan-3-one, 4,4-diphenyl-	MeOH	250(3.48)	44-3711-79
Benzenamine, 4-[4-[2-(4-methoxyphenyl)-ethenyl]-1,3,5-cycloheptatrien-1-yl]-N,N-dimethyl-	EtOH	386(4.615)	78-2269-79
$C_{24}H_{25}NO_4$			
2,3-Naphthalenedicarboxylic acid, 1-[(1,1-dimethylethyl)amino]-4-phen-yl-, dimethyl ester	CH_2Cl_2	239(4.64),264s(4.34), 321(3.89),349s(3.74)	24-3166-79
$C_{24}H_{25}NO_{12}S$			
Cyclobuta[b]azocine-1',2',3,4,7,8-hexa-carboxylic acid, 1,6,6a,8a-tetrahy-dro-1-methyl-6-(2-thioxoethylidene)-, hexamethyl ester	EtOH	220(4.54),298(3.80)	94-2879-79
$C_{24}H_{25}N_3O_{10}$			
1-Azetidineacetic acid, 3-[[[4-(3-ami-no-3-carboxypropoxy)phenyl]oxoacet-yl]amino]-2-(hydroxymethyl)-α-(4-hy-droxyphenyl)-4-oxo-	$EtOH-H_2O$	226(4.27),299(4.20)	23-1932-79
$C_{24}H_{25}N_5O_4$			
Adenosine, N,N-bis(phenylmethyl)-	EtOH	278(4.31)	44-3652-79
$C_{24}H_{26}Br_2$			
Benzene, 1,1'-[1,4-bis(1,1-dimethyleth-yl)-1,2,3-butatriene-1,4-diyl]bis[4-bromo-, (E)-	C_6H_{12}	332(4.38)	24-0567-79
(Z)-	C_6H_{12}	262(4.30),340(4.27)	24-0567-79
$C_{24}H_{26}N_2$			
1,4:5,16-Diethenobenzocyclotetradecene-2,3-dicarbonitrile, 1,4,6,7,8,9,10-11,12,13,14,15-dodecahydro-	EtOH	217(4.29),235s(3.79), 245s(3.68),270s(2.95), 320(2.88)	35-6660-79
Quinolinium, 1,1'-(1,2-ethanediyl)bis-[4,6-dimethyl-, salt with 4-methyl-benzenesulfonic acid (1:2)	EtOH	238(4.54),316(4.05)	104-0566-79
$C_{24}H_{26}N_2O$			
Cinnoline, 4-ethoxy-3-ethyl-1,2,3,4-tetrahydro-1,2-diphenyl-	MeCN	246(3.98),289(3.92)	104-2145-79
$C_{24}H_{26}N_2O_2$			
Quinolinium, 1,1'-(1,2-ethanediyl)bis-[6-methoxy-4-methyl-, salt with 4-methylbenzenesulfonic acid (1:2)	EtOH	241(4.38),313(4.04)	104-0566-79
$C_{24}H_{26}N_2O_3$			
1-Propanone, 1,1'-[azoxybis(4-cyclopro-pyl-2,1-phenylene)]bis-	EtOH	325(3.80)	104-0847-79
$C_{24}H_{26}N_6O_4$			
3H-Purine-3-butanoic acid, α-(1,3-di-hydro-1,3-dioxo-2H-isoindol-2-yl)-6-[(3-methyl-2-butenyl)amino]-, ethyl ester	MeOH	292(4.19)	24-3072-79

Compound	Solvent	$\lambda_{max}(\log \epsilon)$	Ref.
$C_{24}H_{26}O_2$			
3,11:4,10-Dimetheno-1H-cyclohepta[1,2-4,5]dicyclooctene-14-carboxylic acid, 2,5,6,7,8,9,12,13-octahydro-, ethyl ester	EtOH	293(3.97)	35-2128-79
1-Isobenzofuranol, 1,3-dihydro-3,3-bis(1-methylethyl)-1-(1-naphthalenyl)-	50% H_2SO_4	423(4.19)	104-1126-79
1-Isobenzofuranol, 1,3-dihydro-3,3-bis(1-methylethyl)-1-(2-naphthalenyl)-	50% H_2SO_4	373(4.51)	104-1126-79
$C_{24}H_{26}O_2PS$			
Phosphonium, triphenyl-, 1-(dimethylsulfonio)-2-ethoxy-2-oxoethylide, tetrafluoroborate	EtOH	228s(4.51)	104-2169-79
$C_{24}H_{26}O_4S_3$			
Benzene, 1,1'-[thiobis[(3,4-dimethyl-1,3-butadiene-4,1-diyl)sulfonyl]]bis-	n.s.g.	260(4.79),350(4.69)	104-2018-79
$C_{24}H_{26}O_5$			
9(10H)-Anthracenone, 1,8-diacetoxy-10,10-dipropyl-	MeOH	212(4.36),245s(3.89), 273(4.20),310s(3.61)	145-1083-79
$C_{24}H_{26}O_6$			
4H-1-Benzopyran-4-one, 3-(2,4-dimethoxyphenyl)-5,7-dimethoxy-8-(3-methyl-2-butenyl)-	MeOH	264(4.65)	39-0279-79C
$C_{24}H_{26}O_8$			
Butanedioic acid, bis[(3,4-dimethoxyphenyl)methylene]-, dimethyl ester, (E,E)-	EtOH	236(4.29),324(4.43)	2-0202-79
Butanedioic acid, bis[(3,5-dimethoxyphenyl)methylene]-, dimethyl ester, (E,E)-	EtOH	225(4.51),239(4.39)	2-0202-79
2,3-Naphthalenedicarboxylic acid, 1-(3,4-dimethoxyphenyl)-1,2-dihydro-6,7-dimethoxy-, dimethyl ester, trans	EtOH	244(4.32),336(4.15)	2-0202-79
2,3-Naphthalenedicarboxylic acid, 1-(3,5-dimethoxyphenyl)-1,2-dihydro-6,8-dimethoxy-, dimethyl ester	EtOH	242(4.35),295(4.23)	2-0202-79
$C_{24}H_{26}O_{10}$			
9,10-Anthracenedione, 2-[3-acetoxy-1-(dimethoxymethyl)propyl]-1,8-dihydroxy-3,6-dimethoxy-	MeOH	224(4.64),254(4.22), 266(4.34),285(4.53), 322(3.97),447(4.03)	39-0451-79C
$C_{24}H_{26}O_{12}$			
1(9bH)-Dibenzofuranone, 2,6-diacetyl-7-(β-D-glucopyranosyloxy)-3,9-dihydroxy-8,9b-dimethyl-	MeOH	269(4.41)	87-1380-79
$C_{24}H_{26}O_{14}$			
Bergenin pentaacetate	EtOH	210(4.35),255(3.98)	39-2289-79C
$C_{24}H_{27}IN_2O_4$			
L-Tryptophan, N-[(phenylmethoxy)carbonyl]-, 5-iodopentyl ester	EtOH	275(3.74),282(3.78), 291(3.72)	118-0957-79
$C_{24}H_{27}NO$			
Benzenemethanol, α-[1-[(2,2-diphenyl-	EtOH	251(2.69),257(2.75),	4-1525-79

Compound	Solvent	$\lambda_{max}(\log \epsilon)$	Ref.
ethyl)amino]-1-methylethyl]-, hydrochloride (cont.)		264s(2.64)	4-1525-79
$C_{24}H_{27}NO_4$			
1H-Pyrrole-3-carboxylic acid, 2,5-dihydro-2-hydroxy-2-(1-methylethyl)-5-oxo-1,4-bis(phenylmethyl)-, ethyl ester	EtOH	214(4.06)	44-0808-79
$C_{24}H_{27}NO_8$			
Isoquinolinium, 2-[3-ethoxy-2-(ethoxycarbonyl)-1-[2-ethoxy-1-(ethoxycarbonyl)-2-oxoethyl]-3-oxo-1-propenyl]-, hydroxide, inner salt	$CHCl_3$	319(3.6),368(3.4), 495(2.4)	5-1406-79
Quinolinium, 1-[3-ethoxy-2-(ethoxycarbonyl)-1-[2-ethoxy-1-(ethoxycarbonyl)-2-oxoethyl]-3-oxo-1-propenyl]-, hydroxide, inner salt	$CHCl_3$	314(3.5),385(2.1), 504(1.5)	5-1406-79
$C_{24}H_{27}NO_9$			
2-Naphthacenecarboxylic acid, 4-(dimethylamino)-1,4,4a,5,5a,6,11,12a-octahydro-3,5,10,12,12a-pentahydroxy-6-methyl-1,11-dioxo-, ethyl ester	MeOH	265(4.25),360(4.13)	88-2701-79
$C_{24}H_{27}NO_{11}$			
1,3(2H,9bH)-Dibenzofurandione, 6-acetyl-2-(1-aminoethylidene)-7-(β-D-glucopyranosyloxy)-9-hydroxy-8,9b-dimethyl-	MeOH	224(4.32),284(4.30)	87-1380-79
$C_{24}H_{27}N_2O$			
Methylium, bis[4-(dimethylamino)phenyl](4-methoxyphenyl)-, perchlorate	EtOH	238(4.01),294(4.09), 332(3.66),465(4.46), 610(4.98)	65-0860-79
	acetone	462(4.51),610(5.02)	65-0860-79
$C_{24}H_{27}N_3$			
5,9:7,11-Dimethano-1H-1,2,4-triazolo-[4,3-a]azonine, 5,6,7,8,9,10,11,11a-octahydro-11a-methyl-1,3-diphenyl-	MeOH	227(4.07),270(3.86), 347(3.88)	44-3711-79
$C_{24}H_{27}N_5O_8S$			
Guanosine, N-[[(4-methylphenyl)thio]-methyl]-, 2',3',5'-triacetate	EtOH	258(4.30),274s(4.16)	130-0339-79
$C_{24}H_{27}N_7$			
1H-Pyrazole-3-acetonitrile, 4-cyano-1-phenyl-α-(1-piperidinylmethylene)-5-[(1-piperidinylmethylene)amino]-	MeOH	233(4.32),303(4.53)	83-0535-79
$C_{24}H_{27}N_7O_9S_2$			
L-Aspartic acid, 4-[[[[7-[(hydroxyphenylacetyl)amino]-3-[[(1-methyl-1H-tetrazol-5-yl)thio]methyl]-8-oxo-5-thia-1-azabicyclo[4.2.0]oct-2-en-2-yl]carbonyl]oxy]methyl]-, 1-methyl ester, hydrochloride	MeOH	273(3.94)	87-0657-79
$C_{24}H_{27}O_3S$			
Sulfonium, tris(4-hydroxy-3,5-dimethyl-	MeOH	232(3.49),277(4.40)	47-0977-79

Compound	Solvent	λmax(log ε)	Ref.
phenyl)-, tetrafluoroborate (cont.)			47-0977-79
$C_{24}H_{28}$			
Biphenylene, dodecahydro-4a,4b-diphenyl-	hexane	220s(4.11),260(2.66)	35-6383-79
$C_{24}H_{28}N_2O$			
Acridine, 9,10-dihydro-10-methyl-9-[2-(4-morpholinyl)-2-cyclohexen-1-yl]-	EtOH	283(4.06)	103-0541-79
$C_{24}H_{28}N_2O_8$			
4,4'-Bipyridinium, bis[2-ethoxy-1-(ethoxycarbonyl)-2-oxoethylide]	MeCN	250(3.76),560(3.23)	5-0727-79
$C_{24}H_{28}N_2P$			
3H-Indolium, 2-[[[(1,3-dihydro-1,3,3-trimethyl-2H-indol-2-ylidene)methyl]phosphinidene]methyl]-1,3,3-trimethyl-, tetrafluoroborate	$CHCl_3$	585(4.81)	88-0225-79
$C_{24}H_{28}N_2S$			
6H,8H-Pyrimido[2,1-a:4,3-a']diisoquinoline-6-thione, 5,5-diethyl-4b,5,9-13b,15,16-hexahydro-	$CHCl_3$	289(4.11),362(1.76)	5-1702-79
$C_{24}H_{28}N_2S_2$			
1H-Indole, 2,2'-dithiobis[1-methyl-3-propyl-	MeOH	230(3.05),310(1.7)	103-0282-79
$C_{24}H_{28}N_3$			
3H-Indolium, 2-[[[(1,3-dihydro-1,3,3-trimethyl-2H-indol-2-ylidene)methyl]imino]methyl]-1,3,3-trimethyl-, (E,E)-, tetrafluoroborate	$CHCl_3$	603(5.06)	88-0225-79
$C_{24}H_{28}N_6$			
1,4-Benzenediacetonitrile, α,α'-bis-[[(1-piperidinylmethylene)amino]-methylene]-	MeOH	255(4.50),315(4.63), 380(4.90)	83-0535-79
$C_{24}H_{28}O_2$			
1,3-Benzenediol, 2-(3,7-dimethyl-2,6-octadienyl)-5-(2-phenylethenyl)-, (E,E)- (amorphastilbol)	EtOH and EtOH-HCl	238(4.19),316(4.46)	100-0463-79
	EtOH-NaOH	230(4.15),262(4.11), 322(4.25)	100-0463-79
$C_{24}H_{28}O_3$			
3,4(2H,5H)-Furandione, 2,5-bis(1,1-dimethylethyl)-2,5-diphenyl-	C_6H_{12}	528(2.08),540s(2.05), 562s(1.93),572s(1.81)	19-0665-79
	EtOH	249(3.37),280(3.24), 527(2.14),540s(2.10), 562s(1.96)	19-0665-79
	EtOH-55% H_2O	252(3.20),287(3.19), 524(2.16)	19-0665-79
A-Norestr-1(10)-en-2-one, 17β-(benzoyloxy)-	n.s.g.	232(4.52)	22-0157-79
A-Nor-3-oxaestra-1,5(10)-dien-17β-ol, 2-methyl-, benzoate	n.s.g.	212(4.31),222s(4.34), 231(4.39),266s(3.67), 279s(2.92)	22-0157-79
$C_{24}H_{28}O_4$			
Benzene, 4-[2-[2-(3,4-dimethoxyphenyl)-	MeOH	229(4.44),278(4.28),	12-0071-79

Compound	Solvent	λ max (log ε)	Ref.
3-cyclohexen-1-yl]ethenyl]-1,2-dimethoxy-, cis (cont.)		315s(3.78)	12-0071-79
7H-Benz[e]inden-7-one, 3-(benzoyloxy)-1,2,3,3a,4,5,8,9,9a,9b-decahydro-3a-methyl-6-(2-oxopropyl)-, [3S-(3α,3aα,9aα,9bβ)]-	n.s.g.	236(4.35)	22-0157-79
Ferukrin	EtOH	215(4.17),242s(3.44), 252s(3.20),326(4.13)	105-0195-79
$C_{24}H_{28}O_6$			
1H-Phenaleno[1,2-b]furan-1-one, 6-ethoxy-8,9-dihydro-2,3,7-trimethoxy-4,8,8,9-tetramethyl-	EtOH	217(4.64),245(4.29), 259s(4.22),274s(4.11), 283(4.18),292(4.21), 368(4.20),426(4.08)	150-0301-79
1H-Phenalen-1-one, 2-(1,1-dimethyl-2-propenyl)-4-ethoxy-9-hydroxy-3,7,8-trimethoxy-6-methyl-	EtOH	219(4.68),254(4.37), 268s(4.32),381(4.26), 398(4.25),415(4.33)	150-0301-79
$C_{24}H_{28}O_9$			
Eupachifolin B monoacetate	MeOH	205(3.92)	138-1473-79
$C_{24}H_{28}O_{10}$			
1,4-Benzenediol, 5-(3,4-dihydro-6,7,8-trimethoxy-2H-1-benzopyran-3-yl)-2,3-dimethoxy-, diacetate, (S)-	EtOH	285(3.42)	32-0009-79
$C_{24}H_{28}O_{13}$			
Verminoside	MeOH	215(3.93),245s(3.81), 295(3.90),328(4.02)	33-0535-79
$C_{24}H_{29}ClO_{14}$			
1,4-(Epoxymethano)-1H,3H-pyrano[3,4-c]-pyran-8(4H)-one, 3-(chloromethyl)-5,6-dihydro-9-[(2,3,4,6-tetra-O-acetyl-β-D-glucopyranosyl)oxy]-	MeOH	226.5(3.70)	102-1981-79
1,4-(Epoxymethano)-1H,8H-pyrano[3,4-c]-pyran-8-one, 3-(chloromethyl)-3,4,5,6-tetrahydro-9-[(2,3,4,6-tetra-O-acetyl-β-D-glucopyranosyl)oxy]-	MeOH	218.5(3.61)	102-1981-79
$C_{24}H_{29}NO_6$			
Canadine, 8,8-diethyl-	EtOH	233(4.31),288(3.81)	36-0705-79
Floripavidine	EtOH	229s(4.37),273(4.25), 310(4.35)	100-0325-79
$C_{24}H_{29}N_2$			
Pyrrolidinium, 1-[2-(9,10-dihydro-10-methyl-9-acridinyl)cyclohexylidene]-, perchlorate	EtOH	282(3.84),322(3.08)	103-0541-79
$C_{24}H_{29}N_5O_8$			
Adenosine, N-(4-methoxybenzoyl)-2'-O-(tetrahydro-4-methoxy-2H-pyran-4-yl)-	EtOH	289(4.45)	118-0599-79
Adenosine, N-(4-methoxybenzoyl)-3'-O-(tetrahydro-4-methoxy-2H-pyran-4-yl)-	EtOH	290(4.47)	118-0599-79
$C_{24}H_{29}O$			
[1,1'-Biphenyl]-4-yloxy, 3,5-dicyclohexyl-	PrOH	355(4.70),510(3.78)	39-1540-79B

Compound	Solvent	λ_{max}(log ε)	Ref.
$C_{24}H_{30}ClN_3O_2$			
Pentanamide, N-(2-chlorophenyl)-2-[[4-(diethylamino)-2-methylphenyl]imino]-4,4-dimethyl-3-oxo-	BuOAc	432(4.18)	24-3098-79
$C_{24}H_{30}FN_5O_6$			
L-Leucine, N-[N-[4-[(5-fluoro-1,2-dihydro-2-oxo-4-pyrimidinyl)amino]-1,4-dioxobutyl]-L-alanyl-, phenylmethyl ester	EtOH	242(3.93),285(3.52), 348(3.71)	87-1104-79
$C_{24}H_{30}NO_5$			
Isoquinolinium, 4-[2-(3,4-dimethoxyphenyl)-1-ethoxyethylidene]-1,4-dihydro-7,8-dimethoxy-2-methyl-, tetrafluoroborate	EtOH	224(4.23),282(4.13), 360(3.78)	78-1861-79
$C_{24}H_{30}N_2O_4Sn$			
Tin, dicyclohexylbis(2-pyridinecarboxylato-N^1,N^2)-	$CHCl_3$	238(3.74),264(3.99)	131-0165-79D
	MeCN	222(4.19),264(3.97)	131-0165-79D
$C_{24}H_{30}N_2O_{12}$			
1,2,3,4-Butanetetrol, 1-[5-(3,4-diacetoxy-1-butenyl)pyrazinyl]-, tetraacetate, [1S-[1R*(R*),2S*,3R*]]-	EtOH	268(4.19),275(4.17), 295(3.62)	136-0205-79J
$C_{24}H_{30}N_4$			
1H-Indole-2,3-diethanamine, β^2-1H-indol-3-yl-N,N,N',N'-tetramethyl-	EtOH	277s(4.11),284(4.16), 291(4.12)	56-0073-79
$C_{24}H_{30}N_4O_2$			
2H-Isoindol-2-yloxy, 5,5'-azobis[1,3-dihydro-1,1,3,3-tetramethyl-	C_6H_{12}	233(4.38),330(4.42), 428(3.08)	22-0048-79
$C_{24}H_{30}N_4O_3$			
2H-Isoindol-2-yloxy, 5,5'-azoxybis[1,3-dihydro-1,1,3,3-tetramethyl-	C_6H_{12}	235(4.26),335(4.29)	22-0048-79
$C_{24}H_{30}N_4O_7$			
1H-Imidazole-4-carboxylic acid, 1-[5-O-acetyl-3-O-(1-methylethylidene)-β-D-ribofuranosyl]-5-[[(dimethylamino)methylene]amino]-, phenylmethyl ester	MeOH	212(4.32),234(4.11), 300(4.02)	39-1415-79C
$C_{24}H_{30}N_4O_{10}$			
3H-Phenoxazine-1,9-dicarboxamide, 2-amino-N,N'-bis[2-hydroxy-1,1-bis(hydroxymethyl)ethyl]-4,6-dimethyl-3-oxo-	n.s.g.	447(4.48)	104-0951-79
$C_{24}H_{30}O$			
[1,1'-Biphenyl]-4-ol, 3,5-dicyclohexyl-	PrOH	270(4.26)	39-1540-79B
$C_{24}H_{30}O_4$			
9β,10α-Pregna-4,6-diene-3,20-dione, 17α-acetoxy-16-methylene-	MeOH	284(4.43)	54-0078-79
$C_{24}H_{30}O_6$			
2-Butenoic acid, 2-methyl-, 1-(1-hydroxy-1-methylethyl)-4-methyl-6-[(2-	EtOH	218(4.37),244(3.83), 254(3.67),326(4.12)	105-0194-79

Compound	Solvent	λ_{max}(log ε)	Ref.
oxo-2H-1-benzopyran-7-yl)oxy]-4-hexenyl ester, [R-(Z,E)]- (cont.)			105-0194-79
$C_{24}H_{30}O_7$			
9H-10,4a-(Epoxymethano)phenanthren-9-one, 5,6-diacetoxy-1,2,3,4,10,10a-hexahydro-10-hydroxy-1,1-dimethyl-7-(1-methylethyl)-, [4aR-(4aα,10α-10aβ)]-	ether	258(4.12),290(3.33), 298s(3.31)	33-2754-79
$C_{24}H_{30}O_8$			
Coleon O, 19-acetoxy-	EtOH	236(3.93)	33-2374-79
Dibenzo[a,c]cycloocten-5(6H)-one, 7,8-dihydro-6-hydroxy-1,2,3,10,11,12-hexamethoxy-6,7-dimethyl-	EtOH	216(4.62),243s(3.42), 291s(3.32)	94-2695-79
Montafrusin diacetate	EtOH	213(4.15)	102-0843-79
$C_{24}H_{30}O_9$			
Coleon W, 16(or 17)-O-acetyl-	EtOH	264(4.06),286(3.93), 333 (3.73),381(3.95)	33-2374-79
Coleon X, 16(or 17)-O-acetyl-	EtOH	215(4.16),272(3.63), 334(3.79),395(3.73)	33-2374-79
	ether	269(3.65),319(3.80), 385(3.56)	33-2374-79
Hiyodorolactone F	EtOH	210(4.40)(end abs.)	94-2539-79
$C_{24}H_{30}O_{10}$			
2-Propen-1-one, 3-[4-(methoxymethoxy)-phenyl]-1-[3-methoxy-2,4,6-tris(methoxymethoxy)phenyl]-	EtOH	328(4.38)	18-2596-79
$C_{24}H_{30}O_{15}$			
Eustamoside tetraacetate	MeOH	233.0(3.96)	102-1981-79
$C_{24}H_{31}ClO_{15}$			
Eustoside tetraacetate	MeOH	235.0(3.92)	102-1981-79
8-epi-	MeOH	237.0(3.95)	102-1981-79
$C_{24}H_{31}FO_5S$			
Pregna-1,4-diene-3-thione, 9α-fluoro-11β-hydroxy-16α-methyl-17α,20:20,21-bis[methylenebis(oxy)]-	MeCN	331(4.25),580(1.40)	39-1166-79C
$C_{24}H_{31}N_3$			
Cyclohexanecarbonitrile, 4-[5-(4-heptylphenyl)-2-pyrimidinyl]-, trans	EtOH	258(4.32)	64-1535-79B
$C_{24}H_{31}N_3OS$			
1-Butanone, 1-[10-[3-(4-methyl-1-piperazinyl)propyl]-10H-phenothiazin-2-yl]-, dimaleate	MeOH	208(4.71),243(4.40), 278(4.32)	133-0197-79
$C_{24}H_{31}N_3O_2$			
Pentanamide, 2-[[4-(diethylamino)-2-methylphenyl]imino]-4,4-dimethyl-3-oxo-N-phenyl-	BuOAc	424(3.95)	24-3098-79
Pentanamide, 2-[[4-(diethylamino)phenyl]imino]-4,4-dimethyl-N-(4-methylphenyl)-3-oxo-	heptane	414(3.90)	73-1460-79
	EtOH	431(3.93)	73-1460-79

Compound	Solvent	λ_{max}(log ε)	Ref.
$C_{24}H_{31}N_7O_5$			
Alanine, 3-(6-amino-9H-purin-9-yl)-N-[N-[(1,1-dimethylethoxy)carbonyl]-L-phenylalanyl]-, ethyl ester	EtOH	261(4.10)	65-0994-79
$C_{24}H_{32}$			
Benzene, 1,1'-(3-butyl-1-pentyl-1,2-cyclopropanediyl)bis-	EtOH or CCl_4	257(3.32),277(2.73)	104-0080-79
Bicyclo[4.1.0]heptane, 7,7'-[2,4-bis-(1-methylethylidene)-1,3-cyclobutanediylidene]bis-	heptane	207(4.28),245(3.60), 264(3.60)	35-4772-79
$C_{24}H_{32}N_2O_5S_2$			
1H-Pyrrole-3-propanoic acid, 5-[[1,5-dihydro-3-methyl-4-(2-methyl-1,3-dithiolan-2-yl)-5-oxo-2H-pyrrol-2-ylidene]methyl]-2-[(1,1-dimethylethoxy)-carbonyl]-4-methyl-, methyl ester	MeOH	253s(--),261(4.36), 393(4.57),410s(--)	24-2243-79
$C_{24}H_{32}N_2O_7$			
1H-Pyrrole-3-propanoic acid, 5-[[4-(1-acetoxyethyl)-1,5-dihydro-3-methyl-5-oxo-2H-pyrrol-2-ylidene]methyl]-2-[(1,1-dimethylethoxy)carbonyl]-4-methyl-, methyl ester	MeOH	253s(--),260(4.35), 390(4.55),408s(--)	24-2243-79
$C_{24}H_{32}N_4O_2$			
1H-Naphtho[2',1':4,5]indeno[2,1-e]-[1,2,4]triazolo[4,3-b]pyridazin-2-ol, 2,3,4,4a,4b,5,6,6a,13,13a,13b-14,15,15a-tetradecahydro-4a,6a-dimethyl-, acetate	MeOH	214(4.28),293(2.50)	39-1816-79C
$C_{24}H_{32}N_4O_7$			
Diazene, bis[5-(1,1-dimethylethyl)-4-methoxy-2-methyl-3-nitrophenyl]-, 1-oxide	EtOH	235s(4.19),325(4.15)	24-3946-79
Phenol, 2-(1,1-dimethylethyl)-6-[[5-(1,1-dimethylethyl)-4-methoxy-2-methyl-3-nitrophenyl)azo]-3-methoxy-5-methyl-4-nitro-	MeCN	356(4.25),448s(3.64)	24-3946-79
$C_{24}H_{32}O_4$			
Benzene, 4-[2-[2-(3,4-dimethoxyphenyl)-cyclohexyl]ethyl]-1,2-dimethoxy-, cis	MeOH	204(4.54),228(4.18), 278(3.82)	12-0071-79
Spruceanol diacetate	MeOH	220(4.15),278(3.11)	100-0658-79
$C_{24}H_{32}O_4S$			
Pregna-1,4-dien-20-one, 11β-hydroxy-17α,21-[(1-methylethylidene)bis(oxy)]-3-thioxo-	MeOH	332(4.28)	39-1166-79C
$C_{24}H_{32}O_5$			
Feshurin	n.s.g.	220(4.10),245(3.60), 254(3.51),326(4.16)	105-0196-79
$C_{24}H_{32}O_6$			
Dibenzo[a,c]cyclooctene, 5,6,7,8-tetrahydro-1,2,3,10,11,12-hexamethoxy-6,7-dimethyl- (deoxyschizandrin)	EtOH	218(4.66),248(4.16), 284s(3.40)	94-1583-79
	EtOH	218(4.68),248(4.19), 284s(3.43)	94-2695-79

Compound	Solvent	λ_{max}(log ϵ)	Ref.
1,4-Phenanthrenediol, 2-(acetoxymethyl)-4b,5,6,7,8,8a,9,10-octahydro-4b,8,8-trimethyl-, diacetate, (4bS-trans)-	EtOH	220(4.14),256(3.61)	2-0513-79B
$C_{24}H_{32}O_7$			
5α,10α-Pregn-4-ene-2,20-dione, 21-acetoxy-1β,11β-epoxy-17α-hydroxy-11α-methoxy-	MeOH	288(2.32)	35-5019-79
Schizandrin	EtOH	217(4.90),246(4.29), 251(4.30),256s(4.23), 285s(3.44)	94-1383-79
$C_{24}H_{32}O_8$			
Coleon P, 12-O-deacetyl-6-O-acetyl-17-acetoxy-	EtOH	245(3.95)	33-2374-79
Coleon P, 12-O-deacetyl-7-O-acetyl-17-acetoxy-	EtOH	244(4.00)	33-2374-79
Coleon Q, 12-O-deacetyl-7-O-acetyl-19-acetoxy-	EtOH	236(4.03)	33-2374-79
$C_{24}H_{32}O_{12}$			
Boschnaloside, O,O',O",O"'-tetraacetyl-	MeOH	247(4.08)	33-2708-79
$C_{24}H_{32}O_{13}$			
Yuheinoside, O,O',O",O"'-tetraacetyl-	MeOH	242(4.06)	33-2708-79
Tecoside	H_2O	206(3.39)	39-2473-79C
	MeOH	225(4.59),262(4.43), 293(4.14),330(3.26)	39-2473-79C
$C_{24}H_{32}O_{16}$			
Eustomorusside tetraacetate	MeOH	235.5(3.94)	102-1981-79
$C_{24}H_{33}ClO_4S$			
Cyclododecanecarboxylic acid, 1-[2-[(4-chlorophenyl)sulfinyl]ethyl]-2-ethenyl-12-oxo-, methyl ester	EtOH	246(3.92),269s(3.25), 277s(2.92)	33-2630-79
Cyclododecanecarboxylic acid, 3-[2-[(4-chlorophenyl)sulfinyl]ethyl]-12-ethenyl-2-oxo-, methyl ester	EtOH	245(3.86),270s(3.21), 277s(2.92)	33-2630-79
$C_{24}H_{33}ClO_5S$			
Cyclododecanecarboxylic acid, 1-[2-[(4-chlorophenyl)sulfonyl]ethyl]-2-ethenyl-12-oxo-, methyl ester	EtOH	229(4.17),263(2.77), 275(2.62)	33-2630-79
$C_{24}H_{33}NO_2$			
17-Norkaura-1,15-diene-3,12-dione, 13-methyl-2-pyrrolidino-	EtOH	215(4.05),319(3.52)	39-1004-79C
$C_{24}H_{33}NO_3$			
2,4,12-Tridecatrienamide, 13-(1,3-benzodioxol-5-yl)-N-(2-methylpropyl)-, (E,E,E)-	n.s.g.	260(4.75),305(3.97)	2-0538B-79A
$C_{24}H_{33}NO_4$			
Aspochalasin A	EtOH	265(2.61),410(1.09)	33-1501-79
Aspochalasin B (aposterol)	EtOH	225(3.99)	33-1501-79
17,18-Secoapochalasin C, 17,18-didehydro-	EtOH	231(4.09),335s(2.59)	33-1501-79

Compound	Solvent	λ_{max}(log ε)	Ref.
$C_{24}H_{33}N_3O_2S$			
Dixyrazine	MeOH	206(4.44),255(4.49), 308(3.66)	133-0197-79
$C_{24}H_{33}N_4O$			
2H-Isoindol-2-yloxy, 5-[[4-(dimethyl-amino)phenyl]azo]-1,1,3,3-tetraeth-yl-1,3-dihydro-	EtOH	410(4.30)	22-0048-79
	EtOH-HCl	520(4.40)	22-0048-79
$C_{24}H_{34}$			
5,20-Ethenobenzocyclooctadecene, 6,7,8,9,10,11,12,13,14,15,16,17,18-19-tetradecahydro-	EtOH	229(4.66),282(3.67), 290(3.74),301(3.57)	35-6660-79
$C_{24}H_{34}Cl_2N_2O_6$			
1-Piperidinyloxy, 4,4'-[(2,5-dichloro-3,6-dioxo-1,4-cyclohexadiene-1,4-di-ylbis(oxy)]bis[2,2,6,6-tetramethyl-	EtOH	303(4.18),416(2.60)	70-1441-79
1-Piperidinyloxy, 4,4'-[(4,5-dichloro-3,6-dioxo-1,4-cyclohexadiene-1,2-di-ylbis(oxy)]bis[2,2,6,6-tetramethyl-	heptane	303(4.11),419(2.54)	70-1441-79
	EtOH	303(4.10),419(2.59)	70-1441-79
$C_{24}H_{34}N_2O_5S_2$			
1H-Pyrrole-3-propanoic acid, 5-[[2,5-dihydro-3-methyl-4-(2-methyl-1,3-di-thiolan-2-yl)-5-oxo-1H-pyrrol-2-yl]-methyl]-2-[(1,1-dimethylethoxy)carb-onyl]-4-methyl-, methyl ester	MeOH	284(4.11)	24-2243-79
$C_{24}H_{34}N_2O_{20}$			
β-Cellotrioside, 3,4-dinitrophenyl	pH 5	282(3.75)	130-0147-79
$C_{24}H_{34}N_4OS$			
1H-Cyclopenta[5,6]naphtho[1,2-g][1,2,4]-triazolo[5,1-b]quinazolin-1-ol, 2,3-3a,3b,4,5,5a,6,13,13a,13b,14,15,15a-tetradecahydro-1,13a,15a-trimethyl-9-(methylthio)-, [1S-(1α,3aβ,3bα-5aβ,13aα,13bα,15aα)]-	MeOH	212(4.40),227(4.40), 237(4.43),315(4.03)	39-1816-79C
$C_{24}H_{34}O_3$			
Dicyclopenta[3,4:6,7]cycloocta[1,2-d]-1,3-dioxole, 3a,6a,8,9,10,10a,11,11a-octahydro-8-(methoxymethyl)-2,2,6a,11-tetramethyl-4-(1-methylethenyl)-	$CHCl_3$	278(3.44)	32-0101-79
$C_{24}H_{34}O_4$			
Androsta-5,7-dien-17-ol, 3,19-epoxy-3-methoxy-4,4-dimethyl-, acetate, (3β,13α,17α)-	n.s.g.	265(3.91),273(4.06), 283(4.08),296(3.84)	33-2732-79
(3β,13α,17β)-	n.s.g.	265s(3.86),274(4.01), 285(4.03),297(3.81)	33-2732-79
(3β,17β)-	n.s.g.	265s(4.11),274(4.21), 285(4.20),296(3.96)	33-2732-79
$C_{24}H_{34}O_4S$			
Cyclododecanecarboxylic acid, 2-ethen-yl-12-oxo-1-[2-(phenylsulfinyl)eth-yl]-, methyl ester	EtOH	240(3.66),265s(3.30), 271s(2.76)	33-2630-79
Cyclododecanecarboxylic acid, 12-ethen-yl-2-oxo-3-[2-(phenylsulfinyl)ethyl]-,	EtOH	240(3.66),264s(3.11), 271s(2.85)	33-2630-79

Compound	Solvent	$\lambda_{max}(\log \epsilon)$	Ref.
methyl ester (cont.)			33-2630-79
$C_{24}H_{34}O_5$			
5α-Androst-8-en-7-one, 17β-acetoxy-3β,19-epoxy-3β-methoxy-4,4-dimethyl-	n.s.g.	251(3.98)	33-2732-79
5α,13α-Androst-8-en-7-one, 17α-acetoxy-3β,19-epoxy-3α-methoxy-4,4-dimethyl-	n.s.g.	249(4.00)	33-2732-79
17β-	n.s.g.	249(3.92)	33-2732-79
5α-Androst-8(14)-en-7-one, 17β-acetoxy-3β,19-epoxy-3α-methoxy-4,4-dimethyl-	n.s.g.	254(4.04)	33-2732-79
$C_{24}H_{34}O_6$			
Digitoxigenin, 18,20-epoxy-20,22-dihydro-, 3-formate	MeOH	219(2.17)	44-3511-79
6,9-Epoxycyclotetradeca[b]furan-4,5-diol, 4,5,6,7,8,9,10,11,12,15-decahydro-3,6,10,14-tetramethyl-, diacetate, (4R*,5S*,6R*,9S*,10R*,13E)-	EtOH	207(3.86),220s(3.86)	12-2265-79
$C_{24}H_{34}O_7$			
2-Butenoic acid, 3-methyl-4-[tetrahydro-3,4-dihydroxy-5-[[3-(2-hydroxy-1-methylpropyl)oxiranyl]methyl]-2H-pyran-2-yl]-, phenylmethyl ester	EtOH	219(4.15)	39-0308-79C
$C_{24}H_{35}NO_4$			
Aspochalasin C	EtOH	240(3.80)	33-1501-79
Aspochalasin D	EtOH	248(3.92)	33-1501-79
$C_{24}H_{36}O_2$			
Chol-4-ene-3,23-dione	EtOH	240(4.21)	25-0385-79
$C_{24}H_{36}O_3$			
Testosterone pivalate	EtOH	245(4.48)	13-0793-79B
$C_{24}H_{36}O_4$			
Didehydrotrifarin	n.s.g.	252(4.49)	31-1544-79
$C_{24}H_{36}O_6$			
Evillosin acetate	EtOH	209(4.18)	44-1322-79
$C_{24}H_{37}NOS$			
Pregn-4-en-3-one, 20-(2-thiazolidinyl)-	$CHCl_3$	247(3.79)	83-0192-79
$C_{24}H_{38}CuN_2O_2$			
Copper, [[2,2'-[1,2-ethanediylbis(nitrilomethylidyne)]bis[3-methyl-6-(1-methylethyl)cyclohexanonato]](2-)-N,N',O,O']-	n.s.g.	290(4.00),335(4.38), 365(3.95),550(2.56)	65-2433-79
$C_{24}H_{38}N_6O_8$			
1,2,3-Triazinium, 4,5,6-tris(dimethylamino)-2-[3-ethoxy-2-(ethoxycarbonyl)-1-[2-ethoxy-1-(ethoxycarbonyl)-2-oxoethyl]-3-oxo-1-propenyl]-, hydroxide, inner salt	CH_2Cl_2	460(3.30)	24-1535-79
$C_{24}H_{40}N_2O_4$			
1,4-Benzenedicarboxylic acid, 2,5-bis-(hexylamino)-, diethyl ester	EtOH	486(3.71)	48-0905-79

Compound	Solvent	λ_{max}(log ε)	Ref.
$C_{24}H_{40}O_4$			
2H-Pyran-2-one, 3,5-dibutyl-6-(1-butyl-2-oxoheptyl)-4-hydroxy- (elasnin)	EtOH	291(3.89)	35-4386-79
$C_{24}H_{42}O_4$			
2H-Pyran-2-one, 3,5-dibutyl-6-(1-butyl-2-hydroxyheptyl)-4-hydroxy-	EtOH	292(3.81)	35-4386-79
$C_{24}H_{44}N_2O_8$			
10,13-Dioxa-7,16-diazadocosanedioic acid, 7,16-dimethyl-8,15-dioxo-, diethyl ester	n.s.g.	200s(4.15)	33-0754-79
$C_{24}H_{46}N_8$			
Cyclopropenylium, bis[bis(1-methylethyl)amino][4,5,6-tris(dimethylamino)-1,2,3-triazinium-2-yl]-, diperchlorate	CH_2Cl_2	533(4.22)	24-1535-79
$C_{24}H_{46}S_5$			
1,3-Butadiene, 1,1,2,4,4-pentakis[(1,1-dimethylethyl)thio]-	heptane	195(4.45),222(4.22), 285(3.95),360(3.69), 400(3.22)	5-1614-79
$C_{24}H_{48}N_2O_2$			
Octanediamide, N,N,N',N'-tetrabutyl-	H_2O	202(4.23)	33-0754-79
$C_{24}H_{48}N_2O_4$			
Acetamide, 2,2'-[(1,4-butanediylbis-(oxy)]bis[N-heptyl-N-methyl-	H_2O	203(4.23)	33-0754-79
Acetamide, 2,2'-[(1,2-dimethyl-1,2-ethanediyl)bis(oxy)]bis[N-heptyl-N-methyl-	H_2O	203(4.22)	33-0754-79
Acetamide, 2,2'-[1,2-ethanediylbis-(oxy)]bis[N-butyl-N-pentyl-	H_2O	203(4.20)	33-0754-79
$C_{24}H_{56}N_4P_2$			
Hypodiphosphonous tetraamide, octapropyl-	hexane	230(2.66)	22-0241-79I

Compound	Solvent	λ_{max}(log ε)	Ref.
$C_{25}H_{15}BrO_2$			
Spiro[3H-naphtho[2,1-b]pyran-3,9'-[9H]-xanthene], 2-bromo-	EtOAc	295(4.01),325(3.82), 355(3.8),362(3.77), 370(3.83)	104-1132-79
$C_{25}H_{15}ClO_4$			
Naphtho[2,3-c]furan-1,3-dione, 4-(3-chlorophenyl)-9-(4-methylphenyl)-	n.s.g.	226(4.49),245(4.48), 308(3.77)	80-1177-79
$C_{25}H_{15}N$			
Benzo[1]thebenidine, 5-phenyl-	EtOH	215(4.66),246(4.58), 260(4.66),345(3.68), 364(3.62),450(3.78)	103-0526-79
$C_{25}H_{15}NO$			
Benzeneacetonitrile, α-(2-phenyl-5H-naphtho[1,8-bc]furan-5-ylidene)-	MeOH	246(3.9),286(4.0), 419(4.6)	5-0959-79
$C_{25}H_{16}N_2$			
1-Azafluorene, 9-(1-azafluorenylidene-methyl)-	CH_2Cl_2	568(4.29),592(4.28)	24-1473-79
	DMSO-EtOH-NaOEt	538(5.02)	24-1473-79
4-Azafluorene, 9-(4-azafluorenylidene-methyl)-	MeCN	307(4.48)	24-1473-79
	DMSO-EtOH-NaOEt	552(4.99)	24-1473-79
$C_{25}H_{16}O_4$			
5,11-Naphthacenedione, 6-(4-methoxy-phenoxy)-	toluene	480(4.20)	135-0691-79A
5,12-Naphthacenedione, 6-(4-methoxy-phenoxy)-	toluene	400(3.76)	135-0691-79A
$C_{25}H_{16}O_8$			
1H-Naphtho[2",3":4',5']furo[3',2':7,8]-naphtho[2,3-c]pyran-1,8,13-trione, 3,4-dihydro-9,15-dihydroxy-7-meth-oxy-3-methyl-	MeOH	280(4.47),355(3.51), 440(3.64)	88-4989-79
$C_{25}H_{17}ClO_4$			
2,5-Furandione, 3-[(3-chlorophenyl)-phenylmethylene]dihydro-4-[(2-methoxyphenyl)methylene]-	n.s.g.	222(4.58),261(4.23), 313(4.04)	80-1177-79
2,5-Furandione, 3-[(3-chlorophenyl)-phenylmethylene]dihydro-4-[(4-methoxyphenyl)methylene]-	n.s.g.	208(4.44),318(3.95), 416(3.30)	80-1177-79
$C_{25}H_{17}N$			
Benz[g]isoquinoline, 1,3-diphenyl-	EtOH	208(4.48),248(4.65), 282(4.86),331(3.08), 348(3.50),366(3.70), 400(3.56),415(3.43)	103-0526-79
$C_{25}H_{17}N_3O_2$			
3-Pyridinecarbonitrile, 5-benz[cd]indol-2-yl-1,2-dihydro-6-hydroxy-4-methyl-1-(2-methylphenyl)-2-oxo-	DMF	510(3.89)	2-0140-79A
$C_{25}H_{17}N_3O_3$			
3-Pyridinecarbonitrile, 5-benz[cd]indol-2-yl-1,2-dihydro-6-hydroxy-1-(2-meth-oxyphenyl)-4-methyl-2-oxo-	DMF	510(3.87)	2-0140-79A

Compound	Solvent	λ_{max}(log ε)	Ref.
$C_{25}H_{17}N_5O_2$			
Benzo[c]cinnolinium, 5-[[[(4-nitrophenyl)amino]phenylmethylene]amino]-, hydroxide, inner salt	CH_2Cl_2	249(4.59),298(4.18), 310(4.25),324(4.28), 420(4.18)	39-0185-79C
$C_{25}H_{18}BrNO_3$			
Naphtho[1,2-b]furan-3(2H)-one, 4-(4-bromophenyl)-5-hydroxy-2-(methylphenylamino)-	EtOH	218(4.66),244(4.66), 277(4.62),411(3.95)	103-0597-79
$C_{25}H_{18}N_4$			
Benzo[c]cinnolinium, 5-[[phenyl(phenylamino)methylene]amino]-, hydroxide, inner salt	CH_2Cl_2	250(4.72),295(4.13), 307(4.10),321(4.02), 404(4.15)	39-0185-79C
$C_{25}H_{18}O_5$			
9H-Indeno[2,1-c]phenanthren-9-one, 7-acetoxy-5,11-dimethoxy-	n.s.g.	216(4.68),243(4.73), 265(4.32),297(4.24), 331(4.37),353(4.47), 388(3.71),490(3.17)	33-0090-79
$C_{25}H_{18}O_6$			
Dinaphtho[1,2-b:2',3'-d]furan-7,12-diol, 5-methoxy-, diacetate	n.s.g.	262s(4.82),269(5.07), 285s(4.21),298s(3.83), 326(4.01),339(4.07), 358(4.09),375(4.23)	39-2679-79C
$C_{25}H_{19}ClO_5$			
Butanedioic acid, [(3-chlorophenyl)-phenylmethylene][(2-methoxyphenyl)-methylene]-	n.s.g.	210(4.53),274(3.97)	80-1177-79
Butanedioic acid, [(3-chlorophenyl)-phenylmethylene][(4-methoxyphenyl)-methylene]-	n.s.g.	210(4.49),277(4.00), 304(3.00)	80-1177-79
$C_{25}H_{19}F_3N_2O_2$			
Quinazoline, 4-(9-anthracenyl)-3,4-dihydro-2-methyl-, hydrotrifluoroacetate	EtOH	221(4.59),256(5.14), 336(3.57),351(3.86), 368(4.02),390(3.98)	24-1348-79
$C_{25}H_{19}NO_2S$			
1H-Isoindole-1,3(2H)-dione, 2-(3-dibenzo[b,e]thiepin-11(6H)-ylidenepropyl)-, (E)-	MeOH	227(4.53),265s(3.98), 300(3.87)	73-2536-79
$C_{25}H_{19}NO_3$			
Naphtho[1,2-b]furan-3(2H)-one, 5-hydroxy-2-(methylphenylamino)-4-phenyl-	EtOH	223(4.60),242(4.61), 278(4.48),410(3.78)	103-0597-79
$C_{25}H_{19}NO_4$			
4H-[1]Benzopyrano[3,4-d]isoxazole-4-acetic acid, α,α-diphenyl-, methyl ester	MeOH	227(4.8),270(4.6), 325(4.5)	24-1791-79
$C_{25}H_{19}N_2S_2$			
Benzo[1,2-d:5,4-d']bisthiazolium, 3-methyl-2,6-bis(2-phenylethenyl)-, perchlorate	DMF	404(4.37)	126-1441-79
	KBr	268(--),391(--), 604s(--)	126-1441-79
$C_{25}H_{19}N_3O_4$			
Pyridinium, 1-[3-[5-cyano-1,6-dihydro-	EtOH	251(4.26),338(4.17),	2-0100-79A

Compound	Solvent	$\lambda_{max}(\log \epsilon)$	Ref.
2-hydroxy-4-methyl-1-(1-methylethyl)-6-oxo-3-pyridinyl]-1,4-dihydro-1,4-dioxo-2-naphthalenyl]-, hydroxide, inner salt (cont.)		645(3.50)	2-0100-79A
$C_{25}H_{20}ClN$			
25-Azapentacyclo[19.3.1.1^{9,13}.0^{4,16}-0^{6,18}]hexacosa-1(25),2,4,6(18),9,11-13(26),16,19,21,23-undecaene, 26-chloro-	EtOH	246(4.40),251(4.40), 260(4.27),290(3.82)	35-2121-79
$C_{25}H_{20}ClNO_{13}$			
Carbonic acid, 15-chloro-9,10-dihydro-7-oxo-7H-1,3-dioxolo[4',5']indeno-[2',1':4,5]oxazolo[4,3-a]isoquino-line-5b,12,13(15H)-triyl trimethyl ester, (5bα,14bS*,15β)-(±)-	MeOH	216(4.46),252(3.59), 297(3.45)	23-1569-79
$C_{25}H_{20}N_2O$			
Phenol, 2-[5-(2,2-diphenylethenyl)-2-methyl-4-pyrimidinyl]-	MeOH	211(4.4),230(4.3), 298(4.2)	24-1791-79
$C_{25}H_{20}N_2P_2S_2$			
Phosphine sulfide, (diazomethylene)-bis[diphenyl-	C_6H_{12}	268(3.88)	78-0181-79
$C_{25}H_{20}N_3O_5$			
Quinolinium, 1-[(2,4-dinitrophenyl)-methyl]-4-[2-(4-methoxyphenyl)eth-enyl]-, iodide	MeOH	447(4.60)	64-1556-79B
$C_{25}H_{20}N_4$			
1H-Benzimidazole, 1,2-bis(1H-indol-3-ylmethyl)-	MeOH	224(4.32),277(3.18), 283(3.22),289(3.70)	120-0011-79
$C_{25}H_{20}OSi$			
Silane, benzoyltriphenyl-	C_6H_{12}	388(2.07),405(2.35), 424(2.47),440(2.25)	35-0083-79
$C_{25}H_{20}O_4$			
4H-1-Benzopyran-4-one, 3-(1-acetoxy-2,2-diphenylethyl)-	MeOH	220(4.7),305(3.9)	24-1791-79
[1,1'-Binaphthalene]-2-carboxylic acid, 4-acetoxy-, ethyl ester	n.s.g.	222(4.90),235s(4.61), 283(4.10),293(4.03)	33-0090-79
3-Phenanthrenecarboxylic acid, 1-acet-oxy-4-phenyl-, ethyl ester	n.s.g.	208(4.46),223(4.45), 257(4.49),300s(4.01), 340(3.10)	33-0090-79
$C_{25}H_{20}O_5$			
2H-1-Benzopyran-2-acetic acid, 3,4-di-hydro-3-(hydroxymethylene)-4-oxo-α,α-diphenyl-, methyl ester	MeOH	222(4.3),301(3.8), 361(3.7)	24-1791-79
[1]Benzopyrano[3,4-b][1]benzopyran-12-carboxylic acid, 6,6a-dihydro-6a-methoxy-6-phenyl-, methyl ester	EtOH	240(4.23),296(4.07), 307(3.95),342(4.21), 364(4.17)	138-0511-79
$C_{25}H_{21}$			
Cycloheptatrienylium, [8-(3,5-dimethyl-phenyl)-1-naphthalenyl]-, perchlorate	MeCN	224(4.84),274(4.16), 305s(3.92),391(3.83), 465(3.62)	44-2712-79

Compound	Solvent	λ_{max}(log ε)	Ref.
$C_{25}H_{21}NO$			
Benzonitrile, 4-(2,5-dihydro-5,5-dimethyl-2,4-diphenyl-2-furanyl)-	MeOH	238(4.39)	44-4021-79
Pyrrolo[2,1-a]isoquinolin-1(5H)-one, 6,10b-dihydro-10b-methyl-2,3-diphenyl-	MeCN	273(4.07),354(3.85)	88-1213-79
$C_{25}H_{21}NO_2$			
2(1H)-Pyridinone, 1-acetyl-3,4-dihydro-3,4,6-triphenyl-	EtOH	249(4.12)	4-0001-79
$C_{25}H_{21}NO_4$			
2H-1-Benzopyran-2-acetamide, 3,4-dihydro-3-(hydroxymethylene)-6-methyl-4-oxo-α,α-diphenyl-, monoammonium salt	MeOH	218(4.3),316(3.8), 360(3.7)	24-1791-79
Spiro[9H-fluorene-9,1'(8'aH)-indolizine]-2,2'-dicarboxylic acid, 5'-methyl-	n.s.g.	383(4.05)	89-0945-79
$C_{25}H_{21}NO_5$			
Spiro[9H-fluorene-9,1'(8'aH)-indolizine]-2',3'-dicarboxylic acid, 7'-methoxy-, dimethyl ester	n.s.g.	376(3.89)	89-0945-79
$C_{25}H_{21}NS$			
Pyrrolo[2,1-a]isoquinoline-1(5H)-thione, 6,10b-dihydro-10b-methyl-2,3-diphenyl-	MeCN	255(4.12),423(4.12)	88-1213-79
$C_{25}H_{21}N_2O_3$			
Quinolinium, 1-(4-nitrobenzyl)-4-(4-methoxystyryl)-, iodide	MeOH	445(4.57)	64-1556-79B
$C_{25}H_{21}N_3$			
2,4-Diazabicyclo[3.2.0]hept-2-ene-6-carbonitrile, 4-methyl-1,3,5-triphenyl-	EtOH	222s(4.26),266(3.40)	44-0041-79
2,4-Diazabicyclo[3.2.0]hept-3-ene-6-carbonitrile, 2-methyl-1,3,5-triphenyl-	EtOH	222s(4.23),266(3.48)	44-0041-79
$C_{25}H_{21}N_3O$			
1-Propanone, 3-[2-(1H-indol-3-ylmethyl)-1H-benzimidazol-1-yl]-1-phenyl-	MeOH	222(3.25),248(3.98), 277(3.79),284(3.80), 290(3.52)	120-0011-79
$C_{25}H_{21}N_3O_2$			
Benzamide, N-[3-cyano-1,2-dihydro-1-(phenylmethyl)-2-quinolinyl]-4-methoxy-	CH_2Cl_2	241(4.2),255s(4.1), 289s(3.8),299(3.8), 386(3.4)	64-0064-79B
Benzamide, N-[3-cyano-1,4-dihydro-1-(phenylmethyl)-4-quinolinyl]-4-methoxy-	CH_2Cl_2	254(4.2),315(4.1)	64-0064-79B
$C_{25}H_{21}N_5O_2S_2$			
Propanedinitrile, [[4-[[2-acetoxy-3-(2-benzothiazolylthio)propyl](2-cyanoethyl)amino]phenyl]methylene]-	EtOH	417(4.69)	110-1769-79
	EtOH-KOH	335(--)	110-1769-79
	CCl_4	406(--)	110-1769-79
	KBr	426(--)	110-1769-79
$C_{25}H_{22}BrClO_3$			
Benzenepentanoic acid, 4-bromo-β-(4-chlorophenyl)-δ-oxo-α-phenyl-, ethyl ester	EtOH	218s(4.34),256(4.26)	94-2767-79

Compound	Solvent	λmax(log ε)	Ref.
$C_{25}H_{22}ClN_5O_6$			
Adenosine, N-benzoyl-2'-deoxy-, 5'-[(4-chlorophenoxy)acetate]	EtOH	280(4.31)	54-0537-79
$C_{25}H_{22}ClN_5O_7$			
Guanosine, N-benzoyl-2'-deoxy-, 5'-[(4-chlorophenyl)acetate]	EtOH	228(4.38),259(4.17), 266(4.17),289(4.18), 296(4.17)	54-0537-79
$C_{25}H_{22}Cl_4N_5O_7P$			
3'-Adenylic acid, N-benzoyl-2'-deoxy-, 2-chlorophenyl 2,2,2-trichloroethyl ester	MeOH	279(4.31)	54-0537-79
$C_{25}H_{22}Cl_4N_5O_8P$			
3'-Guanylic acid, N-benzoyl-2'-deoxy-, 2-chlorophenyl 2,2,2-trichloroethyl ester	MeOH	237(4.23),257(4.20), 265(4.19),293(4.17)	54-0537-79
$C_{25}H_{22}CuN_6O_4$			
Copper, [12,13,14,15-tetrahydro-2,3-dimethyl-8,18-dinitro-11H-tribenzo-[b,f,m][1,4,8,12]tetraazacyclopentadecinato(2-)-N^5,N^{11},N^{15},N^{21}]-, (SP-4-2)	$CHCl_3$	298(4.43),325(4.40), 420(4.57),460(4.46)	12-2303-79
$C_{25}H_{22}NO$			
Benzo[a]phenanthridinium, 1,2,3,4-tetrahydro-2,2-dimethyl-4-oxo-6-phenyl-, bromide	n.s.g.	232(4.55),291(4.34), 348(3.85)	104-0495-79
chloride	n.s.g.	231(4.55),289(4.23), 350(3.75)	104-0495-79
iodide	n.s.g.	232(4.57),283(4.35), 356(3.78)	104-0495-79
perchlorate	n.s.g.	234(4.84),284(4.40), 358(4.00)	104-0495-79
$C_{25}H_{22}NO_2P$			
Benzenamine, N-[(1-methoxy-2,6-diphenyl-4(1H)-phosphorinylidene)methyl]-	MeOH	403(4.65)	24-1272-79
$C_{25}H_{22}N_2$			
1H-Phenanthro[9,10-d]imidazole, 1,6,9-trimethyl-2-(4-methylphenyl)-	EtOH	255s(4.67),263(4.81), 292(4.25),309(4.14), 349(3.59),366(3.61)	44-0041-79
$C_{25}H_{22}N_2O$			
Cyclopenta[3,4]pyrazolo[1,5-a]pyridin-5-ium, 1,3a,4,9b-tetrahydro-2,6,9b-trimethyl-1-oxo-3,3a-diphenyl-, hydroxide, inner salt	EtOH	206(4.39),276(4.13), 330(3.98),430s(3.46)	88-1765-79
$C_{25}H_{22}N_4O_4$			
1-Imidazolidinecarboxamide, 5,5-dimethyl-2,4-dioxo-N,3-diphenyl-N-[(phenylamino)carbonyl]-	MeCN	228(4.34),244(4.29)	33-1429-79
$C_{25}H_{22}N_4O_8$			
2-Pyridinecarboxylic acid, 5-amino-6-(7-amino-5,8-dihydro-6-methoxy-5,8-dioxo-2-quinolinyl)-4-(2-hydroxy-3,4-dimethoxyphenyl)-3-methyl-	pH 7.5	363(4.18)	36-0853-79
	pH 7.5	385(4.23)(zinc ion added)	36-0853-79

Compound	Solvent	λ_{max}(log ε)	Ref.
$C_{25}H_{22}N_8O_5$			
1H-Pyrrole-2-carboxamide, N-[5-[[(2-cyanophenyl)amino]carbonyl]-1-methyl-1H-pyrrol-3-yl]-1-methyl-4-[[(1-methyl-4-nitro-1H-pyrrol-2-yl)-carbonyl]amino]-	DMF	237(4.35),302(4.37)	87-1296-79
1H-Pyrrole-2-carboxamide, N-[5-[[(3-cyanophenyl)amino]carbonyl]-1-methyl-1H-pyrrol-3-yl]-1-methyl-4-[[(1-methyl-4-nitro-1H-pyrrol-2-yl)-carbonyl]amino]-	DMF	298(4.36)	87-1296-79
1H-Pyrrole-2-carboxamide, N-[5-[[(4-cyanophenyl)amino]carbonyl]-1-methyl-1H-pyrrol-3-yl]-1-methyl-4-[[(1-methyl-4-nitro-1H-pyrrol-2-yl)-carbonyl]amino]-	DMF	292(4.37)	87-1296-79
$C_{25}H_{22}O_3$			
Methanone, [1,4-dihydro-2-(4-methoxyphenyl)-1-naphthalenyl](4-methoxyphenyl)-	EtOH	268(4.34)	87-0962-79
Methanone, [3,4-dihydro-2-(4-methoxyphenyl)-1-naphthalenyl](4-methoxyphenyl)-	EtOH	222(4.36),290(4.45)	87-0962-79
$C_{25}H_{22}O_4$			
[1]Benzopyrano[3,4-b][1]benzopyran, 6a-ethoxy-6,6a-dihydro-6-methoxy-6-phenyl-	EtOH	239(4.29),294(4.16), 332(4.35),350(4.29)	138-1301-79
$C_{25}H_{22}O_5$			
3-Phenanthrenecarboxylic acid, 1,9-dimethoxy-4-(4-methoxyphenyl)-, methyl ester	n.s.g.	230(4.59),254(4.53), 317s(4.17),342s(3.70)	33-0090-79
$C_{25}H_{23}BrO_3$			
Benzenepentanoic acid, 4-bromo-δ-oxo-α,β-diphenyl-, ethyl ester	EtOH	256(4.25)	94-2767-79
$C_{25}H_{23}ClN_4O_3S$			
4H-s-Triazolo[4,3-a][1,4]benzodiazepinium, 8-chloro-1,3-dimethyl-6-phenyl-, tosylate	EtOH	223(4.70),250s(4.12), 262s(3.93),266s(3.90), 271s(3.86),277s(3.78), 285s(3.70),295s(3.50)	44-2688-79
$C_{25}H_{23}ClO_3$			
Benzenepentanoic acid, β-(4-chlorophenyl)-δ-oxo-α-phenyl-, ethyl ester	EtOH	243(4.08)	4-0001-79
$C_{25}H_{23}Cl_2N_3O_4S_2$			
Benzenesulfonamide, 4-chloro-N-[6-[[(4-chlorophenyl)sulfonyl]amino]-1,2,5,6-tetrahydro-5,6-dimethyl-4H-pyrrolo-[3,2,1-ij]quinolin-4-ylidene]-, cis	EtOH	274(4.16),283(4.20), 312(4.27)	39-2387-79C
trans	EtOH	277s(4.14),286(4.23), 310(4.27)	39-2387-79C
$C_{25}H_{23}N$			
Cyclohepta[c]pyrrole, 6-(diphenylmethylene)-2,6-dihydro-1,2,3-trimethyl-	CH_2Cl_2	242(4.33),297(4.33), 363(4.34)	24-2087-79

Compound	Solvent	λmax(log ε)	Ref.
(cont.)	CH_2Cl_2-CF_3COOH	230(4.15),262(4.28),293(4.58),326(4.15),371(3.62),652(3.21)	24-2087-79
$C_{25}H_{23}NO_4S$			
Benzenesulfonamide, N-[2-[(1,3-dihydro-1-oxo-2H-inden-2-ylidene)hydroxymethyl]phenyl]-N-ethyl-4-methyl-	MeOH	203(4.76),231s(--),337(4.24)	83-0254-79
$C_{25}H_{23}NO_5$			
7H-Benz[de]anthracene-1,2-dicarboxylic acid, 3-[(1,1-dimethylethyl)amino]-7-oxo-, dimethyl ester	CH_2Cl_2	310(4.41),323s(3.80),426(4.05)	24-3166-79
$C_{25}H_{23}NO_{10}$			
Pyrido[1,2-a]azepine-6,7,8,9-tetracarboxylic acid, 10-(benzoyloxy)-6,7-dihydro-, tetramethyl ester	MeOH	235(4.41),370s(4.05),396(4.11),490(4.19)	39-0584-79C
	MeOH-$HClO_4$	249(4.34),300(4.00)	39-0584-79C
$C_{25}H_{23}N_3$			
5H-Cyclopenta[d]pyridazine, 1,4-diphenyl-5-(piperidinomethylene)-	MeOH	239(4.25),276(4.19),304s(--),385(4.27)	5-0675-79
$C_{25}H_{23}N_3OS$			
Ethanone, 2-[[6,7-dimethyl-3-(methylamino)-2-quinoxalinyl]thio]-1,2-diphenyl-	EtOH	365(4.1),378(4.1)	103-0102-79
$C_{25}H_{23}N_3O_2S$			
Carbamic acid, [3-[[(2-phenylethyl)amino]thioxomethyl]-1H-indol-2-yl]-, phenylmethyl ester	$CHCl_3$	262(4.38),285(4.34),343(4.12)	103-0179-79
$C_{25}H_{23}N_3O_6$			
Benzoic acid, 4-methyl-, [2,3,3a,9a-tetrahydro-6-imino-3-[(4-methylbenzoyl)oxy]-6H-furo[2',3':4,5]oxazolo-[3,2-a]pyrimidin-2-yl]methyl ester, monohydrochloride	MeOH	242(4.65),270s(4.12)	87-0639-79
$C_{25}H_{23}N_5O_4$			
1H-Pyrazole-5-carboxylic acid, 4,5-dihydro-3-[[(4-nitrophenyl)hydrazono]-phenylmethyl]-4-phenyl-, ethyl ester	EtOH	240s(3.13),260(3.07)	4-0849-79
$C_{25}H_{24}$			
Bicyclo[3.1.0]hexane, 5-methyl-1,2,6-triphenyl-, endo	EtOH	220s(4.24)	35-5743-79
exo	EtOH	220s(4.27)	35-5743-79
Bicyclo[3.1.0]hexane, 6-methyl-1,2,5-triphenyl-, endo	EtOH	220(4.18)	35-5743-79
exo	EtOH	220(4.25)	35-5743-79
Cyclopropane, 3-methyl-1,2-diphenyl-2-(3-phenyl-2-propenyl)-, cis	EtOH	231(4.30)	35-5743-79
trans	EtOH	254(4.27)	35-5743-79
Cyclopropane, 3-methyl-1,2-diphenyl-3-(cis-3-phenyl-2-propenyl)-	EtOH	231(4.33)	35-5743-79
trans	EtOH	246(4.29)	35-5743-79
Cyclopropene, 1-methyl-2,3-diphenyl-3-(3-phenylpropyl)-	EtOH	262(4.21)	35-5743-79

Compound	Solvent	$\lambda_{max}(\log \epsilon)$	Ref.
Cyclopropene, 3-methyl-1,2-diphenyl-3-(3-phenylpropyl)-	EtOH	312(4.38),320(4.45), 337(4.32)	35-5743-79
1H-Indene, 1-methyl-2-phenyl-3-(3-phenylpropyl)-	EtOH	227(4.15),292(4.13)	35-5743-79
1H-Indene, 2-methyl-1-phenyl-3-(3-phenylpropyl)-	EtOH	264(4.02)	35-5743-79
$C_{25}H_{24}ClNS_2$			
8,16-Dithia-28-azapentacyclo[21.3.1-$1^{10,14}.0^{4,18}.0^{6,20}$]octacosa-1(27)-4,6(20),10,12,14(28),18,23,25-nonaene, 27-chloro-	MeCN	268(3.91),280(3.64)	35-2121-79
$C_{25}H_{24}ClN_3O_2$			
Benzenepropanamide, N-(4-chlorophenyl)-α-[[4-(diethylamino)phenyl]imino]-β-oxo-	EtOH	423(4.24)	73-1460-79
$C_{25}H_{24}ClN_3O_8$			
Cytidine, 2'-deoxy-N-(4-methoxybenzoyl)-, 5'-[(4-chlorophenoxy)acetate]	EtOH	287(4.35)	54-0537-79
$C_{25}H_{24}Cl_2F_3N_4O_8P$			
Thymidine, 5'-[2,4-dichlorophenyl [[4-[(trifluoroacetyl)amino]phenyl]methyl]phosphoramidate]	EtOH	238(4.07),257(4.28)	78-2913-79
$C_{25}H_{24}Cl_4N_3O_9P$			
3'-Cytidylic acid, 2'-deoxy-N-(4-methoxybenzoyl)-2-chlorophenyl 2,2,2-trichloroethyl ester	EtOH	289(4.40)	54-0537-79
$C_{25}H_{24}Cl_4O_8$			
Acetic acid, 2,2'-[(2,4-diethyl-1,5-dioxo-1,5-pentanediyl)bis[(2,3-dichloro-4,1-phenylene)oxy]]bis-	MeOH	264(4.23)	83-0633-79
$C_{25}H_{24}CuN_4$			
Copper, [12,13,14,15-tetrahydro-2,3-dimethyl-11H-tribenzo[b,f,m][1,4,8,12]-tetraazacyclopentadecinato(2-)-N^5,N^{11},N^{15},N^{21}]-, (SP-4-2)-	$CHCl_3$	272(4.52),282(4.52), 360(3.90),425(4.04)	12-2303-79
$C_{25}H_{24}N_2$			
1H-Imidazole, 1-methyl-2,4,5-tris(4-methylphenyl)-	EtOH	225s(4.38),286(4.33)	44-0041-79
$C_{25}H_{24}N_2O_3$			
1H-3-Benzazepine, 2,3,4,5-tetrahydro-2,2-dimethyl-3-(4-nitrobenzoyl)-1-phenyl-	EtOH	267(3.98)	4-1525-79
$C_{25}H_{24}N_2O_4$			
2H-1-Benzopyran-2-acetamide, 3,4-dihydro-3-(hydroxymethylene)-6-methyl-4-oxo-α,α-diphenyl-, monoammonium salt	MeOH	218(4.3),316(3.8), 360(3.7)	24-1791-79
$C_{25}H_{24}N_4Ni$			
Nickel, [12,13,14,15-tetrahydro-2,3-dimethyl-11H-tribenzo[b,f,m][1,4,8,12]-tetraazacyclopentadecinato(2-)-	$CHCl_3$	282(4.52),360(3.90), 425(4.04),550(3.00)	12-2303-79

Compound	Solvent	λ max(log ε)	Ref.
N^5,N^{11},N^{15},N^{21}]-, (SP-4-2)- (cont.)			12-2303-79
$C_{25}H_{24}N_4O_2$			
1H-Pyrazole-5-carboxylic acid, 4,5-dihydro-4-phenyl-3-[phenyl(phenylhydrazono)methyl]-, ethyl ester	EtOH	258(3.15),297(3.20)	4-0849-79
$C_{25}H_{24}O$			
Anthracene, 9-(α-tert-butoxybenzyl)-	n.s.g.	332(3.17),351(3.47), 368(3.58),387(3.55)	39-2948-79C
Furan, 2,5-dihydro-2,2-dimethyl-5-(4-methylphenyl)-3,5-diphenyl-	MeOH	253(4.16)	44-4021-79
Methanone, [9-(1,1-dimethylpropyl)-9H-fluoren-9-yl]phenyl-	EtOH	258(4.27),291(3.77), 302(3.57)	118-0616-79
$C_{25}H_{24}O_2$			
11H-Benzo[a]fluoren-11-one, 6b,7,8,9-10,10a-hexahydro-10a-[(4-methoxyphenyl)methyl]-	n.s.g.	287(3.68),300s(3.84), 310(3.93),332s(3.67)	78-1167-79
Furan, 2,5-dihydro-5-(4-methoxyphenyl)-2,2-dimethyl-3,5-diphenyl-	MeOH	253(4.11)	44-4021-79
$C_{25}H_{24}O_3$			
Benzenepentanoic acid, δ-oxo-α,β-diphenyl-, ethyl ester	EtOH	243(4.09)	4-0001-79
$C_{25}H_{24}O_{14}$			
Pteroflavonoloside	MeOH	266(4.35),364(4.28)	94-3130-79
	MeOH-$AlCl_3$	274(--),423(--)	94-3130-79
$C_{25}H_{25}BrN_2O_2$			
Benzenepentanoic acid, 4-bromo-δ-hydrazono-α,β-diphenyl-, ethyl ester	EtOH	269(4.18)	94-2767-79
$C_{25}H_{25}BrO_5$			
Anthra[1,2-b]benzofuran-5,13-dione, 11-bromo-7b,8,9,10,11,11a-hexahydro-6-hydroxy-1-methoxy-11-methyl-8-(1-methylethyl)-, (7bα,8α,11α,11aα)-	MeOH	229(4.53),248(4.12), 457(3.97)	5-2018-79
$C_{25}H_{25}ClN_2O_2$			
Benzenepentanoic acid, β-(4-chlorophenyl)-δ-hydrazono-α-phenyl-, ethyl ester	EtOH	265(4.12)	4-0001-79
$C_{25}H_{25}NO_9$			
Cyclobuta[4,5]pyrrolo[1,2-a]quinoline-7a,8,9,9a-tetracarboxylic acid, 8,9-dihydro-7-(1-oxopropyl)-, tetramethyl ester, (7aα,8α,9β,9aα)-	MeOH	223(4.38),271s(3.93), 282(4.03),301s(4.10), 315(4.21),330(4.19), 412s(3.99),438(4.14), 462(4.16),488(3.94)	39-2171-79C
$C_{25}H_{25}NO_{10}$			
Cyclobuta[4,5]pyrrolo[1,2-a]quinoline-7,7a,8,9,9a-pentacarboxylic acid, 8,9-dihydro-, 7-ethyl 7a,8,9,9a-tetramethyl ester, (7aα,8α,9β,9aα)-	MeOH	220(4.34),268s(4.18), 277(4.24),308(4.22), 321(4.08),404s(3.88), 425(3.96),451(3.96), 481s(3.76)	39-2171-79C
(7aα,8β,9α,9aα)-	MeOH	222(4.34),272(4.18), 297(4.26),309s(4.24), 319(4.06),408s(3.86),	39-2171-79C

Compound	Solvent	$\lambda_{max}(\log \epsilon)$	Ref.
(cont.)		426(3.98),449(3.97), 482s(3.68)	39-2171-79C
	MeOH-HClO$_4$	246(4.57),276(4.08), 298(4.25),301(4.30), 316s(4.28)	39-2171-79C
$C_{25}H_{25}N_3O$			
Benzenepropanamide, N-[4,5-dihydro-1-(phenylmethyl)-1H-pyrazol-3-yl]-β-phenyl-	EtOH	265(4.03)	150-0801-79
Benzenepropanamide, α-[[4-(diethylamino)phenyl]imino]-β-oxo-N-phenyl-	EtOH	438(4.27)	73-1460-79
$C_{25}H_{25}N_3O_4S_2$			
Benzenesulfonamide, N-[4,5-dihydro-1-methyl-1-[[(4-methylphenyl)sulfonyl]amino]pyrrolo[3,2,1-hi]indol-2(1H)-ylidene]-4-methyl-	EtOH	224(4.56),271(4.24), 280(4.19),312(4.00)	39-2387-79C
$C_{25}H_{25}N_3O_4S_3$			
Dispiro[1,3-dioxolane-2,2'-[14,17,20]-trithia[25,26,27]triazatetracyclo-[19.3.1.1^{3,7}.1^{9,13}]heptacosa-1(25)-3,5,7(27),9,11,13(26),21,23]nonaene-8',2"-[1,3]dioxolane]	EtOH	215(4.81),260(5.03), 306(4.61)	44-3816-79
$C_{25}H_{25}N_3O_5S_2$			
Dispiro[1,3-dioxolan-2,2'-[17]oxa[14-20]dithia[25,26,27]triazatetracyclo-[19.3.1.1^{3,7}.1^{9,13}]heptacosa-1(25)-3,5,7(27),9,11,13(26),21,23-nonaene-8',2"-[1,3]dioxolane]	EtOH	215(4.97),260(5.23), 306(4.82)	44-3816-79
$C_{25}H_{25}N_3O_7$			
Dispiro[1,3-dioxolane-2,2'-[14,17,20]-trioxa[25,26,27]triazatetracyclo-[19.3.1.1^{3,7}.1^{9,13}]heptacosa-1(25)-3,5,7(27),9,11,13(26),21,23-nonaene-8',2"-[1,3]dioxolane]	EtOH	225(3.99),275(3.97)	44-3816-79
$C_{25}H_{25}N_3O_7S$			
2(1H)-Quinazolinethione, 3,4-dihydro-4-imino-3-phenyl-1-(2,3,4-tri-O-acetyl-β-D-ribopyranosyl)-	MeOH	208(4.51),219(4.49), 242(4.41),287(4.56)	44-0173-79
$C_{25}H_{25}N_9O_5$			
1H-Pyrrole-2-carboxamide, N-[5-[[[2-(aminoiminomethyl)phenyl]amino[carbonyl]-1-methyl-1H-pyrrol-3-yl]-1-methyl-4-[[(1-methyl-4-nitro-1H-pyrrol-2-yl)carbonyl]amino]-, monohydrochloride	EtOH	236(4.43),298(4.51)	87-1296-79
1H-Pyrrole-2-carboxamide, N-[5-[[[3-(aminoiminomethyl)phenyl]amino]carbonyl]-1-methyl-1H-pyrrol-3-yl]-1-methyl-4-[[(1-methyl-4-nitro-1H-pyrrol-2-yl)carbonyl]amino]-, monohydrochloride	EtOH	238(4.37),302(4.45)	87-1296-79
1H-Pyrrole-2-carboxamide, N-[5-[[[4-(aminoiminomethyl)phenyl]amino]carbonyl]-1-methyl-1H-pyrrol-3-yl]-1-methyl-4-[[(1-methyl-4-nitro-1H-pyrrol-2-yl)carbonyl]amino]-, monohydrochloride	EtOH	242(4.45),300(4.53)	87-1296-79

Compound	Solvent	λ_{max}(log ε)	Ref.
$C_{25}H_{26}Br_2$			
3,4,5,6-Nonatetraene, 3,7-bis(4-bromophenyl)-2,2,8,8-tetramethyl-	C_6H_{12}	252s(4.58),264(4.67), 295s(4.40),355(3.43)	24-0567-79
$C_{25}H_{26}N_2O_2$			
Benzenepentanoic acid, δ-hydrazono-α,β-diphenyl-, ethyl ester	EtOH	266(4.09)	4-0001-79
1H-Pyrrolizine-5-acetamide, N,N-diethyl-2,3-dihydro-α-oxo-6,7-diphenyl-	MeOH	208(4.43),230(4.21), 328(4.24)	83-0896-79
$C_{25}H_{26}N_2O_3$			
1H-Indole-3-acetonitrile, 3-(2-acetoxycyclohexyl)-2,3-dihydro-2-oxo-1-(phenylmethyl)-, form B	EtOH	254(3.86),283s(2.89)	23-1694-79
form A	EtOH	254(--),283s(--)	23-1694-79
$C_{25}H_{26}N_4O_7$			
1H-Pyrazole-4,5-dione, 1-(4-methylphenyl)-3-(1,2,3-triacetoxypropyl)-, 4-(phenylhydrazone), [S-(R*,R*)]-	n.s.g.	207(3.84),252(3.90), 396(3.90)	106-0531-79
$C_{25}H_{26}O$			
Benzene, 1-(2-ethyl-2-methyl-3,3-diphenylcyclopropyl)-4-methoxy-, trans	EtOH	232(4.41),269(3.21), 273(3.22),282(3.24), 290(3.12)	44-1982-79
3-Hexanone, 5-methyl-1,1,1-triphenyl-	MeCN	235(3.31),261(2.92)	78-0177-79
1-Pentene, 3-(4-methoxyphenyl)-3-methyl-1,1-diphenyl-	EtOH	228(4.25),251(4.18), 285(3.62)	44-1982-79
$C_{25}H_{26}O_4$			
1,2-Propanediol, 3-[4-(1,2,3,4-tetrahydro-6-hydroxy-2-phenyl-1-naphthalenyl)phenoxy]-	n.s.g.	279(3.54)	87-1509-79
$C_{25}H_{26}O_5$			
9,10-Anthracenedione, 1,4-dihydroxy-8-methoxy-2-[3-methyl-6-(1-methylethyl)-2-cyclohexen-1-yl]-	MeOH	228(4.44),248(4.26), 280s(--),466(3.98)	5-2018-79
$C_{25}H_{26}O_6$			
[2,6'-Bi-2H-1-benzopyran]-4(3H)-one, 5,7,7'-trihydroxy-2'-methyl-2'-(4-methyl-3-pentenyl)-	MeOH	225(4.49),288(4.19), 320s(3.93)	142-0943-79
	MeOH-NaOMe	319.5(4.50)	142-0943-79
	MeOH-$AlCl_3$	223(4.56),310(4.33), 375(3.54)	142-0943-79
$C_{25}H_{26}O_8$			
Gigantolide	EtOH	202(4.37),211(4.23), 261(4.53)	105-0426-79
$C_{25}H_{27}N$			
1H-3-Benzazepine, 2,3,4,5-tetrahydro-2,2,3-trimethyl-1,5-diphenyl-	EtOH	205(3.98),260s(2.56)	4-1525-79
$C_{25}H_{27}NO$			
4-Piperidinol, 1,4-dimethyl-2,3,6-triphenyl-	EtOH	248-266(2.7-2.8),290s (1.9)	103-0899-79
1-Propanone, 2-(2,3-dihydro-2,2,5-trimethyl-6-phenyl-1H-pyrrolizin-7-yl)-1-phenyl-	MeOH	209(4.30),238(4.25), 272(3.86)	83-0896-79

Compound	Solvent	λ_{max}(log ε)	Ref.
2-Propanone, 3-(4-azatricyclo[4.3.1-1^{3,8}]undec-5-ylidene)-1,1-diphenyl-	MeOH	300(4.43)	44-3711-79
$C_{25}H_{27}NO_3$			
3-Cyclohexene-1-carboxylic acid, 4-[2-[4-(dimethylamino)phenyl]ethenyl]-2-oxo-6-phenyl-, ethyl ester	EtOH	274(4.20),427(4.45)	104-1059-79
$C_{25}H_{27}NO_3S_2$			
Androsta-1,3,5-trien-17-one, 3-[(2-nitrophenyl)dithio]-	MeOH	328(4.02),339(4.00)	39-1166-79C
Estra-1,3,5(10)-trien-17-one, 4-methyl-4-[(2-nitrophenyl)dithio]-	MeOH	343(3.90)	39-1166-79C
$C_{25}H_{27}NO_4S_2$			
Androsta-3,5-diene-11,17-dione, 3-[(2-nitrophenyl)dithio]-	MeOH	243(4.38),350(3.78)	39-1166-79C
$C_{25}H_{27}NO_9$			
Acetamide, 2-acetoxy-N-(2-acetoxy-5,6,7,9-tetrahydro-1,3,10-trimethoxy-9-oxobenzo[a]heptalen-7-yl)-, (S)-	EtOH	245(4.53),353(4.29)	142-0337-79
$C_{25}H_{27}N_2P$			
Cyclopropenylium, bis(dimethylamino)-(triphenylphosphonio)-, diperchlorate	n.s.g.	230(4.62),270(4.51)	89-0472-79
$C_{25}H_{27}N_3O_2$			
β-Alanine, N-[4-(2,2-dicyanoethenyl)-3-methylphenyl]-N-(phenylmethyl)-, butyl ester	EtOH	437(4.71)	110-1769-79
$C_{25}H_{27}N_5O_8$			
Erythrinan-2,8-dione, 1β,15,16-trimethoxy-, 2,4-dinitrophenylhydrazone, cis	MeOH	351(4.58)	24-1110-79
$C_{25}H_{28}$			
3,4,5,6-Nonatetraene, 2,2,8,8-tetramethyl-3,7-diphenyl-, (S)-(+)-	n.s.g.	248(4.6),259(4.6)	24-0567-79
$C_{25}H_{28}ClNO_3S_2$			
Androsta-3,5-dien-17-one, 1-chloro-3-[(2-nitrophenyl)dithio]-	MeOH	247(4.40),350(3.56)	39-1166-79C
$C_{25}H_{28}N_2O_2$			
1H-Indole-2-methanol, 3-[2-(3-ethyl-5,6-dihydro-1(2H)-pyridinyl)ethyl]-, benzoate	EtOH	224(4.61),274(3.94), 284(3.96),293(3.80)	23-0289-79
$C_{25}H_{28}N_2O_4$			
2-Propenoic acid, 2-cyano-3-[4-(3-ethoxy-3-oxopropyl)(phenylmethyl)amino]-2-methylphenyl]-, ethyl ester	EtOH	429(4.67)	110-1769-79
	EtOH-KOH	338(--)	110-1769-79
	CCl_4	420(--)	110-1769-79
	KBr	437(--)	110-1769-79
$C_{25}H_{28}N_2S$			
Thiourea, bis(phenylmethyl)tricyclo-[3.3.1.1^{3,7}]decylidene-	C_6H_{12}	240s(4.12),260(4.06), 295s(3.84)	24-1102-79

Compound	Solvent	λmax(log ε)	Ref.
$C_{25}H_{28}N_8$			
1H-Pyrazole-3-acetonitrile, 4-cyano-1-phenyl-5-[(1-piperidinylmethylene)-amino]-α-[[(1-piperidinylmethylene)-amino]methylene]-	MeOH	249(4.50),340(4.33), 383(4.14)	83-0535-79
$C_{25}H_{28}O_2S_2$			
Androsta-3,5-diene-11,17-dione, 3-(phenyldithio)-	MeOH	246(4.34)	39-1166-79C
$C_{25}H_{28}O_9$			
1H-Phenalene-3-acetic acid, 4-ethoxy-2-(ethoxycarbonyl)-9-hydroxy-7,8-dimethoxy-6-methyl-1-oxo-, ethyl ester	EtOH	215(4.59),237s(4.46), 256s(4.32),269s(4.30), 291s(4.03),380(4.12), 426(4.20)	150-0301-79
$C_{25}H_{28}O_{11}$			
4H-1-Benzopyran-4-one, 2-(3,4-dimethoxyphenyl)-6-β-D-glucopyranosyl-5,7-dimethoxy-	EtOH	290(3.74)	32-0009-79
$C_{25}H_{28}O_{13}$			
Caviunin 7-O-glucoside	MeOH	263(4.30),294s(3.09)	42-0081-79
$C_{25}H_{29}ClN_4O$			
Quinazoline, 6-chloro-2-(4-methylpiperazinomethyl)-4-(6,7,8,9-tetrahydro-5H-benzocyclohepten-2-yl)-, 3-oxide	MeOH	222(4.67),268(4.43), 327(3.83)	73-3604-79
$C_{25}H_{29}IN_2O_4$			
L-Tryptophan, N-[(phenylmethoxy)carbonyl]-, 6-iodohexyl ester	EtOH	274(3.79),282(3.82), 290(3.75)	118-0957-79
$C_{25}H_{29}NO_8$			
Quinolinium, 1-[3-ethoxy-2-(ethoxycarbonyl)-1-[2-ethoxy-1-(ethoxycarbonyl)-2-oxoethyl]-3-oxo-1-propenyl]-2-methyl-, hydroxide, inner salt	$CHCl_3$	317(3.8),381(4.0), 502(2.4)	5-1406-79
$C_{25}H_{29}N_2$			
3H-Indolium, 2-[3-(1,3-dihydro-1,3,3-trimethyl-2H-indol-2-ylidene)-1-propenyl]-1,3,3-trimethyl-, tetrafluoroborate	$CHCl_3$	554(5.14)	88-0225-79
$C_{25}H_{29}N_7O_2$			
3,11-Diazatricyclo[5.3.1.1^{2,6}]dodec-4-ene-8,12-dione, 3,11-bis(4,6-dimethylpyrimidin-2-yl)-10-(2-propenylamino)-	$CHCl_3$	250(4.33),278(4.29)	39-1525-79C
$C_{25}H_{30}$			
Bicyclo[2.2.1]heptane, 2-[bis(3-methylphenyl)methylene]-1,7,7-trimethyl-	MeCN	242.5(3.81)	24-0138-79
$C_{25}H_{30}N_2$			
Acridine, 9,10-dihydro-10-methyl-9-[2-(1-piperidinyl)-2-cyclohexen-1-yl]-	EtOH	285(4.03),318(3.43)	103-0541-79
$C_{25}H_{30}N_2O$			
1H-Pyrrolizine-5-methanol, α-[(diethyl-	MeOH	209(4.42),242(4.30),	83-0896-79

Compound	Solvent	λ_{max}(log ε)	Ref.
amino)methyl]-2,3-dihydro-6,7-diphenyl- (cont.)		268(4.10)	83-0896-79
$C_{25}H_{30}N_2O_3$			
Acetamide, N-[2-[2,3-dihydro-3-(2-hydroxycyclohexyl)-2-oxo-1-(phenylmethyl)-1H-indol-3-yl]ethyl]-, A	EtOH	253(3.89),281s(2.95)	23-1694-79
B	EtOH	254(3.84),280s(3.02)	23-1694-79
$C_{25}H_{30}N_2O_8$			
2-Naphthacenecarboxamide, 4-amino-N-(1,1-dimethylethyl)-1,4,4a,5,5a,6-11,12a-octahydro-3,12,12a-trihydroxy-8,10-dimethoxy-1,11-dioxo-, monohydrochloride (all spectra after one hour standing)	MeOH-HCl	252(4.28),273(4.24), 357(4.19),396s(4.00)	35-2171-79
	MeOH-NaOH	238s(4.21),248(4.22), 277(4.25),365(4.24)	35-2171-79
	MeOH-borax	243(4.28),277(4.25), 337(4.28),406s(3.46)	35-2171-79
$C_{25}H_{30}N_2O_8S$			
5-Thia-1-azabicyclo[4.2.0]oct-2-ene-2-carboxylic acid, 7-[[1-[[(1,1-dimethylethoxy)carbonyl]oxy]-2-phenoxyethylidene]amino]-3-methyl-4,8-dioxo-, 1,1-dimethylethyl ester, (6R-trans)-	EtOH	269(3.69),276(3.72), 294(3.70),317(3.70)	33-2681-79
$C_{25}H_{30}N_3$			
Methylium, tris[4-(dimethylamino)phenyl]-, perchlorate	EtOH	252(4.24),306(4.40), 356(3.15),374(3.08), 592(5.12)	65-0860-79
	acetone	590(5.10)	65-0860-79
$C_{25}H_{30}O_5$			
Andilesin B	EtOH	248(3.40),310(2.85)	39-2113-79C
Benzene, 1-[2-[2-(3,4-dimethoxyphenyl)-3-cyclohexen-1-yl]ethenyl]-2,4,5-trimethoxy-	MeOH	210(4.53),262(4.25), 313(3.94)	12-0071-79
18-Norpregna-4,8,11,13-tetraen-3-one, 20α,21-diacetoxy-17β-methyl-	MeOH	248(4.19)	39-1048-79C
Pregna-4,6,9(11),16-tetraen-3-one, 20α,21-diacetoxy-	MeOH	284(4.33)	39-1048-79C
Pregna-1,4,6-triene-3,11,20-trione, 21-acetoxy-6,16α-dimethyl-	MeOH	226(4.03),258(3.95), 294(4.08)	24-0979-79
$C_{25}H_{30}O_6$			
Andibenin	EtOH	247(3.61),310(2.90)	39-2113-79C
$C_{25}H_{30}O_7$			
19-Norpregna-1,3,5(10)-triene-11,20-dione, 2,21-diacetoxy-17α-hydroxy-1-methyl-	EtOH	267(2.74),276(2.74)	35-5019-79
Talassin A	EtOH	202(4.15),224(4.34), 252(4.25)	105-0426-79
Tricoccin S_{16}	MeOH	208(4.07)	88-4045-79
$C_{25}H_{30}O_{13}$			
Minecoside	MeOH	204(4.15),244(3.98), 298(4.09),328(4.18)	33-0535-79
$C_{25}H_{30}O_{14}$			
10-Dehydrogeniposide tetraacetate	MeOH	227.5(3.77)	94-3115-79

Compound	Solvent	$\lambda_{max}(\log \epsilon)$	Ref.
$C_{25}H_{30}S$			
Spiro[bicyclo[2.2.1]heptane-2,2'-thiiran], 1,7,7-trimethyl-3',3'-bis(3-methylphenyl)-, (1α,2α,4α)-	MeCN	267(3.16),276(3.13)	24-0138-79
$C_{25}H_{31}NO_2$			
1H-Benz[e]inden-3-ol, 2,3,3a,4,8,9,9a-9b-octahydro-7-(1-pyrrolidinyl)-, benzoate, [3S-(3α,3aα,9aα,9bβ)]-	n.s.g.	228(4.23),281(4.41)	22-0157-79
$C_{25}H_{31}N_3O_5$			
Spiro[1H-cyclopent[f]indolizine-7(5H)-1'(2'H)-[4H]pyrrolo[3,2,1-ij]quinoline]-2',6'(5'H)-dione, 2,3,5a,6,8-8a,9,9a-octahydro-7'-hydroxy-4',4',8-8-tetramethyl-5a-nitro-, (5aα,7α,8aα-9aβ)-	MeOH	265(4.02),358(3.79)	39-1751-79C
$C_{25}H_{31}N_7O_7S_2$			
L-Isoleucine, [[[7-[(hydroxyphenylacetyl)amino]-3-[[(1-methyl-1H-tetrazol-5-yl)thio]methyl]-8-oxo-3-thia-1-azabicyclo[4.2.0]oct-2-en-2-yl]carbonyl]oxy]methyl ester, hydrochloride, [6R-[6α,7β(R*)]]-	MeOH	274(3.93)	87-0657-79
L-Leucine, [[[7-[(hydroxyphenylacetyl)-amino]-3-[[(1-methyl-1H-tetrazol-5-yl)thio]methyl]-8-oxo-5-thia-1-azabicyclo[4.2.0]oct-2-en-2-yl]carbonyl]oxy]methyl ester, hydrochloride, [6R-[6α,7β(R*)]]-	EtOH	274(3.97)	87-0657-79
$C_{25}H_{32}NO_5$			
Pyridinium, 4-[2-[4-(2-butoxy-2-oxoethoxy)phenyl]ethenyl]-1-(2-butoxy-2-oxoethyl)-, chloride, (E)-	MeOH	385(4.10)	56-1649-79
Pyridinium, 4-[2-[4-[1-(ethoxycarbonyl)propoxy]phenyl]ethenyl]-1-[1-(ethoxycarbonyl)propyl]-, bromide	MeOH	397(4.40)	56-1649-79
Pyridinium, 4-[2-[4-(1-methyl-2-oxo-2-propoxyethoxy)phenyl]ethenyl]-1-(1-methyl-2-oxo-2-propoxyethyl)-, bromide	MeOH	388(4.35)	56-1649-79
$C_{25}H_{32}N_2O_{14}S$			
2H-Imidazole-2-thione, 1,3-dihydro-1,3-bis(2,3,5-tri-O-acetyl-β-D-ribofuranosyl)-	EtOH	271(4.19)	4-1185-79
	$CHCl_3$	277(4.14)	4-1185-79
$C_{25}H_{32}O_5$			
Andilesin C	EtOH	end absorption	39-2113-79C
18-Nor-5β-pregna-8,11,13-trien-3-one, 20α,21-diacetoxy-17β-methyl-	MeOH	269(2.67)	39-1048-79C
Pregna-4,6-diene-21-carboxylic acid, 17-hydroxy-3-oxo-6-(1-oxopropoxy)-, γ-lactone, (17α)-	MeOH	283(4.18)	44-1597-79
Pregna-1,4,6-triene-3,20-dione, 21-acetoxy-11α-hydroxy-6,16α-dimethyl-	MeOH	226(4.06),262(4.06), 300(4.05)	24-0979-79

Compound	Solvent	λ_{max}(log ε)	Ref.
$C_{25}H_{32}O_5S$			
Pregna-1,3,5-trien-11-one, 3-(ethyl-thio)-17α,20:20,21-bis(methylene-dioxy)-	MeCN	326(3.81)	39-1166-79C
$C_{25}H_{32}O_6$			
Andibenin A	EtOH	end absorption	39-2118-79C
Andibenin C	EtOH	end absorption	39-2118-79C
Andilesin A	EtOH	end absorption	39-2113-79C
Pregna-4,6,9(11)-trien-3-one, 20α,21-diacetoxy-17α-hydroxy-	MeOH	286(4.37)	39-1048-79C
$C_{25}H_{32}O_8$			
6-Benzocyclodeceneacetic acid, 5,12-di-acetoxy-3,4,4a,5,6,9,10,11,12,12a-decahydro-6-hydroxy-α,12a-dimethyl-4,9-bis(methylene)-3-oxo-, methyl ester, [4aR*,5S*,6R*(R*),7E,12S*,12aS*]-	MeOH	232(4.20)	78-1907-79
Clausenolide	EtOH	206(3.8),270(3.64)	77-0246-79
$C_{25}H_{32}O_{10}$			
Repandin A	MeOH	210(4.36)	44-3400-79
Undulatone, 15-deacetyl-	MeOH	223(4.25),240s(4.15)	78-0017-79
$C_{25}H_{33}IO_2$			
Dibenzofuran, 1,3,6-tris(1,1-dimethyl-ethyl)-x-iodo-8-methoxy-	EtOH	256(4.04),266(4.11), 285s(4.16),293(4.35), 317(3.91),330(3.85)	44-0428-79
$C_{25}H_{33}NO_2$			
Estr-4-en-3-one, 17β-hydroxy-, O-(phen-ylmethyl)oxime, (3E)-	EtOH	250(4.36)	78-0233-79
(3Z)-	EtOH	257(4.15)	78-0233-79
$C_{25}H_{33}NO_5S$			
Morpholine, 4-[(11β)-11,17-dihydroxy-3,20-dioxo-21-thioxopregna-1,4-dien-21-yl]-	EtOH	249.5(4.36)	94-1352-79
$C_{25}H_{33}N_3O_7$			
5-Oxa-1-azabicyclo[4.2.0]oct-2-ene-2-carboxylic acid, 7-[[[[(1,1-dimeth-ylethoxy)carbonyl]amino]phenylacet-yl]amino]-3-methyl-8-oxo-, 1,1-di-methylethyl ester, [6R-[6α,7β(R)]]-	EtOH	265(3.87)	39-2268-79C
$C_{25}H_{34}O_2$			
3(2H)-Furanone, 5-[2,6-dimethyl-8-(2,6,6-trimethyl-1-cyclohexen-1-yl)-1,3,5,7-octatetraenyl]-2,2-dimethyl-, (all-E)-	EtOH	408(4.65)	142-0505-79
(Z,E,E,E)-	EtOH	407(4.72)	142-0505-79
$C_{25}H_{34}O_3$			
Benz[6,7]androsta-4,6-dien-3-one, 17-acetoxy-3',6,6',7-tetrahydro-	MeOH	244(4.10)	44-4299-79
19-Norpregn-4-en-20-yn-3-one, 17-(2,2-dimethyl-1-oxopropoxy)-, (17α)-	EtOH	241(3.78)	13-0793-79B
$C_{25}H_{34}O_4$			
Pregna-4,6-diene-21-carboxylic acid,	EtOH	250(3.90),307(4.13)	44-1597-79

Compound	Solvent	λ_{max}(log ε)	Ref.
17-hydroxy-6-(1-methylethoxy)-3-oxo-, γ-lactone, (17α)- (cont.)			44-1597-79
$C_{25}H_{34}O_5$			
Androsta-5,7-dien-3-one, 17,19-diacetoxy-4,4-dimethyl-, (13α,17β)-	n.s.g.	239s(3.21),244s(3.35), 249s(3.51),255s(3.65), 261s(3.73),280(3.88)	33-2732-79
(17β)-	n.s.g.	265s(3.90),273(4.00), 282(2.98),294s(3.73)	33-2732-79
Benzene, 1-[2-[2-(3,4-dimethoxyphenyl)-cyclohexyl]ethyl]-2,4,5-trimethoxy-, cis-(±)-	MeOH	230(4.02),287(3.62)	12-0071-79
$C_{25}H_{34}O_6$			
Androst-8-ene-3,7-dione, 17,19-diacetoxy-4,4-dimethyl-, (5α,17β)-	n.s.g.	250(3.94)	33-2732-79
Androst-8(14)-ene-3,7-dione, 17,19-diacetoxy-4,4-dimethyl-, (5α,13α,17β)-	n.s.g.	257(3.80)	33-2732-79
(5α,17β)-	n.s.g.	260(4.03)	33-2732-79
Pregna-4,9(11)-dien-3-one, 20α,21-diacetoxy-17α-hydroxy-	MeOH	248(4.16)	39-1048-79C
Pregn-5-ene-7,20-dione, 17α-acetoxy-3,3'-(ethylenedioxy)-	EtOH	240(4.11)	150-0501-79
$C_{25}H_{34}O_7$			
10α-Pregn-4-ene-2,20-dione, 21-acetoxy-1β,11β-epoxy-11α-ethoxy-17α-hydroxy-	MeOH	283(2.55)	35-5019-79
$C_{25}H_{34}O_9$			
Castelanone	n.s.g.	239(4.08)	28-0269-79A
$C_{25}H_{35}NO_3S$			
Morpholine, 4-(3,20-dioxo-21-thioxo-pregn-4-en-21-yl)-	EtOH	243(4.34)	94-1352-79
$C_{25}H_{35}NO_4S$			
Morpholine, 4-(17-hydroxy-3,20-dioxo-21-thioxopregn-4-en-21-yl)-	EtOH	245(4.36)	94-1352-79
$C_{25}H_{35}NO_5S$			
Morpholine, 4-[(11β)-11,17-dihydroxy-3,20-dioxo-21-thioxopregn-4-en-21-yl]-	EtOH	247(4.36)	94-1352-79
$C_{25}H_{36}N_4O_4$			
7a-Aza-B-homopregn-5-eno[7a,7-d]tetrazole-3β,20β-diol, diacetate	EtOH	242(4.08)	39-3166-79C
$C_{25}H_{36}N_8O$			
5α-Androst-2-en-17β-ol, 17α-methyl-3-(4H-1,2,4-triazol-4-ylamino)-2-[(4H-1,2,4-triazol-4-ylimino)methyl]-	MeOH	208(3.95),320(4.20)	39-1816-79C
$C_{25}H_{36}O_2$			
6H-Dibenzo[b,d]pyran-1-ol, 3-(1-butyl-1-pentenyl)-6a,7,10,10a-tetrahydro-6,6,9-trimethyl-	EtOH	225(4.62),257(4.15)	2-0250-79A
$C_{25}H_{36}O_3$			
4,6,8,10,12-Tridecapentaen-3-one, 2,5-dihydroxy-2,7,11-trimethyl-13-(2,6,6-	EtOH	405(4.48)	142-0505-79
	EtOH-NaOH	376(--)	142-0505-79

Compound	Solvent	λmax(log ε)	Ref.
trimethyl-1-cyclohexen-1-yl)-, (Z,E,E,E,E)- (cont.)			142-0505-79
(Z,Z,E,E,E)-	EtOH	404(4.58)	142-0505-79
	EtOH-NaOH	370(--)	142-0505-79
$C_{25}H_{36}O_4$			
Pregna-5,7-diene-20-carboxylic acid, 3β-acetoxy-, methyl ester	EtOH	271(4.11),281(4.12), 293(3.88)	44-0643-79
$C_{25}H_{36}O_5$			
Pregna-5,7-diene-3,20-dione, 17-hydroxy-, cyclic bis(1,2-ethanediyl acetal)	MeOH	281.5(4.08)	54-0078-79
(9β,10α)-	MeOH	272(3.97)	54-0078-79
Pregn-5-ene-3,7,20-trione, cyclic 3,20-bis(1,2-ethanediyl acetal)	EtOH	240(4.09)	150-0501-79
$C_{25}H_{36}O_6$			
Digitoxigenin, 18,20-epoxy-20,22-dihydro-, acetate	MeOH	219(2.23)	44-3511-79
3-acetate	MeOH	218(2.69)	44-3511-79
$C_{25}H_{38}NO_2$			
17a-Aza-D-homoandrost-5-en-17a-yloxy, 3β-hydroxy-17,17-di-2-propenyl-	MeOH	235(3.53),443(1.23)	22-0401-79
$C_{25}H_{38}N_2OP$			
Methylium, [bis(1,1-dimethylethyl)phosphinyl]bis[4-(dimethylamino)phenyl]-, perchlorate	MeCN	262(3.92),300s(3.62)	65-1275-79
$C_{25}H_{38}O_2$			
2,6,10,14,18-Eicosapentaenedial, 2,6,10,14,18-pentamethyl-, (E,Z,E,E,E)-	EtOH	233(4.28)	138-1387-79
$C_{25}H_{38}O_3$			
2H-1-Benzopyran-2-one, 4-(hexadecyloxy)-	isooctane	213(4.59),254s(--), 263(4.09),274(4.04), 294s(--),303(3.84), 316s(--)	23-1377-79
	EtOH	213(4.54),257s(--), 264(4.06),276(4.04), 303(3.83),312s(--)	23-1377-79
Ceroplastolic acid	n.s.g.	215(4.274)	25-0592-79
$C_{25}H_{39}NO$			
2-Butenamide, N-cyclohexyl-4-(dodecahydro-3a,6-dimethyl-7H-benz[e]inden-7-ylidene)-, [3aS-[3aα,5aβ,6α,7Z(Z)-9aα,9bβ]]-	hexane	228(3.76)	24-0310-79
$C_{25}H_{39}N_2OP$			
Benzenamine, 4,4'-[[bis(1,1-dimethylethyl)phosphinyl]methylene]bis[N,N-dimethyl-	EtOH	262(4.31),276(4.39), 300s(3.81)	65-1275-79
$C_{25}H_{39}N_2P$			
Benzenamine, 4,4'-[[bis(1,1-dimethylethyl)phosphino]methylene]bis[N,N-dimethyl-	EtOH	267(4.52),300s(3.76), 356(2.54)	65-1275-79

Compound	Solvent	λmax(log ε)	Ref.
$C_{25}H_{40}NO_2$			
17a-Aza-D-homoandrostan-17a-yloxy,	C_6H_{12}	237(3.52),472(1.30)	22-0401-79
3β-hydroxy-17,17-di-2-propenyl-, (5α)-	MeOH	235(3.54),445(1.26)	22-0401-79
17a-Aza-D-homoandrost-4-en-17a-yloxy,	C_6H_{12}	231(4.31),462(1.07)	22-0401-79
3-oxo-17,17-dipropyl-	MeOH	240(4.28),441(1.08)	22-0401-79
$C_{25}H_{40}N_2$			
17a-Aza-D-homopregna-3,5-diene, 3-N-pyrrolidinyl-	MeOH	275(4.36)	39-0305-79C
$C_{25}H_{40}N_2O$			
17a-Aza-D-homopregna-3,5-dien-21-ol, 3-N-pyrrolidinyl-	MeOH	275(4.39)	39-2451-79C
$C_{25}H_{41}NO$			
17a-Aza-D-homoandrost-4-en-3-one, 17,17-dipropyl-	C_6H_{12}	231(4.27),325(1.70), 335f(1.70)	22-0401-79
	MeOH	238(4.24)	22-0401-79
$C_{25}H_{42}NO_2$			
17a-Aza-D-homoandrostan-17a-yloxy,	C_6H_{12}	246(3.26),470(1.05)	22-0401-79
3-oxo-17,17-dipropyl-	MeOH	242(3.20),438(1.08)	22-0401-79
17a-Aza-D-homoandrost-5-en-17a-yloxy,	C_6H_{12}	244(3.25),465(1.06)	22-0401-79
3β-hydroxy-17,17-dipropyl-	MeOH	243(3.33),440(1.12)	22-0401-79
$C_{25}H_{42}N_3O_8P$			
Hexadecanoic acid, 2,3,3a,9-tetrahydro-6-imino-2-[(phosphonooxy)methyl]-6H-furo[2',3':4,5]oxazolo[3,2-a]pyrimidin-3-yl ester, [2R-(2α,3β,3aβ,9aβ)]-	MeOH	235(3.97),264(4.04)	87-0639-79
$C_{25}H_{42}O_2$			
Farnesol, ω-hydroxygeranyl-	EtOH	212(3.85)	138-1387-79
$C_{25}H_{42}O_4$			
4H-Pyran-4-one, 3,5-dibutyl-2-(1-butyl-2-oxoheptyl)-6-methoxy-	EtOH	252(3.90)	35-4386-79
$C_{25}H_{43}NO$			
17a-Aza-D-homo-5α-androstan-3-one,	C_6H_{12}	290(1.79)	22-0401-79
17,17-dipropyl-	MeOH	282(1.93)	22-0401-79
$C_{25}H_{44}NO_2$			
17a-Aza-D-homoandrostan-17a-yloxy,	C_6H_{12}	245(3.28),460(1.13)	22-0401-79
3β-hydroxy-17,17-dipropyl-	MeOH	243(3.31),442(1.16)	22-0401-79

Compound	Solvent	$\lambda_{max}(\log \epsilon)$	Ref.
$C_{26}H_{12}ClN_3O_3$			
Benzimidazo[2,1-a]benz[de]isoquinolin-7-one, 4-chloro-3-phthalimido-	xylene	406(4.17)	153-0043-79
$C_{26}H_{12}Cl_2N_2S_2$			
Dibenzo[c,n]triphenodithiazine, 8,17-dichloro-	H_2SO_4	359(4.83)	40-0432-79
	$o-C_6H_4Cl_2$	632(4.26)	40-0432-79
$C_{26}H_{12}N_4O_2$			
Bisbenzimidazo[2,1-b:1',2'-j]benzo-[lmn][3,8]phenanthroline-6,9-dione	H_2SO_4	246(4.53),328(4.19), 382(4.03),492(4.45)	103-0791-79
Bisbenzimidazo[2,1-b:2',1'-i]benzo-[lmn][3,8]phenanthroline-8,17-dione	H_2SO_4	250(4.49),291(4.57), 382(4.03),474(4.47)	103-0791-79
$C_{26}H_{12}O_2S_2$			
Pyreno[1,10-bc]thiopyran-5(4H)-one, 4-(3-oxobenzo[b]thien-2(3H)-ylidene)-, cis	n.s.g.	551(4.12)	124-0768-79
trans	n.s.g.	657(4.38)	124-0768-79
Pyreno[10,1-bc]thiopyran-3(4H)-one, 4-(3-oxobenzo[b]thien-2(3H)-ylidene)-, cis	n.s.g.	507(4.22)	124-0768-79
trans	n.s.g.	609(4.45)	124-0768-79
$C_{26}H_{13}BrN_2O_4$			
Dinaphtho[2,1-b:2',3'-d]furan-6-carbox-amide, 3-bromo-8,13-dihydro-8,13-di-oxo-N-2-pyridinyl-	dioxan	422(3.83)	46-1208-79
	C_6H_5Cl	428(3.84)	46-1208-79
$C_{26}H_{14}BrF_3N_2O_2$			
Quinazolinium, 4-(6-bromo-1(or 3)-pyr-enyl)-3,4-dihydro-, trifluoroacetate	EtOH	236(4.62),267(4.24), 281(4.44),321(3.72), 336(4.24),354(4.50)	24-1348-79
$C_{26}H_{14}BrNOS$			
9H-Naphtho[3,2,1-kl]acridin-9-one, 2-bromo-6-(phenylthio)-	EtOH	288(4.97),402(4.10), 478(4.35),506(4.37)	103-1227-79
9H-Naphtho[3,2,1-kl]acridin-9-one, 2-bromo-8-(phenylthio)-	EtOH	286(4.79),428(4.39), 478(4.35),506(4.37)	103-1227-79
$C_{26}H_{14}N_2O_4$			
Dinaphtho[2,1-b:2',3'-d]furan-6-carbox-amide, 8,13-dihydro-8,13-dioxo-N-2-	dioxan	428(3.74)	46-1208-79
	$C_2H_4Cl_2$	433(3.80)	46-1208-79
	C_6H_5Cl	435(3.75)	46-1208-79
	DMF	435(3.72)	46-1208-79
	DMSO	435(3.76)	46-1208-79
$C_{26}H_{14}N_2O_7$			
1H-[2]Benzoxepino[3,4-b]pyrrole-2,4,9-(3H)-trione, 1-methyl-3-(1,2,4,9-tetrahydro-1-methyl-2,4,9-trioxo-3H-benz[f]indol-3-ylidene)-	MeCN	226(4.56),255(4.43), 310s(3.99),520(3.45)	103-0759-79
$C_{26}H_{14}N_2S_2$			
Dibenzo[c,n]triphenodithiazine	H_2SO_4	348(4.79)	40-0432-79
	$o-C_6H_4Cl$	630(4.52)	40-0432-79
$C_{26}H_{14}O$			
Diphenaleno[2,1-b:1',2'-d]furan	MeCN	252(3.66),295(3.81), 308(3.96),340(3.51), 398(3.08),424(3.04),	88-2867-79

Compound	Solvent	λ$_{max}$(log ε)	Ref.
(cont.)		520s(--),568(4.01), 614(4.31)	88-2867-79
$C_{26}H_{16}$			
5,6-Benzopicene	EtOH	212(4.65),276(4.88), 293(4.72),305(4.79), 335(4.12),351(3.91), 373(2.88),394(2.63)	70-1784-79
$C_{26}H_{16}Cl_2O_2$			
9(10H)-Anthracenone, 1,3-dichloro-4-hydroxy-10,10-diphenyl-	EtOH	206(4.78),266(4.07), 287(4.03)	104-0139-79
$C_{26}H_{16}N_2O_2$			
Benzoxazole, 2,2'-[1,1'-biphenyl]-4,4'-diylbis-	H_2SO_4	207(4.72),390(3.94)	103-1299-79
5,5'-Bibenzoxazole, 2,2'-diphenyl-	H_2SO_4	261(4.46),346(3.92)	103-1299-79
$C_{26}H_{16}N_2O_3$			
Benzoxazole, 2,2'-(oxydi-4,1-phenylene)bis-	H_2SO_4	200(4.32),345(3.84)	103-1299-79
$C_{26}H_{16}N_2O_4S$			
Benzoxazole, 5,5'-sulfonylbis[2-phenyl-	H_2SO_4	208(4.78),265(3.89)	103-1299-79
$C_{26}H_{16}O_4$			
5,11-Naphthacenedione, 6-(4-acetylphenoxy)-	toluene	480(4.26)	135-0691-79A
5,12-Naphthacenedione, 6-(4-acetylphenoxy)-	toluene	400(3.78)	135-0691-79A
$C_{26}H_{17}F_3N_2O_2$			
Quinazolinium, 4-(1-pyrenyl)-3,4-dihydro-, trifluoroacetate	EtOH	244(4.72),257(4.33), 266(4.47),278(4.61), 318(4.08),328(4.37), 347(4.50),375(2.92)	24-1348-79
$C_{26}H_{18}BrNO_3$			
Benzo[f]quinoline-2-carboxylic acid, 3-(4-bromophenyl)-1-(2-furanyl)-, ethyl ester	EtOH	284(4.62),348(3.80), 367(3.77)	103-0139-79
$C_{26}H_{18}FNO_3$			
Benzo[f]quinoline-2-carboxylic acid, 3-(4-fluorophenyl)-1-(2-furanyl)-, ethyl ester	EtOH	286(4.63),349(3.83), 367(3.77)	103-0139-79
$C_{26}H_{18}N_2$			
9H-Fluoren-2-amine, N-(2,9-dihydro-2-imino-3H-fluoren-9-ylidene)-	MeCN	277(4.3),660(3.4)	18-3208-79
$C_{26}H_{18}N_2OS$			
2H-Naphtho[1,8-bc]thiophen-2-one, 3-ethoxy-, 9H-fluoren-9-ylidenehydrazone	MeOH	208(4.7),231(4.6), 242(4.7),258(4.7), 268(4.6),281(4.5), 292(4.5),318(4.3), 328(4.3),344(4.2), 361(4.2),460(4.6), 477(4.5)	5-1789-79

Compound	Solvent	λ_{max}(log ε)	Ref.
$C_{26}H_{18}N_2O_2$			
Isoquinoline, 2-benzoyl-1,2-dihydro-1-[2-(1H-indol-3-yl)-2-oxoethylidene]-	MeCN	227(4.49),264(4.06)	103-1337-79
$C_{26}H_{18}N_2O_5$			
Benzo[f]quinoline-2-carboxylic acid, 1-(2-furanyl)-3-(4-nitrophenyl)-, ethyl ester	EtOH	290(4.64),348(3.95), 366(3.83)	103-0139-79
$C_{26}H_{18}N_6NiO_4$			
Nickel, [5,6,7,8-tetrahydro-2,11-dinitrodibenzo[f,l]naphtho[2,3-b]-[1,4,8,11]tetraazacyclotetradecinato(2-)-N^5,N^8,N^{14},N^{21}]-, (SP-4-2)-	$CHCl_3$	380(4.00),430(3.85)	12-2303-79
$C_{26}H_{18}O_3$			
Anthra[2,3-b]oxiren-2(1aH)-one, 9,9a-dihydro-9-hydroxy-3,8-diphenyl-, (1aα,9α,9aα)-	ether	256(4.60),302(3.90), 311(3.88),350(3.52)	22-0110-79
(1aα,9β,9aα)-	ether	255(4.60),296(3.91), 304s(3.89),334s(3.41), 345(3.48)	22-0110-79
$C_{26}H_{18}O_4$			
Dibenz[a,h]anthracene-3,4-diol, diacetate	dioxan	282(4.71),290(4.99), 301(5.18),323(4.36), 337(4.27),352(4.19), 374(3.07),394(2.99)	44-3086-79
$C_{26}H_{18}S_2$			
9,9'-Bi-9H-thioxanthene	EtOH	247(4.20),292(3.78)	151-0205-79A
$C_{26}H_{19}ClO_3$			
1(2H)-Anthracenone, 2-chloro-3,4-dihydro-3,4-dihydroxy-9,10-diphenyl-, (2α,3β,4α)-	ether	248(4.65),295(3.92), 325s(3.35),339(3.42)	22-0110-79
(2α,3β,4β)-	ether	250s(4.64),254(4.65), 297(3.91),307s(3.89), 343(3.55),348s(3.54)	22-0110-79
$C_{26}H_{19}NO$			
Cyclopent[d][1,3]oxazine, 2-methyl-4,5,7-triphenyl-	hexane	238(4.40),290(4.65), 405(4.06),517s(3.07)	88-2125-79
Indeno[1,2-b]pyridinium, 9-benzoyl-N-(phenylmethyl)-, hydroxide, inner salt	EtOH	206(5.63),240(5.61), 302(5.60),351(5.64), 378(5.40),520(4.19)	103-1214-79
Indeno[2,3-c]pyridinium, 9-benzoyl-N-(phenylmethyl)-, hydroxide, inner salt	EtOH	206(4.76),226(4.66), 286(4.78),338(4.35), 370(4.35),500(4.19)	103-1214-79
$C_{26}H_{19}NO_3$			
Benzo[f]quinoline-2-carboxylic acid, 1-(2-furanyl)-3-phenyl-, ethyl ester	EtOH	284(4.60),348(3.82), 365(3.82)	103-0139-79
$C_{26}H_{19}NO_3P$			
4H-1,4-Benzoxaphosphorinium, 2-(4-nitrophenyl)-4,4-diphenyl-, perchlorate	MeCN	277(4.43)	78-0775-79
$C_{26}H_{20}$			
Phenanthrene, 4a,4b-dihydro-9,10-diphenyl-	C_6H_{11}Me-isopentane	300(4.2),315(4.3), 450(3.8)	150-1164-79

Compound	Solvent	$\lambda_{max}(\log \epsilon)$	Ref.
Tetraphenylethylene, radical cation	BuCl	494(3.69),929(3.37)	18-2794-79
$C_{26}H_{20}BrClN_2O_2$			
1-Naphthalenecarboxylic acid, 2-[3-(4-bromophenyl)-1-(4-chlorophenyl)-3-oxopropyl]hydrazide	EtOH	222(4.82),260(4.29), 279s(3.91),288s(3.85)	94-0257-79
$C_{26}H_{20}BrNO_3$			
Naphtho[1,2-b]furan-3(2H)-one, 4-(4-bromophenyl)-2-(ethylphenylamino)-5-hydroxy-	EtOH	219(4.66),248(4.63), 278(4.58),410(3.90)	103-0597-79
Naphtho[1,2-b]furan-3(2H)-one, 4-(4-bromophenyl)-5-hydroxy-2-[methyl-(4-methylphenyl)amino]-	EtOH	219(4.71),244(4.67), 277(4.58),412(3.95)	103-0597-79
$C_{26}H_{20}ClN_3O$			
Imidazo[1,2-a]pyrazin-3(7H)-one, 6-(4-chlorophenyl)-2,8-bis(phenylmethyl)-	MeOH	256(4.38),368(3.79), 426(3.89)	69-2204-79
$C_{26}H_{20}Cl_2CoN_4O_4$			
Cobalt, bis[2-chloro-4,5-dihydro-1-methyl-5-oxo-4-[(phenylimino)methyl]-1H-pyrrole-3-carboxaldehydato-N^4,O^5]-, (T-4)-	EtOH-10%DMF	290(4.24),390(4.73)	65-0365-79
	$CHCl_3$	255(--),305(--), 400(--)	65-0365-79
$C_{26}H_{20}Cl_2CuN_4O_4$			
Copper, bis[2-chloro-4,5-dihydro-1-methyl-5-oxo-4-[(phenylimino)methyl]-1H-pyrrole-3-carboxaldehydato-N^4,O^5]-, (T-4)-	EtOH-10%DMF	290(4.26),380(4.36)	65-0365-79
	$CHCl_3$	250(4.39),305(4.61), 390(4.71),560(3.04)	65-0365-79
$C_{26}H_{20}Cl_2N_2O_2Se_2Zn$			
Zinc, bis[2-chloro-4,5-dihydro-1-methyl-4-[(phenylimino)methyl]-5-selenoxo-1H-pyrrole-3-carboxaldehydato-N^4,Se^5]-, (T-4)-	EtOH-10%DMF	280(4.41),340(4.53)	65-0365-79
	$CHCl_3$	255(4.41),340(4.64), 395(4.28)	65-0365-79
$C_{26}H_{20}Cl_2N_4NiO_4$			
Nickel, bis[2-chloro-4,5-dihydro-1-methyl-5-oxo-4-[(phenylimino)methyl]-1H-pyrrole-3-carboxaldehydato-N^4,O^5]-, (T-4)-	EtOH-10%DMF	295(4.27),390(4.79)	65-0365-79
	$CHCl_3$	255(--),305(--), 340(--),405(--)	65-0365-79
$C_{26}H_{20}Cl_2N_4O_2S_2Zn$			
Zinc, bis[2-chloro-4,5-dihydro-1-methyl-4-[(phenylimino)methyl]-5-thioxo-1H-pyrrole-3-carboxaldehydato-N^4,S^5]-, (T-4)-	EtOH-10%DMF	272(4.66),320(4.62), 390(4.42)	65-0365-79
	$CHCl_3$	280s(4.38),320(4.57), 390(4.37)	65-0365-79
$C_{26}H_{20}Cl_2N_4O_4Zn$			
Zinc, bis[2-chloro-4,5-dihydro-1-methyl-5-oxo-4-[(phenylimino)methyl]-1H-pyrrole-3-carboxaldehydato-N^4,O^5]-, (T-4)-	EtOH-10%DMF	297(4.4),400(4.65)	65-0365-79
	$CHCl_3$	250(4.27),305(4.42), 400(4.66)	65-0365-79
$C_{26}H_{20}Cl_4N_4$			
Pyrimidine, 4,4'-(1,3-dichloro-2,4-diphenyl-1,3-cyclobutanediyl)bis[6-chloro-2-methyl-, trans	MeOH	261(4.24)	4-1575-79

Compound	Solvent	λ_{max}(log ε)	Ref.
$C_{26}H_{20}CuN_4$			
Copper, [5,6,7,8-tetrahydrodibenzo-[f,l]naphtho[2,3-b][1,4,8,11]tetra-azacyclotetradecinato(2-)-N^5,N^8,N^{14}-N^{21}]-, (SP-4-2)-	$CHCl_3$	252(4.58),330(4.26),450(4.06),500(3.95)	12-2303-79
$C_{26}H_{20}IN_3O_2$			
Butanamide, N-(4-iodophenyl)-2-[4-(1-naphthalenyl)phenylhydrazono]-	EtOH	248(4.22),278(4.11),390(4.57)	2-0585-79A
$C_{26}H_{20}N_2O_2$			
Benzo[g]phthalazine, 6,9-dimethoxy-1,4-diphenyl-	CH_2Cl_2	287(4.58),359(3.70),375(3.85),416(3.63)	150-3501-79
$C_{26}H_{20}N_2O_2$			
Pyridinium, 1,1'-[(9,10-dihydro-9,10-dioxo-2,3-anthracenediyl)bis(methylene)]bis-, dibromide	H_2O	258(4.75),276(4.17),328(3.73)	78-2255-79
$C_{26}H_{20}N_4$			
Benzo[c]cinnolinium, 5-[[[(2-methylphenyl)amino]phenylmethylene]amino]-, hydroxide, inner salt	CH_2Cl_2	250(4.67),295(4.11),307(4.05),322(3.96),400(4.11)	39-0185-79C
Benzo[c]cinnolinium, 5-[[[(4-methylphenyl)amino]phenylmethylene]amino]-, hydroxide, inner salt	CH_2Cl_2	251(4.66),297(3.85),310(3.78),322(3.60),400(4.15)	39-0185-79C
$C_{26}H_{20}N_4Ni$			
Nickel, [5,6,7,8-tetrahydrodibenzo-[f,l]naphtho[2,3-b][1,4,8,11]tetra-azacyclotetradecinato(2-)-N^5,N^8,N^{14}-N^{21}]-, (SP-4-2)-	$CHCl_3$	264(4.54),296(4.57),348(4.30),436(4.11)	12-2303-79
$C_{26}H_{20}N_8$			
1H-Tetrazolium, 5-[bis(phenylazo)methylene]-1,3-diphenyl-, hydroxide, inner salt	EtOH	287(4.33),470(4.59)	24-2369-79
$C_{26}H_{20}O$			
Diphenaleno[2,1-b:1',2'-d]furan, 4,5,6,10,11,12-hexahydro-	benzene	305(3.38),338(3.40),352(3.77),369(3.89)	88-2867-79
$C_{26}H_{20}OP$			
4H-1,4-Benzoxaphosphorinium, 2,4,4-triphenyl-, bromide	MeCN	261(4.42)	78-0775-79
$C_{26}H_{20}O_2S_2$			
Methanone, [2-(ethylthio)-5-phenyl-3,4-thiophenediyl]bis[phenyl-	CH_2Cl_2	255(4.55),261(4.55)	24-1650-79
$C_{26}H_{20}O_4$			
1H-Indene-1,3(2H)-dione, 2-(3,4-diethoxy-1H-phenalen-1-ylidene)-	MeCN	251(5.6),282(5.6),356(5.6),430(5.5),590(5.3)	83-0288-79
$C_{26}H_{20}O_9$			
Xanthoviridicatin D	MeOH	225(4.06),264(4.36),384(3.91)	88-4989-79
$C_{26}H_{20}Zr$			
Zirconium, bis(η^5-2,4-cyclopentadien-1-	$CHCl_3$	248(4.15),268(3.94),	101-0353-79S

Compound	Solvent	λmax(log ε)	Ref.
yl)bis(phenylethynyl)- (cont.)		310(3.58)	101-0353-79S
$C_{26}H_{21}BrN_2O_2$			
1-Naphthalenecarboxylic acid, 2-[3-(4-bromophenyl)-3-oxo-1-phenylpropyl]-hydrazide	EtOH	222(4.81),261(4.26), 281(4.20),289s(4.19)	94-0257-79
$C_{26}H_{21}ClO_5$			
[1,1'-Binaphthalene]-2-carboxylic acid, 4-acetoxy-6-chloro-4'-methoxy-	n.s.g.	211(5.07),289s(4.21), 300(4.30),322s(4.13)	33-0090-79
3-Phenanthrenecarboxylic acid, 1-acetoxy-4-(4-chlorophenyl)-9-methoxy-, ethyl ester	n.s.g.	228(4.51),261(4.49), 278s(4.18),308(4.07), 336s(3.56)	33-0090-79
$C_{26}H_{21}Cl_3S_4$			
Benzene, 1,1',1"-[[1-[(1,1-dimethylethyl)thio]-1,2,3-butatrien-1-yl-4-ylidene]tris(thio)tris[4-chloro-	heptane	202(4.61),225s(4.41), 403(4.26)	5-1606-79
$C_{26}H_{21}NO_4$			
5(2H)-Oxazolone, 2-(3,4-diethoxy-1H-phenalen-1-ylidene)-4-phenyl-	C_6H_{12}	304(5.3),542(5.0), 590(5.0),640(5.0)	83-0288-79
	MeOH	275(4.8),414(5.2), 605(4.9),655(4.9)	83-0288-79
	MeCN	313(5.1),414(5.3), 554(4.8),602(4.7), 652(4.9)	83-0288-79
$C_{26}H_{21}N_3O$			
Imidazo[1,2-a]pyrazin-3(7H)-one, 6-phenyl-2,8-bis(phenylmethyl)-	MeOH	250(4.38),360(3.80), 430(3.93)	69-2204-79
$C_{26}H_{21}N_3O_4$			
Pyridinium, 1-[3-(1-butyl-5-cyano-1,6-dihydro-2-hydroxy-4-methyl-6-oxo-3-pyridinyl)-1,4-dihydro-1,4-dioxo-2-naphthalenyl]-, hydroxide, inner salt	EtOH	252(4.38),337(4.32), 645(3.58)	2-0100-79A
$C_{26}H_{21}N_5O_5$			
1H-Pyrazole-3-carboxylic acid, 5-[[(4-nitrobenzoyl)hydrazono]phenylmethyl]-4-phenyl-, ethyl ester	EtOH	310(3.18)	4-0849-79
$C_{26}H_{21}N_8$			
1H-Tetrazolium, 5-(1,5-diphenylformazanyl)-1,3-diphenyl-, chloride	EtOH	258(4.27),265(4.29), 311(4.45),456(4.37)	24-2369-79
$C_{26}H_{21}O_4P$			
Phosphonium, [3,6-dihydroxy-2-(methoxycarbonyl)phenyl]triphenyl-, hydroxide, inner salt	EtOH	207(4.80),393(3.78)	33-2350-79
$C_{26}H_{22}ClNO_6$			
3H-2a-Azacyclopenta[ef]heptalene-1,4,5-tricarboxylic acid, 2-chloro-3-phenyl-, 1-ethyl 4,5-dimethyl ester	EtOH	228(4.54),260(4.28), 434(4.38),492s(3.95), 530(3.74),570(3.43)	142-1031-79
$C_{26}H_{22}NOP$			
Ethanone, 1-(4-aminophenyl)-2-(triphenylphosphoranylidene)-	MeOH	275(3.85),334(4.36)	65-2189-79

Compound	Solvent	λ max(log ε)	Ref.
$C_{26}H_{22}N_2$			
9H-Carbazol-9-amine, N-(3',5'-dimethyl-[1,1'-biphenyl]-2-yl)-	n.s.g.	233(4.68),292(4.24), 323(3.62),337(3.59)	39-1536-79C
Cinnoline, 1,2,3,4-tetrahydro-1,2,4-triphenyl-	MeCN	247(4.50),286(4.32)	103-1243-79
$C_{26}H_{22}N_2O_2$			
1-Naphthalenecarboxylic acid, 2-(3-oxo-1,3-diphenylpropyl)hydrazide	EtOH	222(4.85),245s(4.18), 280(3.94),288(3.89)	94-0257-79
$C_{26}H_{22}N_2O_3$			
1H-Cyclopenta[l]phenanthrene-1-carboxylic acid, 2,3-dihydro-1-hydroxy-2-(phenylhydrazono)-, ethyl ester	EtOH	249s(4.83),256(4.94), 279(4.61),287(4.58), 300(4.55),333s(3.85), 349(3.71)	39-2034-79C
$C_{26}H_{22}N_2O_4$			
Benzenamine, N-[5,6-dihydro-9,10-dimethoxy-8H-benzo[g]-1,3-benzodioxolo[5,6-a]quinolizin-8-ylidene)-	EtOH	285(3.95),328(3.75), 370(3.90)	36-0705-79
	EtOH-acid	258(4.06),343(4.06), 395s(3.48),?(3.54)	36-0705-79
$C_{26}H_{22}N_2S_2$			
Benzo[1,2-d:5,4-d']bisthiazolium, 3,5-dimethyl-2,6-bis(2-phenylethenyl)-, diperchlorate	DMF	352(4.41),520(4.05)	126-1465-79
	KBr	428(--)	126-1465-79
Benzothiazolium, 2,2'-(1,4-phenylenedi-2,1-ethenediyl)bis[3-methyl-, diiodide	DMF	263(4.11),300(4.16), 388(4.48),438s(4.31), 466s(4.17)	126-1441-79
	KBr	448(--)	126-1441-79
$C_{26}H_{22}N_4O_3$			
1H-Pyrazole-3-carboxylic acid, 5-[(benzoylhydrazono)phenylmethyl]-4-phenyl-, ethyl ester	EtOH	305(3.29)	4-0849-79
$C_{26}H_{22}OP$			
Phosphonium, (2-oxo-2-phenylethyl)triphenyl-, tetrafluoroborate	n.s.g.	226(4.342),250(4.211), 274(3.674)	104-0332-79
$C_{26}H_{22}O_2$			
2,4-Pentanedione, 3-(9-anthracenylphenylmethyl)-	n.s.g.	335(3.39),352(3.66), 370(3.81),391(3.77)	39-2948-79C
2,4-Pentanedione, 3-[9,10-dihydro-10-(phenylmethylene)-9-anthracenyl]-	n.s.g.	310(4.05)	39-2948-79C
$C_{26}H_{22}O_4S$			
Benzene, 1,1'-sulfonylbis[4-(phenylmethoxy)-	C_6H_{12}	258(4.40)	39-0007-79B
$C_{26}H_{22}O_5$			
2H-1-Benzopyran-2-acetic acid, 3,4-dihydro-3-(hydroxymethylene)-4-oxo-α,α-diphenyl-, ethyl ester	MeOH	221(4.3),303(3.8), 362(3.9)	24-1791-79
[1,1'-Binaphthalene]-2-carboxylic acid, 4-acetoxy-4'-methoxy-, ethyl ester	n.s.g.	212(5.02),290s(4.22), 303(4.28),314s(4.22), 336(3.92),346s(3.70)	33-0090-79
3-Phenanthrenecarboxylic acid, 1-acetoxy-9-methoxy-4-phenyl-, ethyl ester	n.s.g.	228(4.58),260(4.66), 311(4.19),337s(3.62)	33-0090-79
1H,3H-Pyrano[4,3-b][1]benzopyran-3-one, 10-acetoxy-4,4a,10,10a-tetrahydro-4,4-diphenyl-	MeOH	218(4.2),269(3.3)	24-1791-79

Compound	Solvent	λ_{max}(log ε)	Ref.
$C_{26}H_{23}BrN_2O_7S_2$			
3-Butenoic acid, 2-acetyl-2-[(4-bromophenyl)azo]-4,4-bis(phenylsulfonyl)-, ethyl ester	EtOH	275(4.11),420(4.24)	104-0500-79
$C_{26}H_{23}ClN_2O_7S_2$			
3-Butenoic acid, 2-acetyl-2-[(2-chlorophenyl)azo]-4,4-bis(phenylsulfonyl)-, ethyl ester	EtOH	275(3.95),410(4.20)	104-0500-79
3-Butenoic acid, 2-acetyl-2-[(4-chlorophenyl)azo]-4,4-bis(phenylsulfonyl)-, ethyl ester	EtOH	285(3.86),420(4.08)	104-0500-79
$C_{26}H_{23}ClN_4O_5$			
D-erythro-Pentitol, 1,4-anhydro-1-C-(8-chloro-1,2,4-triazolo[4,3-a]pyrazin-3-yl)-2-deoxy-, 3,5-bis(4-methylbenzoate), (R)-	EtOH	280(4.05),305(3.83)	44-1028-79
$C_{26}H_{23}ClO_5$			
1,3-Benzodioxole-5-propanoic acid, β-[2-(4-chlorophenyl)-2-oxoethyl]-α-phenyl-, ethyl ester	EtOH	249(4.27),269-275s(--)	94-2767-79
$C_{26}H_{23}Cl_2N_3O_4S_2$			
Benzenesulfonamide, 4-chloro-N-[10a-[[(4-chlorophenyl)sulfonyl]amino]-4,5,8,9,10,10a-hexahydrocyclopenta-[c]pyrrolo[3,2,1-ij]quinolin-7(7aH)-ylidene]-, trans	EtOH	227(4.51),273(4.09), 285(4.12),310(4.21)	39-2387-79C
Benzenesulfonamide, 4-chloro-N-[2-[[[(4-chlorophenyl)sulfonyl]amino]-methylene]-1'-methylspiro[cyclopentan-1,3'-[3H]indol]-2'(1'H)-ylidene]-	EtOH	226(4.69),275(4.30), 303s(4.15)	39-2154-79C
$C_{26}H_{23}F_3N_4O_4S$			
5-Thia-1-azabicyclo[4.2.0]oct-2-ene-2-carboxylic acid, 4-acetyl-3-methyl-8-oxo-7-[(trifluoroacetyl)amino]-, (diphenylmethylene)methylhydrazide, [4S-(4α,6α,7β)]-	EtOH	241(4.34),258s(4.28), 305(3.92)	39-1629-79C
$C_{26}H_{23}GeN$			
Phenazagermine, 5-ethyl-5,10-dihydro-10,10-diphenyl-	hexane	282(4.38),310(3.9), 320(3.83)	65-0672-79
$C_{26}H_{23}NO$			
Pyrrolo[2,1-a]isoquinolin-1(5H)-one, 10b-ethyl-6,10b-dihydro-2,3-diphenyl-	MeCN	273(3.80),353(3.57)	88-1213-79
$C_{26}H_{23}NOP$			
Phosphonium, [2-(4-aminophenyl)-2-oxoethyl]triphenyl-, chloride	H_2O	275(3.60),334(4.34)	65-2189-79
	MeOH	275(3.48),336(4.44)	65-2189-79
	BuOH	270(3.69),340(4.40)	65-2189-79
	$CHCl_3$	326(4.34)	65-2189-79
hydrochloride	MeOH	275(3.32),336(4.41)	65-2189-79
$C_{26}H_{23}NO_2$			
Benzeneacetamide, N,N-diethyl-α-(10-oxo-9(10H)-phenanthrenylidene)-, (E)-	hexane	235s(3.45),254(3.49), 287s(2.98),334(2.88)	54-0559-79

Compound	Solvent	λ_{max}(log ε)	Ref.
$C_{26}H_{23}NO_4$			
1H-Indole-3-carboxylic acid, 4,5-dihydro-2-methyl-4,5-dioxo-1,6-bis(phenylmethyl)-, ethyl ester	dioxan	335(3.46),486(3.43)	83-0465-79
$C_{26}H_{23}NS$			
Pyrrolo[2,1-a]isoquinoline-1(5H)-thione, 10b-ethyl-6,10b-dihydro-2,3-diphenyl-	MeCN	257(4.07),425(4.10)	88-1213-79
$C_{26}H_{23}NSi$			
Phenazasiline, 5-ethyl-5,10-dihydro-10,10-diphenyl-	hexane	287(4.2),305(4.0), 327(3.8)	65-0672-79
$C_{26}H_{23}NSn$			
Phenazastannine, 5-ethyl-5,10-dihydro-10,10-diphenyl-	hexane	272(4.53),315(3.89), 320(3.20)	65-0672-79
$C_{26}H_{23}N_3O_6$			
L-Tryptophan, N-[(phenylmethoxy)carbonyl]-, (4-nitrophenyl)methyl ester	EtOH	271(3.68),290(3.50)	118-0957-79
$C_{26}H_{23}N_3O_9S_2$			
3-Butenoic acid, 2-acetyl-2-[(2-nitrophenyl)azo]-4,4-bis(phenylsulfonyl)-, ethyl ester	EtOH	267(3.77),380(3.79)	104-0500-79
3-Butenoic acid, 2-acetyl-2-[(4-nitrophenyl)azo]-4,4-bis(phenylsulfonyl)-, ethyl ester	EtOH	272(3.95),382(3.98)	104-0500-79
$C_{26}H_{24}$			
Bicyclo[3.1.0]hexane, 5-methyl-1,6-diphenyl-3-(phenylmethylene)-, exo	EtOH	248(4.18)	35-5743-79
Bicyclo[3.1.0]hexane, 5-methyl-3-methylene-1,2,6-triphenyl-, exo,exo	EtOH	223s(4.35)	35-5743-79
Bicyclo[3.1.0]hexane, 6-methyl-3-methylene-1,2,5-triphenyl-, exo,exo	EtOH	256(3.30)	35-5743-79
Cyclopropene, 3-(2-benzylallyl)-1-methyl-2,2-diphenyl-	EtOH	262(4.24)	35-5743-79
Cyclopropene, 3-(2-benzylallyl)-3-methyl-1,2-diphenyl-	EtOH	228(4.24),238s(4.13), 321(4.39),338(4.26)	35-5743-79
$C_{26}H_{24}Cl_5N_2O_{10}P$			
3'-Thymidylic acid, 2-chlorophenyl 2,2,2-trichloroethyl ester, 5'-[(4-chlorophenoxy)acetate]	MeOH	264(4.05)	54-0537-79
$C_{26}H_{24}NO$			
Benzo[a]phenanthridinium, 1,2,3,4-tetrahydro-2,2-dimethyl-6-(4-methylphenyl)-4-oxo-, bromide	n.s.g.	230(4.83),285(4.65), 354(4.20)	104-0495-79
perchlorate	n.s.g.	232(4.72),284(4.32), 354(4.18)	104-0495-79
$C_{26}H_{24}NO_2$			
Benzo[a]phenanthridinium, 1,2,3,4-tetrahydro-6-(4-methoxyphenyl)-2,2-dimethyl-4-oxo-, bromide	n.s.g.	230(4.55),290(4.37), 252(3.88)	104-0495-79
perchlorate	n.s.g.	228(4.56),284(4.35), 350(3.52)	104-0495-79

Compound	Solvent	λmax(log ε)	Ref.
$C_{26}H_{24}NO_3P$			
Benzenamine, 4-methoxy-N-[(1-methoxy-2,6-diphenyl-4(1H)-phosphorinylidene)-methyl]-, P-oxide	MeOH	250(4.13),412(4.64)	24-1272-79
$C_{26}H_{24}N_2O$			
1H-Indole-2-acetonitrile, 3-[2-(phenylmethoxy)ethyl]-1-(phenylmethyl)-	EtOH	222(4.59),275(3.93),283(3.93),295(3.84)	23-0289-79
$C_{26}H_{24}N_2OS_2$			
Benzenecarbodithioic acid, [4-(dimethylamino)-5-methyl-5-phenyl-2(5H)-oxazolylidene]phenylmethyl ester	MeCN	232(4.32),318(4.44),440(3.46)	33-1236-79
$C_{26}H_{24}N_4O_5$			
Tryptoquivaline N	MeOH	232(4.51),251s(4.25),291(3.95),320s(3.79)	94-1611-79
$C_{26}H_{24}N_8O_3$			
7H-Benzo[e]perimidin-7-one, 6-[(4,6-dimorpholino-1,3,5-triazin-2-yl)amino]-	DMF	467(4.31)	2-0195-79B
$C_{26}H_{24}O_3$			
3,4(2H,5H)-Furandione, 2-(1,1-dimethylethyl)-2,5,5-triphenyl-	C_6H_{12}	253(3.34),279(3.23),532(2.30),540s(2.29),562(2.25)	19-0665-79
$C_{26}H_{24}O_4$			
[1]Benzopyrano[3,4-b][1]benzopyran, 6,6a-diethoxy-6,6a-dihydro-6-phenyl-	EtOH	239(4.40),294(4.20),332(4.39),350(4.32)	138-1301-79
1,4-Naphthacenediol, 2,3,7,10-tetramethyl-, diacetate	$CHCl_3$	270(5.03),276(5.03),287(5.10),302(4.12),314(3.86),329(4.12),345(4.27),378(3.31),399(3.52),424(3.69),454(3.85),483(3.91)	150-3518-79
$C_{26}H_{24}O_5$			
1,3-Benzodioxole-5-propanoic acid, β-(2-oxo-2-phenylethyl)-α-phenyl-, ethyl ester	EtOH	243(4.18)	94-2767-79
$C_{26}H_{24}O_{11}$			
1,4-Ethanoanthracen-2(1H)-one, 4,5,8,9,10-pentaacetoxy-3,4-dihydro-	MeOH	235(4.89),282(4.01)	24-2640-79
$C_{26}H_{24}S_4$			
Benzene, 1,1',1"-[[1-[(1,1-dimethylethyl)thio]-1-buten-3-yne-1,2,4-triyl]-tris(thio)]tris-	heptane	195(4.72),340(4.17)	5-1606-79
$C_{26}H_{25}ClN_2O_4$			
1,3-Benzodioxole-5-propanoic acid, β-[2-(4-chlorophenyl)-2-hydrazonoethyl]-α-phenyl-, ethyl ester	EtOH	276(4.14)	94-2767-79
$C_{26}H_{25}F_3N_2O_5S_2$			
2-Thia-5,7-diazabicyclo[2.2.2]octane-1-carbothioic acid, 6-methoxy-3,3-dimethyl-8-oxo-7-(phenylacetyl)-5-(trifluoroacetyl)-, 5-(phenylmethyl) ester	THF	212(4.38),245s(3.83)	39-0170-79C

Compound	Solvent	$\lambda_{max}(\log \epsilon)$	Ref.
$C_{26}H_{25}NOS$			
2H,6H-[1,3]Thiazino[2,3-a]isoquinoline, 7,11b-dihydro-2-methoxy-11b-methyl-3,4-diphenyl-	MeCN	274(3.83),295(3.90)	88-1213-79
$C_{26}H_{25}NO_2$			
Phenol, 2-(1-morpholino-4,4-diphenyl-1,3-butadienyl)-	MeOH	213(3.7),233(3.6), 340(3.8)	24-1791-79
$C_{26}H_{25}NO_4$			
1H-Indole-3-carboxylic acid, 4,5-dihydro-4-hydroxy-2-methyl-5-oxo-1,4-bis(phenylmethyl)-, ethyl ester	dioxan	247(4.39),332-360(3.63-3.60)	83-0465-79
$C_{26}H_{25}NO_6S$			
L-Cysteine, N-[(phenylmethoxy)carbonyl]-, phenylmethyl ester, phenylmethyl carbonate)	EtOH	243(2.60),248(2.64), 252(2.74),258(2.84), 264(2.76),269(2.56)	118-0957-79
$C_{26}H_{25}NO_7$			
Butanoic acid, 2-(5,6-dihydro-9,10-dimethoxy-8H-benzo[g]-1,3-benzodioxolo-[5,6-a]quinolizin-8-ylidene)-3-oxo-, ethyl ester	EtOH	232(4.53),267(4.62), 337(4.33),432(3.73)	36-0705-79
	EtOH-acid	232(4.60),267(4.48), 352(4.38),440(3.72)	36-0705-79
$C_{26}H_{25}N_3$			
9H-Cyclopenta[1,2-b:4,3-b']dipyridine, 9-(2-butyl-1,3-dimethylcyclohepta-[c]pyrrol-6(2H)-ylidene)-	C_6H_{12}	238(4.48),304(4.42), 482(4.63),512(4.53)	24-2087-79
	CH_2Cl_2	248(4.47),307(4.45), 488(4.61),516(4.54)	24-2087-79
	CH_2Cl_2-CF_3COOH	250(4.36),296(4.67), 344(4.28),378(4.10), 464(3.96),542(4.49)	24-2087-79
$C_{26}H_{25}N_3O_7$			
Acetamide, N-[1-(3,6-di-O-benzoyl-2,5-dideoxy-α-D-erythro-hexofuranosyl)-1,2-dihydro-2-oxo-4-pyrimidinyl]-	EtOH	218(4.44),230(4.47), 248s(--),274(3.72), 282(3.76),330(3.88)	136-0079-79J
β-	EtOH	218(3.45),230(4.49), 282(3.81),300(3.88)	136-0079-79J
$C_{26}H_{26}$			
Cyclopropene, 3-methyl-1,2-diphenyl-3-(4-phenylbutyl)-	EtOH	229(4.22),238(4.10), 312(4.37),321(4.46), 338(4.34)	35-5743-79
9H-Fluorene, 2,7-dimethyl-9-(1-phenylpentylidene)-	$CHCl_3$	255(4.48),265(4.49), 288(4.24),303(4.26), 314(4.23)	24-3490-79
$C_{26}H_{26}N_2$			
Acridine, 9-[(1,3-dihydro-1,3,3-trimethyl-2H-indol-2-ylidene)methyl]-9,10-dihydro-10-methyl-	EtOH	283(4.60)	103-0541-79
$C_{26}H_{26}N_2O$			
4-Oxazolamine, 2-(diphenylmethylene)-5-ethyl-2,5-dihydro-N,N-dimethyl-5-phenyl-	MeCN	228(4.10),333(4.26)	33-1429-79
$C_{26}H_{26}N_2O_4$			
1,3-Benzodioxole-5-propanoic acid, β-(2-	EtOH	265(4.15)	94-2767-79

Compound	Solvent	λ_{max}(log ε)	Ref.
hydrazono-2-phenylethyl)-α-phenyl-, ethyl ester (cont.)			94-2767-79
Pyridinium, 4-(dimethylamino)-1-[1-(diphenylmethylene)-3-methoxy-2-(methoxycarbonyl)-3-oxopropyl]-, hydroxide, inner salt	$CHCl_3$	260(4.4),301(4.4), 403(3.5)	5-1406-79
$C_{26}H_{26}N_2O_5$			
Glycine, N-[N-[(phenylmethoxy)carbonyl]-L-phenylalanyl]-, phenylmethyl ester	EtOH	253(2.58),259(2.68), 262(2.56),265(2.58), 268(2.42)	118-0957-79
$C_{26}H_{26}N_2O_6$			
5H-Indazole-5,5-dicarboxylic acid, 3-(benzoyloxy)-2,4,6,7-tetrahydro-2-phenyl-, diethyl ester	EtOH	240(4.42),254s(4.26)	39-2099-79C
$C_{26}H_{26}N_2O_7$			
1-Azabicyclo[4.2.0]oct-2-ene-2,4-dicarboxylic acid, 3-methyl-8-oxo-7-[(phenoxyacetyl)amino]-, 4-methyl 2-(phenylmethyl) ester	EtOH	268(4.11)	23-0222-79
$C_{26}H_{26}N_8O_5$			
L-Glutamic acid, N-[4-[[(2,4-diamino-6-pteridinyl)methyl](phenylmethyl)-benzoyl]-	pH 1	243(4.33),307(4.47), 345s(4.10)	4-1645-79
	pH 7	258(4.45),304(4.47), 370(3.98)	4-1645-79
	pH 13	259(4.44),305(4.47), 370(3.98)	4-1645-79
$C_{26}H_{26}O$			
Methanone, phenyl[9-(1,1,2-trimethylpropyl)-9H-fluoren-9-yl]-	EtOH	253(4.29),291s(3.83), 303(3.57)	118-0616-79
$C_{26}H_{26}O_2$			
Estra-1,3,5(10),14-tetraen-17-one, 16-(phenylmethylene)-3-methoxy-	MeOH	232(3.26),255(3.07), 333(3.34)	150-2525-79
3(2H)-Furanone, 2-(1,1-dimethylethyl)-dihydro-2,5,5-triphenyl-	C_6H_{12}	253(2.80),258(2.85), 264(2.79),268s(2.70), 284s(2.23),295(2.35), 305(2.42),316(2.40), 329(2.20)	19-0665-79
	EtOH	252(2.82),258(2.85), 264(2.79),267(2.71), 295(2.33),304(2.39), 315(2.37),327(2.16)	19-0665-79
	50% EtOH	252(2.90),258(2.89), 263(2.82),267s(2.74), 295s(2.36),303(2.40), 313s(2.36),325s(2.13)	19-0665-79
$C_{26}H_{26}O_3$			
Benzenepentanoic acid, β-(4-methylphenyl)-δ-oxo-α-phenyl-, ethyl ester	EtOH	242(4.10)	4-0001-79
$C_{26}H_{26}O_4$			
Benzenepentanoic acid, β-(4-methoxyphenyl)-δ-oxo-α-phenyl-, ethyl ester	EtOH	242(4.04)	4-0001-79
Propanedioic acid, (triphenylmethyl)-, diethyl ester	MeCN	235(3.34),260(2.92)	78-0177-79

Compound	Solvent	λ_{max}(log ϵ)	Ref.
$C_{26}H_{27}NO_4$			
Benzo[4,5]cyclohepta[1,2,3-de]naphthalene-1,2-dicarboxylic acid, 3-[(1,1-dimethylethyl)amino]-7,8-dihydro-, dimethyl ester	CH_2Cl_2	253(4.60),273s(4.38), 344(4.09)	24-3166-79
Oxazole, 2,5-dihydro-2,2,4-tris(4-methoxyphenyl)-5,5-dimethyl-	n.s.g.	275(4.32)	88-1619-79
$C_{26}H_{27}NO_7S$			
5,12-Naphthacenedione, 8-acetyl-10-[(3-aminocyclohexyl)thio]-7,8,9,10-tetrahydro-1,6,8,11-tetrahydroxy-	MeOH	234(4.31),253(4.22), 494(3.96),529(3.91)	87-1425-79
$C_{26}H_{27}N_3O_2$			
Benzenepropanamide, α-[[4-(diethylamino)-2-methylphenyl]imino]-β-oxo-N-phenyl-	BuOAc	433(4.20)	24-3098-79
$C_{26}H_{27}N_3O_4S_2$			
Benzenesulfonamide, N,4-dimethyl-N-[1,2,4,5-tetrahydro-1-methyl-2-[(4-methylphenyl)sulfonyl]imino]pyrrolo-[3,2,1-hi]indol-1-yl]-	EtOH	225(4.46),271(4.11), 281(4.07),312(3.85)	39-2387-79C
$C_{26}H_{27}N_9O_4$			
1H-Pyrrole-2-carboxamide, N-[5-[[[2-(aminoiminomethyl)phenyl]amino]carbonyl]-1-methyl-1H-pyrrol-3-yl]-4-[[(4-formylamino)-1-methyl-1H-pyrrol-2-yl]carbonyl]amino]-1-methyl-, monohydrochloride	EtOH	246(4.31),293(4.35)	87-1296-79
1H-Pyrrole-2-carboxamide, N-[5-[[[3-(aminoiminomethyl)phenyl]amino]carbonyl]-1-methyl-1H-pyrrol-3-yl]-4-[[(4-formylamino)-1-methyl-1H-pyrrol-2-yl]carbonyl]amino]-1-methyl-, monohydrochloride	EtOH	235(4.30),289(4.16)	87-1296-79
1H-Pyrrole-2-carboxamide, N-[5-[[[4-(aminoiminomethyl)phenyl]amino]carbonyl]-1-methyl-1H-pyrrol-3-yl]-4-[[(4-formylamino)-1-methyl-1H-pyrrol-2-yl]carbonyl]amino]-1-methyl-, monohydrochloride	EtOH	246(4.38),310(4.46)	87-1296-79
$C_{26}H_{28}IN_3O_7$			
L-Histidine, N,1-bis[(phenylmethoxy)-carbonyl]-, 2-(2-iodoethoxy)ethyl ester	EtOH	243(3.57),268(2.80)	118-0961-79
$C_{26}H_{28}N_2O_2$			
3H-3-Benzazepine-3-carboxamide, N-(4-methoxyphenyl)-2,2-dimethyl-1-phenyl-1,2,4,5-tetrahydro-	EtOH	239(4.25),276-288(3.30)	4-1525-79
Benzenepentanoic acid, δ-hydrazono-β-(4-methylphenyl)-α-phenyl-, ethyl ester	EtOH	266(4.04)	4-0001-79
$C_{26}H_{28}N_2O_3$			
Benzenepentanoic acid, δ-hydrazono-β-(4-methoxyphenyl)-α-phenyl-, ethyl ester	EtOH	267(4.11)	4-0001-79

Compound	Solvent	λ max (log ε)	Ref.
$C_{26}H_{28}N_2O_6S$			
Imidazo[5,1-b]thiazole-3,7-dicarboxylic acid, 2,3,7,7a-tetrahydro-2,2-dimethyl-7-[3-oxo-3-(phenylmethoxy)propyl]-, 3-(phenylmethyl) ester, monohydrochloride, [3S-(3α,7α,7aα)]-	EtOH	230s(3.81)	39-2455-79C
$C_{26}H_{28}N_4O_5$			
2,4(1H,3H)-Pyrimidinedione, 1-[6-(1,3-diphenyl-2-imidazolidinyl)tetrahydro-2,2-dimethylfuro[3,4-d]-1,3-dioxol-4-yl]-, [3aR-(3aα,4α,6α,6aα)]-	EtOH	208(4.23),252(4.49)	33-2788-79
$C_{26}H_{28}N_8O$			
7H-Benzo[e]perimidin-7-one, 6-[[4,6-bis(butylamino)-1,3,5-triazin-2-yl]amino]-	DMF	465(4.30)	2-0195-79B
7H-Benzo[e]perimidin-7-one, 6-[(4,6-bis(diethylamino)-1,3,5-triazin-2-yl]amino]-	DMF	468(4.34)	2-0195-79B
$C_{26}H_{28}O_2$			
1-Isobenzofuranol, 1-[1,1'-biphenyl]-4-yl-1,3-dihydro-3,3-bis(1-methylethyl)-, cation	50% H_2SO_4	407(4.54)	104-1126-79
$C_{26}H_{28}O_2PS$			
Thiophenium, 1-[2-ethoxy-2-oxo-1-(triphenylphosphoranylidene)ethyl]tetrahydro-, tetrafluoroborate	EtOH	226s(4.43)	104-2169-79
$C_{26}H_{28}O_2PSe$			
Selenophenium, 1-[2-ethoxy-2-oxo-1-(triphenylphosphoranylidene)ethyl]tetrahydro-, tetrafluoroborate	EtOH	226s(4.39)	104-2169-79
$C_{26}H_{28}O_9$			
Malaphyllin	EtOH	203(4.29),223(4.35), 264(4.37),296(3.85)	105-0426-79
$C_{26}H_{30}N_2O_2$			
Benzamide, 2-[4-(dimethylamino)benzoyl]-N-tricyclo[3.3.1.1^{3,7}]dec-1-yl-	EtOH	241(4.06),356(4.39)	103-0634-79
	EtOH-N HCl	360(3.5)	103-0634-79
	EtOH-5N HCl	255(4.1)	103-0634-79
$C_{26}H_{30}N_2O_3$			
Acetamide, N-[2-[2,3-dihydro-2-oxo-3-(2-oxocyclohexyl)-1-(phenylmethyl)-1H-indol-3-yl]ethyl]-N-methyl-, A	EtOH	254(3.98),280s(3.26)	23-1694-79
B	EtOH	254(3.98),280s(3.26)	23-1694-79
$C_{26}H_{30}N_5O$			
Cyclopropenylium, bis(diethylamino)(5-oxo-4,6-diphenyl-1,2,3-triazin-2(5H)-yl)-, perchlorate	CH_2Cl_2	327(4.38)	24-1535-79
$C_{26}H_{30}N_6O_2Si$			
9H-Purin-6-amine, 9-[2,3-dideoxy-5-O-[(1,1-dimethylethyl)diphenylsilyl]-2,3-imino-β-D-lyxofuranosyl]-	MeOH	260(4.21)	44-1317-79

Compound	Solvent	$\lambda_{max}(\log \epsilon)$	Ref.
$C_{26}H_{30}N_8O_3Si$			
9H-Purin-6-amine, 9-[3-azido-3-deoxy-5-O-[(1,1-dimethylethyl)diphenylsilyl]-β-D-xylofuranosyl]-	MeOH	260(4.22)	44-1317-79
$C_{26}H_{30}N_{18}O_4$			
Alanine, 3-(6-amino-9H-purin-9-yl)-N-[3-(6-amino-9H-purin-9-yl)-N-[3-(6-amino-9H-purin-9-yl)alanyl]alanyl]-, ethyl ester, tetrahydrochloride	EtOH	260(4.56)	65-1000-79
$C_{26}H_{30}O_2$			
1,1':3',1"-Terphenyl, 4',6'-dimethoxy-2,2",4,4",6,6"-hexamethyl-	$CHCl_3$	288(3.82)	12-1531-79
$C_{26}H_{30}O_4S_3$			
Benzene, 1,1'-[thiobis[(3,4-dimethyl-1,3-butadiene-4,1-diyl)sulfonyl]]-bis[4-methyl-	n.s.g.	255(4.50),346(4.43)	104-2018-79
$C_{26}H_{30}O_{10}$			
2,3-Naphthalenedicarboxylic acid, 1,2-dihydro-6,7,8-trimethoxy-1-(3,4,5-trimethoxyphenyl)-, dimethyl ester	EtOH	244(4.38),307(4.17)	2-0202-79
$C_{26}H_{31}NO_8$			
Quinolinium, 1-[3-ethoxy-2-(ethoxycarbonyl)-1-[2-ethoxy-1-(ethoxycarbonyl)-2-oxoethyl]-3-oxo-1-propenyl]-2,4-dimethyl-, hydroxide, inner salt	$CHCl_3$	317(3.9),379(4.2), 474(2.7)	5-1406-79
Quinolinium, 1-[3-ethoxy-2-(ethoxycarbonyl)-1-[2-ethoxy-1-(ethoxycarbonyl)-2-oxoethyl]-3-oxo-1-propenyl]-2,7-dimethyl-, hydroxide, inner salt	$CHCl_3$	320(3.8),379(3.7), 479(1.2)	5-1406-79
$C_{26}H_{31}NO_{14}$			
Dasycarponin hexaacetate	MeOH	253(4.21)	100-0500-79
Lithospermoside hexaacetate	MeOH	252(4.47)	100-0500-79
$C_{26}H_{31}N_7O_9S_2$			
Glycine, N-[(1,1-dimethylethoxy)carbonyl]-, [[[7-[(hydroxyphenylacetyl)-amino]-3-[[(1-methyl-1H-tetrazol-5-yl)thio]methyl]-8-oxo-5-thia-1-azabicyclo[4.2.0]oct-2-en-2-yl]carbonyl]oxy]methyl ester, [6R-[6α,7β(R*)]]-	MeOH	275(3.91)	87-0657-79
$C_{26}H_{32}AsN$			
Arsinous amide, As-(diphenylmethyl)-N,N-diethyl-As-(2,4,6-trimethylphenyl)-	THF	268(3.01),324(2.84)	89-0395-79
$C_{26}H_{32}N_2O_3$			
Acetamide, N-[2-[2,3-dihydro-3-(2-hydroxycyclohexyl)-2-oxo-1-(phenylmethyl)-1H-indol-3-yl]ethyl]-N-methyl-	EtOH	254(4.00),280s(4.21)	23-1694-79
form B	EtOH	254(3.92),280s(3.21)	23-1694-79
$C_{26}H_{32}N_2O_4$			
2-Hexen-1-one, 3,3'-(1,2-ethanediyldiimino)bis[6-hydroxy-1-phenyl-	MeOH	241(4.23),348(4.57)	44-2073-79

Compound	Solvent	λmax(log ε)	Ref.
$C_{26}H_{32}N_2O_8$			
2-Naphthacenecarboxamide, 4-(dimethylamino)-N-(1,1-dimethylethyl)-1,4,4a-5,5a,6,11,12a-octahydro-3,10,12,12a-tetrahydroxy-8-methoxy-1,11-dioxo-	MeOH-HCl	275(4.18),356(4.34)	35-2171-79
	MeOH-NaOH	275(4.06),300s(3.91), 384(4.23)	35-2171-79
$C_{26}H_{32}N_4O_7$			
1-Azabicyclo[4.2.0]oct-2-ene-2,4,4-tricarboxylic acid, 7-azido-3-methyl-8-oxo-, 4,4-bis(1,1-dimethylethyl) 2-(phenylmethyl) ester, trans	EtOH	271(4.07)	23-0222-79
$C_{26}H_{32}O_5$			
9β,10α-Pregna-3,5,7-trien-20-one, 3,17α-dihydroxy-16-methylene-, 3,17-diacetate	MeOH	238s(--),302s(--), 314(4.32)	54-0078-79
$C_{26}H_{32}O_6$			
Benzene, 1,2,4-trimethoxy-5-[2-[2-(2,4,5-trimethoxyphenyl)-3-cyclohexen-1-yl]ethenyl]-, [1α((E),2α]-	MeOH	210(4.60),260(4.30), 297(4.03)	12-0071-79
Spongia-13(16),14-dien-2-one, 3α,19-diacetoxy-	MeOH	219(3.71)	12-0867-79
$C_{26}H_{32}O_8$			
Cathedulin E_2, 8,15-bis(denicotinyl)-	MeOH	233(4.14)	39-2972-79C
$C_{26}H_{32}O_9$			
D-Homo-16-oxaandrost-5-ene-17-carboxylic acid, 6,9-dihydroxy-4,4,8,17-tetramethyl-12-methylene-3,7,15,17a-tetraoxo-, methyl ester, (17α)-	MeOH	276(3.90)	44-4852-79
$C_{26}H_{32}O_{10}$			
3a,7-Epoxy-3aH-furo[3,2-b]oxocin-3-carboxylic acid, 5-[1,3-dimethyl-6-oxo-6-(tetrahydro-2,4-dioxo-3-furanyl)-2,4-hexadienyl]octahydro-2,6,9a-trimethyl-8-oxo-, methyl ester, [2R-[2α,3α,3aα,5α(1R*,2E,4E),6β,7α,9aβ]]-	EtOH-HCl	232(3.78),350(4.35)	142-0477-79B
	EtOH-NaOH	239(4.17),313(4.23)	142-0477-79B
$C_{26}H_{32}O_{12}$			
β-D-Glucopyranoside, 2-methoxy-4-[tetrahydro-6a-hydroxy-4-(4-hydroxy-3-methoxyphenyl)-1H,3H-furo[3,4-c]furan-1-yl]phenyl, [1R-(1α,3aα,4α,6aα)]-	EtOH	230(4.23),280(3.74)	94-2868-79
$C_{26}H_{32}S_6$			
Dispiro[1,3-dithiolane-2,6'-[6H,12H]dibenzo[b,f][1,5]dithiocin-12',2"-[1,3]-dithiolane], 4,4,4",4",5,5,5",5"-octamethyl-	EtOH	250s(4.22)	18-0496-79
$C_{26}H_{32}Zr$			
Zirconium, bis(cyclohexylethynyl)bis-(η^5-2,4-cyclopentadien-1-yl)-	$CHCl_3$	246(4.01),264(3.72), 298(3.07)	101-0353-79S
$C_{26}H_{33}ClO_{16}$			
1H,3H-Pyrano[3,4-c]pyran-1-one, 5-(1-acetoxy-2-chloroethyl)-4,4a,5,6-tetrahydro-4a-hydroxy-6-[(2,3,4,6-tetra-O-	MeOH	233.5(3.93)	102-1981-79

Compound	Solvent	$\lambda_{max}(\log \epsilon)$	Ref.
acetyl-β-D-glucopyranosyl)oxy]-, [4aR-[4aα,5β(S*),6α]]- (cont.)			102-1981-79
$C_{26}H_{33}NO_2Se$			
4-Azapregn-5-ene-3,20-dione, 6-(phenyl-seleno)-	ether	252(4.23)	88-4931-79
$C_{26}H_{33}NO_3$			
Spiro[cyclohexane-1,3'(5'H)-quinoline]-2,5',6-trione, 1',2',4',6',7',8'-hexa-hydro-4,4,7',7'-tetramethyl-1'-(2-phenylethyl)-	pH 1	307(4.38)	39-1593-79C
	H_2O	316(4.46)	39-1593-79C
	pH 13	319(4.48)	39-1593-79C
$C_{26}H_{33}NO_3Se$			
4-Azapregn-5-ene-3,20-dione, 7-hydroxy-6-(phenylseleno)-, (7α)-	MeOH	249(4.19)	88-4931-79
(7β)-	MeOH	247(4.24)	88-4931-79
4-Azapregn-5-ene-3,20-dione, 6-(phenyl-seleninyl)-	MeOH	220(4.12),252(4.15)	88-4931-79
$C_{26}H_{33}NO_9$			
3a,7-Epoxy-3aH-furo[3,2-b]oxocin-3-carboxylic acid, 5-[6-(2,5-dihydro-4-hydroxy-2-oxo-1H-pyrrol-3-yl)-1,3-dimethyl-6-oxo-2,4-hexadienyl]octa-hydro-2,6,9a-trimethyl-8-oxo-, methyl ester	EtOH-HCl	237(4.02),354(4.53)	142-0477-79B
	EtOH-NaOH	255(4.20),285(4.28), 332(4.30)	142-0477-79B
$C_{26}H_{33}N_3O_3$			
1H-Pyrrole-3-propanoic acid, 5-[[5-[(4-acetyl-3,5-dimethyl-1H-pyrrol-2-yl)-methyl]-4-ethyl-3-methyl-2H-pyrrol-2-ylidene]methyl]-4-methyl-, methyl ester, monohydrobromide	$CHCl_3$-HBr	492(4.70)	104-0970-79
$C_{26}H_{33}N_3O_4$			
Anhydrodihydrocyclopiamine B	MeOH	251(4.21),260(4.21), 280(3.94),287(3.95), 315(3.45),330(3.27)	39-1751-79C
$C_{26}H_{33}N_3O_5$			
Cyclopiamine A	MeOH	230(4.20),261(4.01), 344(3.75)	39-1751-79C
Cyclopiamine B	MeOH	232(4.21),260(4.03), 345(3.76)	39-1751-79C
$C_{26}H_{34}N_2O_3$			
1-Propanone, 1,1'-[azoxybis[4-(1,1-di-methylethyl)-2,1-phenylene]]bis-	EtOH	323(3.79)	104-0847-79
Spiro[cyclopentane-1,1'(2'H)-[4H]pyrro-lo[3,2,1-ij]quinoline-2',3-dione, 7'-methoxy-4',4',5,5-tetramethyl-4-[(1-methyl-2-pyrrolidinyl)methyl]-, [1α,4β(R*)]- (5λ,4ε)	MeOH	249(4.21),262(4.20), 281(3.94),288(3.95), 328(?)	39-1751-79C
$C_{26}H_{34}N_2O_{14}$			
1,2,3,4-Butanetetrol, 1-[5-(2,3,4-tri-acetoxybutyl)pyrazinyl]-, tetraacet-ate	EtOH	268(4.12),275(4.09), 295(3.36)	136-0205-79J
isomer 5a	EtOH	268(4.19),275(4.17), 295(3.62)	136-0205-79J

Compound	Solvent	λmax(log ε)	Ref.
isomer 6a	EtOH	269(4.62),275(4.63), 298(4.30)	136-0205-79J
$C_{26}H_{34}O$			
1,2,3,5,7,11,13-Cyclotetradecaheptaen-9-yn-1-ol, 4,8,11-tris(1,1-dimethylethyl)-	THF at 0°	304s(4.38),331(5.00), 466(4.08),529(2.68), 552(2.70),595(3.50)	88-3169-79
anion	THF, -78°	266(4.17),292(4.18), 334(4.54),373(4.82), 517(4.23),630(4.23)	88-3169-79
$C_{26}H_{34}O_6$			
2H-1-Benzopyran-2-one, 7-[(6-acetoxydecahydro-2-hydroxy-2,5,5,8a-tetramethyl-1-naphthalenyl)methoxy]-	EtOH	218(4.08),242(3.52), 253(3.34),325(4.11)	105-0014-79
Tricoccin S_{22}	MeOH	214(4.23)	88-2015-79
$C_{26}H_{34}O_7$			
Shikodokaurin A acetate	MeOH	232(3.90)	102-0299-79
$C_{26}H_{34}O_8$			
Phenol, 3,3'-(2,3-dimethyl-1,4-butanediyl)bis[5,6-dimethoxy-, diacetate, (R*,S*)-	EtOH	205(4.79),223s(4.22), 274(3.45)	94-1583-79
Shikokaurin B, dehydro-	MeOH	229(3.69)	102-0299-79
$C_{26}H_{34}O_9$			
Coleon Q, 6-O-acetyl-19-acetoxy-	EtOH	236(4.01)	33-2374-79
$C_{26}H_{34}O_{10}$			
Benzo[4,5]cyclodeca[1,2-b]furan-5-carboxaldehyde, 8,9,13-triacetoxy-1,2,3a-6,7,8,8a,9,10,12a,13,13a-dodecahydro-13a-hydroxy-1,8a,12-trimethyl-2-oxo-, (1R*,3aS*,4E,8S*,8aS*,9S*,12aS*,13S*-13aS*)-	MeOH	228(3.93)	78-1907-79
Coleon Q, 12-O-deacetyl-7-O-acetyl-3β,19-diacetoxy-	EtOH	234(4.07)	33-2374-79
Repandin B	MeOH	210(4.36)	44-3400-79
$C_{26}H_{34}O_{11}$			
β-D-Xylopyranoside, [1,2,3,4-tetrahydro-7-hydroxy-1-(4-hydroxy-3,5-dimethoxyphenyl)-3-(hydroxymethyl)-6-methoxy-2-naphthalenyl]methyl [1R-(1α,2β,3α)]-	MeOH	280(3.65)	102-1847-79
$C_{26}H_{34}S$			
Benzene, [[3,7-dimethyl-9-(2,6,6-trimethyl-1-cyclohexen-1-yl)-2,4,6,8-nonatetraenyl]thio]-, (all-E)-	EtOH	332(4.36)	87-1532-79
$C_{26}H_{34}Se$			
Benzene, [[3,7-dimethyl-9-(2,6,6-trimethyl-1-cyclohexen-1-yl)-2,4,6,8-nonatetraenyl]seleno]-, (all-E)-	EtOH	338(4.48)	87-1532-79
$C_{26}H_{35}N$			
1,2,3,5,7,11,13-Cyclotetradecaheptaen-9-yn-1-amine, 4,8,11-tris(1,1-dimethylethyl)-	THF	269(4.01),286s(4.03), 337(4.82),351s(4.73), 495(4.11),544(3.32), 566(3.30),612(3.93)	88-3171-79

Compound	Solvent	λ_{max}(log ε)	Ref.
$C_{26}H_{35}NO_2$			
Androst-4-en-3-one, 17β-hydroxy-, O-(phenylmethyl)oxime, anti	EtOH	252(4.41)	78-0233-79
syn	EtOH	257(4.26)	78-0233-79
$C_{26}H_{35}NO_4S$			
Piperidine, 1-[(11β)-11,17-dihydroxy-3,20-dioxo-21-thioxopregna-1,4-dien-21-yl]-	EtOH	249(4.32)	94-1352-79
$C_{26}H_{35}N_3O_3$			
Spiro[1H-cyclopent[f]indolizine-7(5H),1'(2'H)-[4H]pyrrolo[3,2,1-ij]-quinoline]-2',6'(5'H)-dione, 5a-amino-2,3,5a,6,8,8a,9,9a-octahydro-7'-methoxy-4',4',8,8-tetramethyl-	MeOH	233(4.21),262(4.03), 346(3.76)	39-1751-79C
$C_{26}H_{35}N_3O_5$			
Dihydrocyclopiamine B	MeOH	222(4.39),263(3.57), 288(3.42)	39-1751-79C
$C_{26}H_{35}N_{13}O_6$			
Alanine, 3-(6-amino-9H-purin-9-yl)-N-[N-[3-(6-amino-9H-purin-9-yl)-N-[(1,1-dimethylethoxy)carbonyl]alanyl]-L-alanyl]-, ethyl ester	EtOH	261(4.38)	65-1000-79
$C_{26}H_{36}N_2O_2$			
5α-Androstan-3-one, 17β-hydroxy-17α-methyl-2-(2-pyridinylaminomethylene)-	MeOH	235(3.69),292(3.57), 353(4.13)	39-1816-79C
$C_{26}H_{36}N_2O_4$			
Acetamide, 2,2'-[1,2-ethanediylbis-(oxy)]bis[N-ethyl-N-(1-phenylethyl)-	H_2O	200s(4.45)	33-0754-79
Spiro[cyclopentane-1,1'(2'H)-[4H]pyrrolo[3,2,1-ij]quinoline]-2',3-dione, 5',6'-dihydro-6'-hydroxy-7'-methoxy-4',4',5,5-tetramethyl-4-[(1-methyl-2-pyrrolidinyl)methyl]-	MeOH	221(4.36),264(3.57), 287(3.41)	39-1751-79C
$C_{26}H_{36}O_6$			
Benzene, 1,2,4-trimethoxy-5-[2-[2-(2,4,5-trimethoxyphenyl)cyclohexyl]-ethyl]-, cis-(±)-	MeOH	230(4.17),289(3.93)	12-0071-79
1,5-Biphenylenedicarboxylic acid, 1,4,4a,4b,5,8,8a,8b-octahydro-4b,8b-dimethyl-2,6-bis(2-methylpropyl)-4,8-dioxo-, dimethyl ester, (1α,4aα,4bβ-5β,8aβ,8bα)-(±)-	EtOH	233(4.40)	39-0976-79C
$C_{26}H_{36}O_8$			
Cyclonona[c]pyran-1,9-diol, 4-(1,2-diacetoxy-4-methyl-3-pentenyl)-1,4a,5-6,9,10,11,11a-octahydro-7-methyl-11-methylene]-, 1-acetate	MeOH	214(3.82)	20-0071-79
$C_{26}H_{36}O_{10}$			
Cafestol-2-one, 11-O-(β-D-glucopyranosyl)-	MeOH	276(3.95)	24-1088-79

Compound	Solvent	$\lambda_{max}(\log \epsilon)$	Ref.
$C_{26}H_{36}Zr$			
Zirconium, bis(η^5-2,4-cyclopentadien-1-yl)di-1-octynyl-	$CHCl_3$	248(3.93),264(3.66), 330(3.05)	101-0353-79S
$C_{26}H_{37}NO$			
5α-Androstan-3α-ol, 17β-[(phenylmethylene)amino]-	hexane	211(4.32),247(4.34), 258(4.15),277(3.20), 287(3.04)	44-1690-79
	MeOH	212(4.26),249(4.32), 278s(3.38),287s(3.15)	44-1690-79
$C_{26}H_{37}NO_2$			
5α-Androstan-3α-ol, 17β-[[(2-hydroxyphenyl)methylene]amino]-	hexane	217(4.40),222s(4.36), 258(4.18),263s(4.11), 319(3.71)	44-1690-79
	MeOH	218(4.38),222s(4.36), 257(4.11),262s(4.08), 278(3.76),315(3.56), 401(3.38)	44-1690-79
$C_{26}H_{37}N_3O_5$			
Spiro[cyclopentane-1,1'(2'H)-[4H]pyrrolo[3,2,1-ij]quinolin]-2'-one, 5',6'-dihydro-6'-hydroxy-7'-methoxy-2,2,4'-4'-tetramethyl-3-[(1-methyl-2-pyrrolidinyl)methyl]-4-nitro-	MeOH	222(4.36),263s(3.57), 286(3.41)	39-1751-79C
$C_{26}H_{38}Br_2O_6$			
1,5-Biphenylenedicarboxylic acid, 3,7-dibromododecahydro-4b,8b-dimethyl-2,6-bis(2-methylpropyl)-4,8-dioxo-, dimethyl ester, (1α,2β,3β,4aβ,4bβ-5β,6α,7α,8aβ,8bα)-(±)-	dioxan	320(2.40)	39-0976-79C
$C_{26}H_{38}I_2N_4O_{10}S$			
L-Methionine, N-[N-[N-[N-[(1,1-dimethylethoxy)carbonyl]seryl]-3,5-diiodo-L-tyrosyl-L-seryl]-, methyl ester	EtOH	287(3.45),296(3.44)	33-2460-79
$C_{26}H_{38}O_2$			
27-Norcholesta-5,7,23-trien-25-one, 3β-hydroxy-	EtOH	282(4.08)	65-0202-79
$C_{26}H_{38}O_5$			
Androst-4-ene-1-acetic acid, 3-oxo-17-(1-oxopropoxy)-, ethyl ester, (1α,17β)-	EtOH	242(4.11)	56-0149-79
Androst-5-ene-3,7-dione, 17-[(tetrahydro-2H-pyran-2-yl)oxy]-, cyclic 3-(1,2-ethanediyl acetal), (17β)-	EtOH	240(4.10)	150-0501-79
Androst-5-ene-7,17-dione, 3β-[(tetrahydro-2H-pyran-2-yl)oxy]-, cyclic 17-(1,2-ethanediyl acetal), (3β)-	EtOH	239(4.10)	150-0501-79
Pregn-5-ene-3,7-dione, 17α,20ξ[(1-methylethylidene)bis(oxy)]-, cyclic 3-(1,2-ethanediyl acetal)	EtOH	240(4.10)	150-0501-79
$C_{26}H_{39}DO_2$			
3α,5-Cyclo-26,27-dinor-5α-chloest-22-en-23-one-20-d, 6β-methoxy-, (20R,22E)-	EtOH	227(4.16)	44-2448-79

Compound	Solvent	$\lambda_{max}(\log \epsilon)$	Ref.
$C_{26}H_{39}NO$			
6-Aza-B-homo-19-norcholesta-1,3,5(10)-trien-7-one	EtOH	239(3.78)	114-0319-79C
19-Norcholesta-1,3,5(10)-trien-6-one, oxime	EtOH	255(3.74)	114-0319-79C
$C_{26}H_{39}NO_2S$			
Thiazolidine, 3-acetyl-2-[(20S)-3-oxo-pregn-4-en-20-yl]-	$CHCl_3$	247(4.23)	83-0192-79
$C_{26}H_{39}N_3O_3$			
Spiro[1H-cyclopent[f]indolizine-7(5H)-1'(2'H)-[4H]pyrrolo[3,2,1-ij]quinoline]-2',6'-diol, 5a-amino-2,3,5',5a-6,6',8,8a,9,9a-decahydro-7'-methoxy-4',4',8,8-tetramethyl-	MeOH	310(3.74)	39-1751-79C
	$MeOH-HClO_4$	221(4.15),255(4.05), 297(3.65)	39-1751-79C
isomer 7b	MeOH	240(4.19),250(3.88), 278(3.89),308(3.73)	39-1751-79C
$C_{26}H_{40}N_4O_4$			
2,6(1H,3H)-Pyridinedione, 1-butyl-5-(butylamino)-3-[1-butyl-5-(butylamino)-1,6-dihydro-2,6-dioxo-3(2H)-pyridinylidene]-	$CHCl_3$	286(4.22),636(4.56)	118-0948-79
2,6(1H,3H)-Pyridinedione, 3-[1,6-dihydro-1-(2-methylpropyl)-5-[(2-methylpropyl)amino]-2,6-dioxo-3(2H)-pyridinylidene]-1-(2-methylpropyl)-5-[(2-methylpropyl)amino]-	$CHCl_3$	286(4.23),636(4.55)	118-0948-79
$C_{26}H_{40}O_3$			
2H-1-Benzopyran-2-one, 7-(hexadecyloxy)-4-methyl-	C_6H_{12}	216(4.65),240(3.91), 250(3.79),278(3.92), 288(3.98),310(4.12), 318(4.14),337s(--)	23-1377-79
Ceroplastolic acid, methyl ester	n.s.g.	215(4.337)	25-0592-79
$C_{26}H_{40}O_6$			
1,5-Biphenylenedicarboxylic acid, dodecahydro-4b,8b-dimethyl-2,6-bis(2-methylpropyl)-4,8-dioxo-, dimethyl ester	EtOH	298(1.79)	39-0976-79C
$C_{26}H_{40}O_7$			
Pregn-5-ene-3,8,12,14,17,20-hexol, 20-(2-methyl-2-butenoate)	EtOH	216(4.14)	94-2304-79
$C_{26}H_{41}N_3O_2$			
1,4-Naphthalenedione, 6(or 7)-butyl-2,5,8-tris(butylamino)-	benzene	588(4.13),638(4.44)	138-0627-79
$C_{26}H_{41}N_3O_4$			
Hydrazinecarboxylic acid, [(3β,16α)-16-(acetylamino)-3-hydroxypregn-5-en-20-ylidene]-, ethyl ester	EtOH	228(4.12)	70-0825-79
$C_{26}H_{42}N_2$			
4,4'-Bipyridinium, 1,1'-dioctyl-, dibromide, radical cation	n.s.g.	600(4.16)	39-2704-79C

Compound	Solvent	$\lambda_{max}(\log \epsilon)$	Ref.
$C_{26}H_{42}O$			
A-Norcholest-5-en-3-one	heptane	238(4.00),346(1.49)	35-5515-79
$C_{26}H_{42}O_3$			
Androst-5-en-7-one, 17β-[(4,4-dimethyl-pentyl)oxy]-3β-hydroxy-	MeOH	237(4.12)	44-1590-79
24-Norchol-5-en-7-one, 3β-hydroxy-23-(1-methylethoxy)-	MeOH	237(4.11)	44-1590-79
Pregn-5-en-7-one, 3β-hydroxy-20(S)-(3-methylbutoxy)-	MeOH	237(4.14)	44-1590-79
Pregn-5-en-7-one, 3β-hydroxy-20(S)-21-(2-methylpropoxy)-	MeOH	238(4.10)	44-1590-79
$C_{26}H_{44}N_2O_4$			
1,4-Benzenedicarboxylic acid, 2,5-bis(heptylamino)-, diethyl ester	EtOH	478(3.71)	48-0905-79
$C_{26}H_{45}N_{15}O_{10}$			
Viomycin, 1-guanyl-	H_2O	268(4.39)	94-2551-79
$C_{26}H_{52}N_2O_4$			
Acetamide, 2,2'-[1,2-ethanediylbis-(oxy)]bis[N,N-dipentyl-	H_2O	203(4.18)	33-0754-79

Compound	Solvent	λ_{max}(log ϵ)	Ref.
$C_{27}H_{14}Br_4$			
9H-Fluorene, 2,7-dibromo-9-[(2,7-dibromo-9H-fluoren-9-ylidene)methyl]-	$CHCl_3$	311(4.52)	24-1473-79
	DMSO-EtOH-EtONa	560(5.02)	24-1473-79
$C_{27}H_{15}N_3S$			
2,1-Benzisothiazole-5,6-dicarbonitrile, 3,4,7-triphenyl-	CH_2Cl_2	230(4.48),269(4.66), 369(4.09)	24-0266-79
$C_{27}H_{16}N_2O_2$			
Dibenzo[a,j]phenanthridine, 8-(4-nitrophenyl)-	dioxan	222(3.97),306(4.67), 364(3.92),431(3.88)	103-1007-79
$C_{27}H_{16}N_2O_3$			
Methanone, bis[4-(2-benzoxazolyl)phenyl]-	H_2SO_4	206(4.74),390(3.82)	103-1299-79
$C_{27}H_{17}BrO_2$			
Spiro[2H-1-benzopyran-2,9'-[9H]xanthene], 3-bromo-4-phenyl-	EtOAc	290(4.34),320(3.72)	104-1132-79
$C_{27}H_{17}N$			
Dibenz[a,j]phenanthridine, 8-phenyl-	EtOH	229(4.61),262(4.35), 308(4.61),345(3.71), 361(3.85),380(3.81)	103-1007-79
$C_{27}H_{17}NOS$			
9H-Naphtho[3,2,1-kl]acridin-9-one, 2-methyl-6-(phenylthio)-	$CHCl_3$	242(4.59),286(4.78), 324(3.62),406(3.93), 480s(4.20),504(4.26)	103-1227-79
9H-Naphtho[3,2,1-kl]acridin-9-one, 2-methyl-8-(phenylthio)-	$CHCl_3$	278(4.75),428(4.36), 472(4.13),502(4.12)	103-1227-79
$C_{27}H_{17}NO_3S$			
9H-Naphtho[3,2,1-kl]acridin-9-one, 2-methyl-6-(phenylsulfonyl)-	$CHCl_3$	257(4.49),285(4.39), 389s(3.69),405(3.84), 465s(3.87),490(3.90)	103-1227-79
$C_{27}H_{17}N_3S_2$			
4,7-Epithio-2,1-benzisothiazole-5,6-dicarbonitrile, 4,5,6,7-tetrahydro-3,4,7-triphenyl-, 5-endo,6-exo-	CH_2Cl_2	268(4.22)	24-0266-79
5-exo,6-endo-	CH_2Cl_2	268(4.14)	24-0266-79
$C_{27}H_{18}N_2$			
1H-Phenanthro[9,10d]imidazole, 2-[1,1'-biphenyl]-2-yl-	EtOH	229(4.51),257(4.83), 284(4.26),303(3.91), 340(3.45),357(3.43)	42-1017-79
6H-Pyrido[4,3-b]carbazole, 5,11-diphenyl-	EtOH	270s(3.82),280s(3.95), 287s(4.03),289(4.06), 294s(4.04),335(3.02), 350(2.87),393(3.17)	150-4801-79
	EtOH-HCl	275s(3.72),311(3.96), 344s(2.84),360(2.90), 394(2.76)	150-4801-79
$C_{27}H_{18}N_2O_2$			
Benzoxazole, 5,5'-methylenebis[2-phenyl-	H_2SO_4	218(4.06),320(3.80)	103-1299-79
Dibenzo[a,k]phenanthridine, 5,6-dihydro-4-(4-nitrophenyl)-	dioxan	239(4.48),298(4.58), 340s(4.15),361(4.04),	103-1007-79

Compound	Solvent	λ max (log ε)	Ref.
(cont.)		381(3.97)	103-1007-79
$C_{27}H_{18}O_2$			
Spiro[2H-1-benzopyran-2,9'-[9H]xanthene], 4-phenyl-	EtOAc	287(4.47),320(3.72)	104-0761-79
	EtOAc	287(4.47),322(3.72)	104-1132-79
$C_{27}H_{19}BrN_2O$			
Benzamide, N-[[(4-bromophenyl)imino]-diphenylethylidene]-, (Z,Z)-	EtOH	265(4.13),347s(3.14)	12-2059-79
1H-Imidazole, 1-(4-bromophenyl)-2,4,5-triphenyl-, 3-oxide	MeOH	247(4.48),281s(4.23)	12-2059-79
$C_{27}H_{19}ClN_2O$			
Benzamide, N-[[(4-chlorophenyl)imino]-diphenylethylidene]-, (Z,Z)-	EtOH	270(4.57),355s(3.47)	12-2059-79
1H-Imidazole, 1-(4-chlorophenyl)-2,4,5-triphenyl-, 3-oxide	MeOH	247(4.52),278s(4.10)	12-2059-79
$C_{27}H_{19}F_3N_2O_2$			
Pyrimidinium, 3,4-dihydro-5-methyl-4-(3-perylenyl)-, trifluoroacetate	MeOH	247s(4.34),253(4.47), 393(4.00),415(4.34), 441(4.45)	24-0001-79
$C_{27}H_{19}N$			
Dibenzo[a,j]phenanthridine, 9,14-dihydro-8-phenyl-	EtOH	237(4.41),271(4.62), 325(4.24),351(3.86), 368(3.89)	103-1007-79
$C_{27}H_{19}NO_2S$			
Anthracene, 9-[[(4-nitrophenyl)thio]-phenylmethyl]-	n.s.g.	340(3.95),356(3.97), 377(4.02),396(3.94)	39-2948-79C
2,1-Benzisothiazole-5-carboxylic acid, 3,4,7-triphenyl-, methyl ester	CH_2Cl_2	252(4.51),322(3.89), 362(4.14)	24-0266-79
2,1-Benzisothiazole-6-carboxylic acid, 3,4,7-triphenyl-, methyl ester	CH_2Cl_2	243(4.49),303s(3.85), 314(3.87),365(4.09)	24-0266-79
$C_{27}H_{19}N_3O_6S$			
2-Anthracenesulfonic acid, 1-amino-4-[[2-(benzoylamino)phenyl]-9,10-dihydro-9,10-dioxo-, sodium salt	glycerol	636(4.11)	112-0139-79
2-Anthracenesulfonic acid, 1-amino-4-[[3-(benzoylamino)phenyl]-9,10-dihydro-9,10-dioxo-, sodium salt	glycerol	632(4.12)	112-0139-79
2-Anthracenesulfonic acid, 1-amino-4-[[4-(benzoylamino)phenyl]-9,10-dihydro-9,10-dioxo-, sodium salt	glycerol	637(4.21)	112-0139-79
$C_{27}H_{20}$			
Anthracene, 9-(triphenylmethyl)-	n.s.g.	249(4.09),309(3.96)	39-2948-79C
$C_{27}H_{20}BrNO_4S$			
Benzofuro[2,3,4-def]quinoline-7-sulfonic acid, 2-(4-bromophenyl)-1,2,3,3a-tetrahydro-3a-(2-phenylethenyl)-	MeOH	285(4.53),353(3.85), 367(3.96)	104-2284-79
$C_{27}H_{20}ClNO_4S$			
Benzofuro[2,3,4-def]quinoline-7-sulfonic acid, 2-(4-chlorophenyl)-1,2,3,3a-tetrahydro-3a-(2-phenylethenyl)-	MeOH	285(4.62),350(4.07), 365(4.08)	104-2284-79

Compound	Solvent	$\lambda_{max}(\log \epsilon)$	Ref.
$C_{27}H_{20}FNO_4S$			
Benzofuro[2,3,4-def]quinoline-7-sulfonic acid, 2-(3-fluorophenyl)-1,2,3,3a-tetrahydro-3a-(2-phenylethenyl)-	MeOH	286(4.48),351(3.81), 364(3.90)	104-2284-79
Benzofuro[2,3,4-def]quinoline-7-sulfonic acid, 2-(4-fluorophenyl)-1,2,3,3a-tetrahydro-3a-(2-phenylethenyl)-	MeOH	284(4.50),350(3.91), 363(3.96)	104-2284-79
$C_{27}H_{20}N_2O$			
Benzamide, N-[diphenyl(phenylimino)ethylidene]-, (Z,Z)-	EtOH	262(4.44),345s(3.31)	12-2059-79
1H-Imidazole, 1,2,4,5-tetraphenyl-, 3-oxide	EtOH	248(4.14),278s(3.98)	12-2059-79
$C_{27}H_{20}N_2O_2$			
Dibenzo[a,j]phenanthridine, 7,8,8a,9-tetrahydro-8-(4-nitrophenyl)-	dioxan	257(4.47),284(4.56), 320s(4.08),404(4.10)	103-1007-79
$C_{27}H_{20}N_2O_6S$			
Benzofuro[2,3,4-def]quinoline-7-sulfonic acid, 2-(3-nitrophenyl)-3a-(2-phenylethenyl)-	MeOH	286(4.93),300(4.86), 365(4.32)	104-2284-79
Benzofuro[2,3,4-def]quinoline-7-sulfonic acid, 2-(4-nitrophenyl)-3a-(2-phenylethenyl)-	MeOH	285(4.86),296(4.71), 375(4.05)	104-2284-79
$C_{27}H_{20}N_2O_9$			
Daunorubicin, 5-imino-, hydrochloride	MeOH	220(4.47),233s(--), 252(4.51),307(3.84), 335s(--),357s(--), 520s(--),551(4.22), 592(4.30)	87-0036-79
$C_{27}H_{20}N_4O_3$			
4-Imidazolidinecarboxamide, 2,5-dioxo-1,3,4-triphenyl-N-3-pyridinyl-	MeOH	220(4.52),241(4.41), 276(3.86)	118-0794-79
$C_{27}H_{20}O_2$			
Spiro[2H-1-benzopyran-2,9'-[9H]xanthene], 3,4-dihydro-4-phenyl-	EtOAc	278(3.6)	104-0761-79
$C_{27}H_{20}O_3$			
5,11-Naphthacenedione, 6-(2,4,6-trimethylphenoxy)-	toluene	498(4.11)	135-0691-79A
5,12-Naphthacenedione, 6-(2,4,6-trimethylphenoxy)-	toluene	410(3.83)	135-0691-79A
$C_{27}H_{20}S$			
Anthracene, 9-(phenylmethyl)-10-(phenylthio)-	n.s.g.	264(4.19),330(3.00), 348(3.33),365(3.63), 385(3.83),406(3.83)	39-2948-79C
Anthracene, 9-[phenyl(phenylthio)methyl]-	n.s.g.	268(3.96),338(3.42), 355(3.69),374(3.88), 395(3.84)	39-2948-79C
$C_{27}H_{21}N$			
Dibenzo[a,j]phenanthridine, 7,8,8a,9-tetrahydro-8-phenyl-	EtOH	210(4.57),257(4.48), 286(4.40),327s(4.04), 409(4.15)	103-1007-79

Compound	Solvent	λ_{max}(log ϵ)	Ref.
$C_{27}H_{21}NO$			
9H-Indeno[2,1-c]pyridinium, 1-benzoyl-3-methyl-2-(phenylmethyl)-, hydroxide, inner salt	EtOH	210(4.64),265(4.71), 283(4.59),336(4.19), 370(4.19),490(4.00)	103-1214-79
$C_{27}H_{21}NO_2S_2$			
4,7-Epithio-2,1-benzisothiazole-5-carboxylic acid, 4,5,6,7-tetrahydro-3,4,7-triphenyl-, methyl ester, exo	CH_2Cl_2	265(4.02)	24-0266-79
4,7-Epithio-2,1-benzisothiazole-6-carboxylic acid, 4,5,6,7-tetrahydro-3,4,7-triphenyl-, methyl ester, endo	CH_2Cl_2	263(4.13)	24-0266-79
exo	CH_2Cl_2	264(4.11)	24-0266-79
$C_{27}H_{21}NO_4$			
Naphtho[1,2-b]furan-3(2H)-one, 5-acetoxy-2-(methylphenylamino)-4-phenyl-	EtOH	212(4.48),247(4.58), 272(4.54),380(3.90)	103-0597-79
$C_{27}H_{21}NO_4S$			
Benzofuro[2,3,4-def]quinoline-7-sulfonic acid, 1,2,3,3a-tetrahydro-2-phenyl-3a-(2-phenylethenyl)-	MeOH	285(4.41),352(3.78), 365(3.84)	104-2284-79
$C_{27}H_{21}NO_5$			
1H-Indeno[1,2-g]indolizine-1,2-dicarboxylic acid, 3-benzoyl-4-methyl-, dimethyl ester	$CHCl_3$	266(4.93),295s(4.20), 370s(4.53),400(4.54)	103-0647-79
$C_{27}H_{21}NO_5S$			
Benzofuro[2,3,4-def]quinoline-7-sulfonic acid, 1,2,3,3a-tetrahydro-2-(2-hydroxyphenyl)-3a-(2-phenylethenyl)-	MeOH	300(4.39)	104-2284-79
$C_{27}H_{21}NO_6S$			
Benzofuro[2.3.4-def]quinoline-7-sulfonic acid, 2-(3,4-dihydroxyphenyl)-1,2,3,3a-tetrahydro-3a-(2-phenylethenyl)-	MeOH	350(4.18),365(4.13)	104-2284-79
$C_{27}H_{21}NO_{10}S$			
1H-Pyrrole-3-carboxylic acid, 4-(2-furanylcarbonyl)-1-[1-(2-furanylcarbonyl)-3-methoxy-3-oxo-1-propenyl]-5-[(4-methylphenyl)sulfonyl]-, methyl ester	EtOH	224(4.51),300(4.52)	94-2857-79
$C_{27}H_{21}N_3$			
3H-Benzo[c][1,2,3]triazolo[1,2-a]cinnoline, 3-methyl-2,3-diphenyl-	n.s.g.	255(4.52),398(4.07)	39-0192-79C
$C_{27}H_{22}BrClN_2O_2$			
1-Naphthaleneacetic acid, 2-[3-(4-bromophenyl)-1-(4-chlorophenyl)-3-oxopropyl]hydrazide	EtOH	224(4.84),261(4.24), 272(4.23),282(4.20), 290s(4.04)	94-0257-79
$C_{27}H_{22}Br_2NO$			
Pyridinium, 4-[2-[4-[(4-bromophenyl)methoxy]phenyl]ethenyl]-1-[(4-bromophenyl)methyl]-, bromide, (E)-	MeOH	398(4.15)	56-1649-79

Compound	Solvent	λ_{max}(log ϵ)	Ref.
$C_{27}H_{22}CuN_4$			
Copper, [13,14,15,16-tetrahydro-12H-dibenzo[f,m]naphtho[2,3-b][1,4,8,12]-tetraazacyclopentadecinato(2-)-N^6,N^{12},N^{16},N^{22}]-, (SP-4-2)-	$CHCl_3$	258(4.69),330(4.36), 480(4.34)	12-2303-79
$C_{27}H_{22}N_2O_2$			
Phenol, 2-[5-(2,2-diphenylethenyl)-2-methyl-4-pyrimidinyl]-, acetate	MeOH	204(4.6),232(4.3), 302(4.1)	24-1791-79
$C_{27}H_{22}N_2O_3$			
1(2H)-Naphthalenone, 3,4-dihydro-2-[(2-naphthalenylamino)(4-nitrophenyl)-methyl]-	dioxan	248(4.90),272(4.42), 282(4.45),291(4.39), 345(3.79)	103-1007-79
$C_{27}H_{22}N_2O_4$			
1-Naphthalenecarboxylic acid, 2-[1-(1,3-benzodioxol-5-yl)-3-oxo-3-phenylpropyl]hydrazide	EtOH	222(4.80),245s(4.24), 271s(3.97),280(4.09), 288s(3.89)	94-0257-79
$C_{27}H_{22}N_3O_5$			
Pyridinium, 4-[2-[4-(4-nitrophenyl)-methoxy]phenyl]ethenyl]-1-[(4-nitrophenyl)methyl]-, chloride, (E)-	MeOH	400(4.12)	56-1649-79
$C_{27}H_{22}N_4Ni$			
Nickel, [13,14,15,16-tetrahydro-12H-dibenzo[f,m]naphtho[2,3-b][1,4,8,12]-tetrazacyclopentadecinato(2-)-N^6,N^{12},N^{16},N^{22}]-, (SP-4-2)-	$CHCl_3$	268(4.59),297(4.57), 350(4.04),465(3.95)	12-2303-79
$C_{27}H_{22}O_4$			
4,7-Methanobenzo[3',4']cyclobuta[1',2'-3,4]cyclobuta[1,2-c]furan-1,3,8-trione, 3a,3b,3c,4,7,7a,7b,7c-octahydro-4,7-dimethyl-5,6-diphenyl-	90% EtOH	247(3.95),262(4.00)	12-2659-79
$C_{27}H_{23}BrN_2O_2$			
1-Naphthaleneacetic acid, 2-[3-(4-bromophenyl)-3-oxo-1-phenylpropyl]hydrazide	EtOH	224(4.87),262(4.23), 272(4.06),282(4.10), 290s(3.93)	94-0257-79
$C_{27}H_{23}ClNO_4P$			
1H-Pyrrole-3-acetic acid, 4-chloro-2,5-dihydro-1-methyl-2,5-dioxo-α-(triphenylphosphoranylidene)-, ethyl ester	MeOH	224(3.96),270(4.00), 447(3.90)	48-0797-79
$C_{27}H_{23}ClN_2O_2$			
1-Naphthaleneacetic acid, 2-[1-(4-chlorophenyl)-3-oxo-3-phenylpropyl]hydrazide	EtOH	224(4.83),242(4.24), 273(3.98),282(3.98), 290s(3.98)	94-0257-79
$C_{27}H_{23}NO$			
Methanone, phenyl(1,2,3,8a-tetrahydro-2,3-diphenyl-1-indolizinyl)-	CH_2Cl_2	245(5.08),355(4.84), 445(4.47)	24-2197-79
1(2H)-Naphthalenone, 3,4-dihydro-2-[2-(2-naphthalenylamino)phenylmethyl]-	EtOH	209(4.59),248(4.73), 283(4.03),293(3.98)	103-1007-79
$C_{27}H_{23}NO_2$			
[1,1':4',1"-Terphenyl]-2'-carboxylic	CH_2Cl_2	245s(4.41),284(4.13)	24-0266-79

Compound	Solvent	λ_{max}(log ϵ)	Ref.
acid, 5'-amino-6'-(phenylmethyl)-			24-0266-79
[1,1':4',1"-Terphenyl]-2'-carboxylic acid, 6'-amino-5'-(phenylmethyl)-	CH_2Cl_2	233(4.57),323(3.74)	24-0266-79
$C_{27}H_{23}NO_4$			
Naphtho[1,2-b]furan-3(2H)-one, 2-[ethyl(4-methoxyphenyl)amino]-5-hydroxy-4-phenyl-	EtOH	219(4.67),244(4.57), 278(4.51),407(3.90)	103-0597-79
Naphtho[1,2-b]furan-3(2H)-one, 2-(ethylphenylamino)-5-hydroxy-4-(4-methoxyphenyl)-	EtOH	219(4.72),249(4.64), 278(4.51),414(3.70)	103-0597-79
Naphtho[1,2-b]furan-3(2H)-one, 5-hydroxy-4-(4-methoxyphenyl)-2-[methyl(4-methylphenyl)amino]-	EtOH	220(4.72),249(4.61), 280(4.53),415(3.90)	103-0597-79
$C_{27}H_{23}NO_5$			
1,2-Indolizinedicarboxylic acid, 3-benzoyl-5,8-dimethyl-7-phenyl-, dimethyl ester	EtOH	204(4.62),254(4.86), 334(4.10),370(3.80)	103-0647-79
$C_{27}H_{23}N_2O_2$			
Quinolinium, 1-ethyl-2-[4-(4-nitrophenyl)-2-phenyl-1,3-butadienyl]-, iodide	EtOH	502(4.43),522(4.41)	62-0650-79A
	isoBuOH	504(4.42),530s(--)	62-0650-79A
	dioxan	502(4.41),530s(--)	62-0650-79A
	THF	504(4.41),529s(--)	62-0650-79A
	$CHCl_3$	506(4.42),532s(--)	62-0650-79A
$C_{27}H_{23}N_3O$			
Imidazo[1,2-a]pyrazin-3(7H)-one, 6-(4-methylphenyl)-2,8-bis(phenylmethyl)-	MeOH	248(4.33),355(3.70), 435(3.93)	69-2204-79
$C_{27}H_{23}N_5O_7$			
β-D-Ribofuranuronic acid, 1-deoxy-1-[6-(dibenzoylamino)-9H-purin-9-yl]-2,3-O-(1-methylethylidene)-	MeOH	251(4.60),278s(4.49)	44-4713-79
$C_{27}H_{23}OPS$			
Phosphonium, triphenyl-, 1-(methylthio)-2-oxo-2-phenylethylide	n.s.g.	225s(3.732),270(2.909), 277(2.887),310s(2.756)	65-1740-79
$C_{27}H_{23}OPSe$			
Phosphonium, triphenyl-, 1-(methylseleno)-2-oxo-2-phenylethylide	n.s.g.	225s(3.792),270s(3.065), 278(3.009),317s(2.867)	65-1740-79
$C_{27}H_{24}ClN_5O_6$			
Acetamide, N-[9-[5-O-benzoyl-3-[(benzoyloxy)methyl]-2,3-dideoxy-α-D-erythro-pentofuranosyl]-6-chloro-9H-purin-2-yl]-	MeOH	260(4.05),287(4.10)	87-0518-79
β-	MeOH	260(4.02),283(4.00)	87-0518-79
$C_{27}H_{24}N$			
Quinolinium, 2-(2,4-diphenyl-1,3-butadienyl)-1-ethyl-, iodide	EtOH	525(3.45),561(3.72), 652s(2.59)	62-0650-79A
	isoBuOH	528(3.43),563(4.79)	62-0650-79A
	dioxan	536(3.43),570(3.70)	62-0650-79A
	THF	532(3.45),576(3.78)	62-0650-79A
	$CHCl_3$	534(3.36),566(3.85)	62-0650-79A
$C_{27}H_{24}NO$			
Pyridinium, 1-(4-oxo-1,2,4-triphenyl-	CH_2Cl_2	249(5.15)	24-2197-79

Compound	Solvent	λ_{max}(log ε)	Ref.
butyl)-, perchlorate (cont.)			24-2197-79
Pyridinium, 4-[2-[4-(phenylmethoxy)-phenyl]ethenyl]-1-(phenylmethyl)-, chloride, (E)-	MeOH	395(3.82)	56-1649-79
$C_{27}H_{24}NO_4$			
Benzo[g]-1,3-benzodioxolo[5,6-a]quinolizinium, 5,6-dihydro-9,10-dimethoxy-8-(phenylmethyl)-, bromide	EtOH	285(4.04),365(3.87), 400(3.44),450(3.28)	36-0705-79
$C_{27}H_{24}NO_4P$			
Phosphorin, 1,1-dihydro-1,1-dimethoxy-4-[2-(4-nitrophenyl)ethenyl]-2,6-diphenyl-, (E)-	C_6H_{12}	428(4.45)	24-1272-79
	benzene	475(4.42)	24-1272-79
	MeOH	442(4.45),473(4.45)	24-1272-79
	BuOH	442(4.50),474(4.48)	24-1272-79
	ether	443(4.50)	24-1272-79
	acetone	440(4.44),483(4.45)	24-1272-79
	MeCN	438(4.44),477(4.45)	24-1272-79
	CH_2Cl_2	438(4.35),488(4.36)	24-1272-79
	C_6H_5Br	446(4.30),492(4.33)	24-1272-79
$C_{27}H_{24}N_2$			
Cinnoline, 1,2,3,4-tetrahydro-3-methyl-1,2,4-triphenyl-	MeCN	246(4.34),287(4.19)	104-2145-79
Cinnoline, 1,2,3,4-tetrahydro-4-methyl-1,2,4-triphenyl-	MeCN	255(4.37),282(4.20)	103-1243-79
$C_{27}H_{24}N_2O_2$			
1-Naphthaleneacetic acid, 2-(3-oxo-1,3-diphenylpropyl)hydrazide	EtOH	223(4.76),242(--), 262(3.84),271(4.04), 282(4.12),292(3.95)	94-0257-79
1-Naphthalenecarboxylic acid, 2-[1-(4-methylphenyl)-3-oxo-3-phenylpropyl]-hydrazide	EtOH	223(4.83),245s(4.21), 273(3.93),282(3.99), 290s(3.95)	94-0257-79
$C_{27}H_{24}N_2O_4$			
Benzenamine, N-(5,6-dihydro-9,10-dimethoxy-8H-benzo]g]-1,3-benzodioxolo[5,6-a]quinolizin-8-ylidene)-4-methyl-	EtOH-acid	236(4.50),257(4.40), 342(4.38),420(3.90)	36-0705-79
$C_{27}H_{24}N_2O_8$			
Urea, (2,3,5-tri-O-benzoyl-β-D-ribofuranosyl)-	EtOH	231(4.33),275(3.48)	73-1475-79
$C_{27}H_{24}N_2O_9$			
2-Butenedioic acid, 2-[[1-[3-methoxy-1-(methoxycarbonyl)-3-oxo-1-propenyl]-3,5-diphenyl-1H-pyrazol-4-yl]-oxy]-, dimethyl ester	EtOH	238(4.38),323(4.23)	23-0904-79
Urea, N-hydroxy-N'-(2,3,5-tri-O-benzoyl-β-D-ribofuranosyl)-	EtOH	231(4.37),275(3.46)	73-1475-79
$C_{27}H_{24}N_4O_4$			
1H-Pyrazole-3-carboxylic acid, 5-[[(4-methoxybenzoyl)hydrazono]phenylmethyl]-4-phenyl-, ethyl ester	EtOH	283(3.43)	4-0849-79
$C_{27}H_{24}O$			
Ethanone, 2,2-diphenyl-1-(4,6,8-trimethyl-2-azulenyl)-	benzene	590(3.14)	70-0221-79

Compound	Solvent	λ_{max}(log ε)	Ref.
$C_{27}H_{24}O_5$			
2H-1-Benzopyran-2-acetic acid, 3,4-dihydro-3-(hydroxymethylene)-6-methyl-4-oxo-α,α-diphenyl-, ethyl ester	MeOH	220(4.0),308(3.5)	24-1791-79
$C_{27}H_{24}O_6$			
3-Phenanthrenecarboxylic acid, 1-acetoxy-9-methoxy-4-(4-methoxyphenyl)-, ethyl ester	n.s.g.	230(4.54),255(4.57), 279s(4.32),301s(4.18), 312s(4.13),336s(3.55)	33-0090-79
$C_{27}H_{25}N$			
Benzenamine, 4-(4-[1,1'-biphenyl]-4-yl-1,3,5-cycloheptatrien-1-yl)-N,N-dimethyl-	EtOH	371(4.519)	78-2269-79
[1,1'-Biphenyl]-2-amine, N-(diphenylmethyl)-2',5'-dimethyl-	EtOH	257(4.11)	33-2129-79
$C_{27}H_{25}NO$			
Pyrrolo[2,1-a]isoquinolin-1(5H)-one, 6,10b-dihydro-10b-(1-methylethyl)-2,3-diphenyl-	MeCN	274(4.08),355(3.84)	88-1213-79
$C_{27}H_{25}NO_4$			
1H-Pyrrole-3-carboxylic acid, 2,5-dihydro-2-hydroxy-5-oxo-2-phenyl-1,4-bis(phenylmethyl)-, ethyl ester	EtOH	217(4.16)	44-0808-79
$C_{27}H_{25}NO_8$			
Nogarene	EtOH	239(4.68),260(4.35), 294(4.11),476(4.29), 498(4.27)	44-4030-79
$C_{27}H_{25}NS$			
Pyrrolo[2,1-a]isoquinoline-1(5H)-thione, 6,10b-dihydro-10b-(1-methylethyl)-2,3-diphenyl-	MeCN	255(4.10),423(4.10)	88-1213-79
$C_{27}H_{25}N_3O_8$			
Hydrazinecarboxamide, N-(2,3,5-tri-O-benzoyl-β-D-ribofuranosyl)-	EtOH	231(4.58),275(3.62)	73-1475-79
$C_{27}H_{25}N_4$			
Quinolinium, 4-(1H-benzimidazol-2-yl)-2-[2-[4-(dimethylamino)phenyl]ethenyl]-1-methyl-, iodide	EtOH	565(4.73)	4-1583-79
Quinolinium, 6-(1H-benzimidazol-2-yl)-2-[2-[4-(dimethylamino)phenyl]ethenyl]-1-methyl-, iodide	EtOH	557(4.85)	4-1583-79
Quinolinium, 6-(1H-benzimidazol-2-yl)-4-[2-[4-(dimethylamino)phenyl]ethenyl]-1-methyl-, iodide	EtOH	581(4.61)	4-1583-79
$C_{27}H_{25}O_2P$			
Phosphorin, 1,1-dihydro-1,1-dimethoxy-2,6-diphenyl-4-(2-phenylethenyl)-, (E)-	MeOH	249(4.22),356(4.23), 427(3.88)	24-1272-79
$C_{27}H_{26}BrN_3O_8$			
1H-Indole-3-propanamide, α-(acetylamino)-6-bromo-N-[2-(3,4,5-triacetoxyphenyl)ethenyl]-, [S-(E)]-	MeOH	227(4.77),290(4.57)	23-2325-79

Compound	Solvent	$\lambda_{max}(\log \epsilon)$	Ref.
$C_{27}H_{26}FN_2$			
Quinolinium, 1-ethyl-2-[5-(1-ethyl-2(1H)-quinolinylidene)-3-fluoro-1,3-pentadienyl]-, perchlorate	EtOH	719(4.40)	124-0872-79
$C_{27}H_{26}N_2O_4$			
2,4(1H,3H)-Pyrimidinedione, 1-[2-hydroxy-3-(triphenylmethoxy)propyl]-5-methyl-	n.s.g.	270(3.96)	128-0281-79
$C_{27}H_{26}N_2O_5$			
4,5-Diazatetracyclo[6.2.1.0^{2,7}.0^{3,6}]undec-9-ene-4,5-dicarboxylic acid, 1,8-dimethyl-11-oxo-9,10-diphenyl-, dimethyl ester, (1α,2β,3α,6α,7β,8α)-	90% EtOH	248(3.96),261(4.00)	12-2659-79
$C_{27}H_{26}N_2O_7S_2$			
3-Butenoic acid, 2-acetyl-2-[(4-methylphenyl)azo]-4,4-bis(phenylsulfonyl)-, ethyl ester	EtOH	265(4.09),430(4.29)	104-0500-79
$C_{27}H_{26}N_2O_8S_2$			
3-Butenoic acid, 2-acetyl-2-[(4-methoxyphenyl)azo]-4,4-bis(phenylsulfonyl)-, ethyl ester	EtOH	275(4.07),435(4.28)	104-0500-79
$C_{27}H_{26}N_4O_6$			
Imidazo[4,5-d][1,3]diazepin-8(3H)-one, 3-[2-deoxy-3,5-bis-O-(4-methylbenzoyl)-β-D-erythro-pentofuranosyl]-4,7-dihydro-	MeOH	235(4.71),282(3.48), 300(3.45),350(3.57)	35-6127-79
$C_{27}H_{26}N_4O_8$			
1H-Purine-2,6-dione, 7-(2,3-di-O-benzoyl-6-deoxy-α-L-manno-pyranosyl)-3,7-dihydro-1,3-dimethyl-	MeOH	274(3.90)	39-2682-79C
$C_{27}H_{26}OSi_2$			
Disilane, 1-benzoyl-1,1-dimethyl-2,2,2-triphenyl-	C_6H_{12}	386(2.26),404(2.54), 423(2.66),444(2.45)	35-0083-79
$C_{27}H_{27}NO$			
Phenol, 2-(4,4-diphenyl-1-piperidino-1,3-butadienyl)-	MeOH	230(4.2),342(4.4)	24-1791-79
$C_{27}H_{27}NOS$			
2H,6H-[1,3]Thiazino[2,3-a]isoquinoline, 2-ethoxy-7,11b-dihydro-11b-methyl-3,4-diphenyl-	MeCN	273(3.80),293(3.88)	88-1213-79
2H,6H-[1,3]Thiazino[2,3-a]isoquinoline, 11b-ethyl-7,11b-dihydro-2-methoxy-3,4-diphenyl-	MeCN	274(3.79),297(3.87)	88-1213-79
$C_{27}H_{27}NO_3$			
1H-Indole-2-acetic acid, 3-[2-(phenylmethoxy)ethyl]-1-(phenylmethyl)-, methyl ester	EtOH	224(4.53),277(3.87), 287(3.90),295(3.81)	23-0289-79
$C_{27}H_{27}NO_8$			
Propanedioic acid, (5,6-dihydro-9,10-dimethoxy-8H-benzo[g]-1,3-benzodi-	EtOH	260(4.31),332(4.15), 402(3.7),428s(3.72)	36-0705-79

Compound	Solvent	λ_{max}(log ε)	Ref.
oxolo[5,6-a]quinolizin-8-ylidene)-, diethyl ester (cont.)			36-0705-79
$C_{27}H_{27}N_2O_4PS$			
Phosphorin, 1,1-dihydro-1,1-dimethoxy-4-[[[(4-methylphenyl)sulfonyl]hydrazono]methyl]-2,6-diphenyl-	MeOH	220(4.39),322(4.40), 402(4.17)	24-1272-79
$C_{27}H_{27}N_3O_2$			
Acetamide, N-(3,3-diphenylpropyl)-N-[2-(5-phenyl-1,2,4-oxadiazol-3-yl)-ethyl]-	EtOH	253(4.33)	150-0801-79
Benzamide, N-[[4-(dimethylamino)-5-methyl-5-phenyl-2(5H)-oxazolylidene]phenylmethyl]-N-methyl-	MeCN	231s(4.23),325s(4.43), 335(4.46),348s(4.37)	33-1236-79
$C_{27}H_{27}N_3O_8$			
Benzoic acid, 4-ethoxy-, 2-[[(4-ethoxybenzoyl)oxy]methyl]-2,3,3a,9a-tetrahydro-6-imino-6H-furo[2',3':4,5]oxazolo[3,2-a]pyrimidin-3-yl ester, monohydrochloride, [2R-(2α,3β,3aβ,9aβ)]-	MeOH	262(4.79),273s(4.68)	87-0639-79
$C_{27}H_{27}N_5O_3$			
1,3,5-Triazine-1(2H)-ethanimidamide, tetrahydro-N,N,α,α-tetramethyl-2,4,6-trioxo-N',3,5-triphenyl-	MeCN	260(3.94)	33-1429-79
$C_{27}H_{28}N_2O_2$			
1H-Indole-2-carboxamide, N,N-dimethyl-3-[2-(phenylmethoxy)ethyl]-1-(phenylmethyl)-	EtOH	215(4.55),287(3.97)	23-0289-79
$C_{27}H_{28}N_2O_2S$			
Benzenesulfonic acid, 4-methyl-, (1,5-dimethyl-2,3-diphenyl-2,4-hexadienylidene)hydrazide, (?,Z)-	EtOH	232(4.34),304(4.03)	44-2331-79
$C_{27}H_{28}N_4O_6$			
Formazan, 1,5-bis[2-(carboxymethoxy)-3,5-dimethylphenyl)-3-phenyl-	60% EtOH	496(4.15)	140-1195-79
$C_{27}H_{28}O$			
Methanone, [9-(1,1-dimethylpentyl)-9H-fluoren-9-yl]phenyl-	EtOH	260(4.28),292s(3.78), 303(3.63)	118-0616-79
$C_{27}H_{28}O_5$			
Ethanone, 1-[6-hydroxy-2-[3-(7-methoxy-2,2-dimethyl-2H-1-benzopyran-6-yl)-1-methyl-1-butenyl]-5-benzofuranyl]-, (-)-	$CHCl_3$	240(4.52),267(4.57), 297(4.36),312(4.30)	44-1429-79
$C_{27}H_{28}O_7$			
Giferolide	EtOH	202(4.43),231(4.49), 254s(4.30)	105-0426-79
$C_{27}H_{28}O_{11}$			
5,12-Naphthacenedione, 8-acetyl-10-[(2,6-dideoxy-α-D-ribohexopyranosyl)oxy]-7,8,9,10-tetrahydro-6,8,11-trihydroxy-1-methoxy-	$CHCl_3$	252(4.29),288(3.85), 480(4.02),496(4.01), 530(3.73)	87-0406-79

Compound	Solvent	$\lambda_{max}(\log \epsilon)$	Ref.
5,12-Naphthacenedione, 8-acetyl-10-[(2,6-dideoxy-β-D-ribo-hexopyranosyl)oxy]-7,8,9,10-tetrahydro-6,8,11-trihydroxy-1-methoxy-	$CHCl_3$	253(4.38),289(3.91), 486(4.09),499(4.10), 535(3.87)	87-0406-79
5,12-Naphthacenedione, 8-acetyl-10-[(2,6-dideoxy-α-L-lyxo-hexopyranosyl)oxy]-7,8,9,10-tetrahydro-6,8,11-trihydroxy-1-methoxy-, (8a-cis)-	MeOH	233(4.55),251(4.41), 288(3.96),313(3.56), 327(3.51),385(3.40), 449(3.93),473(4.08), 480(4.08),497(4.09), 517(3.93),532(3.85), 580(2.70)	87-0406-79
$C_{27}H_{29}NO_4$			
7H-Benz[de]anthracene-1,2-dicarboxylic acid, 3-[(1,1-dimethylethyl)amino]-7,7-dimethyl-, dimethyl ester	CH_2Cl_2	254(4.54),270s(4.39), 360(4.21)	24-3166-79
Butanedioic acid, (10,10-dimethyl-9(10H)-anthracenylidene)[(1,1-dimethylethyl)carbonimidoyl]-, dimethyl ester	CH_2Cl_2	266(3.93),321(3.93)	89-0067-79
$C_{27}H_{29}NO_9$			
7-Deoxynogarol	EtOH	236(4.58),261(4.38), 290s(4.00),474(4.16)	44-4030-79
$C_{27}H_{29}NO_{10}$			
Daunorubicin	MeOH	234(4.57),252(4.42), 290(3.93),480(4.08), 495(4.09),532(3.80)	87-0036-79
$C_{27}H_{29}N_2O_2$			
Pyridinium, 3-ethyl-1-[2-[2-(2-methoxy-2-oxoethyl)-1-(phenylmethyl)-1H-indol-3-yl]ethyl]-, iodide	EtOH	265(4.0)	23-0289-79
$C_{27}H_{29}N_3O_2$			
Benzenepropanamide, α-[[4-(diethylamino)-2-methylpropyl]imino]-N-methyl-β-oxo-N-phenyl-	BuOAc	457(4.08)	24-3098-79
$C_{27}H_{29}N_3O_8$			
14,17,20,23,26,29-Hexaoxa-34,35,36-triazatetracyclo[28.3.1.1^{3,7}.1^{9,13}]hexatriaconta-1(34),3,5,7(36),9,11,13(35)-3-,32-nonaene-2,8-dione (or dispiro isomer)	EtOH	220(4.27),275(4.19)	44-3816-79
$C_{27}H_{29}N_6O_3PS$			
Thiourea, N-[bis[(4-methoxyphenyl)amino](2-pyridinylamino)phosphoranylidene]-N'-(4-methoxyphenyl)-	EtOH	217(4.68),227s(4.64), 274(4.60)	64-0297-79B
$C_{27}H_{30}N_2O_4$			
Acetamide, N-[2-[3-(3-formyl-2-oxocyclohexyl)-2,3-dihydro-2-oxo-1-(phenylmethyl)-1H-indol-3-yl]ethyl]-N-methyl-	EtOH	258(4.13),285(4.06)	23-1694-79
	EtOH-NaOH	254(4.04),322(4.29)	23-1694-79
$C_{27}H_{30}N_4O_5S_2$			
S-Benzylthiouronium 1-amino-4-(pentylamino)anthraquinone-2-sulfonate	EtOH	529(4.09),635(4.10)	23-1694-79

Compound	Solvent	λ_{max}(log ϵ)	Ref.
$C_{27}H_{30}O_5$			
1,4-Ethanoanthracene-9,10-dione, 1,4-dihydro-5,8-dihydroxy-1-methyl-6-[3-methyl-6-(1-methylethyl)-2-cyclohex-1-yl]-	MeOH	221(4.50),518(3.77), 555s(--)	5-2018-79
$C_{27}H_{30}O_{15}$			
Multiflorin B	MeOH	267(4.23),300s(3.98), 345(4.06)	95-0439-79
	MeOH-NaOMe	276(4.29),310s(3.90), 325s(4.12),385(4.26)	95-0439-79
$C_{27}H_{31}N_3$			
Cinnoline, 1,2,3,4-tetrahydro-3,3-dimethyl-1,2-diphenyl-4-piperidino-	MeCN	240(4.05),267(4.20), 298(4.02)	103-1243-79
$C_{27}H_{31}N_3O_4S_2$			
Benzenesulfonamide, N-[3,4-dihydro-1,3,3,4-tetramethyl-4-[[(4-methylphenyl)sulfonyl]amino]-2(1H)-quinolinylidene]-4-methyl-	EtOH	222(4.43),282(4.26)	23-0558-79
$C_{27}H_{32}N_2O_3$			
Acetamide, N-[2-[2,3-dihydro-3-(2-methoxy-2-cyclohexen-1-yl)-2-oxo-1-(phenylmethyl)-1H-indol-3-yl]ethyl]-N-methyl-	EtOH	257(3.87),280s(3.38)	23-1694-79
$C_{27}H_{32}N_2O_4$			
Acetamide, N-[2-[3-(2-acetoxycyclohexyl)-2,3-dihydro-2-oxo-1-(phenylmethyl)-1H-indol-3-yl]ethyl]-, A	EtOH	254(3.85),281s(3.11)	23-1694-79
B	EtOH	255(3.84),282s(3.13)	23-1694-79
2-Propenoic acid, 3-[4-[(3-butoxy-3-oxopropyl)(phenylmethyl)amino]-2-methylphenyl]-2-cyano-, ethyl ester	EtOH	428(4.61)	110-1769-79
	EtOH-KOH	338(--)	110-1769-79
	CCl_4	419(--)	110-1769-79
	KBr	435(--)	110-1769-79
$C_{27}H_{32}N_8O_5SSi$			
9H-Purin-6-amine, 9-[3-azido-3-deoxy-5-O-[(1,1-dimethylethyl)diphenylsilyl]-2-O-(methylsulfonyl)-β-D-xylofuranosyl]-	MeOH	259(4.26)	44-1317-79
$C_{27}H_{32}O$			
1H-Inden-1-one, 4-(3,3-diphenyl-2-propenyl)octahydro-4,5,7a-trimethyl-, [3aR-(3aα,4α,5β,7aβ)]-	n.s.g.	252(4.11)	78-2301-79
$C_{27}H_{32}O_3$			
Ent-3β-benzoyloxy-14(13→12)-abeo-beyera-15(16),13(17)-dien-2-one	EtOH	230(4.50),273(3.04), 281(2.94),300s(1.72)	39-1004-79C
$C_{27}H_{32}S_2$			
9,12-Dithiatricyclo[12.3.1.1^{3,7}]nonadeca-1(18),3,5,7(19),14,16-hexaene, 2-(1,7,7-trimethylbicyclo[2.2.1]hept-2-ylidene)-	MeCN	255.5s(4.11)	24-0138-79
$C_{27}H_{32}S_3$			
Dispiro[bicyclo[2.2.1]heptane-2,2'-thi-	MeCN	266s(3.11),275s(2.78)	24-0138-79

Compound	Solvent	λ_{max}(log ϵ)	Ref.
irane-3',2"-[9,12]dithiatricyclo-[12.3.1.1^{3,7}]nonadeca-1(18),3,5-7(19),14,16-hexaene], 1,7,7-tri-methyl- (cont.)			24-0138-79
$C_{27}H_{33}IN_2O_4$			
L-Tryptophan, N-[(phenylmethoxy)carbo-nyl]-, 8-iodooctyl ester	EtOH	275(3.79),282(3.81), 291(3.75)	118-0957-79
$C_{27}H_{33}NO_2$			
Benzenemethanamine, N,N-di-2,4-hexadi-enyl-4-methoxy-α-(4-methoxyphenyl)-, (all-E)-	n.s.g.	230(4.89),274(3.61), 284(3.42)	44-3451-79
$C_{27}H_{33}NO_4S_2$			
Androsta-3,5-dien-17-ol, 3-[(2-nitro-phenyl)dithio]-, acetate, (17β)-	MeOH	243(4.42),350(3.74)	39-1166-79C
$C_{27}H_{33}P$			
Phosphine, tris(2,4,6-trimethylphenyl)-	n.s.g.	313(4.20)	65-1036-79
$C_{27}H_{34}N_2O_5$			
Echitovenedine, 11-methoxy-, (-) (differential spectrum)	EtOH	245(3.98),328(4.15)	78-1151-79
$C_{27}H_{34}O_2S_2$			
Androsta-3,5-dien-17-ol, 3-(phenyldi-thio)-, acetate, (17β)-	MeOH	247(4.31)	39-1166-79C
$C_{27}H_{34}O_4$			
Spiro[cyclopenta[e]cyclopenta[7,8]phen-anthro[10,1-bc]pyran-3(8H),2'(5'H)-furan]-5',8-dione, 1,2,3',3a,4,4',5-5a,5b-6,7,8b,9,10,11,11a,13a,13b-octadecahydro-3a,5b-dimethyl-	MeOH	266(3.70),311(4.09)	44-1597-79
$C_{27}H_{34}O_8$			
Cneorin R	MeOH	208(4.11)	88-2015-79
$C_{27}H_{34}O_9$			
3a,7-Epoxy-3aH-furo[3,2-b]oxocin-3-car-boxylic acid, 5-[6-(2,5-dioxocyclo-pentyl)-1,3-dimethyl-6-oxo-2,4-hexa-dienyl]octahydro-2,6,9a-trimethyl-8-oxo-, methyl ester	EtOH-HCl EtOH-NaOH	228(4.08),357(4.38) 248(4.34),292(4.24), 322(4.25)	142-0477-79B 142-0477-79B
$C_{27}H_{34}O_{11}$			
Undalatone	MeOH	222(4.23),240s(4.14)	78-0017-79
$C_{27}H_{34}O_{12}$			
β-D-Glucopyranoside, 4-[4-(3,4-dimeth-oxyphenyl)tetrahydro-6a-hydroxy-1H-3H-furo[3,4-c]furan-1-yl]-2-methoxy-phenyl, [1R-(1α,3aα,4α,6aα)]-	EtOH	230(4.26),277(3.76)	94-2868-79
$C_{27}H_{35}NO_9$			
3a,7-Epoxy-3aH-furo[3,2-b]oxocin-3-car-boxylic acid, 5-[6-(2,5-dihydro-4-hy-droxy-1-methyl-2-oxo-1H-pyrrol-3-yl]-1,3-dimethyl-6-oxo-2,4-hexadienyl]-octahydro-2,6,9a-trimethyl-8-oxo-, methyl ester	EtOH-HCl EtOH-NaOH	243(3.95),358(4.49) 264(4.25),288(4.25), 336(4.24)	142-0477-79B 142-0477-79B

Compound	Solvent	$\lambda_{max}(\log \epsilon)$	Ref.
3a,7-Epoxy-3aH-furo[3,2-b]oxocin-3-carboxylic acid, 5-[1,3-dimethyl-6-(5-methyl-2,4-dioxo-3-pyrrolidinyl)-6-oxo-2,4-hexadienyl]octahydro-2,6,9a-trimethyl-8-oxo-, methyl ester	EtOH-HCl	236(3.88),352(4.53)	142-0477-79B
	EtOH-NaOH	255(4.15),283(4.23), 330(4.27)	142-0477-79B
3a,7-Epoxy-3aH-furo[3,2-b]oxocin-3-carboxylic acid, 5-[6-(2,4-dioxo-3-piperidinyl)-1,3-dimethyl-6-oxo-2,4-hexadienyl]octahydro-2,6,9a-trimethyl-8-oxo-, methyl ester	EtOH-HCl	246(4.00),346(4.47)	142-0477-79B
	EtOH-NaOH	264(4.38),333(4.17)	142-0477-79B
$C_{27}H_{36}FN_5O_6$			
L-Leucine, N-[N-[4-[(5-fluoro-1,2-dihydro-2-oxo-4-pyrimidinyl)amino]-1,4-dioxobutyl]-L-leucyl]-, phenylmethyl ester	EtOH	244(3.94),293(3.51), 349(3.76)	87-1104-79
$C_{27}H_{36}N_2O_5$			
Aspidospermidine-3-carboxylic acid, 2,3-didehydro-16-methoxy-20-(3-methyl-1-oxobutoxy)-, methyl ester, (5α,12β,19α,20R)-	EtOH	246(3.93),324(4.08)	78-1151-79
$C_{27}H_{36}N_2O_{10}$			
1H-Pyrrole-3-propanoic acid, 5-carboxy-2-[[5-[(1,1-dimethylethoxy)carbonyl]-4-(3-methoxy-3-oxopropyl)-3-methyl-1H-pyrrol-2-yl]methyl]-4-(2-methoxy-2-oxoethyl)-, α-methyl ester	n.s.g.	242(4.01),273(4.35), 290(4.44)	39-1927-79C
$C_{27}H_{36}O_3$			
Benzo[6,7]pregna-4,6-diene-21-carboxylic acid, 3',6,6',7-tetrahydro-17-hydroxy-4'-methyl-3-oxo-, γ-lactone, (6β,7β,17α)-	MeOH	241(4.15)	44-4299-79
Sargaquinal	EtOH	250(4.18)	138-0277-79
$C_{27}H_{36}O_4$			
Sargachromenol	MeOH	263(3.69),332(3.44)	138-0277-79
Sargaquinoic acid	EtOH	251(4.16)	138-0277-79
$C_{27}H_{36}O_{11}$			
Benzo[4,5]cyclodeca[1,2-b]furan-5-carboxylic acid, 8,9,13-triacetoxy-1,2,3a-6,7,8,8a,9,10,12a,13,13a-dodecahydro-13a-hydroxy-1,8a,12-trimethyl-2-oxo-, methyl ester	MeOH	218(3.88)	78-1907-79
$C_{27}H_{36}O_{14}$			
Sylvestroside III	MeOH	237(4.25)	102-0273-79
Sylvestroside IV	MeOH	236(3.99)	102-0273-79
$C_{27}H_{38}O_2$			
2,5-Cyclohexadiene-1,4-dione, 2-methyl-6-(3,7,11,15-tetramethyl-2,6,10,14-hexadecatetraenyl)-, (E,E,E)-	EtOH	252(4.09)	138-1269-79
$C_{27}H_{38}O_3$			
Benz[6,7]androsta-4,6-dien-3-one, 17-acetoxy-3',6,6',7-tetrahydro-4',5'-dimethyl-, (6β,7β,17β)-	MeOH	243(4.13)	44-4299-79

Compound	Solvent	λ_{max}(log ϵ)	Ref.
Spirostan-1,4-dien-3-one, (25R)-	MeOH	245(2.15)	95-0264-79
$C_{27}H_{38}O_4$			
2,5-Cyclohexadiene-1,4-dione, 2-(8,9-dihydroxy-3,7,11,15-tetramethyl-2,6,10,14-hexadecatetraenyl)-6-methyl-	EtOH	253(4.12)	138-1269-79
Stypoldione	MeOH	270(3.39),475(2.95)	88-0145-79
$C_{27}H_{38}O_6$			
Propanedioic acid, [(1α,17β)-17-hydroxy-3-oxoandrosta-4,6-dien-1-yl]-, diethyl ester	EtOH	288(4.45)	56-0149-79
$C_{27}H_{38}O_7$			
Digitoxigenin, 18-acetoxy-, 3-acetate	MeOH	219(4.15)	44-3511-79
5α-Pregn-16-en-20-one, 2α,3β,6β-triacetoxy-	EtOH	239(4.10)	105-0446-79
$C_{27}H_{38}O_{10}$			
6-Benzocyclodecene-6-acetic acid, 1,5,12-triacetoxy-1,2,3,4,4a,5,6,9-10,11,12,12a-dodecahydro-3,6-dihydroxy-α,12a-dimethyl-4,9-bis(methylene)-, methyl ester	MeOH	224(3.56)	78-1907-79
Cyclodeca[3,4]benz[1,2-b]oxirene-10-acetic acid, 3,4,11-triacetoxy-la-2,3,3a,4,5,6,7,10,11,11a,11b-dodecahydro-10-hydroxy-α,3a,11b-trimethyl-7-methylene-, methyl ester	MeOH	224(3.46)	78-1907-79
1H-Cyclopentacyclodecene-5-acetic acid, 1,4,11-triacetoxy-3-formyl-2,3,3a,4-5,8,9,10,11,11a-decahydro-5-hydroxy-α,3,11a-trimethyl-8-methylene-, methyl ester	MeOH	227(4.00)	78-1907-79
$C_{27}H_{39}NO_5S$			
Acetamide, N-[(3β,16α,17α)-3-acetoxy-17-(acetylthio)-20-oxopregn-5-en-16-yl]-	EtOH	238(3.38)	70-0825-79
$C_{27}H_{39}N_3O_6$			
Hydrazinecarboxylic acid, [(3β,16β)-3-acetoxy-3',16-dihydro-2'-oxo-2'H-pregn-5-eno[16,17-d]oxazol-20-ylidene]-, ethyl ester	EtOH	227(3.76)	70-2139-79
Hydrazinecarboxylic acid, 2-[(3β,16β)-3-acetoxy-20-oxo-4'H-pregn-5-eno-[16,17-d]oxazol-2'-yl]-, ethyl ester	EtOH	298(4.00)	70-2139-79
$C_{27}H_{40}Br_2O$			
Cholesta-3,5-dien-7-one, 4,6-dibromo-	EtOH	298(4.18)	39-2727-79C
$C_{27}H_{40}O$			
Cholesta-1,5,7-trien-3-one	EtOH	231(4.07),268(--), 277(3.93)	39-1695-79C
Cholesta-4,6,8(14)-trien-3-one	EtOH	240(3.65),282(3.90), 348(4.41)	12-2017-79
19-Norcholesta-1,3,5(10)-trien-6-one, 1-methyl-	EtOH	256(4.09),302(3.35)	56-0797-79

Compound	Solvent	λ_{max}(log ϵ)	Ref.
$C_{27}H_{40}O_2$			
Cholesta-4,7-diene-3,6-dione	EtOH	209(4.13),277(4.14)	12-2017-79
5α-Cholesta-8(14),9(11)-diene-3,15-dione	n.s.g.	233(4.04),324(3.63)	39-1821-79C
5α-Cholesta-8,14-diene-3,7-dione	n.s.g.	224(4.18),298(3.70)	39-1821-79C
Cholesta-4,6,8(14)-trien-3-one, 9α-hydroxy-	EtOH	342(4.38)	12-2017-79
$C_{27}H_{40}O_3$			
1,4-Benzenediol, 2-(9-hydroxy-3,7,11-15-tetramethyl-2,6,10,14-hexadecatetraenyl)-6-methyl-, (E,E,E)-(-)-	EtOH	290(3.39)	138-1269-79
1,4-Benzenediol, 2-(11-hydroxy-3,7,11-15-tetramethyl-2,6,9,14-hexadecatetraenyl)-6-methyl-, (E,E,E)-, (+)-	EtOH	290(3.29)	138-1269-79
$C_{27}H_{40}O_4$			
1,4-Benzenediol, 2-(8,9-dihydroxy-3,7,11,15-tetramethyl-2,6,10,14-hexadecatetraenyl)-6-methyl-	EtOH	290(3.45)	138-1269-79
Ceroplastolic acid monoacetate	n.s.g.	214(4.215)	25-0592-79
12,18-Diepiscalaradial	MeOH	228(4.03)	31-1277-79
12-Episcalaradial	MeOH	229(4.07)	31-1277-79
$C_{27}H_{40}O_4S$			
Cyclopentadecanecarboxylic acid, 2-ethenyl-15-oxo-1-[2-(phenylsulfinyl)ethyl]-, methyl ester	EtOH	242(3.56),262s(3.08), 266(2.93),273(2.60)	33-2630-79
Cyclopentadecanecarboxylic acid, 15-ethenyl-2-oxo-3-[2-(phenylsulfinyl)-ethyl]-, methyl ester	EtOH	242(3.59),259s(3.18), 266s(2.91),272s(2.58)	33-2630-79
$C_{27}H_{40}O_6$			
Propanedicarboxylic acid, [(1α,17β)-17-hydroxy-17-methyl-3-oxoandrost-4-en-1-yl]-, diethyl ester	EtOH	244(4.11)	56-0149-79
$C_{27}H_{40}O_{12}$			
3-Buten-2-one, 4-[1-hydroxy-2,2,6-trimethyl-6-[(2,3,4,6-tetra-O-acetyl-β-D-glucopyranosyl)oxy]cyclohexyl]-	EtOH	230(4.13)	94-2807-79
$C_{27}H_{40}S$			
Cholesta-1,4,6-triene-3-thione	hexane	354(4.23)	39-1166-79C
$C_{27}H_{41}BrO$			
Cholesta-3,5-dien-7-one, 6-bromo-	EtOH	295(4.08)	39-2727-79C
$C_{27}H_{41}D_3O$			
9,10-Secocholesta-5,7,10(19)-triene-6,19,19-d_3-3-ol, (3β,5E,7E)-	C_6H_{12}	273(4.38)	33-1763-79
$C_{27}H_{41}NO$			
6-Aza-B-homo-19-norcholesta-1,3,5(10)-trien-7-one, 1-methyl-	EtOH	240(3.79)	114-0319-79C
19-Norcholesta-1,3,5(10)-trien-6-one, 1-methyl-, oxime	EtOH	255(3.76)	114-0319-79C
$C_{27}H_{41}NO_3$			
Sevelinone	n.s.g.	250(2.64),300(2.15)	105-0459-79

Compound	Solvent	λ_{max}(log ε)	Ref.
$C_{27}H_{42}O$			
Cholesta-3,5-dien-7-one	EtOH	278(4.04)	39-2727-79C
Cholesta-4,6-dien-3-one	heptane	272(4.46),355(1.80)	35-5515-79
$C_{27}H_{42}O_2$			
5α-Cholesta-8,14-dien-7-one, 3β-hydroxy-	n.s.g.	224(4.19),298(3.70)	39-1821-79C
$C_{27}H_{42}O_3$			
5α-Cholest-8(14)-ene-3,15-dione, 9α-hydroxy-	n.s.g.	254(4.10)	39-1821-79C
$C_{27}H_{42}O_5$			
Silenosterone	EtOH	246(4.05)	105-0700-79
$C_{27}H_{43}ClO$			
Cholest-5-en-7-one, 3β-chloro-	EtOH	235(3.86)	39-2727-79C
$C_{27}H_{43}D$			
5α-Cholesta-1,3-diene-5-d	hexane	262(3.57)	88-2509-79
$C_{27}H_{43}NO_3$			
2H-1-Benzopyran, 3-hexadecyl-2,2-dimethyl-6-nitro-	C_6H_{12}	226(4.16),264(4.35), 272s(--),303(3.77), 341(3.72)	23-1377-79
	EtOH	227(4.17),233s(--), 270(4.30),278s(--), 305(3.79),347(3.75)	23-1377-79
Seveline	n.s.g.	290(2.31)	105-0459-79
$C_{27}H_{44}$			
5α-Cholesta-1,3-diene	heptane	262(3.52)	35-5515-79
	hexane	262(3.58)	88-2509-79
Cholesta-2,4-diene	heptane	265(3.81)	35-5515-79
Cholesta-3,5-diene	heptane	228(4.31),235(4.35), 244(4.15)	35-5515-79
$C_{27}H_{44}O$			
2H-1-Benzopyran, 3-hexadecyl-2,2-dimethyl-	C_6H_{12}	219(4.40),258s(--), 266(3.80),275(3.74), 306(3.65),315s(--)	23-1377-79
Cholest-1-en-3-one	heptane	223(3.98),344(1.45)	35-5515-79
Cholest-4-en-3-one	heptane	232(4.22),337(1.64)	35-5515-79
Cholest-5-en-7-one	heptane	234(4.16)	35-5515-79
Isotachysterin$_3$	C_6H_{12}	279(4.51),290(4.60), 303(4.48)	33-1763-79
Isovitamin D_3	C_6H_{12}	278(4.48),288(4.62), 301(4.51)	33-1763-79
$C_{27}H_{44}O_2$			
Cholesta-5,7-diene-1α,3β-diol	n.s.g.	271(4.01),282(4.05), 294(3.82)	39-1695-79C
5α-Cholest-8-en-7-one, 3β-hydroxy-	EtOH	253(4.00)	44-1282-79
5α-Cholest-8(14)-en-7-one, 3β-hydroxy-	EtOH	262(3.73)	44-1282-79
5α-Cholest-8(14)-en-15-one, 3β-hydroxy-	EtOH	258(4.13)	44-1282-79
$C_{27}H_{44}O_3$			
24-Norchol-5-en-7-one, 23-(1,1-dimethylethoxy)-3β-hydroxy-	MeOH	235(4.14)	44-1590-79
Pregn-5-en-7-one, 20-(3,3-dimethylbutoxy)-3β-hydroxy-, (3β,20S)-	MeOH	237(4.12)	44-1590-79

Compound	Solvent	$\lambda_{max}(\log \epsilon)$	Ref.
$C_{27}H_{44}O_5$			
Cholest-7-en-6-one, 3,14,22,25-tetra- hydroxy- (2-deoxy-α-ecdysone)	EtOH	245(4.12)	105-0700-79
Cholest-8-en-6-one, 3,14,22,25-tetra- hydroxy-, (3β,5β,22R)- (premixister- one)	EtOH	202(3.35)	105-0703-79
$C_{27}H_{44}O_6$			
2-Deoxyecdysterone	EtOH	246(4.10)	105-0700-79
$C_{27}H_{44}O_7$			
Ecdysterone	EtOH	242(3.98)	105-0144-79
$C_{27}H_{44}O_8$			
Integristerone A	EtOH	245(4.09)	105-0144-79
$C_{27}H_{45}NO_2$			
16,28-Secosolanid-22(28)-ene-3,16-diol, (3β,5α,16α)-	EtOH	239(2.41)	12-0597-79
hydrochloride	n.s.g.	218(3.20)	12-0597-79
$C_{27}H_{46}N_2O$			
Solacallinidine	EtOH	239(2.39)	12-0597-79
$C_{27}H_{46}O$			
Cholestan-4-one	heptane	234(3.86)	35-5515-79
$C_{27}H_{46}O_3$			
Pregn-5-en-7-one, 21-(2,2-dimethylprop- oxy)-3β-hydroxy-20(S)-methyl-	MeOH	238(4.12)	44-1590-79
$C_{27}H_{46}O_9$			
Nonanoic acid, 9-[[4-[2-(1,3-dihydroxy- 2-methylbutyl)hexahydro-7-hydroxy-4H- furo[3,2-c]pyran-6-yl]-3-methyl-1- oxo-2-butenyl]oxy]-, methyl ester	EtOH	223(4.16)	39-0838-79C
more polar isomer	EtOH	222(3.99)	39-0838-79C

Compound	Solvent	λ_{max}(log ε)	Ref.
$C_{28}H_5Cl_{15}S_3$			
1-Buten-3-yne, 1-phenyl-1,2,4-tris-(pentachlorophenylthio)-	heptane	216(c.5.0),354(c.4.2)	5-1626-79
$C_{28}H_{13}Br_4N$			
9H-Fluorene-9-acetonitrile, 2,7-dibromo-α-(2,7-dibromo-9H-fluoren-9-ylidene)-	$CHCl_3$	332(4.22)	24-1473-79
	DMSO-EtOH-NaOEt	647(4.69)	24-1473-79
$C_{28}H_{14}F_2OS_2$			
Bisdibenzo[2,3:6,7]thiepino[4,5-b:4',5'-d]furan, 1,9-difluoro-	MeOH	253(4.19),260s(4.18), 320(4.15),340s(4.19)	73-2139-79
$C_{28}H_{15}AsClCr_2O_{10}P$			
Chromium, decacarbonyl[μ-[chloro(triphenylphosphonio)arsino]]di-	n.s.g.	382(3.80)	89-0233-79
$C_{28}H_{16}$			
9,12:15,18-Diethenocycloheptadeca[de]-naphthalene, 7,8,10,20-tetradehydro-	C_6H_{12}	265(4.3),345(4.4), 360s(4.3)	138-1373-79
$C_{28}H_{16}Cl_4S_4$			
1-Buten-3-yne, tetrakis[(4-chlorophenyl)thio]-	heptane	199(4.85),328s(4.64), 349(4.33)	5-1606-79
$C_{28}H_{16}O_3$			
6,13-Pentacenequinone, 5-phenoxy-(photochromic)	toluene	404(3.08)	104-0344-79
$C_{28}H_{16}O_7$			
Dibenzo[b,b']furo[3,2-e:4,5-e']bis-benzofuran-10,13-diol, diacetate	EtOH	218(4.42),232(4.42), 241s(4.34),250s(4.13), 277(3.82),295(4.13), 304(4.35),327s(4.10), 339(4.35),356(4.45)	78-0535-79
$C_{28}H_{17}Cl_2N_5O$			
2H-Benzotriazole, 2-[3-chloro-4-[2-[4-[5-(4-chlorophenyl)-1,2,4-oxadiazol-3-yl]phenyl]ethenyl]phenyl]-	DMF	360(4.80)	33-1411-79
$C_{28}H_{17}Cl_3S_3$			
Benzene, 1,1',1"-[(1-phenyl-1,2,3-butatrien-1-yl-4-ylidene)tris(thio)]-tris[4-chloro-	heptane	200(4.94),421(4.42)	5-1626-79
$C_{28}H_{17}N$			
9H-Fluorene-9-acetonitrile, α-9H-fluoren-9-ylidene-	$CHCl_3$	328(4.58)	24-1473-79
	DMSO-EtOH-NaOEt	653(4.76)	24-1473-79
$C_{28}H_{17}NO$			
9(10H)-Anthracenone, 10-(3-phenyl-1H-isoindol-1-ylidene)-	benzene	434(4.20)	39-0621-79C
$C_{28}H_{17}NO_2$			
5,13-Pentacenedione, 6-(phenylamino)-	toluene	523(3.93),553(3.80)	104-0344-79
$C_{28}H_{17}NO_3S$			
Benzoic acid, 2-[(2-methyl-9-oxo-9H-naphth[3,2,1-kl]acridin-6-yl)thio]-	$CHCl_3$	286(4.72),322s(3.70), 404(3.94),474(4.11),	103-1227-79

Compound	Solvent	λ_{max}(log ε)	Ref.
(cont.)		498(4.18)	103-1227-79
Benzoic acid, 2-[(2-methyl-9-oxo-9H-naphth[3,2,1-kl]acridin-8-yl)thio]-	EtOH	224(4.45),258s(4.35), 278(4.63),426(4.30), 468(4.06),496(4.07)	103-1227-79
$C_{28}H_{17}N_3O_4$			
Pyridinium, 1-[3-(5-cyano-1,6-dihydro-2-hydroxy-4-methyl-6-oxo-1-phenyl-3-pyridinyl)-1,4-dihydro-1,4-dioxo-2-naphthalenyl]-, hydroxide, inner salt	EtOH	254(4.37),338(4.31), 625(3.54)	2-0100-79A
$C_{28}H_{18}ClN_5O$			
2H-Benzotriazole, 2-[3-chloro-4-[2-[4-(3-phenyl-1,2,4-oxadiazol-5-yl)-phenyl]ethenyl]phenyl]-	DMF	363(4.82)	33-1411-79
2H-Benzotriazole, 2-[3-chloro-4-[2-[4-(5-phenyl-1,2,4-oxadiazol-3-yl)-phenyl]ethenyl]phenyl]-	DMF	357(4.79)	33-1411-79
$C_{28}H_{18}N_2$			
9,10-Anthracenedicarbonitrile, 9,10-dihydro-9,10-diphenyl-	MeCN	225s(4.38),252(2.95), 258(3.00),262(3.04), 269(2.92),273s(2.61)	22-0145-79
high melting isomer	MeCN	220s(4.45),253(2.92), 258(2.98),262(2.98), 269(2.87),273s(2.64)	22-0145-79
1H-Isoindole, 3-phenyl-1-(3-phenyl-1H-isoindol-1-ylidene)-	benzene	456(4.48)	39-0621-79C
$C_{28}H_{18}N_2O_2S$			
Benzoxazole, 2-[5-[[4-(5-phenyl-1,2-isoxazol-3-yl)phenyl]ethenyl]-2-thienyl]-	DMF	392(4.79)	33-0779-79
$C_{28}H_{18}N_2O_3$			
Benzoxazole, 2-[5-[[4-(5-phenyl-1,2-isoxazol-3-yl)phenyl]ethenyl]-2-furanyl]-	DMF	381(4.76)	33-0779-79
$C_{28}H_{18}O_2$			
[9,9'-Bianthracene]-10,10'(9H,9'H)-dione	$CHCl_3$	368(4.50)	36-0388-79
$C_{28}H_{18}O_{12}$			
[8,8'-Bi-1H-naphtho[2,3-c]pyran]-1,1',6,6',9,9'-hexone, 3,3',4,4'-tetrahydro-7,7',10,10'-tetrahydroxy-3,3'-dimethyl-	MeOH-HCl	230(4.69),292(4.20), 393(4.05)	24-0957-79
	MeOH-NaOH	236s(--),279(4.57), 390(3.81),464(3.69), 525s(--)	24-0957-79
$C_{28}H_{20}BrN_3O_3$			
4-Imidazolidinecarboxamide, 3-(4-bromophenyl)-2,5-dioxo-N,1,4-triphenyl-	MeOH	232(4.60)	118-0794-79
$C_{28}H_{20}ClN_3O_2S$			
4-Imidazolidinecarbothioamide, N-(4-chlorophenyl)-2,5-dioxo-1,3,4-triphenyl-	MeOH	222(4.60),270(3.99), 282(3.94),310(3.66)	118-0794-79
4-Imidazolidinecarbothioamide, 3-(4-chlorophenyl)-2,5-dioxo-N,1,4-triphenyl-	MeOH	215(4.70),240(4.46), 263(4.17),276(4.08)	118-0794-79

Compound	Solvent	λ max(log ε)	Ref.
$C_{28}H_{20}ClN_3O_3$			
4-Imidazolidinecarboxamide, N-(4-chlorophenyl)-2,5-dioxo-1,3,4-triphenyl-	MeOH	218(4.61),239(4.54)	118-0794-79
4-Imidazolidinecarboxamide, 1-(4-chlorophenyl)-2,5-dioxo-N,3,4-triphenyl-	MeOH	227(4.50),240(4.43)	118-0794-79
$C_{28}H_{20}N_2O$			
9-Anthracenecarboxamide, 10-cyano-9,10-dihydro-9,10-diphenyl-	MeCN	217(4.50),262(3.36), 269(3.27),286(2.92), 308(2.62)	22-0145-79
$C_{28}H_{20}N_2O_3$			
2,4-Imidazolidinedione, 5-benzoyl-1,3,5-triphenyl-	MeOH	230(4.53)	118-0794-79
$C_{28}H_{20}N_4$			
3,11,4,10-[2]Butene[1,4]diylidene-7,14-ethenobenzo[1,2:4,5]dicyclooctene-15,16,18,19-tetracarbonitrile, 1,2,5,6,7,8,9,12,13,14-decahydro-	CH_2Cl_2	291(3.00),375(2.70)	35-2128-79
$C_{28}H_{20}N_6O_2S$			
Benzoic acid, 2-[5-(4,5-diphenyl-2-thiazolyl)-3-(2-pyridinyl)-1-formazano]-	benzene	530(4.29)	106-0790-79
	EtOH	530(4.43)	106-0790-79
	acetone	533(4.34)	106-0790-79
Benzoic acid, 2-[5-(4,5-diphenyl-2-thiazolyl)-3-(3-pyridinyl)-1-formazano]-	EtOH	555(4.28)	106-0790-79
	acetone	558(4.29)	106-0790-79
Benzoic acid, 4-[5-(4,5-diphenyl-2-thiazolyl)-3-(2-pyridinyl)-1-formazano]-	benzene	522(4.28)	106-0790-79
	EtOH	561(4.37)	106-0790-79
	acetone	514(4.40)	106-0790-79
Benzoic acid, 4-[5-(4,5-diphenyl-2-thiazolyl)-3-(3-pyridinyl)-1-formazano]-	benzene	580(4.12)	106-0790-79
	EtOH	588(4.26)	106-0790-79
	acetone	585(4.01)	106-0790-79
$C_{28}H_{20}N_6S_2$			
1H-1,2,4-Triazole, 3,3'-dithiobis[1,5-diphenyl-	n.s.g.	223(4.26),257(3.50)	39-0724-79C
$C_{28}H_{20}O$			
Biphenylene oxide, 2,7-distyryl-	dioxan	320(4.76)	104-1944-79
$C_{28}H_{20}O_2$			
9H-Xanthene, 2-methyl-9-(2-methyl-9H-xanthen-9-ylidene)-	CH_2Cl_2	238(4.13),258(4.09), 284(4.01),370(4.23)	35-0665-79
$C_{28}H_{20}O_3$			
3,4(2H,5H)-Furandione, 3,3,4,4-tetraphenyl-	C_6H_{12}	253(3.50),280(3.32), 533(2.42),562(2.36)	19-0665-79
	EtOH	257s(3.29),264s(3.18), 316s(2.56),531(1.70), 557s(1.61)	19-0665-79
$C_{28}H_{20}S$			
Thiophene, 2,5-bis[2-(2-naphthalenyl)-ethenyl]-	toluene	405(4.68)	103-0729-79
$C_{28}H_{20}S_4$			
1-Buten-3-yne, tetrakis(phenylthio)-	heptane	214(4.77),353(4.36)	5-1606-79
$C_{28}H_{21}N$			
1H-Pyrrole, 2,3,4,5-tetraphenyl-	EtOH	239(4.38),248(4.37)	103-0501-79

Compound	Solvent	$\lambda_{max}(\log \epsilon)$	Ref.
$C_{28}H_{21}NO$			
2H-Pyrrol-2-one, 1,5-dihydro-3,4,5,5-tetraphenyl-	MeOH	225(4.39),255s(4.00)	32-0121-79
3H-Pyrrol-3-one, 1,2-dihydro-2,2,4,5-tetraphenyl-	MeOH	248(4.35),365(3.86)	32-0121-79
$C_{28}H_{21}NO_2$			
9H-Indeno[2,1-c]pyridinium, 9-benzoyl-3-methyl-2-(2-oxo-2-phenylethyl)-, hydroxide, inner salt	EtOH	205(5.13),248(5.01), 286(5.11),340(4.53), 370(4.49),508(4.12)	103-1214-79
9H-Indeno[2,1-c]pyridinium, 9-benzoyl-3-methyl-, 1-benzoyl-2-oxo-2-phenylethylide	EtOH	222(4.70),300(4.96)	103-1214-79
$C_{28}H_{21}N_3O_3$			
4-Imidazolidinecarboxamide, 2,5-dioxo-N,1,3,4-tetraphenyl-	MeOH	229(4.45),242(4.38)	118-0794-79
$C_{28}H_{21}N_5O_3S_2$			
Benzenesulfonic acid, 2-[5-(4,5-diphenyl-2-thiazolyl)-3-phenyl-1-formazano]-	benzene	495(3.97)	106-0790-79
	EtOH	511(4.26)	106-0790-79
	acetone	511(4.22)	106-0790-79
Benzenesulfonic acid, 3-[5-(4,5-diphenyl-2-thiazolyl)-3-phenyl-1-formazano]-	EtOH	577(4.29)	106-0790-79
	acetone	571(4.04)	106-0790-79
Benzenesulfonic acid, 4-[5-(4,5-diphenyl-2-thiazolyl)-3-phenyl-1-formazano]-	EtOH	587(4.24)	106-0790-79
	acetone	571(4.02)	106-0790-79
$C_{28}H_{22}$			
Benz[c]chrysene, 5,6,13,14-tetrahydro-2-phenyl-	C_6H_{12}	220(4.64),247(4.37), 273(3.89),284(4.09), 296(4.18),337(4.55), 350(4.66),368(4.54)	44-4933-79
1,1'-Biphenyl, 4,4'-bis(2-phenylethenyl)-	dioxan	352(4.87)	104-1944-79
Picene, 5,6,13,14-tetrahydro-3-phenyl-	C_6H_{12}	206(4.27),223(4.28), 247(3.81),255(3.76), 289(4.00),301(4.11), 346(4.05),361(4.19), 379(4.07)	44-4933-79
$C_{28}H_{22}BrNO_4$			
Naphtho[1,2-b]furan-3(2H)-one, 5-acetoxy-4-(4-bromophenyl)-2-(ethylphenylamino)-	EtOH	216(4.63),251(4.65), 272(4.59),375(3.78)	103-0597-79
$C_{28}H_{22}ClN_3$			
Benzenamine, 4-chloro-N-[[4-(4,5-dihydro-3,5-diphenyl-1H-pyrazol-1-yl)-phenyl]methylene]-	toluene	330s(4.04),400(4.71)	135-1491-79B
Benzenamine, N-[[4-[3-(4-chlorophenyl)-4,5-dihydro-5-phenyl-1H-pyrazol-1-yl]phenyl]methylene]-	toluene	325s(4.04),397(4.69)	135-1491-79B
$C_{28}H_{22}N_2O$			
Benzamide, N-[diphenyl(phenylimino)ethylidene]-2-methyl-, (Z,Z)-	EtOH	265(4.47),349s(3.33)	12-2059-79
Benzamide, N-[(4-methylphenyl)imino]-diphenylethylidene]-, (Z,Z)-	EtOH	267(4.23),347s(3.41)	12-2059-79

Compound	Solvent	$\lambda_{max}(\log \epsilon)$	Ref.
Cyclopenta[3,4]pyrazolo[1,5-a]quinolin-11-ium, 6b,7,9a,10-tetrahydro-6b,8-dimethyl-7-oxo-9,9a-diphenyl-, hydroxide, inner salt	EtOH	208(4.58),225(4.57), 268(4.20),445(3.51)	88-1765-79
1H-Imidazole, 1-(4-methylphenyl)-2,4,5-triphenyl-, 3-oxide	MeOH	246(4.33),285s(4.09)	12-2059-79
1H-Imidazole, 2-(2-methylphenyl)-1,4,5-triphenyl-, 3-oxide	MeOH	243(4.42)	12-2059-79
$C_{28}H_{22}N_2O_2$			
Benzamide, N-[diphenyl(phenylimino)ethylidene]-4-methoxy-, (Z,Z)-	EtOH	266(4.53)	12-2059-79
Benzamide, N-[[(4-methoxyphenyl)imino]-diphenylethylidene]-, (Z,Z)-	EtOH	266(4.47),341s(3.68)	12-2059-79
1H-Imidazole, 1-(4-methoxyphenyl)-2,4,5-triphenyl-, 3-oxide	MeOH	235(4.46),272s(4.31)	12-2059-79
1H-Imidazole, 2-(4-methoxyphenyl)-1,4,5-triphenyl-, 3-oxide	MeOH	249(4.32),284s(4.18)	12-2059-79
$C_{28}H_{22}N_4$			
1H-Imidazole-5-carbonitrile, 4,5-dihydro-1-methyl-2,4,5-triphenyl-4-(2-pyridinyl)-	EtOH	220s(4.39),260(3.89), 272s(3.78)	44-0041-79
$C_{28}H_{22}N_4O_2$			
Benzenamine, N-[[4-(4,5-dihydro-3,5-diphenyl-1H-pyrazol-1-yl)phenyl]methylene]-4-nitro-	toluene	355s(4.26),420(4.58)	135-1491-79B
Benzenamine, N-[[4-[4,5-dihydro-3-(4-nitrophenyl)-5-phenyl-1H-pyrazol-1-yl]phenyl]methylene]-	toluene	350(4.23),456(4.30)	135-1491-79B
$C_{28}H_{22}N_4S_5$			
Benzo[1,2-d:5,4-d']bisthiazolium, 2,2'-(2,5-thiophenediyldi-2,1-ethenediyl)-bis[3,6-dimethyl-, diiodide	DMF	265(4.71),375(4.29), 440(4.38),549(4.08)	126-1441-79
$C_{28}H_{22}O$			
Ethanone, 1-(2,5,7,8-tetrahydro-5-methyl-1H-acenaphth[5,6-kl]acephenanthrylen-11-yl)-	benzene	323(4.29)	104-0340-79
$C_{28}H_{22}O_2$			
Anthracene, 1,4-dimethoxy-5,8-diphenyl-	CH_2Cl_2	252(4.64),275(4.62), 353(3.55),370(3.80), 400(3.77),418s(3.70)	150-3501-79
$C_{28}H_{22}O_4$			
2-Propenoic acid, 3-(1-naphthalenyl)-, 1,2-ethanediyl ester, (E,E)-	C_6H_{12}	323(4.68)	18-0801-79
(Z,Z)-	C_6H_{12}	296(4.37)	18-0801-79
2-Propenoic acid, 3-(2-naphthalenyl)-, 1,2-ethanediyl ester, (E,E)-	C_6H_{12}	307(4.70)	18-0801-79
$C_{28}H_{23}Cl_3S_4$			
1-Buten-3-yne, 1-cyclohexylthio-1,2,4-tris(4-chlorophenylthio)-	heptane	212(4.55),343(4.24)	5-1606-79
$C_{28}H_{23}NO_2$			
2H-Pyrrole-2,4-diol, 3,4-dihydro-2,3,4,5-tetraphenyl-	MeOH	248(4.28)	32-0121-79

Compound	Solvent	$\lambda_{max}(\log \epsilon)$	Ref.
$C_{28}H_{23}N_3$			
Benzenamine, N-[[4-(4,5-dihydro-3,5-diphenyl-1H-pyrazol-1-yl)phenyl]methylene]-	toluene	315s(4.00),395(4.73)	135-1491-79B
Benzenemethanamine, α-(1,4-diphenyl-5H-cyclopenta[d]pyridazin-5-ylidene)-N,N-dimethyl-	MeOH	257(4.53),332(3.81), 439(4.18)	5-0675-79
$C_{28}H_{23}N_3O_2$			
1H-Imidazole-5-carboxylic acid, 4,5-dihydro-1-methyl-2,4,5-triphenyl-4-(2-pyridinyl)-, hydrochloride	EtOH	232s(4.24),265s(3.99)	44-0041-79
$C_{28}H_{23}N_4S$			
Quinolinium, 4-(1H-benzimidazol-2-yl)-1-methyl-2-[3-(3-methyl-2(3H)-benzothiazolylidene)-1-propenyl]-, iodide	EtOH	605(4.81)	4-1583-79
Quinolinium, 6-(1H-benzimidazol-2-yl)-1-methyl-2-[3-(3-methyl-2(3H)-benzothiazolylidene)-1-propenyl]-, iodide	EtOH	599(5.12)	4-1583-79
Quinolinium, 6-(1H-benzimidazol-2-yl)-1-methyl-4-[3-(3-methyl-2(3H)-benzothiazolylidene)-1-propenyl]-, iodide	EtOH	654(5.14)	4-1583-79
$C_{28}H_{24}$			
1,1'-Biphenyl, 4,4''-(1-methyl-1,2-cyclopropanediyl)bis-	EtOH or CCl_4	239(4.51),250(4.41), 267(4.47)	104-0080-79
$C_{28}H_{24}Br_2$			
1,1':4',1'':4'',1'''-Quaterphenyl, 4,4'''-dibromo-2,2''',5,5'''-tetramethyl-	dioxan	286(4.64)	104-0517-79
$C_{28}H_{24}I_2$			
1,1':4',1'':4'',1'''-Quaterphenyl, 4,4'''-diiodo-2,2''',5,5'''-tetramethyl-	dioxan	288(4.67)	104-0517-79
1,1':4',1'':4'',1'''-Quaterphenyl, 4,4'''-diiodo-2',2'',3,3'''-tetramethyl-	dioxan	281(4.81)	104-0517-79
$C_{28}H_{24}NO_2P$			
Acetamide, N-[4-[(triphenylphosphoranylidene)acetyl]phenyl]-	MeOH	265(4.27),320(4.25)	65-2189-79
$C_{28}H_{24}N_2$			
Ethanone, 1,2-diphenyl-, (1,2-diphenylethylidene)hydrazone	EtOH	218(4.40),269(3.14)	103-0501-79
$C_{28}H_{24}N_2O$			
4H-Indol-4-one, 5-[(diphenylamino)methylene]-1,5,6,7-tetrahydro-2-methyl-1-phenyl-	EtOH	265(3.87),290(3.89), 376(4.14)	4-0913-79
$C_{28}H_{24}N_4$			
1H-Imidazole-2-acetonitrile, 5-(2-cyanoethenyl)-2,5-dihydro-α,1-dimethyl-2,4,5-triphenyl-	EtOH	253(4.18),285s(3.52)	44-0041-79
$C_{28}H_{24}N_4O_3$			
Propanedinitrile, [[4-[[2-acetoxy-3-(2-naphthalenyloxy)propyl](2-cyanoethyl)amino]phenyl]methylene]-	EtOH	417(4.68)	110-1769-79
	EtOH-KOH	331(--)	110-1769-79
	CCl_4	406(--)	110-1769-79
	KBr	426(--)	110-1769-79

Compound	Solvent	λ_{max}(log ε)	Ref.
$C_{28}H_{24}O_2$			
Ethanone, 1-[1,1',2,2'-tetrahydro-6'-(1-hydroxyethyl)[5,5'-biacenaphthylen]-6-yl]-	benzene	290(4.97),303(4.75), 313(3.95),328(3.76)	104-0340-79
$C_{28}H_{24}O_9$			
2,7-Dibenzofurandiol, 1-(2,4-diacetoxyphenyl)-3,4-dimethyl-, diacetate	EtOH	220(4.61),254(4.18), 292(4.25),300(4.21)	1-0271-79
$C_{28}H_{24}O_{16}$			
Benzoic acid, 2,4,5-trihydroxy-, 2'-ester with 3-[(6-deoxy-α-L-mannopyranosyl)oxy]-5,7-dihydroxy-2-(3,4,5-trihydroxyphenyl)-4H-1-benzopyran-4-one	MeOH	258s(--),268(4.41), 356(4.25)	138-0027-79
$C_{28}H_{24}S$			
Thiirane, 2,2-bis(3-methylphenyl)-3,3-diphenyl-	MeCN	295.5(3.82)	24-0138-79
$C_{28}H_{24}Zr$			
Zirconium, bis[(1,2,3,4,5-η)-1-methyl-2,4-cyclopentadien-1-yl]bis(phenylethynyl)-	$CHCl_3$	248(4.09),265(3.94), 290(3.76)	101-0353-79S
$C_{28}H_{25}NO_2P$			
Phosphonium, 2-[4-(acetylamino)phenyl]-2-oxoethyl]triphenyl-, chloride	MeOH	275(4.20),305(4.38)	65-2189-79
$C_{28}H_{25}NO_5$			
1,2-Indolizinedicarboxylic acid, 3-benzoyl-5,8-dimethyl-7-(phenylmethyl)-, dimethyl ester	EtOH	208(5.00),235(5.14), 326(4.28),384(4.20)	103-0647-79
$C_{28}H_{26}$			
5,5'-Biacenaphthylene, 6,6'-diethyl-1,1',2,2'-tetrahydro-	dioxan	293s(--),305(4.05), 317(3.98),330(3.74)	65-1636-79
Bi-2,4,6-cycloheptatrien-1-yl, bis(3-methylphenyl)-	$CHCl_3$	245(4.50),280s(4.10)	39-0262-79B
$C_{28}H_{26}ClN_4O_{10}P$			
Uridine, 2'-O-[(2-nitrophenyl)methyl]-, 3'-(4-chlorophenyl phenylphosphoramidate)	EtOH	260.5(4.21)	35-6409-79
$C_{28}H_{26}N$			
Quinolinium, 1-ethyl-2-[4-(4-methylphenyl)-2-phenyl-1,3-butadienyl]-, iodide	EtOH	526(3.45),563(3.74), 662s(2.30)	62-0650-79A
	isoBuOH	526(3.45),565(3.78), 666s(--)	62-0650-79A
	dioxan	530(3.51),570(3.85), 674s(--)	62-0650-79A
	THF	528(3.48),566(3.79), 668s(--)	62-0650-79A
	$CHCl_3$	529(3.49),568(3.83), 670s(--)	62-0650-79A
$C_{28}H_{26}NO$			
Quinolinium, 1-ethyl-2-[4-(4-methoxyphenyl)-2-phenyl-1,3-butadienyl]-, iodide	EtOH	525(3.30),561(3.55), 600s(2.41)	62-0650-79A
	isoBuOH	527(3.30),566(3.54),	62-0650-79A

Compound	Solvent	λmax(log ε)	Ref.
(cont.)		664s(--)	62-0650-79A
	dioxan	535(3.08),572(3.49), 670s(--)	62-0650-79A
	THF	530(3.15),567(3.62), 667s(--)	62-0650-79A
	$CHCl_3$	530(3.30),570(3.70)	62-0650-79A
$C_{28}H_{26}NOP$			
Benzenamine, 3-[2-[4-(diphenylphosphinyl)phenyl]ethenyl]-N,N-dimethyl-, trans-trans	toluene	320(4.5)	123-0248-79
Benzenamine, 4-[2-[4-(diphenylphosphinyl)phenyl]ethenyl]-N,N-dimethyl-, trans-trans	toluene at 300°K	380(4.6)	123-0248-79
$C_{28}H_{26}N_2O_2$			
1-Naphthaleneacetic acid, 2-[1-(4-methylphenyl)-3-oxo-3-phenylpropyl]hydrazide	EtOH	224(4.87),242(4.14), 272(3.87),282(3.93), 290s(3.78)	94-0257-79
$C_{28}H_{26}N_2O_2S_2$			
Benzothiazolium, 2,2'-[(2,5-dimethoxy-1,4-phenylene)di-2,1-ethenediyl]bis-[3-methyl-, diiodide	DMF	263(4.29),378(4.12), 540(3.61)	126-1441-79
	KBr	494(--)	126-1441-79
diperchlorate	DMF	263(4.10),386(4.28), 489(4.40)	126-1441-79
$C_{28}H_{26}N_2O_7S_2$			
Ceph-3-em-4-carboxylic acid, 7-amino-3-methyl-2-oxo-, diphenylmethyl ester, salt with p-toluenesulfonic acid	EtOH	316(3.75)	87-0743-79
$C_{28}H_{26}N_4O_7S$			
D-Arabinitol, 1,4-anhydro-1-C-[8-[(phenylmethyl)thio]-1,2,4-triazolo[4,3-a]oyrazin-3-yl]-, 2,3-diacetate 5-benzoate, (R)-	EtOH	230(4.32),262(4.00), 315(3.84)	111-0375-79
$C_{28}H_{26}N_4O_9$			
2-Butenedioic acid, 2,2'-(oxydi-1,2(1H)-phthalazinediyl)bis-, tetramethyl ester	MeOH	237(4.10),326(4.14)	150-4772-79
	$MeOH-HClO_4$	239(4.55),286s(3.91), 326(3.92)	150-4772-79
$C_{28}H_{26}O$			
[5,5'-Biacenaphthylene]-6-methanol, 6'-ethyl-1,1',2,2'-tetrahydro-α-methyl-	dioxan	294s(--),305(3.96), 320s(--),330s(--)	65-1636-79
$C_{28}H_{26}OPS$			
Phosphonium, triphenyl-, 1-(dimethylsulfonio)-2-oxo-2-phenylethylide	n.s.g.	264s(4.025),268(4.042), 274s(4.004)	104-0332-79
$C_{28}H_{26}OPSe$			
Phosphonium, triphenyl-, 1-(dimethylselenonio)-2-oxo-2-phenylethylide, tetrafluoroborate	n.s.g.	263s(3.978),268(4.009), 274s(3.990)	104-0332-79
$C_{28}H_{26}OSi_2$			
13H,15H-Diacenaphtho[1',2':1,4:1",2"-2,3]cyclobut[1,2-c][1,2,5]oxadisilole, 6b,6c-dihydro-13,13,15,15-tetramethyl-	C_6H_{12}	222(4.66),302(3.97)	44-4275-79

Compound	Solvent	λ_{max}(log ε)	Ref.
Disiloxane, 1,3-bis(1-acenaphthylenyl)-tetramethyl-	C_6H_{12}	233(4.72),326(4.18)	44-4275-79
$C_{28}H_{26}O_4$			
Propanedioic acid, [9,10-dihydro-10-(phenylmethylene)-9-anthracenyl]-, diethyl ester	n.s.g.	252(1.60),257(1.61), 308(3.88)	39-2948-79C
$C_{28}H_{27}Cl_2N_5O_8$			
9H-Purine, 2,6-dichloro-9-[2,3,5-tri-O-acetyl-5-C-[3-(2,4,6-trimethylphenyl)-5-isoxazolyl]-α-L-ido-pentofuranosyl]-	MeOH	209(4.61),248(3.98), 274(4.01)	136-0141-79H
$C_{28}H_{27}NO_4$			
1H-Indole-2-acetic acid, α-(hydroxymethylene)-3-[2-(phenylmethoxy)ethyl]-1-(phenylmethyl)-, methyl ester	EtOH	225(4.45),275(4.17), 286(4.12),295(4.01)	23-0289-79
$C_{28}H_{27}NO_8$			
7,8,9,10-Fluoranthenetetracarboxylic acid, 6b,10a-dihydro-6b-(1-pyrrolidinyl)-, tetramethyl ester	EtOH	215(4.8),330(3.8)	18-0641-79
$C_{28}H_{27}N_2S_2$			
1H-Pyrrolo[2,1-b]benzothiazolium, 3-[3-(1,2-dihydropyrrolo[2,1-b]benzothiazol-3-yl)-5,5-dimethyl-2-cyclohexen-1-ylidene]-2,3-dihydro-, iodide	MeOH	665(5.33)	104-0774-79
$C_{28}H_{27}N_3O_2$			
Acetamide, N-methyl-N-[2-[2-oxo-1-(phenylmethyl)[3,7'-bi-1H-indol]-3(2H)-yl]ethyl]-	EtOH	259(4.08),285(3.99), 290(3.92)	23-1694-79
$C_{28}H_{27}N_3O_5$			
Glycine, N-[N-[(phenylmethoxy)carbonyl]-L-tryptophyl]-, phenylmethyl ester	EtOH	277(3.74),283(3.76), 292(3.71)	118-0957-79
$C_{28}H_{27}N_3O_9$			
Acetamide, N-[1-(2-O-acetyl-3,6-di-O-benzoyl-5-deoxy-β-D-ribo-hexofuranosyl)-1,2-dihydro-2-oxo-4-pyrimidinyl)-	EtOH	217(4.42),232(4.47), 247s(--),282(3.79), 298(3.81)	136-0079-79J
$C_{28}H_{27}O_2P$			
Phosphorin, 1,1-dihydro-1,1-dimethoxy-4-[2-(4-methylphenyl)ethenyl]-2,6-diphenyl-	MeOH	255(4.25),384(4.25), 426(3.86)	24-1272-79
$C_{28}H_{28}N_2$			
1,4-Benzenedicarboxaldehyde bis(p-styrylethylimine)	$CHCl_3$	267(4.7)	24-2854-79
$C_{28}H_{28}N_2O_4$			
2,4(1H,3H)-Pyrimidinedione, 1-[2-hydroxy-4-(triphenylmethoxy)butyl]-5-methyl-	EtOH	268(3.88)	128-0051-79
$C_{28}H_{28}N_2O_9$			
1-Azabicyclo[4.2.0]oct-2-ene-2,4,4-tricarboxylic acid, 3-methyl-8-oxo-7-	EtOH	269(3.83)	23-0222-79

Compound	Solvent	λ_{max}(log ε)	Ref.
[(phenoxyacetyl)amino]-, 4,4-dimethyl 2-(phenylmethyl) ester, trans (cont.)			23-0222-79
$C_{28}H_{28}N_4O_7$			
Tryptoquivaline D, epideacetyl-, monoacetate	EtOH	217s(4.61),227(4.62), 232s(4.60),255s(4.23), 265s(4.12),276s(4.03), 307(3.58),319(3.48)	94-1611-79
Tryptoquivaline M	MeOH	228(4.51),232(4.49), 255(4.19),278(3.97), 305(3.46),317(3.43)	94-1611-79
$C_{28}H_{29}NOS$			
2H,6H-[1,3]Thiazino[2,3-a]isoquinoline, 7,11b-dihydro-2-methoxy-11b-(1-methylethyl)-3,4-diphenyl-	MeCN	273(3.79),298(3.89)	88-1213-79
$C_{28}H_{29}NO_8$			
Acridinium, 10-[3-ethoxy-2-(ethoxycarbonyl)-1-[2-ethoxy-1-(ethoxycarbonyl)-2-oxoethyl]-3-oxo-1-propenyl]-, hydroxide, inner salt	$CHCl_3$	253(5.2),357(4.0), 647(1.5)	5-1406-79
$C_{28}H_{29}N_2O_2$			
Pyridinium, 3-ethyl-1-[2-[2-[1-(methoxycarbonyl)ethenyl]-1-(phenylmethyl)-1H-indol-3-yl]ethyl]-, iodide	EtOH	265(3.85),285(3.70)	23-0289-79
$C_{28}H_{29}N_2S_2$			
Benzothiazolium, 3-ethyl-2-[2-[3-[(3-ethyl-2(3H)-benzothiazolylidene)ethylidene]-2-methyl-1-cyclopenten-1-yl]ethenyl]-, iodide	MeOH	806(5.41)	104-0351-79
$C_{28}H_{29}N_3O_4S_2$			
Benzenesulfonamide, N-[4,5,8,9,10,10a-hexahydro-10a-[[(4-methylphenyl)sulfonyl]amino]cyclopenta[c]pyrrolo-[3,2,1-ij]quinolin-7(7aH)-ylidene]-4-methyl-, trans	EtOH	272(4.10),304(4.08), 308(4.17)	39-2387-79C
$C_{28}H_{29}N_7O_7S_2$			
L-Phenylalanine, [[[7-[(hydroxyphenylacetyl)amino]-3-[[(1-methyl-1H-tetrazol-5-yl)thio]methyl]-8-oxo-5-thia-1-azabicyclo[4.2.0]oct-2-en-2-yl]-carbonyl]oxy]methyl ester, monohydrochloride	MeOH	274(3.96)	87-0657-79
$C_{28}H_{30}N_2O_3$			
Rhodamine B, hydrochloride	MeOH-NaOH	545(5.06)	151-0467-79A
$C_{28}H_{30}N_2O_4$			
Pyridinium, 4-(dimethylamino)-1-[1-(diphenylmethylene)-3-ethoxy-2-(ethoxycarbonyl)-3-oxopropyl]-, hydroxide, inner salt	$CHCl_3$	258(4.5),300(4.0)	5-1406-79
$C_{28}H_{30}O_6$			
Oxepino[2,3-b]benzofuran-4(10aH)-one, 10a-(benzoyloxy)-2,9-bis(1,1-dimeth-	C_6H_{12}	229(4.28),273(3.87), 284(3.88),297(3.90),	39-0290-79C

Compound	Solvent	$\lambda_{max}(\log \epsilon)$	Ref.
ylethyl)-7-methoxy- (cont.)		386(3.65)	39-0290-79C
$C_{28}H_{30}O_8$			
4H,8H-Benzo[1,2-b:3,4-b']dipyran-4-one, 2-(2,4-dimethoxyphenyl)-3-(2-hydroperoxy-3-methyl-3-butenyl)-5-methoxy-8,8-dimethyl-	MeOH	262(3.95),295s(3.75)	142-1529-79
Ferugolide	EtOH	203(4.39),212(4.38), 216(4.38),232s(4.33), 260(4.50),323(2.29)	105-0426-79
$C_{28}H_{31}NO_{10}$			
5,12-Naphthacenedione, 7-[(3-amino-2,3,6-trideoxy-α-L-lyxo-hexopyranosyl)oxy]-7,8,9,10-tetrahydro-6,9,11-trihydroxy-4-methoxy-9-propionyl-, hydrochloride, (7S,9S)-	MeOH	234(4.53),252(4.37), 290(3.90),478(4.02), 495(4.02),530(3.75)	87-0040-79
Nogarol, 7-con-O-methyl-	EtOH	235(4.67),252(4.45), 257s(4.41),290s(4.03), 478(4.21)	44-4030-79
Nogarol, 7-dis-O-methyl-	EtOH	236(4.70),260(4.38), 288(3.97),476(4.19)	44-4030-79
$C_{28}H_{31}N_2S_2$			
Benzothiazolium, 3-ethyl-2-[[3-[(3-ethyl-2(3H)-benzothiazolylidene)methyl]-5,5-dimethyl-2-cyclohexen-1-ylidene]methyl]-, iodide	MeOH	648(5.21)	104-0774-79
$C_{28}H_{31}N_3O_8$			
Saframycin B	MeOH	269(4.35),368(3.13)	88-2355-79
$C_{28}H_{32}N_2O_4$			
Acetamide, N-[2-[2,3-dihydro-2-oxo-3-[2-oxo-3-(2-oxoethyl)cyclohexyl]-1-(phenylmethyl)-1H-indol-3-yl]ethyl]-N-methyl-	EtOH	254(3.91),280s(3.27)	23-1694-79
$C_{28}H_{32}N_2O_6$			
1H-Imidazolium, 2-[3-ethoxy-1-[2-ethoxy-1-(ethoxycarbonyl)-2-oxoethyl]-2-methyl-3-oxo-1-propenyl]-4,5-dihydro-1,3-diphenyl-, hydroxide, inner salt	$CHCl_3$	323(4.2),434(3.8)	5-1406-79
Pyrimidine, 1,4,5,6-tetrahydro-4-phenyl-4,6-bis(2,4,5-trimethoxyphenyl)-, hydrochloride	EtOH	291(4.14)	24-0001-79
$C_{28}H_{32}O_{15}$			
Spinosin	EtOH	273(4.34),336(4.43)	102-0353-79
	EtOH-NaOEt	235(4.39),273(4.37), 392(4.61)	102-0353-79
	EtOH-NaOAc	273(4.24),338(4.27), 399(4.10)	102-0353-79
	EtOH-NaOAc-H_3BO_3	273(4.29),337(4.38), 403(3.51)	102-0353-79
	EtOH-$AlCl_3$	284(4.26),304(4.24), 355(4.39)	102-0353-79
$C_{28}H_{32}O_{16}$			
Multiflorin A	MeOH	268(4.27),343(4.10)	95-0439-79

Compound	Solvent	λ max(log ε)	Ref.
Multiflorin A (cont.)	MeOH-NaOMe	276(4.32),327s(4.04), 385(4.33)	95-0439-79
$C_{28}H_{33}NO_6$			
1,3-Benzodioxole-5-propanamine, N-(2,2-dimethoxyethyl)-α-[3-methoxy-4-(phenylmethoxy)phenyl]-, (±)-	EtOH	223(4.14),234(4.20), 283(3.92)	78-1857-79
$C_{28}H_{33}N_2O$			
1H-Indole-2-methanaminium, N,N,N-trimethyl-3-[2-(phenylmethoxy)ethyl]-1-(phenylmethyl)-, iodide	EtOH	220(4.68),276(4.01), 292(3.89),304(3.71)	23-0289-79
$C_{28}H_{33}N_5O_4S$			
Benzenesulfonic acid, 4-methyl-, 2-[2,3-dihydro-1,1-dimethyl-9-[(octahydro-1,4-dioxopyrrolo[1,2-a]pyrazin-3-yl)methyl]-1H-pyrrolo[1,2-a]indol-3-yl]hydrazide	EtOH	229(4.50),278(3.68), 286(3.73),293(3.69)	39-3053-79C
less polar isomer	EtOH	229(4.50),278(3.68), 286(3.73),293(3.69)	39-3053-79C
$C_{28}H_{34}N_2$			
19,20-Benzotricyclo[14.2.2.2^{1,16}]docosa-17,19,21-triene-17,18-dicarbonitrile	EtOH	206(4.45),238(3.92), 248s(3.88),293(3.04), 320(2.88)	35-6660-79
1,4:5,20-Diethenobenzocyclooctadecene-2,3-dicarbonitrile, 1,4,6,7,8,9,10-11,12,13,14,15,16,17,18,19-hexadecahydro-	EtOH	212(4.27),233s(3.70), 244s(3.59),270s(2.88), 315(2.85)	35-6660-79
$C_{28}H_{34}N_2O_3S$			
Benzenecarbothioic acid, 4-butoxy-, S-[5-[4-(heptyloxy)phenyl]-2-pyrimidinyl] ester	EtOH	221(4.21),302(4.46)	48-0619-79
$C_{28}H_{34}N_2O_4$			
Benzoic acid, 4-butoxy-, 5-[4-(heptyloxy)phenyl]-2-pyrimidinyl ester	EtOH	279(4.74)	48-0619-79
$C_{28}H_{34}N_4$			
21H-Biline, 10,24-dihydro-1,2,3,7,8-12,13,17,18-nonamethyl-, dihydrobromide	$CHCl_3$-HBr	452(4.62),524(4.99)	104-0970-79
21H,23H-Porphine, 2,3,17,18-tetrahydro-2,2,7,8,12,13,17,17-octamethyl-	EtOH	261s(4.25),276(4.29), 335s(4.42),352s(4.71), 366(4.90),375s(4.85), 396(4.52),480s(3.73), 509(3.94),545(4.17), 584(4.37),632(3.69)	89-0675-79
	EtOH-CF_3COOH	283(4.32),297s(4.26), 332s(4.34),350s(4.60), 365(4.71),380(4.73), 400(5.13),463s(3.55), 488(3.82),520(3.54), 579(4.06),623(4.67)	89-0675-79
$C_{28}H_{34}N_4O_{14}$			
D-Glucose, 2,2'-[(2-amino-4,6-dimethyl-3-oxo-3H-phenoxazine-1,9-diyl)bis-(carbonylimino)]bis[2-deoxy-	n.s.g.	447(4.40)	104-0951-79

Compound	Solvent	λ_{max}(log ϵ)	Ref.
$C_{28}H_{34}O_2$			
1,1':3',1"-Terphenyl, 4',6'-dimethoxy-2,2",3,3",5,5",6,6"-octamethyl-	C_6H_{12}	284(3.80),287(3.79)	12-1531-79
$C_{28}H_{34}O_4$			
Androsta-5,7-diene-3β,17β-diol, 3-acetate 17-benzoate	n.s.g.	280(4.10)	32-0651-79
$C_{28}H_{34}O_6$			
1H-Phenalene-1,3(2H)-dione, 4-ethoxy-9-hydroxy-7,8-dimethoxy-6-methyl-2,2-bis(3-methyl-2-butenyl)-	EtOH	215(4.56),233(4.42), 257(4.64),360(4.12)	150-0301-79
1H-Phenalen-1-one, 4-ethoxy-9-hydroxy-7,8-dimethoxy-6-methyl-2-(3-methyl-2-butenyl)-3-[(3-methyl-2-butenyl)-oxy]-	EtOH	219(4.68),268(4.22), 376(4.17),414(4.16)	150-0301-79
$C_{28}H_{34}O_8$			
2,5-Cyclohexadien-1-one, 2-[[5,7-dihydroxy-2,2-dimethyl-8-(2-methyl-1-oxopropyl)-2H-1-benzopyran-6-yl]-methyl]-3,5-dihydroxy-4,4-dimethyl-6-(2-methyl-1-oxopropyl)-	C_6H_{12}	231(4.46),270(4.54)	39-2563-79C
$C_{28}H_{34}O_9$			
Gomisin B	EtOH	218(4.98),257s(4.24), 292s(3.65)	94-1383-79
Gomisin E	EtOH	213(4.77),290(3.62)	94-2695-79
Gomisin F	EtOH	220(4.77),256s(4.13), 288s(3.42)	94-1383-79
$C_{28}H_{34}O_{10}$			
3a,7-Epoxy-3aH-furo[3,2-b]oxocin-3-carboxylic acid, 5-[6-(3,4-dihydro-6-methyl-2,4-dioxo-2H-pyran-3-yl)-1,3-dimethyl-6-oxo-2,4-hexadienyl]octahydro-2,6,9a-trimethyl-8-oxo-, methyl ester	EtOH-HCl	241(4.02),353(4.39)	142-0477-79B
	EtOH-NaOH	270(4.24),330(4.05)	142-0477-79B
Gomisin D	EtOH	216(4.57),256s(3.94), 294(3.68)	94-1395-79
$C_{28}H_{34}O_{13}$			
β-D-Glucopyranoside, 4-[6a-acetoxytetrahydro-4-(4-hydroxy-3-methoxyphenyl)-1H,3H-furo[3,4-c]furan-1-yl]-2-methoxyphenyl, [1R-(1α,3aα,4α,6aα)]-	EtOH	231(4.31),280(3.83)	94-2868-79
	EtOH-NaOH	254(--),280(--), 292(--)	94-2868-79
$C_{28}H_{35}NO_9$			
3a,7-Epoxy-3aH-furo[3,2-b]oxocin-3-carboxylic acid, 5-[6-(5-ethylidene-2,4-dioxo-3-pyrrolidinyl)-1,3-dimethyl-6-oxo-2,4-hexadienyl]octahydro-2,6,9a-trimethyl-8-oxo-, methyl ester	EtOH-HCl	247(4.15),280(4.27), 356(3.60)	142-0477-79B
	EtOH-NaOH	258(4.33),294(4.52), 346(4.25)	142-0477-79B
$C_{28}H_{35}N_3O_4$			
4-Cyclopentene-1,3-dione, 2-(2-butyl-1,3-dimethylcyclohepta[c]pyrrol-6(2H)-ylidene)-4,5-dimorpholino-	CH_2Cl_2	508(4.53)	83-0120-79
$C_{28}H_{36}N_2O_4$			
2-Hexen-1-one, 3,3'-(1,2-ethanediyldi-	MeOH	252(4.20),352(4.58)	44-2073-79

Compound	Solvent	$\lambda_{max}(\log \epsilon)$	Ref.
imino)bis[6-hydroxy-1-(4-methylphenyl)- (cont.)			44-2073-79
$C_{28}H_{36}N_2O_{13}$			
2,5-Cyclohexadiene-1,4-dione, 2,5-di-1-aziridinyl-3-[1-methoxy-2-[(2,3,4,6-tetra-O-acetyl-β-D-glucopyranosyl)oxy]ethyl]-6-methyl-	EtOH	333(4.15)	87-0406-79
$C_{28}H_{36}N_4O_4$			
Orantine	EtOH and EtOH-HCl	228(4.24),281(3.54), 288s(3.40)	33-2712-79
	EtOH-NaOH	245(--),286(--)	33-2712-79
dihydrochloride	EtOH	228(4.33),282(3.63)	33-2712-79
$C_{28}H_{36}O_4$			
Pregna-4,6-dieno[6,5,4-bc]pyran-21-carboxylic acid, 5',6'-dihydro-17-hydroxy-6'-methyl-6'-(1-methylethenyl)-3-oxo-, γ-lactone, (17α)-	MeOH	263(3.78),317(4.11)	44-1597-79
$C_{28}H_{36}O_8$			
2-Butenoic acid, 2-methyl-, 5,6,7,8-tetrahydro-7-hydroxy-2,3,10,11,12-pentamethoxy-6,7-dimethyldibenzo-[a,c]cycloocten-1-yl ester	EtOH	215(4.72),248s(4.18), 286s(3.14)	94-1576-79
isomer	EtOH	215(4.75),248s(4.21), 285s(3.47)	94-1576-79
$C_{28}H_{36}O_{11}$			
1H-Inden-1-one, 2,3-dihydro-2,5,7-trimethyl-6-[2-[(2,3,4,6-tetra-O-acetyl-β-D-glucopyranosyl)oxy]ethyl]-, (R)-	EtOH	215(4.65),257(4.19), 303(3.40)	94-0592-79
$C_{28}H_{36}O_{18}$			
1H,3H-Pyrano[3,4-c]pyran-1-one, 5-(1,2-diacetoxyethyl)-4,4a,5,6-tetrahydro-4a-hydroxy-6-[(2,3,4,6-tetra-O-acetyl-β-D-glucopyranosyl)oxy]-, [4aR-[4aα,5β(R*),6α]]- (eustomorusside hexaacetate)	MeOH	233.0(3.97)	102-1981-79
(S*)-	MeOH	235.5(3.89)	102-1981-79
$C_{28}H_{36}Zr$			
Zirconium, bis(cyclohexylethynyl)bis-[(1,2,3,4,5-η)-1-methyl-2,4-cyclopentadien-1-yl]-	$CHCl_3$	246(3.99),264(3.72), 304(3.28)	101-0353-79S
$C_{28}H_{37}FO_6S$			
Pregna-1,4-dien-20-one, 9α-fluoro-11β-hydroxy-16β-methyl-17α,21-bis(1-oxopropoxy)-3-thioxo-	MeCN	330(4.28),575(1.38)	39-1166-79C
$C_{28}H_{37}NO$			
Acetamide, N-[4,8,11-tris(1,1-dimethylethyl)-1,2,3,5,7,11,13-cyclotetradecaheptaen-9-yn-1-yl]-	THF	305s(4.42),329s(4.92), 340(5.24),473(4.18), 532(2.53),554(2.68), 599(3.18)	88-3171-79
$C_{28}H_{37}NOS$			
Pregn-4-en-3-one, 20-(2,3-dihydro-2-	$CHCl_3$	246(4.32),316(3.59)	83-0192-79

Compound	Solvent	$\lambda_{max}(\log \epsilon)$	Ref.
benzothiazolyl)- (cont.)			83-0192-79
$C_{28}H_{37}NO_2$			
Carbamic acid, [4,8,11-tris(1,1-dimethyl)-1,2,3,5,7,11,13-tetradecaheptaen-9-yn-1-yl]-, methyl ester	THF	308s(4.42),338(5.21), 470(4.35),532(2.60), 553(2.70),598(2.26)	88-3171-79
$C_{28}H_{37}NO_7$			
5,8-Decanoic acid, 10-[3-[3-[(4-nitrobenzoyl)oxy]-1-octenyl]oxiranyl]-, methyl ester	n.s.g.	260(4.00)	39-0115-79C
5,8,11-Dodecatrienoic acid, 12-[3-[1-[(4-nitrobenzoyl)oxy]hexyl]oxiranyl]-, methyl ester	n.s.g.	260(3.98)	39-0115-79C
5-Heptenoic acid, 7-[3-[6-(4-nitrobenzoyl)oxy]-2,4-undecadienyl]oxiranyl]-, methyl ester	n.s.g.	235(4.35),260(4.05)	39-0115-79C
Oxiranebutanoic acid, 3-[9-[(4-nitrobenzoyl)oxy]-2,5,7-tetradecatrienyl]-, methyl ester	n.s.g.	237(4.41),260(4.13)	39-0115-79C
$C_{28}H_{37}NO_9$			
3a,7-Epoxy-3aH-furo[3,2-b]oxocin-3-carboxylic acid, 5-[6-(5-ethyl-2,4-dioxo-3-pyrrolidinyl)-1,3-dimethyl-6-oxo-2,4-hexadienyl]octahydro-2,6,9a-trimethyl-8-oxo-, methyl ester	EtOH-HCl	238(3.98),354(4.53)	142-0477-79B
	EtOH-NaOH	257(4.18),285(3.88), 334(4.28)	142-0477-79B
$C_{28}H_{37}N_5O_2$			
1-Imidazolidinyloxy, 4-[3-[2,6-bis(dimethylamino)acridinio]-2-oxopropylidene]-2,2,3,5,5-pentamethyl-, iodide	EtOH	224(4.63),270(4.07), 292(4.64),488(4.98)	70-0872-79
$C_{28}H_{38}CuN_2O_2$			
Copper, [[6,6'-[1,6-hexanediylbis(nitrilomethylidyne)]bis[2-methyl-5-(1-methylethenyl)-2-cyclohexen-1-onato]](2-)-N,N',O,O']-	n.s.g.	260(4.24),370(4.64), 400(4.92),575(2.56)	65-2433-79
$C_{28}H_{38}N_4O_{14}$			
D-Glucitol, 1,1'-[(2-amino-4,6-dimethyl-3-oxo-3H-phenoxazine-1,9-diyl)-bis(carbonylimino)]bis[1-deoxy-	n.s.g.	447(4.59)	104-0951-79
$C_{28}H_{38}O_3$			
Benzo[6,7]pregna-4,6-diene-21-carboxylic acid, 3',6,6',7-tetrahydro-17-hydroxy-4,5'-dimethyl-3-oxo-, γ-lactone, (6α,7α,17α)-	MeOH	244(4.16)	44-1382-79
(6β,7β,17α)-	MeOH	240(4.10)	44-1382-79
$C_{28}H_{38}O_6$			
6α,7α:24α,25α-Diepoxywith-2-enolide, 5α-hydroxy-1-oxo-, (22R)-	n.s.g.	225(4.19)	102-1756-79
6α,7α-Epoxywitha-2,24-dienolide, 5α,12β-dihydroxy-1-oxo-, (22R)-	n.s.g.	223(4.22)	102-0283-79
4α-Phorbol-12-octa-2Z,4E-dienoate, 4-deoxy-	MeOH	262(4.37)	100-0112-79
2'H-Pregn-4-eno[6,5,4-bc]pyran-21-carboxylic acid, 5',6'-dihydro-6-hydroperoxy-17-hydroxy-6'-methyl-6'-(1-	MeOH	247(4.00)	44-1597-79

Compound	Solvent	λ max (log ε)	Ref.
methyletheny1)-3-oxo-, γ-lactone, (6β,17α)- (cont.)			44-1597-79
$C_{28}H_{39}NO_6$			
Aspochalasin D, 17O,18O-diacetyl-	EtOH	228s(3.95)	33-1501-79
$C_{28}H_{40}O_3$			
2,5-Cyclohexadiene-1,4-dione, 2-(9-methoxy-3,7,11,15-tetramethyl-2,6-10,14-hexadecatetraenyl)-6-methyl-	EtOH	253(4.17)	138-1269-79
2,5-Cyclohexadiene-1,4-dione, 2-(11-methoxy-3,7,11,15-tetramethyl-2,6-9,14-hexadecatetraenyl)-6-methyl-	EtOH	253(4.20)	138-1269-79
$C_{28}H_{40}O_4$			
2,5-Cyclohexadiene-1,4-dione, 5-(8,9-dihydroxy-3,7,11,15-tetramethyl-2,6,10,14-hexadecatetraenyl)-2,3-dimethyl-	EtOH	255(4.13)	138-1269-79
$C_{28}H_{40}O_6$			
Ergost-24-en-26-oic acid, 6,7-epoxy-5,22-dihydroxy-1-oxo-, δ-lactone, (5α,6α,7α,22R)-	MeOH	227(3.90)	102-0283-79
Margotianin	EtOH	218(3.93)	102-0891-79
Witha-2,24-dienolide, 5α,6β,27-tri-hydroxy-1-oxo-	EtOH	221(4.20)	102-1237-79
$C_{28}H_{40}O_8$			
Colletotrichin, 3-oxo-	EtOH	262(3.88)	39-1494-79C
Ixocarpalactone A	EtOH	218(3.91)	150-1178-79
$C_{28}H_{40}Zr$			
Zirconium, bis[(1,2,3,4,5-η)-1-methyl-2,4-cyclopentadien-1-yl]di-1-octynyl-	$CHCl_3$	248(3.95),264(3.66), 304(3.33)	101-0353-79S
$C_{28}H_{41}NO_2$			
1'H-D-Homoandrost-15-eno[17,17a-c]pyr-rol-12-ol, 1',4,4,8-tetramethyl-, acetate, (5α,12β)-	EtOH	263(4.08)	31-0157-79
$C_{28}H_{42}N_2O_4Sn$			
Tin, dioctylbis(2-pyridinecarboxylato-N^1,O^2)-	$CHCl_3$	238s(3.57),265(3.93)	131-0165-79D
	MeCN	221(4.06),263(3.97)	131-0165-79D
$C_{28}H_{42}N_2S$			
Sulfur diimide, bis[2,5-bis(1,1-dimeth-ylethyl)phenyl]-	hexane	242(4.16),252s(4.11), 392(3.97)	18-1998-79
$C_{28}H_{42}O$			
Ergosta-5,7,9(11),22-tetraen-3-ol, (3β,22E)-	MeOH	311(4.01),324(4.07), 339(3.87)	33-2037-79
$C_{28}H_{42}O_3$			
27-Norcholesta-5,7-dien-25-one, 3β-acetoxy-	EtOH	282(4.06)	65-0202-79
$C_{28}H_{42}O_4$			
Ceroplastolic acid, methyl ester mono-acetate	n.s.g.	217(4.265)	65-0207-79

Compound	Solvent	$\lambda_{max}(\log \epsilon)$	Ref.
$C_{28}H_{43}ClN_2O_6$			
4-Tetradecenamide, N-[2-(chloromethylene)-6-(2,5-dihydro-4-methoxy-2-oxo-1H-pyrrol-1-yl)-4,6-dioxohexyl]-7-methoxy-N-methyl-, [S-(E,E)]-	EtOH	214(4.21),240(4.11)	35-0240-79
	EtOH-base	219(4.57),310(4.32)	35-0240-79
$C_{28}H_{44}O_2$			
9,10-Dioxatricyclo[4.2.1.1[2,5]]decane, 3,4,7,8-tetrakis(2,2-dimethylpropylidene)-	ether	251.5(4.36)	44-2667-79
Ergosta-5,7-dien-3-ol, 22,23-epoxy-	MeOH	271(4.05),281(4.06), 293(3.85)	39-1858-79C
$C_{28}H_{44}O_3$			
Ergosta-7,9(11),22-triene-3β,5α,6α-triol	EtOH	236(4.20),243(4.23), 251(4.05)	44-3657-79
$C_{28}H_{45}N_3O_6Si_2$			
Cytidine, N-benzoyl-2',3'-bis-O-[(1,1-dimethylethyl)dimethylsilyl]-	MeOH-HOAc	260(4.38),303(4.02)	5-1855-79
Cytidine, N-benzoyl-2',5'-bis-O-[(1,1-dimethylethyl)dimethylsilyl]-	MeOH-HOAc	259(4.38),304(4.04)	5-1855-79
Cytidine, N-benzoyl-3',5'-bis-O-[(1,1-dimethylethyl)dimethylsilyl]-	MeOH-HOAc	259(4.38),303(4.04)	5-1855-79
$C_{28}H_{46}$			
Cholest-4-ene, 3-methylene-	heptane	239(4.40)	35-5515-79
Cholest-5-ene, 7-methylene-, (3β,5α)-	heptane	240(4.38)	35-5515-79
$C_{28}H_{46}CuN_2O_2$			
Copper, [[hexamethylenebis(iminomethylidyne)]bismenthonato]-	n.s.g.	310(4.30),345(4.20), 405(3.06),600(2.00), 720(1.80)	65-2433-79
$C_{28}H_{46}N_2S$			
Cholest-2-eno[3,2-d]thiazol-2'-amine, (5α)-	EtOH	262(3.96)	4-0763-79
$C_{28}H_{46}O$			
Vitamin D_4	EtOH	267(4.25)	39-1290-79C
Vitamin D_4 , 5-trans	EtOH	275(4.20)	39-1290-79C
$C_{28}H_{46}O_2$			
2H-1-Benzopyran, 3-hexadecyl-8-methoxy-2,2-dimethyl-	C_6H_{12}	228(4.20),233s(--), 263s(--),270(3.77), 281(3.64),310(3.08)	23-1377-79
	EtOH	226(4.18),269(3.66), 280(3.61),306(3.04)	23-1377-79
2H-1-Benzopyran, 7-(hexadecyloxy)-2,2,4-trimethyl-	isooctane	220(4.43),271(3.89), 277s(--),304(3.88), 313s(--)	23-1377-79
	EtOH	218(4.34),271(3.88), 277s(--),304(3.85), 313s(--)	23-1377-79
$C_{28}H_{50}N_2O_8$			
Hexanoic acid, 6,6'-[1,2-cyclohexanediylbis[oxy(1-oxo-2,1-ethanediyl)(methylimino)]]bis-, diethyl ester	n.s.g.	200s(4.15)	33-0754-79

Compound	Solvent	λ_{max}(log ε)	Ref.
$C_{29}H_7Cl_{15}S_4$			
1-Buten-3-yne, 1-(4-methylphenylthio)-1,2,4-tris(pentachlorophenylthio)-	heptane	192(4.3),212(4.5), 360(3.8)	5-1606-79
$C_{29}H_{16}Cl_3N_3O_2$			
1,2-Benzisoxazole, 6-chloro-3-[3-chloro-4-[2-[4-[5-(4-chlorophenyl)-1,2,4-oxadiazol-3-yl]phenyl]ethenyl]phenyl]-	DMF	340(4.71)	33-1411-79
$C_{29}H_{16}F_6N_2O_2$			
Benzoxazole, 2,2'-[[2,2,2-trifluoro-1-(trifluoromethyl)ethylidene]di-4,1-phenylene]bis-	H_2SO_4	202(3.92),312(3.73)	103-1299-79
$C_{29}H_{17}Cl_2N_3O_2$			
1,2-Benzisoxazole, 6-chloro-3-[4-[2-chloro-4-(5-phenyl-1,3,4-oxadiazol-2-yl)phenyl]ethenyl]phenyl]-	DMF	342(4.72)	33-1411-79
Benzoxazole, 2-[3-chloro-4-[2-[4-[5-(4-chlorophenyl)-1,2,4-oxadiazol-3-yl]-phenyl]ethenyl]phenyl]-	DMF	362(4.79)	33-1411-79
$C_{29}H_{18}ClN_3O_2$			
Benzoxazole, 2-[3-chloro-4-[2-[4-(3-phenyl-1,2,4-oxadiazol-5-yl)phenyl]-ethenyl]phenyl]-	DMF	366(4.82)	33-1411-79
Benzoxazole, 2-[3-chloro-4-[2-[4-(5-phenyl-1,2,4-oxadiazol-3-yl)phenyl]-ethenyl]phenyl]-	DMF	363(4.79)	33-1411-79
Benzoxazole, 2-[4-[2-[4-[5-(4-chlorophenyl)-1,2,4-oxadiazol-3-yl]phenyl]-ethenyl]phenyl]-	DMF	360(4.87),377(4.68)	33-1411-79
Benzoxazole, 5-chloro-2-[4-[2-[4-(5-phenyl-1,2,4-oxadiazol-3-yl)phenyl]-ethenyl]phenyl]-	DMF	362(4.90),379(4.72)	33-1411-79
$C_{29}H_{18}Cl_2N_4O$			
2H-Benzotriazole, 2-[2'-chloro-4"-[3"'-(4-chlorophenyl)isoxazol-5"'-yl]stilben-4'-yl]-	DMF	366(4.83)	33-0779-79
2H-Benzotriazole, 2-[2'-chloro-4"-[5"'-(4-chlorophenyl)isoxazol-3"'-yl]stilben-4'-yl]-	DMF	358(3.80)	33-0779-79
8H-[1,2,4]Triazolo[1,5-a]pyridine, 2-[2'-chloro-4"-[5"'-(4-chlorophenyl)-isoxazol-3"'-yl]syilben-4'yl]-	DMF	337(4.78),350(4.79)	33-0779-79
$C_{29}H_{18}O_6$			
Xylerythrinin acetate	dioxan	265(4.37),397(4.33), 480s(3.03)	1-0006-79
$C_{29}H_{19}ClN_4O$			
2H-Benzotriazole, 2-[2'-chloro-4"-(3"'-phenyl-5"'-isoxazolyl)stilben-4'-yl]-	DMF	367(4.83)	33-0779-79
2H-Benzotriazole, 2-[2'-chloro-4"-(5"'-phenyl-3"'-isoxazolyl)stilben-4'-yl]-	DMF	358(4.79)	33-0779-79
8H-[1,2,4]Triazolo[1,5-a]pyridine, 2-[2'-chloro-4"-(5"'-phenylisoxazol-3"'-yl)stilben-4'-yl]-	DMF	337(4.77),349(4.77)	33-0779-79

Compound	Solvent	$\lambda_{max}(\log \epsilon)$	Ref.
$C_{29}H_{19}Cl_2N_5$			
[1,2,4]Triazolo[1,5-a]pyridine, 2-[3-chloro-4-[2-[4-[1-(4-chlorophenyl)-1H-pyrazol-3-yl]phenyl]ethenyl]-phenyl]-	DMF	360(4.82)	33-1816-79
[1,2,4]Triazolo[1,5-a]pyridine, 2-[3-chloro-4-[2-[4-[3-(4-chlorophenyl)-1H-pyrazol-1-yl]phenyl]ethenyl]-phenyl]-	DMF	356(4.80)	33-1816-79
$C_{29}H_{19}NO_3S$			
Benzoic acid, 2-[(2-methyl-9-oxo-9H-naphtho[3,2,1-kl]acridin-6-yl)thio]-, methyl ester	EtOH	286(4.70),324s(3.64), 400(3.87),472(4.12), 500(4.19)	103-1227-79
Benzoic acid, 2-[(2-methyl-9-oxo-9H-naphtho[3,2,1-kl]acridin-8-yl)thio]-, methyl ester	EtOH	256(4.53),280(4.79), 426(4.39),466(4.13), 496(4.12)	103-1227-79
$C_{29}H_{19}N_3O_2$			
1,2-Benzisoxazole, 3-phenyl-6-[2-[4-(5-phenyl-1,2,4-oxadiazol-3-yl)phenyl]-ethenyl]-	DMF	338(4.75)	33-1411-79
Benzoxazole, 2-[4-[2-[(3-phenyl-1,2,4-oxadiazol-5-yl)phenyl]ethenyl]phenyl]-	DMF	365(4.88),389(4.72)	33-1411-79
Benzoxazole, 2-[4-[2-[(5-phenyl-1,2,4-oxadiazol-3-yl)phenyl]ethenyl]phenyl]-	DMF	360(4.87),378(4.68)	33-1411-79
$C_{29}H_{20}ClN_5$			
[1,2,4]Triazolo[1,5-a]pyridine, 2-[3-chloro-4-[2-[4-(1-phenyl-1H-pyrazol-3-yl)phenyl]ethenyl]phenyl]-	DMF	359(4.79)	33-1816-79
[1,2,4]Triazolo[1,5-a]pyridine, 2-[3-chloro-4-[2-[4-(3-phenyl-1H-pyrazol-1-yl)phenyl]ethenyl]phenyl]-	DMF	358(4.80)	33-1816-79
$C_{29}H_{20}ClN_5O_2$			
2H-Benzotriazole, 2-[3-chloro-4-[2-[4-[3-(4-methoxyphenyl)-1,2,4-oxadiazol-5-yl]phenyl]ethenyl]phenyl]-	DMF	363(4.83)	33-1411-79
2H-Benzotriazole, 2-[3-chloro-4-[2-[4-[5-(4-methoxyphenyl)-1,2,4-oxadiazol-3-yl]phenyl]ethenyl]phenyl]-	DMF	358(4.81)	33-1411-79
2H-Benzotriazole, 2-[3-chloro-4-[2-[4-(5-phenyl-1,2,4-oxadiazol-3-yl)-phenyl]ethenyl]phenyl]-5-methoxy-	DMF	368(4.80)	33-1411-79
$C_{29}H_{20}N_2O_4$			
Benzoxazole, 2-[5'-[4"-(5"'-phenylisoxazol-3"'-yl)styryl]-2'-furanyl]-	DMF	382(4.75),403(4.56)	33-0779-79
$C_{29}H_{20}N_4O$			
2H-Benzotriazole, 2-[4"-(3"'-phenyl-isoxazol-5"'-yl)stilben-4'-yl]-	DMF	368(4.85)	33-0779-79
2H-Benzotriazole, 2-[4"-(5"'-phenyl-isoxazol-3"'-yl)stilben-4'-yl]-	DMF	360(4.83)	33-0779-79
$C_{29}H_{20}O$			
8H-Cyclonona[b]naphthalen-8-one, 5,13-diphenyl-	MeCN	235(4.71),288(4.08)	77-1031-79

Compound	Solvent	λ_{max}(log ε)	Ref.
$C_{29}H_{20}O_5$			
2-Anthracenecarboxaldehyde, 9,10-dihydro-9,10-dioxo-1,4-bis(phenylmethoxy)-	MeOH	206(4.62),250(4.51), 430(3.63)	5-0019-79
$C_{29}H_{20}O_{12}$			
7-Demethylxanthomegnin	MeOH-HCl	228(4.70),290(4.19), 397(4.03)	24-0957-79
	MeOH-NaOH	229s(--),274(4.47), 395s(--),524(3.96)	24-0957-79
$C_{29}H_{21}ClO_4$			
9,10-Anthracenedione, 2-(chloromethyl)-1,4-bis(phenylmethoxy)-	MeOH	205(4.68),253(4.52), 373(3.68)	5-0019-79
$C_{29}H_{21}NO_4S$			
2,1-Benzisothiazole-5,6-dicarboxylic acid, 3,4,7-triphenyl-, dimethyl ester	CH_2Cl_2	253(4.54),305s(3.84), 318(3.91),354(4.09)	24-0266-79
$C_{29}H_{21}N_5$			
2H-Benzotriazole, 2-[4-[2-[4-(1-phenyl-1H-pyrazol-3-yl)phenyl]ethenyl]phenyl]-	DMF	371(4.85)	33-1816-79
2H-Benzotriazole, 2-[4-[2-[4-(3-phenyl-1H-pyrazol-1-yl)phenyl]ethenyl]phenyl]-	DMF	368(4.84)	33-1816-79
$C_{29}H_{21}N_5O_2S$			
Benzoic acid, 2-[5-(4,5-diphenyl-2-thiazolyl)-3-phenyl-1-formazano]-	benzene	590(4.26)	106-0790-79
	EtOH	525(4.34)	106-0790-79
	acetone	525(4.09)	106-0790-79
Benzoic acid, 3-[5-(4,5-diphenyl-2-thiazolyl)-3-phenyl-1-formazano]-	benzene	573(4.17)	106-0790-79
	EtOH	579(4.23)	106-0790-79
	acetone	562(4.16)	106-0790-79
Benzoic acid, 4-[5-(4,5-diphenyl-2-thiazolyl)-3-phenyl-1-formazano]-	benzene	606(4.20)	106-0790-79
	EtOH	592(4.29)	106-0790-79
	acetone	576(4.25)	106-0790-79
$C_{29}H_{22}$			
7H-Dibenzo[a,c]cyclononene, 5,9-diphenyl-	EtOH	245(4.34),265s(4.19), 317(1.95)	78-0667-79
9H-Fluorene, 2,7-bis(2-phenylethenyl)-	dioxan	370(4.98)	104-1944-79
15H-Tetrabenzo[a,c,g,j]cyclotridecene, (E,E)-	EtOH	260(4.45)	78-0667-79
$C_{29}H_{22}N_2O$			
Phenol, 2-[3-(2,2-diphenylethenyl)-1H-1,5-benzodiazepin-4-yl]-	MeOH	222(4.5),241(4.5), 357(4.1)	24-1791-79
Phenol, 2-[4-(2,2-diphenylethenyl)-1-phenyl-1H-pyrazol-5-yl]-	MeOH	310(4.5)	24-1791-79
$C_{29}H_{22}N_2O_2$			
Benzoxazole, 5,5'-(1-methylethylidene)-bis[2-phenyl-	H_2SO_4	227(4.12),342(3.84)	103-1299-79
$C_{29}H_{22}O$			
2-Naphthalenemethanol, 1,3,4-triphenyl-	ether	238(4.75),292(4.03)	78-2101-79
$C_{29}H_{22}O_2$			
5,7:14,16-Dietheno-8H,13H-diindeno[2,1-h:1',2'-i][1,4]dioxacyclotridecin,	MeCN	222(4.68),244(4.35), 267(4.40),302(3.97),	33-2285-79

Compound	Solvent	λ_{max}(log ϵ)	Ref.
10,11-dihydro-, (S)- (cont.)		314(4.08)	33-2285-79
$C_{29}H_{22}O_5$			
9,10-Anthracenedione, 2-(hydroxymethyl)-1,4-bis(phenylmethoxy)-	MeOH	206(4.66),253(4.49), 403(3.67)	5-0019-79
$C_{29}H_{23}ClO_3$			
Anthra[1,2-d]-1,3-dioxol-5(4H)-one, 4-chloro-3a,11b-dihydro-2,2-dimethyl-6,11-diphenyl-, (3aα,4α,11bα)-	ether	224(4.57),254(4.58), 298(3.90),306s(3.89), 332s(3.39),343(3.44)	22-0110-79
$C_{29}H_{23}NO$			
3H-Pyrrol-3-one, 1,2-dihydro-1-methyl-2,2,4,5-tetraphenyl-	MeOH	260(4.15),365(3.92)	32-0121-79
$C_{29}H_{23}NO_4S_2$			
4,7-Epithio-2,1-benzisothiazole-5,6-dicarboxylic acid, 4,5,6,7-tetrahydro-3,4,7-triphenyl-, dimethyl ester, 5-endo,6-endo	CH_2Cl_2	274(4.18)	24-0266-79
5-endo,6-exo	CH_2Cl_2	268(4.16)	24-0266-79
5-exo,6-endo	CH_2Cl_2	265(4.04)	24-0266-79
5-exo,6-exo	CH_2Cl_2	262.5(4.06)	24-0266-79
$C_{29}H_{23}NO_9S$			
2,4-Thiazolidinedione, 3-(2,3,5-tri-O-benzoyl-β-D-ribofuranosyl)-	EtOH	231(4.39),275(3.27)	73-1475-79
$C_{29}H_{23}N_3O_4$			
4-Imidazolidinecarboxamide, N-(4-methoxyphenyl)-2,5-dioxo-1,3,4-triphenyl-	MeOH	218(4.56),264(4.25), 275(4.10)	118-0794-79
$C_{29}H_{23}N_5S$			
2(3H)-Thiazolone, 4,5-diphenyl-, [[(3-methylphenyl)azo]phenylmethylene]hydrazone	EtOH	585(3.96)	106-0790-79
$C_{29}H_{24}N_2$			
1H-Pyrazole, 4,5-dihydro-3,5-diphenyl-1-stilbenyl-	toluene	393(4.62)	135-1491-79B
$C_{29}H_{24}N_2O_6S$			
5-Thia-1-azabicyclo[4.2.0]oct-2-ene-2-carboxylic acid, 3-methyl-4,8-dioxo-7-[(phenoxyacetyl)amino]-, diphenylmethyl ester, (6R-trans)-	EtOH	318(3.87)	87-0743-79
$C_{29}H_{24}N_4O_4S_4$			
5-Thia-1-azabicyclo[4.2.0]oct-2-ene-2-carboxylic acid, 8-oxo-3-[(1,2,3-thiadiazol-5-ylthio)methyl]-7-[(2-thienylacetyl)amino]-, diphenylmethyl ester, (6R-trans)-	MeOH	260(3.95),269(3.95)	87-1214-79
$C_{29}H_{25}NO_4$			
[1,1':4',1"-Terphenyl]-2',3'-dicarboxylic acid, 5'-amino-6'-(phenylmethyl)-, dimethyl ester	CH_2Cl_2	275(3.97)	24-0266-79
$C_{29}H_{25}NO_5$			
Naphtho[1,2-b]furan-3(2H)-one, 5-acet-	EtOH	212(4.53),249(4.48),	103-0597-79

Compound	Solvent	λ_{max}(log ε)	Ref.
oxy-2-[ethyl(4-methoxyphenyl)amino]-4-phenyl- (cont.)		272(4.48),380(3.78)	103-0597-79
Naphtho[1,2-b]furan-3(2H)-one, 5-acetoxy-2-(ethylphenylamino)-4-(4-methoxyphenyl)-	EtOH	216(4.58),253(4.57), 276(4.48),380(3.78)	103-0597-79
$C_{29}H_{25}N_3$			
Benzenamine, N-[[4-(4,5-dihydro-3,5-diphenyl-1H-pyrazol-1-yl)phenyl]methylene]-4-methyl-	toluene	320s(4.02),395(4.72)	135-1491-79B
Benzenamine, N-[[4-[4,5-dihydro-3-(4-methylphenyl)-5-phenyl-1H-pyrazol-1-yl]phenyl]methylene]-	toluene	320s(4.04),393(4.75)	135-1491-79B
$C_{29}H_{25}N_3O$			
Benzenamine, N-[[4-(4,5-dihydro-3,5-diphenyl-1H-pyrazol-1-yl)phenyl]methylene]-	toluene	320s(4.04),395(4.76)	135-1491-79B
Benzenamine, N-[[4-[4,5-dihydro-3-(4-methoxyphenyl)-5-phenyl-1H-pyrazol-1-yl]phenyl]methylene]-	toluene	320s(4.08),395(4.78)	135-1491-79B
$C_{29}H_{25}N_3O_2$			
1H-Imidazole-5-carboxylic acid, 4,5-dihydro-1-methyl-2,4,5-triphenyl-4-(2-pyridinyl)-, methyl ester	EtOH	220s(4.23),263(3.68)	44-0041-79
$C_{29}H_{25}N_5$			
Benzo[c]cinnolinium, 5-[[[[[(1-methylethyl)amino]phenylmethylene]amino]phenylmethylene]amino]-, hydroxide, inner salt	n.s.g.	253(4.94),354(4.29)	39-0185-79C
$C_{29}H_{26}O_2$			
3,5-Cyclohexadiene-1,2-dione, 3-(1,1-dimethylethyl)-5-(triphenylmethyl)-	CCl_4	321(3.65),389(3.30)	44-0428-79
5H-Dibenzo[a,c]cyclononene-5,9-diol, 6,7,8,9-tetrahydro-5,9-diphenyl-	EtOH	254(3.10),260(3.09)	78-0667-79
$C_{29}H_{27}NO_4S$			
Propanedioic acid, (2,4,6-triphenyl-2H-1,3-thiazin-2-yl)-, diethyl ester	EtOH	244(4.41)	18-3767-79
$C_{29}H_{27}N_2O_4S_2$			
Benzo[1,2-d:5,4-d']bisthiazolium, 2,6-bis[2-(2,5-dimethoxyphenyl)ethenyl]-3-methyl-, perchlorate	DMF	262(4.23),312(4.44), 449(4.40)	126-1441-79
	KBr	378(--),476(--)	126-1441-79
$C_{29}H_{28}N_2O_5$			
2,4(1H,3H)-Pyrimidinedione, 1-[2-acetoxy-3-(triphenylmethoxypropyl)]-5-methyl-	n.s.g.	270(3.06)	128-0281-79
$C_{29}H_{28}N_3S_2$			
Benzothiazolium, 2-[2-[2-cyano-3-[(3-ethyl-2(3H)-benzothiazolylidene)ethylidene]-1-cyclohexen-1-yl]ethenyl]-3-ethyl-, bromide	MeOH	884(5.25)	104-0351-79
C H NO			
Phenol, 2-(4,4-diphenyl-1-(1-piperidin-	MeOH	212(4.3),228(4.2),	24-1791-79

Compound	Solvent	λ_{max}(log ϵ)	Ref.
yl)-1,3-butadienyl]-, acetate (cont.)		351(4.4)	24-1791-79
$C_{29}H_{29}NO_7$			
2H-Pyrrole-3,4-dicarboxylic acid, 3,4-dihydro-2,2,5-tris(4-methoxyphenyl)-, dimethyl ester	n.s.g.	272(4.42)	88-1619-79
$C_{29}H_{29}N_2$			
Quinolinium, 2-[4-[4-(dimethylamino)-phenyl]-2-phenyl-1,3-butadienyl]-1-ethyl-, iodide	EtOH	534(4.96)	62-0650-79A
	isoBuOH	532(4.98)	62-0650-79A
	dioxan	523(4.82)	62-0650-79A
	THF	532(4.89)	62-0650-79A
	$CHCl_3$	554(5.00)	62-0650-79A
$C_{29}H_{29}N_5O_8$			
Propanoic acid, 3-(benzoylamino)-, 2-[[3-(benzoylamino)-1-oxopropoxy]-methyl]-2,3,3a,9a-tetrahydro-6-imino-6H-furo[2',3':4,5]oxazolo[3,2-a]pyrim-idin-3-yl ester, monohydrochloride, [2R-(2α,3β,3aβ,9aβ)]-	MeOH	229(4.61),265(4.23)	87-0639-79
$C_{29}H_{30}O_6$			
Pregna-1,4-diene-3,11,20-trione, 17-(benzoyloxy)-21-hydroxy-16-methylene-	MeOH	232(4.42)	145-1662-79
Pregna-1,4,6-triene-3,11,20-trione, 17-(benzoyloxy)-21-hydroxy-16α-methyl-	MeOH	228(4.37),296(4.08)	145-1662-79
$C_{29}H_{30}O_{12}$			
Apiumoside	n.s.g.	265(4.04),320(4.48)	102-1764-79
$C_{29}H_{30}S_4$			
Butatriene, 1-[(1,1-dimethylethyl)thio]-1,4,4-tris(4-methylphenylthio)-	heptane	204(4.75),400(4.44)	5-1606-79
$C_{29}H_{31}NO_5$			
Isohypognavinone, 11-acetyl-	EtOH	230(4.26),275(2.92)	95-0647-79
$C_{29}H_{31}N_2OP$			
Benzenamine, 4,4'-[(diphenylphosphin-yl)methylene]-bis[N,N-dimethyl-	EtOH	267(4.46),305s(3.61)	65-1275-79
$C_{29}H_{31}N_2OS_2$			
Benzothiazolium, 3-ethyl-2-[2-[3-[(3-ethyl-2(3H)-benzothiazolylidene)eth-ylidene]-2-methoxy-1-cyclohexen-1-yl]ethenyl]-, iodide	MeOH	776(5.38)	104-0351-79
$C_{29}H_{31}N_2O_3$			
Pyridinium, 3-ethyl-1-[2-[2-[2-methoxy-1-(methoxycarbonyl)ethenyl]-1-(phen-ylmethyl)-1H-indol-3-yl]ethyl]-, perchlorate, (E)-	EtOH	216(4.59),262(4.03), 285(3.90)	23-0289-79
$C_{29}H_{31}N_2S_2$			
Benzothiazolium, 3-ethyl-2-[2-[3-[(3-ethyl-2(3H)-benzothiazolylidene)eth-ylidene]-2-methyl-1-cyclohexen-1-yl]-ethenyl]-, iodide	MeOH	785(5.49)	104-0351-79

Compound	Solvent	$\lambda_{max}(\log \epsilon)$	Ref.
$C_{29}H_{31}N_5Pd$			
Palladium, [2,3,17,18-tetrahydro-2,2,7,8,12,13,17,17-octamethyl-21H,23H-porphine-5-carbonitrilato-(2-)-N^{21},N^{22},N^{23},N^{24}]-, (SP-4-2)-	EtOH	280(3.82),292s(3.80), 355s(4.42),382(4.77), 505s(3.72),540s(3.99), 576(4.54)	89-0675-79
$C_{29}H_{32}N_2O_{11}$			
Dibenzo[a,c]cycloocten-6-ol, 12-(2,4-dinitrophenoxy)-5,6,7,8-tetrahydro-1,2,3,10,11-pentamethoxy-6,7-dimethyl-	EtOH	212(4.70),250(4.31), 284(4.06),300s(3.98)	94-1576-79
$C_{29}H_{32}N_3S_2$			
Benzothiazolium, 2-[2-[2-(dimethylamino)-3-[(3-ethyl-2(3H)-benzothiazolylidene)ethylidene]-1-cyclopenten-1-yl]ethenyl]-3-ethyl-, iodide	MeOH	684(5.18)	104-0351-79
$C_{29}H_{32}N_5O_4PS$			
Thiourea, N-(4-methoxyphenyl)-N'-[N-(4-methoxyphenyl)-P,P-bis[(4-methoxyphenyl)amino]phosphinimyl]-	EtOH	215(4.84),235s(4.73), 274(4.78)	64-0297-79B
$C_{29}H_{32}O_6$			
Pregna-1,4-diene-3,11,20-trione, 17-(benzoyloxy)-21-hydroxy-16β-methyl-	MeOH	233(4.44)	145-1662-79
$C_{29}H_{32}O_9$			
Malaphyll	EtOH	205(4.57),223(4.70), 262(4.43),295(3.93)	105-0426-79
$C_{29}H_{32}O_{13}$			
Dalbin	MeOH	235(4.03),245s(3.91), 295(4.14)	102-0188-79
$C_{29}H_{33}ClP$			
Phosphonium, [1-chloro-2,3-bis(1,1-dimethylethyl)-2-cyclopropen-1-yl]triphenyl-, tetrafluoroborate	n.s.g.	269(3.83)	89-0472-79
$C_{29}H_{33}NO_5$			
Isohypognavine, 11-acetyl-	EtOH	230(4.03),275(2.84)	95-0647-79
$C_{29}H_{33}NO_7$			
Hernandalinol	EtOH	283(4.24),303(4.16)	100-0325-79
$C_{29}H_{33}NO_7S_2$			
Pregna-1,3,5-trien-20-one, 21-acetoxy-11β,17α-dihydroxy-3-[(2-nitrophenyl)dithio]-	MeOH	330(4.01),340(4.00)	39-1166-79C
$C_{29}H_{33}NO_{10}$			
Nogarol, 7-con-O-ethyl-	EtOH	236(4.58),252(4.53), 258s(4.42),270(4.32), 293(4.06),480(4.22)	44-4030-79
Nogarol, 7-dis-O-ethyl-	EtOH	236(4.64),260(4.35), 288s(3.93),476(4.14)	44-4030-79
$C_{29}H_{33}N_2S_2$			
Benzothiazolium, 3-ethyl-2-[[3-[(3-ethyl-2(3H)-benzothiazolylidene)methyl]-2,5,5-trimethyl-2-cyclohexen-1-yli-	MeOH	657(5.42)	104-0774-79

Compound	Solvent	λ max (log ε)	Ref.
dene]methyl]-, iodide (cont.)			104-0774-79
$C_{29}H_{33}N_3O_9$			
Saframycin C	MeOH	267(4.32),368(3.19)	88-2355-79
$C_{29}H_{34}FN_2$			
3H-Indolium, 1-ethyl-2-[5-(1-ethyl-1,3-dihydro-3,3-dimethyl-2H-indol-2-ylidene)-3-fluoro-1,3-pentadienyl]-3,3-dimethyl-, perchlorate	EtOH	658(4.38)	124-0872-79
$C_{29}H_{34}N_2O_2$			
2-Cyclohexen-1-one, 2,2'-methylenebis-[5,5-dimethyl-3-(phenylamino)-	H_2O	310(4.33)	39-1593-79C
2-Cyclohexen-1-one, 2,2'-methylenebis-[3-[(2-phenylethyl)amino]-	pH 1	282(4.67)	39-1593-79C
	H_2O	292(4.77)	39-1593-79C
$C_{29}H_{34}N_2O_3$			
Acetamide, N-[2-[2,3-dihydro-2-oxo-3-[2-oxo-3-(2-propenyl)cyclohexyl]-1-(phenylmethyl)-1H-indol-3-yl]ethyl]-N-methyl-	EtOH	255(3.85),280s(3.25)	23-1694-79
$C_{29}H_{34}O_6$			
Tavimolidin	EtOH	216(4.29),242(3.63), 253(3.37),352(4.04)	105-0417-79
$C_{29}H_{35}NO_{10}$			
Daunorubicin, N,N-dimethyl-, hydrochloride	MeOH	233(4.59),252(4.42), 288(3.95),478(4.10), 495(4.10),530(3.83)	87-0912-79
$C_{29}H_{35}N_5O_5$			
Ergovaline	CH_2Cl_2	237(4.3),307(3.95)	23-1638-79
$C_{29}H_{35}N_7O_{11}S_2$			
L-Aspartic acid, N-[(1,1-dimethylethoxy)carbonyl]-, 4-[[[[7-[(hydroxyphenylacetyl)amino]-3-[[(1-methyl-1H-tetrazol-5-yl)thio]methyl]-8-oxo-5-thia-1-azabicyclo[4.2.0]oct-2-en-2-yl]carbonyl]oxy]methyl]-, 1-methyl ester, [6R-[6α,7β(R*)]]-	MeOH	272(3.90)	87-0657-79
$C_{29}H_{36}O_3$			
Pregna-4,6-diene-21-carboxylic acid, 4-bicyclo[2.2.1]hept-2-en-7-yl-17-hydroxy-3-oxo-, γ-lactone, [4(anti),17α]-	MeOH	291(4.30)	78-2613-79
$C_{29}H_{36}O_{10}$			
Butanoic acid, 2-hydroxy-2,3-dimethyl-4-[5,6,7,8-tetrahydro-1,2,3-trimethoxy-6,7-dimethyl-5-oxobenzo[3,4]cyclooct[1,2-f][1,3]benzodioxol-13-yl)oxy]-, methyl ester	EtOH	209(4.49),228(4.49), 252s(4.16),273s(3.98), 316s(3.60)	94-2695-79
$C_{29}H_{36}O_{13}$			
β-D-Glucopyranoside, 4-[6a-acetoxy-4-(3,4-dimethoxyphenyl)tetrahydro-1H,3H-furo[3,4-c]furan-1-yl]-2-methoxyphenyl, [1R-(1α,3aα,4α,6aα)]-	EtOH	231(4.25),278(3.68)	94-2868-79

Compound	Solvent	λ_{max}(log ε)	Ref.
$C_{29}H_{37}ClO_{11}$			
1H-Inden-1-one, 6-(2-chloroethyl)-2,3-dihydro-2,5,7-trimethyl-2-[[(2,3,4,6-tetra-O-acetyl-β-D-glucopyranosyl)-oxy]methyl]-, (S)-	EtOH	221(4.55),261(4.14), 306(3.39)	94-0592-79
$C_{29}H_{37}N_7$			
4,5'-Bipyrimidine, 6-phenyl-2,2',4'-tripiperidino-	EtOH	204(4.41),262(4.69), 322(4.12)	103-0671-79
$C_{29}H_{37}N_7O_9S_2$			
5-Thia-1-azabicyclo[4.2.0]oct-2-ene-2-carboxylic acid, 7-(D-mandelamido)-3-[[(1-methyl-1H-tetrazol-5-yl)thio]-methyl]-, N-[(tert-butoxy)carbonyl]-valyloxymethyl ester	MeOH	271(3.88)	87-0657-79
$C_{29}H_{38}N_4O_4$			
Orantine, O-methyl-, (-)- (same in acid and base)	EtOH	229(4.19),247s(3.00), 253(2.92),260s(3.04), 275s(3.48),280(3.54), 288s(3.37)	33-2712-79
$C_{29}H_{38}O_3$			
Pregn-4-ene-21-carboxylic acid, 4-bi-cyclo[2.2.1]hept-2-en-7-yl-17-hydr-oxy-3-oxo-, γ-lactone, [4α(anti),17α]-	MeOH	253.5(4.03)	78-2613-79
Spiro[1,3-dioxolane-2,1'-[1H]indene]-4'-propanol, octahydro-4',5',7'a-trimethyl-α,α-diphenyl-, [3'aR-(3'aα,4'α,5'β,7'aβ)-	n.s.g.	263(3.24),271(3.26), 279(3.18)	78-2301-79
$C_{29}H_{38}O_5$			
Spiro[3H-benz[mn]indeno[5,4-b]xanthene-3,2'(5'H)-furan]-5',8(3aH)-dione, 1,2,3',4,4',5,5a,5b,6,7,8b,9,10,12a-13a,14,14a,14b-octadecahydro-13a-methoxy-3a,5b-dimethyl-, [3S-(3α,3aα-5aβ,5bα,12aβ,13aα,14aα,14bβ)]-	MeOH	246(3.95)	44-1597-79
$C_{29}H_{38}O_{10}$			
Butanoic acid, 2-hydroxy-2,3-dimethyl-4-[(5,6,7,8-tetrahydro-5-hydroxy-1,2,3-trimethoxy-6,7-dimethylbenzo-[3,4]cycloocta[1,2-f][1,3]benzodi-oxol-13-yl)oxy]-, methyl ester	EtOH	214(4.66),255s(3.96), 283(3.55)	94-2695-79
$C_{29}H_{38}O_{11}$			
Butanoic acid, 2-hydroxy-2,3-dimethyl-4-[(5,6,7,8-tetrahydro-5,6-dihydroxy-1,2,3-trimethoxy-6,7-dimethylbenzo-[3,4]cycloocta[1,2-f][1,3]benzodioxol-13-yl)oxy]-, methyl ester	EtOH	217(4.68),255s(3.97), 279s(3.53)	94-1395-79
$C_{29}H_{39}NO_9S$			
3a,7-Epoxy-3aH-furo[3,2-b]oxocin-3-car-boxylic acid, 5-[1,3-dimethyl-6-[5-[2-(methylthio)ethyl]-2,4-dioxo-3-pyrrolidinyl]-6-oxo-2,4-hexadienyl]-octahydro-2,6,9a-trimethyl-8-oxo-, methyl ester	EtOH-HCl	238(3.90),353(4.47)	142-0477-79B
	EtOH-NaOH	258(4.18),279(4.24), 331(4.20)	142-0477-79B

Compound	Solvent	λmax(log ε)	Ref.
$C_{29}H_{39}N_5O_{10}$			
Acetamide, N-[7-[5-O-acetyl-2,3-O-(1-methylethylidene)-β-D-ribofuranosyl]-5-[[(3a,6a-dihydro-2,2-dimethyl-4H-cyclopenta-1,3-dioxol-4-yl)amino]-methyl]-4,7-dihydro-3-(methoxymethyl)-4-oxo-3H-pyrrolo[2,3-d]pyrimidin-2-yl]-	MeOH	265(4.03),293(3.88)	35-3629-79
$C_{29}H_{40}$			
D:A-Friedo-24,25-noroleana-1,3,5,7,9-pentaene, 3-methyl-	C_6H_{12}	229(4.79),239(4.97), 288(4.67),315(4.18), 322(4.01),330(4.23)	2-0504-79B
$C_{29}H_{40}N_2O_{18}S$			
Thiourea, N,N'-bis(2,3,4,6-tetra-O-acetyl-β-D-galactopyranosyl)-	MeOH	253(4.09)	70-0821-79
Thiourea, N,N'-bis(2,3,4,6-tetra-O-acetyl-β-D-glucopyranosyl)-	MeOH	253(4.07)	70-0821-79
$C_{29}H_{40}O_2$			
28-Noroleana-11,13(18),17(22)-triene-3,21-dione	EtOH	338(4.23)	39-2044-79C
$C_{29}H_{40}O_3$			
Benzo[6,7]pregna-4,6-diene-21-carboxylic acid, 3',6,6',7-tetrahydro-17-hydroxy-4',6',6'-trimethyl-3-oxo-, γ-lactone	MeOH	248(4.13)	44-4299-79
19-Norlanosta-2,5,7,9-tetraene-1,11-dione, 7-hydroxy-	EtOH	228(4.21),246s(4.09), 334(3.89)	12-0179-79
Pregna-4,6-diene-21-carboxylic acid, 17-hydroxy-3-oxo-4-(1,1,3-trimethyl-3-butenyl)-, γ-lactone, (17α)-	MeOH	291(4.27)	44-4299-79
Pregn-4-ene-21-carboxylic acid, 4-bicyclo[2.2.1]hept-2-yl-17-hydroxy-3-oxo-, γ-lactone	MeOH	255(4.11)	78-2613-79
$C_{29}H_{40}O_{11}$			
Syriobioside	EtOH	217(4.14)	33-0412-79
$C_{29}H_{42}N_2O_{10}$			
[2,2'-Bi-2H-pyrrole]-4,4'-dipropanoic acid, 5,5'-diacetyl-3,3',4,4'-tetrahydro-3,3'-bis(2-methoxy-2-oxoethyl)-2,3,4'-trimethyl-, dimethyl ester, [2R-[2α(2'R*,3'R*,4'R*),3α,4β]]-	MeOH	214(4.64),278(4.28)	5-1440-79
$C_{29}H_{42}N_4O_4$			
7a-Aza-B-homospirost-5-eno[7a,7-d]tetrazol-3β-ol, acetate, (25R)-	EtOH	242(4.16)	39-3166-79C
$C_{29}H_{42}O_2$			
28-Noroleana-11,13(18),17(22)-trien-21-one, 3α-hydroxy-	EtOH	340(4.66)	39-2044-79C
$C_{29}H_{42}O_6S$			
Cochlioquinone B, 17-(methylthio)-	MeOH	216(3.93),267(3.57), 343(3.54),450(3.00)	32-0565-79

Compound	Solvent	λ_{max}(log ε)	Ref.
$C_{29}H_{42}O_7$			
Propanedioic acid, [(1α,17β)-3-oxo-17-(1-oxopropoxy)androst-4-en-1-yl]-, diethyl ester	EtOH	244(4.11)	56-0149-79
$C_{29}H_{42}O_7S$			
Cochlioquinone B, 11α-hydroxy-17-(methylthio)-	MeOH	224(4.11),264(3.74), 342(3.72),450(3.55)	32-0565-79
$C_{29}H_{43}BrO_7$			
5β-Cholan-24-oic acid, 3α,7α-diacetoxy-12α-bromo-11-oxo-, methyl ester	EtOH	310(2.32)	13-0295-79A
$C_{29}H_{44}O_4$			
5α-Cholesta-8(14),9(11)-dien-7-one, 3β-acetoxy-15α-hydroxy-	EtOH	226(4.04),318(3.41)	44-4447-79
Cholest-8(14)-ene-7,15-dione, 3-acetoxy-	MeOH	259(4.02)	44-3974-79
5α-Cholest-8-en-7-one, 3β-acetoxy-14α,15α-epoxy-	EtOH	246(4.00)	44-4447-79
$C_{29}H_{44}O_5$			
5α-Cholest-8(14)-en-7-one, 3-acetoxy-9,11-epoxy-15-hydroxy-, (3β,5α,11α-15α)-	EtOH	253(3.97)	44-4447-79
$C_{29}H_{44}O_6$			
Silenosterone, 22-acetyl-	EtOH	243(4.07)	105-0700-79
$C_{29}H_{45}BrO_3$			
Cholest-5-en-7-one, 3β-acetoxy-6-bromo-	EtOH	258(3.91)	39-2727-79C
$C_{29}H_{45}ClN_2O_6$			
Malyngamide A	EtOH	213(4.20),265(4.25)	35-0240-79
$C_{29}H_{45}NO_2$			
Androstane-16-ethanimidic acid, N-cyclohexyl-17-hydroxy-3-methoxy-α-methylene-, γ-lactone	EtOH	215(3.76),239s(3.65)	33-1586-79
	EtOH-HCl	232(3.84)	33-1586-79
Androstane-17-propanimidic acid, N-cyclohexyl-3,17-dihydroxy-α-methylene-, γ-lactone, (3β,5α,17α)-	EtOH	216(3.90),236s(3.77)	33-1586-79
	EtOH-HCl	233(4.02)	33-1586-79
Pregn-20-ene-20-carboximidic acid, N-cyclohexyl-16-hydroxy-3-methoxy-, γ-lactone, (3β,5α,16α,17α)-	EtOH	217(3.88),240s(3.78)	33-1586-79
	EtOH-HCl	231(3.99)	33-1586-79
$C_{29}H_{46}$			
D:A-Friedo-25-noroleana-7,9(11)-diene	C_6H_{12}	249(3.96),255(4.04)	39-0060-79C
$C_{29}H_{46}N_2OS$			
Formamide, N-[(5α)-cholest-2-eno[3,2-d]thiazol-2'-yl]-	EtOH	285(3.94)	4-0763-79
$C_{29}H_{46}O$			
Cholesta-3,5,7-triene, 3-ethoxy-	EtOH	215(3.86),281s(--), 322(4.24),337(4.06)	12-2017-79
Stigmasta-5,7,24(28)-trien-3β-ol, (24Z)-	MeOH	262(3.91),270(4.05), 281(4.08),293(3.84)	33-0101-79

Compound	Solvent	$\lambda_{max}(\log \epsilon)$	Ref.
$C_{29}H_{46}O_2$			
Acacidiol	EtOH	248(3.21)	102-1199-79
isomerized by HCl	EtOH	295(3.84)	102-1199-79
Cholesta-4,6-dien-3β-ol, acetate	EtOH?	232(4.35),239(4.39), 247(4.18)	150-0501-79
28-Norolean-12-en-16-one, 3β-hydroxy-	MeOH	288(1.95)	78-0417-79
$C_{29}H_{46}O_3$			
Cholest-4-en-6-one, 3β-acetoxy-	n.s.g.	240(3.85)	56-0139-79
Cholest-5-en-7-one, 3β-acetoxy-	EtOH	235(3.85)	39-2727-79C
5β-Cholest-7-en-6-one, 3β-acetoxy-	n.s.g.	250(4.17)	56-0139-79
5α-Cholest-8(14)-en-15-one, 3β-acetoxy-	MeOH	259(4.15)	44-3974-79
	n.s.g.	260(4.10)	39-1821-79C
$C_{29}H_{46}O_4$			
5α-Cholest-7-en-6-one, 3β-acetoxy-5-hydroxy-	n.s.g.	250(4.11)	56-0139-79
5α,14α-Cholest-7-en-6-one, 3β-acetoxy-14-hydroxy-	n.s.g.	243(4.05)	56-0139-79
5α,14β-Cholest-7-en-6-one, 3β-acetoxy-14-hydroxy-	n.s.g.	243(4.08)	56-0139-79
5β,14β-Cholest-7-en-6-one, 3β-acetoxy-14-hydroxy-	n.s.g.	246(4.06)	56-0139-79
$C_{29}H_{46}O_5$			
5α,14α-Cholest-7-en-6-one, 3β-acetoxy-5,14-dihydroxy-	n.s.g.	250(4.13)	56-0139-79
$C_{29}H_{48}N_2O_2$			
22,26-Epimino-5 -cholest-22(N)-en-16α-ol, 3β-amino-, acetate, (25S)-	EtOH	240(2.44)	12-0597-79
$C_{29}H_{48}N_2S$			
Cholest-2-eno[3,2-d]thiazol-2'-amine, N-methyl-, (5α)-	$CHCl_3$	266(3.63)	4-0763-79

Compound	Solvent	λ_{max}(log ε)	Ref.
$C_{30}H_{11}Cl_4NO_5$			
Anthra[1,9-bc]pyran-2,7-dione, 4,6-dichloro-1-[(2,4-dichloro-1-hydroxy-10-oxo-9(10H)-anthracenylidene)amino]-	C_6H_5Cl	338(3.89),377(3.87), 471(3.83)	104-0923-79
$C_{30}H_{14}F_6O_2$			
9(10H)-Anthracenone, 10-[10-oxo-2-(trifluoromethyl)-9(10H)-anthracenylidene]-3-(trifluoromethyl)-	CH_2Cl_2	234(4.79),260s(4.42), 285s(4.18),304s(4.09), 398(4.19)	44-1941-79
$C_{30}H_{14}N_6O_{12}$			
3H-Indol-3-one, 1-(3,5-dinitrobenzoyl)-2-[1-(3,5-dinitrobenzoyl)-1,3-dihydro-2H-indol-2-ylidene]-1,2-dihydro-, cis	benzene	436(3.45)	18-3397-79 +25-0415-79
trans	benzene	552(3.79)	18-3397-79 +25-0415-79
$C_{30}H_{14}O_2S_2$			
Pyreno[1,10-bc]thiopyran-5(4H)-one, 4-(1-oxonaphtho[2,1-b]thien-2(1H)-ylidene)-, cis	n.s.g.	543(3.96)	124-0768-79
trans	n.s.g.	662(4.46)	124-0768-79
Pyreno[10,1-bc]thiopyran-3(4H)-one, 4-(1-oxonaphtho[2,1-b]thien-2(1H)-ylidene)-, cis	n.s.g.	512(4.18)	124-0768-79
trans	n.s.g.	615(4.40)	124-0768-79
$C_{30}H_{16}F_6O_2$			
[9,9'-Bianthracene]-10,10'(9H,9'H)-dione, 2,2'-bis(trifluoromethyl)-	EtOH	262(4.38),312s(3.85)	44-1941-79
$C_{30}H_{17}Cl_3N_2O_2$			
1,2-Benzisoxazole, 6-chloro-3-[2'-chloro-4"-[3"-(4-chlorophenyl)isoxazol-5"'-yl]stilben-4'-yl]-	DMF	351(4.77)	33-0779-79
$C_{30}H_{17}Cl_4N_3O$			
Benzoxazole, 5-chloro-2-[4-[2-[4-(4,5-dichloro-1-(4-chlorophenyl)-1H-pyrazol-3-yl]phenyl]ethenyl]phenyl]-	DMF	364(4.87)	33-1816-79
$C_{30}H_{18}Cl_2N_2O_2$			
1,2-Benzisoxazole, 6-chloro-3-[2'-chloro-4"-(3"'-phenylisoxazol-5"'-yl)-stilben-4'-yl]-	DMF	353(4.76)	33-0779-79
1,2-Benzisoxazole, 6-chloro-3-[2'-chloro-4"-(5"'-phenylisoxazol-3"'-yl)-stilben-4'-yl]-	DMF	340(4.71)	33-0779-79
Benzoxazole, 2-[2'-chloro-4"-[3"'-(4-chlorophenyl)isoxazol-5"'-yl]stilben-4'-yl]-	DMF	369(4.83)	33-0779-79
Benzoxazole, 2-[2'-chloro-4"-[5"'-(4-chlorophenyl)isoxazol-3"'-yl]stilben-4'-yl]-	DMF	362(4.81)	33-0779-79
$C_{30}H_{18}Cl_2N_4O_2$			
1,2,4-Oxadiazole, 3-[4-[2-[2-chloro-4-[5-(4-chlorophenyl)-1,3,4-oxadiazol-2-yl]phenyl]ethenyl]phenyl]-5-phenyl-	DMF	355(4.78)	33-1411-79

Compound	Solvent	$\lambda_{max}(\log \epsilon)$	Ref.
1,2,4-Oxadiazole, 5-[4-[2-[2-chloro-4-[5-(4-chlorophenyl)-1,3,4-oxadiazol-2-yl]phenyl]ethenyl]phenyl]-3-phenyl-	DMF	360(4.80)	33-1411-79
1,2,4-Oxadiazole, 5-(4-chlorophenyl)-3-[4-[2-[2-chloro-4-(5-phenyl-1,3,4-oxadiazol-2-yl)phenyl]ethenyl]phenyl]-	DMF	354(4.78)	33-1411-79
$C_{30}H_{18}Cl_3N_3O$			
Benzoxazole, 2-[4-[2-[4-(4,5-dichloro-1-(4-chlorophenyl)-1H-pyrazol-3-yl]phenyl]ethenyl]phenyl]-	DMF	362(4.87)	33-1816-79
$C_{30}H_{18}N_2O_4$			
3H-Indol-3-one, 1-benzoyl-2-(1-benzoyl-1,3-dihydro-3-oxo-2H-indol-2-ylidene)-1,2-dihydro-, cis	benzene	460(3.59)	18-3397-79 +25-0415-79
trans	benzene	574(3.76)	18-3397-79
	benzene	574(3.89)	25-0415-79
$C_{30}H_{19}ClN_2O_2$			
1,2-Benzisoxazole, 6-chloro-3-[4"-(5"'-phenylisoxazol-3"'-yl)stilben-4'-yl]-	DMF	342(4.80)	33-0779-79
Benzoxazole, 2-[2'-chloro-4"-(3"'-phenylisoxazol-5"'-yl)stilben-4'-yl]-	DMF	369(4.83)	33-0779-79
Benzoxazole, 2-[2'-chloro-4"-(5"'-phenylisoxazol-3"'-yl)stilben-4'-yl]-	DMF	362(4.81)	33-0779-79
Benzoxazole, 2-[4"-[3"'-(4-chlorophenyl)isoxazol-5"'-yl]stilben-4'-yl]-	DMF	367(4.89),384(4.71)	33-0779-79
Benzoxazole, 2-[4"-[5"'-(4-chlorophenyl)isoxazol-3"'-yl]stilben-4'-yl]-	DMF	358(4.88),377(4.70)	33-0779-79
Benzoxazole, 5-chloro-2-[4"-(3"'-phenylisoxazol-5"'-yl)stilben-4'-yl]-	DMF	368(4.92),387(4.74)	33-0779-79
Benzoxazole, 5-chloro-2-[4"-(5"'-phenylisoxazol-3"'-yl)stilben-4'-yl]-	DMF	360(4.90)	33-0779-79
$C_{30}H_{19}ClN_4O_2$			
1,2,4-Oxadiazole, 3-[4-[2-[2-chloro-4-(5-phenyl-1,3,4-oxadiazol-2-yl)phenyl]ethenyl]phenyl]-5-phenyl-	DMF	355(4.71)	33-1411-79
1,2,4-Oxadiazole, 3-[4-[2-[4-[3-(4-chlorophenyl)-1,2,4-oxadiazol-5-yl]phenyl]ethenyl]phenyl]-5-phenyl-	DMF	348(4.83)	33-1411-79
1,2,4-Oxadiazole, 5-[4-[2-[2-chloro-4-(5-phenyl-1,3,4-oxadiazol-2-yl)phenyl]ethenyl]phenyl]-3-phenyl-	DMF	360(4.79)	33-1411-79
1,2,4-Oxadiazole, 5-[4-[2-[4-[5-(4-chlorophenyl)-1,2,4-oxadiazol-3-yl]phenyl]ethenyl]phenyl]-3-phenyl-	DMF	348(4.84)	33-1411-79
1,2,4-Oxadiazole, 5-(4-chlorophenyl)-3-[4-[2-[4-(5-phenyl-1,3,4-oxadiazol-2-yl)phenyl]ethenyl]phenyl]-	DMF	353(4.85),370(4.76)	33-1411-79
$C_{30}H_{19}ClO$			
Naphtho[2,1-b]furan, 7-chloro-2,4,5-triphenyl-	ether	261(4.50),270s(4.46), 305(4.27),320s(4.25), 350(4.32)	78-2639-79
$C_{30}H_{19}Cl_2N_3O$			
1,2-Benzisoxazole, 6-chloro-3-[3-chloro-4-[2-[4-(1-phenyl-1H-pyrazol-3-yl]phenyl]ethenyl]phenyl]-	DMF	355(4.74)	33-1816-79

Compound	Solvent	$\lambda_{max}(\log \epsilon)$	Ref.
Benzoxazole, 2-[4-[2-[4-[4-chloro-1-(4-chlorophenyl)-1H-pyrazol-3-yl]phenyl]-ethenyl]phenyl]-	DMF	365(4.88)	33-1816-79
Benzoxazole, 5-chloro-2-[4-[2-[4-[1-(4-chlorophenyl)-1H-pyrazol-3-yl]phenyl]-ethenyl]phenyl]-	DMF	372(4.91)	33-1816-79
Benzoxazole, 5-chloro-2-[4-[2-[4-(4-chloro-1-phenyl-1H-pyrazol-3-yl)-phenyl]ethenyl]phenyl]-	DMF	365(4.87)	33-1816-79
$C_{30}H_{19}Cl_2N_3O_3$			
1,2-Benzisoxazole, 6-chloro-3-(3-chloro-4-[2-[4-[5-(4-methoxyphenyl)-1,2,4-oxadiazol-3-yl]phenyl]ethenyl]phenyl]-	DMF	340(4.73)	33-1411-79
$C_{30}H_{19}NO_3$			
5,11-Naphthacenedione, 6-[4-(phenylamino)phenoxy]-	toluene	476(4.26)	135-0691-79A
5,12-Naphthacenedione, 6-[4-(phenylamino)phenoxy]-	toluene	396(3.81)	135-0691-79A
$C_{30}H_{20}$			
Anthracene, 9,9'-(1,2-ethenediyl)bis-	$CHCl_3$	405(4.3)	44-4247-79
1,21:4,6-Dietheno-9,13:14,18-dimethenobenzocycloeicosene, (Z,Z)-	EtOH	206(4.57),238(4.61), 251(4.60),266s(4.52), 308(3.86)	12-0361-79
$C_{30}H_{20}Br_2O$			
Anthracene, 10,10'-dibromo-9,9'-[oxybis(methylene)]bis-	$C_6H_{11}Me$	251(4.84),258(4.87), 341(3.37),359(3.71), 379(3.95),401(4.00)	39-0411-79B
$C_{30}H_{20}ClN_3O$			
1,2-Benzisoxazole, 6-chloro-3-[4-[2-[4-(1-phenyl-1H-pyrazol-3-yl)phenyl]ethenyl]phenyl]-	DMF	355(4.81)	33-1816-79
1,2-Benzisoxazole, 6-chloro-3-[4-[2-[4-(3-phenyl-1H-pyrazol-1-yl)phenyl]ethenyl]phenyl]-	DMF	352(4.80)	33-1816-79
1,2-Benzisoxazole, 6-[2-[4-[1-(4-chlorophenyl)-1H-pyrazol-3-yl]phenyl]-ethenyl]-3-phenyl-	DMF	352(4.81)	33-1816-79
1,2-Benzisoxazole, 6-[2-[4-[3-(4-chlorophenyl)-1H-pyrazol-1-yl]phenyl]-ethenyl]-3-phenyl-	DMF	351(4.79)	33-1816-79
Benzoxazole, 2-[4-[2-[4-[1-(4-chlorophenyl)-1H-pyrazol-3-yl]phenyl]-ethenyl]phenyl]-	DMF	369(4.90)	33-1816-79
Benzoxazole, 2-[4-[2-[4-[3-(4-chlorophenyl)-1H-pyrazol-1-yl]phenyl]-ethenyl]phenyl]-	DMF	368(4.89)	33-1816-79
Benzoxazole, 2-[4-[2-[4-(4-chloro-1-phenyl-1H-pyrazol-3-yl)phenyl]ethenyl]phenyl]-	DMF	364(4.87)	33-1816-79
Benzoxazole, 2-[4-[2-[4-(4-chloro-3-phenyl-1H-pyrazol-1-yl)phenyl]ethenyl]phenyl]-	DMF	365(4.88)	33-1816-79
Benzoxazole, 5-chloro-2-[4-[2-[4-(1-phenyl-1H-pyrazol-3-yl)phenyl]ethenyl]phenyl]-	DMF	372(4.90)	33-1816-79

Compound	Solvent	λ_{max}(log ε)	Ref.
$C_{30}H_{20}ClN_3O_2$			
Benzoxazole, 2-[4-[2-[4-[5-(4-chloro-phenyl)-1,2,4-oxadiazol-3-yl]phenyl]-ethenyl]phenyl]-5-methyl-	DMF	362(4.89)	33-1411-79
$C_{30}H_{20}ClN_3O_3$			
Benzoxazole, 2-[3-chloro-4-[2-[4-[3-(4-methoxyphenyl)-1,2,4-oxadiazol-5-yl]-phenyl]ethenyl]phenyl]-	DMF	366(4.81)	33-1411-79
Benzoxazole, 2-[3-chloro-4-[2-[4-[5-(4-methoxyphenyl)-1,2,4-oxadiazol-3-yl]-phenyl]ethenyl]phenyl]-	DMF	363(4.82)	33-1411-79
Benzoxazole, 2-[4-[2-[4-[5-(4-chloro-phenyl)-1,2,4-oxadiazol-3-yl]phenyl]-ethenyl]phenyl]-5-methoxy-	DMF	365(4.85)	33-1411-79
$C_{30}H_{20}N_2O_2$			
Benzoxazole, 2-[4"-(3"'-phenylisoxazol-5"'-yl)stilben-4'-yl]-	DMF	367(4.91),385(4.73)	33-0779-79
Benzoxazole, 2-[4"-(5"'-phenylisoxazol-3"'-yl)stilben-4'-yl]-	DMF	360(4.89)	33-0779-79
1,2-Benzisoxazole, 3-[4"-(5"'-phenyl-isoxazol-3"'-yl)stilben-4'-yl]-	DMF	340(4.79)	33-0779-79
1,2-Benzisoxazole, 3-phenyl-6-[4'-(3"-phenylisoxazol-5"-yl)styryl]-	DMF	348(4.80)	33-0779-79
1,2-Benzisoxazole, 3-phenyl-6-[4'-(5"-phenylisoxazol-3"-yl)styryl]-	DMF	337(4.77)	33-0779-79
$C_{30}H_{20}N_4O_2$			
1,2,4-Oxadiazole, 3-phenyl-5-[4-[2-[4-(5-phenyl-1,2,4-oxadiazol-3-yl)phen-yl]ethenyl]phenyl]-	DMF	348(4.82)	33-1411-79
1,2,4-Oxadiazole, 5-phenyl-3-[4-[2-[4-(5-phenyl-1,3,4-oxadiazol-2-yl)phen-yl]ethenyl]phenyl]-	DMF	352(4.85),368(4.66)	33-1411-79
$C_{30}H_{20}N_4O_4$			
4H-Pyrazole, 4-(3,5-diphenyl-4H-pyra-zol-4-ylidene)-3,5-diphenyl-, N,N',1,2-tetraoxide	$CHCl_3$	262(4.32),502(4.29)	44-3211-79
$C_{30}H_{20}N_6$			
3,11,4,10-[1,4]Butanediylidene-7,14-ethenobenzo[1,2:4,5]dicyclooctene-15,16,18,18,19,19-hexacarbonitrile, 1,2,5,6,7,8,9,12,13,14-decahydro-	n.s.g.	268(3.20),360(2.54)	35-2128-79
$C_{30}H_{20}N_8$			
Acenaphtho[1,2-e][1,2,4]triazine, 9,9'-(1,4-piperazinediyl)bis-	MeOH	227(4.77),335(4.57), 370(4.11)	83-0147-79
$C_{30}H_{20}O$			
Naphtho[2,1-b]furan, 2,3,5-triphenyl-	ether	240s(4.60),259(4.63), 324s(4.41),346(4.52)	78-2639-79
Spiro[anthracene-9(10H),3'-[3H]benz-[de]anthracen]-10-one, 1',2'-dihydro-	C_6H_{12}	262(5.19),290(3.85), 303(3.79),324(3.18), 339(3.53),356(3.86), 375(4.08),396(4.06)	44-1787-79

Compound	Solvent	λ_{max}(log ε)	Ref.
$C_{30}H_{20}O_2$			
Bianthrone, 2,2'-dimethyl-	CH_2Cl_2	268(4.50),290(4.29), 392(4.21)	44-1941-79
$C_{30}H_{20}O_3$			
1-Naphthalenecarboxaldehyde, 2-(benzoyloxy)-3,4-diphenyl-	ether	230(4.60),255(4.56), 325(4.03)	78-2639-79
$C_{30}H_{20}O_4$			
4H-Anthra[2,3-b]pyran-6,11-dione, 5-hydroxy-3-phenyl-4-(phenylmethyl)-	$CHCl_3$	250(4.63),287(4.62), 300s(4.48),427(4.04)	12-2681-79
5,15-Methano-5H-anthra[2,3-b]benz[f]-oxocin-8,13-dione, 15,16-dihydro-14-hydroxy-17-phenyl-, (5α,15α,17R*)-(±)-	$CHCl_3$	249(4.47),282(4.47), 292s(4.39),416(3.87)	12-2681-79
$C_{30}H_{20}O_5$			
2H-Anthra[2,3-b]pyran-2,6,11-trione, 3,4-dihydro-5-hydroxy-3-phenyl-4-(phenylmethyl)-, trans-(±)-	$CHCl_3$	247(4.63),264(4.72), 400(3.84)	12-2681-79
$C_{30}H_{20}O_6$			
Anthra[2,3-c]furan-1,5,10(3H)-trione, 4,11-bis(phenylmethoxy)-	MeOH	207(4.84),253(4.74), 373(3.83)	5-0019-79
$C_{30}H_{20}O_{12}$			
3,4-Dehydroxanthomegnin	MeOH	246s(4.55),276s(4.31), 390(3.96),434s(3.88)	24-0957-79
	MeOH-NaOH	253(4.45),280s(--), 300s(--),365(3.73), 552(3.98)	24-0957-79
$C_{30}H_{21}BrO$			
Anthracene, 9-[(9-anthracenylmethoxy)-methyl]-10-bromo-	$C_6H_{11}Me$	250(5.28),256(5.21), 350(3.92),360(4.05), 368(4.10),379(4.21), 388(4.10),400(4.21)	39-0411-79B
1H,3H-3a,8[1',2']:9,13b[1",2"]-Dibenzenodibenzo[3,4:7,8]cycloocta[1,2-c]-furan, 8-bromo-8,9-dihydro-	$C_6H_{11}Me$	215(4.84),220(4.77), 250(4.00),258(3.94), 285(2.64)	39-0411-79B
$C_{30}H_{21}ClN_4O_2$			
2H-Benzotriazole, 2-[2'-chloro-4"-[3"'-(4-methoxyphenyl)isoxazol-5"'-yl]-stilben-4'-yl]-	DMF	365(4.83)	33-0779-79
2H-Benzotriazole, 2-[2'-chloro-4"-[5"'-(4-methoxyphenyl)isoxazol-3"'-yl]-stilben-4'-yl]-	DMF	357(3.80)	33-0779-79
2H-Benzotriazole, 5-methoxy-2-[2'-chloro-4"-(3"'-phenylisoxazol-5"'-yl)-stilben-4'-yl]-	DMF	374(4.86)	33-0779-79
2H-Benzotriazole, 5-methoxy-2-[2'-chloro-4"-(5"'-phenylisoxazol-3"'-yl)-stilben-4'-yl]-	DMF	368(4.82)	33-0779-79
8H-[1,2,4]Triazolo[1,5-a]pyridine, 2-[2'-chloro-4"-[5"'-(4-methoxyphenyl)-isoxazol-3"'-yl]stilben-4'-yl]-	DMF	337(4.79),350(4.79)	33-0779-79
$C_{30}H_{21}ClO$			
Furan, 3-(4-chlorophenyl)-2-(1,2-diphenylethenyl)-5-phenyl-	ether	271(4.53),350(4.24)	78-2633-79

Compound	Solvent	$\lambda_{max}(\log \epsilon)$	Ref.
$C_{30}H_{21}N_3O$			
1,2-Benzisoxazole, 3-phenyl-6-[2-[4-(1-phenyl-1H-pyrazol-3-yl)phenyl]ethenyl]-	DMF	352(4.79)	33-1816-79
1,2-Benzisoxazole, 3-phenyl-6-[2-[4-(3-phenyl-1H-pyrazol-1-yl)phenyl]ethenyl]-	DMF	351(4.78)	33-1816-79
1,2-Benzisoxazole, 3-[4-[2-[4-(1-phenyl-1H-pyrazol-3-yl)phenyl]ethenyl]phenyl]-	DMF	354(4.79)	33-1816-79
1,2-Benzisoxazole, 3-[4-[2-[4-(3-phenyl-1H-pyrazol-1-yl)phenyl]ethenyl]phenyl]-	DMF	350(4.80)	33-1816-79
Benzoxazole, 2-[4-[2-[4-(1-phenyl-1H-pyrazol-3-yl)phenyl]ethenyl]phenyl]-	DMF	368(4.89)	33-1816-79
Benzoxazole, 2-[4-[2-[4-(3-phenyl-1H-pyrazol-1-yl)phenyl]ethenyl]phenyl]-	DMF	367(4.90)	33-1816-79
$C_{30}H_{21}N_3O_2$			
Benzoxazole, 5-methyl-2-[4-[2-[4-(3-phenyl-1,2,4-oxadiazol-5-yl)phenyl]ethenyl]phenyl]-	DMF	366(4.89)	33-1411-79
Benzoxazole, 5-methyl-2-[4-[2-[4-(5-phenyl-1,2,4-oxadiazol-3-yl)phenyl]ethenyl]phenyl]-	DMF	362(4.88),380(4.68)	33-1411-79
Benzoxazole, 6-methyl-2-[4-[2-[4-(5-phenyl-1,2,4-oxadiazol-3-yl)phenyl]ethenyl]phenyl]-	DMF	362(4.87)	33-1411-79
Benzoxazole, 7-methyl-2-[4-[2-[4-(5-phenyl-1,2,4-oxadiazol-3-yl)phenyl]ethenyl]phenyl]-	DMF	360(4.87),378(4.67)	33-1411-79
$C_{30}H_{21}N_3O_3$			
1,2-Benzisoxazole, 3-(4-methoxyphenyl)-6-[2-[4-(5-phenyl-1,2,4-oxadiazol-3-yl)phenyl]ethenyl]-	DMF	338(4.75)	33-1411-79
Benzoxazole, 2-[4-[2-[4-[3-(4-methoxyphenyl)-1,2,4-oxadiazol-3-yl]phenyl]ethenyl]phenyl]-	DMF	364(4.89),383(4.71)	33-1411-79
Benzoxazole, 2-[4-[2-[4-[5-(4-methoxyphenyl)-1,2,4-oxadiazol-3-yl]phenyl]ethenyl]phenyl]-	DMF	360(4.89),378(4.70)	33-1411-79
Benzoxazole, 5-methoxy-2-[4-[2-[4-(5-phenyl-1,2,4-oxadiazol-3-yl)phenyl]ethenyl]phenyl]-	DMF	365(4.85)	33-1411-79
$C_{30}H_{22}$			
Anthracene, 9,9'-(1,2-ethanediyl)bis-	C_6H_{12}	248(5.31),256(5.35), 320(3.38),335(3.71), 352(4.02),370(4.32), 391(4.45)	44-4247-79
Stilbene, 4,4'-distyryl-	dioxan	385(4.90)	104-1944-79
$C_{30}H_{22}ClN_5O_3$			
2H-Benzotriazole, 2-[3-chloro-4-[2-[4-[5-(4-methoxyphenyl)-1,2,4-oxadiazol-3-yl]phenyl]ethenyl]phenyl]-5-methoxy-	DMF	368(4.82)	33-1411-79
$C_{30}H_{22}CuN_{12}$			
Copper, (1,10,11,20-tetrahydro-3,13-dimethyl-1,11-diphenyldipyrazolo[4,3-	n.s.g.	430(4.10),490(3.78), 570(2.82)	103-0572-79

Compound	Solvent	λ_{max}(log ε)	Ref.
c:4',3'-j]dipyrido[2,3-f:2',3'-m]-[1,2,5,8,9,12]hexaazacyclotetradecinato(2-)-N[4],N[10],N[14],N[20])-, (SP-4-1)-			103-0572-79
$C_{30}H_{22}N_2O_3$			
[1]Benzopyrano[4,3-c]pyrazole-4-acetic acid, 1,4-dihydro-α,α,1-triphenyl-	MeOH	222(4.3),279(4.1), 319(4.3)	24-1791-79
$C_{30}H_{22}N_4O_2$			
2H-Benzotriazole, 5-methoxy-2-[4-(3-phenyl-1,2-isoxazol-5-yl)stilbenyl]-	DMF	373(4.88)	33-0779-79
2H-Benzotriazole, 5-methoxy-2-[4-(5-phenyl-1,2-isoxazol-3-yl)stilbenyl]-	DMF	368(4.86)	33-0779-79
2H-Benzotriazole, 2-[4-[5-(4-methoxyphenyl)-1,2-isoxazol-3-yl]stilbenyl]-	DMF	360(4.85)	33-0779-79
$C_{30}H_{22}N_4O_4$			
[1,1'-Biphenyl-4,4'-dicarboxaldehyde, 2,2'-dinitro-, bis(4-ethenylphenylimine)	$CHCl_3$	272(4.7),356(4.5)	24-2854-79
$C_{30}H_{22}N_4O_4S_2$			
1H-Indole, 2,2'-dithiobis[1-methyl-3-(4-nitrophenyl)-	dioxan	427(4.39)	103-0282-79
	MeOH	238(--),280(--)	103-0282-79
$C_{30}H_{22}N_{12}Ni$			
Nickel, (1,10,11,20-tetrahydro-3,13-dimethyl-1,11-diphenyldipyrazolo[4,3-c:4',3'-j]dipyrido[2,3-f:2',3'-m]-[1,2,5,8,9,12]hexaazacyclotetradecinato(2-)-N[4],N[10],N[14],N[20])-, (SP-4-1)-	n.s.g.	470(4.61),620(3.57)	103-0572-79
$C_{30}H_{22}N_{12}Pd$			
Palladium, (1,10,11,20-tetrahydro-3,13-dimethyl-1,11-diphenyldipyrazolo[4,3-c:4',3'-j]dipyrido[2,3-f:2',3'-m]-[1,2,5,8,9,12]hexaazacyclotetradecinato(2-)-N[4],N[10],N[14],N[20])-, (SP-4-1)-	n.s.g.	445(4.84),560(3.64)	103-0572-79
$C_{30}H_{22}N_{12}Pt$			
Platinum, (1,10,11,20-tetrahydro-3,13-dimethyl-1,11-diphenyldipyrazolo[4,3-c:4',3'-j]dipyrido[2,3-f:2',3'-m]-[1,2,5,8,9,12]hexaazacyclotetradecinato(2-)-N[4],N[10],N[14],N[20])-, (SP-4-1)-	n.s.g.	420s(4.24),440(4.45), 470s(4.04),620(3.30)	103-0572-79
$C_{30}H_{22}O$			
Anthracene, 1-[(9-anthracenylmethoxy)-methyl]-	$C_6H_{11}Me$	247(5.12),255(5.18), 330(3.54),346(3.91), 362(4.13),366(4.12), 381(4.11),386(4.10)	152-0231-79
photocyclomer	C_6H_{12}	223(4.76),243(4.61), 272(3.96),281(3.87), 314(2.72),327(2.64)	152-0231-79
Anthracene, 9,9'-[oxybis(methylene)]bis-	$C_6H_{11}Me$	255(5.32),388(4.29)	39-0411-79B
9(10H)-Anthracenone, 10-[2-(9-anthracenyl)ethyl]-	C_6H_{12}	250(5.01),257(5.26), 318(3.26),333(3.54), 350(3.85),368(4.08), 388(4.09)	44-4247-79
Furan, 2-(1,2-diphenylethenyl)-3,5-diphenyl-, (1:3 E:Z)	EtOH	272(4.53),348(4.26)	78-2633-79

Compound	Solvent	$\lambda_{max}(\log \epsilon)$	Ref.
Naphtho[2,1-b]furan, 5,5a-dihydro-2,4,5-triphenyl-, cis	ether	245s(4.39),255s(4.26), 288(4.34),308(4.36), 350(3.15)	78-2639-79
$C_{30}H_{22}O_2$			
[9,9'-Bianthracene]-10,10'(9H,9'H)-dione, 2,2'-dimethyl-	EtOH	275(4.30),315s(4.00)	44-1941-79
$C_{30}H_{22}O_4$			
3H,10H-Pyrano[4,3-b][1]benzopyran-3,10-dione, 1,4,4a,10a-tetrahydro-1,4,4-triphenyl-	MeOH	196(4.7),207(4.6), 248(3.9),313(3.5)	24-1791-79
$C_{30}H_{22}O_5$			
2H-Anthra[2,3-b]pyran-6,11-dione, 3,4-dihydro-2α,5-dihydroxy-3β-phenyl-4-(phenylmethyl)-, (4α)-	$CHCl_3$	238(4.39),278(4.45), 407(4.07)	12-2681-79
$C_{30}H_{22}O_6$			
Anthra[2,3-c]furan-5,10-dione, 1,3-dihydro-1-hydroxy-4,11-bis(phenylmethoxy)-	MeOH	206(4.70),256(4.49), 376(3.54)	5-0019-79
$C_{30}H_{22}O_{12}$			
[8,8'-Bi-1H-naphtho[2,3-c]pyran-1,1'-6,6',9,9'-hexone, 3,3',4,4'-tetrahydro-10,10'-dihydroxy-7,7'-dimethoxy-3,3'-dimethyl- (xanthomegnin)	MeOH	275(4.40),395(4.02)	24-0957-79
	MeOH-NaOH	280(4.40),392(3.78), 540(4.00)	24-0957-79
	dioxan	227(4.73),288(4.25), 393(4.03)	24-0957-79
$C_{30}H_{22}O_{13}$			
[3,8'-Bi-4H-1-benzopyran]-4,4'-dione, 2,2'-bis(3,4-dihydroxyphenyl)-2,2',3,3'-tetrahydro-3',5,5',7,7'-pentahydroxy- (manniflavanone)	EtOH	293(4.73),335s(--)	102-1553-79
	EtOH-NaOH	242s(--),335(--)	102-1553-79
	EtOH-NaOAc	335(--)	102-1553-79
$C_{30}H_{23}NO$			
Pyrrolo[2,1-a]isoquinolin-1(5H)-one, 6,10b-dihydro-2,3,10b-triphenyl-	MeCN	274(4.09),360(3.87)	88-1213-79
$C_{30}H_{23}NS$			
Pyrrolo[2,1-a]isoquinoline-1(5H)-thione, 6,10b-dihydro-2,3,10b-triphenyl-	MeCN	255(4.17),435(4.20)	88-1213-79
$C_{30}H_{23}N_3$			
2,4-Diazabicyclo[3.2.0]hept-2-ene-6-carbonitrile, 1,3,4,5-tetraphenyl- (or isomer)	dioxan	273s(3.75),281s(3.69), 298s(3.62)	44-0041-79
$C_{30}H_{23}N_3OS_2$			
4-Thiazolidinone, 5-[(1,3-dihydro-1,3-diphenyl-2H-naphtho[2,3-d]imidazol-2-ylidene)ethylidene]-3-ethyl-2-thioxo-	n.s.g.	533(5.10)	124-0043-79
$C_{30}H_{23}N_5O$			
2H-Benzotriazole, 5-methoxy-2-[4-[2-[4-(1-phenyl-1H-pyrazol-3-yl)phenyl]ethenyl]phenyl]-	DMF	374(4.89)	33-1816-79
2H-Benzotriazole, 5-methoxy-2-[4-[2-[4-(3-phenyl-1H-pyrazol-1-yl)phenyl]ethenyl]phenyl]-	DMF	373(4.89)	33-1816-79

Compound	Solvent	$\lambda_{max}(\log \epsilon)$	Ref.
$C_{30}H_{23}O_3P$			
Phosphorin, 4-formyl-1,1-dihydro-1,1-diphenoxy-2,6-diphenyl-	MeOH	324(4.32),375(4.19)	24-1272-79
$C_{30}H_{23}O_4P$			
Phosphorin, 4-carboxy-1,1-dihydro-1,1-diphenoxy-2,6-diphenyl-	MeOH	293(4.03),378(4.09)	24-1272-79
$C_{30}H_{24}$			
Azulene, 1-phenyl-2,3-bis(phenylmethyl)-	C_6H_{12}	245(4.44),299(4.73), 357(3.82),600(2.44)	138-0171-79
Benzo[1,2:3,4]dicycloheptene, 6,7,12a-12b-tetrahydro-6,7-bis(phenylmethylene)-	EtOH	221(4.04),268(3.62), 323(3.66)	138-0171-79
Bicycloprop-2-ene, 2,2',3,3'-tetraphenyl)- (2'r,3't)	dioxan	225s(4.52),229(4.52), 238(4.41),310(4.35), 320(4.45),338(4.34)	24-2961-79
9,9'-Bifluoren-9-ylidene, 2,2',7,7'-tetramethyl-	benzene	462(4.29)	24-3490-79
[2.2](3,3')Biphenylo(3,6)phenanthrenophane	EtOH	215(4.80),229(4.66), 247s(4.71),252(4.74), 259s(4.69),272s(4.31), 280(4.21),289(4.04), 302(4.11)	12-0361-79
Chrysene, 5,6,11,12-tetrahydro-2,8-diphenyl-	C_6H_{12}	201(4.70),238(4.27), 355(4.62)	44-4933-79
Cyclobuta[5,6]benzo[1,2:3,4]dicycloheptene, 1,2,5,10-tetrahydro-1,2-diphenyl-	C_6H_{12}	264.5(4.76)	138-0171-79
2,5-Etheno-1H-cyclohept[a]azulene, 2,5-dihydro-1-phenyl-11-(phenylmethyl)-	C_6H_{12}	249(4.25),294(4.78), 303(4.79),344(3.65), 359(3.72),402(2.99), 614(2.40)	138-0171-79
Spiro[azulene-1(2H),1'-[2,4,6]cycloheptatriene], 3,8a-dihydro-2,3-bis(phenylmethylene)-	EtOH	223(4.14),270(3.72), 329(3.79)	138-0171-79
$C_{30}H_{24}BrN_3O_6S_3$			
3-Butenenitrile, 2-[(4-bromophenyl)-azo]-4,4-bis[(4-methylphenyl)sulfonyl]-2-(phenylsulfonyl)-	EtOH	265(4.05),330(4.48)	104-1319-79
$C_{30}H_{24}ClNO_3$			
2(1H)-Pyridinone, 6-(4-chlorophenyl)-3-[5-(4-methoxyphenyl)-3-oxo-1-cyclohexen-1-yl]-4-phenyl-	HOAc	246(4.30),308(3.95)	120-0001-79
$C_{30}H_{24}NO_2SSb$			
Antimony, (4-nitrobenzenethiolato-S)-tetraphenyl-	benzene	394(4.2)	70-1585-79
$C_{30}H_{24}N_2$			
[1,1'-Biphenyl]-4,4'-dicarboxaldehyde bis(4-ethenylphenyl)imine	$CHCl_3$	362(4.7)	24-2854-79
$C_{30}H_{24}N_2O$			
Phenol, 2-[3-(2,2-diphenylethenyl)-1H-1,5-benzodiazepin-4-yl]-4-methyl-	MeOH	220(4.6),240(4.6), 357(4.9)	24-1791-79
$C_{30}H_{24}N_2O_2$			
1H-Phenalen-1-one, 3,4-diethoxy-, 9H-	CH_2Cl_2	258(3.6),360(4.6),	83-0288-79

Compound	Solvent	λ_{max}(log ε)	Ref.
fluoren-9-ylidenehydrazone (cont.)		511(4.3)	83-0288-79
1H-Phenalen-1-one, 9-ethoxy-, (9-ethoxy-1H-phenalen-1-ylidene)hydrazone	CH_2Cl_2	288(3.9),250(4.4), 399(4.4),576(4.3), 618(4.3),678(4.4)	83-0288-79
Pyrazine, 2,5-diphenyl-3,6-bis(phenylmethoxy)-	EtOH	235(4.12),268(4.32), 367(4.46)	94-2980-79
$C_{30}H_{24}N_2S_2$			
1H-Indole, 2,2'-dithiobis[1-methyl-3-phenyl-	dioxan	360(4.14)	103-0282-79
	MeOH	227(--),258(--)	103-0282-79
$C_{30}H_{24}N_4S_4$			
Benzo[1,2-d:5,4-d']bisthiazolium, 2,2'-(1,4-phenylenedi-2,1-ethenediyl)bis-[3,6-dimethyl-, diiodide	DMF	295(4.16),393(4.42), 582(3.87)	126-1441-79
$C_{30}H_{24}O_4$			
10H,11H-6a,7,9:11a,1,12-Diethanylylidene-6,11-etheno-2H-pentaleno[1"',6"'-2",3",4"]cyclobuta[1",2":4',5']benzo-[1',2':4,5]cycloocta[1,2,3-cd]pentalene-2,10,15,17-tetrone, 1,5a,6,6b,7-8,8a,9,10b,11b,12,13,13a,13b-tetradecahydro-	MeOH	282(3.48)	88-4595-79
$C_{30}H_{24}O_6$			
9,10-Anthracenedione, 2,3-bis(hydroxymethyl)-1,4-bis(phenylmethoxy)-	MeOH	205(4.74),256(4.51), 376(3.54)	5-0019-79
$C_{30}H_{24}O_8$			
4H-1-Benzopyran-4-one, 3,5,7-trihydroxy-2-[4-methoxy-3,5-bis(phenylmethoxy)phenyl]-	MeOH	256(4.05),355(4.01)	2-0037-79A
$C_{30}H_{24}O_{11}$			
[8,8'-Bi-1H-naphtho[2,3-c]pyran]-1,1',6,9-tetrone, 3,3',4,4'-tetrahydro-9',10,10'-trihydroxy-7,7'-dimethoxy-3,3'-dimethyl-, [R-(R*,R*)]-(viomellein)	MeOH	263(4.67),293s(--), 370s(--),383(4.26)	24-0957-79
	MeOH-NaOH	264(4.64),295s(--), 330(4.81),370s(--), 383(4.20),532(3.91)	24-0957-79
	dioxan	219(4.59),261(4.80), 293s(--),355(4.15), 372(4.19),410s(--)	24-0957-79
$C_{30}H_{25}N_3$			
Benzenamine, N-[[4-[4,5-dihydro-5-phenyl-3-(2-phenylethenyl)-1H-pyrazol-1-yl]phenyl]methylene]-	toluene	330s(4.04),415(4.77)	135-1491-79B
$C_{30}H_{25}N_3O$			
Ethanone, 1-[4-[[[4-(4,5-dihydro-3,5-diphenyl-1H-pyrazol-1-yl)phenyl]methylene]amino]phenyl]-	toluene	320(3.87),405(4.71)	135-1491-79B
$C_{30}H_{26}N_2$			
1H-Pyrazole, 4,5-dihydro-3-(4-methylphenyl)-5-phenyl-1-stilbenyl-	toluene	393(4.69)	135-1491-79B
$C_{30}H_{26}N_2O$			
1H-Pyrazole, 4,5-dihydro-3-(4-methoxyphenyl)-5-phenyl-1-stilbenyl-	toluene	390(4.63)	135-1491-79B

Compound	Solvent	$\lambda_{max}(\log \epsilon)$	Ref.
$C_{30}H_{26}N_2O_4$			
Dispiro[acridine-9(10H),3'-[1,2,5,6]-tetroxocane-7',9"(10"H)-acridine], 10,10"-dimethyl-	CH_2Cl_2	278(4.48)	138-1491-79
$C_{30}H_{26}N_4O_3$			
4-Imidazolidinecarboxamide, 3-[4-(dimethylamino)phenyl]-2,5-dioxo-N,1,4-triphenyl-	MeOH	265(4.49),304(3.78)	118-0794-79
$C_{30}H_{26}O_4$			
1,6-Hexanedione, 1,6-bis(2-hydroxyphenyl)-3,4-diphenyl-	dioxan	252(4.31),325(3.92)	44-1494-79
$C_{30}H_{26}O_6$			
Dichamanetin 5-methyl ether	MeOH	258(3.79),280(3.76), 332(4.02)	100-0264-79
$C_{30}H_{26}O_{10}$			
[8,8'-Bi-1H-naphtho[2,3-c]pyran]-1,1'-dione, 3,3',4,4'-tetrahydro-9,9'-10,10'-tetrahydroxy-7,7'-dimethoxy-3,3'-dimethyl- (vioxanthin)	C_6H_{12}-5% dioxan	271(4.73),310s(--), 350s(--),368(4.14), 385(4.20)	24-0957-79
	MeOH	267(4.79),310s(--), 379(4.24)	24-0957-79
	MeOH-NaOH	267(4.69),332(3.78), 372s(--),388(4.36)	24-0957-79
$C_{30}H_{26}S_3$			
Spiro[9,12-dithiatricyclo[12.3.1.1^{3,7}]-nonadeca-1(18),3,5,7(19),14,16-hexaene-2,2'-thiiran], 3',3'-diphenyl-	MeCN	243(4.34),266(4.04), 318(4.22)	24-0138-79
$C_{30}H_{27}$			
Cyclopropenylium, tris(4-cyclopropylphenyl)-, tetrafluoroborate	EtOH	230(4.33),285s(4.25), 343(4.84),359(4.84)	18-0856-79
$C_{30}H_{27}ClO_5$			
Spiro[benzofuran-2(3H),1'-[2]cyclohexen]-3-one, 7-chloro-4'-(diphenylmethylene)-2',4,6-trimethoxy-6'-methyl-	MeOH	234s(4.07),295(4.35)	39-1166-79C
$C_{30}H_{27}ClO_5S$			
Dispiro[benzofuran-2(3H),1'-[2]cyclohexene-4,2"-thiiran]-3-one, 7-chloro-2',4,6-trimethoxy-6'-methyl-3",3"-diphenyl-	MeOH	214(4.56),237s(4.47), 290(4.32),325(3.69)	39-1166-79C
$C_{30}H_{27}NO_2$			
Pyrrolo[2,1-a]isoquinolin-3(2H)-one, 5,6-dihydro-2-[2-oxo-2-(5,6,7,8-tetrahydro-2-naphthalenyl)ethyl]-1-phenyl-	EtOH	205(5.76),254(5.54)	103-0770-79
$C_{30}H_{27}N_3O_9$			
1,3,5-Benzenetricarboxamide, N,N',N"-tris[(2,3-dihydroxyphenyl)methyl]-	EtOAc	313(4.00)	87-0123-79
$C_{30}H_{28}$			
Benzene, 1,1'-(1,2-ethenediyl)bis[2-(1-phenylethyl)-	C_6H_{12}	256(4.03)	44-3698-79

Compound	Solvent	λ_{max}(log ε)	Ref.
$C_{30}H_{28}Cl_4N_5O_9P$			
3'-Adenylic acid, N-benzoyl-2'-deoxy-, 2-chlorophenyl 2,2,2-trichloroethyl ester, 5'-(4-oxopentanoate)	EtOH	277(4.39)	54-0537-79
$C_{30}H_{28}Cl_4N_5O_{10}P$			
3'-Guanylic acid, N-benzoyl-2'-deoxy-, 2-chlorophenyl 2,2,2-trichloroethyl ester, 5'-(4-oxopentanoate)	EtOH	263(4.34),285(4.28)	54-0537-79
$C_{30}H_{28}N_2$			
2-Propanone, 1,1-diphenyl-, (1-methyl-2,2-diphenylethylidene)hydrazone	EtOH	242(3.90),269(3.19)	103-0501-79
$C_{30}H_{28}N_2O_4$			
Acetamide, 2,2'-[1,2-ethanediylbis-(oxy)]bis[N,N-diphenyl-	H_2O	229(4.32)	33-0754-79
$C_{30}H_{28}N_4$			
1,4-Benzenediamine, N'-[[4-(4,5-dihydro-3,5-diphenyl-1H-pyrazol-1-yl)-phenyl]methylene]-N,N-dimethyl-	toluene	330s(4.11),410(4.68)	135-1491-79B
$C_{30}H_{28}OPSe$			
Phosphonium, triphenyl-, 2-oxo-2-phenyl-1-(tetrahydroselenophenio)ethylide, tetrafluoroborate	n.s.g.	220s(4.477),266(3.927), 272s(3.902)	104-0332-79
$C_{30}H_{28}Si_2$			
1,2-Disilacyclohexa-3,5-diene, 1,2-dimethyl-1,2,3,6-tetraphenyl-, cis	hexane	228(4.46),300(3.96), 356(4.08)	35-0487-79
trans	hexane	236(4.60),305(3.99), 355(4.12)	35-0487-79
$C_{30}H_{29}NO_6$			
1H-Indole-3-carboxylic acid, 4,5-diacetoxy-2-methyl-1,6-bis(phenylmethyl)-, ethyl ester	dioxan	230(4.61),286(4.10)	83-0465-79
$C_{30}H_{29}NO_9$			
Pyrrolo[1,2-a]quinoline-1,3-diacetic acid, 1,2-dihydro-α^1-methoxy-1-(methoxycarbonyl)-α^3-(2-methoxy-2-oxoethylidene)-2-phenyl-, dimethyl ester	MeOH	225(4.32),285(4.00), 384(4.54),473(4.44), 507(4.40)	39-2171-79C
	$MeOH-HClO_4$	205(4.55),270(4.45), 361(4.35)	39-2171-79C
$C_{30}H_{29}N_3O_4$			
[3,7'-Bi-1H-indole]-2'-carboxylic acid, 3-[2-(acetylmethylamino)ethyl]-2,3-dihydro-2-oxo-1-(phenylmethyl)-, methyl ester	EtOH	230s(4.46),258(4.05), 293(4.27)	23-1694-79
$C_{30}H_{29}N_5O_4$			
Adenosine, 3'-O-methyl-5'-O-(triphenylmethyl)-	MeOH	259(4.21)	23-0274-79
$C_{30}H_{30}$			
Bi-2,4,6-cycloheptatrien-1-yl, bis(3,5-dimethylphenyl)-	$CHCl_3$	245(4.51),280s(4.13)	39-0262-79B

Compound	Solvent	$\lambda_{max}(\log \epsilon)$	Ref.
$C_{30}H_{30}Cl_4N_3O_{11}P$			
3'-Cytidylic acid, 2'-deoxy-N-(4-methoxybenzoyl)-, 2-chlorophenyl 2,2,2-trichloroethyl ester, 5'-(4-oxopentanoate)	EtOH	285(4.47)	54-0537-79
$C_{30}H_{30}Cl_4N_4O_9P_2$			
3'-Thymidylic acid, 2-chlorophenyl 2,2,2-trichloroethyl ester, 5'-(N,N'-diphenylphosphorodiamidate)	EtOH	266(4.01)	78-2931-79
$C_{30}H_{30}F_3NO_{11}$			
5,12-Naphthacenedione, 7,8,9,10-tetrahydro-6,9,11-trihydroxy-4-methoxy-9-(1-oxopropyl)-7-[[2,3,6-trideoxy-3-[(trifluoroacetyl)amino]-α-L-lyxo-hexopyranosyl]oxy]-	MeOH	233(4.58),252(4.43), 289(3.95),480(4.08), 496(4.09),531(3.82)	87-0040-79
$C_{30}H_{30}N_2O_4$			
5-Oxa-1-azabicyclo[4.2.0]oct-2-ene-2-carboxylic acid, 8-oxo-7-[(triphenylmethyl)amino]-, 1,1-dimethylethyl ester, (6R-trans)-	EtOH	265(3.68)	39-2268-79C
Pteledimeridine	MeOH	220s(4.79),227(4.84), 266s(4.53),270(4.04), 286(4.05),317(4.06), 330(3.91)	5-1785-79
	MeOH-HCl	220s(4.83),227(4.86), 241s(4.57),270(4.12), 286(4.09),317(4.06), 330(3.96)	5-1785-79
$C_{30}H_{30}N_2O_4S_2$			
Benzo[1,2-d:5,4-d']bisthiazolium, 2,6-bis[2-(2,5-dimethoxyphenyl)ethenyl]-3,5-dimethyl-, diperchlorate	DMF	338(4.32),510(4.14)	126-1465-79
$C_{30}H_{30}N_2O_5$			
Pteledimericine	MeOH	219s(4.45),231(4.76), 252s(4.29),277(3.96), 286(3.99),314(4.16), 327(4.09)	5-1785-79
	MeOH-HCl	219(4.78),234(4.85), 277s(4.11),286(4.17), 310(4.22),327s(4.03)	5-1785-79
2,4(1H,3H)-Pyrimidinedione, 1-[2-acetoxy-4-(triphenylmethoxy)butyl]-5-methyl-	EtOH	266(3.86)	128-0051-79
$C_{30}H_{30}N_4O_8$			
Tryptoquivaline D, epideacetyl-, diacetate	MeOH	228(4.49),233s(4.46), 269(3.94),278s(3.91), 307(3.48),319(3.38)	94-1611-79
$C_{30}H_{31}NO_8$			
Dehydrothaliadine	EtOH	257(4.68),272(4.67), 330(4.24)	100-0325-79
$C_{30}H_{31}N_2S_2$			
Benzothiazolium, 3-ethyl-2-[2-[3-[4-(3-ethyl-2(3H)-benzothiazolylidene)-2-	MeOH	672(4.20)	104-0774-79

Compound	Solvent	λ_{max}(log ε)	Ref.
butenylidene]-1-cyclohexen-1-yl]-ethenyl]-, iodide (cont.)			104-0774-79
$C_{30}H_{32}O_9$			
Gomisin C	EtOH	220(4.76),253s(4.19), 284s(3.58)	94-1383-79
Gomisin G	EtOH	224(4.72),255s(4.08), 280s(3.61),290s(3.35)	94-1383-79
$C_{30}H_{33}NO_8$			
Thaliadine	EtOH	220(4.62),237s(4.48), 277(4.50),300(4.30), 312(4.30),337s(4.01)	100-0325-79
$C_{30}H_{33}NO_{12}$			
Nogalarol, 7-con-O-methyl-	EtOH	236(4.64),252(4.41), 257s(4.39),290s(4.06), 480(4.19)	44-4030-79
$C_{30}H_{33}N_2S_3$			
Benzothiazolium, 3-ethyl-2-[2-[3-[(3-ethyl-2(3H)-benzothiazolylidene)ethylidene]-2-(ethylthio)-1-cyclohexen-1-yl]ethenyl]-, iodide	MeOH	797(5.33)	104-0351-79
$C_{30}H_{33}N_3O_4$			
[3,7'-Bi-1H-indole]-2'-carboxylic acid, 3-[2-(acetylmethylamino)ethyl]-2,3,4',5',6',7'-hexahydro-2-oxo-1-(phenylmethyl)-, methyl ester	EtOH	284.5(4.22)	23-1694-79
$C_{30}H_{34}N_2O_4$			
Acetamide, N-[2-[3-[3-formyl-2-oxo-3-(2-propenyl)cyclohexyl]-2,3-dihydro-2-oxo-1-(phenylmethyl)-1H-indol-3-yl]ethyl]-N-methyl-	EtOH	255(3.92),280s(3.32)	23-1694-79
$C_{30}H_{34}N_2O_8$			
1H-Imidazolium, 2-[3-ethoxy-2-(ethoxycarbonyl)-1-[2-ethoxy-1-(ethoxycarbonyl)-2-oxoethyl]-3-oxo-1-propenyl]-4,5-dihydro-1,3-diphenyl-, hydroxide, inner salt	$CHCl_3$	254(4.4),326(4.2), 442(4.0)	5-1406-79
$C_{30}H_{34}N_3S_2$			
Benzothiazolium, 2-[2-[2-(dimethylamino)-3-[(3-ethyl-2(3H)-benzothiazolylidene)ethylidene]-1-cyclohexen-1-yl]ethenyl]-3-ethyl-, iodide	MeOH	698(5.05)	104-0351-79
$C_{30}H_{34}O_4$			
4H-1-Benzopyran-4-one, 6-(3-methyl-2-butenyl)-7-[(3-methyl-2-butenyl)oxy]-2-[4-[(3-methyl-2-butenyl)oxy]phenyl]-	MeOH	238(3.95),326(4.25)	78-0413-79
$C_{30}H_{34}O_8$			
Dibenzo[a,c]cyclooctene-1,7-diol, 5,6,7,8-tetrahydro-2,3,10,11,12-pentamethoxy-6,7-dimethyl-, 1-benzoate (benzoylgomisin H)	EtOH	217(4.66),250s(4.20), 282s(3.56)	94-1576-79

Compound	Solvent	λ max (log ε)	Ref.
$C_{30}H_{34}O_9$			
3-Benzofuranmethanol, 2,3-dihydro-2-(4-hydroxy-3-methoxyphenyl)-7-methoxy-5-[tetrahydro-4-[(4-hydroxy-3-methoxyphenyl)methyl]-3-(hydroxymethyl)-2-furanyl]- (herpetriol)	n.s.g.	214(--),230(--), 278(4.04),285s(--)	64-1129-79
$C_{30}H_{35}NO_{10}$			
Nogarol, 7-con-O-(1-methylethyl)-	EtOH	236(4.69),259(4.37), 289(3.96),477(4.18)	44-4030-79
Nogarol, 7-con-O-propyl-	EtOH	236(4.73),252(4.53), 258s(4.50),291s(4.12), 479(4.30)	44-4030-79
Nogarol, 7-dis-O-propyl-	EtOH	236(4.65),260(4.36), 290(3.94),477(4.16)	44-4030-79
$C_{30}H_{36}$			
Naphthacene, 5,12-dihydro-1,2,3,4,5,6-7,8,9,10,11-undecamethyl-12-methylene-	C_6H_{12}	220(4.40),249(4.68), 265(4.62),278(4.63), 325(3.82)	44-0007-79
Naphthacene, dodecamethyl-	CH_2Cl_2	272(4.40),308(4.90), 405(3.39),428(3.62), 470(3.44),500(3.73), 537(3.78)	44-0007-79
$C_{30}H_{36}N_2O_5$			
Ibogamine-18-methanol, 3,4-dimethoxy-, benzoate	EtOH	217(4.73),262(4.32), 288(4.21)	36-1403-79
$C_{30}H_{36}N_4O_2$			
21H-Biline-1,19-dione, 3,17-diethyl-22,24-dihydro-2,7,8,12,13,18,22-heptamethyl-, (Z,Z,Z)-	MeOH	360(3.86),575(3.89)	64-1448-79B
	MeOH-CF_3COOH	368(4.08),665(3.90)	64-1448-79B
	MeOH-$Zn(OAc)_2$	360(3.85),608(4.15)	64-1448-79B
$C_{30}H_{36}O_2$			
5,12-Epidioxynaphthacene, 5,12-dihydro-1,2,3,4,5,6,7,8,9,10,11,12-dodecamethyl-	C_6H_{12}	222(4.06),272(4.36), 313(3.43)	44-0007-79
$C_{30}H_{36}O_4$			
9(10H)-Anthracenone, 1,6,8-trihydroxy-3-methyl-2,4,7-tris(3-methyl-2-butenyl)- (ferruanthrone)	$CHCl_3$	240(4.09),256(4.04), 275(3.94),313(3.96), 365(4.15)	78-2143-79
Ferruginin A	$CHCl_3$	245(4.49),267s(4.39), 280s(4.32),320(3.93), 420(4.02)	78-2143-79
Ferruginin B	$CHCl_3$	242(4.19),261(4.00), 411(3.66)	78-2143-79
$C_{30}H_{36}O_5$			
Chalcone, 5'-C-prenyl-2'-hydroxy-4,4'-bis(prenyloxy)-	MeOH	236(4.08),365(4.37)	78-0413-79
$C_{30}H_{36}O_{10}$			
Leptolepisol A	EtOH	281(3.83)	88-0799-79
$C_{30}H_{37}N_5O_5$			
Ergonine	CH_2Cl_2	238(4.31),308(3.95)	23-1638-79

Compound	Solvent	$\lambda_{max}(\log \epsilon)$	Ref.
$C_{30}H_{38}N_2O_2S$			
Benzenecarbothioic acid, 4-hexyl-, S-[5-[4-(heptyloxy)phenyl]-2-pyrimidinyl] ester	EtOH	262(4.27),296(4.44)	48-0619-79
$C_{30}H_{38}N_2O_4$			
Acetamide, N-[2-[2,3-dihydro-2-oxo-1-(phenylmethyl)-3-[2-[(tetrahydro-2H-pyran-2-yl)oxy]cyclohexyl]-1H-indol-3-yl]ethyl]-	EtOH	255(3.98),280s(3.34)	23-1694-79
$C_{30}H_{38}O_4$			
Pristimerinene	MeOH	256(4.05),446(4.09)	39-3127-79C
$C_{30}H_{38}O_5$			
Hydroxypristimerinene	MeOH	256(4.05),446(4.09)	39-3127-79C
$C_{30}H_{38}O_{10}$			
Conferoside	n.s.g.	220(4.27),242(3.70), 253(3.63),297(4.01), 325(4.22)	105-0414-79
$C_{30}H_{38}O_{11}$			
Leptolepisol B	EtOH	280(3.78)	88-0799-79
$C_{30}H_{39}ClN_2O_9$			
Maytanacine	MeOH	233(4.48),240s(4.45), 252(4.44),280(3.75), 288(3.75)	78-1079-79
$C_{30}H_{39}NO_{11}$			
2-Pyrrolidinepropanoic acid, tetrahydro-4-[4-methyl-6-[octahydro-3-(methoxycarbonyl)-2,6,9a-trimethyl-8-oxo-3a,7-epoxy-3aH-furo[3,2-b]oxocin-5-yl]-1-oxo-2,4-heptadienyl]-3,5-dioxo-, methyl ester	EtOH-HCl	237(3.88),353(4.41)	142-0477-79B
	EtOH-NaOH	260(4.14),279(4.24), 330(4.15)	142-0477-79B
$C_{30}H_{39}N_7O_9S_2$			
L-Isoleucine, N-[(1,1-dimethylethoxy)-carbonyl]-, [[[7-[(hydroxyphenylacetyl)amino]-3-[[(1-methyl-1H-tetrazol-5-yl)thio]methyl]-8-oxo-5-thia-1-azabicyclo[4.2.0]oct-2-en-2-yl]carbonyl]-oxy]methyl ester, [6R-(6α,7β(R*)]-	MeOH	270(3.89)	87-0657-79
L-Leucine, N-[(1,1-dimethylethoxy)carbonyl]-, [[[7-[(hydroxyphenylacetyl)-amino½-3-[[(1-methyl-1H-tetrazol-5-yl)thio]methyl]-8-oxo-5-thia-1-azabicyclo[4.2.0]oct-2-en-2-yl]carbonyl]-oxy]methyl ester, [6R-(6α,7β(R*)]-	MeOH	273(3.90)	87-0657-79
$C_{30}H_{39}P$			
Phosphine, tris(2,3,5,6-tetramethylphenyl)-	n.s.g.	318(4.17)	65-1036-79
$C_{30}H_{40}AsN_2$			
3H-Indolium, 1,3,3-triethyl-2-[[[(1,3-3-triethyl-1,3-dihydro-2H-indol-2-ylidene)methyl]arsinidene]methyl]-, tetrafluoroborate	$CHCl_3$	665(4.77)	88-0225-79

Compound	Solvent	$\lambda_{max}(\log \epsilon)$	Ref.
$C_{30}H_{40}N_3O_{12}P$			
2(1H)-Pyrimidinone, 4-amino-1-[5-O-[[[(11β)-11,17-dihydroxy-3,20-dioxopregna-1,4-dien-21-yl]oxy]hydroxyphosphinyl]-β-D-arabinofuranosyl]-, monoammonium salt	pH 1	250s(4.22),268(4.25)	87-1428-79
	H_2O	242(4.31),260s(4.26)	87-1428-79
	pH 13	240(4.29),260s(4.23)	87-1428-79
$C_{30}H_{40}O_3$			
2'H-Naphtho[2',1':4,5]pregn-6-ene-21-carboxylic acid, 3',5',6',7',8',8'a-hexahydro-17-hydroxy-3-oxo-, γ-lactone	MeOH	242.5(4.11)	44-4299-79
$C_{30}H_{40}O_5$			
Pristimerin, 21-hydroxy-	EtOH	250(3.94),421(4.08)	39-3127-79C
$C_{30}H_{40}O_7$			
2,4-Octadienoic acid, 9a-acetoxy-1a,1b,4,4a,5,7a,7b.8,9,9a-decahydro-7b-hydroxy-3-(hydroxymethyl)-1,1,6,8-tetramethyl-5-oxo-1H-cyclopropa[3,4]-benz[1,2-e]azulen-9-yl ester	MeOH	262(4.49)	100-0112-79
$C_{30}H_{40}O_9$			
3a,7-Epoxy-3aH-furo[3,2-b]oxocin-3-carboxylic acid, 5-[6-(4,4-dimethyl-2,6-dioxocyclohexyl)-1,3-dimethyl-6-oxo-2,4-hexadienyl]octahydro-2,6,9a-trimethyl-8-oxo-, methyl ester	EtOH-HCl	251(4.11),346(4.33)	142-0477-79B
	EtOH-NaOH	271(4.50),328(3.90)	142-0477-79B
3a,7-Epoxy-3aH-furo[3,2-b]oxocin-3-carboxylic acid, 5-[6-[(5,5-dimethyl-3-oxo-1-cyclohexen-1-yl)oxy]-1,3-dimethyl-6-oxo-2,4-hexadienyl]octahydro-2,6,9a-trimethyl-8-oxo-, methyl ester	n.s.g.	276.5(4.53)	142-0477-79B
Isocarpalactone A acetate	EtOH	218(3.92)	150-1178-79
$C_{30}H_{40}O_{10}$			
Affinoside B	MeOH	211(4.15),282(3.92)	94-2463-79
$C_{30}H_{41}N_7O_6$			
L-Valinamide, N^2-[[(1-carboxy-2-phenylethyl)amino]carbonyl]-L-arginyl-N-(1-formyl-2-phenylethyl)-	80% MeOH	247(2.56),252(2.54), 258(2.71),264(2.61), 268(2.48)	88-0625-79
$C_{30}H_{41}N_7O_7$			
L-Phenylalanine, N-[N-[N^2-[[(1-carboxy-2-phenylethyl)amino]carbonyl]-L-arginyl]-L-valyl]-, (S)-	H_2O	247(2.43),252(2.54), 258(2.61),264(2.50), 268(2.34)	88-0625-79
$C_{30}H_{42}N_2O_2$			
Alfileramine	EtOH	212(2.68),283(5.50), 290s(5.30)	78-1487-79
$C_{30}H_{42}N_2O_9$			
Herbimycin	MeOH	270(4.30),393(3.21)	88-4323-79
$C_{30}H_{42}N_4O_{14}$			
D-Glucitol, 1,1'-[(2-amino-4,6-dimethyl-3-oxo-3H-phenoxazine-1,9-diyl)bis-[carbonyl(methylimino)]]bis[1-deoxy-	n.s.g.	452(4.10)	104-0951-79

Compound	Solvent	$\lambda_{max}(\log \epsilon)$	Ref.
$C_{30}H_{42}O_3$			
19-Norlanosta-2,5,7,9-tetraene-1,11-dione, 7-methoxy-	EtOH	231(4.31),248(4.24), 330(3.78)	12-0179-79
$C_{30}H_{42}O_4$			
Ferruginin A, hexahydro-	$CHCl_3$	241(4.45),263(4.34), 282(4.27),422(3.98)	78-2143-79
$C_{30}H_{42}O_8$			
Cardanolide, 3-[(5,6-dihydro-3-methoxy-6-methyl-5-oxo-2H-pyran-2-yl)oxy]-18,20-epoxy-14-hydroxy-	MeOH	260(3.65)	44-3511-79
$C_{30}H_{44}N_2O_{25}$			
β-Cellotetraoside, 3,4-dinitrophenyl	pH 5	283(3.75)	130-0147-79
$C_{30}H_{44}O_2$			
19-Norlanosta-1,5,7,9-tetraen-3-one, 7-methoxy-	EtOH	258(4.33),265(4.2), 350(3.90)	12-0179-79
19-Norlanosta-2,5,7,9-tetraen-1-one, 7-methoxy-	EtOH	225(4.08),243(3.91), 306(3.79)	12-0179-79
$C_{30}H_{44}O_4$			
Papyriogenin C	EtOH	243s(--),252(4.18)	39-2044-79C
$C_{30}H_{44}O_7$			
Oleaside A	MeOH	211(4.28)	94-1604-79
$C_{30}H_{44}O_8$			
Oleaside B	MeOH	207(4.28)	94-1604-79
Simplexin	MeOH	244(3.91)	12-2495-79
$C_{30}H_{44}O_9$			
Neriifolin-4'-one, 18,20-epoxy-20,22-dihydro-	MeOH	214.5(2.96)	44-3511-79
$C_{30}H_{45}N_5O_7$			
Hydrazinecarboxylic acid, [(3β,16β)-3-acetoxy-2'-[2-(ethoxycarbonyl)hydrazino]-4'H-pregn-5-eno[16,17-d]oxazol-20-ylidene]-, ethyl ester	EtOH	227(4.42)	70-2139-79
$C_{30}H_{46}N_2O$			
2-Azetidinone, 1-menthyl-4-(menthylimino)-3-methyl-3-phenyl-	C_6H_{12}	221(4.11),263s(2.56), 269s(2.34)	56-0643-79
$C_{30}H_{46}N_2S$			
Sulfur diimide, bis[2,4-bis(1,1-dimethylethyl)-6-methylphenyl]-	hexane	317(3.74),409(3.82)	18-2002-79
$C_{30}H_{46}O$			
19-Nor-4,5-secolanosta-4(28),5,7,9,11-pentaen-3-ol, 5-methyl-	EtOH	274(4.07)	39-0646-79C
19-Nor-4,5-secolanosta-5,7,9,11-tetraen-3-one, 5-methyl-	EtOH	274(4.04)	39-0646-79C
$C_{30}H_{46}O_2$			
Ergosteryl B_2 acetate	EtOH	252(4.26)	118-0265-79
A'-Neogammacer-17(21)-ene-3,16-dione	EtOH	257(3.91)	102-1363-79
19-Norlanosta-5,7,9-trien-1-one, 7-methoxy-	EtOH	235(4.1),280(3.88)	12-0179-79

Compound	Solvent	λ_{max}(log ε)	Ref.
19-Norlanosta-5,7,9-trien-3-one, 7-methoxy-	EtOH	280(4.32),296(3.22)	12-0179-79
$C_{30}H_{46}O_3$			
Ergosta-5,7-dien-3-ol, 22,23-epoxy-, acetate, (3β)-	MeOH	271(4.10),281(4.12), 293(3.89)	39-1858-79C
$C_{30}H_{46}O_5$			
25,26,27-Trinor-C_{14a}-homo-B-norlanost-8-en-24-oic acid, 3β-acetoxy-14a-oxo-, methyl ester	EtOH	252(4.04)	56-1203-79
$C_{30}H_{46}O_9$			
Neriifolin, 18,20-epoxy-20,22-dihydro-	MeOH	219(2.89)	44-3511-79
Ruvoside	MeOH	222(4.04)	44-3511-79
$C_{30}H_{47}N_3O_7Si_2$			
Cytidine, N-benzoyl-2',5'-bis-O-[(1,1-dimethylethyl)dimethylsilyl]-, 3'-acetate	MeOH-HOAc	261(4.39),303(4.01)	5-1855-79
Cytidine, N-benzoyl-3',5'-bis-O-[(1,1-dimethylethyl)dimethylsilyl]-, 2'-acetate	MeOH-HOAc	261(4.38),303(4.01)	5-1855-79
$C_{30}H_{47}N_5O_6Si_2$			
Adenosine, 2',5'-bis-O-[(1,1-dimethylethyl)dimethylsilyl]-N-(4-methoxybenzoyl)-	EtOH	289(4.52)	118-0599-79
Adenosine, 3',5'-bis-O-[(1,1-dimethylethyl)dimethylsilyl]-N-(4-methoxybenzoyl)-	EtOH	288(4.49)	118-0599-79
$C_{30}H_{48}N_2O_8$			
Cyclopropenylium, bis[bis(1-methylethyl)amino][3-ethoxy-2-(ethoxycarbonyl)-1-[2-ethoxy-1-(ethoxycarbonyl)-2-oxoethyl]-1-propenyl]-, hydroxide, inner salt	$CHCl_3$	410(4.2)	5-1406-79
$C_{30}H_{48}N_4O_4$			
2,6(1H,3H)-Pyridinedione, 3-[1,6-dihydro-2,6-dioxo-1-pentyl-5-(pentylamino)-3(2H)-pyridinylidene]-1-pentyl-5-(pentylamino)-	$CHCl_3$	286(4.17),636(4.49)	118-0948-79
2,6(1H,3H)-Pyridinedione, 3-[1,6-dihydro-1-(3-methylbutyl)-5-[(3-methylbutyl)amino]-2,6-dioxo-3(2H)-pyridinylidene]-1-(3-methylbutyl)-5-[(3-methylbutyl)amino]-	$CHCl_3$	286(4.07),636(4.40)	118-0948-79
$C_{30}H_{48}O_2$			
2,14,17,29-Cyclotriacontatetraene-1,16-dione, (all-E)-	EtOH	248(4.58)	33-2661-79
Lup-20(30)-en-29-al, 3β-hydroxy-	n.s.g.	225(3.9)	102-1239-79
19-Norlanosta-5,7,9-trien-3β-ol, 7-methoxy-	EtOH	276(3.98),278s(3.91)	12-0179-79
$C_{30}H_{50}CuN_2O_2$			
Copper, [[octamethylenebis(iminoethylidyne)]bismenthonato]-	n.s.g.	308(4.36),338(4.25), 405(3.09),620(2.04)	65-2433-79

Compound	Solvent	λ max (log ε)	Ref.
$C_{30}H_{50}N_2$			
Cycloocta[1,2-c:5,6-c']dipyrrole, 4,5,9,10-tetrakis(1,1-dimethylethyl)-2,4,5,7,9,10-hexahydro-2,7-dimethyl-, (4α,5β,9α,10β)-	EtOH	227(4.34)	44-2667-79
$C_{30}H_{50}O$			
Cholestan-3-one, 2-(1-methylethylidene)-	heptane	246(3.90),323(1.74)	35-5515-79
$C_{30}H_{50}O_3$			
19-Norlanost-5-en-7-one, 3,11-dihydroxy-9-methyl-, (3β,9β,11β)-	EtOH	247(4.13)	39-0007-79C
$C_{30}H_{50}O_9$			
Nonanoic acid, 9-[[4-[hexahydro-7-hydroxy-2-(2,2,5,6-tetramethyl-1,3-dioxan-4-yl)-4H-furo[3,2-c]pyran-6-yl]-3-methyl-1-oxo-2-butenyl]-oxy]-, methyl ester	EtOH	223(4.14)	39-0838-79C
$C_{30}H_{52}CuN_2O_2$			
Copper, bis[[(butylamino)methylene]-menthonato]-	benzene	308(4.35),335(4.24), 410(3.10),635(2.00)	65-2427-79
Copper, bis[[(tert-butylamino)methylene]menthonato]-	benzene	324(4.38),340(4.20), 440(2.80),515(2.96), 800(2.51)	65-2427-79
$C_{30}H_{52}N_2O_3$			
3-Azetidinecarboxylic acid, 3-(1,1-dimethylethyl)-1-[5-methyl-2-(1-methylethyl)cyclohexyl]-2-[[5-methyl-2-(1-methylethyl)cyclohexyl]imino]-4-oxo-, ethyl ester	C_6H_{12}	214(3.35),262(3.59)	56-0643-79

Compound	Solvent	$\lambda_{max}(\log \epsilon)$	Ref.
$C_{31}H_{18}Cl_4N_4O$			
1,3,4-Oxadiazole, 2-(4-chlorophenyl)-5-[4-[2-[4-[4,5-dichloro-1-(4-chlorophenyl)-1H-pyrazol-3-yl]phenyl]ethenyl]phenyl]-	DMF	357(4.86)	33-1816-79
$C_{31}H_{19}BrO_2$			
Spiro[3H-naphtho[2,1-b]pyran-3,9'-[9H]-xanthene], 2-bromo-1-phenyl-	EtOAc	290(4.25),312(3.97), 327(4.01),358(4.00), 370(3.92)	104-1132-79
$C_{31}H_{19}Cl_2N_3O_2$			
1,2,4-Oxadiazole, 3-(4-chlorophenyl)-5-[4"-[5"'-(4-chlorophenyl)isoxazol-3"'-yl]stilben-4'-yl]-	DMF	349(4.83)	33-0779-79
1,3,4-Oxadiazole, 2-(4-chlorophenyl)-5-[4"-[5"'-(4-chlorophenyl)isoxazol-3"'-yl]stiben-4'-yl]-	DMF	353(4.90)	33-0779-79
1,3,4-Oxadiazole, 2-[2'-chloro-4"-[3"'-(4-chlorophenyl)isoxazol-5"'-yl)stilben-4'-yl]-	DMF	362(4.82)	33-0779-79
1,3,4-Oxadiazole, 2-[2'-chloro-4"-[3"'-phenylisoxazol-5"'-yl)stilben-4'-yl]-5-(4-chlorophenyl)-	DMF	363(4.82)	33-0779-79
1,3,4-Oxadiazole, 2-[2'-chloro-4"-[5"'-(4-chlorophenyl)isoxazol-3"'-yl]-stilben-4'-yl]-5-phenyl-	DMF	355(4.87)	33-0779-79
1,3,4-Oxadiazole, 2-[2'-chloro-4"-[5"'-phenylisoxazol-3"'-yl)-5-(4-chlorophenyl)-	DMF	355(4.79)	33-0779-79
$C_{31}H_{19}Cl_3N_4O$			
2H-1,2,3-Triazole, 2-[2'-chloro-4"-[5"'-(4-chlorophenyl)isoxazol-3"'-yl]stilben-4'-yl]-5-chloro-4-phenyl-	DMF	355(4.81)	33-0779-79
1,3,4-Oxadiazole, 2-[4-[2-[4-[4-chloro-1-(4-chlorophenyl)-1H-pyrazol-3-yl]-phenyl]ethenyl]phenyl]-5-(4-chlorophenyl)-	DMF	360(4.85)	33-1816-79
1,3,4-Oxadiazole, 2-[4-[2-[4-[4,5-dichloro-1-(4-chlorophenyl)-1H-pyrazol-3-yl]phenyl]ethenyl]phenyl]-5-phenyl-	DMF	355(4.85)	33-1816-79
$C_{31}H_{20}ClN_3O_2$			
1,2,4-Oxadiazole, 3-(4-chlorophenyl)-5-[4"-(3"'-phenylisoxazol-5"'-yl)stilben-4'-yl]-	DMF	358(4.85)	33-0779-79
1,2,4-Oxadiazole, 3-(4-chlorophenyl)-5-[4"-(5"'-phenylisoxazol-3"'-yl)stilben-4'-yl]-	DMF	350(4.83)	33-0779-79
1,2,4-Oxadiazole, 3-phenyl-5-[4"-[3"'-(4-chlorophenyl)isoxazol-5"'-yl]-stilben-4'-yl]-	DMF	357(4.86)	33-0779-79
1,2,4-Oxadiazole, 3-phenyl-5-[4"-[5"'-(4-chlorophenyl)isoxazol-3"'-yl]-stilben-4'-yl]-	DMF	348(4.83)	33-0779-79
1,3,4-Oxadiazole, 2-(4-chlorophenyl)-5-[4"-(3"'-phenylisoxazol-5"'-yl)stilbem-4'-yl]-	DMF	360(4.89)	33-0779-79
1,3,4-Oxadiazole, 2-(4-chlorophenyl)-5-	DMF	354(4.87)	33-0779-79

Compound	Solvent	λ_{max}(log ε)	Ref.
[4"-(5"'-phenylisoxazol-3"'-yl)stilben-4'-yl]- (cont.)			33-0779-79
1,3,4-Oxadiazole, 2-[2'-chloro-4"-[3"'-phenylisoxazol-5"'-yl)stilben-4'-yl]-5-phenyl-	DMF	363(4.79)	33-0779-79
1,3,4-Oxadiazole, 2-[2'-chloro-4"-[5"'-phenylisoxazol-3"'-yl)stilben-4'-yl]-5-phenyl-	DMF	354(4.77)	33-0779-79
1,3,4-Oxadiazole, 2-phenyl-5-[4"-[5"'-(4-chlorophenyl)isoxazol-3"'-yl]-stilben-4'-yl]-	DMF	353(4.87)	33-0779-79
$C_{31}H_{20}Cl_2N_2O_3$			
1,2-Benzisoxazole, 6-chloro-3-[2'-chloro-3-[2'-chloro-4"-[3"'-(4-methoxyphenyl)isoxazol-5"'-yl]stilben-4'-yl]-	DMF	347(4.76)	33-0779-79
$C_{31}H_{20}Cl_2N_4O$			
1,3,4-Oxadiazole, 2-[4-[2-[4-[4-chloro-1-(4-chlorophenyl)-1H-pyrazol-3-yl]-phenyl]ethenyl]phenyl]-5-phenyl-	DMF	359(4.82)	33-1816-79
1,3,4-Oxadiazole, 2-(4-chlorophenyl)-5-[3-chloro-4-[2-[4-(1-phenyl-1H-pyrazol-3-yl)phenyl]ethenyl]phenyl]-	DMF	368(4.79)	33-1816-79
1,3,4-Oxadiazole, 2-(4-chlorophenyl)-5-[4-[2-[4-[1-(4-chlorophenyl)-1H-pyrazol-3-yl]phenyl]ethenyl]phenyl]-	DMF	364(4.88)	33-1816-79
2H-1,2,3-Triazole, 2-[2'-chloro-4"-(3"'-phenylisoxazol-5"'-yl)stilben-4'-yl]-4-phenyl-5-chloro-	DMF	362(4.83)	33-0779-79
2H-1,2,3-Triazole, 2-[2'-chloro-4"-(5"'-phenylisoxazol-3"'-yl)stilben-4'-yl]-4-phenyl-5-chloro-	DMF	353(4.81)	33-0779-79
$C_{31}H_{20}Cl_3N_3O$			
Benzoxazole, 2-[4-[2-[4-(4,5-dichloro-1-(4-chlorophenyl)-1H-pyrazol-3-yl]-phenyl]ethenyl]phenyl]-5-methyl-	DMF	364(4.88)	33-1816-79
Benzoxazole, 2-[4-[2-[4-(4,5-dichloro-1-(4-chlorophenyl)-1H-pyrazol-3-yl]-phenyl]ethenyl]phenyl]-6-methyl-	DMF	365(4.88)	33-1816-79
$C_{31}H_{20}Cl_3N_3O_2$			
Benzoxazole, 2-[4-[2-[4-(4,5-dichloro-1-(4-chlorophenyl)-1H-pyrazol-3-yl]-phenyl]ethenyl]phenyl]-5-methoxy-	DMF	367(4.87)	33-1816-79
$C_{31}H_{20}Cl_3N_5$			
2H-1,2,3-Triazole, 4-chloro-2-[3-chloro-4-[2-[4-[1-(4-chlorophenyl)-1H-pyrazol-3-yl]phenyl]ethenyl]phenyl]-5-phenyl-	DMF	365(4.83)	33-1816-79
2H-1,2,3-Triazole, 4-chloro-2-[3-chloro-4-[2-[4-[3-(4-chlorophenyl)-1H-pyrazol-1-yl]phenyl]ethenyl]phenyl]-5-phenyl-	DMF	364(4.83)	33-1816-79
$C_{31}H_{20}N_4$			
Pyrazino[2',3':4,5]pyrrolo[1,2-a]quinoxaline, 6,9,10-triphenyl-	EtOH	252s(4.19),280(4.27), 302s(4.17),365s(3.85),	78-2463-79

Compound	Solvent	$\lambda_{max}(\log \epsilon)$	Ref.
(cont.)		385(3.97),412s(3.76), 430(3.70),454(3.49)	78-2463-79
$C_{31}H_{20}O_2$			
Spiro[anthracene-9(10H),3'-[3H]benz-[de]anthracen]-10-one, 7'-methoxy-	C_6H_{12}	268(5.04),375(3.58), 397(3.89),420(4.14), 448(4.15)	44-1787-79
$C_{31}H_{21}ClN_2O$			
1H-Pyrazole, 1-[4-[2-[4-(2-benzofuran-yl)phenyl]ethenyl]phenyl]-3-(4-chlorophenyl)-	DMF	371(4.92)	33-1816-79
1H-Pyrazole, 3-[4-[2-[4-(2-benzofuran-yl)phenyl]ethenyl]phenyl]-1-(4-chlorophenyl)-	DMF	373(4.94),392(4.77)	33-1816-79
1H-Pyrazole, 1-[4-[2-[4-(5-chloro-2-benzofuranyl)phenyl]ethenyl]phenyl]-3-phenyl-	DMF	372(4.93)	33-1816-79
1H-Pyrazole, 3-[4-[2-[4-(5-chloro-2-benzofuranyl)phenyl]ethenyl]phenyl]-1-phenyl-	DMF	374(4.94),392(4.77)	33-1816-79
$C_{31}H_{21}ClN_2O_2$			
Benzoxazole, 2-[4"-[3"'-(4-chlorophen-yl)isoxazol-5"'-yl]stilben-4'-yl]-5-methyl-	DMF	367(4.92),386(4.74)	33-0779-79
Benzoxazole, 2-[4"-[5"'-(4-chlorophen-yl)isoxazol-3"'-yl]stilben-4'-yl]-5-methyl-	DMF	362(4.88),380(4.69)	33-0779-79
$C_{31}H_{21}ClN_2O_3$			
Benzoxazole, 2-[2'-chloro-4"-[3"'-(4-methoxyphenyl)isoxazol-5"'-yl]stilb-en-4'-yl]-	DMF	368(4.81)	33-0779-79
$C_{31}H_{21}ClN_4O$			
1,2,4-Oxadiazole, 3-(4-chlorophenyl)-5-[4-[2-[4-(1-phenyl-1H-pyrazol-3-yl)-phenyl]ethenyl]phenyl]-	DMF	364(4.81)	33-1816-79
1,2,4-Oxadiazole, 3-(4-chlorophenyl)-5-[4-[2-[4-(3-phenyl-1H-pyrazol-1-yl)-phenyl]ethenyl]phenyl]-	DMF	362(4.78)	33-1816-79
1,2,4-Oxadiazole, 5-(4-chlorophenyl)-3-[4-[2-[4-(1-phenyl-1H-pyrazol-3-yl)-phenyl]ethenyl]phenyl]-	DMF	354(4.82)	33-1816-79
1,2,4-Oxadiazole, 5-[4-[2-[4-[1-(4-chlorophenyl)-1H-pyrazol-3-yl)-phenyl]ethenyl]phenyl]-3-phenyl-	DMF	362(4.83)	33-1816-79
1,2,4-Oxadiazole, 5-[4-[2-[4-[3-(4-chlorophenyl)-1H-pyrazol-1-yl)-phenyl]ethenyl]phenyl]-3-phenyl-	DMF	359(4.80)	33-1816-79
1,3,4-Oxadiazole, 2-(4-chlorophenyl)-5-[4-[2-[4-(1-phenyl-1H-pyrazol-3-yl)-phenyl]ethenyl]phenyl]-	DMF	364(4.88)	33-1816-79
1,3,4-Oxadiazole, 2-(4-chlorophenyl)-5-[4-[2-[4-(3-phenyl-1H-pyrazol-1-yl)-phenyl]ethenyl]phenyl]-	DMF	364(4.88)	33-1816-79
1,3,4-Oxadiazole, 2-[3-chloro-4-[2-[4-(1-phenyl-1H-pyrazol-3-yl)phenyl]-ethenyl]phenyl]-5-phenyl-	DMF	365(4.74)	33-1816-79

Compound	Solvent	$\lambda_{max}(\log \epsilon)$	Ref.
1,3,4-Oxadiazole, 2-[4-[2-[4-[1-(4-chlorophenyl)-1H-pyrazol-3-yl]phenyl]-ethenyl]phenyl]-5-phenyl-	DMF	363(4.88)	33-1816-79
1,3,4-Oxadiazole, 2-[4-[2-[4-[3-(4-chlorophenyl)-1H-pyrazol-1-yl]phenyl]-ethenyl]phenyl]-5-phenyl-	DMF	362(4.86)	33-1816-79
2H-1,2,3-Triazole, 2-[2'-chloro-4"-(3"'-phenylisoxazol-5"'-yl)stilben-4'-yl]-4-phenyl-	DMF	360(4.76)	33-0779-79
2H-1,2,3-Triazole, 2-[2'-chloro-4"-(5"'-phenylisoxazol-3"'-yl)stilben-4'-yl]-4-phenyl-	DMF	355(4.79)	33-0779-79
$C_{31}H_{21}ClN_4O_3$			
1,2,4-Oxadiazole, 3-[4-[2-[2-chloro-4-[5-(4-methoxyphenyl)-1,3,4-oxadiazol-2-yl]phenyl]ethenyl]phenyl]-5-phenyl-	DMF	355(4.79)	33-1411-79
1,2,4-Oxadiazole, 5-[4-[2-[2-chloro-4-[5-(4-methoxyphenyl)-1,3,4-oxadiazol-2-yl]phenyl]ethenyl]phenyl]-3-phenyl-	DMF	362(4.80)	33-1411-79
1,2,4-Oxadiazole, 3-[4-[2-[2-chloro-4-(5-phenyl-1,3,4-oxadiazol-2-yl)phenyl]ethenyl]phenyl]-5-(4-methoxyphenyl)-	DMF	357(4.78)	33-1411-79
1,2,4-Oxadiazole, 5-[4-[2-[2-chloro-4-(5-phenyl-1,3,4-oxadiazol-2-yl)phenyl]ethenyl]phenyl]-3-(4-methoxyphenyl)-	DMF	360(4.80)	33-1411-79
$C_{31}H_{21}Cl_2N_3O_2$			
Benzoxazole, 2-[4-[2-[4-[4-chloro-1-(4-chlorophenyl)-1H-pyrazol-3-yl]phenyl]-ethenyl]phenyl]-5-methoxy-	DMF	370(4.88)	33-1816-79
$C_{31}H_{21}Cl_2N_5$			
2H-1,2,3-Triazole, 2-[3-chloro-4-[2-[4-[1-(4-chlorophenyl)-1H-pyrazol-3-yl]-phenyl]ethenyl]phenyl]-4-phenyl-	DMF	365(4.85)	33-1816-79
2H-1,2,3-Triazole, 2-[3-chloro-4-[2-[4-[3-(4-chlorophenyl)-1H-pyrazol-1-yl]-phenyl]ethenyl]phenyl]-4-phenyl-	DMF	361(4.79)	33-1816-79
2H-1,2,3-Triazole, 4-chloro-2-[3-chloro-4-[2-[4-(1-phenyl-1H-pyrazol-3-yl)-phenyl]ethenyl]phenyl]-5-phenyl-	DMF	364(4.82)	33-1816-79
$C_{31}H_{21}NO_2$			
Isoxazole, 3-[4"-(5"'-benzofuran-2"'-yl)stilben-4'-yl]-5-phenyl-	DMF	365(4.85)	33-0779-79
$C_{31}H_{21}NO_6$			
1,4-Naphthalenedione, 2-acetyl-3-[4-[(3-acetyl-1,4-dihydro-1,4-dioxo-2-naphthalenyl)amino]-2-methylphenyl]-	dioxan	256(4.53),263s(4.5), 272s(4.5),330s(4.0), 428(3.83)	5-0503-79
1,4-Naphthalenedione, 2-acetyl-3-[4-[(3-acetyl-1,4-dihydro-1,4-dioxo-2-naphthalenyl)amino]-3-methylphenyl]-	dioxan	247s(4.5),255(4.57), 266(4.57),276s(4.5), 332s(4.0),445(3.78)	5-0503-79
$C_{31}H_{21}N_3O_2$			
1,2,4-Oxadiazole, 3-phenyl-5-[4"-(3"'-phenylisoxazol-5"'-yl)stilben-4'-yl]-	DMF	359(4.83)	33-0779-79

Compound	Solvent	λ_{max}(log ϵ)	Ref.
1,2,4-Oxadiazole, 3-phenyl-5-[4"-(5"'-phenylisoxazol-3"'-yl)stilben-4'-yl]-	DMF	349(4.81)	33-0779-79
1,3,4-Oxadiazole, 2-phenyl-5-[4"-(3"'-phenylisoxazol-5"'-yl)stilben-4'-yl]-	DMF	360(4.89),378(4.71)	33-0779-79
1,3,4-Oxadiazole, 2-phenyl-5-[4"-(5"'-phenylisoxazol-3"'-yl)stilben-4'-yl]-	DMF	353(4.86)	33-0779-79
$C_{31}H_{22}$			
Phenanthrene, 9-[4-(4-methylphenyl)-3-buten-1-ynyl]-1-phenyl-	MeOH	237s(4.50),252s(4.52), 260(4.56),282s(4.58), 289(4.59),341(4.48)	78-1537-79
Triphenylene, 1-(4-methylphenyl)-12-phenyl-	MeOH	259(4.68),269(4.74), 289(4.58)	78-1537-79
$C_{31}H_{22}ClN_3O$			
Benzoxazole, 2-[4-[2-[4-[1-(4-chlorophenyl)-1H-pyrazol-3-yl]phenyl]ethenyl]phenyl]-5-methyl-	DMF	370(4.91)	33-1816-79
Benzoxazole, 2-[4-[2-[4-[1-(4-chlorophenyl)-1H-pyrazol-3-yl]phenyl]ethenyl]phenyl]-6-methyl-	DMF	371(4.92)	33-1816-79
Benzoxazole, 2-[4-[2-[4-[1-(4-chlorophenyl)-1H-pyrazol-3-yl]phenyl]ethenyl]phenyl]-7-methyl-	DMF	370(4.90)	33-1816-79
Benzoxazole, 2-[4-[2-[4-[3-(4-chlorophenyl)-1H-pyrazol-1-yl]phenyl]ethenyl]phenyl]-5-methyl-	DMF	369(4.90)	33-1816-79
Benzoxazole, 2-[4-[2-[4-(4-chloro-1-phenyl-1H-pyrazol-3-yl)phenyl]ethenyl]phenyl]-5-methyl-	DMF	365(4.88)	33-1816-79
Benzoxazole, 2-[4-[2-[4-(4-chloro-1-phenyl-1H-pyrazol-3-yl)phenyl]ethenyl]phenyl]-6-methyl-	DMF	365(4.88)	33-1816-79
Benzoxazole, 2-[4-[2-[4-(4-chloro-3-phenyl-1H-pyrazol-1-yl)phenyl]ethenyl]phenyl]-5-methyl-	DMF	367(4.89)	33-1816-79
Benzoxazole, 2-[4-[2-[4-(4-chloro-3-phenyl-1H-pyrazol-1-yl)phenyl]ethenyl]phenyl]-6-methyl-	DMF	368(4.89)	33-1816-79
$C_{31}H_{22}ClN_3O_2$			
Benzoxazole, 2-[4-[2-[4-[1-(4-chlorophenyl)-1H-pyrazol-3-yl]phenyl]ethenyl]phenyl]-5-methoxy-	DMF	373(4.91)	33-1816-79
Benzoxazole, 2-[4-[2-[4-(4-chloro-1-phenyl-1H-pyrazol-3-yl)phenyl]ethenyl]phenyl]-5-methoxy-	DMF	368(4.87)	33-1816-79
$C_{31}H_{22}ClN_5$			
2H-1,2,3-Triazole, 2-[3-chloro-4-[2-[4-(1-phenyl-1H-pyrazol-3-yl)phenyl]ethenyl]phenyl]-4-phenyl-	DMF	365(4.85)	33-1816-79
2H-1,2,3-Triazole, 2-[3-chloro-4-[2-[4-(3-phenyl-1H-pyrazol-1-yl)phenyl]ethenyl]phenyl]-4-phenyl-	DMF	360(4.78)	33-1816-79
$C_{31}H_{22}N_2$			
1,1-Cyclopropanedicarbonitrile, 3-(2,2-diphenylethenyl)-2,2-diphenyl-	EtOH	267.5(4.28)	35-6367-79
Propanedinitrile, bis(2,2-diphenylethenyl)-	ether	261(4.39)	35-6367-79

Compound	Solvent	λ max (log ε)	Ref.
Propanedinitrile, (2,2,4,4-tetraphenyl-3-butenylidene)-	C_6H_{12}	253(4.20)	35-6367-79
Propanedinitrile, [(2,2,3,3-tetraphenylcyclopropyl)methylene]-	EtOH	225(4.37),267(4.01)	35-6367-79
$C_{31}H_{22}N_2O$			
1H-Pyrazole, 1-[4-[2-[4-(2-benzofuranyl)phenyl]ethenyl]phenyl]-3-phenyl-	DMF	371(4.92)	33-1816-79
1H-Pyrazole, 3-[4-[2-[4-(2-benzofuranyl)phenyl]ethenyl]phenyl]-1-phenyl-	DMF	373(4.93)	33-1816-79
$C_{31}H_{22}N_2O_2$			
1,2-Benzisoxazole, 6-methyl-3-[4"-(5"'-phenylisoxazol-3"'-yl)stilben-4'-yl]-	DMF	342(4.78)	33-0779-79
Benzoxazole, 2-[4"-(3"'-phenylisoxazol-5"'-yl)stilben-4'-yl]-5-methyl-	DMF	368(4.91),387(4.73)	33-0779-79
Benzoxazole, 2-[4"-(3"'-phenylisoxazol-5"'-yl)stilben-4'-yl]-6-methyl-	DMF	368(4.92),387(4.73)	33-0779-79
Benzoxazole, 2-[4"-(3"'-phenylisoxazol-5"'-yl)stilben-4'-yl]-7-methyl-	DMF	367(4.91),386(4.72)	33-0779-79
Benzoxazole, 2-[4"-(5"'-phenylisoxazol-3"'-yl)stilben-4'-yl]-5-methyl-	DMF	361(4.89)	33-0779-79
Benzoxazole, 2-[4"-(5"'-phenylisoxazol-3"'-yl)stilben-4'-yl]-6-methyl-	DMF	362(4.89)	33-0779-79
Benzoxazole, 2-[4"-(5"'-phenylisoxazol-3"'-yl)stilben-4'-yl]-7-methyl-	DMF	360(4.88),378(4.68)	33-0779-79
$C_{31}H_{22}N_2O_3$			
1,2-Benzisoxazole, 3-(4-methoxyphenyl)-6-[4-(5"-phenylisoxazol-3"-yl)styryl]-	DMF	338(4.78)	33-0779-79
1,2-Benzisoxazole, 3-phenyl-6-[4'-[5"-(4-methoxyphenyl)isoxazol-3"-yl]-styryl]-	DMF	337(4.79)	33-0779-79
Benzoxazole, 2-[4"-[3"'-(4-methoxyphenyl)isoxazol-5"'-yl]stilben-4'-yl]-	DMF	366(4.91),385(4.73)	33-0779-79
Benzoxazole, 2-[4"-[5"'-(4-methoxyphenyl)isoxazol-3"'-yl]stilben-4'-yl]-	DMF	358(4.89),377(4.70)	33-0779-79
Benzoxazole, 2-[4"-(3"'-phenylisoxazol-5"'-yl)stilben-4'-yl]-5-methoxy-	DMF	371(4.90)	33-0779-79
Benzoxazole, 2-[4"-(5"'-phenylisoxazol-3"'-yl)stilben-4'-yl]-5-methoxy-	DMF	365(4.86)	33-0779-79
$C_{31}H_{22}N_4O$			
1,2,4-Oxadiazole, 3-phenyl-5-[4-[2-[4-(1-phenyl-1H-pyrazol-3-yl)phenyl]ethenyl]phenyl]-	DMF	363(4.80)	33-1816-79
1,2,4-Oxadiazole, 3-phenyl-5-[4-[2-[4-(3-phenyl-1H-pyrazol-1-yl)phenyl]ethenyl]phenyl]-	DMF	362(4.80)	33-1816-79
1,2,4-Oxadiazole, 5-phenyl-3-[4-[2-[4-(1-phenyl-1H-pyrazol-3-yl)phenyl]ethenyl]phenyl]-	DMF	353(4.81)	33-1816-79
1,3,4-Oxadiazole, 2-phenyl-5-[4-[2-[4-(1-phenyl-1H-pyrazol-3-yl)phenyl]ethenyl]phenyl]-	DMF	363(4.86)	33-1816-79
1,3,4-Oxadiazole, 2-phenyl-5-[4-[2-[4-(3-phenyl-1H-pyrazol-1-yl)phenyl]ethenyl]phenyl]-	DMF	362(4.85)	33-1816-79
$C_{31}H_{22}N_4O_3$			
1,2,4-Oxadiazole, 3-[4-[2-[4-[3-(4-meth-	DMF	348(4.83)	33-1411-79

Compound	Solvent	λ_{max}(log ϵ)	Ref.
oxyphenyl)-1,2,4-oxadiazol-5-yl]-phenyl]ethenyl]phenyl]-5-phenyl-			33-1411-79
1,2,4-Oxadiazole, 5-[4-[2-[4-[5-(4-methoxyphenyl)-1,2,4-oxadiazol-3-yl]-phenyl]ethenyl]phenyl]-3-phenyl-	DMF	348(4.83)	33-1411-79
1,2,4-Oxadiazole, 5-(4-methoxyphenyl)-3-[4-[2-[4-(5-phenyl-1,3,4-oxadiazol-2-yl)phenyl]ethenyl]phenyl]-	DMF	352(4.87),370(4.67)	33-1411-79
$C_{31}H_{22}O$			
Naphtho[2,1-b]furan, 7-methyl-2,4,5-triphenyl-	ether	258(4.52),266s(4.45), 310s(4.32),322(4.36), 342(4.42),355(4.49)	78-2639-79
Spiro[anthracene-9(10H),3'-[3H]benz-[de]anthracen]-10-one, 1',2'-dihydro-7'-methyl-	C_6H_{12}	266(5.16),291(3.88), 304(3.79),332(3.15), 347(3.51),365(3.86), 385(4.10),407(4.10)	44-1787-79
$C_{31}H_{22}O_2$			
Spiro[anthracene-9(10H),3'-[3H]benz-[de]anthracen]-10-one, 1',2'-dihydro-7'-methoxy-	C_6H_{12}	266(5.16),291(3.86), 304(3.78),334(3.18), 350(3.53),368(3.85), 388(4.07),410(4.05)	44-1787-79
$C_{31}H_{22}O_3$			
1-Naphthalenecarboxaldehyde, 2-(benzoyloxy)-6-methyl-3,4-diphenyl-	ether	235(4.70),255s(4.57), 330(4.07),385(3.45)	78-2639-79
$C_{31}H_{23}$			
5,13[1',2']:6,12[1",2"]-Dibenzeno-5H-cyclohept[b]anthracenylium, 5a,6-12,12a,13,?-hexahydro-	CH_2Cl_2	334(3.61)	88-4747-79
isomer	CH_2Cl_2	316(3.60)	88-4747-79
$C_{31}H_{23}BrO$			
Anthracene, 9-[(10-bromo-9-anthracenylmethoxy)methyl]-10-methyl-	$C_6H_{11}Me$	252(5.14),258(5.15), 340(3.61),358(3.94), 378(4.18),400(4.22)	39-0411-79B
$C_{31}H_{23}ClN_4O$			
2H-Benzotriazole, 5-methoxy-2-[4-[5-(4-methoxyphenyl)-1,2-benzisoxazol-3-yl]chlorostilbenyl]-	DMF	368(4.83)	33-0779-79
$C_{31}H_{23}N_3O$			
1,2-Benzisoxazole, 5-methyl-3-[4-[2-[4-(1-phenyl-1H-pyrazol-3-yl)phenyl]-ethenyl]phenyl]-	DMF	353(4.82)	33-1816-79
1,2-Benzisoxazole, 5-methyl-3-[4-[2-[4-(3-phenyl-1H-pyrazol-1-yl)phenyl]-ethenyl]phenyl]-	DMF	350(4.81)	33-1816-79
Benzoxazole, 5-methyl-2-[4-[2-[4-(1-phenyl-1H-pyrazol-3-yl)phenyl]-ethenyl]phenyl]-	DMF	370(4.90)	33-1816-79
Benzoxazole, 5-methyl-2-[4-[2-[4-(3-phenyl-1H-pyrazol-1-yl)phenyl]-ethenyl]phenyl]-	DMF	370(4.89)	33-1816-79
Benzoxazole, 6-methyl-2-[4-[2-[4-(1-phenyl-1H-pyrazol-3-yl)phenyl]-ethenyl]phenyl]-	DMF	371(4.90)	33-1816-79

Compound	Solvent	$\lambda_{max}(\log \epsilon)$	Ref.
Benzoxazole, 6-methyl-2-[4-[2-[4-(3-phenyl-1H-pyrazol-1-yl)phenyl]ethenyl]phenyl]-	DMF	370(4.90)	33-1816-79
Benzoxazole, 7-methyl-2-[4-[2-[4-(1-phenyl-1H-pyrazol-3-yl)phenyl]ethenyl]phenyl]-	DMF	368(4.88)	33-1816-79
Benzoxazole, 7-methyl-2-[4-[2-[4-(3-phenyl-1H-pyrazol-1-yl)phenyl]ethenyl]phenyl]-	DMF	367(4.88)	33-1816-79
$C_{31}H_{23}N_3O_2$			
1,2-Benzisoxazole, 3-(4-methoxyphenyl)-6-[2-[4-(1-phenyl-1H-pyrazol-3-yl)phenyl]ethenyl]-	DMF	352(4.80)	33-1816-79
1,2-Benzisoxazole, 3-(4-methoxyphenyl)-6-[2-[4-(3-phenyl-1H-pyrazol-1-yl)phenyl]ethenyl]-	DMF	351(4.79)	33-1816-79
Benzoxazole, 5,6-dimethyl-2-[4-[2-[4-(5-phenyl-1,2,4-oxadiazol-3-yl)phenyl]ethenyl]phenyl]-	DMF	364(4.87)	33-1411-79
Benzoxazole, 5,7-dimethyl-2-[4-[2-[4-(5-phenyl-1,2,4-oxadiazol-3-yl)phenyl]ethenyl]phenyl]-	DMF	362(4.87),380(4.67)	33-1411-79
Benzoxazole, 5-methoxy-2-[4-[2-[4-(1-phenyl-1H-pyrazol-3-yl)phenyl]ethenyl]phenyl]-	DMF	373(4.90)	33-1816-79
Benzoxazole, 5-methoxy-2-[4-[2-[4-(3-phenyl-1H-pyrazol-1-yl)phenyl]ethenyl]phenyl]-	DMF	373(4.90)	33-1816-79
$C_{31}H_{23}N_3O_2S$			
Benzenesulfonic acid, 4-methyl-, (2,4-diphenyl-5H-indeno[1,2-b]pyridin-4-ylidene)hydrazide	EtOH	212(4.50),227(4.49), 258(4.40),320(4.00), 390(3.86)	103-0777-79
$C_{31}H_{23}N_3O_3$			
Benzoxazole, 2-[4-[2-[4-[3-(4-methoxyphenyl)-1,2,4-oxadiazol-5-yl]phenyl]ethenyl]phenyl]-5-methyl-	DMF	367(4.90),386(4.72)	33-1411-79
Benzoxazole, 2-[4-[2-[4-[5-(4-methoxyphenyl)-1,2,4-oxadiazol-3-yl]phenyl]ethenyl]phenyl]-5-methyl-	DMF	362(4.89),379(4.70)	33-1411-79
$C_{31}H_{23}N_3O_4$			
Benzoxazole, 5-methoxy-2-[4-[2-[4-[5-(4-methoxyphenyl)-1,2,4-oxadiazol-3-yl]phenyl]ethenyl]phenyl]-	DMF	365(4.87)	33-1411-79
$C_{31}H_{23}N_3O_6$			
1-Naphthalenecarboxylic acid, [2,3,3a-9a-tetrahydro-6-imino-3-[(1-naphthalenylcarbonyl)oxy]-6H-furo[2',3'-4,5]oxazolo[3,2-a]pyrimidin-2-yl]methyl ester, [2R-(2α,3β,3aβ,9aβ)]-, monotetrafluoroborate	MeOH	216s(4.77),235s(4.56), 270(4.00),302(3.97)	87-0639-79
$C_{31}H_{24}$			
Benzene, [(4,4-diphenyl-2,5-cyclohexadien-1-ylidene)phenylmethyl]-	EtOH	233(4.05),246(4.09), 260(3.93),312(4.44)	35-1841-79
Benzene, 1,1'-[4-(diphenylmethylene)bicyclo[3.1.0]hex-2-en-6-ylidene]bis-	EtOH	321(4.32)	35-1841-79

Compound	Solvent	λ_{max}(log ε)	Ref.
$C_{31}H_{24}ClN_5O_2$			
2H-Benzotriazole, 2-[4-[2-[4-[1-(4-chlorophenyl)-1H-pyrazol-3-yl]phenyl]ethenyl]phenyl]-5,6-dimethoxy-	DMF	375(4.96)	33-1816-79
$C_{31}H_{24}N_2O_2$			
Phenol, 2-[3-(2,2-diphenylethenyl)-1H-1,5-benzodiazepin-4-yl]-, acetate	MeOH	209(4.7),241(4.5), 352(4.1)	24-1791-79
$C_{31}H_{24}N_2O_3$			
[1]Benzopyrano[4,3-c]pyrazole-4-acetic acid, 1,4-dihydro-8-methyl-α,α,1-triphenyl-	MeOH	201(4.7),285(4.2), 327(4.3)	24-1791-79
[1]Benzopyrano[4,3-c]pyrazole-4-acetic acid, 1,4-dihydro-α,α,1-triphenyl-, methyl ester	MeOH	215(4.5),277(4.2), 317(4.3)	24-1791-79
$C_{31}H_{24}N_3O_3S_6$			
Methylium, tris[[4-(4-methoxyphenyl)-1,3-dithiol-2-ylidene]amino]-, tetrafluoroborate	MeCN	260(4.70),292(4.58), 515(4.70)	48-0827-79
$C_{31}H_{24}N_3S_6$			
Methylium, tris[[4-(4-methylphenyl)-1,3-dithiol-2-ylidene]amino]-, tetrafluoroborate	MeCN	246(4.64),287(4.47), 504(4.71)	48-0827-79
$C_{31}H_{24}N_4O_3$			
2H-Benzotriazole, 5,6-dimethoxy-2-[4-(5-phenylisoxazol-3-yl)stilbenyl]-	DMF	370(4.92)	33-0779-79
2H-Benzotriazole, 2-[4-[5-(4-methoxyphenyl)isoxazol-3-yl]stilbenyl]-5-methoxy-	DMF	367(4.86)	33-0779-79
$C_{31}H_{24}O$			
Anthracene, 9-[(9-anthracenylmethoxy)-methyl]-10-methyl-	$C_6H_{11}Me$	249(4.96),256(4.95), 348(3.92),357(3.99), 367(4.11),376(4.15), 387(4.09),397(4.15)	39-0411-79B
1H,3H-3a,8[1',2']:9,13b[1",2"]-Dibenzenodibenzo[3,4:7,8]cycloocta[1,2-c]-furan, 8,9-dihydro-8-methyl-	$C_6H_{11}Me$	220(4.45),258(3.66), 275(3.22),290(2.88)	39-0411-79B
Furan, 2-(1,2-diphenylethenyl)-3-(4-methylphenyl)-5-phenyl-, (1:3 E:Z)-	ether	273(4.52),350(4.21)	78-2633-79
Naphtho[2,1-b]furan, 5,5a-dihydro-7-methyl-2,4,5-triphenyl-	ether	248(4.45),258s(4.37), 290(4.41),310(4.39)	78-2639-79
$C_{31}H_{24}O_2$			
9(10H)-Anthracenone, 10-[2-(10-methoxy-9-anthracenyl)ethyl]-	C_6H_{12}	254(5.04),262(5.29), 346(3.54),362(3.85), 381(4.07),403(4.06)	44-4247-79
$C_{31}H_{24}O_5$			
9,10-Anthracenedione, 2-(1-oxopropyl)-1,4-bis(phenylmethoxy)-	MeOH	208(4.72),252(4.58), 402(3.75)	5-0019-79
$C_{31}H_{24}O_7$			
2-Anthraceneacetic acid, 9,10-dihydro-α-hydroxy-9,10-dioxo-1,4-bis(phenylmethoxy)-, methyl ester	MeOH	206(4.60),253(4.45), 403(3.62)	5-0035-79

Compound	Solvent	λ max(log ε)	Ref.
$C_{31}H_{24}O_{10}$			
Aurasperone D	EtOH	238(4.70),280(4.71), 323(4.18),380(3.85)	98-1347-79
	EtOH-AlCl$_3$	243s(4.67),285(4.58), 419(3.56)	98-1347-79
$C_{31}H_{25}NO$			
Pyrrolo[2,1-a]isoquinolin-1(5H)-one, 6,10b-dihydro-2,3-diphenyl-10b-(phenylmethyl)-	MeCN	273(4.06),357(3.84)	88-1213-79
$C_{31}H_{25}NO_8S$			
1H-Pyrrole-3-carboxylic acid, 4-benzoyl-1-(1-benzoyl-3-methoxy-3-oxo-1-propenyl)-5-[(4-methylphenyl)sulfonyl]-, methyl ester	EtOH	236(4.48),380(4.39)	94-2857-79
$C_{31}H_{25}NS$			
Pyrrolo[2,1-a]isoquinoline-1(5H)-thione, 6,10b-dihydro-2,3-diphenyl-10b-(phenylmethyl)-	MeCN	255(4.06),428(4.04)	88-1213-79
$C_{31}H_{25}N_5O_2$			
2H-Benzotriazole, 5,6-dimethoxy-2-[4-[2-[4-(1-phenyl-1H-pyrazol-3-yl)-phenyl]ethenyl]phenyl]-	DMF	377(4.94)	33-1816-79
2H-Benzotriazole, 5,6-dimethoxy-2-[4-[2-[4-(3-phenyl-1H-pyrazol-1-yl)-phenyl]ethenyl]phenyl]-	DMF	375(4.94)	33-1816-79
$C_{31}H_{25}N_5O_4$			
Adenosine, N-(benzo[a]pyren-6-ylmethyl)-	EtOH	266(4.73),276(4.58), 288(4.67),300(4.70), 354(4.11),373(4.42), 393(4.46),406(4.93)	44-3202-79
Adenosine, 1-(benzo[a]pyren-6-ylmethyl)-N,6-didehydro-1,6-dihydro-	EtOH	254(4.74),267(4.79), 278(4.58),291(4.68), 303(4.73),361(4.16), 380(4.42),400(4.41), 408(4.31)	44-3202-79
$C_{31}H_{25}N_5O_8$			
Guanosine, N-benzoyl-, 3',5'-dibenzoate	EtOH	232(4.56),257(4.19), 284(4.18),297(4.14)	39-2088-79C
$C_{31}H_{25}N_5O_{10}$			
2H-Isoindole-2-propanoic acid, 1,3-dihydro-1,3-dioxo-, 2-[[3-(1,3-dihydro-1,3-dioxo-2H-isoindol-2-yl)-1-oxopropoxy]methyl]-2,3,3a,9a-tetrahydro-6-imino-6H-furo[2',3':4,5]oxazolo[3,2-a]pyrimidin-3-yl ester, tetrafluoroborate	MeOH	219(4.71),233(4.37), 241s(4.22),266(3.89)	87-0639-79
$C_{31}H_{25}O_4P$			
Phosphorin, 1,1-dihydro-4-(methoxycarbonyl)-1,1-diphenoxy-2,6-diphenyl-	MeOH	297(4.17),376(4.22)	24-1272-79
$C_{31}H_{26}ClN_3O_6S_3$			
3-Butenenitrile, 2-[(4-chlorophenyl)-	EtOH	265(4.02),327(4.50)	104-1319-79

Compound	Solvent	$\lambda_{max}(\log \epsilon)$	Ref.
azo]-2,4,4-tris(4-methylphenyl)sul-fonyl]- (cont.)			104-1319-79
$C_{31}H_{26}N_2$			
1H-Pyrazole, 4,5-dihydro-5-phenyl-3-(2-phenylethenyl)-1-stilbenyl-	toluene	417(4.76)	135-1491-79B
$C_{31}H_{26}N_4O_8S_3$			
3-Butenenitrile, 2,4,4-tris[(4-methyl-phenyl)sulfonyl]-2-[(4-nitrophenyl)-azo]-	EtOH	260(4.30),327(4.30)	104-1319-79
$C_{31}H_{26}O_3$			
5,7:17,19-Dietheno-8H,16H-diindeno-[2,1-k:1',2'-l][1,4,7]trioxacyclo-hexadecin, 10,11,13,14-tetrahydro-,(S)-	n.s.g.	221(4.62),267(4.45), 277(4.42),298(4.07), 310(4.27)	33-2285-79
$C_{31}H_{26}O_5$			
9,10-Anthracenedione, 2-(1-hydroxyprop-yl)-1,4-bis(phenylmethoxy)-	MeOH	206(4.60),252(4.46), 310s(--),402(3.77)	5-0019-79
$C_{31}H_{26}O_6$			
4H-1-Benzopyran-4-one, 3-[2,4-dimeth-oxy-3-(phenylmethoxy)phenyl]-7-(phen-ylmethoxy)-	EtOH	241s(4.16),249s(4.14), 308(3.79)	102-0815-79
$C_{31}H_{26}S_3$			
Butatriene, 1,1,4-tris(4-methylphenyl-thio)-1-phenyl-	heptane	197(4.60),423(4.12)	5-1626-79
$C_{31}H_{27}NOS$			
2H,6H-[1,3-Thiazino[2,3-a]isoquinoline, 7,11b-dihydro-2-methoxy-3,4,11b-tri-phenyl-	MeCN	276(3.81),297(3.84)	88-1213-79
$C_{31}H_{28}N_4$			
1H-Imidazole-5-carbonitrile, 4,5-di-hydro-1-methyl-2,4,5-tris(4-methyl-phenyl)-4-(2-pyridinyl)-	EtOH	228(4.45),259(3.97), 265s(3.95),272s(3.86)	44-0041-79
$C_{31}H_{28}N_4O_6$			
2,4(1H,3H)-Pteridinedione, 1-[2-deoxy-5-O-[(4-methoxyphenyl)diphenylmeth-yl]-α-D-erythro-pentofuranosyl]-	MeOH	232(4.49),317(3.88)	33-1171-79
β-	MeOH	232(4.40),317(3.80)	33-1171-79
$C_{31}H_{28}N_6O_5S$			
5-Thia-1-azabicyclo[4.2.0]oct-2-ene-2-carboxylic acid, 3-[[(1-methyl-1H-tetrazol-5-yl)oxy]methyl]-8-oxo-7-[(phenylacetyl)amino]-, diphenyl-methyl ester, (6R-trans)-	CH_2Cl_2	282(3.96)	87-0757-79
$C_{31}H_{28}O_2$			
1,4-Pentadiene, 3,3-dimethoxy-1,1,5,5-tetraphenyl-	C_6H_{12}	251(4.32)	35-6367-79
$C_{31}H_{28}O_4$			
2-Buten-1-one, 1-[4-methoxy-2-(phenyl-methoxy)phenyl]-3-[4-(phenylmethoxy)-phenyl]-	EtOH	233(4.31),283(4.03), 322(4.15)	78-0531-79

Compound	Solvent	λ_{max}(log ε)	Ref.
$C_{31}H_{28}O_6$			
4H-1-Benzopyran-4-one, 3-[2,4-dimethoxy-3-(phenylmethoxy)phenyl]-2,3-dihydro-7-(phenylmethoxy)-, (±)-	EtOH	233s(4.59),274(4.52), 317s(4.31)	102-0815-79
$C_{31}H_{29}N_5O_{10}$			
Benzamide, N-[9-[2,3-di-O-acetyl-3-C-(acetoxymethyl)-5-O-benzoyl-β-D-xylofuranosyl]-9H-purin-6-yl]-	EtOH	211s(--),227(4.33), 260s(--),278(4.24)	33-0689-79
$C_{31}H_{30}NO_2$			
Isoquinolinium, 6-methoxy-7-(phenylmethoxy)-2-[4-(4-phenylmethyl)phenylmethyl]-	EtOH	250(4.37),313(4.08), 365(4.05)	39-0283-79C
	EtOH-NaOH	282(3.75)	39-0283-79C
$C_{31}H_{30}N_2O_6S_3$			
Androsta-3,5-diene-11,17-dione, 3-[(2-nitrophenyl)dithio]-6-[(2-nitrophenyl)thio]-	MeOH	242(4.34),275s(4.20), 355(3.78)	39-1166-79C
$C_{31}H_{30}O_5$			
2H-1-Benzopyran, 3-[2,4-dimethoxy-3-(phenylmethoxy)phenyl]-3,4-dihydro-7-(phenylmethoxy)-	EtOH	283(4.13)	102-0815-79
$C_{31}H_{31}N_2O_5P$			
1H-Pyrrole-3-acetic acid, 2,5-dihydro-1-methyl-4-(4-morpholinyl)-2,5-dioxo-α-(triphenylphosphoranylidene)-, ethyl ester	MeOH	223(4.79),260(4.32), 415(3.78)	48-0795-79
$C_{31}H_{31}N_3O_4$			
[3,7'-Bi-1H-indole]-2'-carboxylic acid, 3-[2-(acetylmethylamino)ethyl]-2,3-dihydro-2-oxo-1-(phenylmethyl)-, ethyl ester	EtOH	293.5(4.26)	23-1694-79
$C_{31}H_{31}O_8P$			
Phosphonium, [3-ethoxy-2-(ethoxycarbonyl)-1-[2-methoxy-1-(methoxycarbonyl)-2-oxoethyl]-3-oxo-1-propenyl]triphenyl-, hydroxide, inner salt	$CHCl_3$	480(3.3)	5-1406-79
$C_{31}H_{32}As_2O_2$			
Arsine, [(2,2-dimethyl-1,3-dioxolane-4,5-diyl)bis(methylene)]bis[diphenyl-, (4S-trans)-	EtOH	241(4.37)	118-0350-79
$C_{31}H_{32}NO_4PS$			
1H-Pyrrole-3-acetic acid, 4-(butylthio)-2,5-dihydro-1-methyl-2,5-dioxo-α-(triphenylphosphoranylidene)-, ethyl ester	MeOH	223(4.98),270(4.23), 460(3.92)	48-0795-79
$C_{31}H_{32}N_2O_4$			
5-Oxa-1-azabicyclo[4.2.0]oct-2-ene-2-carboxylic acid, 3-methyl-8-oxo-7-[(triphenylmethyl)amino]-, 1,1-dimethylethyl ester, (6R-trans)-	EtOH	268(3.81)	39-2268-79C

Compound	Solvent	$\lambda_{max}(\log \epsilon)$	Ref.
$C_{31}H_{32}N_4O_2$			
Roxburghine D	EtOH	224(4.89),284(4.61), 290(4.57)	102-1385-79
Roxburghine X	EtOH	226(4.91),284(4.60), 292(4.58)	102-1385-79
$C_{31}H_{32}N_4O_4$			
Thymidine, 3'-O-benzyl-5'-deoxy-5,5'-(N,N'-diphenylethylenediamino)-	MeOH	253(4.57)	44-1309-79
$C_{31}H_{32}O_2$			
2,4-Cyclohexadien-1-one, 2-(1,1-dimethylethyl)-6-methoxy-6-methyl-4-(triphenylmethyl)-	$CHCl_3$	270s(4.57),277(4.59), 310(4.63),370(3.46)	44-0428-79
$C_{31}H_{32}O_7$			
Pregna-1,4,6-triene-3,11,20-trione, 21-acetoxy-17-(benzoyloxy)-16α-methyl-	MeOH	229(4.38),296(4.32)	145-1662-79
16β-	MeOH	232(4.38),296(4.07)	145-1662-79
$C_{31}H_{32}O_{13}$			
Daunomycinone, 7-O-(3,4-di-O-acetyl-2,6-dideoxy-α-L-lyxo-hexopyranosyl)-	MeOH	233(4.56),251(4.43), 288(3.97),313(3.45), 327(3.53),388(3.45), 450(3.95),473(4.09), 480(4.09),496(4.10), 519(3.91),532(3.85), 578(2.60)	87-0406-79
$C_{31}H_{33}BrO_7$			
Pregna-1,4-diene-3,11,20-trione, 21-acetoxy-17-(benzoyloxy)-7-bromo-16-methyl-, (7α,16α)-	MeOH	232(4.44)	145-1662-79
(7α,16β)-	MeOH	235(4.45)	145-1662-79
$C_{31}H_{33}ClO_7$			
Pregna-1,4-diene-3,11,20-trione, 21-acetoxy-17-(benzoyloxy)-7-chloro-16-methyl-, (7α,16β)-	MeOH	233(4.48)	145-1662-79
$C_{31}H_{33}NO_6$			
D-allo-2-Octenoic acid, 3-amino-4,7-anhydro-2,3-dideoxy-5,6-O-(1-methylethylidene)-8-O-(triphenylmethyl)-, methyl ester	EtOH	274(4.22)	44-4854-79
$C_{31}H_{33}N_3O_4$			
Acetamide, N-[2-[1-benzyl-3-[2-(ethoxycarbonyl)-4,5,6,7-tetrahydroindol-7-yl]oxindol-3-yl]ethyl]-N-methyl-	EtOH	286(4.29)	23-1694-79
$C_{31}H_{34}O_7$			
Pregna-1,4-diene-3,11,20-trione, 21-acetoxy-17-(benzoyloxy)-16α-methyl-	MeOH	233(4.45)	145-1662-79
16β-	MeOH	234(4.47)	145-1662-79
Pregna-1,4,6-triene-3,20-dione, 21-acetoxy-17-(benzoyloxy)-11-hydroxy-16-methyl-, (11β,16α)-	MeOH	229(4.35),296(4.04)	145-1662-79
(11β,16β)-	MeOH	230(4.34),290(4.05)	145-1662-79

Compound	Solvent	λ_{max}(log ϵ)	Ref.
$C_{31}H_{35}BrO_7$			
Pregna-1,4-diene-3,20-dione, 21-acetoxy-17-(benzoyloxy)-7-bromo-11-hydroxy-16-methyl-, (7α,11β,16α)-	MeOH	233(4.43)	145-1662-79
(7α,11β,16β)-	MeOH	235(4.42)	145-1662-79
$C_{31}H_{35}ClO_7$			
Pregna-1,4-diene-3,20-dione, 21-acetoxy-17-(benzoyloxy)-7-chloro-11-hydroxy-16-methyl-, (7α,11β,16α)-	MeOH	233(4.41)	145-1662-79
(7α,11β,16β)-	MeOH	235(4.43)	145-1662-79
$C_{31}H_{35}FO_7$			
Pregna-1,4-diene-3,20-dione, 21-acetoxy-17-(benzoyloxy)-7-fluoro-11-hydroxy-16α-methyl-	MeOH	232(4.43)	145-1662-79
$C_{31}H_{35}IO_7$			
Pregna-1,4-diene-3,20-dione, 21-acetoxy-17-(benzoyloxy)-11-hydroxy-7-iodo-16-methyl-, (7α,11β,16α)-	MeOH	233(4.39)	145-1662-79
$C_{31}H_{35}NO_6$			
Isohypognavine, diacetyl-	EtOH	231(4.11),275(2.96)	95-0647-79
$C_{31}H_{35}NO_{12}$			
Nogalarol, 7-con-O-ethyl-	EtOH	236(4.66),258(4.34), 288s(4.03),480(4.17)	44-4030-79
Nogalarol, 7-dis-O-ethyl-	EtOH	236(4.68),253(4.40), 257s(4.40),290(4.02), 478(4.21)	44-4030-79
$C_{31}H_{35}N_3O_6$			
Benzoic acid, 4-(1,1-dimethylethyl)-, 2-[[[4-(1,1-dimethylethyl)benzoyl]-oxy]methyl]-2,3,3a,9a-tetrahydro-6-imino-6H-furo[2',3':4,5]oxazolo[3,2-a]pyrimidin-3-yl ester, hydrochloride, [2R-(2α,3β,3aβ,9aβ)]-	MeOH	243(4.67),270s(4.14)	87-0639-79
$C_{31}H_{35}N_3O_{13}$			
Aconitan-3-one, 8-acetoxy-14-(benzoyl-oxy)-1,2-didehydro-13,15-dihydroxy-6,16-dimethoxy-4-(methoxymethyl)-2-nitro-20-nitroso-, (6α,14α,15α,16β)-	EtOH	230(4.2),343(3.4)	138-1163-79
$C_{31}H_{36}N_2O_7$			
Echitoveniline, (-)- (differential spectrum)	EtOH	228(3.90),300(3.92), 330(4.15)	78-1151-79
$C_{31}H_{36}O$			
2-Azulenecarboxaldehyde, 1,4-dihydro-3,8-dimethyl-5-(1-methylethyl)-4-[[1-methyl-7-(1-methylethyl)-4-azulenyl]methyl]-	C_6H_{12}	205(4.50),246(4.44), 287(4.61),305s(4.17), 341s(4.09),353(4.17), 366s(4.14),543s(2.43), 568s(2.58),592s(2.67), 610(2.73),632(2.69), 667(2.69),698s(2.41), 739(2.28)	18-1748-79

Compound	Solvent	λ max(log ε)	Ref.
2-Azulenecarboxaldehyde, 3,6-dihydro-1,4-dimethyl-7-(1-methylethyl)-6-[[1-methyl-7-(1-methylethyl)-4-azulenyl]methyl]-	C_6H_{12}	202(4.44),249s(4.51), 285(4.62),289s(4.61), 303s(4.18),346s(4.10), 352(4.14),368s(4.03), 543s(2.47),565s(2.60), 591s(2.69),609(2.75), 632(2.70),666(2.68), 699s(2.38),738(2.26)	18-1748-79
$C_{31}H_{36}O_7$			
Pregna-1,4-diene-3,20-dione, 21-acetoxy-17-(benzoyloxy)-11-hydroxy-16-methyl-, (11β,16α)-	MeOH	233(4.43)	145-1662-79
(11β,16β)-	MeOH	234(4.44)	145-1662-79
Shikodokaurin B benzoate	MeOH	228(4.28),273(3.29)	102-0299-79
$C_{31}H_{38}N_2O_5$			
Ibogamine-18-carboxylic acid, 13-[(3,4-dimethoxyphenyl)methyl]-12-methoxy-, methyl ester	EtOH	224(4.49),283(4.09), 296s(4.00)	36-1403-79
$C_{31}H_{38}N_4O_2$			
21H-Biline-1,19-dione, 3,8,12,17-tetraethyl-22,24-dihydro-2,7,13,18-tetramethyl- (lactim form)	MeOH	355(4.35),615(4.45)	5-1560-79
zinc complex	MeOH	369(4.64),687(4.57)	5-1560-79
$C_{31}H_{38}N_{18}O_6$			
Alanine, 3-(6-amino-9H-purin-9-yl)-N-[3-(6-amino-9H-purin-9-yl)-N-[3-(6-amino-9H-purin-9-yl)-N-[(1,1-dimethylethoxy)carbonyl]alanyl]alanyl]-, ethyl ester	EtOH	260(4.56)	65-1000-79
$C_{31}H_{39}N$			
Benzo[c]phenanthridine, 6-tetradecyl-	EtOH	212(4.77),240(4.70), 254(4.75),264(4.70), 327s(3.67),343(3.47), 360(3.44)	39-1070-79C
Benzo[i]phenanthridine, 5-tetradecyl-	EtOH	215(4.97),221(4.96), 255(5.01),266(5.16), 310(4.25),329(4.23), 340(3.80),360(3.62)	39-1070-79C
$C_{31}H_{39}N_5O_5$			
Ergoptine	CH_2Cl_2	238(4.34),308(3.98)	23-1638-79
$C_{31}H_{40}O_9$			
Benzo[3,4]cycloocta[1,2-f][1,3]benzodioxol-5(6H)-one, 7,8-dihydro-1,2,3-trimethoxy-6,7-dimethyl-13-[2-(2,2,4-trimethyl-1,3-dioxolan-4-yl)propoxy]-	EtOH	210(4.55),229(4.52), 250s(4.17),272s(3.99), 319s(3.58)	94-2695-79
$C_{31}H_{40}O_{10}$			
Benzo[3,4]cycloocta[1,2-f][1,3]benzodioxol-5(6H)-one, 7,8-dihydro-6-hydroxy-1,2,3-trimethoxy-6,7-dimethyl-13-[2-(2,2,4-trimethyl-1,3-dioxolan-4-yl)propoxy]-	EtOH	216(4.56),250s(4.15), 295s(3.44)	94-2695-79

Compound	Solvent	λ_{max}(log ε)	Ref.
$C_{31}H_{41}ClN_2O_9$			
Maytansinol propanoate	MeOH	233(4.48),240s(4.45), 252(4.44),280(3.76), 288(3.76)	78-1079-79
$C_{31}H_{41}IN_2O_4$			
L-Tryptophan, N-[(phenylmethoxy)carbonyl]-, 12-iododecyl ester	EtOH	274(3.77),282(3.79), 291(3.73)	118-0957-79
$C_{31}H_{41}N_3O_6$			
1H-Pyrrole-3-propanoic acid, 5-[[4-(3-methoxy-3-oxopropyl)-2-[[4-(3-methoxy-3-oxopropyl)-3,5-dimethyl-1H-pyrrol-2-yl]methylene]-3-methyl-2H-pyrrol-5-yl]methyl]-2,4-dimethyl-, methyl ester, hydrobromide	$CHCl_3$-HBr	364(3.91),487(4.85)	104-0970-79
$C_{31}H_{42}N_2O_3$			
13-Oxadispiro[5.0.5.1]tridecen-1-one, 2-[[3-(1-hydroxycyclohexyl)-2-(phenylhydrazono)-3-cyclohexen-1-yl]methyl]-, [2α(R*),6α]-	hexane	248(3.87),300(4.14), 327(4.24)	104-0676-79
$C_{31}H_{42}N_2O_5$			
13-Oxadispiro[5.0.5.1]tridecan-1-one, 2-[[2-hydroperoxy-3-(1-hydroxycyclohexyl)-2-(phenylazo)-3-cyclohexen-1-yl]methyl]-	hexane	326(4.54),338(4.53), 431(2.47)	104-0676-79
$C_{31}H_{42}N_4O_5$			
Scutianine H	n.s.g.	none	102-0473-79
$C_{31}H_{42}O_4$			
19-Norlanosta-2,5,7,9-tetraene-1,11-dione, 7-acetoxy-	EtOH	228(4.23),248(4.1), 338(3.89)	12-0179-79
$C_{31}H_{42}O_{10}$			
Benzo[3,4]cycloocta[1,2-f][1,3]benzodioxole-5,6-diol, 5,6,7,8-tetrahydro-1,2,3-trimethoxy-6,7-dimethyl-13-[2-(2,2,4-trimethyl-1,3-dioxolan-4-yl)propoxy]-	EtOH	214(4.74),256s(4.04), 283s(3.51)	94-2695-79
$C_{31}H_{44}N_2O_3$			
13-Oxadispiro[5.0.5.1]tridecan-1-one, 2-[[1'-hydroxy-2-(phenylhydrazono)-[1,1'-biphenyl]-3-yl]methyl]-, [2R-[2α(1R*,3R*),6β]]-	hexane	248(3.93),300(4.11), 330(4.27)	104-0676-79
$C_{31}H_{44}N_2O_8$			
2-Butenedioic acid, 2-methyl-, bis[8-methyl-6-[(3-methyl-1-oxo-2-butenyl)-oxy]-8-azabicyclo[3.2.1]oct-3-yl] ester (schizanthin B)	EtOH	221(4.52)	102-0171-79
$C_{31}H_{44}O_8S$			
Cochlioquinone A_1, 17-(methylthio)-	MeOH	224(3.98),274(3.66), 343(3.48),450(2.97)	32-0565-79
$C_{31}H_{45}NO_8$			
Stephanthraniline B	EtOH	222(4.54),253(5.05)	94-2304-79

Compound	Solvent	$\lambda_{max}(\log \epsilon)$	Ref.
$C_{31}H_{46}O_2$			
Vitamin K_1	DMF	410(3.82)	104-1621-79
$C_{31}H_{46}O_3$			
28-Noroleana-12,17-dien-16-one, 3β-acetoxy-	EtOH	298(3.87)	78-0417-79
$C_{31}H_{46}O_5$			
9,11-Anhydrofusidic acid	EtOH	204(4.19),225s(3.92)	78-2419-79
$C_{31}H_{46}O_6$			
Fusidic acid, 3-oxo-	EtOH	204(4.02),225s(3.88)	78-2419-79
Fusidic acid, 11-oxo-	EtOH	204(4.04),225s(3.84)	78-2419-79
Fusidic acid, 9,11-anhydro-9α,11α-epoxy-	EtOH	204(4.04),225s(3.90)	78-2419-79
Fusidic acid, 9,11-anhydro-12-hydroxy-	EtOH	205(4.20),225s(3.80)	78-2419-79
Pseudofusidic acid, 7,8-dehydro-	EtOH	204(4.18),225s(3.91)	78-2419-79
$C_{31}H_{46}O_7$			
Fusilactidic acid	EtOH	208(4.00),225s(3.83)	78-2419-79
$C_{31}H_{46}O_{13}$			
Aeginetoside pentaacetate	EtOH	237(4.58)	94-2807-79
2,4-Pentadienoic acid, 5-(1-hydroxy-2,2,6-trimethyl-6-[(2,3,4,6-tetra-O-acetyl-β-D-glucopyranosyl)oxy]-cyclohexyl]-3-methyl-, ethyl ester, cis-trans	EtOH	269(4.13)	94-2807-79
trans-trans	EtOH	268(4.39)	94-2807-79
$C_{31}H_{47}N_3O_6$			
10-Undecenoic acid, [2,3,3a,9a-tetra-hydro-6-imino-3-[(1-oxo-10-undecen-yl)oxy]-6H-furo[2',3':4,5]oxazolo-[3,2-a]pyrimidin-2-yl]methyl ester, monohydrochloride, [2R-(2α,3β,3aβ-9aβ)]-	MeOH	235(4.00),264(4.07)	87-0639-79
$C_{31}H_{48}N_2O_7$			
"Sch 23831"	n.s.g.	229(3.94)	88-2767-79
$C_{31}H_{48}O_3$			
28-Norolean-12-en-16-one, 3β-acetoxy-	MeOH	292(1.74)	78-0417-79
28-Norolean-17-en-16-one, 3β-acetoxy-	EtOH	251(3.74)	78-0417-79
$C_{31}H_{48}O_4$			
C(14a)-Homo-B-norchola-8(14a),9(11)-di-ene-3,24-diol, 4,4,14-trimethyl-, diacetate, (3β,5α)-	EtOH	260(3.90)	56-1203-79
$C_{31}H_{48}O_6$			
3-Epifusidic acid	EtOH	204(3.99),225(3.87)	78-2419-79
11-Epifusidic acid	EtOH	204(3.99),225s(3.85)	78-2419-79
Fusidic acid, 24,24-dihydro-11-oxo-	EtOH	214(3.90)	78-2419-79
$C_{31}H_{48}O_7$			
α-Ecdysone, 3,22-diacetyl-2-deoxy-	EtOH	243(4.04)	105-0700-79
Isofusilactidic acid, 24,25-dihydro-	EtOH	214(3.88)	78-2419-79
$C_{31}H_{48}O_8$			
Ecdysterone, 3,22-diacetyl-2-deoxy-	EtOH	243(4.10)	105-0700-79

Compound	Solvent	λ_{max}(log ε)	Ref.
$C_{31}H_{49}Br_2N_3O_6$			
Undecanoic acid, 11-bromo-, 2-[[(11-bromo-1-oxoundecyl)oxy]methyl]-2,3,3a,9a-tetrahydro-6-imino-6H-furo-[2',3':4,5]oxazolo[3,2-a]pyrimidin-3-yl ester, monohydrochloride, [2R-(2α,3β,3aβ,9aβ)]-	MeOH	236(3.97),264(4.05)	87-0639-79
$C_{31}H_{49}NO_4$			
22,26-Epimino-5α-chloest-22(N)-ene-3β,16α-diol, diacetate, (25S)-	EtOH	240(2.40)	12-0597-79
$C_{31}H_{50}N_6O_{10}$			
1-Piperidinyloxy, 4-[[[3-(2-deoxy-β-D-erythro-pentofuranosyl)-3,6-dihydro-2,6-dioxo-5-[2-oxo-2-[(2,2,6,6-tetramethyl-1-oxy-4-piperidinyl)amino]ethoxy]-1(2H)-pyrimidinyl]acetyl]amino]-2,2,6,6-tetramethyl-	pH 7	275(3.90)	33-1677-79
$C_{31}H_{50}N_6O_{11}$			
1-Piperidinyloxy, 4-[[[3,6-dihydro-2,6-dioxo-3-β-D-ribofuranosyl-5-[2-[(2,2,6,6-tetramethyl-1-oxo-4-piperidinyl)amino]-2-oxoethoxy]-1(2H)-pyrimidinyl]acetyl]amino]-2,2,6,6-tetramethyl-	pH 7	275(3.90)	33-1677-79
$C_{31}H_{50}O_3$			
Alnuselide	MeOH	220(1.54)	18-1153-79
C(14a)-Homo-B-norchola-8(14a),9(11)-dien-24-ol, 3-ethoxy-4,4,14-trimethyl-, acetate, (3β,5α)-	EtOH	262(3.91)	56-1203-79
28-Noroleanan-16-one, 3β-acetoxy-	MeOH	288(2.31)	78-0417-79

Compound	Solvent	$\lambda_{max}(\log \epsilon)$	Ref.
$C_{32}H_{17}N_5O_8$			
Benzo[lmn][3,8]phenanthroline-1,3,6,8-(2H,7H)-tetrone, 2,7-bis(4-nitrophenyl)-4-(phenylamino)-	$CHCl_3$	516(4.10)	104-2279-79
$C_{32}H_{18}BrNOS_2$			
9H-Naphth[3,2,1-kl]acridin-9-one, 2-bromo-6,8-bis(phenylthio)-	EtOH	292(4.60),432(4.07), 460(3.87),496(4.01), 528(4.05)	103-1227-79
$C_{32}H_{18}N_4O_6$			
Benzo[lmn][3,8]phenanthroline-1,3,6,8-(2H,7H)-tetrone, 4-[(3-nitrophenyl)-amino]-2,7-diphenyl-	$CHCl_3$	502(4.23)	104-2279-79
Benzo[lmn][3,8]phenanthroline-1,3,6,8-(2H,7H)-tetrone, 4-[(4-nitrophenyl)-amino]-2,7-diphenyl-	$CHCl_3$	507(4.27)	104-2279-79
$C_{32}H_{18}O_6$			
Methanone, benzo[1,2-b:4,5-b']bisbenzofuran-6,12-diylbis[(2-hydroxyphenyl)-	dioxan	224(4.64),265(4.34), 295(4.24),355(4.26)	1-0405-79
$C_{32}H_{19}Cl_2N_5O$			
2H-Naphtho[1,2-d]triazole, 2-[3-chloro-4-[2-[4-[5-(4-chlorophenyl)-1,2,4-oxadiazol-3-yl]phenyl]ethenyl]phenyl]-	DMF	322(4.45),373(4.83)	33-1411-79
$C_{32}H_{19}F_3O_3$			
Acetic acid, trifluoro-, 1',2'-dihydro-10-oxospiro[anthracene-9(10H),3'-[3H]benz[de]anthracen]-7'-yl ester	C_6H_{12}	263(5.19),289(3.86), 301(3.63),328(3.20), 343(3.52),361(3.85), 381(4.07),402(4.04)	44-1787-79
$C_{32}H_{19}N_3O_4$			
Benzo[lmn][3,8]phenanthroline-1,3,6,8-(2H,7H)-tetrone, 2,7-diphenyl-4-(phenylamino)-	$CHCl_3$	514(4.17)	104-2279-79
$C_{32}H_{20}ClN_5O$			
2H-Naphtho[1,2-d]triazole, 2-[3-chloro-4-[2-[4-(5-phenyl-1,2,4-oxadiazol-3-yl)phenyl]ethenyl]phenyl]-	DMF	323(4.44),373(4.83)	33-1411-79
$C_{32}H_{20}N_2O_2$			
1H-Phenalen-1-one, 9,9'-(1,2-phenylenediimino)bis-	n.s.g.	277(4.35),355(4.36), 443(4.24),462(4.16)	44-1704-79
$C_{32}H_{20}O_2$			
Methanone, 1,8-naphthalenediylbis[1-naphthalenyl-	EtOH	216(5.02),230s(4.79), 250s(4.35),316(4.28)	18-3314-79
$C_{32}H_{20}O_3$			
Spiro[anthracene-9(10H),3'-[3H]benz-[de]anthracen]-10-one	C_6H_{12}	267(5.03),370(3.56), 392(3.90),416(4.19), 442(4.23)	44-1787-79
$C_{32}H_{21}ClN_2O_2$			
Isoxazole, 5-(4-chlorophenyl)-3-[4"-(5"'-phenylisoxazol-2"'-yl)stilben-4'-yl]-	DMF	367(4.84)	33-0779-79

Compound	Solvent	λ_{max}(log ε)	Ref.
Isoxazole, 5-phenyl-3-[4"-[3"'-(4-chlorophenyl)isoxazol-5"'-yl]stilben-4'-yl]-	DMF	351(4.81)	33-0779-79
$C_{32}H_{21}Cl_2N_3O$			
Isoxazole, 5-(4-chlorophenyl)-3-[4-[2-[4-[1-(4-chlorophenyl)-1H-pyrazol-3-yl]phenyl]ethenyl]phenyl]-	DMF	353(4.87)	33-1816-79
$C_{32}H_{22}ClN_3O$			
Isoxazole, 3-(4-chlorophenyl)-5-[4-[2-[4-(1-phenyl-1H-pyrazol-3-yl)phenyl]ethenyl]phenyl]-	DMF	363(4.87)	33-1816-79
Isoxazole, 3-(4-chlorophenyl)-5-[4-[2-[4-(3-phenyl-1H-pyrazol-1-yl)phenyl]ethenyl]phenyl]-	DMF	360(4.86)	33-1816-79
Isoxazole, 5-(4-chlorophenyl)-3-[4-[2-[4-(1-phenyl-1H-pyrazol-3-yl)phenyl]ethenyl]phenyl]-	DMF	353(4.85)	33-1816-79
Isoxazole, 5-(4-chlorophenyl)-3-[4-[2-[4-(3-phenyl-1H-pyrazol-1-yl)phenyl]ethenyl]phenyl]-	DMF	351(4.84)	33-1816-79
Isoxazole,3-[4-[2-[4-[3-(4-chlorophenyl)-1H-pyrazol-1-yl]phenyl]ethenyl]phenyl]-5-phenyl-	DMF	352(4.85)	33-1816-79
Isoxazole, 5-[4-[2-[4-[1-(4-chlorophenyl)-1H-pyrazol-3-yl]phenyl]ethenyl]phenyl]-3-phenyl-	DMF	362(4.88)	33-1816-79
Isoxazole, 5-[4-[2-[4-[3-(4-chlorophenyl)-1H-pyrazol-1-yl]phenyl]ethenyl]phenyl]-3-phenyl-	DMF	359(4.87)	33-1816-79
Oxazole, 2-[4-[2-[4-[1-(4-chlorophenyl)-1H-pyrazol-3-yl]phenyl]ethenyl]phenyl]-5-phenyl-	DMF	375(4.90)	33-1816-79
$C_{32}H_{22}ClN_3O_3$			
1,2,4-Oxadiazole, 3-(4-chlorophenyl)-5-[4"-[5"'-(4-methoxyphenyl)isoxazol-3"'-yl]stilben-4'-yl]-	DMF	349(4.84)	33-0779-79
1,2,4-Oxadiazole, 3-(4-methoxyphenyl)-5-[4"-[5"'-(4-chlorophenyl)isoxazol-3"'-yl]stilben-4'-yl]-	DMF	348(4.84)	33-0779-79
1,3,4-Oxadiazole, 2-[2'-chloro-4"-[3"'-(4-methoxyphenyl)isoxazol-5"'-yl]-stilben-4'-yl]-5-phenyl-	DMF	362(4.81)	33-0779-79
1,3,4-Oxadiazole, 2-[2'-chloro-4"-[5"'-(4-methoxyphenyl)isoxazol-3"'-yl]-stilben-4'-yl]-5-phenyl-	DMF	355(4.79)	33-0779-79
1,3,4-Oxadiazole, 2-[2'-chloro-4"-(3"'-phenylisoxazol-5"'-yl)stilben-4'-yl]-5-(4-methoxyphenyl)-	DMF	365(4.84)	33-0779-79
1,3,4-Oxadiazole, 2-[2'-chloro-4"-(5"'-phenylisoxazol-3"'-yl)stilben-4'-yl]-5-(4-methoxyphenyl)-	DMF	358(4.80)	33-0779-79
1,3,4-Oxadiazole, 2-(4-chlorophenyl)-5-[4"-[5"'-(4-methoxyphenyl)isoxazol-3"'-yl]stilben-4'-yl]-	DMF	353(4.89)	33-0779-79
1,3,4-Oxadiazole, 2-(4-methoxyphenyl)-5-[4"-[5"'-(4-chlorophenyl)isoxazol-3"'-yl]stilben-4'-yl]-	DMF	356(4.88)	33-0779-79

Compound	Solvent	λ_{max}(log ε)	Ref.
$C_{32}H_{22}Cl_2N_4O_2$			
2H-1,2,3-Triazole, 2-[2'-chloro-4"-[5"'-(4-methoxyphenyl)isoxazol-3"'-yl]stilben-4'-yl]-4-phenyl-5-chloro-	DMF	355(4.83)	33-0779-79
$C_{32}H_{22}N_2O_2$			
Isoxazole, 5-phenyl-3-[4"-(3"'-phenylisoxazol-5"'-yl)stilben-4'-yl]-	DMF	350(4.84)	33-0779-79
Isoxazole, 5-phenyl-3-[4"-(5"'-phenyloxazol-2"'-yl)stilben-4'-yl]-	DMF	368(4.83)	33-0779-79
$C_{32}H_{22}O_3$			
Spiro[anthracene-9(10H),3'-[3H]benz[de]anthracen]-10-one, 7'-acetoxy-1',2'-dihydro-	C_6H_{12}	264(5.16),290(3.81), 303(3.73),329(3.11), 345(3.49),362(3.84), 382(4.08),404(4.06)	44-1787-79
$C_{32}H_{23}ClN_2O_2$			
Benzoxazole, 2-[4"-[3"'-(4-chlorophenyl)isoxazol-5"'-yl]stilben-4'-yl]-5,7-dimethyl-	DMF	368(4.91),387(4.72)	33-0779-79
Benzoxazole, 2-[4"-[5"'-(4-chlorophenyl)isoxazol-3"'-yl]stilben-4'-yl]-5,7-dimethyl-	DMF	363(4.88),380(4.69)	33-0779-79
$C_{32}H_{23}ClN_4O_2$			
1,3,4-Oxadiazole, 2-[3-chloro-4-[2-[4-(1-phenyl-1H-pyrazol-3-yl)phenyl]ethenyl]phenyl]-5-(4-methoxyphenyl)-	DMF	368(4.82)	33-1816-79
1,3,4-Oxadiazole, 2-[4-[2-[4-[1-(4-chlorophenyl)-1H-pyrazol-3-yl]phenyl]ethenyl]phenyl]-5-(4-methoxyphenyl)-	DMF	365(4.90)	33-1816-79
$C_{32}H_{23}ClN_4O_4$			
1,2,4-Oxadiazole, 5-[4-[2-[2-chloro-4-[5-(5-methoxyphenyl)-1,3,4-oxadiazol-2-yl]phenyl]ethenyl]phenyl]-3-(4-methoxyphenyl)-	DMF	363(4.81)	33-1411-79
$C_{32}H_{23}NO$			
9-Anthracenecarbonitrile, 10-[[(10-methyl-9-anthracenyl)methoxy]methyl]-	$C_6H_{11}Me$	252(4.92),258(4.93), 360(3.81),377(3.99), 386(3.98),398(3.97), 408(3.95)	39-0411-79B
5H-Indeno[1,2-c]pyridine, 5-(4-methoxyphenyl)methylene]-1,3-diphenyl-	EtOH	224s(4.9),256(4.86), 286(4.82),320s(4.6), 370(4.4)	103-0899-79
$C_{32}H_{23}NO_2$			
Isoxazole, 3-[4"-(5"'-methylbenzofuran-2"'-yl)stilben-4'-yl]-5-phenyl-	DMF	368(4.87)	33-0779-79
$C_{32}H_{23}NO_3$			
Isoxazole, 3-[4"-(benzofuran-2"'-yl)-stilben-4'-yl]-5-(4-methoxyphenyl)-	DMF	366(4.88)	33-0779-79
Isoxazole, 3-[4"-(5"'-methoxybenzofuran-2"'-yl)stilben-4'-yl]-5-phenyl-	DMF	370(4.88)	33-0779-79
$C_{32}H_{23}NO_4$			
Naphtho[1,2-b]furan-3(2H)-one, 5-(benzoyloxy)-2-(methoxyphenylamino)-4-phenyl-	EtOH	239(4.69),272(4.40), 379(3.78)	103-0597-79

Compound	Solvent	λ_{max}(log ϵ)	Ref.
$C_{32}H_{23}NO_8$			
1,4-Naphthalenedione, 2-acetyl-3-[4-(3-acetyl-1,4-dihydro-1,4-dioxo-2-naphthalenyl)amino]-3,5-dimethoxyphenyl]-	dioxan	246(4.51),253(4.50), 261s(4.4),296(4.44), 479(3.73)	5-0503-79
$C_{32}H_{23}N_3O$			
Isoxazole, 3-phenyl-5-[4-[2-[4-(1-phenyl-1H-pyrazol-3-yl)phenyl]ethenyl]-phenyl]-	DMF	362(4.87)	33-1816-79
Isoxazole, 3-phenyl-5-[4-[2-[4-(3-phenyl-1H-pyrazol-1-yl)phenyl]ethenyl]-phenyl]-	DMF	360(4.85)	33-1816-79
Isoxazole, 5-phenyl-3-[4-[2-[4-(1-phenyl-1H-pyrazol-3-yl)phenyl]ethenyl]-phenyl]-	DMF	353(4.84)	33-1816-79
Isoxazole, 5-phenyl-3-[4-[2-[4-(3-phenyl-1H-pyrazol-1-yl)phenyl]ethenyl]-phenyl]-	DMF	352(4.83)	33-1816-79
Oxazole, 5-phenyl-2-[4-[2-[4-(1-phenyl-1H-pyrazol-3-yl)phenyl]ethenyl]-phenyl]-	DMF	373(4.89)	33-1816-79
Oxazole, 5-phenyl-2-[4-[2-[4-(3-phenyl-1H-pyrazol-1-yl)phenyl]ethenyl]-phenyl]-	DMF	373(4.88)	33-1816-79
$C_{32}H_{23}N_3O_3$			
1,2,4-Oxadiazole, 3-(4-methoxyphenyl)-5-[4"-(3"'-phenylisoxazol-5"'-yl)-stilben-4'-yl]-	DMF	358(4.85)	33-0779-79
1,2,4-Oxadiazole, 3-(4-methoxyphenyl)-5-[4"-(5"'-phenylisoxazol-3"'-yl)-stilben-4'-yl]-	DMF	350(4.83)	33-0779-79
1,2,4-Oxadiazole, 3-phenyl-5-[4"-[3"'-(4-methoxyphenyl)-5"'-isoxazol-yl]stilben-4'-yl]-	DMF	358(4.83)	33-0779-79
1,2,4-Oxadiazole, 3-phenyl-5-[4"-[5"'-(4-methoxyphenyl)-3"'-isoxazol-yl]stilben-4'-yl]-	DMF	350(4.84)	33-0779-79
1,3,4-Oxadiazole, 2-(2-methoxyphenyl)-5-[4"-(5"'-phenylisoxazol-3"'-yl)-stilben-4'-yl]-	DMF	353(4.84)	33-0779-79
1,3,4-Oxadiazole, 2-(3-methoxyphenyl)-5-[4"-(5"'-phenylisoxazol-3"'-yl)-stilben-4'-yl]-	DMF	355(4.86)	33-0779-79
1,3,4-Oxadiazole, 2-(4-methoxyphenyl)-5-[4"-(5"'-phenylisoxazol-3"'-yl)-stilben-4'-yl]-	DMF	357(4.87)	33-0779-79
1,3,4-Oxadiazole, 2-(4-methoxyphenyl)-5-[4"-(3"'-phenylisoxazol-5"'-yl)-stilben-4'-yl]-	DMF	363(4.91)	33-0779-79
1,3,4-Oxadiazole, 2-phenyl-5-[4"-[3"'-(4-methoxyphenyl)isoxazol-5"'-yl]stilben-4'-yl]-	DMF	359(4.89)	33-0779-79
1,3,4-Oxadiazole, 2-phenyl-5-[4"-[5"'-(4-methoxyphenyl)isoxazol-3"'-yl]stilben-4'-yl]-	DMF	352(4.87)	33-0779-79
$C_{32}H_{23}N_5$			
Benzo[c]cinnolinium, 5-[[phenyl[[phenyl(phenylamino)methylene]amino]methylene]amino]-, hydroxide, inner salt	n.s.g.	247(4.75),297(4.07), 310(4.04),324(3.92), 431(4.11)	39-0185-79C

Compound	Solvent	$\lambda_{max}(\log \epsilon)$	Ref.
$C_{32}H_{23}N_7O_{13}S$			
β-D-arabino-Hexopyranoside, 1H-purin-6-yl 2-deoxy-1-thio-, 3,4,6-tris(4-nitrobenzoate)	$CHCl_3$	295(3.45)	136-0089-79B
$C_{32}H_{24}$			
Pentacyclo[20.2.2.2^{4,7}.2^{10,13}.2^{16,19}]-dotriaconta-2,4,6,8,10,12,14,16,18-20,22,24,25,27,29,31-hexadecaene	C_6H_{12} or EtOH	303(4.76)	1-0443-79
Phenanthrene, 9-[4-(3,5-dimethylphenyl)-3-buten-1-ynyl]-1-phenyl-, (E)-	MeOH	252s(4.49),260(4.53), 281s(4.55),289(4.57), 341(4.46)	78-1537-79
Triphenylene, 1-(3,5-dimethylphenyl)-12-phenyl-	MeOH	261(4.69),268(4.76), 289(4.57)	78-1537-79
$C_{32}H_{24}ClN_3O$			
Benzoxazole, 2-[4-[2-[4-[3-(4-chlorophenyl)-1H-pyrazol-1-yl]phenyl]ethenyl]phenyl]-5,7-dimethyl-	DMF	369(4.89)	33-1816-79
Benzoxazole, 2-[4-[2-[4-(4-chloro-3-phenyl-1H-pyrazol-1-yl)phenyl]ethenyl]phenyl]-5,6-dimethyl-	DMF	369(4.89)	33-1816-79
$C_{32}H_{24}N_2O_2$			
Benzoxazole, 2-[4"-(5"'-phenylisoxazol-3"'-yl)stilben-4'-yl]-5,6-dimethyl-	DMF	365(4.88)	33-0779-79
Benzoxazole, 2-[4"-(3"'-phenylisoxazol-5"'-yl)stilben-4'-yl]-5,7-dimethyl-	DMF	368(4.91),388(4.73)	33-0779-79
Benzoxazole, 2-[4"-(5"'-phenylisoxazol-3"'-yl)stilben-4'-yl]-5,7-dimethyl-	DMF	363(4.88)	33-0779-79
1H-Pyrazole, 1-[4-[2-[4-(5-methoxy-2-benzofuranyl)phenyl]ethenyl]phenyl]-3-phenyl-	DMF	374(4.93)	33-1816-79
1H-Pyrazole, 3-[4-[2-[4-(5-methoxy-2-benzofuranyl)phenyl]ethenyl]phenyl]-1-phenyl-	DMF	374(4.94),393(4.77)	33-1816-79
$C_{32}H_{24}N_2O_3$			
Benzoxazole, 2-[4"-[3"'-(4-methoxyphenyl)isoxazol-5"'-yl)stilben-4'-yl]-5-methyl-	DMF	368(4.92),387(4.75)	33-0779-79
Benzoxazole, 2-[4"-[3"'-(4-methoxyphenyl)isoxazol-5"'-yl)stilben-4'-yl]-7-methyl-	DMF	365(4.95),385(4.76)	33-0779-79
Benzoxazole, 2-[4"-[5"'-(4-methoxyphenyl)isoxazol-3"'-yl)stilben-4'-yl]-5-methyl-	DMF	360(4.89),378(4.69)	33-0779-79
Benzoxazole, 2-[4"-[5"'-(4-methoxyphenyl)isoxazol-3"'-yl)stilben-4'-yl]-7-methyl-	DMF	360(4.89),378(4.69)	33-0779-79
$C_{32}H_{24}N_2O_4$			
Benzoxazole, 2-[4"-[3"'-(4-methoxyphenyl)isoxazol-5"'-yl]stilben-4'-yl]-5-methoxy-	DMF	370(4.91)	33-0779-79
Benzoxazole, 2-[4"-[5"'-(4-methoxyphenyl)isoxazol-3"'-yl]stilben]4'-yl]-5-methoxy-	DMF	365(4.88)	33-0779-79

Compound	Solvent	λ_{max}(log ε)	Ref.
$C_{32}H_{24}N_4$			
1H-Pyrazole, 1,1'-(1,2-ethenediyldi-4,1-phenylene)bis[3-phenyl-	DMF	357(4.89)	33-1816-79
1H-Pyrazole, 3,3'-(1,2-ethenediyldi-4,1-phenylene)bis[1-phenyl-	DMF	359(4.90)	33-1816-79
1H-Pyrazole, 1-phenyl-3-[4-[2-[4-(3-phenyl-1H-pyrazol-1-yl)phenyl]ethenyl]phenyl]-	DMF	358(4.89)	33-1816-79
$C_{32}H_{24}N_4O_2$			
1,2,4-Oxadiazole, 3-(4-methoxyphenyl)-5-[4-[2-[4-(1-phenyl-1H-pyrazol-3-yl)phenyl]ethenyl]phenyl]-	DMF	362(4.82)	33-1816-79
1,2,4-Oxadiazole, 3-(4-methoxyphenyl)-5-[4-[2-[4-(3-phenyl-1H-pyrazol-1-yl)phenyl]ethenyl]phenyl]-	DMF	362(4.82)	33-1816-79
1,2,4-Oxadiazole, 5-(4-methoxyphenyl)-3-[4-[2-[4-(1-phenyl-1H-pyrazol-3-yl)phenyl]ethenyl]phenyl]-	DMF	353(4.83)	33-1816-79
1,3,4-Oxadiazole, 2-(2-methoxyphenyl)-5-[4-[2-[4-(1-phenyl-1H-pyrazol-3-yl)phenyl]ethenyl]phenyl]-	DMF	362(4.86)	33-1816-79
1,3,4-Oxadiazole, 2-(3-methoxyphenyl)-5-[4-[2-[4-(1-phenyl-1H-pyrazol-3-yl)phenyl]ethenyl]phenyl]-	DMF	364(4.86)	33-1816-79
1,3,4-Oxadiazole, 2-(4-methoxyphenyl)-5-[4-[2-[4-(1-phenyl-1H-pyrazol-3-yl)phenyl]ethenyl]phenyl]-	DMF	365(4.89)	33-1816-79
1,3,4-Oxadiazole, 2-(4-methoxyphenyl)-5-[4-[2-[4-(3-phenyl-1H-pyrazol-1-yl)phenyl]ethenyl]phenyl]-	DMF	366(4.87)	33-1816-79
$C_{32}H_{24}N_4O_4$			
1,2,4-Oxadiazole, 5-(4-methoxyphenyl)-3-[4-[2-[4-[5-(4-methoxyphenyl)-1,3,4-oxadiazol-2-yl]phenyl]ethenyl]phenyl]-	DMF	357(4.87)	33-1411-79
$C_{32}H_{24}N_6O_6S_2$			
1-Naphthalenesulfonic acid, 3,3'-[[1,1'-biphenyl]-4,4'-diylbis(azo)]bis[4-amino- (Congo Red)	n.s.g.	235(4.6),342(4.5), 500(4.7)	69-5197-79
$C_{32}H_{24}O_2$			
Anthracene, 9,9'-(1,2-ethenediyl)bis-[10-methoxy-	$CHCl_3$	417(4.3)	44-4247-79
$C_{32}H_{24}S$			
Thiophene, 2,5-bis(2-[1,1'-biphenyl]-4-ylethenyl)-, (E,E)-	toluene	415(4.83)	103-0729-79
$C_{32}H_{24}Si$			
Silane, 9-anthracenyltriphenyl-	CCl_4	342(3.54),356(3.83), 374(4.01),394(3.98)	78-2131-79
$C_{32}H_{24}Sn$			
Stannane, 9-anthracenyltriphenyl-	CCl_4	338(3.51),354(3.82), 371(3.99),391(3.97)	78-2131-79
$C_{32}H_{25}ClNO_4P$			
1H-Pyrrole-3-acetic acid, 4-chloro-2,5-dihydro-2,5-dioxo-1-phenyl-α-(triphen-	MeOH	223(4.71),270(3.95), 450(3.83)	48-0797-79

Compound	Solvent	$\lambda_{max}(\log \epsilon)$	Ref.
ylphosphoranylidene)-, ethyl ester			48-0797-79
$C_{32}H_{25}N_3O_3$			
Benzoxazole, 2-[4-[2-[4-[5-(4-methoxy-phenyl)-1,2,4-oxadiazol-3-yl]phenyl]-ethenyl]phenyl]-5,7-dimethyl-	DMF	362(4.88)	33-1411-79
$C_{32}H_{25}OPSe$			
Phosphonium, triphenyl-, 2-oxo-2-phen-yl-1-(phenylseleno)ethylide	n.s.g.	225s(3.892),270(2.945), 278s(2.914)	65-1740-79
$C_{32}H_{26}Br_2N_4O_2$			
Dibenzo[b,j][1,5,9,13]tetraazacyclo-hexadecine-6,16(5H,7H)-dione, 2,12-dibromo-8,15,17,18-tetrahydro-10,20-diphenyl-	DMF	281s(--),320(3.99)	30-0105-79
$C_{32}H_{26}ClNO_6$			
2H-Pyran-3-carboxylic acid, 6-[6-(4-chlorophenyl)-1,2-dihydro-2-oxo-4-phenyl-3-pyridinyl]-3,4-dihydro-4-(4-methoxyphenyl)-2-oxo-, ethyl ester	HOAc	262(4.47),306(4.25)	120-0001-79
$C_{32}H_{26}N_2O_{10}$			
Uridine, 5-acetyl-, 2',3',5'-tribenzoate	EtOH-acid	284(4.17)	78-1125-79
	EtOH-base	284(4.04)	78-1125-79
$C_{32}H_{26}N_4O_4$			
2H-Benzotriazole, 5,6-dimethoxy-2-[4"-[5"'-(4-methoxyphenyl)isoxazol-3"'-yl]stilben-4'-yl]-	DMF	369(4.89)	33-0779-79
[1,1'-Biphenyl]-4,4'-dicarboxaldehyde, 2,2'-dinitro-, bis[(4-ethenylphenyl)-methyl]imine	$CHCl_3$	257(4.9)	24-2854-79
$C_{32}H_{26}N_6O_6$			
Dibenzo[b,j][1,5,9,13]tetraazacyclo-hexadecine-6,16(5H,7H)-dione, 8,15,17,18-tetrahydro-2,12-dinitro-10,20-diphenyl-	DMF	281s(--),338(4.42)	30-0105-79
$C_{32}H_{26}O_2$			
Anthracene, 9,9'-(1,2-ethanediyl)bis-[10-methoxy-	C_6H_{12}	253(5.27),262(5.30), 350(3.74),366(4.02), 387(4.27),410(4.31)	44-4247-79
$C_{32}H_{26}O_4$			
[2,2'-Bi-4H-1-benzopyran]-4,4'-dione, 2,2',3,3'-tetrahydro-6,6'-dimethyl-2,2'-diphenyl-	MeOH	220(4.20),256(3.68), 333(3.22)	77-0333-79
$C_{32}H_{26}O_8$			
[9,9'-Bianthracene]-10,10'(9H,9'H)-di-one, 4,4',5,5'-tetrahydroxy-2,2'-di-methoxy-7,7'-dimethyl-	MeOH	279(3.85),360(3.95)	98-1342-79
$C_{32}H_{26}O_{10}$			
Aurasperone A	EtOH	225(4.52),258(4.42), 280(4.53),325(3.90), 400(3.68)	98-1347-79

Compound	Solvent	$\lambda_{max}(\log \epsilon)$	Ref.
Isoaurosperone A	EtOH	255(4.53),275(4.59), 388(3.54)	98-1347-79
$C_{32}H_{27}O_2P$			
Phosphorin, 1,1-dihydro-1,1-diphenoxy-2,6-diphenyl-4-(1-propenyl)-	MeOH	417(3.94)	24-1272-79
$C_{32}H_{28}$			
Anthracene, 1,2,3,4,4a,10-hexahydro-9,10,10-triphenyl-	ether	265(3.90),271(3.94), 276(3.96),283(3.98)	78-2101-79
[2]Paracyclophane-1,9-diene	EtOH	270(4.19),310(3.99)	1-0391-79
$C_{32}H_{28}N_2O_2$			
[6,6'-Bi-6H-pyrrolo[3,2,1-de]acridine]-6,6'-diol, 1,1',2,2'-tetrahydro-1,1'-dimethyl-	EtOH	212(4.1),262(3.65), 285(3.9)	103-1223-79
Pyrazine, 2,5-bis(phenylmethoxy)-3,6-bis(phenylmethyl)-	EtOH	230s(4.57),280(3.85), 324(4.46)	94-2980-79
$C_{32}H_{28}N_2O_2S_2$			
1H-Indole, 2,2'-dithiobis[3-(4-methoxy-phenyl)-1-methyl-	dioxan	355(4.14)	103-0282-79
	MeOH	230(--),260(--)	103-0282-79
$C_{32}H_{28}N_2O_5$			
1H-Indole-2-methanol, 3-[2-(phenylmeth-oxy)ethyl]-1-(phenylmethyl)-, 4-ni-trobenzoate	EtOH	224(4.63),268(4.30), 300(3.96)	23-0289-79
$C_{32}H_{28}N_2O_8S$			
2(1H)-Pyrimidinone, 5-ethyl-3,4-dihy-dro-4-thioxo-1-(2,3,5-tri-O-benzoyl-α-D-arabinofuranosyl)-	MeOH	275(3.46),336(4.05)	87-0647-79
$C_{32}H_{28}N_2O_9$			
2,4(1H,3H)-Pyrimidinedione, 5-ethyl-1-(2,3,5-tri-O-benzoyl-α-D-arabino-furanosyl)-	MeOH	265(4.13)	87-0647-79
$C_{32}H_{28}N_2S_2$			
1H-Indole, 2,2'-dithiobis[1-methyl-3-(2-methylphenyl)-	dioxan	355(4.00)	103-0282-79
	MeOH	228(--),285(--)	103-0282-79
$C_{32}H_{28}N_4O_2S_4$			
Benzo[1,2-d:5,4-d']bisthiazolium, 2,2'-[(2,5-dimethoxy-1,4-phenylene)di-2,1-ethenediyl]bis[3,6-dimethyl-, diiodide	DMF	295(4.08),385(4.44), 508(4.57)	126-1441-79
$C_{32}H_{28}N_4O_7$			
1-Azabicyclo[4.2.0]oct-2-ene-2,4,4-tri-carboxylic acid, 7-azido-3-methyl-8-oxo-, tris(phenylmethyl) ester, trans	EtOH	270(4.04)	23-0222-79
$C_{32}H_{28}O_2$			
9H-Xanthene, 2-(1-methylethyl)-9-[2-(1-methylethyl)-9H-xanthen-9-ylidene]-	CH_2Cl_2	235(4.25),256(4.15), 283(4.03),368(4.24)	35-0665-79
$C_{32}H_{28}O_5$			
9,10-Anthracenedione, 2-(1-hydroxybut-yl)-1,4-bis(phenylmethoxy)-	MeOH	207(4.72),251(4.51), 401(3.79)	5-0019-79

Compound	Solvent	$\lambda_{max}(\log \epsilon)$	Ref.
$C_{32}H_{28}O_{11}$			
Aurasperone E	EtOH	230(4.86),282(5.17), 322(4.35),330(4.31), 400(4.29)	98-1347-79
$C_{32}H_{28}S_4$			
1-Buten-3-yne, tetrakis(4-methylphenylthio)-	heptane	201(4.61),210(4.65), 348(4.29)	5-1606-79
$C_{32}H_{29}NOS$			
2H,6H-[1,3]Thiazino[2,3-a]isoquinoline, 7,11b-dihydro-2-methoxy-3,4-diphenyl-11b-(phenylmethyl)-	MeCN	275(3.79),300(3.88)	88-1213-79
$C_{32}H_{29}NO_3$			
1H-Indole-2-methanol, 3-[2-(phenylmethoxy)ethyl]-1-(phenylmethyl)-, benzoate	EtOH	225(4.66),275(4.16), 300(3.86)	23-0289-79
$C_{32}H_{29}NO_7$			
L-Tyrosine, N-[(phenylmethoxy)carbonyl]-, phenylmethyl ester phenylmethyl carbonate	EtOH	258(2.88),264(3.01), 268(2.97),270(2.99), 273(2.83)	118-0957-79
$C_{32}H_{29}O_2P$			
Phosphorin, 1,1-dihydro-1,1-diphenoxy-2,6-diphenyl-4-propyl-	MeOH	408(4.22)	24-1272-79
$C_{32}H_{30}$			
Bi-2,4,6-cycloheptatrien-1-yl, bis(4-cyclopropylphenyl)-	$CHCl_3$	250(4.56),290s(4.23)	39-0262-79B
1,1'-Biphenyl, 4,4'-bis[2-(2,4-dimethylphenyl)ethenyl]-	dioxan	326(4.77)	104-1944-79
Pentacyclo[20.2.2.2^{4,7}.2^{10,13}.2^{16,19}]-dotriaconta-2,4,6,10,12,16,18,22,24-25,27,29,31-tridecaene	EtOH	269(4.03)	1-0391-79
$C_{32}H_{30}OSi_2$			
Disiloxane, 1,3-di-9-anthracenyl-1,1,3,3-tetramethyl-	$C_6H_{11}Me$	257(5.45),334(3.77), 350(4.07),378(4.26), 388(4.22)	152-0231-79
photocyclomer	ether	225(4.67),252(4.56), 273(3.82),283(3.75), 297(3.71),307(3.54), 320(2.98),348(2.82)	152-0231-79
$C_{32}H_{31}NO$			
1H-3-Benzazepine, 3-(diphenylacetyl)-2,3,4,5-tetrahydro-2,2-dimethyl-1-phenyl-	EtOH	260(3.04)	4-1525-79
$C_{32}H_{31}N_3O_2$			
1H-Imidazole-5-carboxylic acid, 4,5-dihydro-1-methyl-2,4,5-tris(4-methylphenyl)-4-(2-pyridinyl)-, methyl ester	EtOH	222s(4.34),265(3.79)	44-0041-79
$C_{32}H_{31}N_3O_5$			
4H-Pyrrolo[2,3-d]pyrimidin-4-one, 1,7-dihydro-7-[2,3,5-tris-O-(phenylmethyl)-α-D-arabinofuranosyl]-	MeOH	258(3.98),275s(3.82)	24-3432-79
β-	MeOH	258(3.99),275s(3.85)	24-3432-79

Compound	Solvent	λmax(log ε)	Ref.
$C_{32}H_{32}N_2O_5$			
Acetamide, 2,2'-[oxybis(2,1-ethanediyl-oxy)]bis[N,N-diphenyl-	H_2O	229(4.28)	33-0754-79
$C_{32}H_{34}N_2O_6$			
2,4(1H,3H)-Pyrimidinedione, 5-ethyl-1-[2,3,5-tris-O-(phenylmethyl)-β-D-arabinofuranosyl]-	MeOH	265(3.99)	87-0647-79
$C_{32}H_{34}N_2O_7S$			
2-Naphthacenecarboxamide, N-(1,1-dimethylethyl)-1,4,4a,5,5a,6,11,12a-octahydro-3,12-dihydroxy-8,10-dimethoxy-1,11-dioxo-4-[(phenylthioxomethyl)amino]- (isomer 38a)	MeOH-HCl	236(4.32),250(4.32), 276(4.34),320(4.11), 434(4.32)	35-2171-79
	MeOH-HCl after 135 minutes	234(4.42),248(4.42), 272(4.38),320(4.13), 407(4.11),426(4.17), 462(3.75)	35-2171-79
(changing spectrum)	MeOH-NaOH	232(4.41),278(4.24), 443(4.32),478(4.24)	35-2171-79
	MeOH-borax	233(4.36),284(4.23), 438s(4.42),461(4.57), 485(4.51)	35-2171-79
	MeOH-borax after 10 minutes	234(4.34),282(4.20), 440(4.42),462(4.59), 485(4.56)	35-2171-79
$C_{32}H_{34}N_2O_8S$			
2-Naphthacenecarboxamide, N-(1,1-dimethylethyl)-1,4,4a,5,5a,6,11,12a-octahydro-3,12,12a-trihydroxy-8,10-dimethoxy-1,11-dioxo-4-[(phenylthioxomethyl)amino]-, (4α,4aβ,5aβ,12aβ)-(±)- (all spectra after one hour standing)	MeOH-HCl	250(4.42),277(4.35), 353(4.21),400s(3.83)	35-2171-79
	MeOH-NaOH	243(4.45),277(4.39), 365(4.26)	35-2171-79
	MeOH-borax	244(4.49),279(4.40), 337(4.30),400s(3.51)	35-2171-79
$C_{32}H_{34}N_2O_9$			
2-Naphthacenecarboxamide, 4-(benzoylamino)-N-(1,1-dimethylethyl)-1,4,4a-5,5a,6,11,12a-octahydro-3,12,12a-trihydroxy-8,10-dimethoxy-1,11-dioxo-, (4α,4aβ,5aβ,12aβ)-(±)- (all spectra after one hour standing)	MeOH-HCl	250(4.38),272s(4.31), 357(4.25),397s(3.92)	35-2171-79
	MeOH-NaOH	233(4.42),275(4.29), 365(4.26)	35-2171-79
	MeOH-borax	239(4.45),276(4.31), 337(4.27),402s(3.40)	35-2171-79
$C_{32}H_{34}O$			
Androsta-1,4-dien-17-one, 3-(diphenylmethylene)-	MeOH	248(4.00),313(4.36)	39-1166-79C
$C_{32}H_{35}NO_6$			
2-Propenoic acid, 3-amino-3-(2,3-O-isopropylidene-5-O-trityl-β-D-ribofuranosyl)-, ethyl ester	EtOH	274(4.25)	44-4854-79
$C_{32}H_{36}N_4O_9$			
4-Oxazolecarboxamide, N-[4-[(2,3-dihydroxybenzoyl)amino]butyl]-N-[3-[(2,3-dihydroxybenzoyl)amino]propyl]-4,5-dihydro-2-(2-hydroxyphenyl)-5-methyl-, (4S-trans)-	EtOH	250(4.43),309(4.01)	88-4805-79
hydrochloride	EtOH	253(4.48),316(4.01)	88-4805-79

Compound	Solvent	λ_{max}(log ε)	Ref.
$C_{32}H_{36}O_{16}$			
Veronicoside pentaacetate	$CHCl_3$	205(4.18),231(4.21), 275(3.11)	33-0530-79
$C_{32}H_{37}BrO_7$			
Pregna-1,4-diene-3,20-dione, 17-(benzoyloxy)-7-bromo-11-hydroxy-16-methyl-21-(1-oxopropoxy)-, (7α,11β,16α)-	MeOH	233(4.45)	145-1662-79
$C_{32}H_{37}NO_9$			
3a,7-Epoxy-3aH-furo[3,2-b]oxocin-3-carboxylic acid, 5-[1,3-dimethyl-6-(2,4-dioxo-5-phenyl-3-pyrrolidinyl)-6-oxo-2,4-hexadienyl]octahydro-2,6,9a-trimethyl-8-oxo-, methyl ester	EtOH-HCl	240(3.91),355(4.45)	142-0477-79B
	EtOH-NaOH	260(4.17),281(4.19), 333(4.23)	142-0477-79B
$C_{32}H_{37}NO_{10}$			
Cathedulin E 8	MeOH	227(4.15),256(4.43), 264(3.48),270s(3.43), 283s(2.95)	39-2965-79C
$C_{32}H_{37}NO_{12}$			
Nogalarol, 7-con-O-propyl-	EtOH	236(4.68),258(4.36), 287(4.01),481(4.18)	44-4030-79
Nogalarol, 7-dis-O-propyl-	EtOH	236(4.69),259(4.35), 288s(3.95),479(4.16)	44-4030-79
$C_{32}H_{37}N_7O_9S_2$			
3-Cephem-4-carboxylic acid, 7-(D-mandelamido)-3-[[(1-methyl-1H-tetrazol-5-yl)thio]methyl]-, N-[(tert-butoxy)-carbonyl]phenylalanyloxymethyl ester	MeOH	274(3.95)	87-0657-79
$C_{32}H_{38}N_2O_4$			
Acetic acid, [3-(diethylaminomethylene)-3,4-dihydro-4-oxo-2H-1-benzopyran-2-yl]diphenyl-, diethylamine salt	MeOH	219(4.3),327(3.7), 382(4.1)	24-1791-79
$C_{32}H_{38}N_2O_8$			
Echitoveniline, 11-methoxy-, (-)-	EtOH	242(3.62),327(3.95)	78-1151-79
$C_{32}H_{38}O_2$			
1H,8H-Benzo[1,2-c:3,4-c']bis[2]benzopyran, 4,4a,8a,9,12,12a,14,14a-octahydro-3,8,8,11,14,14-hexamethyl-5-phenyl-	EtOH	210(4.51),229(4.35), 290(3.38)	2-0250-79A
$C_{32}H_{40}MgN_8$			
Magnesium, [2,7,12,17-tetrakis(1,1-dimethylethyl)-21H,23H-porphyrazinato-(2-)-N^{21},N^{22},N^{23},N^{24}]-, (SP-4-1-)-	EtOH	333(4.94),542(4.35), 591(5.24)	104-0962-79
$C_{32}H_{40}MgN_8O_4$			
Magnesium, [2,7,12,17-tetrakis(1,1-dimethylethoxy)-21H,23H-porphyrazinato-(2-)-N^{21},N^{22},N^{23},N^{24}]-, (SP-4-1)-	$CHCl_3$	340(4.82),565(4.25), 612(4.67)	104-0962-79
$C_{32}H_{40}N_4$			
6H-Isoindolo[2,1-a]indole-11-ethanamine, 6a,7,8,10a-tetrahydro-N,7,7,9-tetra-	n.s.g.	230(4.80),251s(4.39), 285(4.39),293(4.38)	100-0092-79

Compound	Solvent	λ$_{max}$(log ε)	Ref.
methyl-6-[3-[2-(methylamino)ethyl]-1H-indol-2-yl]- (borreverine)			100-0092-79
Isoborreverine	n.s.g.	226(4.72),288(4.15), 294(4.15)	100-0092-79
$C_{32}H_{40}N_4O_2$			
21H-Biline-1,19-dione, 3,8,12,17-tetraethyl-22,24-dihydro-2,7,13,18,21-pentamethyl-, (E,Z,Z)-	MeOH	320(4.23),365(4.31), 595(4.20)	64-1448-79B
(Z,Z,Z)-	MeOH	320s(4.23),365(4.37), 595(3.99)	64-1448-79B
	MeOH-CF_3COOH	325s(4.20),360(4.26), 624(4.45)	64-1448-79B
	MeOH-$Zn(OAc)_2$	335s(4.20),370(4.32), 635s(4.08),682(4.26)	64-1448-79B
$C_{32}H_{40}N_4O_6$			
Orantine, N(6),N(10)-diacetyl-	EtOH	227(4.53),283(3.71), 289(3.56)	33-2712-79
	EtOH-NaOH	247(--),285(--)	33-2712-79
$C_{32}H_{40}O_6$			
D:A-Friedo-24.25-dinoroleana-1,3,5,7,9-pentaen-29-oic acid, 2,3-dimethoxy-17-methyl-11,21-dioxo-, methyl ester, (20α)-	$CDCl_3$	252s(4.16),268(4.32), 280(4.42),331.5(3.90), 332s(3.89)	39-3127-79C
$C_{32}H_{41}N_3O_5$			
L-Tryptophan, N^{α}-(benzyloxycarbonyl)-N^{in}-formyl-, dicyclohexylamine salt	MeOH-HCl	300(3.72)	63-0013-79
$C_{32}H_{42}N_4O$			
1H,5H-4b,9b-(Iminoethano)indeno[1,2-b]-indol-3-ol, 2,3,4,4a,10,10a-hexahydro-1,1,3,13-tetramethyl-10-[3-[2-(methylamino)ethyl]-1H-indol-2-yl]-	EtOH	226(4.52),251s(3.97), 285(4.07),293(4.06)	102-2066-79
6H-Isoindolo[2,1-a]indol-9-ol, 6a,7,8-9,10,10a-hexahydro-N,7,7,9-tetramethyl-6-[3-[2-(methylamino)ethyl]-1H-indol-2-yl]-	EtOH	225(4.69),286(4.14), 294(4.15)	102-2066-79
$C_{32}H_{42}N_8$			
21H,23H-Porphyrazine, 2,7,12,17-tetrakis(1,1-dimethylethyl)-	hexane	333(4.90),512s(4.00), 521s(4.03),547(4.79), 568(4.00),583(3.96), 620(5.00)	104-0962-79
$C_{32}H_{42}N_8O_4$			
21H,23H-Porphyrazine, 2,7,12,17-tetrakis(1,1-dimethylethoxy)-	$CHCl_3$	331(4.76),574(4.36), 594(4.46),646(4.57)	104-0962-79
$C_{32}H_{42}O_4$			
Isopristimerinene II, di-O-methyl-	MeOH	239(4.90),288(4.00), 332s(3.40)	39-3127-79C
Isopristimerinene III, di-O-methyl-	$CHCl_3$	256(4.6),309(4.0)	39-3127-79C
$C_{32}H_{43}ClN_2O_9$			
Ansamitocin P-3	MeOH	233(4.48),240s(4.45), 252(4.44),280(3.76), 288(3.76)	78-1079-79

Compound	Solvent	$\lambda_{max}(\log \epsilon)$	Ref.
Ansamitocin P-3'	MeOH	233(4.48),240s(4.45), 252(4.44),280(3.76), 288(3.76)	78-1079-79
$C_{32}H_{44}MgN_{12}$			
Magnesium, [N,N,N',N',N",N",N"',N"'-octaethyl-21H,23H-porphyrazine-2,7,12,17-tetraaminato(2-)-N^{21},N^{22},N^{23},N^{24}]-, (SP-4-1)-	$CHCl_3$	338(4.99),462(4.36), 662(4.49),716(4.72)	104-0962-79
Magnesium, [N,N',N",N"'-tetrakis(1,1-dimethylethyl)-21H,23H-porphyrazine-2,7,12,17-tetraaminato(2-)-N^{21},N^{22}-N^{23},N^{24}]-, (SP-4-1)-	$CHCl_3$	336(5.12),466(4.22), 660(4.37),710(4.93)	104-0962-79
$C_{32}H_{44}N_6$			
Cyclopropenylium, [5-[bis(1-methylethyl)amino]-4,5-diphenyl-1,2,3-triazinium-2-yl]bis(diethylamino)-, diperchlorate	CH_2Cl_2	442(4.22)	24-1535-79
$C_{32}H_{44}O_4$			
19-Norcholesta-1,3,5,7,9-pentaen-11-one, 1-acetoxy-7-methoxy-3,4,14-trimethyl-	EtOH	220(4.58),256(4.35), 330(4.01)	12-0179-79
29-Nordammara-3,9(11),12,17(20),24-pentaen-21-oic acid, 16-acetoxy-, methyl ester, (8α,14β,16β,17Z)-	EtOH	204(4.08),235(3.65), 272(3.59),355(3.96)	78-2419-79
$C_{32}H_{44}O_5$			
Isopristimerin II, 21-hydroxy-di-O-methyl-	MeOH	233(4.56),288(3.61), 324(2.84)	39-3127-79C
Isopristimerin III, 21-hydroxy-di-O-methyl-	MeOH	254(4.50),298(3.90)	39-3127-79C
$C_{32}H_{44}O_8$			
Acnistoferin, diacetyl-	EtOH	220(4.29)	102-1237-79
$C_{32}H_{45}NO_9$			
3a,7-Epoxy-3aH-furo[3,2-b]oxocin-3-carboxylic acid, 5-[6-(5-hexyl-2,4-dioxo-3-pyrrolidinyl)-1,3-dimethyl-6-oxo-2,4-hexadienyl]octahydro-2,6,9a-trimethyl-8-oxo-, methyl ester	EtOH-HCl	236(3.91),353(4.49)	142-0477-79B
	EtOH-NaOH	256(4.20),280(4.27), 331(4.24)	142-0477-79B
$C_{32}H_{45}N_5O_9$			
Guanosine, 3',4'-didehydro-3'-deoxy-N-(2,2-dimethyl-1-oxopropyl)-, 2'-[3'-(2,2-dimethyl-1-oxopropoxy-4,4-dimethyl-2-pentenoate] 5'-(2,2-dimethylpropanoate)	MeOH	253(4.22),278s(4.07)	24-0625-79
$C_{32}H_{46}IN_5O_9$			
2-Pentenoic acid, 3-(2,2-dimethyl-1-oxopropoxy)-4,4-dimethyl-, ester with N-[9-[2-deoxy-5-O-(2,2-dimethyl-1-oxopropyl)-2-iodo-β-D-ribofuranosyl]-6,9-dihydro-6-oxo-1H-purin-2-yl]-2,2-dimethylpropanamide (plus isomer)	MeOH	257(4.24),280s(4.12)	24-0625-79
$C_{32}H_{46}N_4O_2$			
2H-Isoindol-2-yloxy, 5,5'-azobis[1,1,3-3-tetraethyl-1,3-dihydro-	C_6H_{12}	235(4.27),335(4.34), 435(2.95)	22-0048-79

Compound	Solvent	λ_{max}(log ϵ)	Ref.
(cont.)	MeOH	235(4.38),335(4.43), 430(2.95)	22-0048-79
$C_{32}H_{46}N_4O_3$			
2H-Isoindol-2-yloxy, 5,5'-azoxybis- [1,1,3,3-tetraethyl-1,3-dihydro-	C_6H_{12}	235(4.26),337(4.32)	22-0048-79
	MeOH	235(4.26),335(4.35)	22-0048-79
$C_{32}H_{46}O_3$			
19-Norcholesta-1,3,5,7,9-pentaen-1-ol, 7-methoxy-3,4,14α-trimethyl-, acetate	EtOH	245(4.46),285(3.73)	12-0179-79
$C_{32}H_{46}O_{10}$			
Peruvoside 2'-monoacetate	MeOH	223(4.07)	44-3511-79
$C_{32}H_{48}O_3$			
B(9a)-Homo-19-norlanosta-1(10),5,8-tri-en-7-one, 3β-acetoxy-	EtOH	297(4.15)	39-0007-79C
$C_{32}H_{48}O_4$			
Multiflora-7,9(11)-dien-29-oic acid, 3α-acetoxy-	EtOH	234(4.04),241(4.08), 249(3.91)	102-1843-79
$C_{32}H_{48}O_5$			
Ergosta-7,9(11),22-triene-3,5,6-triol, 3,6-diacetate, (3β,5α,6α,22E)-	EtOH	236(4.20),243(4.23), 251(4.05)	44-3657-79
Ergosta-7,14,22-triene-3,5,6-triol, 3,6-diacetate, (3β,5α,6α,22E)-	EtOH	242(3.99)	44-3657-79
$C_{32}H_{48}O_6$			
29-Nordammara-17(20),24-dien-21-oic acid, 16-acetoxy-3-hydroxy-11-oxo-, methyl ester (11-ketofusidic acid methyl ester)	EtOH	204(4.01),225s(3.89)	78-2419-79
29-Nordammara-17(20),24-dien-21-oic acid, 16-acetoxy-11-hydroxy-3-oxo-, methyl ester	EtOH	204(4.01),225(3.95)	78-2419-79
$C_{32}H_{48}O_7$			
C-Homo-29-nor-12-oxadammara-17(20),24-dien-21-oic acid, 16-acetoxy-3-hy-droxy-11-oxo-, methyl ester (fusi-lactidic acid methyl ester)	EtOH	205(4.03),225s(3.87)	78-2419-79
$C_{32}H_{48}O_{10}$			
Cardanolide, 3-[(2-acetoxy-6-deoxy-3-O-methyl-α-L-glucopyranosyl)oxy]-18,20-epoxy-14-hydroxy-, (3β,5β)-	MeOH	215(2.94)	44-3511-79
$C_{32}H_{50}N_8$			
4H-1,2,4-Triazol-4-amine, N-[[(5α)-4H-1,2,4-triazol-4-ylamino)cholest-2-en-2-yl]methylene]-	MeOH	207(4.01),321(4.21)	39-1816-79C
$C_{32}H_{50}O_3$			
B(9a)-Homo-19-norlanosta-1(10),8-dien-7-one, 3β-acetoxy-	EtOH	252(3.90)	39-0007-79C
B(9a)-Homo-19-norlanosta-1(10),9(11)-dien-7-one, 3β-acetoxy-	EtOH	296(1.58)	39-0007-79C
B(9a)-Homo-19-norlanosta-9(11),9a-dien-7-one, 3β-acetoxy-	EtOH	232s(4.12),238(4.28), 243s(4.13)	39-0007-79C

Compound	Solvent	λ$_{max}$(log ε)	Ref.
Lanosta-5,8-dien-7-one, 3β-acetoxy-	EtOH	249(4.04),280s(3.40)	12-0179-79
5α-Lanosta-8,11-dien-7-one, 3β-acetoxy-	EtOH	315(3.52)	12-0179-79
Lup-20(30)-en-29-al, 3β-acetoxy-	n.s.g.	225(3.8)	102-1239-79
18-Norlanosta-8,13(17)-dien-7-one, 3β-acetoxy-12β-methyl-	EtOH	249(4.08)	39-0007-79C
19-Norlanosta-5,7,9-trien-3-ol, 7-methoxy-, acetate, (3β)-	EtOH	280s(3.53),283(4.10)	12-0179-79
Urs-20(30)-en-21-one, 3-acetoxy-, (3β,18α,19α)-	EtOH	235(3.67)	2-0078-79A
$C_{32}H_{50}O_4$			
Lanost-8-ene-7,11-dione, 3β-acetoxy-	EtOH	271(4.01)	56-1203-79
19-Norlanost-5-ene-3,7-dione, 11-acetoxy-9-methyl-	n.s.g.	245(4.02)	39-1222-79C
19-Norlanost-5-ene-7,11-dione, 3-acetoxy-9-methyl-, (3β,9β,10α)-	n.s.g.	243(4.12)	39-1222-79C
Urs-12-en-28-oic acid, 3β-acetoxy-	MeOH	end absorption	64-1320-79B
$C_{32}H_{50}O_5$			
Ergosta-7,22-diene-3,5,6-triol, 3,6-diacetate, (3β,5α,6α,22E)-	EtOH	236(4.09),243(4.12), 251(3.98)	44-3657-79
$C_{32}H_{50}O_6$			
3-Epifusidic acid, methyl ester	EtOH	204(4.00),225s(3.92)	78-2419-79
11-Epifusidic acid, methyl ester	EtOH	204(4.00),225s(3.91)	78-2419-79
$C_{32}H_{50}O_7$			
Fusilactidic acid, 24,25-dihydro-, methyl ester	EtOH	215(3.97)	78-2419-79
Isofusilactidic acid, 24,25-dihydro-, methyl ester	EtOH	216(3.85)	78-2419-79
$C_{32}H_{51}BrO_3$			
5α-Lanost-8-en-7-one, 3β-acetoxy-11β-bromo-	EtOH	255(3.89)	12-0179-79
$C_{32}H_{52}O_2$			
C(14a)-Homo-B-norlanosta-8(14a),9(11)-dien-3-ol, acetate, (3β)-	EtOH	260(3.90)	56-1203-79
$C_{32}H_{52}O_3$			
Cholest-5-en-7-one, 3-(tetrahydropyranyloxy)-	EtOH	239(4.10)	150-0501-79
C(14a)-Homo-B-norlanost-8-en-14a-one, 3β-acetoxy-	EtOH	251(4.02)	56-1203-79
5α-Lanost-8-en-7-one, 3β-acetoxy-	EtOH	225(4.01)	12-0179-79
$C_{32}H_{52}O_4$			
19-Norlanost-5-en-7-one, 3-acetoxy-11-hydroxy-9-methyl-, (3β,9β,10α,11β)-	n.s.g.	244(4.05)	39-1222-79C
(3β,9β,11β)-	EtOH	243(4.13)	39-0007-79C
19-Norlanost-5-en-7-one, 11-acetoxy-3-hydroxy-9-methyl-, (3β,9β,11β)-	EtOH	245(4.13)	39-0007-79C
$C_{32}H_{54}N_2O_2$			
Docosanamide, N-[2-(5-hydroxy-1H-indol-3-yl)ethyl]-	n.s.g.	278.5(3.77)	98-0012-79
$C_{32}H_{54}O$			
C(14a)-Homo-B-norlanosta-8(14a),9(11)-diene, 3β-ethoxy-	EtOH	261(3.91)	56-1203-79

Compound	Solvent	λ_{max}(log ϵ)	Ref.
$C_{33}H_{20}ClN_3O_2$			
Naphth[1,2-d]oxazole, 2-[4-[2-[4-[5-(4-chlorophenyl)-1,2,4-oxadiazol-3-yl]-phenyl]ethenyl]phenyl]-	DMF	320(4.42),375(4.84)	33-1411-79
$C_{33}H_{20}Cl_2N_4O$			
2H-Naphtho[1,2-d]triazole, 2-[2'-chloro-4"-[3"'-(4-chlorophenyl)isoxazol-5"'-yl]stilben-4'-yl]-	DMF	331(4.47),378(4.87)	33-0779-79
2H-Naphtho[1,2-d]triazole, 2-[2'-chloro-4"-[5"'-(4-chlorophenyl)isoxazol-3"'-yl]stilben-4'-yl]-	DMF	324(4.47),373(4.84)	33-0779-79
$C_{33}H_{21}ClN_4O$			
2H-Naphtho[1,2-d]triazole, 2-[2'-chloro-4"-(3"'-phenylisoxazol-5"'-yl)-stilben-4'-yl]-	DMF	331(4.46),378(4.87)	33-0779-79
2H-Naphtho[1,2-d]triazole, 2-[2'-chloro-4"-(5"'-phenylisoxazol-3"'-yl)-stilben-4'-yl]-	DMF	324(4.43),374(4.83)	33-0779-79
$C_{33}H_{21}NOS_2$			
9H-Naphtho[3,2,1-kl]acridin-9-one, 2-methyl-6,8-bis(phenylthio)-	$CHCl_3$	290(4.80),430(4.30), 458s(4.09),494(4.23), 520(4.23)	103-1227-79
$C_{33}H_{21}N_3O_2$			
Naphth[1,2-d]oxazole, 2-[4-[2-[4-(5-phenyl-1,2,4-oxadiazol-3-yl)phenyl]-ethenyl]phenyl]-	DMF	320(4.42),375(4.84)	33-1411-79
$C_{33}H_{21}N_3O_4$			
Benzo[lmn][3,8]phenanthridine-1,3,6,8-(2H,7H)-tetrone, 4-[(4-methylphenyl)-amino]-	$CHCl_3$	518(4.16)	104-2279-79
$C_{33}H_{22}ClN_5$			
2H-Naphtho[1,2-d]triazole, 2-[3-chloro-4-[2-[4-(1-phenyl-1H-pyrazol-3-yl)-phenyl]ethenyl]phenyl]-	DMF	379(4.86)	33-1816-79
2H-Naphtho[1,2-d]triazole, 2-[3-chloro-4-[2-[4-(3-phenyl-1H-pyrazol-1-yl)-phenyl]ethenyl]phenyl]-	DMF	379(4.86)	33-1816-79
$C_{33}H_{22}ClN_5O_2$			
2H-Naphtho[1,2-d]triazole, 2-[3-chloro-4-[2-[4-[3-(4-methoxyphenyl)-1,2,4-oxadiazol-5-yl]phenyl]ethenyl]phenyl]-	DMF	330(4.45),376(4.86)	33-1411-79
2H-Naphtho[1,2-d]triazole, 2-[3-chloro-4-[2-[4-[5-(4-methoxyphenyl)-1,2,4-oxadiazol-3-yl]phenyl]ethenyl]phenyl]-	DMF	323(4.47),372(4.84)	33-1411-79
$C_{33}H_{22}N_2O_2S_2$			
4,8-Epithio-4H-pyrrolo[3,4-f]-2,1-benzisothiazole-5,7(4aH,6H)-dione, 7a,8-dihydro-3,4,6,8-tetraphenyl-, endo-endo	n.s.g.	265(4.09)	24-0266-79
exo,exo-	n.s.g.	265(4.13)	24-0266-79
$C_{33}H_{22}N_4O$			
2H-Naphtho[1,2-d]triazole, 2-[4"-(5"'-	DMF	324(4.48),372(4.86)	33-0779-79

Compound	Solvent	λ_{max}(log ε)	Ref.
phenylisoxazol-3"'-yl)stilben-4'-yl]-			33-0779-79
$C_{33}H_{22}O_9$			
9,10-Anthracenedione, 2,2'-(4-oxopent-ylidene)bis[1,4-dihydroxy-	MeOH	234s(--),251(4.74), 254s(--),285(4.20), 486(4.20),516s(--)	5-0019-79
$C_{33}H_{23}N_5$			
2H-Naphtho[1,2-d]triazole, 2-[4-[2-[4-(1-phenyl-1H-pyrazol-3-yl)phen-yl]ethenyl]phenyl]-	DMF	332(4.46),378(4.89)	33-1816-79
2H-Naphtho[1,2-d]triazole, 2-[4-[2-[4-(3-phenyl-1H-pyrazol-1-yl)phen-yl]ethenyl]phenyl]-	DMF	332(4.46),377(4.89)	33-1816-79
$C_{33}H_{24}ClN_3O_4$			
1,3,4-Oxadiazole, 2-[2'-chloro-4"-[3"'-(4-methoxyphenyl)isoxazol-5"'-yl]stilben-4'-yl]-5-(4-methoxyphenyl)-	DMF	362(4.83)	33-0779-79
$C_{33}H_{24}NO_2P$			
4H-1-Benzopyran-4-one, 2-phenyl-3-[(triphenylphosphoranylidene)amino]-	$CHCl_3$	285(4.07),337s(--), 409(3.94)	5-0162-79
$C_{33}H_{24}N_2O_3$			
Isoxazole, 5-(4-methoxyphenyl)-3-[4"-(3"'-phenylisoxazol-5"'-yl)-stilben-4'-yl]-	DMF	350(4.86),368(4.67)	33-0779-79
Isoxazole, 5-(4-methoxyphenyl)-3-[4"-(5"'-phenyloxazol-2"'-yl)-stilben-4'-yl]-	DMF	367(4.85)	33-0779-79
Isoxazole, 5-phenyl-3-[4"-[3"'-(4-meth-oxyphenyl)isoxazol-5"'-yl]stilben-4'-yl]-	DMF	351(4.87)	33-0779-79
$C_{33}H_{24}N_4$			
1H-Imidazole-5-carbonitrile, 4,5-di-hydro-1,2,4,5-tetraphenyl-4-(2-pyri-dinyl)-	EtOH	230s(4.44),255s(4.28), 298s(3.72)	44-0041-79
$C_{33}H_{25}ClP$			
Phosphonium, (1-chloro-2,3-diphenyl-2-cyclopropen-1-yl)triphenyl-, tetrafluoroborate	n.s.g.	310(4.28)	89-0472-79
$C_{33}H_{25}Cl_2N_3O_2$			
Benzoxazole, 2-[3-chloro-4-[2-[4-[5-(4-chlorophenyl)-1,2,4-oxadiazol-3-yl]-phenyl]ethenyl]phenyl]-5-(1,1-di-methylethyl)-	DMF	363(4.80)	33-1411-79
$C_{33}H_{25}NO$			
Methanone, (1',8'a-dihydro-2'-phenyl-spiro[9H-fluoren-9,3'(2'H)-indoliz-in]-1'-yl)phenyl-	CH_2Cl_2	265(5.01),357(4.87), 450(4.63)	24-2197-79
$C_{33}H_{25}N_3O_2$			
Isoxazole, 3-(4-methoxyphenyl)-5-[4-[2-[4-(1-phenyl-1H-pyrazol-3-yl)phenyl]-ethenyl]phenyl]-	DMF	360(4.88)	33-1816-79

Compound	Solvent	$\lambda_{max}(\log \epsilon)$	Ref.
Isoxazole, 3-(4-methoxyphenyl)-5-[4-[2-[4-(3-phenyl-1H-pyrazol-1-yl)phenyl]ethenyl]phenyl]-	DMF	358(4.87)	33-1816-79
Isoxazole, 5-(4-methoxyphenyl)-3-[4-[2-[4-(1-phenyl-1H-pyrazol-3-yl)phenyl]ethenyl]phenyl]-	DMF	353(4.86)	33-1816-79
Isoxazole, 5-(4-methoxyphenyl)-3-[4-[2-[4-(3-phenyl-1H-pyrazol-1-yl)phenyl]ethenyl]phenyl]-	DMF	291(4.41),350(4.86)	33-1816-79
$C_{33}H_{25}N_3O_4$			
1,2,4-Oxadiazole, 3-(4-methoxyphenyl)-5-[4"-[5"'-(4-methoxyphenyl)isoxazol-3"'-yl]stilben-4'-yl]-	DMF	348(4.84)	33-0779-79
1,3,4-Oxadiazole, 2-(4-methoxyphenyl)-5-[4"-[3"'-(4-methoxyphenyl)isoxazol-5"'-yl]stilben-4'-yl]-	DMF	361(4.89)	33-0779-79
1,3,4-Oxadiazole, 2-(4-methoxyphenyl)-5-[4"-[5"'-(4-methoxyphenyl)isoxazol-3"'-yl]stilben-4'-yl]-	DMF	355(4.89)	33-0779-79
$C_{33}H_{26}$			
Phenanthrene, 1-phenyl-9-[4-(2,4,6-trimethylphenyl)-3-buten-1-ynyl]-, cis	MeOH	253(4.65),259(4.68), 280(4.50),292(4.52), 333(4.02)	78-1537-79
trans	MeOH	238(4.52),260(4.53), 292(4.52),345(4.48)	78-1537-79
Triphenylene, 1-phenyl-12-(2,4,6-trimethylphenyl)-	MeOH	262s(4.70),269(4.75), 283s(4.59)	78-1537-79
$C_{33}H_{26}ClN_3O_2$			
Benzoxazole, 2-[3-chloro-4-[2-[4-(5-phenyl-1,2,4-oxadiazol-3-yl)phenyl]ethenyl]phenyl]-5-(1,1-dimethylethyl)-	DMF	363(4.81)	33-1411-79
$C_{33}H_{26}NO_2P$			
4H-1-Benzopyran-4-one, 2,3-dihydro-2-phenyl-3-[(phenylphosphoranylidene)amino]-, trans	EtOH	250(4.04),332(3.51)	5-0174-79
$C_{33}H_{26}N_2O_2$			
Benzoxazole, 2-[4"-(3"'-phenylisoxazol-5"'-yl)stilben-4'-yl]-5-(1-methylethyl)-	DMF	366(4.92),386(4.73)	33-0779-79
Benzoxazole, 2-[4"-(3"'-phenylisoxazol-5"'-yl)stilben-4'-yl]-5-propyl-	DMF	367(4.91),386(4.73)	33-0779-79
Benzoxazole, 2-[4"-(5"'-phenylisoxazol-3"'-yl)stilben-4'-yl]-5-propyl-	DMF	361(4.89)	33-0779-79
$C_{33}H_{26}N_2O_3$			
Benzoxazole, 2-[4"-[3"'-(4-methoxyphenyl)isoxazol-5"'-yl]stilben-4'-yl]-5,7-dimethyl-	DMF	369(4.92),388(4.73)	33-0779-79
Benzoxazole, 2-[4"-[5"'-(4-methoxyphenyl)isoxazol-3"'-yl]stilben-4'-yl]-5,7-dimethyl-	DMF	362(4.89),380(4.70)	33-0779-79
$C_{33}H_{26}O_2Si$			
Spiro[anthracene-9(10H),3'-[3H]benz[de]anthracen]-10-one, 7'-[(dimethylsilyl)oxy]-	C_6H_{12}	271(5.03),370(3.48), 388(3.72),410(3.88), 432(4.08),458(4.03)	44-1787-79

Compound	Solvent	$\lambda_{max}(\log \epsilon)$	Ref.
$C_{33}H_{27}ClNO_4P$			
1H-Pyrrole-3-acetic acid, 4-chloro-2,5-dihydro-2,5-dioxo-1-(phenylmethyl)-α-(triphenylphosphoranylidene)-, ethyl ester	MeOH	225(4.63),270(3.78), 450(3.75)	48-0797-79
$C_{33}H_{27}Cl_5N_5O_9P$			
3'-Adenylic acid, N-benzoyl-2'-deoxy-, 2-chlorophenyl 2,2,2-trichloroethyl ester, 5'-[(4-chlorophenoxy)acetate]	MeOH	279(4.35)	54-0537-79
$C_{33}H_{27}Cl_5N_5O_{10}P$			
3'-Guanylic acid, N-benzoyl-2'-deoxy-, 2-chlorophenyl 2,2,2-trichloroethyl ester, 5'-[(4-chlorophenoxy)acetate]	MeOH	257(4.19),264(4.20), 287(4.18)	54-0537-79
$C_{33}H_{27}Fe_3$			
Cyclopropenylium, triferrocenyl-, perchlorate	CH_2Cl_2	309(4.42),363(3.98), 520(3.85)	78-0733-79
$C_{33}H_{27}N_3O_2$			
Benzoxazole, 5-(1,1-dimethylethyl)-2-[4-[2-[4-(5-phenyl-1,2,4-oxadiazol-3-yl)phenyl]ethenylphenyl]-	DMF	362(4.88),380(4.69)	33-1411-79
$C_{33}H_{27}N_3O_7$			
β-D-Ribofuranosylamine, N-1H-benzimid-azol-2-yl-, 2,3,5-tribenzoate	MeOH	230(4.5),280(3.8), 297(3.9)	94-1153-79
$C_{33}H_{28}N_2O_5$			
Methanone, (octahydro-4a-methyl-2,6-di-phenylfuro[2,3-d:4,5-d']diisoxazole-3,7-diyl)bis[phenyl-, (3α,3aα,4aβ-7β,7aβ,7bα)-	MeOH	248(4.65)	142-1005-79
$C_{33}H_{28}N_3$			
1H-Naphth[2,3-d]imidazolium, 2-[2-[4-(dimethylamino)phenyl]ethenyl]-1,3-diphenyl-, perchlorate	n.s.g.	492(4.69)	124-0043-79
$C_{33}H_{28}N_4O_9S$			
Isothiazolo[3,4-d]pyrimidine-4,6(5H,7H)-dione, 5,7-dimethyl-3-[(2,3,5-tri-O-benzoyl-β-D-ribofuranosyl)amino]-	dioxan	230(4.5),260(4.2), 277(4.2),310(4.2)	94-1147-79
$C_{33}H_{28}OPSe$			
Phosphonium, triphenyl-, 1-(methylphen-ylselenonio)-2-oxo-2-phenylethylide, tetrafluoroborate	n.s.g.	220s(4.699),261(4.052), 267(4.053)	104-0332-79
$C_{33}H_{28}O_2Si$			
Spiro[anthracene-9(10H),3'-[3H]benz-[de]anthracen]-10-one, 1',2'-dihy-dro-7'-[(trimethylsilyl)oxy]-	C_6H_{12}	268(5.09),292(3.87), 305(3.77),340(3.20), 359(3.58),376(3.85), 398(3.96),422(3.91)	44-1787-79
$C_{33}H_{28}O_6$			
Anthra[2,3-e][1,3]dioxepin-7,12-dione, 1,5-dihydro-3,3-dimethyl-6,13-bis-(phenylmethoxy)-	MeOH	206(4.58),257(4.41), 377(3.52)	5-0019-79

Compound	Solvent	$\lambda_{max}(\log \epsilon)$	Ref.
$C_{33}H_{29}Cl_5N_3O_{11}P$			
3'-Cytidylic acid, 2'-deoxy-N-(4-methoxybenzoyl)-, 2-chlorophenyl 2,2,2-trichloroethyl ester, 5'-[(4-chlorophenoxy)acetate]-	EtOH	287(4.34)	54-0537-79
$C_{33}H_{29}N_3O_7S$			
Thiourea, N-(2-aminophenyl)-N'-(2,3,5-tri-O-benzoyl-β-D-ribofuranosyl)-	MeOH	231(4.7),282(3.9), 301(3.9)	94-1153-79
$C_{33}H_{29}N_5O_7$			
Benzonitrile, 2-[(2,3,4-tris-O-[(phenylamino)carbonyl]-β-D-ribofuranosyl]amino]-	MeOH	219(4.68),236(4.64), 317(3.85)	44-0173-79
$C_{33}H_{29}N_5O_9$			
1H-Purine-2,6-dione, 3,7-dihydro-1,3-dimethyl-8-[(2,3,5-tri-O-benzoyl-β-D-ribofuranosyl)amino]-	MeOH	231(5.0),282(3.8), 302(3.7)	94-1153-79
$C_{33}H_{30}$			
9H-Fluorene, 2-(1-methylethyl)-9-[[2-(1-methylethyl)-9H-fluoren-9-ylidene]methyl]-	$CHCl_3$	318(4.56)	24-1473-79
$C_{33}H_{30}N_2O_9S$			
4-Isothiazolecarboxylic acid, 3-methyl-5-[(2,3,5-tri-O-benzoyl-β-D-ribofuranosyl)amino]-, ethyl ester	dioxan	230(4.5),275(4.5), 380(2.7)	94-1147-79
$C_{33}H_{30}N_4O_8$			
Uridine, 4-[(1-methylethylidene)hydrazone], 2',3',5'-tribenzoate	EtOH	283(4.26)	39-2088-79C
$C_{33}H_{30}O_2Si$			
9(10H)-Anthracenone, 10-[2-[10-[(trimethylsilyl)oxy]-9-anthracenyl]-ethyl]-	C_6H_{12}	256(4.96),265(5.24), 355(3.61),372(3.86), 392(4.00),417(3.92)	44-4247-79
$C_{33}H_{30}O_4$			
5,7:20,22-Dietheno-8H,19H-diindeno[2,1-n:1',2'-o][1,4,7,10]tetraoxacycloundecin, 10,11,13,14,16,17-hexahydro-, (R)-	MeCN	267(4.50),277(4.51), 298(4.21),310(4.35)	33-2285-79
$C_{33}H_{31}NO_3Si_2$			
6H-[1,2,5]Oxadisilolo[3,4-d]azepine-6-carboxylic acid, 1,3,3a,8a-tetrahydro-1,1,3,3-tetraphenyl-, ethyl ester, trans	EtOH	244(4.3),254(4.2), 260(4.1),265(4.0), 272(3.8)	142-0263-79
$C_{33}H_{31}N_2S_2$			
Benzothiazolium, 3-ethyl-2-[2-[3-[(3-ethyl-2(3H)-benzothiazolylidene]ethylidene]-2-phenyl-1-cyclopenten-1-yl]ethenyl]-, iodide	MeOH	808(5.51)	104-0351-79
$C_{33}H_{32}N_2O_5$			
L-Phenylalanine, N-[N-[(phenylmethoxy)-carbonyl]-L-phenylalanyl]-, phenylmethyl ester	EtOH	248(2.14),252(2.26), 258(2.35),265(2.25), 268(2.06)	118-0957-79

Compound	Solvent	$\lambda_{max}(\log \epsilon)$	Ref.
$C_{33}H_{32}N_2O_9S$			
2-Butenoic acid, 3-amino-2-[thioxo-[(2,3,5-tri-O-benzoyl-β-D-ribofuranosyl)amino]methyl]-, ethyl ester	dioxan	228(4.6),275(4.3),385(2.6)	94-1147-79
$C_{33}H_{32}N_4O_6$			
2,4(1H,3H)-Pteridinedione, 1-[2-deoxy-5-O-[(4-methoxyphenyl)diphenylmethyl]-α-D-ribofuranosyl]-6,7-dimethyl-	MeOH	230(4.43),324(3.93)	33-1171-79
β-	MeOH	231(4.44),324(3.96)	33-1171-79
$C_{33}H_{33}ClN_7O_{10}P$			
Guanosine, N-(2-methyl-1-oxopropyl)-2'-O-[(2-nitrophenyl)methyl]-, 3'-(4-chlorophenyl phenylphosphoramidate)	EtOH	260.5(4.34)	35-6409-79
$C_{33}H_{33}NO_4Si_2$			
1H-Azepine-1-carboxylic acid, 4,5-dihydro-4,5-bis(hydroxydiphenylsilyl)-, ethyl ester, trans	EtOH	244s(4.4),248(4.4),254(4.3),260(4.2),265(4.0),271(3.9)	142-0263-79
$C_{33}H_{33}N_3O_5$			
7H-Pyrrolo[2,3-d]pyrimidine, 4-methoxy-7-[2,3,5-tris-O-(phenylmethyl)-α-D-arabinofuranosyl]-	MeOH	262(3.85)	24-3432-79
β-	MeOH	262(3.85)	24-3432-79
$C_{33}H_{33}N_5O_5$			
Cytidine, N^4-benzoyl-5'-deoxy-5',5'-(N,N'-diphenylethenediamino)-2',3'-O-isopropylidene-	MeOH	254(4.72),297(4.11)	44-1309-79
$C_{33}H_{34}N_4O_6$			
Biliverdin IXa	MeOH	278(4.25),315(4.36),376(4.70),665(4.16)	31-0009-79
	+ CF_3COOH	307(4.27),376(4.79),698(4.46)	31-0009-79
$C_{33}H_{34}O_5$			
2-Pentanone, 1,5-bis[4-methoxy-3-(phenylmethoxy)phenyl]-	EtOH	208(4.65),225s(4.22),280(3.75)	39-0662-79C
$C_{33}H_{35}N_2O$			
Quinolinium, 1-ethyl-2-[2-[3-[(1-ethyl-2(1H)-quinolinylidene)ethylidene]-2-methoxy-1-cyclohexen-1-yl]ethenyl]-, iodide	MeOH	837(5.34)	104-0351-79
$C_{33}H_{35}N_5O_6$			
Ergotamine, 8-hydroxy-	EtOH	261(3.95),381(3.57)	73-2255-79
$C_{33}H_{35}O_8P$			
Phosphonium, [3-ethoxy-2-(ethoxycarbonyl)-1-[2-ethoxy-1-(ethoxycarbonyl)-2-oxoethyl]-3-oxo-1-propenyl]triphenyl-, hydroxide, inner salt	$CHCl_3$	485(3.2)	5-1406-79
$C_{33}H_{36}N_2O_3$			
1H-Indole-2-acetic acid, 3-[2-(phenylmethoxy)ethyl]-1-(phenylmethyl)-α-(1-piperidinylmethylene)-, methyl ester	EtOH	283(4.30)	23-0289-79

Compound	Solvent	λ max(log ε)	Ref.
$C_{33}H_{36}O_4$			
Benzene, 1,1'-(1,5-pentanediyl)bis[4-methoxy-3-(phenylmethoxy)-	C_6H_{12}	207(4.49),225s(4.01), 278(3.51)	39-0662-79C
$C_{33}H_{37}NO_9$			
3a,7-Epoxy-3aH-furo[3,2-b]oxocin-3-carboxylic acid, 5-[1,3-dimethyl-6-[2,4-dioxo-5-(phenylmethylene)-3-pyrrolidinyl]-6-oxo-2,4-hexadienyl]octahydro-2,6,9a-trimethyl-8-oxo-, methyl ester	EtOH-HCl	227(4.05),360(4.65)	142-0477-79B
	EtOH-NaOH	243(4.15),293(4.43), 333(4.61)	142-0477-79B
$C_{33}H_{37}N_5$			
21H,23H-Porphine-5-carbonitrile, 2,7,12,17-tetraethyl-3,8,13,18-tetramethyl-	CH_2Cl_2	402(5.17),511(4.60), 547(4.10),580(3.75), 633(4.06)	35-5953-79
$C_{33}H_{39}BrO_7$			
Pregna-1,4-diene-3,20-dione, 17-(benzoyloxy)-7-bromo-11-hydroxy-16-methyl-21-(1-oxobutoxy)-, (7α,11β,16α)-	MeOH	234(4.43)	145-1662-79
$C_{33}H_{39}N_2O$			
3H-Indolium, 2-[2-[3-[(1,3-dihydro-1,3,3-trimethyl-2H-indol-2-ylidene)-ethylidene]-2-methoxy-1-cyclohexen-1-yl]ethenyl]-1,3,3-trimethyl-, perchlorate	MeOH	758(5.38)	104-0351-79
$C_{33}H_{39}O_4P$			
Pregn-4-ene-3,20-dione, 17-[(diphenylphosphinyl)oxy]-	n.s.g.	241(4.11)	39-1159-79C
$C_{33}H_{40}N_2O_4$			
Acetic acid, [3-(diethylaminomethylene)-3,4-dihydro-6-methyl-4-oxo-2H-1-benzopyran-2-yl]diphenyl-, diethylamine salt	MeOH	222(4.3),338(3.8), 388(4.1)	24-1791-79
$C_{33}H_{40}N_2O_9$			
3-Epireserpine	MeCN	266(4.26),296(4.02)	35-6404-79
$C_{33}H_{40}O_3$			
1H,8H-Benzo[1,2-c:3,4-c']bis[2]benzopyran, 4,4a,8a,9,12,12a,14,14a-octahydro-5-(4-methoxyphenyl)-3,8,8,11-14,14-hexamethyl-	EtOH	213(4.48),232(4.38), 265(3.63)	2-0250-79A
$C_{33}H_{40}O_{20}$			
Isovitexin, 2"-O-glucosyl-, 7-O-galactoside	MeOH	272(3.63),332(3.64)	102-0907-79
	MeOH-MeONa	233s(--),255s(--), 271(--),392(--)	102-0907-79
$C_{33}H_{42}N_4$			
Borreverine, 4-methyl-	EtOH	226(4.53),250s(3.96), 286(4.01),294(4.01)	102-1559-79
Isoborreverine, 4-methyl-	EtOH	225(4.79),286(4.23), 294(4.23)	102-1559-79
$C_{33}H_{42}N_4O_6$			
Orantine, N(6),N(10)-diacetyl-O(34)-	EtOH	230(4.32),275s(3.49),	33-2712-79

Compound	Solvent	$\lambda_{max}(\log \epsilon)$	Ref.
methyl- (cont.)		281(3.55),289s(3.38)	33-2712-79
$C_{33}H_{43}N_2P$			
Cyclopropenylium, bis[bis(1-methylethyl)amino](triphenylphosphonio)-	n.s.g.	235(4.65),277(4.62)	89-0472-79
$C_{33}H_{44}N_4O_6$			
16,17-Secoorantine, N(6),N(10)-diacetyl-O(34)-methyl-	EtOH	222(4.38),278(3.61), 283(3.61)	33-2712-79
	EtOH-NaOH	258(--),284(--), 303(--)	33-2712-79
$C_{33}H_{44}O_5$			
19-Norcholesta-1,3,5,7,9-pentaen-11-one, 1,7-diacetoxy-3,4,14α-trimethyl-	EtOH	248(4.1),280(3.5)	12-0179-79
$C_{33}H_{45}ClN_2O_9$			
Maytansine, 3-de[2-(acetylmethylamino)-1-oxopropoxy]-3-(3-methyl-1-oxobutoxy)-	MeOH	233(4.48),240s(4.45), 252(4.44),280(3.76), 288(3.75)	78-1079-79
$(C_{33}H_{45}N_5O_7)_n$			
Poly[imino[1-(1-methylethyl)-2-oxo-1,2-ethanediyl]imino[2-oxo-1-[4-[[(phenylmethoxy)carbonyl]amino]butyl]-1,2-ethanediyl]imino[2-oxo-1-[4-[[(phenylmethoxy)carbonyl]amino]butyl]-1,2-ethanediyl]], (S)-	CF_3CH_2OH	188(4.7),200s(4.0), 257f(2.3)	126-2893-79
$C_{33}H_{46}O_6$			
1,4-Benzenediol, 2-(9-acetoxy-3,7,11-15-tetramethyl-2,6,10,14-hexadecatetraenyl]-6-methyl-, diacetate, (E,E,E)-(+)-	EtOH	262(2.78)	138-1269-79
$C_{33}H_{46}O_{19}$			
Cantleyoside	MeOH	235(4.31)	102-0273-79
$C_{33}H_{48}NO_2$			
Oxazolidinium, 3,3,4-trimethyl-2-[(20S)-3-oxopregn-4-en-20-yl]-5-phenyl-, iodide	$CHCl_3$	247(4.37)	83-0192-79
$C_{33}H_{48}O_5$			
19-Norlanosta-5,7,9-trien-11-one, 3β,7-diacetoxy-	EtOH	263(3.9),303s(3.38)	12-0179-79
$C_{33}H_{48}O_{19}$			
Sylvestroside I	EtOH	236(4.32)	102-0273-79
$C_{33}H_{50}O_4$			
19-Norlanosta-5,7,9-triene-3β,7-diol, diacetate	EtOH	268(2.77),276s(2.72)	12-0179-79
$C_{33}H_{50}O_5$			
18αH-Oleanolic acid, 11-oxo-, acetate, methyl ester	EtOH	247(3.93)	2-0112-79B
β-	EtOH	252(4.2)	2-0112-79B

Compound	Solvent	λ_{max}(log ε)	Ref.
$C_{33}H_{51}ClN_3O_8$			
1-Piperidinyloxy, 4,4',4"-[(5-chloro-3,6-dioxo-1,4-cyclohexadiene-1,2,4-triyl)tris(oxy)]tris[2,2,6,6-tetramethyl-	heptane	306(4.11),435(2.60)	70-1441-79
	EtOH	305(4.12),430(2.63)	70-1441-79
$C_{33}H_{51}NO_5$			
16,28-Secosolanid-22-ene-3,16-diol, 28-acetyl-, diacetate, (3β,5α,16α)-	EtOH	236(3.87)	12-0597-79
$C_{33}H_{52}N_2O$			
Diazene, (3α,5α)-cholestan-3-ylphenyl-, 2-oxide	C_6H_{12}	246(4.00)	39-2030-79C
(3β,5α)-	C_6H_{12}	247(4.03)	39-2030-79C
$C_{33}H_{52}N_2O_4$			
Acetamide, N-[(3β,5α,16α)-28-acetyl-16-acetoxy-16,28-secosolanid-22-en-3-yl]-	EtOH	235(3.90)	12-0597-79
$C_{33}H_{52}O_3$			
2H-Pyran, 2-[[(3β)-22,23-epoxyergosta-5,7-dien-3-yl]oxy]tetrahydro-	MeOH	271(4.10),282(4.11), 293(3.89)	39-1858-79C
$C_{33}H_{53}NO_6$			
Acetamide, N-[(3β,5α,16α,25S)-3,16-diacetoxy-22-oxocholestan-26-yl]-	EtOH	288(1.86)	12-0597-79

Compound	Solvent	λ_{max}(log ε)	Ref.
$C_{34}H_{20}BrCl_5S_5$			
1,3-Butadiene, 3-bromo-1,1,2,4,4-pentakis(4-chlorophenylthio)-	heptane	200(4.98),225s(4.71), 282(4.44)	5-1614-79
1,3-Butadiene, 4-bromo-1,1,2,3,4-pentakis(4-chlorophenylthio)-	heptane	199(5.00),228(4.74), 288(4.45)	5-1614-79
$C_{34}H_{20}Cl_6S_5$			
1,3-Butadiene, 3-chloro-1,1,2,4,4-pentakis(4-chlorophenylthio)-	heptane	201(4.81),224s(4.64), 267(4.42)	5-1614-79
1,3-Butadiene, 4-chloro-1,1,2,3,4-pentakis(4-chlorophenylthio)-	heptane	200(4.97),225(4.82), 275(4.51)	5-1614-79
$C_{34}H_{21}ClN_2O_2$			
Naphth[1,2-d]oxazole, 2-[4"-[3"'-(4-chlorophenyl)isoxazol-5"'-yl]stilben-4'-yl]-	DMF	325(4.41),380(4.91)	33-0779-79
Naphth[1,2-d]oxazole, 2-[4"-[5"'-(4-chlorophenyl)isoxazol-3"'-yl]stilben-4'-yl]-	DMF	322(4.46),375(4.87)	33-0779-79
$C_{34}H_{21}Cl_5S_5$			
1,3-Butadiene, 1,1,2,3,4-pentakis(4-chlorophenylthio)-	heptane	199(4.79),270(4.48)	5-1614-79
1,3-Butadiene, 1,1,2,4,4-pentakis(4-chlorophenylthio)-	heptane	203(4.91),255(4.70), 271s(4.46)	5-1614-79
$C_{34}H_{21}NO_6$			
1,4-Naphthalenedione, 2-acetyl-3-[4-[(3-acetyl-1,4-dihydro-1,4-dioxo-2-naphthalenyl)amino]-1-naphthalenyl-	dioxan	225(4.77),253(4.53), 263s(4.4),293(4.4), 437(3.72)	5-0503-79
$C_{34}H_{21}N_3O_5$			
1,4:5,8-Naphthalenetetracarboxylic acid diimide, N,N'-diphenyl-2-(N-acetylphenylamino)-	$CHCl_3$	430(3.63)	104-2279-79
$C_{34}H_{22}N_2$			
[1,1'-Biphenyl]-4,4'-dicarboxaldehyde, bis(p-styrylethanimine)	n.s.g.	254(4.5)	24-2854-79
$C_{34}H_{22}N_2O_2$			
Benzoxazole, 2-[4'-[4"-(5"'-phenylisoxazol-3"'-yl)styryl]naphthalen-1'-yl]-	DMF	380(4.67)	33-0779-79
Naphth[1,2-d]oxazole, 2-[4"-(3"'-phenylisoxazol-5"'-yl)stilben-4'-yl]-	DMF	326(4.38),380(4.90)	33-0779-79
Naphth[1,2-d]oxazole, 2-[4"-(5"'-phenylisoxazol-3"'-yl)stilben-4'-yl]-	DMF	322(4.44),375(4.86)	33-0779-79
$C_{34}H_{23}ClN_4O_2$			
2H-Naphtho[1,2-d]triazole, 2-[2'-chloro-4"-[3"'-(4-methoxyphenyl)isoxazol-5"'-yl]stilben-4'-yl]-	DMF	370(4.48),378(4.88)	33-0779-79
2H-Naphtho[1,2-d]triazole, 2-[2'-chloro-4"-[5"'-(4-methoxyphenyl)isoxazol-3"'-yl]stilben-4'-yl]-	DMF	323(4.51),373(4.85)	33-0779-79
$C_{34}H_{23}N_3O_3$			
Naphth[1,2-d]oxazole, 2-[4-[2-[4-[5-(4-methoxyphenyl)-1,2,4-oxadiazol-3-yl]phenyl]ethenyl]phenyl]-	DMF	320(4.46),374(4.86)	33-1411-79

Compound	Solvent	λ_{max}(log ε)	Ref.
$C_{34}H_{23}N_3O_6$			
Benzo[1mn][3,8]phenanthroline-1,3,6,8-(2H,7H)-tetrone, 2,7-bis(4-methoxyphenyl)-4-(phenylamino)-	$CHCl_3$	516(4.09)	104-2279-79
$C_{34}H_{24}N_4O_2$			
2H-Naphtho[1,2-d]triazole, 2-[4"-[5"'-(4-methoxyphenyl)isoxazol-3"'-yl]stilben-4'-yl]-	DMF	323(4.53),370(4.87)	33-0779-79
$C_{34}H_{24}O_4$			
9-Anthracenol, 10,10'-(1,2-ethenediyl)-bis-, diacetate	$CHCl_3$	410(4.3)	44-4247-79
$C_{34}H_{26}$			
Naphthalene, 1-(1,3,6-cycloheptatrien-1-yl)-4-(3,4-diphenyl-1,3-cyclopentadien-1-yl)-	MeCN	310(4.17),352(4.28)	39-0889-79C
Naphthalene, 1-(1,3,6-cycloheptatrien-1-yl)-5-(3,4-diphenyl-1,3-cyclopentadien-1-yl)-	MeCN	310s(4.15),347(4.24)	39-0889-79C
$C_{34}H_{26}Cl_2N_2O_2$			
Benzoxazole, 2-[2'-chloro-4"-[3"'-(4-chlorophenyl)isoxazol-5"'-yl]stilben-4'-yl]-5-(1,1-dimethylethyl)-	DMF	369(4.85)	33-0779-79
$C_{34}H_{26}CoO$			
Cobaltocenium, 1-hydroxy-2,3,4,5-tetraphenyl-	50% EtOH-6M HCl	232(4.44),332(4.27)	101-0107-79J
$C_{34}H_{26}F_4$			
1,1':4',1":4",1"':4"",1""-Quinquephenyl, 2",3",5",6"-tetrafluoro-2,2"",5,5""-tetramethyl-	n.s.g.	280(4.67)	104-0517-79
$C_{34}H_{26}N_2O_4$			
Butanedioic acid, (5H-dibenzo[a,d]cyclohepten-5-ylidenehydrazono)(diphenylmethylene)-, dimethyl ester	CH_2Cl_2	233(4.62),275(4.46), 297(4.39),375(3.98)	88-1571-79
Isoxazole, 5-(4-methoxyphenyl)-3-[4"-(3"'-phenylisoxazol-5"'-yl)stilben-4'-yl]-	DMF	352(4.89),368(4.70)	33-0779-79
$C_{34}H_{26}N_2O_8$			
D-Allose, 2,5-anhydro-1-C-1H-indazol-3-yl-, 3,4,6-tribenzoate	EtOH	206(4.35),230(4.61), 272s(4.14),283(4.22), 304(4.32)	4-0081-79
$C_{34}H_{26}N_4O$			
Benzo[c]cinnolinium, 5-[(3-methyl-4-oxo-1,2,3-triphenyl-2-azetidinyl)-amino]-, hydroxide, inner salt	n.s.g.	251(4.66),296(3.87), 308(3.87),322(3.79), 374(4.09)	39-0192-79C
$C_{34}H_{26}O_4$			
9-Anthracenol, 10,10'-(1,2-ethanediyl)-bis-, diacetate	C_6H_{12}	253(5.27),261(5.27), 340(3.68),357(4.03), 379(4.33),403(4.39)	44-4247-79
$C_{34}H_{26}S_5$			
1,3-Butadiene, 1,1,2,3,4-pentakis(phen-	heptane	200(4.81),263(4.38)	5-1614-79

Compound	Solvent	λmax(log ε)	Ref.
ylthio)- (cont.)			5-1614-79
1,3-Butadiene, 1,1,2,4,4-pentakis(phenylthio)-	heptane	199(4.91),265(4.39)	5-1614-79
$C_{34}H_{27}ClN_2O_2$			
Benzoxazole, 2-[2'-chloro-4"-(3"'-phenylisoxazol-5"'-yl)stilben-4'-yl]-5-(1,1-dimethylethyl)-	DMF	370(4.84)	33-0779-79
Benzoxazole, 2-[2'-chloro-4"-(5"'-phenylisoxazol-3"'-yl)stilben-4'-yl]-5-(1,1-dimethylethyl)-	DMF	363(4.81)	33-0779-79
$C_{34}H_{27}NO_2$			
Methanone, [3-[(1,1-dimethylethyl)amino]-1,2-fluoranthenediyl]bis[phenyl-	CH_2Cl_2	257(4.74),311(4.09), 388(3.92)	24-3166-79
$C_{34}H_{27}N_2O_4PS_2$			
1H-Pyrrole-3-acetic acid, 4-(2-benzothiazolylthio)-2,5-dihydro-1-methyl-2,5-dioxo-α-(triphenylphosphoranylidene)-, ethyl ester	MeOH	223(4.80),268(4.36), 460(4.00)	48-0795-79
$C_{34}H_{27}N_3$			
Benzenamine, N-[[4-(3-[1,1'-biphenyl]-4-yl-4,5-dihydro-5-phenyl-1H-pyrazol-1-yl)phenyl]methylene]-	toluene	330s(4.10),405(4.82)	135-1491-79B
$C_{34}H_{28}Br_2$			
p-Quinquephenyl, 4,4""-dibromo-2,2"",5,5""-tetramethyl-	dioxan	301(4.79)	104-0517-79
$C_{34}H_{28}ClN_3O_3$			
Benzoxazole, 2-[3-chloro-4-[2-[4-[5-(4-methoxyphenyl)-1,2,4-oxadiazol-3-yl]-phenyl]ethenyl]phenyl]-5-(1,1-dimethylethyl)-	DMF	363(4.80)	33-1411-79
$C_{34}H_{28}I_2$			
p-Quinquephenyl, 4,4""-diiodo-2,2"",5,5""-tetramethyl-	dioxan	303(4.81)	104-0517-79
$C_{34}H_{28}N_2O_2$			
Benzoxazole, 2-[4"-(3"'-phenyl-5"'-isoxazolyl)stilben-4'-yl]-5-(1,1-dimethylethyl)-	DMF	368(4.92),387(4.74)	33-0779-79
Benzoxazole, 2-[4"-(5"'-phenyl-3"'-isoxazolyl)stilben-4'-yl]-5-(1,1-dimethylethyl)-	DMF	362(4.89)	33-0779-79
$C_{34}H_{28}N_2O_4$			
Butanedioic acid, [(10,11-dihydro-5H-dibenzo[a,d]cyclohepten-5-ylidene)-hydrazono]diphenylmethylene]-, dimethyl ester	CH_2Cl_2	232(4.43),257(4.32), 308(4.27),375(3.73)	88-1571-79
$C_{34}H_{28}N_4O_2$			
1,2,4-Oxadiazole, 3-[4-[2-[4-[3-[4-(1,1-dimethylethyl)phenyl]-1,2,4-oxadiazol-5-yl]phenyl]ethenyl]phenyl]-5-phenyl-	DMF	348(4.81)	33-1411-79

Compound	Solvent	$\lambda_{max}(\log \epsilon)$	Ref.
$C_{34}H_{30}N_2O_4$			
1H-Imidazolium, 2-[1-(diphenylmethylene)-3-methoxy-2-(methoxycarbonyl)-3-oxopropyl]-4,5-dihydro-1,3-diphenyl-, hydroxide, inner salt	$CHCl_3$	259(4.4),290(4.3), 482(3.6)	5-1406-79
$C_{34}H_{30}N_2O_5$			
1,2-Dehydromicranthine	MeOH or EtOH	335(3.4)	100-0001-79
$C_{34}H_{30}N_3OP$			
Ethanone, 1-[4-[[4-(dimethylamino)phenyl]azo]phenyl]-2-(triphenylphosphoranylidene)-	MeOH	265(4.20),440(4.52)	65-2189-79
$C_{34}H_{30}O_2PSe$			
Phosphonium, triphenyl-, 1-(diphenylselenonio)-2-ethoxy-2-oxoethylide, tetrafluoroborate	EtOH	225s(4.63),265(3.94)	104-2169-79
$C_{34}H_{30}O_4$			
Anthracene, 9,9'-[1,2-ethanediylbis(oxy-2,1-ethanediyloxy)]bis-	C_6H_{12}	249(5.23),257(5.47), 320(3.32),335(3.71), 351(4.03),370(4.23), 390(4.18)	108-0220-79
	benzene	392(4.20)	108-0220-79
	EtOH	256(5.47),389(4.17)	108-0220-79
$C_{34}H_{31}N_3OP$			
Phosphonium, [2-[4-[[4-(dimethylamino)phenyl]azo]phenyl]-2-oxoethyl]triphenyl-, iodide	MeOH	275(4.21),450(4.49)	65-2189-79
$C_{34}H_{32}N_2O_5$			
Micranthine	MeOH	286(3.76)	100-0001-79
Tricordatine	MeOH or EtOH	227(4.60),275s(3.69), 284(3.71),304(3.44)	100-0001-79
Triolobine, 12'-O-demethyl-	MeOH or EtOH	233(4.73),275(3.80), 289(3.84),306s(3.64)	100-0001-79
$C_{34}H_{32}N_4O_2$			
Dibenzo[b,j][1,5,9,13]tetraazacyclohexadecine-6,16(5H,7H)-dione, 8,15,17-18-tetrahydro-2,12-dimethyl-10,20-diphenyl-	DMF	280s(--),329(3.89)	30-0105-79
$C_{34}H_{32}O_2$			
9H-Xanthene, 2-(1,1-dimethylethyl)-9-[2-(1,1-dimethylethyl)-9H-xanthen-9-ylidene]-	CH_2Cl_2	237(4.14),258(4.03), 283(3.93),370(4.16)	35-0665-79
$C_{34}H_{33}N_2S_2$			
Benzothiazolium, 3-ethyl-2-[2-[3-[(3-ethyl-2(3H)-benzothiazolylidene)ethylidene]-2-phenyl-1-cyclohexen-1-yl]-ethenyl]-, iodide	MeOH	782(5.48)	104-0351-79
$C_{34}H_{33}N_2S_3$			
Benzothiazolium, 3-ethyl-2-[2-[3-[(3-ethyl-2(3H)-benzothiazolylidene)ethylidene]-2-phenyl-1-cyclohexen-1-	MeOH	805(5.42)	104-0351-79

Compound	Solvent	λ_{max}(log ε)	Ref.
yl]ethenyl]-, iodide (cont.)			104-0351-79
$C_{34}H_{34}$			
Bi-2,4,6-cycloheptatrien-1-yl, bis(4-cyclopropyl-3-methylphenyl)-	$CHCl_3$	248(4.50),290s(4.16)	39-0262-79B
$C_{34}H_{34}N_2O_6$			
N,N'-Bisnoraromaline	MeOH	285(3.88)	100-0001-79
$C_{34}H_{34}O_8$			
Benz[3,3a]indeno[1,7,6-cde]fluorene-2,3,9,10-tetracarboxylic acid, 1a,3a,10b,10c-tetrahydro-5,8,11,14-tetramethyl-, tetramethyl ester	EtOH	390(4.00),430(4.02)	39-0673-79C
$C_{34}H_{35}NO_{16}$			
Benzofuro[3,2-f]-1,2-benzisoxazol-4(4aH)-one, 8-acetyl-5-acetoxy-3,4a,6-trimethyl-7-[(2,3,4,6-tetra-O-acetyl-β-D-glucopyranosyl)oxy]-	MeOH	218(4.48),247(4.13), 297(3.80),358(3.53)	87-1380-79
$C_{34}H_{35}N_3O_5S$			
7H-Pyrrolo[2,3-d]pyrimidine, 4-methoxy-2-(methylthio)-7-[2,3,5-tris-O-(phenylmethyl)-α-D-arabinofuranosyl]-	MeOH	237(4.18),282(4.09)	24-3432-79
β-	MeOH	238(4.19),282(4.11)	24-3432-79
4H-Pyrrolo[2,3-d]pyrimidin-4-one, 1,7-dihydro-5-methyl-2-(methylthio)-7-[2,3,5-tris-O-(phenylmethyl)-β-D-ribofuranosyl]-	MeOH	278(4.09),298(4.13)	35-3629-79
$C_{34}H_{36}N_2O_6$			
α-D-Glucopyranoside, methyl 6-deoxy-6-(phenyl-ONN-azoxy)-2,3,4-tris-O-(phenylmethyl)-	n.s.g.	247(4.11)	39-2030-79C
Lindoldhamine	MeOH	205(4.65),220s(4.39), 280(3.91)	100-0001-79
$C_{34}H_{36}Si_2$			
Silane, (12,13-dihydro-7,12[1',2']benzeno-6,13-ethenobenzo[5,6]cycloocta-[1,2-b]naphthalene-5,7(6H)-diyl)-bis[trimethyl-	THF	240(3.60),251(3.49), 254(3.48),258(3.46), 284(2.94)	152-0231-79
$C_{34}H_{38}CoN_4O_4$			
Cobalt, [8-methyl octadehydro-1,2,3,7-13,17,18,19-octamethyl-8,12-corrindipropanoato(2-)-N^{21},N^{22},N^{23},N^{24}]-, (SP-4-3)-, perchlorate	$CHCl_3$	280(4.38),350(4.26), 490(4.11)	65-2398-79
Cobalt, [2-methyl octadehydro-1,3,7,8-12,13,17,19-octamethyl-2,18-corrindipropanoato(2-)-N^{21},N^{22},N^{23},N^{24}]-, (SP-4-3)-, perchlorate	$CHCl_3$	277(4.32),350(4.23), 495(4.00)	65-2398-79
$C_{34}H_{38}N_4NiO_4$			
Nickel, [8-methyl octadehydro-1,2,3,7-13,17,18,19-octamethyl-8,12-corrindipropanoato(2-)-N^{21},N^{22},N^{23},N^{24}]-, (SP-4-3)-, perchlorate	$CHCl_3$	274(4.41),352(4.41), 565(4.08)	65-2398-79

Compound	Solvent	$\lambda_{max}(\log \epsilon)$	Ref.
$C_{34}H_{38}N_4O_3$			
3-Phorbinepropanoic acid, 9,14-diethyl-4,8,13,18-tetramethyl-20-oxo-, methyl ester, (3S-trans)-	dioxan	406(4.06),501(4.03), 531(3.99),599(3.90), 655(4.71)	5-1992-79
$C_{38}H_{40}FNO_8S_2$			
Pregna-1,3,5-trien-20-one, 9α-fluoro-11β-hydroxy-16β-methyl-3-[(2-nitrophenyl)dithio]-17α,21-bis(1-oxopropoxy)-	MeOH	270s(4.01),329(4.04), 340(4.02)	39-1166-79C
$C_{34}H_{40}N_2O_4$			
2-Naphthalenecarboxylic acid, 6,6'-(1,6-hexanediyl)bis[4-amino-1-methyl-, diethyl ester	EtOH	244(4.62),261(4.62), 340(3.63)	44-4469-79
	EtOH-HCl	240(4.99),290(4.15), 335(3.15)	44-4469-79
$C_{34}H_{42}BrN_5O_2Pd$			
Palladium, [1,1-dimethylethyl 19-bromo-1-cyano-1,2,3,7,8,23-hexahydro-1,2,2-7,7,12,13,17,18-nonamethyl-21H-biline-10-carboxylato(2-)-N^{21},N^{22},N^{23},N^{24}]-	MeCN	298(4.14),325(4.05), 380(4.31),405(4.26), 430s(4.21),507s(3.49), 562s(3.99),609(4.35)	89-0675-79
$C_{34}H_{44}N_4$			
Isoborreverine, 4,4'-dimethyl-	EtOH	224(4.65),286(4.11), 294(4.10)	102-1559-79
$C_{34}H_{46}N_2O_6$			
Isostachysterin$_3$ 3,5-dinitrobenzoate	C_6H_{12}	280(4.49),290(3.61), 303(4.47)	33-1763-79
Isovitamin D_3 3,5-dinitrobenzoate	C_6H_{12}	277(4.54),288(4.60), 301(4.52)	33-1763-79
$C_{34}H_{46}N_4O_6$			
1,6,10,22-Tetraazatricyclo[9.7.6-$1^{12,16}$]pentacosa-12,14,16(25)-triene-18,23-dione, 6,10-diacetyl-15-methoxy-17-[(4-methoxyphenyl)methyl]-, [11S-(11R*,17R*)]-	EtOH	225(4.41),277(3.57), 282(3.55)	33-2712-79
$C_{34}H_{46}O_2$			
[1,1':3',1"-Terphenyl]-4,4"-diol, 3,3",5,5"-tetrakis(1,1-dimethylethyl)-	THF	268(4.57)	18-1853-79
$C_{34}H_{46}O_4$			
2,5-Cyclohexadien-1-one, 4,4'-(1,3-phenylene)bis[2,6-bis(1,1-dimethylethyl)-4-hydroxy-	THF	231(4.50)	18-1853-79
$C_{34}H_{48}O_6$			
Oleana-9(11),13(18)-diene-12,19-dione, 3β,16β-diacetoxy-	EtOH	278(4.35)	56-2465-79
Oleana-11,13(18)-dien-29-oic acid, 3-acetoxy-6-oxo-, anhydride with acetic acid, (3β,20α)-	MeOH	208(3.96),227(3.70), 259(2.72),268(2.60)	64-1320-79B
$C_{34}H_{48}O_7$			
18αH-Acacic acid, 11-oxo-, lactone, diacetate	EtOH	240(3.85)	2-0112-79B

Compound	Solvent	λ max (log ε)	Ref.
18βH-Acacic acid, 11-oxo-, lactone, diacetate	EtOH	245(4.12)	2-0112-79B
$C_{34}H_{48}O_8$			
Cholest-7-en-6-one, 2,3,5,14,20-pentahydroxy-22,24-[(phenylmethylene)bis(oxy)]-, [2β,3β,5β,22R(R),24S]-	EtOH	243(4.03)	12-0779-79
Cholest-7-en-6-one, 2,3,5,14,24-pentahydroxy-20,22-[(phenylmethylene)bis(oxy)]-, (2β,3β,5β,22R,24S)-	EtOH	242(4.02)	12-0779-79
$C_{34}H_{48}O_{10}$			
Simplexin 5,20-diacetate	MeOH	243(3.77)	12-2495-79
$C_{34}H_{50}N_2O_2$			
Phenol, 2-[[[(3β,5α,22β,25S)-spirosolan-3-yl]imino]methyl]-	EtOH	224(4.20),255(4.11), 316(3.61),400(3.03)	12-0611-79
Phenol, 4-[[[(3β,5α,22β,25S)-spirosolan-3-yl]imino]methyl]-	EtOH	220(4.07),271(4.27), 384(3.62)	12-0611-79
16,28-Secosolanid-22(28)-en-16-ol, 3-[[(2-hydroxyphenyl)methylene]amino]-, (3β,5α,16α)-	EtOH	225(4.18),255(4.10), 316(3.58),400(3.18)	12-0597-79
$C_{34}H_{50}O_6$			
Urs-13(18)-en-28-oic acid, 2,3-diacetoxy-20-hydroxy-, δ-lactone, (2α,3β-19ξ)-	MeOH	207(4.00),227(3.78)	64-1320-79B
$C_{34}H_{50}O_{10}$			
Simplexin, 15,16-dihydro-, 5,20-diacetate	MeOH	243(3.77)	12-2495-79
$C_{34}H_{50}O_{11}$			
Cardanolide, 3-[(2,4-diacetoxy-6-deoxy-3-O-methyl-α-L-glucopyranosyl)oxy]-18,20-epoxy-14-hydroxy-, (3β,5β)-	MeOH	218(2.78)	44-3511-79
$C_{34}H_{52}O_4$			
B(9a)-Homo-19-norlanosta-1(10),7,9(11)-triene-3β,7-diol, diacetate	EtOH	248(4.13)	39-0007-79C
Multiflora-7,9(11)-dien-29-oic acid, 3α-acetoxy-, ethyl ester	EtOH	233(3.84),240(3.88), 248(3.66)	102-1843-79
18-Norlanosta-6,8,13(17)-triene-3,7-diol, 12-methyl-, diacetate, (3β,12β)-	EtOH	262(3.60)	39-0007-79C
$C_{34}H_{52}O_6$			
Corosolic acid acetate	MeOH	204(3.82)	64-1320-79B
5α-Cucurbit-1(10)-ene-2,7-dione, 3β,11β-diacetoxy-	n.s.g.	243(3.99)	39-1222-79C
$C_{34}H_{54}O_5$			
10α-Cucurbit-5-en-7-one, 3β,11β-diacetate	n.s.g.	245(4.13)	39-1222-79C
10β-	n.s.g.	243(4.01)	39-1222-79C
19-Norlanost-5-en-7-one, 3,11-diacetoxy-9-methyl-, (3β,9β,11β)-	EtOH	243(4.13)	39-0007-79C
$C_{34}H_{56}S_5$			
1,3-Butadiene, 1,1,2,4,4-pentakis(cycylhexylthio)-	heptane	194(4.50),274(4.09)	5-1614-79

Compound	Solvent	$\lambda_{max}(\log \epsilon)$	Ref.
$C_{35}H_{22}$			
11H-Benzo[a]fluorene, 11-(11H-benzo[a]-fluoren-11-ylidenemethyl)-	CH_2Cl_2	357(3.90)	24-1473-79
	DMSO-EtOH-NaOEt	625(4.55)	24-1473-79
$C_{35}H_{22}ClN_3O_2$			
Benzoxazole, 2-[4-[2-[4-[5-(4-chloro-phenyl)-1,2,4-oxadiazol-3-yl]phenyl]-ethenyl]phenyl]-5-phenyl-	DMF	364(4.91),382(4.72)	33-1411-79
Benzoxazole, 2-[4-[2-[4-[5-(4-chloro-phenyl)-1,2,4-oxadiazol-3-yl]phenyl]-ethenyl]phenyl]-6-phenyl-	DMF	367(4.92)	33-1411-79
$C_{35}H_{22}O_6$			
1,8,9-Anthracenetriol, tribenzoate	$CHCl_3$	260(5.06),325(3.34), 340(3.54),357(3.83), 375(4.01),396(3.94)	145-1083-79
$C_{35}H_{23}N_3O_2$			
Benzoxazole, 5-phenyl-2-[4-[2-[4-(5-phenyl-1,2,4-oxadiazol-3-yl)phenyl]-ethenyl]phenyl]-	DMF	363(4.90),382(4.72)	33-1411-79
Benzoxazole, 6-phenyl-2-[4-[2-[4-(5-phenyl-1,2,4-oxadiazol-3-yl)phenyl]-ethenyl]phenyl]-	DMF	368(4.90)	33-1411-79
Benzoxazole, 7-phenyl-2-[4-[2-[4-(5-phenyl-1,2,4-oxadiazol-3-yl)phenyl]-ethenyl]phenyl]-	DMF	361(4.88),380(4.69)	33-1411-79
$C_{35}H_{24}ClN_5$			
[1,2,4]Triazolo[1,5-a]pyridine, 2-[3-chloro-4-[2-[4-(3,5-diphenyl-1H-pyrazol-1-yl)phenyl]ethenyl]phenyl]-	DMF	345(4.74)	33-1816-79
$C_{35}H_{24}N_2O_2$			
Benzoxazole, 2-[4'-[4"-(5"'-phenylisox-azol-3"'-yl)styryl]naphthalen-1'-yl]-5-methyl-	DMF	382(4.68)	33-0779-79
$C_{35}H_{24}N_2O_3$			
Benzoxazole, 2-[4'-[4"-[5"'-(4-methoxy-phenyl)isoxazol-3"'-yl]styryl]-1'-naphthalenyl]-	DMF	380(4.68)	33-0779-79
Naphth[1,2-d]oxazole, 2-[4"-[3"'-(4-methoxyphenyl)isoxazol-5"'-yl]stil-ben-4'-yl]-	DMF	325(4.39),379(4.90)	33-0779-79
Naphth[1,2-d]oxazole, 2-[4"-[5"'-(4-methoxyphenyl)isoxazol-3"'-yl]stil-ben-4'-yl]-	DMF	322(4.50),376(4.88)	33-0779-79
$C_{35}H_{25}N_5$			
2H-Benzotriazole, 2-[4-[2-[4-(1,3-di-phenyl-1H-pyrazol-5-yl)phenyl]eth-enyl]phenyl]-	DMF	363(4.80)	33-1816-79
$C_{35}H_{28}N_2$			
1H-Pyrazole, 4,5-dihydro-3-(p-biphen-ylyl)-5-phenyl-1-stilbenyl-	toluene	405(4.58)	135-1491-79B
$C_{35}H_{29}ClN_2O_3$			
Benzoxazole, 2-[2'-chloro-4"-[3"'-(4-	DMF	370(4.83)	33-0779-79

Compound	Solvent	λ_{max}(log ϵ)	Ref.
methoxyphenyl)isoxazol-5"'-yl]stilben-4'-yl]-5-(1,1-dimethylethyl)-			33-0779-79
$C_{35}H_{29}N_3O_2$			
1,2,4-Oxadiazole, 3-(p-tert-butylphenyl)-5-[4"-(3"'-phenylisoxazol-5"'-yl)stilben-4'-yl]-	DMF	357(4.85)	33-0779-79
1,2,4-Oxadiazole, 3-(p-tert-butylphenyl)-5-[4"-(5"'-phenylisoxazol-3"'-yl)stilben-4'-yl]-	DMF	350(4.83)	33-0779-79
1,3,4-Oxadiazole, 2-(p-tert-butylphenyl)-5-[4"-(3"'-phenylisoxazol-5"'-yl)stilben-4'-yl]-	DMF	362(4.89)	33-0779-79
1,3,4-Oxadiazole, 2-(p-tert-butylphenyl)-5-[4"-(5"'-phenylisoxazol-3"'-yl)stilben-4'-yl]-	DMF	354(4.87)	33-0779-79
$C_{35}H_{30}N_2O_2$			
Benzoxazole, 2-[4"-(3"'-phenylisoxazol-5"'-yl)stilben-4'-yl]-5-methyl-7-(1,1-dimethylethyl)-	DMF	368(4.91),387(4.72)	33-0779-79
Benzoxazole, 2-[4"-(3"'-phenylisoxazol-5"'-yl)stilben-4'-yl]-7-methyl-5-(1,1-dimethylethyl)-	DMF	368(4.91),387(4.72)	33-0779-79
Benzoxazole, 2-[4"-(5"'-phenylisoxazol-3"'-yl)stilben-4'-yl]-5-methyl-7-(1,1-dimethylethyl)-	DMF	364(4.85)	33-0779-79
Benzoxazole, 2-[4"-(5"'-phenylisoxazol-3"'-yl)stilben-4'-yl]-7-methyl-5-(1,1-dimethylethyl)-	DMF	363(4.89)	33-0779-79
$C_{35}H_{30}N_2O_5$			
Trigilletimine	MeOH or EtOH	210(4.72),232s(4.67), 273s(4.21),311s(3.46), 351(3.05)	100-0001-79
$C_{35}H_{30}O_2$			
1H-Cyclohepta[b]cyclopropa[c]furan-1-methanol, 1a,2,3a,4-tetrahydro-α,α,2,2-tetraphenyl-	MeOH	260(4.07)	18-0151-79
1H-Cyclohepta[b]cyclopropa[c]furan-1-methanol, 1a,2,3a,8-tetrahydro-α,α,2,2-tetraphenyl-	MeOH	255(4.18)	18-0151-79
1H-Cyclohepta[b]cyclopropa[c]furan-1-methanol, 1a,2,7,8-tetrahydro-α,α,2,2-tetraphenyl-	MeOH	277(4.10)	18-0151-79
$C_{35}H_{30}O_{10}$			
α-D-Glucopyranoside, methyl, 2,3,4,6-tetrabenzoate	EtOH	231(4.59)	136-0001-79I
β-	EtOH	231(4.58)	136-0001-79I
$C_{35}H_{31}ClN_5O_{10}P$			
Cytidine, N-benzoyl-2'-O-[(2-nitrophenyl)methyl]-, 3'-(4-chlorophenyl phenylphosphoramidate)	EtOH	261(4.49),302(4.08)	35-6409-79
diastereomer	EtOH	261(4.48),302(4.06)	35-6409-79
$C_{35}H_{32}O_2PSe$			
Phosphonium, triphenyl-, 2-ethoxy-2-oxo-1-[phenyl(phenylmethyl)selenonio)eth-	EtOH	227s(4.64)	104-2169-79

Compound	Solvent	$\lambda_{max}(\log \epsilon)$	Ref.
ylide, tetrafluoroborate (cont.)			104-2169-79
$C_{35}H_{34}N_2OP$			
Methylium, bis[4-(dimethylamino)phenyl][4-(diphenylphosphinyl)phenyl]-, perchlorate	EtOH	262(4.16),318(4.39), 430(4.21),636(4.75)	65-0860-79
	acetone	430(4.21),634(4.84)	65-0860-79
$C_{35}H_{34}N_2O_5$			
Cocsuline (eferine)	MeOH or EtOH	234(4.72),275s(3.73), 289(3.77),307s(3.58)	100-0001-79
Micrantine, O-methyl-	MeOH	286(3.78)	100-0001-79
Nortilliacorine A	EtOH	215(4.80),235s(4.69), 293(4.00)	100-0001-79
Pseudotiliarine	MeOH or EtOH	212(4.75),236s(4.67), 292(3.99)	100-0001-79
Trilobine	EtOH	287(3.75)	100-0001-79
	EtOH	275s(3.96),288(3.97), 305(3.81)	100-0399-79
$C_{35}H_{34}N_2P$			
Methylium, bis[4-(dimethylamino)phenyl][4-(diphenylphosphino)phenyl]-, perchlorate	EtOH	261(4.15),314(4.15), 454(4.16),628(4.78)	65-0860-79
	acetone	450(4.37),624(5.00)	65-0860-79
$C_{35}H_{34}O_5$			
9,9'-Spirobifluorene, 2,2'-(2,5,8,11,14-pentaoxapentadecano)-	MeCN	211(4.80),221(4.85), 267(4.52),277(4.51), 298(4.17),310(4.35)	33-2285-79
$C_{35}H_{36}Br_2N_4O_4$			
21H,23H-Porphine-2,18-dipropanoic acid, 8-(1,2-dibromoethenyl)-3,7,12,13,17-pentamethyl-, dimethyl ester	$CHCl_3$	406(5.30),505(4.04), 542(4.21),567(3.95), 624(3.20)	65-0767-79
$C_{35}H_{36}N_2O_6$			
Cycleacurine	EtOH	284(3.83)	100-0001-79
Daphnoline	MeOH	285(3.92)	100-0001-79
Obamegine, 2-N-nor-	MeOH	283(3.84)	100-0001-79
Peinamine, 7-O-demethyl-	MeOH	284(3.95)	100-0001-79
$C_{35}H_{38}N_4O_4$			
9,13-Phorbinedipropanoic acid, 3,4-didehydro-3,4,8,14,18-pentamethyl-, dimethyl ester	$CHCl_3$	401(5.35),501(4.19), 536(3.65),564(3.83), 618(3.63)	65-0767-79
$C_{35}H_{38}N_4O_6$			
Biliverdin IXα, dimethyl ester, Zn complex	pH 8	385(4.63),705(4.51)	41-0097-79
	pH 10	400(4.57),795(4.32)	41-0097-79
$C_{35}H_{40}Br_2N_4O_4$			
21H-Biline-8,12-dipropanoic acid, 2-(1,2-dibromoethenyl)-10,24-dihydro-1,3,7,13,17,18-hexamethyl-, dimethyl ester, hydrobromide	$CHCl_3$	457(4.94),525(5.57)	65-0767-79
$C_{35}H_{40}N_4O_4$			
Pyrophaeophorbide a, 3-ethyl-20-(hydroxymethyl)-, methyl ester	dioxan	410(5.00),510(3.89), 541(4.04),608(3.76), 665(4.66)	5-1992-79

Compound	Solvent	λ_{max}(log ε)	Ref.
$C_{35}H_{41}CoN_4O_4$			
Cobalt(1+), [dimethyl octadehydro-1,2,3,7,13,17,18,19-octamethyl-8,12-corrindipropanoato-N^{21},N^{22},N^{23},N^{24}]-, (SP-4-3)-, perchlorate	$CHCl_3$	280(4.38),350(4.26), 490(4.11)	65-2398-79
Cobalt(1+), [dimethyl octadehydro-1,3,7,8,12,13,17,19-octamethyl-2,18-corrindipropanoato-N^{21},N^{22},N^{23},N^{24}]-, (SP-4-3)-, perchlorate	$CHCl_3$	282(4.46),350(4.31), 495(4.10)	65-2398-79
$C_{35}H_{41}N_4NiO_4$			
Nickel(1+), [dimethyl octadehydro-1,2,3,7,13,17,18,19-octamethyl-8,12-corrindipropanoato-N^{21},N^{22},N^{23},N^{24}]-, (SP-4-3)-, perchlorate	$CHCl_3$	274(4.42),352(4.43), 565(4.08)	65-2398-79
Nickel(1+), [dimethyl octadehydro-1,3,7,8,12,13,17,19-octamethyl-2,18-corrindipropanoato-N^{21},N^{22},N^{23},N^{24}]-, (SP-4-3)-, perchlorate	$CHCl_3$	279(4.51),353(4.49), 564(4.14)	65-2398-79
$C_{35}H_{42}N_4O_6$			
Phycoerythrobiline, dimethyl ester, (2R,16R)-	MeOH	305s(--),318(4.28), 331s(--),500s(--), 530(4.53)	24-2243-79
	MeOH-HCl	328(4.27),386s(--), 594(4.69),600s(--)	24-2243-79
$C_{35}H_{42}O_{16}$			
Hydroxypinoresinol monomethyl ether 4'-β-D-glucoside, tetraacetate, (+)-	EtOH	226(4.13),279(3.65)	94-2868-79
$C_{35}H_{44}O_{10}$			
Ohchinolide B	EtOH	210(4.36)(end abs.)	138-1137-79
$C_{35}H_{44}O_{14}$			
Deglucosyrioside, tri-O-acetyl-	EtOH	213(--),283s(2.34)	33-0412-79
$C_{35}H_{44}O_{18}$			
Sylvestroside IV tetraacetate	MeOH	233(3.97)	102-0273-79
	MeOH-NaOMe	272(--)	102-0273-79
$C_{35}H_{45}N_2O_6$			
Cycleahomine (chloride)	MeOH	284(4.08)	100-0001-79
$C_{35}H_{47}NO_2$			
1'H-D-Homoandrost-15-eno[17,17a-c]pyrrol-12-ol, 4,4,8-trimethyl-1'-(2-phenylethyl)-, acetate, (5α,12β)-	EtOH	262(4.07)	31-0157-79
$C_{35}H_{48}O_3$			
Ergosta-5,7-dien-22-one, 3β-(benzoyloxy)-	EtOH	227(4.05),262(3.87), 271(4.00),281(4.01), 293(3.76)	39-0935-79C
$C_{35}H_{48}O_8$			
1,4-Benzenediol, 2-(8,9-diacetoxy-3,7,11,15-tetramethyl-2,6,10,14-heptadecatetraenyl)-6-methyl-, diacetate	EtOH	260(2.77)	138-1269-79

Compound	Solvent	λ_{max}(log ε)	Ref.
$C_{35}H_{49}N_3O_3$			
4a,13b-Etheno-1H,9H-benzo[c]cyclopenta-[h][1,2,4]triazolo[1,2-a]cinnolin-1,3(2H)-dione, 11-(1,5-dimethylhex-yl)-5,6,7,8,8a,8b,10,10a,11,12,13,13a-dodecahydro-6-hydroxy-8a,10a-dimethyl-2-phenyl-	MeOH	255(3.68)	39-1858-79C
$C_{35}H_{50}O_2$			
1H,8H-Benzo[1,2-c:3,4-c']bis[2]benzo-pyran, 5-(1-butyl-1-pentenyl)-4,4a-8a,9,12,12a,14,14a-octahydro-3,8,8-11,14,14-hexamethyl-	EtOH	223(4.46),293(3.38)	2-0250-79A
$C_{35}H_{50}O_3$			
Ergosta-5,7-diene-3,22-diol, 3-benz-oate, (3β,22R)-	EtOH	229(4.04),264(3.92), 272(4.04),282(4.04), 294(3.79)	39-0935-79C
(3β,22S)-	EtOH	229(4.14),264(4.02), 272(4.14),282(4.15), 294(3.90)	39-0935-79C
Ergosta-5,7-diene-3,23-diol, 3-benz-oate, (3β,22R)-	EtOH	229(4.00),264(3.83), 272(3.96),282(3.97), 294(3.70)	39-0935-79C
$C_{35}H_{50}O_{20}$			
Sylvestroside II	EtOH	238(4.38)	102-0273-79
$C_{35}H_{52}O_7$			
18αH-Echinocystic acid, 11-oxo-, methyl ester, diacetate	EtOH	246(3.80)	2-0112-79B
β-	EtOH	251(4.1)	2-0112-79B
18βH-Machaerinic acid, 11-oxo-, methyl ester, diacetate	EtOH	251(3.42)	2-0112-79B
$C_{35}H_{53}NO_{13}$			
Tetrin A, 24-demethyl-24-ethyl-(tetramycin)	MeOH	280(4.40),290(4.73), 304(4.93),318(4.88)	78-1851-79
$C_{35}H_{63}NO_{13}$			
Tetramycin, decahydro-	MeOH	208(4.25)	78-1851-79

Compound	Solvent	λ max(log ε)	Ref.
$C_{36}H_{18}N_4O_2$			
[10,10'-Bi-7H-benzimidazo[2,1-a]benz-[de]isoquinoline]-7,7'-dione (or isomer)	H_2SO_4	245(4.83),312(4.52), 428(4.08)	103-0791-79
$C_{36}H_{18}N_4O_3$			
7H-Benzimidazo[2,1-a]benz[de]isoquino-lin-7-one, 10,10'-oxybis- (or isomer)	H_2SO_4	231(4.86),305(4.49), 416(4.74)	103-0791-79
$C_{36}H_{18}N_4O_4S$			
7H-Benzimidazo[2,1-a]benz[de]isoquino-lin-7-one, 10,10'-sulfonylbis- (or isomer)	H_2SO_4	235(4.53),304(3.78), 405(4.50)	103-0791-79
$C_{36}H_{22}Cl_3N_3O$			
Benzoxazole, 2-[4-[2-[4-[4,5-dichloro-1-(4-chlorophenyl)-1H-pyrazol-3-yl]-phenyl]ethenyl]phenyl]-5-phenyl-	DMF	366(4.90)	33-1816-79
Benzoxazole, 2-[4-[2-[4-[4,5-dichloro-1-(4-chlorophenyl)-1H-pyrazol-3-yl]-phenyl]ethenyl]phenyl]-6-phenyl-	DMF	371(4.91)	33-1816-79
Benzoxazole, 2-[4-[2-[4-[4,5-dichloro-1-(4-chlorophenyl)-1H-pyrazol-3-yl]-phenyl]ethenyl]phenyl]-7-phenyl-	DMF	364(4.87)	33-1816-79
$C_{36}H_{22}N_2$			
3,5-Cyclopentadiene-1,3-dicarbonitrile, 2-[4-(2,4,6-cycloheptatrien-1-ylid-ene)-1(4H)-naphthalenylidene]-4,5-diphenyl-	MeCN	268(4.58),370(3.92), 644(3.81)	39-0889-79C
3,5-Cyclopentadiene-1,3-dicarbonitrile, 2-[5-(2,4,6-cycloheptatrien-1-yli-ene)-1(5H)-naphthalenylidene)-4,5-diphenyl-	CF_3COOH	464(3.87)	39-0889-79C
$C_{36}H_{23}ClN_2O_2$			
Benzoxazole, 2-[4"-[3"'-(4-chlorophen-yl)isoxazol-5"'-yl]stilben]4'-yl]-5-phenyl-	DMF	370(4.94),389(4.76)	33-0779-79
Benzoxazole, 2-[4"-[3"'-(4-chlorophen-yl)isoxazol-5"'-yl]stilben]-4'-yl]-7-phenyl-	DMF	368(3.91),387(3.72)	33-0779-79
Benzoxazole, 2-[4"-[5"'-(4-chlorophen-yl)isoxazol-3"'-yl]stilben]-4'-yl]-7-phenyl-	DMF	362(4.89),378(4.70)	33-0779-79
$C_{36}H_{23}ClN_4O$			
2-Oxabicyclo[2.2.2]oct-7-ene-5,5,6,6-tetracarbonitrile, 8-(4-chlorophenyl)-1,3-diphenyl-3-(phenylmethyl)-	ether	265(4.52),335(3.57)	78-2633-79
$C_{36}H_{23}ClN_4O_2$			
1,2,4-Oxadiazole, 3-[4-[2-[4-(5-[1,1'-biphenyl]-4-yl-1,3,4-oxadiazol-2-yl)-2-chlorophenyl]ethenyl]phenyl]-5-phenyl-	DMF	358(4.83)	33-1411-79
1,2,4-Oxadiazole, 5-[4-[2-[4-(5-[1,1'-biphenyl]-4-yl-1,3,4-oxadiazol-2-yl)-2-chlorophenyl]ethenyl]phenyl]-3-phenyl-	DMF	362(4.81)	33-1411-79

Compound	Solvent	$\lambda_{max}(\log \epsilon)$	Ref.
$C_{36}H_{23}Cl_2N_3O$			
1,2-Benzisoxazole, 6-chloro-3-[3-chloro-4-[2-[4-(1,3-diphenyl-1H-pyrazol-5-yl)phenyl]ethenyl]phenyl]-	DMF	344(4.70)	33-1816-79
Benzoxazole, 2-[4-[2-[4-[4-chloro-1-(4-chlorophenyl)-1H-pyrazol-5-yl]phenyl]ethenyl]phenyl]-5-phenyl-	DMF	368(4.91)	33-1816-79
Benzoxazole, 2-[4-[2-[4-[4-chloro-1-(4-chlorophenyl)-1H-pyrazol-5-yl]phenyl]ethenyl]phenyl]-6-phenyl-	DMF	373(4.92)	33-1816-79
$C_{36}H_{24}ClN_3O$			
1,2-Benzisoxazole, 6-chloro-3-[4-[2-[4-(1,3-diphenyl-1H-pyrazol-5-yl)phenyl]ethenyl]phenyl]-	DMF	345(4.73)	33-1816-79
Benzoxazole, 2-[4-[2-[4-[1-(4-chlorophenyl)-1H-pyrazol-3-yl]phenyl]ethenyl]phenyl]-5-phenyl-	DMF	373(4.94)	33-1816-79
Benzoxazole, 2-[4-[2-[4-[3-(4-chlorophenyl)-1H-pyrazol-1-yl]phenyl]ethenyl]phenyl]-5-phenyl-	DMF	370(4.92)	33-1816-79
Benzoxazole, 2-[4-[2-[4-(4-chloro-1-phenyl-1H-pyrazol-3-yl)phenyl]ethenyl]phenyl]-5-phenyl-	DMF	367(4.90)	33-1816-79
$C_{36}H_{24}N_2O_2$			
1,2-Benzisoxazole, 3-(p-biphenylyl)-6-[4'-(5"-phenylisoxazol-3"-yl)styryl]-	DMF	339(4.81)	33-0779-79
Benzoxazole, 2-[4"-(3"'-phenylisoxazol-5"'-yl)stilben-4'-yl]-5-phenyl-	DMF	370(4.94),388(4.76)	33-0779-79
Benzoxazole, 2-[4"-(3"'-phenylisoxazol-5"'-yl)stilben-4'-yl]-6-phenyl-	DMF	374(4.94)	33-0779-79
Benzoxazole, 2-[4"-(3"'-phenylisoxazol-5"'-yl)stilben-4'-yl]-7-phenyl-	DMF	367(4.91),386(4.72)	33-0779-79
Benzoxazole, 2-[4"-(5"'-phenylisoxazol-3"'-yl)stilben-4'-yl]-5-phenyl-	DMF	363(4.91)	33-0779-79
Benzoxazole, 2-[4"-(5"'-phenylisoxazol-3"'-yl)stilben-4'-yl]-6-phenyl-	DMF	368(4.91)	33-0779-79
Benzoxazole, 2-[4"-(5"'-phenylisoxazol-3"'-yl)stilben-4'-yl]-7-phenyl-	DMF	362(4.88),378(4.69)	33-0779-79
$C_{36}H_{24}N_4O$			
2-Oxabicyclo[2.2.2]oct-7-ene-5,5,6,6-tetracarbonitrile, 1,3,8-triphenyl-3-(phenylmethyl)-	ether	260(4.29),330(3.30)	78-2633-79
$C_{36}H_{24}N_4O_2$			
1,2,4-Oxadiazole, 3-[4-[2-[4-(3-[1,1'-biphenyl]-4-yl-1,2,4-oxadiazol-5-yl)phenyl]ethenyl]phenyl]-5-phenyl-	DMF	348(4.85)	33-1411-79
$C_{36}H_{24}S$			
Thiophene, 2,5-bis[2-(9-anthracenyl)ethenyl]-, (E,E)-	toluene	420(4.40)	103-0729-79
$C_{36}H_{25}N_3O$			
1,2-Benzisoxazole, 3-[4-[2-[4-(1,3-diphenyl-1H-pyrazol-5-yl)phenyl]ethenyl]phenyl]-	DMF	343(4.72)	33-1816-79

Compound	Solvent	$\lambda_{max}(\log \epsilon)$	Ref.
1,2-Benzisoxazole, 3-[4-[2-[4-(3,5-diphenyl-1H-pyrazol-1-yl)phenyl]ethenyl]phenyl]-	DMF	342(4.73)	33-1816-79
1,2-Benzisoxazole, 6-[2-[4-(1,3-diphenyl-1H-pyrazol-5-yl)phenyl]ethenyl]-3-phenyl-	DMF	343(4.70)	33-1816-79
1,2-Benzisoxazole, 6-[2-[4-(1,5-diphenyl-1H-pyrazol-3-yl)phenyl]ethenyl]-3-phenyl-	DMF	348(4.77)	33-1816-79
1,2-Benzisoxazole, 6-[2-[4-(3,5-diphenyl-1H-pyrazol-1-yl)phenyl]ethenyl]-3-phenyl-	DMF	340(4.70)	33-1816-79
Benzoxazole, 2-[4-[2-[4-(1,3-diphenyl-1H-pyrazol-5-yl)phenyl]ethenyl]phenyl]-	DMF	360(4.83)	33-1816-79
Benzoxazole, 2-[4-[2-[4-(1,5-diphenyl-1H-pyrazol-3-yl)phenyl]ethenyl]phenyl]-	DMF	367(4.88)	33-1816-79
Benzoxazole, 2-[4-[2-[4-(3,5-diphenyl-1H-pyrazol-1-yl)phenyl]ethenyl]phenyl]-	DMF	359(4.83)	33-1816-79
Benzoxazole, 5-phenyl-2-[4-[2-[4-(1-phenyl-1H-pyrazol-3-yl)phenyl]ethenyl]phenyl]-	DMF	372(4.93)	33-1816-79
Benzoxazole, 6-phenyl-2-[4-[2-[4-(1-phenyl-1H-pyrazol-3-yl)phenyl]ethenyl]phenyl]-	DMF	377(4.94)	33-1816-79
Benzoxazole, 7-phenyl-2-[4-[2-[4-(1-phenyl-1H-pyrazol-3-yl)phenyl]ethenyl]phenyl]-	DMF	370(4.88)	33-1816-79
Benzoxazole, 5-phenyl-2-[4-[2-[4-(3-phenyl-1H-pyrazol-1-yl)phenyl]ethenyl]phenyl]-	DMF	370(4.91)	33-1816-79
Benzoxazole, 6-phenyl-2-[4-[2-[4-(3-phenyl-1H-pyrazol-1-yl)phenyl]ethenyl]phenyl]-	DMF	375(4.93)	33-1816-79
Benzoxazole, 7-phenyl-2-[4-[2-[4-(3-phenyl-1H-pyrazol-1-yl)phenyl]ethenyl]phenyl]-	DMF	369(4.87)	33-1816-79
$C_{36}H_{25}N_3O_3$			
Benzoxazole, 2-[4-[2-[4-[5-(4-methoxyphenyl)-1,2,4-oxadiazol-3-yl]phenyl]ethenyl]phenyl]-5-phenyl-	DMF	363(4.92),382(4.73)	33-1411-79
Benzoxazole, 2-[4-[2-[4-[5-(4-methoxyphenyl)-1,2,4-oxadiazol-3-yl]phenyl]ethenyl]phenyl]-6-phenyl-	DMF	368(4.92)	33-1411-79
Benzoxazole, 2-[4-[2-[4-[5-(4-methoxyphenyl)-1,2,4-oxadiazol-3-yl]phenyl]ethenyl]phenyl]-7-phenyl-	DMF	361(4.88)	33-1411-79
$C_{36}H_{26}ClN_5O$			
2H-Benzotriazole, 2-[3-chloro-4-[2-[4-(1,3-diphenyl-1H-pyrazol-5-yl)phenyl]ethenyl]phenyl]-5-methoxy-	DMF	370(4.79)	33-1816-79
$C_{36}H_{26}N_8$			
1,10-Phenanthroline-4,7-diamine, M,N'-bis[4-(phenylazo)phenyl]-	isopentanol	275(4.53),400(4.71)	140-0391-79

Compound	Solvent	$\lambda_{max}(\log \epsilon)$	Ref.
$C_{36}H_{26}O$			
Anthracene, 9-[(9-anthracenylmethoxy)-methyl]-10-phenyl-	$C_6H_{11}Me$	248(5.17),255(5.22), 355(4.00),367(4.14), 373(4.18),387(4.13), 394(4.19)	39-0411-79B
1H,3H-3a,8[1',2']:9,13b[1",2"]-Dibenzenodibenzo[3,4:7,8]cycloocta[1,2-c]-furan, 8,9-dihydro-8-phenyl-	$C_6H_{11}Me$	211(4.80),255(3.83), 270(3.04),305(2.62)	39-0411-79B
$C_{36}H_{26}O_6$			
Methanone, (2,8-dimethylbenzo[1,2-b:4,5-b']bisbenzofuran-6,12-diyl)-bis[(2-hydroxy-5-methylphenyl)-	dioxan	227(4.76),268(4.47), 301(4.35),364(4.38)	1-0405-79
$C_{36}H_{26}O_{10}$			
[9,9'-Bianthracene]-10,10'(9H,9'H)-di-one, 4,4',5,5'-tetraacetoxy-	MeOH	260(4.27),273s(4.26)	145-1083-79
$C_{36}H_{27}N_5$			
Methanamine, N,N-dimethyl-1-(1,4,5,8-tetraphenyl-9H-cyclopenta[1,2-d:3,4-d']dipyridazin-9-ylidene)-	MeOH	219(4.54),273(4.56), 342(3.81),450(4.16)	5-0675-79
$C_{36}H_{27}N_5O$			
2H-Benzotriazole, 2-[4-[2-[4-(1,3-di-phenylpyrazol-5-yl)phenyl]ethenyl]-phenyl]-5-methoxy-	DMF	369(4.85)	33-1816-79
$C_{36}H_{28}N_3$			
1H-Naphth[2,3-d]imidazolium, 2-[3-(1-methyl-2(1H)-quinolinylidene)-1-pro-penyl]-1,3-diphenyl-, perchlorate	n.s.g.	571(5.16)	124-0043-79
$C_{36}H_{29}N_5$			
Ethenamine, 2,2-bis(3,6-diphenyl-4-pyri-dazinyl)-N,N-dimethyl-	MeOH	264(4.32),370(4.00), 411s(3.81)	5-0675-79
$C_{36}H_{30}$			
1,1'-Biphenyl, 4,4'-[1,4-phenylene-bis(2-methyl-2,1-ethenediyl)]bis-	dioxan	312(4.80)	104-1944-79
$C_{36}H_{31}ClN_7O_9P$			
Adenosine, N-benzoyl-2'-O-[(2-nitro-phenyl)methyl]-, 3'-(4-chlorophenyl)-phosphoramidate	EtOH	279.5(4.43)	35-6409-79
$C_{36}H_{32}N_4$			
Cycloocta[1,2-d:5,6-d']dipyridazine, 2,4a,5,6,8,10a,11,12-octahydro-1,4,7,10-tetraphenyl-	MeOH	325(4.06)	78-0277-79
	MeOH-HCl	230(4.53),292s(4.12)	78-0277-79
$C_{36}H_{34}F_3NO_{11}$			
5,12-Naphthacenedione, 7,8,9,10-tetra-hydro-6,8,11-trihydroxy-1-methoxy-8-(1-oxo-3-phenylpropyl)-10-[[2,3,6-trideoxy-3-[(trifluoroacetyl)amino]-α-L-lyxo-hexopyranosyl]oxy]-, (8S-cis)-	MeOH	234(4.57),252(4.43), 289(3.96),479(4.10), 495(4.10),530(3.84)	87-0040-79
$C_{36}H_{34}N_2O_4$			
1H-Imidazolium, 2-[1-(diphenylmethyl-	$CHCl_3$	260(4.4),300(4.3),	5-1406-79

Compound	Solvent	λ$_{max}$(log ε)	Ref.
ene)-3-ethoxy-2-(ethoxycarbonyl)-3-oxopropyl]-4,5-dihydro-1,3-diphenyl-, hydroxide, inner salt (cont.)		488(3.5)	5-1406-79
$C_{36}H_{34}N_2O_6$			
Sciadoline	MeOH or EtOH	275(3.94),283s(3.88), 326s(3.77),335(3.78)	100-0001-79
Stebisimine	MeOH	238(4.71),279(4.38)	100-0001-79
$C_{36}H_{34}N_2O_7$			
[1,1'-Biphenyl]-3-carboxaldehyde, 2'-hydroxy-6-methoxy-5'-[(1,2,3,4,9,10-11,12-octahydro-6-methoxy-2,11-dimethyl-12-oxo[1,4]dioxino[2,3-g:6,5-h']diisoquinolin-1-yl)methyl]-, (R)-	MeOH	220(4.08),286s(3.44), 312s(3.16)	100-0116-79
$C_{36}H_{34}O_5$			
Anthracene, 9,9'-[oxybis(2,1-ethanediyloxy-2,1-ethanediyloxy)]bis-	C_6H_{12}	249(5.24),257(5.48), 320(3.29),335(3.72), 351(4.04),370(4.24), 390(4.19)	108-0220-79
	benzene	392(4.19)	108-0220-79
	MeOH	256(5.47),389(4.16)	108-0220-79
$C_{36}H_{35}N_3$			
Tetramethylammonium 1-(cyclohepta-1,3,6-trienyl)-4-(2,5-dicyano-3,4-diphenylcyclopentadienido)naphthalene	MeCN	270(4.54),366(4.06)	39-0889-79C
$C_{36}H_{36}N_2O_5$			
Dinklacorine	MeOH or EtOH	222(4.70),236s(4.68), 294(3.97)	100-0001-79
Micranthine, N,O-dimethyl-	MeOH	286(3.85)	100-0001-79
Tiliacorine	MeOH	295(3.91)	100-0001-79
Tiliacorinine	MeOH	290(3.95)	100-0001-79
$C_{36}H_{36}N_2O_6$			
Cepharanoline	MeOH	282(3.90)	100-0001-79
Tiliafunimine	MeOH	212(4.77),238s(4.46), 285(3.99),319s(3.85)	100-0001-79
$C_{36}H_{36}O_2Si_2$			
Silane, [1,2-ethenediylbis(10,9-anthracenediyloxy)]bis[trimethyl-	$CHCl_3$	425(4.3)	44-4247-79
$C_{36}H_{37}BOSSe$			
Dimethylsulfonium benzoyldimethylselenoniomethylide, tetraphenylborate	n.s.g.	260(4.071),265s(4.063), 274s(3.987)	104-0332-79
$C_{36}H_{37}BOS_2$			
Dimethylsulfonium benzoyldimethylsulfoniomethylide, tetraphenylborate	n.s.g.	259(4.114)	104-0332-79
$C_{36}H_{37}BrO_7$			
Pregna-1,4-diene-3,20-dione, 17,21-bis(benzoyloxy)-7-bromo-11-hydroxy-16-methyl-, (7α,11β,16α)-	MeOH	232(4.60)	145-1662-79
$C_{36}H_{38}$			
Bi-2,4,6-cycloheptatrien-1-yl, bis(4-cyclopropyl-3,5-dimethylphenyl)-	$CHCl_3$	247(4.55),290s(4.18)	39-0262-79B

Compound	Solvent	λ_{max}(log ϵ)	Ref.
Cyclohexadeca[a]naphthalene, 10,11,17-18,19,20-hexadehydro-9,12,16-tris-(1,1-dimethylethyl)-	C_6H_{12}	235(4.45),292(4.51), 324(4.85),362(4.56), 408s(4.46),600(3.15)	88-4217-79
$C_{36}H_{38}N_2O_6$			
Aromoline	MeOH or EtOH	208(4.94),228s(4.69), 285(3.95)	100-0001-79
Atherospermoline	MeOH	284(3.97)	100-0001-79
Baluchistine, (+)-	EtOH	283(3.67)	31-1137-79
	EtOH-base	290(3.80)	31-1137-79
Curine, (-)-	MeOH or EtOH	206(4.95),225s(4.61), 282(3.98)	100-0001-79
Daphnandrine	MeOH	285(3.91)	100-0001-79
Dryadodaphnine	MeOH	285(3.90)	100-0001-79
Hayatine	MeOH	277(3.73),283(3.75)	100-0001-79
Isochondodendrine	MeOH	211(4.72),231s(4.58), 278(3.73),285(3.72)	100-0001-79
Isothalicberine, 7-O-demethyl-	EtOH	285(3.88)	32-0567-79
Krukovine	MeOH	285(3.82)	100-0001-79
Macolidine	MeOH	284(3.93)	100-0001-79
2-N-Norberbamine	MeOH	282(3.83)	100-0001-79
Norpanurensine	MeOH or EtOH	223(4.04),240(4.30), 288(4.10)	100-0001-79
Obamegine	MeOH	280(3.19)	100-0001-79
Peinamine	MeOH	282(3.90)	100-0001-79
Peinamine, 7-O-demethyl-N-methyl-	MeOH	284(3.90)	100-0001-79
Sepeerine	MeOH	284(3.79)	100-0001-79
$C_{36}H_{38}N_{12}$			
21H,23H-Porphyrazine-2,7,12,17-tetra-carbonitrile, 3,8,13,18-tetrakis-[(1,1-dimethylethyl)amino]-	$CHCl_3$	352(4.94),540(4.11), 576(4.77),650(4.98)	65-1233-79
$C_{36}H_{38}O_2Si_2$			
Silane, [1,2-ethanediylbis(10,9-anthra-cenediyloxy)]bis[trimethyl-	C_6H_{12}	254(5.25),260(5.23), 353(3.72),369(4.03), 392(4.21),418(4.24)	44-4247-79
$C_{36}H_{39}N_3O_6S$			
7H-Pyrrolo[2,3-d]pyrimidine, 4-(meth-oxymethoxy)-5-methyl-2-(methylthio)-7-[2,3,5-tris-O-(phenylmethyl)-β-D-ribofuranosyl]-	MeOH	247(4.33),287(4.09)	35-3629-79
4H-Pyrrolo[2,3-d]pyrimidin-4-one, 3,7-dihydro-3-(methoxymethyl)-5-methyl-2-(methylthio)-7-[2,3,5-tris-O-(phen-ylmethyl)-β-D-ribofuranosyl]-	MeOH	278s(3.92),308(4.05)	35-3629-79
$C_{36}H_{40}N_2O_6$			
Magnoline	MeOH or EtOH	224(4.24),239(4.25), 287(4.01),320s(3.25)	100-0001-79
$C_{36}H_{40}N_4O_4$			
9,13-Phorbinedipropanoic acid, 3,4-di-dehydro-3-ethyl-4,8,14,18-tetrameth-yl-, dimethyl ester	$CHCl_3$	402(5.36),502(4.24), 538(3.62),567(3.86), 620(3.68)	65-0767-79
$C_{36}H_{40}N_4O_5$			
21H,23H-Porphine-2,18-dipropanoic acid, 8-acetyl-12-ethyl-3,7,13,17-tetra-methyl-, dimethyl ester	$CHCl_3$	411(5.27),512(3.99), 552(4.11),580(3.95), 642(3.08)	65-0767-79

Compound	Solvent	$\lambda_{max}(\log \epsilon)$	Ref.
$C_{36}H_{40}O_5$			
Pregna-1,4-dien-20-one, 21-acetoxy-3-(diphenylmethylene)-11β,17-dihydroxy-	MeOH	247(4.06),312(3.40)	39-1166-79C
$C_{36}H_{42}N_4O_4$			
3-Phorbinepropanoic acid, 9,14-diethyl-6-(methoxymethyl)-4,8,13,18-tetramethyl-20-oxo-, methyl ester, (3S-trans)-	dioxan	410(4.98),508(3.86), 540(4.01),608(3.76), 664(4.64)	5-1992-79
$C_{36}H_{42}N_{16}$			
21H,23H-Porphyrazine-2,7,12,18-tetracarbonitrile, 3,8,13,17-tetrakis-[(1,1-dimethylethyl)amino]-	$CHCl_3$	334(4.91),400(4.24), 450(4.26),648(4.30), 682(4.42),744(4.60), 774(4.68)	65-1233-79
$C_{36}H_{43}CoN_4O_5$			
Cobalt(1+), [2-(2-hydroxyethyl) 18-methyl octadehydro-1,3,7,8,12,13,17-19-octamethyl-2,18-corrindipropanoato-N^{21},N^{22},N^{23},N^{24}]-, (SP-4-3)-, perchlorate	$CHCl_3$	280(4.41),350(4.29), 495(4.05)	65-2398-79
Cobalt(1+), [8-(2-hydroxyethyl) 12-methyl octadehydro-1,2,3,7,13,17,18-19-octamethyl-8,12-corrindipropanoato-N^{21},N^{22},N^{23},N^{24}]-, (SP-4-3)-, perchlorate	$CHCl_3$	280(4.39),351(4.25), 495(4.00)	65-2398-79
$C_{36}H_{43}N_4NiO_5$			
Nickel(1+), [8-(2-hydroxyethyl) 12-methyl octadehydro-1,2,3,7,13,17,18-19-octamethyl-8,12-corrindipropanoato-N^{21},N^{22},N^{23},N^{24}]-, (SP-4-3)-, perchlorate	$CHCl_3$	274(4.43),352(4.34), 560(4.10)	65-2398-79
$C_{36}H_{44}N_2O_{12}$			
Pyrromethane-5,5'-dicarboxylic acid, 3,4'-bis(2-methoxycarbonylethyl)-3',4-bis(methoxycarbonylmethyl)-, 5-benzyl 5'-tert-butyl ester	n.s.g.	241(4.00),273(4.40), 289(4.51)	39-1927-79C
$C_{36}H_{44}N_4O_5$			
21H-Biline-8,12-dipropanoic acid, 18-acetyl-2-ethyl-10,24-dihydro-1,3,7-13,17-pentamethyl-, dimethyl ester, dihydrobromide	$CHCl_3$-1%HBr	450(4.81),520(5.11)	65-0767-79
$C_{36}H_{45}NO_8$			
Pregnane-3,8,12,14,17,20-hexol, 12-(3-phenyl-2-propenoate) 20-(3-pyridinecarboxylate) (dihydrogagaminin)	EtOH	218(4.26),282(4.23)	94-2304-79
$C_{36}H_{46}N_4$			
Porphine, octaethyl-	benzene	400(5.20),498(4.16), 532(4.03),568(3.83), 596(3.18),622(3.76)	101-0311-79P
$C_{36}H_{47}NO_{17}$			
Cathedulin K15	MeOH	221(3.92),264(3.59)	39-2965-79C

Compound	Solvent	λ_{max}(log ϵ)	Ref.
$C_{36}H_{47}N_5$			
21H,23H-Porphin-21-amine, 2,3,7,8,12-13,17,18-octaethyl-	toluene	408(5.15),510(3.98),545(3.76),573(3.83),628(3.77)	78-1455-79
$C_{36}H_{48}CoN_8O_{12}$			
meso-Tetranitrooctaethylporphyrin cobalt(III) hydroxide trihydrate	CH_2Cl_2	410(4.50),545(3.82),580(3.79),671(3.72)	78-1251-79
$C_{36}H_{48}MgN_8S_4$			
Magnesium, [2,7,12,17-tetrakis(1,1-dimethylpropyl)thio]-21H,23H-porphyrazinato(2-)-N^{21},N^{22},N^{23},N^{24}]-, (SP-4-1)-	$CHCl_3$	350(4.89),649(4.74)	104-0962-79
$C_{36}H_{48}N_6O_{12}$			
Octanedioic acid, bis[[3-(2,2-dimethyl-1-oxopropoxy)-2,3,3a,9a-tetrahydro-6-imino-6H-furo[2',3':4,5]oxazolo[3,2-a]pyrimidin-2-yl]methyl] ester, dihydrochloride	MeOH	235(4.32),264(4.38)	87-0639-79
$C_{36}H_{49}O_2$			
[1,1":3',1"-Terphenyl]-2'-yloxy, 5'-(octadecyloxy)-	PrOH	405(4.40),650(3.38) (anom.)	39-1540-79B
$C_{36}H_{50}O_2$			
[1,1':3',1"-Terphenyl]-2'-ol, 5'-(octadecyloxy)-	PrOH	315(3.85)	39-1540-79B
$C_{36}H_{50}O_{10}$			
Huratoxin, 12-acetoxy-	MeOH	236(4.27),261(4.09),272(4.09),282(3.97)	12-2495-79
$C_{36}H_{52}O_3$			
Cholest-4-en-3-one, 6α-acetyl-6β-(4-methoxyphenyl)-	MeOH	228(4.20),243s(4.04),271s(3.59),279s(3.49)	12-1561-79
Cholest-4-en-3-one, 6β-acetyl-6α-(4-methoxyphenyl)-	MeOH	229(4.27),274(3.65)	12-1561-79
$C_{36}H_{54}O_7$			
Urs-20-en-30-al, 3,16,28-triacetoxy-, (3β,16β,18α,19α)-	EtOH	231(4.16)	56-2465-79
$C_{36}H_{54}O_{12}$			
Oleaside C	MeOH	208(4.26)	94-1604-79
$C_{36}H_{54}O_{13}$			
Oleaside D	MeOH	207(4.16)	94-1604-79
$C_{36}H_{58}N_2S$			
Sulfur diimide, bis[2,4,6-tris(1,1-dimethylethyl)phenyl]-	hexane	332(3.88),414(3.70)	18-1998-79
$C_{36}H_{62}O_4$			
2-Propenoic acid, 3-(4-hydroxy-3-methoxyphenyl)-, hexacosyl ester	EtOH	220(4.07),239(4.01),330(4.27)	95-0500-79

Compound	Solvent	λ_{max}(log ε)	Ref.
$C_{37}H_{20}N_4O_2$			
7H-Benzimidazo[2,1-a]benz[de]isoquinolin-7-one, 10,10'-methylenebis- (or isomer)	H_2SO_4	305(4.44),420(4.56)	103-0791-79
$C_{37}H_{23}Cl_2N_3O_2$			
1,2,4-Oxadiazole, 3-[4-[2-[2-chloro-4-(4,5-diphenyl-2-oxazolyl)phenyl]ethenyl]phenyl]-5-(4-chlorophenyl)-	DMF	366(4.73)	33-1411-79
$C_{37}H_{24}ClN_3O_2$			
1,2,4-Oxadiazole, 3-[4-[2-[2-chloro-4-(3,5-diphenyl-2-oxazolyl)phenyl]ethenyl]phenyl]-5-phenyl-	DMF	368(4.73)	33-1411-79
1,2,4-Oxadiazole, 5-[4-[2-[2-chloro-4-(4,5-diphenyl-2-oxazolyl)phenyl]ethenyl]phenyl]-3-phenyl-	DMF	372(4.72)	33-1411-79
1,3,4-Oxadiazole, 2-[2'-chloro-4"-(3"'-phenylisoxazol-5"'-yl)stilben-4'-yl]-5-(p-biphenylyl)-	DMF	365(4.87)	33-0779-79
1,3,4-Oxadiazole, 2-[2'-chloro-4"-(5"'-phenylisoxazol-3"'-yl)stilben-4'-yl]-5-(p-biphenylyl)-	DMF	358(4.84)	33-0779-79
$C_{37}H_{25}ClN_2O$			
1H-Pyrazole, 5-[4-[2-[4-(5-chloro-2-benzofuranyl)phenyl]ethenyl]phenyl]-1,3-diphenyl-	DMF	367(4.88)	33-1816-79
$C_{37}H_{25}ClN_4O$			
1,2,4-Oxadiazole, 3-(4-chlorophenyl)-5-[4-[2-[4-(1,3-diphenyl-1H-pyrazol-5-yl)phenyl]ethenyl]phenyl]-	DMF	353(4.76)	33-1816-79
1,3,4-Oxadiazole, 2-[1,1'-biphenyl]-4-yl-5-[3-chloro-4-[2-[4-(1-phenyl-1H-pyrazol-3-yl)phenyl]ethenyl]phenyl]-	DMF	370(4.82)	33-1816-79
1,3,4-Oxadiazole, 2-[1,1'-biphenyl]-4-yl-5-[4-[2-[4-[1-(4-chlorophenyl)-1H-pyrazol-3-yl]phenyl]ethenyl]phenyl]-	DMF	367(4.92)	33-1816-79
1,3,4-Oxadiazole, 2-(4-chlorophenyl)-5-[4-[2-[4-(1,3-diphenyl-1H-pyrazol-5-yl)phenyl]ethenyl]phenyl]-	DMF	355(4.82)	33-1816-79
2H-1,2,3-Triazole, 2-[2'-chloro-4"-(3"'-phenylisoxazol-5"'-yl)stilben-4'-yl]-4,5-diphenyl-	DMF	365(4.85)	33-0779-79
2H-1,2,3-Triazole, 2-[2'-chloro-4"-(5"'-phenylisoxazol-3"'-yl)stilben-4'-yl]-4,5-diphenyl-	DMF	358(4.84)	33-0779-79
$C_{37}H_{25}Cl_2N_5$			
2H-1,2,3-Triazole, 4-chloro-2-[3-chloro-4-[2-[4-(1,3-diphenyl-1H-pyrazol-5-yl)phenyl]ethenyl]phenyl]-5-phenyl-	DMF	355(4.77)	33-1816-79
$C_{37}H_{25}NO$			
9-Anthracenecarbonitrile, 10-[[(10-phenyl-9-anthracenyl)methoxy]methyl]-	$C_6H_{11}Me$	252(4.99),258(4.98), 370(3.99),378(4.07), 386(4.07),399(4.04), 408(4.05)	39-0411-79B

Compound	Solvent	λ max (log ε)	Ref.
$C_{37}H_{25}NO_5S_2$			
Benzoic acid, 2,2'-[(2-methyl-9-oxo-9H-naphtho[3,2,1-kl]acridine-6,8-diyl)-bis(thio)]bis-, dimethyl ester	EtOH	240(4.65),289(4.78), 433(4.35),494(4.23), 527(4.27)	103-1227-79
$C_{37}H_{25}N_3O_2$			
1,2,4-Oxadiazole, 3-(p-biphenylyl)-5-[4"-(3"'-phenylisoxazol-5"'-yl)stilben-4'-yl]-	DMF	357(4.88)	33-0779-79
1,2,4-Oxadiazole, 3-(p-biphenylyl)-5-[4"-(5"'-phenylisoxazol-3"'-yl)stilben-4'-yl]-	DMF	350(4.85)	33-0779-79
1,3,4-Oxadiazole, 2-(p-biphenylyl)-5-[4"-(5"'-phenylisoxazol-3"'-yl)stilben-4'-yl]-	DMF	357(4.91)	33-0779-79
$C_{37}H_{26}ClN_5$			
2H-1,2,3-Triazole, 2-[3-chloro-4-[2-[4-(1,3-diphenyl-1H-pyrazol-5-yl)-phenyl]ethenyl]phenyl]-4-phenyl-	DMF	355(4.79)	33-1816-79
2H-1,2,3-Triazole, 2-[3-chloro-4-[2-[4-(3,5-diphenyl-1H-pyrazol-1-yl)-phenyl]ethenyl]phenyl]-4-phenyl-	DMF	354(4.79)	33-1816-79
2H-1,2,3-Triazole, 2-[3-chloro-4-[2-[4-(1-phenyl-1H-pyrazol-3-yl)phenyl]ethenyl]phenyl]-4,5-diphenyl-	DMF	367(4.86)	33-1816-79
2H-1,2,3-Triazole, 2-[3-chloro-4-[2-[4-(3-phenyl-1H-pyrazol-1-yl)phenyl]ethenyl]phenyl]-4,5-diphenyl-	DMF	365(4.86)	33-1816-79
$C_{37}H_{26}N_2O$			
1H-Pyrazole, 1-[4-[2-[4-(2-benzofuranyl)phenyl]ethenyl]phenyl]-3,5-diphenyl-	DMF	365(4.86)	33-1816-79
1H-Pyrazole, 3-[4-[2-[4-(2-benzofuranyl)phenyl]ethenyl]phenyl]-1,5-diphenyl-	DMF	372(4.92)	33-1816-79
1H-Pyrazole, 5-[4-[2-[4-(2-benzofuranyl)phenyl]ethenyl]phenyl]-1,3-diphenyl-	DMF	367(4.86)	33-1816-79
1H-Pyrazole, 1-phenyl-3-[4-[2-[4-(5-phenyl-2-benzofuranyl)phenyl]ethenyl]phenyl]-	DMF	374(4.96),394(4.79)	33-1816-79
1H-Pyrazole, 3-phenyl-1-[4-[2-[4-(5-phenyl-2-benzofuranyl)phenyl]ethenyl]phenyl]-	DMF	373(4.94)	33-1816-79
$C_{37}H_{26}N_2O_3$			
Benzoxazole, 2-[4"-[3"'-(4-methoxyphenyl)isoxazol-5"'-yl]stilben-4'-yl]-5-phenyl-	DMF	369(4.95),389(4.77)	33-0779-79
Benzoxazole, 2-[4"-[3"'-(4-methoxyphenyl)isoxazol-5"'-yl]stilben-4'-yl]-7-phenyl-	DMF	366(4.92),387(4.74)	33-0779-79
Benzoxazole, 2-[4"-[5"'-(4-methoxyphenyl)isoxazol-3"'-yl]stilben-4'-yl]-5-phenyl-	DMF	362(4.92),380(4.74)	33-0779-79
Benzoxazole, 2-[4"-[5"'-(4-methoxyphenyl)isoxazol-3"'-yl]stilben-4'-yl]-7-phenyl-	DMF	360(4.90),379(4.71)	33-0779-79

Compound	Solvent	$\lambda_{max}(\log \epsilon)$	Ref.
$C_{37}H_{26}N_4O$			
2-Oxabicyclo[2.2.2]oct-7-ene-5,5,6,6-tetracarbonitrile, 8-(4-methylphenyl)-1,3-diphenyl-3-(phenylmethyl)-	ether	267(4.45),330(3.28)	78-2633-79
1,2,4-Oxadiazole, 3-[1,1'-biphenyl]-4-yl-5-[4-[2-[4-(1-phenyl-1H-pyrazol-3-yl)phenyl]ethenyl]phenyl]-	DMF	363(4.81)	33-1816-79
1,2,4-Oxadiazole, 3-[1,1'-biphenyl]-4-yl-5-[4-[2-[4-(3-phenyl-1H-pyrazol-1-yl)phenyl]ethenyl]phenyl]-	DMF	362(4.83)	33-1816-79
1,2,4-Oxadiazole, 3-[4-[2-[4-(1,5-diphenyl-1H-pyrazol-3-yl)phenyl]ethenyl]phenyl]-5-phenyl-	DMF	351(4.80)	33-1816-79
1,2,4-Oxadiazole, 5-[4-[2-[4-(1,3-diphenyl-1H-pyrazol-5-yl)phenyl]ethenyl]phenyl]-3-phenyl-	DMF	352(4.75)	33-1816-79
1,2,4-Oxadiazole, 5-[4-[2-[4-(3,5-diphenyl-1H-pyrazol-1-yl)phenyl]ethenyl]phenyl]-3-phenyl-	DMF	350(4.75)	33-1816-79
1,3,4-Oxadiazole, 2-[1,1'-biphenyl]-4-yl-5-[4-[2-[4-(1-phenyl-1H-pyrazol-3-yl)phenyl]ethenyl]phenyl]-	DMF	367(4.91)	33-1816-79
1,3,4-Oxadiazole, 2-[4-[2-[4-(1,3-diphenyl-1H-pyrazol-5-yl)phenyl]ethenyl]phenyl]-5-phenyl-	DMF	355(4.79)	33-1816-79
1,3,4-Oxadiazole, 2-[4-[2-[4-(3,5-diphenyl-1H-pyrazol-1-yl)phenyl]ethenyl]phenyl]-5-phenyl-	DMF	352(4.79)	33-1816-79
$C_{37}H_{27}N_3O$			
1,2-Benzisoxazole, 3-[4-[2-[4-(1,3-diphenyl-1H-pyrazol-5-yl)phenyl]ethenyl]phenyl]-5-phenyl-	DMF	343(4.68)	33-1816-79
Benzoxazole, 2-[4-[2-[4-(1,3-diphenyl-1H-pyrazol-5-yl)phenyl]ethenyl]phenyl]-5-methyl-	DMF	363(4.84)	33-1816-79
Benzoxazole, 2-[4-[2-[4-(1,3-diphenyl-1H-pyrazol-5-yl)phenyl]ethenyl]phenyl]-6-methyl-	DMF	363(4.84)	33-1816-79
Benzoxazole, 2-[4-[2-[4-(1,5-diphenyl-1H-pyrazol-3-yl)phenyl]ethenyl]phenyl]-5-methyl-	DMF	369(4.90)	33-1816-79
Benzoxazole, 2-[4-[2-[4-(1,5-diphenyl-1H-pyrazol-3-yl)phenyl]ethenyl]phenyl]-6-methyl-	DMF	368(4.87)	33-1816-79
Benzoxazole, 2-[4-[2-[4-(1,5-diphenyl-1H-pyrazol-3-yl)phenyl]ethenyl]phenyl]-7-methyl-	DMF	367(4.89)	33-1816-79
Benzoxazole, 2-[4-[2-[4-(3,5-diphenyl-1H-pyrazol-1-yl)phenyl]ethenyl]phenyl]-5-methyl-	DMF	360(4.84)	33-1816-79
Benzoxazole, 2-[4-[2-[4-(3,5-diphenyl-1H-pyrazol-1-yl)phenyl]ethenyl]phenyl]-6-methyl-	DMF	360(4.85)	33-1816-79
$C_{37}H_{27}N_3O_2$			
1,2-Benzisoxazole, 6-[2-[4-(1,3-diphenyl-1H-pyrazol-5-yl)phenyl]ethenyl]-3-(4-methoxyphenyl)-	DMF	343(4.72)	33-1816-79
Benzoxazole, 2-[4-[2-[4-(1,3-diphenyl-1H-pyrazol-5-yl)phenyl]ethenyl]phen-	DMF	367(4.84)	33-1816-79

Compound	Solvent	λ_{max}(log ε)	Ref.
yl]-5-methoxy- (cont.)			33-1816-79
Benzoxazole, 2-[4-[2-[4-(1,5-diphenyl-1H-pyrazol-3-yl)phenyl]ethenyl]-phenyl]-5-methoxy-	DMF	373(4.88)	33-1816-79
$C_{37}H_{28}$			
Toluene, pentaphenyl-	MeCN	233(4.66)	44-2483-79
$C_{37}H_{28}O$			
Ethanone, 1-(1,2,3,4,5-pentaphenyl-2,4-cyclopentadien-1-yl)-	MeCN	247(4.39),265s(4.26), 340(4.00)	44-2483-79
$C_{37}H_{29}N_5O_2$			
2H-Benzotriazole, 2-[4-[2-[4-(1,3-di-phenyl-1H-pyrazol-5-yl)phenyl]ethen-yl]phenyl]-5,6-dimethoxy-	DMF	371(4.89)	33-1816-79
2H-Benzotriazole, 2-[4-[2-[4-(3,5-di-phenyl-1H-pyrazol-1-yl)phenyl]ethen-yl]phenyl]-5,6-dimethoxy-	DMF	370(4.88)	33-1816-79
$C_{37}H_{30}$			
Benzene, 1,1',1",1"',1""-(5-ethylidene-1,3-pentadiene-1,2,3,4,5-pentayl)-pentakis-	MeCN	255(4.46),326s(--)	44-2483-79
1,3-Cyclohexadiene, 6-methyl-1,2,3,4,5-pentaphenyl-, trans	MeCN	230s(--),315(4.04)	44-2483-79
1H-Cyclopent[c]indene, 5,5a-dihydro-1-methyl-2,3,4,5-tetraphenyl-, (1α,5β,5aα,9aR*)-	MeCN	255s(4.34),262s(4.32), 267s(4.28),272s(4.25), 313(4.28)	44-2483-79
$C_{37}H_{30}OSi_2$			
Disilane, benzoylpentaphenyl-	C_6H_{12}	389(2.12),407(2.42), 423(2.53),445(2.37)	35-0083-79
$C_{37}H_{30}O_{10}$			
Benzoic acid, 3,4,5-trihydroxy-, 2,2'-bis(3,4-dihydroxyphenyl)-3,3',4,4'-tetrahydro-3,5,5',7,7'-pentahydroxy-[4,8'-bi-2H-1-benzopyran]-3'-yl ester, [2R-[2α,3α,4β(2'R*,3'R*)]]-	MeOH	206(4.69),225(4.65), 253(4.75),403(4.09)	5-0019-79
$C_{37}H_{32}$			
1H-Cyclopent[c]indene, 5,5a,8,9-tetra-hydro-1-methyl-2,3,4,5-tetraphenyl-, (1α,5β,5aα,9aR*)-	MeCN	312(4.34)	44-2483-79
$C_{37}H_{33}N_2O_2$			
Quinolinium, 1-(4-ethoxyphenyl)-2-[3-[1-(4-ethoxyphenyl)-2(1H)-quinolin-ylidene]-1-propenyl]-, perchlorate	EtOH	570(5.18),616(5.41)	104-1160-79
$C_{37}H_{34}$			
1H-Cyclopent[c]indene, 5,5a,6,7,8,9-hexahydro-1-methyl-2,3,4,5-tetra-phenyl-, (1α,5β,5aα,9aR*)-	MeCN	312(4.31)	44-2483-79
$C_{37}H_{35}N_2S_2$			
Naphtho[1,2-d]thiazolium, 1-ethyl-2-[2-[3-[(1-ethylnaphtho[1,2-d]thiazol-2(1H)-ylidene]-2-methyl-1-cyclohexen-1-yl]ethenyl]-, chloride	MeOH	817(5.38)	104-0351-79

Compound	Solvent	$\lambda_{max}(\log \epsilon)$	Ref.
$C_{37}H_{37}N_5O_{10}$			
2H-Isoindole-2-hexanoic acid, 1,3-dihydro-1,3-dioxo-, 2-[[[6-(1,3-dihydro-1,3-dioxo-2H-isoindol-2-yl)-1-oxohexyl]oxy]methyl]-2,3,3a,9a-tetrahydro-6-imino-6H-furo[2',3':4,5]oxazolo[3,2-a]pyrimidin-3-yl ester, [2R-(2α,3β,3aα,9aβ)]-, tetrafluoroborate	MeOH	220(4.67),234s(4.28), 242s(4.15),267(3.87)	87-0639-79
$C_{37}H_{38}N_2O_6$			
Cissampareine	MeOH	282(4.0),320s(3.60)	100-0001-79
Coclobine	MeOH or EtOH	230(5.0),274(4.15), 300s(3.84)	100-0001-79
Epistephanine, (+)-	MeOH	233(4.53),282(4.16)	100-0001-79
Epistephanine, (-)-	MeOH	284(4.23)	100-0001-79
Ocotosine	MeOH or EtOH	233(4.55),282(4.01), 298s(3.00)	100-0001-79
Thalmethine, O-methyl-	MeOH	280(4.13),314(3.87)	100-0001-79
$C_{37}H_{38}N_2O_7$			
Thalsimidine	MeOH	280(4.12),312(3.76)	100-0001-79
$C_{37}H_{38}O_6$			
9,9'-Spirobifluorene, 2,2'-(2,5,8,11-14,17-hexaoxaoctadecano)-, (-)-	MeCN	268(4.52),276(4.51), 299(4.18),311(4.34)	33-2285-79
$C_{37}H_{39}N_2$			
3H-Indolium, 2-[2-[3-[(1,3-dihydro-1,3,3-trimethyl-2H-indol-2-ylidene)-ethylidene]-2-phenyl-1-cyclopenten-1-yl]ethenyl]-1,3,3-trimethyl-, perchlorate	MeOH	785(5.45)	104-0351-79
$C_{37}H_{40}N_2O_6$			
Berbamine	MeOH	284(3.79)	100-0001-79
Curine, 12'-O-methyl-	MeOH	279(3.95),284(3.95)	100-0001-79
Cycleadrine	MeOH	282(3.81)	100-0001-79
Cycleanorine	MeOH	282(4.01)	100-0001-79
Cycleapeltine	MeOH	282(3.72)	100-0001-79
Dryadine	MeOH	285(3.92)	100-0001-79
Fangchinoline	MeOH	236s(4.51),282(4.01)	100-0001-79
Hayatidine	80% EtOH	280(3.07)	100-0001-79
Hayatinine	pH 1	280(4.16)	100-0001-79
Homoaromoline	MeOH	284(3.93)	100-0001-79
Isothalicberine	EtOH	284(3.98)	32-0567-79
Nemuarine	MeOH	211(4.87),284(3.98)	100-0001-79
Norcycleanine, (-)-	MeOH	229(4.76),276(3.84)	100-0001-79
2-Nortetrandrine	MeOH	227(4.53),282(3.88)	100-0001-79
Ocotine	MeOH	224(4.60),284(4.04)	100-0001-79
Oxyacanthine	MeOH or EtOH	206(4.94),238s(5.45), 282(3.92)	100-0001-79
Pakistanine	EtOH	206(4.69),218(4.61), 270s(4.13),277(4.21), 307(4.07)	100-0133-79
Panurensine	MeOH or EtOH	225(4.38),238(4.55), 284(4.22)	100-0001-79
Penduline	MeOH	284(3.84)	100-0001-79
Phlebicine	MeOH	292(3.93)	100-0001-79
Pycnamine	MeOH or EtOH	229s(4.59),282(3.99), 292(3.88)	100-0001-79

Compound	Solvent	λ_{max}(log ϵ)	Ref.
Repandine	MeOH	284(3.83)	100-0001-79
Sciadenine	MeOH	277(3.48),283(3.47)	100-0001-79
Thalicberine	MeOH	282(3.81)	100-0001-79
Thalmine	MeOH	286(3.65)	100-0001-79
Thalrugosamine	MeOH	282(3.91)	100-0001-79
Thalrugosine	MeOH	282(3.94)	100-0001-79
Tiliageine	MeOH or EtOH	212(4.83),231s(4.60), 288(4.03),295s(3.96)	100-0001-79
$C_{37}H_{40}N_2O_7$			
Thalidezine, N-demethyl-	MeOH	282(3.84)	100-0001-79
Thaligosidine	MeOH	275(3.72),283(3.72)	100-0001-79
Thalisopidine	MeOH	285(4.04)	100-0001-79
$C_{37}H_{40}N_4O_7$			
Acetamide, N-[4,7-dihydro-3-(methoxymethyl)-5-methyl-4-oxo-7-[2,3,5-tris-O-(phenylmethyl)-β-D-ribofuranosyl]-3H-pyrrolo[2,3-d]pyrimidin-2-yl]-	MeOH	275(3.78),304(3.93)	35-3629-79
$C_{37}H_{40}N_5O_8PS$			
Benzoic acid, 4,4',4"-[[[[[4-(ethoxycarbonyl)phenyl]amino]thioxomethyl]-phosphinimylidyne]triimino]tris-, triethyl ester	EtOH	224(4.95),269(4.45)	64-0297-79B
$C_{37}H_{41}FeN_5O_6$			
Iron, chloro[dimethyl 7,12-diethyl-3,8,13,17-tetramethyl(nitromethyl)-21H,23H-porphinato(2-)-N^{21},N^{22},N^{23}-N^{24}]-, chloride	CH_2Cl_2	378(4.99),510(3.90), 535(3.89),638(3.59)	78-1251-79
$C_{37}H_{42}Cl_2N_2O_6$			
Tubocurarine chloride, (+)-	MeOH	225(4.56),282(3.90)	36-0655-79
$C_{37}H_{42}N_2O_6$			
Dauricine, N^1-demethyl-	MeOH	283(4.0)	100-0001-79
Daurinoline	MeOH	284(3.95)	100-0001-79
Grisabine	MeOH or EtOH	224(4.25),237(4.21), 287(4.21)	100-0001-79
Isoliensinine	MeOH or EtOH	286(4.04)	100-0001-79
Macoline (dichloride)	MeOH	282(3.92)	100-0001-79
Northalibrine	MeOH	284(3.70)	100-0001-79
$C_{37}H_{42}N_2O_7$			
Magnolamine	MeOH	284(4.11)	100-0001-79
Thaligosine	MeOH	282(3.86)	100-0001-79
$C_{37}H_{42}N_4O_6$			
21H,23H-Porphine-2,8,12-tripropanoic acid, 3,7,13,17,18-pentamethyl-, trimethyl ester	$CHCl_3$	400(5.29),499(4.17), 535(4.01),570(3.83), 625(3.62)	104-0970-79
$C_{37}H_{42}O_4$			
Pregna-1,4-dien-20-one, 3-(diphenylmethylene)-11β-hydroxy-17α,21-[(1-methylethylidene)dioxy]-	MeOH	248(4.04),312(4.38)	39-1166-79C
$C_{37}H_{42}O_{19}$			
Minecoside hexaacetate	$CHCl_3$	204(4.21),228(4.11), 310(4.28)	33-0535-79

Compound	Solvent	λ_{max}(log ε)	Ref.
$C_{37}H_{44}N_4O_6$			
Chlorin e_6, 3-ethyl-, trimethyl ester	dioxan	398(4.20),497(4.10), 524(3.49),599(3.80), 653(4.66)	5-1992-79
$C_{37}H_{44}O_{17}$			
β-D-Glucopyranoside, 4-[6a-acetoxy-4-(3,4-dimethoxyphényl)tetrahydro-1H,3H-furo[3,4-c]furan-1-yl]-, 2-methoxyphenyl, tetraacetate	EtOH	229(4.20),278(3.70)	94-2868-79
$C_{37}H_{45}N_5$			
21H,23H-Porphine-5-carbonitrile, 2,3,7,8,12,13,17,18-octaethyl-	CH_2Cl_2	404(5.09),512(4.02), 548(4.13),579(3.79), 632(4.11)	35-5953-79
$C_{37}H_{45}N_5S$			
Thiocyanic acid, 2,3,7,8,12,13,17,18-octaethyl-21H,23H-porphin-5-yl ester	CH_2Cl_2	405(5.09),512(3.93), 548(3.97),580(3.65), 631(3.84)	35-5953-79
$C_{37}H_{46}N_4O_6$			
21H-Biline-2,8,12-tripropanoic acid, 10,24-dihydro-1,3,7,13,17,18-hexamethyl-, trimethyl ester, dihydrobromide	$CHCl_3$-HBr	455(4.59),524(5.29)	104-0970-79
$C_{37}H_{46}O_{19}$			
Sylvestroside III pentaacetate	MeOH	238(4.28)	102-0273-79
$C_{37}H_{47}InN_4$			
Indium, methyl[2,3,7,8,12,13,17,18-octaethyl-21H,23H-porphinato(2-)-N^{21},N^{22},N^{23},N^{24}]-, (SP-5-31)-	$CHCl_3$	354(4.69),428(5.39), 515(3.40),554(4.24), 588(3.95)	101-0311-79P
$C_{37}H_{47}NO_{14}$			
Nogamycin, dis-	EtOH	236(4.71),259(4.41), 290(4.00),478(4.21)	44-4030-79
1"β-Nogamycin, con-	EtOH	236(4.71),258(4.38), 292s(3.99),478(4.19)	44-4030-79
$C_{37}H_{47}N_5O$			
21H,23H-Porphine-5-carboxaldehyde, 2,3,7,8,12,13,17,18-octaethyl-, oxime	CH_2Cl_2	402(5.19),503(4.15), 536(3.96),570(3.78), 623(3.62)	35-5953-79
$C_{37}H_{48}N_4O_2$			
2-Cyclohexen-1-one, 6,6'-methylenebis-[2-(1-hydroxycyclohexyl)-, bis(phenylhydrazone)	hexane	247(3.65),298(3.91), 323(4.00)	104-0676-79
Spiro[cyclohexane-1,3'-[3H]indazol]-2-ol, 6',6"'-methylenebis[2,3'a,4-5',6',7'-hexahydro-2-phenyl-	hexane	284(4.89)	104-0457-79
$C_{37}H_{48}O_{15}$			
Syriobioside, tetra-O-acetyl-	EtOH	213(4.23)	33-0412-79
$C_{37}H_{51}NO_{12}$			
Geldanamycin, 7-O-acetyl-22-acetyl-18,21-diacetoxy-7-O-de(aminocarbonyl)-	MeOH	271(4.23)	88-4323-79

Compound	Solvent	$\lambda_{max}(\log \epsilon)$	Ref.
18,21-didehydro-17-demethoxy-18,21-dideoxy-15-methoxy-11-O-methyl-(geldanamycin) (cont.)			88-4323-79
$C_{37}H_{52}N_2O_{11}$			
Cashmiradelphine	EtOH	253(4.15),310(3.74)	100-0615-79
$C_{37}H_{52}O_3$			
Phenol, 4-[bis(3,5-di-tert-butyl-4-hydroxyphenyl)methyl]-2,6-dimethyl-	C_6H_{12}	278(3.77)	18-1911-79
$C_{37}H_{52}O_6$			
Toxistylide A	MeOH	270(2.85)	88-3619-79
Toxistylide B	MeOH	270(2.96)	88-3619-79

Compound	Solvent	λ_{max}(log ϵ)	Ref.
$C_{38}H_{24}Cl_2N_2O_2$			
Isoxazole, 5-[2"-chloro-4"-(4"',5"'-diphenyloxazol-2"'-yl)stilben-4'-yl]-3-(4-chlorophenyl)-	DMF	375(4.80)	33-0779-79
$C_{38}H_{24}O_2$			
Benz[a]anthracen-12(7H)-one, 9-methyl-7-(9-methyl-12-oxobenz[a]anthracen-7(12H)-ylidene)-	CH_2Cl_2	250(4.53),265s(4.48), 300(4.34),325s(4.15), 406(4.24)	44-1941-79
5(12H)-Naphthacenone, 2-methyl-12-(3-methyl-12-oxo-5(12H)-naphthacenylidene)-	CH_2Cl_2	248(4.93),277s(4.66), 298s(4.59),350s(4.05), 420(4.05)	44-1941-79
$C_{38}H_{25}ClN_2O_2$			
Isoxazole, 3-[2"-chloro-4"-(4"',5"'-diphenyloxazol-2"'-yl)stilben-4'-yl]-5-phenyl-	DMF	367(4.74)	33-0779-79
Isoxazole, 5-[2"-chloro-4"-(4"',5"'-diphenyloxazol-2"'-yl)stilben-4'-yl]-3-phenyl-	DMF	375(4.79)	33-0779-79
$C_{38}H_{26}ClN_3O$			
Isoxazole, 3-(4-chlorophenyl)-5-[4-[2-[4-(1,3-diphenyl-1H-pyrazol-5-yl)-phenyl]ethenyl]phenyl]-	DMF	353(4.81)	33-1816-79
Isoxazole, 5-(4-chlorophenyl)-3-[4-[2-[4-(1,3-diphenyl-1H-pyrazol-5-yl)-phenyl]ethenyl]phenyl]-	DMF	343(4.77)	33-1816-79
Isoxazole, 5-(4-chloro-phenyl)-3-[4-[2-[4-(1,5-diphenyl-1H-pyrazol-3-yl)-phenyl]ethenyl]phenyl]-	DMF	350(4.85)	33-1816-79
Oxazole, 2-[3-chloro-4-[2-[4-(1-phenyl-1H-pyrazol-3-yl)phenyl]ethenyl]-phenyl]-4,5-diphenyl-	DMF	377(4.81)	33-1816-79
Oxazole, 2-[3-chloro-4-[2-[4-(3-phenyl-1H-pyrazol-1-yl)phenyl]ethenyl]-phenyl]-4,5-diphenyl-	DMF	375(4.80)	33-1816-79
$C_{38}H_{26}ClN_3O_3$			
1,2,4-Oxadiazole, 3-[4-[2-[2-chloro-4-(4,5-diphenyl-2-oxazolyl)phenyl]-ethenyl]phenyl]-5-(4-methoxyphenyl)-	DMF	367(4.76)	33-1411-79
1,2,4-Oxadiazole, 5-[4-[2-[2-chloro-4-(4,5-diphenyl-2-oxazolyl)phenyl]-ethenyl]phenyl]-3-(4-methoxyphenyl)-	DMF	372(4.75)	33-1411-79
$C_{38}H_{26}N_2$			
Dibenz[2,3:6,7]-s-indaceno[1,8-bc:5,4-b'c']dipyridine, 3,10-dihydro-3,10-bis(phenylmethyl)-	EtOH	212(4.56),246(4.28), 291(4.06),330(4.27), 377(3.86),615(4.23)	103-1214-79
Dibenz[2,3:6,7]-s-indaceno[4,5-bc:8,1'-b'c']dipyridine, 1,8-dihydro-1,8-bis(phenylmethyl)-	EtOH	206(4.82),280(4.78), 500(3.66),660(4.57)	103-1214-79
$C_{38}H_{26}N_2O$			
Cyclopenta[3,4]pyrazolo[1,5-a]quinolin-11-ium, 6b,7,9a,10-tetrahydro-7-oxo-6b,8,9,9a-tetraphenyl-, hydroxide, inner salt	EtOH	205(4.73),225(4.70), 278(4.33),450(3.93)	88-1765-79

Compound	Solvent	λ_{max}(log ϵ)	Ref.
$C_{38}H_{26}N_2O_2$			
Isoxazole, 3-[4"-[3"'-(p-biphenylyl)-isoxazol-5"'-yl]stilben-4'-yl]-	DMF	350(4.88)	33-0779-79
Isoxazole, 3-[4"-(4"',5"'-diphenyloxa-zol-2"'-yl)syilben-4'-yl]-5-phenyl-	DMF	367(4.80)	33-0779-79
Isoxazole, 5-[4"-(4"',5"'-diphenyloxa-zol-2"'-yl)stilben-4'-yl]-3-phenyl-	DMF	372(4.85)	33-0779-79
$C_{38}H_{26}O_2$			
[7,7'-Bibenz[a]anthracene]-12,12'-(7H,7'H)-dione, 9,9'-dimethyl-	CH_2Cl_2	236(4.62),260s(4.45), 295(4.21),338(4.23)	44-1941-79
[5,5'-Binaphthacene]-12,12'(5H,5'H)-di-one, 3,3'-dimethyl-	CH_2Cl_2	234(4.83),265(4.73), 317(4.41),360(3.79)	44-1941-79
$C_{38}H_{27}NO_3$			
Isoxazole, 5-(4-methoxyphenyl)-3-[4"-(4"',5"'-diphenyloxazol-2"'-yl)stil-ben-4'-yl]-	DMF	368(4.90)	33-0779-79
$C_{38}H_{27}N_3O$			
Isoxazole, 3-[1,1'-biphenyl]-4-yl-5-[4-[2-[4-(1-phenyl-1H-pyrazol-3-yl)phenyl]ethenyl]phenyl]-	DMF	362(4.90)	33-1816-79
Isoxazole, 3-[1,1'-biphenyl]-4-yl-5-[4-[2-[4-(3-phenyl-1H-pyrazol-1-yl)phenyl]ethenyl]phenyl]-	DMF	360(4.89)	33-1816-79
Isoxazole, 3-[4-[2-[4-(1,3-diphenyl-1H-pyrazol-5-yl)phenyl]ethenyl]-phenyl]-5-phenyl-	DMF	342(4.76)	33-1816-79
Isoxazole, 3-[4-[2-[4-(3,5-diphenyl-1H-pyrazol-1-yl)phenyl]ethenyl]-phenyl]-5-phenyl-	DMF	340(4.76)	33-1816-79
Isoxazole, 5-[4-[2-[4-(1,3-diphenyl-1H-pyrazol-5-yl)phenyl]ethenyl]-phenyl]-3-phenyl-	DMF	352(4.81)	33-1816-79
Isoxazole, 5-[4-[2-[4-(1,5-diphenyl-1H-pyrazol-3-yl)phenyl]ethenyl]-phenyl]-3-phenyl-	DMF	358(4.86)	33-1816-79
Isoxazole, 5-[4-[2-[4-(3,5-diphenyl-1H-pyrazol-1-yl)phenyl]ethenyl]-phenyl]-3-phenyl-	DMF	350(4.80)	33-1816-79
Oxazole, 4,5-diphenyl-2-[4-[2-[4-(1-phenyl-1H-pyrazol-3-yl)phenyl]eth-enyl]phenyl]-	DMF	375(4.86)	33-1816-79
Oxazole, 4,5-diphenyl-2-[4-[2-[4-(3-phenyl-1H-pyrazol-1-yl)phenyl]eth-enyl]phenyl]-	DMF	374(4.86)	33-1816-79
Oxazole, 2-[4-[2-[4-(1,3-diphenyl-1H-pyrazol-5-yl)phenyl]ethenyl]phenyl]-5-phenyl-	DMF	368(4.81)	33-1816-79
$C_{38}H_{28}Br_2N_2O$			
1,2-Diazabicyclo[4.3.1]deca-3,8-dien-10-one, 3,9-bis(4-bromophenyl)-5,6,7-triphenyl-	EtOH	261(4.51)	94-2767-79
$C_{38}H_{28}Br_2O_3$			
2H-Pyran-2-one, 6-(4-bromophenyl)-3-[3-(4-bromophenyl)-3-oxo-1-phenyl-propyl]-3,4-dihydro-3,4-diphenyl-	EtOH	258(4.48)	94-2767-79

Compound	Solvent	$\lambda_{max}(\log \epsilon)$	Ref.
$C_{38}H_{28}N_2O$			
7H-Cyclopenta[3,4]pyrazolo[1,5-a]quino-lin-7-one, 6a,6b,9,10-tetrahydro-6b,8,9,9a-tetraphenyl-	EtOH	205(4.70),231(4.67), 269s(4.21),317s(4.02)	88-1765-79
$C_{38}H_{28}N_2O_2$			
Benzo[g]phthalazine, 6,9-dimethoxy-1,4,5,10-tetraphenyl-	CH_2Cl_2	275(4.5),326(4.0), 411(3.86),432s(3.74)	150-3501-79
	HCl	275(4.57),324(4.43), 431(3.88),538(3.65)	150-3501-79
1H-Pyrazole, 5-[4-[2-[4-(5-methoxy-2-benzofuranyl)phenyl]ethenyl]phenyl]-1,3-diphenyl-	DMF	370(4.86)	33-1816-79
$C_{38}H_{28}N_4$			
1H-Pyrazole, 1,5-diphenyl-3-[4-[2-[4-(1-phenyl-1H-pyrazol-3-yl)-phenyl]ethenyl]phenyl]-	DMF	358(4.89)	33-1816-79
1H-Pyrazole, 1,5-diphenyl-3-[4-[2-[4-(3-phenyl-1H-pyrazol-1-yl)-phenyl]ethenyl]phenyl]-	DMF	357(4.89)	33-1816-79
$C_{38}H_{28}N_4O_2$			
1,2,4-Oxadiazole, 5-[4-[2-[4-(1,3-di-phenyl-1H-pyrazol-5-yl)phenyl]eth-enyl]phenyl]-3-(4-methoxyphenyl)-	DMF	353(4.77)	33-1816-79
1,3,4-Oxadiazole, 2-[4-[2-[4-(1,3-di-phenyl-1H-pyrazol-5-yl)phenyl]eth-enyl]phenyl]-5-(4-methoxyphenyl)-	DMF	357(4.82)	33-1816-79
$C_{38}H_{29}N_3O$			
Benzoxazole, 2-[4-[2-[4-(1,3-diphenyl-1H-pyrazol-5-yl)phenyl]ethenyl]-phenyl]-5,7-dimethyl-	DMF	364(4.84)	33-1816-79
Benzoxazole, 2-[4-[2-[4-(3,5-diphenyl-1H-pyrazol-1-yl)phenyl]ethenyl]-phenyl]-5,7-dimethyl-	DMF	360(4.84)	33-1816-79
$C_{38}H_{30}O$			
Cyclobut[f]isobenzofuran, 4-(1,1-di-methylethyl)-1,3,5,6-tetraphenyl-	$CHCl_3$	292(4.45),330(4.35), 436(3.93)	138-1451-79
perchlorate	CH_2Cl_2	298(4.42),331(4.32), 400(4.08),632(4.32), 700s(4.11)	138-1451-79
$C_{38}H_{30}OPSe$			
Phosphonium, triphenyl-, 1-(diphenyl-selenonio)-2-oxo-2-phenylethylide, tetrafluoroborate	n.s.g.	264(4.079),288s(3.875)	104-0332-79
$C_{38}H_{30}O_6$			
2-Anthraceneacetic acid, 9,10-dihydro-9,10-dioxo-1,4-bis(phenylmethoxy)-α-(phenylmethyl)-, methyl ester	MeOH	207(4.70),252(4.53), 402(3.77)	5-0035-79
$C_{38}H_{30}S$			
Cyclobuta[4,5]benzo[1,2-c]thiophene, 4-(1,1-dimethylethyl)-1,3,5,6-tetra-phenyl-	$CHCl_3$	294(4.34),337(4.37), 432(3.70)	138-1451-79
perchlorate	$CHCl_3$	426(4.84),560(4.94), 650s(4.09),694s(3.86)	138-1451-79

Compound	Solvent	λ_{max}(log ϵ)	Ref.
$C_{38}H_{32}N_4O_4$			
2,6(1H,3H)-Pyridinedione, 3-[1,6-dihydro-2,6-dioxo-1-(phenylmethyl)-5-[(phenylmethyl)amino]-3(2H)-pyridinylidene]-1-(phenylmethyl)-5-[(phenylmethyl)amino]-	$CHCl_3$	277(3.69),625(3.94)	118-0948-79
$C_{38}H_{32}O$			
Cyclobut[f]isobenzofuran, 4-(1,1-dimethylethyl)-1,7a-dihydro-1,3,5,6-tetraphenyl-	$CHCl_3$	298(4.28),311(4.29), 375s(3.94)	138-1451-79
$C_{38}H_{36}N_2O_8$			
[1,1'-Biphenyl]-3-carboxaldehyde, 2'-acetoxy-6-methoxy-5'-[(1,2,3,4,9,10-11,12-octahydro-6-methoxy-2,11-dimethyl-12-oxo[1,4]dioxino[2,3-g:6,5-h']diisoquinolin-1-yl)methyl]-, (R)-	MeOH	228(4.27),279s(3.81), 313s(3.38)	100-0116-79
Thalfine	MeOH	260(4.58),348(3.86)	100-0001-79
$C_{38}H_{38}O_6$			
3,6,9,12-Tetraoxatetradecane, 1,14-bis-(9-anthracenyloxy)-	C_6H_{12}	249(5.23),257(5.48), 320(3.29),335(3.72), 351(4.03),370(4.23), 390(4.18)	108-0220-79
	benzene	392(4.18)	108-0220-79
	MeOH	256(5.48),389(4.17)	108-0220-79
$C_{38}H_{40}As_2O_2Rh$			
Rhodium(1+), [(2,3,5,6-η)-bicyclo-[2.2.1]hepta-2,5-diene][[(2,2-dimethyl-1,3-dioxolane-4,5-diyl)bis-(methylene)]bis[diphenylarsine]-As-As']-, tetrafluoroborate	EtOH	246(4.03),460(2.62)	118-0350-79
$C_{38}H_{40}N_2O_6$			
Insularine	MeOH or EtOH	209(4.68),229s(4.56), 276(3.64)	100-0001-79
$C_{38}H_{40}N_2O_7$			
Tenuipine, (+)-	MeOH	280(3.82)	100-0001-79
Thalsimine	MeOH	282(4.23),312(3.90)	100-0001-79
$C_{38}H_{40}N_2O_8$			
Thalibrunimine	MeOH or EtOH	241(4.48),283(4.02), 300s(3.91)	100-0001-79
$C_{38}H_{40}N_2O_{11}$			
Cathedulin E2	MeOH	225(4.36),260s(3.75), 264(3.79),270s(3.69), 282s(3.18)	39-2965-79C
	MeOH-H_2SO_4	227(4.24),258s(4.02), 262(4.05),268s(3.97), 282s(3.18)	39-2965-79C
$C_{38}H_{41}N_2$			
3H-Indolium, 2-[2-[3-[(1,3-dihydro-1,3,3-trimethyl-2H-indol-2-ylidene]-ethylidene]-2-phenyl-1-cyclohexen-1-yl]ethenyl]-1,3,3-trimethyl-, perchlorate	MeOH	754(5.52)	104-0351-79

Compound	Solvent	$\lambda_{max}(\log \epsilon)$	Ref.
$C_{38}H_{42}N_2O_6$			
Cycleanine	MeOH or EtOH	232s(4.87),276(3.89), 285s(3.83)	100-0001-79
Funiferine	MeOH or EtOH	233s(4.64),286(4.15), 292s(4.12)	100-0001-79
Isotetrandrine	MeOH or EtOH	206(4.97),238s(4.38), 282(3.85)	100-0001-79
Isothalicberine, O-methyl-	EtOH	285(3.98)	32-0567-79
Pakistanamine	EtOH	206(4.86),225s(4.63), 280(4.12),310s(3.61)	100-0133-79
Pakistananine, 1-O-methyl-	EtOH	207(4.88),225s(4.75), 270s(4.28),277(4.37), 304(4.16)	100-0133-79
Phaeanthine	MeOH or EtOH	206(3.98),236s(4.44), 282(3.91)	100-0001-79
Repandine, O-methyl-	MeOH or EtOH	206(5.11),233s(4.65), 282(3.81)	100-0001-79
Rodiasine	MeOH or EtOH	233(4.41),285(4.07), 292s(4.01)	100-0001-79
Tetrandrine, (+)-	MeOH	214(4.78),283(3.91)	100-0001-79
	MeOH	230(4.40),282(3.89)	100-0001-79
Thalicberine, O-methyl-	MeOH	278(3.65)	100-0001-79
$C_{38}H_{42}N_2O_7$			
Funiferine N-oxide	MeOH	261(4.75),288(3.95)	100-0001-79
Isothalidezine	MeOH	282(3.99)	100-0001-79
Thalictrimine (thalfoetidine)	MeOH	275(3.87),285(3.87)	100-0001-79
Thalidezine	MeOH	283(4.02)	100-0001-79
Thaligosinine	MeOH	282(3.90)	100-0001-79
Thalisamine	MeOH	284(4.60)	100-0001-79
Thalisopine	MeOH	284(3.65)	100-0001-79
Thalrugosidine	MeOH	275(3.99),282(3.99)	100-0001-79
$C_{38}H_{42}N_3$			
3H-Indolium, 2-[2-[3-[(1,3-dihydro-1,3,3-trimethyl-2H-indol-2-ylidene)-ethylidene]-2-(phenylamino)-1-cyclohexen-1-yl]ethenyl]-1,3,3-trimethyl-, iodide	MeOH	736(5.21)	104-0351-79
$C_{38}H_{42}O_{20}$			
Verminoside heptaacetate	$CHCl_3$	203(4.13),282(4.09)	33-0535-79
$C_{38}H_{43}N_2O_6$			
Oblongamine	MeOH	284(3.97)	100-0001-79
$C_{38}H_{44}N_2O_6$			
Dauricine	MeOH	283(4.0)	100-0001-79
Thalibrine	MeOH	284(3.90)	100-0001-79
$C_{38}H_{44}N_2O_7$			
Thalirugine	MeOH	280(3.81)	100-0001-79
$C_{38}H_{44}O_{18}$			
β-D-Glucopyranoside, 4-[6a-acetoxy-4-(4-acetoxy-3-methoxyphenyl)tetrahydro-1H,3H-furo[3,4-c]furan-1-yl]-2-methoxyphenyl, tetraacetate	EtOH	220(4.26),275(3.75), 279(3.74)	94-2868-79

Compound	Solvent	λ_{max}(log ε)	Ref.
$C_{38}H_{46}O_4S$			
Androsta-3,5-diene-11,17-dione, 3,3'-thiobis-	MeOH	239(4.26),248(4.23), 270(4.12),297s(3.93)	39-1166-79C
$C_{38}H_{46}O_{16}$			
Pseudrelone B	n.s.g.	261(3.46)	102-1574-79
$C_{38}H_{47}NO_{16}$			
Nogalamycinic acid	EtOH	236(4.60),269(4.33), 291s(3.94),482(4.13)	44-4030-79
$C_{38}H_{49}InN_4$			
Indium, ethyl[2,3,7,8,12,13,17,18-octa-ethyl-21H,23H-porphinato(2-)-N^{21},N^{22}-N^{23},N^{24}]-, (SP-5-31)-	benzene	365(4.77),435(5.16), 520(3.38),558(4.25), 592(3.81)	101-0311-79P
$C_{38}H_{54}N_2$			
Naphthacene-1,4:7,10-diimine, 13,14-di-butyl-1,4,7,10-tetrahydro-1,2,3,4,5-6,7,8,9,10,11,12-dodecamethyl-	hexane	219(4.38),262(4.75), 265(4.76),268(4.81), 285(4.04),295(4.10)	44-0007-79
$C_{38}H_{68}O_3$			
Triacontanoic acid, 2-(4-hydroxyphenyl)-ethyl ester	EtOH	226(4.00),279(3.39)	95-0500-79
	EtOH-NaOH	246(4.07),298(3.47)	95-0500-79

Compound	Solvent	λ_{max}(log ϵ)	Ref.
$C_{39}H_{18}F_6N_4O_2$			
7H-Benzimidazo[2,1-a]benz[de]isoquinolin-7-one, 10,10'-[2,2,2-trifluoro-1-(trifluoromethyl)ethylidene]bis-, (or isomer)	H_2SO_4	231(4.86),303(4.36), 412(4.66)	103-0791-79
$C_{39}H_{26}ClN_5$			
2H-Naphtho[1,2-d]triazole, 2-[3-chloro-4-[2-[4-(1,3-diphenyl-1H-pyrazol-5-yl)phenyl]ethenyl]phenyl]-	DMF	375(4.81)	33-1816-79
$C_{39}H_{26}N_2O_2$			
Benzoxazole, 5,5'-(diphenylmethylene)-bis[2-phenyl-	H_2SO_4	205(4.44),278(3.67)	103-1299-79
$C_{39}H_{27}N_5$			
2H-Naphtho[1,2-d]triazole, 2-[4-[2-[4-(1,3-diphenyl-1H-pyrazol-5-yl)-phenyl]ethenyl]phenyl]-	DMF	373(4.83)	33-1816-79
2H-Naphtho[1,2-d]triazole, 2-[4-[2-[4-(1,5-diphenyl-1H-pyrazol-3-yl)-phenyl]ethenyl]phenyl]-	DMF	329(4.43),377(4.88)	33-1816-79
2H-Naphtho[1,2-d]triazole, 2-[4-[2-[4-(3,5-diphenyl-1H-pyrazol-1-yl)-phenyl]ethenyl]phenyl]-	DMF	372(4.84)	33-1816-79
$C_{39}H_{28}N_4O$			
Benzo[c]cinnolinium, 5-[(4-oxo-1,2,3,3-tetraphenyl-2-azetidinyl)amino]-, hydroxide, inner salt	n.s.g.	250(4.72),297(3.99), 308(3.92),322(3.83), 392(4.13),412(4.02)	39-0192-79C
$C_{39}H_{29}N_3O_2$			
Isoxazole, 3-[4-[2-[4-(1,3-diphenyl-1H-pyrazol-5-yl)phenyl]ethenyl]phenyl]-5-(4-methoxyphenyl)-	DMF	343(4.78)	33-1816-79
Isoxazole, 5-[4-[2-[4-(1,3-diphenyl-1H-pyrazol-5-yl)phenyl]ethenyl]phenyl]-3-(4-methoxyphenyl)-	DMF	353(4.82)	33-1816-79
$C_{39}H_{34}N_2$			
1H-Pyrazole, 5,5'-methylenebis[2,3-dihydro-6,7-diphenyl-	ether	207(4.85),244(4.68), 277(4.43)	83-0896-79
$C_{39}H_{36}S_5$			
1,3-Butadiene, 1,1,2,3,4-pentakis(4-methylphenylthio)-	heptane	202(4.90),273(4.45)	5-1614-79
1,3-Butadiene, 1,1,2,4,4-pentakis(4-methylphenylthio)-	heptane	200(4.93),265(4.46)	5-1614-79
$C_{39}H_{37}N_2O_2$			
Quinolinium, 1-[4-(1-methylethoxy)phenyl]-2-[3-[1-[4-(1-methylethoxy)phenyl]-2(1H)-quinolinylidene]-1-propenyl]-, perchlorate	EtOH	572(5.13),616(5.43)	104-1160-79
Quinolinium, 1-(4-propoxyphenyl)-2-[3-[1-(4-propoxyphenyl)-2(1H)-quinolinylidene]-1-propenyl]-, perchlorate	EtOH	572(5.16),615(5.34)	104-1160-79
$C_{39}H_{37}N_7O_{13}$			
Biliverdin IXa, picric acid complex	MeOH	376(4.78),676(4.30)	31-0009-79

Compound	Solvent	λ max(log ε)	Ref.
$C_{39}H_{40}O_{10}$			
Cauferoside	n.s.g.	217(4.35),245(3.74), 254(3.47),297(4.01), 326(4.24)	105-0414-79
$C_{39}H_{40}O_{17}$			
Apiumoside pentaacetate	n.s.g.	280(4.59),295(4.56), 320(4.27)	102-1764-79
$C_{39}H_{42}N_2O_8$			
Pennsylpavoline	EtOH	230(4.47),280s(4.06), 288(4.13),306s(4.01), 320s(3.96)	100-0133-79
Thalfinine	MeOH	282(3.76)	100-0001-79
$C_{39}H_{44}ClN_2O_6$			
Berbanaminium, 2'-(chloromethyl)-6,6',7,12-tetramethoxy-2,2'-dimethyl-, chloride	MeOH	283(3.88)	100-0001-79
$C_{39}H_{44}N_2O_6$			
Pakistanine, 1,10-di-O-methyl-	EtOH	215(4.60),270s(4.27), 277(4.29),301(4.09)	100-0133-79
$C_{39}H_{44}N_2O_7$			
Calafatine (same spectrum in base)	MeOH	258(3.32),281(3.82)	142-1559-79
Hernandezine	MeOH	209(4.99),283(3.90)	100-0001-79
Thalidasine	MeOH	275(3.66),282(3.66)	100-0001-79
Thaliracebine	MeOH	278(3.90)	100-0001-79
Thalrugosaminine	MeOH or EtOH	205(4.89),227s(4.51), 282(3.94)	100-0001-79
$C_{39}H_{44}N_2O_8$			
Pennsylvanamine	MeOH	276s(4.07),284(4.17), 297s(4.11),312s(4.06)	100-0133-79
Revolutopine	MeOH	281(4.40),302(4.24), 314s(4.15)	100-0133-79
Thalibrunine	MeOH or EtOH	205(5.04),242s(--), 282(3.93)	100-0001-79
Thalictrogamine	EtOH	230s(4.39),277(4.11), 298s(3.98),307s(3.82)	100-0133-79
Thalipine	EtOH	282(4.49),303s(4.34), 316s(4.19)	100-0133-79
$C_{39}H_{46}N_2O_6$			
Dauricine, O-methyl-	EtOH	283(4.04)	100-0001-79
$C_{39}H_{46}N_2O_7$			
Thaliruginine	MeOH	281(3.90)	100-0001-79
$C_{39}H_{46}N_2O_8$			
Thalirugidine	MeOH	278(2.82)	100-0001-79
$C_{39}H_{48}N_6$			
21H,23H-Porphine, 2,3,7,8,12,13,17,18-octaethyl-5-(1H-imidazol-1-yl)-	CH_2Cl_2	400(5.18),500(4.12), 535(3.94),569(3.80), 622(3.67)	35-5953-79
$C_{39}H_{51}InN_4$			
Indium, (1-methylethyl)[2,3,7,8,12,13-	$CHCl_3$	372(4.95),439(4.99),	101-0311-79P

Compound	Solvent	$\lambda_{max}(\log \epsilon)$	Ref.
17,18-octaethyl-21H,23H-porphinato-(2-)-N^{21},N^{22},N^{23},N^{24}]-, (SP-5-31)-		525(3.53),564(4.25), 595(3.72)	101-0311-79P
$C_{39}H_{51}N_3O_8$			
Benzoic acid, 4-(octyloxy)-, [2,3,3a,9a-tetrahydro-6-imino-3-[[4-(octyloxy)-benzoyl]oxy]-6H-furo[2',3':4,5]oxazolo[3,2-a]pyrimidin-2-yl]methyl ester, monohydrochloride, [2R-(2α,3β,3aβ,9aβ)]-	MeOH	262(4.71),273s(4.62)	87-0639-79
$C_{39}H_{51}N_3O_{12}$			
1H-Pyrrole-3-propanoic acid, 2-[(1,1-dimethylethoxy)carbonyl]-5-[[3-(2-methoxy-2-oxoethyl)-2-[[4-(2-methoxy-2-oxoethyl)-3-(3-methoxy-3-oxopropyl)-5-methyl-1H-pyrrol-2-yl]methylene]-4-(3-methoxy-3-oxopropyl)-2H-pyrrol-5-yl]methyl]-4-methyl-, methyl ester, monohydrobromide	n.s.g.	280(4.21),362(3.73), 498(4.83)	39-1927-79C
$C_{39}H_{63}N_3O_{10}$			
Butanedioic acid, 2-[[1,4-dioxo-4-(undecyloxy)butoxy]methyl]-2,3,3a,9a-tetrahydro-6-imino-6H-furo[2',3':4,5]-oxazolo[3,2-a]pyrimidin-3-yl undecyl ester, monohydrochloride, [2R-(2α,3β,3aβ,9aβ)]-	MeOH	235(3.98),264(4.05)	87-0639-79
Undecanoic acid, 11-(1-oxobutoxy)-, [2,3,3a,9a-tetrahydro-6-imino-3-[[1-oxo-11-(1-oxobutoxy)undecyl]-oxy]-6H-furo[2',3':4,5]oxazolo[3,2-a]pyrimidin-2-yl]methyl ester, hydrochloride, [2R-(2α,3β,3aβ,9aβ)]-	MeOH	236(3.98),264(4.05)	87-0639-79
$C_{39}H_{65}N_5O_8$			
Undecanoic acid, 11-[(1-oxobutyl)amino]-, [2,3,3a,9a-tetrahydro-6-imino-3-[[1-oxo-11-[(1-oxobutyl)amino]undecyl]oxy]-6H-furo[2',3':4,5]oxazolo-[3,2-a]pyrimidin-2-yl]methyl ester, hydrochloride, [2R-(2α,3β,3aβ,9aβ)]-	MeOH	235(4.02),264(4.07)	87-0639-79
$C_{39}H_{67}N_3O_6S_2$			
Undecanoic acid, 11-(butylthio)-, 2-[[[11-(butylthio)-1-oxoundecyl]oxy]-methyl]-2,3,3a,9a-tetrahydro-6-imino-6H-furo[2',3':4,5]oxazolo[3,2-a]-pyrimidin-3-yl ester, hydrochloride, [2R-(2α,3β,3aβ,9aβ)]-	MeOH	236(4.00),264(4.08)	87-0639-79
$C_{39}H_{67}N_3O_8$			
Propanoic acid, 3-(dodecyloxy)-, 2-[[3-(dodecyloxy)-1-oxopropoxy]methyl]-2,3,3a,9a-tetrahydro-6-imino-6H-furo-[2',3':4,5]oxazolo[3,2-a]pyrimidin-3-yl ester, hydrochloride, [2R-(2α,3β,3aβ,9aβ)-	MeOH	235(4.04),263(4.09)	87-0639-79

Compound	Solvent	λ_{max}(log ϵ)	Ref.
$C_{40}H_{27}N$			
2H-Isoindole, 1,3-diphenyl-2-(10-phenyl-9-anthracenyl)-	benzene	366s(4.23),380(4.33), 400s(4.16)	39-0621-79C
$C_{40}H_{27}NO$			
Methanone, phenyl[2-[phenyl[(10-phenyl-9-anthracenyl)imino]methyl]phenyl]-	dioxan	264(4.86),384s(3.75), 403(3.92),420s(3.90)	39-0621-79C
$C_{40}H_{28}$			
[2](1,4)Naphthaleno[2]paracyclo[2](1,4)-naphthaleno[2]paracyclophanetetraene	C_6H_{12} or EtOH	295(4.04)	1-0443-79
[2])1,5)Naphthaleno[2]paracyclo[2](1,5)-naphthaleno[2]paracyclophanetetraene	C_6H_{12} or EtOH	287(4.13)	1-0443-79
[2](2,6)Naphthaleno[2]paracyclo[2](2,6)-naphthaleno[2]paracyclophanetetraene	C_6H_{12} or EtOH	315(4.78)	1-0443-79
$C_{40}H_{30}$			
1,3-Butadiene, 1,1,2,3,4,4-hexaphenyl-	ether	270(4.64),416(4.72)	104-1867-79
$C_{40}H_{30}N_2$			
Dibenz[2,3:6,7]-s-indaceno[4,5-bc:8,1-b'c']dipyridine, 1,8-dihydro-2,9-dimethyl-1,8-bis(phenylmethyl)-	EtOH	208(4.77),280(4.80), 391(3.85),504(3.88), 674(4.69)	103-1214-79
$C_{40}H_{30}N_2O_5$			
1,2-Diazabicyclo[4.3.1]deca-3,8-dien-10-one, 3,7-bis(1,3-benzodioxol-5-yl)-5,6,9-triphenyl-	EtOH	241(4.53),282s(4.10)	94-2767-79
$C_{40}H_{30}O_7$			
2H-Pyran-2-one, 4-(1,3-benzodioxol-5-yl)-3-[1-(1,3-benzodioxol-5-yl)-3-oxo-3-phenylpropyl]-3,4-dihydro-3,6-diphenyl-	EtOH	246(4.48),288(4.00)	94-2767-79
$C_{40}H_{32}$			
Pentacyclo[28.2.2.2^{6,9}.2^{16,17}.2^{22,25}]-tetraconta-2,4,6,8,10,12,14,16,18,20-22,24,26,28,30,32,33,35,37,39-eicosaene, (Z,Z,Z,Z,E,E,E,E)-	C_6H_{12}	345(4.88),360(4.88)	1-0464-79
$C_{40}H_{32}I_2$			
p-Sexiphenyl, 4,4'''''-diiodo-2,2'''''-5,5'''''-tetramethyl-	C_6H_5Cl	312(4.75)	104-0517-79
$C_{40}H_{34}O_{14}$			
[9,9'-Bi-11H-benzofuro[2,3-b][1]benzopyran]-11,11'-dione, 10b,10'b-diacetoxy-5a,5'a,10b,10'b-tetrahydro-3,3',8,8'-tetramethoxy-5a,5'a-dimethyl-	MeOH	289(4.52)	18-0529-79
$C_{40}H_{35}N_3$			
Tetramethylammonium 1-(cyclohepta-1,3,6-trienyl)-5-(2,5-dicyano-3,4-diphenylcyclopentadienido)naphthalene	MeCN	271(4.54),370s(3.97)	39-0889-79C
$C_{40}H_{36}N_2O_9$			
1-Azabicyclo[4.2.0]oct-2-ene-2,4,4-tricarboxylic acid, 3-methyl-8-oxo-7-	EtOH	269(4.16)	23-0222-79

Compound	Solvent	λ_{max}(log ε)	Ref.
[(phenoxyacetyl)amino]-, tris(phenylmethyl) ester, trans (cont.)			23-0222-79
$C_{40}H_{38}Br_2N_4$			
Quinolinium, 1,1'-(1,2-ethanediyl)bis-[6-bromo-4-[2-[4-(dimethylamino)phenyl]ethenyl]-, salt with 4-methylbenzenesulfonic acid (1:2)	EtOH	586(4.89)	104-0566-79
$C_{40}H_{38}N_6O_4$			
Quinolinium, 1,1'-(1,2-ethanediyl)bis-[4-[2-[4-(dimethylamino)phenyl]ethenyl]-6-nitro-, salt with 4-methylbenzenesulfonic acid (1:2)	EtOH	592(5.01)	104-0566-79
$C_{40}H_{38}O_4P_2$			
Phosphorin, 4,4'-(1,2-ethenediyl)bis-[1,1-dihydro-1,1-dimethoxy-2,6-diphenyl-, (E)-	MeOH	325(4.75),389(4.00)	24-1272-79
$C_{40}H_{40}N_2O_9$			
Oxothalicarpine	EtOH	237(4.52),271(4.44), 285s(4.34),343(3.93)	100-0133-79
$C_{40}H_{40}N_4$			
Quinolinium, 1,1'-(1,2-ethanediyl)bis-[4-[2-[4-(dimethylamino)phenyl]ethenyl]-, salt with 4-methylbenzenesulfonic acid (1:2)	EtOH	580(5.12)	104-0566-79
$C_{40}H_{40}O_{12}$			
Compd., m. 148-155°	EtOH	340(3.92)	39-0673-79C
$C_{40}H_{42}O_7$			
3,6,9,12,15-Pentaoxaheptadecane, 1,17-bis(9-anthracenyloxy)-	C_6H_{12}	249(5.23),257(5.48), 320(3.29),335(3.72), 351(4.03),370(4.23), 390(4.18)	108-0220-79
	benzene	392(4.16)	108-0220-79
	MeOH	256(5.44),389(4.13)	108-0220-79
$C_{40}H_{44}ClFeN_8O_{12}$			
Iron, chloro[dimethyl 7,12-diethyl-3,8,13,17-tetramethyl-5,10,15,20-tetrakis(nitromethyl)-21H,23H-porphine-2,18-dipropanoato(2-)-N^{21},N^{22},N^{23},N^{24}]-, (SP-5-13)-	CH_2Cl_2	375(4.56),510(3.53), 545(3.46),642(3.11)	78-1251-79
$C_{40}H_{44}N_2O_8$			
Pennsylpavine	EtOH	230(4.62),280s(4.38), 288(4.40),308s(4.23), 320s(4.15)	100-0133-79
Thalmelatine, dehydro-	EtOH	268(4.57),330(4.15)	100-0133-79
$C_{40}H_{44}N_4O_3$			
Pleiocorine, N(1')-demethyl-	EtOH	243(4.12),295(3.48), 333(3.73)	102-1729-79
	EtOH-$HClO_4$	240(--),293(--), 323(--)	102-1729-79

Compound	Solvent	$\lambda_{max}(\log \epsilon)$	Ref.
$C_{40}H_{44}O_{12}$			
Herpetetrol	n.s.g.	214(--),235s(--), 281(4.09),285s(--)	64-1129-79C
$C_{40}H_{46}FeN_6O_3$			
Hemin-6(7)-(6-aminohexyl)amide, chloride, hydrochloride	$CHCl_3$-EtOH	399(5.05),470(3.80), 510(3.91),540(3.88), 588(3.37),641(3.56)	104-0741-79
$C_{40}H_{46}N_2O_8$			
Fetidine	EtOH	220(4.80),280(4.36), 305(4.24)	100-0133-79
Pennsylvanine	EtOH	284(4.26),304(4.18), 320s(4.05)	100-0133-79
Thalictropine	EtOH	225(4.46),278(4.12), 298s(3.88),310s(3.70)	100-0133-79
Thalidoxine	MeOH	275(4.23),296s(4.08), 310s(4.02)	100-0133-79
Thalilutidine	MeOH	280(4.38),304s(4.21)	100-0133-79
Thalirevoline	MeOH	270s(4.31),280(4.40), 301(4.24),310s(4.18)	100-0133-79
Thalistyline, N-demethyl-	MeOH	282(3.81)	100-0001-79
$C_{40}H_{46}N_4O_3$			
Isostrychnobiline, 12'-hydroxy-	MeOH	212(4.64),250(4.17), 290(3.7),308s(3.43)	102-0515-79
$C_{40}H_{47}N_2O_8$			
Thalirabine (cation)	MeOH	207(4.99),276(3.82), 283(3.80)	100-0001-79
$C_{40}H_{48}ClFeN_8O_{12}$			
Iron, chloro[2,3,7,8,12,13,17,18-octaethyl-5,10,15,20-tetrakis(nitromethyl)-21H,23H-porphinato(2-)-N^{21},N^{22}-N^{23},N^{24}]-, (SP-5-12)-	CH_2Cl_2	375(4.84),510(3.92), 644(3.58)	78-1251-79
$C_{40}H_{48}ClN_8O_8Tl$			
Thallium. chloro(2,3,7,8,12,13,17,18-octaethyl-5,10,15,20-tetrakis(nitromethyl)-21H,23H-porphinato(2-)-N^{21},N^{22},N^{23},N^{24}]-, (SP-5-12)-	CH_2Cl_2	426(5.00),516(3.90), 556(3.74),591(3.54)	78-1251-79
$C_{40}H_{48}O_2$			
4-Hexen-3-one, 6,6'-[8,13-bis(1,1-dimethylethyl)-5,7,13,15-cyclohexadecatetraene-2,9,11-triyne-1,4-diylidene]bis[2,2-dimethyl-	THF	237(4.17),281(4.45), 306s(4.24),380(4.99)	88-4213-79
$C_{40}H_{49}IN_4O_8$			
21H-Biline-2,8,12,17-tetrapropanoic acid, 10,24-dihydro-19-iodo-1,3,7-8,13,18-pentamethyl-, tetramethyl ester, dihydrobromide	$CHCl_3$-HBr	460(4.97),537(5.17)	104-0970-79
$C_{40}H_{50}$			
Cholesta-1,4,6-triene, 3-(diphenylmethylene)-	MeOH	213(4.30),250(3.85), 333(4.34)	39-1166-79C
$C_{40}H_{51}NO_{19}$			
Cathedulin K2	MeOH	221(3.89),265(3.57)	39-2965-79C

Compound	Solvent	$\lambda_{max}(\log \epsilon)$	Ref.
$C_{40}H_{52}N_4O_2$			
2H-Isoindol-2-yloxy, 5,5'-[1,4-phenylenebis(methylidynenitrilo)]bis-[1,1,3,3-tetraethyl-1,3-dihydro-	C_6H_{12}	233(4.43),295(4.46), 350(4.54)	22-0048-79
$C_{40}H_{53}InN_4$			
Indium, butyl[2,3,7,8,12,13,17,18-octaethyl-21H,23H-porphinato(2-)-$N^{21},N^{22},N^{23},N^{24}$]-, (SP-5-31)-	benzene	365(4.77),435(5.15), 520(3.38),559(4.25), 594(3.81)	101-0311-79P
Indium, (1,1-dimethylethyl)[2,3,7,8-12,13,17,18-octaethyl-21H,23H-porphinato(2-)-$N^{21},N^{22},N^{23},N^{24}$]-, (SP-5-31)-	benzene	377(4.98),443(4.79), 565(4.13),594(3.56)	101-0311-79P
$C_{40}H_{58}O_2$			
β,ψ-Carotene, 5,6-dihydro-5,6-dihydroxy-, (5R,6R)-, (all-E)	EtOH	279(4.58),431(5.05), 456(5.25),488(5.21)	33-2534-79
$C_{40}H_{60}O_7$			
Acacigenin B	EtOH	220(3.03)	102-0463-79

Compound	Solvent	λ max(log ε)	Ref.
$C_{41}H_{32}O_3$			
6,10-Etheno-9H-cyclopent[1,7a]indeno-[5,6-c]furan-7,9(1H)-dione, 5,5a,6-6a,9a,10-hexahydro-1-methyl-2,3,4,5-tetraphenyl-, (1α,5β,5aα,6β,6aα-9aα,10β,10aS*)-	MeCN	220s(4.28),235(4.04), 319(4.25)	44-2483-79
$C_{41}H_{34}N_2O_{17}$			
5,12-Naphthacenedione, 8-acetyl-10-[[2,6-dideoxy-3,4-bis-O-(4-nitro-benzoyl)-α-D-ribo-hexopyranosyl]-oxy]-7,8,9,10-tetrahydro-6,8,11-trihydroxy-1-methoxy-, (8S-cis)-	$CHCl_3$	253(4.60),483(4.05), 498(4.05),532(3.79)	87-0406-79
β-	$CHCl_3$	253(4.64),488(4.04), 505(4.04),540(3.79)	87-0406-79
$C_{41}H_{39}BOSSe$			
Dimethylsulfonium (benzoylmethylphenyl-selenoniomethylide), tetraphenylborate	n.s.g.	220s(4.398),257(3.808), 264(3.798)	104-0332-79
$C_{41}H_{41}NO_{10}$			
5,12-Naphthacenedione, 8-acetyl-10-[[3-[bis(phenylmethyl)amino]-2,3,6-tride-oxy-α-L-lyxo-hexopyranosyl]oxy]-7,8,9,10-tetrahydro-6,8,11-trihydroxy-1-methoxy-, (8S-cis)-, hydrochloride	MeOH	233(4.60),252(4.43), 289(3.95),478(4.10), 495(4.10),530(--)	87-0912-79
$C_{41}H_{41}N_2O_2$			
Quinolinium, 1-(4-butoxyphenyl)-2-[3-[1-(4-butoxyphenyl)-2(1H)-quino-linylidene]-1-propenyl]-, perchlorate	EtOH	572(5.12),616(5.41)	104-1160-79
$C_{41}H_{46}N_2O_8$			
Dehydrothalicarpine	EtOH	268(4.82),331(4.34)	100-0133-79
$C_{41}H_{46}N_4O_5$			
Pleiocorine	EtOH	247(4.19),297(3.43), 342(3.83)	102-1729-79
Pleiocraline	EtOH	247(4.14),298(3.60), 330(3.80)	102-1729-79
	EtOH-HCl	234(4.12),283(3.58), 305(3.58)	102-1729-79
$C_{41}H_{47}FeN_7O_4$			
Hemin-6(7)-(7-aminoenanthohydrazide), chloride	DMF	402(5.13),463(3.95), 513(3.88),590(3.28), 650(3.46)	104-0741-79
$C_{41}H_{48}N_2O_8$			
Thalicarpine	EtOH	282(4.33),301(4.22)	100-0133-79
Thalirevolutine	EtOH	270s(4.31),280(4.38), 302(4.21),315s(4.10)	100-0133-79
$C_{41}H_{48}N_2O_9$			
Thaliadanine	EtOH	281(4.33),302(4.18), 312(4.11)	100-0133-79
Thalilutine	EtOH	282(4.40),303s(4.28), 312s(4.23)	100-0133-79
$C_{41}H_{49}N_2O_8$			
Thalistyline (chloride)	MeOH	276(3.86),283(3.84)	100-0001-79

Compound	Solvent	λ_{max}(log ε)	Ref.
$C_{41}H_{50}N_4O_{10}$			
21H-Biline-2,8,12,17-tetrapropanoic acid, 19-carboxy-10,24-dihydro-1,3,7,13,18-pentamethyl-, α²,α⁸,α¹²-α¹⁷-tetramethyl ester, dihydrobromide	$CHCl_3$-HBr	455(4.83),527(4.96)	104-0970-79
$C_{41}H_{50}N_5$			
Pyridinium, 1-(2,3,7,8,12,13,17,18-octaethyl-21H,23H-porphin-5-yl)-, chloride	CH_2Cl_2	402(5.18),505(4.16), 537(4.06),566(3.93), 616(3.92)	35-5953-79
$C_{41}H_{54}N_2O_{11}$			
25-O-Deacetylrifamycin S, compd. with 1,3,5-tri-tert-butylhexahydro-1,3,5-triazine	pH 6.1	227(4.54),273(4.29), 311(4.21),356(4.22), 569(4.06)	138-1313-79
$C_{41}H_{54}N_4O_2$			
15,21-Diazapentacyclo[21.4.4.4^{8,13}-0^{10,33}.0^{25,29}]pentatriaconta-8,10-12,23,25,27,28,30,32,34-decaene-14,22-dione, 11,30-bis(dimethylamino)-15,21,24,32-tetramethyl-, isomer A	EtOH-H_2SO_4	285(3.94),328(3.15)	44-4469-79
	EtOH-NaOH	246(3.48),313(3.92)	44-4469-79
isomer B	EtOH-H_2SO_4	285(4.00),328(3.26)	44-4469-79
	EtOH-NaOH	247(4.52),315(3.88)	44-4469-79
$C_{41}H_{57}N_3O_4$			
4a,13b-Etheno-1H,9H-benzo[c]cyclopenta-[h][1,2,4]triazolo[1,2-a]cinnoline-1,3(2H)-dione, 5,6,7,8,8a,8b,10,10a-11,12,13,13a-dodecahydro-8a,10a-dimethyl-2-phenyl-6-[(tetrahydro-2H-pyran-2-yl)oxy]-11-(1,4,5-trimethyl-2-hexenyl)-, [4aS-[4aα,6α,8aα,8bβ-10aα,11α(1S*,2E,4S*),13aβ,13bα]]-	MeOH	256(3.60)	39-1858-79C
$C_{41}H_{58}N_2O_2$			
Benzamide, N,N'-[(2α,3β,5α)-cholestane-2,3-diyl]bis-	MeCN-dioxan (9:1)	229(4.09),225(4.12)	119-0093-79
(2β,3β,5α)-	MeCN-dioxan (9:1)	226(4.11),231(4.10)	119-0093-79
$C_{41}H_{59}N_3O_5$			
4a,13b-Etheno-1H,9H-benzo[c]cyclopenta-[h][1,2,4]triazolo[1,2-a]cinnoline-1,3(2H)-dione, 5,6,7,8,8a,8b,10,10a-11,12,13,13a-dodecahydro-11-(2-hydroxy-1,4,5-trimethylhexyl)-8a,10a-dimethyl-2-phenyl-6-[(tetrahydro-2H-pyran-2-yl)oxy]-	MeOH	255(3.86)	39-1858-79C
$C_{41}H_{71}N_3O_6$			
Hexadecanoic acid, [2,3,3a,9a-tetrahydro-6-imino-3-[(1-oxohexadecyl)oxy]-6H-furo[2',3':4,5]oxazolo[3,2-a]pyrimidin-2-yl]methyl ester, [2R-(2α-3β,3aβ,9aβ)]-, hydrochloride	MeOH	236(4.00),264(4.06)	87-0639-79

Compound	Solvent	λ max (log ε)	Ref.
$C_{42}H_{29}N_3O$			
1,2-Benzisoxazole, 3-[1,1'-biphenyl]-4-yl-6-[2-[4-(1,3-diphenyl-1H-pyrazol-5-yl)phenyl]ethenyl]-	DMF	343(4.74)	33-1816-79
Benzoxazole, 2-[4-[2-[4-(1,3-diphenyl-1H-pyrazol-5-yl)phenyl]ethenyl]-phenyl]-5-phenyl-	DMF	365(4.88)	33-1816-79
Benzoxazole, 2-[4-[2-[4-(1,5-diphenyl-1H-pyrazol-3-yl)phenyl]ethenyl]-phenyl]-5-phenyl-	DMF	370(4.92)	33-1816-79
$C_{42}H_{30}$			
Naphthacene, 5,11-dihydro-5,6,11,12-tetraphenyl-	ether	233s(4.40),245s(4.30), 356(4.17)	78-2093-79
$C_{42}H_{30}O$			
Anthracene, 9,9'-[oxybis(methylene)]-bis[10-phenyl-	$C_6H_{11}Me$	253(5.23),258(5.27), 340(3.87),357(4.18), 376(4.39),397(4.40)	39-0411-79B
Anthracene, 9,9'-[oxybis(phenylmethylene)]bis-	n.s.g.	268(--),336(3.67), 352(3.96),370(4.13), 391(4.1)	39-2948-79C
$C_{42}H_{30}O_2$			
Naphtho[2,3-c]furan-1-ol, 1,3-dihydro-1,3,3,4,9-pentaphenyl-	ether	238(4.85),270s(3.77), 280s(3.89),289(3.99), 297s(3.91)	78-2101-79
$C_{42}H_{30}S_6$			
Benzene, hexakis(phenylthio)-	CCl_4	323(2.03)	39-1011-79B
$C_{42}H_{32}$			
Benzene, 1,1',1",1"'-[(3,4-diphenyl-1,2-cyclobutanediylidene)dimethanetetrayl]tetrakis-, cis	ether	261(4.40),353(4.31)	78-2093-79
trans	ether	262(4.45),356(4.24)	78-2093-79
Benzene, 1,1',1"-[3-(diphenylmethylene)-2-phenyl-4-(phenylmethylene)-cyclobutylidene]bis-, (Z)-	ether	230s(4.08),249(4.03), 350(4.15)	78-2093-79
Naphthacene, 5,5a,6,11-tetrahydro-5,5,11,12-tetraphenyl-	ether	263(3.90),271(3.96), 276(4.02),284(4.06)	78-2101-79
Naphthalene, 2,3-bis(diphenylmethyl)-1-phenyl-	ether	238(4.91),264(3.90), 270(3.86),275(3.85), 287(3.86),296s(3.72)	78-2101-79
Naphthalene, 2-(2,2-diphenylethyl)-1,3,4-triphenyl-	ether	240(4.70),293(3.95)	78-2101-79
Naphthalene, 2-(diphenylmethyl)-1,4-diphenyl-3-(phenylmethyl)-	ether	237(4.83),271(3.83), 292(3.97)	78-2101-79
$C_{42}H_{32}N_2O$			
1,2-Diazabicyclo[4.3.1]deca-3,8-dien-10-one, 6-(1-naphthalenyl)-3,5,7,9-tetraphenyl-	EtOH	225(4.86),249(4.43), 272s(4.24),273(4.17), 294s(4.03)	94-2767-79
$C_{42}H_{32}O$			
2-Naphthalenemethanol, 3-(diphenylmethyl)- ,1,4-triphenyl-	ether	240(4.82),267(3.89), 284(3.91),292(3.95)	78-2101-79
$C_{42}H_{32}O_3$			
2H-Pyran-2-one, 3,4-dihydro-3-(1-naphthalenyl)-3-(3-oxo-1,3-diphenylprop-	EtOH	225(4.83),249(4.44), 284(4.21)	94-2767-79

Compound	Solvent	λ_{max}(log ϵ)	Ref.
yl)-4,6-diphenyl- (cont.)			94-2767-79
$C_{42}H_{34}N_2S_4$			
15,16-Diazatricyclo[9.3.1.1^{4,8}]hexadeca-1(15),2,4,6,8(16),9,11,13-octaene, 2,3,9,10-tetrakis[(phenylmethyl)thio]-	90% EtOH	275(4.27),314(4.55), 347s(4.15)	12-1241-79
$C_{42}H_{36}O_2P_2Pt$			
Platinum, bis(3-hydroxy-1-propynyl)bis-(triphenylphosphine)-, (SP-4-1)-	$CHCl_3$	316(3.65)	101-0101-79B
$C_{42}H_{36}Zr$			
Zirconium, bis(η^5-2,4-cyclopentadien-1-yl)bis(4,4-diphenyl-1-butynyl)-	$CHCl_3$	250(4.01),270(3.87), 305(3.28)	101-0353-79S
$C_{42}H_{37}N_2O_2$			
Naphth[1,2-d]oxazolium, 1-ethyl-2-[2-[3-[(1-ethylnaphth[1,2-d]oxazol-2(1H)-ylidene)ethylidene]-2-phenyl-1-cyclohexen-1-yl]ethenyl]-, iodide	MeOH	732(5.41)	104-0351-79
$C_{42}H_{38}O$			
Cyclobut[f]isobenzofuran, 4,7-bis(1,1-dimethylethyl)-1,3,5,6-tetraphenyl-	$CHCl_3$	260(4.40),296(4.49), 370(3.93)	138-1451-79
$C_{42}H_{38}S$			
Cyclobuta[4,5]benzo[1,2-c]thiophene, 4,7-bis(1,1-dimethylethyl)-1,3,5,6-tetraphenyl-	$CHCl_3$	257(4.36),318(4.46), 390(3.62)	138-1451-79
$C_{42}H_{38}Se$			
Cyclobuta[4,5]benzo[1,2-b]selenophene, 4,7-bis(1,1-dimethylethyl)-2,3,5,6-tetraphenyl-	$CHCl_3$	265(4.28),323(3.45), 415(2.63)	138-1451-79
$C_{42}H_{40}O$			
Cyclobuta[f]benzofuran, 4,7-bis(1,1-dimethylethyl)-2,3-dihydro-2,3,5,6-tetraphenyl-	$CHCl_3$	265(4.37),304(4.43), 355s(4.05),425s(3.18)	138-1451-79
$C_{42}H_{42}Br_2N_2O_8$			
[1,1'-Binaphthalene]-4,4'-diamine, N,N'-bis[(2-bromo-4,5-dimethoxyphenyl)methyl]-6,6',7,7'-tetramethoxy-	EtOH	205(5.00),220(4.24), 239s(4.84),263(4.68), 331(4.27)	44-0293-79
$C_{42}H_{42}Cu_2N_6O_{12}$			
Copper, bis[μ-[4-[[2-hydroxy-2-(4-nitrophenyl)-1-[[[(phenylamino)carbonyl]oxy]methyl]ethyl]imino]-2-pentanonato(2-)]]di-	DMSO	284(4.11),318(4.09), 606(1.96)	94-1245-79
$C_{42}H_{42}N_4O_2$			
Sungucine	EtOH	218(4.87),265(3.84), 292(4.02),305(4.01)	88-4227-79
$C_{42}H_{44}N_2O_8$			
[1,1'-Binamphthalene]-4,4'-diamine, N,N'-bis[(3,4-dimethoxyphenyl)methyl]-6,6',7,7'-tetramethoxy-	EtOH	202(4.92),221(4.85), 263(4.61),333(4.19)	44-0293-79

Compound	Solvent	$\lambda_{max}(\log \epsilon)$	Ref.
$C_{42}H_{44}N_4$			
Quinolinium, 1,1'-(1,2-ethanediyl)bis-[4-[2-[4-(dimethylamino)phenyl]ethenyl]-6-methyl-, salt with 4-methylbenzenesulfonic acid (1:2)	EtOH	578(4.91)	104-0566-79
$C_{42}H_{44}N_4O_2$			
Quinolinium, 1,1'-(1,2-ethanediyl)bis-[4-[2-[4-(dimethylamino)phenyl]ethenyl]-6-methoxy-, salt with 4-methylbenzenesulfonic acid (1:2)	EtOH	580(4.94)	104-0566-79
$C_{42}H_{47}FeN_5O_5$			
Methyl hemin-6(7)-(7-aminoenanthate), chloride	$CHCl_3$-EtOH	402(5.08),471(4.11), 496(4.08),547(3.91), 590(3.83),639(3.57)	104-0741-79
$C_{42}H_{47}N_3O_7Si$			
Cytidine, N-benzoyl-2'-O-[(1,1-dimethylethyl)dimethylsilyl]-5'-O-[(4-methoxyphenyl)diphenylmethyl]-	MeOH-HOAc	259(4.42),305(4.08)	5-1855-79
Cytidine, N-benzoyl-3'-O-[(1,1-dimethylethyl)dimethylsilyl]-5'-O-[(4-methoxyphenyl)diphenylmethyl]-	MeOH-HOAc	259(4.40),305(4.07)	5-1855-79
$C_{42}H_{48}$			
Bicyclo[12.10.2]hexacosa-1(25),2,4,10-12,14(26),15,17,21,23,25-undecaene-6,8,19-triyne, 5,10,18,21-tetrakis-(1,1-dimethylethyl)-	THF	233(4.22),240(4.23), 265(4.17),278(4.17), 304s(4.57),316(4.68), 329s(4.62),384(5.09), 407(5.29),676(3.65), 750s(3.49),830s(3.18)	88-4213-79
$C_{42}H_{49}InN_4$			
Indium, [2,3,7,8,12,13,17,18-octaethyl-21H,23H-porphinato(2-)-N^{21},N^{22},N^{23}-N^{24}]phenyl-, (SP-5-31)-	$CHCl_3$	354(4.66),424(5.42), 512(3.45),551(4.26), 587(3.98)	101-0311-79B
$C_{42}H_{50}N_2O_9$			
Adiantifoline	EtOH	283(4.51),302(4.39), 312(4.34)	100-0133-79
$C_{42}H_{50}N_2O_{10}$			
Thalmineline	EtOH	283(5.46?)	100-0133-79
$C_{42}H_{53}NO_{20}$			
Cathedulin Y1	MeOH	221(3.91),265(3.58)	39-2965-79C
$C_{42}H_{54}O_8S$			
Pregna-1,4-diene-3,20-dione, 21,21'-thiobis[11,17-dihydroxy-, (11β)-(11'β)	EtOH	244(4.51)	94-1352-79
$C_{42}H_{54}O_8S_2$			
Pregna-1,4-diene-3,20-dione, 21,21'-dithiobis[11,17-dihydroxy-, (11β)-(11'β)	EtOH	242(4.54)	94-1352-79
$C_{42}H_{58}O_6S_2$			
Pregn-4-ene-3,20-dione, 21,21'-dithiobis[17-hydroxy-	EtOH	241(4.49)	94-1352-79

Compound	Solvent	λ_{max}(log ε)	Ref.
$C_{42}H_{58}O_8S_2$			
Pregn-4-ene-3,20-dione, 21,21'-dithio-bis[11,17-dihydroxy-, (11β)-(11'β)	EtOH	242(4.51)	94-1352-79
$C_{42}H_{64}O_{17}$			
Oleaside E	MeOH	208(4.33)	94-1604-79
$C_{42}H_{69}NO_5$			
16,28-Secosolanid-22-ene-3,16-diol, 28-(2,2-dimethyl-1-oxopropyl)-, bis(2,2-dimethylpropanoate), (3β,5α,16α)-	EtOH	237(3.79)	12-0597-79
$C_{42}H_{72}O_4$			
2H-1-Benzopyran-2-one, 5,7-bis(hexa-decyloxy)-4-methyl-	C_6H_{12}	212(4.45),242(3.89), 252(3.83),307(4.16), 313(4.15),328s(--)	23-1377-79
	EtOH	212(4.47),245(3.85), 254(3.82),321(4.22)	23-1377-79
2H-1-Benzopyran-2-one, 7,8-bis(hexa-decyloxy)-4-methyl-	C_6H_{12}	220s(--),247(3.95), 257(3.94),303(4.16), 314s(--)	23-1377-79
$C_{42}H_{76}O_2$			
2,5-Cyclohexadiene-1,4-dione, 2,5-di-octadecyl-	$CHCl_3$	262(4.23),302(3.00), 345(2.90),400(1.7)	104-1736-79
2,5-Cyclohexadiene-1,4-dione, 2,6-di-octadecyl-	$CHCl_3$	263(4.24),335(3.03), 450(1.48)	104-1736-79
$C_{42}H_{78}O_2$			
1,4-Benzenediol, 2,5-dioctadecyl-	$CHCl_3$	292(3.79)	104-1736-79
1,4-Benzenediol, 2,6-dioctadecyl-	$CHCl_3$	295(3.7)	104-1736-79
$C_{42}H_{89}N_5O_{10}Si_7$			
Adenosine, N-[3-methyl-4-[[2,3,4,6-tetrakis-O-(trimethylsilyl)-β-D-glucopyranosyl]oxy]butyl]-2',3',5'-tris-O-(trimethylsilyl)-	pH 1	264(4.20)	102-0819-79
	pH 13	269(4.18)	102-0819-79
	EtOH	268(4.16)	102-0819-79

Compound	Solvent	λ_{max}(log ε)	Ref.
$C_{43}H_{30}ClN_5$			
2H-1,2,3-Triazole, 2-[3-chloro-4-[2-[4-(1,3-diphenyl-1H-pyrazol-5-yl)phenyl]ethenyl]phenyl]-4,5-diphenyl-	DMF	357(4.80)	33-1816-79
2H-1,2,3-Triazole, 2-[3-chloro-4-[2-[4-(1,5-diphenyl-1H-pyrazol-3-yl)phenyl]ethenyl]phenyl]-4,5-diphenyl-	DMF	367(4.86)	33-1816-79
2H-1,2,3-Triazole, 2-[3-chloro-4-[2-[4-(3,5-diphenyl-1H-pyrazol-1-yl)phenyl]ethenyl]phenyl]-4,5-diphenyl-	DMF	357(4.81)	33-1816-79
$C_{43}H_{30}N_2O$			
1H-Pyrazole, 1,3-diphenyl-5-[4-[2-[4-(5-phenyl-2-benzofuranyl)phenyl]ethenyl]phenyl]-	DMF	370(4.94)	33-1816-79
$C_{43}H_{30}N_4O$			
1,2,4-Oxadiazole, 3-[1,1'-biphenyl]-4-yl-5-[4-[2-[4-(1,3-diphenyl-1H-pyrazol-5-yl)phenyl]ethenyl]phenyl]-	DMF	353(4.79)	33-1816-79
$C_{43}H_{36}N_4O_6$			
2,4(1H,3H)-Pteridinedione, 1-[2-deoxy-5-O-[(4-methoxyphenyl)diphenylmethyl]-α-D-erythro-pentofuranosyl]-6,7-diphenyl-	MeOH	227(4.59),273(4.24), 357(4.11)	33-1171-79
β-	MeOH	227(4.59),273(4.22), 359(4.11)	33-1171-79
$C_{43}H_{40}F_3NO_{11}$			
5,12-Naphthacenedione, 7,8,9,10-tetrahydro-6,8,11-trihydroxy-1-methoxy-8-[1-oxo-3-phenyl-2-(phenylmethyl)propyl]-10-[[2,3,6-trideoxy-3-[(trifluoroacetyl)amino]-α-L-lyxo-hexopyranosyl]oxy]-, (8S-cis)-	MeOH	235(4.59),253(4.46), 289(3.99),480(4.13), 498(4.13),531(3.89)	87-0040-79
$C_{43}H_{42}O_{22}$			
Carthamin	EtOH	390(4.5),515(5.0)	138-0201-79
$C_{43}H_{50}N_4O_{10}$			
4',20',21'-Trinor-4',5'-secovincaleukoblastine, 3',5'-dioxo-	EtOH	213(4.66),268(4.15), 284(4.08),294(4.00), 310(3.67)	23-1682-79
$C_{43}H_{51}N_5O_2SZn$			
Zinc, [4-methyl-N-(2,3,7,8,12,13,17,18-octaethyl-21H,23H-porphin-21-yl)benzenesulfonamidato(2-)-N^{21},N^{22},N^{23},N^{24}]-, (SP-4-1)-	toluene	413(5.27),530(3.97), 565(4.08),610(4.05)	78-1455-79
$C_{43}H_{53}N_5O_2S$			
Benzenesulfonamide, 4-methyl-N-(2,3,7,8,12,13,17,18-octaethyl-21H,23H-porphin-21-yl)-	toluene	407(5.10),532(3.96), 568(4.17),612(3.43)	78-1455-79
$C_{43}H_{56}N_2O_{12}$			
Rifamycin S deriv. A	pH 6.1	227(4.54),272(4.30), 310(4.21),356(4.22), 568(4.05)	138-1313-79

Compound	Solvent	λ_{max}(log ε)	Ref.
$C_{43}H_{62}O_3$			
2,5-Cyclohexadien-1-one, 4-[bis[3,5-bis(1,1-dimethylethyl)-4-hydroxyphenyl]methylene]-2,6-bis(1,1-dimethylethyl)-	THF	434(4.50)	18-1911-79
$C_{43}H_{64}O_3$			
Phenol, 4,4',4"-methylidynetris[2,6-bis(1,1-dimethylethyl)-	C_6H_{12}	278(3.77)	18-1911-79
$C_{43}H_{64}O_8$			
Acacigenin B, methyl ester, acetate	EtOH	219(3.21)	102-0463-79
$C_{43}H_{80}N_3O_{10}P$			
Phosphoric acid, mono[2,3-bis(hexadecyloxy)propyl]-, mono[2-[[(2,4-dinitrophenyl)amino]ethyl] ester	MeOH	349(4.06)	106-0287-79

Compound	Solvent	λ max(log ε)	Ref.
$C_{44}H_{24}Cl_4N_2S_2$			
21,23-Dithiaporpyrin, tetrakis(4-chlorophenyl)-	n.s.g.	436(5.39),514(4.38), 548(3.83),633(3.27), 696(3.55)	39-1066-79C
$C_{44}H_{24}F_4N_2S_2$			
21,23-Dithiaporphyrin, tetrakis(4-fluorophenyl)-	n.s.g.	435(5.46),513(4.47), 546(3.85),632(3.32), 696(3.67)	39-1066-79C
$C_{44}H_{26}F_2N_2S_2$			
21,23-Dithiaporphyrin, α,β-bis(4-fluorophenyl)-γ,δ-diphenyl-	n.s.g.	435(5.48),513(4.49), 547(3.86),632(3.32), 696(3.68)	39-1066-79C
$C_{44}H_{27}BrCuN_4$			
Copper, [2-bromo-5,10,15,20-tetraphenyl-21H,23H-porphinato(2-)-N^{21},N^{22}-N^{23},N^{24}]-, (SP-4-2)-	CH_2Cl_2	416(4.61),541(4.29), 575(3.52)	35-3857-79
$C_{44}H_{27}CuN_5O_2$			
Copper, 2-nitro-5,10,15,20-tetraphenyl-21H,23H-porphinato(2-)-N^{21},N^{22},N^{23}-N^{24}]-, (OC-6-23)-	CH_2Cl_2	420(5.27),547(4.11), 582(3.92)	35-3857-79
$C_{44}H_{28}N_2S_2$			
21,23-Dithiaporphyrin, tetraphenyl-	n.s.g.	435(5.47),515(4.47), 548(3.86),635(3.34), 699(3.59)	39-1066-79C
$C_{44}H_{29}ClN_4$			
21H,23H-Porphine, 2-chloro-5,10,15,20-tetraphenyl-	CH_2Cl_2	417(5.55),517(4.35), 552(3.86),595(3.81), 651(3.72)	35-3857-79
$C_{44}H_{29}N_5O_2$			
21H,23H-Porphine, 2-nitro-5,10,15,20-tetraphenyl-	CH_2Cl_2	426(5.34),527(4.18), 565(3.60)	35-3857-79
$C_{44}H_{30}$			
Hexabenzo[d,f,jk,o,q,uv]dodecalene, (all-E)-	CH_2Cl_2	280(4.84)	44-1936-79
(E,E,Z,Z)-	CH_2Cl_2	270(4.79)	44-1936-79
$C_{44}H_{30}ClN_3O$			
Oxazole, 2-[3-chloro-4-[2-[4-(1,3-diphenyl-1H-pyrazol-5-yl)phenyl-ethenyl]phenyl]-4,5-diphenyl-	DMF	370(4.73)	33-1816-79
$C_{44}H_{30}N_4$			
21H,23H-Porphine, 5,10,15,20-tetraphenyl-	benzene	419(5.67),515(4.27), 548(3.91),592(3.72), 647(3.53)	101-0311-79P
$C_{44}H_{31}N_3O$			
Isoxazole, 3-[1,1'-biphenyl]-4-yl-5-[4-[2-[4-(1,3-diphenyl-1H-pyrazol-5-yl)-phenyl]-	DMF	353(4.84)	33-1816-79
Oxazole, 2-[4-[2-[4-(1,3-diphenyl-1H-pyrazol-5-yl)phenyl]ethenyl]phenyl]-4,5-diphenyl-	DMF	369(4.80)	33-1816-79

Compound	Solvent	$\lambda_{max}(\log \epsilon)$	Ref.
$C_{44}H_{32}N_4$			
1H-Pyrazole, 3,3'-(1,2-ethenediyldi-4,1-phenylene)bis[1,5-diphenyl-	DMF	356(4.90)	33-1816-79
$C_{44}H_{34}N_2O_2$			
1,2-Diazabicyclo[4.3.1]deca-3,8-dien-10-one, 2-acetyl-6-(1-naphthalenyl)-3,5,7,9-tetraphenyl-	EtOH	254(4.50)	94-2767-79
$C_{44}H_{34}N_2Zr$			
Zirconium, bis(4-cyano-4,4-diphenyl-1-butynyl)bis(η^5-2,4-cyclopentadien-1-yl)-	$CHCl_3$	248(4.16),264(4.02), 304(3.69)	101-0353-79S
$C_{44}H_{36}N_2O$			
1,2-Diazabicyclo[4.3.1]deca-3,8-dien-10-one, 5,7-bis(4-methylphenyl)-6-(1-naphthalenyl)-3,9-diphenyl-	EtOH	246(4.43),262s(4.19), 282s(4.17),294s(4.08)	94-2767-79
$C_{44}H_{36}O_3$			
2H-Pyran-2-one, 3,4-dihydro-4-(4-methylphenyl)-3-[1-(4-methylphenyl)-3-oxo-3-phenylpropyl]-3-(1-naphthalenyl)-6-phenyl-	EtOH	224(4.84),246s(4.55), 273(4.31),285(4.28), 291s(4.22)	94-2767-79
$C_{44}H_{38}N_2O_{10}$			
Fagopyrin diacetate	pyridine	562(4.40),603(4.74)	88-1575-79
$C_{44}H_{39}N$			
1-Azaoctacyclo[10.10.10.$2^{2,5}$.$2^{8,11}$-$2^{13,16}$.$2^{19,22}$.$2^{23,26}$.$2^{29,32}$]tetratetraconta-2,4,8,10,13,15,19,21,23,25,29-31,33,35,37,39,41,43-octadecaene, 12-methyl-	$CHCl_3$	299(4.53)	88-1561-79
radical cation	$CHCl_3$	705(3.43)	88-1561-79
$C_{44}H_{40}N_4O_4$			
Cycloocta[1,2-d:5,6-d']dipyridazine, 2,3,8,9-tetraacetyl-2,3,5,6,8,9,11-12-octahydro-1,4,7,10-tetraphenyl-	MeOH	217(4.65),290(4.53)	78-0277-79
$C_{44}H_{40}O_2P_2Pt$			
Platinum, bis(3-hydroxy-1-butynyl)bis-(triphenylphosphine)-, (SP-4-1)-	$CHCl_3$	317(3.79)	101-0101-79B
$C_{44}H_{40}Zr$			
Zirconium, bis(4,4-diphenyl-1-butynyl)-bis[(1,2,3,4,5-η)-1-methyl-2,4-cyclopentadien-1-yl]-	$CHCl_3$	245(4.04),262(3.94), 304(3.35)	101-0353-79S
$C_{44}H_{44}O$			
Cyclobuta[f]benzofuran, 1,7-bis(1,1-dimethylethyl)-2,7a-dihydro-2,7a-dimethyl-2,3,5,6-tetraphenyl-	$CHCl_3$	256(4.35),275(4.32), 320s(4.06)	138-1451-79
$C_{44}H_{49}InN_4$			
Indium, [2,3,7,8,12,13,17,18-octaethyl-21H,23H-porphinato(2-)-N^{21},N^{22},N^{23}-N^{24}](phenylethynyl)-, (SP-5-31)-	benzene	345(4.49),415(5.63), 508(3.40),547(4.30), 584(4.26)	101-0311-79P

Compound	Solvent	λ_{max}(log ε)	Ref.
$C_{44}H_{51}InN_4$			
Indium, [2,3,7,8,12,13,17,18-octaethyl-21H-23H-porphinato(2-)-N^{21},N^{22},N^{23}-N^{24}](2-phenylethenyl)-, (SP-5-31)-	benzene	354(4.60),426(5.39), 514(3.30),554(4.25), 589(3.99)	101-0311-79P
$C_{44}H_{52}S_4$			
1-Buten-3-yne, tetrakis(4-tert-butylphenylthio)-	heptane	199(4.83),348(4.19)	5-1606-79
$C_{44}H_{54}N_2O_{30}$			
β-Cellotrioside, deacetyl-, 3,4-dinitrophenyl	MeOH	282(3.80)	130-0147-79
$C_{44}H_{54}O_7$			
27-Norlanosta-8,16-diene-15,23-dione, 3,28-bis(benzoyloxy)-24-methoxy-	EtOH	230(4.49)	32-0391-79
$C_{44}H_{60}CuN_4$			
Copper, [2,7,12,17-tetramethyl-3,8,13-18-tetrapentyl-21H,23H-porphinato-(2-)-N^{21},N^{22},N^{23},N^{24}]-, (SP-4-1)-	CH_2Cl_2	399(5.58),526(4.13), 562(4.43)	44-2077-79
$C_{44}H_{62}N_4$			
21H,23H-Porphine, 2,7,12,17-tetramethyl-3,8,13,18-tetrapentyl-	CH_2Cl_2	398(5.23),498(4.13), 532(4.00),567(3.84), 593(3.11),620(3.69)	44-2077-79
$C_{44}H_{78}O_3$			
2H-1-Benzopyran, 5,7-bis(hexadecyloxy)-2,2,4-trimethyl-	isooctane	233(4.65),240s(--), 278(4.41)	23-1377-79
2H-1-Benzopyran, 7,8-bis(hexadecyloxy)-2,2,4-trimethyl-	C_6H_{12}	223(4.47),272(4.04), 282s(--),300(3.59), 316s(--)	23-1377-79
	EtOH	223(4.49),272(4.03), 280s(--),300(3.60), 312s(--)	23-1377-79

Compound	Solvent	$\lambda_{max}(\log \epsilon)$	Ref.
$C_{45}H_{27}CuN_5$			
Copper, [5,10,15,20-tetraphenyl-21H-23H-porphine-2-carbonitrilato(2-)-N^{21},N^{22},N^{23},N^{24}]-, (SP-4-2)-	CH_2Cl_2	420(5.67),510(3.75), 545(4.32),583(4.10)	35-3857-79
$C_{45}H_{27}CuN_5S$			
Copper, [5,10,15,20-tetraphenyl-21H-23H-porphin-2-yl thiocyanato(2-)-N^{21},N^{22},N^{23},N^{24}]-, (SP-4-2)-	CH_2Cl_2	415(5.53),542(4.30), 575(3.67)	35-3857-79
$C_{45}H_{29}N_5S$			
Thiocyanic acid, 5,10,15,20-tetraphen-yl-21H,23H-porphin-2-yl ester	CH_2Cl_2	420(5.48),519(4.32), 554(3.66),595(3.78), 652(3.76)	35-3857-79
$C_{45}H_{31}InN_4$			
Indium, methyl[5,10,15,20-tetraphenyl-21H,23H-porphinato(2-)-N^{21},N^{22},N^{23}-N^{24}]-, (SP-5-31)-	$CHCl_3$	343(4.53),439(5.67), 538(3.60),578(4.19), 623(4.10)	101-0311-79P
$C_{45}H_{52}N_4O_8$			
5-Norcatharanthine, 3'-vindolinyl-	EtOH	225(4.73),258(4.24), 286(4.03),293(4.03), 307s(--)	23-2572-79
	EtOH-acid	262(4.32),281(4.03), 288(4.03),308(3.81)	23-2572-79
5'-Norcatharantine, 6'-vindolinyl-	EtOH	223(4.85),263(4.43), 275(4.26),283(4.23), 298(3.89)	23-2572-79
	EtOH-acid	221(4.89),272(4.51), 281(4.30),299(4.06)	23-2572-79
$C_{45}H_{60}CuN_4O$			
Copper, [2,7,12,17-tetramethyl-3,8,13-18-tetrapentyl-21H,23H-porphine-5-carboxaldehydato(2-)-N^{21},N^{22},N^{23},N^{24}]-, (SP-4-2)-	CH_2Cl_2	402(4.36),530(3.97), 567(4.16),636(3.46)	44-2077-79
$C_{45}H_{61}N_5O_8$			
Undecanoic acid, 11-(benzoylamino)-, 2-[[[11-(benzoylamino)-1-oxoundecyl]-oxy]methyl]-2,3,3a,9a-tetrahydro-6-imino-6H-furo[2',3':4,5]oxazolo[3,2-a]pyrimidin-3-yl ester, [2R-(2α,3β,3aβ,9aβ)]-, monotetrafluoro-borate	MeOH	230(4.50),265(4.11)	87-0639-79
$C_{45}H_{62}CuN_4O$			
Copper, [2,7,12,17-tetramethyl-3,8,13-18-tetrapentyl-21H,23H-porphine-5-methanolato(2-)-N^{21},N^{22},N^{23},N^{24}]-, (SP-4-2)-	CH_2Cl_2	405(5.49),533(4.07), 573(4.24)	44-2077-79
$C_{45}H_{62}N_4O$			
21H,23H-Porphine-5-carboxaldehyde, 2,7,12,17-tetramethyl-3,8,13,18-tetrapentyl-	CH_2Cl_2	402(5.07),503(3.92), 537(3.76),574(3.71), 625(3.51),657(3.20)	44-2077-79
$C_{45}H_{64}N_4O$			
21H,23H-Porphine-5-methanol, 2,7,12,17-	CH_2Cl_2	403(5.21),505(4.12),	44-2077-79

Compound	Solvent	λ_{max}(log ε)	Ref.
tetramethyl-3,8,13,18-tetrapentyl- (cont.)		541(3.94),575(3.78), 628(3.63)	44-2077-79
$C_{45}H_{65}N_5O_{10}S_2$			
Undecanoic acid, 11-[[(4-methylphenyl)-sulfonyl]amino]-, [2,3,3a,9a-tetrahydro-6-imino-3-[[11-[[(4-methylphenyl)sulfonyl]amino]-1-oxoundecyl]-oxy]-4H-furo[2',3':4,5]oxazolo[3,2-a]pyrimidin-2-yl]methyl ester, [2R-(2α,3β,3aβ,9aβ)]-	MeOH	229(4.54),264(4.14)	87-0639-79
$C_{45}H_{75}N_3O_{10}$			
Hexadecanedioic acid, 2-[[(16-ethoxy-1,16-dioxohexadecyl)oxy]methyl]-2,3-3a,9a-tetrahydro-6-imino-6H-furo-[2',3':4,5]oxazolo[3,2-a]pyrimidin-3-yl ethyl ester, monohydrochloride, [2R-(2α,3β,3aβ,9aβ)]-	MeOH	235(3.96),264(4.01)	87-0639-79
$C_{46}H_{30}Cl_2N_2O_2S_2$			
21,23-Dithiaporphyrin, α,β-bis(4-chlorophenyl)-γ,δ-bis(4-methoxyphenyl)-	n.s.g.	439(4.45),517(4.37), 555(4.00),634(3.27), 700(3.71)	39-1066-79C
$C_{46}H_{30}F_2N_2O_2S_2$			
21,23-Dithiaporphyrin, α,β-bis(4-fluorophenyl)-γ,δ-bis(4-methoxyphenyl)-	n.s.g.	438(5.46),517(4.39), 552(4.01),635(3.29), 700(3.76)	39-1066-79C
$C_{46}H_{32}N_2O_2S_2$			
21,23-Dithiaporphyrin, α,β-bis(4-methoxyphenyl)-γ,δ-diphenyl-	n.s.g.	438(5.42),516(4.37), 552(3.95),635(3.23), 700(3.69)	39-1066-79C
$C_{46}H_{33}InN_4$			
Indium, ethyl[5,10,15,20-tetraphenyl-21H,23H-porphinato(2-)-N^{21},N^{22},N^{23}-N^{24}]-, (SP-5-31)-	$CHCl_3$	355(4.56),445(5.47), 545(3.51),584(4.07), 628(4.14)	101-0311-79P
$C_{46}H_{38}N_2Zr$			
Zirconium, bis(4-cyano-4,4-diphenyl-1-butynyl)bis[(1,2,3,4,5-η)-1-methyl-2,4-cyclopentadien-1-yl]-	$CHCl_3$	250(4.18),268(4.07), 308(3.81)	101-0353-79S
$C_{46}H_{40}N_2O_4$			
2,4(1H,3H)-Pyrimidinedione, 1-[2,3-bis(triphenylmethoxy)propyl]-5-methyl-	n.s.g.	270(3.96)	128-0281-79
$C_{46}H_{40}P_2Pt$			
Platinum, bis(3-methyl-3-buten-1-ynyl)-bis(triphenylphosphine)-, (SP-4-1)-	$CHCl_3$	341(4.05)	101-0101-79B
$C_{46}H_{41}BOSe_2$			
Dimethylselenonium (benzoyldiphenylselenoniomethylide), tetraphenylborate	n.s.g.	257s(3.932),264(3.925), 272s(3.968)	104-0332-79
$C_{46}H_{42}N_2O_6$			
1,2-Ethenediamine, N,N'-bis[bis[4-meth-	n.s.g.	278(4.55),413(3.68)	88-1619-79

Compound	Solvent	λ_{max}(log ϵ)	Ref.
oxyphenyl)methylene]-1,2-bis(4-methoxyphenyl)- (cont.)			88-1619-79
$C_{46}H_{44}O_2P_2Pt$			
Platinum, bis(4-hydroxy-1-pentynyl)-bis(triphenylphosphine)-, (SP-4-1)-	$CHCl_3$	319(3.77)	101-0101-79B
$C_{46}H_{50}O_{25}$			
Tamarixetin 7-O-rutinoside, peracetate	MeOH	228(4.208),255(4.044), 315(4.22)	102-1248-79
$C_{46}H_{54}N_4O_{10}$			
Leurosine, 19'-oxo-	EtOH	214(4.66),262(4.13), 284(4.05),294(4.00), 309s(3.74)	23-1682-79
$C_{46}H_{54}N_4O_{11}$			
4',5'-Secovincaleukoblastine, 4'-deoxy-3',4',5'-trioxo-	EtOH	207(4.70),260(4.20), 277(4.11),293(4.03), 308(3.70)	23-1682-79
$C_{46}H_{56}N_4O_9$			
Leurosidine, 19'-oxo-4'-deoxy-	EtOH	212(4.72),263(4.13), 284(4.08),294(4.03), 311(3.92)	23-1682-79
$C_{46}H_{56}N_4O_{11}$			
4',5'-Secovincaleukoblastine, 4'-deoxy-3'-hydroxy-4',5'-dioxo-, (3'R)-	EtOH	212(4.72),268(4.19), 284(4.14),294(4.08), 310(3.80)	23-1682-79
$C_{46}H_{56}N_4O_{14}$			
21H-Biline-3,8,13,17-tetrapropanoic acid, 10,23-dihydro-2,7,8-tris(2-methoxy-2-oxoethyl)-1,12-dimethyl-, tetramethyl ester, dihydrobromide	$CHCl_3$-HBr	372(4.17),457(4.46), 523(5.15)	39-1927-79C
$C_{46}H_{58}N_4O_{11}$			
4',5'-Secovincaleukoblastine, 3'-hydroxy-5'-oxo-, (3'R,4'ξ)-	EtOH	212(4.65),267(4.11), 284(4.06),295(4.00), 310(3.65)	23-1682-79
$C_{46}H_{60}ClFeN_8O_2$			
Hemin di-(6-aminohexyl)amide, hydrochloride	$CHCl_3$-EtOH	399(5.05),475(3.88), 547(3.69),590(3.63), 640(3.32)	104-0741-79
$C_{47}H_{25}CoN_7$			
Cobalt, [5,10,15,20-tetraphenyl-21H-23H-porphine-2,7,12-tricarbonitrilato(2-)-N^{21},N^{22},N^{23},N^{24}]-, (SP-4-2)-	CH_2Cl_2	433(5.03),612(4.17), 635(4.13)	35-3857-79
$C_{47}H_{35}InN_4$			
Indium, (1-methylethyl)[5,10,15,20-tetraphenyl-21H,23H-porphinato(2-)-N^{21},N^{22},N^{23},N^{24}]-, (SP-5-31)-	$CHCl_3$	383(4.82),451(5.31), 550(3.57),590(4.07), 636(4.18)	101-0311-79P
$C_{47}H_{56}N_2O_{14}$			
Hedamycin, 3',3",11-tri-O-acetyl-	EtOH	213(4.55),240(4.56), 263(4.55),369(3.94)	33-2525-79

Compound	Solvent	$\lambda_{max}(\log \epsilon)$	Ref.
$C_{47}H_{57}N_5O_{10}$			
2H-Isoindole-2-undecanoic acid, 1,3-dihydro-1,3-dioxo-, 2-[[[11-(1,3-dihydro-1,3-dioxo-2H-isoindol-2-yl)-1-oxoundecyl]oxy]methyl]-2,3,3a,9a-tetrahydro-6-imino-6H-furo[2',3'-4,5]oxazolo[3,2-a]pyrimidin-3-yl ester, [2R-(2α,3β,3aβ,9aβ)]-	MeOH	220(4.83),234s(4.48), 242s(4.35),267(4.00)	87-0639-79
$C_{47}H_{66}N_4O_2$			
21H,23H-Porphine-5-methanol, 2,7,12,17-tetramethyl-3,8,13,18-tetrapentyl-	CH_2Cl_2	404(5.20),506(4.12), 541(3.97),576(3.78), 629(3.72)	44-2077-79
$C_{47}H_{68}N_4O$			
21H,23H-Porphine, 5-(ethoxymethyl)-2,7,12,17-tetramethyl-3,8,13,18-tetrapentyl-	CH_2Cl_2	404(5.19),505(4.07), 540(3.90),575(3.77), 628(3.60),659(2.85)	44-2077-79
$C_{48}H_{24}$			
Kekulene	$C_6H_3Cl_3$ (1,2,4)	320(5.2),388(4.3)	89-0699-79
$C_{48}H_{24}FeN_8$			
Iron(1+), [5,10,15,20-tetraphenyl-21H-23H-porphine-2,7,12,17-tetracarbonitrilato(2-)-N^{21},N^{22},N^{23},N^{24}]-, chloride, (SP-4-1)-	CH_2Cl_2	433(4.95),675(4.29)	35-3857-79
$C_{48}H_{24}MnN_8$			
Manganese(1+), [5,10,15,20-tetraphenyl-21H,23H-porphine-2,7,12,17-tetracarbonitrilato(2-)-N^{21},N^{22},N^{23},N^{24}]-, chloride, (SP-4-1)-	CH_2Cl_2	400(4.81),510(5.11), 610(4.07),675(4.15), 713(4.33)	35-3857-79
$C_{48}H_{32}$			
[2_4](2,6)Naphthalenophanetetraene	C_6H_{12} or EtOH	335(4.13)	1-0443-79
$C_{48}H_{36}N_2O_4S_2$			
21,23-Dithiaporphyrin, tetrakis(4-methoxyphenyl)-	n.s.g.	441(4.43),519(4.34), 555(4.07),638(3.20), 704(3.76)	39-1066-79C
$C_{48}H_{36}N_5S$			
1H-Naphth[2,3-d]imidazolium, 2-[3-[5-(2-benzothiazolyl)-3-ethyl-1,3-dihydro-1-phenyl-2H-benzimidazol-2-ylidene]-1-propenyl]-1,3-diphenyl-, iodide	n.s.g.	544(5.24)	124-0043-79
$C_{48}H_{37}InN_4$			
Indium, butyl[5,10,15,20-tetraphenyl-21H,23H-porphinato(2-)-N^{21},N^{22},N^{23}-N^{24}]-, (SP-5-31)-	$CHCl_3$	356(4.63),445(5.53), 544(3.56),583(4.13), 627(4.18)	101-0311-79P
Indium, (1,1-dimethylethyl)[5,10,15,20-tetraphenyl-21H,23H-porphinato(2-)-N^{21},N^{22},N^{23},N^{24}]-, (SP-5-31)-	$CHCl_3$	393(5.00),453(5.13), 551(3.58),592(3.99), 639(5.14)	101-0311-79P
$C_{48}H_{40}N_2O_{16}$			
[12,12'-Biindolo[2,1-a]isoquinoline]-	EtOH	228(4.67),257(4.48),	142-1413-79

Compound	Solvent	λ$_{max}$(log ε)	Ref.
2,2',3,3',9,9',10,10'-octol, 5,5',6-6'-tetrahydro-, octaacetate (cont.)		332(4.64)	142-1413-79
$C_{48}H_{40}N_4O_8P_4$			
1,3,5,7,2,4,6,8-Tetraazatetraphosphocine, 2,2,4,4,6,6,8,8-octahydro-2,2,4,4,6,6,8,8-octaphenoxy-	EtOAc	253.7(3.38)(not a max.)	116-0108-79
$C_{48}H_{42}N_2O_{12}$			
Fagopyrin tetraacetate	$CHCl_3$	468(4.50),549(4.32), 591(4.56)	88-1575-79
$C_{48}H_{42}S_6$			
Benzene, hexakis[(4-methylphenyl)thio]-	CCl_4	325(2.16)	39-1011-79B
$C_{48}H_{46}Br_2N_4$			
Quinolinium, 1,1'-(1,2-ethanediyl)bis-[6-bromo-4-[3-(1,3-dihydro-1,3,3-trimethyl-2H-indol-2-ylidene)-1-propenyl]-, salt with 4-methylbenzenesulfonic acid (1:2)	EtOH	575(4.92),636(5.24)	104-0566-79
$C_{48}H_{46}N_6O_4$			
Quinolinium, 1,1'-(1,2-ethanediyl)bis-[4-[3-(1,3-dihydro-1,3,3-trimethyl-2H-indol-2-ylidene)-1-propenyl]-6-nitro-, salt with 4-methylbenzenesulfonic acid (1:2)	EtOH	575(4.84),638(5.14)	104-0566-79
$C_{48}H_{50}ClFeN_{10}O_6$			
Iron, chloro[[dimethyl N,N'-[(7,12-diethenyl-3,8,13,17-tetramethyl-21H-23H-porphine-2,18-diyl)bis[(1-oxo-3,1-propanediyl)imino]]bis[L-histidinato]](2-)]-	$CHCl_3$-EtOH	404(4.99),484(4.08), 595(3.76)	104-0741-79
$C_{48}H_{58}ClFe N_6O_6$			
Iron, chloro[methyl 7-[[3-[7,12-diethenyl-18-[3-[[1-(methoxycarbonyl)-3-(methylthio)propyl]amino]-3-oxopropyl]-3,7,13,17-tetramethyl-21H,23H-porphin-2-yl]-1-oxopropyl]amino]-heptanoato(2-)-N^{21},N^{22},N^{23},N^{24}]-	$CHCl_3$-EtOH	402(5.25),469(4.14), 495(4.15),592(3.89)	104-0741-79
$C_{48}H_{58}N_4O_{12}$			
4',5'-Secovincaleukoblastine, 3'-acetoxy-4'-deoxy-4',5'-dioxo-, (3'R)-	EtOH	213(4.73),270(4.21), 285(4.17),294(4.10), 310(3.81)	23-1682-79
$C_{48}H_{58}N_4O_{16}$			
21H-Biline-3,7,12,17-tetrapropanoic acid, 10,24-dihydro-1-(methoxycarbonyl)-2,13,18-tris(2-methoxy-2-oxoethyl)-8,19-dimethyl-, tetramethyl ester, dihydrobromide	$CHCl_3$-HBr	373(4.11),456(4.57), 526(5.07)	39-1927-79C
$C_{48}H_{80}MgN_{16}$			
Porphyrazine, octakis(tert-butylamino)-, magnesium complex	$CHCl_3$	346(5.08),623(4.95)	104-0962-79

Compound	Solvent	λ_{max}(log ϵ)	Ref.
$C_{48}H_{84}N_6$			
[1,1':2',1"-Tercyclopropene]-3,3',3"-triylium, 3'-[bis[bis(1-methylethyl)-amino]cyclopropenyliumyl]-2,2",3,3"-tetrakis[bis(1-methylethyl)amino]-, (deloc-1,2,3"1',2',3':1",2",3")-, tetraperchlorate	n.s.g.	347(4.52)	89-0473-79
$C_{49}H_{35}N_4$			
1H-Naphth[2,3-d]imidazolium, 2-[3-(1,3-dihydro-1,3-diphenyl-2H-naphth[2,3-d]imidazol-2-ylidene)-1-propenyl]-1,3-diphenyl-, iodide	n.s.g.	542(5.23)	124-0043-79
$C_{49}H_{45}NO_2S$			
2H-Cyclobut[f]isoindole, 4,7-bis(1,1-dimethylethyl)-2-[(4-methylphenyl)-sulfonyl]-1,3,5,6-tetraphenyl-	$CHCl_3$	243(4.43),260(4.42), 309(4.55),377(3.86)	138-1451-79
$C_{49}H_{50}N_9O_{13}P$			
Uridine, P-(2-cyanoethyl)-2'-deoxy-5,6-[(1,2-dimethyl-1,2-ethenediyl)dinitrilo]-5,6-dihydrouridylyl-(5'→3')-2'-deoxy-5,6-[(1,2-dimethyl-1,2-ethenediyl)dinitrilo]-5,6-dihydro-5'-O-[(4-methoxyphenyl)diphenylmethyl]-	MeOH	234(4.65),256(4.70), 270s(4.69),325(4.19)	33-1179-79
$C_{49}H_{62}O_{27}$			
Cantleyoside octaacetate	MeOH	233(4.24)	102-0273-79
$C_{49}H_{66}N_{14}O_{13}S$			
α-Melanotropin(pig), 2-de-L-tyrosine-3-de-L-serine-11-de-L-lysine-12-de-L-proline-13-de-L-valinamide-, monohydrochloride	pH 13	280(3.74),289(3.71)	33-2460-79
$C_{50}H_{20}CoN_8O_8$			
Cobalt, [[5,5'-(29H,31H-phthalocyanine-diyl)dicarbonyl]bis[1,3-isobenzofurandionato]](2-)-N^{29},N^{30},N^{31},N^{32}]-	N-Mepyrrolidone	330(3.81),608(3.55), 660(3.84),678(3.38)	126-2073-79
$C_{50}H_{20}CuN_8O_8$			
Copper, [[5,5'-(29H,31H-phthalocyanine-diyl)dicarbonyl]bis[1,3-isobenzofurandionato]](2-)-N^{29},N^{30},N^{31},N^{32}]-	N-Mepyrrolidone	350(3.74),610(3.53), 640(3.86),675(3.97), 683(3.95)	126-2073-79
$C_{50}H_{20}N_8NiO_8$			
Nickel, [[5,5'-(29H,31H-phthalocyanine-diyl)dicarbonyl]bis[1,3-isobenzofurandionato]](2-)-N^{29},N^{30},N^{31},N^{32}]-	N-Mepyrrolidone	340(3.64),605(3.46), 635(3.52),670(3.92), 680(3.85)	126-2073-79
$C_{50}H_{22}CoN_{10}O_6$			
Cobalt, [[5,5'-(29H,31H-phthalocyanine-diyl)dicarbonyl]bis[1H-isoindole-1,3-(2H)-dionato]](2-)-N^{29},N^{30},N^{31},N^{32}]-	N-Mepyrrolidone	328(3.64),596(3.16), 634(3.27),664(3.73),	126-2073-79
$C_{50}H_{22}CuN_{10}O_6$			
Copper, [[5,5'-(29H,31H-phthalocyanine-diyl)dicarbonyl]bis[1H-isoindole-1,3-(2H)-dionato]](2-)-N^{29},N^{30},N^{31},N^{32}]-	N-Mepyrrolidone	342(3.36),610(3.11), 638(3.18),674(3.59), 680(3.70)	126-2073-79

Compound	Solvent	$\lambda_{max}(\log \epsilon)$	Ref.
$C_{50}H_{22}N_{10}NiO_6$			
Nickel, [[5,5'-(29H,31H-phthalocyanine-diyl)dicarbonyl]bis[1H-isoindole-1,3-(2H)-dionato]](2-)-N^{29},N^{30},N^{31},N^{32}]-	N-Mepyrrol-idone	326(3.18),600(2.98), 630(2.99),664(3.37)	126-2073-79
$C_{50}H_{33}InN_4$			
Indium, phenyl[5,10,15,20-tetraphenyl-21H,23H-porphinato(2-)-N^{21},N^{22},N^{23}-N^{24}]-, (SP-5-31)-	$CHCl_3$	343(4.56),439(5.73), 535(3.53),577(4.23), 619(4.17)	101-0311-79P
$C_{50}H_{52}N_4$			
Quinolinium, 1,1'-(1,2-ethanediyl)bis-[4-[3-(1,3-dihydro-1,3,3-trimethyl-2H-indol-2-ylidene)-1-propenyl]-6-methyl-, salt with 4-methylbenzene-sulfonic acid (1:2)	EtOH	588(4.98),642(5.25)	104-0566-79
$C_{50}H_{52}N_4O_2$			
Quinolinium, 1,1'-(1,2-ethanediyl)bis-[4-[3-(1,3-dihydro-1,3,3-trimethyl-2H-indol-2-ylidene)-1-propenyl]-6-methoxy-, salt with 4-methylbenzene-sulfonic acid (1:2)	EtOH	587(4.72),644(5.08)	104-0566-79
$C_{50}H_{56}N_2O_{21}$			
Cathedulin E4, 2-deacetyl-	EtOH	215(4.51),267(4.07), 295s(3.73)	39-2982-79C
$C_{50}H_{62}N_4O_{13}$			
4',5'-Secovincaleukoblastine, 3'-acet-oxy-5'-oxo-, 4'-acetate, (3'R,4'ξ)-	EtOH	212(4.67),269(4.10), 284(4.08),294(4.03), 309(3.70)	23-1682-79
$C_{50}H_{64}O_8$			
Naphth[2",1":4',5']indeno[2',1':1,2]-naphtho[1',2':7,8]fluoreno[3,4-c]-furan-7(1H)-one, 2,4-diacetoxy-6b-(2,5-dihydro-5-oxo-3-furanyl)-2,3,4-4a,4b,5,6,6a,6b,6c,9,9c,10,11,11a-11b,12,13,14,15,15a,16,17,17a,18a-18b,19b,20,21,21a-triacontahydro-4a,6a,9c,11b-tetramethyl-	EtOH	214(4.21)	94-2975-79
$C_{50}H_{68}O_{10}$			
16,17-Dehydrodigitoxigenin, 3-acetate, dimer	EtOH	217(4.20)	94-2975-79
$C_{50}H_{80}O_{28}$			
Pregn-16-en-20-one, 3-[(O-β-D-glucopyr-anosyl-(1→2)-O-β-D-glucopyranosyl-(1→2)-O-[β-D-xylopyranosyl-(1→3)]-O-β-D-glucopyranosyl-(1→4)-β-D-galacto-pyranosyl)oxy]-2,6-dihydroxy-, (2α,3β,5α,6β)-	EtOH	239(3.84)	105-0446-79
$C_{51}H_{36}ClN_4$			
1H-Naphth[2,3-d]imidazolium, 2-[3-chlo-ro-5-(1,3-dihydro-1,3-diphenyl-2H-naphth[2,3-d]imidazol-2-ylidene)-1,3-pentadienyl]-1,3-diphenyl-, iodide	n.s.g.	631(5.50)	124-0043-79

Compound	Solvent	λmax(log ε)	Ref.
$C_{51}H_{37}N_4$			
1H-Naphth[2,3-d]imidazolium, 2-[5-(1,3-dihydro-1,3-diphenyl-2H-naphth[2,3-d]imidazol-2-ylidene)-1,3-pentadienyl]-1,3-diphenyl-, iodide	n.s.g.	640(5.48)	124-0043-79
$C_{51}H_{39}N_5O_2S$			
Benzenesulfonamide, N-(12,13-dihydro-5,10,15,20-tetraphenyl-21H,23H-porphin-21-yl)-4-methyl-	toluene	427(5.12),442(5.15), 550s(3.96),568(4.09), 582(4.15),634(4.10)	78-1455-79
$C_{51}H_{47}N_{10}O_{12}P$			
Adenosine, P-(2-cyanoethyl)-2'-deoxy-5,6-(1,2-ethenediyldinitrilo)-5,6-dihydrouridylyl-(5'→-3')-N-benzoyl-2'-deoxy-5'-O-[(4-methoxyphenyl)diphenylmethyl]-	MeOH	231(4.61),278(4.33), 318(3.89)	33-1179-79
$C_{51}H_{60}N_4O_7$			
Vobasan-17-oic acid, 3-[18-[[(3,4-dimethoxybenzoyl)oxy]methyl]-12-methoxyibogamin-13-yl]-, methyl ester	EtOH	218(4.77),263(4.31), 288(4.29)	36-1403-79
$C_{52}H_{28}N_4Zn$			
Zinc, [37H,39H-tetranaphtho[2,3-b:2',3'-g:2",3"-l:2"',3"'-q]porphinato(2-)-N^{37},N^{38},N^{39},N^{40}]-, (SP-4-2)-	DMF	439(4.67),640(3.83), 667(3.79),701(4.82)	65-2467-79
$C_{52}H_{33}InN_4$			
Indium, (phenylethynyl)[5,10,15,20-tetraphenyl-21H,23H-porphinato(2-)-N^{21},N^{22},N^{23},N^{24}]-, (SP-5-31)-	benzene	322(4.36),432(5.51), 528(3.57),568(4.32), 610(4.08)	101-0311-79P
$C_{52}H_{35}InN_4$			
Indium, (2-phenylethenyl)[5,10,15,20-tetraphenyl-21H,23H-porphinato(2-)-N^{21},N^{22},N^{23},N^{24}]-, (SP-5-31)-	$CHCl_3$	340(4.51),439(5.70), 538(3.54),578(4.21), 621(4.14)	101-0311-79P
$C_{52}H_{40}P_2Pt$			
Platinum, bis(phenylethynyl)bis(triphenylphosphine)-	$CHCl_3$	348(4.39)	101-0101-79B
$C_{52}H_{42}N_4$			
1H-Pyrazole, 1,1'-[1,4-phenylenebis(2,1-ethenediyl-4,1-phenylene)]bis[4,5-dihydro-3,5-diphenyl-	n.s.g.	430(4.9)	103-0435-79
$C_{52}H_{52}CuN_4$			
Copper, [2,9,16,23-tetrakis(1,1-dimethylethyl)-29H,31H-tetrabenzo[b,g,l,q]-porphinato(2-)-N^{29},N^{30},N^{31},N^{32}]-, (SP-4-1)-	benzene	394(4.68),420(5.23), 459(4.69),570(4.18), 624(4.98),638(4.46)	104-0570-79
$C_{52}H_{52}N_4Ni$			
Nickel, [2,9,16,23-tetrakis(1,1-dimethylethyl)-29H,31H-tetrabenzo[b,g,l,q]-porphinato(2-)-N^{29},N^{30},N^{31},N^{32}]-, (SP-4-1)- (also other metal chelates)	benzene	416(5.27),474(4.46), 566(4.25),622(5.02)	104-0570-79
$C_{52}H_{52}N_4Zn$			
Zinc, [2,9,16,23-tetrakis(1,1-dimethyl-	hexane	233(5.12),252s(4.75),	104-0570-79

Compound	Solvent	$\lambda_{max}(\log \epsilon)$	Ref.
ethyl)-29H,31H-tetrabenzo[b,g,l,q]-porphinato(2-)-N^{29},N^{30},N^{31},N^{32}]-, (SP-4-1)-		262s(4.74),267s(4.73), 316(4.53),401(5.03), 412(5.38),453(4.17), 577(4.17),623(5.07)	104-0570-79
$C_{52}H_{54}N_4$			
29H,31H-Tetrabenzo[b,g,l,q]porphine, 2,9,16,23-tetrakis(1,1-dimethylethyl)-	hexane	230(4.98),239(4.62), 250(4.62),271(4.58), 340(4.29),382(4.72), 387(4.70),411(5.35), 426(5.33),446(4.61), 542(3.95),555(3.97), 568f(3.97),594(4.84), 602(4.69),610f(4.48), 662(4.81)	104-0570-79
$C_{52}H_{58}N_2O_{22}$			
Cathedulin E4	EtOH	215(4.61),268(4.08)	39-2965-79C
$C_{52}H_{62}O_{24}$			
9H-Xanthen-9-one, 1-hydroxy-7-methoxy-2,8-bis(3-methyl-2-butenyl)-3,6-bis-[(2,3,4,6-tetra-O-acetyl-β-D-glucopyranosyl)oxy]-	EtOH	240(4.45),261(4.52), 304(4.32),355(3.78)	100-0361-79
$C_{52}H_{63}N_6O_{12}P$			
5'-Thymidylic acid, monoanhydride with N,N'-dicyclohexylcarbamimidic acid, 2-(3,4-dihydro-5-methyl-2,4-dioxo-1(2H)-pyrimidinyl)-1-[(triphenylmethoxy)methyl]ethyl ester, 3'-acetate	n.s.g.	268(4.08)	128-0281-79
$C_{52}H_{64}N_4O_{14}$			
4',5'-Secovincaleukoblastine, 3'-acetoxy-5'-oxo-, 3,4'-diacetate, (3'R-4'ξ)-	EtOH	212(4.70),267(4.15), 284(4.11),294(4.06), 310(3.73)	23-1682-79
$C_{52}H_{73}BrN_4O_{16}$			
Decobalto-10-bromo-5,6-dioxomonosecocobyrinic acid, heptamethyl ester	MeOH	252(4.04),346(3.99)	5-0811-79
$C_{52}H_{74}N_4O_{16}$			
Decobalto-5,6-dioxomonosecocobyrinic acid, heptamethyl ester	MeOH	260(4.08),373(4.14)	5-0811-79
$C_{52}H_{76}CuN_4$			
Copper, [2,7,12,17-tetraheptyl-3,8,13-18-tetramethyl-21H,23H-porphinato-(2-)-N^{21},N^{22},N^{23},N^{24}]-, (SP-4-1)-	CH_2Cl_2	398(5.59),525(4.13), 561(4.43)	44-2077-79
$C_{52}H_{78}N_2O_4$			
3H-Indol-3-one, 2-[1,3-dihydro-3-oxo-1-(1-oxooctadecyl)-2H-indol-2-ylidene]-1,2-dihydro-1-(1-oxooctadecyl)-, cis	benzene benzene	435(3.59) 437(3.59)	18-3397-79 25-0415-79
trans	benzene	567(3.85)	18-3397-79 +25-0415-79
$C_{52}H_{78}N_4$			
21H,23H-Porphine, 2,7,12,17-tetraheptyl-3,8,13,18-tetramethyl-	CH_2Cl_2	398(5.23),497(4.15) 531(4.01),566(3.83),	44-2077-79

Compound	Solvent	λ_{max}(log ε)	Ref.
(cont.)		593(3.11),620(3.72)	44-2077-79
$C_{52}H_{81}N_7O_{13}$ Echinocandin D	MeOH	193(4.98),224s(4.12), 278(3.24)	33-1252-79
$C_{52}H_{81}N_7O_{15}$ Echinocandin C	MeOH	193(4.97),226s(4.12), 278(3.20)	33-1252-79
$C_{52}H_{81}N_7O_{16}$ Echinocandin B	MeOH	194(5.01),226s(4.13), 276(3.17)	33-1252-79
$C_{52}H_{85}N_7O_{13}$ Echinocandin D, tetrahydro-	MeOH	193(4.94),224s(4.02), 278(3.20)	33-1252-79
$C_{52}H_{85}N_7O_{15}$ Echinocandin C, tetrahydro-	MeOH	194(4.92),227s(4.09), 278(3.27)	33-1252-79
$C_{52}H_{85}N_7O_{16}$ Echinocandin B, tetrahydro-	MeOH	194(4.88),227s(4.03), 277(3.12)	33-1252-79
$C_{53}H_{39}N_4$ 1H-Naphth[2,3-d]imidazolium, 2-[7-(1,3-dihydro-1,3-diphenyl-2H-naphth[2,3-d]imidazol-2-ylidene)-1,3,5-heptatrienyl]-1,3-diphenyl-, iodide	n.s.g.	745(5.47)	124-0043-79
$C_{53}H_{41}N_4O_2$ 1H-Naphth[2,3-d]imidazolium, 2-[5-(1,3-dihydro-1,3-diphenyl-2H-naphth[2,3-d]imidazol-2-ylidene)-3-(2-hydroxyethoxy)-1,3-pentadienyl]-1,3-diphenyl-, iodide	n.s.g.	652(5.48)	124-0043-79
$C_{53}H_{51}N_{10}O_{12}P$ Adenosine, P-(2-cyanoethyl)-2'-deoxy-5,6-[(1,2-dimethyl-1,2-ethenediyl)-dinitrilo]-5,6-dihydrouridylyl-(5'→3')-N-benzoyl-2'-deoxy-5'-O-[(4-methoxyphenyl)diphenylmethyl]-	MeOH	230(4.66),280(4.43), 325(3.95)	33-1179-79
$C_{53}H_{62}N_2O_{23}$ 2-Pyridinepropanoic acid, 3-(methoxycarbonyl)-α,β-dimethyl-, 19,20-diacetoxy-24-(2-acetoxy-2-methyl-1-oxopropoxy)-5,14,15,17,18,19,20,23-octahydro-17,25-dihydroxy-15-(hydroxymethyl)-8,27-dimethoxy-15,17-dimethyl-11,23-dioxo-7,10-etheno-13,20a-14,16-dimethano-11H,13H,21H-[1,5]-[11,16]benzotetraoxacyclononadecino-[14,13-c]pyridin-18-yl ester	EtOH	215(4.59),267(4.10), 291s(3.74)	39-2982-79C
$C_{53}H_{65}N_6O_{12}P$ 5'-Thymidylic acid, (cyclohexylamino)-(cyclohexylimino)methyl, 1-[(3,4-di-	EtOH	269(4.22)	128-0051-79

Compound	Solvent	$\lambda_{max}(\log \epsilon)$	Ref.
hydro-5-methyl-2,4-dioxo-1(2H)-pyrimidinyl)methyl]-3-(triphenylmethoxy)propyl ester, 3'-acetate (cont.)			128-0051-79
$C_{53}H_{76}CuN_4O$			
Copper, [2,7,12,17-tetraheptyl-3,8,13-18-tetramethyl-21H,23H-porphine-5-carboxaldehydato(2-)-N[21],N[22],N[23]-N[24]]-, (SP-4-2)-	CH_2Cl_2	404(5.38),530(4.00), 567(4.18),634(3.49)	44-2077-79
$C_{53}H_{78}N_4O$			
21H,23H-Porphine-5-carboxaldehyde, 2,7,12,17-tetraheptyl-3,8,13,18-tetramethyl-	CH_2Cl_2	403(5.13),504(3.97), 538(3.83),573(3.77), 626(3.58),659(3.30)	44-2077-79
$C_{53}H_{80}N_4O$			
21H,23H-Porphine-5-methanol, 2,7,12,17-tetraheptyl-3,8,13,18-tetramethyl-	CH_2Cl_2	404(5.22),506(4.13), 542(3.93),576(3.79), 628(3.64)	44-2077-79
$C_{54}H_{36}O_2$			
9,11:15,17:26,28:32,34-Tetraetheno-12H,14H,29H,31H-tetraindeno[2,1-e:1',2'-f:2",1"-o:1"',2"'-p][1,11]-dioxacycloeicosin, [4bS-(4bR*,21bR*)]-	MeCN	241(4.72),267(4.77), 277(4.76),299(4.43), 311(4.64)	33-2285-79
$C_{54}H_{40}$			
1,3,5-Hexatriene, 1,1,2,3,4,5,6,6-octaphenyl-	ether	254(4.74),318(4.64), 380(4.46)	104-1867-79
$C_{54}H_{44}O_2P_2Pt$			
Platinum, bis(3-hydroxy-3-phenyl-1-propynyl)bis(triphenylphosphine)-, (SP-4-1)-	$CHCl_3$	313(3.92)	101-0101-79B
$C_{54}H_{60}N_2O_{23}$			
Cathedulin E3	EtOH	215(4.61),268(4.11), 293s(3.77)	39-2965-79C
$C_{54}H_{60}N_4P$			
Phosphonium, (2,3,7,8,12,13,17,18-octaethyl-21H,23H-porphin-5-yl)triphenyl-, chloride	CH_2Cl_2	421(5.07),608(3.91), 677(4.22)	35-5953-79
$C_{54}H_{62}N_2O_{23}$			
Evonine, O^9,O^{15}-dideacetyl-8-deoxy-8-[(4-hydroxy-3,5-dimethoxybenzoyl)-oxy]-, 9-(2-acetoxy-2-methylpropanoate) 15-(4-methyl-3-pyridinecarboxylate), (8α)-	EtOH	221(4.52),275(4.10), 285s(4.06)	39-2982-79C
	EtOH-NaOH	213s(4.46),262s(3.83), 337(4.28)	39-2982-79C
$C_{54}H_{72}BrCoN_6O_{16}$			
Monosecocobyrinic acid, 10-bromodicyano-5,6-dioxo-, heptamethyl ester	MeOH	337(4.13),509(4.05)	5-0811-79
$C_{54}H_{73}CoN_6O_{16}$			
Monosecocobyrinic acid, dicyano-5,6-dioxo-, heptamethyl ester	MeOH	269(3.79),288(3.70), 326(3.77),481(3.74)	5-0811-79

Compound	Solvent	λ_{max}(log ϵ)	Ref.
$C_{54}H_{76}O_{12}$			
Digitoxigenin, 16,17-dehydro-21-ethoxy-, 3-acetate, dimer, (R)-	EtOH	213(4.07)	94-2975-79
(S)-	EtOH	212(4.10)	94-2975-79
$C_{54}H_{86}O_{27}S$			
Holothurin A, sodium salt	MeOH	none above 210 nm	88-1419-79
$C_{55}H_{82}N_4O_2$			
21H,23H-Porphine-5-methanol, 2,7,12,17-tetraheptyl-3,8,13,18-tetramethyl-, acetate	CH_2Cl_2	404(5.23),506(4.13), 542(3.98),576(3.79), 629(3.72)	44-2077-79
$C_{56}H_{40}$			
5,36[1',2']:18,23[1",2"]-Dibenzeno-10,13:28,31-diethenodibenzo[a,q]-cyclodotriacontene, (E,E,E,E,Z,Z,Z,Z)-	C_6H_{12}	260(5.16)	1-0464-79
$C_{56}H_{43}N_4$			
1H-Naphth[2,3-d]imidazolium, 2-[2-[3-[(1,3-dihydro-1,3-diphenyl-2H-naphth-[2,3-d]imidazol-2-ylidene)ethylid-ene]-1-cyclohexen-1-yl]ethenyl]-1,3-diphenyl-, iodide	n.s.g.	755(5.55)	124-0043-79
$C_{56}H_{56}P_2Pt$			
Platinum, di-1,9-decadiynylbis(triphen-ylphosphine)-, (SP-4-1)-	$CHCl_3$	323(3.76)	101-0101-79B
$C_{56}H_{70}N_2O_{38}$			
β-Cellotetraoside, 3,4-dinitrophenyl, trideca-O-acetyl deriv.	MeOH	284(3.8)	130-0147-79
$C_{56}H_{80}N_{14}O_{14}S$			
Glycine, N-[N-[N^2-[N-[N-[N-[N-[(1,1-di-methylethoxy)carbonyl]-L-seryl-L-methionyl]-L-α-glutamyl]-L-histi-dyl]-L-phenylalanyl]-L-arginyl]-L-tryptophyl]-, 5-(1,1-dimethylethyl) ester, monohydrochloride	M HOAc	280(3.73)	33-2460-79
$C_{56}H_{88}MgN_8S_8$			
Magnesium, [2,3,7,8,12,13,17,18-octa-kis[(1,1-dimethylpropyl)thio]-21H-23H-porphyrazinato(2-)-N^{21},N^{22},N^{23}-N^{24}]-, (SP-4-1)-	$CHCl_3$	365(4.98),651(4.90)	104-0962-79
$C_{57}H_{62}N_2O_{22}$			
Cathedulin E6	EtOH	217(4.66),265(4.25), 287s(3.83)	39-2965-79C
$C_{58}H_{44}O_4$			
9,11:18,20:29,31:38,40-Tetraetheno-12H,17H,32H,37H-tetraindeno[2,1-h:1',2'-i:2",1"-u:1"',2"'-v][1,4-14,17]tetraoxacyclohexacosin, 14,15,34,35-tetrahydro-, [4bS-(4bR*,24bR*)]-	MeCN	221(4.99),242(4.64), 267(4.66),278(4.64), 299(4.29),311(4.47)	33-2285-79

Compound	Solvent	λ_{max}(log ϵ)	Ref.
$C_{58}H_{104}N_4O_4$			
2,6(1H,3H)-Pyridinedione, 1-dodecyl-5-(dodecylamino)-3-[1-dodecyl-5-(dodecylamino)-1,6-dihydro-2,6-dioxo-3(2H)-pyridinylidene]-	$CHCl_3$	285(3.02),635(3.30)	118-0948-79
$C_{61}H_{45}N_4$			
1H-Naphth[2,3-d]imidazolium, 2-[2-[3-[(1,3-dihydro-1,3-diphenyl-2H-naphth-[2,3-d]imidazol-2-ylidene)ethylidene]-2-phenyl-1-cyclopenten-1-yl]-ethenyl]-1,3-diphenyl-, iodide	n.s.g.	801(5.53)	124-0043-79
$C_{61}H_{74}Cl_2O_{33}$			
Flambamycin	EtOH	288(3.24)	78-0105-79
$C_{61}H_{78}N_6O_{12}$			
21H-Biline-2,7,13,17-tetrapropanoic acid, 5,15,19,23-tetrahydro-19-[[4-(3-methoxy-3-oxopropyl)-5-[[4-(3-methoxy-3-oxopropyl)-3,5-dimethyl-1H-pyrrol-2-yl]methyl]-2-methyl-1H-pyrrol-2-yl]methylene]-1,3,8,12,18-pentamethyl-, tetramethyl ester, dihydrobromide	$CHCl_3$-HBr	368(4.18),448(4.64), 528(4.79)	104-0970-79
$C_{61}H_{88}Cl_2O_{32}$			
Avilamycin A	MeOH	227(4.15),286(3.33), 300s(3.1)	33-0001-79
$C_{61}H_{90}Cl_2O_{32}$			
Avilamycin C	MeOH	228(4.12),284(3.33), 300s(3.12)	33-0001-79
$C_{62}H_{30}CoN_{10}O_6$			
Cobalt, [5,5'-(29H,31H-phthalocyanine-diyldicarbonyl)bis[2-phenyl-1H-isoindole-1,3(2H)-dionato]]-	N-Mepyrrolidone	330(3.74),605(3.36), 635(3.46),666(3.93), 683(3.90)	126-2073-79
$C_{62}H_{30}CuN_{10}O_6$			
Copper, [5,5'-(29H,31H-phthalocyanine-diyldicarbonyl)bis[2-phenyl-1H-isoindole-1,3(2H)-dionato]]-	N-Mepyrrolidone	342(3.73),611(3.48), 636(3.50),673(3.92), 682(3.86)	126-2073-79
$C_{62}H_{30}N_{10}NiO_6$			
Nickel, [5,5'-(29H,31H-phthalocyanine-diyldicarbonyl)bis[2-phenyl-1H-isoindole-1,3(2H)-dionato]]-	N-Mepyrrolidone	325(3.52),610(3.33), 638(3.40),665(3.80)	126-2073-79
$C_{62}H_{52}O_6$			
9,11:21,23:32,34:44,46-Tetraetheno-12H,20H,35H,43H-tetraindeno[2,1-k:1',2'-1:2",1"-a_1:1"',2"'-b_1]-[1,4,7,17,20,23]hexaoxacyclodotriacontin, 14,15,17,18,37,38,40,41-octahydro-, [4bS-(4bR*,27bR*)]-	MeCN	221(4.97),242(4.61), 267(4.64),277(4.63), 299(4.28),311(4.45)	33-2285-79
$C_{62}H_{62}ClO_2P_2Rh$			
Rhodium, chloro[4,4'-(η^2-1,2-ethenediylidene)bis[2,6-bis(1-methylethyl)-2,5-cyclohexadien-1-one]]bis(triphenylphosphine)-	$CHCl_3$	265(--),350(--), 525(--),547(4.53)	35-4888-79

Compound	Solvent	λ_{max}(log ε)	Ref.
$C_{62}H_{86}N_{12}O_{16}$			
Actinomycin D	$CHCl_3$	424(4.33),442(4.36)	87-0797-79
$C_{63}H_{55}N_{10}O_{12}P$			
3'-Adenylic acid, N-benzoyl-2'-deoxy-5'-O-[(4-methoxyphenyl)diphenylmethyl]-, mono(2-cyanoethyl) ester, 3'→5'-ester with 1-(2-deoxy-β-D-erythro-pentofuranosyl)-6,7-diphenyl-2,4(1H,3H)-pteridinedione	MeOH	228(4.66),278(4.49), 361(4.07)	33-1179-79
5'-Adenylic acid, N-benzoyl-2'-deoxy-, mono(2-cyanoethyl) ester, 5'→3'-ester with 1-[2-deoxy-5-O-[(4-methoxyphenyl)diphenylmethyl]-β-D-erythro-pentofuranosyl]-6,7-diphenyl-2,4(1H,3H)-pteridinedione	MeOH	228(4.76),278(4.59), 360(4.11)	33-1179-79
$C_{64}H_{56}Cu_4N_8O_{20}$			
Copper, [μ_3-[2-[[(2-hydroxyphenyl)methylene]amino]-1-(4-nitrophenyl)-1,3-propanediolato(2-)]]tetra-	DMSO	270(4.25),362(4.29), 622(2.17)	94-1245-79
$C_{64}H_{86}N_{12}O_{17}$			
L-Valine, L-threonyl-D-valyl-L-prolyl-N-methylglycyl-N-methyl-, ξ-lactone, 1,1'-diamide with 10,12-dimethyl-2-oxo-2H,6H-1,4-oxazino[3,2-b]phenoxazine-5,7-dicarboxylic acid	$CHCl_3$	394(3.90),501(3.67)	87-0797-79
$C_{65}H_{87}FN_{12}O_{17}$			
L-Valine, L-threonyl-D-valyl-L-prolyl-N-methylglycyl-N-methyl-, ξ-lactone, 1,1'-diamide with 3-(fluoromethyl)-10,12-dimethyl-2-oxo-2H,6H-1,4-oxazino[3,2-b]phenoxazine-5,7-dicarboxylic acid	$CHCl_3$	526(3.84)	87-0797-79
$C_{65}H_{88}N_{12}O_{17}$			
L-Valine, [(3,10,12-trimethyl-2-oxo-2H,6H-1,4-oxazino[3,2-b]phenoxazine-5,7-diyl)dicarbonyl]bis[1-threonyl-D-valyl-L-prolyl-N-methylglycyl-N-methyl-, di-ξ-lactone	$CHCl_3$	320(3.94),393(3.79), 495(3.86)	87-0797-79
$C_{66}H_{70}ClO_2P_2Rh$			
Rhodium, chloro[4,4'-(η^2-1,2-ethenediylidene)bis[2,6-bis(1,1-dimethylethyl)-2,5-cyclohexadien-1-one]]-bis(triphenylphosphine)	$CHCl_3$	263(--),345(--), 510(--),540(4.55)	35-4888-79
$C_{66}H_{88}N_{12}O_{19}$			
L-Valine, L-threonyl-D-valyl-L-prolyl-N-methylglycyl-N-methyl-, ξ-lactone, (1→5)(1'→7)-diamide with 3-(carboxymethyl)-10,12-dimethyl-2-oxo-2H,6H-1,4-oxazino[3,2-b]phenoxazine-5,7-dicarboxylic acid	$CHCl_3$	320(3.94),395(3.81), 500(3.85)	87-0797-79
$C_{66}H_{90}N_{12}O_{17}$			
L-Valine, L-threonyl-D-valyl-L-prolyl-	$CHCl_3$	316(3.98),488(3.85)	87-0797-79

Compound	Solvent	$\lambda_{max}(\log \epsilon)$	Ref.
N-methylglycyl-N-methyl-, ξ-lactone, 1,1'-diamide with 3-ethyl-10,12-dimethyl-2-oxo-2H,6H-1,4-oxazino[3,2-b]phenoxazine-5,7-dicarboxylic acid (cont.)			87-0797-79
$C_{67}H_{90}N_{12}O_{19}$			
L-Valine, L-threonyl-D-valyl-L-prolyl-N-methylglycyl-N-methyl-, ξ-lactone, (1→5),(1'→7)-diamide with 3-(2-carboxyethyl)-10,12-dimethyl-2-oxo-2H-6H-1,4-oxazino[3,2-b]phenoxazine-5,7-dicarboxylic acid	$CHCl_3$	351(3.94),398(3.95), 509(3.91)	87-0797-79
$C_{67}H_{99}N_{19}O_{18}S_2$			
L-Valinamide, L-seryl-L-methionyl-L-α-glutamyl-L-histidyl-L-phenylalanyl-L-arginyl-L-tryptophylglycyl-N^6-[[2-(methylsulfonyl)ethoxy]carbonyl]-L-lysyl-L-prolyl-, dihydrochloride	M HOAc	280(3.83),289(3.68)	33-2460-79
$C_{68}H_{48}Cl_8N_8O_4$			
4,14,24,34,41,44,46,48-Octaazanonacyclo[$34.4.2^{2,35}.2^{5,12}.2^{15,22}.2^{25,32}.0.0^{6,11}.0^{16,21}.0^{26,31}$]octatetraconta-2(42),6,8,10,12(47),16,18,20,22(45)-26,28,30,32(43),36,38,40-hexadecaene-3,13,23,33-tetrone	CH_2Cl_2	235(4.6),269(4.5), 322(4.6)	64-1593-79B
$C_{68}H_{50}$			
1,3,5,7-Octatetraene, 1,1,2,3,4,5,6-7,8,8-decaphenyl-	ether	254(4.92),356(4.04)	104-1867-79
$C_{70}H_{90}N_{12}O_{17}$			
L-Valine, L-threonyl-D-valyl-L-prolyl-N-methylglycyl-N-methyl-, ξ-lactone, 1,1'-diamide with 10,12-dimethyl-2-oxo-3-phenyl-2H.6H-1,4-oxazino[3,2-b]phenoxazine-5,7-dicarboxylic acid	$CHCl_3$	349(4.11),527(3.83)	87-0797-79
$C_{71}H_{102}N_{13}O_{17}$			
Actinomycin D, N-(2,2,6,6-tetramethyl-1-oxo-4-piperidinyl)-	pH 7.4	198(4.86),248(4.51), 434(4.24)	87-1051-79
	MeOH	245(4.57),435(4.20), 455(4.19)	87-1051-79
$C_{72}H_{101}N_{19}O_{16}S$			
L-Valinamide, N-[3-(4-hydroxyphenyl)-1-oxopropyl]-L-seryl-L-methionyl-L-α-glutamyl-L-histidyl-L-phenylalanyl-L-arginyl-L-tryptophylglycyl-L-lysyl-L-prolyl-, diacetate	M HOAc	280(3.83)	33-2460-79
$C_{72}H_{105}N_{15}O_{20}S_2$			
Glycine, N-[N-[N^2-[N-[N-[N-[N-[N-[N-[N-[(1,1-dimethylethoxy)carbonyl]-L-seryl-L-tyrosyl]-L-seryl-L-methionyl]-L-α-glutamyl]-L-histidyl]-L-phenylalanyl]-L-arginyl]-L-leucyl]-, 5-(1,1-dimethylethyl) 1-[2-[(4-methylphenyl)sulfonyl]ethyl] ester, hydrochloride	M HOAc	269(3.19),275(3.23), 283s(3.03)	33-2452-79

Compound	Solvent	λ_{max}(log ε)	Ref.
$C_{72}H_{110}N_{20}O_{19}S$			
α-Melanotropin (pig), 9-L-leucine, diacetate	M HOAc	276(3.21)	33-2452-79
$C_{73}H_{107}N_{14}O_{17}$			
Actinomycin D, N-[2-[(2,2,6,6-tetramethyl-1-oxo-4-piperidinyl)amino]-ethyl]-	pH 7.7	199(4.83),240(4.38), 442(4.07)	87-1051-79
	MeOH	245(4.38),435(4.04)	87-1051-79
$C_{74}H_{102}I_2N_{20}O_{17}$			
L-Valinamide, N-acetyl-3,5-diiodo-L-tyrosyl-L-seryl-L-norvalyl-L-α-glutamyl-L-histidyl-L-phenylalanyl-L-arginyl-L-tryptophylglycyl-L-lysyl-L-prolyl-, diacetate	pH 13	280(3.82),289(3.79)	33-2460-79
$C_{74}H_{102}I_2N_{20}O_{17}S$			
L-Valinamide, N-acetyl-3,5-diiodo-L-tyrosyl-L-seryl-L-methionyl-L-α-glutamyl-L-histidyl-L-phenylalanyl-L-arginyl-L-tryptophylglycyl-L-lysyl-L-prolyl-, dihydrochloride	M HOAc	280(3.85)	33-2460-79
$C_{74}H_{104}N_{20}O_{17}$			
L-Valinamide, N-acetyl-L-tyrosyl-L-seryl-L-norvalyl-L-α-glutamyl-L-histidyl-L-phenylalanyl-L-arginyl-L-tryptophylglycyl-L-lysyl-L-prolyl-, diacetate	pH 13	280(3.94),289(3.81)	33-2460-79
$C_{74}H_{104}N_{20}O_{17}S$			
L-Valinamide, N-acetyl-L-tyrosyl-L-seryl-L-methionyl-L-α-glutamyl-L-histidyl-L-phenylalanyl-L-arginyl-L-tryptophylglycyl-L-lysyl-L-prolyl-, diacetate	pH 13	280(3.83),289s(3.91)	33-2460-79
$C_{74}H_{109}N_{14}O_{17}$			
Actinomycin D, N-[3-[(2,2,6,6-tetramethyl-1-oxy-4-piperidinyl)amino]-propyl]-	pH 7.7	199(4.76),243(4.43), 361(4.25),443(4.02)	87-1051-79
	MeOH	245(4.46),359(4.27), 431(4.01)	87-1051-79
$C_{76}H_{46}N_4$			
21H,23H-Porphine, 5,10,15,20-tetra-9-anthracenyl-	$CHCl_3$	427(5.51),519(4.60), 550(4.20),594(4.18), 658(4.23)	88-3725-79
$C_{76}H_{64}Cl_8N_8O_{12}$			
4,14,24,34,41,44,46,48-Octaazanonacyclo[$34.4.2^{2,35}.2^{5,12}.2^{15,22}.2^{25,32}.0.0^{6,11}.0^{16,21}.0^{26,31}$]octatetraconta-2(42),6,8,10,12(47),16,18,20,22(45)-26,28,30,32(43),36,38,40-hexadecaene-3,13,23,33-tetrone	CH_2Cl_2	231(4.6),252(4.7), 327(4.4)	64-1593-79B
$C_{76}H_{115}N_{19}O_{20}S_2$			
L-Valinamide, N-[(1,1-dimethylethoxy)-carbonyl]-L-seryl-L-methionyl-L-α-glutamyl-L-histidyl-L-phenylalanyl-	M HOAc	280(3.73)	33-2460-79

Compound	Solvent	$\lambda_{max}(\log \epsilon)$	Ref.
L-arginyl-L-tryptophylglycyl-N^6-[[2-(methylsulfonyl)ethoxy]carbonyl]-L-lysyl-L-prolyl-, 1,1-dimethylethyl ester, monohydrochloride (cont.)			33-2460-79
$C_{77}H_{107}I_2N_{21}O_{19}S$			
α-Melanotropin (pig), 1-(N-acetyl-D-serine-2-(3,5-diiodo-L-tyrosine)-diacetate	M HOAc	281(3.86),288(3.83)	33-2460-79
	pH 13	281(3.80),289(3.81), 310(3.70)	33-2460-79
$C_{77}H_{108}IN_{21}O_{19}S$			
α-Melanotropin (pig), 2-(3-iodo-L-tyrosine)-, diacetate	pH 13	281(3.82),289(3.82)	33-2460-79
$C_{77}H_{109}N_{21}O_{19}S$			
α-Melanotropin, 1-(N-acetyl-D-serine)-, diacetate	pH 13	281(3.84),289(3.82)	33-2460-79
$C_{83}H_{130}N_{20}O_{24}S_2$			
α^{1-13}-Corticotropin, N-[(1,1-dimethylethyl)carbonyl]-9-L-leucine-11-[N -[[2-(methylsulfonyl)ethoxy]carbonyl]-L-lysine]-13-L-valinamide, 1,1-dimethylethyl ester, hydrochloride	M HOAc	275(3.20)	33-2452-79
$C_{84}H_{66}N_{12}O_6$			
Diazene, [1,2,3,4,5,6-benzenehexaylhexakis(methyleneoxy-4,1-phenylene)]-hexakis[phenyl-	$CHCl_3$	341(5.07),440(4.02)	88-2335-79
$C_{86}H_{124}IN_{21}O_{21}S$			
α-Melanotropin (pig), 2-(3-iodo-L-tyrosine)-11-[N^6-[(1,1-dimethylethoxy)-carbonyl]-L-lysine]-, 1,1-dimethylethyl ester, monohydrochloride	10% HOAc	281(3.81),288(3.76)	33-2460-79
$C_{88}H_{127}I_2N_{21}O_{24}S_2$			
α^{1-13}-Corticotropin, 1-[N-[(1,1-dimethylethoxy)carbonyl]-D-serine]-2-(3,5-diiodo-L-tyrosine)-11-[N^6-[[2-(methylsulfonyl)ethoxy]carbonyl]-L-lysine]-13-L-valinamide-, 1,1-dimethylethyl ester	M HOAc	281(3.91)	33-2460-79
$C_{124}H_{124}N_{12}O_{32}$			
Nonacyclo[43.3.1.1^{3,7}.1^{9,13}.1^{15,19}.1^{21,25}.1^{27,31}.1^{33,37}.1^{39,43}]hexapentaconta-1(49),3,5,7(56),9,11,13-(55),15,17,19(54),21,23,25(53),27-29,31(52),33,35,37(51),39,41,43(50)-45,47-tetracosaene-49,50,51,52,53-54,55,56-octol, 5,11,17,23,29,35-41,47-octakis(1,1-dimethylethyl)-, hexakis(2,4-dinitrophenyl) ether	MeCN	218(4.93),249(4.56), 280(4.64)	44-3962-79

1- -79, Acta Chem. Scand. B, 33 (1979)
0006 J. Gripenberg et al.
0057 H. Lund and C. Degrand
0079 G. Barta-Szalai et al.
0138 P. Kolsaker and P.O. Ellingsen
0256 T. Olsson and O. Wennerström
0271 H.-E. Högberg and P. Komlos
0277 C.J. Calleman and C.A. Wachtmeister
0294 H. Hjeds and P. Krogsgaard-Larsen
0299 T. Laerum et al.
0305 J. Becher
0307 J.E. Mänsson et al.
0313 A. Osbirk and E.B. Pedersen
0319 K.G. Jensen and E.P. Pedersen
0365 H. Breivik et al.
0391 K. Ankner et al.
0405 J. Bergman et al.
0443 D. Tanner et al.
0460 Ø.H. Johansen and K. Undheim
0464 D. Tanner et al.
0515 M. Gacek and K. Undheim
0551 J. Johansen and S. Liaaen-Jensen
0695 J.R. Andersen et al.

1- 79A, Acta Chem. Scand. A, 33 (1979)
0137 K.A. Jensen and E. Larsen

2- 79A, Indian J. Chem. Sect. B, 17 (1979)
0037 S.R. Gupta et al.
0067 M.C. Moorjani et al.
0078 P.P. Pai and G.H. Kulkarni
0079 M. Pardhasaradhi and B.M. Choudary
0100 N.R. Ayyangar et al.
0111 P. Bhattacharyya et al.
0113 J. Banerji et al.
0123 A.C. Jain et al.
0140 N.R. Ayyangar et al.
0168 D. Kumari et al.
0175 A. Patra et al.
0198 A.S. Shirwaiker and A.B. Kulkarni
0202 P.A. Ganeshpure
0222 A.K. Sen and G. Chattopadhyay
0226 A. Mitra and M.D. Gupta
0250 P. Unnikrishnan et al.
0295 B.H. Bhide and V.P. Gupta
0298 S.K. Talapatra et al.
0299 P.N. Sharma et al.
0324 S.R. Ramadas and P.K. Sujeeth
0349 P. Hanumanthu and C.V. Ratnam
0360 A.R. Modi and R.N. Usgaonkar
0385B A. Patra et al.
0410 A.S. Gupta and J.R. Merchant
0415 K.V. Sastry et al.
0430 V.H. Belgaonkar and R.N. Usgaonkar
0503 B.R. Pai et al.
0523 R.P. Soni and J.P. Saxena
0525 B.R. Pai et al.
0538B S. Dasgupta and A.B. Ray
0541 A. Chatterjee et al.
0585 I.I. Abd El-Gawad et al.
0593 S.H. Etaiw et al.
0638 A. Patra et al.
0642 U.C. Mashelkar and R.N. Usgaonkar
0651 A. Chatterjee et al.

2- -79A', Indian J. Chem. Sect A, 17 (1979)
0502 M.S. Masoud et al.

2- -79B, Indian J. Chem. Sect. B, 18 (1979)
0011 K.L. Bhat et al.
0016 R.B. Gupta and R.N. Khanna
0039 P.B. Talukdar et al.
0071 P.B. Kelkar et al.
0076 S.C. Chibber and R.P. Sharma
0082 A. Chatterjee and J. Padhi
0087 A. Chatterjee and S. Bandyopadhyay
0112 A.S.R. Anjaneyulu et al.
0115 N.S. Narasimhan et al.
0122 E.I. Enayat and H.A. Abdel-Hamid
0131 N. Latif et al.
0152 V. Dabral, H. Ila and N. Anand
0180 M.V. Naidu and G.S.K. Rao
0183 P.C. Chakroborti
0195 N.R. Ayyangar et al.
0233 A. Mitra and S.B. Das
0292 A.S.R. Anjaneyulu and NM.N. Rao
0307 A.K. Sen and G. Chattopadhyay
0320 G.B.V. Subramanian et al.
0338 A.A.H. Saeed and G.Y. Matti
0456 S.S. Patwardhan and R.N. Usgaonkar
0504 P. Sengupta et al.
0513 C.B. Rao et al.
0525 D. Roy and R.N. Khanna
0529 C.S.R. Iyer et al.
0552 D. Adinarayana and D. Gunasekar
0552B D. Roy and R.N. Khanna

2- -79B', Indian J. Chem. Sect. A, 18 (1979)
0480 D. Roy

3- -79, Anal. Chem., 51 (1979)
0007 D.F. Fritz et al.

4- -79, J. Heterocyclic Chem., 16 (1979)
0001 Y.A. Al-Farkh et al.
0033 S.Sunder and N.P. Peet
0065 J.P. Chupp and S. Metz
0081 G. Alonso et al.
0087 D.R. Elmaleh et al.
0093 A. Bargagna et al.
0123 A.S. Shawali, A.A. Fahmi and N.F. Eweiss
0133 J.H. Maguire and R.L. McKee
0137 G. Bernath et al.
0177 L. Mosti, P. Schenone and G. Menozzi
0183 C.H. Chen and B.A. Donatelli
0217 F. Evangelisti et al.
0225 L.R. Caswell et al.
0239 T.J. Delia and W.D. Munslow
0253 D. Donati et al.
0257 J.R. Patton and K.H. Dudley
0293 S. Romani et al.
0297 F. Morlacchi et al.
0339 R.F. Lauer and G. Zenchoff
0353 J.A. Montgomery and H.J. Thomas
0403 R. Milcent and C. Redeuilh
0411 H. Tanaka and T. Ueda
0413 G. Cauquis et al.

0417 M. Poje and K. Balenovic
0427 J. Daunis et al.
0433 G.R. Lenz
0449 S.S. Parmar and S.P. Singh
0471 V. Horak et al.
0481 H. Feuer et al.
0487 Y. Kawase et al.
0505 S. Gelin and P. Pollet
0517 T. Yamazaki et al.
0527 T. Yamazaki et al.
0555 C.A. Lovelette
0567 K. Anzai
0591 G. Bettoni et al.
0599 L.H. Klemm and R.F. Lawrence
0625 S.P. Singh et al.
0637 T. Terasawa and T. Okada
0657 C. Deshayes and S. Gelin
0689 M. Iwao and T. Kuraishi
0737 I.E. El-Kholy et al.
0763 P. Catsoulacos and D. Kallias
0807 D.A. Smith and T.L. Spencer
0811 B.S. Huang et al.
0835 O. Migliara et al.
0839 H. Stetter and A. Landscheidt
0849 I.E. El-Kholy et al.
0913 L. Mosto, P. Schenone and G. Menozzi
0945 F.A. Devillanova and G. Verani
0949 V. Shankarnarayan and J.R. Merchant
1001 F. Sparatore and R. Cerri
1005 R. Cerri, A. Boido and F. Sparatore
1009 S. Mataka et al.
1025 C.O. Okafor
1049 E.K. Ryu and T.J. Bardos
1059 C.V. Greco and J.R. Mehta
1081 P.M. Weintraub
1105 O. Migliara, S. Petruso and V. Sprio
1113 J. Kagan and B, Melnick
1117 G. Gelin et al.
1153 J.S. Amato et al.
1169 J. Matsumoto, S. Mishio and S. Minami
1185 G. Gosselin et al.
1217 D. Maume et al.
1235 T. Nakano and A. Martin
1281 J.H. Looker et al.
1335 B. Chantegrel and S. Gelin
1353 H. Agui and T. Nakagome
1365 F. Yoneda et al.
1385 G. Elitropi and S. Tricerri
1423 T.P. Culbertson
1455 M.J. Winchester
1477 L. Baiocchi, G. Picconi and G. Palazzo
1525 G. Bobowski et al.
1545 G. Elitropi, E. Panto and S. Tricerri
1575 T. Kato et al.
1579 E. Barni and P. Savarino
1583 E. Barni and P. Savarino
1611 C. Bellec et al.
1645 J.C. Parham et al.
1649 C.A. Lovelette

5- -79, Ann. Chem. Liebigs (1979)
0019 K. Krohn and C. Hemme
0035 K. Krohn and C. Hemme
0063 H. Gotthardt and F. Reiter
0083 H. Quast et al.
0162 T. Patonay et al.
0174 G. Litkei et al.
0248 W. Walter and O.H. Bauer
0297 W. Tochtermann and H. Maasland
0503 M. Pardo et al.
0533 P. Hildenbrand
0554 D. Dopp and E. Brugger
0564 R. Buck et al.
0595 R. Matusch et al.
0608 G. Rucker and U. Molls
0617 S.R. Kuhlmey et al.
0650 H. Gotthardt and F. Reiter
0656 G. Ege et al.
0675 M. Bachmann and H. Neunhoeffer
0727 S. Hunig and W. Schenk
0769 P. Dimroth and V. Radtke
0811 R.P. Hinze et al.
0927 P. Rosenmund and E. Jadri
0959 R. Neidlein and E. Bernhard
0965 R. Neidlein and L. Seguil-Carnargo
0973 C. Engelfried et al.
1048 H.-J. Teuber et al.
1067 W.-R. Knappe
1085 K.-D. Gundermann and H. Giesecke
1212 H. Budzikiewicz et al.
1258 H.A. Staab and V.M. Schwendemann
1370 K.W. Henneke et al.
1388 R. Gompper and U. Wolf
1406 R. Gompper and U. Wolf
1440 G. Bartels
1443 P. Studt
1518 S. Romani et al.
1534 K. Gewald and P. Bellmann
1560 H. Falk and T. Schlederer
1606 A. Roedig and G. Zaby
1614 A. Roedig and G. Zaby
1626 A. Roedig and G. Zaby
1643 P. Rosenmund et al.
1657 W. Böll and H. König
1696 F. Lübbe et al.
1702 E. Schaumann and F.-F. Grabley
1715 E. Schaumann and F.-F. Grabley
1785 I. Mester et al.
1789 R. Neidlein and L. Seguil-Camargo
1802 R.W. Grauert
1855 W. Kohler and W. Pfleiderer
1872 K. Ienaga and W. Pfleiderer
1890 P. Eilbracht and P. Dahler
1945 M. Baumann et al.
1992 U. Jürgens et al.
2018 K. Krohn and A. Rösner

7- -79, Ann. chim.(Rome), 69 (1979)
0563 L. Pentimalli and G. Milani

9- -79, Appl. Spectroscopy, 33 (1979)
0561 D.M. Rackham

12- -79, Australian J. Chem., 32 (1979)
0071 T. Amatayakul et al.
0133 W.H. Cherry et al.
0145 W.H. Cherry and Q.N. Porter
0179 P.S. Cooper et al.
0217 R.M. Carman and J.K.L. Maynard

0345 L.K. Dyall and C.J. Pullin
0361 D.N. Leach and J.A. Reiss
0399 I.A. Blair and C.J. Seaborn
0459 G.B. Barlin
0545 I.H. Pitman and N.B. Juin
0575 D.W. Cameron et al.
0597 G.J. Bird et al.
0611 G.J. Bird et al.
0643 L.K. Dyall
0653 B.F. Bowden et al.
0681 R. Olstein and E.F.M. Stephenson
0779 J.W. Blunt et al.
0817 A.L. Cossey et al.
0823 L.N. Mander and L.T. Palmer
0849 M.G. Banwell and B. Halton
0867 R. Kazlauskas et al.
1067 J.R. Davy et al.
1079 K.G. Lewis and C.E. Mulquiney
1093 D.J. Collins and W.A. Matthews
1107 D.J. Collins et al.
1159 M. Fawzy El-Newaihy et al.
1231 H.-D. Becker et al.
1241 H.J.J.-B. Martel et al.
1273 A. Ahond et al.
1281 D.J. Bell et al.
1307 K. Healey and I.C. Calder
1487 R.K. Norris and D. Randles
1521 H.C. Bell et al.
1531 H.C. Bell et al.
1551 H.C. Bell et al.
1561 H.C. Bell et al.
1601 D.E. Rivett et al.
1627 E.L. Ghisalberti et al.
1709 P.J. Newcombe and R.K. Norris
1727 K.-C. Chang et al.
1749 E.R. Cole et al.
1767 R.J. Armstrong et al.
1775 D. St.C. Black et al.
1785 D. St.C. Black et al.
1795 D. St.C. Black and N.A. Blackman
1827 I.R.C. Bick et al.
1841 R.G. Cooke and I.J. Dagley
1949 R.K. Norris and R.J. Smyth-King
2003 E. Dimitriadis and R.A. Massy-Westropp
2017 J.F. Kinnear et al.
2025 D.St.C. Black et al.
2035 D.St.C. Black and N.A. Blackman
2041 D.St.C. Black et al.
2049 W.B. Cowden and N.W. Jacobsen
2059 A.D. Woolhouse
2071 I.R.C. Bick et al.
2079 K.D. Croft et al.
2203 M.R. Grimmett et al.
2265 B.F. Bowden et al.
2303 D. St.C. Black et al.
2317 R.W. Read and W.C. Taylor
2323 P. Bogan and R.E. Gall
2413 R.K. Norris and D. Randles
2483 R.A. Eade and H.-P. Pham
2495 P.W. Freeman et al.
2507 R.D. Allan et al.
2523 I.R.C. Bick et al.
2537 I.R.C. Bick et al.
2545 P. Bates et al.
2637 R.F. Martin and D.P. Kelly
2647 P.J. Newcombe and R.K. Norris
2659 R.N. Warrener et al.
2675 R. Bishop and A.E. Landers
2681 A. Castonguay and Y. Berger
2689 M.G. Banwell and B. Halton
2713 D.J. Brown et al.
2735 R.W. Dunlop et al.
2771 J.H. Lister
2793 R.C. Cambie et al.

13- -79A, Steroids, 33 (1979)
0153 S.R. Ramadas and S. Padmanabhan
0295 G. Halperin
0361 G.V. Bhide
0467 M. Mori et al.
0601 P.S. Jogdeo and G.V. Bhide

13- -79B, Steroids, 34 (1979)
0199 D.F. Covey
0347 M. Numazawa and Y. Osawa
0361 W.-H. Chiu and M.E. Wolff
0485 K.M. Lewis and R.D. Archer
0619 P.S. Jogdeo and G.V. Bhide
0729 P.S. Jogdeo and G.V. Bhide
0793 J. Muller and J.E. Herz

18- -79, Bull. Chem. Soc. Japan, 52 (1979)
0107 K. Imatuki et al.
0111 K. Imatuku et al.
0127 T. Masamune et al.
0135 T. Masamune et al.
0151 T. Toda et al.
0160 H. Nakazumi and T. Kitao
0175 R. Okazaki et al.
0181 T. Sugimoto and S. Matsuura
0204 T. Tanabe et al.
0208 H. Takei et al.
0253 A. Mukoh et al.
0257 S. Kurokawa and A.G. Anderson, Jr.
0259 T. Tanabe et al.
0329 A. Kuboyama
0462 M. Nakatani and T. Hase
0496 R. Okazaki et al.
0516 Y. Inukai et al.
0529 K. Kurosawa and F. Araki
0584 B.K. Deshmukh and R.B. Kharat
0608 A.K. Banerjee et al.
0641 U. Tsuge and H. Watanabe
0789 A. Yabe
0801 H. Tanaka et al.
0811 K. Kusuda and A. Roedig
0856 K. Komatsu et al.
0867 T. Sugimoto et al.
0930 S. Smolinski and A. Czarny
1126 T. Sone et al.
1153 T. Suga and T. Hirata
1156 T. Nozoe et al.
1165 F. Ogura et al.
1182 Y. Ishizaki et al.
1203 A.C. Jain et al.
1549 K. Kohara et al.
1573 K. Yasukouchi et al.
1588 T. Kubota et al.
1601 Y. Tanimoto et al.
1748 S. Kurokawa
1796 A. Kuboyama and H. Matsumoto

1853 K. Mukai et al.
1867 T. Tezuka and T. Nozoe
1911 K. Mukai
1964 A. Horinaka and K. Naya
1972 A. Yamane et al.
1998 Y. Inagaki et al.
2002 Y. Inagaki et al.
2023 T. Uyehara et al.
2033 R.P. Soni and J.P. Saxena
2169 Y. Itoh et al.
2173 K.K. Bhattacharya and P.K. Sen
2372 A. Horinaka et al.
2447 K. Imafuku et al.
2596 H. Obara et al.
2657 Y. Inukai et al.
2794 H. Suzuki et al.
2933 T. Sugimoto et al.
2950 T. Horie et al.
2962 T. Uyehara et al.
3015 T. Kishi et al.
3019 Y. Miyagi et al.
3096 R.P. Soni and J.P. Saxena
3123 T. Someya et al.
3127 T. Tsuyuki et al.
3129 T. Sato et al.
3208 K. Yasukouchi et al.
3314 M. Kubo and T. Sato
3355 T. Uyehara and Y. Kitahara
3397 Y. Omote et al.
3597 T. Ibata and R. Sato
3615 Y. Inagaki et al.
3640 K.-T. Kang et al.
3728 M.N. Basyouni and A. El-Khamry
3755 H. Hirota et al.
3765 M. Oda and Y. Kanao
3767 I. Shibuya

19- -79, Bull. Acad. Polon. Sci., Ser. Chim., 27 (1979)
0045 E. Dawidziak et al.
0109 W.Z. Antkowiak and S. Szwarc
0249 D. Maciejewska and L. Skulski
0665 W. Jasiobedzki and J. Wozniak-Kornacka
0793 E. Wagner and M.K. Kalinowski

20- -79, Bull. soc. chim. Belges, 88 (1979)
0071 J.C. Brackman et al.
0087 L. De Taeye et al.
0093 P. Sarlet and J. Hannart
0883 S.M. Al-Mousawi et al.
0905 G. Beynon et al.

22- -79, Bull. soc. chim. France, Pt. II, (1979)
0015 J. Garnero and D. Joulai
0017 M. Genas et al.
0048 A.M. Giroud and A. Rassat
0056 J. Favero et al.
0110 A. Defoin and J. Rigaudy
0119 M. Hauteville and J. Chopin
0125 M. Hauteville et al.
0145 G. Cauquis and D. Serve
0157 J. Canceill et al.
0373 R. Martin
0401 D. Martin-Borret et al.
0520 B. Rouot and G. Leclerc
0559 J. Cossy and J.P. Pete
0627 M. Pfau et al.
0651 M. Cariou

22- -79I, Bull. soc. chim. France, Part I, (1979)
0241 D. Troy et al.
0375 D. Fompeydie et al.

23- -79, Can. J. Chem., 57 (1979)
0044 B. Gregory et al.
0222 T.W. Doyle et al.
0227 T.W. Doyle et al.
0274 M.J. Robins et al.
0289 J.P. Kutney et al.
0300 J.P. Kutney et al.
0360 M. Mukai et al.
0506 R.S. McDonald and E.V. Martin
0558 T.S. Cameron et al.
0904 P.J. Fagan et al.
0999 E. Buncel et al.
1186 W.J. Leigh and D.R. Arnold
1377 H.P. Pommier et al.
1403 J.A. Pincock and K.P. Murray
1451 G.A. Poulton et al.
1569 D. Dime and S. McLean
1638 R. Brunner et al.
1642 J.W. Skiles et al.
1647 P. Chinnasamy and M. Shamma
1682 J.P. Kutney et al.
1694 P.K. Battey et al.
1707 R.E. Schwartz et al.
1932 G.H. Hakimelahi and G. Just
1939 G.H. Hakimelahi and G. Just
1980 J.T. Edward and S.C. Wong
2260 R.A. McClelland et al.
2325 R.J. Andersen and R.J. Stonard
2512 E. Buncel et al.
2572 R.Z. Andriamialisoa et al.
2593 P. Aleksandrowicz et al.
2669 T.J. Greenhough et al.
2734 F.H. Al-Hajjar et al.
2804 C.O. Bender and S.F. O'Shea
2853 P. Yates and H. Akusi
3296 C.A. Demerson and L.G. Humber
3308 J. Das et al.
3332 W.A. Ayer and S.P. Lee

24- -79, Chem. Ber., 112 (1979)
0001 W.P.K. Girke
0138 M. Altzmüller and F. Vögtle
0175 G. Boche and D. Martens
0260 H. Gotthardt et al.
0266 H. Gotthardt and F. Reiter
0310 G. Quinkert et al.
0349 R. Neidlein and G. Humburg
0376 E. Medina and G. Spiteller
0389 G. Speier and Z. Tyeklar
0445 H. Hansen et al.
0484 K. Klemm et al.
0517 J. Goerdeler and W. Lobach
0532 A. Malchow et al.
0567 K. Bertsch et al.

0577 J. Mettay et al.
0625 R. Mengel and W. Muhs
0700 F. Seela et al.
0734 D. Schumann et al.
0781 H. Hofmann and H. Gaube
0799 U. Lüpke and F. Seela
0862 H.D. Scharf et al.
0957 A. Zeeck et al.
0979 K. Kieslich et al.
0990 G. Seitz et al.
1088 H. Richter and G. Spiteller
1102 A.Q. Hussein et al.
1110 A. Mondon et al.
1126 A. Mondon et al.
1168 F.G. Klärner et al.
1193 H. Gotthardt and F. Reiter
1206 H. Gotthardt and F. Reiter
1226 S. Hünig and G. Schenk
1272 K. Dimroth et al.
1329 A. Mondon and H.J. Nestler
1348 W.P.K. Girke
1473 H. Bauer et al.
1477 F.A. Neugebauer and H. Fischer
1495 M. Braun
1499 Z. Kazimierczuk and W. Pfleiderer
1514 R. Gompper and K. Schönfinger
1529 R. Gompper and K. Schönfinger
1535 R. Gompper and K. Schönfinger
1550 W. Gramlich and H. Plieninger
1571 W. Gramlich and H. Plieninger
1635 H. Gotthardt and F. Reiter
1650 H. Gotthardt et al.
1712 W. Sucrow et al.
1719 W. Sucrow et al.
1791 F. Eiden and E, Breugst
1889 H. Hammer et al.
1902 E. Bolsing et al.
1956 A.Q. Hussein and J.C. Jochims
1981 H.J. Degen et al.
2087 G. Seitz et al.
2197 J. Curtze et al.
2243 A. Gossauer and E. Klahr
2369 F.A. Neugebauer et al.
2465 W. Flitsch et al.
2472 A. Mondon et al.
2631 K. Junghans et al.
2640 K. Krohn et al.
2718 N. Wiberg et al.
2741 A. Roedig et al.
2750 W. Pfleiderer
2854 G. Wulff et al.
2907 H. Paulsen and W. Lüttke
2913 E. Hofer
2961 G. Boche et al.
2997 E. Vilsmaier et al.
3072 F. Seela and D. Hasselmann
3098 H.H. Credner et al.
3166 G. Ege and K. Gilbert
3237 U. Wolf et al.
3286 H. Böshagen and W. Geiger
3293 J. Leitich et al.
3432 U. Lüpke and F. Seela
3453 E. Krohn and K. Tolkiehn
3480 H. Duttmann and P. Weyerstahl
3486 R. Hohlbrugger and W. Klotzer
3490 R. Knorr et al.
3526 U. Lüpke and F. Seela
3743 F. Seela and Q.H.T. Thi
3748 E.C. Herrmann and G.A. Hoyer
3795 S. Mohr et al.
3895 H.A. Staab et al.
3907 H.A. Staab et al.
3946 D. Döpp et al.

25- -79, Chem. and Ind.(London), (1979)
0057 D.W. Theobald
0058 J.R. Merchant and M.S. Venkatesh
0347 O.L. Tombesi
0351 J.R. Merchant et al.
0385 A.B. Turner
0415 Y. Omote et al.
0478 J.R. Merchant and M.S. Venkatesh
0592 L. Quijano et al.
0667 D.P. Chakraborty et al.
0744 K.K. Seth et al.
0854 S. Ghosal et al.

27- -79, Chimia, 33 (1979)
0324 W. Bernhard et al.

28- -79A, Compt. rend., 288 (1979)
0053 D. Bondon et al.
0057 A. Tixidre et al.
0133 A. Leibenguth et al.
0269 J. Polonsky et al.

28- -79B, Compt. rend., 289 (1979)
0255 M. Cariou

30- -79, Doklady Akad. Nauk S.S.S.R., 244-249 (1979)
0046 A.A. Akhrem et al.
0105 K.B. Yatsimirskii et al.
0254 V.N. Charushin et al.

31- -79, Experientia, 35 (1979)
0009 P. Manitto and D. Monti
0157 F. Cafieri et al.
0298 G. Cimino et al.
1137 G.A. Miana et al.
1277 G. Cimino et al.
1278 E.G. Boeren et al.
1418 Z. Neiman
1420 Y. Asakawa and T. Takemoto
1543 K.K. Bhattacharya and P.K. Sen
1544 R.J. Wells and K.D. Barrow

32- -79, Gazz. chim. ital, 109 (1979)
0009 A. Lupi et al.
0013 G. Ortaggi and R. Marcee
0101 G. Randazzo et al.
0121 G. Adembri et al.
0151 G. Assante et al.
0175 G.F. Bettinetti et al.
0195 E. Dradi et al.
0301 F.D. Monache et al.
0329 A. Carotti et al.
0351 A.B. Hamman et al.
0357 G.M. Gasparini
0391 M. Parrilli et al.
0565 L. Canonica et al.
0567 R. Torres et al.

0651 R. Caputo et al.

33- -79, Helv. Chim. Acta, 62 (1979)
0001 W. Heilman et al.
0021 G. Vernin et al.
0086 S. Chaloupka and H. Heimgartner
0090 V.B. Baghos et al.
0101 C. Delseth et al.
0119 R. Mariaca and K. Schaffner
0160 U. Schmid et al.
0205 M. Riediker and W. Graf
0234 E. Georgarakis et al.
0271 T. Doppler et al.
0304 T. Doppler et al.
0314 T. Doppler et al.
0391 B. Jackson et al.
0412 P. Brown et al.
0442 F. Kienele and P. Rosen
0481 H.P. Ros et al.
0511 A. Chollet et al.
0530 O. Sticher and F.V. Afifi-Yazar
0535 O. Sticher and F.V. Afifi-Yazar
0553 B. Frei et al.
0593 A.J.W.G. Visser and F. Müller
0689 J.M.J. Tronchet and J.F. Tronchet
0718 W. Rutsch et al.
0754 U. Oesch and W. Simon
0768 G. Mukherjee-Müller et al.
0779 H. Berger and A.E. Siegrist
0833 J.M.J. Tronchet et al.
0852 M. Karpf and A.S. Dreiding
0965 H.G. Capraro and A. Brossi
0971 J.M.J. Tronchet et al.
0977 J.M.J. Tronchet and B. Gentile
1129 K.K. Chexal et al.
1171 R. Charubala and W. Pfleiderer
1179 R. Charubala and W. Pfleiderer
1217 E.H.F. Escher et al.
1236 J. Lukac and H. Heimgartner
1252 R. Traber et al.
1298 J.M.J. Tronchet and B. Gentile
1303 J.M.J. Tronchet et al.
1330 H. Wyler and U. Meuer
1396 M. Goetz et al.
1401 J.M.J. Tronchet and O.R. Martin
1411 H. Berger and A.E. Siegrist
1429 G. Mukherjee-Müller et al.
1493 W. Oppolzer et al.
1501 W. Keller-Schierlein and E. Kupfer
1525 E. Kupfer and W. Keller-Schierlein
1549 M. Gerecke and A. Brossi
1570 C. Siv et al.
1586 M. Riediker and W. Graf
1632 J.M.J. Tronchet and M.A.M. Massoud
1645 B. Frei et al.
1668 B. Frei et al.
1677 A.J. Ozinskas and A.M. Bobst
1763 W. Reischl and E. Zbiral
1785 K.K. Chexal et al.
1816 R.B. Palmberg and A.E. Siegrist
2025 K.B. Becker and M.K. Hohermuth
2037 C. Delseth et al.
2061 S. Escher et al.
2091 J.M.J. Tronchet and B. Gentile
2129 M. Märky et al.
2174 E. Stamm et al.
2211 A.A. Hofmann et al.
2285 V. Prelog and D. Bedekovic
2325 P. Metzinger and C.H. Eugster
2341 O. Pilet et al.
2350 P. Müller et al.
2374 T. Miyase et al.
2452 A. Eberle and R. Schwyzer
2460 A. Eberle and W. Hubscher
2525 M. Zehnder et al.
2534 W. Eschenmoser et al.
2539 R. Kyburz et al.
2581 S. Jolidon and H.-J. Hansen
2613 H. Bader and H.-J. Hansen
2630 J. Bruhn et al.
2661 G. Büchi and H. Wüest
2681 I. Ernest
2708 Y. Ozaki et al.
2712 P. Dätwyler et al.
2732 G. Acklin and W. Graf
2754 F. Yoshizaki et al.
2788 J.M.J. Tronchet and M.J. Valero
2833 P. Müller et al.

34- -79, J. Chem. Eng. Data, 24 (1979)
0072 R. Pande and S.G. Tandon
0250 R.K. Jain and Y.K. Agrawal

35- -79, J. Am. Chem. Soc., 101 (1979)
0083 A.G. Brook et al.
0147 M. Nakazaki et al.
0237 S.K. Yang et al.
0240 J.H. Cardellina, II, et al.
0378 P.J. Wagner and B.J. Scheve
0390 L.A. Carpino and H.-W. Chen
0487 H. Sakurai et al.
0665 I. Agranat and Y. Tapuhi
0689 H. Muxfeldt et al.
0717 D.A. Jaeger et al.
0770 W. Nutakul et al.
0996 F.-T. Liu and N.J. Leonard
1047 G.R. Newkome et al.
1259 H.A. Bates and H. Rapoport
1544 J.L. Herrmann et al.
1820 R.P. Steiner et al.
1841 H.E. Zimmerman and D.R. Diehl
1904 D.R. Anderson et al.
2121 I.D. Reingold et al.
2128 R. Gray and V. Boekelheide
2171 B. Glatz et al.
2210 F. DiNinno et al.
2284 A. Rauk et al.
2383 I.M. Takakis and W.C. Agosta
2470 D.R. Boyd and G.A. Berchtold
2682 Z. Rappoport and P. Peled
2784 R.G. Powell et al.
3000 A.G. Sherwood et al.
3097 S. Mitra and R.G. Lawton
3125 P.F.T. Schirch et al.
3126 Y. Sekine et al.
3136 M. Nakagawa et al.
3206 M. Krumpole and J. Rocek
3261 R.L. Coffin et al.
3277 K.K. de Fonseka et al.
3306 M.L. Kaplan et al.
3315 J.J. Tufariello et al.
3402 K. Kakinuma et al.

3607 P.S. Mariano and A.A. Leone
3629 T. Ohgi et al.
3651 R.N. Alder and R.B. Sessions
3847 R.A. Epstein et al.
3857 A. Giraudeau et al.
3893 W.H. Rastetter and T.J. Richard
4013 M. Okada et al.
4386 S. Omura et al.
4419 W.T. Ashton et al.
4472 G.R. Newkome et al.
4720 S.B. Mahato et al.
4772 P.J. Stang and T.E. Fisk
4888 L. Hagelee et al.
5019 J.R. Willaims et al.
5059 K. Nishino et al.
5078 A. Kini et al.
5186 H.E. Smith et al.
5370 E. Wenkert et al.
5515 J. Gawronski et al.
5660 M.I. Kanischev et al.
5703 R.E. Swaim and W.P. Weber
5717 T.W. Lewis et al.
5725 K.W. Ho and P. de Mayo
5743 A. Padwa et al.
5953 K.M. Smith et al.
5972 L.A. Paquette et al.
6068 G. Moad et al.
6127 D.C. Baker and S.R. Putt
6136 R.R. Izac and J.J. Sims
6144 R. Dietrich and S.J. Benkovic
6296 M. Lang et al.
6301 I. Ernest et al.
6306 H.R. Pfaendler et al.
6367 H.E. Zimmerman et al.
6383 W.G. Dauben et al.
6404 B.A. Pearlman
6409 E. Ohtsuka et al.
6445 Y. Kobayashi et al.
6475 E.A. Truesdale and R.S. Hutton
6660 K.B. Wiberg and M.J. O'Donnell
6710 N. Cohen et al.
6742 M.R. Uskokovic et al.
6748 E.J. Corey et al.
6767 G. Buchi and P.-S. Chu
6991 L.A. Paquette et al.
7013 S. Danishefsky et al.
7036 A. Ohno et al.
7129 R.D. Little and G.W. Muller
7130 M.C. Pirrung
7323 M. Caswell and G.L. Schmir
7332 I. Saito et al.
7347 S.F. Nelsen et al.
7367 J.M. Hornback and G.S. Proehl
7510 J.A. Barltrop et al.
7521 J.A. Barltrop et al.
7684 J. Nakayama et al.

36- -79, J. Pharm. Sci., 68 (1979)
0036 J.R. Dimmock et al.
0247 M.M. Chien et al.
0388 H.M. Elsabbagh et al.
0499 W.-H. Hong and D.H. Szulczewski
0655 J. Naghaway and T.O. Soine
0668 Y.F. Shealy and C.A. O'Dell
0705 J.L. Moniot et al.
0715 T.G. Waddell et al.
0816 D.R. Hwang and J.S. Driscoll
0845 J.V. Earley et al.
0853 K.V. Rao
1039 W.O. Landen, Jr. and D.S. Caine
1144 L.R. Wantland and S.D. Hersh
1306 K.W. Street, Jr. and G.H. Schenk
1403 D.G.I. Kingston and S.M. Sami
1453 P.L. Warner, Jr.

39- -79B, J. Chem. Soc., Perkin Trans. II (1979)
0007 A.S. Amiri and J.M. Mellor
0151 P. Baas and H. Cerfontain
0156 P. Baas and H. Cerfontain
0163 L. Forlani et al.
0217 I.W. Jones and J.C. Tebby
0219 G. Lousiglio et al.
0262 K. Komatsu et al.
0304 K.C. Brown and J.F. Corbett
0308 K.C. Brown and J.F. Corbett
0393 P.B. Koster et al.
0411 A. Castellan et al.
0501 I.W. Jones and J.C. Tebby
0717 C.W. Spangler et al.
0792 G. Fukata et al.
0810 C.W. Spangler et al.
0862 L. Carlsen et al.
0907 G. Barth et al.
1005 K. Takeuchi et al.
1011 A.D.U. Hardy et al.
1025 P. Baas and H. Cerfontain
1089 J.D. Palmer and A.J. Waring
1103 J.H. Barlow et al.
1298 N.P. Smith and I.D.R. Stevens
1395 A.C. Hopkinson et al.
1402 K. Takagi and Y. Ogata
1540 V.A. Kuz'min et al.
1545 A.A.M. Roof et al.
1665 F. Mossini et al.
1686 F.P.A. Zweegers et al.

39- -79C, J. Chem. Soc., Perkin Trans. I, 1979)
0007 G.V. Baddeley et al.
0043 T.M.H. Liu et al.
0060 P. Sengupta et al.
0062 D.W. Knight and G. Pattenden
0084 D.W. Knight and G. Pattenden
0089 D.R. Gedge and G. Pattenden
0115 J.E. Baldwin et al.
0170 A.G.M. Barrett
0185 J.J. Barr and R.C. Storr
0192 J.J. Barr and R.C. Storr
0237 P.A. Reddy and G.S. Krishna Rao
0266 G.W. Kirby et al.
0274 G. Gowda and T.B.H. McMurry
0279 A.C. Jain et al.
0283 S. Natarajan et al.
0290 F.R. Hewgill et al.
0305 H. Singh et al.
0308 J.P. Clayton et al.
0323 T. Ishida and K. Wada
0337 J.F. Grove and M. Pople
0376 G.A. Taylor
0399 A.R. Katritzky et al.
0451 P.S. Steyn et al.

0464	L. Crombie et al.
0472	L. Crombie et al.
0478	L. Crombie et al.
0488	R. Bonnett et al.
0508	N.K. Hamer
0544	F. Elvazi and K.M. Smith
0584	R.M. Acheson et al.
0591	R.M. Acheson et al.
0595	R.M. Acheson et al.
0599	G. Jones and W.H. McKinley
0603	G.A.F. Roberts
0621	A.R. Forrester et al.
0646	D.R. Crump
0652	A.G.M. Barrett et al.
0662	A.G.M. Barrett et al.
0673	D.W. Jones
0677	S.R. Baker et al.
0686	L. Crombie and R.V. Dove
0692	T. Takeshima et al.
0696	K.Y. Chu and J. Griffiths
0702	G. Green-Buckley and J. Griffiths
0719	R.G.F. Giles et al.
0724	E. Cawkill et al.
0732	R.N. Hanley et al.
0736	R.N. Hanley et al.
0741	R.N. Hanley et al.
0744	R.N. Hanley et al.
0775	A.M. Maione et al.
0807	A.J. Birch et al.
0823	R. Effenberger and T.J. Simpson
0829	I. Fleming and M. Woolias
0838	J.P. Clayton et al.
0885	F. Bondavalli et al.
0889	T. Sakae et al.
0922	A. Albert and A.M. Trotter
0926	R.M. Christie et al.
0935	A.A.L. Gunatilaka and A.F. Mateos
0956	K. Masuda et al.
0976	M.J. Begley et al.
0990	T. Terasawa and T. Okada
1004	L.P. L. Piacenza et al.
1043	Y. Girard et al.
1048	H.T.A. Cheung et al.
1056	M.A. Alkhader et al.
1063	K. Psotta et al.
1066	A. Ulman and J. Manassen
1070	J.H. Boyer and J.R. Patel
1120	R.W. Clarke et al.
1147	M. Ohashi et al.
1150	T. Laerum and K. Undheim
1154	K. Wada and T. Ishida
1159	D.H.R. Barton et al.
1166	D.H.R. Barton et al.
1192	G.G. Alenge et al.
1199	Y. Maki et al.
1222	Z. Paryzek
1228	R.E. van der Stoel and H.C. van der Plas
1233	T.J. Simpson
1250	J.A. Elvidge et al.
1273	D.J. Field and D.W. Jones
1290	P.J. Kocienski et al.
1305	O. Prakash et al.
1322	A.B. Turner and S. Kerr
1326	G.M. Buchan and A.B. Turner
1333	A.B. Turner
1351	J. Burdon et al.
1364	J.H. Gorvin and D.P. Whalley
1389	M.J. Gait et al.
1395	M. Viriot-Villaume et al.
1407	M. Fetizon et al.
1411	J.V. Greenhill and M.L. Mohamed
1415	G. Shaw et al.
1478	Y. Maki and M. Sako
1481	A.A. Chalmers et al.
1494	R. Goddard et al.
1499	D.W. Allen and B.G. Hutley
1525	A.R. Katritzky et al.
1536	L. Benati et al.
1542	L.H. Zalkow et al.
1593	I. Chaaban et al.
1597	G. Cainelli et al.
1629	A.G.M. Barrett
1634	G.J. Lofthouse et al.
1659	M.M. Campbell et al.
1695	D.W. Guest and D.H. Williams
1698	C.W.F. Leung et al.
1729	G. Cardillo et al.
1751	R.F. Bond et al.
1762	S. Rajappa et al.
1774	R.E. Corbett et al.
1816	J.S. Bajwa and P.J. Sykes
1821	M. Anastasia et al.
1833	E.E. Glover et al.
1837	B.A. McAndrew
1852	C.D. Maycock and R.J. Stoodley
1858	M. Tada and A. Oikawa
1871	T.L. Gilchrist et al.
1885	J.L. Markham and P.G. Sammo
1889	J.L. Markham and P.G. Sammo
1918	J.R. Bearder et al.
1927	A.R. Battersby et al.
1969	R. Bonnett and P. Nicolaidou
1990	P. Gregory and D. Thorp
2027	G. Casiraghi et al.
2030	D.H.R. Barton et al.
2034	L.A. Cort and M.A. Mahesar
2044	S. Amagaya et al.
2048	J.F. Grove and M. Pople
2064	J.F. Kingston et al.
2088	Y. Ishido et al.
2099	V. Skaric and V. Turjak-Zebic
2107	T. Nakano et al.
2113	A.W. Dunn et al.
2118	T.J. Simpson
2136	L. Crombie et al.
2154	G.A. Bahadur et al.
2162	T. Iwakuma et al.
2171	R.M. Acheson and G. Proctor
2215	S. Chimichi and R. Nesi
2219	M. Ohashi et al.
2268	C.L. Branch and M.J. Pearson
2282	P.M. Hardy et al.
2289	S.R. Landor et al.
2313	P.A. Ramaiah et al.
2334	D.H. Reid et al.
2340	A.G. Briggs et al.
2349	K. Masuda et al.
2361	N.I. Viswanathan and V. Balakrishnan
2378	A.G.M. Barrett et al.
2387	A.S. Bailey et al.

2393 R.E. van der Stoel and H.C. van der Plas
2401 R.J. Bushby and M.D. Pollard
2411 R.B. Herbert et al.
2429 B. Lythgoe and I. Waterhouse
2449 R.M. Letcher and K.-M. Wong
2451 H. Singh et al.
2455 P.H. Bentley et al.
2473 K.S. Verma et al.
2481 S.A. Martin et al.
2506 M. Driver et al.
2526 C. Marquez and S. Valverde
2528 A.R. Katritzky et al.
2535 A.R. Katritzky et al.
2542 M.C. Carre et al.
2563 T. Meikle and R. Stevens
2606 U. Chiacchio et al.
2652 A. Matsuo et al.
2664 B.F. Coles et al.
2672 N.C. De and G.B. Chheda
2679 O.C. Musgrave and D. Skoyles
2682 J. Herscovici and K. Antonakis
2696 E. Malan and D.G. Roux
2704 R.D. Balanson et al.
2708 F. Stansfield and M.D. Coomassie
2727 Shafiullah et al.
2744 I.G.C. Coutts et al.
2756 B. Iddon et al.
2881 M.M. El-Abadelah et al.
2902 T. Sheradsky et al.
2909 R.J.S. Beer et al.
2914 S. Chatterjee et al.
2948 M. Takagi et al.
2965 R.L. Baxter et al.
2972 R.L. Baxter et al.
2982 R.L. Baxter et al.
2995 G. Ashworth et al.
3017 R.S. Atkinson and J.E. Miller
3042 M.M. Campbell et al.
3048 P.G. Sammes and A.C. Weedon
3053 P.G. Sammes and A.C. Weedon
3061 M. Ikeda et al.
3077 P.F. Newton and G.H. Whitham
3107 T. Brown et al.
3127 F.D. Monache et al.
3155 S.J. Martinez and J.A. Joule
3166 H. Singh et al.
3207 D.G. Hawkins et al.

40- -79, Nippon Kagaku Kaishi (1979)
0255 J. Iwamura et al.
0389 I. Shibuya
0398 Y. Yokoyama
0432 H. Nishi and M. Murayama
0915 T. Oda et al.
1437 H. Imai et al.
1728 M. Tajima et al.
1774 Y. Inukai

41- -79, J. Chim. Phys., 76 (1979)
0097 C. Petrier et al.

42- -79, J. Indian Chem. Soc., 56 (1979)
0052 K.P. Sanghvi et al.
0056 K.P. Sanghvi and K.N. Trivedi
0068 S. Banerjee and G. Bagavant
0081 M. Radhakrishniah
0328 P. Bhattacharyya et al.
0505 K.U. Joseph and V.V. Samayajulu
0708 N.R. Naik et al.
0871 J.P. Saxena et al.
0907 A. Mitra and R.M. Ray
1017 B. Dash et al.
1217 D.P. Chakraborty et al.

44- -79, J. Org. Chem., 44 (1979)
0001 H. Hart et al.
0007 A. Sy and H. Hart
0016 M. Nakazaki et al.
0025 K.C. Brown and J.F. Corbett
0041 Y. Ito and T. Matsuura
0084 P.C. Wade et al.
0088 P.C. Wade et al.
0120 V. Horak and W.B. Manning
0124 F.S. Mariano et al.
0168 L.J. Chinn and K.W. Salamon
0173 J.P. Ferris et al.
0255 A. Padwa and H. Ku
0285 C.N. Filer et al.
0293 J.M. Quante et al.
0302 E.C. Taylor and A.J. Cocuzza
0317 E. Buncel and B. Menon
0368 M. Sasaoka and H. Hart
0400 S.D. Dimitijevich et al.
0428 H.D. Becker and K. Gustafsson
0435 A. Srinivasan and A.D. Broom
0447 G.F. Weber and S.S. Hall
0452 H. Kuritani et al.
0497 D.L. Evans et al.
0502 G.R. Newkome and J.M. Roper
0514 T.E. O'Boyle et al.
0569 D.F. Aycock and G.P. Jurch, Jr.
0604 B. Fuchs and G. Scharf
0610 T.-L. Ju and J.L. Kice
0626 K.T. Potts and J.L. Marshall
0632 M.S. Raasch
0643 M.A. Apfel
0691 A.M. Kuck and E.A. Forlano
0699 W.B. Manning et al.
0808 S. Gelin and R. Gelin
0825 G.F. Field
0827 Y. Ohtsuka
0880 D.J. Sandman et al.
0894 S.R. Ditto et al.
0907 W.D. Graham et al.
0930 M. Sato et al.
0958 W.F. Johns and K.W. Salamon
0964 D.B. Stierle and D.J. Faulkner
0968 B.N. Ravi and D.J. Faulkner
0970 S. Senda et al.
0989 A.A. Frimer et al.
0999 W.H. Rastetter et al.
1028 T. Huynh-Dinh et al.
1063 M.E. Kuehne et al.
1108 J.C. Craig and S.D. Hurt
1118 J. Rolcach et al.
1125 E.C. Taylor and A.J. Cocuzza
1162 I.W. Elliott, Jr.
1170 S.A. Monti and S.-C. Chen
1202 D.H. Aue et al.
1208 D. Bellus
1218 E.M. Gordon and J. Plusec

1273 J.P. Ferris et al.
1282 M. Tsuda et al.
1294 I.M. Takakis and W.C. Agosta
1301 R.D. Youssefych et al.
1309 G.H. Jones et al.
1317 M.J. Robins et al.
1322 P.C. Manchand et al.
1354 H.H. Sun and W. Fenicel
1358 W.E. Noland et al.
1359 D.A. Herold and R.D. Rieke
1382 G.R. Lenz
1388 R.A.E. Ceustermans et al.
1404 T. Adachi et al.
1414 D.E. Bergstrom and K.F. Rash
1417 K. Suyama and S. Adachi
1424 T. Sasaki et al.
1429 C. Steelink and G.P. Marshall
1450 M.F. Zady and J.L. Wong
1458 J.F. Bunnett and S. Sridharan
1476 D.C. Green
1494 J.G. Sweeney et al.
1502 J.T. Valko and J. Wolinsky
1590 J.H. Dygos and B.N. Desai
1597 G.R. Lenz
1604 Z. Goldschmid and M. Shefi
1704 K.D. Franz
1737 K. Anzai
1761 S.W.H. Damji
1779 R.L. Amey and J.C. Martin
1787 H.D. Becker and D. Sanchez
1842 T.L. Gibson and L.L. Smith
1855 R.A. McClelland and M. Ahmad
1892 J.L. Fourrey and P. Jouin
1915 M. Yoshida et al.
1931 A.R. Miller
1934 A.R. Miller
1936 I. Agranat et al.
1941 I. Agranat and Y. Tapuhi
1977 P. de Mayo et al.
1982 H.E. Zimmerman et al.
1992 U.R. Ghatak et al.
2019 T. Nishitani et al.
2034 G.O. Spessard et al.
2039 M. Imazawa and F. Eckstein
2044 J. Finer et al.
2073 M.R. Detty
2077 K.M. Smith and G.M.F. Bisset
2087 G. Bartoli et al.
2150 G.M. Muschik et al.
2153 R.L. Hannan et al.
2160 M. Nakazaki et al.
2176 D.R. Bender et al,
2219 B. Rodriguez et al.
2238 K. Hermann and H. Wynberg
2300 A. Buquet et al.
2331 H.E. Zimmerman and M.C. Hovey
2381 J. Elzinga and H. Hogeveen
2391 J.L. Pyle et al.
2441 R.G. Gaughan and C.D. Poulter
2448 I.J. Massey and C. Djerassi
2457 H.C. Dalzell et al.
2468 N. Langlois and R.Z. Andriamiali-soa
2483 N.F. Woolsey et al.
2491 F. Wudl et al.
2498 W.W. Paudler et al.
2522 J. Foos et al.
2575 W. Vichnewski et al.
2629 M.S. Raasch
2667 P.J. Garratt and S.B. Neoh
2683 J.A. Moore et al.
2688 J.B. Hester, Jr. et al.
2712 K. Komatsu et al.
2722 H. Hart et al.
2732 P. Bey et al.
2784 W. Herz et al.
2798 J.T. Baker and S. Sifniades
2807 P. Gosselin et al.
2838 D.L. Snitman et al.
2896 E. Maccarone et al.
2902 H. Kimoto and L.A. Cohen
2920 G. Ortaggi et al.
2929 P. Crabbe et al.
2941 J.W. Lyga and J.A. Secrist, III
2983 A. Nishinaga et al.
2989 G.E. Keyser and N.J. Leonard
3031 H.O. House et al.
3053 S. Gelin
3086 N.G. Kundu
3100 L.M. Beacham, III
3109 B.N. Ravi et al.
3113 W.E. Epstein and L.A. Gaudioso
3202 R.E. Royer et al.
3211 G.R. Stevenson et al.
3244 M.Z.A. Badr et al.
3256 O.S. Tee and S. Banerjee
3261 J.H. Markgraf et al.
3281 A. Padwa et al.
3310 H.J. Shine and S.-M. Wu
3324 R.C. Moschel et al.
3400 F.C. Seman et al.
3410 H. Feuer and R.M. McMillan
3451 B.M. Trost and E. Keinan
3511 A. Cruz et al.
3576 L. Duhamel et al.
3652 T. Endo and J. Zemlicka
3657 M. Anastasia et al.
3666 J.L. Martin et al.
3687 Z. Rappoport et al.
3698 J.M. Hornback et al.
3711 T. Sasaki et al.
3715 Y.M. Sheikh et al.
3741 U. Hengartner et al.
3748 U. Hengartner et al.
3755 R. Davis and K.G. Untch
3765 P. Mangeney et al.
3790 A.C. Hsu and M.P. Cava
3793 H.O. House et al.
3812 G.R. Newkome et al.
3816 G.R. Newkome et al.
3826 M.-I. Lim et al.
3830 K. Senga et al.
3835 J.B. Holtwick et al.
3847 J.J. Krutak et al.
3908 M.N. Paddon-Row et al.
3952 F.S. El-Feraly
3957 P. Wiriyachitra et al.
3959 J.V. Silverton and M. Ziffer
3962 R. Muthukrishnan and C.D. Gutsche
3970 S.J. Kirsch and H. Schelling
3974 R.J. Chorrat and B.N. Desai
3994 H.D.H. Showalter et al.

4005 N. Cohen et al.
4021 A. Padwa and T. Brookhart
4030 P.F. Wiley et al.
4039 J.H. Cardllina, II et al.
4042 B.D. MacKenzie et al.
4046 B.-S. Huang and J.C. Parham
4116 G. Büchi and H. Wüest
4123 L. Thijs et al.
4191 H.A. Albrecht et al.
4212 J. Jernow et al.
4233 P.S. Engel
4243 Y. Takeuchi et al.
4247 H.D. Becker et al.
4254 D.L. Schuster and J. Eriksen
4275 M. Laguerre et al.
4299 G.R. Lenz
4332 A. Castonguay and H.V. Vunakis
4337 J.L. Moniot and M. Shamma
4343 J.L. Moniot et al.
4347 J.L. Moniot et al.
4351 T.J. Cousineau and J.A. Secrist, III
4359 L.M. Lerner
4378 J.P. Ferris et al.
4381 J.P. Ferris et al.
4385 H. Tahuchi and S.Y. Wang
4402 W.E. Noland and S.R. Wann
4420 L. Bonaccina et al.
4435 D.F. Eaton and B.E. Smart
4438 J.F. Hansen et al.
4440 I. Willner et al.
4447 M. Anastasia et al.
4452 K.-K. Law et al.
4458 D. Davalian and C.H. Hitchcock
4469 D.S. Kemp et al.
4477 T.S. Cantrell and J.V. Silverton
4481 C.H. Heathcock et al.
4511 J.E. Saavedra
4547 S.Y.K. Tam et al.
4557 Y. Fukuda et al.
4562 U.R. Ghatak and P.C. Chakraborti
4588 N. Nakazaki et al.
4609 R.H. Foster and N.J. Leonard
4713 K. Kondo and I. Inoue
4742 R.M. Coates and C.W. Hutchins
4852 J.P. Springer et al.
4854 S.Y.K. Tam et al.
4871 Y. Ohtsuka et al.
4899 J.W. Wilt and V.P. Narutis
4933 T.A. Lyle and G.H. Daub
4981 D. Caine et al.
4988 D. Davalian and C.H. Heathcock

46- -79, J. Phys. Chem., 83 (1979)
0810 M. Takakusa
1208 R.O. Loutfy and J.H. Sharp
1213 R.R. da Silva et al.
1821 F.P.A. Zweegers and C.A.G.O. Varmo
2176 T. Gangwer

47- -79, J. Polymer Sci., Polymer Chem. Ed., 17 (1979)
0351 P.P. Umrigar et al.
0777 H.W. Gibson et al.
0905 M. Akashi et al.
0977 J.V. Crivello and J.H.W. Lam
1047 J.V. Crivello and J.H.W. Lam
1739 C.G. Overberger and Y. Inaki
1963 P. Kovacic and K.N. McFarland
2877 J.V. Crivello and J.H.W. Lam
2893 I. Lukac et al.
3845 J.V. Crivello and J.H.W. Lam

48- -79, J. prakt. Chem., 321 (1979)
0001 K.D. Schleinitz et al.
0071 K. Gewald and J. Oelsner
0117 W. Abraham et al.
0127 A.K. Fateen et al.
0175 K.E. Malterud
0249 J. Beger et al.
0353 S. Andreae and H. Seeboth
0437 J. Jamrozik
0443 H.H. Rüttinger et al.
0488 D. Cech et al.
0495 H. Wilde et al.
0619 H. Zaschke et al.
0695 H. Schäfer et al.
0797 M. Augustin et al.
0827 E. Fänghänel et al.
0881 H. Dorn and R. Ozegowski
0905 H. Ulbricht et al.
0959 J. Beger et al.
1039 A. Attin et al.

49- -79, Monatsh. Chem., 110 (1979)
0051 R. Ott et al.
0201 J.M. Ribo and F. Trull
0279 S. Smolinski and B. Rys
0567 H. Reinshagen and A. Stutz
0577 H. Reinshagen et al.
0613 F. Wille et al.
0699 D. Braun et al.
0739 R. Peltzmann et al.
0947 H. Budzikiewicz et al.
1057 R. Martin et al.
1127 H. Falk et al.
1189 K. Gewald et al.
1233 G.P. Blümer and M. Zander
1367 J. Lichtescheidl and N. Getoff
1387 O.S. Wolfbeis and H. Junek

51- -79, Naturwiss., 66 (1979)
0364 W. Thies

54- -79, Rec. trav. chim., 98 (1979)
0055 R.S. Sukhai and L. Brandsma
0071 G.A. Harff et al.
0078 S.J. Halkes et al.
0187 M. Sindler-Kulyk and W.H. Laarhoven
0192 P. Courtot et al.
0316 M.S. Brouwer et al.
0341 B.H. Bakker et al.
0346 P. Chaquin et al.
0423 J.T.M. Evers and A. Mackor
0452 M. Sindler-Kulyk and W.H. Laarhoven
0496 H. Bieräugel and U.K. Pandit
0537 J.F.M. de Rooij et al.
0559 W. Verboom and H.J.T. Bos

56- -79, Polish J. Chem., 53 (1979)
0027 H.F. Campbell et al.

0057 A.R. Katritzky et al.
0073 D.L. Crookes et al.
0079 M. Hanaoka et al.
0107 J.W. ApSimon and K. Yamasaki
0139 W.J. Rodewald et al.
0149 M. Kocor et al.
0229 W. Basinski and Z. Jerzmanowska
0265 O. Achmatowicz, Jr. and M.H. Burzynska
0403 J. Gronowska et al.
0415 M. Ciszewska and M. Gajewsku
0503 K. Krowicki
0529 K. Golankiewicz et al.
0533 A. Erndt et al.
0631 Z. Krawczyk and C. Betzecki
0643 Z. Krawczyk and C. Betzecki
0701 K. Krowicki
0797 W.J. Rodewald et al.
0839 Z. Bankowska and M. Jedrzejewska
0849 S. Goszczynski et al.
0989 T. Skarzynska-Klentak and T. Wider-nik
1033 Z. Witczak and M. Krolikowska
1147 T. Kiersznicki and A. Rajca
1203 W.J. Rodewald and J.J. Jagodzinski
1221 W.E. Hahn and M. Jatczak
1649 E. Wyrzykiewicz et al.
1729 W.E. Hahn and E. Kozlowska-Gramsz
1751 W.E. Harn and Kryczka
1895 E. Poradowska et al.
1913 J.B. Chylinska
2021 L. Jablonski
2121 R. Balicki and P. Nantka-Namirski
2159 G.D. Pandey and K.P. Tiwari
2251 Z. Bankowska and M. Jedrzejewska
2340 E. Salwinska and J. Suwinski
2385 S. Mejer et al.
2465 J. St. Pyrek
2597 R.S. Kharsan and R.K. Mishra

59- -79, Spectrochim. Acta, 35A (1979)
0421 K.C. Brown et al.
0509 J. Barrett and F.S. Deghaidy
0603 J.A. Groves and W.F. Smyth
0663 U. Chandra Singh et al.

60- -79, J. Chem. Soc., Faraday Trans. II (1979)
0058 E.J.J. Groenin and W.N. Koelman

61- -79, Ber. Bunsen Gesell. Phys. Chem., 83 (1979)
0417 G. Kossmehl et al.
0776 D. Dudek et al.

62- -79A, Z. phys. Chem.(Leipzig), 260 (1979)
0650 M.S.A. Abd-El-Mottaleb et al.

63- -79, Z. physiol. Chem., 360 (1979)
0013 M. Low and L. Kistaludy
0621 K. Haase-Aschoff and F. Lingens
0721 J.B. Hansen et al.
0787 L. Moroder et al.

64- -79B, Z. Naturforsch., 34b (1979)
0064 W.H. Gündel and H. Berenbold
0102 U. Wolf et al.
0297 F.I. Abdel-Hay et al.
0573 T. Madach and H. Vahrenkamp
0624 F. Dallacker et al.
1019 W.-H. Gündel
1145 H. Hofmann and R. Heidrich
1320 M. Manzoor-i-Khuda and G. Habermehl
1448 H. Falk and K. Thirring
1473 W.H. Gündel
1535 A. Villiger et al.
1556 H. Güsten and D. Schulte-Frohlinde
1576 R. Hänsel et al.
1580 M. Mittelbach and H. Junek
1587 W.H. Gündel and H. Berenbold
1593 W.H. Gündel and H. Berenbold

64- -79C, Z. Naturforsch., 34c (1979)
0288 M.M. El-Olemy and J. Reisch
0311 H. Rimpler and B. Schafer
0670 M. Wenzel et al.
1129 M. Kaouadji et al.

65- -79, Zhur. Obshchei Khim., 49 (1979) (English translation pagination)
0068 V.V. Dorokhova et al.
0146 I.I. Lapkin et al.
0188 K.I. Pashkevich et al.
0202 N.A. Bogoslavskii et al.
0275 L.M. Sergienko et al.
0365 A.V. El'tsov et al.
0464 L.N. Markovskii et al.
0479 G.V. Ratovskii et al.
0672 V.O. Reikhsfel'd et al.
0767 V.D. Rumyantseva et al.
0916 V.A. Petukhov et al.
0989 Y.P. Shvachkin and E.N. Olsuf'eva
0994 Y.P. Shvachkin et al.
1000 E.N. Olsuf'eva and Y.P. Shvachkin
1036 A.I. Bokanov and B.I. Stepanov
1225 V.V. Kalmykov and V.A. Ivanov
1233 V.N. Kopranenkov et al.
1275 N.N. Bychkov et al.
1333 E.A. Kirichenko
1407 V.D. Orlov et al.
1600 A.P. Apsitis and D.K. Mutsenietse
1636 E.Y. Khmel'nitskaya ey al.
1658 G.D. Glebova et al.
1740 N.N. Magdesieva and V.A. Danilenko
1760 A.V. Chernova et al.
1828 N.V. Varentsova et al.
1964 B.A. Khaskin et al.
2000 G.A. Chmutova et al.
2056 Z.V. Bezuglaya et al.
2127 E.S. Petrov et al.
2189 V.V. Kormachev et al.
2398 N.D. Pekel' and T.A. Melent'eva
2427 G.V. Panova et al.
2433 G.V. Panova et al.
2467 V.N. Kopranenkov et al.

69- -79, Biochemistry, 18 (1979)

0632 H. Hayatsu and M. Shiragami
1019 W.G. Hanstein et al.
1094 G. Jones et al.
1288 J.A. Maasen
1431 K.R. Hanson et al.
2838 A.J. Grant and L.M. Lerner
2843 G.L. Nelsetuen
4733 S. Ghisla et al.
5197 R.A. Edwards and R. Woody
5332 Y.H. Wong et al.

70- -79, Izvest. Akad. Nauk S.S.S.R., 28 (1979)
0129 E.S. Neupokoeva et al.
0208 G.I. Shchukin and L.B. Volodarskii
0214 G.I. Shchukin and L.B. Volodarskii
0221 Y.N. Porshnev et al.
0315 G.N. Dolenko et al.
0353 N.Y. Grigor'eva et al.
0509 U.M. Dzhemilev et al.
0594 E.V. Polunin et al.
0758 Z.A. Krusnaya et al.
0821 S.E. Zurabyan et al.
0825 A.V. Kamernitskii et al.
0848 L.B. Volodarskii et al.
0854 U.M. Dzhemilev et al.
0872 V.A. Reznikov and L.B. Volodarskii
0944 T.I. Kedrova et al.
1271 V.I. Lozinskii et al.
1282 V.B. Luzhkov
1441 V.A. Golubev et al.
1479 M.G. Voronkove et al.
1585 L.M. Epshtein et al.
1610 G.V. Ratovskii et al.
1636 O.V. Lyubinskaya et al.
1668 G.F. Bannikov et al.
1784 T.S. Skorokhodova et al.
1916 F.M. Stoyanovich and M.A. Marakatkina
1931 E.S. Domnina et al.
1973 M.M. Litvak et al.
2139 Z.I. Istomina and A.M. Turuta
2352 A.V. Zibarev et al.
2452 G.V. Kryshtal'
2521 I.A. Grigor'ev et al.
2526 A.Y. Lazaris et al.
2602 M.G. Voronkov et al.

73- -79, Coll. Czech. Chem. Comm., 44 (1979)
0269 J. Farkas
0424 L. Stibranyi et al.
0439 J. Brokes et al.
0593 A. Holy
0781 E. Svatek et al.
0873 I. Danihel and J. Kuthan
0918 V. Konecny et al.
1318 M. Poctova
1413 J. Vavrova et al.
1423 D. Ilavsky et al.
1460 J. Korinek et al.
1475 H. Hrebabecky et al.
1613 V. Rehak and V. Kaderabek
1634 H. Pischel et al.
1761 V. Konecny and S. Varkonda
1805 A. Krutosikova et al.
2096 J. Hrabovsky and J. Kovac
2108 M. Protiva et al.
2124 J.O. Jilek et al.
2139 I. Cervena et al.
2211 J. Krejcoves et al.
2221 R. Princ and O. Exner
2238 M. Ferles and O. Kocian
2255 A. Krajicek et al.
2426 I. Basnak and J. Farkas
2438 J. Slouka
2507 A. Jurasek et al.
2511 J. Prosek et al.
2536 M. Rajsner et al.
2550 A. Holy and M. Vanecek
2677 V. Valenta et al.
2689 V. Valenta et al.
2815 M. Meloun and J. Chylkova
2846 A. Holy
2946 O. Cervinka et al.
2987 M. Protiva et al.
2997 M. Rajsner et al.
3008 V. Valenta et al.
3023 H. Pischel et al.
3288 D. Ilavsky et al.
3301 F. Povazanec et al.
3604 Z. Vejdelek et al.
3617 K. Sindelar et al.

74- -79B, Mikrochim. Acta II (1979)
0403 P.W. Beaupre

77- -79, J. Chem. Soc., Chem. Comm. (1979)
0135 T. Saito and T. Fujii
0165 S. Ghosal and S. Banerjee
0174 A. Matsuo et al.
0221 B.S. Holla and S.Y. Ambekar
0222 A. Mathew et al.
0246 D.P. Chakraborty et al.
0271 D.S. Wise and L.B. Townsend
0276 M. Essiz et al.
0285 B.J. Van Keulen et al.
0302 P.H. Ruehle et al.
0333 I. Yokoe et al.
0428 R.E. Markwell
0441 G.J. Kruger et al.
0516 E.M. Engler et al.
0528 R.H. Bradbury et al.
0534 T. Tsuchiya et al.
0642 D.A. Taylor and J.A. Joule
0645 A.G.M. Barrett et al.
0659 I. Brown and J.S. Mitchell
0663 P.C. Cherry et al.
0665 C.M.D. Beels et al.
0666 S.R. Baker et al.
0726 H. Kaise et al.
0823 M. Lancaster and D.J.H. Smith
0903 A. Gold et al.
1027 G. Saito and J.P. Ferraris
1030 N.F. Haley
1031 A.G. Anastassiou et al.
1061 D. Brewer et al.
1062 R.D. Chambers et al.
1084 P.H. Helferty et al.
1102 K.A. Lerstrup and L. Henriksen
1135 H.C. Hansen and A. Senning

78- -79, Tetrahedron, 35 (1979)
0017 M.C. Wani et al.
0025 H.D. Scharf et al.
0059 R. Szargan et al.
0063 K. Schwetlick et al.
0105 W.D. Ollis et al.
0155 H. Vermeer et al.
0177 G. Bidan, G. Cauquis and M. Genies
0181 B. Divisia
0233 A. Bodor and A. Barabas
0241 J.W. Barton et al.
0263 Y. Kashman
0277 S. Satish, A. Mitra and M.V. George
0341 H. Sliwa and A. Tartar
0385 H.D. Scharf and J. Janus
0413 A.C. Jain, R.C. Gupta and R. Khazanchi
0417 P.J. Hylands and A.M. Salama
0437 R.M. Smith
0463 D.A. Lightner and Y.T. Park
0511 F.A. Devillanova and G. Verani
0531 A. Pelter et al.
0535 H. Erdtman and H.E. Hogberg
0609 R.T. Luibrand et al.
0621 M.E. Jung and B. Gaede
0633 D. Herlem and F. Khuong-Huu
0641 P. Rasoanaivo et al.
0667 M. Rabinovitz et al.
0697 R.D.H. Murray and K.W.M. Lawrie
0733 I. Agranat et al.
0775 M.B. Marszak and M. Simalty
0815 I. Salazar and E. Diaz
0823 M. Suzuki et al.
0861 R. Cooper et al.
0869 J. Becher, C. Dreier and O. Simonsen
0949 K. Takeuchi et al.
0961 C. Agami et al.
0979 R. Misra, R.C. Pandey and S. Dev
0985 R. Misra, R.C. Pandey and S. Dev
0989 L. De Taeye et al.
1079 M. Asai et al.
1125 A.S. Jones et al.
1151 P.L. Majumder et al.
1167 M. Essiz et al.
1177 R.J. Atkins and G.I. Fray
1199 R.J.S. Beer et al.
1251 J.C. Fanning et al.
1273 S. Yamada and C. Kaneko
1331 P. Bouchet et al.
1449 K.C. Joshi et al.
1455 H.J. Callot
1483 J. Jernow et al.
1487 M.A. Caolo and F.P. Stermitz
1523 J. Becher and M.C. Christensen
1537 A.H.A. Tinnemans and W.H. Laarhoven
1551 P.S. Steyn, P.L. Wessels and W.F.O. Marass
1665 B.S. Joshi et al.
1777 A.V.B. Sankaram, A.S. Rao and J.N. Shoolery
1851 K. Dornberger et al.
1857 S.F. Dyke and P. Warren
1861 S.F. Dyke et al.
1869 I. Kapovits et al.
1875 I. Kapovits et al.
1899 M. Pfau and J. Ughetto-Monfrin
1907 S.J. Wratten and D.J. Faulkner
2027 G. Jones and P. Rafferty
2061 G. Casiraghi et al.
2071 P. Jacques et al.
2093 P. Capdevielle and J. Rigaudy
2101 P. Capdevielle and J. Rigaudy
2131 M. Lotfi and R.M.G. Roberts
2143 F. Delle Monache et al.
2237 M. Yoshida et al.
2255 H.D. Scharf and R. Weitz
2269 W. Abraham et al.
2285 A. Laurent et al.
2301 R. Misra, R.C. Pandey and S. Dev
2311 A.R. Bremb er et al.
2359 I. Willner and M. Rabinovitz
2419 W.O. Godtfredsen et al.
2463 R.K. Anderson et al.
2493 A. Nishinaga et al.
2501 J.C. Arnould et al.
2539 T.I. Gray et al.
2545 C. Galeffi et al.
2555 S.F. Dyke and P. Warren
2571 M.M. El Abadelah et al.
2613 G.R. Lenz
2633 F. Fournier et al.
2639 F. Fournier et al.
2655 B. Cazes and S. Julia
2901 J.N. Denis and A. Krief
2913 J.F.M. De Roou et al.
2931 J.F.M. De Rooij et al.

80- -79, Revue Roumaine Chim., 24 (1979)
0059 I. Dragota and I. Niculescu-Duvaz
0137 T. Nicolaescu et al.
0453 N.A. Shams
1027 H.W. Langfeld
1061 E. Pop et al.
1143 D. Belarbi et al.
1177 A.M. El-Abbady et al.
1329 H.W. Langfeld
1485 N.F. Eweiss et al.
1491 M.R. Mahmoud and R. Abd-Elhamide

83- -79, Arch. Pharm., 312 (1979)
0039 A. Keutzberger and D. Wiedemann
0076 H. Fenner and W. Oppermann
0120 G. Seitz et al.
0147 V.J. Ram
0192 Y. Golander et al.
0219 H. Möhrle and J. Gerloff
0240 E. Reimann
0248 K. Görlitzer et al.
0254 K. Görlitzer
0273 J. Knabe and A. Ecker
0282 U. Pindur and B. Unterhalt
0288 R. Neidlein and Z. Behzadi
0302 F. Eiden and F. Meinel
0319 Y. Golander et al.
0385 E. von Angerer and W. Wiegrebe
0426 A. Kreutzberger and A. Tantawy
0431 U. Kücklander
0465 U. Kücklander
0498 G. Dannhardt and R. Obergrusberger
0515 U. Kücklander and W. Hühnermann
0535 A. Kreutzberger and D. Wiedemann

0555 G. Schneider and M. Willems
0586 V.J. Ram et al.
0591 F. Eiden and E.G. Teupe
0619 K.C. Liu et al.
0633 K. Gorlitzer and G. Hobbel
0662 F. Eiden and M. Dürr
0708 F. Eiden and M. Dürr
0726 V.J. Ram
0776 K.C. Liu et al.
0842 K. Gekeler and J. Metz
0896 G. Dunnhardt and R. Obergrusberger
0971 P. Nickel et al.
1037 H. Auterhoff and J. Thimnes
1054 F. Moll and A. Esperester

86- -79, Talanta, 26 (1979)
0081 E.A. Neves and D.W. Franco
0297 A. Corsini and R.M. Cassidy
0341 J.M. Poirier and J.-F. Verchere
0349 J.M. Poirier and J.-F. Verchere
0479 T. Yoshino et al.
0921 H. Nakamura et al.

87- -79, J. Med. Chem., 22 (1979)
0028 R.K.Y. Zee-Cheng and C.C. Cheng
0032 A.M. Crider et al.
0036 G.L. Tong et al.
0040 T.H. Smith et al.
0048 M. Nakagura et al.
0063 M.E. Flaugh et al.
0123 M.C. Venuti et al.
0263 P.F. Juby et al.
0273 D.C. Baker et al.
0316 P.F. Torrence et al.
0406 E.-F. Fuchs et al.
0491 M. Yoshimoto et al.
0496 F.G. de las Heras et al.
0501 R.K. Zee-Cheng et al.
0505 D.L. Temple et al.
0514 A.M. Mian et al.
0518 E.M. Acton et al.
0569 L.K.T. Lam et al.
0592 M. Bobek et al.
0618 S. Choi et al.
0621 A. Hampton et al.
0639 K. Kondo et al.
0647 J. Kulikowski et al.
0657 W.J. Wheeler et al.
0731 C. Temple, Jr. et al.
0741 S.C. Lin et al.
0743 C.U. Kim et al.
0757 M. Narisada et al.
0797 S.K. Sengupta et al.
0807 M.T. Garcia-Lopez et al.
0850 M.G. Nair et al.
0869 J.E. Martinelli et al.
0874 J.E. Martinelli et al.
0912 G.L. Tong et al.
0918 C.W. Mosher et al.
0922 E.M. Acton et al.
0958 M.S. Poonian et al.
0962 C.D. Jones et al.
0966 C.G. Pitt et al.
1051 B.K. Sinha et al.
1104 A.S. Steinfeld et al.
1109 J.A. Montgomery and H.J. Thomas
1134 J.S. Park et al.
1214 G.S. Lewis and P.H. Nelson
1230 J.A. Beisler et al.
1244 S. Nesnow
1273 R.F. Schinazi et al.
1296 M. Bialer et al.
1306 H.P. Benschop et al.
1330 A.F. Cook et al.
1354 L.A. Mitscher et al.
1380 M. Takai et al.
1390 J.B. Hester, Jr and P. von Voigtlander
1422 R.A. Earl and E.B. Townsend
1425 J.M. Essery et al.
1428 C.I. Hong et al.
1435 W.J. Leanza et al.
1509 T. Tatee et al.
1524 A. Hampton et al.
1529 A. Hampton and D. Picker
1532 S.C. Welch and J.M. Gruber
1538 R.M. Kanojia et al.
1541 C.B. Brouillette et al.
1545 H. Rosemeyer and F. Seela

88- -79, Tetrahedron Letters (1979)
0053 E. Nagarajan et al.
0143 R.P. Thummel and D.K. Kohli
0145 W.H. Gerwick et al.
0151 T. Miyashi et al.
0155 T. Miyashi et al.
0225 N. Gamon and C. Reichardt
0271 P.B.J. Driessen and H. Hogeveen
0279 D.H.R. Barton et al.
0391 P.H. Bentley et al.
0405 A. daC. Pinto et al.
0561 J.-P. Hagenbuch and P. Vogel
0565 P. Geetha et al.
0605 F.M. Unger et al.
0625 T. Watanabe et al.
0629 D.J. Collins and J. Sjovall
0661 L. Crombie et al.
0685 H.H. Sun and W. Fenical
0711 D.E. Minter et al.
0745 C.L. Pedersen
0779 D. Kaufmann and A. de Meijere
0799 K. Miki et al.
0863 T. Ishigami et al.
0867 M. Kato et al.
0871 A. Sekiguchi et al.
0921 R. Gompper and R. Sobotta
0941 R. Briere et al.
0963 F. Cafieri et al.
0981 W. Oppolzer et al.
1025 O. Campos and J.M. Cook
1051 T. Sato and S. Ito
1055 Y. Fukazawa et al.
1113 N. Kato et al.
1125 S. Inayama et al.
1177 B.M. Goldschmidt et al.
1209 A.F. Mourad and H. Hopf
1213 T. Eicher and D. Krause
1223 J. Brugidou et al.
1303 J.M. Ribo and L. Vinuesa
1305 A. Krebs and W. Ruger
1389 E. Brown et al.
1419 I. Kitagawa et al.

1445 G. Jones et al.
1453 T.J. King et al.
1477 R.B. Nader and M.K. Kaloustian
1529 D.N. Reinhoudt et al.
1561 F. Vogtle and J. Winkel
1571 G. Ege et al.
1575 H. Brockmann and H. Lackner
1587 A. Laurent et al.
1619 T. Kitamura et al.
1649 C.M. Beechan and J.J. Sims
1701 R. Furuta et al.
1765 Y. Yamashita and M. Masumura
1773 M. Katayama and S. Marumo
1875 S. Albanesi et al.
1889 P.H. Bentley et al.
1931 W.Z. Antkowiak and W.P. Gessner
1939 W.G.L. Aalbersberg and K.P.C. Vollhardt
2003 C.J. Simmons et al.
2007 J.H. Cardellina, II and R.E. Moore
2015 B. Epe and A. Mondon
2075 M. Franck-Neumann and J.J. Lohmann
2105 D.F. Corey et al.
2125 H.B. Eckhardt and H. Perst
2247 D. Shiengthong et al.
2317 E.J. Corey and G. Schmidt
2335 E. Weber et al.
2347 H.D. Martin et al.
2355 T. Arai et al.
2385 N. Cong-Danh et al.
2389 J.C. Moutet and G. Reveroy
2401 M. Sakakibara and K. Mori
2415 M. Yoshifuji et al.
2427 B.S. Joshi et al.
2457 E. Hickmann et al.
2481 A. Stoessl et al.
2485 P.A. Wender et al.
2493 J.P. Marino and J.R. Kostusyk
2509 A.W. Burgstahler and M.E. Sanders
2511 C.H. Brieskorn and R. Hofmann
2513 H.A. Staab et al.
2557 I. Hermecz et al.
2603 Y. Yamada et al.
2677 P. Beslin et al.
2701 A. Brandt et al.
2741 F.E. Ziegler et al.
2767 M.S. Puar et al.
2849 M. Croisy-Delcey et al.
2867 A.S. Kende et al.
2897 T. Sato et al.
2965 A.G. Schultz et al.
2983 A. Inada et al.
3053 N.J. Eggers and A.J. Jones
3141 G. Markl et al.
3159 N. Cong-Danh et al.
3169 Y. Onishi et al.
3171 T. Satake et al.
3197 J. Borges et al.
3233 M.S.R. Nair and S.T. Carey
3319 L. Duhamel and J. Valnot
3345 B.A. Burke et al.
3401 P.G. Gassman et al.
3457 H. Ogawa et al.
3549 H.I.X. Mager
3571 J.W. Barton and D.J. Lapham
3579 A. Alemany et al.
3619 G. Cimino et al.
3669 T. Sato et al.
3673 R. Okazaki et al.
3725 J.M. Cense and R. LeQuan
3819 R.E. Lehr et al.
3891 I. Bryson et al.
3921 Y. Gopichand and F.J. Schmitz
4045 B. Epe and A. Mondon
4049 W. Eberbach et al.
4053 R. Bingmann et al.
4117 D. Panek-Janc and J. Koziol
4141 P. Warner and S.-C. Chang
4213 M. Iyoda et al.
4217 Y. Aso et al.
4227 J. Lamotte et al.
4269 H. Wagner et al.
4323 S. Omura et al.
4399 T. Osawa et al.
4407 A.S. Bailey et al.
4415 A.J. Jones et al.
4457 P.G. Gassman and M.J. Mullins
4493 M. Behforouz and R. Benrashid
4521 M. Murugesan and M. Shamma
4527 E. Leete
4529 W. Flitsch and E.R. Gesing
4533 P. Carrupt and P. Vogel
4545 W. Pritschins and W. Grimme
4587 P. Slosse and C. Hootele
4589 L. Castedo et al.
4595 G. Mehta et al.
4675 M. Takasugi et al.
4701 R.A. Ross and P.J. Scheuer
4747 K. Komatsu et al.
4781 M. Poje and B. Rocic
4787 K.N. Tantry et al.
4789 J. Dalling et al.
4805 T. Peterson and J.B. Neilands
4847 J. Gumułka et al.
4857 R.G. Visser and H.G.T. Bos
4879 A. Islam et al.
4915 J.H. Cardellina, II et al.
4931 T.G. Back and N. Ibrahim
4989 M.E. Stack et al.
4999 K. Yamamura et al.
5035 J.S. Davies et al.

89- -79, Angew. Chem.(Intl. Ed.), 18 (1979)
0067 G. Ege and K. Gilbert
0156 R. Gompper and K. Bichlmayer
0161 K. Hafner et al.
0162 K. Hafner et al.
0214 M. Hanke and C. Jutz
0233 J. von Seyerl and G. Huttner
0311 G. Schröder and W. Witt
0312 W. Gilb and G. Schröder
0329 J. Kleinschroth and H. Hopf
0331 R. Huisgen et al.
0395 T.C. Klebach et al.
0396 U.H. Brinker and I. Fleischhauer
0411 A. Naiman and K.P.C. Vollhardt
0413 J. Rigaudy et al.
0472 R. Weiss et al.
0473 R. Weiss et al.
0545 E. Vogel et al.
0675 F.P. Montforts et al.
0699 C. Krieger et al.

0945 G. Hauck and H. Dürr
0946 K. Nakasuji et al.
0964 M. Breuninger et al.

90- -79, J. Inorg. Nucl. Chem., 41 (1979)
0549 A. Sarpotdar and J.G. Burr
0815 M.F. Iskander et al.

93- -79, J. Appl. Chem. U.S.S.R., 52 (1979)
0333 A.V. El'tsov and T.A. Yurre
0903 R.I. Vlyazlo et al.
1271 E.E. Nifant'ev et al.

94- -79, Chem. Pharm. Bull. Japan, 27 (1979)
0144 I. Murakoshi et al.
0183 A. Matsuda et al.
0242 K. Matoba et al.
0257 Y.A. Al-Farkh et al.
0274 C. Iwata et al.
0275 J. Endo et al.
0331 K. Yamakawa et al.
0346 H. Ishii et al.
0351 H. Sayo et al.
0403 S. Tamura and E. Takeda
0541 E. Suzuki and M. Okada
0592 M. Kuroyanagi et al.
0676 Y. Tamura et al.
0682 H. Yamashita et al.
0783 T. Miura et al.
0793 H. Saikachi et al.
0870 T. Takahashi et al.
0899 H. Nomura et al.
0946 C. Kaneko et al.
0984 K. Hata et al.
1147 H. Takahashi et al.
1153 H. Takahashi et al.
1245 K. Tanaka et al.
1252 M. Arisawa et al.
1255 M. Ichikawa et al.
1316 A. Ohta et al.
1328 T. Naka and Y. Furukawa
1352 M. Obayashi et al.
1378 A. Ohta et al.
1383 Y. Ikeya et al.
1395 Y. Ikeya et al.
1448 T. Momose et al.
1576 Y. Ikewa et al.
1583 Y. Ikewa et al.
1604 F. Abe and T. Yamauchi
1611 M. Yamazaki et al.
1683 K. Masuda et al.
1688 K. Masuda et al.
1747 K. Yamakawa and T. Satoh
1792 T. Kurihara et al.
1813 C. Kaneko et al.
1824 M. Tanno and S. Kamiya
1847 T. Fujii et al.
1965 T. Naka and Y. Furukawa
1982 M. Hori et al.
2027 A. Ohta et al.
2143 Y. Kurasawa et al.
2183 T. Tsuchiya et al.
2194 N. Takao and K. Iwasa
2229 N. Oda et al.
2304 S. Tetrada and H. Mitsuhashi
2316 H. Sayo et al.
2382 M. Kobayashi et al.
2442 T. Kurechi et al.
2463 T. Yamauchi et al.
2497 T. Fujii and S. Yoshifuji
2539 T. Takahashi et al.
2551 T. Kitagawa et al.
2589 H. Natsugari et al.
2596 A. Ohta et al.
2618 H. Natsugari and Y. Kuwada
2627 A. Ohta et al.
2647 M. Ikehara et al.
2695 Y. Ikewa et al.
2767 F.H. Al-Hajjar et al.
2775 H. Nakayama et al.
2807 T. Endo et al.
2857 H. Saikachi et al.
2868 M. Chiba et al.
2874 N. Tanaka et al.
2879 K. Mizuyama et al.
2927 H. Natsugari et al.
2954 K. Endo et al.
2975 T. Hashimoto et al.
2980 A. Ohta et al.
3029 H. Ishii et al.
3078 A. Tanaka and T. Usui
3115 K. Inoue et al.
3130 A. Hiraoka and M. Maeda

95- -79, J. Pharm. Soc. Japan, 99 (1979)
0038 K. Kashima et al.
0102 J. Kunitomo et al.
0264 M. Takahira et al.
0439 S. Takagi et al.
0500 K. Inoue et al.
0515 Y. Tominaga et al.
0540 Y. Tominaga et al.
0647 S.I. Sakai et al.
0657 M. Iinuma and S. Matsuura
0674 H. Yamaguchi et al.
0699 S. Nagai et al.
0705 S. Nagai et al.
0813 S. Fukushima et al.
0818 Y. Sakamoto and T. Kurihara
0880 K. Kubo et al.
0989 H. Okuda et al.
1081 Y. Tominaga et al.
1234 S. Hidaki et al.

97- -79, Z. Chemie, 19 (1979)
0020 A.R. Katritzky et al.
0059 J. Bodeker et al.
0096 K. Brosche et al.
0106 M. von Janta-Lipinski et al.
0109 S.L. Spassov et al.
0192 E. Fanghanel and H. Poleschner
0226 R. Uhlemann and H. Bukowsky
0289 H. Viola and R. Mayer
0446 J. Wrubel and R. Mayer
0451 H.-J. Siemann et al.
0452B J. Wrubel

98- -79, J. Agr. Food Chem., 27 (1979)
0012 P. Folstar et al.
0201 P.M. Scott et al.
0699 H.G. Rast et al.

0999 R.H. Cox et al.
1342 M. Bachmann et al.
1347 S. Ghosal et al.

99- -79, Theor. Exptl. Chem., 15 (1979)
0043 V.A. Shagun et al.
0055 E.A. Romanenko et al.
0573 L.E. Bodeskul et al.

100- -79, J. Natural Products, 42 (1979)
0001 K.P. Guha et al.
0092 F. Tillequin et al.
0112 A.D. Kinghorn
0116 D. Dwuma-Badu et al.
0126 S.F. El-Naggar and R.W. Doskotch
0133 H. Guinaudeau et al.
0159 A. Kato et al.
0163 C.-H. Chen et al.
0174 A. Shafiee et al.
0197 Y.A.H. Mohamed et al.
0203 L.H. Zalkow et al.
0264 H.N. El-Sohly et al.
0274 J.M. Cassady et al.
0279 W.W. Epstein and E.E. Ubben Jenkins
0301 H. Nielsen and P. Arends
0320 P.W. LeQuesne et al.
0325 H. Guinaudeau et al.
0361 B.R. Pai et al.
0374 K. Nozawa and S. Nakajima
0378 G.C. Hokanson
0385 A.B. Beck et al.
0399 S. Dasgupta et al.
0427 J.M. Cassady et al.
0430 R. Torres et al.
0450 M.A. Elsohly et al.
0463 M. Kemal et al.
0475 S.P. Gunaselera
0496 D.G.I. Kingston et al.
0500 J. Wu et al.
0540 P.M. Subramanian and G.S. Misra
0615 M. Shamma et al.
0627 C.E. Snipes et al.
0643 M.M. Chien and J.P. Rosazza
0658 S.P. Gunasekera et al.

101- -79B, J. Organomet. Chem., 165 (1979)
0101 M.V. Russo and A. Furlain

101- -79C, J. Organomet. Chem., 166 (1979)
0139 G.W.H. Cheeseman and S.G. Greenberg

101- -79E, J. Organomet. Chem., 168 (1979)
0177 D. Maetens et al.

101- -79J, J. Organomet. Chem., 173 (1979)
0107 J.E. Sheats et al.
0199 R.D. Wilson et al.

101- -79K, J. Organomet. Chem., 174 (1979)
0027 W.E. Fristad et al.

101- -79N, J. Organomet. Chem., 177 (1979)
0211 M. Julia et al.

101- -79R, J. Organomet. Chem., 181 (1979)
0223 J. Halpern and R.A. Jewsbury

101- -79S, J. Organomet. Chem., 182 (1979)
0353 R. Jiminez et al.

102- -79, Phytochemistry, 18 (1979)
0129 W. Vichnewski et al.
0139 M.H.A. Elgamal
0149 M.A.F. Jalal et al.
0171 H. Ripperger
0175 E.K. Adesogan
0181 V.K. Gujral et al.
0182 A.A.L. Gunatilaka et al.
0188 S.S. Chibber and U. Khera
0217 H. Iwamura et al.
0273 S.R. Jensen et al.
0279 M. Rohr et al.
0283 M.A. Qurishi et al.
0285 Y. Asakawa and T. Takemoto
0293 M. De Bernardi et al.
0299 T. Fujita et al.
0311 G. Assante et al.
0328 M. Rohr and P. Naegeli
0338 A. Ulubelen et al.
0351 D. deB. Correa et al.
0352 S.K. Garg et al.
0353 W.S. Woo et al.
0365 S. Bhanumati et al.
0366 S.J. Torrance et al.
0463 A.S.R. Anjaneyulu et al.
0473 A.F. Morel et al.
0488 D. Takaoka et al.
0494 S. Tandon and R.P. Rastogi
0503 S. Ghosal et al.
0515 M. Tits et al.
0617 F.X. Woolard et al.
0663 T.C.P. Tomassini and M.E.D. Matos
0681 N. Ohno et al.
0684 M. Pardhasaradhi and L. Krishnakumari
0688 W.E. Campbell and G.M.L. Cragg
0694 M. Sarkar and D.P. Chakraborty
0695 V.B. Pandey et al.
0699 I. Murakoshi et al.
0700 A.B. Ray et al.
0815 A. Maranduba et al.
0819 C.C. Duke et al.
0843 L. Quijano et al.
0859 G. Savona et al.
0867 R. Tschesche et al.
0881 F.S. El-Feraly et al.
0891 M. Rodriguez and M. Pinar
0907 H. Wagner et al.
1007 Y. Asakawa et al.
1015 M.F.L. de Almeida et al.
1017 Y.A.G.P. Gunawardana
1029 S. Ghosal and K. Biswas
1037 G.D. Manners and L. Jurd
1073 B.A. Burke and H. Parkins
1089 H. Ronsch and W. Schade
1195 E. Lemmich
1199 A.S.R. Anjaneyulu et al.
1211 M. Ishii et al.
1215 L.V. Puyvelde et al.
1237 G.J. Bukovits and E.G. Gros
1239 D.L. Kulshreshtha

1240 T. Yamauchi et al.
1245 A. Nagar et al.
1248 R. Tschesche et al.
1251 S. Asen et al.
1265 H. Iwamura et al.
1337 W. Herz et al.
1349 Y. Asakawa et al.
1363 M.K. Choudhury and P. Chakrabarti
1385 W.H.M.W. Herath et al.
1415 A. Ahond et al.
1495 H. Erdtman and J. Harmatha
1527 R. Martinez J. et al.
1547 O. Olsen and H. Sørensen
1553 E.G. Crichton and P.G. Waterman
1559 F. Tillequin and M. Koch
1574 D.A.H. Taylor
1579 K.L. Stevens et al.
1580 S.K. Garg et al.
1584 P.K. Bhaumik et al.
1681 Y. Asakawa et al.
1691 J.A. Hembree et al.
1729 J. Vercauterin et al.
1741 E. Rodriguez et al.
1743 W. Herz and N. Kumar
1745 L. Quijano et al.
1756 M.A. Qurishi et al.
1764 S.K. Karg et al.
1765 M.S. Kemp et al.
1768 M.F. Grundon and H.M. Okely
1835 M.C. Garcia-Alvarez et al.
1843 P.J. Hylands and M.T. Oskoui
1847 V. Vecchietti et al.
1886 E.K. Adesogan and B.I. Alo
1899 E. Besson et al.
1981 S. Uesato et al.
2033 M.T. Chinag et al.
2036 A.C. Pinto et al.
2053 P. Junior
2066 F. Tillequin and M. Koch

103- -79, <u>Khim. Geterosikl. Soedin.</u>, <u>15</u> (1979)
0013 A.F. Oleinik et al.
0028 B.M. Krasovitskii and V.M. Shershukov
0037 V.G. Beilin et al.
0041 G.G. Dvoryantseva et al.
0056 Z.V. Bren' et al.
0076 A.A. Prokopov and L.N. Yakhontov
0087 A.N. Kost et al.
0092 V.V. Martin and L.B. Volodarskii
0102 E.M. Peresleni et al.
0111 V.V. Dovlatyan and A.V. Doulatyan
0139 N.S. Kozlov et al.
0166 M.M. Medvedeva et al.
0173 E.V. Braude and M.A. Gal'bershtam
0179 T. Jagodzinski et al.
0188 V.I. Mukhanove et al.
0215 B.L. Moldarer and M.E. Aronzon
0226 D.Y. Sniker et al.
0276 L.G. Yudin et al.
0282 A.N. Kost et al.
0302 R.M. Mirzametova et al.
0310 V.A. Azimov et al.
0316 N.S. Prostakov et al.
0384 N.Y. Kvitko et al.
0421 N.S. Prostakove et al.
0429 G.K. Lebedeva et al.
0435 R.A. Minakova et al.
0443 V.K. Ivanova et al.
0488 I.A. Aleksandrova et al.
0501 I.I. Grandberg et al.
0518 P.B. Terent'ev et al.
0526 N.S. Prostakov et al.
0541 O.N. Chupakhin et al.
0544 I.Y. Kvitko et al.
0551 M.A. Mikhaleva et al.
0572 V.M. Dziomko et al.
0597 E.Y. Lokmane et al.
0611 I.N. Azerbaev et al.
0634 G.A. Karlivan et al.
0642 T.E. Khoshtariya et al.
0647 N.S. Prostakov et al.
0654 V.M. Dziomko et al.
0657 V.M. Dziomko and B.K. Berestevich
0671 M.A. Mikhaleva et al.
0677 V.F. Sedova and V.P. Mamaev
0681 G.N. Kurilo et al.
0685 V.A. Bakulev et al.
0696 V.S. Velezheva et al.
0697 F.G. Yaremenko et al.
0729 L.Y. Malkes et al.
0731 Y.L. Gol'dfarb et al.
0741 L.B. Shagalov et al.
0747 V.N. Eraksina et al.
0759 A.I. Shakhnovich et al.
0764 S.D. Moshchitskii and A.A. Zeikan'
0770 S.G. Agbalyan and R.D. Khachikyan
0773 T.V. Stupnikova et al.
0777 N.S. Prostakove et al.
0780 R.G. Glushkov et al.
0791 A.L. Rusanov et al.
0794 I.K. Yurgevits et al.
0798 A.F. Mishnev et al.
0805 V.I. Nifontov et al.
0807 V.A. Bakulev et al.
0808 V.F. Sedova et al.
0811 L.T. Gorb et al.
0842 V.A. Zagorevskii et al.
0864 A.V. Yudashkin et al.
0872 L.T. Gorb et al.
0879 N.N. Pogodaeva et al.
0883 O.D. Zhilina et al.
0888 V.P. Chetverikov et al.
0890 M.I. Sikharulidze et al.
0894 T.M. Alyab'eva et al.
0899 N.S. Prostakov et al.
0926 R.A. Zhuk et al.
0961 V. Dauksas et al.
0966 V.N. Sheinker et al.
0968 S.D. Sokolov and S.M. Vinogradova
0970 P.L. Trakhtenberg et al.
0978 B.K. Strelets et al.
0989 S.A. Samsoniya et al.
0994 V.S. Velezheva et al.
0997 S.S. Kiselev et al.
1007 N.S. Kozlov et al.
1025 A.Y. Tikhonov et al.
1070 V.I. Shvedov et al.
1074 V.I. Shvedov et al.
1078 V.I. Shvedov et al.
1081 L.T. Gorb et al.

1097 M.I. Sikharulidze et al.
1101 M.A. Gal'bershtam et al.
1113 L.G. Yudin et al.
1117 A.N. Kost et al.
1120 A.F. Bekhli et al.
1142 L.D. Garaeva et al.
1147 L.D. Garaeva and M.N. Preobrazhenskaya
1153 A.L. Fridman et al.
1173 N.E. Kolabova and L.V. Goncharenko
1185 A.Y. Ermishov and I.L. Shegal
1187 A.N. Borisevich and P.S. Pel'kis
1193 A.N. Grinev et al.
1197 S.D. Moshchitskii et al.
1208 B.M. Gutsulyak and V.N. Chuchina
1214 N.S. Prostakov et al.
1223 T.M. Alyab'eva et al.
1227 L.V. Ektova et al.
1231 M.V. Gorelik and V.I. Rybinov
1243 K.M. Zelenin and V.N. Verbov
1260 A.I. Kost et al.
1261 G.V. Grishina et al.
1299 V.V. Korshak et al.
1303 B.M. Krasovitskii et al.
1329 M.A. Gal'bershtam et al.
1337 T.V. Stupnikova and Z.M. Skorobogatova
1361 I.A. Korbulch et al.

104- -79, <u>Zhur. Organ. Khim.</u>, <u>15</u> (1979)
0039 Y.S. Ol'dekop et al.
0043 L.A. Badovskaya et al.
0080 I.I. Grandberg et al.
0101 T.P. Shapirovskaya et al.
0120 Z.F. Solomko et al.
0139 M.G. Gorelik et al.
0147 M.V. Gorelik et al.
0164 V.M. Berestovitskaya et al.
0178 E.R. Zakhs et al.
0183 O.N. Chupakhin et al.
0240 Y.A. Ol'dekop et al.
0311 M.S. Tovbis et al.
0332 N.N. Magdesieva and V.A. Danilenko
0340 G.N. Vorozhtsov et al.
0343 K.A. Balodis et al.
0344 Y.E. Gerasimenko and N.T. Poteleshchenko
0351 Y.L. Slominskii
0361 V.A. Buevich et al.
0364 L.B. Volodarskii et al.
0370 R.G. Dubenko and P.S. Pel'kis
0395 V.N. Kokin and A.V. Reznichenko
0396 F.M. Suidova and A.D. Magai
0454 L.N. Chernova et al.
0457 T.I. Akimova et al.
0487 V.N. Drozd and N.V. Grandberg
0495 B.M. Gutsulyak and M.V. Mel'nik
0500 V.M. Neplyuev
0510 A.M. Galushko and N.S. Dokunikhin
0517 E.A. Andreeshchev et al.
0535 A.I. Mikhaleva et al.
0541 N.N. Magdesieva et al.
0558 V.P. Shchipanov et al.
0566 L.I. Rogovik et al.
0570 V.N. Kopranenkov et al.
0578 A.D. Bulat et al.
0586 V.N. Drozd and N.V. Grandberg
0615 Y.A. Ol'dekop et al.
0618 G.A. Tolstikov et al.
0676 T.I. Akimova and M.N. Tilichenko
0685 S.V. Morozov et al.
0733 A.M. Platoshkin et al.
0741 A.E. Vasil'ev et al.
0751 I.Y. Shirobokov et al.
0761 N.D. Dmitrieva et al.
0765 A.B. Tomchin and G.A. Shirokii
0774 Y.L. Slominskii et al.
0784 R.I. Bodina et al.
0847 S.S. Mochalov et al.
0887 R.N. Khelevin
0919 V.M. Neplyuev et al.
0923 M.V. Gorelik et al.
0937 D.A. Oparin et al.
0951 S.S. Tsymbalova et al.
0955 V.N. Drozd et al.
0962 V.N. Kopranenkov et al.
0967 A.F. Mironov et al.
0970 A.F. Mironov et al.
0981 Y.A. Ol'dekop et al.
1037 U.M. Dzhemilev et al.
1041 U.M. Dzhemilev et al.
1059 V.D. Orlov and V.N. Tishchenko
1082 I.M. Bazarova et al.
1121 Y.A. Failkov et al.
1126 A. Fabrycy et al.
1132 N.D. Dmitrieva et al.
1140 N.P. Shusherina et al.
1144 B.O. Kraiz and A.L. Remizov
1160 M.I. Rogovik and L.I. Rogovik
1166 N.A. Shenberg et al.
1168 G.K. Khisomutdinov et al.
1237 A.A. Potekhin and S; I. Zhdanov
1247 A.A. Akhrem et al.
1290 V.N. Kovtonyuk et al.
1310 N.F. Salakhutdinov et al.
1315 V.A. Beuvich et al.
1319 V.M. Neplyuev et al.
1324 R.G. Dubenko et al.
1341 I.I. Brunovlenskaya et al.
1344 S.M. Ramsh et al.
1396 M.V. Gorelik et al.
1416 K.M. Dyumaev et al.
1437 G.A. Suboch et al.
1462 G.P. Sharnin et al.
1495 V.S. Fedenko et al.
1514 L.M. Gornostaev et al.
1594 V.A. Mironov et al.
1621 I.B. Afanas'ev and N.I. Polozova
1669 S.M. Makin et al.
1703 A.N. Detsina et al.
1715 I.M. Andreeva et al.
1730 V.K. Shchel'tsyn et al.
1736 R.E. Valter et al.
1740 V.K. Daukshas et al.
1744 G.N. Vorozhtsov et al.
1793 V.P. Shchipanov
1798 M.V. Povstyanoi et al.
1805 V.E. Statsyuk et al.
1859 A.S. Polyanskaya et al.
1867 M.M. Kremlev et al.
1915 A.N. Frolov et al.
1926 E.R. Zakhs et al.
1934 N.E. Akhmetova et al.

1944 E.N. Bokeriya et al.
1964 O.V. Zakharova et al.
1973 I.B. Repinskaya et al.
1983 V.F. Shner et al.
2000 V.P. Shchipanov et al.
2018 A.D. Bulat et al.
2023 A.A. Solov'yanov et al.
2066 V.A. Khrustalev et al.
2073 V.A. Khrustalev et al.
2145 K.N. Zelenin et al.
2169 N.N. Magdesieva and R.A. Kyandzhstsian
2174 N.N. Magdesieva and N.G. Chovnikova
2179 L.N. Baeva et al.
2187 I.I. Maletina et al.
2203 L.N. Koikov et al.
2204 G.K. Khisamutdinov et al.
2279 E.F. Bondarenko et al.
2284 V.I. Letunov
2288 N.K. Genkina et al.
2292 N.A. Saldobol
2316 V.N. Knyazaev et al.
2346 M.L. Petrov et al.

105- -79, Khim. Prirodn. Soedin., 15 (1979)
0014 A.A. Nabiev et al.
0091 I.A. Israilov et al.
0127 Z.A. Kuliev et al.
0135 G.V. Sagitdinova et al.
0144 Y.D. Kholodova et al.
0194 T.K. Khasanov et al.
0195 N.V. Veselovskaya et al.
0196 A.S. Kadyrov et al.
0367 I.A. Israilov et al.
0370 K.A. Kadyrov and S.A. Khamidkhodzhaev
0414 Z.A. Kuliev et al.
0417 T.K. Khasanov et al.
0426 A.A. Savina et al.
0446 G.V. Pirtskhalava et al.
0459 K. Samikove et al.
0513 K.A. Kadyrov et al.
0577 S.L. Kasymov et al.
0635 L.I. Dukhovlinova et al.
0639 V.A. Bandyukova
0644 P.D. Fraishtat and S.A. Popravko
0656 D.M. Razakova et al.
0691 E.N. Manukov et al.
0700 Z. Saatov et al.
0703 Z. Saatov et al.
0716 D.M. Razakova et al.
0771 G.V. Sagitdinova et al.
0783 M. Alimova et al.

106- -79, Die Pharmazie, 34 (1979)
0008 P. Richter and G. Wagner
0022 H.-P. Schmauder et al.
0027 J. Kracmar et al.
0188 L. Jahodar and I. Leifertova
0194 P. Proksa et al.
0221 E. Schötter and D. Herndek
0287 H.J. Rüger et al.
0390 S. Leistner et al.
0435 H. Ripperger
0447B G. Kitanov and C. Achtardjiev
0531 M.A. El Sekily
0537 S. El-Dine and S.M. El-Khawass
0577 H. Ripperger
0663 P. Richter and W. Buhrow
0790 S. Johne et al.
0841 N.Q. Chien and G. Adam
0844 S. Leistner and G. Wagner
0847 P. Richter and K. Gerisch

107- -79, Synthetic Comm., 9 (1979)
0077 K.K. Bhattacharya and P.K. Sen
0081 O.S. Park and L.A. Maldonado
0129 G. Roberge and P. Brassard
0317 E. Guittet and S. Julia
0505 E. Wenkert et al.
0603 W. Sucrow and K.-P. Grosz
0825 H. Klein and R. Wiartalla
0877 D.J. Crouse et al.
0895 G.D. Pandey and K.P. Tiwari

108- -79, Israel J. Chem., 18 (1979)
0220 J.P. Desvergne and H. Bonas-Laurent

110- -79, Russian J. Phys. Chem., 53 (1979)
0097 I.I. Dmitrieva et al.
0188 I.I. Dmitrieva et al.
1769 G.N. Rodionova et al.

111- -79, European J. Med. Chem., 14 (1979)
0053 G. Nannini et al.
0123 C. Chavis et al.
0151 M. Garcia-Lopez et al.
0157 P. Krogsgaard-Larsen and T. Roldskov-Christiansen
0375 G. Doukhan et al.
0411 J.C. Eriks et al.
0543 M.C. Carre et al.

112- -79, Spectroscopy Letters, 12 (1979)
0139 M. Nakashima and J.F. Roach

114- -79A, Acta Chem. Acad. Sci. Hung., 99 (1979)
0029 A. Antus-Ercsenyi and I. Bitter
0043 Z. Pal et al.
0407 T. Veszpremi et al.

114- -79B, Acta Chem. Acad. Sci. Hung., 100 (1979)
0089 S. Solyom et al.
0421 F. Joo and M.T. Beck

114- -79C, Acta Chem. Acad. Sci. Hung., 101 (1979)
0319 Shafiullah and Islamuddin
0387 G. Kalaus et al.

114- -79D, Acta Chem. Acad. Sci. Hung., 102 (1979)
0127 Z. Pal et al.
0187 E.R. David et al.
0195 T. Veszpremi et al.
0305 L. Hazai et al.

116- -79, Macromolecules, 12 (1979)

0108 J.P. O'Brien et al.

117- -79, Org. Preps. Procedures Intl., 11 (1979)
0077 S. Nakajima et al.
0247 N. Aggarwal and D.W.H. MacDowell
0255 E.H. Vickery et al.

118- -79, Synthesis (1979)
0120 Y. Tamura et al.
0122 M. Schaefer et al.
0130 L. Bemi et al.
0148 G. Roberge and P. Brassard
0177 H. Willner and M. Halpern
0265 D.H.R. Barton et al.
0267 R.I. Zhdanov et al.
0269 R.I. Zhdanov et al.
0279 J. Kosanyi et al.
0295 G.F. Field and W.J. Zally
0350 B.A. Murrer et al.
0359 J.S. Davidson
0361 G. Seitz et al.
0374 J.M. Hook et al.
0376 G. Ege et al.
0440 C. Deshayes and S. Gelin
0442 H. Boshagen and W. Geiger
0531 H. Yamashita et al.
0545 M. Heberlein et al.
0581 M. Eckstein and A. Drabczynska
0584 B. Chantegrel and S. Gelin
0589 N.S. Narasimhan and P.S. Chandra-chood
0599 J.A.J. den Hartog and J.H. van Boom
0616 S. Akabori and M. Ohtomi
0666 M.T. Shipchandler
0695 G. Schill et al.
0708 M.V. Naidu and G.S. KrisnaRao
0794 J. Moskal and A. Moskal
0824 G. Casiraghi et al.
0830 F. Bondavalli et al.
0889 M. Payard and J. Couquelet
0903 N.S. Narasimhan and S.P. Bhagwat
0948 C.-G. Dieris and H.-D. Scharf
0957 V. Bocchi et al.
0961 V. Bocchi et al.
0987 D. Middlemiss

119- -79, S. African J. Chem., 32 (1979)
0093 G.M.L. Cragg

120- -79, Pakistan J. Sci. Ind. Research, 22 (1979)
0001 A. Essawy et al.
0011 H.Q. Izhar et al.
0189 B. Robinson and M.V. Zubair

121- -79, J. Macromol. Sci., Pt. A, 13 (1979)
0001 H. Ohnishi and T. Otsu
0203 T. Simionescu et al.
0351 G.B. Butler
0503 Y. Ito and T. Saegusa
0573 Y. Morishima and C.G. Overberger

123- -79, Moscow U. Chem. Bull., 34 (1979)
0070 A.P. Golovina et al.
0248 L. Alder et al.

124- -79, Ukrain. Khim. Zhur., 45 (1979)
0043 Y. Slominsky et al.
0048 I.V. Alekseeva et al.
0225 A.V. Bogatsky et al.
0231 L.K. Mushkalo et al.
0447 L.N. Vostrova et al.
0768 V.D. Parmonov et al.
0871 I.V. Smolanka et al.
0872 M.M. Kul'chitsky
1093 V.D. Orlov et al.
1214 M.I. Shenbor et al.

125- -79, Inorg. Chem., 18 (1979)
0120 M.H. Chisholm et al.
2165 J.S. Plotkin et al.

126- -79, Makromol. Chem., 180 (1979)
0079 C. Bonnans-Plaisana et al.
0325 M. Hattori and M. Kinoshita
1441 G. Kossmehl et al.
1465 G. Kossmehl et al.
1651 O. Nuyken et al.
2073 H. Shirai et al.
2303 M. Hattori et al.
2323 M. Hattori and M. Kinoshita
2883 R. Ciaschi et al.
2893 R. Ciaschi and M. D'Alagni
2903 M. D'Alagni
2979 T. Hamaya and S. Yamada

128- -79, Croatica Chem. Acta, 52 (1979)
0051 V. Skaric and Z. Raza
0281 V. Skaric et al.

130- -79, Bioorg. Chem., 8 (1979)
0009 J. Engels
0147 B. Capon and J.W. Thomson
0311 J.A. Gudgeon et al.
0339 P.K. Bridson and C.B. Reese

131- -79D, J. Mol. Structure, 54 (1979)
0077 G. Uray et al.

133- -79, Pharm. Acta Helv., 54 (1979)
0197 B. Kreyenbuhl et al.

135- -79A, J. Appl. Spectroscopy S.S.S.R., 30 (1979)
0220 B.E. Zaitsev et al.
0691 Y.E. Gerasimenko et al.

135- -79B, J. Appl. Spectroscopy S.S.S.R., 31 (1979)
1004 K.G. Bogolitsyn and I.M. Bokhovkin
1183 B.V. Lopatin et al.
1491 L.A. Kutulya et al.

136- -79A, Carbohydrate Research, 68 (1979)
0061 T. Halmos and K. Antonakis
0087 M.A. El Sekily and S. Mancy
0141 V.C. Borlaza et al.
0331 J.G. Buchanan and D.R. Clark

136- -79B, Carbohydrate Research, 69 (1979)

0055 F.J. Lopez Aparicio et al.
0071 F.M. Unger et al.
0089 P.A. Lartey and L. Fedor
0117 D.C. Baker and D. Horton
0235 F.J. Lopez Aparicino et al.
0287 J.M.J. Tronchet et al.

136- -79C, Carbohydrate Research, 70 (1979)
0059 D. Horton et al.
0263 M. Bobek et al.

136- -79D, Carbohydrate Research, 71 (1979)
0169 F. Shafizadeh et al.

136- -79E, Carbohydrate Research, 72 (1979)
0272 R.R. Schmidt and R. Angerbauer

136- -79F, Carbohydrate Research, 73 (1979)
0113 T. Adachi et al.

136- -79G, Carbohydrate Research, 74 (1979)
0117 H. Rosemeyer and F. Seela
0127 A. Faure et al.

136- -79H, Carbohydrate Research, 75 (1979)
0101 J.N. Dominguez and L.N. Owen
0141 D. Horton and J.-H. Tsai
0151 D. Horton and J.-H. Tsai
0314 R. Mengel and U. Krahmer
0325 L. Somogyi et al.

136- -79I, Carbohydrate Research, 76 (1979)
0001 C.A. White et al.

136- -79J, Carbohydrate Research, 77 (1979)
0079 S. David and G. de Sennyev
0205 S.J. Eitelman and M.S. Feather
0234 C. De Gourcy et al.

137- -79, Finnish Chem. Letters (1979)
0118 R. Raunio et al.
0147 T. Laitalainen and T. Simonen

138- -79, Chemistry Letters (1979)
0027 T. Isobe et al.
0043 K. Kato et al.
0073 A. Matsuo et al.
0081 M. Koreeda et al.
0171 T. Toda et al.
0201 H. Obara and J. Onodera
0221 K.D. Franz
0241 A. Ohsawa et al.
0277 T. Kusumi et al.
0301 T. Suzuki and E. Kurosawa
0419 S. Takano et al.
0511 K. Shibata et al.
0537 E. Todo et al.
0541 T. Shinmyozu et al.
0595 M. Tashiro and T. Yamato
0627 M. Matsuoka et al.
0771 Y. Nesumi et al.
0807 M. Kimura et al.
0855 M. Hirama et al.
0859 A. Kawamata et al.
0931 M. Murakami and S. Nishida
1021 J. Inanaga
1035 J. Ojima et al.
1077 S. Oae et al.
1097 K. Maruyama et al.
1137 M. Ochi et al.
1163 T. Amiya et al.
1213 M. Takahashi and S. Watanabe
1269 M. Ishitsuka et al.
1283 T. Ohgi et al.
1301 K. Shibata et al.
1313 G. Tsukamoto et al.
1373 A. Kasahara et al.
1387 L. Quijano et al.
1427 M. Oda et al.
1451 F. Toda and K. Tanaka
1469 K. Ito et al.
1473 K. Ito et al.
1491 E.H. White et al.
1503 K. Ito et al.

139- -79, P,S and Related Elements, 7 (1979)
0195 T.W. Ku and D. Swern

140- -79, J. Anal. Chem. S.S.S.R., 34 (1979)
0391 P.Y. Pustovar
0807 M.A. Matveets et al.
1133 L.N. Savoskina et al.
1195 Y.M. Ostrovskaya et al.
1436 E.A. Shpak and V.A. Satsyuk
1489 V.D. Bakalov et al.
1562 E.A. Shpak et al.

142- -79A, Heterocycles, 12 (1979)
0239 K. Nagahara and A. Takada
0263 K. Saito and K. Takahashi
0269 M. Afzal et al.
0337 P. Sedmera and F. Santavy
0343 T.R. Bok and W.N. Spetkamp
0353 B. Danieli et al.
0397 T. Kurihara and Y. Sakamoto
0401 Y. Tominaga et al.
0453 K. Harano et al.
0471 T. Kaneko et al.
0485 H. Okuda et al.
0497 M. Hanaoka et al.
0503 Y. Tominaga et al.
0505 M. Ito et al.
0691 F. Yoneda et al.
0815 S. Karady et al.
0929 J. Bhattacharyya and S.C. Pakrashi
0943 T. Nomura and T. Fukai
1001 W.A. Romanchick and M.M. Joullie
1005 L. Fisera et al.
1027 T. Hino et al.
1031 N. Abe and T. Nishiwaki
1033 L.A. Mitscher et al.
1141 G.I. Dmitrienko
1203 V.K. Ahluwalia et al.
1315 M. Shibuya and S. Kubota
1407 I. Hermecz and Z. Meszaros
1413 C.-P. Mak and A. Brossi
1423 Y. Tsuda et al.
1427 T. Jano and Y. Horiguchi
1483 G.D. Pandey and K.P. Tiwari
1529 T. Nomura et al.

1539 M. Tsukayama et al.
1543 T. Fujii et al.
1559 V. Fajardo et al.

142- -79B, Heterocycles, 13 (1979)
0141 T. Sato and R. Noyori
0187 E. Kaji and S. Zen
0191 H. Okawara et al.
0227 J.C. Sheehan et al.
0333 K. Isono and S. Suzuki
0353 A. Terahara et al.
0411 K. Takahashi and T. Kametani
0477 S. Nakagawa et al.

144- -79, Mol. Photochem., 9 (1978-9)
0111 N.J. Turro et al.
0227 J.F. Graf and C.P. Lillya

145- -79, Arzneimittel. Forsch., 29 (1979)
0001 K. Klemm et al.
0187 N.A. Jonsson et al.
0463 H. Hamacher
0983 P. Kourounakis et al.
1083 W. Wiegrebe et al.
1659 J.C. Vezin et al.
1662 B.N. Lutsky et al.

146- -79, J. Chem. Tech. Biotech., 29 (1979)
0031 T. Fujita et al.
0100 T. Fujita et al.

149- -79A, Photochem. Photobiol., 29 (1979)
0233 G. Tollin et al.
0389 C. Petrier et al.
0447 A. Sarpotdar and J.G. Burr
0531 A.A. Schothorst et al.
0695 H. Matsumoto et al.

149- -79B, Photochem. Photobiol., 30 (1979)
0251 M.P. Pileni et al.
0645 M.T. Sa E Melo et al.
0689 P.K. Das et al.

150- -79, J. Chem. Research(M), (1979)
0201 J.E.T. Corrie
0301 D.D. Halton and G.A. Morrison
0413 S.H. Hedges and R.B. Herbert
0501 E. Mappus and C. Cuilleron
0801 D. Korbonits et al.
1164 D. Billen et al.
1178 I. Kirson et al.
1451 H. McNab et al.
1579 S.R. James
1713 D. Mulvagh et al.
1732 T. Takeshima et al.
2525 J.R. Bull et al.
2567 J.L. Fourrey et al.
2685 J.E. Knapp et al.
2935 H. Singh et al.
3501 D. Villessot and Y. LePage
3518 D. Villessot and Y. LePage
3643 V.K. Krohn
3686 M.L. Viriot
3782 R. Grandi et al.
3801 C.A. Dewar and C.J. Suckling
3901 R.M. Acheson et al.
4772 P.J. Abbott et al.
4801 D.A. Taylor et al.

150- -79S, J. Chem. Research(S), (1979)
0110 E. Suzuki et al.
0212 T. Takeshima et al.
0272 F. Terrier et al.
0410 T. Takeshima et al.

151- -79A, J. Photochem., 10 (1979)
0205 U. Bruhlmann and J.R. Huber
0467 P.R. Hammond

151- -79B, J. Photochem., 11 (1979)
0039 L.L. Costanzo et al.
0197 K.-H. Grellmann et al.
0313 E.P. Gibson and J.H. Turnbull

152- -79, Nouveau J. Chim., 3 (1979)
0047 Y.M. Saunier et al.
0115 F. Bellamy et al.
0231 A. Castellan et al.
0287 A. Grabowska et al.
0647 M. Maxfield et al.
0785 J. Ficini et al.

153- -79, Bull. Univ. Osaka Prefecture, Sec. A, 28 (1979)
0033 M. Matsuoka et al.
0043 H. Nakazumi et al.
0173 H. Nakazumi et al.
0199 J. Nakaya and M. Uehara